Glencoe Science

Physical Science with Earth Science

Features of *Physical Science with Earth Science*

- **Mastering Standardized Tests** is based on the National Science Standards and contains methods for content review and test prep, chapter tests to assess content mastery, and practice standardized tests to allow students to become accustomed to standardized test formats.
- **Interactive Chalkboard** CD-ROM provides customizable Microsoft® PowerPoint® presentations correlated to the National Science Standards.
- **TeacherWorks™** CD-ROM is a complete lesson planner and resource center correlated to the National Science Standards.
- **StudentWorks™ Plus** CD-ROM provides an all-in-one interactive Student Edition and student resources—a backpack solution in Spanish and English.
- **Reading Essentials, An Interactive Student Textbook** presents each chapter at a lower reading level to help struggling readers master the content.
- **Video Labs, Virtual Labs,** the **Science Lab Manual,** the **Probeware Lab Manual,** and the **Science Inquiry Lab Manual** provide additional opportunities to learn and practice laboratory techniques.

Log on to gpescience.com

SAFETY SYMBOLS

SAFETY SYMBOLS	HAZARD	EXAMPLES	PRECAUTION	REMEDY
DISPOSAL	Special disposal procedures need to be followed.	certain chemicals, living organisms	Do not dispose of these materials in the sink or trash can.	Dispose of wastes as directed by your teacher.
BIOLOGICAL	Organisms or other biological materials that might be harmful to humans	bacteria, fungi, blood, unpreserved tissues, plant materials	Avoid skin contact with these materials. Wear mask or gloves.	Notify your teacher if you suspect contact with material. Wash hands thoroughly.
EXTREME TEMPERATURE	Objects that can burn skin by being too cold or too hot	boiling liquids, hot plates, dry ice, liquid nitrogen	Use proper protection when handling.	Go to your teacher for first aid.
SHARP OBJECT	Use of tools or glassware that can easily puncture or slice skin	razor blades, pins, scalpels, pointed tools, dissecting probes, broken glass	Practice common-sense behavior and follow guidelines for use of the tool.	Go to your teacher for first aid.
FUME	Possible danger to respiratory tract from fumes	ammonia, acetone, nail polish remover, heated sulfur, moth balls	Make sure there is good ventilation. Never smell fumes directly. Wear a mask.	Leave foul area and notify your teacher immediately.
ELECTRICAL	Possible danger from electrical shock or burn	improper grounding, liquid spills, short circuits, exposed wires	Double-check setup with teacher. Check condition of wires and apparatus.	Do not attempt to fix electrical problems. Notify your teacher immediately.
IRRITANT	Substances that can irritate the skin or mucous membranes of the respiratory tract	pollen, moth balls, steel wool, fiberglass, potassium permanganate	Wear dust mask and gloves. Practice extra care when handling these materials.	Go to your teacher for first aid.
CHEMICAL	Chemicals can react with and destroy tissue and other materials	bleaches such as hydrogen peroxide; acids such as sulfuric acid, hydrochloric acid; bases such as ammonia, sodium hydroxide	Wear goggles, gloves, and an apron.	Immediately flush the affected area with water and notify your teacher.
TOXIC	Substance may be poisonous if touched, inhaled, or swallowed.	mercury, many metal compounds, iodine, poinsettia plant parts	Follow your teacher's instructions.	Always wash hands thoroughly after use. Go to your teacher for first aid.
FLAMMABLE	Flammable chemicals may be ignited by open flame, spark, or exposed heat.	alcohol, kerosene, potassium permanganate	Avoid open flames and heat when using flammable chemicals.	Notify your teacher immediately. Use fire safety equipment if applicable.
OPEN FLAME	Open flame in use, may cause fire.	hair, clothing, paper, synthetic materials	Tie back hair and loose clothing. Follow teacher's instruction on lighting and extinguishing flames.	Notify your teacher immediately. Use fire safety equipment if applicable.

Eye Safety
Proper eye protection should be worn at all times by anyone performing or observing science activities.

Clothing Protection
This symbol appears when substances could stain or burn clothing.

Animal Safety
This symbol appears when safety of animals and students must be ensured.

Handwashing
After the lab, wash hands with soap and water before removing goggles.

McGraw Hill Glencoe

New York, New York Columbus, Ohio Chicago, Illinois Peoria, Illinois Woodland Hills, California

Glencoe Science

Physical Science with Earth Science

Moonrise over a rocky Pacific coast serves as the background for a color-enhanced image that shows the emulsifying property of a detergent and a computer-generated model of the chemical structure of vitamin B_6.

Glencoe

The McGraw·Hill Companies

Send all inquiries to:
Glencoe/McGraw-Hill
8787 Orion Place
Columbus, OH 43240-4027

ISBN: 0-07-868554-0 (Student Edition)
ISBN: 0-07-868555-9 (Teacher Wraparound Edition)

Printed in the United States of America.

1 2 3 4 5 6 7 8 9 10 071/043 09 08 07 06 05

Authors

NATIONAL GEOGRAPHIC
Education Division
Washington, D.C.

Marilyn Thompson, EdD
Assistant Professor, College of Education
Arizona State University
Tempe, AZ

Ralph M. Feather, Jr., PhD
Assistant Professor, Physics Department
Indiana University of Pennsylvania
Indiana, PA

Dinah Zike
Educational Consultant
Dinah-Might Activities, Inc.
San Antonio, TX

Charles William McLaughlin, PhD
Senior Lecturer
University of Nebraska
Lincoln, NE

Teacher Advisory Board

Glencoe's National Teacher Advisory Board gave the authors, editorial staff, and the design team feedback on the content and design of the Student Edition. They were instrumental in providing valuable input toward the development of the 2006 edition of ***Glencoe Physical Science with Earth Science.*** We thank these teachers for their hard work and creative suggestions.

Melissa Shirley
Olentangy Liberty High School
Powell, OH

JoAnn Alverson
Pipestone Senior High
Pipestone, MN

Chuck Cambria
Springfield North High School
Springfield, OH

Susan Gleason
Middletown High School
Middletown, DE

Christy Saddic
Conestoga High School
Berwyn, PA

Laura Schmitmeyer
Memorial High School
St. Marys, OH

Jackie Barge
Walter Payton High School
Chicago, IL

Contributing Authors

Nancy Ross-Flanigan
Science Writer
Detroit, MI

Tina C. Hopper
Science and Health Writer
Rockwell, TX

Steve Hardesty
Adjunct Professor
Valencia Community College
Orlando, FL

Sharon Nicholson, PhD
Heinz and Katharina Lettau Professor of Climatology
Meteorology Department
Florida State University
Tallahassee, FL

Margaret K. Zorn
Science Writer
Yorktown, VA

Consultants

SCIENCE

Jack Cooper
Ennis High School
Ennis, TX

Elle Feth, MS
Columbus State Community College
Columbus, OH

David G. Haase, PhD
North Carolina State University
Raleigh, NC

William C. Keel, PhD
University of Alabama
Tuscaloosa, AL

Steve Letro
Meteorologist in Charge
WFO, National Weather Service
Jacksonville, FL

Madelaine Meek
Physics Consultant Editor
Lebanon, OH

Cheryl Wistrom, PhD
St. Joseph's College
Rensselaer, IN

Carl Zorn, PhD
Staff Scientist
Jefferson Laboratory
Newport News, VA

MATH

Michael Hopper, DEng.
Manager of Aircraft Certification
L-3 Communications
Greenville, TX

READING

Constance Cain, EdD
Literacy Coordinator
University of Central Florida
Tallahassee, FL

Maria Grant, EdD
Hoover High School
San Diego State University
San Diego, CA

ReLeah Lent, MS
Literacy Coordinator
University of Central Florida
Tallahassee, FL

SAFETY

Jack A. Gerlovich
Professor Science Education Safety
Drake University
Des Moines, IA

Denis McElroy
Assistant Professor Technology Education
Graceland University
Independence, MO

LAB TESTERS

Timothy Eimer
Phil-Mont Christina Academy
Erdenheim, PA

Nicholas Hainen
Worthington High School, Retired
Worthington, OH

James Marshall
Ohio State University
Columbus, OH

Jack Minot
Bexley High School
Bexley, OH

Reviewers

Sharla Adams
IPC Teacher
Allen High School
Allen, TX

Tom Bright
Concord High School
Charlotte, NC

Nora M. Prestinari Burchett
Saint Luke School
McLean, VA

Louise Chapman
Mainland High School
Daytona Beach, FL

Obioma Chukwu
J.H. Rose High School
Greenville, NC

Sandra Curtis
Atlantic High School
Port Orange, FL

Inga Dainton
Merrilville High School
Merrilville, IN

Robin Dillon
Hanover Central High School
Cedar Lake, IN

Dwight Dutton
East Chapel Hill High School
Chapel Hill, NC

Tracy Ebert
Robert Hungerford Preparatory High School
Eatonville, FL

Carolyn Elliott
South Iredell High School
Statesville, NC

Sueanne Esposito
Tipton High School
Tipton, IN

Kye Ewing
The Star Farm
Venus, FL

George Gabb
Great Bridge Middle School
Chesapeake Public Schools
Chesapeake, VA

Jan Gilliland
Alonso High School
Tampa, FL

Erick Hueck
Miami Senior High School
Miami, FL

Felecia Joiner
Judson High School
Converse, TX

Joe Kowalski
James "Nikki" Rowe High School
McAllen, TX

Bernie Leverett
Sublette High School
Sublette, KS

Jeff McKay
Spruce Creek High School
Port Orange, FL

Mike McKee
Cypress Creek High School
Orlando, FL

Armando S Miccoli, III
Adairsville High School
Adairsville, GA

Jane Nelson
University High School
Orlando, FL

Jim Nelson
University High School
Orlando, FL

Alicia K. Parker
New Smyrna Beach High School
New Smyrna Beach, FL

Annette Parrott
Lakeside High School
Atlanta, GA

Tom Schultz
Charlevoix High School
Charlevoix, MI

Ben Stofcheck
Citrus County Schools
Inverness, FL

Clabe Webb
Permian High School
Ector County ISD
Odessa, TX

Kim Wimpey
North Gwinnett High School
Suwanee, GA

Teacher Handbook

Table of Contents

Dynamic Instruction

The consistent instructional strategies in each chapter strengthen students' learning—from the beginning of each chapter where students see "Chapter Preview," to the end where they have a chance to test the knowledge they have acquired and prepare for the next lesson.

Chapter Preview at the beginning of each chapter introduces the main concepts.

Science Journal promotes writing and critical-thinking skills.

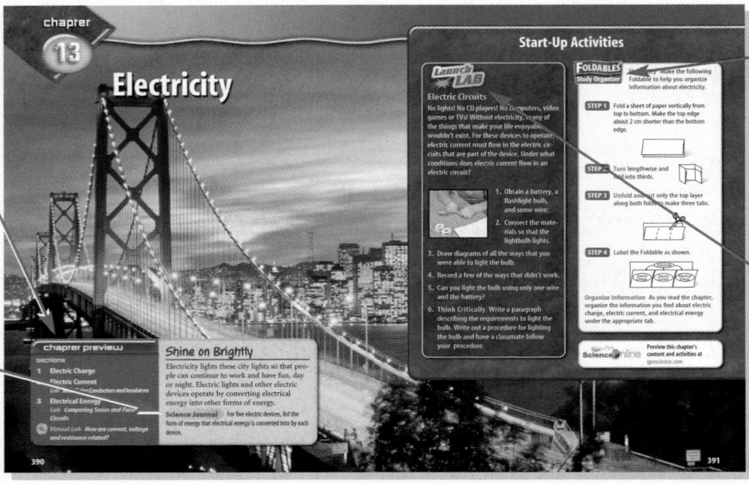

Dinah Zike's Foldables™ let students create interactive study guides.

Launch Lab gives students an opportunity to explore new ideas at the beginning of the chapter.

What You'll Learn at the beginning of each section introduces the main concepts.

Why It's Important provides an answer to "Why do we have to learn this?"

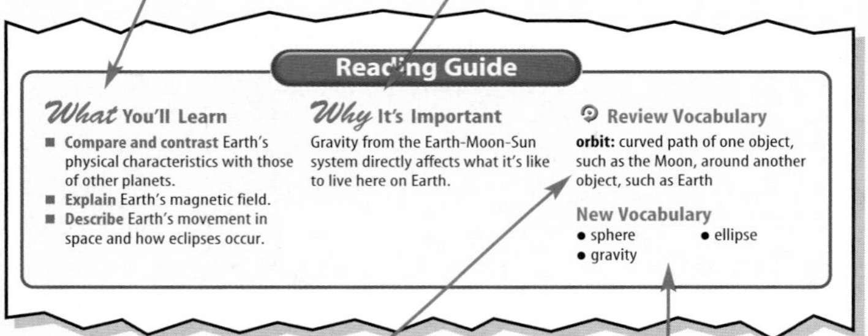

Reading Guide

What You'll Learn
- **Compare and contrast** Earth's physical characteristics with those of other planets.
- **Explain** Earth's magnetic field.
- **Describe** Earth's movement in space and how eclipses occur.

Why It's Important
Gravity from the Earth-Moon-Sun system directly affects what it's like to live here on Earth.

Review Vocabulary
orbit: curved path of one object, such as the Moon, around another object, such as Earth

New Vocabulary
- sphere
- ellipse
- gravity

Review Vocabulary reviews a term that helps students better understand section content.

New Vocabulary highlights new terms students will learn in the section.

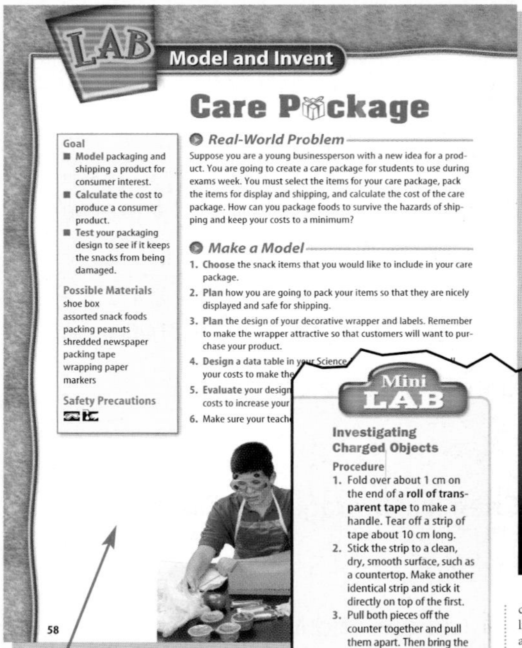

LAB Model and Invent

Care Package

Goal
- **Model** packaging and shipping a product for consumer interest.
- **Calculate** the cost to produce a consumer product.
- **Test** your packaging design to see if it keeps the snacks from being damaged.

Possible Materials
shoe box
assorted snack foods
packing peanuts
shredded newspaper
packing tape
wrapping paper
markers

Safety Precautions

Real-World Problem
Suppose you are a young businessperson with a new idea for a product. You are going to create a care package for students to use during exams week. You must select the items for your care package, pack the items for display and shipping, and calculate the cost of the care package. How can you package foods to survive the hazards of shipping and keep your costs to a minimum?

Make a Model
1. **Choose** the snack items that you would like to include in your care package.
2. **Plan** how you are going to pack your items so that they are nicely displayed and safe for shipping.
3. **Plan** the design of your decorative wrapper and labels. Remember to make the wrapper attractive so that customers will want to purchase your product.
4. **Design** a data table in your Science ... your costs to make the ...
5. **Evaluate** your design ... costs to increase your ...
6. Make sure your teach...

58

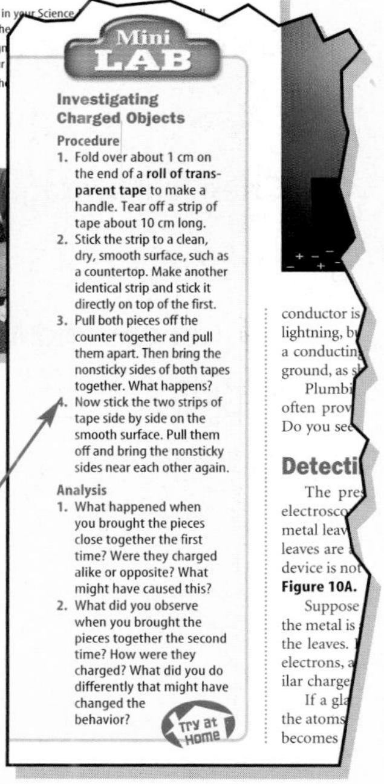

Mini LAB

Investigating Charged Objects

Procedure
1. Fold over about 1 cm on the end of a **roll of transparent tape** to make a handle. Tear off a strip of tape about 10 cm long.
2. Stick the strip to a clean, dry, smooth surface, such as a countertop. Make another identical strip and stick it directly on top of the first.
3. Pull both pieces off the counter together and pull them apart. Then bring the nonsticky sides of both tapes together. What happens?
4. Now stick the two strips of tape side by side on the smooth surface. Pull them off and bring the nonsticky sides near each other again.

Analysis
1. What happened when you brought the pieces close together the first time? Were they charged alike or opposite? What might have caused this?
2. What did you observe when you brought the pieces together the second time? How were they charged? What did you do differently that might have changed the behavior?

Try at Home

Labs Whether students are designing their own experiments or following well-tested procedures, they'll learn and practice science processes.

MiniLABs offer students quick and easy-to-do ways to clarify concepts and reinforce skills.

Multilevel Review and Assessment

Each chapter provides five pages of review and testing to help you evaluate students' knowledge and ability to apply science concepts.

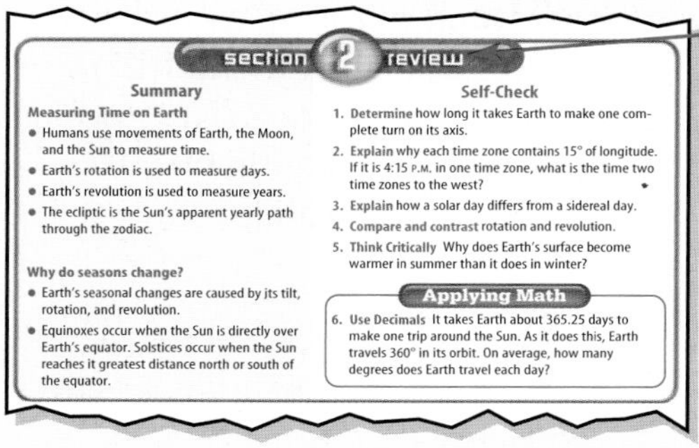

Section Review

- Summary pinpoints important concepts in the section.
- Skill-based questions promote critical thinking skills.

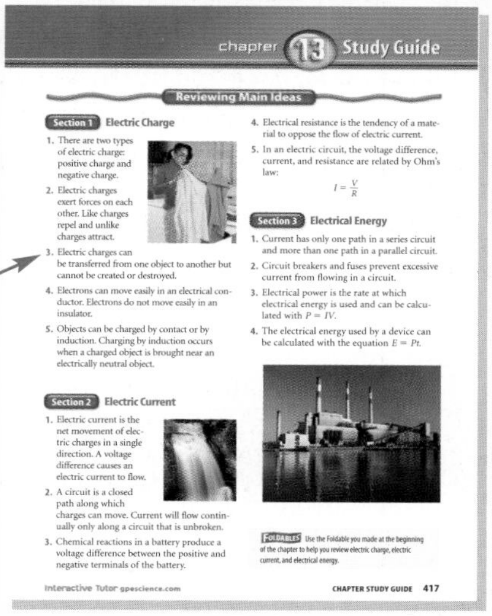

Study Guide

- Main idea summary of each section
- Concept mapping activity to help students visualize the main ideas

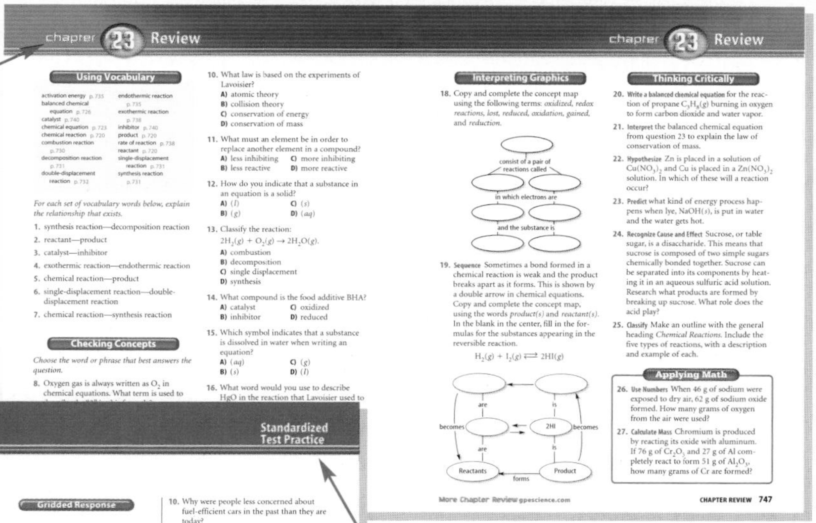

Chapter Review

- Using Vocabulary
- Checking Concepts
- Thinking Critically
- Performance Activities
- Applying Math

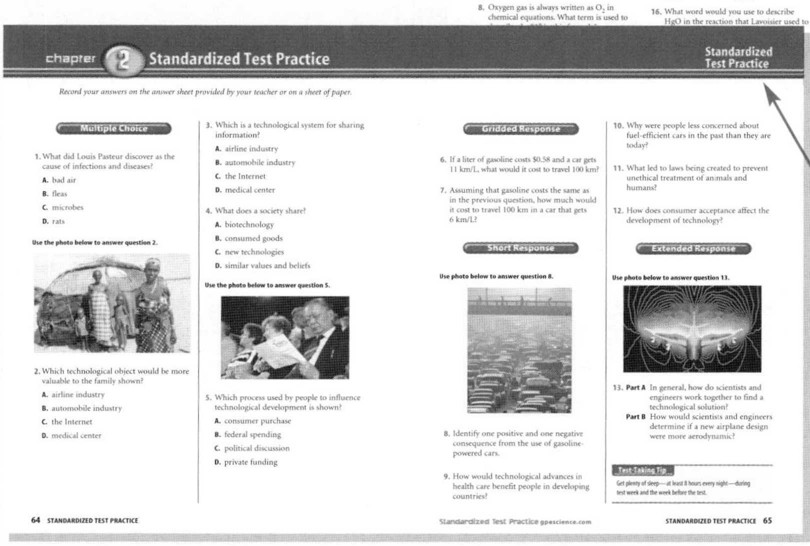

Standardized Test Practice

- Multiple Choice
- Gridded Response
- Short Response
- Extended Response

Time-Saving Teacher Resources

Glencoe Science provides an extensive array of support materials and resources designed to help you create and customize your science course quickly and easily.

FAST FILE Chapter Resources

For each chapter, Chapter Resources contain key reproducible masters along with additional teaching strategies, teacher support, and answer keys.

Reproducible Student Resources include:

- Worksheets for all MiniLABs and Labs
- *Directed Reading for Content Mastery* (in English and Spanish), *Reinforcement* and *Enrichment* worksheets for each chapter
- *Section Focus, Teaching,* and *Assessment Transparencies* masters
- Chapter Review and Chapter Test masters

Teacher Support and Planning includes:

- Additional student preparation materials for each chapter
- Spanish Resources provide translations of all objectives, vocabulary, and main ideas
- Answer keys and teaching strategies

TeacherWorks™

This CD-ROM is your all-in-one teacher resource center. Personalize a lesson plan, access resources from the *Teacher Wraparound Edition*, connect to the Internet, or make a to-do list. These are only a few of the many features that can assist you in the planning and organizing of your lessons.

Includes:

- A calendar feature
- Access to all program blackline masters
- Standards correlations and more

Teacher Wraparound Edition

The *Teacher Wraparound Edition* is your key to the teaching resources available. In addition to teaching strategies and suggestions, the *Teacher Wraparound Edition* provides a guide for all print and software materials available for each lesson.

Transparencies

- Section Focus Transparency
- Assessment Transparency
- Teaching Transparency
- Transparency masters and worksheets

ExamView® *Pro Testmaker* CD-ROM

- Create, edit, and customize tests
- Create multiple versions of tests
- Translate tests from English to Spanish and vice versa
- Build tests aligned with state standards

Video Labs

- Step-by-step lab procedures for selected *Student Edition* labs
- Lab safety skills
- Teacher support
- Troubleshooting advice

Technology Support

StudentWorks Plus

This CD-ROM is a valuable resource for students to access content online and use online resources to continue learning chapter concepts.

Includes:

- Complete *Student Edition* on CD-ROM
- Full read of *Student Edition* in English and summaries of each chapter in Spanish
- Links to online activities and resources
- Access to all student worksheets

INTERACTIVE CHALKBOARD PowerPoint® Presentations

This CD-ROM brings Microsoft® PowerPoint® presentations right to your door. With the large number of graphics provided, students can use a visual approach to learning chapter content.

Includes:

- A pre-made presentation for every chapter
- Image bank and interactive graphics
- Animations and audio clips
- All new section and chapter questions
- Standardized test practice
- Transparencies
- Foldables™ directions
- Links to gpescience.com

TechCONNECT

Using TechCONNECT, your students develop computer skills as they reinforce basic language arts, math, science, and social studies concepts. TechCONNECT provides a solution for incorporating technology in the classroom, as states and districts fulfill *No Child Left Behind* (NCLB) requirements. This legislation sets the goal that "every student be technologically literate by the time the student finishes the eighth grade" and requires that states "improve the capacity to integrate technology into their curriculum and instruction."

Visit the Web site for a FREE tour—techconnect.glencoe.com

Virtual Labs CD-ROM Program

The *Virtual Labs* CD-ROM contains a collection of labs that allow students to complete labs that are too expensive, take too long to complete, or might be too dangerous in a classroom laboratory.

Science Online

gpescience.com

For students:

- Prescreened Internet sites (Web links) that correlate to text chapters
- Interactive activities that review chapter concepts
- Internet Labs where students can share data with each other
- Access to *Student Edition* online
- Interactive self-check quizzes for each chapter section as well as the entire chapter

For teachers:

- *WebQuest* activities
- Teacher Forum for teachers to share activities and ideas

McGraw Hill Learning Network mhln.com

mhln.com is an online teaching and learning space for teachers, students, and parents.

- For students, mhln.com provides an interactive online textbook. This means a lighter student backpack.
- For teachers, mhln.com provides a customizable online learning space for posting assignments, web-based instruction, student resources, and a class calendar.
- For parents, mhln.com provides tools to help their child succeed in school. Parents have instant access to their child's progress and daily assignments.

Help Your Students with Reading and Writing

Glencoe Science increases science literacy, improves reading comprehension, and deepens students' understanding of ideas and concepts. The reading strategies are active, constructive, and engaging.

In the *Student Edition*

Reading Checks stimulate quick recall and keep students focused on the main idea.

✔ **Reading Check**

Caption Questions offer a visual approach to learning. Students are asked to recall what they have read by interpreting the visual.

> **Figure 18** Three allotropes of carbon are depicted here.
> **Identify** *the geometric shapes that make up each allotrope.*

Science Journals provide opportunities to write responses to questions that require critical thinking, to conduct research and write about it, or to practice creative writing skills.

Skill Words such as *compare and contrast, describe, explain,* and *state* are included in the Self Check at the end of each section, in the goals of each Lab, and in the chapter reviews.

Technology Support

Vocabulary PuzzleMaker allows you to create crossword puzzles, jumble puzzles, or word searches in minutes to review chapter vocabulary. The puzzles can be printed or played on the computer screen.

Reading Support Workbooks

Reading Essentials provides summaries of each section of the textbook, focusing on the most important scientific concepts.

Reading and Writing Skills Activities provides teachers with effective strategies for building students' skills in reading and writing about science.

Science Notebook presents a step-by-step approach to improving student note-taking ability with strategies based on the Cornell note-taking model. This workbook builds scientific and academic vocabulary skills, scientific writing skills, and ability in reading for critical content. Bloom's Hierarchy of Learning is used to indicate strategy levels.

In the *Teacher Wraparound Edition*

Project CRISS™ (**Cr**eating **I**ndependence through **S**tudent-Owned **S**trategies) strategies are highlighted in the Unit Openers where an activity is supplied that relates to unit content. For more information about Project CRISS™, visit www.projectcriss.com.

Use Science Words features encourage students to look up biology terms. Use these as a pre-reading activity, or have students keep a vocabulary journal.

> **Use Science Words**
> **Word Origin** Have students find the origin of the word *friction.* The word friction comes from the Latin word fricare, which means "to rub."

Additional Science Journal writing activities promote writing and critical thinking skills and extend the *Student Edition* journaling activity.

Active Reading Strategies utilize a variety of learning styles, and encourage cooperative learning and intrapersonal reflection on chapter content.

Making Concept Maps and Charts

Bubble Map Students brainstorm and organize words in clusters to describe concepts.

Flow Chart Students logically analyze and draw a sequence of events.

Cause-and-Effect Chart Students visually represent the causes and effects of an event or process.

Supporting-Idea Chart Students make a concept map to analyze relationships between a whole and its parts.

Network-Tree Concept Map Students show a hierarchy and use branching procedures.

Events-Chain Concept Map Students order steps or stages in a linear procedure.

Cycle Concept Map Students show how a series of events interact.

Spider Concept Map Students use for brainstorming and grouping nonrelated terms to a central idea.

Using the Science Journal

Double-Reference Journal Students read and record ideas.

Metacognition Students analyze what and how they have learned.

Learning Journal Students create notes and reflect on the content.

Problem-Solution Journal Students analyze problems and suggest workable solutions.

Speculation About Effects/Prediction Journal Students examine events and speculate about their possible long-term effects.

Synthesis Journal Students reflect on a project, a paper, or a performance task and plan how to apply what they have learned to their own lives.

Reflective Journal Students identify what they learned in an activity and record responses.

Quickwrites Students use spontaneous writing to discover what they already know.

Collaborative Learning Strategies

Pair of Pairs Partners respond to a question and compare their response to other pairs and to the class.

Write-Draw-Discuss Students write about and draw a picture of a concept, then share it with the class.

Active Reading

Learning Reading Have students divide a sheet of paper in half. Have them record research notes, lecture notes, and vocabulary terms related to the laws of motion in the left column. Tell them to use the right column to respond, interpret, question, and analyze left-column entries. L2 **Intrapersonal**

Four-Corner Discussion The class works in four groups to debate a complex issue.

Jigsaw Students work in groups to become experts on a portion of text and share what they've learned with the class.

Buddy Interviews Students interview one another to find out what strategies they use to learn the text.

Reciprocal Teaching Students take turns reading a section of text, retelling it in their own words, then asking questions about it.

News Summary Students are given several minutes to summarize, retell, or analyze an activity for a "TV" audience.

ReQuest The teacher reads aloud an article or story. Student pairs then construct discussion questions and review the content.

Assessment

Glencoe Science offers the Glencoe Assessment Advantage, a system designed to give you all the tools you need to prepare your students for success in any testing situation.

In the *Student Edition*

Section Review and **Applying Math** questions appear in every chapter.

> **Applying Math**
>
> **5. Solve One-Step Equations** The overall charge on the polyatomic sulfate ion, found in some acids, is 2^{-}. Its formula is SO_4^{2-}. If the oxygen ion has a 2^{-} oxidation number, determine the oxidation number of sulfur in this polyatomic ion.

Chapter Review questions help you evaluate students' knowledge and ability to apply science concepts.

Standardized Test Practice questions at the end of each chapter provide students with additional opportunities to practice their test-taking skills.

In the *Teacher Wraparound Edition*

Assessments located throughout the *Teacher Wraparound Edition* provide methods for assessing students' comprehension with Performance, Process, and Content exercises.

> **✔ Assessment**
>
> **Content** Many benefits result from nuclear applications in medicine, but there are disadvantages, too. Ask students to write newspaper articles explaining how radiation can cause as well as treat cancer. Possible answers: It can cause mutations in cell structures, leading to tumor formation, or it can kill cancer cells. Use **PASC,** p. 141.

Teacher Classroom Resources

Performance Assessment in the Science Classroom

- Guidelines for assessing the performance of a task
- Reproducible activities for evaluating students
- Sample rubrics and checklists

***Fast File* Chapter Resources** provides six pages of assessement for every chapter including *Testing Concepts, Applying Concepts,* and *Writing Skills.*

Technology Support

MindJogger Videoquizzes are interactive video quizzes set in game show format. Each is designed for the full range of student learning styles.

***ExamView® Pro Testmaker* CD-ROM** for Windows® and Macintosh® provides an easy way to create, edit, and customize your tests. Select your own test items by State Standard, or write and edit your own. Translate tests from English to Spanish and vice versa.

Science Holistic Rubrics

The scoring rubrics below describe the characteristics of the answers required for each possible score for Short- and Extended-Response tasks.

Short-Response Tasks	
2 Points:	A score of two indicates that the student has demonstrated a thorough understanding of the scientific concepts and/or procedures embodied in the task. The student has completed the task correctly, in a scientifically sound manner. When required, student explanations and/or interpretations are clear and complete. The response may contain minor flaws that do not detract from the demonstration of a thorough understanding.
1 Point:	A score of one indicates that the student has provided a response that is only partially correct. For example, the student may arrive at an acceptable conclusion or provide an adequate interpretation, but may demonstrate some misunderstanding of the underlying scientific concepts and/or procedures. Conversely, a student may arrive at an unacceptable conclusion or provide a faulty interpretation, but could have applied appropriate and scientifically sound concepts and/or procedures.
0 Points:	A score of zero indicates that the student has provided a response that demonstrates no understanding of the science embodied in the task. The student explanation may be incorrect, uninterpretable, or contain clear misunderstandings of the underlying scientific concepts and/or procedures.

Extended-Response Tasks	
4 Points:	A score of four indicates that the student has demonstrated a thorough understanding of the scientific concepts and/or procedures embodied in the task. The student has completed the task correctly, used scientifically sound procedures, and provided clear and complete explanations and interpretations. The response may contain minor flaws that do not detract from a demonstration of a thorough understanding.
3 Points:	A score of three indicates that the student has demonstrated an understanding of the scientific concepts and/or procedures embodied in the task. The student's response to the task is essentially correct, but the scientific procedures, explanations, and/or interpretations provided are not thorough. The response may contain minor flaws that reflect inattentiveness or indicate some misunderstanding of the underlying scientific concepts and/or procedures.
2 Points:	A score of two indicates that the student has demonstrated only a partial understanding of the scientific concepts and/or procedures embodied in the task. Although the student may have arrived at an acceptable conclusion or provided an adequate interpretation of the task, the student's work lacks an essential understanding of the underlying scientific concepts and/or procedures. The response may contain errors related to misunderstanding important aspects of the task, misuse of scientific procedures/processes, or faulty interpretations of results.
1 Point:	A score of one indicates that the student has demonstrated a very limited understanding of the scientific concepts and/or procedures embodied in the task. The student's response is incomplete and exhibits many flaws. Although the student's response has addressed some of the conditions of the task, the student has reached an inadequate conclusion and/or provided reasoning that is faulty or incomplete. The response exhibits many flaws or may be incomplete.
0 Points:	A score of zero indicates that the student has provided a response that demonstrates no understanding of the science embodied in the task. The student explanation may be incorrect, uninterpretable, or contain clear misunderstandings of the underlying scientific concepts and/or procedures.

Meeting Individual Needs

Teaching Strategies

Following each suggested assessment and activity, ability levels are supplied to accommodate all students.

- LS Multiple Learning Styles logos are used throughout the text to indicate strategies that address different learning styles.
- L1 Level 1 activities should be appropriate for students with learning difficulties.
- L2 Level 2 activities should be within the ability range of all students.
- L3 Level 3 activities are designed for above-average students.
- ELL English-Language Learners activities should be within the ability range of English-Language Learners or students who speak English as a second language (ESL).
- COOP LEARN Cooperative Learning activities are designed for small group work.
- PBL Problem-Based Learning activities apply real-world situations to learning.
- P Portfolio strategies represent student products that can be placed into a best-work portfolio.

Identifying Misconceptions

These short, diagnostic, and perscriptive lessons target common science misconceptions.

IDENTIFYING **Misconceptions**

Necessary Metals Students may think it strange that metals are needed by the body. Explain that the metals calcium, potassium, and sodium, for example, help transmit electrical signals within the nervous system.

Multiple Learning Styles

Look for these italicized designations under various activities to help you target your lessons to each student's preferred learning style.

- ***Kinesthetic*** learners learn through touch, movement, and manipulating objects.
- ***Visual-Spatial*** learners think in terms of images, illustrations, and models.
- ***Interpersonal*** learners understand and work well with other people.
- ***Intrapersonal*** learners can analyze their own strengths and weaknesses and may prefer to work on their own.
- ***Linguistic*** learners write clearly and easily understand the written word.
- ***Logical-Mathematical*** learners understand numbers easily and have highly-developed reasoning skills.

Daily Interventions

Found at the end of each chapter section, this feature is designed to intercept students who are struggling and prescribe a system to help them get back on track. *Reteach* provides reinforcement of the section's concepts through visual activities.

DAILY INTERVENTION

Check for Understanding

Kinesthetic Have a student light a match and allow it to burn. Also, place an ice cube in a glass container and allow it to melt. Have students explain what type of changes took place with each item and describe the final properties of each.

Differentiated Instruction

These activities present various teaching strategies designed to help you meet the special needs of students with learning disabilities, physical challenges, visual impairment, and hearing impairment. Challenge activities provide opportunities for students who excel to engage in activities and research projects that extend the chapter's concepts. English-language learners in the classroom will also find exercises that bridge the gap between language barriers and the chapter content.

Differentiated Instruction

English-Language Learners Have students make flashcards with the name of a gland on one side and the hormone it produces on the other. Student pairs can quiz each other using the flashcards.

Cultural Diversity

These readings provide insights into the unique ways in which people of different ethnicities and cultural heritage have approached science. The intent of these features is to build awareness and appreciation for the global community in which we live.

Cultural Diversity

Tsunami! Tsunamis occur in many areas around the world and have been reported since ancient times. One of the earliest record tsunamis struck Syria around 2,000 B.C. Thera, one of the Cyclades Islands in the Mediterranean, may be the remnant of a volcano that erupted—causing tsunamis that ended the Minoan civilization on Crete. Tsunami is a Japanese word for "harbor wave." Many have struck the Japanese shore. Because Japan is an island nation, the threat of tsunamis is a national safety concern. Today, by using expected tsunami characteristics, the Japan Meteorological Agency can forecast tsunami heights for the Japanese coastline. This provides residents with the knowledge necessary to move a safe distance away from the shore.

Inquiry-Based Science

The call for more inquiry-based science by the *National Science Education Standards* has been met by Glencoe Science.

Glencoe Science recognizes the importance of conducting inquiry-based science activities in the classroom. The process of doing inquiry models actual science practice, encouraging problem-solving strategies and developing critical thinking skills. Inquiry gets students actively involved in the learning process by allowing them to determine materials, procedures, or the topics and questions they want to investigate.

Inquiry can range from a very structured activity for those students who need more guidance to a more open-ended approach where students lead the investigations. Glencoe Science recognizes that the inquiry activities suggested will not look the same in every classroom. We encourage teachers to modify the suggested activities in a manner that best supports your students.

Glencoe also provides teachers with Alternative Inquiry Labs, teaching strategies or suggestions for making existing labs more inquiry-based.

Alternative Inquiry Lab

Extend the Experience To make this Lab an Inquiry Lab, have students examine the magnetic field around the motor, using a compass or iron fillings. Test the armature and rotor before final assembly, as it will be difficult to fit the compass inside the motor. Encourage students to make various adaptations to the motor. Ask them to figure out how to make the motor spin the other way, spin faster, and spin slower. How could the motor be turned into a generator? How could they make the motor consume less power? Finally, students might research how these issues are handled by industry or other questions they find interesting.

Foldables™

Foldables™ are easy-to-make, three-dimensional, interactive graphic organizers that students create out of simple sheets of paper. These unique hands-on tools for studying and reviewing were created exclusively for Glencoe by education specialist Dinah Zike.

Research Behind Foldables™

According to research (Bransford, 1979; Corno, 1994), study strategies help students understand, organize, remember and apply new information presented in science textbooks. Some study strategies include concept mapping, highlighting, outlining, note taking, summarizing, and underlining (Peverly, Brobst, Graham & Shaw, 2003). Glencoe Science offers Dinah Zike's Foldables™ Study Organizers as an organizational tool and study guide for students.

Build Prereading Skills

- Encourages students to prepare for what they will be learning
- Gives students an opportunity to recall what they already know about a subject

Encourage Active Reading and Writing

- Practices basic reading and writing skills
- Develops skills in finding and reporting main ideas
- Organizes information
- Reviews key vocabulary terms

Summarize Content for Review

- Creates a comprehensive, interactive snapshot of the chapter
- Provides preparation support for chapter, unit, and end-of-course exams, as well as standardized tests

FOLDABLES™ Study Organizer

Acids, Bases, and Salts The very essence of life, DNA, is an acid. You also may be familiar with ascorbic acid, or vitamin C. Make the following Foldable to compare and contrast the characteristics of acids, bases, and salts.

STEP 1 **Fold** one sheet of paper lengthwise.

STEP 2 **Fold** into thirds.

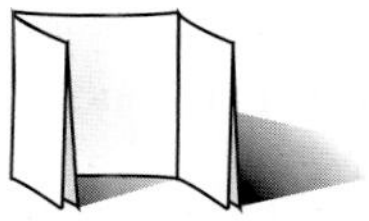

STEP 3 **Unfold** and **draw** overlapping ovals. Cut the top sheet along the folds.

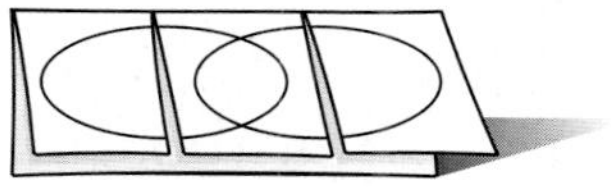

STEP 4 **Label** the ovals *Acids, Salts,* and *Bases.*

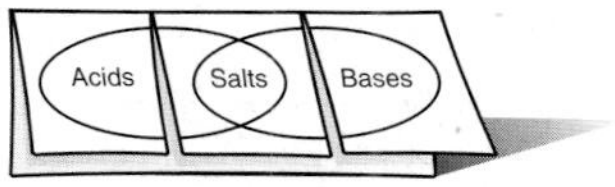

Construct a Venn Diagram As you read the chapter, list the characteristics of acids, bases, and salts under the appropriate tabs.

Dinah Zike's *Teaching with Foldables™ Science*

- Sample presentations of Foldables™ instructions
- Ideas on how to incorporate Foldables™ into your lessons
- Easy-to-read folding instruction pages

Educational Partnerships

NATIONAL GEOGRAPHIC

Some topics in the chapter either require or benefit from a larger, more detailed visual explanation. The National Geographic Society has created *Visualizing* features that call out an important concept from the chapter and illustrate it in a way that will inform, excite, and motivate your students.

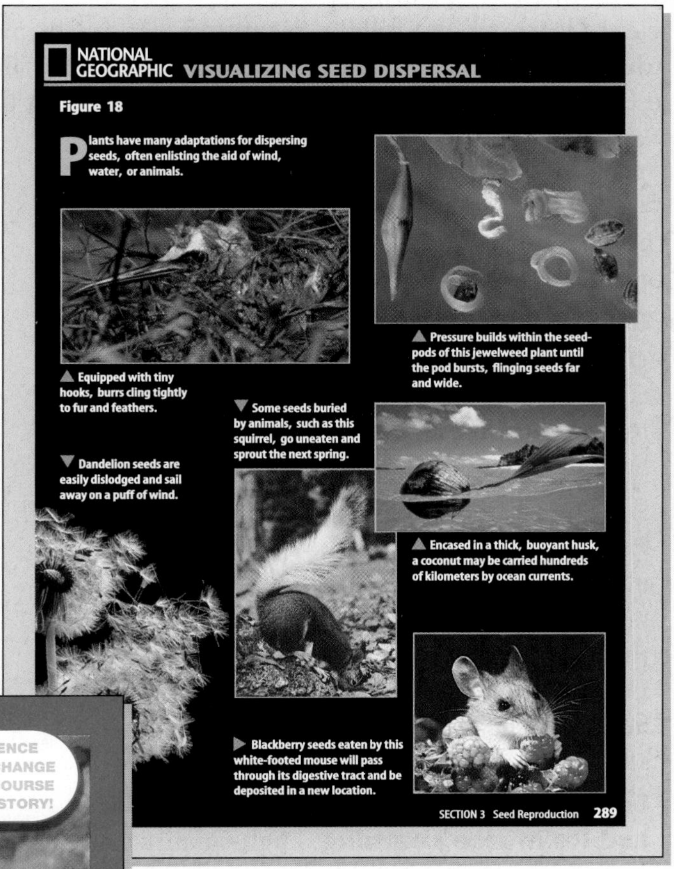
NATIONAL GEOGRAPHIC VISUALIZING SEED DISPERSAL

Figure 18

Plants have many adaptations for dispersing seeds, often enlisting the aid of wind, water, or animals.

▲ Equipped with tiny hooks, burrs cling tightly to fur and feathers.

▲ Pressure builds within the seedpods of this jewelweed plant until the pod bursts, flinging seeds far and wide.

▼ Some seeds buried by animals, such as this squirrel, go uneaten and sprout the next spring.

▼ Dandelion seeds are easily dislodged and sail away on a puff of wind.

▲ Encased in a thick, buoyant husk, a coconut may be carried hundreds of kilometers by ocean currents.

▶ Blackberry seeds eaten by this white-footed mouse will pass through its digestive tract and be deposited in a new location.

SECTION 3 Seed Reproduction 289

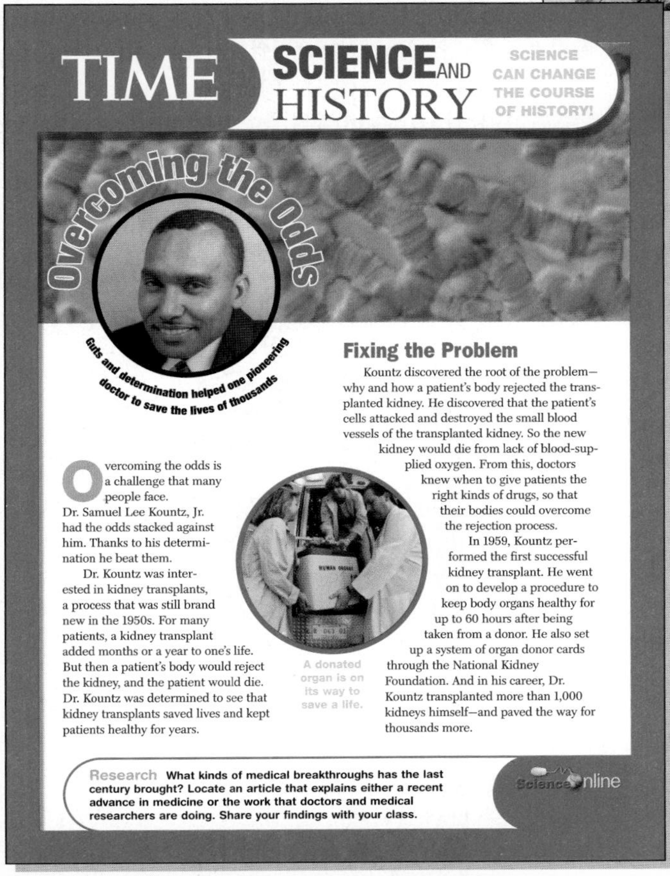
TIME SCIENCE AND HISTORY

SCIENCE CAN CHANGE THE COURSE OF HISTORY!

Overcoming the Odds

Guts and determination helped one pioneering doctor to save the lives of thousands

Overcoming the odds is a challenge that many people face. Dr. Samuel Lee Kountz, Jr. had the odds stacked against him. Thanks to his determination he beat them.

Dr. Kountz was interested in kidney transplants, a process that was still brand new in the 1950s. For many patients, a kidney transplant added months or a year to one's life. But then a patient's body would reject the kidney, and the patient would die. Dr. Kountz was determined to see that kidney transplants saved lives and kept patients healthy for years.

A donated organ is on its way to save a life.

Fixing the Problem

Kountz discovered the root of the problem—why and how a patient's body rejected the transplanted kidney. He discovered that the patient's cells attacked and destroyed the small blood vessels of the transplanted kidney. So the new kidney would die from lack of blood-supplied oxygen. From this, doctors knew when to give patients the right kinds of drugs, so that their bodies could overcome the rejection process.

In 1959, Kountz performed the first successful kidney transplant. He went on to develop a procedure to keep body organs healthy for up to 60 hours after being taken from a donor. He also set up a system of organ donor cards through the National Kidney Foundation. And in his career, Dr. Kountz transplanted more than 1,000 kidneys himself—and paved the way for thousands more.

Research What kinds of medical breakthroughs has the last century brought? Locate an article that explains either a recent advance in medicine or the work that doctors and medical researchers are doing. Share your findings with your class.

Science Online

TIME

TIME Magazine brings science topics and history together to further explain the chapter's main ideas and show how science relates to real life.

Research-Based Learning Strategies

Glencoe Science incorporates the most current and applicable educational research on science learning and follows recommendations from the American Association for the Advancement of Science and the National Science Teachers Association. The following research-based strategies can be found throughout the text.

Learning Strategies

The following research-based strategies can be found throughout the text:

- **Using Prior Knowledge** Glencoe Science encourages students to use their prior knowledge to learn information because this adds relevance to the material. Students are referred back to other parts of the text or to their own real-life experiences.
- **Practicing Important Tasks** By offering students an opportunity to practice important tasks using a variety of labs and activities in the *Student Edition, Teacher Wraparound Edition,* ancillaries and technology, Glencoe Science makes learning fun and relevant for students.
- **Using Visuals to Communicate, Organize, and Reinforce Learning** High-quality art and photos throughout the text communicate concepts more efficiently and reinforce learning, while allowing students to organize information.
- **Motivating Students to Achieve** Active strategies and real-world experiences motivate students to achieve. Throughout Glencoe's programs, students are encouraged to apply their knowledge in ways that will motivate them to learn.
- **Developing Decoding and Reading Comprehension Strategies** Throughout the text, students are supplied with caption questions, reading checks, and other strategies to aid in comprehension.
- **Using Study Strategies** Through the use of highlighting, outlining, note-taking, summarizing, and other such strategies, students can monitor their own progress and organize information more effectively, thereby increasing their scientific literacy. These strategies are found throughout the text and ancillaries.

The use of these strategies within Glencoe Science will help teachers to achieve the goals set forth by the *National Science Education Standards.*

White Paper

The Glencoe Science White Paper outlines the educational strategies on which this program was based. This document provides specific examples from the *Student Edition, Teacher Wraparound Edition,* ancillary program, and technology resources, highlighting extensive use of educationally sound strategies that help students learn science.

Spencer Grant/PhotoEdit, Inc.

Field Research and Testing

Feedback from students, teachers, curriculum supervisors, department chairpersons, parents, learning specialists, and science content experts is invaluable in the development of Glencoe's science programs.

Prior to Publication

- Detailed classroom teacher and curriculum supervisor **surveys** are conducted by independently contracted researchers.
- A **nationwide panel** of science teachers, curriculum supervisors, and department chairpersons provide countless hours of feedback and assistance throughout program development.
- A wide range of **educator and content reviewers** provide in-depth reviews of and suggestions for manuscripts and pre-publication versions of Glencoe's science programs.
- **Face-to-face interviews** with science teachers provide insight into teachers' day-to-day challenges.

After Publication

- Field tests are conducted in which students and teachers use a pre-publication manuscript in the classroom.
- Follow-up interviews, observations, and surveys of Glencoe users provide ongoing opportunities for program development and verification of program success.

Field-Test Results

- Field-test research indicates that test scores increased among students using Glencoe's science programs.
- Nine out of ten students earned higher scores after using Glencoe programs.
- Scores improved among both male and female students.
- Scores improved among both minority and non-minority students.
- Overall, the gap closed between the average pre-test score and a perfect score. Stated differently, on average, **scores increased after students used Glencoe's science programs.**

KS Studios

National Education Standards

How Glencoe Science Aligns with the National Science Education Standards

The correlations below show the close alignment between Glencoe Science and the grade-appropriate standards. Glencoe Science allows students to discover concepts within each of the content standards and gives students opportunities to make connections among the science disciplines. Hands-on activities and inquiry-based lessons reinforce the science processes emphasized in the standards.

Correlation of *Physical Science with Earth Science* to the National Science Education Standards.

Content Standard	Chapter and Section
(UCP) Unifying Concepts and Processes	
1. Systems, order, and organization	1-1, 1-2, 1-3, 2-1, 2-2, 2-3, 3-1, 3-2, 3-3, 4-1, 4-2, 4-3, 5-1, 5-2, 6-1, 6-2, 6-3, 7-1, 7-2, 7-3, 8-1, 8-2, 8-3, 8-4, 9-1, 9-2, 9-3, 9-4, 10-1, 10-2, 10-3, 11-1, 11-2, 11-3, 11-4, 12-1, 12-2, 12-3, 12-4, 14-1, 14-2, 14-3, 15-1, 15-2, 15-3, 16-1, 16-2, 16-3, 17-1, 17-2, 17-3, 17-4, 18-1, 18-2, 19-1, 19-2, 19-3, 20-1, 20-2, 20-3, 20-4, 21-1, 21-2, 21-3, 21-4, 22-1, 22-2, 22-3, 23-1, 23-2, 23-3, 23-4, 24-1, 24-2, 24-3, 24-4, 25-1, 25-2, 25-3, 25-4, 26-1, 26-2, 26-3, 26-4
2. Evidence, models, and explanation	1-1, 1-2, 1-3, 2-1, 2-2, 2-3, 3-1, 3-2, 3-3, 4-1, 4-2, 4-3, 5-1, 5-2, 6-1, 6-2, 6-3, 7-1, 7-2, 7-3, 8-1, 8-2, 8-3, 8-4, 9-1, 9-2, 9-3, 9-4, 10-1, 10-2, 10-3, 11-1, 11-2, 11-3, 11-4, 12-1, 12-2, 12-3, 12-4, 13-1, 13-2, 13-3, 14-1, 14-2, 14-3, 15-1, 15-2, 15-3, 16-1, 16-2, 16-3, 17-1, 17-2, 17-3, 17-4, 18-1, 18-2, 19-1, 19-2, 19-3, 20-1, 20-2, 20-3, 20-4, 21-1, 21-2, 21-3, 21-4, 22-1, 22-2, 22-3, 23-1, 23-2, 23-3, 23-4, 24-1, 24-2, 24-3, 24-4, 25-1, 25-2, 25-3, 25-4, 26-1, 26-2, 26-3, 26-4
3. Change, consistency, and measurement	1-1, 1-2, 1-3, 2-1, 2-2, 2-3, 3-1, 3-2, 3-3, 4-1, 4-2, 4-3, 5-1, 5-2, 6-1, 6-2, 6-3, 7-1, 7-2, 7-3, 8-1, 8-2, 8-3, 8-4, 9-1, 9-2, 9-3, 9-4, 10-1, 10-2, 10-3, 11-1, 11-2, 11-3, 11-4, 12-1, 12-2, 12-3, 12-4, 13-1, 13-2, 13-3, 14-1, 14-2, 14-3, 15-1, 15-2, 15-3, 16-1, 16-2, 16-3, 17-1, 17-2, 17-3, 17-4, 18-1, 18-2, 19-1, 19-2, 19-3, 20-1, 20-2, 20-3, 20-4, 21-1, 21-2, 21-3, 21-4, 21-3, 21-4, 22-1, 22-2, 22-3, 23-1, 23-2, 23-3, 23-4, 24-1, 24-2, 24-3, 24-4, 25-1, 25-2, 25-3, 25-4, 26-1, 26-2, 26-3, 26-4
4. Evolution and equilibrium	2-1, 2-2, 2-3, 7-3, 8-1, 8-2, 8-3, 8-4, 12-2, 12-3, 12-4, 17-4, 23-1, 23-2, 23-3, 23-4, 26-2, 26-3, 26-4
5. Form and function	1-1, 1-2, 1-3, 2-1, 2-2, 2-3, 4-1, 4-2, 4-3, 5-1, 5-2, 6-1, 6-2, 6-3, 7-1, 7-2, 7-3, 8-1, 8-2, 8-3, 8-4, 9-1, 9-2, 9-3, 9-4, 10-1, 10-2, 10-3, 11-1, 11-2, 11-3, 11-4, 12-1, 12-2, 12-3, 12-4, 13-1, 13-2, 13-3, 14-1, 14-2, 14-3, 15-1, 15-2, 15-3, 16-1, 16-2, 16-3, 17-1, 17-2, 17-3, 17-4, 18-1, 19-1, 19-2, 19-3, 20-1, 20-2, 20-3, 20-4, 22-1, 22-2, 22-3, 23-1, 23-2, 23-3, 23-4, 24-1, 24-2, 24-3, 24-4, 25-1, 25-2, 25-3, 25-4, 26-2, 26-3, 26-4
(A) Science as Inquiry	
1. Abilities necessary to do scientific inquiry	1-1, 1-2, 1-3, 2-1, 2-2, 2-3, 3-1, 3-2, 3-3, 4-1, 4-2, 4-3, 5-1, 5-2, 6-1, 6-2, 6-3, 7-1, 7-2, 7-3, 8-1, 8-2, 8-3, 8-4, 9-1, 9-2, 9-3, 9-4,10-1, 10-2, 10-3, 11-1, 11-2, 11-3, 11-4, 12-1, 12-2, 12-3, 12-4, 13-1, 13-2, 13-3, 14-1, 14-2, 14-3, 15-1, 15-2, 15-3, 16-1, 16-2, 16-3, 17-1, 17-2, 17-3, 17-4, 18-1, 19-1, 19-2, 19-3, 20-1, 20-2, 20-3, 20-4, 21-1, 21-2, 21-3, 21-4, 22-1, 22-2, 22-3, 23-1, 23-2, 23-3, 23-4, 24-1, 24-2, 24-3, 24-4, 25-1, 25-2, 25-3, 25-4, 26-1, 26-2, 26-3, 26-4
2. Understandings about scientific theory	1-1, 1-2, 1-3, 2-1, 2-2, 2-3, 3-1, 3-2, 3-3, 4-1, 4-2, 4-3, 5-1, 5-2, 6-1, 6-2, 6-3, 7-1, 7-2, 7-3, 8-1, 8-2, 8-3, 8-4, 9-1, 9-2, 9-3, 9-4, 10-1, 10-2, 10-3, 11-1, 11-2, 11-3, 11-4, 12-1, 12-2, 12-3, 12-4, 13-1, 13-2, 13-3, 14-1, 14-2, 14-3, 15-1, 15-2, 15-3, 16-1, 16-2, 16-3, 17-1, 17-2, 17-3, 17-4, 18-1, 19-1, 19-2, 19-3, 20-1, 20-2, 20-3, 20-4, 21-1, 21-2, 21-3, 21-4, 22-1, 22-2, 22-3, 23-1, 23-2, 23-3, 23-4, 24-1, 24-2, 24-3, 24-4, 25-1, 25-2, 25-3, 25-4, 26-1, 26-2, 26-3, 26-4
(B) Physical Science	
1. Structure of Atoms	16-2, 21-4, 24-1, 25-1, 25-2, 25-3, 25-4
2. Structure and properties of matter	4-1, 5-1, 5-2, 9-1, 9-2, 9-3, 9-4, 10-1, 10-2, 10-3, 11-2, 11-3, 11-4, 13-1, 13-2, 13-3, 14-1, 14-2, 14-3, 15-1, 15-2, 15-3, 16-1, 16-2, 18-1, 18-2, 19-1, 19-2, 19-3, 21-4, 22-1, 22-2, 23-1, 23-2, 23-3, 23-4, 24-1, 24-2, 24-3, 24-4, 25-1, 25-2, 25-3, 25-4, 26-1
3. Chemical reactions	18-2, 20-1, 21-1, 23-1, 23-2, 23-3, 23-4, 24-1, 24-3, 24-4
4. Motion and forces	3-1, 3-2, 3-3, 4-1, 4-2, 4-3, 5-1, 5-2, 6-1, 6-2, 6-3, 8-1, 8-3, 9-1, 9-3, 9-4, 10-1, 10-2, 10-3, 13-1, 13-2, 13-3, 14-1, 14-2, 14-3, 15-1, 15-2, 15-3, 17-2, 17-3, 22-1, 22-2, 22-3, 26-1, 25-4, 26-2
5. Conservation of energy and increase in disorder	5-2, 9-1, 9-2, 9-4, 10-1, 10-3, 19-1, 19-2, 19-3
6. Interactions of energy and matter	6-1, 6-2, 6-3, 9-1, 9-2, 9-3, 10-1, 10-2, 10-3, 11-2, 11-4, 13-3, 15-1, 15-2, 15-3, 17-2, 17-3, 18-2, 19-1, 19-2, 19-3, 22-1, 22-2, 22-3, 23-3, 23-4, 24-2, 26-4
(C) Life Science	
1. Biological Evolution	8-4
2. Matter, energy, and organization in living systems	8-4, 17-3
3. The behavior of organisms	8-4, 11-4, 17-1
(D) Earth and Space Science	
1. Energy in the Earth system	7-1, 12-1, 12-2, 12-3, 12-4, 14-1, 15-1, 16-1, 16-3, 17-1, 17-2, 17-3, 17-4, 20-1, 20-2, 20-3, 20-4, 21-2
2. Geochemical cycles	12-4, 16-1, 16-3, 17-1, 17-2, 20-1, 20-2, 20-3, 20-4, 21-2, 21-3

National Education Standards

3. The origin and evolution of the Earth system	7-1, 7-3, 8-1, 8-2, 8-3, 8-4, 12-2, 12-3, 12-4, 14-1, 16-1, 16-3, 17-4, 21-4
4. The origin and evolution of the universe	7-3, 8-1, 8-3, 8-4, 26-4
(E) Science and Technology	
1. Abilities of technological design	2-1, 2-2, 2-3, 12-2, 21-4
2. Understandings about science and technology	2-1, 2-2, 2-3
(F) Science in Personal and Social Perspectives	
1. Personal and community health	11-1, 22-2, 25-3, 25-4, 26-1, 26-2, 26-4
2. Population growth	16-2, 16-3, 26-4
3. Natural Resources	20-1
4. Environmental quality	16-2, 16-3, 17-4, 21-3
5. Natural and human-induced hazards	1-1, 2-2, 12-2, 12-4, 17-4, 21-3
6. Science and technology in local, national, and global challenges	13-3, 2-1, 2-2, 2-3, 12-2, 26-1, 26-2
(G) History and Nature of Science	
1. Science as a human endeavor	22-4
2. Nature of scientific knowledge	1-1, 1-2, 1-3, 2-2, 2-3, 3-3, 21-4, 23-4
3. History of science	5-2, 8-1, 8-2, 8-3, 9-2, 10-3, 14-2, 14-3, 15-1, 15-3, 19-1, 19-2, 19-3, 20-1, 22-3, 23-1, 23-4, 25-1, 25-4, 26-3, 26-4

How Glencoe Science Aligns with the NCTM Standards for Grades 9–12

Throughout Glencoe Science, each Applying Math activity provides students with the opportunity to practice and apply some of the mathematical concepts and applications described in the NCTM Standards. These activities serve to reinforce mathematical skills in real-life situations, thus preparing students to meet their needs in an ever-changing world.

Correlation of *Physical Science with Earth Science* to NCTM Standards

Math Standard	Page
1. Number and Operations	24, 33, 63, 72, 93, 102, 116, 123, 130, 132, 149, 156, 158, 181, 198, 213, 220, 247, 255, 258, 283, 297, 315, 325, 349, 357, 385, 411, 412, 419, 451, 459, 481, 513, 537, 545, 565, 603, 621, 641, 665, 681, 728, 747, 781, 798, 813, 820
2. Algebra	24, 33, 72, 93, 102, 116, 123, 130, 132, 149, 156, 158, 181, 198, 220, 255, 258, 283, 297, 315, 325, 357, 385, 411, 412, 419, 451, 481, 537, 565, 573, 705, 715, 728, 747, 781, 845
3. Geometry	255, 258
4. Measurement	16, 33, 213, 247, 349, 545, 603, 621, 641, 665, 681, 757
5. Data Analysis and Probability	24, 283, 513
6. Problem Solving	573, 705, 715, 757, 798, 813
7. Reasoning and Proof	16, 24, 72, 102, 116, 130, 132, 156, 162, 198, 220, 255, 258, 297, 325, 357, 411, 412, 459, 537, 565, 621, 665, 705, 728, 757, 798, 820
8. Communication	507, 775
9. Connections	24, 33, 63, 72, 93, 102, 116, 123, 130, 132, 149, 156, 158, 181, 198, 213, 220, 247, 283, 297, 315, 325, 349, 357, 385, 411, 412, 419, 451, 481, 513, 537, 545, 565, 573, 603, 621, 641, 665, 681, 705, 715, 728, 747, 757, 781, 798, 813, 820, 845
10. Representation	220, 728, 747

Learning in the Laboratory

In the *Student Edition*

Working in the lab is perhaps the most exciting part of science. Labs and MiniLABs give your students the hands-on opportunity to create, investigate, and explore science. Students will learn new material, while having fun.

Traditional Labs provide guided inquiry as students hypothesize, plan investigations, and collect and analyze data.

Design Your Own Labs challenge students to design their own experiments that will provide answers to lab problems.

Model and Invent Labs allow students to create a model or invent a product that can demonstrate scientific concepts.

Use the Internet Labs help students share and retrieve data from others around the country and world, by posting data they have collected on gpescience.com. These activities show students the possible range of data, importance of collecting large amounts of data, and data analysis.

MiniLABs and **Applying Science** activities are a quick way for students to practice specific process skills as they learn science concepts. Many of them can be classroom demonstrations or homework assignments.

In the *Teacher Wraparound Edition*

Quick Demos allow students to visualize biology concepts.

Inquiry Labs in each chapter can be used to support inquiry-based science or as alternatives to traditional labs.

Technology Support

Virtual Labs CD-ROM includes a collection of interactive activities involving major chapter themes that allow students to understand science concepts in a virtual setting. These labs provide a way to conduct experiments without classroom time, cost, and safety constraints.

Video Labs show students step-by-step lab procedures while emphasizing important lab safety skills. The lab videos also include teacher support, troubleshooting advice, and expected outcomes.

Additional Resources

Laboratory Activities offer a variety of traditional laboratory experiences that reinforce the biology principles in the text. The *Teacher Wraparound Edition* provides full support.

Probeware Labs present activities for students to explore scientific concepts using a probeware data collection system. These hand-held systems provide a fast and simple way to collect, view, and analyze data in the classroom or during a field investigation. Integrating technology in the classroom is made simple with step-by-step instructions for setting up and using probeware.

Science Inquiry Lab Manual gives students the opportunity to become increasingly independent in stating hypotheses, designing and performing experiments, and collecting and analyzing data.

Safety in the Laboratory

All activities are designed to minimize dangers in the laboratory. Careful laboratory planning and management by both the instructor and the student are essential to a safe laboratory experience. **Local, state, and federal laboratory safety laws and regulations must be strictly followed.** The information provided here is one of the many resources to which you can refer for information about laboratory safety.

Classroom and Laboratory Preparation

1. Label and store chemicals properly and securely. See p. 20T.
2. Store equipment properly and securely and other thing.
   a. Clean and dry all equipment before storing.
   b. Protect electronic equipment and microscopes from dust, humidity, and extreme temperatures.
   c. Number, catalog, and organize equipment.
3. Ensure adequate work space for each student.
4. Ensure adequate classroom and storeroom ventilation.
5. Explain and post safety and evacuation guidelines along with expectations of conduct.
6. Ensure that all safety equipment is functioning properly and is clearly visible.
7. Provide hot plates as a heat source whenever possible. If gas burners are used, know where the central gas supply shutoff valve is located.
8. Ensure that each workstation has a GFCI-protected electrical source.
9. Provide safety goggles consistent with ANSI Standard Z87.1 for each student, including students who wear corrective lenses.

First Day of Class (with students)

1. Distribute and discuss safety rules, safety symbols, and first aid guidelines. Have students to review safety symbols and guidelines.
2. Review safe use of equipment and chemicals.
3. Review use and location of safety equipment.
4. Discuss safe disposal of materials and laboratory cleanup policy.
5. Discuss proper laboratory attitude and conduct.
6. Document students' understanding of the preceding points. Have students sign a safety contract and return it.

Before Each MiniLAB or Lab

1. Perform each investigation yourself before assigning it.
2. Arrange the lab in such a way that equipment and supplies are clearly labeled and easily accessible.
3. Have available only equipment and supplies needed to complete the assigned investigation.
4. Review the procedure with students, emphasizing any caution statements or safety symbols that appear.
5. Be sure all students know the proper procedures to follow if an accident should occur.
6. Provide containers for disposing of chemicals, waste products, and biological specimens. Disposal methods should meet local guidelines.

During the MiniLAB or Lab

1. Make sure the lab is clean and free of clutter.
2. Insist that students wear goggles and aprons.
3. Never allow a student to work alone in the lab.
4. Never allow students to use a cutting device with more than one edge.
5. Students should not point the open end of a heated test tube toward anyone.
6. Remove broken glassware or frayed cords from use. Also clean up any spills immediately. Dilute solutions with water before removing.
7. Be sure all glassware that is to be heated is of a heat-treated type that will not shatter.
8. Remind students that hot glassware looks cool.
9. Prohibit eating and drinking in the lab.

After the MiniLAB or Lab

1. Be sure that the lab is clean.
2. Be certain that students have returned all equipment and disposed of broken glassware and chemicals properly.
3. Be sure that all hot plates and electrical connections are off.
4. Insist that each student wash his or her hands when lab work is completed.

Chemical Storage and Disposal

General Guidelines

Be sure to store all chemicals properly. The following are guidelines commonly used. Your school, city, county, or state may have additional requirements for handling chemicals. It is the responsibility of each teacher to become informed of the rules or guidelines in effect in his or her area.

1. Separate chemicals by reaction type. Strong acids should be stored together. Likewise, strong bases should be stored together and should be separated from acids. Oxidants should be stored away from easily oxidized materials, and so on.
2. Be sure all chemicals are stored in labeled containers indicating contents, concentration, source, date purchased (or prepared), any precautions for handling and storage, and expiration date.
3. Dispose of any outdated or waste chemicals properly according to accepted disposal procedures.
4. Do not store chemicals above eye level.
5. Wood shelving is preferable to metal. All shelving should be firmly attached to the wall and should have anti-roll edges.
6. Store only those chemicals that you plan to use.
7. Hazardous chemicals require special storage containers and conditions. Be sure to know which chemicals those are and the accepted practices for your area. Some substances must be stored outside the building.
8. When working with chemicals or preparing solutions, observe the same general safety precautions that you would expect from students. These include wearing an apron and goggles. Wear gloves and use the fume hood when necessary. Students will want to do as you do whether they admit it or not.
9. If you are a new teacher in a particular laboratory, it is your responsibility to survey the chemicals stored there to be sure they are stored properly. If not, they should be disposed of. Consult the rules and laws in your area concerning which chemicals can be kept in your classroom. For disposal, consult up-to-date disposal information from state and federal governments.

Disposal of Chemicals

Local, state, and federal laws regulate the proper disposal of chemicals. These laws should be consulted before chemical disposal is attempted. Although many substances encountered in the science classroom can be flushed down the drain with plenty of water, it is not safe to assume that this is always true. Teachers who use chemicals should consult the following book from the National Research Council:

Prudent Practices in the Laboratory. Washington, DC: National Academy Press, 1995. This book is useful and was revised in 1995. Current laws in your area would, of course, supersede the information in this book.

DISCLAIMER

Glencoe Publishing Company makes no claims to the completeness of this discussion of laboratory safety and chemical storage. The material presented is not all-inclusive, nor does it address all of the hazards associated with handling, storing, and disposing of chemicals, or with laboratory management.

Clement Mok/PictureQuest

Preparation of Solutions

It is important to use safe laboratory techniques when handling all chemicals. Always check the MSDS (Material Safety Data Sheet) for each chemical before using it in the classroom. Many substances might appear harmless, but might be toxic, corrosive, or very reactive. Chemicals should never be ingested. Use proper techniques to smell any chemical, wear safety goggles and an apron in the laboratory, and observe the following precautions.

1. **Dilution of Acids and Bases** When diluting acids with water, always add the acids to the water. Never add water to acids. When sulfuric acid and sodium hydroxide are added to water, a large amount of thermal energy is released. Use extra care when handling these substances.

2. **Poisonous and Corrosive Liquids or Vapors** Use a fume hood if possible. Examples include hydrochloric acid, acetic acid, nitric acid, and ammonium hydroxide.

3. **Poisonous and Corrosive to Eyes, Lungs, and Skin** Examples include acids, bases, silver nitrate, iodine, and potassium permanganate.

Bromthymol blue: Add 0.5 g bromthymol blue powder to 500 mL distilled water to make a BTB stock solution. Dilute 40 mL BTB stock solution to 2 L with distilled water. Solution should be bright blue. If not, add one drop of NaOH at a time, swirling to mix. Check color.

Hydrochloric acid (HCL) solution: To make a 5% solution, add 13.6 mL concentrated HCl to 73 mL water while stirring. To make a 0.1*M* solution, add 1 mL concentrated hydrochloric acid to 100 mL water while stirring.

Iodine solution/Iodine stain: Dilute 1 part Lugol's solution with 15 parts water.

Limewater solution: Add up to 1 gallon of distilled or tap water to 1 teaspoon of calcium hydroxide (Limewater is a saturated solution; a teaspoon will yield a fully saturated solution if you use one gallon of water or less.). Shake the jar vigorously for one to two minutes, then let it stand for 24 hours. Pour the clearer portion off the top of the solution through a coffee filter or filter paper, being careful not to stir up any sediment. Repeat the filtering if necessary to produce a clear limewater solution.

Lugol's solution: Dissolve 10 g potassium iodide in 100 mL distilled water. Then add and dissolve 5 g iodine. Store in dark bottle. Keeps indefinitely.

Phenolphthalein indicator: From a drug store, buy a package of any laxative that contains phenolphthalein. To make 1% solution, mash 4 tablets and pour the powder into 10 mL of rubbing alcohol. Let mixture soak for 15 minutes. Pour liquid into and store in a dropper bottle.

Potassium permanganate: For a 0.01*M* solution of potassium permanganate, dissolve 0.15 g $KMnO_4$ in 100 mL water.

Red cabbage concentrate: Put 5 leaves of red cabbage in a pot. Add 1 L of water, bring to a boil, and simmer until water turns a deep purple. Pour liquid through a strainer or piece of cheesecloth into a storage bottle. Keep refrigerated.

Salt solution: For a 3.5% salt (NaCl) solution that simulates the concentration of ocean water, dissolve 35 g of salt (NaCl) in 965 mL of water. For a 1% solution (weak), dissolve 1 g of salt (NaCl) in 99 mL of water. For a 6% solution, dissolve 6 g of salt (NaCl) in 94 mL of water.

Silver nitrate solution: To make a 10% solution, put 5 g of silver nitrate in 50 mL of distilled water.

Sugar solution: Add 1 tablespoon of sugar to 1 cup of warm water in a deep jar or flask. Stir to dissolve.

Sodium hydroxide (dilute): To make a 1% solution, dissolve 1 g NaOH in 99 mL of water.

Equipment and Materials List

These easy-to-use tables of equipment and consumable materials can help you prepare for your science classes for the year. Refer to the Chapter Organizer in front of each chapter for a list of equipment and materials used for each laboratory activity in the chapter.

Consumables

Material	Launch Lab (Chapter)	MiniLAB (Chapter-Section)	Lab (Chapter-Section)
adding machine tape	8, 21		
agar gel	23		
alum			24-4
aluminum foil		3-3, 14-1, 16-1	15-2
ammonia	24		
antacid tablet		24-3	
baking soda			23-4
balloon	9	22-2	23-4, 26-4
butter		9-3	
cabbage indicator (homemade)			24-4
can of food	6-2		
candies (various colors)		25-1	
candle		16-1	9-3
cardboard	24	17-2	6-3
cardboard box			5-1, 16-3
cardboard tube	26		14-3
chalk	7		
clay		25-3	
cloth		14-1, 16-3, 19-3	
coffee can	16		
construction paper (various colors)	15, 25	19-1	7-2, 16-3
copper bromide (crystals)		23-4	
cotton swab	24		
cream of tartar			24-4
dilute hydrochloric acid: HCl		24-3	20-4
envelope (large)	19		
filter paper		18-2	18-1, 24-4
food coloring	18, 22	17-1	17-1
fruit preservative			24-4
hydrogen peroxide: H_2O_2 (3%)			23-4
index cards, 3-in × 5-in		23-1	
index cards, 4-in × 6-in		22-1	
leaf		19-3	
manganese dioxide: MnO_2			23-4
milk		12-4	
nail (iron, aluminum)	23		20-1, 20-4
pancake mix		12-4	
paper (graph)		8-1	12-4
paper (white)			12-4

Equipment and Materials List

Material	Launch Lab (Chapter)	MiniLAB (Chapter-Section)	Lab (Chapter-Section)
paper, 11-in × 17-in			19-3
paper clip	5, 10	3-3, 5-2, 14-1, 19-3	11-3
pepper			9-3, 18-1
phenolphthalein	24		
plaster of paris		22-3	
plastic sheet (clear)			8-2
plate (paper)		9-1	
rice		26-2	
rock		3-3	
rock samples			20-4
salt		1-3, 9-1, 21-1, 20-3	18-1
sand		15-2	8-4, 23-4
soil			8-4
splint (wooden)			23-4
steel wool	5		
string		4-2, 11-1	
sugar (granulated, cubes)	25	21-1, 25-1	18-1, 24-4
taffy (large bar)		12-2	
tape (double-sided)		26-1	
tape (electrical)	5		
tape (masking)		3-1, 4-2, 9-2	4-3, 5-1, 11-3, 24-4
tape (transparent)	25	23-1	8-2
thread		14-1	
universal indicator		24-3	
vegetable oil	22		
vinegar	24	23-4	
water (distilled)			24-4
waxed paper			24-4
wire	13	13-2	13-2, 14-3
wool		22-2	
Nonconsumables			
ammeter			14-3
baking sheet		3-3, 21-2	
balance	4	5-1	3-3, 4-3, 5-1, 6-3, 18-1
ball (plastic, slotted)		4-1	
ball (rubber)			4-3, 5-1
ball (white)		7-3	
baseball		19-3	4-2
battery	5, 13	13-2	13-2
bead (plastic)		9-3	
beaker, 10-mL			17-1
beaker, 150-mL		15-2, 16-1	23-4
beaker, 200-mL	18	17-1	
beaker, 250-mL		24-3, 25-3	18-1, 23-4, 24-4
beaker, 400-mL			9-4
beaker, 500-mL	9	9-3	9-3, 17-1
beaker, 1000-mL			17-1
binder clip			26-4

Material	Launch Lab (Chapter)	MiniLAB (Chapter-Section)	Lab (Chapter-Section)
block (wooden)		3-3	
board		4-1	
bottle (plastic)			23-4
bowl		1-3, 9-2, 22-3	15-2
broom handles	6		
calculator			12-4
can opener (manual)		6-2	
cart		4-1	
coiled spring toy			10-2
coins		5-1	6-3, 20-1, 20-4
colored pencils			19-3
compass		1-3	12-4
copper wire stirrer			24-4
crayon		19-3	
cup (clear, plastic)		1-3	8-4
cup (foam)		14-1	9-4
dominoes			25-3
drinking glass	17	21-1, 24-2	
dropper		18-2	17-1
eraser		3-3	
evaporating dish	18		
feather		19-3	
flashlight bulb	13	7-2	13-2, 15-2
funnel		12-4	18-1
geologic cross-sections			21-4
glass plate			20-1, 20-4
globe		7-2	
golf ball		19-3	
graduated cylinder	22	1-2	18-1, 23-4, 24-4
hair dryer		22-3	
hammer (rubber)		22-3	
hot plate	18	12-4	9-3, 9-4, 17-1, 23-4, 24-4
H-R diagrams (star temperature and brightness diagrams)			26-2
iron filings			18-1
ladle			17-1
lamp		7-3	7-2
lenses		26-1	
lightbulb		13-2	
lightbulb holder			13-2
magnet	14	14-1	14-3, 18-1
magnifying lens		20-1	8-4, 18-1, 20-4
mallet		10-3	
map of the Hawaiian Islands			12-4
map of the Moon			7-3
marbles	10	19-3, 25-3	
marker (erasable)			8-2
marker (permanent)		9-2, 18-2	23-4, 26-4

Material	Launch Lab (Chapter)	MiniLAB (Chapter-Section)	Lab (Chapter-Section)
meterstick	3, 7, 8, 25	4-2	10-2, 10-3, 5-1
microwave		15-2	
mineral samples			20-1
Mohs hardness scale			20-1
pan		12-4	
paring knife			9-4
pencil		1-2, 1-3	
periodic table			22-1
photograph of Mars			8-2
pie plate		10-2	
plane mirror			11-3
plate		18-2	
porcelain tile (unglazed)			20-1, 20-4
protractor		1-3	7-2, 11-3
Reference Handbook: *Minerals*			20-1
ring stand		14-1	24-4
rope (several meters)	6		10-3
rubber band	5-1	4-1	
ruler (metric)	11	1-3, 3-3	6-3, 12-4, 12-4, 19-3
sauce pan and lid		20-3	
saucer		20-3	
scissors	16		4-2, 8-2, 14-3
softball	4		4-3
spoon (metal)		11-1, 9-3, 20-3, 21-1	
spoon (small, plastic)		9-3	23-4
spoon (wooden)		9-3	
spring scale			3-3
stopwatch or watch with a second hand	3, 4	3-1, 6-1, 12-4, 21-1	4-2, 4-3, 10-2, 10-3, 16-3, 23-4, 25-3
tape measure	1, 9		23-4
teaspoon			24-4
television and remote control		15-1	
tennis ball	4		4-3, 5-1
test tube		11-3, 23-4	23-4, 24-4
test tube holder			24-4
test tube rack			23-4, 24-4
test tube stopper		11-3	
thermal mitt		20-3	9-4, 17-1
thermometer	16	1-3, 16-1	7-2, 8-2, 9-4, 16-3, 24-4
tongs	5		
toy car		3-1	
tuning fork		10-3	
turntable		17-2	

Suppliers

Equipment Suppliers

American Science & Surplus
P.O. Box 1030
Skokie, IL 60076
(847) 647-0011
www.sciplus.com

Bio-Rad Laboratories
2000 Alfred Nobel Dr.
Life Science Group
Hercules, CA 94547
(800) 424-6723
www.bio-rad.com

Carolina Biological Supply Co.
2700 York Road
Burlington, NC 27215
(800) 334-5551
www.carolina.com

Chem Scientific, LLC
1250 Washington St.
Norwood, MA 02062
(888) 527-5827
www.chemscientific.com

Edmund Scientific Company
60 Pearce Ave.
Tonawanda, NY 14150
(800) 728-6999
www.edmundscientific.com

Fisher Science Education
Educational Materials Division
4500 Turnberry Dr.
Hanover Park, IL 60133
(800) 955-1177
www.fisheredu.com

Flinn Scientific
P.O. Box 219
770 N. Raddant Rd.
Batavia, IL 60510
(800) 452-1261
www.flinnsci.com

Frey Scientific, Div. of Beckley Cardy
P.O. Box 8101
Mansfield, OH 44901
(800) 225-FREY (3739)
www.freyscientific.com

Nasco Science
901 Janesville Avenue
P.O. Box 901
Fort Atkinson, WI 53538-0901
(800) 558-9595
www.enasco.com

Nebraska Scientific
3823 Leavenworth St.
Omaha, NE 68105-1180
(800) 228-7117
nebraskascientific.com

PASCO Scientific
10101 Foothills Blvd.
Roseville, CA 95747
(800) 772-8700
www.pasco.com

Sargent-Welch/VWR Scientific Products
P.O. Box 5229
Buffalo Grove, IL 60089-5229
(800) SAR-GENT 727-4368
www.SargentWelch.com

Science Kit and Boreal Laboratories
777 East Park Dr.
P.O. Box 5003
Tonawanda, NY 14150
(800) 828-7777
www.sciencekit.com

Ward's Natural Science Est.
5100 W. Henrietta Road
P.O. Box 92912
Rochester, NY 14692-9012
(800) 962-2660
www.wardsci.com

Audiovisual Distributors

Bullfrog Films
P.O. Box 149
Oley, PA 19547
(800) 543-FROG (3764)
www.bullfrogfilms.com

Coronet/MTI Film & Video
2349 Chaffee Dr.
St. Louis, MO 63146
(800) 221-1274
www.phoenixlearninggroup.com

Discovery Channel School
1 Discovery Place
Silver Springs, MD 20910
(240) 662-2000
www.discoveryschool.com

Films for the Humanities and Sciences
P.O. Box 2053
Princeton, NJ 08543
(800) 257-5126
www.films.com

Flinn Scientific
P.O. Box 219
770 N. Raddant Rd.
Batavia, IL 60510
(800) 452-1261
www.flinnsci.com

Frey Scientific, Div. of Beckley Cardy
P.O. Box 8101
Mansfield, OH 44901
(800) 225-FREY (3739)
www.freyscientific.com

Media Design Associates
1731 15th St.
Suite 220
Boulder, CO 80302
(866) 546-9151
www.indra.com

National Geographic Society Educational Services
1145 17th Street, N.W.
Washington, DC 20036-4688
(800) 647-5463
www.nationalgeographic.com

Scholastic, Inc.
557 Broadway
New York, NY 10012-3999
(800) 246-2986
www.scholastic.com

Videodiscovery Inc.
920 N. 34th St.
Seattle, WA 98103
(800) 548-3472
www.videodiscovery.com

Software Distributors

Boreal Laboratories, Ltd.
399 Vansickle Rd.
St. Catharines, Ontario,
L2S 3T4
Canada
(800) 387-9393
boreal.com

Educational Activities, Inc.
1937 Grand Ave.
P.O. Box 87
Baldwin, NY 11510
(800) 645-3739
www.edact.com

IBM Education
1133 Westchester Ave.
White Plains, NY 10604
(800) 426-4968
www.solutions.ibm.com/k12

J. Weston Walch, Publisher
40 Walch Dr.
P.O. Box 658
Portland, ME 04104-0658
(800) 341-6094
www.walch.com

Scholastic, Inc.
557 Broadway
New York, NY 10012-3999
(800) 246-2986
www.scholastic.com

Sunburst Technology, Inc.
1550 Executive Drive
Elgin, IL 60123
(888) 492-8817
www.SUNBURST.com

Contents In Brief

unit 1 Science and Technology—2

In each chapter, look for these opportunities for review and assessment:
- Reading Checks
- Caption Questions
- Section Review
- Chapter Study Guide
- Chapter Review
- Standardized Test Practice
- Online practice at gpescience.com

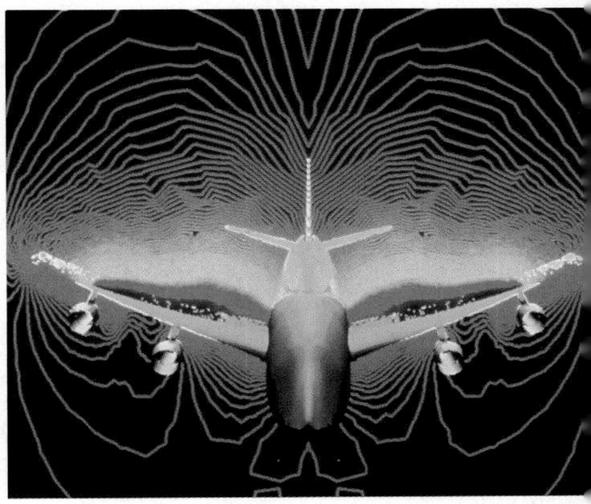

unit 2 Motion, Forces, and Energy—66

Contents

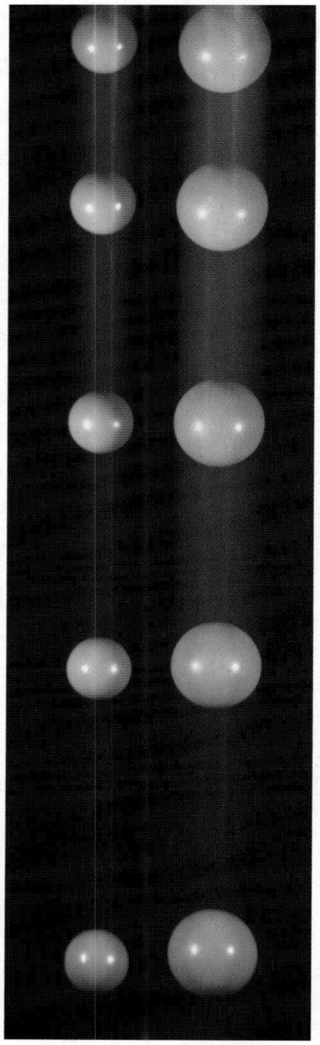

The Solar System—216

In each chapter, look for these opportunities for review and assessment:

- Reading Checks
- Caption Questions
- Section Review
- Chapter Study Guide
- Chapter Review
- Standardized Test Practice
- Online practice at gpescience.com

Unit 3 Energy in Motion—250

Heat and States of Matter—252

Waves—286

Contents

chapter 14 Magnetism—422

chapter 15 Electromagnetic Radiation—454

chapter 16 Energy Sources—484

chapter 17 Weather and Climate—516

In each chapter, look for these opportunities for review and assessment:

- Reading Checks
- Caption Questions
- Section Review
- Chapter Study Guide
- Chapter Review
- Standardized Test Practice
- Online practice at gpescience.com

Contents

Contents

unit 5 Matter and Earth Materials—548

chapter 18 Classification of Matter—550

chapter 19 Properties of Atoms and the Periodic Table—576

chapter 20 Earth Materials—606

In each chapter, look for these opportunities for review and assessment:
- Reading Checks
- Caption Questions
- Section Review
- Chapter Study Guide
- Chapter Review
- Standardized Test Practice
- Online practice at gpescience.com

Contents

Student Resources—848

In each chapter, look for these opportunities for review and assessment:
- Reading Checks
- Caption Questions
- Section Review
- Chapter Study Guide
- Chapter Review
- Standardized Test Practice
- Online practice at gpescience.com

Cross-Curricular Readings

NATIONAL GEOGRAPHIC Unit Openers

NATIONAL GEOGRAPHIC VISUALIZING

TIME SCIENCE AND Society

TIME SCIENCE AND HISTORY

Oops! Accidents in SCIENCE

Science and Language Arts

SCIENCE Stats

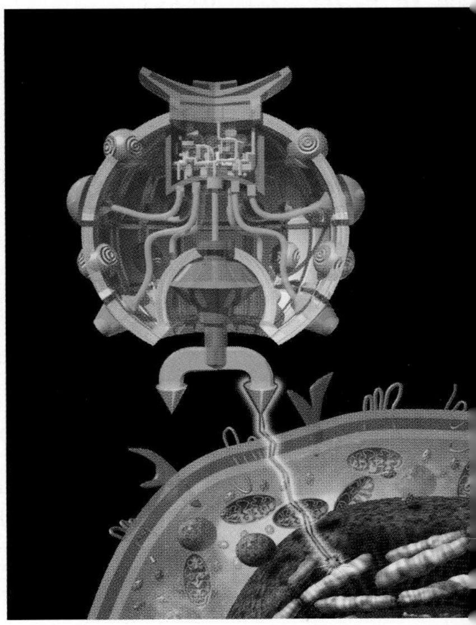

available as a video lab

Launch LAB

Mini LAB

Content Details

Mini LAB Try at Home

Content Details

(video lab icon) available as a video lab

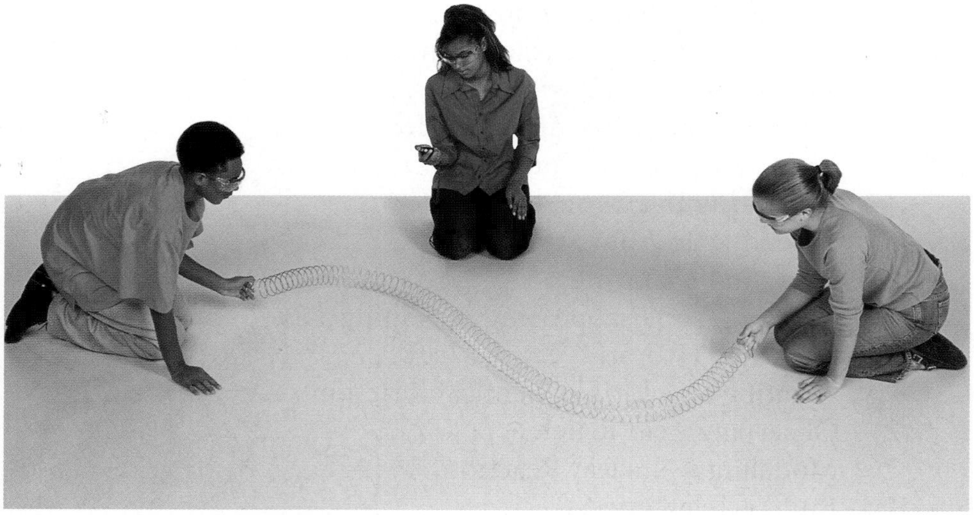

Traditional Labs

Design Your Own Labs

Model and Invent Labs

Use the Internet Labs

Activities

Applying Math

Applying Science

INTEGRATE

Science Online

Standardized Test Practice

Unit Contents

WebQuest While completing **Recycling Plastics,** students will investigate the history of plastics, what defines the seven classes of plastics and their uses, the chemistry behind plastics, and how they can be recycled–compared to paper, glass, and aluminum. Completing a table listing each type of plastic, its normal use, and into what it can be recycled might help students become more active, responsible, and aware citizens.

unit 1 Science and Technology

How Are Billiards & Bottles Connected?

2

PROJECT CRISS℠

Study Skills

Active Reading Questions will arise in the students' minds as they read. Encourage students to write these questions in their Science Journals to aid in their understanding of the diversity of matter. Questions about elements, organic compounds, and newly-developed and versatile materials can be addressed in a whole-class discussion.

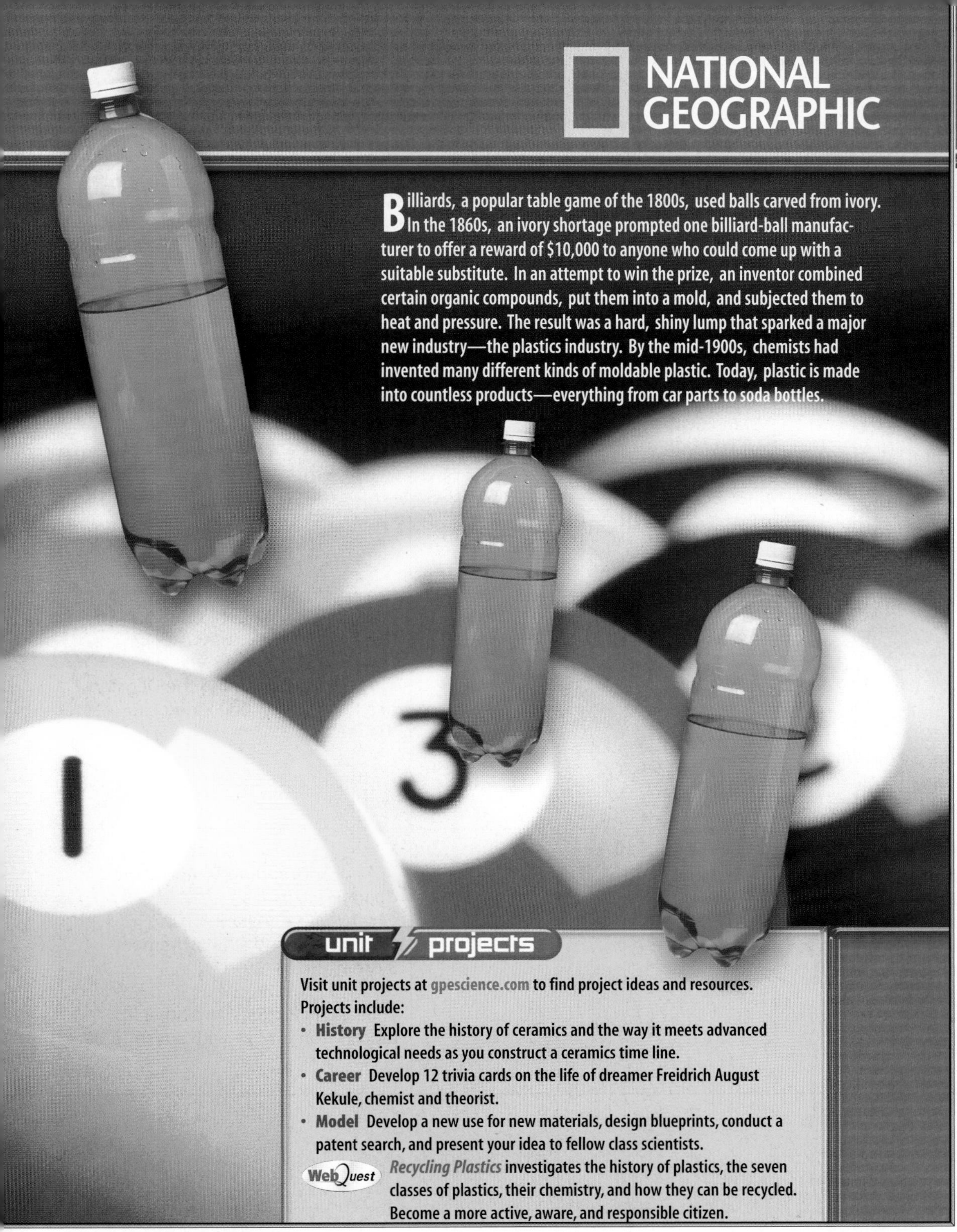

NATIONAL GEOGRAPHIC

Billiards, a popular table game of the 1800s, used balls carved from ivory. In the 1860s, an ivory shortage prompted one billiard-ball manufacturer to offer a reward of $10,000 to anyone who could come up with a suitable substitute. In an attempt to win the prize, an inventor combined certain organic compounds, put them into a mold, and subjected them to heat and pressure. The result was a hard, shiny lump that sparked a major new industry—the plastics industry. By the mid-1900s, chemists had invented many different kinds of moldable plastic. Today, plastic is made into countless products—everything from car parts to soda bottles.

unit projects

Visit unit projects at gpescience.com to find project ideas and resources. Projects include:

- **History** Explore the history of ceramics and the way it meets advanced technological needs as you construct a ceramics time line.
- **Career** Develop 12 trivia cards on the life of dreamer Freidrich August Kekule, chemist and theorist.
- **Model** Develop a new use for new materials, design blueprints, conduct a patent search, and present your idea to fellow class scientists.

WebQuest *Recycling Plastics* investigates the history of plastics, the seven classes of plastics, their chemistry, and how they can be recycled. Become a more active, aware, and responsible citizen.

unit projects

History Have students explore the use of ceramics in society. Have students construct a time line of 20 uses of this ancient material and how it is being used in new and creative ways with constantly changing technology.

Career Ask students to research Freidrich August Kekule and his contribution to chemistry and theory. Have students develop 12 interesting facts about Kekule and present them in a question-and-answer-trivia format.

Model Working with a partner, have students design a unique use for ceramics, polymers, alloys, or other new materials. Have students draw a "blueprint," conduct a patent search for similar devices, and then modify their design based on their research. Using visual aids, students may then host presentations of their new product to fellow class scientists.

Additional Resources Visit unit projects at gpescience.com for more information, resources, and assessment rubrics.

NATIONAL GEOGRAPHIC **How Are Billiards & Bottles Connected?**

- Ask students how they can identify plastics. Have them write down their thoughts and revise them as they study more about different types of materials.
- Ask students to define the term *diverse.* Emphasize to students that matter is diverse, and different types of matter can be classified into even more diverse categories.
- Ask students how the plastic in a billiard ball differs from that in a bottle. Point out that the term *plastic* refers to a type of material, not a specific one.

chapter 1 Organizer

Section/Objectives	Standards		Labs/Features
	National	State/Local	
Chapter Opener	See p. 16T–17T for a Key to Standards.		**Launch Lab:** Understanding Measurements, p. 5 **Foldables,** p. 5
Section 1 The Methods of Science 1 session .5 block 1. **Identify** the steps scientists often use to solve problems. 2. **Describe** why scientists use variables. 3. **Compare and contrast** science and technology.	National Content Standards: UCP.1–3, UCP.5, A.1, A.2, F.5, G.2		**Science Online,** p. 7 **Integrate History,** p. 9 **Integrate Earth Science,** p. 11 **Science Online,** p. 12
Section 2 Standards of Measurement 2 sessions 1 block 4. **Name** the prefixes used in SI and indicate what multiple of ten each one represents. 5. **Identify** SI units and symbols for length, volume, mass, density, time, and temperature. 6. **Convert** related SI units.	National Content Standards: UCP.1–3, UCP.5, A.1, A.2, G.2		**Applying Math:** Centimeters, p. 16 **Integrate Earth Science,** p. 17 **Science Online,** p. 18 **MiniLAB:** Determining the Density of a Pencil, p. 19 Video Lab **Visualizing SI Dimensions,** p. 20
Section 3 Communicating with Graphs 2 sessions 1 block 7. **Identify** three types of graphs and explain the ways they are used. 8. **Distinguish** between dependent and independent variables. 9. **Analyze** data using the various types of graphs.	National Content Standards: UCP.1–3, UCP.5, A.1, A.2, G.2		**Applying Math:** Temperature, p. 24 **MiniLAB:** Graphing Temperature Change, p. 25 **Lab:** What's my graph?, p. 27 **Lab:** Developing a Measurement System, pp. 28–29 **Science and Language Arts:** Thinking in Pictures: and other reports from my life with autism, p. 30

StudentWorks Plus

Glencoe Exclusive! TeacherWorks™ All-In-One Planner and Resource Center

Lab Materials	Reproducible Resources	Section Assessment	Technology
Launch Lab: yardstick, tape measure	**Chapter *Fast File* Resources** Foldables Worksheet, p. 17 Note-taking Worksheets, pp. 33–34 Directed Reading Overview, p. 19		TeacherWorks includes: • Interactive Teacher Edition • Lesson Planner with calendar • Access to all program blacklines • Correlations to standards • Web links
Need materials? Contact Science Kit at 1-800-828-7777 or www.sciencekit.com.	**Chapter *Fast File* Resources** Transparency Activity, p. 44 Enrichment, p. 30 Reinforcement, p. 27 Directed Reading, p. 20 **Cultural Diversity,** p. 29 **Science Inquiry Labs,** pp. 13–14	**Performance** Applying Math, p. 13 **Content** Section Review, p. 13	Section Focus Transparency Virtual Labs CD-ROM Interactive Chalkboard CD-ROM StudentWorks Plus
MiniLAB: unsharpened pencil, 100-mL graduated cylinder, 90 mL water	**Chapter *Fast File* Resources** Transparency Activity, p. 45 MiniLAB, p. 3 Enrichment, p. 31 Reinforcement, p. 28 Directed Reading, p. 20 Lab Activity, pp. 9–12	**Portfolio** Make a Model, p. 16 **Performance** Applying Math, p. 16 MiniLAB, p. 19 Applying Math, p. 21 **Content** Section Review, p. 21	Section Focus Transparency Interactive Chalkboard CD-ROM StudentWorks Plus Video Lab
MiniLAB: water, plastic bowl, table salt, clear-plastic cup, thermometer **Lab:** ruler, protractor, pencil, compass, circle template **Lab:** string, scissors, marking pen, masking tape, miscellaneous objects for standards	**Chapter *Fast File* Resources** Transparency Activity, p. 46 MiniLAB, p. 4 Enrichment, p. 32 Reinforcement, p. 29 Directed Reading, pp. 21, 22 Lab Worksheets, pp. 5–6, 7–8 Transparency Activity, pp. 47–48 Lab Activity, pp. 13–16	**Portfolio** Science Journal, p. 24 Assessment, p. 29 **Performance** Applying Math, p. 24 MiniLAB, p. 25 Applying Math, p. 26 **Content** Section Review, p. 26	Section Focus Transparency Teaching Transparency Interactive Chalkboard CD-ROM StudentWorks Plus

End of Chapter Assessment

Blackline Masters	Technology	Professional Series
Chapter *Fast File* Resources Chapter Review, pp. 37–38 Chapter Tests, pp. 39–42 **Standardized Test Practice,** pp. 8–11	MindJogger Videoquiz Virtual Labs CD-ROM Exam*View*® Pro Testmaker TeacherWorks CD-ROM Interactive Chalkboard CD-ROM	**Performance Assessment in the Science Classroom (PASC)**

Transparencies

Section Focus

Section 1 Section Focus Transparency **Splendid Science** Chapter 1

Scientists work in different areas and different ways. These photos illustrate the three main divisions of science—life science, Earth science, and physical science. Scientists often work in more than one area, requiring them to have a broad base of knowledge. A biologist, for example, needs to know a good deal of chemistry to understand cell functions.

1. Volcanoes are a topic studied in Earth science. Why might you need to know some physical science when studying volcanoes?
2. What is the general purpose of science?
3. What do the three divisions of science have in common?

L2

The Nature of Science

Section 2 Section Focus Transparency **Pick a Scale and Go with It** Chapter 1

What does it mean if someone says that the temperature is thirty-two degrees? It depends entirely on the scale that they're using. Referring to a temperature of 32 might mean that it's a hot summer's day or that it's so cold that even oxygen is frozen solid.

1. Label the three pictures *32°F, 32°C,* and *32 K.*
2. Why must a measurement include the units in order to be meaningful?
3. What kind of units do you use to measure length? Mass?

L2

The Nature of Science

Section 3 Section Focus Transparency **Data by Graph** Chapter 1

Sometimes the best way to communicate information is with a graph. Circle graphs are a good way to show the parts of a whole—in this case, the U.S. population by age.

1. What information does the circle graph provide? Could you have obtained that information by looking at the photograph?
2. How else could you display these data?
3. Would it be useful to list all the people in the U.S. along with their ages? Why or why not?

L2

The Nature of Science

This is a representation of key blackline masters available in the Teacher Classroom Resources. See Resource Manager boxes within the chapter for additional information.

Assessment

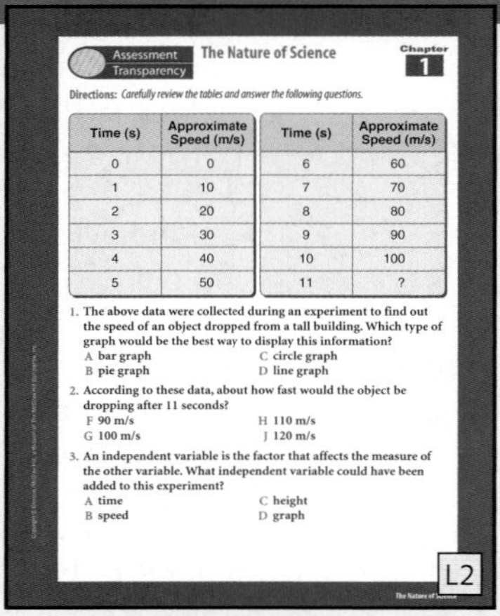
Assessment Transparency **The Nature of Science** Chapter 1

Directions: Carefully review the tables and answer the following questions.

Time (s)	Approximate Speed (m/s)
0	0
1	10
2	20
3	30
4	40
5	50

Time (s)	Approximate Speed (m/s)
6	60
7	70
8	80
9	90
10	100
11	?

1. The above data were collected during an experiment to find out the speed of an object dropped from a tall building. Which type of graph would be the best way to display this information?
   A bar graph C circle graph
   B pie graph D line graph
2. According to these data, about how fast would the object be dropping after 11 seconds?
   F 90 m/s H 110 m/s
   G 100 m/s J 120 m/s
3. An independent variable is the factor that affects the measure of the other variable. What independent variable could have been added to this experiment?
   A time C height
   B speed D graph

L2

The Nature of Science

Teaching

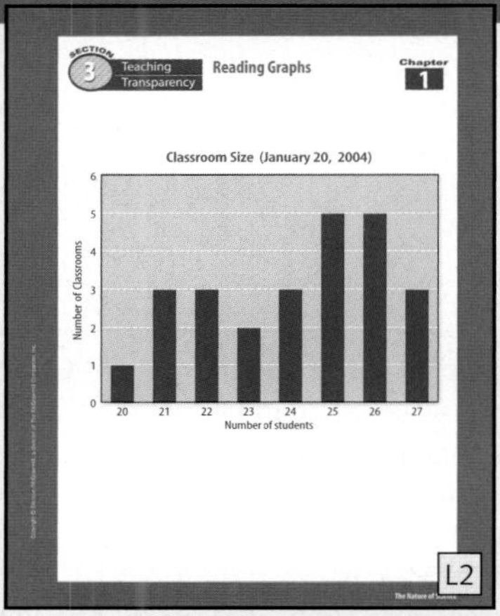
Section 3 Teaching Transparency **Reading Graphs** Chapter 1

L2

The Nature of Science

Key to Teaching Strategies

The following designations will help you decide which activities are appropriate for your students.

- L1 Level 1 activities should be appropriate for students with learning difficulties.
- L2 Level 2 activities should be within the ability range of all students.
- L3 Level 3 activities are designed for above-average students.
- ELL ELL activities should be within the ability range of English Language Learners.
- COOP LEARN Cooperative Learning activities are designed for small group work.
- LS Multiple Learning Styles logos, as described on page 12T, are used throughout to indicate strategies that address different learning styles.
- P These strategies represent student products that can be placed into a best-work portfolio.
- PBL Problem-Based Learning activities apply real-world situations to learning.

Hands-on Activities

Student Text Lab Worksheet

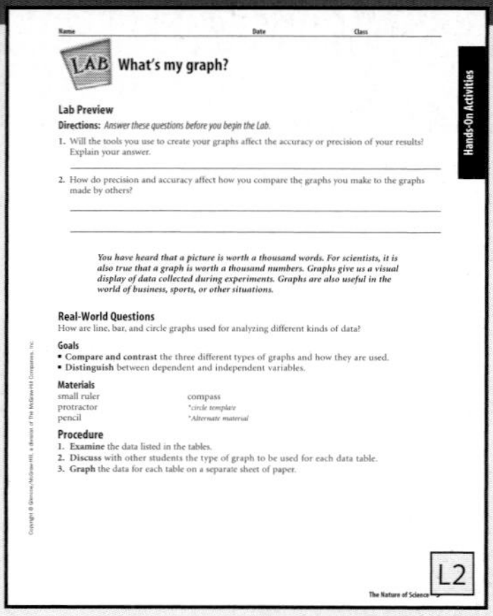
Name Date Class

LAB **What's my graph?**

Hands-On Activities

Lab Preview

Directions: *Answer these questions before you begin the Lab.*

1. Will the tools you use to create your graphs affect the accuracy or precision of your results? Explain your answer.
2. How do precision and accuracy affect how you compare the graphs you make to the graphs made by others?

You have heard that a picture is worth a thousand words. For scientists, it is also true that a graph is worth a thousand numbers. Graphs give us a visual display of data collected during experiments. Graphs are also useful in the world of business, sports, or other situations.

Real-World Questions
How are line, bar, and circle graphs used for analyzing different kinds of data?

Goals
- **Compare and contrast** the three different types of graphs and how they are used.
- **Distinguish** between dependent and independent variables.

Materials
small ruler
protractor
pencil
compass
*circle template
*Alternate material

Procedure
1. **Examine** the data listed in the tables.
2. **Discuss** with other students the type of graph to be used for each data table.
3. **Graph** the data for each table on a separate sheet of paper.

L2

The Nature of Science

Laboratory Activities

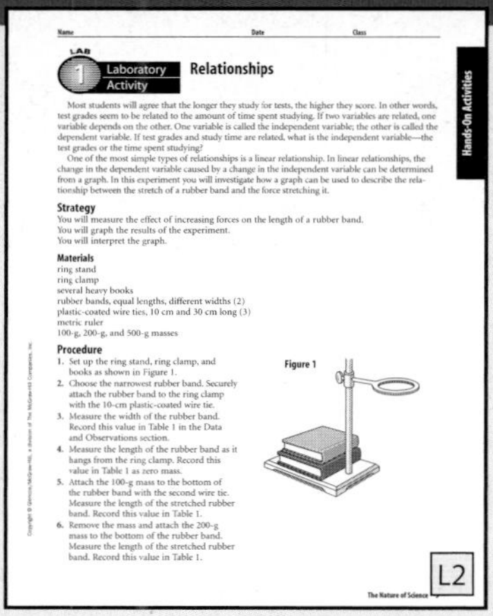
Name Date Class

LAB 1 Laboratory Activity **Relationships**

Hands-On Activities

Most students will agree that the longer they study for tests, the higher they score. In other words, test grades seem to be related to the amount of time spent studying. If two variables are related, one variable depends on the other. One variable is called the independent variable; the other is called the dependent variable. If test grades and study time are related, what is the independent variable—the test grades or the time spent studying?

One of the most simple types of relationships is a linear relationship. In linear relationships, the change in the dependent variable caused by a change in the independent variable can be determined from a graph. In this experiment you will investigate how a graph can be used to describe the relationship between the stretch of a rubber band and the force stretching it.

Strategy
You will measure the effect of increasing forces on the length of a rubber band.
You will graph the results of the experiment.
You will interpret the graph.

Materials
ring stand
ring clamp
several heavy books
rubber bands, equal lengths, different widths (2)
plastic-coated wire ties, 10 cm and 30 cm long (3)
metric ruler
100-g, 200-g, and 500-g masses

Procedure
1. Set up the ring stand, ring clamp, and books as shown in Figure 1.
2. Choose the narrowest rubber band. Securely attach the rubber band to the ring clamp with the 10-cm plastic-coated wire tie.
3. Measure the width of the rubber band. Record this value in Table 1 in the Data and Observations section.
4. Measure the length of the rubber band as it hangs from the ring clamp. Record this value in Table 1 as zero mass.
5. Attach the 100-g mass to the bottom of the rubber band with the second wire tie. Measure the length of the stretched rubber band. Record this value in Table 1.
6. Remove the mass and attach the 200-g mass to the bottom of the rubber band. Measure the length of the stretched rubber band. Record this value in Table 1.

Figure 1

L2

The Nature of Science

Meeting Different Ability Levels

Content Outline

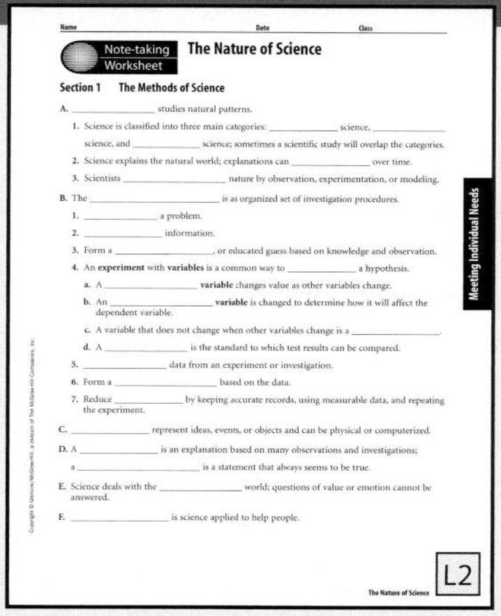

Reinforcement

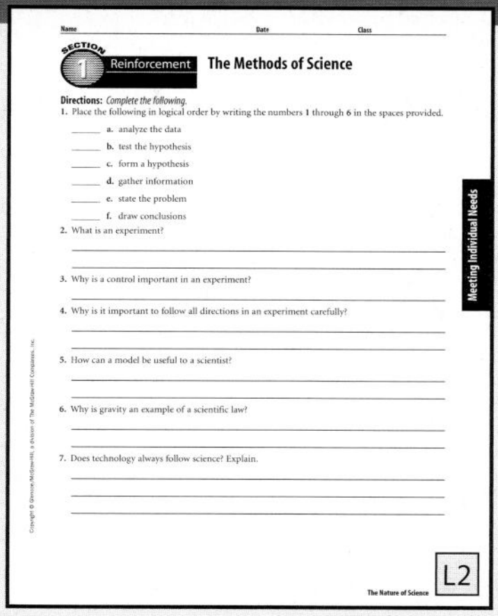

Enrichment

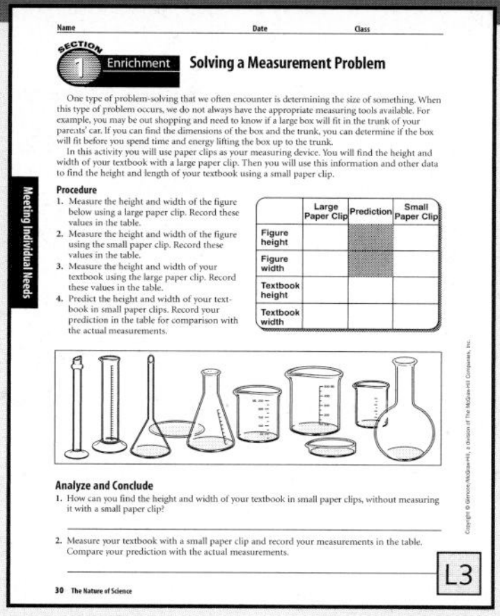

Directed Reading (English/Spanish)

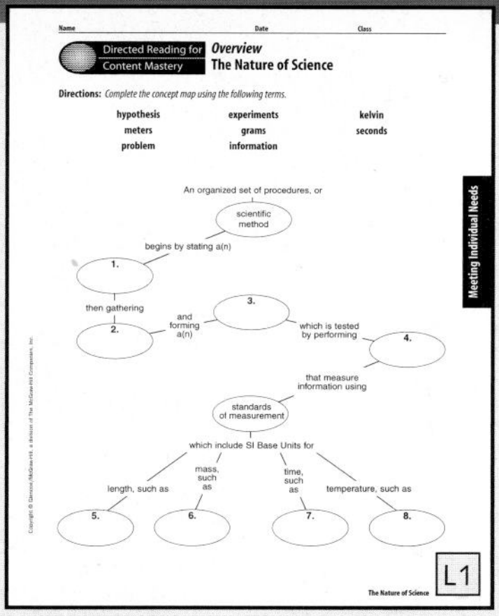

Study Guide

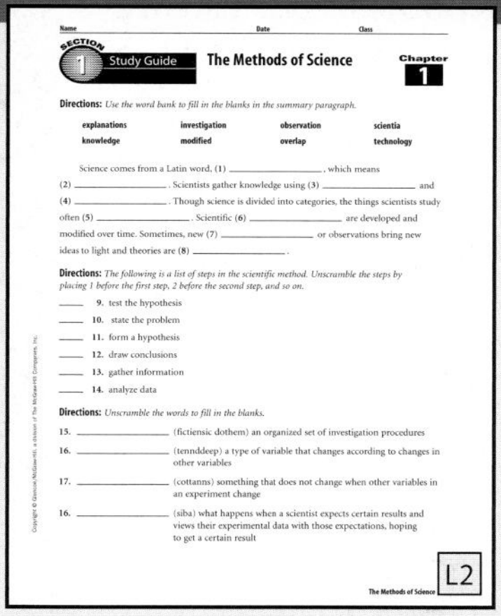

Reading Essentials

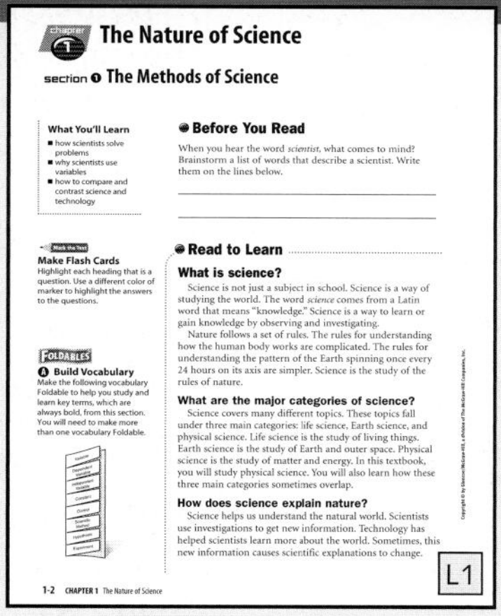

Assessment

Test Practice Workbook

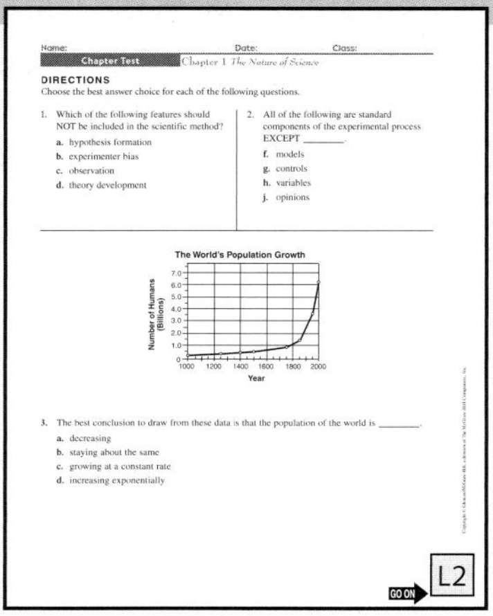

Chapter Review

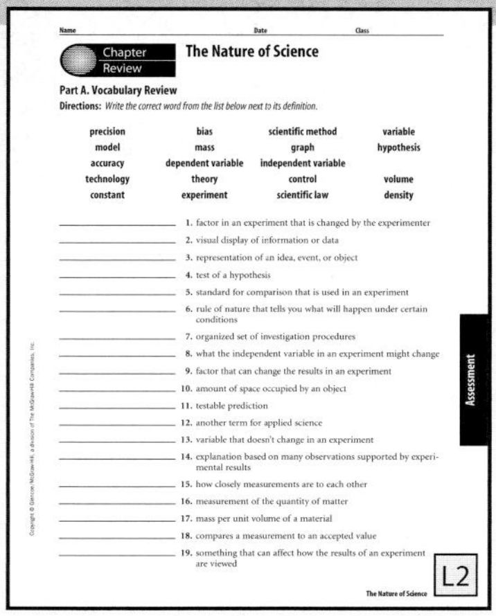

Chapter Tests

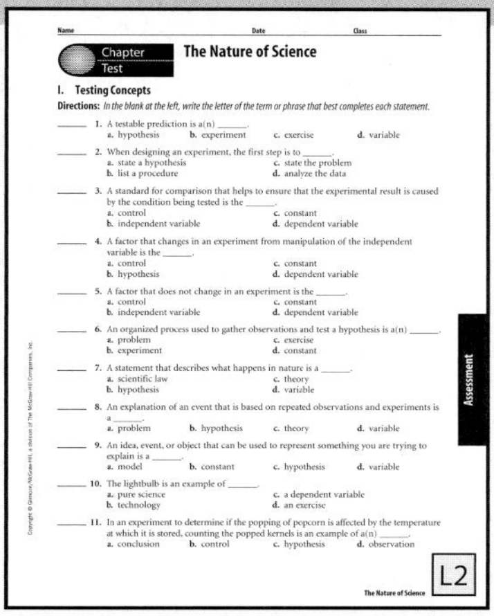

Science Content Background

section 1 The Methods of Science

Scientific Methods

Many science educators are no longer using the term "the scientific method." This is because there is really no one method; an astronomer works in ways that are very different from those of a medical researcher. Also, science does not always proceed in the linear manner described by "the scientific method." The term "scientific methods" indicates that a variety of approaches are employed in scientific inquiry.

Investigations will sometimes use a null hypothesis. This null hypothesis is usually the opposite of the scientist's hypothesis for what will happen in the investigation. Thus if a medical researcher thinks Drug PR will help cure disease PQ, a null hypothesis could be that there will be no difference in symptoms between people who received PR and those who didn't receive it. If the data show that the null hypothesis is false, then this is evidence that the original hypothesis may be correct.

The term *experiment* should be reserved for occasions when scientists or students manipulate a variable to see the result. The independent variable is the thing or variable that is changed. This is done to see the effect on the dependent variable.

In human drug experiments, a drug is given to a treatment group and a placebo is given to a control group. A placebo is something, such as a sugar pill, that resembles medication but contains no drug. It is given because people often get better just because they believe they are taking something that will help even though they are not. The people in the drug experiment don't know whether they are taking the new drug or the placebo.

Using Science—Technology

Pure science is often contrasted with applied science. Pure science seeks knowledge just for the sake of knowledge. Applied science seeks to develop technologies that improve people's lives.

While science certainly leads to the development of technologies, technologies also lead to the development of science. The invention of the light microscope advanced the field of cell biology. Other technologies that have influenced science include gel electrophoresis, telescopes, and particle accelerators.

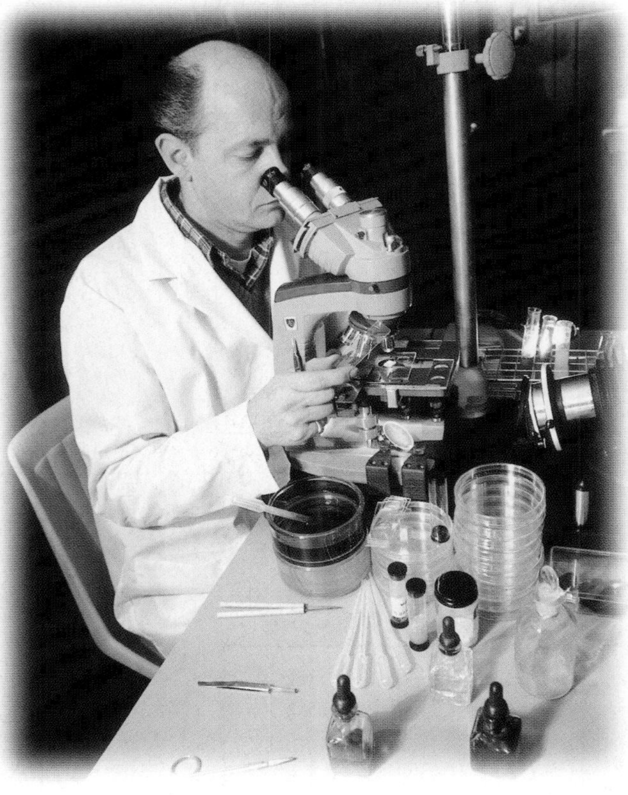

Barry L. Runk/Grant Heilman Photography, Inc.

section 2 Standards of Measurement

Measurement Systems

The SI system of measurement allows easy conversions among SI units. The SI system stops being easy when measurements are converted into English units. A gram is approximately the mass of one regular-size paper clip. A kilometer is 2.5 times around an Olympic track. A liter is just a bit more than a quart of milk.

Measuring Distance

A common metric unit for area is the hectare. One hectare is equal to 10,000 square meters.

Measuring Time and Temperature

Three systems of units are commonly used for temperature. Almost all the people in the world use the Celsius system. People in the United States use the Fahrenheit system. While United States scientists typically use the Celsius or Kelvin system, many United States meteorologists use Fahrenheit. The Kelvin is the official SI unit for temperature.

Measuring Matter

Water has a density of 1 g/cm^3, so if you didn't have a scale you could measure 5 g of water by using a graduated cylinder to measure 5 mL, which is 5 cm^3, of water. Objects that have a density greater than 1 g/cm^3 sink in water and those with a lower density float.

section 3 Communicating with Graphs

Choosing the Right Graph

Line graphs are appropriate for continuous data. Continuous data are numerical data that have an uninterrupted range of values such as time of travel, growth in height of a plant, or current flow in a wire. Bar graphs are appropriate for categorical or nominal data. These are data that fall into defined categories or that have specific names such as boys and girls, types of primates, or types of fruits.

Teacher to Teacher

Erin Peters, Lead Science Teacher
Williamsburg Middle School
Arlington, VA

"When discussing the nature of science it is important to distinguish between observation and inference. Place raisins in carbonated water with yellow food coloring and lead the students to believe that they are 'sewer slugs,' (fictitious) animals that purify sewage. When the students realize the 'animals' are fictitious, begin to analyze which of their statements were observations and which statements were inferences. In addition, discuss what statements are appropriate for a scientific discussion, as opposed to everyday conversations."

Erin Peters

chapter content resources

Internet Resources

For additional content background, visit gpescience.com to:

- access your book online
- find references to related articles in popular science magazines
- access Web links with related content background
- access current events with science journal topics

Print Resources

Science and Technology, by Oxford University, 1993

Classroom Critters and the Scientific Method, by Sally Kneidel, Fulcrum Publishers, 1999

The Wild Side—Weird Science, by Henry Billings, Jamestown Publishers, 2001

chapter 1

Chapter Vocabulary

scientific method, p. 7
hypothesis, p. 8
experiment, p. 8
variable, p. 9
dependent variable, p. 9
independent variable, p. 9
constant, p. 9
control, p. 9
bias, p. 10
model, p. 11
theory, p. 12
scientific law, p. 12
technology, p. 13
precision, p. 14
accuracy, p.14
volume, p. 18
mass, p. 19
density, p. 19
graph, p. 22

Science Journal Student responses will vary, but may include learning about the universe, or studying the weather.

INTERACTIVE CHALKBOARD with Image Bank

PowerPoint® Presentations

This CD-ROM is an editable Microsoft® PowerPoint® presentation that includes:

- a pre-made presentation for every chapter
- interactive graphics
- animations
- audio clips
- image bank
- all new section and chapter questions
- Standardized Test Practice
- transparencies
- Foldables directions
- links to gpescience.com

chapter 1

The Nature of Science

chapter preview

sections

Out of This World

The space program was developed in response to many unanswered questions. Scientists have worked together to develop ways in which to answer those questions. In this chapter, you will learn how scientists learn about the natural world.

Science Journal Look at the picture above. Write in your Science Journal why scientists study space.

4

Theme Connection

Systems and Interactions Scientific methods provide a system for observing interactions in the world, testing those observations, and forming hypotheses, theories, and laws about how and why interactions occur and have the consequences they do.

About the Photo

Space Program The space program was developed in response to many unanswered questions. Scientists all over the world have worked together to develop ways in which to answer some of those questions. In this chapter, you will learn how scientists learn about the natural world, the system that has been developed to standardize measurements, and how patterns are detected in data.

Start-Up Activities

Launch LAB

Understanding Measurements

Before there were measurement standards, people used parts of the body for measuring items. The length from the tip of the elbow to the end of the middle finger was a *cubit*. Egyptians used this measurement in construction. The *foot* was the length of a man's foot and was used to measure distance. How does the length of your classroom differ when measured using several students' feet?

1. Estimate the distance in feet across the classroom. Record this number in your Science Journal.
2. Walk across your classroom by placing the heel of one foot against the toes of your other foot. Count and record the number of steps in your Science Journal.
3. Measure the lengths of your two feet and average them. Calculate the distance of the classroom by multiplying the average length of your feet by the number of steps.
4. Measure the distance across the classroom using a tape measure.
5. **Think Critically** Compare the distance across the classroom using your foot with the distance using other classmates' feet. How does your calculated measurement compare to your classmates' calculated measurements and to the actual measurement?

FOLDABLES™ Study Organizer

Scientific Processes Make the following Foldable to help identify what you already know, what you want to know, and what you learned about science.

STEP 1 **Fold** a sheet of paper vertically from side to side. Make the front edge about 1.25 cm shorter than the back edge.

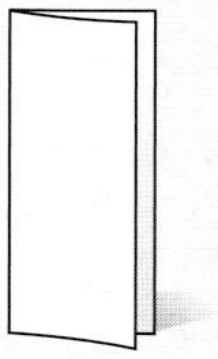

STEP 2 **Turn** lengthwise and **fold** into thirds.

STEP 3 **Unfold and cut** only the top layer along both folds to make three tabs. **Label** each tab.

Identify Questions Before you read the chapter, write what you already know about science under the left tab of your Foldable, and write questions about what you'd like to know under the center tab. After you read the chapter, list what you learned under the right tab.

Science Online | Preview this chapter's content and activities at gpescience.com

Launch LAB

Purpose Use the Launch Lab activity to introduce students to nonstandard measuring units. L1 ELL COOP LEARN

LS **Interpersonal**

Materials yardstick, tape measure

Teaching Strategy Have students estimate the length of the classroom before making any measurements. Have students work in groups.

Think Critically

Students should recognize that each person's foot will not be the same length and will give a different measurement for the classroom. The calculated measurement should be about the same because a standard measurement was used.

Assessment

Oral Have students draw cartoons that explain the limitations of the measurements they made. It is difficult to measure fractions of units accurately and to compare data from groups that use different units. Use **Performance Assessment in the Science Classroom,** p. 133.

FOLDABLES™ Study Organizer **Dinah Zike Study Fold**

Student preparation materials for this Foldable are available in the **Chapter *Fast File* Resources.**

section 1 The Methods of Science

1 Motivate

INTERACTIVE CHALKBOARD PowerPoint® Presentations An editable Microsoft® PowerPoint® presentation is available on **Interactive Chalkboard** CD-ROM.

Bellringer

Section Focus Transparencies also are available on the Interactive Chalkboard CD-ROM. L2 ELL

SECTION 1 Section Focus Transparency **Splendid Science** Chapter 1

Scientists work in different areas and different ways. These photos illustrate the three main divisions of science—life science, Earth science, and physical science. Scientists often work in more than one area, requiring them to have a broad base of knowledge. A biologist, for example, needs to know a good deal of chemistry to understand cell functions.

1. **Volcanoes are a topic studied in Earth science. Why might you need to know some physical science when studying volcanoes?**
2. **What is the general purpose of science?**
3. **What do the three divisions of science have in common?**

L2

The Nature of Science

Reading Preview

Tie to Prior Knowledge
What is science? Discuss with students what they believe science to be. Have them compare their ideas with the definition of science given in the text.

Content Specific Words Preview and discuss **Figure 3** to help students see that *experiment* is not listed on this flow-chart for the scientific method. Explain that an experiment is just one way of testing a hypothesis or a possible solution to a problem. Then, locate the six new vocabulary words related to an experiment in the text.

Reading Guide

What **You'll Learn**
- **Identify** the steps scientists often use to solve problems.
- **Describe** why scientists use variables.
- **Compare and contrast** science and technology.

Why **It's Important**
Using scientific methods will help you solve problems.

Review Vocabulary
investigation: to observe or study by close examination

New Vocabulary
- scientific method
- hypothesis
- experiment
- variable
- dependent variable
- independent variable
- constant
- control
- bias
- model
- theory
- scientific law
- technology

What is science?

Science is not just a subject in school. It is a method for studying the natural world. After all, science comes from the Latin word *scientia,* which means "knowledge." Science is a process that uses observation and investigation to gain knowledge about events in nature.

Nature follows a set of rules. Many rules, such as those concerning how the human body works, are complex. Other rules, such as the fact that Earth rotates about once every 24 h, are much simpler. Scientists ask questions to learn about the natural world.

Major Categories of Science Science covers many different topics that can be classified according to three main categories. (1) Life science deals with living things. (2) Earth science investigates Earth and space. (3) Physical science deals with matter and energy. In this textbook, you will study mainly physical science. Sometimes, though, a scientific study will overlap the categories. One scientist, for example, might study the motions of the human body to understand how to build better artificial limbs. Is this scientist studying energy and matter or how muscles operate? She is studying both life science and physical science. It is not always clear what kind of science you are using, as shown in **Figure 1.**

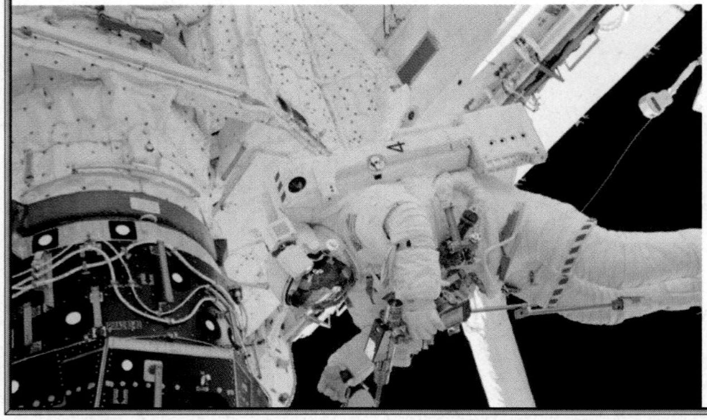

Figure 1 Astronaut Michael Lopez-Alegria uses a pistol-grip tool on the *International Space Station.*
Observe *What evidence do you see of the three main branches of science in the photograph?*

Section 1 Resource Manager

Chapter *Fast File* Resources
Transparency Activity, p. 44
Note-taking Worksheets, pp. 33–34
Enrichment, p. 30
Directed Reading for Content Mastery, pp. 19–20
Reinforcement, p. 27
Reading and Writing Skill Activities, p. 37
Cultural Diversity, p. 29
Science Inquiry Labs, pp. 13–14

Science Explains Nature Scientific explanations help you understand the natural world. Sometimes these explanations must be modified. As more is learned about the natural world, some of the earlier explanations might be found to be incomplete or new technology might provide more accurate answers.

For example, look at **Figure 2.** In the late eighteenth century, most scientists thought that heat was an invisible fluid with no mass. Scientists observed that heat seems to flow like a fluid. It also moves away from a warm body in all directions, just as a fluid moves outward when you spill it on the floor.

However, the heat fluid idea did not explain everything. If heat was an actual fluid, an iron bar at a temperature of 1,000°C should have more mass than it does at 100°C because it would have more of the heat fluid in it. Eighteenth-century scientists thought they were not able to measure the small mass of the heat fluid on the balances they had. When additional investigations showed no difference in mass, scientists had to change the explanation.

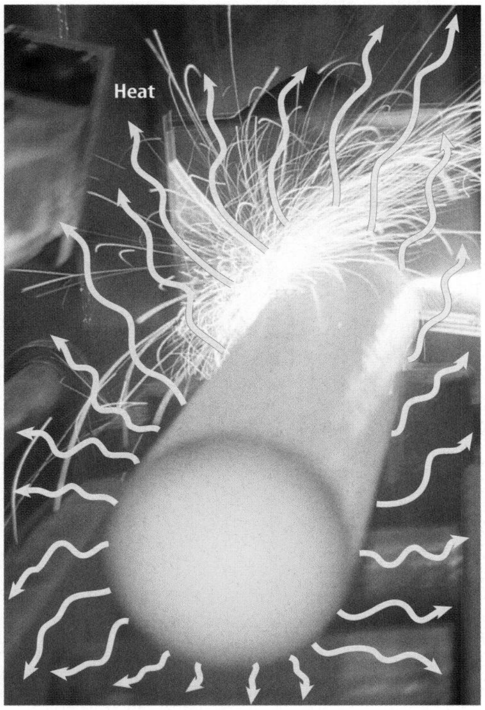

Figure 2 Many years ago, scientists thought that heat, such as in this metal rod, was a fluid.
Infer *how heat acts like a fluid.*

Investigations Scientists learn new information about the natural world by performing investigations, which can be done many different ways. Some investigations involve simply observing something that occurs and recording the observations, such as in a journal. Other investigations involve setting up experiments that test the effect of one thing on another. Some investigations involve building a model that resembles something in the natural world and then testing the model to see how it acts. Often, a scientist will use something from all three types of investigations when attempting to learn about the natural world.

Reading Check *Why do scientific explanations change?*

Science Online

Topic: Prediction
Visit gpescience.com for Web links to information about why leaves change color in the autumn.

Activity Fill a glass with cold water and add a few drops of blue or red food coloring. Cut a piece of celery and place it in the glass. Over the next few days, observe what happens to the celery. Make a prediction about why this occurs. Support your answer with evidence.

Scientific Methods

Although scientists do not always follow a rigid set of steps, investigations often follow a general pattern. An organized set of investigation procedures is called a **scientific method.** Six common steps found in scientific methods are shown in **Figure 3.** A scientist might add new steps, repeat some steps many times, or skip steps altogether when doing an investigation.

2 Teach

Activity

Venn Diagram Have students work as a class or in large groups. Have each group make a Venn diagram representing the three main branches of science. Place three overlapping circles on a large sheet of paper or a bulletin board and label each circle with one major category of science. Have them use pictures from newspapers and magazines to fill in the areas on the diagram. Be sure the overlap areas of the circles are large enough to accommodate examples that apply to more than one branch of science. Be sure students can justify each placement. L1 ELL COOP LEARN

LS **Visual-Spatial**

Caption Answers

Figure 1 physical science—pistol grip tool and other instruments; Earth science—event taking place in space; life science—space suit that allows a human body to survive in space

Figure 2 It flows from one location to another.

Reading Check

Answer Scientists are constantly learning new information by performing investigations.

Visual Learning

Figure 2 Discuss with students ways scientists study heat. Point out that scientists study the structure of the materials through which heat travels, why heat travels through them, and what heat really is. L1

LS **Logical-Mathematical**

Differentiated Instruction

English-Language Learners While science can answer many questions about how things work, what they are made of, and where things come from, it cannot answer questions that are opinion-based. Science cannot answer questions about art, politics, or literature. Science cannot tell you what is right, wrong, good, or bad. Have students brainstorm both questions that science can answer and those that science cannot answer. Ask students to explain why science can answer some questions, but not others. ELL L1

Use an Analogy

Finding Class Ask students to describe how they found their different classrooms on the first day of school in this building. Explain that their methods are analogous to the way the scientific methods discussed in this section are used.

Use Science Words

Word Origin The word *experiment* is from the Latin word *experimentum*, which means "proof or test." Have students write entries in their Science Journals explaining how the meaning of the word reflects the meaning of its root. L2 LS **Linguistic**

Fun Fact

Experiments can be done to confirm a hypothesis about how an independent variable affects a dependent variable. They can also be done to confirm a null hypothesis. A null hypothesis states that the independent variable does not affect the dependent variable.

Discussion

Hypothesis Confirmed Why are results that do not confirm a hypothesis important? These experimental results can help scientists adjust and restate hypotheses. L2 LS **Logical-Mathematical**

Caption Answer

Figure 3 Form and test a new hypothesis.

Reading Strategy

Outline Have students outline this section in their Science Journals, using headings and subheadings. The title should be The Methods of Science. Tell students to write each highlighted vocabulary word in the outline and include a definition by jotting down key words or phrases from the text as they read.

Figure 3 The series of procedures shown here is one way to use scientific methods to solve a problem.
Explain *what should be done if your hypothesis is not supported.*

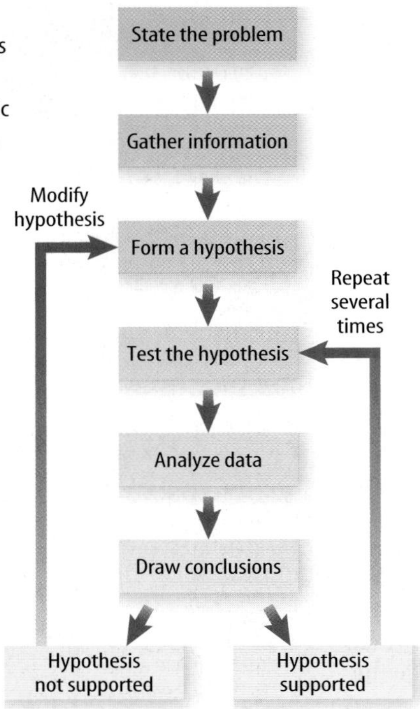

Stating a Problem Many scientific investigations begin when someone observes an event in nature and wonders why or how it occurs. Then the question of "why" or "how" is the problem. Sometimes a statement of a problem arises from an activity that is not working. Some early work on guided missiles showed that the instruments in the nose of the missiles did not always work. The problem statement involved finding a material to protect the instruments from the harsh conditions of flight.

Later, National Aeronautics and Space Administration (NASA) scientists made a similar problem statement. They wanted to build a new vehicle—the space shuttle—that could carry people to outer space and back again. Guided missiles did not have this capability. NASA needed to find a material for the outer surface of the space shuttle that could withstand the heat and forces of re-entry into Earth's atmosphere.

Researching and Gathering Information Before testing a hypothesis, it is useful to learn as much as possible about the background of the problem. Have others found information that will help determine what tests to do and what tests will not be helpful? The NASA scientists gathered information about melting points and other properties of the various materials that might be used. In many cases, tests had to be performed to learn the properties of new, recently created materials.

Forming a Hypothesis A **hypothesis** is a possible explanation for a problem using what you know and what you observe. NASA scientists knew that a ceramic coating had been found to solve the guided missile problem. They hypothesized that a ceramic material also might work on the space shuttle.

Testing a Hypothesis Some hypotheses can be tested by making observations. Others can be tested by building a model and relating it to real-life situations. One common way to test a hypothesis is to perform an experiment. An **experiment** tests the effect of one thing on another using controlled conditions.

Cultural Diversity

Herbal Medicine Principles of science have been used to solve problems throughout the world and throughout history. In the rain forests of Central and South America, plants are used to promote healing. For thousands of years the local people have observed and tested plants and learned which ones can be used for medicines. Today scientists from industries that specialize in manufacturing prescription drugs are working with these herbal healers to identify the materials in the plants that have medicinal value.

Variables An experiment usually contains at least two variables. A **variable** is a factor that can cause a change in the results of an experiment. You might set up an experiment to determine the amount of fertilizer that will help plants grow the biggest. Before you begin your tests, you would need to think of all the factors that might cause the plants to grow bigger. Possible factors include plant type, amount of sunlight, amount of water, room temperature, type of soil, and type of fertilizer.

In this experiment, the amount of growth is the **dependent variable** because its value changes according to the changes in the other variables. The variable you change to see how it will affect the dependent variable is called the **independent variable.**

Constants and Controls To be sure you are testing to see how fertilizer affects growth, you must keep the other possible factors the same. A factor that does not change when other variables change is called a **constant.** You might set up one trial, using the same soil and type of plant. Each plant is given the same amount of sunlight and water and is kept at the same temperature. These are constants. Three of the plants receive a different amount of fertilizer, which is the independent variable.

The fourth plant is not fertilized. This plant is a control. A **control** is the standard by which the test results can be compared. Suppose after several days, the three fertilized plants grow between 2 and 3 cm. If the unfertilized plant grows 1.5 cm, you might infer that the growth of the fertilized plants was due to the fertilizers.

How might the NASA scientists set up an experiment to solve the problem of the damaged tiles shown in **Figure 4?** What are possible variables, constants, and controls?

Reading Check *Why is a control used in an experiment?*

INTEGRATE History

Classification Systems Through observations of living organisms, Aristotle designed a classification system. Systems used today group organisms according to variables such as habits and physical and chemical features. Research to learn recent reclassifications of organisms. Share your findings with your class.

Figure 4 NASA has had an ongoing mission to improve the space shuttle. A technician is replacing tiles damaged upon re-entry into Earth's atmosphere.

Activity

Create a Hypothesis Organize the class into teams and give each team a large index card on which to write a problem for an experiment. Have teams exchange their cards. Each team should generate a hypothesis for the question they hold and write it on the card. Have students exchange cards with a different group. Ask each team to devise an experiment based on the question and hypothesis on the card the team now has. Students should be sure to identify the constants, independent variable, dependent variable, and control in the experiment. L2 COOP LEARN LS **Logical-Mathematical**

INTEGRATE History

Classification Systems The science that deals with the naming and classifying of organisms is called taxonomy. Taxonomists continually collect and analyze data, sometimes changing the way organisms are classified as a result of their findings. Fungi, for example, were classified as plants until data convinced scientists to put fungi in their own kingdom.

Text Question Answer

They might make tiles of many different materials and subject them all to the heat and other stresses encountered by the shuttle. The variables would be the materials used, the constants would be the conditions to which the tiles were subjected, and scientists could use additional tiles that are made from the same materials as the tested tiles for the controls.

Reading Check

Answer A control is a standard to which test results can be compared.

Active Reading

ReQuest To improve listening skills, have students listen carefully as you read the discussion of scientific methods in this section. After the reading, have students construct questions to be discussed in class. You can have students reread the section and participate in the questioning with other students.

Use Science Words

Word Meaning Some of the terms used when analyzing data are *mean*, *mode*, *median*, and *average*. These terms have slightly different meanings and can be confusing. Have students define each one. *mean:* a value that is computed by dividing the sum of a set of values by the number of values; *mode:* the most frequent value of a set of data; *median:* a value in an ordered set of values below and above which there is an equal number of values, or, if there is no one middle number, a value which is the arithmetic mean of the two middle values; *average:* same as mean. L2 LS **Linguistic**

Quick Demo

The Scientific Method

Material thermometer, two beakers of hot water, one stirrer, stopwatch, ice cubes

Estimated Time 15 minutes

Procedure Do ice cubes melt faster in hot water when stirred or when left untouched? Perform the steps of the scientific method out of order in front of the class. Ask students to rank the steps in the order they should have occurred. Have them explain why it makes a difference if the scientific method is performed out of order. Repeat the steps in the order the students ranked them. Ask students which way makes more sense.

Caption Answer

Figure 5 Answers may include: meetings, journals, presentations.

Reading Check

Answer A bias occurs when what the scientist expects changes how the results are viewed.

Figure 5 An exciting and important part of investigating something is sharing your ideas with others, as this student is doing at a science fair.
Identify *possible methods of how scientists can share their research data.*

Analyzing the Data An important part of every experiment includes recording observations and organizing the test data into easy-to-read tables and graphs. Later in this chapter you will study ways to display data. When you are making and recording observations, you should include all results, even unexpected ones. Many important discoveries have been made from unexpected occurrences.

Interpreting the data and analyzing the observations is an important step. If the data are not organized in a logical manner, wrong conclusions can be drawn. No matter how well a scientist communicates and shares that data, someone else might not agree with the data. Scientists share their data through reports and conferences. In **Figure 5,** a student is displaying her data.

Drawing Conclusions Based on the analysis of your data, you decide whether or not your hypothesis is supported. When lives are at stake, such as with the space shuttle, you must be very sure of your results. For the hypothesis to be considered valid and widely accepted, the experiment must result in the exact same data every time it is repeated. If your experiment does not support your hypothesis, you must reconsider the hypothesis. Perhaps it needs to be revised or your experiment needs to be conducted differently.

Being Objective Scientists also should be careful to reduce bias in their experiments. A **bias** occurs when what the scientist expects changes how the results are viewed. This expectation might cause a scientist to select a result from one trial over those from other trials. Bias also might be found if the advantages of a product being tested are used in a promotion and the drawbacks are not presented.

Scientists can lessen bias by running as many trials as possible and by keeping accurate notes of each observation made. Valid experiments also must have data that are measurable. For example, a scientist performing a global warming study must base his or her data on accurate measures of global temperature. This allows others to compare the results to data they obtain from a similar experiment. Most importantly, the experiment must be repeatable. Findings are supportable when other scientists perform the same experiment and get the same results.

Reading Check *What is bias in science?*

Curriculum Connection

Language Arts Emphasize to students that being objective is important in reporting information in all areas. Have them search through magazines and newspapers and find articles in which the writer's bias has influenced the article. L2 LS **Linguistic**

Differentiated Instruction

Challenge When analyzing the results of many different trials, scientists use the methods of statistics. One of the most useful tools of statistics is normal distribution. Have students find out what this tool is. A normal distribution is a distribution of values that produces a symmetrical bell-shaped curve. It shows the distribution of values that results from many random variables. L3 LS **Logical-Mathematical**

10 CHAPTER 1 The Nature of Science

Visualizing with Models

Sometimes, scientists cannot see everything that they are testing. They might be observing something that is too large, too small, or takes too much time to see completely. In these cases, scientists use models. A **model** represents an idea, event, or object to help people better understand it.

Models in History Models have been used throughout history. One scientist, Lord Kelvin, who lived in England in the 1800s, was famous for making models. To model his idea of how light moves through space, he put balls into a bowl of jelly and encouraged people to move the balls around with their hands. Kelvin's work to explain the nature of temperature and heat still is used today.

High-Tech Models Scientific models don't always have to be something you can touch. Today, many scientists use computers to build models. NASA experiments involving space flight would not be practical without computers. The complex equations would take far too long to calculate by hand, and errors could be introduced much too easily.

Another type of model is a simulator, like the one shown in **Figure 6.** An airplane simulator enables pilots to practice problem solving with various situations and conditions they might encounter when in the air. This model will react the way a plane does when it flies. It gives pilots a safe way to test different reactions and to practice certain procedures before they fly a real plane.

INTEGRATE Earth Science

Computer Models Meteorology has changed greatly due to computer modeling. Using special computer programs, meteorologists now are able to more accurately predict disastrous weather. In your Science Journal, describe how computer models might help save lives.

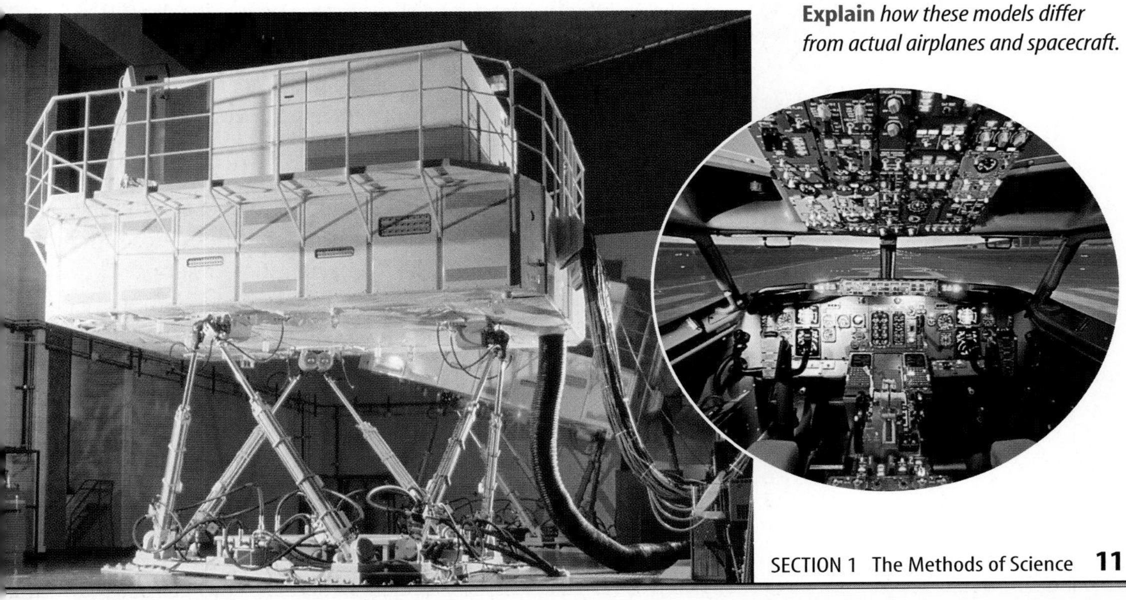

Figure 6 Pilots and astronauts use flight simulators for training. **Explain** *how these models differ from actual airplanes and spacecraft.*

INTEGRATE Earth Science

Computer Models Journal entries should include that predictions of severe weather, such as tornadoes, hurricanes, and flooding rains, can warn residents of an area to take precautions or evacuate the area.

Activity

Studying Models Have students make posters showing situations in which models are used to study something too large to study directly, too small to be studied directly, and too dangerous to be studied directly. Possible answers: the solar system, which is too large to be studied directly; the tiny particles that make up matter, which are too small to be studied directly; and a plane crash, which is too dangerous to be studied directly L2 LS **Visual-Spatial**

Caption Answer

Figure 6 They don't always mimic the real situation exactly. They also don't cause any damage to people or materials when the pilot makes a mistake and crashes.

Discussion

Modeling with Computers Why are computers useful for modeling situations? Computers can slow down or speed up action and can show how a process changes over time. They also can be programmed to make predictions based on data put into them. L2 LS **Logical-Mathematical**

Science Journal

Universal Theories Have students investigate theories about the origin of the universe and explain why these theories are not scientific laws. The current main theory is the Big Bang Theory. This theory is not a law because it tries to explain how or why something happens. A law simply describes a pattern. L2 LS **Logical-Mathematical**

Visual Learning

Figure 6 Ask students whether they have used a driving simulator in a video game. Ask them to explain what it taught them about driving and why it does not really equip them to drive. The simulation might give them practice in steering, accelerating, and stopping, but it does not involve roadway experience with other cars. L2 LS **Visual-Spatial**

Inquiry Lab

The Path of Theory Development

Purpose To have students get a better grasp of the evolution of scientific knowledge and the application of scientific method.

Possible Materials index cards

Safety Precautions

- As this lab may involve social commentary, caution students to remain objective.
- Have students use topics from news items only, not from observations about events within the school or about their peers. Make a rule against 'picking on' individuals.

Estimated Time one class period

Teaching Strategies

- Have students record at least three observations about a psychological, social, or scientific phenomenon in their experience.
- Mix the cards up and have students suggest an experiment that could be done to test a hypothesis for each observation. Encourage objective discussion of the viability of each experiment suggested.
- The game can demonstrate that a hypothesis can't be proven, only disproved.
- For each hypothesis that students disprove with observations, have them create a further hypothesis. Explain that this is how real science develops.

For additional inquiry activities, see *Science Inquiry Lab Manual*.

Virtual Labs

Data Collection *How is a controlled experiment performed?*

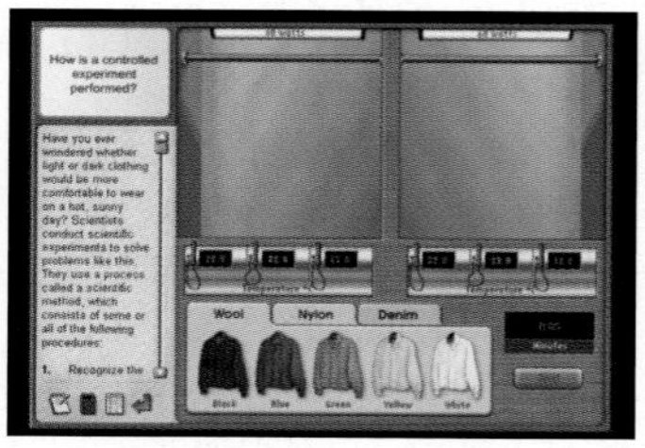

Science Online

Topic: Archimedes' Principle

Visit gpescience.com for Web links to information about Archimedes' principle.

Activity Place a full soft-drink bottle, water bottle, or container of milk in a tub of water. What happens to the pop bottle or milk container? Would you classify Archimedes' principle as a scientific theory or scientific law?

Scientific Theories and Laws

A scientific **theory** is an explanation of things or events based on knowledge gained from many observations and investigations. It is not a guess. If scientists repeat an investigation and the results always support the hypothesis, the hypothesis can be called a theory. Just because a scientific theory has data supporting it does not mean it will never change. Recall that the theory about heat being a fluid was discarded after further experiments. As new information becomes available, theories can be modified. A theory accepted today might at some time in the future also be discarded.

A **scientific law** is a statement about what happens in nature and that seems to be true all the time. Laws tell you what will happen under certain conditions, but they don't explain why or how something happens. Gravity is an example of a scientific law. The law of gravity says that any one mass will attract another mass. To date, no experiments have been performed that disprove the law of gravity.

A theory can be used to explain a law. For example, many theories have been proposed to explain how the law of gravity works. Even so, there are few theories in science and even fewer laws.

Reading Check ***What is the difference between a scientific theory and a scientific law?***

Figure 7 Science can't answer all questions.
Analyze *Can anyone prove that you like artwork? Explain.*

The Limitations of Science

Science can help you explain many things about the world, but science cannot explain or solve everything. Although it's the scientist's job to make hypotheses, the scientist also has to make sure his or her hypotheses can be tested and verified. How do you prove that people will like a play or a piece of music? You cannot and science cannot.

Most questions about emotions and values are not scientific questions. They cannot be tested. You might take a survey to get people's opinions about such questions, but that would not prove that the opinions are true for everyone. A survey might predict that you will like the art in **Figure 7,** but science cannot prove that you or others will.

Post Reading

Discussion After reading Using Science and Technology, take time to discuss additional scientific advances that may be controversial. Identify ethical issues that would be challenging topics for debate. Talk about personal values, ethics, and bias related to a controversial issue. How can expert scientists ignore their personal values?

12 CHAPTER 1 The Nature of Science

Using Science—Technology

Many people use the terms *science* and *technology* interchangeably, but they are not the same. **Technology** is the application of science to help people. For example, when a chemist develops a new, lightweight material that can withstand great amounts of heat, science is used. When that material is used on the space shuttle, technology is applied. **Figure 8** shows other examples of technology.

Technology doesn't always follow science, however. Sometimes the process of discovery can be reversed. One important historic example of science following technology is the development of the steam engine. The inventors of the steam engine had little idea of how it worked. They just knew that steam from boiling water could move the engine. Because the steam engine became so important to industry, scientists began analyzing how it worked. Lord Kelvin, James Prescott Joule, and Sadi Carnot, who lived in the 1800s, learned so much from the steam engine that they developed revolutionary ideas about the nature of heat.

Science and technology do not always produce positive results. The benefits of some technological advances, such as nuclear technology and genetic engineering, are subjects of debate. Being more knowledgeable about science can help society address these issues as they arise.

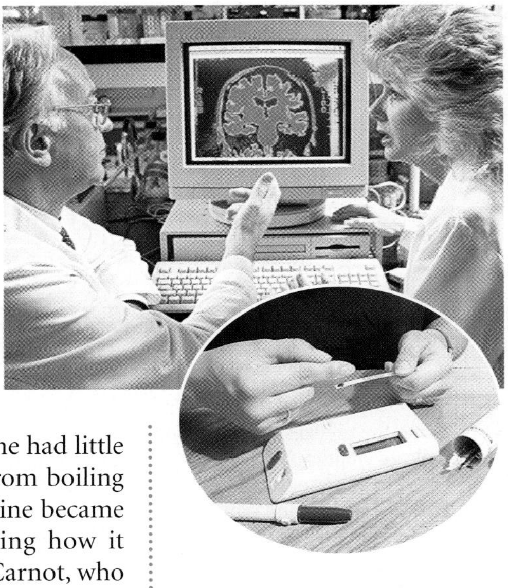

Figure 8 Technology is the application of science.
Identify *the type of science (life, Earth, or physical) that is applied in these examples of technology.*

section 1 review

Summary

What is science?

- Scientists ask questions and perform investigations to learn more about the natural world.

Scientific Methods

- Scientists perform the six-step scientific method to test their hypotheses.

Visualizing with Models

- Models help scientists visualize concepts.

Scientific Theories and Laws

- A theory is a possible explanation for observations, while a scientific law describes a pattern but does not explain why things happen.

Using Science—Technology

- Technology is the application of science in our everyday lives.

Self Check

1. **Define** the first step a scientist usually takes to solve a problem.
2. **Explain** why a control is needed in a valid experiment.
3. **Think Critically** What is the dependent variable in an experiment that shows how the volume of gas changes with changes in temperature?

Applying Math

4. **Find the Average** You perform an experiment to determine how many breaths a fish takes per minute. Your experiment yields the following data: minute 1: 65 breaths; minute 2: 73 breaths; minute 3: 67 breaths; minute 4: 71 breaths; minute 5: 62 breaths. Calculate the average number of breaths that the fish takes per minute.

More Section Review gpescience.com

section 1 review

1. Identify the problem.
2. to provide a standard against which test results can be compared
3. volume of gas
4. The fish takes an average of 68 breaths per minute.

Reading Check

Answer A theory can change if its supporting data changes. A law is assumed to be true and doesn't change. Also, a law tells what happens but does not explain why. Theories try to explain why things happen.

Caption Answers

Figure 7 No, it cannot be tested.

Figure 8 The top picture shows applications of physical science (computer) and life science (medical image). The lower picture shows the application of physical science (instruments) and life science (measuring levels of sugar in blood).

3 Assess

DAILY INTERVENTION

Check for Understanding

Visual-Spatia Review with students the scientific method. On sparate sheets of paper, write the parts of the scientific method. Have students place these sheets on a chart in the correct order.

Reteach

Freezing Water Ask students to design an experiment that will determine whether hot water freezes faster than cold water does. Make sure that constants include the amount of water, the size and kind of container, the amount of time in the freezer, and the freezer used. L2 IS **Logical-Mathematical**

Assessment

Performance Have students design and perform an experiment to determine whether microwave popcorn pops better when it has been frozen. Have them identify constants, variables, and a control for the experiment. Use **PASC,** p. 95.

section 2

Standards of Measurement

Reading Guide

What You'll Learn
- **Name** the prefixes used in SI and indicate what multiple of ten each one represents.
- **Identify** SI units and symbols for length, volume, mass, density, time, and temperature.
- **Convert** related SI units.

Why It's Important
By using uniform standards, nations can exchange goods and compare information easily.

Review Vocabulary
measurement: the dimensions, capacity, or amount of something

New Vocabulary
- precision
- accuracy
- volume
- mass
- density

Units and Standards

A standard is an exact quantity that people agree to use to compare measurements. Look at **Figure 9.** Suppose you and a friend want to make some measurements to find out whether a desk will fit through a doorway. You have no ruler, so you decide to use your hands as measuring tools. Using the width of his hands, your friend measures the doorway and says it is 8 hands wide. Using the width of your hands, you measure the desk and find it is $7\frac{3}{4}$ hands wide. Will the desk fit through the doorway? You can't be sure. What went wrong? Even though you both used hands to measure, you didn't check to see whether your hands were the same width as your friend's.

Figure 9 Hands are a convenient measuring tool, but using them can lead to misunderstanding.

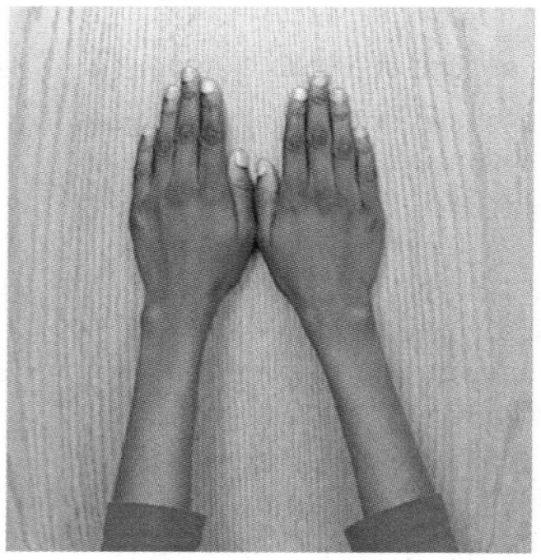

Precision and Accuracy

You are watching an archery event. The first person shoots five bull's-eyes in a row. The second person does not hit the bull's-eye at all, but the arrows all are in a similar location. What can be said about these two participants? The first person's aim was both precise and accurate. The second person's aim was only precise. **Precision** describes how closely measurements are to each other and how carefully measurements were made. **Accuracy** compares a measurement to the real or accepted value. When taking measurements, it is important to be precise and accurate.

1 Motivate

INTERACTIVE CHALKBOARD PowerPoint® Presentations An editable Microsoft® PowerPoint® presentation is available on **Interactive Chalkboard** CD-ROM.

Bellringer

Section Focus Transparencies also are available on the Interactive Chalkboard CD-ROM. L2 ELL

Section 2 Section Focus Transparency — Pick a Scale and Go with It — Chapter 1

What does it mean if someone says that the temperature is thirty-two degrees? It depends entirely on the scale that they're using. Referring to a temperature of 32 might mean that it's a hot summer's day or that it's so cold that even oxygen is frozen solid.

1. Label the three pictures *32°F, 32°C,* and *32 K.*
2. Why must a measurement include the units in order to be meaningful?
3. What kind of units do you use to measure length? Mass? L2

The Nature of Science

Reading Preview

Tie to Prior Knowledge

Measuring Students are familiar with measurements. Ask them to name the units they commonly use to measure length, mass, volume, and temperature.

Visualize Focus students' attention on the review and new vocabulary words. Activate prior knowledge about length, volume, mass and density by reading together and discussing **Figure 15**, Visualizing Dimensions. Make associations between the illustrations and the concepts of volume, mass, and density.

Section 2 Resource Manager

Chapter *Fast File* Resources
- Transparency Activity, p. 45
- Enrichment, p. 31
- Directed Reading for Content Mastery, p. 20
- MiniLAB, p. 3
- Lab Activity, pp. 9–12
- Reinforcement, p. 28

Physical Science Critical Thinking/Problem Solving, p. 2

Mathematics Skill Activities, p. 61

Reading and Writing Skills Activities, pp. 13, 41

International System of Units

In 1960, an improved version of the metric system was devised. Known as the International System of Units, this system is often abbreviated SI, from the French *Le Systeme Internationale d'Unites.* SI is an improved, accepted version of the metric system that is based on multiples of ten. It is understood by scientists throughout the world. The standard kilogram, which is kept in Sèvres, France, is shown in **Figure 10.** All kilograms used throughout the world must be exactly the same as the kilogram kept in France.

Each type of SI measurement has a base unit. The meter is the base unit of length. Every type of quantity measured in SI has a symbol for that unit. These names and symbols for the seven base units are shown in **Table 1.** All other SI units are obtained from these seven units.

Figure 10 The standard for mass, the kilogram, and other standards are kept at the International Bureau of Weights and Measures in Sèvres, France. **Explain** *the purpose of a standard.*

SI Prefixes The SI system is easy to use because it is based on multiples of ten. Prefixes are used with the names of the units to indicate what multiple of ten should be used with the units. For example, the prefix *kilo-* means "1,000." This means that one kilometer equals 1,000 meters. Likewise, one kilogram equals 1,000 grams. Because *deci-* means "one-tenth," one decimeter equals one-tenth of a meter. A decigram equals one-tenth of a gram. The most frequently used prefixes are shown in **Table 2.**

Reading Check *How many meters are in 1 km? How many grams are in 1 dg?*

Table 1 SI Base Units

Quantity Measured	Unit	Symbol
Length	meter	m
Mass	kilogram	kg
Time	second	s
Electric current	ampere	A
Temperature	kelvin	K
Amount of substance	mole	mol
Intensity of light	candela	cd

Table 2 Common SI Prefixes

Prefix	Symbol	Multiplying Factor
Kilo-	k	1,000
Deci-	d	0.1
Centi-	c	0.01
Milli-	m	0.001
Micro-	μ	0.000 001
Nano-	n	0.000 000 001

2 Teach

IDENTIFYING Misconceptions

SI Precision Students may think that SI is more precise than the English system because scientists use it. Point out that both systems can yield equally precise measurements. For instance, a micrometer used by machinists can measure the diameters of bolts to the nearest 0.0001 inch. Scientists use SI because it is easier to use and easier to convert units. Have students measure the length of their textbook using a metric ruler and a ruler calibrated in inches. Have them compare results and note that both measurements can be precise.

Caption Answer

Figure 10 It provides an accepted and understood value for a base unit.

Reading Check

Answer 1,000; one tenth

Reading Strategy

Double-Entry Notes Ask students to take notes on this section by dividing their papers with a vertical line. Students should write bold headings in the left column. On the right side, students should include vocabulary definitions, formulas, words in italics, summaries, and responses that correlate to the headings.

Science Journal

Standards Have students record in their Science Journals the physical standards for mass, length, and time. The standard mass is the 1 kg of platinum-iridium alloy shown in **Figure 10.** The standard length, 1 meter, is defined as the distance light travels in a vacuum in 1/299,792,458 of a second. The standard time, 1 second, is defined as 9,192,631,770 periods of the radiation of cesium-133 atoms. L3

Differentiated Instruction

Challenge Have students research the standardization of currency. When did it occur? Why? They can compare the need for standard units of measurement with the need for standard currency. It is believed that the first standard coins were produced in Lydia, part of present-day Turkey, in the 600s B.C. The coins were standardized so people knew the exact value of the metal pieces. L3 LS **Linguistic**

Caption Answer

Figure 11 3.1 cm; 31 mm

Make a Model

Measurment System Model a new metric measurement system. Organize the class into groups and have each group choose an object to be the basis for its new metric standard of length. Have students make or draw models showing a unit, a deciunit, a centiunit, and a kilounit. L2
LS **Visual-Spatial** P

Applying Math

Math Standards

National: 4

Answers to Practice Problems

1. 1 cm = 10mm
   11 cm × 10 mm/cm = 110 mm
2. 1 mi = 1.6 km
   20,000 mi × 1.6 km = 32000 km

Discussion

Measuring Day Time Point out to students that while in SI the units for time less than 1 s are divided into multiples of ten (the millisecond, nanosecond, etc.), the units for time greater than 1 s are not. Have each student devise a metric system for measuring the amount of time in a day. Accept all responses in which time is divided into units that are multiples of ten. L3 LS **Logical-Mathematical**

Reading Check

Answer avoiding large digit numbers and numbers with many decimal places

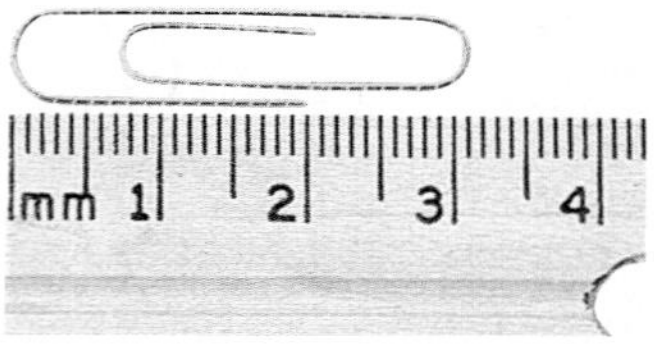

Figure 11 One centimeter contains 10 mm.
Determine *the length of the paper clip in centimeters and in millimeters.*

Converting Between SI Units Sometimes quantities are measured using different units, as shown in **Figure 11.** A conversion factor is a ratio that is equal to one and is used to change one unit to another. For example, there are 1,000 mL in 1 L, so 1,000 mL = 1 L. If both sides in this equation are divided by 1 L, the equation becomes:

$$\frac{1{,}000\text{ mL}}{1\text{ L}} = 1$$

To convert units, you multiply by the appropriate conversion factor. For example, to convert 1.255 L to mL, multiply 1.255 L by a conversion factor. Use the conversion factor with new units (mL) in the numerator and the old units (L) in the denominator.

$$1.255\ \cancel{\text{L}} \times \frac{1{,}000\text{ mL}}{1\ \cancel{\text{L}}} = 1{,}255\text{ mL}$$

Applying Math — Convert Units

CENTIMETERS How long in centimeters is a 3,075 mm rope?

IDENTIFY known values and the unknown value

Identify the known values:

The rope measures 3,075 mm; 1 m = 100 cm = 1,000 mm

Identify the unknown value:

How long is the rope in cm?

SOLVE the problem

This is the equation you need to use:

$$?\text{ cm} = 3{,}075\text{ mm} \times \frac{100\text{ cm}}{1{,}000\text{ mm}}$$

Cancel units and multiply:

$$3{,}075\ \cancel{\text{mm}} \times \frac{1\cancel{00}\text{ cm}}{1{,}0\cancel{00}\ \cancel{\text{mm}}} = 307.5\text{ cm}$$

CHECK your answer

Does your answer seem reasonable? Check your answer by multiplying the answer by $\frac{1{,}000\text{ mm}}{100\text{ cm}}$. Did you calculate the original length in millimeters?

Practice Problems

1. Your pencil is 11 cm long. How long is it in millimeters?
2. The Bering Land Bridge National Preserve is a summer home to birds. Some birds migrate 20,000 miles. Assume 1 mile equals 1.6 kilometers. Calculate the distance birds fly in kilometers.

For more practice problems, go to page 879 and visit Math Practice at gpescience.com.

Teacher FYI

Early Measurement Early measurements were based on body parts. One of the earliest measurements ever recorded was length. The Egyptian cubit was derived from the length of the arm from the elbow to the outstretched fingertips. France's unit of length was the meter, which was defined as being one ten-millionth part of a quarter of Earth's circumference. The production of this standard required a very careful survey to be done which took several years. As more accurate instruments became available, the standard was called into question.

16 CHAPTER 1 The Nature of Science

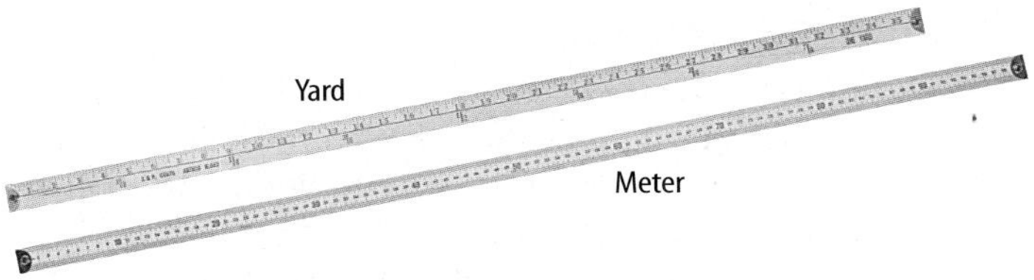

Figure 12 One meter is slightly longer than 1 yard, and 100 m is slightly longer than a football field. **Predict** *whether your time for a 100-m dash would be slightly more or less than your time for a 100-yard dash.*

Measuring Distance

The word *length* is used in many different ways. For example, the length of a novel is the number of pages or words it contains. In scientific measurement, length is the distance between two points. That distance might be the diameter of a hair or the distance from Earth to the Moon. The SI base unit of length is the meter, m. A baseball bat is about 1 m long. Metric rulers and metersticks are used to measure length. **Figure 12** compares a meter and a yard.

Choosing a Unit of Length As shown in **Figure 13,** the size of the unit you measure with will depend on the size of the object being measured. For example, the diameter of a shirt button is about 1 cm. You probably also would use the centimeter to measure the length of your pencil and the meter to measure the length of your classroom. What unit would you use to measure the distance from your home to school? You probably would want to use a unit larger than a meter. The kilometer, km, which is 1,000 m, is used to measure these kinds of distances.

By choosing an appropriate unit, you avoid large-digit numbers and numbers with many decimal places. Twenty-one kilometers is easier to deal with than 21,000 m, and 13 mm is easier to use than 0.013 m.

Reading Check *Why is choosing the correct unit of length important?*

INTEGRATE Earth Science

Astronomical Units The standard measurement for the distance from Earth to the Sun is called the astronomical unit, AU. The distance is about 150 billion (1.5×10^{11}) m. In your Science Journal, calculate what 1 AU would equal in kilometers.

Figure 13 The size of the object being measured determines which unit you will measure in. A tape measure measures in meters. The micrometer, shown on the left, measures in small lengths. **State** *what unit you think it measures.*

Caption Answers

Figure 12 slightly more

Figure 13 micrometers

Activity

Rulers Distribute metric rulers and have students identify the millimeter, centimeter, and decimeter markings on the ruler. Have them measure common objects. As they are measuring, have each student choose an object that best represents a centimeter. Allow them to make estimations and use their rulers to check their estimations. L2 LS **Kinesthetic**

INTEGRATE Earth Science

Astronomical Units Venus is 0.72 AU from the Sun and Pluto is 39.6 AU from the Sun. 1 AU is about 1.5×10^8 km = 150,000,000 km.

Career Astronomers study objects where they cannot use all of their senses. They cannot touch or smell stars, comets, or planets other than Earth. Astronomers do need good observations skills. The majority of the astronomers do not look through telescopes. They teach and do research in colleges and universities.

Quick Demo
Accurate Measurements

Materials meterstick, tape measure, round object

Estimated Time five minutes

Purpose Use a meterstick to measure the circumperence of a round object. Repeat the measurement with a metric tape measure. Ask the students to explain why the measurement made with the tape measure is more accurate. The meterstick can't bend to accurately measure the curved surface. L1 ELL LS **Logical-Mathematical**

Cultural Diversity

Length Through Time Accurate length measurement was important for ancient engineering projects, such as the Nazca lines, the pyramids in Central America and Africa, and the great public buildings found in many cultures. Have students identify some of the units of length used in the ancient world. Lengths used include the cubit and the Roman mile. L2 LS **Linguistic**

Visual Learning

Figure 12 Discuss with students the difference between a meter and a yard. Measure the distance across the classroom or blackboard in both meters and yards and make sure students understand the measurements. Review with students how to convert meters into yards.

Activity

Relative Volume Provide a number of irregularly-shaped containers and a graduated cylinder. Have each student make a hypothesis about the relative volumes of the containers and write down the hypothesis. Then have students test their hypotheses by measuring the volume of each container. Tell them to fill each container completely with water, pour the water into the graduated cylinder, and measure the amount the container held. L2 LS **Kinesthetic**

Caption Answer

Figure 14 1,000 cm^3 are in 1 dm^3.

Science Online

Topic: International System of Units
Visit gpescience.com for Web links to information about the International System of Units.

Activity Measure four different things in your classroom using a different unit—distance, volume, time, or temperature—for each. Use each unit only once. Write the measurements down and using the common prefixes in **Table 2**, convert them to different units.

Measuring Volume

The amount of space occupied by an object is called its **volume.** If you want to know the volume of a solid rectangle, such as a brick, you measure its length, width, and height and multiply the three numbers and their units together ($V = l \times w \times h$). For a brick, your measurements probably would be in centimeters. The volume would then be expressed in cubic centimeters, cm^3. To find out how much a moving van can carry, your measurements probably would be in meters, and the volume would be expressed in cubic meters, m^3, because when you multiply, you add exponents.

Measuring Liquid Volume How do you measure the volume of a liquid? A liquid has no sides to measure. In measuring a liquid's volume, you are indicating the capacity of the container that holds that amount of liquid. The most common units for expressing liquid volumes are liters and milliliters. These are measurements used in canned and bottled foods. A liter occupies the same volume as a cubic decimeter, dm^3. A cubic decimeter is a cube that is 1 dm, or 10 cm, on each side, as in **Figure 14.**

Look at **Figure 14.** One liter is equal to 1,000 mL. A cubic decimeter, dm^3, is equal to 1,000 cm^3. Because 1 L = 1 dm^3, it follows that

$$1 \text{ mL} = 1 \text{ cm}^3$$

Sometimes, liquid volumes such as doses of medicine are expressed in cubic centimeters.

Suppose you wanted to convert a measurement in liters to cubic centimeters. You would use conversion factors to convert L to mL and then mL to cm^3.

$$1.5 \cancel{\text{L}} \times \frac{1{,}000 \cancel{\text{mL}}}{1 \cancel{\text{L}}} \times \frac{1 \text{ cm}^3}{1 \cancel{\text{mL}}} = 1{,}500 \text{ cm}^3$$

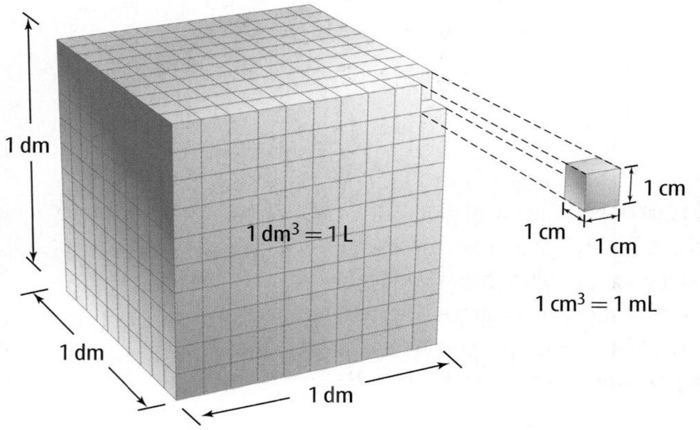

Figure 14 The large cube has a volume of 1 dm^3, which is equivalent to 1 L. **Calculate** *the cubic centimeters (cm^3) in the large cube.*

Curriculum Connection

Math Have students find and record the equations for determining the volumes of shapes such as a cylinder, sphere, square pyramid, and cone. The equation for calculating the volume of a cylinder is $\pi r^2 h$. The equation for the volume of a sphere is $\frac{4}{3}\pi r^3$. The equation for the volume of a square pyramid is $\frac{1}{3}bh$. The equation for the volume of a cone is $\frac{1}{3}\pi r^2 h$. L3 LS **Logical-Mathematical**

Table 3 Densities of Some Materials at 20°C

Material	Density (g/cm^3)	Material	Density (g/cm^3)
Hydrogen	0.000 09	Aluminum	2.7
Oxygen	0.001 4	Iron	7.9
Water	1.0	Gold	19.3

Measuring Matter

A table-tennis ball and a golf ball have about the same volume. But if you pick them up, you will notice a difference. The golf ball has more mass. **Mass** is a measurement of the quantity of matter in an object. The mass of the golf ball, which is about 45 g, is almost 18 times the mass of the table-tennis ball, which is about 2.5 g. To visualize SI units, see **Figure 15** on the following page.

Density A cube of polished aluminum and a cube of silver that are the same size not only look similar but also have the same volume. The mass and volume of an object can be used to find the density of the material the object is made of. **Density** is the mass per unit volume of a material. You find density by dividing an object's mass by the object's volume. For example, the density of an object having a mass of 10 g and a volume of 2 cm^3 is 5 g/cm^3. **Table 3** lists the densities of some familiar materials.

Reading Check *How is density determined?*

Derived Units The measurement unit for density, g/cm^3, is a combination of SI units. A unit obtained by combining different SI units is called a derived unit. An SI unit multiplied by itself also is a derived unit. Thus the liter, which is based on the cubic decimeter, is a derived unit. A meter cubed, expressed with an exponent—m^3—is a derived unit.

Measuring Time and Temperature

It is often necessary to keep track of how long it takes for something to happen, or whether something heats up or cools down. These measurements involve time and temperature.

Time is the interval between two events. The SI unit for time is the second. In the laboratory, you will use a stopwatch or a clock with a second hand to measure time.

Mini LAB

Determining the Density of a Pencil

Procedure

1. Find a **pencil** that will fit in a **100-mL graduated cylinder** below the 90-mL mark.
2. Measure the mass of the pencil in grams.
3. Put 90 mL of **water** (initial volume) into the 100-mL graduated cylinder. Lower the pencil, eraser first, into the cylinder. Push the pencil down until it is just submerged. Hold it there and record the final volume to the nearest tenth of a milliliter.

Analysis

1. Determine the water displaced by the pencil by subtracting the initial volume from the final volume.
2. Calculate the pencil's density by dividing its mass by the volume of water displaced.
3. Is the density of the pencil greater than or less than the density of water? How do you know?

Mini LAB

Purpose Students measure the mass and volume of a pencil and use these data to find its density. L1 ELL LS **Logical-Mathematical**

Materials water, 100-mL graduated cylinder, unsharpened pencil, balance

Teaching Strategy The mass measurement should be made using a dry pencil.

Analysis

1. Students should use the equation $d = m/v$. Remind them that 1 mL = 1 cm^3.
2. Check students' paper.
3. Because the pencil floats, its density is less than that of water. Also, its calculated density is less than that of water—1.0.

Assessment

Performance Have students use the same procedure to test the density of another object such as a cork or a rubber stopper. If possible, they could compare their results with the density given in **Table 3** on this page or another density table. Use **Performance Assessment in the Science Classroom,** p. 97.

Reading Check

Answer divide mass by volume

Curriculum Connection

Math The SI prefix *pico-* is used for tiny measurements. The diameter of a hydrogen nucleus is about 78 picometers. Have students find out what *pico-* means and find the diameter of a hydrogen atom in meters. The prefix means one-trillionth. A hydrogen atom has a diameter of 78 trillionths (78×10^{-12}) of a meter. L2 LS **Logical-Mathematical**

Differentiated Instruction

Behaviorally Disordered Have these students read through the lab a day or two before the class does it. Show them how it works and ask whether they have any questions. Make sure they understand the purpose of the water. When they do the lab, pair them with students who work well in the lab.

NATIONAL GEOGRAPHIC

Visualizing SI Dimensions

Have students examine the pictures and read the captions. Then ask the following questions.

In what units would you measure your height? meters The distance a runner covered in a marathon? kilometers The mass of a pencil? grams

Why wouldn't you measure the distance from Dallas, Texas to Miami, Florida in millimeters? The number of millimeters would be an extremely large number, too big to be able to visualize. What unit should you use? kilometers

Activity

Different Measurements Set up three stations and allow groups to rotate through them. One station should have a balance and several objects that students can mass. Another station should have several containers of liquids and a graduated cylinder so they can measure volumes. The third station should have a metric ruler and meterstick and several objects whose lengths students can determine. Have students measure the objects and compare their measurements when all have finished. L1

LS **Kinesthetic**

NATIONAL GEOGRAPHIC **VISUALIZING SI DIMENSIONS**

Figure 15

The characteristics of most of these everyday objects are measured using an international system known as SI dimensions. These dimensions measure length, volume, mass, density, and time. Celsius is not an SI unit but is widely used in scientific work.

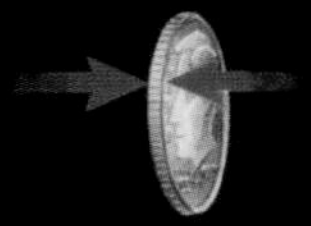

MILLIMETERS **A dime is about 1 mm thick.**

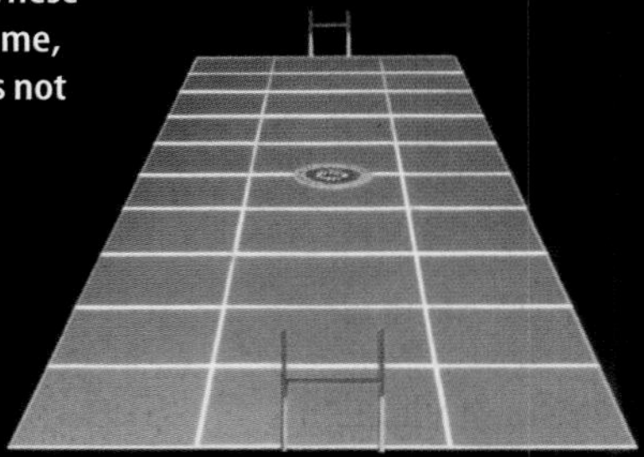

METERS **A football field is about 91 m long.**

KILOMETERS **The distance from your house to a store can be measured in kilometers.**

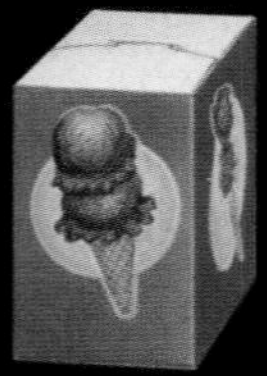

LITERS **This carton holds 1.98 L of frozen yogurt.**

MILLILITERS **A teaspoonful of medicine is about 5 mL.**

GRAMS/METER **This stone sinks because it is denser—has more grams per cubic meter—than water.**

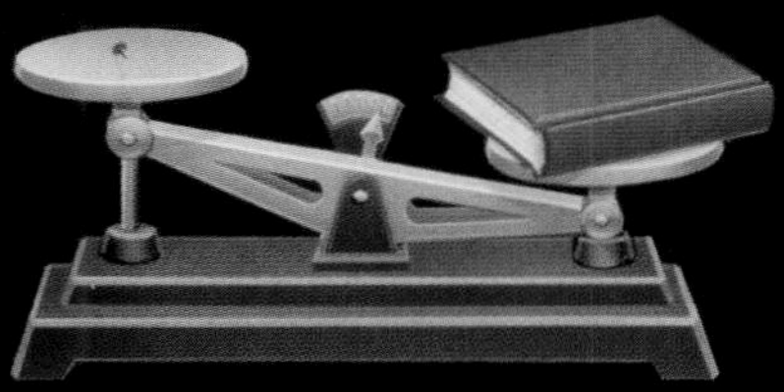

GRAMS **The mass of a thumbtack and the mass of a textbook can be expressed in grams.**

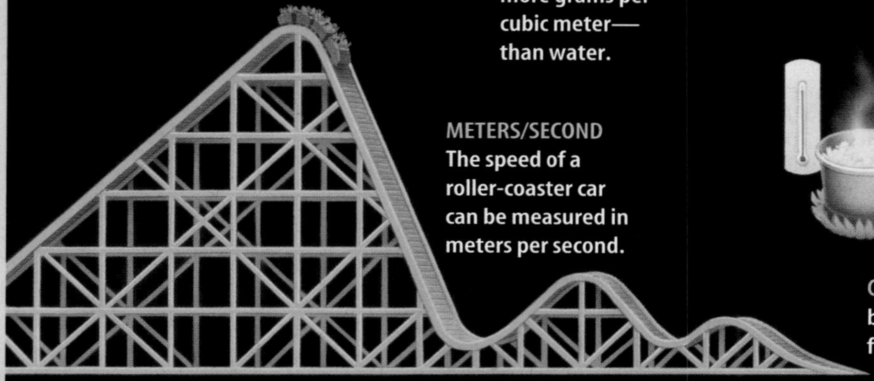

METERS/SECOND **The speed of a roller-coaster car can be measured in meters per second.**

CELSIUS **Water boils at 100°C and freezes at 0°C.**

Differentiated Instruction

Challenge Have students find the high temperature for the day in Fahrenheit, Celsius, and Kelvin. They can obtain the temperature, probably in Fahrenheit, from a weather report. Have them use the following equations: $C = 5(F - 32)/9$; $C + 273 = K$. L3 LS **Logical-Mathematical**

Post Reading

Creating Charts After reading the section on time and temperature, have students make a chart that shows Fahrenheit, Celsius, and Kelvin temperatures for the boiling point of water (212°F), an extremely hot day (100°F), a perfect day (72°F), a chilly day (45°F), a freezing day (32°F) and dangerously cold days (0°F).

What's Hot and What's Not You will learn the scientific meaning of the word *temperature* in a later chapter. For now, think of temperature as a measure of how hot or how cold something is.

Look at **Figure 16.** For most scientific work, temperature is measured on the Celsius (C) scale. On this scale, the freezing point of water is 0°C, and the boiling point of water is 100°C. Between these points, the scale is divided into 100 equal divisions. Each one represents 1°C. On the Celsius scale, the average human body temperature is 37°C, and a typical room temperature is between 20°C and 25°C.

Kelvin and Fahrenheit The SI unit of temperature is the kelvin (K). Zero on the Kelvin scale (0 K) is the coldest possible temperature, also known as absolute zero. Absolute zero is equal to −273°C, which is 273° below the freezing point of water.

Most laboratory thermometers are marked only with the Celsius scale. Because the divisions on the two scales are the same size, the Kelvin temperature can be found by adding 273 to the Celsius reading. So, on the Kelvin scale, water freezes at 273 K and boils at 373 K. Notice that degree symbols are not used with the Kelvin scale.

The temperature measurement you are probably most familiar with is the Fahrenheit scale, which was based roughly on the temperature of the human body, 98.6°.

Reading Check *What is the relationship between the Celsius scale and the Kelvin scale?*

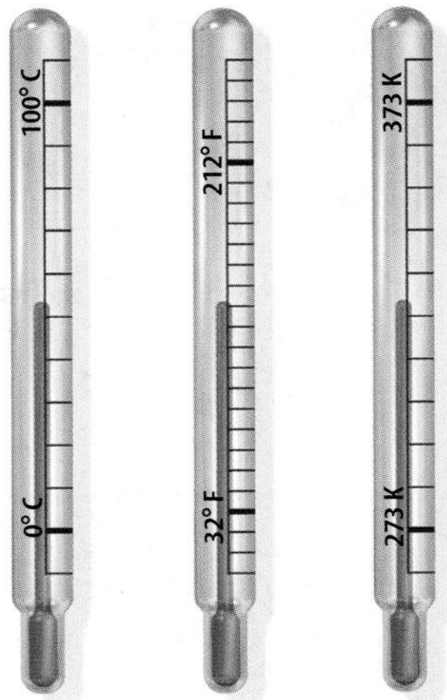

Figure 16 These three thermometers illustrate the scales of temperature between the freezing and boiling points of water. **Compare** *the boiling points of the three scales.*

section 2 review

Summary

Precision and Accuracy

- Precision is the description of how close measurements are to each other.

International System of Units

- The International System of Units, or SI, was established to provide a standard of measurement and reduce confusion.
- Conversion factors are used to change one unit to another and involve using a ratio equal to 1.

Measuring

- The size of an object being measured determines which unit you will measure in.

Self Check

1. **Explain** why it is important to have exact standards of measurement.
2. **Explain** why density is a derived unit.
3. **Think Critically** Using a metric ruler, measure a shoe box and a pad of paper. Find the volume of each in cubic centimeters. Then convert the units to mL.

Applying Math

4. **Convert Units** Make the following conversions: 27°C to Kelvin, 20 dg to milligrams, and 3 m to decimeters.
5. **Calculate Density** What is the density of an unknown metal that has a mass of 158 g and a volume of 20 mL? Use **Table 3** to identify this metal.

More Section Review gpescience.com

Caption Answer

Figure 16 The boiling point of water is 373 K, 100°C, and 212°F.

Reading Check

Answer The units are the same size, but zero on the Kelvin scale is 273 units lower than zero on the Celsius scale.

3 Assess

DAILY INTERVENTION

Check for Understanding

Kinesthetic Being able to convert between SI units is important in understanding how scientists operate on a daily basis. Have students measure various objects in centimenters. Then have students convert from centimeters to meter, from meter to kilometer, and centimeter to kilometer.

Reteach

Have each student calculate his or her mass in kilograms. Tell students that at Earth's surface, an object weighing 1 pound has a mass of 0.45 kg. Sample: A student weighing 120 pounds has a mass of 54 kg. L2 LS **Logical-Mathematical**

Assessment

Performance Have students develop their own standards and units for measuring time. Have them evaluate their units in terms of how easy it is to replicate results using their standards. Use **PASC**, p. 117.

section 2 review

1. They provide a consistent, known, and accepted value for a base unit.
2. It is obtained by combining two SI units.
3. Check students' work.
4. 300 K; 2000 mg; 30 dm
5. 158.0 g/20.0 mL = 7.90 g/mL; iron

section 3

Communicating with Graphs

1 Motivate

INTERACTIVE CHALKBOARD PowerPoint® Presentations An editable Microsoft® PowerPoint® presentation is available on **Interactive Chalkboard** CD-ROM.

Bellringer

Section Focus Transparencies also are available on the Interactive Chalkboard CD-ROM. L2 ELL

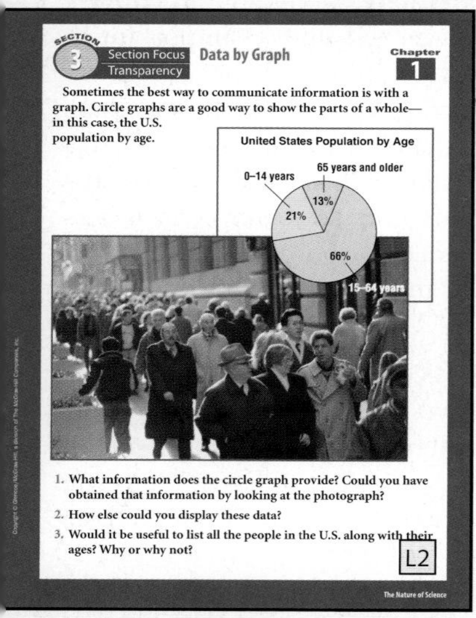
SECTION 3 Section Focus Transparency **Data by Graph** Chapter 1

Sometimes the best way to communicate information is with a graph. Circle graphs are a good way to show the parts of a whole—in this case, the U.S. population by age.

1. **What information does the circle graph provide? Could you have obtained that information by looking at the photograph?**
2. **How else could you display these data?**
3. **Would it be useful to list all the people in the U.S. along with their ages? Why or why not?** L2

The Nature of Science

Reading Preview

Tie to Prior Knowledge

Finding Graphs Assign students to find graphs in newspapers and magazines and bring them to class. Have student groups develop a classification system for the graphs. L1 IN **Interpersonal**

Charts and Graphs Preview the text and identify types of graphs and illustrations in this section. Ask "Have you ever used or seen any others types of graphs?" Students may think of picture graphs and coordinate graphs. Have students talk about the differences between a chart and a graph.

Reading Guide

What You'll Learn

- **Identify** three types of graphs and explain the ways they are used.
- **Distinguish** between dependent and independent variables.
- **Analyze** data using the various types of graphs.

Why It's Important

Graphs are a quick way to communicate a lot of information in a small amount of space.

Review Vocabulary

data: information gathered during an investigation or observation

New Vocabulary

- graph

A Visual Display

Scientists often graph the results of their experiments because they can detect patterns in the data easier in a graph than in a table. A **graph** is a visual display of information or data. **Figure 17** is a graph that shows a girl walking her dog. The horizontal axis, or the *x*-axis, measures time. Time is the independent variable because as it changes, it affects the measure of another variable. The distance from home that the girl and the dog walk is the other variable. It is the dependent variable and is measured on the vertical axis, or *y*-axis.

Graphs are useful for displaying numerical information in business, science, sports, advertising, and many everyday situations. Different kinds of graphs—line, bar, and circle—are appropriate for displaying different types of information.

Reading Check *What are three common types of graphs?*

Figure 17 This graph tells the story of the motion that takes place when a girl takes her dog for an 8-min walk.

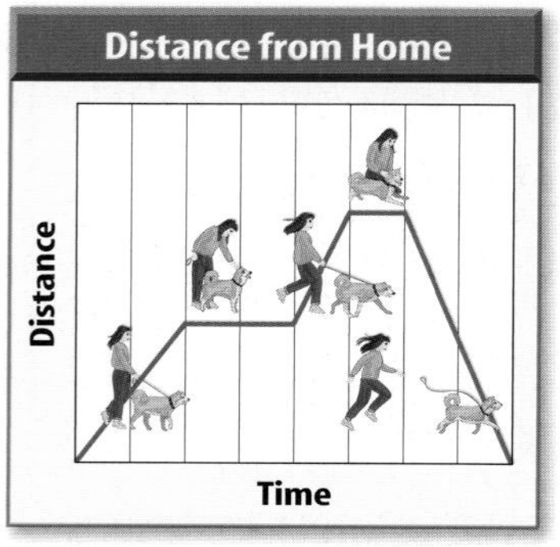

Graphs are useful for displaying numerical information in business, science, sports, advertising, and many other everyday situations. Graphs make it easier to understand complex patterns by displaying data in a visual manner. Scientists often graph their data to detect patterns that would not have been evident in a table. Different graphs use different methods for displaying information. The conclusions drawn from graphs must be based on accurate information and reasonable scales.

Section 3 Resource Manager

Chapter *FAST FILE* Resources

- Transparency Activity, pp. 46, 47–48
- Directed Reading for Content Mastery, pp. 21–22
- MiniLAB, p. 4
- Enrichment, p. 32
- Reinforcement, p. 29
- Lab Activity, pp. 13–16
- Lab Worksheet, pp. 5–6, 7–8

Lab Management and Safety, p. 71

Reading and Writing Skill Activities, p. 47

Line Graphs

A line graph can show any relationship where the dependent variable changes due to a change in the independent variable. Line graphs often show how a relationship between variables changes over time. You can use a line graph to track many things, such as how certain stocks perform or how the population changes over any period of time—a month, a week, or a year.

You can show more than one event on the same graph as long as the relationship between the variables is identical. Suppose a builder had three choices of thermostats for a new school. He wanted to test them to know which was the best brand to install throughout the building. He installed a different thermostat in classrooms A, B, and C. He set each thermostat at 20°C. He turned the furnace on and checked the temperatures in the three rooms every 5 min for 25 min. He recorded his data in **Table 4.**

Table 4 Room Temperature

Time*	Classroom Temperature (C°) A	B	C
0	16	16	16
5	17	17	16.5
10	19	19	17
15	20	21	17.5
20	20	23	18
25	20	25	18.5

*minutes after turning on heat

The builder then plotted the data on a graph. He could see from the table that the data did not vary much for the three classrooms. So he chose small intervals for the *y*-axis and left part of the scale out (the part between 0° and 15°), as shown in **Figure 18.** This allowed him to spread out the area on the graph where the data points lie. You easily can see the contrast in the colors of the three lines and their relationship to the black horizontal line. The black line represents the thermostat setting and is the control. The control is what the resulting room temperature of the classrooms should be if the thermostats are working efficiently.

Figure 18 The room temperatures of classrooms A, B, and C are shown in contrast to the thermostat setting of 20°C.
Identify *the thermostat that achieved its temperature setting the quickest.*

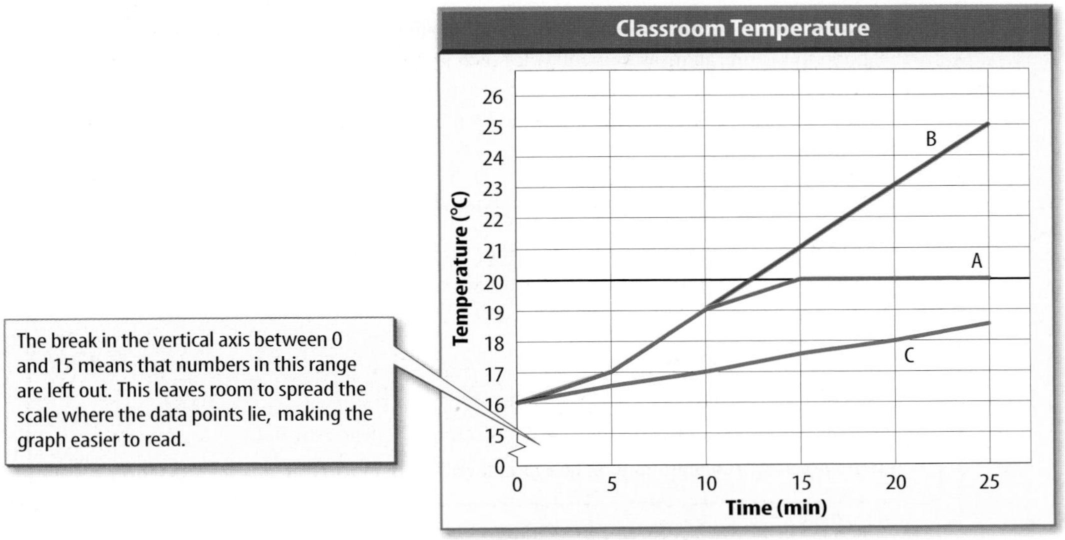

2 Teach

Reading Check

Answer line, bar, and circle graphs

Caption Answer

Figure 18 thermostat A

Discussion

Interpolation v. Extrapolation Explain to students that interpolation is reading graph values between data points, and extrapolation is reading graph values beyond data points. Ask students which process is likely to produce more error. Extrapolation; it goes beyond what has actually been measured in an experiment. L3 LS **Logical-Mathematical**

Activity

Graphing Have students look in the newspaper for information that can be presented as graphs. Have each student explain why they chose that particular graph. Examples can be weather data, motor vehicle ads, or sports statistics.

Reading Strategy

Summarize Ask students to write a summary sentence in their Science Journals after studying the line graph in **Figure 18**, the bar graph in **Figure 20**, and the circle graph in **Figure 21**. Have students compare their summary statements.

Visual Learning

Figure 18 Have students practice interpolation (finding data between reference points) and extrapolation (finding data past the range of the reference points) by examining the data provided. Ask them what they would expect the temperature to be in the classroom using thermostat A after 8 min and after 30 min. 18°C and 20°C L3 ELL LS **Visual-Spatial**

Differentiated Instruction

Challenge Graphs are not always a completely objective presentation of data. Graphs are frequently used in advertising to conceal or distort data. Ask students to think of ways that information could be emphasized or underplayed on a graph. A stretched-out vertical scale would emphasize highs and lows. A compressed vertical scale would conceal them. L2 ELL LS **Logical-Mathematical**

Quick Demo
Data Tables

Materials none

Estimated Time ten minutes

Purpose Use students' clothing or shoes to demonstrate how to make a data table. For example, you could collect data such as shoe type, shoe color, sleeve length, or clothing type. After completing the data table, complete a bar graph of the information. Reinforce the idea that a bar graph rather than a line graph would be used because a line graph must contain two sets of numbers, while a bar graph can use categories. L2 ELL LS **Visual-Spatial**

Applying Math

Math Standards

National: 1, 2, 5, 9

Answer to Practice Problem

1. Students could use either bar graphs or line graphs to represent this data. In either case, running time should be on the y-axis and year should be on the x-axis.
2. Check students' work.
3. The difference in time is 1.2h.
   % Improvement =
   1.2 h/5.2 h × 100 = 23.1%

Teacher FYI

Charts and Graphs The earliest surviving chart, an illustration of the orbits of the planets over time, dates back to the tenth century. The art of charting and graphing didn't appear again until the 18th century with the introduction of the modern economics graph by William Playfair.

Figure 19 Graphing calculators are valuable tools for making graphs.

Constructing Line Graphs Besides choosing a scale that makes a graph readable, as illustrated in **Figure 18,** other factors are involved in constructing useful graphs. The most important factor in making a line graph is always using the x-axis for the independent variable. The y-axis always is used for the dependent variable. Because the points in a line graph are related, you connect the points.

Another factor in constructing a graph involves units of measurement. For example, you might use a Celsius thermometer for one part of your experiment and a Fahrenheit thermometer for another. But you must first convert your temperature readings to the same unit of measurement before you make your graph.

In the past, graphs had to be made by hand, with each point plotted individually. Today, scientists use a variety of tools, such as computers and graphing calculators like the one shown in **Figure 19,** to help them draw graphs.

Applying Math — Make and Use Graphs

TEMPERATURE In an experiment, you checked the air temperature at certain hours of the day. At 8 A.M., the temperature was 27°C; at noon, the temperature was 32°C; and at 4 P.M., the temperature was 30°C. Graph the results of your experiment.

IDENTIFY known values

time = independent variable, which is the x-axis

temperature = dependent variable, which is the y-axis

GRAPH the problem

Graph time on the x-axis and temperature on the y-axis. Mark the equal increments on the graph to include all measurements. Plot each point on the graph by finding the time on the x-axis and moving up until you find the recorded temperature on the y-axis. Place a point there. Continue placing points on the graph. Then connect the points from left to right.

Practice Problems

As you train for a marathon, you compare your previous times. In year one, you ran it in 5.2 h; in year two, you ran it in 5 h; in year three, you ran it in 4.8 h; in year four, you ran it in 4.3 h; and in year five, you ran it in 4 h.

1. Make a table of your data.
2. Graph the results of your marathon races.
3. Calculate your percentage of improvement from year one to year five.

For more practice problems, go to page 879 and visit Math Practice at gpescience.com.

Science Journal

Birth Months Take a class survey of the month in which each student's birthday occurs and tally these data on the board. Have students record this information in their Science Journals. Ask each student to make both a bar graph and a circle graph to show the information. L2 LS **Logical-Mathematical** P

Differentiated Instruction

Learning Disabled Have students conduct a survey in class to determine how many of their peers walk to class, how many ride a bike, get a ride, and take the bus. After students gather their data, have them determine which graph will best display the data. Why did they choose that particular graph? What made the other graphs a bad choice?

24 CHAPTER 1 The Nature of Science

Bar Graphs

A bar graph is useful for comparing information collected by counting. For example, suppose you counted the number of students in every classroom in your school on a particular day and organized your data as in **Table 5.** You could show these data in a bar graph like the one shown in **Figure 20.** Uses for bar graphs include comparisons of oil or crop productions, costs, or data in promotional materials. Each bar represents a quantity counted at a particular time, which should be stated on the graph. As on a line graph, the independent variable is plotted on the x-axis and the dependent variable is plotted on the y-axis.

Recall that you might need to place a break in the scale of the graph to better illustrate your results. For example, if your data were 1,002, 1,010, 1,030, and 1,040 and the intervals on the scale were every 100 units, you might not be able to see the difference from one bar to another. If you had a break in the scale and started your data range at 1,000 with intervals of ten units, you could make a more accurate comparison.

Reading Check ***Describe possible data where using a bar graph would be better than using a line graph.***

Table 5 Classroom Size

Number of Students	Number of Classrooms
20	1
21	3
22	3
23	2
24	3
25	5
26	5
27	3

Figure 20 The height of each bar corresponds to the number of classrooms having a particular number of students.

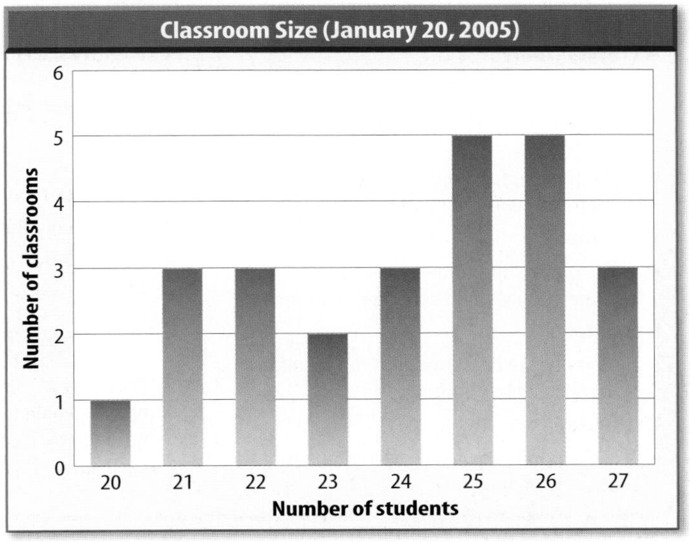

Mini LAB

Graphing Temperature Change

Procedure

1. Add 1-c of **cold water** to a **medium-sized plastic bowl.** Add 1/2 c of **ice** to the water. Put 2 tbs of **table salt** into the iced water.
2. Fill a **clear-plastic cup** 2/3 full with **room temperature water.** Measure the temperature of the water using a **thermometer.** Place the plastic cup with the thermometer into the bowl of iced water. Make sure the iced water surrounds the liquid in the cup. Do not allow any iced water into the cup.
3. Measure and record the temperature every 30 s for 5 min.

Analysis

1. Identify the dependent and independent variables.
2. Make a line graph of the data recorded in step 3.

Try at Home

Mini LAB

Purpose Students measure the change in temperature over time and graph the data. L1 ELL IN Visual-Spatial

Materials cold water, room-temperature water, table salt, medium-size plastic bowl, clear-plastic cup, alcohol thermometer, graph paper, timer with second hand

Teaching Strategy Show students how to estimate a reading between marks on the thermometer.

Analysis

1. dependent variable—temperature; independent variable—time
2. Check students' work. The graph will show decreasing temperature as time increases. The slope of the line would be negative.

Assessment

Process Have students sketch a graph of what they would observe if they heated the water in an open container. The graph will show increasing temperature as time increases. The slope of the line would be positive.

Try at Home

Reading Check

Answer Answers will vary but might include the number of points scored by the local football team for each game of the season.

LAB DEMONSTRATION

Purpose to show students how to draw circle graphs

Preparation Write the following data on the board: Of the people who attended a play, 42 were under 10 years old; 27 were ages 11 to 20, and 11 were over 21.

Procedure Determine what percentage of the whole each part represents (percentage = part ÷ whole × 100%). For those under 10, this is 42/80 × 100% = 52%. A circle contains 360°. To find the number of degrees needed to show each percentage, change the percentage to a decimal number and multiply it by 360°. For those under 10, 360° × 0.52 = 187°.

Assessment

What percentage of the audience were ages 11 to 20? $\frac{27}{80}$ × 100% = 34% from 11 to 20 Over 21? $\frac{11}{80}$ × 100% = 14% How many degrees of the circle graph are required for each of these groups? 360° × 0.34 = 122° from 11 to 20; 360° × 0.14 = 50° over 21

Caption Answer

Figure 21 180°

Post Reading

Cooperative Learning In groups, have students talk about a sports activity that is familiar to them. Ask students to write the three types of graphs in their notes and tell what type of sports information could be illustrated by each type of graph. What title and labels would be needed for the graphs? Share results as a group.

3 Assess

DAILY INTERVENTION

Check for Understanding

Logical-Mathematical Tell students that four students scored a D on a test, ten scored a C, seven scored a B, and four scored an A. Have each student make a bar graph and a circle graph of the data. L2

Reteach

Candle Wicks Stick ten birthday cake candles in holders in a long piece of plastic foam. Light the second candle and let it burn for only 5 s. Light the remaining candles in turn, letting the third candle burn for 10 s, the fourth for 15 s, etc. Remove the candles from the holders, clip their wicks, and place them side-by-side, bases aligned, on an overhead projector. Discuss with students what the silhouette displays. L2

LS **Visual-Spatial**

Assessment

Performance Have students find a graph in a newspaper or a magazine. Identify the kind of graph and explain what the graph shows. Use **PASC,** p. 113.

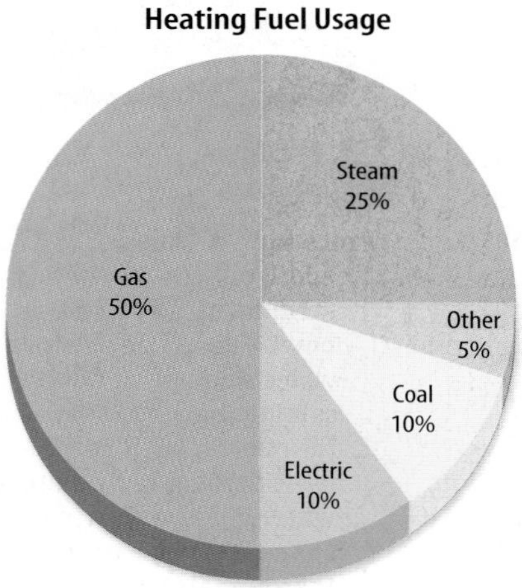

Figure 21 A circle graph shows the different parts of a whole quantity.
Calculate *the angle of gas usage.*

Circle Graphs

A circle graph, or pie graph, is used to show how some fixed quantity is broken down into parts. The circular pie represents the total. The slices represent the parts and usually are represented as percentages of the total.

Figure 21 illustrates how a circle graph could be used to show the percentage of buildings in a neighborhood using each of a variety of heating fuels. You easily can see that more buildings use gas heat than any other kind of heating fuel system. What else does the graph tell you?

To create a circle graph, you start with the total of what you are analyzing. There are 72 buildings in the neighborhood. For each type of heating fuel, you divide the number of buildings using each type of fuel by the total (72). You then multiply that decimal by 360° to determine the angle that the decimal makes in the circle. Eighteen buildings use steam. Therefore, $(18 \div 72) \times 360° = 90°$ on the circle graph. You then would measure 90° on the circle with your protractor to show 25 percent.

When you use graphs, think carefully about the conclusions you can draw from them. You want to make sure your conclusions are based on accurate information and that you use scales that help make your graph easy to read.

section 3 review

Summary

A Visual Display

- Graphs are a visual representation of data.
- Scientists often graph their data to detect patterns.
- The type of graph used is based on the conclusions you want to identify.

Line Graphs

- A line graph shows how a relationship between two variables changes over time.

Bar Graphs

- Bar graphs are best used to compare information collected by counting.

Circle Graphs

- A circle graph shows how a fixed quantity is broken down into parts.

Self Check

1. **Identify** the kind of graph that would best show the results of a survey of 144 people where 75 ride a bus, 45 drive cars, 15 carpool, and 9 walk to work.
2. **State** which type of variable is plotted on the *x*-axis and which type is plotted on the *y*-axis.
3. **Explain** why the points in a line graph are connected.
4. **Think Critically** How are line, bar, and circle graphs similar? How are they different?

Applying Math

5. **Percentage** In a survey, it was reported that 56 out of 245 people would rather drink orange juice in the morning than coffee. Calculate what percentage of a circle graph this data would occupy.

More Section Review gpescience.com

section 3 review

1. bar graph
2. The independent variable is shown on the *x*-axis and the dependent variable is shown on the *y*-axis.
3. Points are connected because they are related.
4. All three graphs are used to display data. A line graph shows relation-ships between two variables. A bar graph can be used to compare information. A circle graph can be used to show percentages.
5. 22.9%

LAB

What's my graph?

You have heard that a picture is worth a thousand words. For scientists, it is also true that a graph is worth a thousand numbers. Graphs give us a visual display of data collected during experiments. Graphs are also useful in the world of business, sports, and other situations.

Real-World Problem

How are line, bar, and circle graphs used for analyzing different kinds of data?

Goals

- **Compare and contrast** the three different types of graphs and how they are used.
- **Distinguish** between dependent and independent variables.

Materials

Science Journal
small ruler
protractor
pencil
compass
*circle template

Alternate material

Procedure

1. Copy the data tables into your Science Journal. Examine the data listed in the tables.
2. **Discuss** with other students the type of graph to be used for each data table.
3. **Graph** the data for each table in your Science Journal.

Data Table 1 Home Energy Use

Type of Energy Use	Percentage
Heating and Cooling	44%
Water Heating	14%
Refrigerator	9%
Light Cooking and Other	33%

Data Table 2 Motion of an Object

Time (s)	Distance (m)
0	0
5	3
10	6
15	9

Data Table 3 Average Number of tornadoes by month

Month	Average # of Tornadoes
March	53
April	107
May	176
June	168
July	94

Conclude and Apply

1. **Explain** why you chose the type of graph you made for each data table.
2. **Define** the independent and dependent variables.
3. **Discuss** the advantages of looking at a graph instead of just looking at numbers in a data table.

Communicating Your Data

As a class, compare the type of graph made for each data table.

BENCH TESTED

Real-World Problem

Purpose Students demonstrate how line, bar, and circle graphs are used for analyzing different kinds of data.

Process Skills analyze results, classify, communicate, design, draw and label, interpret data, list, make and use graphs, organize data, summarize, record

Time Required one class period.

Alternate Material circle template for circle graph

Procedure

Teaching Strategy Have students discuss and debate their selection of graph type for the three data tables. Have students work independently when making their graphs.

Conclude and Apply

1. Circle graph: shows total percentage is broken down by parts. Line graph: shows change in relationship of a variable over time. Bar graph: compares information collected by counting.
2. For the line graph choice, time is the independent variable and distance is the dependent variable.
3. Visual image can be used to quickly analyze data.

Assessment

Performance Give students data to determine the proper graph to use. Have them explain why they selected the graph they used. Use **Performance Assessment in the Science Classroom,** p. 111.

Communicating Your Data

Have students gather and plot data of local interest.

BENCH TESTED

Real-World Problem

Purpose Students will design and carry out an experiment to show the necessary components of an acceptable measurement system. L1 COOP LEARN

LS Interpersonal

Process Skills measure, collect and organize data, make and use tables, separate and control variables, communicate, form operational definitions, make models, use numbers, classify, observe and infer

Time Required one class period to brainstorm; one-half to one class period to complete the activity and summarize results

Materials Have various colors of string available.

Form a Hypothesis

Possible Hypothesis Students may hypothesize that using a defined measurement standard will make it possible for other students to measure objects consistently.

Test Your Hypothesis

Possible Procedures Choose an object such as a piece of chalk, a paper clip, or a book as the standard. Mark the units on the string with a marker or tape. Try several different-sized scale divisions of the base unit to measure halves, quarters, and tenths of units.

LAB Design Your Own

Developing a Measurement System

Goals

- **Design** an experiment that involves devising and testing your own measurement system for length.
- **Measure** various objects with the string measurement system.

Possible Materials

string
scissors
marking pen
masking tape
miscellaneous objects for standards

Safety Precautions

Real-World Problem

To develop the International System of Units, people had to agree on set standards and basic definitions of scale. If you had to develop a new measurement system, people would have to agree with your new standards and definitions. In this lab, your team will use string to devise and test its own SI (String International) system for measuring length. What are the requirements for designing a new measurement system using string?

Form a Hypothesis

Based on your knowledge of measurement standards and systems, form a hypothesis that explains how exact units help keep measuring consistent.

Test Your Hypothesis

Make a Plan

1. As a group, agree upon and write out the hypothesis statement.
2. As a group, list the steps that you need to take to test your hypothesis. Be specific, describing exactly what you will do at each step.
3. Make a list of the materials that you will need.

Alternative Inquiry Lab

Real-World Connection Have students research and discuss why other standards in science are necessary. Examples include graphing rules, writing in pen in permanently bound laboratory notebooks (the debacle of the Cold Fusion experiments is a good illustration), and standards in experimental procedures and reporting format. Researching the history of standards of measurement in antiquity also can be fascinating. Possible topics include the precision of the construction of the Egyptian pyramids, geometry, astronomy, and monolithic construction, the ancient Chinese, the Mayans, the ancient Muslim scientists, and units for trade and barter.

Using Scientific Methods

4. **Design** a data table in your Science Journal so it is ready to use as your group collects data.
5. As you read over your plan, be sure you have chosen an object in your classroom to serve as a standard. It should be in the same size range as what you will measure.
6. Consider how you will mark scale divisions on your string. Plan to use different pieces of string to try different-sized scale divisions.
7. What is your new unit of measurement called? Come up with an abbreviation for your unit. What will you name the smaller scale divisions?
8. What objects will you measure with your new unit? Be sure to include objects longer and shorter than your string. Will you measure each object more than once to test consistency? Will you measure the same object as another group and compare your findings?

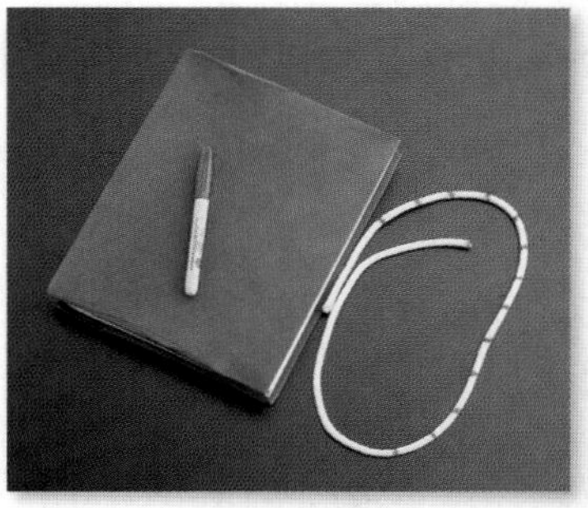

Follow Your Plan

1. Make sure your teacher approves your plan before you start.
2. Carry out the experiment as it has been planned.
3. **Record** observations that you make and complete the data table in your Science Journal.

Analyze Your Data

1. **Explain** which of your string scale systems will provide the most accurate measurement of small objects.
2. **Describe** how you recorded measurements that were between two whole numbers of your units.

Conclude and Apply

1. **Explain** why, when sharing your results with other groups, it is important for them to know what you used as a standard.
2. **Infer** how it is possible for different numbers to represent the same length of an object.

Communicating Your Data

Compare your conclusions with other students' conclusions. Are there differences? Explain how these may have occurred.

Teaching Strategy Use heavy string to make handling easy. Be sure metersticks and other standard measuring devices are not available to students. Encourage students to use common classroom objects as standards.

Expected Outcome Students will devise and test a measuring system that other groups can use to make consistent measurements. They may encounter errors due to stretching of the string and estimating between units.

Discussion Discuss with students that measurements between two marked units will include one estimated digit. Different people using the same measuring device will be more likely to get the same measurement if the scale divisions are small. The ability to measure and get the same answer is called precision.

Analyze Your Data

1. the system with the smallest divisions, because it is the most precise
2. The final digit was estimated.

Error Analysis Have students analyze how errors could result from the method used to mark their string into smaller units.

Conclude and Apply

1. so they can reproduce your results
2. When the size of the unit of measurement varies, the number of units used to measure an object also must vary.

Assessment

Portfolio Have students tape a sample of their measuring string to an explanation of their standard and measuring system. Then have them write about any problems they solved in the process of developing this system. Students should include this paper in their portfolio. Use **Performance Assessment in the Science Classroom,** p. 159.

Communicating Your Data

To test their measurement systems, have students exchange strings and use them to measure the same item.

Understanding Literature

Identifying the Main Head Possible answer: The main idea of this selection is that thinking in pictures—has allowed Temple Grandin to solve design problems as an equipment designer.

Answers to Questions

1. They think in pictures.
2. photographs at the cow's eye level
3. kites and model airplanes
4. **Linking Science and Writing** Remind students that maps and pictures can be models as well as three-dimensional objects.

INTEGRATE Physics

Modeling The design and use of models can help people predict the characteristics of any system. Because a model can be built, tested, and modified at a reasonably low cost, scientists, architects, and other designers use models to predict the performance of a prototype. If the results obtained from a model are to be applicable to the prototype, a strict set of conditions must be met by the model or the deviations from these conditions must be considered when predicting the behavior of the prototype.

Science and Language Arts

Thinking in Pictures: and other reports from my life with autism[1]

By Temple Grandin

Temple Grandin is an animal scientist and writer who also happens to be autistic. People with autism are said to think in pictures.

I think in pictures. Words are like a second language to me. I translate both spoken and written words into full-color movies, complete with sound, which run like a VCR tape in my head. When somebody speaks to me, his words are instantly translated into pictures. Language-based thinkers often find this phenomenon difficult to understand, but in my job as equipment designer for the livestock industry, visual thinking is a tremendous advantage.

. . . I credit my visualization abilities with helping me understand the animals I work with. Early in my career I used a camera to help give me the animals' perspective as they walked through a chute for their veterinary treatment. I would kneel down and take pictures through the chute from the cow's eye level. Using the photos, I was able to figure out which things scared the cattle.

Every design problem I've ever solved started with my ability to visualize and see the world in pictures. I started designing things as a child, when I was always experimenting with new kinds of kites and model airplanes.

1 Autism is a complex developmental disability that usually appears during the first three years of life. Children and adults with autism typically have difficulties in communicating with others and relating to the outside world.

Understanding Literature

Identifying the Main Idea The most important idea expressed in a paragraph or essay is the main idea. The main idea in a reading might be clearly stated, but sometimes the reader has to summarize the contents of a reading in order to determine its main idea. What do you think is the main idea of the passage?

Respond to the Reading

1. How do people with autism think differently from other people?
2. What did the author use to see from a cow's point of view?
3. What did the author use for models to design things when she was a child?
4. **Linking Science and Writing** Research the use of a scientific model. Write a paragraph stating the main ideas and listing supporting details.

INTEGRATE Physics

Models enable scientists to see things that are too big, too small, or too complex. Scientists might build models of DNA, airplanes, or other equipment. Temple Grandin's visual thinking and ability to make models enable her to predict how things will work when they are put together.

Resources for Teachers and Students

Dr. Temple Grandin Video-Visual Thinking of a Person with Autism, by Temple Grandin, Future Horizons, 1999

Unraveling the Mystery of Autism and Pervasive Development Disorder: A Mother's Story of Research and Recovery, by Karyn Seroussi and Bernard Rimland Ph.D., Simon & Shuster, 2000

Reviewing Main Ideas

Section 1 The Methods of Science

1. Science is a way of learning about the natural world, such as the hurricane shown below, through investigation.

2. Scientific investigations can involve making observations, testing models, or conducting experiments.
3. Scientific experiments investigate the effect of one variable on another. All other variables are kept constant.
4. Scientific laws are repeated patterns in nature. Theories attempt to explain how and why these patterns develop.

Section 2 Standards of Measurement

1. A standard of measurement is an exact quantity that people agree to use as a basis of comparison. The International System of Units, or SI, was established to provide a standard and reduce confusion.
2. When a standard of measurement is established, all measurements are compared to the same exact quantity—the standard. Therefore, all measurements can be compared with one another.
3. The most commonly used SI units include length—meter, volume—liter, mass—kilogram, and time—second.
4. Any SI unit can be converted to any other related SI unit by multiplying by the appropriate conversion factor. These towers are 45,190 cm in height, which is equal to 451.9 m.

5. Precision is the description of how close measurements are to each other. Accuracy is comparing a measurement to the real or accepted value.

Section 3 Communicating with Graphs

1. Graphs are visual representations of data that make it easier for scientists to detect patterns.
2. Line graphs show continuous changes among related variables. Bar graphs are used to show data collected by counting. Circle graphs show how a fixed quantity can be broken into parts.
3. To create a circle graph, you have to determine the angles for your data.
4. In a line graph, the independent variable is always plotted on the horizontal x-axis. The dependent variable is always plotted on the vertical y-axis.

FOLDABLES™ Use the Foldable that you made at the beginning of this chapter to help you review scientific processes.

chapter 1 Study Guide

Reviewing Main Ideas

Summary statements can be used by students to review the major concepts of the chapter.

Science Online

Visit gpescience.com
More Section Review
Interactive Tutor
Vocabulary PuzzleMaker
More Chapter Review
Standardized Test Practice

Assessment Transparency

For additional assessment questions, use the *Assessment Transparency* located in the transparency book.

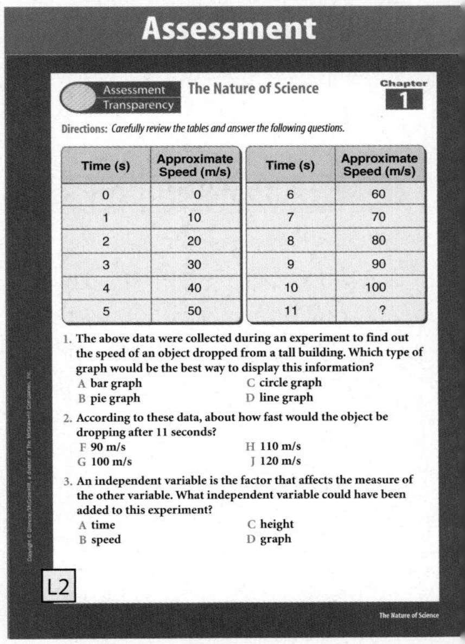

Assessment

Assessment Transparency — The Nature of Science — Chapter 1

Directions: *Carefully review the tables and answer the following questions.*

Time (s)	Approximate Speed (m/s)	Time (s)	Approximate Speed (m/s)
0	0	6	60
1	10	7	70
2	20	8	80
3	30	9	90
4	40	10	100
5	50	11	?

1. The above data were collected during an experiment to find out the speed of an object dropped from a tall building. Which type of graph would be the best way to display this information?
   A bar graph C circle graph
   B pie graph D line graph
2. According to these data, about how fast would the object be dropping after 11 seconds?
   F 90 m/s H 110 m/s
   G 100 m/s J 120 m/s
3. An independent variable is the factor that affects the measure of the other variable. What independent variable could have been added to this experiment?
   A time C height
   B speed D graph

L2

The Nature of Science

FOLDABLES™ Have students use the Foldables that they made at the beginning of the chapter to help them review scientific processes.

Using Vocabulary

1. accuracy
2. volume
3. technology
4. mass
5. dependent variable
6. graph
7. experiment
8. constant
9. density
10. hypothesis

Checking Concepts

11. C
12. D
13. C
14. D
15. A
16. B
17. D

Interpreting Graphics

18. Independent variable: pot; constant: vegetables; ingredients; dependent variable: heat required, iron content, taste, cooking time
19. See student page.

Thinking Critically

20. Possible answer: The next king's arm would be a different length.
21. Possible advantages: SI is based on powers of 10 conversion is easy because the same prefixes are used for all types of measurements most countries use it. Possible disadvantages: Conversion to SI would be expensive; people are reluctant to change from a familiar system.
22. Bias occurs when a scientist's expectations about the experiment change how he views the results. Running multiple trials, keeping accurate records of measurable data, and designing experiments that can be repeated reduces bias and helps validate data.

chapter 1 Review

Using Vocabulary

accuracy p. 14	mass p. 19
bias p. 10	model p. 11
constant p. 9	precision p. 14
control p. 9	scientific law p. 12
density p. 19	scientific method p. 7
dependent variable p. 9	technology p. 13
experiment p. 8	theory p. 12
graph p. 22	variable p. 9
hypothesis p. 8	volume p. 18
independent variable p. 9	

Match each phrase with the correct term from the list of vocabulary words.

1. comparing a measurement to the real or accepted value
2. the amount of space occupied by an object
3. application of science to help people
4. the amount of matter in an object
5. a variable that changes as another variable changes
6. a visual display of data
7. a test set up under controlled conditions
8. a variable that does **NOT** change as another variable changes
9. mass per unit volume
10. an educated guess using what you know and observe

Checking Concepts

Choose the word or phrase that best answers the question.

11. Which question **CANNOT** be answered by science?
    A) How do birds fly?
    B) How does a clock work?
    C) Is this a good song?
    D) What is an atom?

12. Which is an example of an SI unit?
    A) foot **C)** pound
    B) gallon **D)** second

13. One one-thousandth is expressed by which prefix?
    A) centi- **C)** milli-
    B) kilo- **D)** nano-

14. What is SI based on?
    A) English units **C)** powers of five
    B) inches **D)** powers of ten

15. What is the symbol for deciliter?
    A) dL **C)** dkL
    B) dcL **D)** Ld

16. Which is **NOT** a derived unit?
    A) dm^3 **C)** cm^3
    B) m **D)** g/mL

17. Which is **NOT** equal to 1,000 mL?
    A) 1 L **C)** 1 dm^3
    B) 100 cL **D)** 1 cm^3

Interpreting Graphics

Use the photo below to answer question 18.

18. **Define** The illustrations above show the items needed for an investigation. Which item is the independent variable? Which items are the constants? What might a dependent variable be?

Vocabulary PuzzleMaker gpescience.com

Use the Exam*View*® Pro Testmaker CD-ROM to:

- create multiple versions of tests
- create modified tests with one mouse click for inclusion students
- edit existing questions and add your own questions
- build tests aligned with state standards using built-in State Curriculum Tags
- change English tests to Spanish with one mouse click and vice versa

19. Concept Map Copy and complete this concept map on scientific methods.

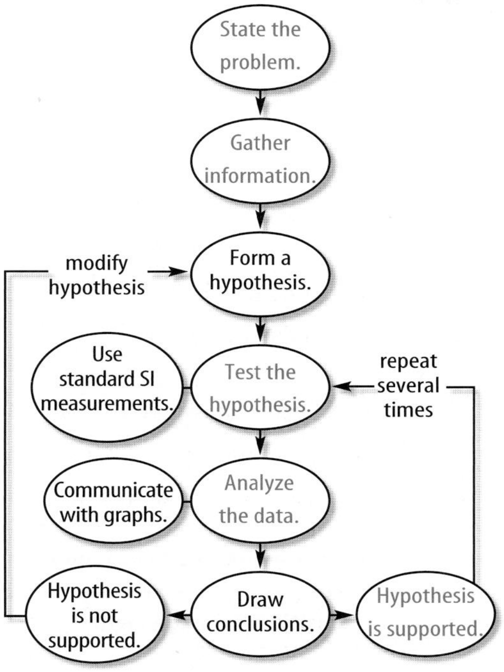

Thinking Critically

20. Communicate Standards of measurement used during the Middle Ages often were based on such things as the length of the king's arm. How would you go about convincing people to use a different system of standard units?

21. Analyze What are some advantages and disadvantages of adopting SI in the United States?

22. Identify when bias occurs in scientific experimentation. Describe steps scientists can take to reduce bias and validate experimental data.

23. Demonstrate Not all objects have a volume that is measured easily. If you were to determine the mass, volume, and density of your textbook, a container of milk, and an air-filled balloon, how would you do it?

24. Apply Suppose you set a glass of water in direct sunlight for 2 h and measure its temperature every 10 min. What type of graph would you use to display your data? What would the dependent variable be? What would the independent variable be?

25. Form a Hypothesis A metal sphere is found to have a density of 5.2 g/cm^3 at 25°C and a density of 5.1 g/cm^3 at 50°C. Form a hypothesis to explain this observation. How could you test your hypothesis?

26. Compare and contrast the ease with which conversions can be made among SI units versus conversions among units in the English system.

Applying Math

27. Convert Units Make the following conversions.

A) 1,500 mL to L
B) 2 km to cm
C) 5.8 dg to mg
D) 22°C to K

28. Calculate the density of an object having a mass of 17 g and a volume of 3 cm^3.

Use the illustration below to answer question 29.

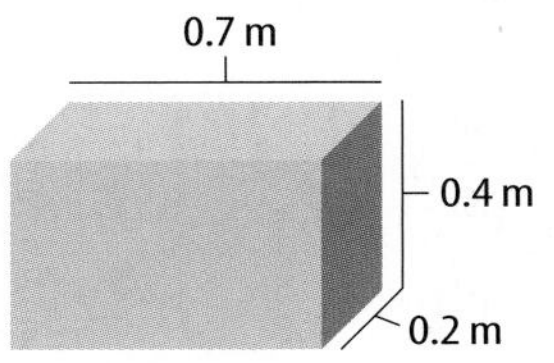

29. Solve Find the dimensions of the box in centimeters. Then find its volume in cubic centimeters.

Assessment Resources

Reproducible Masters

Chapter *Fast File* Resources
Chapter Review, pp. 39–40
Chapter Tests, pp. 41–44
Assessment Transparency Activity, p. 51

Glencoe Science Web site
Chapter Review Test
Standardized Test Practice

Glencoe Technology
Assessment Transparency
Exam*View*® Pro Testmaker
MindJogger Videoquiz
Interactive Chalkboard

chapter 1 Review

Thinking Critically

23. Textbook volume could be determined by multiplying its length, width, and height. The volume of the balloon could be determined by measuring the volume of water it displaces. The volume of any irregular object, such as the milk carton, must be determined indirectly. If the object is not harmed by water, volume can be measured by water displacement.

24. A line graph; time would be the independent variable and temperature would be the dependent variable.

25. The metal expands when heated. The hypothesis can be tested by measuring the volume of the ball at the two temperatures.

26. SI measurements are based on powers of ten. There are many different divisions in the English system. Thus, it is easier to convert in SI than in the English system.

Applying Math

Math Standards

National: 1, 2, 4, 9

27. a. 1.5 L
b. 200,000 cm
c. 580 mg
d. 295 K

28. $D = \frac{m}{V}$

$m = 17\text{ g} \qquad V = 3\text{ cm}^3$

$D = \frac{17\text{ g}}{3\text{ cm}^3} = 5.67\text{ g/cm}^3$

29. 0.4 m = 40 cm;
0.2 m = 20 cm;
0.7 m = 70 cm
V = length × width × height
V = 40 cm × 70 cm × 20 cm
= 56,000 cm3

Answer Sheet An answer sheet can be found at **gpescience.com**.

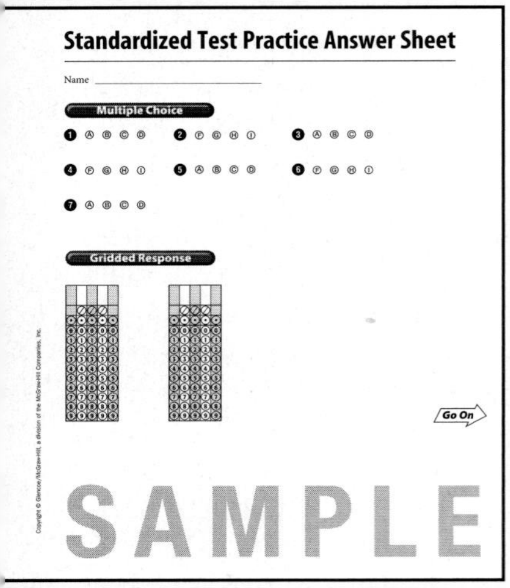

Multiple Choice

1. B
2. C
3. B
4. C
5. B
6. B
7. C

Gridded Response

8. 64cm^3

chapter 1 Standardized Test Practice

Record your answers on the answer sheet provided by your teacher or on a sheet of paper.

Multiple Choice

Students drop objects from a height and measure the time it takes each to reach the ground.

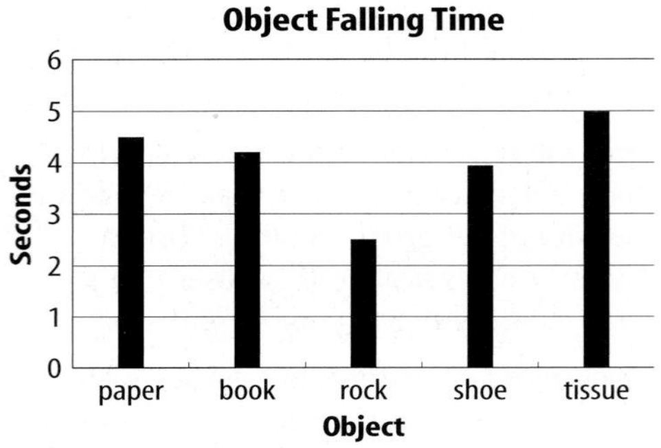

1. What is the dependent variable in this experiment?

A. drop height

B. falling time

C. paper

D. shoe

2. Which graph is most useful for showing how the relationship between independent and dependent variables changes over time?

A. bar graph

B. circle graph

C. line graph

D. pictograph

Test-Taking Tip

Recheck Your Answers Double check your answers before turning in the test.

3. Which is a statement about something that happens in nature which seems to be true all the time?

A. theory

B. scientific law

C. hypothesis

D. conclusion

4. Which best defines mass?

A. the amount of space occupied by an object

B. the distance between two points

C. the quantity of matter in an object

D. the interval between two events

Use the graph below to answer questions 5 and 6.

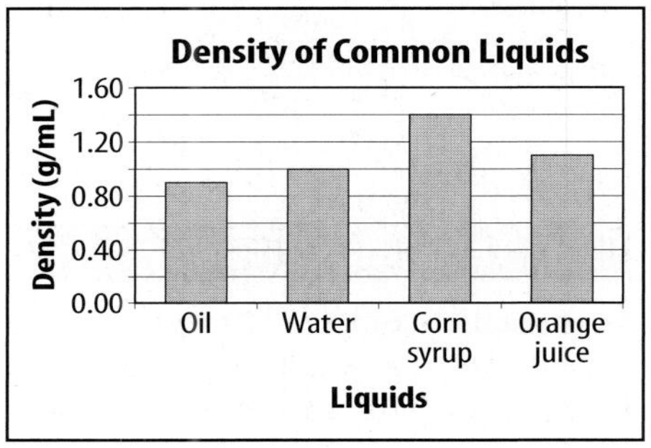

5. Which two liquids have the highest and the lowest densities?

A. oil and water

B. oil and corn syrup

C. orange juice and water

D. corn syrup and orange juice

6. Convert 615 mg to grams.
   A. 0.00615 g
   B. 0.615 g
   C. 6.15 g
   D. 61.5 g

7. What does the symbol *ns* represent?
   A. microsecond
   B. millisecond
   C. nanosecond
   D. picosecond

Gridded Response

8. Calculate the volume of the cube shown.

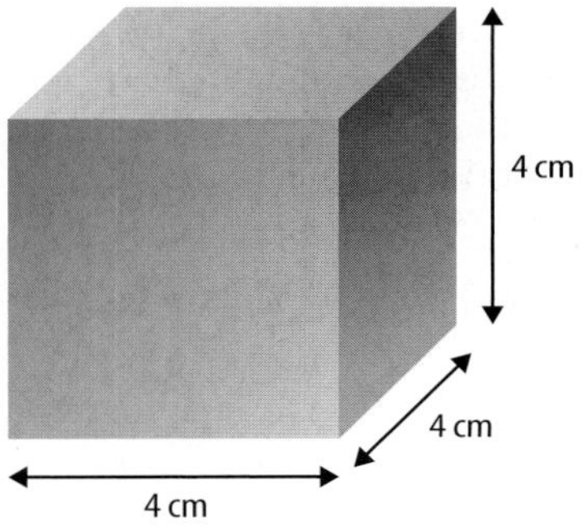

Short Response

9. Describe several ways scientists use investigations to learn about the natural world.

10. Why do scientists use graphs when analyzing data?

Extended Response

11. You must decide what items to pack for a hiking and camping trip. Space is limited, and you must carry all items during hikes. What measurements are important in your preparation?

12. What is the standard unit shown in this illustration? Why is it kept under cover in a vacuum-sealed container?

13. Define the term *technology.* Identify three ways that technology makes your life easier, safer, or more enjoyable.

14. Describe the three major categories into which science is classified. Which branches of science would be most important to an environmental engineer? Why?

15. A friend frequently misses the morning school bus. Use the scientific method to address this problem.

Extended Response

11. The length, width, and height of the packing areas help determine which items will fit in which spaces. The volume or total amount of space in the duffel bag and car also determine the items which will fit into each. Mass is important, as massive objects which must be carried on hikes will be difficult to manage.

12. This is the kilogram, the standard for mass. It is covered in a vacuum-sealed container to prevent any erosion or corrosion with air, and to keep airborne materials from settling on it, changing its mass.

13. Technology is the application of science to help people. Examples of technology are nearly limitless, but may be grouped into categories including medical tools, equipment designed for entertainment, modes of transportation, or home appliances.

14. Life science deals with living things, Earth science with Earth and space, and physical science with matter and energy. An environmental engineer would be connected with all three branches. For example, he might study how heat and waste materials emitted by an industrial plant (physical science) affect the air, water, and soil (Earth Science) and living organisms (life science) near the plant.

15. *The Problem:* Your friend misses the morning school bus. *Gather information:* Learn about the time and location of the bus' arrival and the morning routines in the home. *Possible hypothesis:* Your friend should wake earlier, lay her clothes out the night before, or leave the house earlier in order to make the bus. *Test hypotheses, analyze data, and conclude.* Test each hypothesis several times over different mornings. If your friend consistently catches the bus, you can conclude that the hypothesis tested was supported.

Short Response

9. A scientist may make and record observations about something that is taking place. She might set up an experiment or build a model, run tests, and gather data about her observations.

10. It is easier to detect patterns when examining data in graph form than chart form.

Rubrics

For more help evaluating Short- and Extended-Response questions, see the rubrics on p. 10T.

chapter 2 Organizer

Section/Objectives	Standards		Labs/Features
	National	State/Local	
Chapter Opener	See pp. 16T–17T for a Key to Standards.		**Launch Lab:** Technology in Your Life, p. 37 **Foldables,** p. 37
Section 1 Science and Technology 1 session .5 block 1. **Discuss** how the study of science leads to a better understanding of natural events. 2. **Describe** the different types of technology. 3. **Explain** why the value of technology may differ for different people and at different times.	National Content Standards: UCP.1–5, A.1, A.2, E.1, E.2, F.6		**MiniLAB:** Researching the Past, p. 40 **Visualizing Technology Supplying Basic Needs,** p. 44 **Science Online,** p. 45
Section 2 Forces that Shape Technology 2 sessions 1 block 4. **Discuss** how funds for science research come from the federal govermment, private industries, and private foundations. 5. **Explain** how consumers affect technological development. 6. **Describe** the importance of responsible technological development.	National Content Standards: UCP.1–5, A.1 A.2, E.1, E.2, F.5, F.6, G.2 G.3		**MiniLAB:** Evaluating the Benefits and Consequences of Technology, p. 47 **Integrate Environment,** p. 48 **Applying Science:** What impact does the accident at Chernobyl have on the future of nuclear power?, p. 49 **Science Online,** p. 50 **Lab:** Who contributes CO_2?, p. 51
Section 3 Developing Technology 3 sessions 1.5 blocks 7. **Discuss** how the roles of a scientist and an engineer differ. 8. **Explain** how technological problems often create a demand for new scientific knowledge. 9. **Describe** the general process used to find technical solutions to problems or human needs.	National Content Standards: UCP.1–5, A.1 A.2, E.1, E.2, F.6		**Integrate Life Science,** p. 54 **Integrate Career,** p. 56 **Lab:** Care Package, pp. 58–59 Video Lab **Oops! Accidents in Science:** A Slippery Situation, p. 60

StudentWorks Plus — Glencoe Exclusive! TeacherWorks™ All-In-One Planner and Resource Center

Lab Materials	Reproducible Resources	Section Assessment	Technology
Launch Lab: Science Journal, pencil	**Chapter *FAST FILE* Resources** Foldables Worksheet, p. 13 Directed Reading Overview, p. 15 Note-taking Worksheets, pp. 30–31	Glencoe's Assessment Advantage	TeacherWorks includes: • Interactive Teacher Edition • Lesson Planner with calendar • Access to all program blacklines • Correlations to standards • Web links
MiniLAB: Science Journal, pencil or pen	**Chapter *FAST FILE* Resources** Transparency Activity, pp. 40 MiniLAB, p. 3 Lab Activity, pp. 9–10 Enrichment, p. 26 Reinforcement, p. 23 Directed Reading, p. 16	**Portfolio** Activity, p. 41 **Performance** MiniLAB, p. 40 Applying Math, p. 45 **Content** Section Review, p. 45	
MiniLAB: Science Journal, pencil **Lab:** Science Journal, pencil or pen Need materials? Contact Science Kit at 1-800-828-7777 or www.sciencekit.com.	**Chapter *FAST FILE* Resources** Transparency Activity, pp. 41, 43–44 MiniLAB, p. 4 Enrichment, p. 27 Reinforcement, p. 24 Directed Reading, p. 16 Lab Worksheets, pp. 5–6 **Life Science Critical Thinking/Problem Solving,** p. 4	**Portfolio** Check for Understanding, p. 50 **Performance** MiniLAB, p. 47 Applying Science, p. 49 Applying Math, p. 50 **Content** Section Review, p. 50	Section Focus Transparency Teaching Transparency Interactive Chalkboard CD-ROM StudentWorks Plus
Lab: packages of snack foods, shoe box, packing peanuts, shredded newspaper, packing tape, wrapping paper, markers	**Chapter *FAST FILE* Resources** Transparency Activity, p. 42 Lab Activity, pp. 11–12 Enrichment, p. 28 Reinforcement, p. 25 Directed Reading, p. 17 Lab Worksheets, pp. 7–8 **Home and Community Involvement,** p. 27	**Portfolio** Differentiated Instruction, p. 56 **Performance** Applying Math, p. 57 **Content** Section Review, p. 57	Section Focus Transparency Interactive Chalkboard CD-ROM StudentWorks Plus Video Lab

End of Chapter Assessment

Blackline Masters	Technology	Professional Series
Chapter *FAST FILE* Resources Chapter Review, pp. 33–34 Chapter Tests, pp. 35–38 **Standardized Test Practice,** pp. 12–15	MindJogger Videoquiz Exam*View*® Pro Testmaker TeacherWorks CD-ROM Interactive Chalkboard CD-ROM	**Performance Assessment in the Science Classroom (PASC)**

Transparencies

Section Focus

Section 1 Section Focus Transparency — Air Traffic Controller — Chapter 2

The air traffic control system is a vast network of people and equipment that ensures the safe operation of commercial and private aircraft. Air traffic controllers coordinate the movement of air traffic to make certain that planes stay a safe distance apart. Their immediate concern is safety, but controllers also must direct planes efficiently to minimize delays. Some regulate airport traffic; others regulate flights between airports.

1. What are the four types of technology indicated in this picture?
2. What is the difference between science and technology?

L2

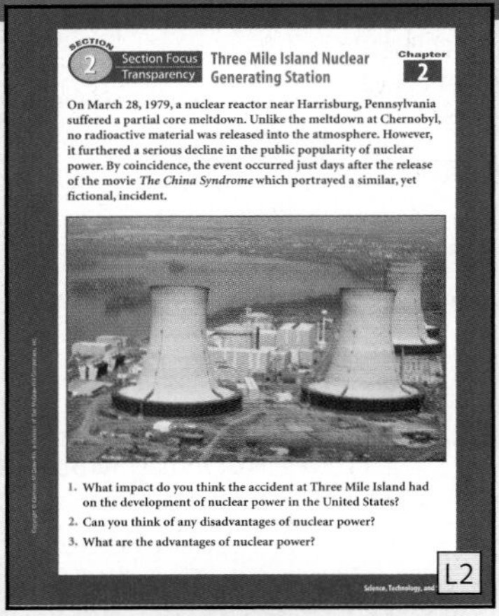
Section 2 Section Focus Transparency — Three Mile Island Nuclear Generating Station — Chapter 2

On March 28, 1979, a nuclear reactor near Harrisburg, Pennsylvania suffered a partial core meltdown. Unlike the meltdown at Chernobyl, no radioactive material was released into the atmosphere. However, it furthered a serious decline in the public popularity of nuclear power. By coincidence, the event occurred just days after the release of the movie *The China Syndrome* which portrayed a similar, yet fictional, incident.

1. What impact do you think the accident at Three Mile Island had on the development of nuclear power in the United States?
2. Can you think of any disadvantages of nuclear power?
3. What are the advantages of nuclear power?

L2

Section 3 Section Focus Transparency — Challenger Space Shuttle — Chapter 2

On Jan. 28, 1986, the space shuttle Challenger exploded with seven crew members aboard. The explosion on the $1.2 billion shuttle came at one minute, 15 seconds after launch when the shuttle was about 11 miles high and nine miles down range from the Kennedy Space Center. It was the 25th shuttle flight and tenth for Challenger. The disaster was the worst for NASA since the first Apollo moon capsule burned on its launch pad Jan. 27, 1967, killing three astronauts.

1. On February 1, 2003 NASA lost another space shuttle, the Columbia. What, if anything, could have prevented this disaster after what was learned about Challenger?
2. What are the differences in the design of the Challenger and the design of a commercial jumbo jet? Why are the designs different?

L2

This is a representation of key blackline masters available in the Teacher Classroom Resources. See Resource Manager boxes within the chapter for additional information.

Assessment

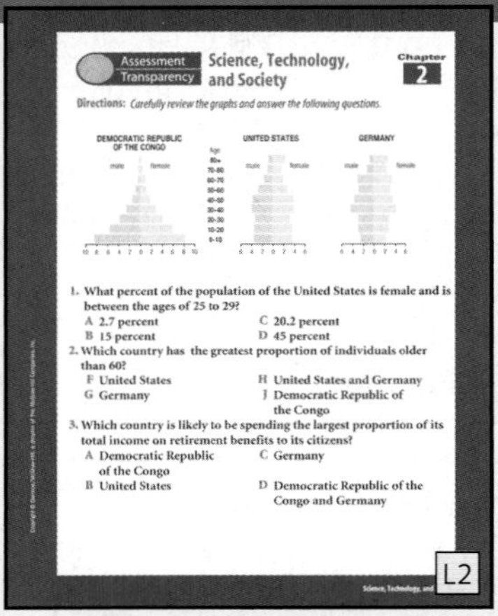
Assessment Transparency — Science, Technology, and Society — Chapter 2

Directions: Carefully review the graphs and answer the following questions.

1. What percent of the population of the United States is female and is between the ages of 25 to 29?
A 2.7 percent C 20.2 percent
B 15 percent D 45 percent
2. Which country has the greatest proportion of individuals older than 60?
F United States H United States and Germany
G Germany J Democratic Republic of the Congo
3. Which country is likely to be spending the largest proportion of its total income on retirement benefits to its citizens?
A Democratic Republic of the Congo C Germany
B United States D Democratic Republic of the Congo and Germany

L2

Teaching

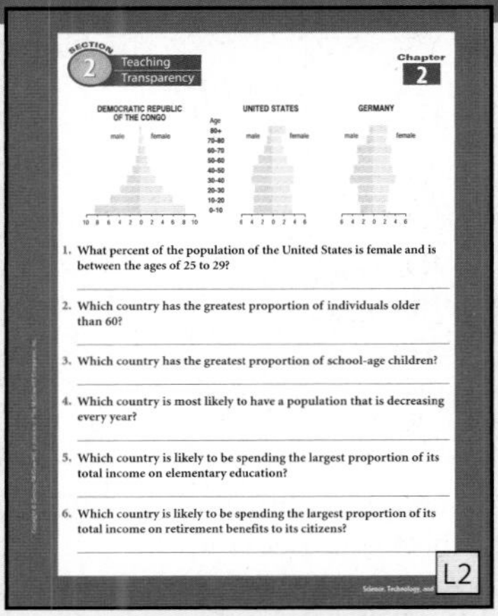
Section 2 Teaching Transparency — Chapter 2

1. What percent of the population of the United States is female and is between the ages of 25 to 29?
2. Which country has the greatest proportion of individuals older than 60?
3. Which country has the greatest proportion of school-age children?
4. Which country is most likely to have a population that is decreasing every year?
5. Which country is likely to be spending the largest proportion of its total income on elementary education?
6. Which country is likely to be spending the largest proportion of its total income on retirement benefits to its citizens?

L2

Key to Teaching Strategies

The following designations will help you decide which activities are appropriate for your students.

- L1 Level 1 activities should be appropriate for students with learning difficulties.
- L2 Level 2 activities should be within the ability range of all students.
- L3 Level 3 activities are designed for above-average students.
- ELL ELL activities should be within the ability range of English Language Learners.
- COOP LEARN Cooperative Learning activities are designed for small group work.
- LS Multiple Learning Styles logos, as described on page 12T, are used throughout to indicate strategies that address different learning styles.
- P These strategies represent student products that can be placed into a best-work portfolio.
- PBL Problem-Based Learning activities apply real-world situations to learning.

Hands-on Activities

Student Text Lab Worksheet

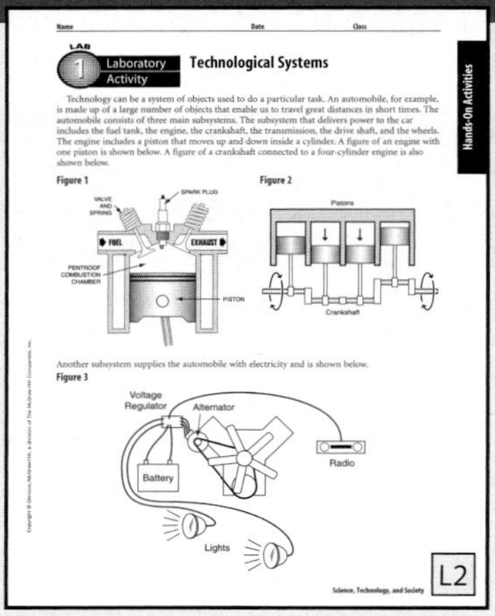
Lab 1 Laboratory Activity — Technological Systems

Technology can be a system of objects used to do a particular task. An automobile, for example, is made up of a large number of objects that enable us to travel great distances in short times. The automobile consists of three main subsystems. The subsystem that delivers power to the car includes the fuel tank, the engine, the crankshaft, the transmission, the drive shaft, and the wheels. The engine includes a piston that moves up and down inside a cylinder. A figure of an engine with one piston is shown below. A figure of a crankshaft connected to a four-cylinder engine is also shown below.

Another subsystem supplies the automobile with electricity and is shown below.

Figure 3

L2

Laboratory Activities

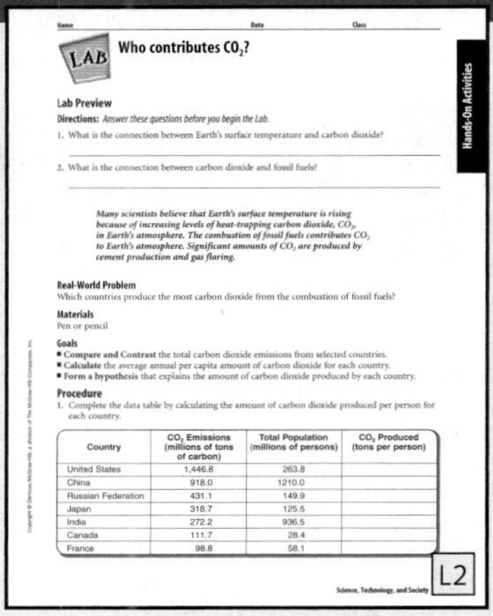
LAB — Who contributes CO_2?

Lab Preview

Directions: Answer these questions before you begin the Lab.

1. What is the connection between Earth's surface temperature and carbon dioxide?
2. What is the connection between carbon dioxide and fossil fuels?

Many scientists believe that Earth's surface temperature is rising because of increasing levels of heat-trapping carbon dioxide, CO_2, in Earth's atmosphere. The combustion of fossil fuels contributes CO_2 to Earth's atmosphere. Significant amounts of CO_2 are produced by cement production and gas flaring.

Real-World Problem
Which countries produce the most carbon dioxide from the combustion of fossil fuels?

Materials
Pen or pencil

Goals
- Compare and Contrast the total carbon dioxide emissions from selected countries.
- Calculate the average annual per capita amount of carbon dioxide for each country.
- Form a hypothesis that explains the amount of carbon dioxide produced by each country.

Procedure
1. Complete the data table by calculating the amount of carbon dioxide produced per person for each country.

Country	CO_2 Emissions (millions of tons of carbon)	Total Population (millions of persons)	CO_2 Produced (tons per person)
United States	1,446.8	263.8	
China	918.0	1210.0	
Russian Federation	431.1	149.9	
Japan	318.7	125.5	
India	272.2	936.5	
Canada	111.7	28.4	
France	98.8	58.1	

L2

Meeting Different Ability Levels

Content Outline

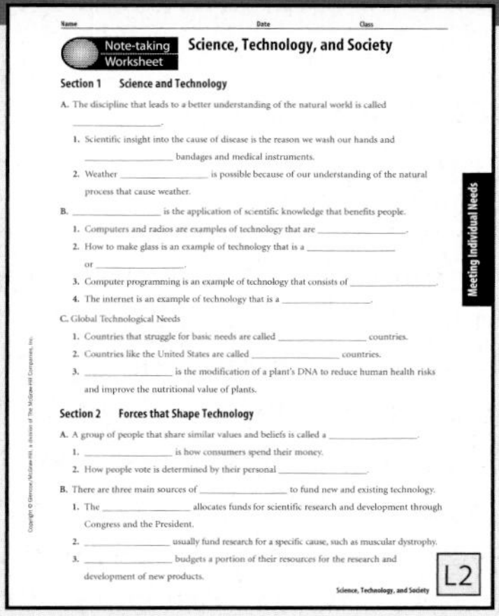
Note-taking Worksheet
Science, Technology, and Society
L2

Reinforcement

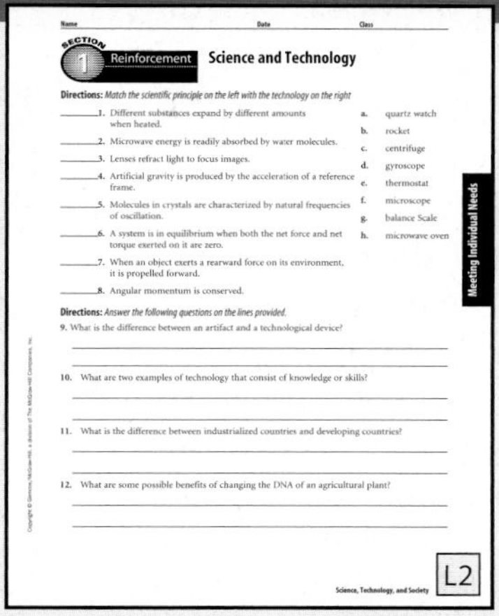
Section 1 Reinforcement
Science and Technology
L2

Enrichment

Section 1 Enrichment
Science and Technology
L1

Directed Reading (English/Spanish)

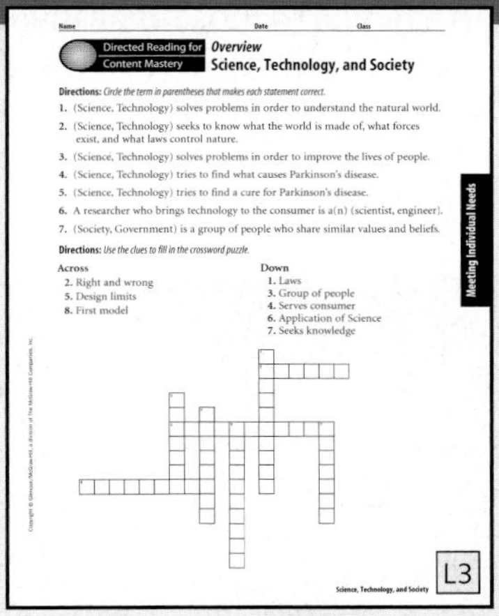
Directed Reading for Content Mastery
Overview
Science, Technology, and Society
L3

Study Guide

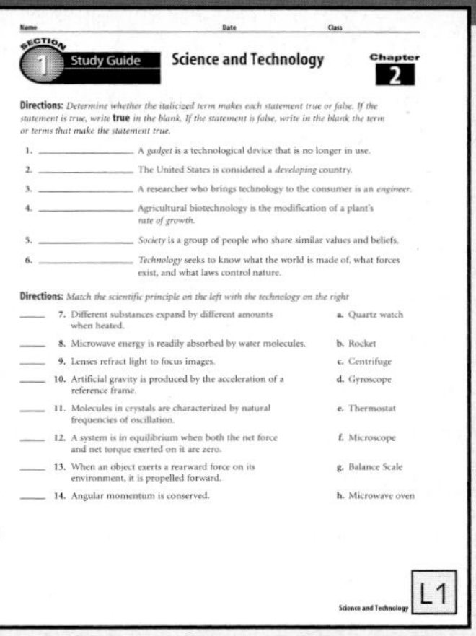
Section 1 Study Guide
Science and Technology
Chapter 2
L1

Reading Essentials

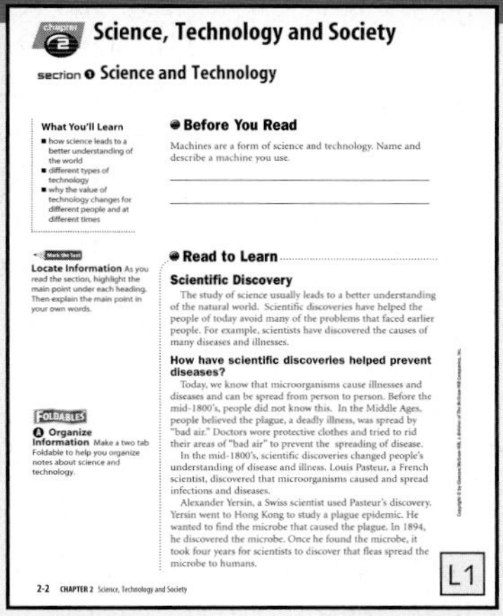
Chapter 2 Science, Technology and Society
Section 1 Science and Technology
Before You Read
Read to Learn
L1

Assessment

Test Practice Workbook

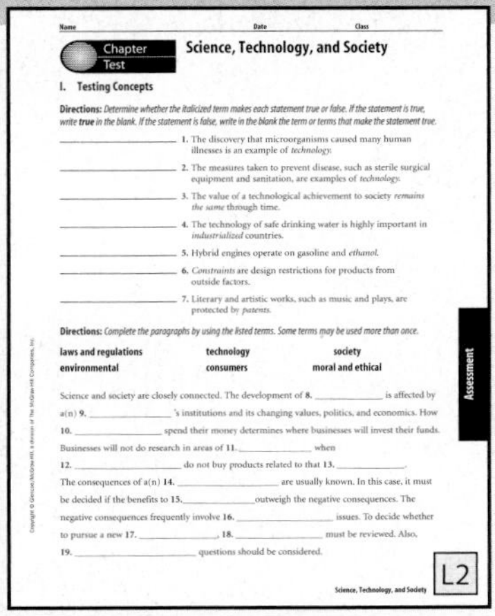
Chapter Test
Science, Technology, and Society
L2

Chapter Review

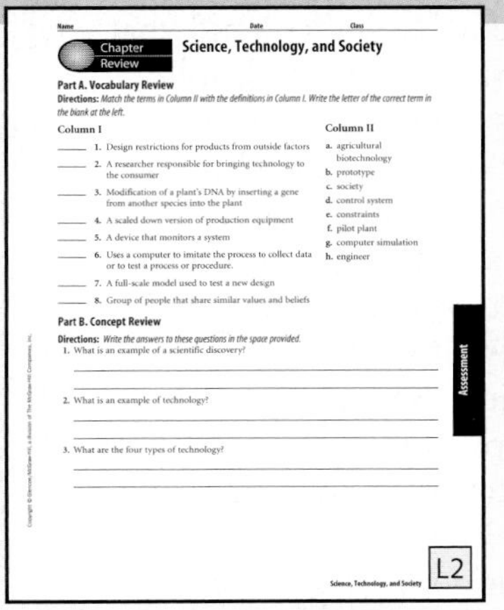
Chapter Review
Science, Technology, and Society
L2

Chapter Tests

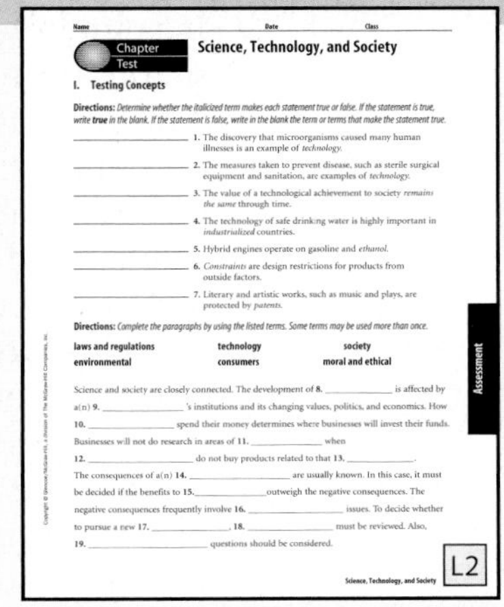
Chapter Test
Science, Technology, and Society
L2

Science Content Background

section 1 Science and Technology

Understanding Science and Technology

Many students do not understand the connection between science and technology. Science usually is the practice of learning new scientific information about how the natural world works. For example, finding the virus that causes a particular strain of influenza is considered science. Technology is the use of science to solve a human need or solve a problem. Finding a vaccine for a particular strain of influenza is an example of technology.

History and Scientific Achievements

History is full of examples of how science led to a better understanding of why something occurs. For example, influenza has caused many deaths through the centuries. A pandemic during the 1918-1919 flu season caused about 20 million deaths worldwide. Now scientists are able to isolate the specific virus that causes a particular strain of flu and make a vaccine for it. Flu outbreaks still occur, but the number of deaths has dropped dramatically since the process for developing flu vaccines has been developed.

This example shows how science and technology go hand-in-hand. The scientific discovery of finding the virus that causes a strain of flu was the scientific information needed for the technology of the vaccine to be developed.

Types of Technology

It is important for students to understand that there are many different types of technology. The term technology is a universal term that encompasses many different things. Technology can be an object, a method of doing a task, the skill needed to perform a task, or a system that includes all of the other types of technology.

This airplane pilot is sitting in an airplane that is a technological object. She has the technological skills needed to operate this aircraft. The act of going from one location to another by airplane is technology. She also is part of a system of transportation that is considered technology.

section 2 Forces that Shape Technology

Technology and Society

Developments in technology often are driven by society. In the example of the flu vaccine, the needs of society fueled the scientific search for the cause of flu which ultimately led to the vaccine. Members of society are not always in agreement in the value of scientific research. Controversial scientific investigations are hotly debated by people on both sides of the issue. Some scientific investigations, such as stem-cell research, are strictly regulated. Other types of research, particularly those that involve human subjects, are forbidden by law. Society can demand that scientific research and technology be pursued or they can demand that research stop.

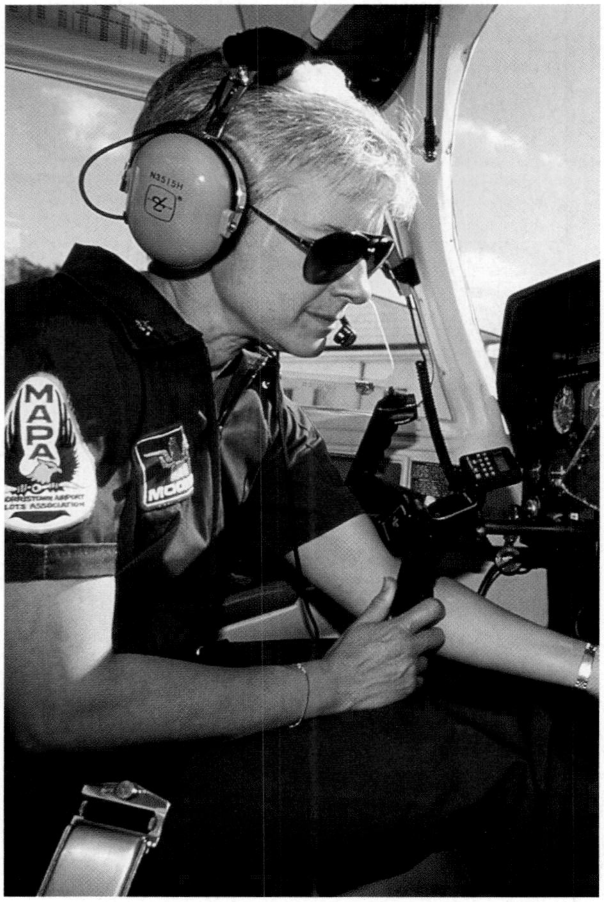

section 3 Developing Technology Methods

Scientists and engineers do not develop technology in a haphazard fashion. They use methods similar to the scientific method in their development process. Many professionals from the fields of science, engineering, and business work together to produce products that are marketable, safe, reliable, and environmentally friendly.

Product Protection

Intellectual property such as new technology is legally protected by patent laws. Patent laws give companies exclusive rights to manufacture their products without unfair competition from other companies. These laws give companies the opportunity to recover the investment costs in developing the new product.

chapter content resources

Internet Resources

For additional content background, visit gpescience.com to:

- access your book online
- find references to related articles in popular science magazines
- access Web links with related content background
- access current events with science journal topics

Print Resources

Science and Technology in World History: An Introduction, by James E. McClellan and Harold Dorn, John Hopkins University Press, 1999

Science, Technology, and Democracy, by Daniel Lee Kleinman, State University of New York Press, 2000

Taking Sides: Controversial Issues in Science, Technology, and Society, by Thomas A. Easton (editor), McGraw-Hill, 2002

chapter 2

Chapter Vocabulary

agricultural biotechnology, p. 45
society, p. 46
engineer, p. 53
constraints, p. 55
computer simulation, p. 55
prototype, p. 56
pilot plant, p. 56
control system, p. 56

Science Journal Student responses may vary, such as using the nanotubes to keep coffee mugs warm, clothes that can keep a person warm in winter, or defroster for front windshield on a car.

INTERACTIVE CHALKBOARD with Image Bank

PowerPoint® Presentations

This CD-ROM is an editable Microsoft® PowerPoint® presentation that includes:

- a pre-made presentation for every chapter
- interactive graphics
- animations
- audio clips
- image bank
- all new section and chapter questions
- Standardized Test Practice
- transparencies
- Foldables directions
- links to gpescience.com

chapter 2

Science, Technology, and Society

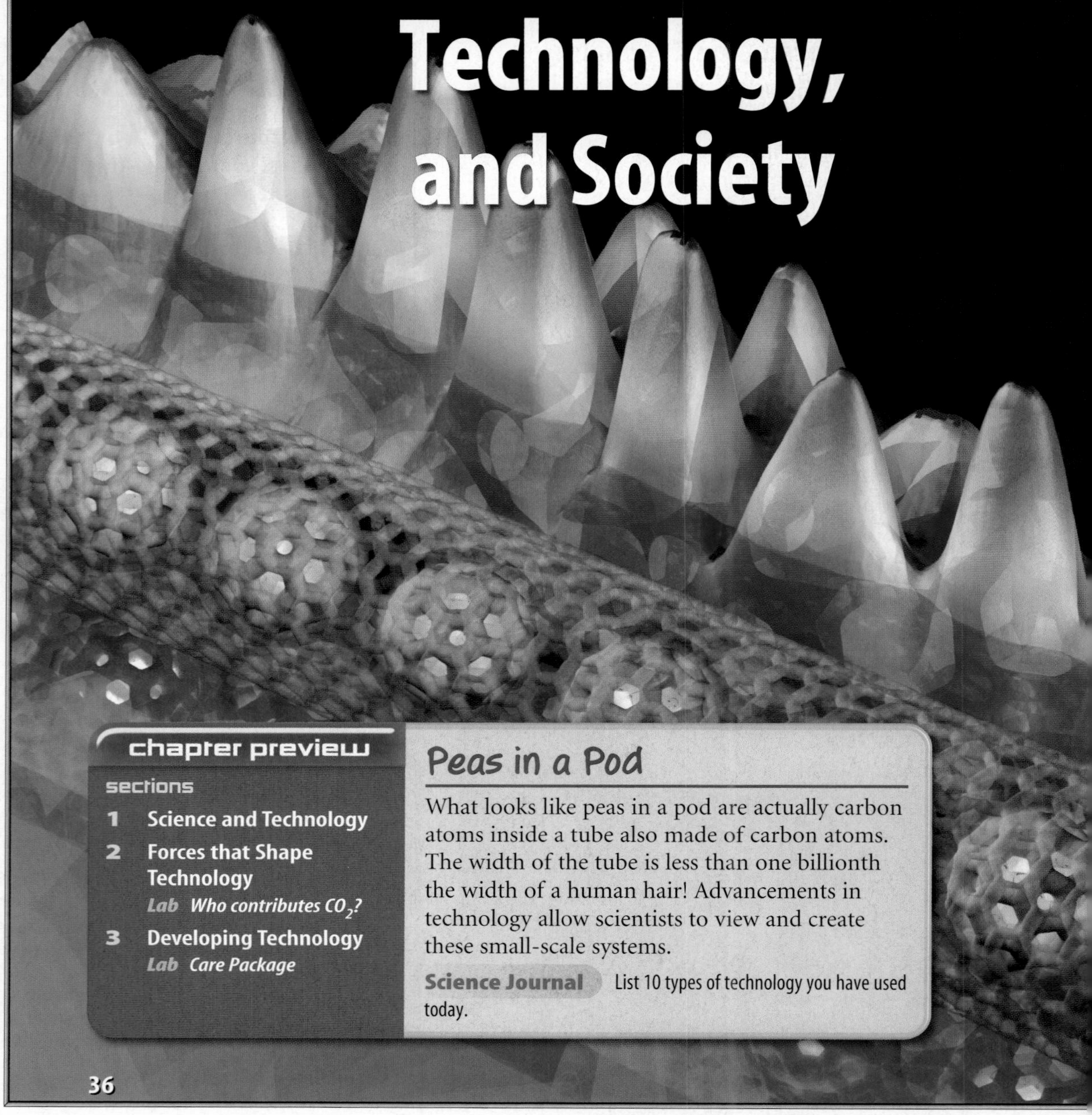

chapter preview

sections

Peas in a Pod

What looks like peas in a pod are actually carbon atoms inside a tube also made of carbon atoms. The width of the tube is less than one billionth the width of a human hair! Advancements in technology allow scientists to view and create these small-scale systems.

Science Journal List 10 types of technology you have used today.

36

Theme Connection

Science and Technology Science and technology are interdependent. Advances in technology often are the result of advances in science. Advances in science often are accomplished because there is a need for new technology.

About the Photo

Nanotechnology The photo is a computer model of carbon atoms in the shaped of buckyballs inserted into a nanotube made from carbon atoms. Discovered in 1991, carbon nanotubes are 100 times stronger and six times lighter than steel and have the potential to revolutionize science and technology. Nanotechnology is expected to affect everything from how doctors treat diseases to how engineers design cars.

Start-Up Activities

Launch LAB

Technology in Your Life

You probably do not think about how technology affects your life. You use many types of technology every day without realizing it. How much technology do you use?

1. Make a list of everything that you do from the time that you get home from school until you go to bed.
2. Circle the items on the list that involve some type of technology.
3. Select two of the items and identify the technologies involved in the item. For example, the technologies involved in a television may be the wiring or the wave that transports the signal.
4. **Thinking Critically** Write a list of activities that you could do after school if none of the technologies that you listed were available.

Science Online Preview this chapter's content and activities at gpescience.com

FOLDABLES™ Study Organizer

Science and Technology Make the following Foldable to help organize information about science and technology.

STEP 1 **Fold** a sheet of paper vertically in half from top to bottom.

STEP 2 **Fold** in half from side to side with the fold at the top.

STEP 3 **Unfold** the paper once. **Cut** only the fold of the top flap to make two tabs.

STEP 4 **Turn** the paper vertically and label the flaps *Science* and *Technology*.

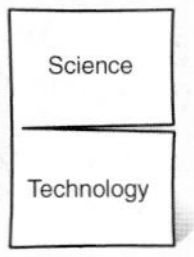

Read for Main Ideas As you read the chapter, list the characteristics of science and technology under the appropriate flap.

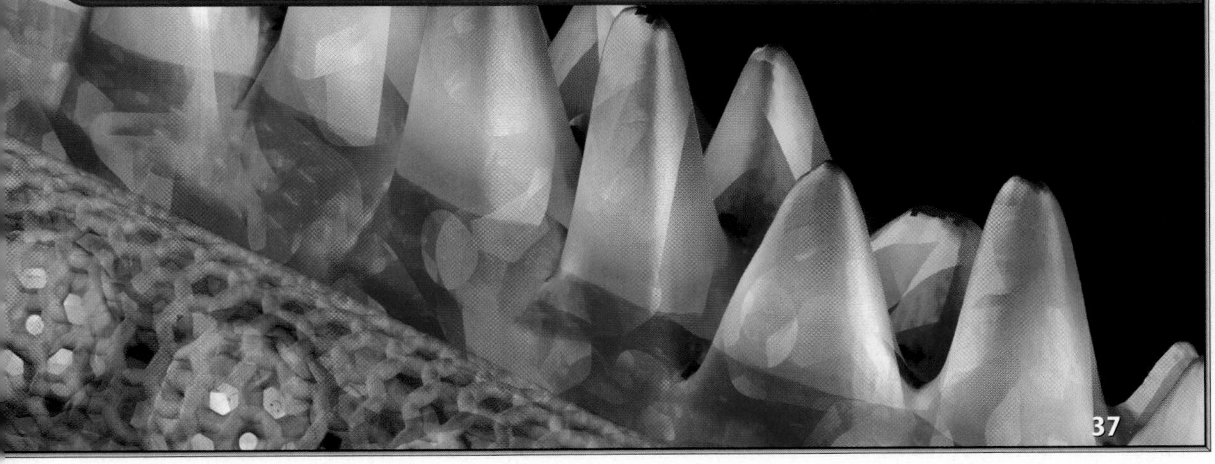

37

Launch LAB

Purpose Use this launch lab to demonstrate to students the abundance of technology that surrounds them.

Preparation Have students make a list of their activities the day before this lab.

Materials Science Journal, pencil

Teaching Strategy

- Ask student volunteers to give definitions for science and technology.
- After students have completed this lesson, have them look at their activities and see if they should make changes.

Think Critically

Possible answers: read a book, go for a walk, play outdoors, visit a friend

Assessment

Oral Ask students how would life differ if the medical technology that we have today were not available? Possible answer: The conditions would be similar to those of the Middle Ages and earlier. Many infants and children would die of childhood diseases and the life expectancy of adults would be much lower. Use **Performance Assessment in the Science Classroom,** p. 91.

section 1

Science and Technology

1 Motivate

INTERACTIVE CHALKBOARD PowerPoint® Presentations An editable Microsoft® PowerPoint® presentation is available on **Interactive Chalkboard** CD-ROM.

Bellringer

Section Focus Transparencies also are available on the Interactive Chalkboard CD-ROM. L2 ELL

SECTION 1 Section Focus Transparency — Air Traffic Controller — Chapter 2

The air traffic control system is a vast network of people and equipment that ensures the safe operation of commercial and private aircraft. Air traffic controllers coordinate the movement of air traffic to make certain that planes stay a safe distance apart. Their immediate concern is safety, but controllers also must direct planes efficiently to minimize delays. Some regulate airport traffic; others regulate flights between airports.

1. What are the four types of technology indicated in this picture?
2. What is the difference between science and technology?

L2

Reading Preview

Tie to Prior Knowledge

Science Ask students to recall the meaning of science and the various tools that scientists use. In this section they will learn the difference between science and technology.

Prediction Have students break the new vocabulary term *agricultural biotechnology* into parts to determine meaning. Have students define *agricultural*, *bio*, and *technology*. Then, ask students to predict the meaning for the whole term. After reading, have students decide if their guesses were right.

Reading Guide

What You'll Learn

- **Discuss** how the study of science leads to a better understanding of natural events.
- **Describe** the different types of technology.
- **Explain** why the value of technology may differ for different people and at different times.

Why It's Important

Science provides information, insight, and analytical skills to help people understand the possible causes and effects of natural events.

Review Vocabulary

technology: the application of science to help people

New Vocabulary

- agricultural biotechnology

Figure 1 Physicians in the Middle Ages treated people who had the plague. The beak in the protective mask contains a mixture of materials to filter the "bad air."
Contrast *the methods used to help prevent the spread of diseases during the Middle Ages against methods used today.*

Scientific Discovery

The study of science usually leads to a better understanding of the world around you. For example, some scientists in the Middle Ages believed that the plague was spread by breathing "bad air". Doctors wore protective clothing to protect themselves, as shown in **Figure 1.** Various measures were taken by local doctors to rid homes of this "bad air" in an attempt to stop the plague. History is full of breakthroughs in science that have changed the course of human history. One such breakthrough is the discovery that microorganisms cause illnesses and disease. Before the mid-1800s, people had no idea that microorganisms caused many human illnesses. Many diseases were easily passed from person to person because people had no idea why the disease was spreading.

In the mid-1800s, Louis Pasteur, a French scientist, discovered the cause of most infectious diseases. He informed the public that microorganisms brought about infections and diseases. Knowing how infectious diseases spread, Alexandre Yersin, a bacteriologist, traveled to Hong Kong. A plague epidemic was underway. He was hoping to isolate the bacteria that caused this disease. In 1894, Yersin was able to isolate the microbe that caused the disease. Once scientists discovered what was causing the disease, they could focus on how the disease spread through the population. It took another four years before scientists discovered that fleas spread this microbe to humans.

Section 1 Resource Manager

Chapter *FAST FILE* Resources

Transparency Activity, p. 40
Note-taking Worksheets, pp. 30–31
MiniLAB, p. 3
Lab Activity, pp. 9–10
Enrichment, p. 26
Reinforcement, p. 23
Directed Reading for Content Mastery, pp. 15, 16
Earth Science Critical Thinking/Problem Solving, p. 11
Physical Science Critical Thinking/Problem Solving, p. 1
Lab Management and Safety, pp. 58–60
Mathematics Skills Activities, pp. 7–8

Scientific Insight

Once scientists found the source of the plague, scientists brought the information to the public's attention. The information provided an explanation of why the plague occurred. Outbreaks of the plague took place throughout history. One outbreak in the 14th century killed approximately one-fourth of the population of Europe. When people clearly understood why the disease was spreading, actions could be taken to stop the disease.

Disease Prevention Today The fact that microbes spread illnesses is not news today. Young children are taught to wash their hands before eating. Restrooms contain water, soap, and towels to use to prevent the spread of microbes. Sterile bandages, cleansers, and medicines are sold in stores for use on injuries to prevent infection. Doctors and hospitals use sterile instruments for each patient to prevent the spread of disease. These measures are taken now because we know how contagious diseases are spread from person to person and what causes infections in wounds.

Weather Forecasting Scientific insight also is used in many other ways, including weather forecasting. If you had lived in the 1800s, you only could have guessed the type of weather that was approaching by looking at the sky. Today, meteorologists use a variety of specialized instruments to predict the weather. Their instruments can detect approaching conditions that are dangerous. With advance warning, people can seek shelter or leave areas that are threatened by violent weather. **Figure 2** demonstrates the importance of forecasting dangerous weather conditions.

Science has changed the way people respond to natural events, such as the spread of microbes and hazardous weather. The study of science can lead to an understanding of why a natural process occurs. Once there is a clear understanding, people learn how to respond to the event and try to control the outcome.

Reading Check ***What is another example of science being used to change people's behavior?***

Figure 2 In 1900, a hurricane struck Galveston, Texas, killing about 8,000 people. Today early-warning systems alert people of an approaching storm, which saves many lives.
Identify *a type of hazardous weather that occurs in your area that requires an early-warning system.*

Caption Answer

Figure 1 During the Middle Ages, people did not know about washing their hands, covering their mouths, or clean and sterilize medical instruments. In order to prevent diseases today, people are vaccinated. Medical instruments are sterilized.

2 Teach

Discussion

Disease Prevention What are additional examples of things that are done to prevent the spread of illnesses and diseases? Accept all reasonable responses.

What are additional examples of science giving people insight into why or how something occurs? Accept all reasonable responses.

Reading Check

Answer Possible answers: seat belts in vehicles, car seats for infants

Caption Answer

Figure 2 Possible answers: tornadoes, floods, thunderstorms with lightning and hail

Curriculum Connection

History Before satellites and radar, people used observations of nature to predict the weather. They did not know why things happened, but they noted patterns. For example, they knew rain often follows a halo around the moon. Have students research other weather folklore and make posters describing what they find.

Reading Strategy

Double-Entry Notes Ask students to create a two-column chart as they read the text under the headings Scientific Insight and What is Technology? In the left column, they should take specific notes from the text, focusing on main ideas. In the right column, they should record comments, opinions, and sketches.

Mini LAB

Purpose Students will discover that many technological advances have occurred in recent years.

Materials Science Journal, pen or pencil.

Teaching Strategy Encourage students to spend time writing thoughtful questions.

Analysis

Check students' responses.

Assessment

Content Have students search for contrasting photographs that depict technology in the past and the technology of today. For example, students may find a photograph of someone writing a letter or sending a telegraph. The other photograph could be of someone using a cell phone or email. Use **Performance Assessment in the Science Classroom,** p. 89.

Try at Home

Reading Check

Answer Possible answers: transistor radio, electric lamp, digital thermometer, electric toaster, microwave oven

Caption Answer

Figure 3 technological methods or techniques

Mini LAB

Researching the Past

Procedure

1. Prepare at least five questions to ask a senior citizen about technology when he or she was a teenager.
2. Perform the interview.
3. Write the responses to your questions in your **Science Journal**.

Analysis

Compare and contrast at least five differences in technology between then and now.

Try at Home

What is technology?

The terms *science* and *technology* often are used interchangeably. However, these terms have very different definitions. Science is an exploration process. Scientific processes are used to gain knowledge to explain and predict natural occurrences. Scientists often pursue scientific knowledge for the sake of learning new information. There may or may not be a plan to use the knowledge.

When scientific knowledge is used to solve a human need or problem, as shown in **Figure 3,** the result is referred to as technology. Technology is the application of scientific knowledge of materials and processes to benefit people. Given this definition, is an aspirin tablet technology? Is a car technology? What about the national highway system? Although these examples appear to be very different, they all represent examples of technology. Technology can be:

- any human-made object (such as a radio, computer, or pen),
- methods or techniques for making any object or tool (such as the process for making glass or ceramics),
- knowledge or skills needed to operate a human-made object (such as the skills needed to pilot an airplane), or
- a system of people and objects used to do a particular task (such as the Internet, which is a system to share information).

Technological Objects? The value of a technological object changes through time. What is considered technology today might be considered an antique tomorrow. For example, special feathers called quills were used long ago to write with ink. The quill pen was the height of technology for over one thousand years. Then, in the middle of the nineteenth century, metallic pens and writing points came into use. The modern ballpoint pen was not widely used until the 1940s.

Reading Check *What are five additional objects that are considered technology?*

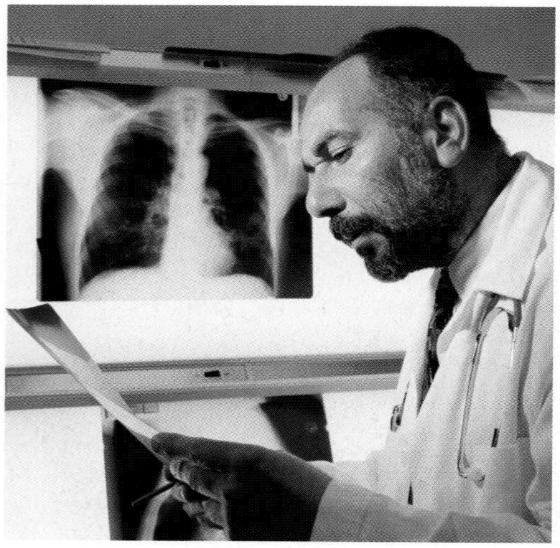

Figure 3 This figure shows technology. This image is a technological object. The knowledge needed to create and interpret this image is technology.
Identify *the technologies used to make a car.*

Differentiated Instruction

English-Language Learners Have ELL students create a poster showing different types of technology. The poster should have something to represent a technological object, method or technique, knowledge or skill, and a technological system.

Figure 4 Technology changes through time. As new scientific knowledge and techniques are learned, the processes used to create objects change.
Identify *another process used to create objects that has changed through time.*

Technological Methods or Techniques Just as writing instruments have changed through time, so have techniques for performing various tasks. **Figure 4** shows the results of how the techniques for making books have changed. Long ago, people would sit for hours copying each page of a book by hand. They used whatever writing materials were available during that time. Books were expensive and bought only by the very rich. Today, books can be created in different ways. They can be made on a computer, printed with a computer printer, and bound with a simple machine. Modern printing presses are used to produce the majority of books used today, including your textbook.

The methods used to print books have changed through time. Each technique is technology. Other techniques that characterize technology are using a compact disc to store information, using a refrigerator to preserve food, and using email to correspond with friends.

Technological Knowledge or Skills Technology also can be the knowledge or skills needed to perform a task. For example, computer skills are needed to use the software that is used to make books and other documents. Printing press operators must use their skills to print books successfully. Anytime a complex machine is used to perform a task, technological skills must be used by the operator.

Technological Systems A network of people and objects that work together to perform a task also is technology. One example of this technology is the Internet. The Internet is a collection of computers and software that is used to exchange information. A technological system is a collection of the other types of technology that are combined to perform a specific function. The airline industry is an example of technological systems. This industry is a collection of objects, methods, systems, knowledge, and procedures. The airports, pilots, fuel, and ticketing process form a technology system that is used to move people and goods.

Activity

Technology Have students look in a library for copies of scientific journals such as *Nature*, *Discover*, *Scientific American*, or *Popular Science*. Have them write a paragraph describing three scientific achievements and three technological achievements. Have students share their paragraphs with the class. P

Quick Demo

Types of Technology

Materials a computer.

Estimated Time 5 minutes

Procedure Use a desktop or laptop computer as something that represents all types of technology. Point out the following information to students. The computer represents a technological object. The use of the computer to calculate grades is an example of a new method or technique for doing something. The knowledge or skill that the teacher has to use the computer represents a knowledge or skill needed to operate a human-made object. Using the computer to communicate with other people in the school system about grades, class schedules, etc. represents a technological system.

Caption Answer

Figure 4 Possible answer: Tools used to be handmade by a single person, now they are manufactured on assembly lines in a factory.

Visual Learning

Figure 4 Johannes Guttenberg, an artisan and inventor, modernized the printing of books. His invention, known as the Guttenberg press, remained the standard until the twentieth century. The printing press was a wooden frame that contained a series of blocks. Each block had a single raised letter on its face. Ink was then rolled over the blocks where the letters were transferred to a sheet of paper. Guttenberg's invention allowed the price of printed materials to drop which meant that more people could afford books.

Fun Fact

The library in ancient Alexandria, Egypt held most of the ancient writings of its time. It is thought to have had 500,000 volumes or rolls and an annex containing another 43,000 volumes. Many ancient works have survived to modern times because of this great library.

Reading Check

Answer Possible answers: inexpensive portable water filtration systems and inexpensive electrical generation systems

Global Technological Needs

The example of how books were made explained how technology has changed through the ages. The value of technology may differ for different people and at different times. The technology that is valued in the United States is not necessarily valued in other parts of the world. The needs for technology are different in developing and industrialized countries.

Developing Countries The people of some countries work hard for basic needs such as food, shelter, clothing, safe drinking water, and health care. For example, the Kenyan family shown in **Figure 5** lives without electricity and running water in their home. Health care is limited for many families in Africa. The lack of health care results in a life expectancy for rural Kenyans to be in the mid-forties. Tropical diseases, as well as infection by the human immunodeficiency virus (HIV) are a severe problem. In addition, droughts often cause shortages of food supplies in some parts of this country.

Technological solutions in developing countries focus on supplying basic needs for these families. Technology that would supply adequate and safe drinking water and food supplies would be valued. Increasing the accessibility of basic health care would improve the quality of life and increase the life expectancy in developing countries. The technology valued by rural people contrast with the technology valued by people in industrialized Kenyan cities.

Reading Check *What are two examples of technology that would be valued in developing countries?*

Figure 5 The technological needs of this Kenyan family center around providing the basic needs for survival, such as provisions for safe water and food supplies, health care, education, and a safe environment in which to live and work.

42 CHAPTER 2 Science, Technology, and Society

Industrialized Countries The United States is considered an industrialized country. Technology gives people the ability to clean polluted waters. Improving the quality of the food supply is also valued. But the level of urgency and focus appears to differ in developing countries. Most areas of the United States have adequate and safe water and food supplies. Most homes have electricity and running water. Quality health care is available to many people. The life expectancy of Americans is the late-seventies.

Look at the home in **Figure 6** and compare it to the home shown on the previous page. Does one of the homes have more technology? Look at the materials used to build each home. The materials used to build the home in **Figure 6** are technology, too.

Because the needs for survival are met in industrialized nations, money often is spent on technology. Technology is designed to improve the quality of life of individuals. Most homes in the United States contain many different types of technology, including computers, telephones, and televisions. People living in industrialized countries may value faster and faster computers. They may value small devices such as compact discs that store large amounts of information. Advances in health care can improve the quality of life due to the ability to cure diseases. Money is spent on such medical procedures as cosmetic surgery to remove wrinkles, and eye surgery so that a person no longer has to wear glasses.

Contrasting Needs As you can see, the human needs for developing and industrialized countries are very different. Both developing and industrialized countries value technologies that supply basic human needs as discussed in **Figure 7.** The actual technology required in each country may be very different.

Figure 6 The basic needs for survival are available in industrialized nations. In these countries, value is placed on technology that improves the quality of life such as devices that make tasks easier and devices that provide entertainment.
Describe *three technological objects that you value that would be of less value to the Kenyan family on the previous page. Explain your answers.*

IDENTIFYING Misconceptions

Africa Students may think that all the inhabitants of Africa live in rural areas like those shown in Figure 5. Africa is a diverse continent that contains large, modern cities, as well as rural, undeveloped areas.

Caption Answer

Figure 6 Possible answers: portable compact disc player, DVD player, or television; There is no electrical power available and they cannot afford to purchase batteries for these items.

Cultural Diversity

Contributions from Africa Egypt, which is located in Northern Africa, was the location of one of the greatest civilizations in history. Ancient Egyptians built the great pyramids, compiled a vast library in Alexandria, and built a thriving economy. Have students research the contributions to the world made by ancient Egyptians.

NATIONAL GEOGRAPHIC

Visualizing Technology Supplying Basic Needs

Have students examine the pictures and read the captions. Then ask the following questions.

How does modern agriculture increase yields over traditional methods? Modern agriculture uses large tractors instead of horses, large farms instead of small ones, chemical fertilizers instead of organic fertilizers, special pesticides, and specially engineered seed.

How does the construction of roads affect the other technologies? Roads allow for transportation of food, medicines, parts, tractors, and workers. Without roads, other technologies can be difficult to implement.

Activity

Divide the classroom into several groups and ask them to do the following exercise. If you were in charge of bringing technology to a developing country and could only bring one technology a year, in what order would you bring the technologies? Why?

Post Reading

Science Journal Technological advances range from the invention of the ballpoint pen to the invention of the television. Ask students to think about the technological advancements they have seen in their lives. Have them respond to this prompt: How has technology changed your life?

NATIONAL GEOGRAPHIC **VISUALIZING TECHNOLOGY SUPPLYING BASIC NEEDS**

Figure 7

Technology is used to help supply the basic requirements of people across the globe. Many of life's necessities that we take for granted in the United States are lacking or inadequate in other countries.

▲ Modern Agriculture **Farming with tractors on vast fields and using pesticides and specially engineered seed can increase the amount of food a country produces.**

▲ Water Treatment **Polluted water can cause diseases. Treating the water with chlorine kills germs.**

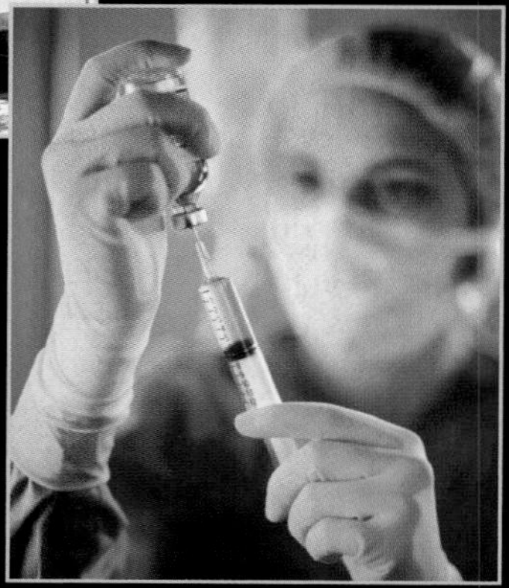

◀ Vaccines **Diseases like polio, measles, and tetanus kill hundreds of thousands of people a year. Vaccines cause the human body to make antibodies for a specific bacteria or virus. If this bacteria or virus enters the body, the antibodies destroy it.**

▲ Power Plants **Electricity is necessary for many technologies. Electricity can be produced in many ways including burning coal, using moving water, absorbing the heat of solar rays, and using heat deep in the earth.**

▲ Transportation Systems **Technology allows countries to build roads, airports, and canals that let food, medicine, and information travel quickly to where it is needed.**

44 **CHAPTER 2** Science, Technology, and Society

Differentiated Instruction

Challenge Have students make a detailed list of the pros and cons of using technology to move from a developing country to a developed country. Pros include more food, longer life spans, new conveniences and job creation. Cons include pollution, cultural disruption, ecological damage, forced relocation, and diseases of the wealthy like obesity and diabetes. Ask students to evaluate how the pros and cons would affect their decision to implement a technology.

Bioengineering and Food Can technology stop world hunger and starvation? Agricultural biotechnology can increase the yields of farm crops. It also can increase the nutritional value of the food produced. **Agricultural biotechnology** is a collection of scientific techniques, including genetic engineering, that are used to create, improve, or modify plants, animals, and microorganisms. For example, changing the DNA of a plant such as corn can improve its tolerance to drought. Other benefits could make it disease and insect resistant, or improve its nutritional value. The end result may be a higher crop yield and a product that provides more nutritional value per serving.

Genetically altering plant species is a highly controversial practice. Some people argue that the practice is too dangerous. They argue that humans should not alter species that occur naturally on Earth. Others argue that new species could harm natural ecosystems. New crops could pose human health risks such as food allergies or toxins.

A discussion also exists over whether more food really is needed to feed the world population. One argument is that enough food is produced, but it is not equally distributed throughout the world. As you can see, using technology to solve human problems is not always an easy task. Often there are many obstacles and issues involved.

Science Online

Topic: Biotech Foods
Visit gpescience.com for Web links to information about agricultural biotechnology and biotech foods.

Activity Create a pamphlet explaining the risks and benefits of biotech foods.

section 1 review

Summary

Scientific Discovery
- The study of science leads to a better understanding of natural events that occur.

Scientific Insight
- Once there is an understanding of why a natural process occurs, people learn how to respond to the event and try to control the outcome.
- Scientific insight changes human behavior.

What is technology?
- Technology can be an object, a technique, a skill, or a system.
- The value of technological objects varies over time.

Global Technological Needs
- Technological needs vary around the world.

Self Check

1. **Describe** a situation in which scientific insight changed people's understanding, resulting in behavior change in response to a natural event or process.
2. **Classify** List the types of technology and give at least two examples of each type.
3. **Explain** why the types of technology valued varies from location to location.
4. **Think Critically** Cell phones are a technology that is popular throughout the world. Would this technology be of use in rural areas of the world? Explain your answer.

Applying Math

5. **Calculate** Approximately 38 million people are infected with HIV worldwide. Two-thirds of this group lives in sub-Saharan Africa. Calculate how many sub-Saharans are affected.

More Section Review gpescience.com

3 Assess

DAILY INTERVENTION

Check for Understanding

Interpersonal Divide the class into small groups. Have each group compile and share a list of items or actions that are scientific achievements and a list of items or actions that are technological achievements.

Reteach

Technology Write examples of technology, such as radio or Internet, on the board. Ask students to identify the type of technology represented. Radio is a human-made technology object. The Internet is an example of a technological system.

Assessment

Content Divide the students into small groups. Have students debate whether or not agricultural biotechnology should be used for food crops. Half of each group should be assigned "for biotechnology development" and the other half should be "against biotechnology development." Allow each group some time to brainstorm their ideas before the debate begins. Use **PASC,** p.,169

section 1 review

1. Possible answer: Today people understand that microbes transmit illnesses and disease. People now take precautions against spreading microbes.
2. Possible answer: object, ball-point pen; method, building a house; knowledge, driving a car; system, airport
3. Locations around the world vary in the amount of technology and resources that are available to the public. For instance, many locations do not have electrical power in homes. Any electrical device would be useless in these locations and not valued.
4. It would be of value only in the large cities. In the rural areas, there is no electrical power and the people do not have the money to buy cell phones. There are few areas in which the phones would work because the entire country does not have cell phone coverage.
5. approximately 27 million

section 2 Forces that Shape Technology

1 Motivate

INTERACTIVE CHALKBOARD An editable Microsoft® PowerPoint® presentation is available on **Interactive Chalkboard** CD-ROM.

Bellringer

Section Focus Transparencies also are available on the Interactive Chalkboard CD-ROM. L2 ELL

Section 2 Section Focus Transparency — Three Mile Island Nuclear Generating Station — Chapter 2

On March 28, 1979, a nuclear reactor near Harrisburg, Pennsylvania suffered a partial core meltdown. Unlike the meltdown at Chernobyl, no radioactive material was released into the atmosphere. However, it furthered a serious decline in the public popularity of nuclear power. By coincidence, the event occurred just days after the release of the movie *The China Syndrome* which portrayed a similar, yet fictional, incident.

1. What impact do you think the accident at Three Mile Island had on the development of nuclear power in the United States?
2. Can you think of any disadvantages of nuclear power?
3. What are the advantages of nuclear power?

L2

Reading Preview

Tie to Prior Knowledge

Ecosystems Remind students that an ecosystem consists of the living and nonliving parts of an environment that are interdependent. Altering an ecosystem affects the organisms, including humans, that depend on that physical environment for survival.

Word Map Have students make a concept map with the new vocabulary word *society* in the center. Have them connect three large ovals to the word. Ask students to write the definition in one oval. In another, have them create a sentence using the term. In the last oval, have students make a sketch of the word's meaning.

Reading Guide

What You'll Learn

- **Discuss** how funds for science research come from the federal government, private industries, and private foundations.
- **Explain** how consumers affect technological development.
- **Describe** the importance of responsible technological development.

Why It's Important

Society and economic forces influence which technologies will be developed and used.

Review Vocabulary

ecosystem: a complex community of organisms that function together in a particular environment

New Vocabulary

- society

Social Forces that Shape Technology

Science and society are closely connected. **Society** is a group of people that share similar values and beliefs. Discoveries in science and technology bring about changes in society. In turn, society affects how new technologies develop. The development of technology is affected by society and its changing values, politics, and economics.

In the past 100 years, attitudes in the United States have changed toward automobiles. Many people were able to own cars due to the changes in technology and manufacturing. As car ownership increased, so did fossil-fuel consumption. With rising gasoline prices, some consumers began buying more fuel-efficient cars. The automotive industry has researched and developed technologies that make cars more fuel-efficient. Today we have hybrid cars that use both gasoline and electricity.

Figure 8 Consumers often decide which technologies will be developed. If consumers do not purchase a product, additional money usually will not be spent on the production or improvement of the product.

Consumer Acceptance Purchasing technology is a direct way in which people support the development of technology, as shown in **Figure 8.** For example, if consumers continue to purchase fuel-efficient cars, additional money will be spent on improving the technology. If consumers fail to buy a product, companies usually will not spend additional money on that type of technology.

Section 2 Resource Manager

Chapter *FAST FILE* Resources
- Transparency Activity, pp. 41, 43–44
- MiniLAB, p. 4
- Enrichment, p. 27
- Reinforcement, p. 24
- Directed Reading for Content Mastery, p. 16
- Lab Worksheets, pp. 5–6

Life Science Critical Thinking/Problem Solving, p. 4

Reading and Writing Skills Activities, pp. 9–10

Personal Values People will support the development of technologies that agree with their personal values, directly and indirectly. For example, people vote for a congressional candidate based upon the candidate's views on various issues. This is an indirect way in which people's personal values influence how technology projects receive funding. People support the development of technology directly when they give their money to organizations committed to a specific project, such as cancer research.

Reading Check *How do the personal values of consumers influence which technologies will be developed?*

Economic Forces that Shape Technology

Many factors influence how much money is spent on technology. Before funding is given for a project, several questions should be answered. What is the benefit for this product? What is the cost? Who will buy this product? All these questions should be answered before money is given for a project. Various methods exist to fund new and existing technology.

Federal Government One way in which funds are allocated for research and development of technology is through the federal government. Every year, Congress and the president place large amounts of money in the federal budget for scientific research and development. These funds are reserved for specific types of research, such as agriculture, defense, energy, and transportation. This money is given to companies and institutions in the form of contracts and grants to do specific types of research. Citizens can influence elected officials by telling them how they want the official to vote, as shown in **Figure 9.**

Private Foundations Some scientific research is funded using money from private foundations. A private foundation, which is an organization not associated with the government, is a group of people who work together for a common goal. Funds are raised for various types of disease research, such as breast cancer and muscular dystrophy. Money is raised by events such as races and telethons. Many private foundations focus on research for a specific cause.

Mini LAB

Evaluating the Benefits and Consequences of Technology

Procedure

1. Choose a technology that you value and do not want to live without.
2. Make a two-column table. Label one column *Benefits* and the other column *Consequences.*
3. Provide at least three entries for each column.

Analysis

1. Do the benefits of the technology outweigh the consequences? Explain.
2. Infer who funded the development of your technology. Explain.
3. Infer how you may influence future funding on this type of technology.

Figure 9 Participating in the political process is one way in which people can influence which technologies are developed and which are not.
Explain *how voting for someone in the Congress influences which technologies will be developed.*

2 Teach

Reading Check

Answer People influence the development of technology indirectly when they vote for members of Congress. They influence technology directly by giving their money to various organizations.

Mini LAB

Purpose Students reflect on the benefits and consequences of a technology that they do not want to live without.

Materials Science Journal, pencil

Teaching Strategy

- Encourage students to think about the raw materials that are used to make the product.
- Encourage students to think about environmental consequences their technology may have.
- After all of the above are considered, the students should evaluate the benefits and consequences of their technology.

Analysis

1. Accept all reasonable responses.
2. Answers will vary.
3. In most cases, purchasing the item will impact the future funding of similar technologies.

Assessment

Oral Is it possible to improve the benefits and reduce the consequences for your chosen technology? Answers will vary

Caption Answer

Figure 9 Members of Congress are elected by the voters in their districts. These representatives vote on the federal budget which funds many types of technology. Voting is an indirect way that people affect which technologies will be developed.

Activity

Current Issues Have students research a technological issue that is part of an election debate. The issue can be part of a local, state, or federal election. Have students find arguments from both sides of the debate.

Teacher FYI

DDT The pesticide DDT was used to kill disease-carrying and crop-eating insects. DDT was successful in reducing the number of cases of yellow fever, typhus, malaria, and other diseases carried by insects in many parts of the world. DDT was banned or strictly regulated after it was discovered that it was adversely affecting animals, such as the bald eagle.

INTEGRATE Environment

Environmental Protection Agency The EPA does more than just protect the health of humans and the environment. The organization develops and enforces regulations. They offer financial assistance through grants to states, non-profit organizations, and educational institutions for environmental projects. The scientists who work for EPA perform environmental research.

INTEGRATE Environment

Environmental Protection Agency The purpose of the EPA is to protect human health and the environment. The EPA was established in 1970 by the White House and Congress. Cleaner air and water, along with cleaner land, were things that U.S. citizens have demanded. Prior to the establishment of the EPA, the government had no organized method to reduce pollutants. Research the water quality for your city or state.

Private Industries Research and development also is funded by private industries. Industries budget a portion of their profits for research and development. Investing in research and development often makes money for the company. Bringing new products to the marketplace is one way companies make profits.

Responsible Technology

Humans have the ability to invent tools and processes that can have an impact on other living things. Humans are part of many ecosystems on Earth. It is important that any technology that is used does not destroy the environment, as shown in **Figure 10.** It is important that both positive and negative consequences of a particular technology be considered.

Environmental Issues Sometimes the consequences of technology are known, but the benefits are perceived to outweigh the risks. One example of technology that has both positive and negative consequences is gasoline-powered cars. Gasoline-powered cars give the benefit of reliable transportation. The negative consequences are the environmental problems created by drilling for oil, air pollution, and disposal of unwanted cars. The disposal of used petroleum products, such as motor oil, also is a problem.

Sometimes the benefits of technology are known immediately, but the consequences are not known for a period of time. For example, at one time, the pesticide DDT was eagerly accepted by people. It killed insects that were damaging agricultural crops. The fact that DDT was damaging the environment was not known immediately. When the damage was discovered, DDT was banned and other pesticides were developed. Consumers and voters have a responsibility to weigh the benefits and consequences of technology. They play a major role in determining which technologies are used and which are rejected.

Figure 10 In March 1989, approximately 42,000 kiloliters of oil were spilled in Prince William Sound, Alaska. Animals, such as ducks and birds, are affected by human-made environmental disasters.

Visual Learning

Figure 10 No one knows the exact number of wildlife harmed or killed by the oil spill. Oil can injure wildlife by coating the fur and feathers, causing them to ingest the oil while trying to clean themselves, or by making them incapable to protect themselves. Liquid dish detergent is used to clean the oil from the animals. Have students research to determine which wildlife has not yet recovered from the oil spill.

Differentiated Instruction

Learning Disabled Pair students with learning disabilities with other students that can assist them in finding the Ukraine on the globe or atlas.

INTEGRATE History

The Chernobyl Accident Possibly the worst technological accident in modern times occurred on April 26, 1986, at the Chernobyl nuclear power plant in the Ukraine. Large areas of land were contaminated and more than 400,000 people had to be relocated. The city of Pripyat had to be abandoned, as shown in **Figure 11.** An accumulation of radioactive fallout in the upper layers of soil has destroyed important farmland. Groundwater and surface waters were contaminated. Some water wells had to be sealed. Structures had to be built to prevent rivers and streams in the area from contaminating additional rivers in the watershed, which led to the Black Sea.

The radiation also affected many animals and plants around Chernobyl. As the radiation diminished, plants and animals started to repopulate the area.

Reading Check *Why did the residents near the accident have to move?*

Figure 11 This town once was home to about 45,000 residents. It is now abandoned because radioactive contamination has made it unsafe to live in.
Identify *possible health effects that Ukrainians faced.*

Applying Science

What impact does the accident at Chernobyl have on the future of nuclear power?

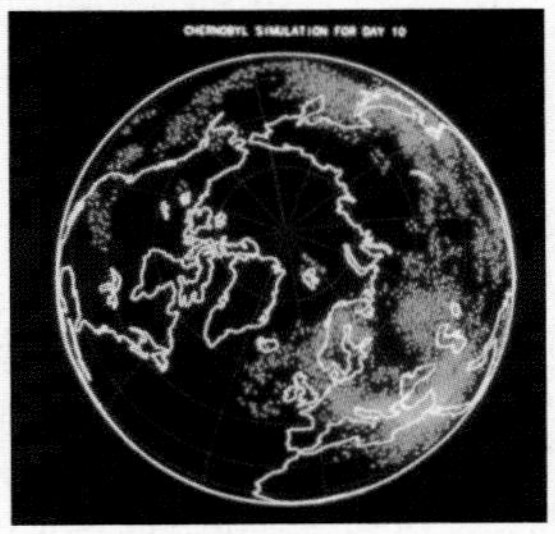

The nuclear accident at Chernobyl in 1986 demonstrates the far-reaching impact of a nuclear disaster. Not only were the residents and environment surrounding the facility influenced, but nuclear fallout was spread across most of the northern hemisphere. Parts of the USSR and Europe were seriously affected.

Identifying the Problem

Many countries, including the United States, use nuclear power as a source of electric power. Is it important for industrialized countries, such as the United States, that have vast resources and knowledge about nuclear power generation, to assist developing countries in their nuclear power generation programs?

Solving the Problem

1. What are the benefits and consequences of allowing developing countries that do not have the experience that developed countries have to develop nuclear power on their own?
2. What are the benefits and consequences of assisting developing countries?

Discussion

Responsibility How does the Chernobyl accident exemplify irresponsible technology? Safeguards were not in place to prevent the accident from occurring.

Applying Science

Answers

1. Possible answers: Benefits—Safe systems can be built based on proven technologies without the risk of a preventable nuclear disaster. Consequences—Developing countries may build an unsafe system because they do not have the knowledge or experience needed to build safe systems.
2. Benefits—Many countries benefit because a safe system is built and a tragedy similar to Chernobyl is averted. Consequences—Developing countries may use the technology to develop nuclear weapon systems.

Caption Answer

Figure 11 leukemia, thyroid cancer, cancer, genetic problems, radiation poisoning

INTEGRATE History **Content Background**

The radioactive elements that were released into the air were iodine-131, cesium-137, and strontium-90. Due to this release, much of the area will remain uninhabited for centuries. The land affected by the accident is approximately the size of Kentucky. The reactor, which caused the accident, is buried in a concrete tomb. It will remain radioactive for centuries.

Reading Strategy

Panel Discussion After students read the text titled Responsible Technology, form a panel of students to respond to the following prompt: Space exploration poses risks to society and to the astronaut. Are the benefits worth the risks? Have the class add to the discussion by asking questions to the panel.

Curriculum Connection

Geography Have students find the location of the Chernobyl nuclear power plant on a globe or in an atlas. It is located in the country of Ukraine, which was once part of the Soviet Union. Have students identify the countries surrounding the Ukraine.

Post Reading

Essay Have students consider technology issues they have read about that might be controversial. Ask them to write an essay in which they present their opinions regarding the issue. For instance, an essay topic might involve the engineering of disease-resistant wheat through crossbreeding.

3 Assess

DAILY INTERVENTION

Check for Understanding

Linguistic Write a paragraph explaining why morality and ethics are important in science. P

Reteach

Responsible Technology Have students explain why humans must practice responsible technology. Because humans can have an enormous impact on other living things through the use of technology.

Assessment

Content Have students work in small groups to write a newspaper article about the nuclear disaster at Chernobyl. Use **PASC,** p. 141.

Science Online

Topic: Morals and Ethics in Science

Visit gpescience.com for Web links to information about morals and ethics in science.

Activity Choose a topic and write an essay describing the moral and ethical arguments surrounding the topic.

Moral and Ethical Issues When people need to distinguish between right and wrong, what is fair, and what is in the best interest of all people, moral and ethical issues are raised. Ethical issues in science pose questions and establish rules about how scientific hypotheses should be tested and how society should use scientific knowledge.

Ethics help scientists establish standards that they agree to follow when they collect, analyze, and report data. Scientists are expected to conduct investigations honestly and openly. Honesty is important because scientists share the results of their investigations with each other. As a result, one scientist's dishonesty can harm the investigations of many scientists.

Other ethical questions in science concern the use of animals and humans in scientific investigations. In the past, the inhumane treatment of humans and animals in experiments has led to public outcry. For example, human test subjects have been subjected to experiments against their will, or without informing them of risks associated with the research or the true nature of the experiments. Ethical questions about these practices helped to create laws and guidelines to prevent unethical treatment of both humans and animals in scientific research.

section 2 review

Summary

Social and Economic Forces that Shape Technology

- Societal and economic forces influence which technologies will be developed and used.
- The federal government, private foundations, and private industries fund research and development of technology.
- Consumers influence which technologies will be developed by their voting and buying habits.

Responsible Technology

- Humans must be responsible in their technological choices because the technology may have an enormous impact on other living things and the environment.
- The risks and benefits of technology must be considered before developing and using it.
- Consumers and scientists must consider moral and ethical issues when choosing which technologies should be developed.

Self Check

1. **Describe** how private citizens have a voice in which projects the federal government will fund.
2. **Explain** how you can influence whether or not funding will be spent on developing certain technology.
3. **Describe** a situation in which technology had unexpected consequences.
4. **Think Critically** Many products carry a message on their label that no animals or humans were used in the testing of the product. Is this good or bad for the consumer? Explain your answer.

Applying Math

5. **Use Percentages** In 2001, approximately \$41 million was spent by the Department of Defense for Research, Development, Test, and Evaluation. If the total amount of money spent by the department was over \$305 million, what percent of the defense budget does this represent?

 More Section Review gpescience.com

section 2 review

1. Private citizens have an indirect voice because they elect the people that make the decisions.
2. You can influence funding by voting and by contributing money to private foundations that are involved in developing the technology.
3. Possible answer: Gasoline-powered cars created smog and air-pollution problems.
4. This can be good and bad. It is good because humans and animals were not harmed in the testing. It is bad because the product may not have been fully tested before it was sold to the consumer.
5. 13 percent

Who contributes CO_2?

Many scientists believe that Earth's surface temperature is rising because of increasing levels of heat-trapping carbon dioxide, CO_2, in Earth's atmosphere. The combustion of fossil-fuels contributes CO_2 to Earth's atmosphere. Significant amounts of CO_2 are produced by cement production and gas flaring.

Real-World Problem

Which countries produce the most carbon dioxide from the combustion of fossil fuels?

Goals

- **Compare and contrast** the total carbon dioxide emissions from selected countries.
- **Calculate** the average annual per capita amount of carbon dioxide for each country.
- **Form a hypothesis** that explains the amount of carbon dioxide produced by each country.

Materials

Science Journal
pen or pencil

Procedure

1. Copy and complete the data table in your Science Journal by calculating the amount of carbon dioxide produced per person for each country.
2. **Formulate** a hypothesis that explains the amount of carbon dioxide produced by the inhabitants of the countries listed in the table. For each country, consider the following factors: size; population density; transportation requirements; heating and cooling requirements; development and industry; means of generating electricity.

Countries CO_2 Emissions

Country	CO_2 Emissions (millions of tons of carbon)	Total Population (millions of) persons)	CO_2 Produced (tons/person)
United States	1,446.8	263.8	5.48
China	918.0	1,210.0	0.76
Russian Federation	431.1	149.9	2.88
Japan	318.7	125.5	2.54
India	272.2	936.5	0.29
Canada	111.7	28.4	3.93
France	98.8	58.1	1.70

Conclude and Apply

1. **Graph** the data of carbon dioxide produced per person using a bar graph.
2. **Think Critically** Why might more developed, industrial countries have more carbon dioxide produced per person?
3. **Evaluate** Did the results obtained from your calculations support your hypothesis?

Communicating Your Data

Compare your bar graphs with those of other students. Discuss any differences, particularly if some students used computer graphing programs to prepare their graphs.

BENCH TESTED

Real-World Problem

Purpose Students compare total and per capita carbon dioxide emissions of selected countries, evaluate their results, and graph their data.

Process Skills analyze results, communicate, compare and contrast, evaluate, form hypotheses, interpret data, make and use graphs, think critically, calculate

Time Required 45 minutes

Procedure

Teaching Strategies

- Suggest that students work in pairs or groups to make and check their calculations and discuss the comparative amount of CO2 produced for various countries.
- Have students work individually to prepare their graphs and write answers to questions.

Conclude and Apply

1. See student page for the amount of carbon dioxide produced per person. Check students' work for the bar graph.
2. Answers will vary. In general, more developed and industrialized countries tend to have higher CO2 emissions. Persons living in these countries drive more automobiles and use more power-consuming conveniences and devices.
3. Answers will vary.

Assessment

Oral Have students formulate and present ideas regarding ways that countries and individuals can reduce their carbon dioxide emissions and, thereby, do their part to combat global warming.

Communicating Your Data

Have students prepare their bar graphs using computer graphing programs. Emphasize that data and results should be presented clearly and concisely for others to follow and understand.

section 3

Developing Technology

Reading Guide

What You'll Learn

- **Discuss** how the roles of a scientist and an engineer differ.
- **Explain** how technological problems often create a demand for new scientific knowledge.
- **Describe** the general process used to find technical solutions to problems or human needs.

Why It's Important

Understanding how technology is developed can help you make better decisions as a consumer.

Review Vocabulary

system: a group of devices that work together to perform a specific function

New Vocabulary

- engineer
- constraints
- computer simulation
- prototype
- pilot plant
- control system

Scientists and Engineers

How do a scientist and an engineer differ? This may seem to be a very odd question, but it is important to learn the roles of these two types of professionals. Recall that a scientist is someone who has knowledge about science. He or she works to learn more information about science. Scientists may not know how or if the results of their work will be used, but they pursue knowledge for the sake of learning new things.

Scientists have knowledge of scientific principles. Most scientists have some knowledge of basic chemistry, physics, and biology. Many scientists specialize in one area of science. For example, a scientist may have a chemistry background but specialize in Earth science. This scientist will study the chemical and physical changes that occur on Earth. An Earth scientist may specialize even further and study topics such as glaciers, earthquakes, or volcanoes.

Scientists often work in research laboratories doing research. In addition, scientists also work in the field, as shown in **Figure 12.** An Earth scientist is an example of a scientist that would conduct investigations and research in the field, as well as in the laboratory.

Figure 12 This meteorologist is collecting data on an approaching tornado. This information can be used in the study of tornadoes and how to protect people and property from damage.

Reading Check *What is a scientist?*

1 Motivate

An editable Microsoft® PowerPoint® presentation is available on **Interactive Chalkboard** CD-ROM.

Bellringer

Section Focus Transparencies also are available on the Interactive Chalkboard CD-ROM. L2 ELL

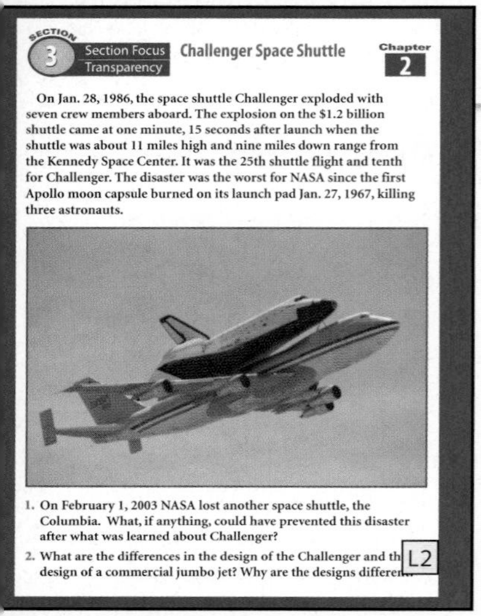

Section 3 Section Focus Transparency — Challenger Space Shuttle — Chapter 2

On Jan. 28, 1986, the space shuttle Challenger exploded with seven crew members aboard. The explosion on the $1.2 billion shuttle came at one minute, 15 seconds after launch when the shuttle was about 11 miles high and nine miles down range from the Kennedy Space Center. It was the 25th shuttle flight and tenth for Challenger. The disaster was the worst for NASA since the first Apollo moon capsule burned on its launch pad Jan. 27, 1967, killing three astronauts.

1. On February 1, 2003 NASA lost another space shuttle, the Columbia. What, if anything, could have prevented this disaster after what was learned about Challenger?
2. What are the differences in the design of the Challenger and th[e] design of a commercial jumbo jet? Why are the designs differen[t?] L2

Reading Preview

Tie to Prior Knowledge

Scientific Methods Tell students that finding a solution to a technological problem is much like using the scientific method in research. Both processes are very methodical and deliberate.

Word Associations Have students write a new vocabulary word in the center of a sheet of paper. They should draw four lines emanating from the central term. Each line will extend to words associated with the vocabulary term. For example, *engineer* might be associated with "problem solver" or "analytical."

Section 3 Resource Manager

Chapter *Fast File* Resources

Transparency Activity, p. 42
Lab Activity, pp. 11–12
Enrichment, p. 28
Reinforcement, p. 25
Directed Reading for Content Mastery, p. 17
Lab Worksheets, pp. 7–8

Home and Community Involvement, p. 27

Performance Assessment in the Science Classroom, pp. 46–47

Engineers A researcher who is responsible for bringing technology to the consumer is called an **engineer.** Using scientific information or an idea, an engineer creates a way to solve a problem or to produce a product. For example, decreasing petroleum deposits and high prices for gasoline have created a demand for cars that get better gas mileage. Engineers are working to improve an engine called a hybrid. The hybrid engine operates on electricity and gasoline or diesel to power the car. Fuel efficiency increases by combining the two power sources. Cars currently are available using this technology. As this example demonstrates, consumers want cars with better gas mileage. Engineers worked to create technology that would satisfy this consumer demand.

Figure 13 New technology often creates a demand for even more technology. Many technological advances have been made in the automobile since 1950.
Identify *at least three different technological advances that have been made in the automobile since 1950.*

Technological problems often create a demand for new scientific knowledge. Time and money are devoted to finding new scientific information, which makes it possible for scientists to extend their research in a way that advances science. Many unexpected discoveries happened when scientists were looking for a technical solution. In addition, new technology often creates a need for even more technology, as shown in **Figure 13.**

Engineers not only design automobiles, they work in many areas of science. There are aeronautical, aerospace, biomedical, chemical, computer, electrical, mechanical, and many other types of engineers. At some point of the manufacturing process, engineers are involved in the development of the products you use every day.

Reading Check *How do scientists and engineers differ?*

2 Teach

Reading Check

Answer A scientist is someone who has knowledge of science and works to learn more information about science.

Discussion

Demand for New Technology What is another example of where technology created a demand for new technology? Possible answer: The invention of the airplane has created a continuous demand for new technology. How has the demand for technology led to advances in science? Possible answer: The advances made in air travel made it possible to go to space. Many advances in space science have been made because of our ability to do space travel.

Caption Answer

Figure 13 Possible answers: automatic transmission, catalytic converter to control emissions, power doors and locks

Reading Check

Answer Scientists study science to find new information and engineers use science to solve human needs or mass produce products.

Teacher FYI

Marketing A driving force in the development of technology is whether or not the product or technology will sell. Marketing considerations often override other issues in the development of technology.

Differentiated Instruction

Learning Disabled The vocabulary in this section is complex. Have students create an illustrated glossary of the terms. Students can write the word and definition on an index card. Students should draw an illustration or glue a photo on the card that illustrates the meaning of the word.

Fun Fact

One of the first scientific societies formed in Italy in 1603. The purpose of the *Accademia del Cimento* was to exchange scientific information.

INTEGRATE Life Science

Young Owl Gets Help Research on animals is beneficial in several ways. Zoo and domestic animals can be treated with new technologies when the need arises. Species of animals that are near extinction can be saved and can produce offspring.

Inquiry Lab

Finding Solutions

Purpose to model the process for finding a solution

Possible Materials poster board, newspaper ads

Estimated Time 1 week

Teaching Strategies

Students have a budget of $500.00 to design the perfect bedroom for a friend. They are to propose solutions, identify constraints, comply with all rules set by the friend and the friend's parents, and create a scale drawing to make sure that everything fits in the room. Encourage students to cut pictures out of the newspaper showing prices for items they want to purchase.

For additional inquiry activities, see *Science Inquiry Lab Manual.*

Caption Answer

Figure 14 scientific method

Reading Check

Answer to find a possible solution

INTEGRATE Life Science

Young Owl Gets Help Technology can be used in unusual ways. A young, great-horned owl was observed sitting on a fence for several days without moving. It seems the owl could not see and could not search for food. Veterinarians removed the owl's cataracts and fitted the owl with new artificial lenses. The owl recovered and was returned to the wild. Research other medical procedures that can be used to help animals.

Finding Solutions

Scientists and engineers work together to find technological solutions, as shown in **Figure 14.** They often use a system much like the scientific method. The general process is outlined in this section. However, there are many variations to this procedure, just as there are many kinds of technical problems.

Identifying the Problem The first step in finding a technical solution is to define clearly the problem that you are trying to solve. The problem must have a narrow enough focus so that a solution is possible. For example, it would not be helpful to define the problem as, "Create and build a new vehicle." This definition of the problem is too broad. What type of vehicle is needed? Should the vehicle be designed to carry passengers or heavy loads or both? What type of fuel should the new vehicle use? What types of materials should be used to construct the vehicle? Is there a market for the vehicle once it is built? All of these questions and many more should be answered in the definition of the problem. A better statement of the problem may be, "Build a new passenger vehicle from readily available materials that has an improved gas mileage of at least 20 percent over current, similar-size models and is competitively priced."

Proposing Solutions Once the problem is clearly defined, the search for the solution can begin. This is not always an easy process. There are many factors to consider when searching for the best solution to a problem. The best solution must be found while working with many limitations.

Reading Check *Why is it important to have a clearly defined problem?*

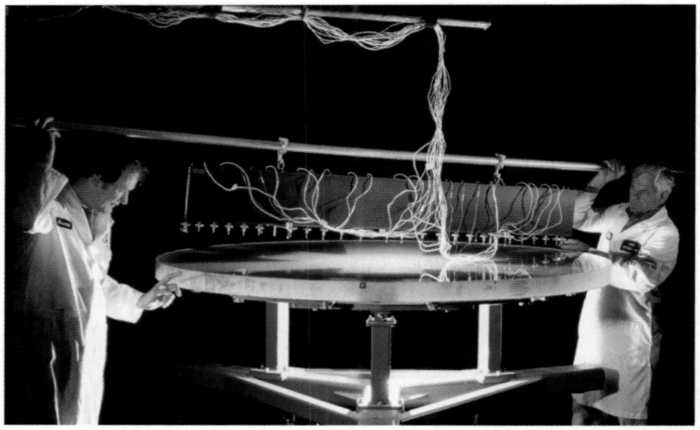

Figure 14 Scientists and engineers work together to solve technical problems.
Identify *the type of system scientists and engineers use to find technological solutions.*

LAB DEMONSTRATION

Purpose to test the strength of two types of thread.

Materials spool of cotton thread; spool of nylon thread; ring stand; ring; assorted small weights.

Procedure Attach the ring to the top of the ring stand. Tie the cotton thread to the ring stand. Cut the thread so that it will not touch the table after the weights are attached. Measure the length of the string. Attach weights to the string until the string breaks. Record the total amount of weight attached. Repeat the procedure with the same length of nylon string.

Expected Outcome The nylon thread supports more weight.

Assessment

Which thread would provide the strongest seam? nylon.

Constraints Design restrictions for products from outside factors are known as **constraints.** Examples of constraints are cost, environmental impact, and available materials. Constraints also include limited time to complete the task, limited funding, and design changes that must be made to satisfy laws and regulations. In addition, working with too little information or technical data can be constraints. Some designs may be perfect solutions but they cannot be built. Some materials may not be available or do not exist. Money may not be available. The solution to the problem may be a compromise because of many design constraints.

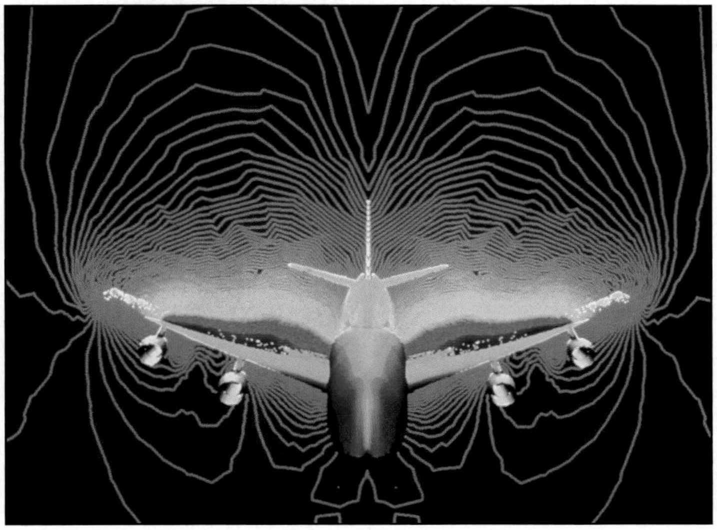

Figure 15 This is a computer simulation of an aircraft in a wind tunnel. The lines and colors surrounding the aircraft show airflow and turbulence. Scientists who use computer simulation can work to improve the aircraft design.
List *other ways that a computer simulation can be used.*

Performance Testing Once design ideas are accepted, drawings or models usually are constructed. These are carefully evaluated to identify possible design flaws. It is important to find design flaws as early in the process as possible. The later a design flaw is found in the process, the more expensive it is to correct.

After the drawing or model has been thoroughly evaluated, the design must be tested to make sure everything operates as planned. Many ways exist to performance test a design. The type of performance test used depends upon the design. For example, a chemical process may be tested initially by using a computer simulation. A **computer simulation** uses a computer to imitate the process to collect data or to test a process or procedure. Computer software is designed to mimic the processes in the design, as shown in **Figure 15.**

Complying with Laws and Regulations Local communities, states, and the federal government have laws and regulations regarding manufacturing processes, products, or buildings. These regulations often cover topics such as worker safety, environmental protection, product transportation, and how pleasing the manufacturing facility looks in the community. Products also must meet ethical or moral standards in their production, testing, and use. All of these factors must be considered when designing technology.

Reading Strategy

Set a Purpose Have students scan the following sections: Identifying the Problem, Proposing Solutions, and Constraints. Remind them to pay attention to headings, bold print, and figures. Have them set the purpose by writing down what they expect to learn from each section. As they read, have each student note if his or her purpose has been met.

Activity

Product Features and Solutions Show the students a laptop computer bag. Allow students to examine the bag closely. Have students make a list of features that the bag must have to protect the laptop computer. Then, have students make a list of features the bag has that are added for convenience such as pen holders, straps, etc.

Quick Demo

The Best Protection

Materials polyester batting (used in quilting), sheet of firm foam (used in upholstery)

Estimated Time 10 minutes

Procedure Engineers must select the best materials for a product. Allow students to examine both materials. Ask students which would be the best material to place in a laptop computer bag to protect the computer. Place both samples on a desk or table. Place a laptop computer or a heavy textbook to simulate a computer on each material. Which material is depressed less? the foam Which material would provide more protection for the computer? the foam Why? The foam will absorb more force which will protect the computer.

Caption Answer

Figure 15 testing cars, wind speed test on airplanes, designing a house, designing clothes

Visual Learning

Figure 15 Computer simulation or modeling started with the Manhattan Project. Scientists used the computer to simulate the process of nuclear detonation. Today, researchers use computer modeling to study all areas of natural science and social science.

Science Journal

Local Laws Have students attend a local planning and zoning meeting. Have students write in their journals the different laws that citizens and companies are required to follow when building or remodeling a structure.

Make a Model

Bridges Have students make a model of a bridge using toothpicks and glue. Students' bridges should span a distance of 30 cm. Have students design a way to performance test the bridges to see which bridge will support the most weight.

Use Science Words

Word Origin The prefix *proto* means "first in time". Have students write entries in their Science Journals explaining how the meaning of the word prototype is derived from the mean of its prefix and root word.

Use an Analogy

Control Systems Tell students that control systems are similar to traffic lights and stop signs on streets. Both are designed to control the flow of objects and processes.

INTEGRATE Career

Flight-Test Engineer A flight test engineer must have an engineering degree from a college or university. Additional training in flight testing usually is required before an engineer begins to work as a flight test engineer.

Caption Answer

Figure 16 A prototype allows engineers and scientists to thoroughly performance test a design before it goes into production.

Post Reading

Cooperative Projects Have groups of three to four students choose a profession in the field of science or engineering. Students might choose, for example, a civil engineer. Have them develop a presentation that discusses both the challenges and rewards of the profession.

Figure 16 This robot, which is 39 cm tall, can be controlled by a cellular phone or by voice commands. The robot can be used in schools to teach about engineering and computer programming.
Explain *why it is important to make a prototype of a new product.*

INTEGRATE Career

Flight-Test Engineer
One of the crew members responsible for flight-testing an airplane or helicopter prototype is a flight-test engineer. The flight-test engineer is responsible for planning the test, acquiring the test equipment, writing the test plan, conducting the test, and then writing the test report. Research the educational requirements of a flight-test engineer.

Prototypes and Pilot Plants Constructing a prototype or manufacturing in a pilot plant are methods of performance testing. A **prototype** is a full-scale model that is used to test a new product such as a new car design or a new airplane product. A prototype, as shown in **Figure 16,** is the first full-scale product that is built. A **pilot plant** is a smaller version of the real production equipment that closely models actual manufacturing conditions. A pilot plant would be used to test a new manufacturing process, such as a production line to produce a new medicine.

Limiting System Failure Performance testing is one way to limit system failures. A system is a group of devices that work together to perform a specific function. Other ways to limit system failures are to put redundant systems within a design. A redundant system performs the same function within a design. These systems are used for important processes that would force the entire system to shut down if there is a failure. When redundancy is built into the design, if one part fails the other system will take over, keeping the entire system from failing.

Control systems, such as a fail safe system, also are incorporated into designs to keep the system from failing. A **control system** is a device or collection of devices that monitors a system. This device makes corrections to keep the system operating at preset conditions. A simple control system is the thermostat on an air conditioner or heater. An air conditioner thermostat turns the unit on when the air temperature rises to a preset high temperature. When the air temperature drops to the preset low temperature, the unit is turned off. Control systems can be simple, like a thermostat, or very complicated, like an elaborate computer system that controls heating and cooling. The purpose of control systems is to keep the system operating at desired conditions.

Active Reading

ReQuest To improve listening skills, have students listen carefully as you read the discussion about limiting system failure in this section. After the reading, have students construct questions to be discussed in class. You can have students reread the section and participate in the questioning with other students.

Differentiated Instruction

Challenge Have students research the process that is required to get a patent on a new invention. Have students prepare an informative visual aid that can be presented to the class that explains the process. P

Intellectual Property Once a new product is introduced, it is important that a company protects its investment. Research and development of a new product is costly. Often, it takes years to bring a new product to the consumer. Companies protect their rights to sell their new product or process by applying for a patent. A patent is a legal document granted by the government giving an inventor the exclusive right to make, use, and sell an invention for a specific number of years. In the United States, a new patent lasts for 20 years. A patent allows a company to get the money back that they have spent on creating the new product or process.

A patent is one example of intellectual property. Intellectual property is any type of creative work that has financial value and is protected by law. Patent laws protect technological inventions. Copyright laws protect literary and artistic works such as music, plays, poetry, and novels. The compact discs shown in **Figure 17** are examples of copyrighted products. Trademark laws protect words or symbols that identify brands, goods, or services in the marketplace.

Figure 17 Music compact discs are copyrighted. Copyright protection lasts for the author's life plus an additional seventy years after the author's death.

Reading Check *What are three types of intellectual property, and can you give an example of each type?*

Reading Check

Answer patents—the chemical process to make a new medicine such as a high blood pressure medication; copyright—this text-book; trademark—the Nike swoosh

section 3 review

Summary

Scientists and Engineers

- Scientists seek new scientific knowledge, but they may not have a plan to use that knowledge.
- Engineers use science to find solutions to problems or human needs.
- Technical problems often create a demand for new scientific knowledge.

Finding Solutions

- Scientists and engineers often work together to solve technical problems.
- Performance testing often is conducted using models and computer simulations to reduce the chance of system failure.
- Intellectual property such as technology, music, and symbols that identify products is protected by law.
- Companies protect their investment in technology with a patent.

Self Check

1. **Compare and contrast** the roles of scientists and engineers.
2. **Describe** a specific situation in which new technology created a demand for even more technology.
3. **Describe** Briefly describe the general process that is used to find technological solutions.
4. **Think Critically** Some foreign countries do not have intellectual property laws. It is common for people in these countries to illegally manufacture goods that are protected in the United States and sell them to consumers. Explain how this financially harms companies in the United States as well as the consumer.

Applying Math

5. **Use Percentages** The U.S. Customs and Border Protection made 6,500 seizures of merchandise in violation of intellectual property rights in the year 2003. This was an increase of about 700 seizures over the previous year. What was the percentage increase in the number of seizures from 2002 to 2003?

More Section Review gpescience.com

3 Assess

DAILY INTERVENTION

Check for Understanding

Interpersonal Divide students into small groups. Have students create a flow chart that describes the process for developing technology. Check students' charts.

Reteach

Scientists and Engineers Have students write a description of the work of a scientist and the work of an engineer on two pieces of paper. Have students exchange papers with a neighbor. See if the neighbor can identify which description is that of an engineer and which is that of a scientist.

Assessment

Oral Why is it important for a design to be performance tested? to find design flaws and to make sure the design works as intended

section 3 review

1. Both scientists and engineers use scientific knowledge in their work. Scientists usually work to discover new scientific information. Engineers usually use science to solve human problems or needs.
2. The introduction of the automobile has created a continuous demand for new technology.
3. Scientists and engineers identify the problem, find the best solution, performance test the solution, test a prototype or create a pilot plant, and produce the item.
4. It harms the companies because they do not get the profits from the product. It harms the consumer because the quality of the product is usually inferior in counterfeit products.
5. 12 percent

BENCH TESTED

Real-World Problem

Purpose Students will design and make a model of a package that can be safely shipped to a consumer.

Process Skills observe, use numbers, communicate, infer, formulate models, recognize cause and effect, make and use a table, communicate

Time Required one class period

Materials Encourage each student to bring a large package of snacks to share. This will give students an assortment of items to choose from. Students should provide the cost of the items they bring, so that a cost analysis of the gift packages can be calculated.

Safety Precautions Remind students not to eat in the lab and not to eat the lab materials.

Make a Model

Possible Procedures Set the possible materials on a table for students to get their own supplies. You may want to have pictures of gift packages from catalogs that are currently sold on display. This may give the students inspiration and ideas.

LAB Model and Invent

Care Package

Goal
- **Model** packaging and shipping a product for consumer interest.
- **Calculate** the cost to produce a consumer product.
- **Test** your packaging design to see if it keeps the snacks from being damaged.

Possible Materials
shoe box
assorted snack foods
packing peanuts
shredded newspaper
packing tape
wrapping paper
markers

Safety Precautions

Real-World Problem

Suppose you are a young businessperson with a new idea for a product. You are going to create a care package for students to use during exams week. You must select the items for your care package, pack the items for display and shipping, and calculate the cost of the care package. How can you package foods to survive the hazards of shipping and keep your costs to a minimum?

Make a Model

1. **Choose** the snack items that you would like to include in your care package.
2. **Plan** how you are going to pack your items so that they are nicely displayed and safe for shipping.
3. **Plan** the design of your decorative wrapper and labels. Remember to make the wrapper attractive so that customers will want to purchase your product.
4. **Design** a data table in your Science Journal to keep track of all your costs to make the care package.
5. **Evaluate** your design plan. Determine if there are ways to cut costs to increase your profit.
6. Make sure your teacher approves your plan before you start.

Sample Data Table:

Food Item	Unit Cost	# of Items	Total Cost
Candy bar	$0.89	2	$1.78
Potato chips	$1.39	1	$1.39
Cookies	$0.75	2	$1.50

Test Your Model

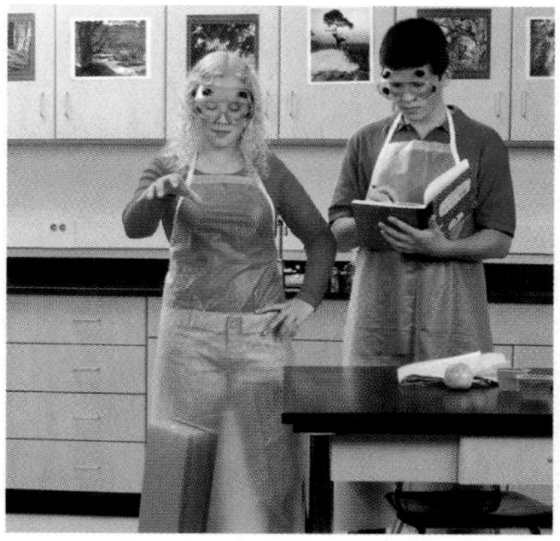

1. Assemble the items that you need to carry out your plan.
2. Pack the materials according to your plan. Do not put on the decorative wrapper until after you have tested your package.
3. After you have carefully packed your box, test to make sure that everything is secure. Drop the box from the height of your lab table five times.
4. Unwrap your box to see if anything is damaged. If the contents are broken, determine changes that can be made to improve your design.
5. If needed, retest your new design. After the drop tests are successful, apply your wrapper and labels.

Analyze Your Data

1. **Calculate** the cost of your package.
2. **Determine** the constraints of your design.

Conclude and Apply

1. **Explain** how you can improve your design. Consider cost, contents of package, and packaging.
2. **Determine** under what conditions the contents of your package may be damaged. For example, if your package contains chocolate, the package cannot be shipped during hot summer months. What changes can you make to your design to remove the shipping constraints?
3. **Infer** what would happen to the contents of your package if the package were dropped from heights taller than your lab table.

Communicating Your Data

Present your design to your classmates. Compare your design to those of your classmates. Look for ways that you could improve your design.

Communicating Your Data

Students should be able to get ideas from other students on how to improve their designs. The changes may be cosmetic or functional.

Teaching Strategies

- Encourage students to be creative in their designs.
- This lab provides an opportunity for students that are gifted in art and design to be leaders in a science activity.

Test Your Model

Expected Outcome Students will build a model of a gift box that can be safely shipped through the mail without damaging the contents of the box.

Analyze Your Data

1. The cost of the gift boxes will vary.
2. Constraints will vary. Students should look at the shelf life of their products, risks from temperature extremes, and damage to fruits in transit, if fruits are included in the packages.

Conclude and Apply

1. Ask students to record the answers to this section and discuss them in small groups.
2. Ask students to record the answers to this section and discuss them in small groups.
3. Ask students to record the answers to this section and discuss them in small groups.

Assessment

Content Have students work in small groups to make advertising flyers for their gift packages. Use **PASC,** p. 129.

Content Background

Teflon® is just one of many polymers. The first polymer was a natural one—the sap from the rubber tree. It has been used by South American Indians for hundreds of years. In 1839, Charles Goodyear discovered how to vulcanize rubber by heating it with sulfur. The result was a much stronger and more durable substance. The first plastic polymer was synthesized in 1907. Since then, the uses and kinds of polymers have greatly increased. Nylon, polystyrene (used in disposable coffee cups), polyester, epoxies and glues, polyvinyl chloride (PVC) pipe, and silicone are just a few examples.

Activity

Slippery Experiment Give groups of students a length of Teflon® tape and an assortment of other tapes and glues. Apply the tapes and glues to the Teflon® tape. Will anything stick to it?

WARNING: *Be careful when using super glue. If students get superglue on their hands, fingernail polish remover will remove the glue.*

Analyze the Event

Discuss with the class how some accidents are good (like the discovery of Teflon®) and how some are bad (like discovering that CFCs are harmful to the ozone layer). Ask how polymers can have so many different applications. Polymers can be used for many applications because their physical and chemical properties can be modified. Polymers are composed of long chains of monomers. If the composition or arrangement of monomers is changed, the properties of the polymer will change.

Oops! Accidents in SCIENCE

SOMETIMES GREAT DISCOVERIES HAPPEN BY ACCIDENT!

A Slippery Situation

Oddly enough, one of the slipperiest substances, Teflon®, was discovered by accident. Teflon was discovered in 1938 by Roy Plunkett, a research scientist. He was trying to improve the chemicals that refrigerators use to stay cool. He experimented with dozens of chemicals. One day, he noticed a gas cylinder that wouldn't operate. When he took the cylinder apart, he found that a white, slippery powder had clogged it.

Instead of being frustrated by a glitch in his experiment, Plunkett took the time to test this strange substance. What he found was amazing. This substance turned out to be extremely resistant to heat and highly inert. A substance that is inert will not react with other substances.

Why is Teflon resistant to heat and corrosion? Because it is a polymer.

Polymers are compounds with long strings of a repeating unit, like a chain. This makes them very strong. This is why Teflon can withstand high temperatures and corrosion. Plastics are another example of a very strong polymer.

At first, scientists were skeptical about any practical uses for Teflon because it was so difficult to manufacture and therefore, very expensive. However, that changed when the Manhattan Project (the group of scientists who developed the atomic bomb) needed a substance that was heat resistant and chemically inert. This was the perfect job for Teflon. Since then, Teflon has found its way into many items, including the space shuttle, surgical implants, stain guards, and, of course, easy-to-clean pots and pans.

Look **With a partner, walk around the room and make a list of objects that are made from polymers. The length of the list will surprise you. Your teacher can help you find many polymers.**

For more information, visit gpescience.com

Look Polymers are everywhere and include all plastics, glues, and rubbers, as well as PVC pipes used in plumbing, polystyrene cups, stainguard on fabrics and carpets, and polyester and rayon fabrics.

Resources for Teachers and Students

American plastic: A cultural history, by Jeffery L. Meikle, Rutgers University Press, 1995

Giant Molecules: Here There and Everywhere, by Alexander Yu, San Diego Academic Press, 1997

Reviewing Main Ideas

Section 1 Science and Technology

1. The study of science leads to a better understanding of the world around you.
2. Scientists bring information and insight to the public's attention and provide an understanding of why an event occurs. The knowledge that microbes cause illness and diseases changed people's behavior. Today we take precautions to prevent the spread of microbes by washing our hands often and covering our mouth when we cough.

3. Once people understand why an event or natural process occurs, they can respond and try to control the outcome.
4. Technology can be an object, a method or technique for making an object or tool, the knowledge or skill needed to operate a human-made object, or a system of people or objects that perform a task.
5. The value of technology varies over time and from location to location. This electric guitar may be valued by some in industrialized nations, but people in developing countries do not have electricity in their homes. This technology would be useless to them.

Section 2 Forces that Shape Technology

1. Funding for scientific research and technology comes from the federal government, private industries, and private foundations.
2. Consumers affect which technologies will be developed by their voting and buying habits.
3. Humans can have an enormous impact on other living things and must practice responsible technology.
4. The consequences of technology may be known immediately, but sometimes they are not known for a period of time.
5. Moral and ethical issues should be considered when doing scientific research or developing technology.

Section 3 Developing Technology

1. Scientists and engineers have different roles in developing technology.
2. Technological problems often create a demand for new scientific knowledge.

3. Scientists and engineers use a methodical process to develop technology. Performance testing is an important part of this process that reduces or prevents product failure.

FOLDABLES™ Use the Foldable that you made at the beginning of this chapter to help you review science, technology, and society.

chapter 2 Study Guide

Reviewing Main Ideas

Summary statements can be used by students to review the major concepts of the chapter.

Science Online

Visit gpescience.com
More Section Review
Interactive Tutor
Vocabulary PuzzleMaker
More Chapter Review
Standardized Test Practice

Assessment Transparency

For additional assessment questions, use the *Assessment Transparency* located in the transparency book.

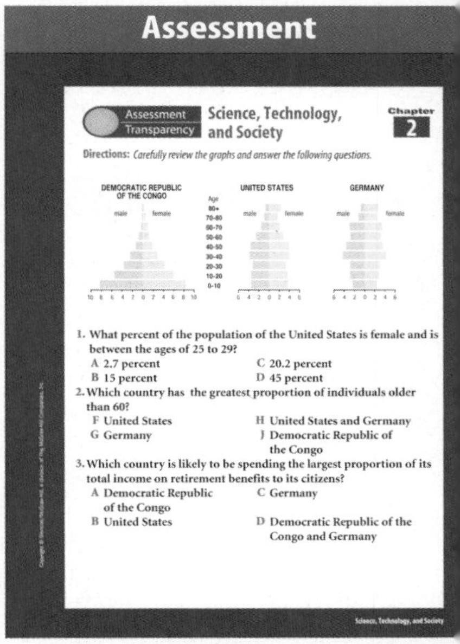
Assessment

Assessment Transparency — Science, Technology, and Society — Chapter 2

Directions: *Carefully review the graphs and answer the following questions.*

1. What percent of the population of the United States is female and is between the ages of 25 to 29?
   A 2.7 percent
   B 15 percent
   C 20.2 percent
   D 45 percent
2. Which country has the greatest proportion of individuals older than 60?
   F United States
   G Germany
   H United States and Germany
   J Democratic Republic of the Congo
3. Which country is likely to be spending the largest proportion of its total income on retirement benefits to its citizens?
   A Democratic Republic of the Congo
   B United States
   C Germany
   D Democratic Republic of the Congo and Germany

Science, Technology, and Society

FOLDABLES™ Have students use their Foldables to review the main ideas in the chapter. Explain the difference between science and technology.

Using Vocabulary

1. engineer
2. computer simulation
3. society
4. constraints
5. prototype
6. pilot plant
7. control system

Checking Concepts

8. B	13. B
9. C	14. A
10. A	15. A
11. B	16. C
12. D	

Interpreting Graphics

17. See student page.
18. Science—finding the composition of Saturn's rings and finding the human genes that cause a birth defect; Technology—developing the vehicle that can fly to Saturn and producing a medicine that can cure a disease.

Thinking Critically

19. The protective clothing seems ridiculous to us because we know the cause of the disease today. The people of that time did not know the cause and were willing to accept an explanation that seemed reasonable to them.
20. Possible answer: Scientific knowledge explained how the temperature of the ocean affects the development of hurricanes.
21. Possible answers: object—calculator; method or technique—using a calculator to solve a math problem; knowledge or skill—the knowledge of how to use the calculator; system—NASA control center during a space mission

chapter 2 Review

Using Vocabulary

agricultural biotechnology p. 45
computer simulation p. 55
constraints p. 55
control system p. 56
engineer p. 53
pilot plant p. 56
prototype p. 56
society p. 46

Answer each question using the correct vocabulary word(s).

1. Which professional in science devises a way to use scientific knowledge to solve a problem or mass-produce a product?
2. What is performance-testing using a computer to imitate the process called?
3. What is the name of a group of people that share similar values and beliefs?
4. What is the term for design limitations put on the design by outside factors?
5. What is the full-scale model that is used to performance-test a new car design called?
6. What is the name of a scaled-down version of real production equipment that closely models actual manufacturing conditions?
7. What is a device that monitors a system to keep it operating at preset conditions called?

Checking Concepts

Choose the word or phrase that best answers the question.

8. Which represents technology?
   A) canary
   B) digital camera
   C) eating an apple
   D) native grass
9. Which technological object would be most valued in a developing country?
   A) compact discs
   B) electric can opener
   C) portable water purifier
   D) video recorder
10. What is a collection of scientific techniques that are used to create, improve, or modify plants, animals, and microorganisms?
   A) agricultural biotechnology
   B) agricultural cloning
   C) agricultural prototype
   D) agricultural simulation
11. Which is NOT normally a source of funding for technology?
   A) federal government
   B) local government
   C) private foundation
   D) private industry
12. Which is NOT considered part of moral and ethical considerations?
   A) doing what is cost effective
   B) doing what is fair
   C) doing what is honest
   D) doing what is right
13. What is the term for limitations put on the design of a product from outside factors?
   A) conflicts
   B) constraints
   C) parameters
   D) specifications
14. A thermostat on an air conditioner is an example of which of the following?
   A) control system
   B) environmental system
   C) monitoring system
   D) on/off system
15. What are patents legal protection for?
   A) new medicine
   B) new novels
   C) new product symbol
   D) new songs
16. Which does NOT represent technology?
   A) calculator
   B) computer program
   C) granite rock
   D) compact discs

62 CHAPTER REVIEW

Vocabulary PuzzleMaker gpescience.com

Use the Exam*View*® Pro Test Bank CD-ROM to:

- create multiple versions of tests
- create modified tests with one mouse click for inclusion students
- edit existing questions and add your own questions
- build tests aligned with state standards using built-in State Curriculum Tags
- change English tests to Spanish with one mouse click and vice versa

Interpreting Graphics

17. Copy and complete the following concept map on technology.

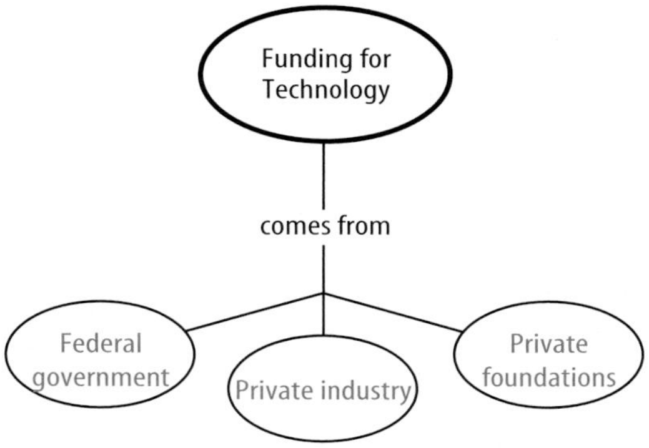

18. **Make a table** classifying each of the following actions as science or technology: finding the composition of Saturn's rings, developing the vehicle that can travel to Saturn, finding the human genes that cause a birth defect, and producing a medicine that can cure a disease.

Thinking Critically

19. **Draw Conclusions** Explain why technology of the past, such as the protective clothing shown in **Figure 1,** seems ridiculous to us today even though the people of the time accepted the technology as reasonable.
20. **Describe** one way in which scientific knowledge has changed people's understanding of a natural process or event.
21. **Describe** each type of technology and give a new example of each type.
22. **Explain** why the aircraft radar used by air-traffic controllers represents all types of technology.
23. **Explain** why the value of technology may differ for people living in different parts of the world.
24. **List** three technological items that you value that would not be important in a developing country such as Kenya.
25. **Describe** how technology can be used to supply basic human needs for survival to those who are in need.
26. **Explain** why ethics are important to scientists.
27. **Explain** how citizens of a local community can influence the development of new technology.
28. **Explain** During the mid 1970s, gasoline was in short supply. The price for gasoline increased. Automobile manufacturers produced smaller, fuel-efficient cars. The crisis soon was over and the smaller cars did not sell well. Explain how consumers' actions determined where the manufacturers spent their research funds.
29. **Explain** What type of intellectual property is protected by copyright? How does a copyright differ from a patent?

Applying Math

30. **Calculate** A hybrid car gets 20 km/L in city driving. The same model that is gasoline-powered gets 14 km/L in city driving. If gasoline costs $0.53 per liter, how much money would be saved per year if you drove 19,000 km of city driving?
31. **Calculate** How many liters of gasoline would be saved using the hybrid car instead of the gasoline-powered car?

chapter Review 2

22. The radar is an object. Radar is a new technique used to monitor vehicles. The air traffic control system is a collection of objects and people that make air travel safe.
23. People in different parts of the world have different needs and have different resources available to them.
24. Possible answers: television, cell phone, and telephone
25. Possible answer: Medicines can be distributed to those in need to cure diseases and illnesses.
26. Some countries do not allow genetically-altered foods into their countries. They fear the consequences of genetically-altered foods.
27. Possible answer: Tests should be conducted on the effects of the crops on the environment and the short- and long-term effects on humans that eat the foods.
28. Since consumers were not buying the smaller cars, manufacturers spent their research dollars on other technologies.
29. Copyrights protect literary and artistic works, whereas patents protect technological inventions.

Applying Math

Math Standards

National: 1, 9

30. $215.71

    Gas-powered car: (19,000 km / 14 km/L) × $0.53/L = $719.21

    Hybrid car: (19,000 km / 20 km/L) × $0.53/L = $503.50

    Cost difference = $719.21 − 503.50 = $215.71
31. 407 liters

    Gas-powered car: (19,000 km / 14 km/L) = 1357 L

    Hybrid car: (19,000 km / 20 km/L) = 950 L

    Fuel difference = 1,357 L − 950 L = 407 L

Assessment Resources

Reproducible Masters

Chapter *Fast File* Resources
- Chapter Review, pp. 33–34
- Chapter Tests, pp. 35–38
- Assessment Transparency Activity, p. 45

Glencoe Science Web site
- Chapter Review Test
- Standardized Test Practice

Glencoe Technology

- Assessment Transparency
- Exam*View*® Pro Testmaker
- MindJogger Videoquiz
- Interactive Chalkboard

Answer Sheet An answer sheet can be found at **gpescience.com**.

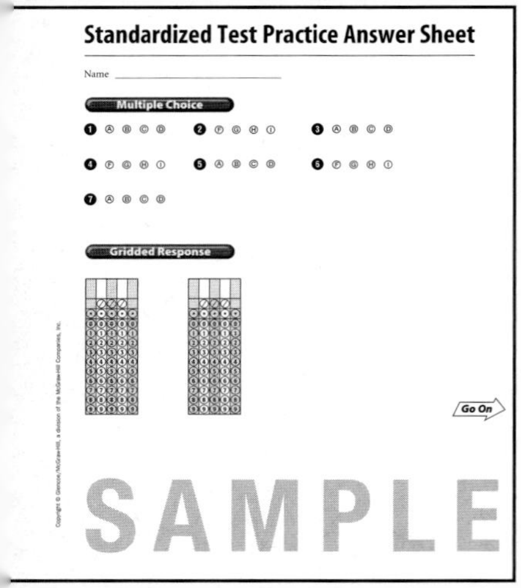
Standardized Test Practice Answer Sheet

Name

Multiple Choice

Gridded Response

Go On

SAMPLE

Multiple Choice

1. C
2. D
3. C
4. D
5. C

Gridded Response

6. $5.27
7. $9.67

Record your answers on the answer sheet provided by your teacher or on a sheet of paper.

Multiple Choice

1. What did Louis Pasteur discover as the cause of infections and diseases?

A. bad air

B. fleas

C. microbes

D. rats

Use the photo below to answer question 2.

2. Which technological object would be more valuable to the family shown?

A. airline industry

B. automobile industry

C. the Internet

D. medical center

3. Which is a technological system for sharing information?

A. airline industry

B. automobile industry

C. the Internet

D. medical center

4. What does a society share?

A. biotechnology

B. consumed goods

C. new technologies

D. similar values and beliefs

Use the photo below to answer question 5.

5. Which process used by people to influence technological development is shown?

A. consumer purchase

B. federal spending

C. political discussion

D. private funding

Gridded Response

6. If a liter of gasoline costs $0.58 and a car gets 11 km/L, what would it cost to travel 100 km?

7. Assuming that gasoline costs the same as in the previous question, how much would it cost to travel 100 km in a car that gets 6 km/L?

Short Response

Use photo below to answer question 8.

8. Identify one positive and one negative consequence from the use of gasoline-powered cars.

9. How would technological advances in health care benefit people in developing countries?

10. Why were people less concerned about fuel-efficient cars in the past than they are today?

11. What led to laws being created to prevent unethical treatment of animals and humans?

12. How does consumer acceptance affect the development of technology?

Extended Response

Use photo below to answer question 13.

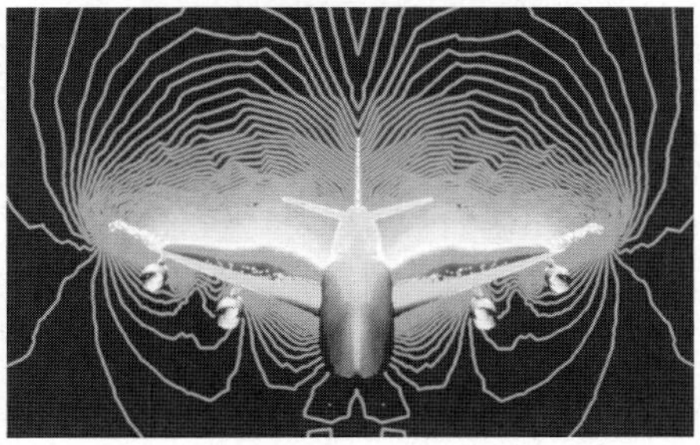

13. **Part A** In general, how do scientists and engineers work together to find a technological solution?
Part B How would scientists and engineers determine if a new airplane design were more aerodynamic?

Test-Taking Tip

Get plenty of sleep—at least 8 hours every night—during test week and the week before the test.

Short Response

8. Possible answer: positive consequence—ease of transportation; negative consequence—air pollution
9. They would improve the quality of life and increase life expectancy.
10. Gasoline prices were low and fossil fuels consumption was down.
11. Human test subjects have been subjected to experiments against their will and animals have been subjected to unnecessary pain during experiments.
12. If consumers purchase new technologies, additional money is spent on improving the technology. If consumers do not purchase new technologies, companies will not spend additional money on that technology.

Extended Response

13. **Part A:** Scientists and engineers would work together and use a system similar to the scientific method. They would identify the problem, propose solutions, deal with design constraints, comply with laws and regulations, test design ideas, and build prototypes.
Part B: They would build a model of the new aerodynamic design and test its capabilities in a wind tunnel where the flow of air around the new design could be measured.

Rubrics

For more help evaluating Short- and Extended-Response questions, see the rubrics on p. 9T.

unit 2

Unit Contents

WebQuest ***Roller Coaster Physics*** is an investigation of coaster design, laws of motion, gravity, velocity, and acceleration. Students will use virtual programming to engineer, test, and evaluate roller coaster simulations. As a culminating activity, students will create their own roller coaster model and report on their results.

unit 2

Motion, Forces, and Energy

How Are Waffles & Running Shoes Connected?

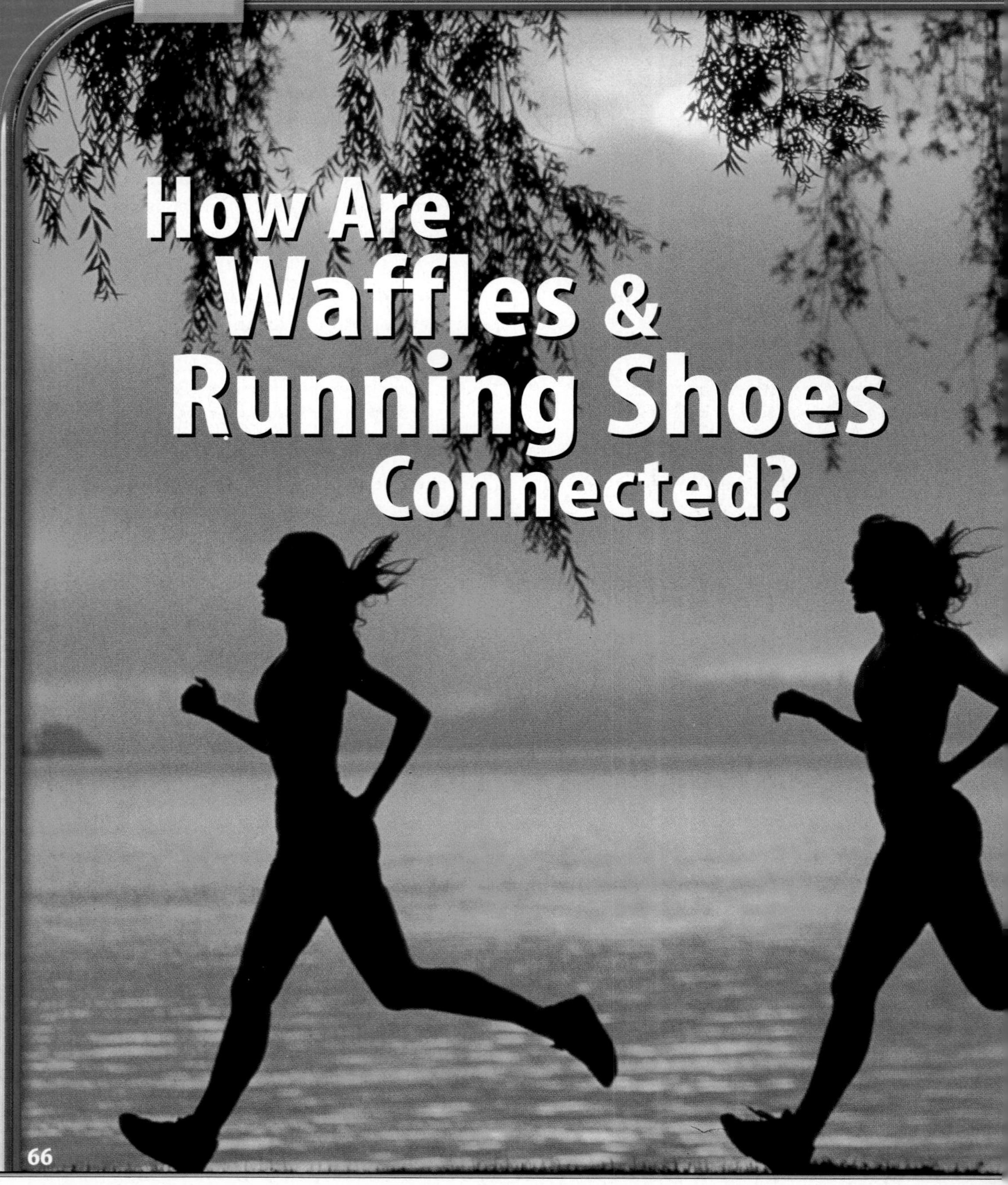

66

PROJECT CRISS[SM]

Study Skills

Use of Graphics Changing words into pictures enables students to synthesize ideas. After finishing the unit, students in cooperative teams can use large sheets of paper and colored markers to map a selected topic through pictures, words, and diagrams. The various topics could include motion, speed, energy, friction, velocity, force, Newton's laws, inertia, work, and machines. Teams share their free-form maps with the class.

For centuries, shoes were made mostly of leather, cloth, or wood. These shoes helped protect feet, but they didn't provide much traction on slippery surfaces. In the early twentieth century, manufacturers began putting rubber on the bottom of canvas shoes, creating the first "sneakers." Sneakers provided good traction, but the rubber soles could be heavy—especially for athletes. One morning in the 1970s, an athletic coach stared at the waffles on the breakfast table and had an idea for a rubber sole that would be lighter in weight but would still provide traction. That's how the first waffle soles were born. Waffle soles soon became a world standard for running shoes.

unit projects

Visit unit projects at gpescience.com to find project ideas and resources.
Projects include:

- **Career** Explore the field of mechanical engineering through sports. Create an advertisement for your aerodynamic sports equipment.
- **Technology** Create a brochure showing five different shoe treads with reference to particular sports and environmental conditions.
- **Model** Design and build a model of a space station on the Moon or on a planet in our solar system.

WebQuest Using virtual programming, *Roller Coaster Physics* provides an opportunity to engineer, test, and evaluate roller coaster design, and then build your own three-dimensional coaster.

NATIONAL GEOGRAPHIC How Are Waffles & Running Shoes Connected?

- Ask students how many of them have slipped when wearing an old pair of running shoes because the tread was worn.
- Have students compare the tread pattern in several pairs of their shoes and hypothesize how each affects friction. Ask them how the intended surface affects what type of tread is on the shoe.

unit projects

Career Have students explore the careers available to mechanical engineers in sports—equipment designer or participant. Have students write an advertisement for their particular sport and its equip-ment, stating why their friction and aerodynamic design is the best for that sport and its conditions. Some choices include car racing, rollerblading, iceskating, bike racing, skiing, bobsledding, boating, or monster-truck competition.

Technology Ask students to examine, sketch, or do rubbings of a variety of soles of shoes. Have students research and then draw conclusions about how the different treads affect the friction between the shoe and the ground. Have students create a brochure showing five different shoe treads with an explanation about how each type of sole might suit a shoe to a particular activity or environmental condition. Students should analyze how today's technology has made advancements in shoe design, sports, and safety possible.

Model Ask students to design and build a model of a space station on the Moon or a planet in our solar system. Students should research the surface, atmosphere quality, and temperature ranges, as well as the length of day and seasons. Presentation of student models should address each characteristic of the Moon or planet and how the space station's design meets these characteristics.

Additional Resources Visit unit projects at gpescience.com for more information, resources, and assessment rubrics.

chapter 3 Organizer

Section/Objectives	Standards		Lab/Features
	National	State/Local	
Chapter Opener	See pp. 16T-17T for a Key to Standards.		**Launch Lab:** Compare Speeds, p. 69 **Foldables,** p. 69
Section 1 Describing Motion 2 sessions 1 block 1. **Distinguish** between distance and displacement. 2. **Calculate** average speed. 3. **Explain** the difference between speed and velocity. 4. **Interpret** motion graphs.	National Content Standards: UCP.1-3, A.1, A.2, B.4		**MiniLAB:** Measuring Average Speed, p. 71 **Applying Math:** Average Speed, p. 72 **Science Online,** p. 72 **Integrate Astronomy,** p. 74 **Science Online,** p. 75
Section 2 Acceleration 1 session 1 block 5. **Identify** how acceleration, time, and velocity are related. 6. **Describe** how to calculate the average acceleration of an object. 7. **Explain** how positive and negative acceleration affect motion.	National Content Standards: UCP.1-3, A.1, A.2, B.4		**Integrate History,** p. 77 **Visualizing Acceleration,** p. 78
Section 3 Motion and Forces 3 sessions 1 block 8. **Explain** how forces and motion are related. 9. **Compare and contrast** static friction and sliding friction. 10. **Describe** the effects of air resistance on falling objects.	National Content Standards: UCP.1-3, A.1, A.2, B.4, G.3		**Science Online,** p. 82 **MiniLAB:** Comparing Friction, p. 83 **Lab:** Force and Acceleration. p. 87 Video Lab **Lab:** Comparing Motion from Different Forces, pp. 88-89 **Science and Language Arts:** A Brave and Startling Truth, p. 90

StudentWorks Plus

Glencoe Exclusive!
TeacherWorks™
All-In-One Planner and Resource Center

Lab Materials	Reproducible Resources	Section Assessment	Technology
Launch Lab: meterstick, stopwatch	**Chapter *Fast File* Resources** Foldables Worksheet, p. 17 Note-taking Worksheets, pp. 33–35 Directed Reading Overview, p. 19	Glencoe's Assessment Advantage	TeacherWorks includes: • Interactive Teacher Edition • Lesson Planner with calendar • Access to all program blacklines • Correlations to standards • Web links
MiniLAB: tape, toy car, stopwatch, meterstick *Need materials?* Contact Science Kit at 1-800-828-7777 or www.sciencekit.com.	**Chapter *Fast File* Resources** Transparency Activity, p. 44 MiniLAB, p. 3 Enrichment, p. 30 Reinforcement, p. 27 Directed Reading, p. 20 Lab Activity, pp. 9–12 Transparency Activity, pp. 47–48	**Portfolio** Differentiated Instruction, p. 73 **Performance** MiniLAB, p. 71 Applying Math, p. 72 Applying Math, p. 75 **Content** Section Review, p. 75	Section Focus Transparency Teaching Transparency Virtual Labs CD-ROM Interactive Chalkboard CD-ROM StudentWorks Plus
MiniLAB: ice cube, rock, eraser, wood block, aluminum foil, metal or plastic tray, metric ruler	**Chapter *Fast File* Resources** Transparency Activity, p. 45 MiniLAB, p. 4 Enrichment, p. 31 Reinforcement, p. 28 Directed Reading, p. 21 Lab Activity, pp. 13–15 Science Inquiry Labs, pp. 23–24	**Portfolio** Differentiated Instruction, p. 78 Check for Understanding, p. 80 **Performance** Applying Math, p. 80 **Content** Section Review, p. 80	Section Focus Transparency Interactive Chalkboard CD-ROM StudentWorks Plus
Lab: tape, paper clip, 10-N spring scale, large book, balance **Lab:** toy car, ramps, springs or rubber bands, string, stopwatch, meterstick, graph paper	**Chapter *Fast File* Resources** Transparency Activity, p. 46 Enrichment, p. 32 Reinforcement, p. 29 Directed Reading, pp. 21, 22 Lab Worksheets, pp. 5–6, 7–8	**Performance** MiniLAB, p. 83 Applying Math, p. 86 **Content** Section Review, p. 86	Section Focus Transparency Interactive Chalkboard CD-ROM StudentWorks Plus Video Lab

End of Chapter Assessment

Glencoe's Assessment Advantage

Blackline Masters	Technology	Professional Series
Chapter *Fast File* Resources Chapter Review, pp. 37–38 Chapter Tests, pp. 39–42 **Standardized Test Practice,** pp. 16–19	MindJogger Videoquiz Virtual Labs CD-ROM Exam*View*® Pro Testmaker TeacherWorks CD-ROM Interactive Chalkboard CD-ROM	**Performance Assessment in the Science Classroom (PASC)**

Transparencies

Section Focus

Section 1 Section Focus Transparency — How about a rematch? — Chapter 3

In Aesop's fable "The Tortoise and the Hare," a tortoise and a hare have a race. The hare bounds far ahead of the tortoise and then, sure of victory, lies down to rest under a tree. The tortoise passes the resting hare and wins the race.

1. Which animal ran faster?
2. How does the motion of a car racing on an oval track change?

L2

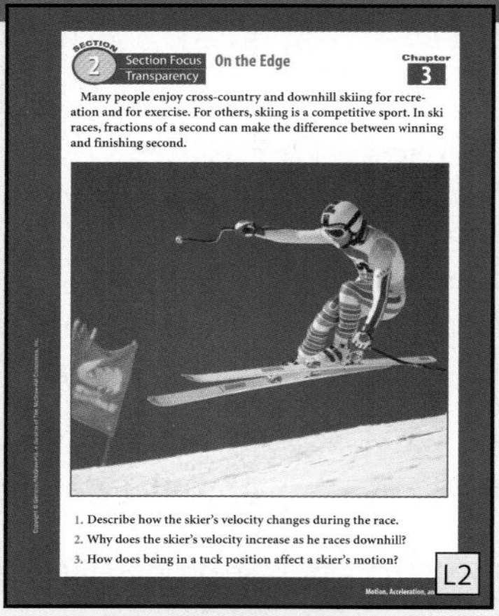
Section 2 Section Focus Transparency — On the Edge — Chapter 3

Many people enjoy cross-country and downhill skiing for recreation and for exercise. For others, skiing is a competitive sport. In ski races, fractions of a second can make the difference between winning and finishing second.

1. Describe how the skier's velocity changes during the race.
2. Why does the skier's velocity increase as he races downhill?
3. How does being in a tuck position affect a skier's motion?

L2

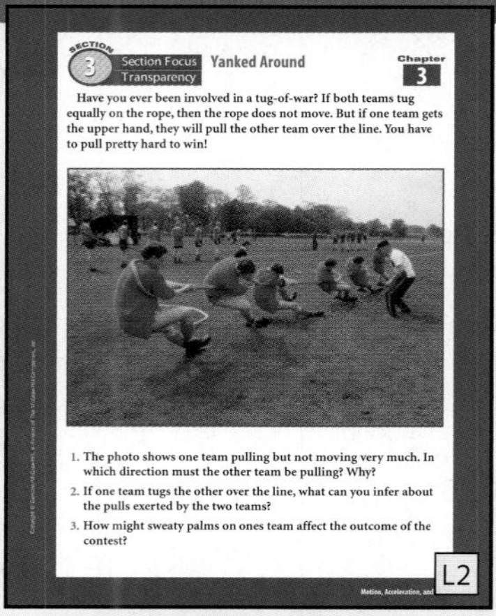
Section 3 Section Focus Transparency — Yanked Around — Chapter 3

Have you ever been involved in a tug-of-war? If both teams tug equally on the rope, then the rope does not move. But if one team gets the upper hand, they will pull the other team over the line. You have to pull pretty hard to win!

1. The photo shows one team pulling but not moving very much. In which direction must the other team be pulling? Why?
2. If one team tugs the other over the line, what can you infer about the pulls exerted by the two teams?
3. How might sweaty palms on ones team affect the outcome of the contest?

L2

This is a representation of key blackline masters available in the Teacher Classroom Resources. See Resource Manager boxes within the chapter for additional information.

Assessment

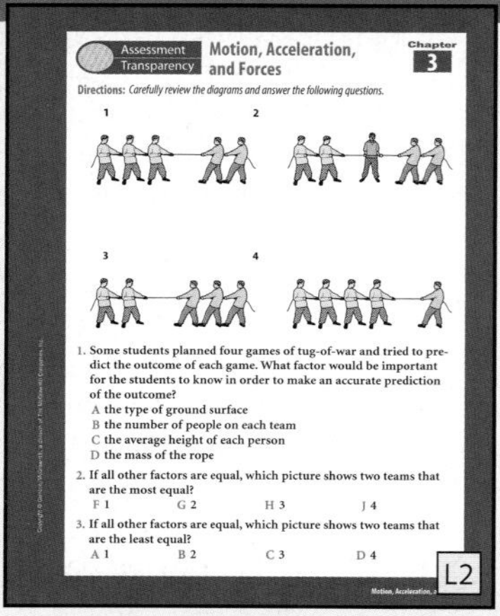
Assessment Transparency — Motion, Acceleration, and Forces — Chapter 3

Directions: *Carefully review the diagrams and answer the following questions.*

1. Some students planned four games of tug-of-war and tried to predict the outcome of each game. What factor would be important for the students to know in order to make an accurate prediction of the outcome?
   A the type of ground surface
   B the number of people on each team
   C the average height of each person
   D the mass of the rope
2. If all other factors are equal, which picture shows two teams that are the most equal?
   F 1 G 2 H 3 J 4
3. If all other factors are equal, which picture shows two teams that are the least equal?
   A 1 B 2 C 3 D 4

L2

Teaching

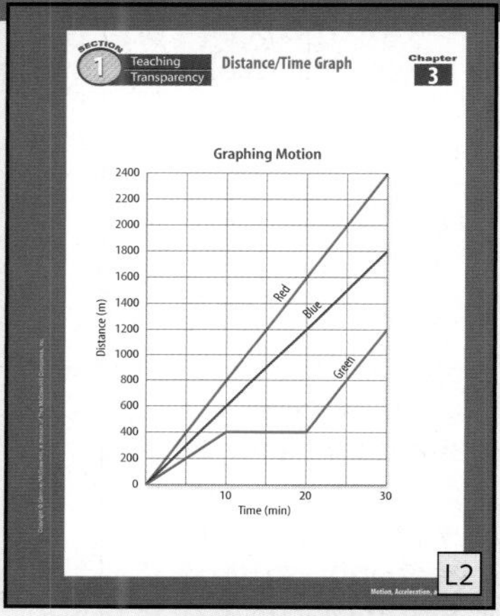

L2

Key to Teaching Strategies

The following designations will help you decide which activities are appropriate for your students.

- L1 Level 1 activities should be appropriate for students with learning difficulties.
- L2 Level 2 activities should be within the ability range of all students.
- L3 Level 3 activities are designed for above-average students.
- ELL ELL activities should be within the ability range of English Language Learners.
- COOP LEARN Cooperative Learning activities are designed for small group work.
- LS Multiple Learning Styles logos, as described on page 12T, are used throughout to indicate strategies that address different learning styles.
- P These strategies represent student products that can be placed into a best-work portfolio.
- PBL Problem-Based Learning activities apply real-world situations to learning.

Hands-on Activities

Student Text Lab Worksheet

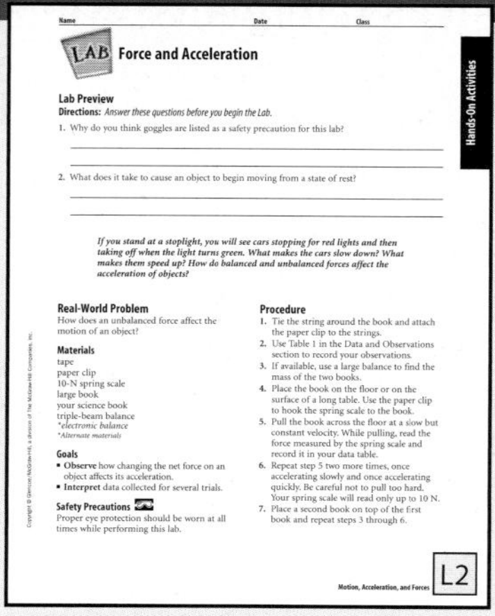
LAB — Force and Acceleration

Lab Preview

Directions: *Answer these questions before you begin the Lab.*

1. Why do you think goggles are listed as a safety precaution for this lab?
2. What does it take to cause an object to begin moving from a state of rest?

If you stand at a stoplight, you will see cars stopping for red lights and then taking off when the light turns green. What makes the cars slow down? What makes them speed up? How do balanced and unbalanced forces affect the acceleration of objects?

L2

Laboratory Activities

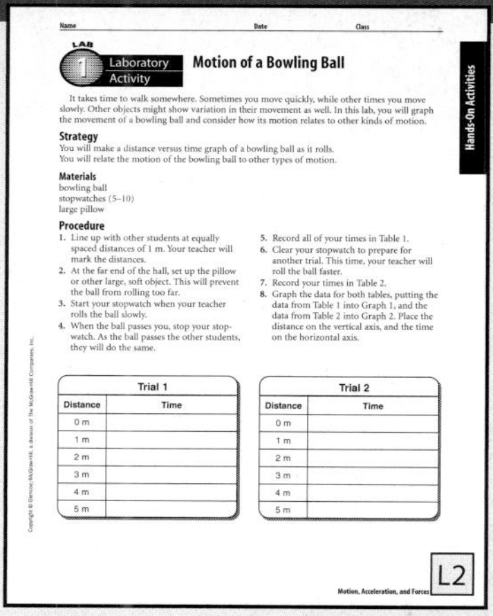
Lab 1 Laboratory Activity — Motion of a Bowling Ball

Trial 1	
Distance	Time
0 m	
1 m	
2 m	
3 m	
4 m	
5 m	

Trial 2	
Distance	Time
0 m	
1 m	
2 m	
3 m	
4 m	
5 m	

L2

Meeting Different Ability Levels

Content Outline

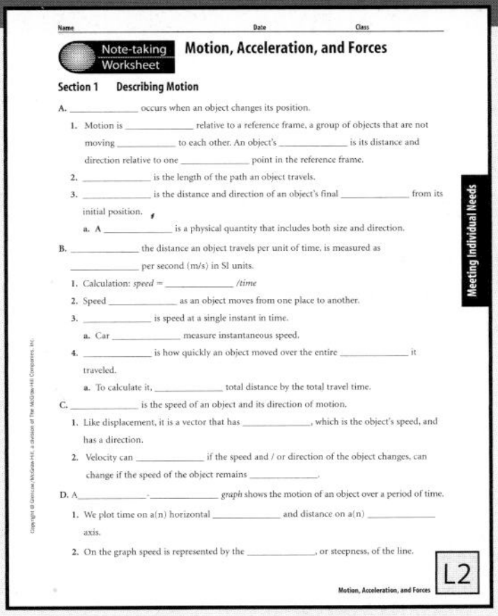

Reinforcement

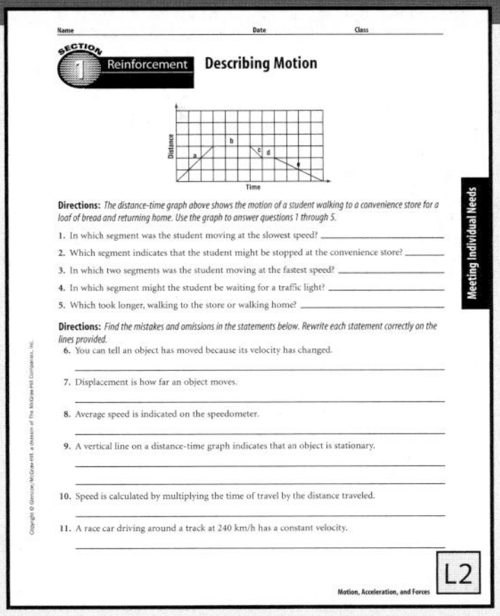

Enrichment

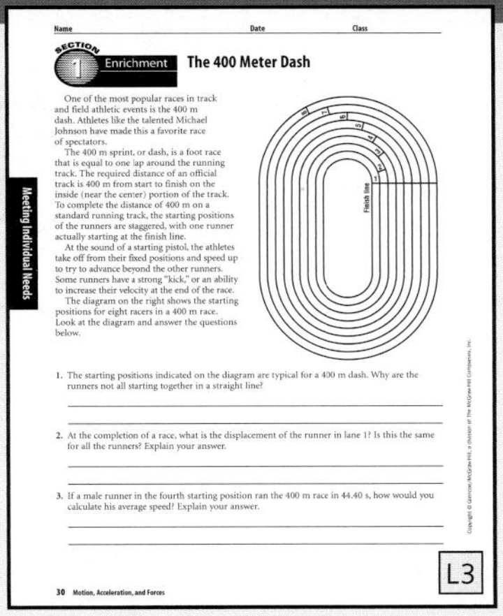

Directed Reading (English/Spanish)

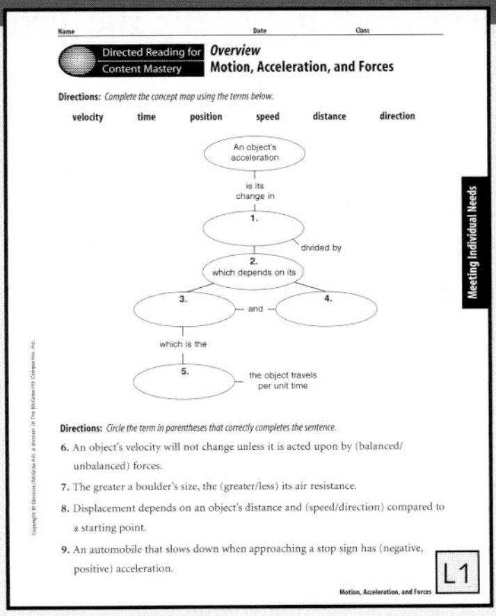

Study Guide

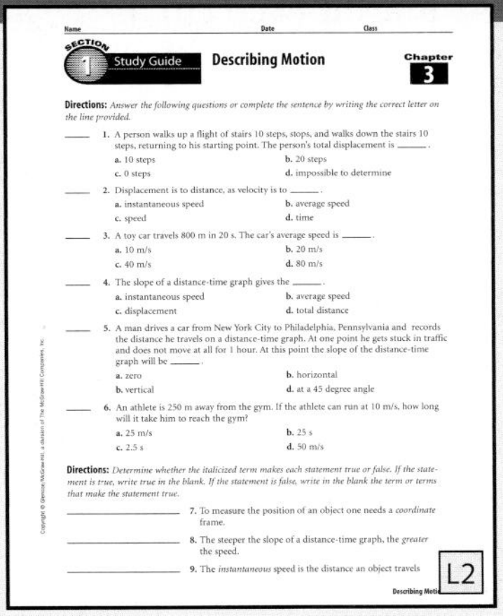

Reading Essentials

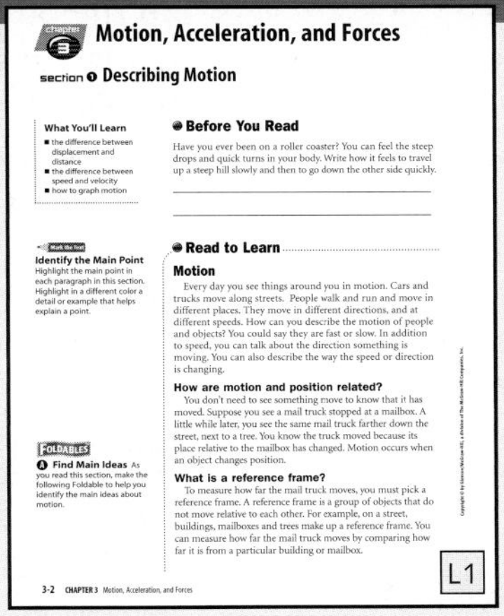

Assessment

Test Practice Workbook

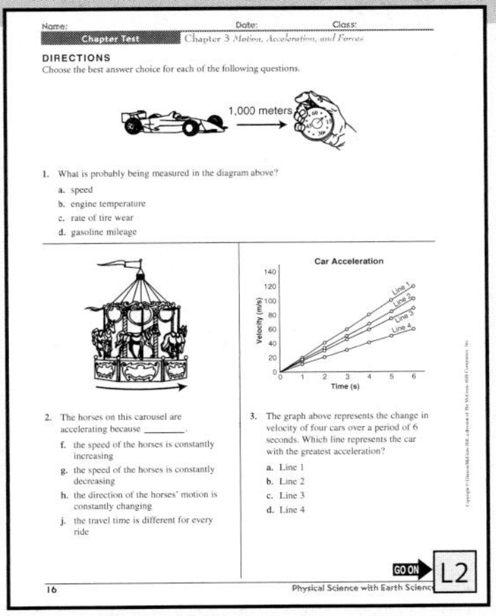

Chapter Review

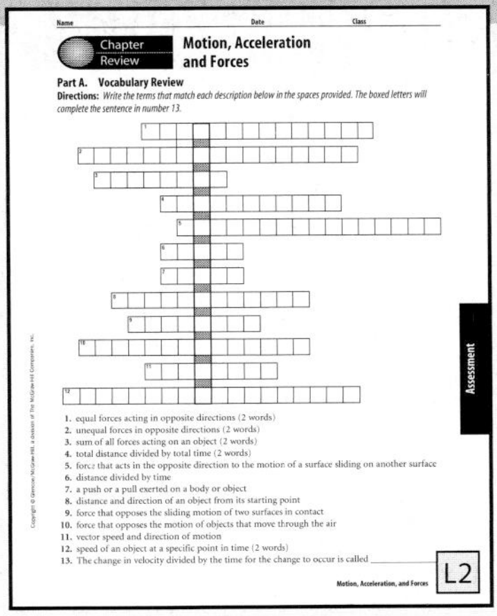

Chapter Tests

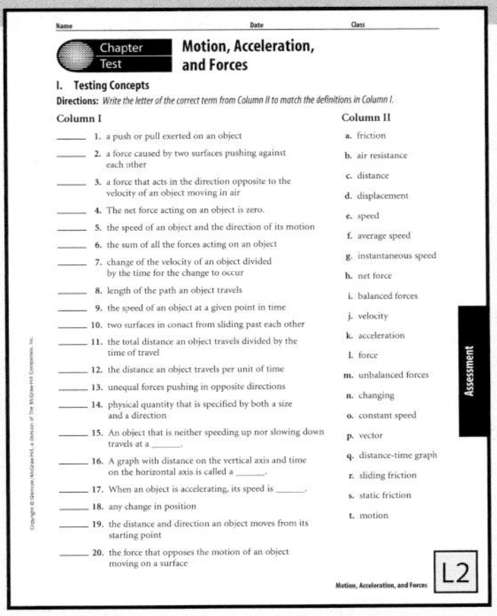

Science Content Background

section 1 Describing Motion

Distance v. Displacement

A vector quantity has both magnitude and direction, such as a displacement of 15 km east and a velocity of 7 m/s west. Scalar quantities have magnitude only, such as a distance of 5 km and a speed of 6 m/s. The terms distance and displacement have different meanings. Consider a car going around a round racetrack. The distance the car travels can be read from its odometer, but the car's displacement is its straight-line distance and direction from its starting point. For each lap the odometer increases. But for each lap its displacement at first increases, and then decreases and becomes zero as it returns to the starting point. Speed and velocity also can be contrasted easily. The car traveling around the track may have a constant speed, but its velocity is constantly changing because its direction is constantly changing.

section 2 Acceleration

Acceleration, Speed and Velocity

An object will move with constant velocity unless a force acts on it. A planet orbiting a star experiences the force of gravity between the star and the planet. This force causes the object to accelerate toward the star and not fly off in straight-line motion.

Acceleration units show changes in velocity divided by time. If velocity is expressed as meters/second and time in seconds, then acceleration is expressed with units of meters per second per second. This is equivalent to m/s/s or (m/s $\times$ 1/s) or m/s^2.

section 3 Motion and Forces

Air Resistance

When people jump out of high-altitude airplanes, they don't keep accelerating. The faster they fall, the greater the air resistance acting on them, so their acceleration decreases as they fall. Eventually a skydiver stops accelerating and achieves a constant velocity called the terminal velocity. For humans, terminal velocity is about 53 m/s or 190 km/h. It's a good thing a skydiver's velocity slows to only 5 to 10 m/s after the parachute opens!

chapter content resources

Internet Resources

For additional content background, visit gpescience.com to:

- access your book online
- find references to related articles in popular science magazines
- access Web links with related content background
- access current events with science journal topics

Print Resources

Eyewitness: Force and Motion, by Peter Lafferty, Doris Kindersley Publishing, 2000

Sports Science Projects: The Physics of Balls in Motion (Science Fair Success), by Madeline Goodstein, Enslow Publishers, Inc., 1999

The Science of Soccer, by John Wesson, Institute of Physics Publishing, 2002

The Physics of Hockey, by Alain Hache, John Hopkins University Press, 2002

IDENTIFYING Misconceptions

Find Out What Students Think

Students may think that...

Distance and displacement are the same thing.

Speed and velocity are the same thing.

Students are familiar with scalar quantities and vector quantities, but terms such as *displacement* and *velocity* may cause confusion. Also, the term *velocity* is frequently used as though it were the same as *speed*. Finally, the terms *displacement* and *distance* sound similar, which may cause confusion between them.

Discussion

Tell students that a turtle and a hare start a race at the same time. The turtle goes straight to the finish line. The hare starts off and deviates along the way. They both finish the race at the same time. Discuss which had the greatest average speed during the race.

Promote Understanding

Activity

Distance Versus Time

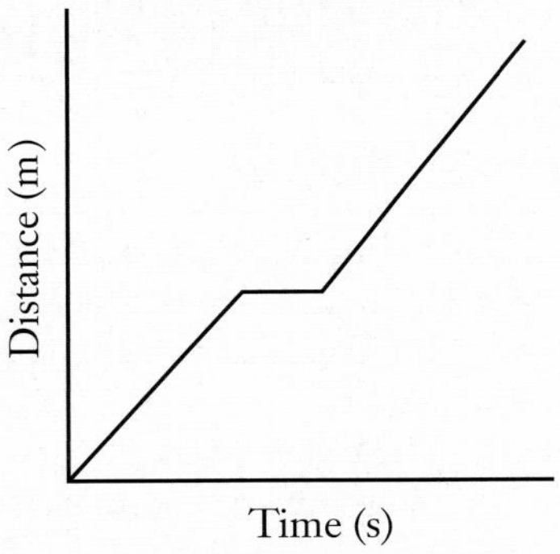

Displacement Versus Time

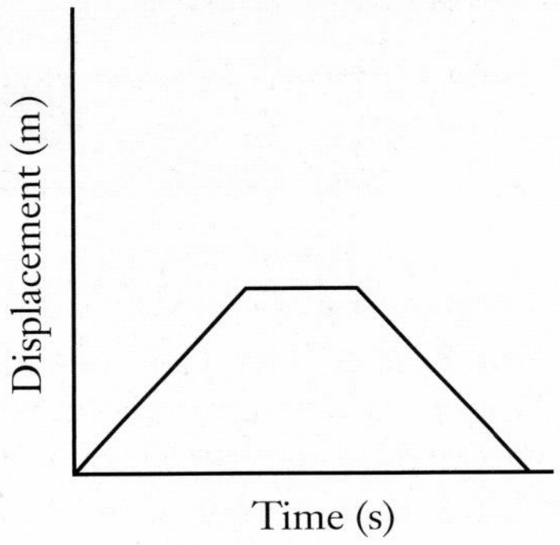

- Draw the graphs to the left on the board. Explain that the distance-time graph and the displacement-time graph each show Samantha's walking motion after she left her house.
- Ask students to supply a possible story to describe Samantha's motion. Ask them what she might be doing when the lines of both graphs are horizontal.
- Students should see that the distance-time graph and the displacement-time graph for the same motion look very different. In this case the distance traveled is how far Samantha actually walked. Her displacement shows how far she is from her house.
- A plausible story for both graphs is: Samantha walks with constant speed directly away from her house, then rests a bit, and then walks with constant speed directly back to her house. L2

Assess

After completing the chapter, see *Identifying Misconceptions* in the Study Guide at the end of the chapter.

Chapter Vocabulary

displacement, p.71
vector, p. 71
speed, p. 71
instantaneous speed, p. 71
average speed, p. 72
velocity, p. 73
acceleration, p. 76
force, p. 81
net force, p. 82
balanced forces, p. 82
unbalanced forces, p. 82
friction, p. 83
static friction, p. 84
sliding friction, p. 84
air resistance, p. 85

Science Journal Roller coasters and bumper cars provide examples of quick velocity and acceleration changes. Ferris wheels provide an example of constant speed but changing velocity and acceleration due to the constant change in the direction of the passengers.

INTERACTIVE CHALKBOARD with Image Bank

PowerPoint® Presentations

This CD-ROM is an editable Microsoft® PowerPoint® presentation that includes:

- a pre-made presentation for every chapter
- interactive graphics
- animations
- audio clips
- image bank
- all new section and chapter questions
- Standardized Test Practice
- transparencies
- Foldables directions
- links to gpescience.com

chapter 3

Motion, Acceleration, and Forces

chapter preview

sections

1 Describing Motion
2 Acceleration
3 Motion and Forces
Lab *Force and Acceleration*
Lab *Comparing Motion from Different Forces*
Virtual Lab *What is the relationship between distance, average speed, and time?*

Taking the Plunge

You probably don't think of an amusement park as a physics laboratory. The fast speeds, quick turns, and plunging falls are a great place to study the laws of gravity and motion. In fact, engineers use these laws when they are designing and building amusement park rides.

Science Journal Write a paragraph describing three rides in an amusement park and how the rides cause you to move.

68

Theme Connection

Stability and Change An object will have a constant velocity unless the object is acted upon by an unbalanced outside force.

About the Photo

Amusement Park Physics The fast speeds, sharp turns, and plunging falls in amusement park rides may seem dangerous, but they are very safe. Engineers use the laws of motion to design the rides so that the passengers experience the thrill but are not in danger of getting hurt.

Start-Up Activities

Launch LAB

Compare Speeds

A cheetah can run at a speed of almost 120 km/h and is the fastest runner in the world. A horse can reach a speed of 64 km/h; an elephant's top speed is about 40 km/h; and the fastest snake slithers at a speed of about 3 km/h. The speed of an object is calculated by dividing the distance the object travels by the time it takes it to move that distance. How does your speed compare to the speeds of these animals?

1. Use a meterstick to mark off 10 m.
2. Have your partner use a stopwatch to determine how fast you run 10 m.
3. Divide 10 m by your time in seconds to calculate your speed in m/s.
4. Multiply your answer by 3.6 to determine your speed in km/h.
5. **Think Critically** Write a paragraph in your Science Journal comparing your speed with the maximum speed of a cheetah, horse, elephant, and snake. Could you win a race with any of them?

Science Online — Preview this chapter's content and activities at gpescience.com

FOLDABLES™ Study Organizer

Motion Many things are in motion in your everyday life. Make the following Foldable to help you better understand motion as you read the chapter.

STEP 1 **Fold** a sheet of paper in half lengthwise. Make the back edge about 1.25 cm longer than the front edge.

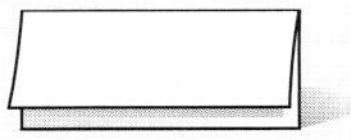

STEP 2 **Fold** in half, then fold in half again to make three folds.

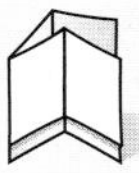

STEP 3 **Unfold and cut** only the top layer along the three folds to make four tabs.

STEP 4 **Label** the tabs.

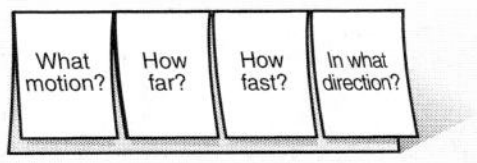

Identify Questions Before you read the chapter, select a motion you can observe and write it under the left tab. As you read the chapter, write answers to the other questions under the appropriate tabs.

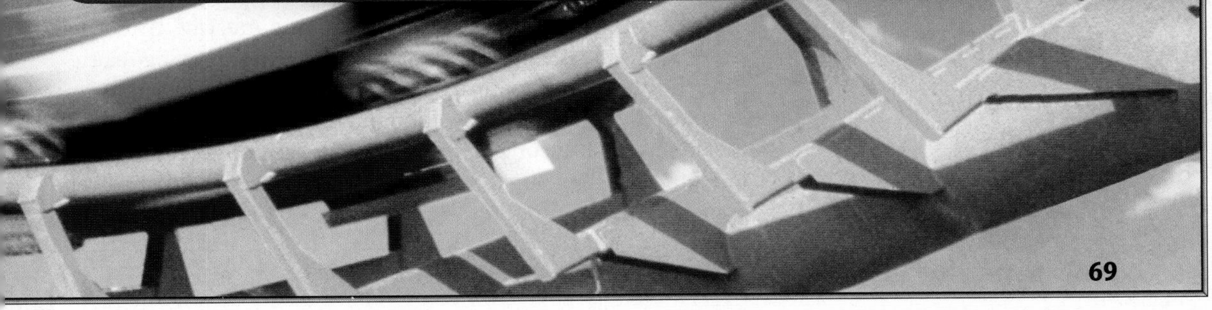

69

Launch LAB

Purpose Use the Launch Lab to introduce students to the relationship between motion and speed. L2 IN **Kinesthetic**

Preparation Find a location outside where groups of students will have room to mark off their 10-m distances. Assign each group a specific location.

Materials meterstick, stopwatch, calculator

Teaching Strategy Stage a contest between the five students with the greatest speeds to determine the fastest student in the class. Post the top speeds on a classroom bulletin board.

Think Critically

Students would lose races with a cheetah, horse, or elephant. They would win races with a snake.

Assessment

Oral Have students infer a formula for determining the speed of moving objects. Use **Performance Assessment in the Science Classroom,** p. 101.

FOLDABLES™ Study Organizer **Dinah Zike Study Fold**

Student preparation materials for this Foldable are available in the **Chapter *Fast File* Resources.**

section 1

Describing Motion

Reading Guide

What You'll Learn

- **Distinguish** between distance and displacement.
- **Calculate** average speed.
- **Explain** the difference between speed and velocity.
- **Interpret** motion graphs.

Why It's Important

Understanding the nature of motion and how to describe it helps you understand why motion occurs.

Review Vocabulary

instantaneous: occurring at a particular instant of time

New Vocabulary

- displacement
- vector
- speed
- instantaneous speed
- average speed
- velocity

Figure 1 This mail truck is in motion.

Infer *How do you know the mail truck has moved?*

Motion

Every day you see objects and people in motion. Cars, buses, and trucks move along streets and highways. People around you walk and run and move in different directions. How would you describe the motion of the people and objects around you? One way to describe motion is to say that it is fast or slow. However, sometimes you might need to know the speed of an object, as well as the direction in which it is moving. It also might be important to know how the motion of something is changing.

Motion is a Change in Position You don't always need to see something move to know that motion has taken place. For example, suppose you see a mail truck stopped next to a mailbox, as in **Figure 1.** A little while later, you see the same truck stopped farther along the street. Although you didn't see the truck move, you know it moved because its position relative to the mailbox changed. Motion occurs when an object changes position.

Position Depends on a Reference Frame To measure the position of an object, a reference frame must be chosen. A reference frame is a group of objects that are not moving relative to each other. One point in the reference frame is chosen as the reference point. Then the position of an object is the distance and the direction of the object from the reference point. For example, in **Figure 1** the mailbox, the tree, and the houses can form a reference frame because they aren't moving relative to each other.

1 Motivate

INTERACTIVE CHALKBOARD An editable Microsoft® PowerPoint® presentation is available on **Interactive Chalkboard** CD-ROM.

Bellringer

Section Focus Transparencies also are available on the Interactive Chalkboard CD-ROM. L2 ELL

Section 1 Section Focus Transparency — How about a rematch? — Chapter 3

In Aesop's fable "The Tortoise and the Hare," a tortoise and a hare have a race. The hare bounds far ahead of the tortoise and then, sure of victory, lies down to rest under a tree. The tortoise passes the resting hare and wins the race.

1. Which animal ran faster?
2. How does the motion of a car racing on an oval track chang[e] L2

Motion, Acceleration, and Forces

Reading Preview

Tie to Prior Knowledge

Speed Limits Ask students to name the speed limits near the school, near their homes, or on an interstate highway. Discuss with students the units, such as miles per hour or kilometers per hour, used in speed limits. Tell students they will learn about measuring speed. L1

Facets of Meaning Have students predict meaning for new vocabulary. The words will be familiar in an everyday sense, such as *speed* meaning "swiftness." In physics, however, the definitions may differ. Point out that *speed* in physics means "distance traveled divided by the time traveled."

Section 1 Resource Manager

Chapter *FAST FILE* Resources

Transparency Activity, pp. 44, 47–48

Directed Reading for Content Mastery, pp. 19–20

Note-taking Worksheets, pp. 33–35

MiniLAB, p. 3

Mathematics Skill Activities, p. 11

Physical Science Critical Thinking/Problem Solving, p. 2

Life Science Critical Thinking/Problem Solving, p. 14

Motion is Relative The motion of an object depends on the reference frame that is chosen. For example, suppose you are sitting in a moving car. You are not moving if the car is the reference frame, but you are moving relative to the ground. Using the Sun as a reference frame, Earth is moving at a speed of 30 km/s. However, the Sun also is moving relative to a reference frame centered on the Milky Way Galaxy. Your motion would be different in each of these reference frames. However, there is no special reference frame that really is at rest compared to all other reference frames. As a result, an object does not have absolute motion, but only motion relative to a chosen reference frame.

Distance and Displacement Suppose a runner jogs to the 50-m mark and then turns around and runs back to the 20-m mark, as shown in **Figure 2.** How far did the runner travel? For a moving object, distance is the length of the path the object travels. The runner traveled a distance of 50 m plus 30 m, or 80 m. However, even though she ran 80 m, she is only 20 m from the starting line. Her final position is 20 m north of her initial position. **Displacement** is the distance and direction of an object's final position from its initial position. The runner's displacement is 20 m north.

Displacement includes both a size and a direction. The size of the displacement is the distance between the initial and final position. A quantity that is specified by both a size and a direction is a **vector.** Displacement includes both a size and a direction and is an example of a vector. However, distance is a physical quantity that does not include a direction and isn't a vector.

Reading Check *How do distance and displacement differ?*

Mini LAB

Measuring Average Speed

Procedure
1. Mark a starting point on the floor with **tape.** Place a **toy car** at the starting point.
2. Give the toy car a gentle push forward. At the same time, start a **stopwatch.**
3. Record the time it takes for the car to come to a stop.
4. Use a **meterstick** to measure the distance the car traveled.

Analysis
Calculate the average speed of the car in m/s. How does the average speed depend on the direction of motion?

Speed

To describe how fast something is moving, you need to know how far it travels in a given amount of time. **Speed** is the distance an object travels per unit of time. In SI units, the unit of speed is meters per second (m/s). Usually the speed of an object changes as it moves from one place to another.

One way to describe the speed of an object is to measure its speed at a single instant of time. The **instantaneous speed** of an object is the speed at a single instant of time. A car's speedometer measures the instantaneous speed of the car.

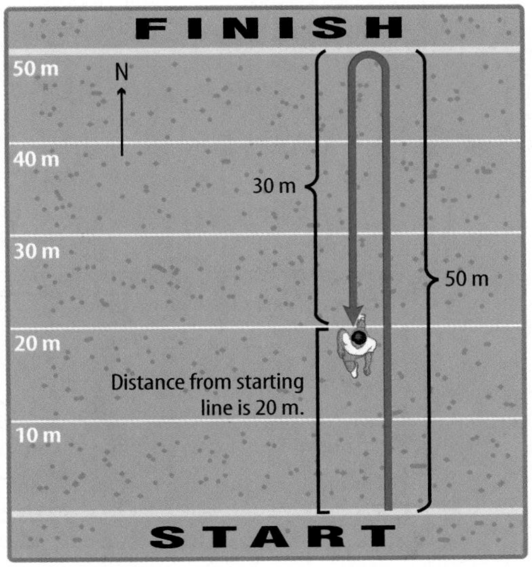

Figure 2 The runner's displacement is 20 m north of the starting line. However, the total distance traveled is 80 m.

2 Teach

Caption Answer

Figure 1 Its position relative to the mailbox changed.

Use Science Words

Word Usage Students may have difficulty with the term *relative* when it is used to describe an object's motion or position. Have them discuss what the word means. Possible answers are "dependent upon" or "with reference to." L1 ELL IS **Linguistic**

Mini LAB

Purpose Students will calculate the average speed of a car. L2

Materials tape, toy car, stopwatch, pencil, meterstick

Teaching Strategy Try to use cars that will travel in a straight line when pushed gently.

Analysis

average speed = distance/time; The speed would be the same if the car traveled in the opposite direction.

Assessment

Process Have students use their observations to hypothesize why the car eventually comes to a rest. Use **Performance Assessment in the Science Classroom,** p. 93.

Reading Check

Answer Distance describes how far an object has moved; displacement includes distance and direction of an object's change in position from its starting point.

Visual Learning

Figure 2 Help students understand the information presented in **Figure 2.** As you read the description from the text, have these students follow the path of the runner with their fingers. Then ask the students how far the runner ran and how far she is from the starting line. 80 m; 20 m L2

SECTION 1 Describing Motion 71

IDENTIFYING Misconceptions

Word Differences Students may think that distance and displacement are the same. They may also think speed and velocity are the same. Refer to page F at the beginning of this chapter for teaching strategies that address this misconception.

Activity

Different Rates Review the concept of rate by having students measure their breathing rates. Discuss other rates, such as heart rate (pulse) and interest rates. Discuss the units that describe these rates and point out similarities in the units. They are all a number of something per time. L2 LS **Logical-Mathematical**

Applying Math

Math Standards

National: 1, 2, 9

Answers to Practice Problems

1. 8.0 m/s
2. 0.25 h or 15 min

Use an Analogy

Lined Paper Explain to students that using a reference point to describe motion is analogous to using lines on paper to write. The lines on the paper provide a reference point to keep your writing on a straight line. L2

Science Online

Topic: Running Speeds

Visit gpescience.com for Web links to information about the speeds of various animals.

Activity Make a table comparing the top speed of various animals.

Average Speed Another way to describe the motion of an object is to determine the object's average speed. The average speed describes how quickly an object moved over the entire distance it traveled. The **average speed** of any object is the total distance traveled divided by the total travel time:

Average Speed Equation

$$\text{average speed (in meters/second)} = \frac{\text{total distance (in meters)}}{\text{total time (in seconds)}}$$

$$\bar{v} = \frac{d}{t}$$

The units of average speed are always a distance unit divided by a time unit. Sometimes it is more convenient to express average speed in units other than m/s, such as kilometers per hour (km/h).

Applying Math — Solve a One-Step Equation

AVERAGE SPEED What is the average speed of a car that travels a distance of 750 m in 25 s?

IDENTIFY known values and the unknown value

Identify the known values:

travels a distance of 750 m → means → $d = 750$ m

in 25 s → means → $t = 25$ s

Identify the unknown value:

What is the average speed? → means → $\bar{v} = ?$ m/s

SOLVE the problem

Substitute the given values of distance and time into the average speed equation:

$$\bar{v} = \frac{d}{t} = \frac{750\text{ m}}{25\text{ s}} = 30\text{ m/s}$$

CHECK your answer:

Does your answer seem reasonable? Check your answer by multiplying the time by the average speed. The result should be the distance given in the problem.

Practice Problems

1. An elevator travels a distance of 220 m from the first floor to the 60th floor in 27.5 s. What is the elevator's average speed?
2. A motorcyclist travels with an average speed of 20 km/h. If the cyclist is going to a friend's house 5 km away, how long does it take the cyclist to make the trip?

For more practice problems, go to page 879 and visit Math Practice at gpescience.com.

Cultural Diversity

The Olympics Runners from all over the world participate in track and field events in the Olympics every four years. Have students research the winners and their times and speeds for a track and field event of their choice for the past five summer Olympics. They should combine their research into a bulletin board display and creatively relate it to information in this chapter. L2

Differentiated Instruction

Learning Disabled Perform the calculations for determining average speed on the board to help students understand the process before doing it themselves. After you have done the procedure several times, ask students to do the calculations on their own. L2

Velocity

You turn on the TV and see a news story about a hurricane, such as the one in **Figure 3,** that is approaching land with a speed of 10 km/h. The eye of the hurricane is located 450 km east of your location. Should you take shelter?

If you know only the hurricane's speed and location, you don't have enough information to answer the question. To decide whether the hurricane will reach your location, you need to know the direction in which the storm is moving. In other words, you need to know the velocity of the hurricane. The **velocity** of an object is the speed of the object and its direction of motion. Just like displacement, velocity is a vector that has a size and a direction. The size of an object's velocity is the object's speed.

Objects have different velocities if they are moving at different speeds, or in different directions. The people on the up escalator and the down escalator in **Figure 4** are moving with the same speed, but in opposite directions. As a result, the people on the up escalator and the down escalator have a different velocity.

The velocity of an object can change even if the speed of the object remains constant. For example, look at **Figure 4.** The race car has a constant speed as it goes around an oval track. Even though the speed remains constant, the velocity changes because the direction of the car's motion is changing.

Reading Check ***How are velocity and speed different?***

Figure 3 The speed of a hurricane is not enough information to plot the hurricane's path. The direction of its motion also must be known.

Figure 4 The velocity of an object depends on both its speed and its direction of motion.
Describe *how the car's velocity changes as the car travels from the starting line to the top of the figure.*

The people on these two escalators have the same speed. However, their velocities are different because they are traveling in opposite directions.

The velocity of this car changes because its direction of motion is changing.

Quick Demo
Car Ramps

Materials three ramps of various lengths at least 2 m long, toy car, stopwatch, meterstick

Estimated Time 15 minutes

Procedure Make three ramps of various lengths, each at least 2 m long. Start a toy car rolling down one of the ramps. Time the car's motion with a stopwatch. Measure the distance covered by the car. Write the distance traveled and time elapsed on the board. Repeat the activity with each of the three ramps. Have students determine the average speed for the three runs by dividing the total distance traveled by the total time. L2

Discussion

Speed Units Remind students that when the equation for speed is rearranged, we have $t = d/v$. How do time units emerge from this equation? $m / (m/s) = m \times s/m = s$

Reading Check

Answer Velocity includes direction; speed does not.

Virtual Labs

d = st *What is the relationship between distance, average speed, and time?*

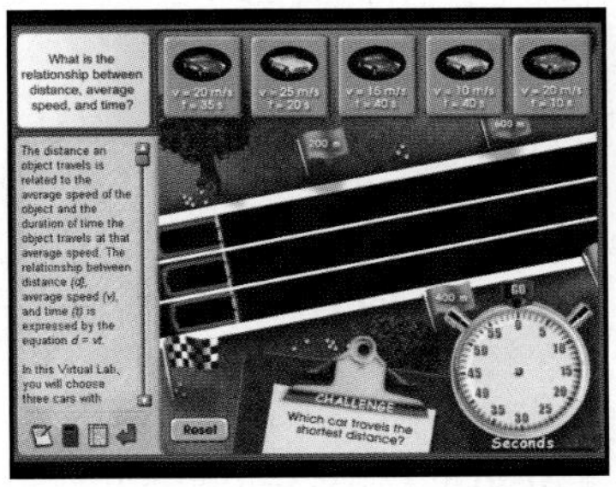

Differentiated Instruction

English-Language Learners Have students cut photographs out of magazines showing some type of motion. Have students create a decorative collage of their photos. L1 P

Curriculum Connection

Geography Geographers use lines of latitude and longitude to help them describe displacement on Earth. Have students find out how early seafarers determined their latitude and longitude. To find their latitude they used the positions of the stars and the Sun. They had no way to determine longitude until an accurate chronometer was developed in the mid-1700s. L3 LS **Linguistic**

Caption Answer

Figure 4 The velocity is to the right at the start line and to the left at the top of the figure. The magnitude of the velocity does not change.

IDENTIFYING Misconceptions

Average Speed Students sometimes interpret the height of a distance-time graph as its slope. The steepness of the straight line of a distance-time graph is the slope. This shows the average speed. The height of the line is the farthest distance the object has traveled in the positive direction.

Visual Learning

Figure 5 In addition to finding the average speed over the entire 30-min period, students can find the average speed over any time period by dividing the change in distance during the period by the amount of time. What is Julie's average speed during the period 15 min to 25 min? 40 m/min Students should also notice that the instantaneous speed at any point in time is the slope of the line at that point. What is the instantaneous speed of Mary at $t = 5$ min? 80 m/min L2 LS **Visual-Spatial**

Caption Answer

Figure 5 On Julie's graph there is a slope of zero between 10 min and 20 min, which represents a speed of 0 m/min.

INTEGRATE Astronomy

Orbital Speeds The average orbital speed of a planet decreases as the radius of the orbit increases.

Research Have students investigate how astronomers study planets outside the solar system. Ask students to present their findings to the class in an oral report.

Figure 5 The slope of a line on a distance-time graph gives the speed of an object in motion. **Identify** *the part of the graph that shows one of the swimmers resting for 10 min.*

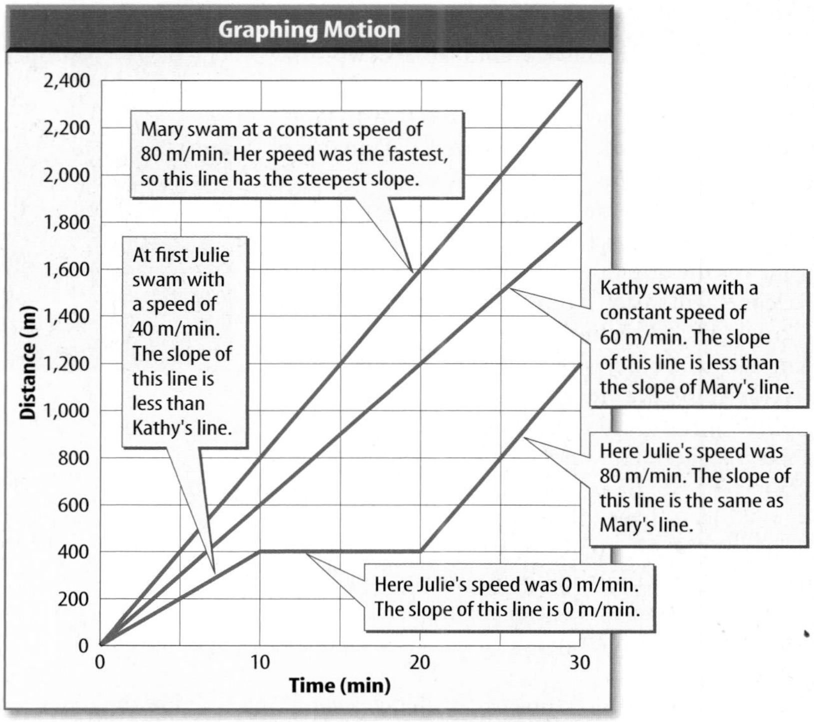

Graphing Motion

The motion of an object over a period of time can be shown on a distance-time graph. Time is plotted along the horizontal axis of the graph and the distance traveled is plotted along the vertical axis of the graph. If the object moves with constant speed, the increase in distance over equal time intervals is the same. As a result, the line representing the object's motion is a straight line.

For example, the graph shown in **Figure 5** represents the motion of three swimmers during a 30-min workout. The straight red line represents the motion of Mary, who swam with a constant speed of 80 m/min over the 30-min workout. The straight blue line represents the motion of Kathy, who swam with a constant speed of 60 m/min during the workout.

The graph shows that the line representing the motion of the faster swimmer is steeper. The steepness of a line on a graph is the slope of the line. The slope of a line on a distance-time graph equals the speed. A horizontal line on a distance-time graph has zero slope, and represents an object at rest. Because Mary has a larger speed than Kathy, the line representing her motion has a larger slope.

INTEGRATE Astronomy

Orbital Speeds Size, mass, composition, and orbital radius are some of the ways astronomers classify planets. Astronomers also measure the speed of a planet relative to the Sun. Make a table of the average orbital speeds and orbital radii of the nine planets in the solar system. How are distance from the Sun and orbital speed related?

Teacher FYI

Vertical Speed It is impossible to have a vertical line on a distance-time graph. It would mean the object moved a distance in zero time. To do this, the object would have to go infinitely fast.

Reading Strategy

Clarify Text After students read this page, have them clarify the meanings of *instantaneous speed, average speed* and *velocity* by providing examples of each term. Students should share examples with the class and chart ideas to display in the classroom.

Changing Speed The green line represents the motion of Julie, who did not swim at a constant speed. She covered 400 m at a constant speed during the first 10 min, rested for the next 10 min, and then covered 800 m during the final 10 min. During the first 10 min, her speed was less than Mary's or Kathy's, so her line has a smaller slope. During the middle period her speed is zero, so her line over this interval is horizontal and has zero slope. During the last time interval she swam as fast as Mary, so that part of her line has the same slope.

Plotting a Distance-Time Graph On a distance-time graph, the distance is plotted on the vertical axis and the time on the horizontal axis. Each axis must have a scale that covers the range of numbers to be plotted. In **Figure 5** the distance scale must range from 0 to 2,400 m and the time scale must range from 0 to 30 min. Then, each axis can be divided into equal time intervals to represent the data. Once the scales for each axis are in place, the data points can be plotted. After plotting the data points, draw a line connecting the points.

Science Online

Topic: Olympic Swimming Speeds

Visit gpescience.com for Web links to information about the speeds of Olympic swimmers over the past 60 years.

Activity Make a speed-year graph showing the swimming speeds over time. Are there any trends in the speed data?

section 1 review

Summary

Position and Motion

- The position of an object is determined relative to a reference point.
- Motion occurs when an object changes its position relative to a reference point.
- Distance is the length of the path an object has traveled. Displacement is the distance and direction of a change in position.

Average Speed and Velocity

- Average speed is the total distance traveled divided by the total time:

$$\bar{v} = \frac{d}{t}$$

- The velocity of an object includes the object's speed and its direction of motion relative to a reference point.

Graphing Motion

- On a distance-time graph, time is the horizontal axis and distance is the vertical axis.
- The slope of a line plotted on a distance-time graph is the speed.

Self Check

1. **Infer** whether the size of an object's displacement could be greater than the distance the object travels.
2. **Describe** the motion represented by a horizontal line on a distance-time graph.
3. **Explain** whether, during a trip, a car's instantaneous speed can ever be greater than its average speed.
4. **Describe** the difference between average speed and constant speed.
5. **Think Critically** You are walking toward the back of a bus that is moving forward with a constant velocity. Describe your motion relative to the bus and relative to a point on the ground.

Applying Math

6. **Calculate Average Speed** Michiko walked a distance of 1.60 km in 30 min. Find her average speed in m/s.
7. **Calculate Distance** A car travels at an average speed of 30.0 m/s for 0.8 h. Find the total distance traveled in km.

section 1 review

1. No. The displacement equals the distance only if the object moves in a straight line in a single direction. Otherwise, the displacement is less than the distance.
2. The slope is zero, corresponding to a speed of zero.
3. Yes. The instantaneous speed at various times can be greater or less than the average speed.
4. Average speed is total distance traveled divided by total time; the instantaneous speed can be changing. Constant speed means that the instantaneous speed doesn't change.
5. Relative to the bus, you move backward at your walking speed. Relative to the ground, you move in the same direction as the bus with a speed equal to the bus speed minus your walking speed.
6. 0.89 m/s
7. 86.4 km

Post Reading

Graphs Have students create their own distance v. time graphs to demonstrate an object's motion. Graphs should be annotated with a written description.

3 Assess

DAILY INTERVENTION

Check for Understanding

Linguistic Have students write a short narrative that could be used to explain the difference between distance and displacement to a younger sibling or to someone in the class that doesn't understand the difference. L2

Reteach

Calculating Average Speed Have students calculate the average speed of a windup or battery-operated toy car using metersticks and a wall clock. L2 IS **Logical-Mathematical**

Assessment

Process Provide students with the following problem: Suppose a bus is traveling through the city. It travels 100 km in the first 2 h and 120 km in the second 2 h. It stops for 1 h, then it finishes the route by going 100 km in 2 h. Draw a distance-time graph of the bus's motion.

Answer:

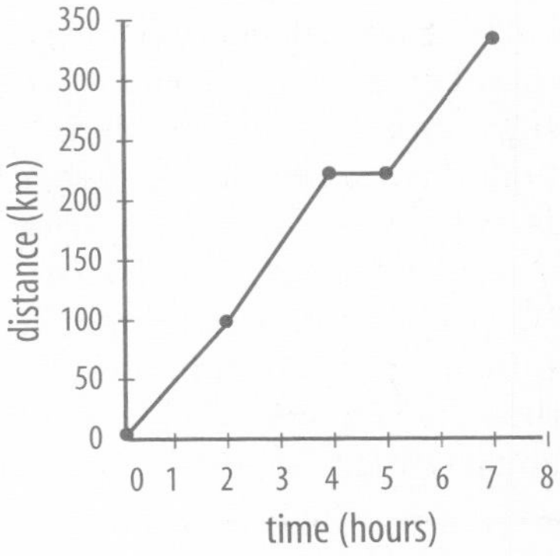

Use **PASC**, p. 111. L2

1 Motivate

An editable Microsoft® PowerPoint® presentation is available on **Interactive Chalkboard** CD-ROM.

Bellringer

Section Focus Transparencies also are available on the Interactive Chalkboard CD-ROM. L2 ELL

Section 2 Section Focus Transparency — On the Edge — Chapter 3

Many people enjoy cross-country and downhill skiing for recreation and for exercise. For others, skiing is a competitive sport. In ski races, fractions of a second can make the difference between winning and finishing second.

1. Describe how the skier's velocity changes during the race.
2. Why does the skier's velocity increase as he races downhill?
3. How does being in a tuck position affect a skier's motion? L2

Motion, Acceleration, and Forces

Reading Preview

Tie to Prior Knowledge

Floor It Have a student explain the phrase "stepping on the gas." Relate the function of the accelerator to the motion of a car. L2

Activate Background Knowledge Have students write what they know about *acceleration.* Introduce the physics definition: *acceleration is the change in velocity divided by the time it takes for the change to occur.* Discuss how this definition is similar to or different from their preconceived ideas of acceleration.

section 2

Acceleration

Reading Guide

What You'll Learn
- **Identify** how acceleration, time, and velocity are related.
- **Describe** how to calculate the average acceleration of an object.
- **Explain** how positive and negative acceleration affect motion.

Why It's Important

Acceleration occurs all around you as objects speed up, slow down, or change direction.

Review Vocabulary

velocity: a vector with a size that is an object's speed and a direction that is the direction of an object's motion

New Vocabulary
- acceleration

Acceleration, Speed, and Velocity

A car at a stoplight starts moving when the light finally turns green. When the car started moving, the car's velocity increased and the car was accelerating. **Acceleration** is the change in velocity divided by the time for the change to occur.

Remember that velocity is a vector that includes both the speed and direction of motion. So a change in velocity can either be a change in speed or a change in direction of motion. Acceleration occurs when the speed of an object changes or its direction of motion changes.

Reading Check ***When does acceleration occur?***

Just as velocity has a size and direction, acceleration also is a vector that has a size and direction. **Figure 6** shows how acceleration can cause an object to speed up or slow down.

Figure 6 These cars are both accelerating because their speed is changing.
Infer *how the car would move if its acceleration were zero.*

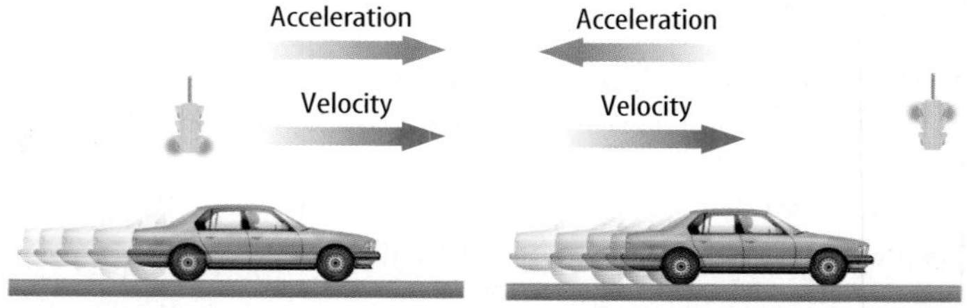

The car speeds up when the acceleration and velocity are in the same direction.

The car slows down when the acceleration and velocity are in opposite directions.

Section 2 Resource Manager

Chapter *Fast File* Resources
- Transparency Activity, p. 45
- MiniLAB, p. 4
- Enrichment, p. 31
- Lab Activity, pp. 13–15
- Directed Reading for Content Mastery, p. 21
- Reinforcement, p. 28

Performance Assessment in the Science Classroom, p. 37

Science Inquiry Labs, pp. 23–24

Changing Direction A change in velocity can be either a change in how fast something is moving or a change in the direction of movement. Any time a moving object changes direction, its velocity changes and it is accelerating. Think about a horse on a carousel. Although the horse's speed remains constant, the horse is accelerating because it is changing direction constantly as it travels in a circular path, as shown in **Figure 7.** Another example is the motion of Earth around the Sun in a nearly circular path. As a result, the direction of Earth's velocity is continually changing. This means that Earth is accelerating as it orbits the Sun.

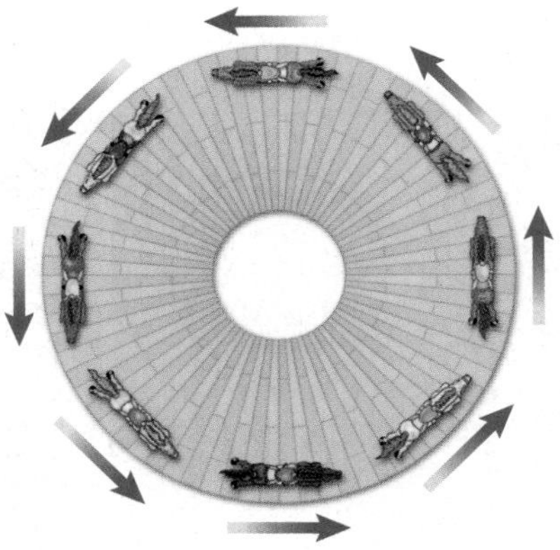

Figure 7 The speed of each horse on this carousel is constant but each is accelerating because the direction of its velocity is changing.

Calculating Acceleration

When an object moves from one place to another, it might speed up, slow down, and change direction many times. Each change in velocity causes the acceleration of the object to change. When acceleration is changing, the size of the average acceleration over some period of time can be calculated. If the direction of motion of an object doesn't change, the size of its average acceleration can be calculated using the following equation:

Acceleration Equation

average acceleration (in m/s²) = $\dfrac{\text{(final velocity (in m/s)} - \text{initial velocity (in m/s))}}{\text{(final time (s)} - \text{initial time (s))}}$

$$\bar{a} = \frac{(v_f - v_i)}{(t_f - t_i)}$$

In this equation, v_i is the size of the velocity at the start of the time period and v_f is the size of the velocity at the end of the time period. For motion in a single direction, v_i is the same as the initial speed, and v_f is the same as the final speed. In SI units, acceleration has units of m/s^2—meters per second squared. An acceleration of 1 m/s^2 means that the velocity of the object increases by 1 m/s each second. If the object was initially at rest, its velocity would be 1 m/s after 1 s, 2 m/s after 2 s, and so on.

Speed-Time Graphs For an object moving in one direction, the acceleration can be found from a speed-time graph. For this type of graph, the vertical axis is the object's speed and the horizontal axis is the time. Then the slope of the plotted line is the size of the object's acceleration. **Figure 8** shows some examples of speed-time graphs.

INTEGRATE History

Aircraft Carriers In 1911, American pilot Eugene Ely successfully landed on a specially equipped deck on the battleship *Pennsylvania.* Today, huge aircraft carriers provide floating landing strips for military airplanes. Carriers must be equipped to provide large accelerations, both positive and negative, to the jets launched from their decks. Research the accelerations provided by modern carriers as they launch and land aircraft.

2 Teach

Reading Check

Answer Acceleration occurs whenever ther is a change in speed or direction of motion.

Caption Answer

Figure 6 The car would move with a constant velocity.

INTEGRATE History

Aircraft Carriers The U.S. Navy was not alone in the development of aircraft carriers. During World War I, the British navy converted a merchant-ship hull into the first aircraft carrier with an unobstructed flight deck, the HMS *Argus.* The first U.S. carrier, the USS *Langley,* joined the fleet in March 1922. The Japanese built the first carrier from the keel up, the *Hosyo.* It entered service in December 1922. Modern carriers provide accelerations between 30 m/s^2 and 40 m/s^2, or three to four gs.

Discussion

Acceleration Tell students that, as in the case of speed and velocity, acceleration can be constant or changing, and one can measure instantaneous acceleration as well as average acceleration. Ask students to give examples of constant acceleration, instantaneous acceleration, and average acceleration. constant acceleration—free fall; instantaneous acceleration—the acceleration of a falling rock after it has been falling for 3 s; average acceleration—final velocity of the falling rock when it hits the ground divided by the total time it was falling L3

LS **Logical-Mathematical**

Curriculum Connection

Physical Education Most sports rely on the ability of people to make quick changes in acceleration. Have students find out some of the equipment used in different sports to make acceleration easier. starting blocks for runners and swimmers; cleats on shoes for runners, soccer players, football players, and baseball players; rubber-soled shoes for basketball players; special clothing for reducing wind resistance for all racers L2

Reading Strategy

Dialogue with the Text As students read Calculating Acceleration, have them write down questions or ideas for the author. For instance, a student might ask the author: Why is it important to know these concepts? More specifically, why do you say to subtract final velocity from initial velocity?

NATIONAL GEOGRAPHIC

Visualizing Acceleration

Have students examine the pictures and read the captions. Then ask the following questions.

In the graphs for A, B, and C, how are the slopes of the lines and the accelerations of the objects related? The slope of the line is positive if acceleration is positive, negative if acceleration is negative, and zero if there is no acceleration.

In the graph for B, what is the numerical value of the acceleration of the ball? The numerical value is the same as the acceleration due to gravity, 9.8 m/s^2.

What is the relationship between the graphs for B and C? The acceleration of both balls is due to the pull of gravity. Graph B has a positive acceleration due to gravity or + 9/8 m/s^2 and graph C has a negative acceleration due to gravity or − 9.8 m/s^2.

Activity

Rap Songs Have students work in pairs to make up rap songs containing descriptions of the relationship between different types of acceleration and their corresponding graphs. L2 LS **Auditory-Musical**

Teacher FYI

Feeling Acceleration In the aerospace industry, the accelerations experienced by astronauts and pilots are often expressed as multiples of g. The acceleration, caused by gravity (g), acting on an object falling freely near Earth's surface is about 9.78 m/s^2. Vertical accelerations as low as 3 g can cause pilots to black out.

NATIONAL GEOGRAPHIC **VISUALIZING ACCELERATION**

Figure 8

Acceleration can be positive, negative, or zero depending on whether an object is speeding up, slowing down, or moving at a constant speed. If the speed of an object is plotted on a graph, with time along the horizontal axis, the slope of the line is related to the acceleration.

A The car in the photograph on the right is maintaining a constant speed of about 90 km/h. Because the speed is constant, the car's acceleration is zero. A graph of the car's speed with time is a horizontal line.

B The green graph shows how the speed of a bouncing ball changes with time as it falls from the top of a bounce. The ball speeds up as gravity pulls the ball downward, so the acceleration is positive. For positive acceleration, the plotted line slopes upward to the right.

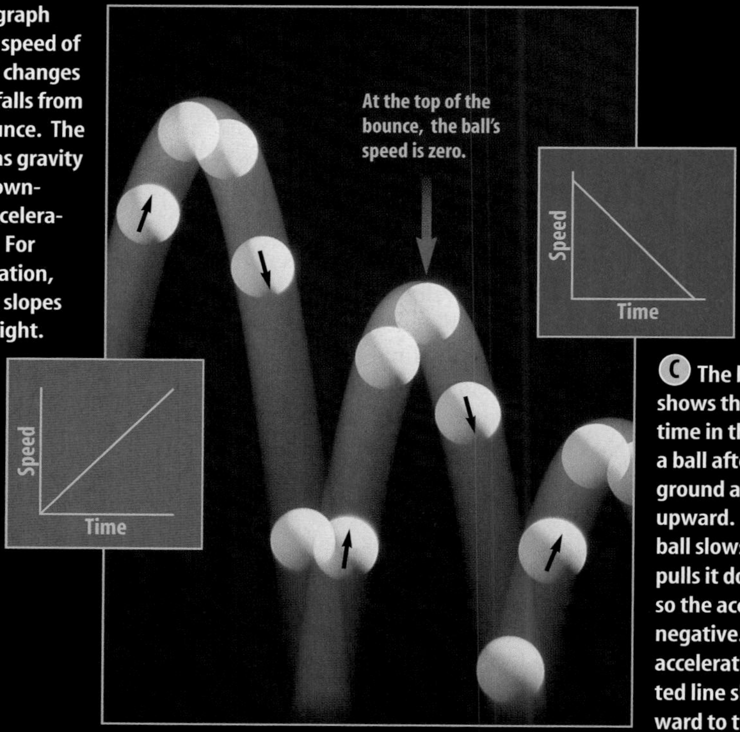

C The blue graph shows the change with time in the speed of a ball after it hits the ground and bounces upward. The climbing ball slows as gravity pulls it downward, so the acceleration is negative. For negative acceleration, the plotted line slopes downward to the right.

78 **CHAPTER 3** Motion, Acceleration, and Forces

Differentiated Instruction

Challenge Have students find out what type of information can be obtained by finding the area under a speed-time graph. Explain why this could be a useful tool for scientists. Construct a speed-time graph and find the distance traveled by the object. The numerical value of the area under a speed-time graph is the distance traveled by the object. L3 P LS **Logical-Mathematical**

Visually Impaired Have a student helper read the text for each graph. Have the helper move his or her finger along the graph while the other student gently lays his or her hand on top of the helper's hand. This can help the visually-impaired student "see" the graph.

Calculating Positive Acceleration How is the acceleration for an object that is speeding up different from that of an object that is slowing down? Suppose the jet airliner in **Figure 9** starts at rest and moves down the runway in a single direction. After accelerating for 20 s, it reaches a speed of 80 m/s. Because it started from rest, its initial speed was zero. The jetliner's average acceleration can be calculated as follows:

$$\bar{a} = \frac{(v_f - v_i)}{(t_f - t_i)} = \frac{(80 \text{ m/s} - 0 \text{ m/s})}{20 \text{ s}} = 4 \text{ m/s}^2$$

The airliner is speeding up, so the final speed is greater than the initial speed and the acceleration is a positive number.

Calculating Negative Acceleration Now imagine that the skateboarder in **Figure 9** is moving in a straight line at a constant speed of 3 m/s and comes to a stop in 2 s. The final speed is zero and the initial speed was 3 m/s. The skateboarder's acceleration is calculated as follows:

$$\bar{a} = \frac{(v_f - v_i)}{(t_f - t_i)} = \frac{(0 \text{ m/s} - 3 \text{ m/s})}{2 \text{ s}} = -1.5 \text{ m/s}^2$$

The skateboarder is slowing down, so the final speed is less than the initial speed and the acceleration is a negative number. For an object moving in one direction, the acceleration will be a positive number if an object is speeding up and a negative number if the object is slowing down.

Figure 9 A speed-time graph tells you if acceleration is a positive or negative number.
Infer *what a steeper slope indicates on a speed-time graph.*

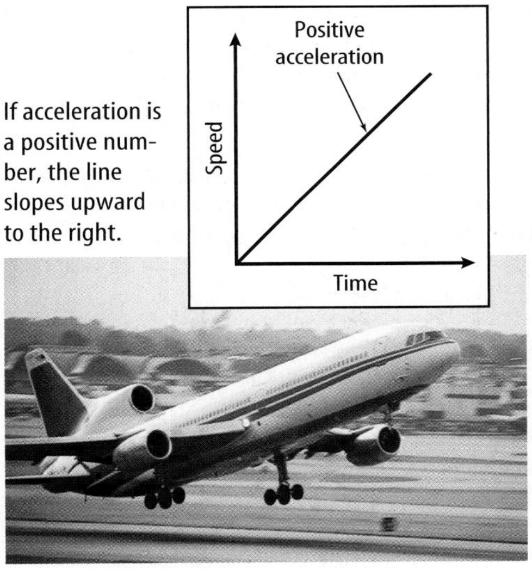

Visual Learning

Figure 9 Review with students the graphs in **Figure 9.** Then ask a volunteer to draw on the board the speed-time graph for a car that starts at 0 km/h, accelerates to 30 km/h over a period of 2 min, runs at 30 km/h for 10 min, then takes 30 s to stop. L2

Quick Demo
Sphere Acceleration

Materials about 2 m of clear-plastic tubing, small spheres that can freely roll through tubing

Estimated Time 10 minutes

Procedure Have two students hold the tubing in a U-shape. Put a sphere in one end of the tubing. Point out to the students that the sphere has positive acceleration as it rolls downhill in the tubing. The sphere has negative acceleration as it starts to go uphill in the tubing.

Caption Answer

Figure 9 A steeper slope means a larger acceleration.

Post Reading

Extended Research Ask students to research roller coaster design. Have them develop a poster or written report that explains how design is tied to acceleration. Suggest that they use design information from existing roller coasters to support their ideas.

LAB DEMONSTRATION

Purpose to demonstrate making a table and graph from distance-time measurements

Materials 8 socks, stopwatch, meterstick

Preparation Mark a starting line where you have room to walk.

Procedure Begin walking slowly, then steadily increase your speed. Drop a sock every 3 s. Measure the distance from the starting line to each sock. On the board, make a table and a distance-time graph of the data.

Expected Outcome The distance between socks will increase for each 3-s interval.

Teaching Strategy Reassure students that walking speeds vary and any distance interval they measure is acceptable.

Assessment

What is the slope of the line after 6 s? The slope will vary with the data. What does this show? speed Use **PASC,** p. 111. L2

Reading Check

Answer They are accelerated.

3 Assess

DAILY INTERVENTION

Check for Understanding

Kinesthetic Have students work in groups to discuss acceleration experienced by a tennis ball as it is dropped and bounces. Because the velocity of the ball changes direction as it bounces, students must include the direction of the ball's motion when they calculate acceleration. If down is the positive direction, the ball's acceleration is positive when it falls. When the ball rises, its velocity becomes less negative as it moves upward, so its acceleration is positive. When the ball is in contact with the floor, its acceleration is negative as it slows down in the positive (down) direction, and then speeds up in the negative (up) direction. Have students make a labeled poster illustrating the tennis ball's positive then negative acceleration cycle—a pattern that repeats itself with each bounce. L3 COOP LEARN P LS **Interpersonal**

Reteach

Have students demonstrate three ways to accelerate while walking. speeding up, slowing down, changing direction L1 LS **Kinesthetic**

Assessment

Process Think about how motion is affected by gravitational acceleration. Water on Earth falls from a waterfall with an acceleration of 9.8 m/s^2. The gravity of Mars is two-fifths that of Earth. If water were on the surface of Mars, would water fall from a waterfall faster, more slowly, or at the same rate? more slowly. Use **Performance Assessment in the Science Classroom,** p. 89. L2

Figure 10 Cars on this roller coaster can reach a speed of about 150 km/h in 4 s.

Amusement Park Acceleration

Riding roller coasters in amusement parks can give you the feeling of danger, but these rides are designed to be safe. Engineers use the laws of physics to design amusement park rides that are thrilling, but harmless. Roller coasters are constructed of steel or wood. Because wood is not as rigid as steel, wooden roller coasters do not have hills that are as high and steep as some steel roller coasters have. As a result, the highest speeds and accelerations usually are produced on steel roller coasters.

Steel roller coasters can offer multiple steep drops and inversion loops, which give the rider large accelerations. As the rider moves down a steep hill or an inversion loop, he or she will accelerate toward the ground due to gravity. When riders go around a sharp turn, they also are accelerated. This acceleration makes them feel as if a force is pushing them toward the side of the car. **Figure 10** shows the fastest roller coaster in the United States.

Reading Check *What happens when riders on a roller coaster go around a sharp turn?*

section 2 review

Summary

Acceleration, Speed, and Velocity

- Acceleration is the change in velocity divided by the time needed for the change to occur.
- A change in velocity occurs when an object changes its speed or direction of motion.
- The speed of an object increases if the acceleration is in the same direction as the velocity.
- The speed of an object decreases if the acceleration and the velocity of the object are in opposite directions.

Calculating Acceleration

- The average acceleration of an object can be calculated using this equation:

$$\bar{a} = \frac{(v_f - v_i)}{(t_f - t_i)}$$

- When an object moving in a straight line speeds up, its acceleration is positive
- When an object moving in a straight line slows down, its acceleration is negative.

Self Check

1. **Determine** whether you are accelerating as Earth rotates once every 24 h.
2. **Determine** the change in velocity of a car that starts at rest and has a final velocity of 20 m/s north.
3. **Explain** why streets and highways have speed limits rather than velocity limits.
4. **Describe** the motion of an object that has an acceleration of 0 m/s^2.
5. **Think Critically** Suppose a car is accelerating so that its speed is increasing. Describe the plotted line of the motion of the car on a distance-time graph.

Applying Math

6. **Calculate Acceleration** A ball is dropped from a cliff and reaches a speed of 29.4 m/s after 3.0 s. What is the ball's average acceleration?
7. **Calculate Speed** A sprinter runs with an average acceleration of 4.5 m/s^2. What is the sprinter's speed 2 s after leaving the starting blocks?

More Section Review gpescience.com

section 2 review

1. Yes, you are accelerating.
2. 20 m/s north
3. Velocity includes direction, so to have a velocity limit there would have to be some limit as to the direction in which a car was moving, as well as speed.
4. It's moving in a straight line with constant speed.
5. The plot would be a curved line sloping upward whose slope is increasing.
6. 9.8 m/s^2
7. 9.0 m/s

section 3

Motion and Forces

Reading Guide

What You'll Learn

- **Explain** how forces and motion are related.
- **Compare and contrast** static friction and sliding friction.
- **Describe** the effects of air resistance on falling objects.

Why It's Important

All changes in motion are caused by the forces that act on objects.

Review Vocabulary

vector: a quantity that includes both a size and a direction

New Vocabulary

- force
- net force
- balanced forces
- unbalanced forces
- friction
- static friction
- sliding friction
- air resistance

What is force?

When you shoot a basketball or kick a soccer ball, you are exerting a force on an object. In fact, every push or pull you exert results in a force being applied to some object. A **force** is a push or pull that one object exerts on another. Just like velocity and acceleration, force also is a vector that has a size and a direction. The size of a force often is called the strength of the force. The direction of a force is the direction in which the push or pull is applied. For example, when you lift your backpack, you apply an upward force. In SI units, force is measured in newtons (N). You have to apply a force of about 3 N to lift a full can of soft drink.

Changing Motion What happens to the motion of an object when you exert a force on it? A force can cause the motion of an object to change, as in **Figure 11.** The racket strikes the ball with a force that causes the ball to stop and then move in the opposite direction. If you have played billiards, you know that you can cause a ball at rest to roll into a pocket by striking it with another ball. The force applied by the moving ball causes the ball at rest to move in the direction of the force. In these cases, the velocities of the tennis ball and the billiard ball were changed by a force.

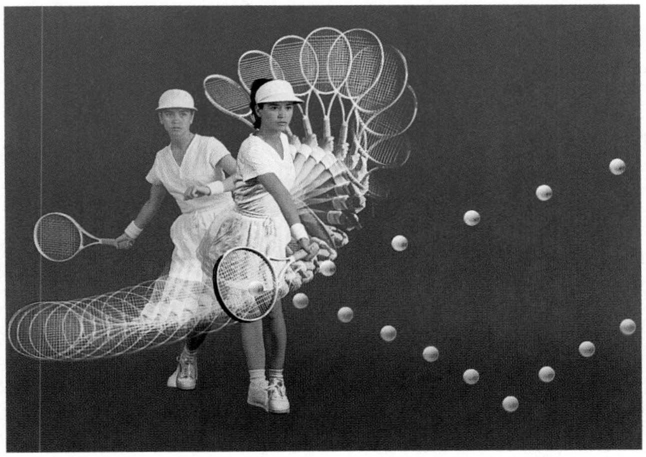

Figure 11 This ball is hit with a force. The racket strikes the ball with a force in the opposite direction of its motion. As a result, the ball changes the direction it is moving.

Section 3 Resource Manager

Chapter *Fast File* Resources

- Transparency Activity, p. 46
- Enrichment, p. 32
- Reinforcement, p. 29
- Directed Reading for Content Mastery, pp. 21–22
- Lab Worksheets, pp. 5–6, 7–8
- **Home and Community Involvement,** p. 41
- **Earth Science Critical Thinking/Problem Solving,** p. 9
- **Cultural Diversity,** p. 63

1 Motivate

INTERACTIVE CHALKBOARD PowerPoint® Presentations An editable Microsoft® PowerPoint® presentation is available on **Interactive Chalkboard** CD-ROM.

Bellringer

Section Focus Transparencies also are available on the Interactive Chalkboard CD-ROM. L2 ELL

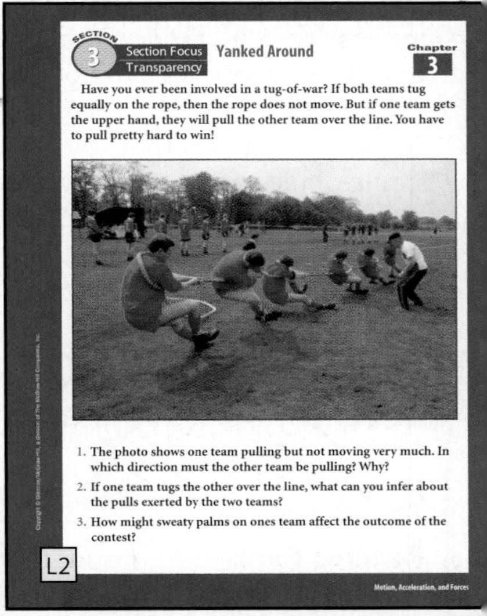

Section 3 Section Focus Transparency **Yanked Around** Chapter 3

Have you ever been involved in a tug-of-war? If both teams tug equally on the rope, then the rope does not move. But if one team gets the upper hand, they will pull the other team over the line. You have to pull pretty hard to win!

1. The photo shows one team pulling but not moving very much. In which direction must the other team be pulling? Why?
2. If one team tugs the other over the line, what can you infer about the pulls exerted by the two teams?
3. How might sweaty palms on ones team affect the outcome of the contest?

L2

Motion, Acceleration, and Forces

Reading Preview

Tie to Prior Knowledge

Changing Velocity Ask students to describe things they could do to change the velocity of a soccer ball. Point out that in each case, they are using a push or a pull to change the ball's motion. Tell students that pushing and pulling are forces, and this section discusses how forces change an object's motion. L2

Visualizing Text Have students choose two new vocabulary words to visualize and illustrate. For instance, for *force* students might think of a falling acorn hitting the ground. For *balanced forces,* they might visualize two people pushing on opposite sides of a box with the same force.

2 Teach

Reading Check

Answer Student answers will vary. possible answers: force of gravity on a falling object

Quick Demo

Upward and Downward Forces

Materials spring scale, objects with various masses

Estimated Time 10 minutes

Procedure Hold up a spring scale and hang objects of different masses from it. Have a student read the force required to hold up each object. Explain that the upward force exerted by the spring of the spring scale balances the downward gravitational force on the object.

IDENTIFYING Misconceptions

Balanced Forces The point to emphasize is that a condition of zero velocity (constant velocity of zero) is not any different, in terms of net force acting on the object, than an object moving at a constant, non-zero velocity. Explain that any constant velocity means that the forces acting on the object are balanced.

Make a Model

Rough Surfaces Students can use modeling clay to show how two surfaces that appear to be smooth and in complete contact are, in fact, microscopically rough. The models should show the bumps and dips on the surfaces and how the surfaces only touch on a small number of the bumps. L2 IS **Kinesthetic**

Figure 12 Forces can be balanced and unbalanced.

→ + ← = 0
Net Force = 0

A These students are pushing on the box with an equal force but in opposite directions. Because the forces are balanced, the box does not move.

→ + ← = →
Net Force = →

B These students are pushing on the box with unequal forces in opposite directions. The box will be moved in the direction of the larger force.

→ + → = →
Net Force = →

C These students are pushing on the box in the same direction. The combined forces will cause the box to move.

Science Online

Topic: Forces and Fault Lines

Visit gpescience.com for Web links to information about the unbalanced forces that occur along Earth's fault lines.

Activity Use inexpensive materials such as bars of soap to model the forces and movements along the fault lines. Share your models and demonstrations with your class.

Balanced Forces Force does not always change velocity. In **Figure 12A,** two students are pushing on opposite sides of a box. Both students are pushing with an equal force but in opposite directions. When two or more forces act on an object at the same time, the forces combine to form the **net force.** The net force on the box in **Figure 12A** is zero because the two forces cancel each other. Forces on an object that are equal in size and opposite in direction are called **balanced forces.**

Unbalanced Forces Another example of how forces combine is shown in **Figure 12B.** When two students are pushing with unequal forces in opposite directions, a net force occurs in the direction of the larger force. When forces combine to produce a net force that is not zero, the forces acting on the object are **unbalanced forces.** The net force that causes the box to accelerate will be the difference between the two forces because they are in opposite directions.

In **Figure 12C,** the students are pushing on the box in the same direction. These forces are combined, or added together, because they are exerted on the box in the same direction. The net force that acts on this box is found by adding the two forces together.

Reading Check *Give another example of an unbalanced force.*

Visual Learning

Figure 12 Tell students that the net force acting on an object is called the resultant force. In **Figure 12A,** the forces are equal and in opposite directions, so the resultant force is zero. In **Figure 12B,** you can calculate the resultant force by subtracting the smaller force from the larger one. How would you calculate the resultant force in **Figure 12C?** Add the two forces together. L2 IS **Visual-Spatial**

Teacher FYI

Plate Tectonics Scientists do not fully understand the driving force behind the movement of the plates. There appear to be three factors contributing to the movement of the plates: the pull of gravity, convection currents in the mantle, and thermal plumes or vertical columns of molten material in the mantle.

Unbalanced Forces Change Velocity When the forces acting on an object are balanced, the velocity of an object doesn't change. If you and a friend push on a door from opposite sides with the same size force, the door doesn't move. The net force is zero and the forces are balanced. But if you push harder, the door moves in the direction of your push. The velocity the door, or any object, changes only when the forces on it are unbalanced.

Friction

Suppose you give a skateboard a push with your hand. The skateboard speeds up as you push it and then keeps moving after it leaves your hand. What happens to the skateboard's speed if it is moving on a flat, level surface? You know the answer. The skateboard slows down and finally stops.

After it left your hand, the skateboard's velocity changed because the forces acting on it were unbalanced. The unbalanced force that slowed the skateboard was friction. **Friction** is the force that opposes the sliding motion of two surfaces that are in contact.

What causes friction? The size of the frictional force exerted by one surface on another depends on the materials the surfaces are made from and the roughness of the surfaces. All surfaces have bumps and dips, including highly-polished metal surfaces that seem very smooth. When two surfaces are in contact, sticking occurs where the bumps and dips touch each other. This causes microwelds to form between the two surface. These microwelds tend to make the surfaces stick together and cause friction to occur.

The frictional force between two surfaces increases when the force pushing the surfaces together increases, as shown in **Figure 13.** When the surfaces are pushed together with more force, more of the bumps and dips come into contact. This increases the strength of the microwelds.

Mini LAB

Comparing Friction

Procedure

1. Place an **ice cube,** a **rock,** an **eraser,** a **wood block,** and a square of **aluminum foil** at one end of a **metal or plastic tray.**
2. Slowly lift the end of the tray with the items.
3. Have a partner use a **metric ruler** to measure the height of the raised end of the tray at which each object begins to slide. Record your measurements.

Analysis

1. List the height at which each object began to slide.
2. How did the height at which objects began to slide depend on the roughness of the objects?
3. How did the forces due to static and sliding friction compare for each object?

Try at Home

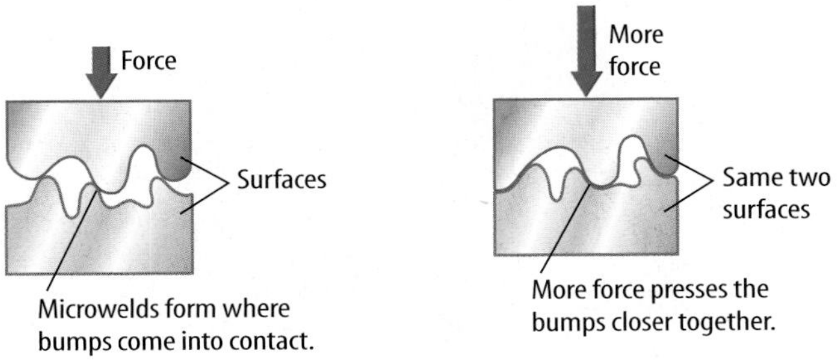

Figure 13 Friction is due to the microwelds that form between two surfaces in contact. These microwelds become stronger when the force pushing the surfaces together increases.
Explain *how the area of contact between the surfaces changes when they are pushed together with a larger force.*

Mini LAB

Purpose Students observe the effect of friction on several materials. L2 LS **Kinesthetic**

Materials ice cube, rock, eraser, wood block, square of aluminum foil, metal or plastic tray, metric ruler

Teaching Strategy Have an empty jar or beaker available for the ice cubes.

Analysis

1. The ice cube should slide first, followed by the aluminum foil, rock, wood block, and eraser.
2. The rougher the object, the higher it was before it began to slide.
3. Static friction was greater than sliding friction for all materials.

Assessment

Oral Ask students to list several ways to increase the friction between tires and ice. Put chains on tires, make tires with steel grips, add sand or some other abrasive to ice, add weight to the car. Use **Performance Assessment in the Science Classroom,** p. 93.

Try at Home

Caption Answer

Figure 13 The area of contact increases.

LAB DEMONSTRATION

Purpose to observe properties of friction

Materials 2 heavy wood blocks (about 10 cm × 15 cm × 5 cm thick), 2 nails, spring scale, string, strip of sandpaper as wide as the blocks, smooth surface

Procedure Pound nails in the center of one 5-cm side and one 15-cm side of one wood block. Attach the spring scale and pull the block across a smooth surface. Record the force. Repeat on a rough surface with the second block on top. Repeat with the block on its end.

Expected Outcome There is more friction on a rough surface. Friction doubles if the mass doubles. The area of contact doesn't affect friction.

Assessment

What would happen if a third block were placed on top of the second block? The frictional force would triple.

SECTION 3 Motion and Forces **83**

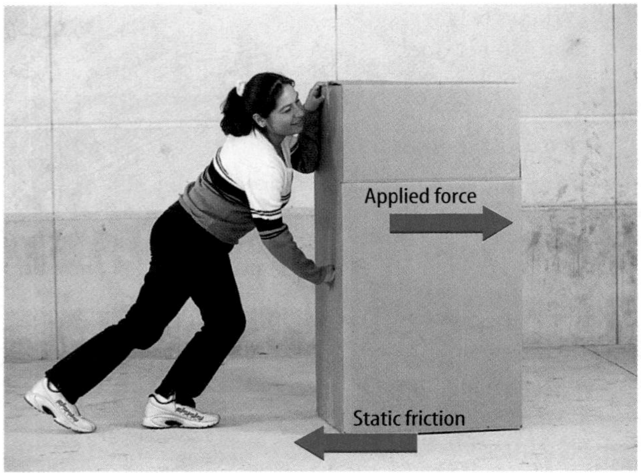

Figure 14 The static friction force balances the applied force so the box doesn't move.
Infer *the net force on the box.*

Static Friction Suppose you push on a heavy box, like the one in **Figure 14,** and it doesn't budge. The velocity of the box didn't change, so another force is acting on the box that balances your push. This force is a frictional force called static friction that is due to the microwelds that have formed between the box and the floor. **Static friction** is the frictional force that prevents two surfaces in contact from sliding past each other. In this case, the box didn't move because your push is not large enough to break the microwelds between the two surfaces.

Sliding Friction You and a friend push together on the box and the box slides along the floor, as shown in **Figure 15.** As the box slides on the floor, another frictional force—sliding friction—opposes the motion of the box. **Sliding friction** is the force that acts in the opposite direction to the motion of a surface sliding on another surface. If you stop pushing, sliding friction causes the box to slow down and stop. The force due to sliding friction between two surfaces is smaller than the force due to static friction.

Reading Check *Sliding friction always is in what direction?*

Rolling Friction When an object rolls over a surface, a frictional force due to rolling friction slows the object down. Rolling friction usually is much less than sliding friction. This is why it is easier to move a heavy object if it is on wheels.

Figure 15 Sliding friction acts on the sliding box in the direction opposite to the motion of the box.

IDENTIFYING Misconceptions

Effect of Surface Area on Friction Friction is nearly independent of the surface area of contact. Friction depends on the microscopic contact areas on the microscopic welds that form when the surfaces are pushed together. If the microscopic contact area increases, more welds are formed. However, because pressure equals force divided by area, the pressure pushing the surfaces together decreases. This causes the contact area on each weld to become smaller so that the total microscopic contact area remains nearly unchanged.

Caption Answer

Figure 14 The net force is zero.

Using Science Words

Word Origin Have students find the origin of the word *friction.* The word friction comes from the Latin word fricare, which means "to rub." L2 LS **Linguistic**

Reading Strategy

Discussion Groups Organize students into groups of four. Assign a discussion leader and recorder. Have them use the following prompt to begin a discussion: What is friction? Have the recorder write a summary statement that outlines the main points of the conversation.

Reading Check

Answer opposite the direction of motion

Differentiated Instruction

Challenge In general, the smoother two surfaces are, the less friction there is between them. However, if surfaces are extremely smooth, they actually have more friction between them. Have students rub two new glass slides together and compare this to the resistance felt when rubbing older, scratched slides together. Ask them to explain this effect. Extremely smooth surfaces have a greater true contact area (more bumps are in contact). L3 LS **Kinesthetic**

Air Resistance

When an object falls toward Earth, it is pulled downward by the force due to gravity. However, a type of frictional force called **air resistance** opposes the motion of objects that move through the air. Air resistance causes objects to fall with different accelerations and different speeds. If there were no air resistance, then all objects, like the apple and feather shown in **Figure 16,** would fall with the same acceleration.

Air resistance acts in the direction opposite to the velocity of an object moving in air. If an object is falling downward, air resistance acts upward on the object. The size of the air resistance force depends on the size and shape of an object. Imagine dropping two identical plastic bags. One is crumpled into a ball and the other is spread out. When the bags are dropped, the crumpled bag falls faster than the spread-out bag. The downward force of gravity on both bags is the same, but the upward force of air resistance on the crumpled bag is less. As a result, the net downward force on the crumpled bag is greater, as shown in **Figure 17.**

The amount of air resistance on an object depends on the speed, size, and shape of the object. Air resistance, not the object's mass, is why feathers, leaves, and sheets of paper fall more slowly than pennies, acorns, and apples.

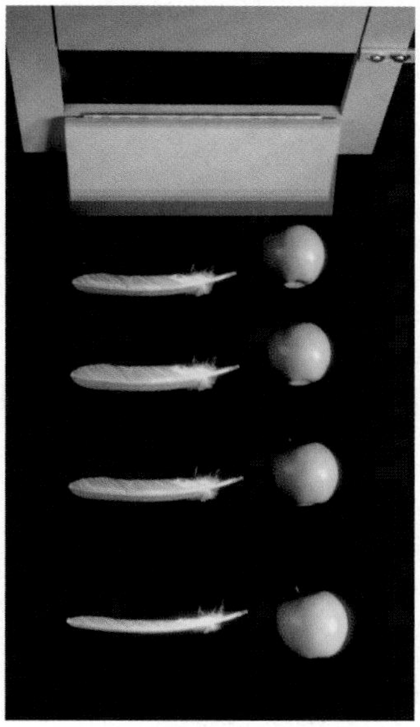

Figure 16 This photograph shows an apple and a feather falling in a vacuum. The photograph was taken with a strobe light that flashes on and off at a steady rate. Because there is no air resistance in a vacuum, the feather and the apple fall with the same acceleration.

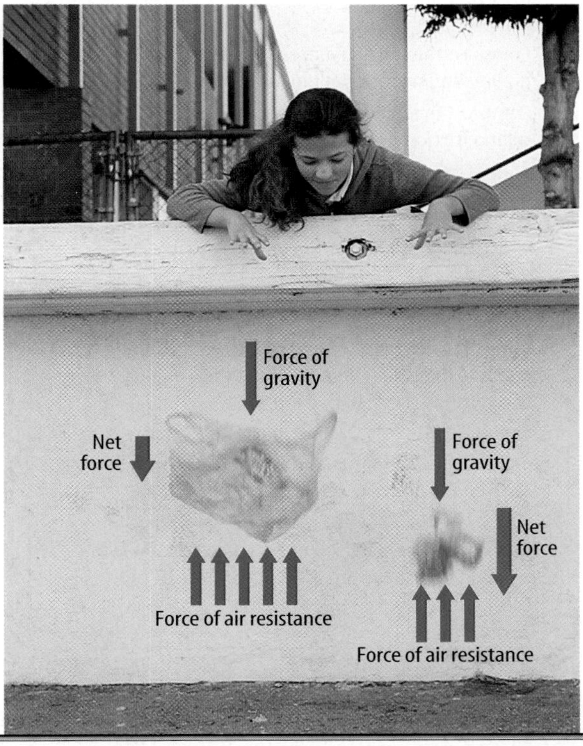

Figure 17 Because the bag on the left has a greater surface area, the bag on the left has more air resistance acting on it as it falls.

Activity

Air Resistance Have students show how air resistance affects the way an object falls by making a parachute out of string and cloth and attaching it to a small object. Suggest that students compare the rates at which the object falls when it is attached to the parachute and when it is not. L1 ELL LS **Kinesthetic**

Inquiry Lab

Controlling Motion

Purpose To design a device that will control the motion of a marble and keep it in motion for exactly 3 min

Possible Materials Students will choose their own materials. Suggestions: cardboard sheets, cardboard tubes, pizza delivery boxes, plastic tubing

Estimated Time 2 class periods; outside class time may be required.

Teaching Strategies

- Divide the class into small groups. Students can use a variety of schemes to keep their marble in motion. The goal is to keep the marble in motion exactly 3 min, so the students will have to fine-tune their device. Encourage students to use gravity, springs, catapults, mouse traps, etc. to make their device fun.

For additional inquiry activities, see Science Inquiry Lab Manual.

Post Reading

Graphic Organizer Using the terms *balanced and unbalanced forces, friction,* and *air resistance* as central themes, have students develop a concept map with branches to words or ideas that provide details and explanations. Allow students to use illustrations to augment their chart.

Active Reading

ReQuest Have students listen carefully as you read an interesting story or newsworthy item aloud. After the reading, students, alone or in groups, can formulate questions to discuss. Have students participate in a ReQuest related to friction, air resistance, or terminal velocity.

Science Journal

Falling Objects Have students describe in their Science Journals how the velocity and acceleration of an object change as it falls from a tall building. Initially, velocity increases causing the air resistance force to increase until it equals the force of gravity. The velocity is then constant and acceleration is zero until the object hits the ground. L2 LS **Logical-Mathematical**

Discussion

Terminal Velocity What happens to an object's velocity and acceleration when the object reaches terminal velocity? The object's velocity remains constant, so its acceleration is zero.

3 Assess

DAILY INTERVENTION

Check for Understanding

Kinesthetic Have (or draw on the board) three boxes that are the same size but have different masses. Ask how the students could tell which is heaviest without actually picking it up. You could push it along the floor. If the boxes are made from the same material so that the frictional force varies only with the weight of the box, the most difficult to push is the heaviest.

Reteach

Friction Have students demonstrate how rolling friction is less than sliding friction by pulling a rubber band attached to a toy car. If the car is pulled on its wheels, the rubber band barely extends. If the car is pulled on its top, the rubber band extends much more. L2 ELL IS **Kinesthetic**

✔ Assessment

Oral Have students work in small groups to discuss various sports they enjoy. They should explain how static, sliding, and rolling friction are important for the sport. Use **PASC,** p. 89.

Figure 18 When the sky diver reaches terminal velocity, the force due to air resistance balances the force due to gravity.

Terminal Velocity As an object falls, the downward force of gravity causes the object to accelerate. For example, after falling 2,000 m, without the effects of air resistance a skydiver's speed would be almost 200 m/s, or more than 700 km/h.

However, as the speed of a falling object increases, the upward force of air resistance also increases. This causes the net force on a sky diver to decrease as the sky diver falls. Finally, the upward air resistance force becomes large enough to balance the downward force of gravity. The net force on the object is zero, and the velocity of the object doesn't change. The object falls with a constant velocity called the terminal velocity. The terminal velocity is the highest velocity the falling object will reach.

The terminal velocity depends on the size, shape, and mass of the falling object. The air resistance force on an open parachute, like the one in **Figure 18,** is much larger than the air resistance on the a sky diver with a closed parachute. With the parachute open, the terminal velocity of the sky diver becomes small enough that the sky diver can land safely.

section 3 review

Summary

Balanced and Unbalanced Forces

- A force is a push or a pull that one object exerts on another object.
- The net force on an object is the combination of all the forces acting on the object.
- When the net force on an object is zero, the forces acting on the object are balanced.
- When the net force on an object is not zero, the forces acting on the object are unbalanced.
- Unbalanced forces cause the velocity of an object to change.

Friction

- Friction is the force that opposes motion between two surfaces that are touching each other.
- Friction depends on the types of surfaces and the force pressing the surfaces together.
- Static friction prevents surfaces that are in contact from sliding past each other.

Air Resistance

- Air resistance is a force that acts on objects that move through the air.

Self Check

1. **Explain** why the frictional force between two surfaces increases when the force pushing the surfaces together increases.
2. **Compare** the force of air resistance and the force of gravity on an object falling at its terminal velocity.
3. **Compare** the size of forces due to static, sliding, and rolling friction between two surfaces.
4. **Think Critically** What is the net force on a car stopped at a stop sign? What is the net force on a car moving in a straight line with a constant speed?

Applying Math

5. **Calculate Net Force** Two students push on a box in the same direction, and another pushes on the box in the opposite direction. What is the net force on the box if each pushes with a force of 50 N?
6. **Calculate Sliding Friction** You push a box with a force of 80 N. If the net force on the box is 50 N, what is the force on the box due to sliding friction?
7. **Calculate Acceleration** The downward force of gravity and the upward force of air resistance on a falling ball are both 5 N. What is the ball's acceleration?

 More Section Review gpescience.com

section 3 review

1. The contact area between the surfaces increases and more microwelds are formed.
2. The two forces are equal and in opposite directions.
3. Static is greater than sliding which is greater than rolling.
4. The net force is 0 N in both cases.
5. 50 N in the direction the two students are pushing.
6. 30 N in the opposite direction of the 80 N force.
7. 0 m/s^2 (Net force is 0 N.)

LAB

Force AND ACCELERATION

If you stand at a stoplight, you will see cars stopping for red lights and then taking off when the light turns green. What makes the cars slow down? What makes them speed up? How do balanced and unbalanced forces affect the acceleration of objects?

Real-World Problem

How does an unbalanced force affect the motion of an object?

Goals

- **Observe** how changing the net force on an object affects its acceleration.
- **Interpret** data collected for several trials.

Materials

tape	this science book
paper clip	triple-beam balance
10-N spring scale	**electronic balance*
large book	**Alternate materials*

Safety Precautions

Proper eye protection should be worn at all times while performing this lab.

Procedure

1. Tie the string around the book and attach the paper clip to the string.
2. Prepare a data table with the following headings: *Force, Mass.*
3. If available, use a large balance to find the mass of the two books.
4. Place the book on the floor or on the surface of a long table. Use the paper clip to hook the spring scale to the book.

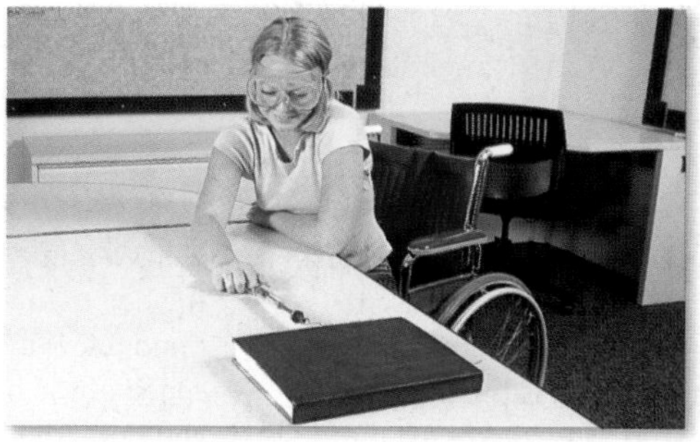

5. Pull the book across the floor or table at a slow but constant velocity. While pulling, read the force measured by the spring scale and record it in your data table.
6. Repeat step 5 two more times, once accelerating slowly and once accelerating quickly. Be careful not to pull too hard. Your spring scale will read only up to 10 N.
7. Place a second book on top of the first book and repeat steps 3 through 6.

Conclude and Apply

1. **Organize** the pulling forces from greatest to least for each set of trials. What is the relationship between the net force and the acceleration of the book?
2. **Explain** how adding the second book changed your results.

Communicating Your Data

Compare your conclusions with those of other students in your class.

BENCH TESTED

Video Lab available for this Lab.

Real-World Problem

Purpose Students will observe the relationship between mass, force, and acceleration. L2

Process Skills observe, compare, infer

Time Required 40 minutes

Procedure

Safety Precautions Students should wear safety goggles while this activity is in progress.

Teaching Strategy Remind students that the spring scale only reads up to 10 N, so they must not pull too hard.

Conclude and Apply

1. As force increased, so did the acceleration.
2. When the second book was added, the force should have increased. If the second book has approximately the same mass as the first book, the force should have doubled.

Communicating Your Data

Have students discuss with one another any differences in their results and possible reasons for the differences.

Assessment

Process Ask students to infer how the pulling force would change if a book with less mass were pulled. Less force would be required. How would it be different if three of the science books were pulled? More force would be required. Use **Performance Assessment in the Science Classroom,** p. 89. L2

LAB Design Your Own

Comparing Motion from Different Forces

Goals
- **Identify** several forces that you can use to propel a small toy car across the floor.
- **Demonstrate** the motion of the toy car using each of the forces.
- **Graph** the position versus time for each force.
- **Compare** the motion of the toy car resulting from each force.

Possible Materials
small toy car
ramps or boards of different lengths
springs or rubber bands
string
stopwatch
meterstick or tape measure
graph paper

Safety Precautions

Real-World Problem

Think about a small ball. How many ways could you exert a force on the ball to make it move? You could throw it, kick it, roll it down a ramp, blow it with a large fan, etc. Do you think the distance and speed of the ball's motion will be the same for all of these forces? Do you think the acceleration of the ball would be the same for all of these types of forces?

Form a Hypothesis

Based on your reading and observations, state a hypothesis about how a force can be applied that will cause a toy car to go fastest.

Test Your Hypothesis

Make a Plan

1. As a group, agree upon the hypothesis and decide how you will test it. Identify which results will confirm the hypothesis that you have written.
2. **List** the steps you will need to test your hypothesis. Be sure to include a control run. Be specific. Describe exactly what you will do in each step. List your materials.
3. **Prepare** a data table in your Science Journal to record your observations.

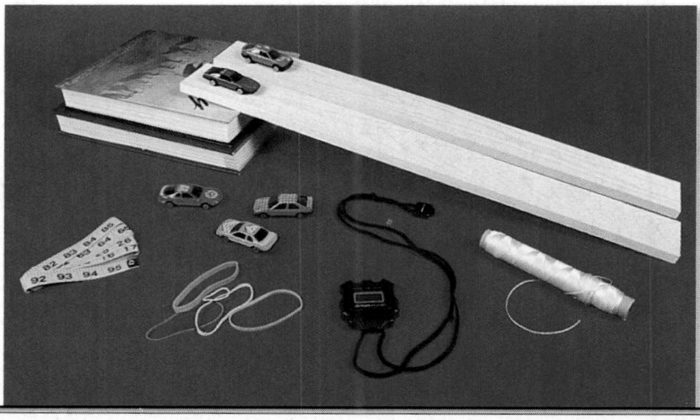

BENCH TESTED

Real-World Problem

Purpose Demonstrate how the motion of a toy car is affected by different forces. L2 LS **Kinesthetic**

Process Skills form a hypothesis, design an experiment, separate and control variables, interpret data, measure, use numbers, observe, infer, compare and contrast, recognize cause and effect, communicate, make and use tables, make and use graphs

Time Required 30 minutes to plan the experiment and 45 minutes to make measurements and graph data

Possible Materials Try small springs from molecular model sets to propel the cars by flipping one end of the spring against the car while holding the other end securely.

Use thin springs with loose windings so that they can be easily retracted and released to push the car forward. The string can be used to sharply tug the car. Rubber bands can be used, but they will provide less momentum.

Data Table:

Force Used	Distance	Time	Speed
1			
2			
3			
4			

Form a Hypothesis

Possible Hypothesis Students might hypothesize that the force of the spring will cause the car to go fastest.

Alternative Inquiry Lab

Real-World Connection To make the lab an inquiry lab, give the students more personal investment into the problem by connecting it to the real world. Tell the students that they are designing a race track for a new type of car racing. They are to design a new race track that will allow stock cars to break speed records in racing. Students should consider safe but innovative ways to increase the speeds of the race cars. L2

Using Scientific Methods

4. **Read** the entire experiment to make sure all steps are in logical order and will lead to a useful conclusion.
5. **Identify** all constants, variables, and controls of the experiment. Keep in mind that you will need to have measurements at multiple points. These points are needed to graph your results. You should make sure to have several data points taken after you stop applying the force and before the car starts to slow down. It might be useful to have several students taking measurements, making each responsible for one or two points.

Follow Your Plan

1. Make sure your teacher approves your plan before you start.
2. Carry out the experiment as planned.
3. While doing the experiment, record your observations and complete the data tables in your Science Journal.

Analyze Your Data

1. **Graph** the position of the car versus time for each of the forces you applied. How can you use the graphs to compare the speeds of the toy car?
2. **Calculate** the speed of the toy car over the same time interval for each of the forces that you applied. How do the speeds compare?

Conclude and Apply

1. **Evaluate** Did the speed of the toy car vary depending upon the force applied to it?
2. **Determine** For any particular force, did the speed of the toy car change over time? If so, how did the speed change? Describe how you can use your graphs to answer these questions.
3. **Draw Conclusions** Did your results support your hypothesis? Why or why not?

Communicating Your Data

Compare your data with those of other students. **Discuss** how the forces you applied might be different from those others applied and how that affected your results.

Test Your Hypothesis

Possible Procedures Position students with stopwatches at points along a track to determine when the car reaches that point. One student will provide the initial force to the car by releasing a spring against it, tugging it with a string, etc.

Teaching Strategy Encourage students to provide a sufficient force to enable the car to travel the entire length of the track they have made.

Expected Outcome Although results will vary greatly, students should be able to determine the average speed of the car for each force.

Analyze Your Data

1. Some graphs will show a slight increase in speed. Others will show a decrease in speed.
2. Students should calculate the average speed using $v = d/t$.

Error Analysis Ask students to compare their results with other groups and discuss ways the differences could be minimized.

Conclude and Apply

1. yes
2. Answers will vary.
3. Answers will depend on student hypotheses.

Assessment

Process Ask students to draw diagrams showing how fiction, gravity, and inertia influenced the motion of the car. Use **Performance Assessment in the Science Classroom,** p. 127. L2

Communicating Your Data

Have students use graphics software to prepare a poster explaining their experiment and the results. Posters should contain sketches showing forces on the car. They might also include graphs of the data. L2

Understanding Literature

Descriptive Writing Angelou is telling us that the power that people have to make changes for better lives is more significant than the universe and the special places people have built on Earth.

Respond to the Reading

1. small, lonely, miniscule, kithless, wayward, floating
2. people
3. **Linking Science and Writing** Remind students that the Moon revolves around Earth. Therefore, their poems should describe how the Moon might see the Sun come and go as it moves around Earth.

INTEGRATE Physics **Motion** In the Middle Ages, most people thought Earth stood still and that the sky moved around Earth. It is now known that the daily movement of the stars is due to Earth's rotation on its axis. At the same time that Earth rotates, it revolves about the Sun. Earth follows the Sun in its wanderings through the heavens. The Sun revolves around the center of the Milky Way. Earth, a satellite of the Sun, takes part in this journey.

Science and Language Arts

"A Brave and Startling Truth"

by Maya Angelou

We, this people, on a small and lonely planet
Traveling through casual space
Past aloof stars, across the way of indifferent suns
To a destination where all signs tell us
It is possible and imperative that we learn
A brave and startling truth …

When we come to it
Then we will confess that not the Pyramids
With their stones set in mysterious perfection …
Not the Grand Canyon
Kindled into delicious color
By Western sunsets
These are not the only wonders of the world …

When we come to it
We, this people, on this minuscule and kithless[1] globe …
We this people on this mote[2] of matter

When we come to it
We, this people, on this wayward[3], floating body
Created on this earth, of this earth
Have the power to fashion for this earth
A climate where every man and every woman
Can live freely without sanctimonious piety[4]
Without crippling fear

When we come to it
We must confess that we are the possible
We are the miraculous, the true wonder of the world
That is when, and only when
We come to it.

Understanding Literature

Descriptive Writing The poet names some special places on Earth. These places, although marvelous, fall short of being really wonderful. How does Angelou contrast Earth's position within the universe to emphasize the importance of people?

Respond to the Reading

1. What adjectives does the poet use to describe Earth?
2. What does the poet believe are the true wonders of the world?
3. **Linking Science and Writing** Write a six-line poem that describes Earth's movement from the point of view of the Moon.

INTEGRATE Physics Sometimes a person doesn't need to see movement to know that something has moved. Even though we don't necessarily see Earth's movement, we know Earth moves relative to a reference point such as the Sun. If the Sun is the reference point, Earth moves because the Sun appears to change its position in the sky. The poem describes Earth's movement from a reference point outside of Earth, somewhere in space.

1 to be without friends or neighbors
2 small particle
3 wanting one's own way in spite of the advice or wishes of another
4 a self-important show of being religious

Resources for Teachers and Students

"On the Pulse of Morning" from *The Complete Collected Poems of Maya Angelou*, Maya Angelou, Random House, Inc., 1994

Space Travel, edited by Ben Bova with Anthony R. Lewis, Writer's Digest Books, 1997

Roller Coaster, by David Bennett, Chartwell Books, 1998

Reviewing Main Ideas

Section 1 Describing Motion

1. Motion is a change of position of a body. Distance is the measure of how far an object moved. Displacement is the distance and direction of an object's change in position from the starting point.
2. A reference point must be specified in order to determine an object's position.
3. The average speed of an object can be calculated from this equation:

$$\bar{v} = \frac{d}{t}$$

4. Velocity is a vector that includes the speed and direction of a moving object.
5. The slope of a line on a distance-time graph is equal to the speed.

Section 2 Acceleration

1. Acceleration occurs when an object changes speed or changes direction.
2. An object speeds up if its acceleration is in the direction of its motion.
3. An object slows down if its acceleration is opposite to the direction of its motion.
4. Acceleration is the rate of change of velocity, and is calculated from this equation:

$$\bar{a} = \frac{v_f - v_i}{(t_f - t_i)}$$

Section 3 Motion and Forces

1. A force is a push or a pull.
2. The net force acting on an object is the combination of all the forces acting on the object.
3. The forces on an object are balanced if the net force is zero.
4. Sliding friction is a force opposing the sliding motion of two surfaces in contact. Static friction prevents surfaces in contact from sliding past each other.
5. Air resistance opposes the motion of objects that move in the air.

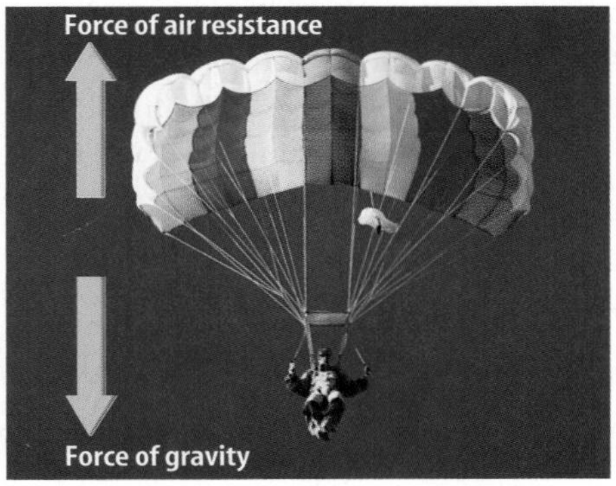

FOLDABLES Use the Foldable that you made at the beginning of this chapter to help you review motion.

Identifying Misconceptions

Assess

After students have done the activity on page F and completed the chapter, perform this activity.

Materials protractor, paper, ruler, string

Procedure Have each student use the protractor to draw a large circle and label four points 90 degrees apart *A*, *B*, *C* and *D*. Have them place an object at point A. Their mission is to find the object's distance traveled and displacement at points B, C and D as it travels around the circle.

Expected Outcome Use the string to measure the circle or use the formula $c = 2\pi r$. L2

chapter 3 Study Guide

Reviewing Main Ideas

Summary statements can be used by students to review the major concepts of the chapter.

Science Online

Visit gpescience.com
More Section Review
Interactive Tutor
Vocabulary PuzzleMaker
More Chapter Review
Standardized Test Practice

Assessment Transparency

For additional assessment questions, use the *Assessment Transparency* located in the transparency book.

Assessment

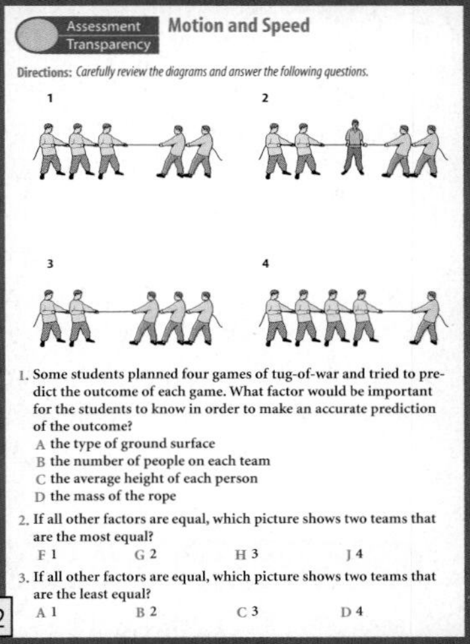
Assessment Transparency **Motion and Speed**

Directions: *Carefully review the diagrams and answer the following questions.*

1 2 3 4

1. Some students planned four games of tug-of-war and tried to predict the outcome of each game. What factor would be important for the students to know in order to make an accurate prediction of the outcome?
   A the type of ground surface
   B the number of people on each team
   C the average height of each person
   D the mass of the rope
2. If all other factors are equal, which picture shows two teams that are the most equal?
   F 1 G 2 H 3 J 4
3. If all other factors are equal, which picture shows two teams that are the least equal?
   A 1 B 2 C 3 D 4

L2

Motion and Speed

FOLDABLES Have students use their Foldables to review the content of the chapter. On the back, have them write five facts they have learned about motion.

Using Vocabulary

1. Both tell how distance changes with time. Velocity includes the direction.
2. Displacement is distance and direction from a starting point. Distance is the length of the path followed by the object.
3. Both describe rate of change in position. Average speed refers to total distance traveled divided by total time elapsed. Instantaneous speed refers to speed at a given point in time.
4. Balanced forces are forces on an object that cancel each other out. Net force is the sum of all forces acting on an object.
5. Velocity is the speed and direction of an object. Acceleration is how the velocity changes with time.
6. Velocity is the speed and direction of an object. Instantaneous speed is how fast an object moves at a given point in time.
7. Both are forces that oppose the motion of surfaces that are touching each other. Static friction is the force between two surfaces that are not moving relative to one another. Sliding friction is the force opposing the motion of one surface as it slides over another surface.
8. Both are forces that tend to oppose motion. Friction is between surfaces. Air resistance is the force acting to oppose the motion of an object as it moves through air.

Checking Concepts

9. A
10. B
11. C
12. B
13. A
14. C
15. C

Using Vocabulary

acceleration p. 76
air resistance p. 85
average speed p. 72
balanced forces p. 82
displacement p. 71
force p. 81
friction p. 83
instantaneous speed p. 71
net force p. 82
sliding friction p. 84
speed p. 71
static friction p. 84
unbalanced forces p. 82
vector p. 71
velocity p. 72

Compare and contrast the following pairs of vocabulary words.

1. speed—velocity
2. distance—displacement
3. average speed—instantaneous speed
4. balanced force—net force
5. acceleration—velocity
6. velocity—instantaneous speed
7. static friction—sliding friction
8. friction—air resistance

Checking Concepts

Choose the word or phrase that best answers the question.

9. Which of the following do you calculate when you divide the total distance traveled by the total travel time?
   A) average speed
   B) constant speed
   C) variable speed
   D) instantaneous speed

10. Which term below best describes the forces on an object with a net force of zero?
   A) inertia
   B) balanced forces
   C) acceleration
   D) unbalanced forces

11. Which of the following is a proper unit of acceleration?
   A) s/km^2
   B) km/h
   C) m/s^2
   D) cm/s

12. Which of the following is not used in calculating acceleration?
   A) initial velocity
   B) average speed
   C) time interval
   D) final velocity

13. In which of the following conditions does the car NOT accelerate?
   A) A car moves at 80 km/h on a flat, straight highway.
   B) The car slows from 80 km/h to 35 km/h.
   C) The car turns a corner.
   D) The car speeds up from 35 km/h to 80 km/h.

14. What is the slope of a line on a distance-time graph?
   A) displacement
   B) force
   C) speed
   D) acceleration

15. How can speed be defined?
   A) acceleration/time
   B) change in velocity/time
   C) distance/time
   D) displacement/time

Interpreting Graphics

Use the table below to answer question 16.

Distance-Time for Runners

Time (s)	1	2	3	4
Sally's distance (m)	2	4	6	8
Alonzo's distance (m)	1	2	2	4

16. **Graph** the motion of both runners on a distance-time graph. What is the average speed of each runner? Which runner stops briefly? Over what time interval do they both have the same speed?

Vocabulary PuzzleMaker gpescience.com

Use the ExamView® Pro Test Bank CD-ROM to:

- create multiple versions of tests
- create modified tests with one mouse click for inclusion students
- edit existing questions and add your own questions
- build tests aligned with state standards using built-in State Curriculum Tags
- change English tests to Spanish with one mouse click and vice versa

17. Copy and complete this concept map on motion.

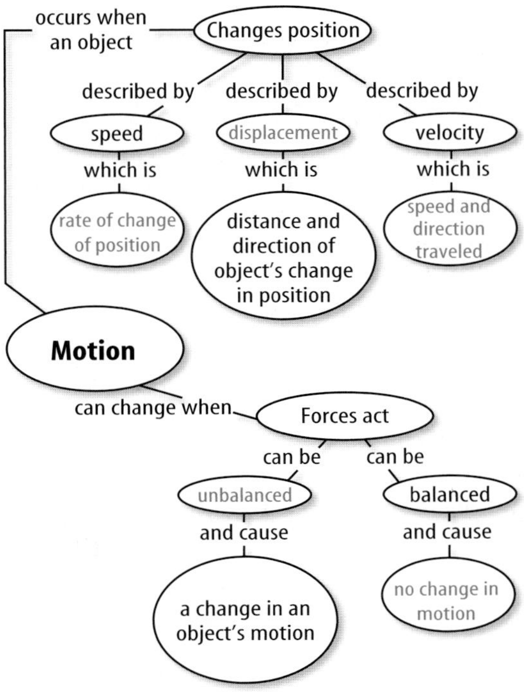

Thinking Critically

18. **Evaluate** Which of the following represents the greatest speed: 20 m/s, 200 cm/s, or 0.2 km/s?

19. **Describe** a line on a distance-time graph representing an object that is not moving.

20. **Infer** You push a book on a table so that its velocity is constant. If the force you apply is 15 N, what is the force due to sliding friction?

21. **Determine** If you walked 20 m, took a book from a library table, turned around and walked back to your seat, what are the distance traveled and displacement?

22. **Explain** When you are describing the rate that a race car goes around a track, should you use the term *speed* or *velocity* to describe the motion?

Applying Math

23. **Calculate Speed** A cyclist must travel 800 km. How many days will the trip take if the cyclist travels 8 h/day at an average speed of 16 km/h?

24. **Calculate Acceleration** A satellite's speed is 10,000 m/s. After 1 min, it is 5,000 m/s. What is the satellite's acceleration?

25. **Calculate Displacement** A cyclist leaves home and rides due east for a distance of 45 km. She returns home on the same bike path. If the entire trip takes 4 h, what is her average speed? What is her displacement?

26. **Calculate Velocity** The return trip of the cyclist in question 13 took 30 min longer than her trip east, although her total time was still 4 h. What was her velocity in each direction?

Use the graph below to answer question 27.

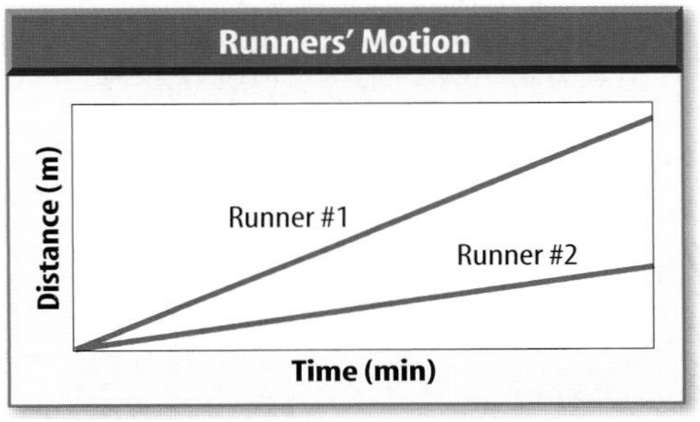

27. **Interpret a Graph** Use the graph to determine which runner had the greatest speed.

Assessment Resources

Reproducible Masters

Chapter *Fast File* Resources
Chapter Review, pp. 39–40
Chapter Tests, pp. 41–44
Assessment Transparency Activity, p. 51

Glencoe Science Web site
Chapter Review Test
Standardized Test Practice

Glencoe Technology
Assessment Transparency
Exam*View*® Pro Testmaker
MindJogger Videoquiz
Interactive Chalkboard

Interpreting Graphics

16. Sally's average speed is 2 m/s and Alonzo's is 1 m/s. Alonzo stops briefly; they run at the same speed from 3 s to 4 s.

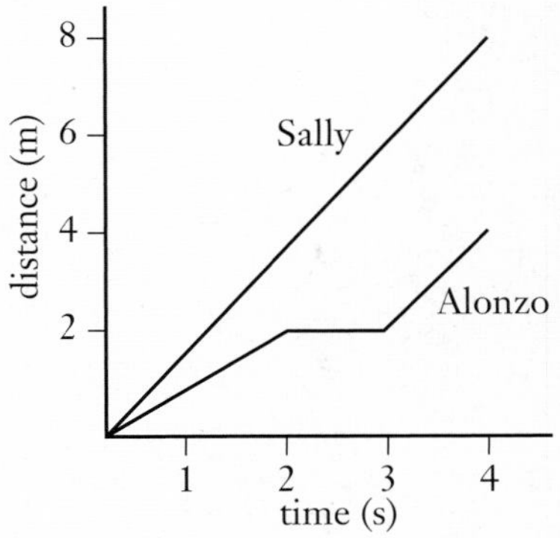

17. See student page.

Thinking Critically

18. 0.2 km/s
19. The line would be horizontal.
20. 15 N
21. distance traveled, 40 m; displacement, 0 m
22. Speed, because the velocity is constantly changing due to the constant change of direction.

Applying Math

Math Standards

National: 1, 2, 9

23. time = 800 km/16km/h = 50 h; at 8 h/day, total time is 6 days 2 hours
24. about $-83.3\ m/s^2$
25. 22.5 km/h; displacement is 0 km
26. Time there is 1.75 hours; time back is 2.25 hours; velocity there is 25.7 km/h; velocity back is 20 km/h.
27. Runner 1 because of the greater slope on the graph.

Answer Sheet An answer sheet can be found at **gpescience.com**.

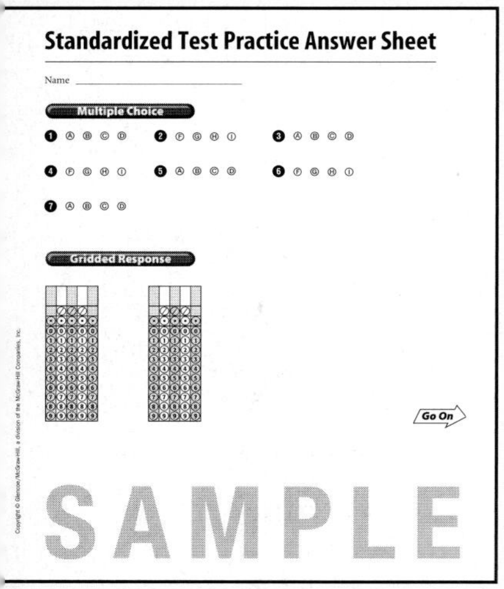
Standardized Test Practice Answer Sheet

Name

Multiple Choice

Gridded Response

Go On

SAMPLE

Multiple Choice

1. B
2. C
3. C
4. B
5. A
6. C
7. B
8. C

chapter 3 Standardized Test Practice

Record your answers on the answer sheet provided by your teacher or on a sheet of paper.

Multiple Choice

1. Sound travels at a speed of 330 m/s. How long does it take for the sound of thunder to travel 1,485 m?

A. 45 s

B. 4.5 s

C. 4,900 s

D. 0.22 s

Use the graph below to answer questions 2–4.

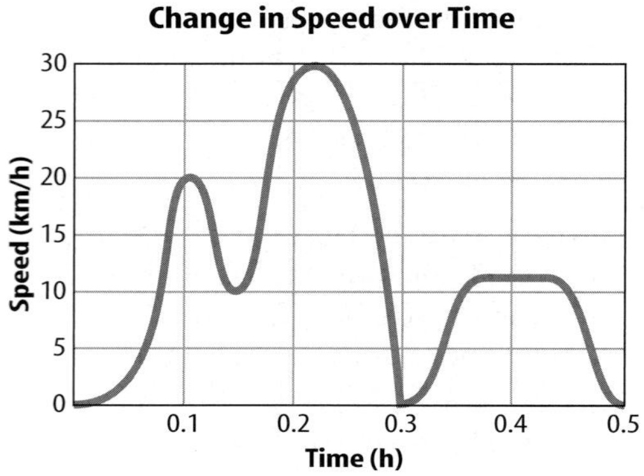

2. The graph shows how a cyclist's speed changed over 0.5 h. What is the cyclist's average speed if the trip was 6 km?

A. 3 km/h

B. 10 km/h

C. 12 km/h

D. 20 km/h

Test-Taking Tip

Read Carefully Read each question carefully for full understanding.

3. Once the trip was started, how many times did the cyclist stop?

A. 0

B. 4

C. 2

D. 5

4. What was the fastest speed the cyclist traveled?

A. 20 km/h

B. 30 km/h

C. 12 km/h

D. 10 km/h

Use the table below to answer questions 5 and 6.

Runner	Distance covered (km)	Time (min)
Daisy	12.5	42
Jane	7.8	38
Bill	10.5	32
Joe	8.9	30

5. What is Daisy's average speed?

A. 0.30 km/min

B. 530 km/min

C. 3.0 km/min

D. 3.4 km/min

6. Which runner has the fastest average speed?

A. Daisy

B. Jane

C. Bill

D. Joe

7. A skier is going down a hill at a speed of 9 m/s. The hill gets steeper and her speed increases to 18 m/s in 3 s. What is her acceleration?

A. 9 m/s^2

B. 3 m/s^2

C. 27 m/s^2

D. 6 m/s^2

8. Which of the following best describes an object with constant velocity?

A. It is changing direction.

B. Its acceleration is increasing.

C. Its acceleration is zero.

D. Its acceleration is negative.

Gridded Response

9. If a car is traveling at a speed of 40 km/h and then comes to a stop in 5 s, what is its acceleration in m/s^2?

Short Response

Use the table below to answer question10.

Car	Mass (kg)	Stopping Distance(m)
A	1,000	80
B	1,250	100
C	1,500	120
D	2,000	160

10. What is the relationship between a car's mass and its stopping distance?

11. If the speedometer on a car indicates a constant speed, can you be sure the car is not accelerating? Explain.

Extended Response

Use the graph below to answer question 12.

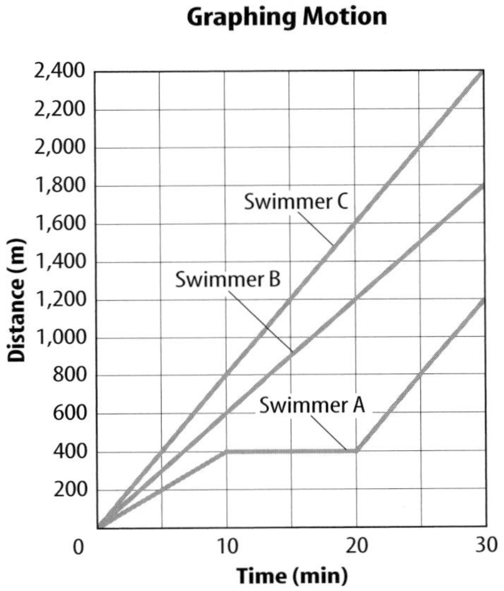

12. The graph shows the motion of three swimmers during a 30-min workout. Describe the motion of the three swimmers.

13. Where would you place the location of a reference point in order to describe the motion of a space probe traveling from Earth to Jupiter? Explain your choice.

Gridded Response

9. 2.2

Short Response

10. The greater the mass of the car, the greater the stopping distance.

11. No, because the car could be accelerating if it is changing direction.

Extended Response

12. Swimmer A swam at a constant rate of 40 m/min for 10 min., rested for 10 min., then swam at a constant rate of 80 m/min for 10 min. Swimmer B swam at a constant rate of 60m/min for 30 min. Swimmer C swam at a constant rate of 80m/min for 30 min.

13. Possible answer: at the Sun, because Earth and Jupiter move with respect to the Sun

Rubrics

For more help evaluating Short- and Extended-Response questions, see the rubrics on p. 9T.

chapter 4 Organizer

Section/Objectives	Standards: National	Standards: State/Local	Labs/Features
Chapter Opener	See pp. 16T–17T for a Key to Standards.		**Launch Lab:** The Force of Gravity, p. 97 **Foldables,** p. 97
Section 1 The First Two Laws of Motion 2 sessions 1 block 1. **Define** Newton's first law of motion. 2. **Explain** how inertia and mass are related. 3. **Define** Newton's second law of motion. 4. **Apply** Newton's second law of motion.	National Content Standards: UCP.1–3, UCP.5, A.1, A.2, B.2, B.4		**MiniLAB:** Observing Inertia, p. 99 **Science Online,** p. 101 **Applying Math:** The Acceleration of a Sled, p. 102
Section 2 Gravity 2 sessions 1 block 5. **Describe** the gravitational force. 6. **Distinguish** between mass and weight. 7. **Explain** why objects that are thrown will follow a curved path. 8. **Compare** circular motion with motion in a straight line.	National Content Standards: UCP.1–3, UCP.5, A.1, A.2, B.4		**Science Online,** p. 105 **Integrate Earth Science,** p. 108 **MiniLAB:** Observing Centripetal Force, p. 110 **Lab:** Gravity and Air Resistance, p. 112
Section 3 The Third Law of Motion 2 sessions 1 block 9. **State** Newton's third law of motion. 10. **Identify** action and reaction forces. 11. **Calculate** momentum. 12. **Recognize** when momentum is conserved.	National Content Standards: UCP.1–3, UCP.5, A.1, A.2, B.4		**Integrate Career,** p. 114 **Visualizing Rocket Motion,** p. 115 **Applying Math:** The Momentum of a Sprinter, p. 116 **Lab:** The Momentum of Colliding Objects, pp. 118–119 Video Lab **Science and History:** Newton and the Plague, p. 120

StudentWorks Plus

Glencoe Exclusive! TeacherWorks™ All-In-One Planner and Resource Center

Lab Materials	Reproducible Resources	Section Assessment	Technology
Launch Lab: stopwatch, softball, tennis ball, a piece of crumpled paper, a flat sheet of paper, meterstick	**Chapter *Fast File* Resources** Foldables Worksheet, p. 17 Directed Reading Overview, p. 19 Note-taking Worksheets, pp. 33–35	Glencoe's Assessment Advantage	TeacherWorks includes: • Interactive Teacher Edition • Lesson Planner with calendar • Access to all program blacklines • Correlations to standards • Web links
MiniLAB: board, textbooks, small cart, small object, rubber bands	**Chapter *Fast File* Resources** Transparency Activity, p. 44 MiniLAB, p. 3 Enrichment, p. 30 Reinforcement, p. 27 Directed Reading, p. 20 **Reading and Writing Skill Activities**, p. 49	**Portfolio** Differental Instructions, p. 100 **Perfomance** MiniLAB, p. 99 Applying Math, p. 102 Applying Math, p. 103 **Content** Section Review, p. 103	Section Focus Transparency Teaching Transparency Interactive Chalkboard CD-ROM StudentWorks Plus
MiniLAB: string, meterstick, plastic slotted ball **Lab:** 4 equal-sized sheets of paper, scissors, meterstick, stopwatch, masking tape *Need materials?* Contact Science Kit at 1-800-828-7777 or www.sciencekit.com.	**Chapter *Fast File* Resources** Transparency Activity, p. 45 MiniLAB, p. 4 Enrichment, p. 31 Reinforcement, p. 28 Directed Reading, p. 21 Transparency Activity, pp. 47–48 Lab Worksheet, pp. 5–6 Lab Activity, pp. 9–12 **Life Science Critical Thinking/ Problem Solving,** p. 14 **Earth Science Critical Thinking/ Problem Solving,** p. 5 **Cultural Diversity,** p. 25	**Portfolio** Curriculumn Connection, p. 108 Reteach, p. 111 **Performance** MiniLAB, p. 110 Applying Math, p. 111 **Content** Section Review, p. 111	Section Focus Transparency Interactive Chalkboard CD-ROM StudentWorks Plus
Lab: meterstick, softball, racquetball, tennis ball, baseball, stopwatch, masking tape, balance	**Chapter *Fast File* Resources** Transparency Activity, p. 46 Enrichment, p. 32 Reinforcement, p. 29 Directed Reading, p. 22 Lab Worksheet, pp. 7–8 Lab Activity, pp. 13–16 **Home and Community Involvement,** p. 49	**Portfolio** Activity, p. 115 **Performance** Applying Math, p. 116 Applying Math, p. 117 **Content** Section Review, p. 117	Section Focus Transparency Virtual Labs CD-ROM Interactive Chalkboard CD-ROM StudentWorks Plus Video Lab

End of Chapter Assessment

Glencoe's Assessment Advantage

Blackline Masters	Technology	Professional Series
Chapter *Fast File* Resources Chapter Review, pp. 37–38 Chapter Tests, pp. 39–42 **Standardized Test Practice,** pp. 20–23	MindJogger Videoquiz Virtual Labs CD-ROM Exam*View*® Pro Testmaker TeacherWorks CD-ROM Interactive Chalkboard CD-ROM	**Performance Assessment in the Science Classroom (PASC)**

Transparencies

Section Focus

Section 1 Section Focus Transparency — Something He Could Sink His Teeth Into! — Chapter 4

In 1999, Krishna Gopal Shrivestava of India set an unverified world record by pulling a ship with a mass of 244,000 kg with his teeth! His efforts can teach us about force, mass, and acceleration.

1. What would happen if the man were pulling a small rowboat instead of a large ship?
2. When he stops pulling, will the ship stop moving? Explain.
3. What direction is the ship moving? Why?

L2

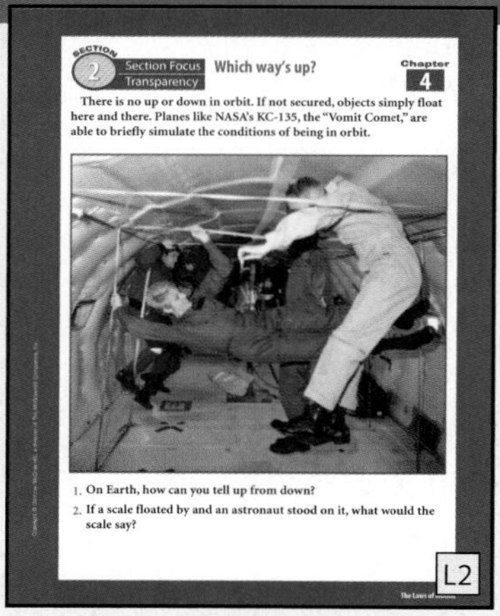
Section 2 Section Focus Transparency — Which way's up? — Chapter 4

There is no up or down in orbit. If not secured, objects simply float here and there. Planes like NASA's KC-135, the "Vomit Comet," are able to briefly simulate the conditions of being in orbit.

1. On Earth, how can you tell up from down?
2. If a scale floated by and an astronaut stood on it, what would the scale say?

L2

Section 3 Section Focus Transparency — Fighting Fire — Chapter 4

It takes more than one firefighter to aim a fire hose. The force of the water shooting out of the nozzle causes a reaction that can be difficult to control.

1. Describe what happens if you step from a canoe or small boat onto a dock.
2. Does a garden hose need more than one person to hold it? What's the difference between a garden hose and a fire hose?
3. What would happen if the firefighters dropped the hose?

L2

This is a representation of key blackline masters available in the Teacher Classroom Resources. See Resource Manager boxes within the chapter for additional information.

Assessment

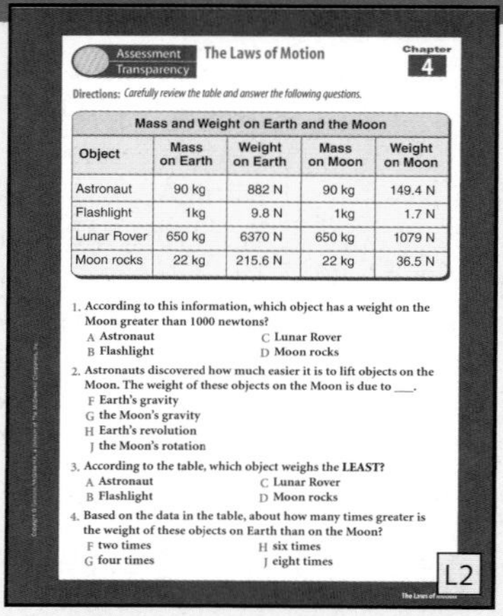
Assessment Transparency — The Laws of Motion — Chapter 4

Directions: *Carefully review the table and answer the following questions.*

Mass and Weight on Earth and the Moon

Object	Mass on Earth	Weight on Earth	Mass on Moon	Weight on Moon
Astronaut	90 kg	882 N	90 kg	149.4 N
Flashlight	1kg	9.8 N	1kg	1.7 N
Lunar Rover	650 kg	6370 N	650 kg	1079 N
Moon rocks	22 kg	215.6 N	22 kg	36.5 N

1. According to this information, which object has a weight on the Moon greater than 1000 newtons?
   A Astronaut C Lunar Rover
   B Flashlight D Moon rocks
2. Astronauts discovered how much easier it is to lift objects on the Moon. The weight of these objects on the Moon is due to ___.
   F Earth's gravity
   G the Moon's gravity
   H Earth's revolution
   J the Moon's rotation
3. According to the table, which object weighs the LEAST?
   A Astronaut C Lunar Rover
   B Flashlight D Moon rocks
4. Based on the data in the table, about how many times greater is the weight of these objects on Earth than on the Moon?
   F two times H six times
   G four times J eight times

L2

Teaching

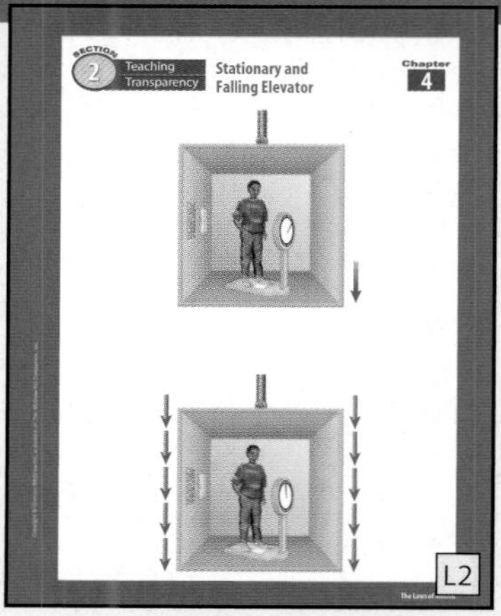
Section 2 Teaching Transparency — Stationary and Falling Elevator — Chapter 4

L2

Key to Teaching Strategies

The following designations will help you decide which activities are appropriate for your students.

- L1 Level 1 activities should be appropriate for students with learning difficulties.
- L2 Level 2 activities should be within the ability range of all students.
- L3 Level 3 activities are designed for above-average students.
- ELL ELL activities should be within the ability range of English Language Learners.
- COOP LEARN Cooperative Learning activities are designed for small group work.
- LS Multiple Learning Styles logos, as described on page 12T, are used throughout to indicate strategies that address different learning styles.
- P These strategies represent student products that can be placed into a best-work portfolio.
- PBL Problem-Based Learning activities apply real-world situations to learning.

Hands-on Activities

Student Text Lab Worksheet

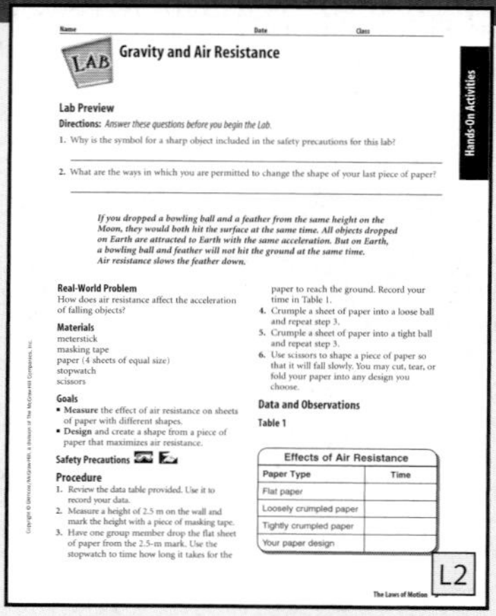
Name Date Class

LAB Gravity and Air Resistance

Hands-On Activities

Lab Preview

Directions: *Answer these questions before you begin the Lab.*

1. Why is the symbol for a sharp object included in the safety precautions for this lab?
2. What are the ways in which you are permitted to change the shape of your last piece of paper?

If you dropped a bowling ball and a feather from the same height on the Moon, they would both hit the surface at the same time. All objects dropped on Earth are attracted to Earth with the same acceleration. But on Earth, a bowling ball and feather will not hit the ground at the same time. Air resistance slows the feather down.

Real-World Problem
How does air resistance affect the acceleration of falling objects?

Materials
meterstick
masking tape
paper (4 sheets of equal size)
stopwatch
scissors

Goals
- **Measure** the effect of air resistance on sheets of paper with different shapes.
- **Design** and create a shape from a piece of paper that maximizes air resistance.

Safety Precautions

Procedure
1. Review the data table provided. Use it to record your data.
2. Measure a height of 2.5 m on the wall and mark the height with a piece of masking tape.
3. Have one group member drop the flat sheet of paper from the 2.5-m mark. Use the stopwatch to time how long it takes for the paper to reach the ground. Record your time in Table 1.
4. Crumple a sheet of paper into a loose ball and repeat step 3.
5. Crumple a sheet of paper into a tight ball and repeat step 3.
6. Use scissors to shape a piece of paper so that it will fall slowly. You may cut, tear, or fold your paper into any design you choose.

Data and Observations

Table 1

Effects of Air Resistance

Paper Type	Time
Flat paper	
Loosely crumpled paper	
Tightly crumpled paper	
Your paper design	

L2

The Laws of Motion

Laboratory Activities

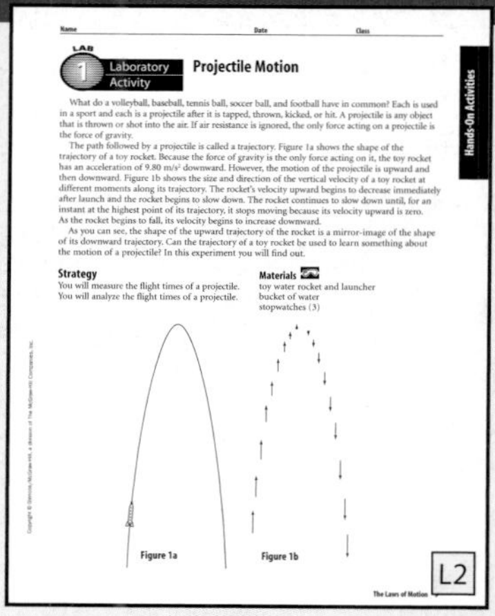
Name Date Class

LAB 1 Laboratory Activity — Projectile Motion

Hands-On Activities

What do a volleyball, baseball, tennis ball, soccer ball, and football have in common? Each is used in a sport and each is a projectile after it is tapped, thrown, kicked, or hit. A projectile is any object that is thrown or shot into the air. If air resistance is ignored, the only force acting on a projectile is the force of gravity.

The path followed by a projectile is called a trajectory. Figure 1a shows the shape of the trajectory of a toy rocket. Because the force of gravity is the only force acting on it, the toy rocket has an acceleration of 9.80 m/s^2 downward. However, the motion of the projectile is upward and then downward. Figure 1b shows the size and direction of the vertical velocity of a toy rocket at different moments along its trajectory. The rocket's velocity upward begins to decrease immediately after launch and the rocket begins to slow down. The rocket continues to slow down until, for an instant at the highest point of its trajectory, it stops moving because its velocity upward is zero. As the rocket begins to fall, its velocity begins to increase downward.

As you can see, the shape of the upward trajectory of the rocket is a mirror-image of the shape of its downward trajectory. Can the trajectory of a toy rocket be used to learn something about the motion of a projectile? In this experiment you will find out.

Strategy
You will measure the flight times of a projectile.
You will analyze the flight times of a projectile.

Materials
toy water rocket and launcher
bucket of water
stopwatches (3)

Figure 1a

Figure 1b

L2

The Laws of Motion

Meeting Different Ability Levels

Content Outline

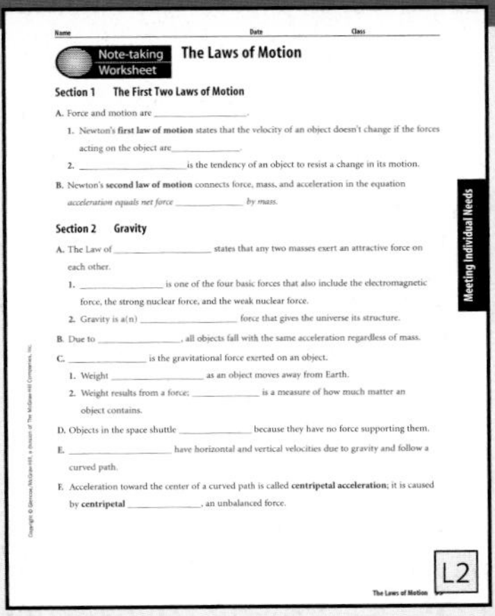

Reinforcement

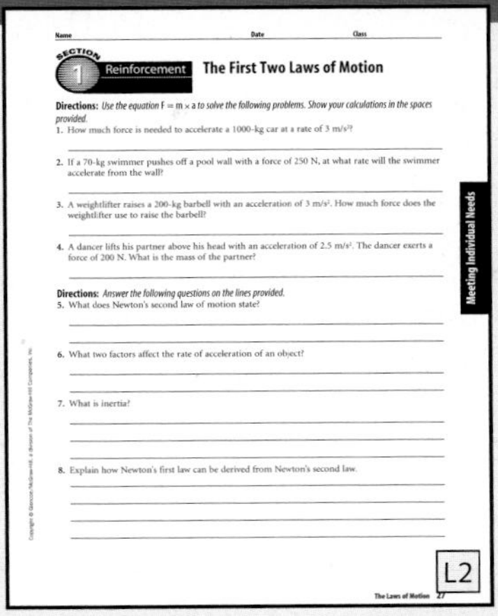

Enrichment

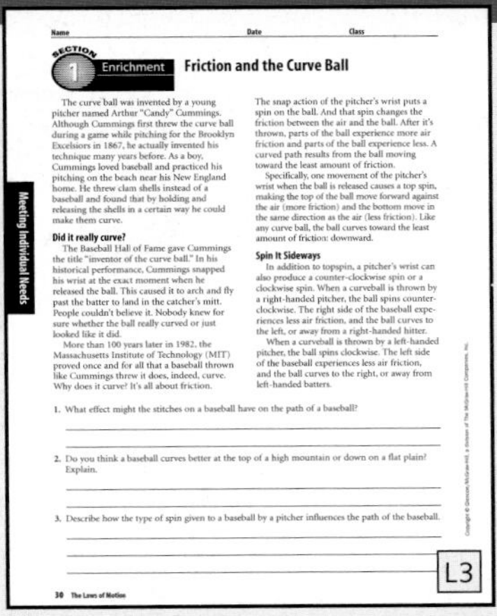

Directed Reading (English/Spanish)

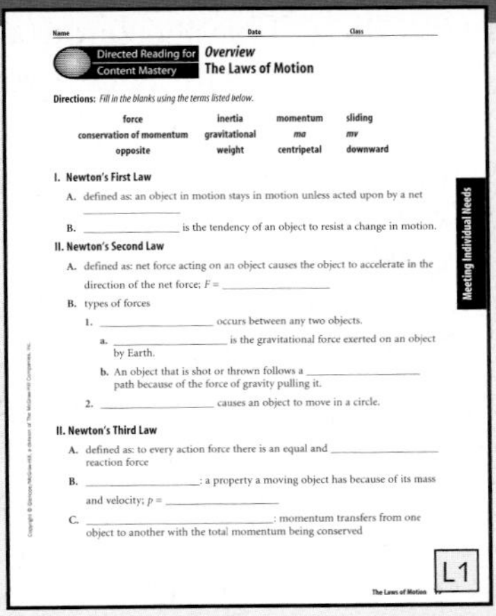

Study Guide

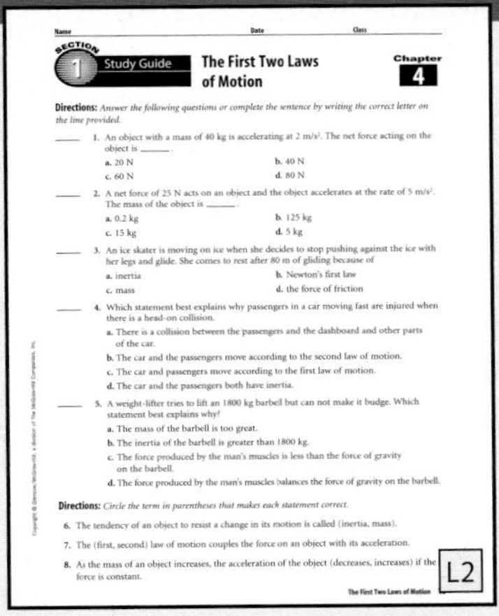

Reading Essentials

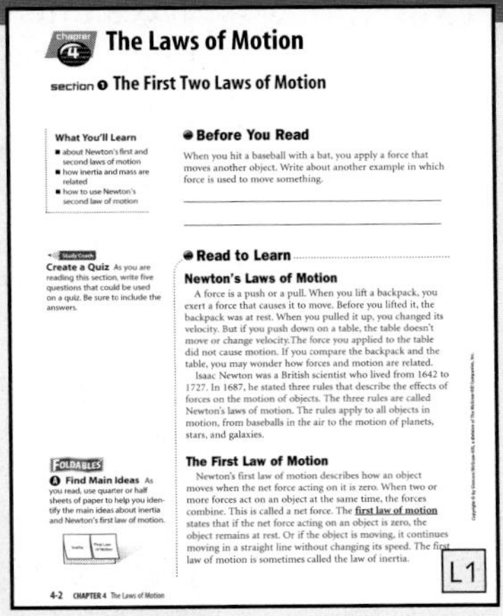

Assessment

Test Practice Workbook

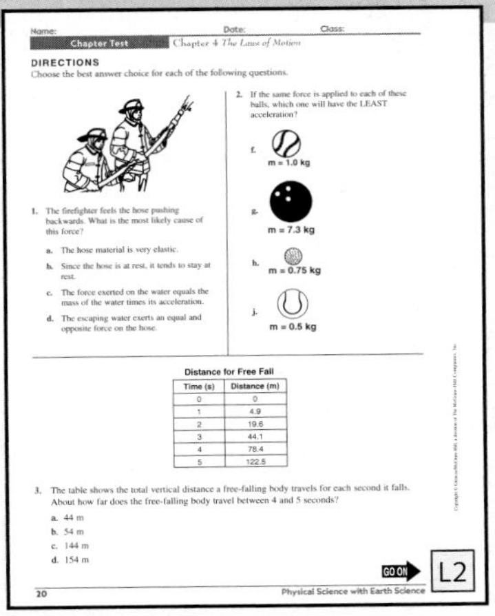

Chapter Review

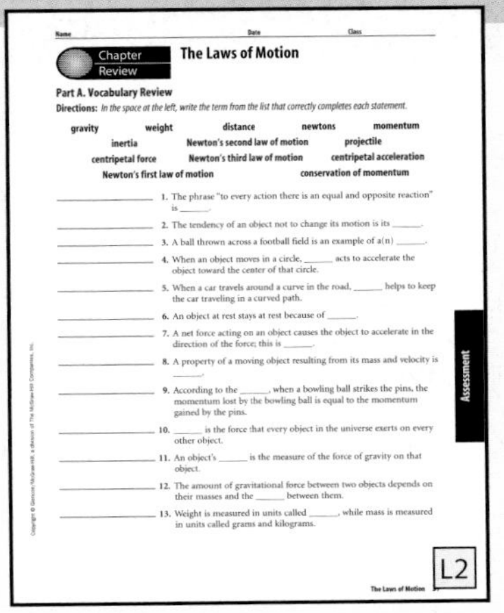

Chapter Tests

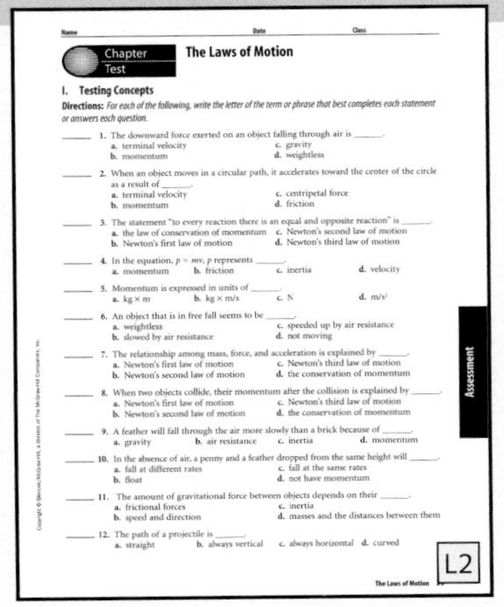

Science Content Background

section 1

The First Two Laws of Motion

Force, Mass, and Acceleration

Dynamics is the study of motion produced by forces. It comes from the Greek word *dynamis*, which means "strength or power." Words such as *dynamite* and *dynamo* share these origins.

Newton's Second Law

It follows from this law that if an object is accelerating, there must be a force acting on it. Engines produce forces to make cars positively accelerate. The brakes produce forces to cause negative acceleration. A planet moving with constant speed around a star is constantly changing direction and therefore is accelerating toward the star. This acceleration is due to the force of gravity between the star and the planet.

A force of one newton is equal to one kilogram meter per second squared ($1\ N = 1\ kg\ m/s^2$). Thus, when dividing force by mass, the kg units cancel, leaving the acceleration units of m/s^2.

section 2

Gravity

The Law of Gravitation

Newton described the gravitational force between two objects and the distance between them with the following equation: force of gravity = $G \times (mass_1) \times (mass_2) / (\text{distance between them})^2$. G is the universal gravitational constant. If the mass of one of the objects quadruples, the force of gravity quadruples. If the distance between the objects quadruples, the force of gravity is reduced by one-sixteenth.

Gravitational Acceleration

The average acceleration due to gravity on Earth is $9.8\ m/s^2$. This value varies slightly with location. In general the greater the distance from Earth's center, the lower the value, which means gravitational acceleration is smaller on a mountain than in a valley. The acceleration at the equator tends to be less than at the poles. This is because Earth is not a perfect sphere; its poles are somewhat pushed together. The acceleration due to gravity on Mercury is $3.8\ m/s^2$, while on Jupiter it is $22.9\ m/s^2$.

Newton's second law can be used to explain why all objects, regardless of mass, fall with the same acceleration due to gravity. Objects with a large mass have a greater gravitational force acting on them. However, although the force is great, so is the mass. These offset each other, causing all objects to fall with the same acceleration.

Centripetal Force

An object in circular motion is sometimes said

chapter content resources

Internet Resources

For additional content background, visit gpescience.com to:

- access your book online
- find references to related articles in popular science magazines
- access Web links with related content background
- access current events with science journal topics

Print Resources

Forces and Motion by Peter Lafferty, Raintree Steck-Vaughn Publishers, 2001

Science Projects About the Physics of Sports by Robert Gardner, Enslow Publishers, Inc., 2000

Gravity the Universal Force by Don Nardo, Lucent Books, 1990

Awesome Experiments in Force & Motion by Michael DiSpezio, Sterling Publishing Co., 1998 to be experiencing centrifugal force, which really doesn't exist. If you swing a bucket of water on a string, the water seems to be pushed outward, but this is due to the water's inertia. If tends to move in a straight-line motion while the bucket is pulled in by the centripetal force of the string. This causes the water to remain at the bottom of the bucket.

section 2 The Third Law of Motion

Newton's Third Law

The recoil of a rifle is an interesting application of Newton's laws. When fired, the rifle "kicks back" into the shoulder of the shooter. If the rifle hurts the shoulder, should the shooter use a more-massive or a less-massive gun? If the guns are firing the same bullets with the same accelerations, the more-massive gun will give less kickback. The recoil force will be the same, but the more-massive gun will not accelerate as much ($a = F/m$).

Finding Planets with Newton's Laws

Newton's third law is now being used to find planets in other solar systems. The planets are not directly seen, but their presence is inferred from the behavior of the stars in that solar system. More than 50 planets in other solar systems have been found this way.

Momentum

To hit a homerun, a softball player must impart the maximum momentum from his or her body and the bat to the ball. To do this, each player must find the bat that gives him or her the best combination of mass and speed. A heavier bat has more mass but the player may not be able to swing it as fast as a lighter bat.

A force applied over time, also called an impulse, can change momentum.The momentum change depends on the size of the net force acting on an object and the time over which the net force acts. A large force acting for a short time and a small force acting for a longer time can cause equal changes in momentum. The formula describing this relationship is $F \times t = m\ \Delta v$. In softball, following through on a swing can increase the amount of time the bat stays in contact with the ball, and this causes a greater velocity gain by the ball.

Teacher to Teacher
Sarah Vandermeer
St. Charles High School
Columbus, OH

"I have one of the smaller and one of the larger students in the class each take a 100-N spring scale. We hook the two scales together, and each students pulls as hard as possible. A third student reads each of the scales and, sure enough, they have the same reading. This is true even if the stronger student causes the smaller one to slide along the floor. You can also get two bathroom scales and place them bottom to bottom between the students. When they push on the scales, against each other, the two scales show the same force."

Sarah Vandermeer

David Young–Wolff/PhotoEdit

chapter 4

Chapter Vocabulary

first law of motion, p. 98
inertia, p. 99
second law of motion, p. 102
gravity, p. 104
weight, p. 106
centripetal acceleration, p. 110
centripetal force, p. 110
third law of motion, p. 113
momentum, p. 116
law of conservation of momentum, p. 116

Science Journal A car with a front that crumples in a crash is safer. It provides a longer distance and a longer time over which a car can slow down.

INTERACTIVE CHALKBOARD with Image Bank

PowerPoint® Presentations

This CD-ROM is an editable Microsoft® PowerPoint® presentation that includes:

- a pre-made presentation for every chapter
- interactive graphics
- animations
- audio clips
- image bank
- all new section and chapter questions
- Standardized Test Practice
- transparencies
- Foldables directions
- links to gpescience.com

chapter 4

The Laws of Motion

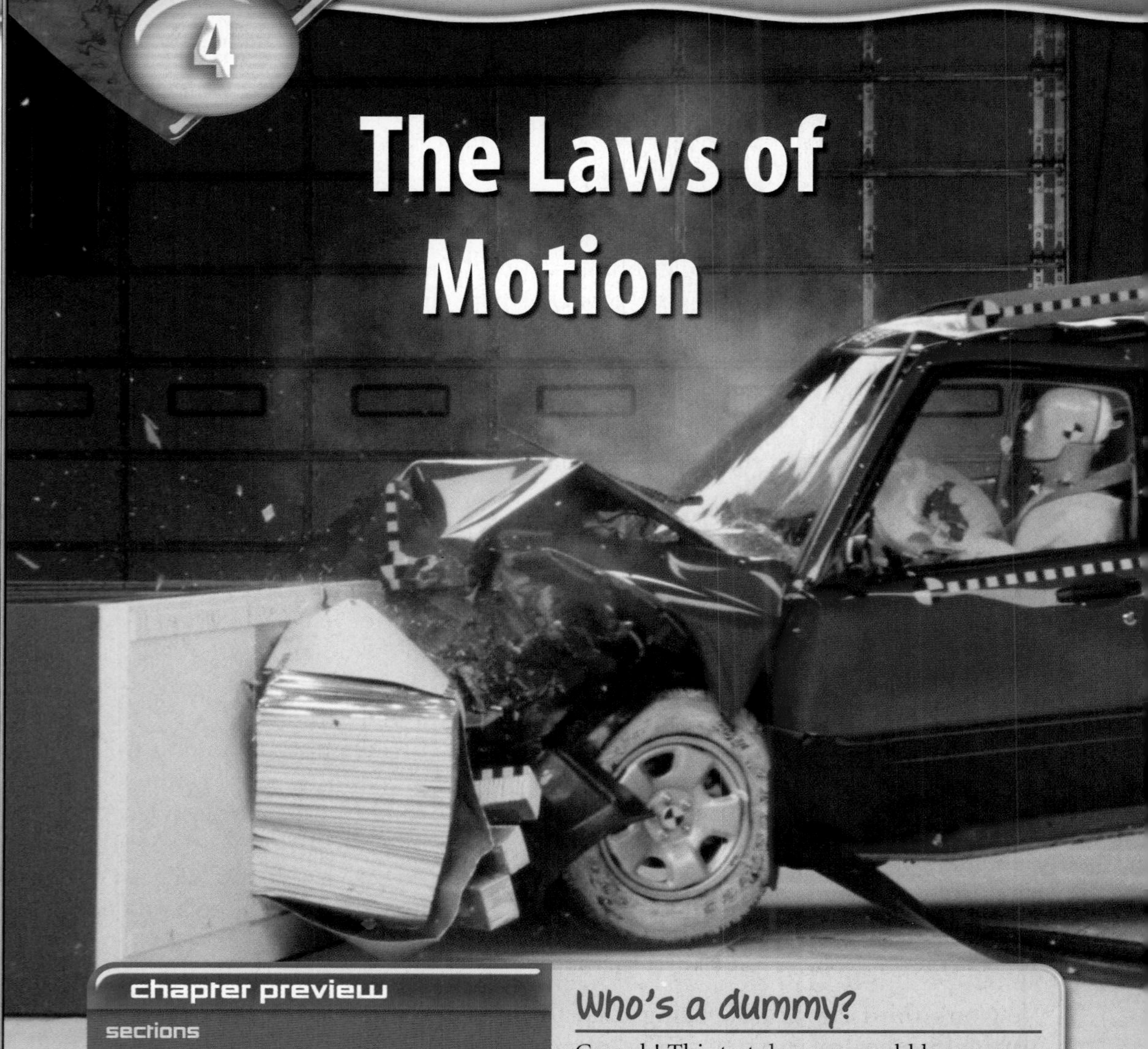

chapter preview

sections

Who's a dummy?

Crunch! This test dummy would have some explaining to do if this were a traffic accident. But in a test crash, the dummy plays an important role. The forces acting on it during a crash are measured and analyzed in order to learn how to make cars safer.

Science Journal Explain which would be a safer car—a car with a front that crumples in a crash, or one with a front that doesn't crumple.

96

Theme Connection

Stability and Change Newton established his three laws of motion by considering common patterns of change in all motion. Newton's laws can be used to analyze and predict changes in the motion of objects.

About the Photo

Crash Forces During a car crash, the forces exerted on the car's occupants can be enormous. The size of the force depends on the speed of the car, the stopping distance, and the mass of the occupant. If a car moving at 30 mph crashes, a 160-lb driver without a seat belt could experience a force equal to 150 times the force of gravity.

Start-Up Activities

Launch LAB

The Force of Gravity

The force of Earth's gravity pulls all objects downward. However, objects such as rocks seem to fall faster than feathers or leaves. Do objects with more mass fall faster?

1. Measure the mass of a softball, a tennis ball, and a flat sheet of paper. Copy the data table below and record the masses.
2. Drop the softball from a height of 2.5 m and use a stopwatch to measure the time it takes for the softball to hit the floor. Record the time in your data table.
3. Repeat step 2 using the tennis ball and the flat sheet of paper. Record the times in your data table.
4. Crumple the flat sheet of paper into a ball, and measure the time for the crumpled paper to fall 2.5 m. Record the time in your data table.
5. **Think Critically** Write a paragraph comparing the times it took each item to fall 2.5 m. From your data, infer if the speed of a falling object depends on the object's mass.

Falling Object Data

Object	Mass	Time
Softball		
Tennis ball		
Flat paper		
Crumpled paper		

FOLDABLES™ Study Organizer

The Laws of Motion Make the following Foldable to help you better understand Newton's laws of motion as you read the chapter.

STEP 1 **Fold** the top of a vertical piece of paper down and the bottom up to divide the paper into thirds.

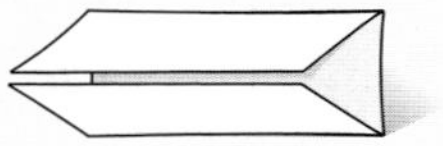

STEP 2 **Unfold and label** the rows *First Law, Second Law, Third Law.*

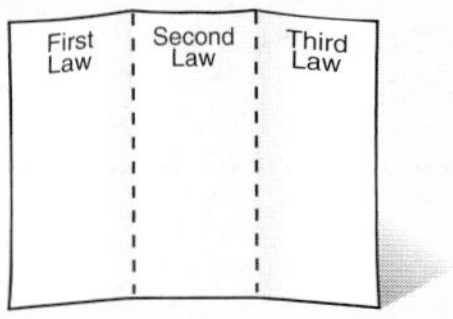

Find Main Ideas As you read the chapter, list the main ideas in the sections on the laws of motion under the appropriate column.

Science Online
Preview this chapter's content and activities at gpescience.com

Launch LAB

Purpose Use the Launch Lab to introduce students to the phenomenon that, neglecting air resistance, objects with different masses fall with the same acceleration. L2 LS **Visual-Spatial**

Preparation Find a suitable location, such as a stairwell, from which students can drop the balls. Measure a distance of 2.5 m above the floor, and mark the height with a piece of tape.

Materials softball, meterstick, tennis ball, paper, stopwatch

Teaching Strategy Have students do this lab in pairs so one student can drop the balls while the other observes and determines which object hit the ground first.

Think Critically

Although they differ in mass, the softball, tennis ball, and crumpled paper ball will fall at nearly the same velocity. Air resistance prevents the flat paper from falling with the same velocity as the crumpled paper ball.

Assessment

Process Have students make bar graphs of the data they obtained in this activity. Use **Performance Assessment in the Science Classroom,** p. 111.

FOLDABLES™ Study Organizer — Dinah Zike Study Fold

Student preparation materials for this Foldable are available in the Chapter *Fast File* Resources.

1 Motivate

INTERACTIVE CHALKBOARD PowerPoint® Presentations An editable Microsoft® PowerPoint® presentation is available on **Interactive Chalkboard** CD-ROM.

Bellringer

Section Focus Transparencies also are available on the Interactive Chalkboard CD-ROM. L2 ELL

SECTION 1 Section Focus Transparency **Something He Could Sink His Teeth Into!** Chapter 4

In 1999, Krishna Gopal Shrivestava of India set an unverified world record by pulling a ship with a mass of 244,000 kg with his teeth! His efforts can teach us about force, mass, and acceleration.

1. **What would happen if the man were pulling a small rowboat instead of a large ship?**
2. **When he stops pulling, will the ship stop moving? Explain.** L2
3. **What direction is the ship moving? Why?**

The Laws of Motion

Reading Preview

Tie to Prior Knowledge

Movement Ask students how they move heavy objects. In this section, they will learn how the mass of an object affects how easy it is to move and why some objects keep moving while others stop.

Set a Purpose Have students scan the text to find the new vocabulary words. Be sure they look carefully at figures and headings for clues to meaning. Using ideas gleaned from scanning, have students develop questions that incorporate the vocabulary terms. As students read the text, they should answer each other's questions.

section 1

The First Two Laws of Motion

Reading Guide

What You'll Learn

- **Define** Newton's first law of motion.
- **Explain** how inertia and mass are related.
- **Define** Newton's second law of motion.
- **Apply** Newton's second law of motion.

Why It's Important

Newton's first two laws of motion explain how forces cause the motion of objects to change.

Review Vocabulary

net force: the combination of all forces acting on an object

New Vocabulary

- first law of motion
- inertia
- second law of motion

Newton's Laws of Motion

When you lift a backpack, you exert a force on an object and cause it to move. The backpack initially was at rest. The force you exerted caused its velocity to change. But if you push downward on a table, the table doesn't move. The force you applied did not cause the velocity of the table to change. How are forces and motion related?

The British scientist Isaac Newton, who lived from 1642 to 1727, published a set of three rules in 1687 that explained how forces and motion are related. These three rules are called Newton's laws of motion. They apply to the motion of all objects you encounter every day, such as those in **Figure 1,** as well as to the motion of planets, stars, and galaxies.

Figure 1 Newton's laws of motion apply to all objects, including the volleyball and the volleyball players.

The First Law of Motion

Newton's first law of motion describes how an object moves when the net force acting on it is zero. According to Newton's **first law of motion,** if the net force acting on an object is zero, the object remains at rest, or if the object is moving, it continues moving in a straight line with constant speed. The first law of motion means that if the forces acting on an object are balanced, then the velocity of the object doesn't change.

Section 2 Resource Manager

Chapter *FAST FILE* Resources

Transparency Activity, p. 44

Note-taking Worksheets, pp. 33–35

Directed Reading for Content Mastery, pp. 19–20

MiniLAB, p. 3

Enrichment, p. 30

Reinforcement, p. 27

Home and Community Involvement, p. 39

Reading and Writing Skills Activities, p. 49

Only Unbalanced Forces Change Velocity The first law of motion connects forces with changes in motion. For example, suppose a skateboard is at rest. The skateboard doesn't move until you give it a push. Then the velocity of the skateboard increases while you are pushing it. The forces on the skateboard are unbalanced while you are pushing on it. As a result, the velocity of the skateboard changes as its speed increases.

However, after the skateboard leaves your hand, it slows down and stops. It might seem that the skateboard stops moving because there are no forces acting on it. However, there is an unbalanced frictional force that acts on the skateboard as it rolls. This is the force that causes the skateboard to stop. The unbalanced frictional force causes the velocity of the skateboard to change as its speed decreases. The velocity of an object changes only when there are unbalanced forces acting on it.

Inertia and Mass

All objects have a property called inertia. **Inertia** is the tendency of an object to resist a change in its motion. The dirt bike in **Figure 2** has inertia that tends to keep it moving with a constant velocity when its rider tries to steer around a curve. The inertia of an object depends on the object's mass. The greater the mass of an object, the greater its inertia.

For example, a bowling ball has more mass than a volleyball. Which would be harder to stop—a volleyball or a bowling ball rolling at the same speed? You would have to exert a greater force on the bowling ball to make it stop. The bowling ball has more inertia than the volleyball because it has more mass.

Reading Check *How does the inertia of an object depend on the object's mass?*

Figure 2 Inertia causes the bike to move in a straight line despite the efforts of the rider to steer the bike around the curve.

Mini LAB

Observing Inertia

Procedure

1. Create an inclined plane using a **board** and **textbooks.**
2. Place a small object in a **cart** and let the cart roll down the plane. Record the results.
3. Secure the object in the cart with rubber bands. Let the cart roll down the plane and record your results.

Analysis

1. Identify the forces acting on the object in the cart in both runs.
2. Explain how safety belts reduce the risk of injury in a car crash.

2 Teach

Mini LAB

Purpose Students will observe the effect of inertia. L2 IS **Kinesthetic**

Materials board, textbooks, block, small object, cart, rubber bands

Teaching Strategy Be sure the students' ramps are not so steep they are unable to observe the motion of the object and cart as it comes to a sudden stop.

Analysis

1. Without rubber bands, the forces are gravity and the force exerted by the cart on the object. When the cart hits the wall, the object continues moving until the stop block exerts a force on it. The rubber bands exert an additional force on the object. Because the rubber bands can stretch, the object slows down over a longer period of time, reducing the stopping force.
2. In a crash, seat belts reduce the stopping force and decrease damage to passengers.

Assessment

Process Ask students to make diagrams of each run of the cart. Have them use labeled arrows to indicate the forces. Use **PASC,** p. 127.

Reading Check

Answer the greater the object's mass, the greater its inertia

Reading Strategy

Determine Importance After students read about inertia, ask them to come up with three points they think are particularly important in this section and explain why. Have partners compare their lists and then share with the class.

Visual Learning

Figure 2 Have students sketch the situation depicted in **Figure 2,** then add arrows to their drawings to indicate the forces acting on the bike. Have a student read the caption describing the picture and ask the students if their arrows are consistent with this explanation.

Teacher FYI

Although the law of inertia is called Newton's first law, Galileo formulated it before Newton was even born. In his writings, Newton credited Galileo for the idea.

Caption Answer

Figure 3 same as the velocity of the cart and boxes just before the cart stopped

Make a Model

Inertia Have students use their textbooks to model the situation in **Figure 3**. Stack one book on top of the other. Gently accelerate the stack by pushing on the bottom book, then bring the bottom book to a sudden stop and observe the motion of the top book.

Figure 3 The inertia of the boxes causes them to keep moving after the cart has been brought to a sudden stop.
Describe *the velocity of the boxes just after the cart stops.*

Inertia and the First Law of Motion According to the first law of motion, the velocity of an object doesn't change unless the forces acting on the object are unbalanced. In other words, if you observe a change in an object's velocity, you know an unbalanced force acted on it. This is similar to the definition of inertia—an object resists a change in its motion. As a result, the first law of motion sometimes is called the law of inertia.

Inertia and the first law of motion explain why the boxes in **Figure 3** slide off the cart when the cart comes to a sudden stop. The student applies an unbalanced force to the cart that makes it stop. However, the inertia of the boxes causes them to keep moving even after the cart stops.

What happens in a crash?

The first law of motion can explain what happens in a car crash. When a car traveling 50 km/h collides head-on with something solid, the car crumples, slows down, and stops within about 0.1 s. Any passenger not wearing a safety belt continues to move forward at the same speed the car was traveling. Within about 0.02 s after the car stops, unbelted passengers slam into the dashboard, windshield, or steering wheel, as shown in **Figure 4.** Passengers in the back seat might slam into the backs of the front seats. Because of their inertia, they are traveling at the car's original speed of 50 km/h—about the same speed they would reach falling from a three-story building.

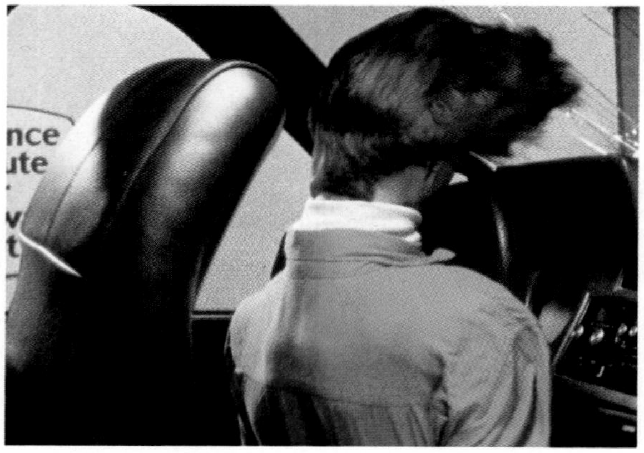

Figure 4 This crash test dummy is not restrained in this low-speed crash. Inertia causes the dummy to slam into the steering wheel.

Differentiated Instruction

Challenge Have students prepare a diagram showing the four forces acting on an ice-skater skating forward. Explain why the skater is able to move forward for a relatively long period of time. Possible answer: The four forces are gravity pulling down on the skater, the ice pushing up, the ice pushing forward in response to the skater's push on the ice, and friction pulling the skater back. Since the ice provides relatively little friction, the skater's inertia keeps him or her moving forward for a relatively long time. L3 LS **Logical-Mathematical** P

Safety Belts In **Figure 5** the crash test dummies are restrained with safety belts. As a result, they slow down at the same rate that the car slows down. However, the force exerted on a person that slows from 50 km/h to 0 km/h in 0.1 s is about 14 times as large as the force of gravity on the person. To further reduce the force acting on a person, the seat belt loosens slightly, increasing the time it takes to slow the person. Increasing the time needed to stop reduces the force exerted on the person. The safety belt also prevents the person from being thrown out of the car. Car-safety experts say that about half the people who die in car crashes would survive if they wore safety belts.

Figure 5 These crash test dummies were restrained with safety belts in this crash. This prevented the dummies from hitting the dashboard or windshield.

Reading Check ***What are two advantages of wearing a safety belt in a crash?***

The Second Law of Motion

According to Newton's first law of motion, unbalanced forces cause the velocity of an object to change. Newton's second law of motion describes how the net force on an object, its mass, and its acceleration are related.

Force and Acceleration What's different about throwing a ball horizontally as hard as you can and tossing it gently? When you throw hard, the net force on the ball is greater than when you toss it. Also, the ball has a greater velocity when it leaves your hand. As a result, the hard-thrown ball has a greater change in velocity, and this change can occur over a shorter period of time. Recall that acceleration is the change in velocity divided by the time needed for the change to occur. So, a hard-thrown ball has a greater acceleration than a gently-thrown ball.

Mass and Acceleration If you throw a baseball and a softball with the same amount of force, why does the baseball move faster? A softball has more mass than a baseball. Even though the net force exerted on both balls is the same, the softball has less velocity when it leaves your hand than the baseball does. If it takes the same amount of time to throw both balls, the acceleration of the softball is less than that of the baseball. So, the acceleration of an object depends on its mass, as well as the net force exerted on it. Net force, mass, and acceleration are related.

Science Online

Topic: Motion in Sports
Visit gpescience.com for Web links to information about methods used to analyze the motions of athletes.

Activity Choose a sport and write a report on how analyzing the motions involved in the sport can improve performance and reduce injuries.

Activity

Safety Belts Contact your local state patrol office to have an officer speak to the class about the advantages of wearing safety belts. Tell the officer ahead of time that you are studying the forces experienced by a person during a crash so that topic can be addressed. Afterward, have students write in their Science Journal about what they have learned from the officer. L2 LS
Auditory-Musical

Discussion

Air Bags How do air bags prevent injuries during a car crash? Air bags increase the time over which a force acts to slow the motion of a body. The increased time decreases the force required to stop the body, thus reducing the chance for serious injury. L3 LS
Logical-Mathematical

Reading Check

Answer decreases the magnitude of the force necessary to stop the passenger (increases the time over which the acceleration takes place); prevents the passenger from being thrown out of the car

Quick Demo
Newton's Second Law

Materials flexible plastic ruler, table-tennis ball, golf ball, flat surface

Estimated Time five minutes

Procedure Place a flexed ruler next to a golf ball and release the ruler. Observe the motion of the ball, and measure the distance it travels. Repeat using a table tennis ball. Be sure to keep the launch force constant by bending the ruler back the same amount each time. L2 ELL IS **Visual-Spatial**

Applying Math

Math Standards

National: 1, 2, 9

Answers to Practice Problems

1. 4 m/s^2
2. 28,800 N
3. 1,500 kg

The Second Law of Motion

Newton's **second law of motion** states that the acceleration of an object is in the same direction as the net force on the object, and that the acceleration can be calculated from the following equation:

Newton's Second Law of Motion

$$\text{acceleration (in meters/second}^2) = \frac{\text{net force (in newtons)}}{\text{mass (in kilograms)}}$$

$$a = \frac{F_{net}}{m}$$

Applying Math — Solve a Simple Equation

THE ACCELERATION OF A SLED You push a friend on a sled. Your friend and the sled together have a mass of 70 kg. If the net force on the sled is 35 N, what is the sled's acceleration?

IDENTIFY known values and the unknown value

Identify the known values:

The net force on the sled is 35 N means $F_{net} = 35$ N

Your friend and the sled together have a mass of 70 kg means $m = 70$ kg

Identify the unknown value:

What is the sled's acceleration? means $a = ?\ \text{m/s}^2$

SOLVE the problem

Substitute the known values $F_{net} = 35$ N and $m = 70$ kg into the equation for Newton's second law of motion:

$$a = \frac{F_{net}}{m} = \frac{35 \text{ N}}{70 \text{ kg}} = 0.5\frac{\text{N}}{\text{kg}} = 0.5\frac{\cancel{\text{kg}}\text{ m}}{\text{s}^2} \times \frac{1}{\cancel{\text{kg}}} = 0.5 \text{ m/s}^2$$

CHECK your answer

Does your answer seem reasonable? Check your answer by multiplying the acceleration you calculated by the mass given in the problem. The result should be the net force given in the problem.

Practice Problems

1. If the mass of a helicopter is 4,500 kg, and the net force on it is 18,000 N, what is the helicopter's acceleration?
2. What is the net force on a dragster with a mass of 900 kg if its acceleration is 32.0 m/s^2?
3. A car is being pulled by a tow truck. What is the car's mass if the net force on the car is 3,000 N and it has an acceleration of 2.0 m/s^2?

For more practice problems go to page 879, and visit Math Practice at gpescience.com.

LAB DEMONSTRATION

Purpose observe how unbalanced forces affect the velocity of an object

Materials video camera and player, cart, binders, books, metric tape measure

Preparation Film a cart rolling down a slope and then rolling up another slope, with a tape measure placed along the path.

Procedure Show the video one frame at a time. Have students compare the distances the cart moves between each frame on the two slopes.

Expected Outcome The cart moves farther between each frame as it goes downhill and moves a shorter distance between each frame as it goes uphill.

Assessment

What is the direction of the net force acting on the car in each section of the path? in the direction of motion when it is rolling downhill; opposite the motion when it is rolling uphill. L2 IS **Visual-Spatial**

Calculating Net Force with the Second Law Newton's second law also can be used to calculate the net force if mass and acceleration are known. To do this, the equation for Newton's second law must be solved for the net force, *F*. To solve for the net force, multiply both sides of the above equation by the mass:

$$\cancel{m} \times \frac{F_{net}}{\cancel{m}} = ma$$

The mass, *m*, on the left side cancels, giving the equation:

$$F_{net} = ma$$

For example, when the tennis player in **Figure 6** hits a ball, the ball might be in contact with the racket for only a few thousandths of a second. Because the ball's velocity changes over such a short period of time, the ball's acceleration could be as high as 5,000 m/s^2. The ball's mass is 0.06 kg, so the net force exerted on the ball would be:

$$F_{net} = ma = (0.06\ \text{kg})\ (5{,}000\ \text{m/s}^2) = 300\ \text{kg m/s}^2 = 300\ \text{N}$$

Figure 6 The tennis racket exerts a force on the ball that causes it to accelerate.

section 1 review

Summary

Inertia and the First Law of Motion

- According to Newton's first law of motion, the velocity of an object does not change unless an unbalanced net force acts on the object.
- The inertia of an object is the tendency of the object to resist a change in motion.
- The larger the mass of an object, the greater its inertia.
- In a car crash, inertia causes an unrestrained passenger to continue moving at the speed of the car before the crash.

The Second Law of Motion

- The acceleration of an object depends on the mass of the object and the net force exerted on the object.
- According to Newton's second law of motion, the acceleration of an object is in the direction of the net force on the object, and can be calculated from this equation:

$$a = \frac{F_{net}}{m}$$

Self Check

1. **Infer** whether the inertia of an object changes as the object's velocity changes.
2. **Determine** whether or not there must be an unbalanced force acting on any object that is moving. Explain.
3. **Determine** whether or not there can be forces acting on an object that is at rest. Explain.
4. **Infer** the net force on a refrigerator if you push on the refrigerator and it doesn't move.
5. **Think Critically** Describe three situations in which a force changes the velocity of an object. Let at least one of the situations involve the force due to gravity.

Applying Math

6. **Calculate Mass** You push yourself on a skateboard with a force of 30 N and accelerate at 0.5 m/s^2. Find the mass of you and the skateboard together.
7. **Calculate Net Force** You push a book that has a mass of 2.0 kg so that it has an acceleration of 1.0 m/s^2. What is the net force on the book?

More Section Review gpescience.com

Post Reading

Fix-Up Strategy Model this strategy with a challenging section of text. Tell students you will reread the section aloud to enhance meaning. As you read, identify and talk about confusing parts. Sound out words, slow down, and ask questions. Next, allow students to practice the strategy using another section.

3 Assess

DAILY INTERVENTION

Check For Understanding

Auditory-Musical Divide students into small groups. Have students create a song that explains balanced and unbalanced forces. Students may perform their songs for the class as a review. L2

Reteach

Tie a string around a book and suspend it. Cut the string. Ask students to describe the forces acting on the book before and after you cut the string. Before the string was cut, the force of gravity was pulling down on the book. The string exerted an equal upward force on the book. Since these forces were equal and opposite in direction, the book was at rest. After the string was cut, there was no upward force on the book. The force of gravity was not opposed, so the book fell to the floor. L1 ELL IN **Visual-Spatial**

Assessment

Oral Have students discuss the forces that enable a kite to stay in the air. Gravity pulls down on the kite. The wind blowing on the surface area of the kite results in an upward net force on the kite. This upward net force allows the kite to overcome gravity and fly. The tension in the string prevents the kite from flying away. Use **PASC,** p. 143.

section 1 review

1. No; the inertia is related to the amount of mass and doesn't change.
2. If an object is moving with a constant velocity, then no unbalanced force is acting on it.
3. An object can be a trest if the forces acting on it are balanced.
4. The net force is zero.
5. Possible answers: force exerted by baseball bat changes velocity of pitched ball, gravity causes ball thrown upward to fall, force exerted by person lifting book from desk
6. 60 kg
7. 2 N

section 2 Gravity

1 Motivate

INTERACTIVE CHALKBOARD PowerPoint® Presentations An editable Microsoft® PowerPoint® presentation is available on **Interactive Chalkboard** CD-ROM.

Bellringer

Section Focus Transparencies also are available on the Interactive Chalkboard CD-ROM. L2 ELL

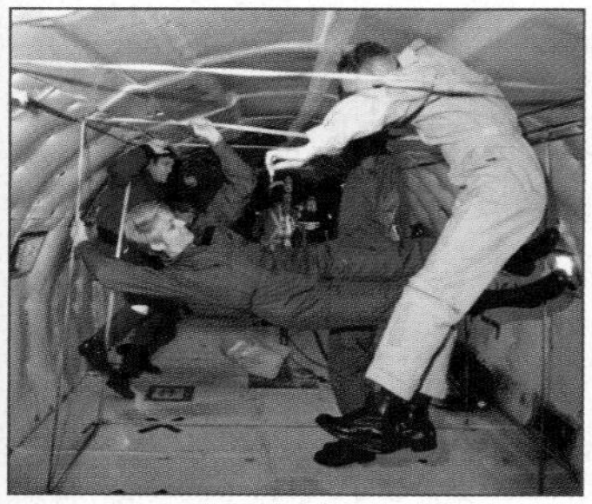
Section 2 Section Focus Transparency — Which way's up? — Chapter 4

There is no up or down in orbit. If not secured, objects simply float here and there. Planes like NASA's KC-135, the "Vomit Comet," are able to briefly simulate the conditions of being in orbit.

1. On Earth, how can you tell up from down?
2. If a scale floated by and an astronaut stood on it, what would the scale say?

L2

The Laws of Motion

Reading Preview

Tie to Prior Knowledge

Gravity's Effect on a Football Ask students to describe how a football must be thrown for a long pass. Explain that in this section they will learn how the force of gravity affects the motion of projectiles such as a football.

Word Relationships Ask students to determine the relationships between the new vocabulary words. For instance, students might suggest that weight is the pull of gravity. Allow them to use the text to develop their ideas. Have students share with the class.

Reading Guide

What You'll Learn

- **Describe** the gravitational force.
- **Distinguish** between mass and weight.
- **Explain** why objects that are thrown will follow a curved path.
- **Compare** circular motion with motion in a straight line.

Why It's Important

There is a gravitational force between you and every other object in the universe.

Review Vocabulary

acceleration: the rate of change of velocity which occurs when an object changes speed or direction

New Vocabulary

- gravity
- weight
- centripetal acceleration
- centripetal force

Figure 7 The gravitational force between two objects depends on their masses and the distance between them.

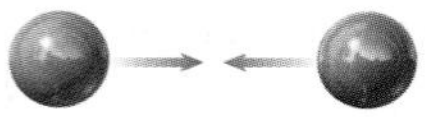

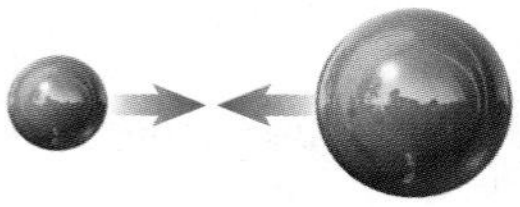

Increasing the mass of either object increases the gravitational force between them.

If the objects are closer together, the gravitational force between them increases.

What is gravity?

There's a lot about you that's attractive. At this moment, you are exerting an attractive force on everything around you—your desk, your classmates, even the planet Jupiter millions of kilometers away. It's the attractive force of gravity.

Anything that has mass is attracted by the force of gravity. **Gravity** is an attractive force between any two objects that depends on the masses of the objects and the distance between them. This force increases as the mass of either object increases, or as the objects move closer, as shown in **Figure 7.**

You can't feel any gravitational attraction between you and this book because the force is weak. Only Earth is both close enough and has a large enough mass that you can feel its gravitational attraction. While the Sun has much more mass than Earth, the Sun is too far away to exert a noticeable gravitational attraction on you. And while this book is close, it doesn't have enough mass to exert an attraction you can feel.

Gravity—A Basic Force Gravity is one of the four basic forces. The other basic forces are the electromagnetic force, the strong nuclear force, and the weak nuclear force. The two nuclear forces only act on particles in the nuclei of atoms. Electricity and magnetism are caused by the electromagnetic force. Chemical interactions between atoms and molecules also are due to the electromagnetic force.

Section 2 Resource Manager

Chapter *FAST FILE* Resources

Transparency Activities, pp. 45, 47–48
Directed Reading for Content Mastery, p. 21
MiniLAB, p. 4
Enrichment, p. 31
Lab Worksheet, pp. 5–6
Lab Activity, pp. 9–12
Life Science Critical Thinking/Problem Solving, p. 14
Earth Science Critical Thinking/Problem Solving, p. 5
Cultural Diversity, p. 25

104 CHAPTER 4 The Laws of Motion

The Law of Universal Gravitation

For thousands of years, people have observed the night sky and collected data on the motions of the stars and planets. Isaac Newton used some of these data on the motions of planets to formulate the law of universal gravitation, which he published in 1687. This law can be written as the following equation.

The Law of Universal Gravitation

$$\text{gravitational force} = (\text{constant}) \times \frac{(\text{mass 1}) \times (\text{mass 2})}{(\text{distance})^2}$$

$$F = G\frac{m_1 m_2}{d^2}$$

In this equation G is a constant called the universal gravitational constant, and d is the distance between the two masses, m_1 and m_2. The law of universal gravitation enables the force of gravity to be calculated between any two objects if their masses and the distance between them are known.

The Range of Gravity According to the law of universal gravitation, the gravitational force between two masses decreases rapidly as the distance between the masses increases. For example, if the distance between two objects increases from 1 m to 2 m, the gravitational force between them becomes one fourth as large. If the distance increases from 1 m to 10 m, the gravitational force between the objects is one hundredth as large. However, no matter how far apart two objects are, the gravitational force between them never completely disappears. As a result, gravity is called a long-range force.

Reading Check *Why is gravity called a long-range force?*

INTEGRATE Astronomy

Finding Other Planets Earth's motion around the Sun is affected by the gravitational pulls of the other planets in the solar system. In the same way, the motion of every planet in the solar system is affected by the gravitational pulls of all the other planets.

In the 1840s the most distant planet known was Uranus. The motion of Uranus calculated from the law of universal gravitation disagreed slightly with its observed motion. Some astronomers suggested that there must be an undiscovered planet affecting the motion of Uranus. Using the law of universal gravitation and Newton's laws of motion, two astronomers independently calculated the orbit of this planet. As a result of these calculations, the planet Neptune, shown in **Figure 8,** was found in 1846.

Science Online

Topic: Gravity on Other Planets

Visit gpescience.com for Web links to information about the gravitational acceleration near the surface of different planets in the solar system.

Activity Make a graph with the gravitational acceleration on the *y*-axis, and the planet's mass on the *x*-axis. Infer from your graph how the gravitational acceleration depends on a planet's mass.

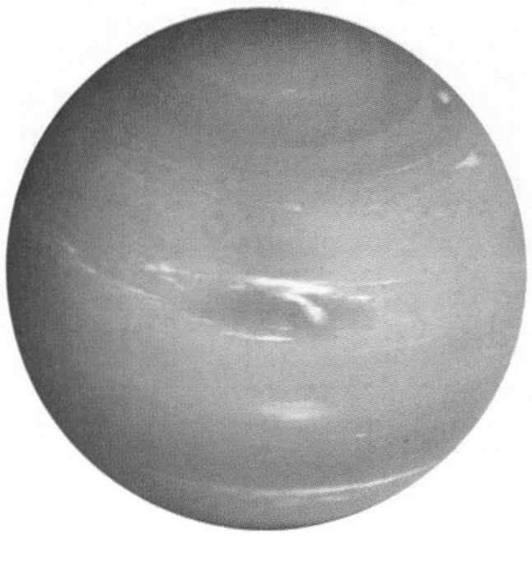

Figure 8 The location of the planet Neptune in the night sky was correctly predicted using Newton's laws of motion and the law of universal gravitation.

2 Teach

Quick Demo

Gravitational Acceleration

Materials water, bucket, plastic cup

Estimated Time five minutes

Procedure Punch a hole in the bottom of the cup. Place your finger over the hole and fill the cup with water. Hold the cup as high over your head as you can, and let it drop into the bucket. Have students observe that the water and the cup fall at the same rate, so no water drains out of the cup as it falls. L2 ELL IS

Visual-Spatial

Reading Check

Answer It never disappears, regardless of distance between objects.

INTEGRATE Astronomy

Content Background

Finding Other Planets Astronomers use several techniques to find evidence of planets outside the solar system. Some rely on measuring the periodic motion of the star due to the planet's gravitational pull as it orbits the star. Other techniques measure the slight dimming of a star as a planet passes between the star and the telescope. Using these techniques, astronomers have discovered over 125 extrasolar planets.

Fun Fact

Newton's law of gravitation states that the gravitational attraction between two objects is $F = G(m_1 m_2)/d^2$, where d is the distance between the two objects and G is the universal gravitational constant. In 1798, Henry Cavendish performed experiments that verified Newton's law. Based on his work and the work of others, the value of G is now known to be approximately $6.67 \times 10^{-11} \text{m}^3/\text{kg}\cdot\text{s}^2$.

Reading Strategy

Determine Main Ideas Have students read The Law of Gravitation, Earth's Gravitational Acceleration, Weightlessness and Free Fall, Projectile Motion, and Centripetal Force. Ask students to write two to four sentences describing the main ideas of each section. Bold print, captions, and headings offer clues to main ideas.

Differentiated Instruction

Challenge Have students show how Newton's first law can be derived from Newton's second law. Newton's second law says F = ma. If F = 0 then a = 0. If a = 0 the velocity of the object doesn't change. It remains at rest or continues to move in a straight line at constant velocity. L3 IS

Logical-Mathematical

Quick Demo

Mass and Falling Speed

Materials golf ball, table-tennis ball

Estimated Time 15 minutes

Procedure Bring a golf ball and a table tennis ball to class. Have volunteers determine the mass of each ball and write it on the board. Then drop both balls from the same height for the class to observe. Have the class decide whether one ball hit the floor before the other. L2 LS **Visual-Spatial**

Text Question Answer

The bowling ball and the marble would hit the ground at the same time. They have the same acceleration, so their velocities are the same as they fall.

IDENTIFYING Misconceptions

Mass v. Weight People in Europe and other places that use SI units usually express their weight in kilograms. This is technically incorrect, as the kilogram is a unit of mass, not weight.

Activity

Weight Conversion Have students calculate their mass in kilograms, then use their answers to calculate their weightin newtons. Make sure students know that the weight of one kilogram is 2.2 pounds. L2 LS **Logical-Mathematical**

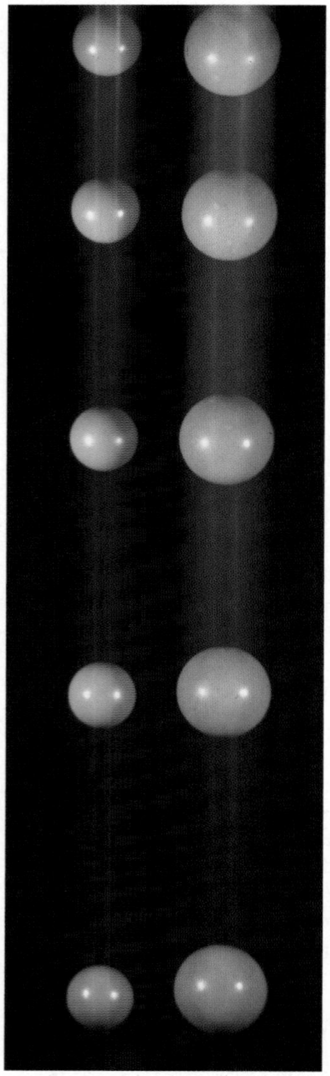

Figure 9 Time-lapse photography shows that two balls of different masses fall at the same rate.

Earth's Gravitational Acceleration

If you dropped a bowling ball and a marble at the same time, which would hit the ground first? Suppose the effects of air resistance are small enough to be ignored. When all forces except gravity acting on an a falling object can be ignored, the object is said to be in free fall. Then all objects near Earth's surface would fall with the same acceleration, just like the two balls in **Figure 9.**

Close to Earth's surface, the acceleration of an object in free fall is 9.8 m/s^2. This acceleration is the gravitational acceleration and is given the symbol g. By the second law of motion, the gravitational force exerted by Earth on a falling object is the object's mass times the gravitational acceleration. The gravitational force can be calculated from this equation:

Gravitational Force Equation

gravitational force (N) = mass (kg) × gravitational acceleration (m/s^2)

$$F = mg$$

For example, the gravitational force on a skydiver with a mass of 60 kg would be

$$F = mg = (60 \text{ kg})\ (9.8 \text{ m/s}^2) = 588 \text{ N}$$

Weight Even if you are not falling, the force due to Earth's gravity still is pulling you downward. If you are standing on a floor, the net force on you is zero. The force due to Earth's gravity pulls you downward, but the floor exerts an upward force on you that balances gravity's downward pull.

Whether you are standing, jumping, or falling, Earth exerts a gravitational force on you. The gravitational force exerted on an object is called the object's **weight.** The weight of an object on Earth is equal to the gravitational force exerted by Earth on the object. As a result, near Earth's surface an object's weight can be calculated from this equation:

Weight Equation

weight (N) = mass (kg) × gravitational acceleration (m/s^2)

$$W = mg$$

On Earth, where g equals 9.8 m/s^2, a cassette tape weighs about 0.5 N, a backpack full of books could weigh 100 N, and a jumbo jet weighs about 3.4 million N.

Differentiated Instruction

Challenge Ask students to identify the force that opposes gravity and enables objects to float in water. The buoyant force of the water acts on an object with a force equal to the weight of the water displaced by the object. If the buoyant force is equal to the force of gravity pulling on the object, the object will float. This occurs when the object is less dense than water. L3 LS **Logical-Mathematical**

Science Journal

Lower Gravity Ask students to imagine that, during the next few days, the gravitational force of Earth gradually becomes half of what it is now. Have students write in their Science Journals about the changes that might take place. Students might describe balls bouncing higher, people jumping higher, increased ease of walking and running.

Weight and Mass Weight and mass are not the same. Weight is a force and mass is a measure of the amount of matter an object contains. However, according to the weight equation on the previous page, weight and mass are related. Weight increases as mass increases.

The weight of an object usually is the gravitational force between the object and Earth. But the weight of an object can change, depending on the gravitational force on the object. For example, the acceleration due to gravity on the Moon is 1.6 m/s^2, about one sixth as large as Earth's gravitational acceleration. As a result, a person, like the astronaut in **Figure 10,** would weigh only about one sixth as much on the Moon as on Earth. **Table 1** shows how various weights on Earth would be different on the Moon and some of the planets.

Reading Check *How are weight and mass related?*

Weightlessness and Free Fall

You've probably seen pictures of astronauts and equipment floating inside the space shuttle. Any item that is not fastened down seems to float throughout the cabin. They are said to be experiencing the sensation of weightlessness.

However, for a typical mission, the shuttle orbits Earth at an altitude of about 400 km. According the law of universal gravitation, at 400-km altitude the force of Earth's gravity is about 90 percent as strong as it is at Earth's surface. So an astronaut with a mass of 80 kg still would weigh about 700 N in orbit, compared with a weight of about 780 N at Earth's surface.

Figure 10 On the Moon, the gravitational force on the astronaut is less than it is on Earth. As a result, the astronaut can take longer steps and jump higher than on Earth.
Describe *how the astronaut's mass and weight on the Moon compare to his mass and weight on Earth.*

Table 1 Weight Comparison Table

Weight on Earth (N)	Weight on Other Bodies in the Solar System (N)				
	Moon	Venus	Mars	Jupiter	Saturn
75	12	68	28	190	87
100	17	90	38	254	116
150	25	135	57	381	174
500	84	450	190	1,270	580
700	119	630	266	1,778	812
2,000	333	1,800	760	5,080	2,320

Discussion

Weight and Mass Why is it that an object has mass in and of itself, but must interact with another object for it to have weight? Mass is a measure of the amount of matter an object contains. Weight is a measure of gravitational force, which only occurs between objects.

Activity

Collecting Data To help students become familiar with the relationship between an object's mass and its weight on Earth, have groups of students work together to make a table listing the weights and masses of various objects. Students should first use a balance to determine the object's mass in kilograms and then calculate the weight by multiplying the mass by 9.8 m/s^2. L2 ELL IS **Kinesthetic**

Reading Check

Answer Weight equals mass times acceleration due to gravity.

Quick Demo
Simulating Gravity

Materials marble, shallow pan

Estimated Time 15 minutes

Procedure One way to overcome weightlessness in space is to build a space station in the shape of a large, doughnut-shaped ring called a torus. If the torus is set spinning in outer space, the centripetal force would cause people inside to feel as if they are being pushed toward the outer wall, simulating gravity. Demonstrate this to students by swirling a marble in a shallow pan. L3 IS **Visual-Spatial**

Caption Answer

Figure 10 mass is the same; weight is less on the moon

Teacher FYI

Acceleration Due to Gravity Near Earth's surface, acceleration due to gravity (g) is approximately 9.8 m/s^2. This value varies by only a fraction of a percent even on top of Mount Everest. The value of *g* decreases as you travel away from Earth's surface. At a height of 1,000 km, it is about 3/4 the value at Earth's surface.

Active Reading

Reflective Journal In this strategy, students record their responses to various activities and what they learned from each. Have them divide sheets of paper into five columns: *What I Did, What I Learned, Questions I Have, What Surprised Me,* and *Overall Response.* Have students write a reflective journal entry for the activities about gravity in this section.

Activity

Using a Spring Scale Have students hang an object from a spring scale to determine its weight. Next, have them compare this with the force recorded on the scale when the object is moved rapidly up and rapidly down. Have students explain the results. The downward force exerted by the object on the scale is the force recorded on the scale, and equals the upward force exerted by the scale on the object. When the object isn't accelerating, the scale exerts an upward force on the object equal to its weight. When the object is accelerating upward, the upward force on the object exerted by the scale is greater than its weight. When the object is accelerating downward, the upward force on the object exerted by the scale is less than its weight. L3 IN **Logical-Mathematical**

INTEGRATE Earth Science

Gravity and Earth's Atmosphere The force of gravity also has caused the shape of the Earth and other bodies in the solar system to be spherical. During Earth's formation, gravity caused denser material such as iron and nickel to sink toward the center of earth, where they now form Earth's core. Less dense materials such as silicates and water were left at Earth's surface, where they now form Earth's crust and oceans.

Use Science Words

Word Origins Ask students to find the origin of the word *projectile*. The word projectile comes from the Latin prefix *pro-*, which means "forward," and the Latin verb *iacere*, which means "to throw." L2 IN **Linguistic**

Reading Check

Answer gravitational force

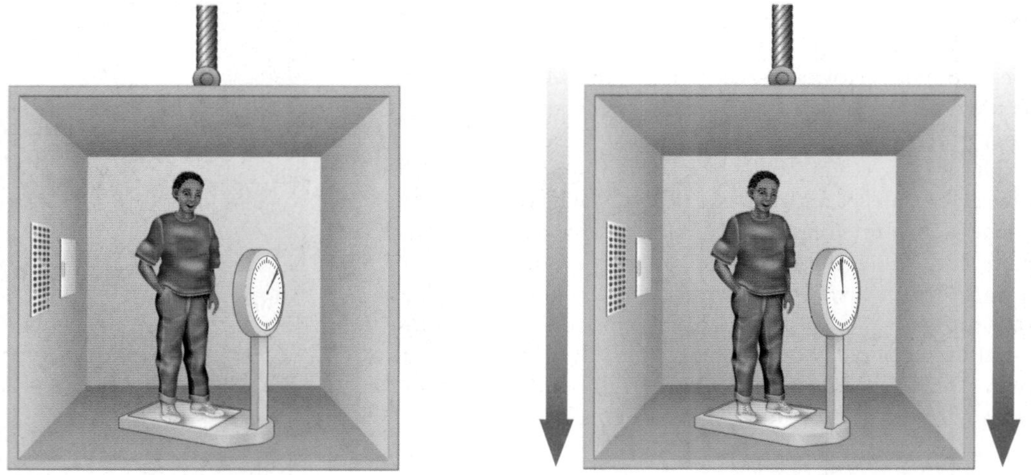

A When the elevator is stationary, the scale shows the boy's weight.

B If the elevator were in free fall, the scale would show a zero weight.

Figure 11 The boy and the scale no longer exert forces on each other when they both are in free fall. As a result, the boy seems to be weightless.

Floating in Space Why do objects seem weightless in orbit? Think about measuring your weight. When you stand on a scale, as in **Figure 11A,** the net force on you is zero. The scale exerts an upward force on you equal to your weight. Now suppose you stand on a scale in an elevator that is in free fall, as shown in **Figure 11B.** Then the only force acting on you is the gravitational force. You and the scale no longer exert forces on each other. The scale would show zero weight, even though the gravitational force on you hasn't changed.

Reading Check *What is the only force on an object in free fall?*

A space shuttle in orbit is in free fall, but it is falling around Earth, rather than straight downward. Everything in the orbiting space shuttle is falling around Earth at the same rate, in the same way you and the scale were falling in the elevator. Objects in the shuttle seem to be floating because they are all falling with the same acceleration.

INTEGRATE Earth Science

Gravity and Earth's Atmosphere Apart from simply keeping your feet on the ground, gravity is important for life on Earth for other reasons, too. Because Earth has a sufficient gravitational pull, it can hold around it the oxygen/nitrogen atmosphere necessary for sustaining life. Research other ways in which gravity has played a role in the formation of Earth.

Projectile Motion

If you've tossed a ball to someone, you've probably noticed that thrown objects don't always travel in straight lines. They curve downward. Anything that's thrown or shot through the air is called a projectile. Earth's gravity causes projectiles to follow a curved path.

Curriculum Connection

Health Pictures of objects floating around in a spaceship make weightlessness look like fun, but weightlessness can have an adverse effect on the health of astronauts. Have students research this problem and prepare a report about some effects. Some problems astronauts experience are loss of bone density and muscle atrophy. L2 P IN **Linguistic**

Figure 12 The pitcher gives the ball a horizontal motion. Gravity, however, is pulling the ball down. The combination of these two motions causes the ball to move in a curved path.

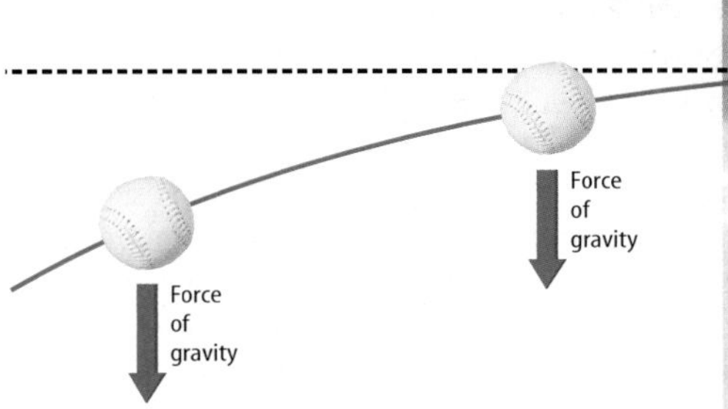

Horizontal and Vertical Motions When you throw a ball, like the pitcher in **Figure 12,** the force exerted by your hand pushes the ball forward. This force gives the ball horizontal motion. After you let go of the ball, no force accelerates it forward, so its horizontal velocity is constant, if you ignore air resistance.

However, when you let go of the ball, gravity can accelerate it downward, giving it vertical motion. Now the ball has constant horizontal velocity but increasing vertical velocity. Gravity exerts an unbalanced force on the ball, changing the direction of its path from only forward to forward and downward. The result of these two motions is that the ball appears to travel in a curve, even though its horizontal and vertical motions are completely independent of each other.

Horizontal and Vertical Distance If you were to throw a ball as hard as you could from shoulder height in a perfectly horizontal direction, would it take longer to reach the ground than if you dropped a ball from the same height? Surprisingly, it won't. A thrown ball and one dropped will hit the ground at the same time. Both balls in **Figure 13** travel the same vertical distance in the same amount of time. However, the ball thrown horizontally travels a greater horizontal distance than the ball that is dropped.

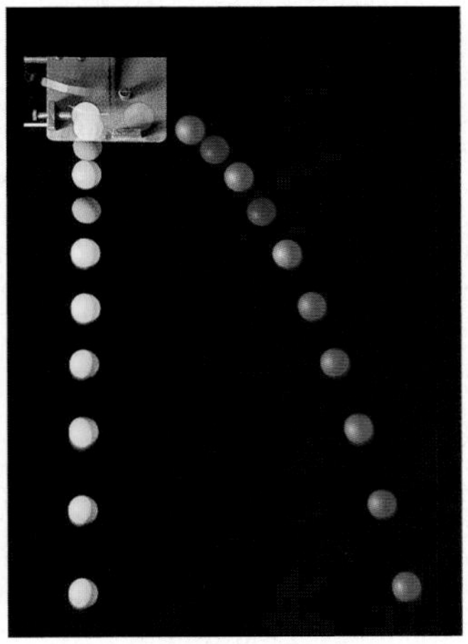

Figure 13 Multiflash photography shows that each ball has the same acceleration downward, whether it's thrown or dropped.

Inquiry Lab

Distance and Launch Angle

Purpose Students design an experiment to show how the horizontal distance traveled by a projectile is affected by its initial launch angle.

Possible Materials meterstick, protractor, rubber bands, boards about 5 cm × 12 cm, nails small rubber stopper or a toy rubber-tipped dart gun

Estimated Time one class period

Possible Procedure

1. Have students build a slingshot using the board, nails, and rubber band to launch the rubber stopper (or use the dart gun).
2. Launch the rubber stopper at different angles from the same elevation. Keep the launch force the same.
3. Measure the horizontal distance traveled by the projectile at each angle.
4. Plot the results on a graph of angle versus distance.
5. Infer which angles give the greatest horizontal distance.

Teaching Strategy Wear protective eye gear and caution students not to aim at anything breakable or each other. They should find that complementary angles give the same horizontal distance. L3 LS **Logical-Mathematical**

For additional inquiry activities, see *Science Inquiry Lab Manual*.

Visual Learning

Figure 13 Point out that the spacing of the balls with respect to the horizontal is identical. This shows that the balls have the same vertical acceleration. The horizontal and vertical accelerations are separate. Ask students what the result would be if one of the balls had greater mass. The result would be the same. L2 LS **Visual-Spatial**

Differentiated Instruction

Challenge Have students explain the following problem, using both diagrams and written expression: If one bullet is dropped from the same altitude and at the same time that an identical bullet is fired horizontally from a gun, they both hit the ground at the same time (but not the same place). Which bullet will hit first if one is fired at an upward angle at the same time the second is dropped? When the gun is fired horizontally, both bullets have the same initial vertical speed (0) and the same vertical acceleration (9.8 m/s^2). They land at the same time. When one bullet is fired at an upward angle, they do not have the same initial vertical speed. L3 LS **Logical-Mathematical**

SECTION 2 Gravity **109**

Use Science Words

Word Usage Have students explain how the definition of the word centripetal describes the force exerted on a ball on a string that you swing around your head. Centripetal means "moving toward the center." The tension in the string pulls the ball toward the center. L2 LS **Linguistic**

Caption Answer

Figure 14 gravity; force exerted by the wall of the tube on the ball

Mini LAB

Purpose to observe the effect of centripetal force

Materials string; plastic, slotted golf ball

Teaching Strategy Suggest to students that they perform this experiment outside.

Analysis

1. centripetal force
2. The faster the ball swings, the more tension there is on the string.

Assessment

Process Show students a picture of a satellite in orbit. Ask them to diagram the forces acting on the satellite. The centripetal force of Earth's gravity pulls the satellite toward Earth. Use **PASC,** p. 127.

Try at Home

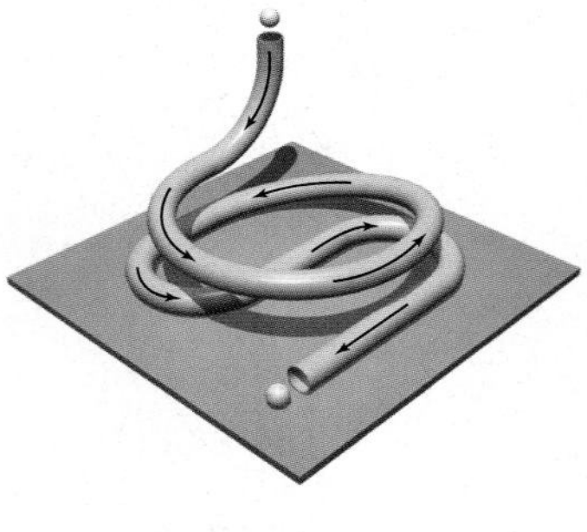

Figure 14 When the ball moves through the curved portions of the tube, it is accelerating because its velocity is changing. **Identify** *the forces acting on the ball as it falls through the tube.*

Centripetal Force

Look at the path the ball follows as it travels through the curved tube in **Figure 14.** The ball may accelerate in the straight sections of the pipe maze if it speeds up or slows down. However, when the ball enters a curve, even if its speed does not change, it is accelerating because its direction is changing. When the ball goes around a curve, the change in the direction of the velocity is toward the center of the curve. Acceleration toward the center of a curved or circular path is called **centripetal acceleration.**

According to the second law of motion, when the ball has centripetal acceleration, the direction of the net force on the ball also must be toward the center of the curved path. The net force exerted toward the center of a curved path is called a **centripetal force.** For the ball moving through the tube, the centripetal force is the force exerted by the walls of the tube on the ball.

Centripetal Force and Traction When a car rounds a curve on a highway, a centripetal force must be acting on the car to keep it moving in a curved path. This centripetal force is the frictional force, or the traction, between the tires and the road surface. If the road is slippery and the frictional force is small, the centripetal force might not be large enough to keep the car moving around the curve. Then the car will slide in a straight line. Anything that moves in a circle, such as the people on the amusement park ride in **Figure 15,** is doing so because a centripetal force is accelerating it toward the center.

Mini LAB

Observing Centripetal Force

Procedure

1. Thread a **string** about 1 m long through the holes of a **plastic, slotted ball.**
2. Swing the ball in a vertical circle.
3. Swing the ball at different speeds and observe the motion of the ball and the tension in the string.

Analysis

1. What force does the string exert on the ball when the ball is at the top, sides, and bottom of the swing?
2. How does the tension in the string depend on the speed of the ball?

Try at Home

Figure 15 Centripetal force keeps these riders moving in a circle.

Differentiated Instruction

Learning Disabled Make sure students realize that as an object moves in a circle, its change in direction is toward the center of the circle. Students can show this by moving a brick along the edge of a large circle. Every time they move the brick, they must twist it a bit so it fits on the circle. This twist shows the change in direction.

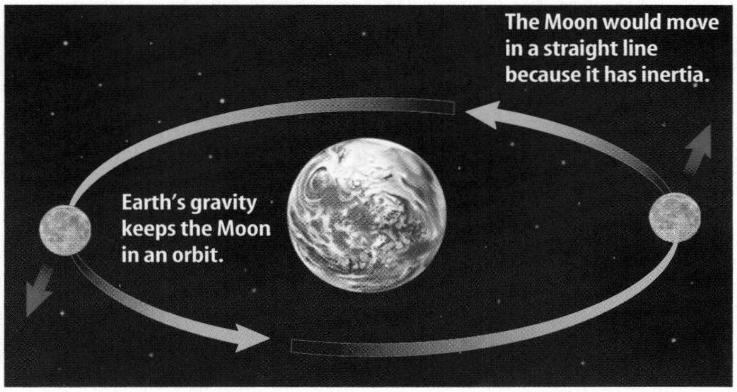

Figure 16 The Moon would move in a straight line except that Earth's gravity keeps pulling it toward Earth. This gives the Moon a nearly circular orbit.

Gravity Can Be a Centripetal Force Imagine whirling an object tied to a string above your head. The string exerts a centripetal force on the object that keeps it moving in a circular path. In the same way, Earth's gravity exerts a centripetal force on the Moon that keeps it moving in a nearly circular orbit, as shown in **Figure 16.**

section 2 review

Summary

Gravity

- According to the law of universal gravitation, the gravitational force between two objects depends on the masses of the objects and the distance between them.
- The acceleration due to gravity near Earth's surface has the value 9.8 m/s^2.
- Near Earth's surface, the gravitational force on an object with mass, m, is given by:

$$F = mg$$

Weight

- The weight of an object is related to its mass according to the equation:

$$W = mg$$

- An object in orbit seems to be weightless because it is falling around Earth.

Projectile Motion and Centripetal Force

- Projectiles follow a curved path because their horizontal motion is constant, but gravity causes the vertical motion to be changing.
- The net force on an object moving in a circular path is called the centripetal force.

Self Check

1. **Describe** how the gravitational force between two objects depends on the mass of the objects and the distance between them.
2. **Distinguish** between the mass of an object and the object's weight.
3. **Explain** what causes the path of a projectile to be curved.
4. **Describe** the force that causes the planets to stay in orbit around the Sun.
5. **Think Critically** Suppose Earth's mass increased, but its diameter didn't change. How would the acceleration due to gravity near Earth's surface change?

Applying Math

6. **Calculate Weight** On Earth, what is the weight of a large-screen TV that has a mass of 75 kg?
7. **Calculate Gravity on Mars** Find the acceleration due to gravity on Mars if a person with a mass of 60.0 kg weighs 222 N on Mars.
8. **Calculate Force** Find the force exerted by a rope on a 10-kg mass that is hanging from the rope.

More Section Review gpescience.com

Post Reading

Illustrations Have students create graphics or illustrations to explain the key ideas behind the following concepts: gravity, weight, projectile motion, and centripetal force. Remind students to use labeling to highlight central themes. Display illustrations for all to see.

3 Assess

DAILY INTERVENTION

Check For Understanding

Visual-Kinesthetic Toss a tennis ball gently across the room to a student who will catch it. Ask the students to describe the vertical motion of the ball. Did it ever speed up, slow down, or stop vertically? It slowed down on the way up, stopped and then sped up on the way down. Ask them to describe the horizontal motion in similar terms. What causes the change in vertical motion of the ball? gravity Is there any horizontal force once the ball is released? no

Reteach

Measure the Fall Have students measure the distance that either of the two balls shown in **Figure 9** fell between each flash. They can use a bar graph to show distance fallen versus flash number. Ask them to explain how this graph supports the idea that the balls are accelerating downward. The balls fall farther between successive flashes. L2 ELL P IS **Logical-Mathematical**

section 2 review

1. It increases as the mass of one or both objects increases, and it decreases as the distance between the objects increases.
2. Mass is a measure of the amount of matter an object contains. Weight is a measure of the force of gravity on an object. Weight changes if the gravitational force changes.
3. Gravity causes the vertical velocity of the projectile to change.
4. The Sun's gravitational force keeps them in orbit.
5. Standing on Earth's surface, you would be attracted by a larger mass, so the force of Earth's gravity and the acceleration of gravity would be greater.
6. Weight $= mg = 75\,kg \times 9.8\,m/s^2 = 735\,N$
7. $a = F/m = (222\,N)/(60\,kg) = 3.7\,m/s^2$
8. $F = ma = 10.0\,kg \times 9.8\,m/s^2 = 98\,N$

Assessment

Oral Ask students to explain why the astronauts and everything else in the space shuttle behave as if they were weightless. Everything in the shuttle is in free fall as the shuttle orbits Earth. Use **PASC,** p. 143.

BENCH TESTED

Real-World Problem

Purpose Students will observe the effect of air resistance on the gravitational acceleration of different shaped sheets of paper. L2 LS **Kinesthetic**

Process Skills measure, recognize cause and effect, formulate models, compare, infer

Time Required 30 minutes

Alternate Materials Make sure the sheets of paper are identical.

Safety Precautions Caution students to be careful when standing on stools or ladders.

Procedure

Teaching Strategies Stage a contest to determine which design maximizes the effect of air resistance. Have students practice timing the falling paper before entering data in their tables.

Troubleshooting Have students do at least three trials for each paper drop and record the average time in their data table.

Conclude and Apply

1. expected outcome: (in order of decreasing time) own design, flat paper, loosely crumpled, tightly crumpled
2. Shapes with greater exposed surface areas create more air resistance and fall more slowly.
3. Answers will vary.

LAB

GRAVITY AND AIR RESISTANCE

If you dropped a bowling ball and a feather from the same height on the Moon, they would both hit the surface at the same time. All objects dropped on Earth are attracted to Earth with the same acceleration. But on Earth, a bowling ball and a feather will not hit the ground at the same time. Air resistance slows the feather down.

Real-World Problem

How does air resistance affect the acceleration of falling objects?

Goals

- **Measure** the effect of air resistance on sheets of paper with different shapes.
- **Design** and create a shape from a piece of paper that maximizes air resistance.

Materials

paper (4 sheets of equal size)
scissors
meterstick
stopwatch
masking tape

Safety Precautions

Procedure

1. Copy the data table above in your Science Journal, or create it on a computer.
2. Measure a height of 2.5m on the wall and mark the height with a piece of masking tape.
3. Have one group member drop the flat sheet of paper from the 2.5-m mark. Use the stopwatch to time how long it takes for the paper to reach the ground. Record your time in your data table.

Effects of Air Resistance

Paper Type	Time
Flat paper	
Loosely crumpled paper	
Tightly crumpled paper	
Your paper design	

4. Crumple a sheet of paper into a loose ball and repeat step 3.
5. Crumple a sheet of paper into a tight ball and repeat step 3.
6. Use scissors to shape a piece of paper so that it will fall slowly. You may cut, tear, or fold your paper into any design you choose.

Conclude and Apply

1. **Compare** the falling times of the different sheets of paper.
2. **Explain** why the different-shaped papers fell at different speeds.
3. **Explain** how your design caused the force of air resistance on the paper to be greater than the air resistance on the other paper shapes.

Communicating Your Data

Compare your paper design with the designs created by your classmates. As a class, compile a list of characteristics that increase air resistance.

Assessment

Process Show students several photographs of falling sky divers and ask them to analyze the sky divers' body positions and infer the order of their velocities. Use **PASC,** p. 89.

Communicating Your Data

Encourage students to electronically represent their design using the appropriate software.

section 3

The Third Law of Motion

Reading Guide

What You'll Learn
- **State** Newton's third law of motion.
- **Identify** action and reaction forces.
- **Calculate** momentum.
- **Recognize** when momentum is conserved.

Why It's Important

The third law of motion explains how you affect Earth when you walk, and how Earth affects you.

Review Vocabulary

velocity: describes the speed and direction of a moving object

New Vocabulary
- third law of motion
- momentum
- law of conservation of momentum

Newton's Third Law

Push against a wall and what happens? If the wall is sturdy enough, usually nothing happens. If you pushed against a wall while wearing roller skates, you would go rolling backward. Your action on the wall produced a reaction—movement backward. This is a demonstration of Newton's third law of motion.

The **third law of motion** describes action-reaction pairs this way: When one object exerts a force on a second object, the second one exerts a force on the first that is equal in strength and opposite in direction. Another way to say this is "to every action force there is an equal and opposite reaction force."

Action and Reaction When a force is applied in nature, a reaction force occurs at the same time. When you jump on a trampoline, for example, you exert a downward force on the trampoline. Simultaneously, the trampoline exerts an equal force upward, sending you high into the air.

Action and reaction forces are acting on the two skaters in **Figure 17.** The male skater is pulling upward on the female skater, while the female skater is pulling downward on the male skater. The two forces are equal, but in opposite directions.

Figure 17 According to Newton's third law of motion, the two skaters exert forces on each other. The two forces are equal, but in opposite directions.

1 Motivate

INTERACTIVE CHALKBOARD PowerPoint® Presentations An editable Microsoft® PowerPoint® presentation is available on **Interactive Chalkboard** CD-ROM.

Bellringer

Section Focus Transparencies also are available on the Interactive Chalkboard CD-ROM. L2 ELL

SECTION 3 Section Focus Transparency **Fighting Fire** Chapter 4

It takes more than one firefighter to aim a fire hose. The force of the water shooting out of the nozzle causes a reaction that can be difficult to control.

1. Describe what happens if you step from a canoe or small boat onto a dock.
2. Does a garden hose need more than one person to hold it? What's the difference between a garden hose and a fire hose?
3. What would happen if the firefighters dropped the hose?

L2

The Laws of Motion

Reading Preview

Tie to Prior Knowledge

Motion of Different Objects Have students recall the motions of an untied, inflated balloon and a rocket. Tell them that the forces pushing these objects are governed by Newton's third law. In this section they will learn more about the third law.

Word Wall Post new vocabulary words on a chart or board. Play a game to encourage vocabulary development. For example, offer a clue to the meaning of a word. Ask students to guess the word. Continue giving clues until students identify the word. Allow students to take your place as they guess the word.

Section 3 Resource Manager

Chapter *FAST FILE* Resources
- Transparency Activity, p. 46
- Directed Reading for Content Mastery, p. 22
- Enrichment, p. 32
- Reinforcement, p. 29
- Lab Worksheet, pp. 7–8
- Lab Activity, pp. 13–16
- **Home and Community Involvement,** p. 49

2 Teach

Text Question Answer

She pushes the water backward.

INTEGRATE Career

Space Medicine Some scientists think that living in outer space may arrest the spread of arthritis and be beneficial because stress on bones is much smaller than on Earth. Medical research is being carried out in outer space that could lead to a better understanding of diseases such as sickle-cell anemia.

Research Have students research the different kinds of medical projects done on space-shuttle missions.

Reading Check

Answer they are acting on different objects

Caption Answer

Figure 18 opposite the direction of expelled gas

Visual Learning

Figure 18 Review the forces that move the car shown here. Draw the car on the board, and indicate gas particles inside the rocket engine. Emphasize that the action force is the rocket engine pushing the gas particles, and the reaction force is the gas particles against the rocket engine. L2 LS **Visual-Spatial**

INTEGRATE Career

Space Medicine Astronauts who stay in outer space for extended periods of time may develop health problems. Their muscles, for example, may begin to weaken because they don't have to exert as much force to get the same reaction as they do on Earth. A branch of medicine called space medicine deals with the possible health problems that astronauts may experience. Research some other health risks that are involved in going into outer space.

Action and Reaction Forces Don't Cancel If action and reaction forces are equal, you might wonder how some things ever happen. For example, how does a swimmer move through the water in a pool if each time she pushes on the water, the water pushes back on her? According to the third law of motion, action and reaction forces act on different objects. Thus, even though the forces are equal, they are not balanced because they act on different objects. In the case of the swimmer, as she "acts" on the water, the "reaction" of the water pushes her forward. Thus, a net force, or unbalanced force, acts on her so a change in her motion occurs. As the swimmer moves forward in the water, how does she make the water move?

Reading Check *Why don't action and reaction forces cancel?*

Rocket Propulsion Suppose you are standing on skates holding a softball. You exert a force on the softball when you throw the softball. According to Newton's third law, the softball exerts a force on you. This force pushes you in the direction opposite the softball's motion. Rockets use the same principle to move even in the vacuum of outer space. In the rocket engine, burning fuel produces hot gases. The rocket engine exerts a force on these gases and causes them to escape out the back of the rocket. By Newton's third law, the gases exert a force on the rocket and push it forward. The car in **Figure 18** uses a rocket engine to propel it forward. **Figure 19** shows how rockets were used to travel to the Moon.

Figure 18 Newton's third law enables the rocket engine to push the car forward. The rocket engine pushes the hot gases produced by burning fuel backward out of the engine's nozzle. By the third law, the gases exert a force of equal size on the engine in the forward direction.
Infer *the direction of the car's acceleration when the rocket engine is fired.*

Science Journal

Newton's Third Law Have students use Newton's third law to describe the similarities between a person walking on a sidewalk and a fish swimming in the ocean. A person exerts a force on the sidewalk, and the sidewalk pushes back on the person, moving the person forward. A fish pushes on water, and the reaction force of the water on the fish propels the fish forward. L1 LS **Linguistic**

Reading Strategy

Science Journal As students read this chapter, ask them to develop a log of their reading. The log should include main points, sketches, questions regarding the text, and any other thoughts they have as they read the text. Read the logs and respond to students' efforts without assigning a grade.

NATIONAL GEOGRAPHIC

VISUALIZING ROCKET MOTION

Figure 19

On the afternoon of July 16, 1969, *Apollo 11* lifted off from Cape Kennedy, Florida, bound for the Moon. Eight days later, the spacecraft returned to Earth, splashing down safely in the Pacific Ocean. The motion of the spacecraft to the Moon and back is governed by Newton's laws of motion.

◀ *Apollo 11* roars toward the Moon. At launch, a rocket's engines must produce enough force and acceleration to overcome the pull of Earth's gravity. A rocket's liftoff is an illustration of Newton's third law: For every action there is an equal and opposite reaction.

▲ As *Apollo* rises, it burns fuel and ejects its rocket booster engines. This decreases its mass, and helps *Apollo* move faster. This is Newton's second law in action: As mass decreases, acceleration can increase.

▶ The lunar module uses other engines to slow down and ease into a soft touchdown on the Moon. A day later, the same engines lift the lunar module again into outer space.

▲ The lunar module returns to the *Apollo* spacecraft, which fires its engines to start it moving toward Earth. As the spacecraft gets closer to Earth, the gravitational force exerted by Earth becomes larger, continually increasing the acceleration of the spacecraft.

NATIONAL GEOGRAPHIC

Visualizing Rocket Motion

Have students examine the pictures and read the captions. Then ask the following questions.

When *Apollo 11* was launched, what were the equal and opposite forces? The thrust from the rocket engines pushed on the rocket and the rocket pushed back.

As *Apollo* ejected its spent rocket booster, what equation described the relationship between mass and acceleration? $F = ma$

As the rocket returns to Earth, why is the rocket able to shut off its engines? The rocket will continue to move toward Earth after the engines are turned off because of inertia.

Activity

Apollo 11 Have the students write a poem about the *Apollo 11* mission and Newton's laws of motion. L2 LS **Linguistics** P

Fun Fact

Squid and octopuses use Newton's third law as a means of propulsion. They take in water and forcibly expel it through a siphon in a sudden spurt that pushes them through the water. Squid are very streamlined and can achieve speeds of 37 km/h.

Quick Demo

Newton's Third Law

Materials party balloons, tape, 15-m piece of string, plastic straw, two vertical supports

Estimated Time two minutes

Procedure Put the string though the straw and stretch it between two vertical supports about 10 m apart. Blow up the balloon and tape it to the straw. Let go and have the students observe that air molecules pushing against the front of the balloon propel it backward.

Differentiated Instruction

English-Language Learners Have students write a sentence that describes or includes each of the following words, and then organize the sentences into a paragraph about space travel: rocket, force, spacecraft, booster rocket, gravity, planet, the Moon.

Cultural Diversity

And the Rockets' Red Glare... Centuries ago, the Chinese invented gunpowder. Although it was first used during celebrations, gunpowder was quickly adapted for war purposes. By the fourteenth century, Chinese armies were using it in rockets. When the gunpowder ignited, it expelled hot gases, which propelled the rockets forward.

IDENTIFYING Misconceptions

Force and Momentum Many students confuse the ideas of force and momentum. Sometimes when comparing two moving objects, students will say that one object has more force than the other, when they really should say that the object has more momentum than the other. Be alert for statements such as these during class discussions and help the students to use the scientific terms correctly and precisely.

Discussion

Momentum in Football Momentum is important to football players. What is the advantage of a football player having a large momentum? It makes it harder to change the player's velocity.

Applying Math

Math Standards

National: 1, 2, 9

Answers to Practice Problems

1. 36,400 kg·m/s
2. 40 m/s
3. 65 kg

Virtual Labs

Crash! *How is momentum conserved in a vehicle collision?*

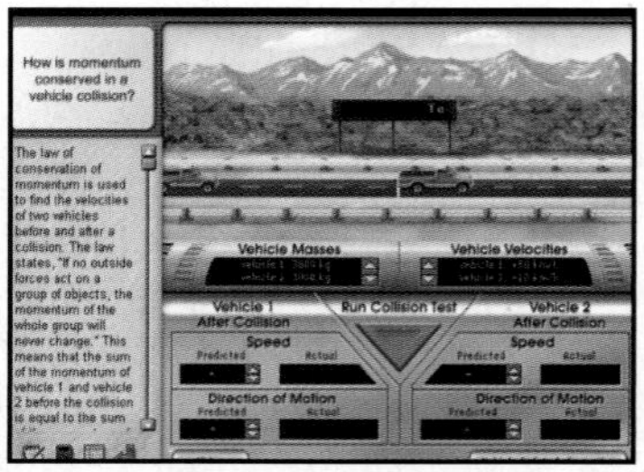

Momentum

A moving object has a property called momentum that is related to how much force is needed to change its motion. The **momentum** of an object is the product of its mass and velocity. Momentum is given the symbol p and can be calculated with the following equation:

Momentum Equation

momentum (kg m/s) = mass (kg) × velocity (m/s)

$$p = mv$$

The unit for momentum is kg·m/s. Notice that momentum has a direction because velocity has a direction.

Applying Math — Solve a Simple Equation

THE MOMENTUM OF A SPRINTER At the end of a race, a sprinter with a mass of 80 kg has a speed of 10 m/s. What is the sprinter's momentum?

IDENTIFY known values and the unknown value

Identify the known values:

a sprinter with a mass of 80 kg means $m = 80$ kg

has a speed of 10 m/s means $v = 10$ m/s

Identify the unknown value:

What is the sprinter's momentum? means $p = ?$ kg•m/s

SOLVE the problem

Substitute the known values $m = 80$ kg and $v = 10$ m/s into the momentum equation:

$$p = mv = (80 \text{ kg})(10 \text{ m/s}) = 800 \text{ kg•m/s}$$

CHECK your answer

Does your answer seem reasonable? Check your answer by dividing the momentum you calculated by the mass given in the problem. The result should be the speed given in the problem.

Practice Problems

1. What is the momentum of a car with a mass of 1,300 kg traveling at a speed of 28 m/s?
2. A baseball thrown by a pitcher has a momentum of 6.0 kg•m/s. If the baseball's mass is 0.15 kg, what is the baseball's speed?
3. What is the mass of a person walking at a speed of 0.8 m/s if their momentum is 52.0 kg•m/s?

For more practice problems go to page 879, and visit Math Practice at gpescience.com.

Differentiated Instruction

Challenge Newton actually worded his second law as force equals the change in momentum divided by the change in time. Explain how this is equivalent to $F = ma$. F = ma; Δp = mΔv; F = Δp/t; F = m(Δv)/ t; a = Δv/t so F = ma L3 LS **Logical-Mathematical**

Post Reading

Science Journal After reading Newton's Third Law, Momentum, and the Law of Conservation of Momentum, have students work in teams to create a demonstration that illustrates the main ideas behind these concepts. Remind students to follow the text when designing their projects. They may also use outside resources.

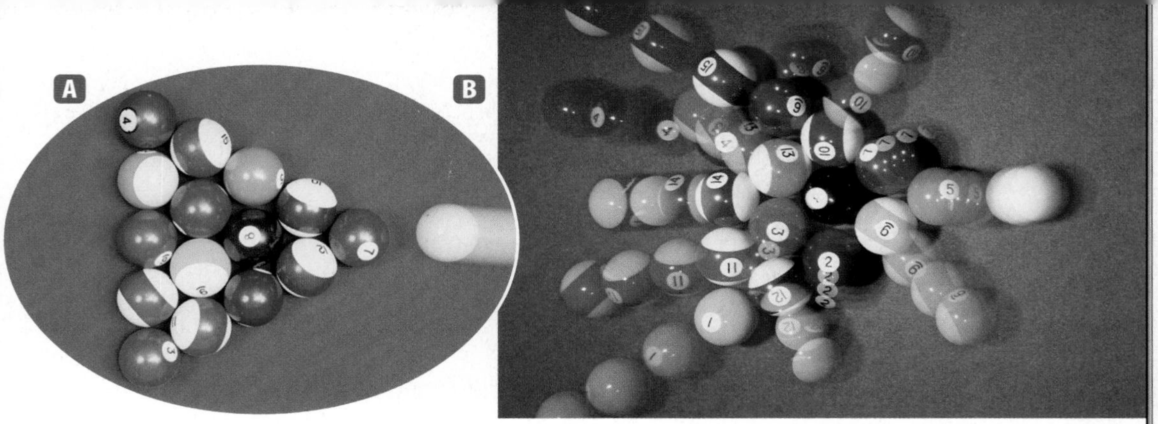

Law of Conservation of Momentum The momentum of an object doesn't change unless its mass, velocity, or both change. Momentum, however, can be transferred from one object to another. Consider the game of pool shown in **Figure 20.**

When the cue ball hits the group of balls that are motionless, the cue ball slows down and the rest of the balls begin to move. The momentum the group of balls gained is equal to the momentum that the cue ball lost. The total momentum of all the balls just before and after the collision would be the same. If no other forces act on the balls, their total momentum is conserved—it isn't lost or created. This is the **law of conservation of momentum**—if a group of objects exerts forces only on each other, their total momentum doesn't change.

Figure 20 Momentum is transferred in collisions. **A** Before the collision, only the cue ball has momentum. **B** When the cue ball strikes the other balls, it transfers some of its momentum to them.

section 3 review

Summary

Newton's Third Law

- According to Newton's third law of motion, for every action force, there is an equal and opposite reaction force.
- Action and reaction forces act on different objects.

Momentum

- The momentum of an object is the product of its mass and velocity:

$$p = mv$$

The Law of Conservation of Momentum

- According to the law of conservation of momentum, if objects exert forces only on each other, their total momentum is conserved.
- In a collision, momentum is transferred from one object to another.

Self Check

1. **Determine** You push against a wall with a force of 50 N. If the wall doesn't move, what is the net force on you?
2. **Explain** how a rocket can move through outer space where there is no matter for it to push on.
3. **Compare** the momentum of a 6,300-kg elephant walking 0.11 m/s and a 50-kg dolphin swimming 10.4 m/s.
4. **Describe** what happens to the momentum of two billiard balls that collide.
5. **Think Critically** A ballet director assigns slow, graceful steps to larger dancers, and quick movements to smaller dancers. Why is this plan successful?

Applying Math

6. **Calculate Momentum** What is the momentum of a 100-kg football player running at a speed of 4 m/s?

Visual Learning

Figure 20 Point out that the balls scatter left and right as they are deflected by the cue ball. Tell students that momentum is conserved separately in each direction. Since the balls have the same mass, the sum of the forward velocities of the balls equals the cue ball's initial forward velocity. The sum of the left velocities is equal to the sum of the right velocities. Why do the balls eventually slow and stop? friction

3 Assess

DAILY INTERVENTION

Check for Understanding

Visual-Kinesthetic Have two students of different sizes stand facing one another and push on each others' hands, palm to palm, without either student pushing the other over. Ask who is exerting the larger force. They both exert the same force. Have one student stand in stockinged feet so that he or she slides when pushed. Now which one exerts the greater force? They are still the same. If the forces are the same, why does one move and not the other? One has a higher frictional force keeping him or her stationary.

Reteach

Action/Reaction Ask students to draw and explain action/reaction force arrows for a box sitting on the ground and for a person running. L2 IS **Visual-Spatial**

section 3 review

1. You are not accelerating, so $F_{net} = 0$. The wall pushes back on you with a force equal to the force you push on it. The static friction between your feet and the floor keeps you from moving.
2. The rocket exerts a force on gas molecules, pushing them backward. The gas molecules exert a force on the rocket, pushing it forward.
3. The dolphin's momentum is $p = (50\text{ kg})(10.4\text{ m/s}) = 520\text{ kg·m/s}$. The elephant's momentum is $p = (6{,}300\text{ kg})(0.11\text{ m/s}) = 693\text{ kg·m/s}$.
4. The two balls exchange momentum.
5. It takes less force for a person with less mass to move quickly than for a person with more mass to do so.
6. $p = mv = 100\text{ kg} \times 4\text{ m/s} = 400\text{ kg m/s}$

Assessment

Process Provide students with photographs of various types of activities or collisions. Have them describe how momentum is conserved in each situation. Use **PASC,** p. 89.

SECTION 3 The Third Law of Motion 117

BENCH TESTED

Video Lab available.

Real-World Problem

Purpose Students will observe the effects of mass and velocity on the momentum of rolling objects. L2 LS **Kinesthetic**

Process Skills observe, measure, compare, use numbers, use space/time relationship, sequence, recognize cause and effect, infer

Time Required one class period

Alternate Materials A foam rubber ball, golf ball, or hockey ball could replace the tennis ball and racquetball.

Safety Precautions Caution students never to throw the balls during the activity and to roll the baseball only when other students are clear of the ball's path.

Procedure

Teaching Strategy Have students practice rolling the balls at different speeds and rolling the balls into the softball. Clear away floor space in your room or take students outside to provide enough space for each group.

LAB

The Momentum of Colliding Objects

Goals

- **Observe** and calculate the momentum of different balls.
- **Compare** the results of collisions involving different amounts of momentum.

Materials

meterstick
softball
racquetball
tennis ball
baseball
stopwatch
masking tape
balance

Safety Precautions

Real-World Problem

Many scientists hypothesize that dinosaurs became extinct 65 million years ago when an asteroid collided with Earth. The asteroid's diameter was probably no more than 10 km. Earth's diameter is more than 12,700 km. How could an object that size change Earth's climate enough to cause the extinction of animals that had dominated life on Earth for 140 million years? The asteroid could have caused such damage because it may have been traveling at a velocity of 50 m/s, and had a huge amount of momentum. The combination of an object's velocity and mass will determine how much force it can exert. How do the mass and velocity of a moving object affect its momentum?

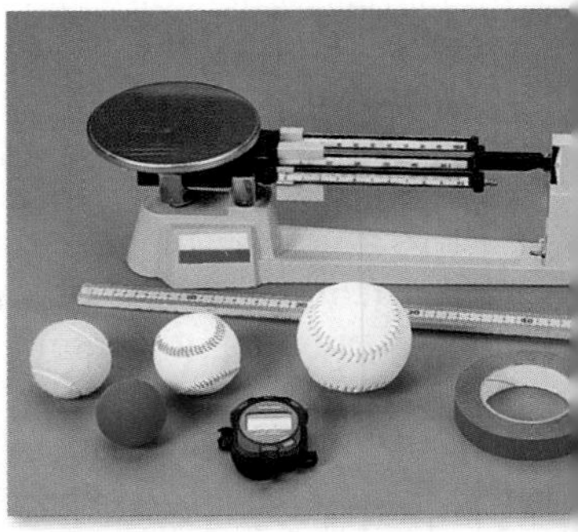

Momentum of Colliding Balls

Action	Time	Velocity	Mass	Momentum	Distance Softball Moved
Racquetball rolled slowly			0.04		
Racquetball rolled quickly			0.04		
Tennis ball rolled slowly	Answers will vary.	Answers will vary.	0.06	Answers will vary.	Answers will vary.
Tennis ball rolled quickly			0.06		
Baseball rolled slowly			0.14		
Baseball rolled quickly			0.14		

Active Reading

Synthesis Journal In this strategy, students reflect on a project, a paper, or a performance task and plan for personal application. Have each student divide a sheet of paper into three sections labeled *What I did*, *What I learned*, and *How I can use it*. Have students write a Synthesis Journal related to this lab.

Alternative Inquiry Lab

Momentum Supply students with the materials listed for this lab, and ask them to find a way to give each ball the same momentum. Have them design a data table and a method to test when the momentum of each ball is equal to the others.

Using Scientific Methods

Procedure

1. Copy the data table on the previous page in your Science Journal.
2. Use the balance to measure the mass of the racquetball, tennis ball, and baseball. Record these masses in your data table.
3. Measure a 2-m distance on the floor and mark it with two pieces of masking tape.
4. Place the softball on one piece of tape. Starting from the other piece of tape, slowly roll the racquetball toward the center of the softball.
5. Use a stopwatch to time how long it takes the racquetball to roll the 2-m distance and hit the softball. Record this time in your data table.
6. Measure and record the distance the racquetball moved the softball.
7. Repeat steps 4–6, rolling the racquetball quickly.
8. Repeat steps 4–6, rolling the tennis ball slowly, then quickly.
9. Repeat steps 4–6, rolling the baseball slowly, then quickly.

Distance Softball Moved and Momentum of Colliding Ball

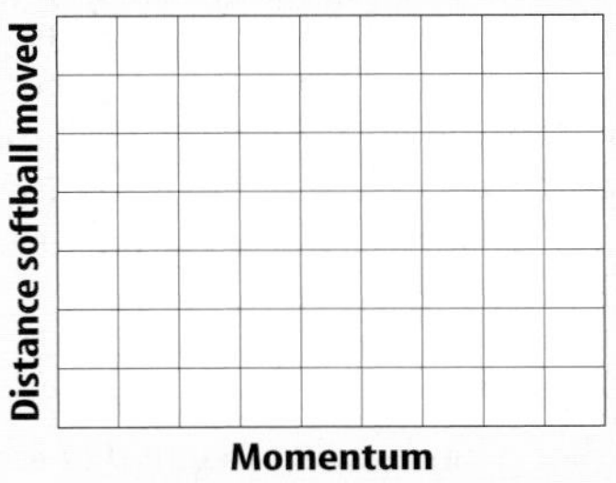

Analyze Your Data

1. **Calculate** the momentum for each type of ball and action using the formula $p = mv$. Record your calculations in the data table.
2. **Graph** the relationship between the momentum of each ball and the distance the softball was moved using a graph like the one shown.

Conclude and Apply

1. **Infer** from your graph how the distance the softball moves after each collision depends on the momentum of the ball that hits it.
2. **Explain** how the motion of the balls after they collide can be determined by Newton's laws of motion.

Communicating Your Data

Compare your graph with the graphs made by other students in your class. **Discuss** why the graphs might look different.

119

Tie to Prior Knowledge Students will be aware that more massive moving objects and objects traveling with greater speeds will produce more force.

Analyze Your Data

Expected Outcome The high velocity baseball will have the greatest momentum, and the slow velocity racquetball will have the least momentum.

Answer to Questions

1. Calculations should show that the momentum of a ball increases as its speed increases.
2. The graph should have a positive (diagonally upward) slope.

Error Analysis Have students compare their graphs with other lab groups. Ask which of their predictions matched their results, and have them explain those that did not. Have students identify possible sources of measurement, timing or procedural errors.

Conclude and Apply

1. The graph should show that as the momentum of the colliding ball increases, so does the distance the softball moves.
2. By the third law of motion, when the balls collide, they exert the same force on each other. The softball has the larger mass, so according to the second law its acceleration will be less than the smaller ball.

✓ Assessment

Oral Ask students if it is possible for an object to have a negative value for momentum. Yes; velocity has both direction and magnitude. Once a positive direction is chosen, velocity in the opposite direction is negative and momentum is negative. Use **PASC,** p. 143.

Communicating Your Data

Divide the class into small groups for the discussion so that all students have the opportunity to describe their experiences with the sports.

TIME

Content Background

Newton's three laws of motion and the law of universal gravitation have proven to be able to describe the motion of objects ranging from galaxies to raindrops. Newton believed that the forces involved in the behavior of ordinary objects, such as the forces that caused an apple to fall from a tree, were the same forces that controlled the motions of planets and moons. The law of universal gravitation and the three laws of motion applied to all objects. Newton also believed that matter was made of indivisible particles and that the forces of gravity, electricity and magnetism determined the behavior of these particles.

Newton was correct in that gravity, electricity and magnetism also act at the atomic level. However, the gravitational force is so much weaker than the electromagnetic force that it can be ignored at the atomic level. In addition, there are two other forces, the strong and the weak nuclear forces, that are involved in nuclear reactions that were unknown to Newton.

Historical Significance

What Newton contributed to science during his first 25 years cannot be underestimated. More than 300 years later, scientists and engineers still use his laws to understand natural phenomena and to design and develop new technologies.

TIME **SCIENCE** AND HISTORY

SCIENCE CAN CHANGE THE COURSE OF HISTORY!

Newton and the Plague

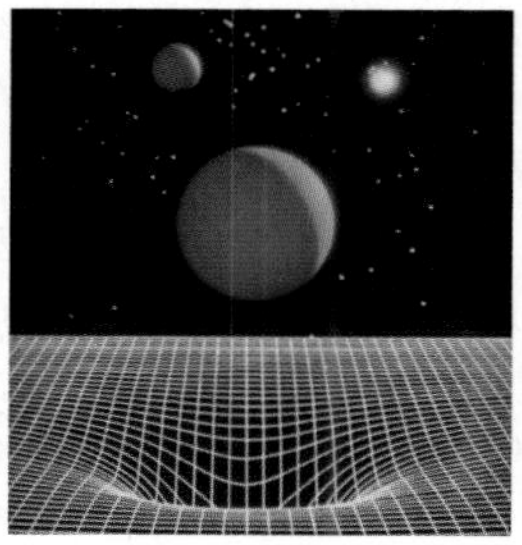

In Einstein's theory of general relativity, gravity is due to a distortion in space-time.

In 1665, the bubonic plague swept through England and other parts of Europe. Isaac Newton, then a 23-year-old university student, returned to his family's farm until Cambridge university reopened. To occupy his time, Newton made a list of 22 questions. During the next 18 months, Newton buried himself in the search for answers. And in that brief time, Newton developed calculus, the three laws of motion, and the universal law of gravitation!

The Laws of Motion

Earlier philosophers thought that force was necessary to keep an object moving. By analyzing the data collected by Galileo and others, Newton realized that forces did not cause motion. Instead, forces cause a change in motion. Newton came to understand that force and acceleration were related and that objects exert equal and opposite forces on each other. Newton's three laws of motion were able to explain how all things moved, from an apple falling from a tree to the motions of the moon and the planets, in terms of force, mass, and acceleration.

Isaac Newton was a university student when he developed the laws of motion.

What is gravity?

Using the calculus and data on the motion of the planets, Newton deduced the law of universal gravitation. This law enabled the force of gravity between any two objects to be calculated, if their masses and the distance between them were known.

Newton was able to show mathematically that the law of universal gravitation predicted that the planets' orbits should be ellipses, just as Johannes Kepler had discovered two generations earlier. The application of Newton's laws of motion and the law of universal gravitation also were able to explain phenomena such as tides, the motion of the moon and the planets, and the bulge at the Earth's equator.

A Different View of Gravity

In 1916, Albert Einstein proposed a different model for gravity called the general theory of relativity. In Einstein's model, objects create distortions in space-time, like a bowling ball dropped on a sheet. What we see as the force of gravity is the motion of an object on distorted space-time. Today, Einstein's theory is used to help explain the nature of the big bang and the structure of the universe.

Investigate **Research how both Newton's law of gravitation and Einstein's general theory of relativity have been used to develop the current model of the universe.**

TIME

For more information, visit gpescience.com

Investigate The existence of dark matter has been hypothesized to explain the rotations and motions of galaxies that seem to violate Newton's laws of motion. For Newton's laws to be satisfied, these galaxies must contain additional matter that has not been detected directly. Einstein's general theory of relativity explains how the structure of space-time changed as the universe expanded after the big bang.

Resources for Teachers and Students

Isaac Newton: The Greatest Scientist of All Time Margaret Jean Anderson, Enslow Publishers, Incorporated, 1996

Albert Einstein: Physicist and Genius. Joyce Goldenstern, Enslow Publishers, Incorporated, 1994

Reviewing Main Ideas

Section 1 The First Two Laws of Motion

1. According to the first law of motion, the velocity of an object doesn't change unless an unbalanced net force acts on the object.
2. Inertia is the tendency of an object to resist a change in its motion.
3. The second law of motion states that a net force causes an object to accelerate in the direction of the net force and that the acceleration is given by

$$a = \frac{F_{net}}{m}$$

4. Projectiles travel in a curved path because of their horizontal motion and vertical acceleration due to gravity.
5. The centripetal force is the net force on an object in circular motion and is directed toward the center of the circular path.

Section 2 Gravity

1. Gravity is an attractive force between any two objects with mass. The gravitational force depends on the masses of the objects and the distance between them.
2. The gravitational acceleration, g, near Earth's surface equals 9.8 m/s^2. The force of gravity on an object with mass, m, is:

$$F = mg$$

3. The weight of an object near Earth's surface is:

$$W = mg$$

Section 3 The Third Law of Motion

1. Newton's third law of motion states that for every action there is an equal and opposite reaction.
2. The momentum of an object can be calculated by the equation $p = mv$.

3. When two objects collide, momentum can be conserved. Some of the momentum from one object is transferred to the other.

FOLDABLES™ Use the Foldable that you made at the beginning of this chapter to help you review the laws of motion.

chapter Study Guide 4

Reviewing Main Ideas

Summary statements can be used by students to review the major concepts of the chapter.

Science Online

Visit gpescience.com
More Section Review
Interactive Tutor
Vocabulary PuzzleMaker
More Chapter Review
Standardized Test Practice

Assessment Transparency

For additional assessment questions, use the *Assessment Transparency* located in the transparency book.

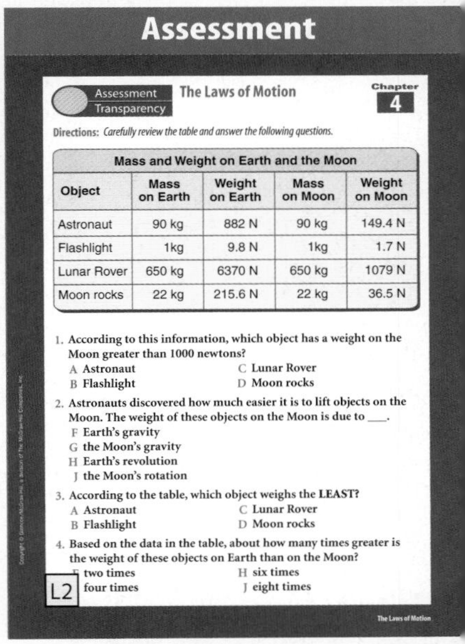

Assessment

Assessment Transparency — The Laws of Motion — Chapter 4

Directions: *Carefully review the table and answer the following questions.*

Mass and Weight on Earth and the Moon

Object	Mass on Earth	Weight on Earth	Mass on Moon	Weight on Moon
Astronaut	90 kg	882 N	90 kg	149.4 N
Flashlight	1kg	9.8 N	1kg	1.7 N
Lunar Rover	650 kg	6370 N	650 kg	1079 N
Moon rocks	22 kg	215.6 N	22 kg	36.5 N

1. According to this information, which object has a weight on the Moon greater than 1000 newtons?
   A Astronaut C Lunar Rover
   B Flashlight D Moon rocks
2. Astronauts discovered how much easier it is to lift objects on the Moon. The weight of these objects on the Moon is due to ____.
   F Earth's gravity
   G the Moon's gravity
   H Earth's revolution
   J the Moon's rotation
3. According to the table, which object weighs the LEAST?
   A Astronaut C Lunar Rover
   B Flashlight D Moon rocks
4. Based on the data in the table, about how many times greater is the weight of these objects on Earth than on the Moon?
   F two times H six times
   four times J eight times

L2

The Laws of Motion

FOLDABLES™ Have students use their Foldables to review the content of the chapter. Have students work in pairs to describe situations illustrating each of the three laws of motion.

Using Vocabulary

1. Newton's third law of motion
2. momentum
3. weight
4. centripetal force
5. gravity
6. Newton's second law of motion

Checking Concepts

7. D	11. B
8. A	12. C
9. B	13. A
10. B	14. C

Interpreting Graphics

15. See student page.
16. C

Using Vocabulary

centripetal acceleration p. 110	law of conservation of momentum p. 117
centripetal force p. 110	momentum p. 116
first law of motion p. 98	second law of motion p. 102
gravity p. 104	third law of motion p. 113
inertia p. 99	weight p. 106

Complete each statement using a word(s) from the vocabulary list above.

1. The way in which objects exert forces on each other is described by _________.
2. The _________ of an object depends on its mass and velocity.
3. The _________ of an object is different on other planets in the solar system.
4. When an object moves in a circular path, the net force is called a(n) _________.
5. The attractive force between two objects that depends on their masses and the distance between them is _________.
6. _________ relates the net force exerted on an object to its mass and acceleration.

Checking Concepts

Choose the best answer for each question.

7. What is the gravitational force exerted on an object called?
   A) centripetal force **C)** momentum
   B) friction **D)** weight
8. Which of the following best describes why projectiles move in a curved path?
   A) They have horizontal velocity and vertical acceleration.
   B) They have momentum.
   C) They have mass.
   D) They have weight.
9. Which of the following explains why astronauts seem weightless in orbit?
   A) Earth's gravity is much less in orbit.
   B) The space shuttle is in free fall.
   C) The gravity of Earth and the Sun cancel.
   D) The centripetal force on the shuttle balances Earth's gravity.
10. Which of the following exerts the strongest gravitational force on you?
   A) the Moon **C)** the Sun
   B) Earth **D)** this book

Use the graph below to answer question 11.

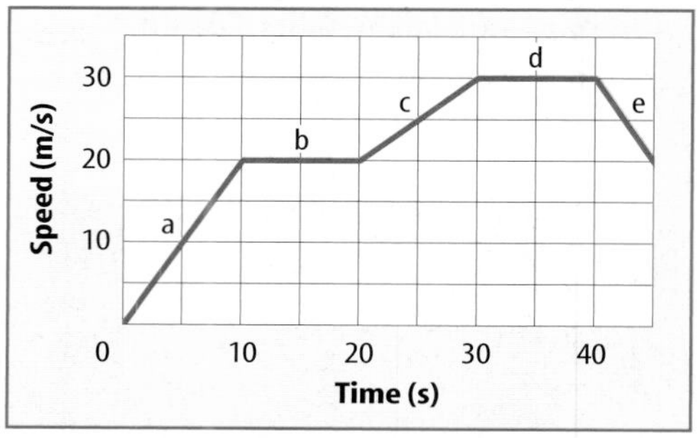

11. The graph shows the speed of a car moving in a straight line. Over which segments are the forces on the car balanced?
   A) A and C **C)** C and E
   B) B and D **D)** D only
12. Which of the following is true about an object in free fall?
   A) Its acceleration depends on its mass.
   B) It has no inertia.
   C) It pulls on Earth, and Earth pulls on it.
   D) Its momentum is constant.
13. The acceleration of an object is in the same direction as which of the following?
   A) net force **C)** static friction
   B) air resistance **D)** gravity
14. Which of the following is NOT a force?
   A) weight **C)** momentum
   B) friction **D)** air resistance

Use the ExamView® Pro Test Bank CD-ROM to:

- create multiple versions of tests
- create modified tests with one mouse click for inclusion students
- edit existing questions and add your own questions
- build tests aligned with state standards using built-in State Curriculum Tags
- change English tests to Spanish with one mouse click and vice versa

Interpreting Graphics

15. Copy and complete the following concept map on forces.

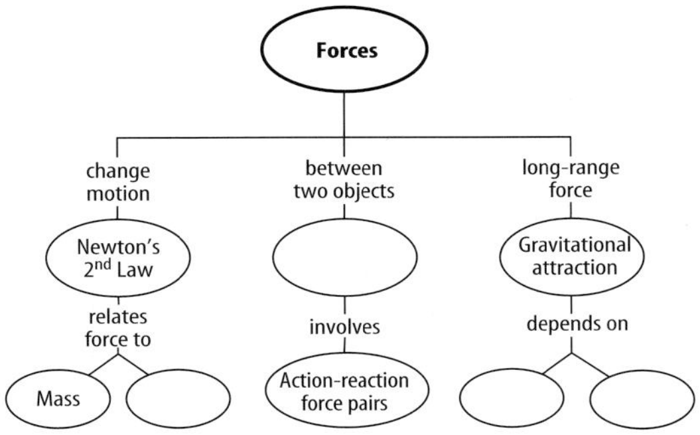

Use the table below to answer questions 16–18.

Time of Fall for Dropped Objects		
Object	**Mass (g)**	**Time of Fall (s)**
A	5.0	2.0
B	5.0	1.0
C	30.0	0.5
D	35.0	1.5

16. If the objects in the data table above all fell the same distance, which object fell with the greatest average speed?

Thinking Critically

17. **Describe** the forces acting on a softball after it leaves the pitcher's hand. Ignore the effects of air resistance.

18. **Determine** the direction of the net force on a book sliding on a table if the book is slowing down.

19. **Explain** whether there can be any forces acting on a car moving in a straight line with constant speed.

20. **Explain** You pull a door open. If the force the door exerts on you is equal to the force you exert on the door, why don't you move?

21. **Predict** Suppose you are standing on a bathroom scale next to a sink. How does the reading on the scale change if you push down on the sink?

22. **Describe** the action and reaction force pairs involved when an object falls toward Earth. Ignore the effects of air resistance.

Applying Math

23. **Calculate Mass** Find your mass if a scale on Earth reads 650 N when you stand on it.

24. **Calculate Acceleration of Gravity** You weigh yourself at the top of a high mountain and the scale reads 720 N. If your mass is 75 kg, what is the acceleration of gravity at your location?

Use the figure below to answer question 25.

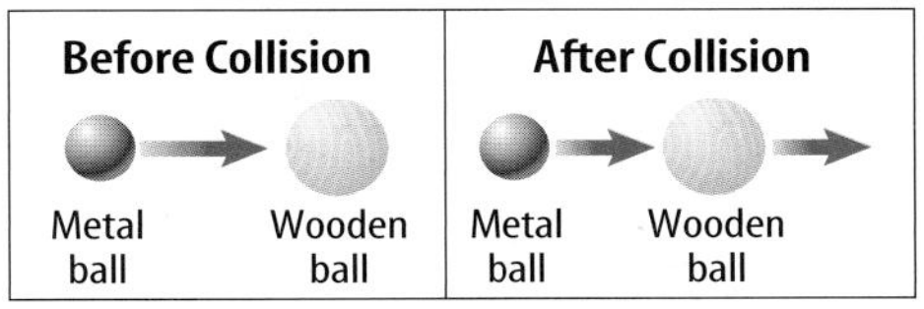

25. **Calculate Speed** The 2-kg metal ball moving at a speed of 3 m/s strikes a 1-kg wooden ball that is at rest. After the collision, the speed of the metal ball is 1 m/s. Assuming momentum is conserved, what is the speed of the wooden ball?

26. **Calculate Mass** Find the mass of a car that has a speed of 30 m/s and a momentum of 45,000 kg·m/s.

27. **Calculate Sliding Friction** A box being pushed with a force of 85 N slides along the floor with a constant speed. What is the force of sliding friction on the box?

Assessment Resources

Reproducible Masters

Chapter *Fast File* Resources
- Chapter Review, pp. 37–38
- Chapter Tests, pp. 39–42
- Assessment Transparency Activity, p. 49

Glencoe Science Web site
- Chapter Review Test
- Standardized Test Practice

Glencoe Technology
- Assessment Transparency
- Exam*View*® Pro Testmaker
- MindJogger Videoquiz
- Interactive Chalkboard

chapter 4 Review

Thinking Critically

17. The only force acting on the ball is the force of gravity.
18. The book is slowing down, so the acceleration is in the direction opposite the motion. The net force is in the same direction as the acceleration.
19. Yes, there can be forces acting on the car, but the forces are balanced so that the net force is zero.
20. The force of static friction between your feet and the floor balances the force the door exerts on you.
21. The reading on the scale decreases because the sink pushes up on you. The upward force exerted by the scale and the sink now balance your weight, so the force exerted by the scale decreases.
22. Earth pulls on the object and the object pulls on Earth.

Applying Math

Math Standards

National: 1, 2, 9

23. $m = \frac{F}{g} = \frac{(650\ N)}{(9.8\ m/s^2)} = 66.3\ kg$

24. $g = \frac{F}{m} = \frac{(720\ N)}{(75\ kg)} = 9.6\ m/s^2$

25. $m_1v_1 = m_1v_1' + m_2v_2$

$2\ kg \times 3\ m/s = 6\ kg\ m/s$

$2\ kg \times 1\ m/s = 2\ kg\ m/s$

$6\ kg\ m/s - 2\ kg\ m/s = 4\ kg\ m/s$

$\frac{(4\ kg\ m/s)}{1\ kg} = 4\ m/s$

26. $m = \frac{p}{v} = \frac{(45{,}000\ kg\ m/s)}{(30\ m/s)} = 1500\ kg$

27. $F = 85\ N$

Answer Sheet An answer sheet can be found at **gpescience.com**.

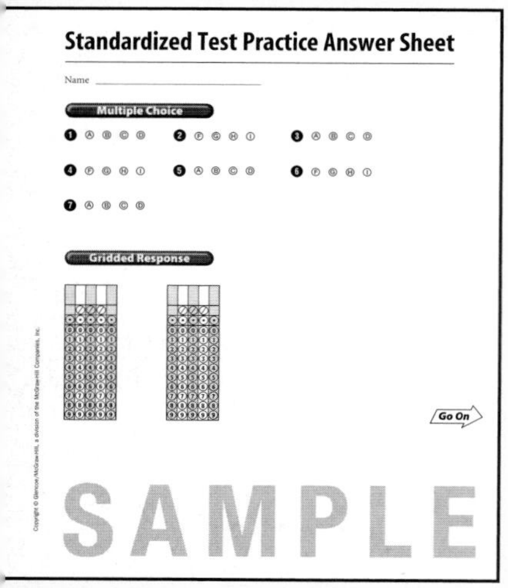

Multiple Choice

1. C
2. A
3. C
4. C
5. A
6. B

chapter 4 Standardized Test Practice

Record your answers on the answer sheet provided by your teacher or on a sheet of paper.

Multiple Choice

1. The net force on an object moving with constant speed in circular motion is in which direction?
   - **A.** downward
   - **B.** opposite to the object's motion
   - **C.** toward the center of the circle
   - **D.** in the direction of the object's velocity

Use the table below to answer questions 2–4.

Object in Free Fall with Air Resistance	
Time (s)	**Speed (m/s)**
0	0
1	9.1
2	15.1
3	18.1
4	19.3
5	19.9

2. Over which of the following time intervals is the acceleration of the object the greatest?
   - **A.** 0 s to 1 s
   - **B.** 1 s to 2 s
   - **C.** 4 s to 5 s
   - **D.** The acceleration is constant.

Test-Taking Tip

Keep Track of Time If you are taking a timed test, keep track of time. If you find you are spending too much time on a multiple-choice question, mark your best guess and move on.

3. Over which of the following time intervals is the net force on the object the smallest?
   - **A.** 0 s to 1 s
   - **B.** 1 s to 2 s
   - **C.** 4 s to 5 s
   - **D.** The force is constant.

4. According to the trend in these data, which of the following values is most likely the speed of the object after falling for 6 s?
   - **A.** 26.7 m/s
   - **B.** 15.1 m/s
   - **C.** 20.1 m/s
   - **D.** 0 m/s

5. Which of the following would cause the gravitational force between object A and object B to increase?
   - **A.** Decrease the distance between them.
   - **B.** Increase the distance between them.
   - **C.** Decrease the mass of object A.
   - **D.** Decrease the mass of both objects.

Use the graphs below to answer question 6.

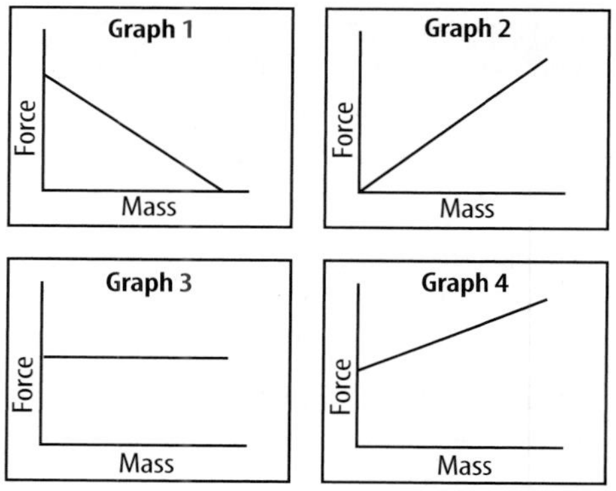

124 STANDARDIZED TEST PRACTICE

6. Which of the graphs on the previous page shows how the force on an object changes if the mass increases and the acceleration stays constant?

   A. Graph 1

   B. Graph 2

   C. Graph 3

   D. Graph 4

Gridded Response

7. You are pushing a 30-kg wooden crate across the floor. The force of sliding friction on the crate is 90 N. How much force, in newtons, must you exert on the crate to keep it moving with a constant velocity?

8. A skydiver with a mass of 60 kg jumps from an airplane. Five seconds after jumping, the force of air resistance on the skydiver is 300 N. What is the skydiver's acceleration in m/s^2 five seconds after jumping?

Short Response

Use the figure below to answer question 9.

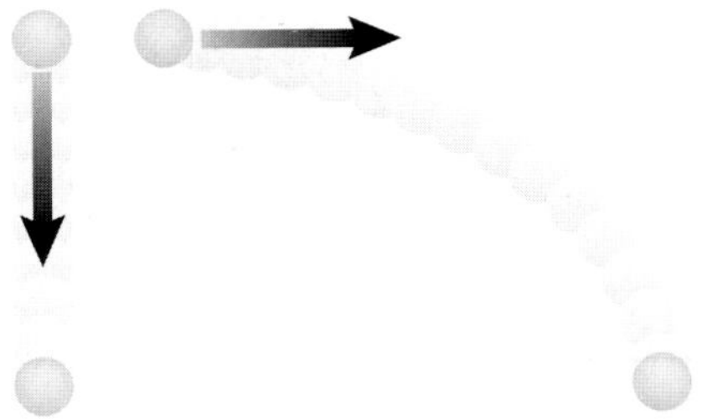

9. Two balls are at the same height. One ball is dropped and the other initially moves horizontally, as shown in the figure. After 1 s, which ball has fallen the greatest vertical distance?

10. How does the acceleration of gravity 5,000 km above Earth's surface compare with the acceleration of gravity at Earth's surface?

Extended Response

Use the graph below to answer question 11.

Speed of Sliding Book

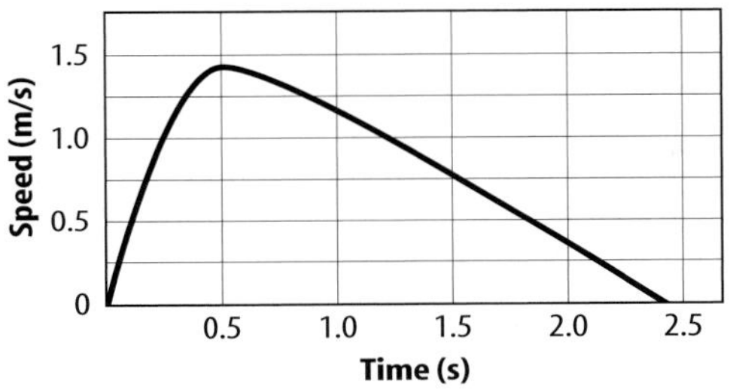

11. The graph above shows the how the speed of a book changes as it slides across a table. Over what time interval is the net force on the book in the opposite direction of the book's motion?

12. When the space shuttle is launched from Earth, the rocket engines burn fuel and apply a constant force on the shuttle until they burn out. Explain why the shuttles acceleration increases while the rocket engines are burning fuel.

chapter 4

Standardized Test Practice

Gridded Response

7. 90

8. Force of gravity on skydiver = (60 kg)($9.8\ m/s^2$) = 588 N, net force on skydiver = 588 N – 300 N = 288 N, a = Fnet / m = (288 N)/(60 kg) = $4.8\ m/s^2$

Short Response

9. Both balls have fallen the same distance after 1 s. Their vertical motion is independent of their horizontal motion.

10. It is less, because an object at this height is farther from Earth than an object at Earth's surface. According to the law of universal gravitation, the force of gravity decreases as the distance between objects increases. Because the force of gravity decreases, the acceleration due to gravity decreases.

Extended Response

11. After 0.5 s, the book is slowing down, so the acceleration and the net force are opposite to the book's direction of motion.

12. The mass of the rockets is decreasing as the fuel burns, but the force exerted by the rocket engines remains the same. By the second law of motion, the acceleration then must increase.

Rubrics

For more help evaluating Short- and Extended-Response questions, see the rubrics on p. 9T.

chapter 5 Organizer

Section/Objectives	Standards: National	Standards: State/Local	Labs/Features
Chapter Opener	See pp. 16T–17T for a Key to Standards		**Launch Lab:** Energy Conversions, p. 127 **Foldables,** p. 127
Section 1 The Nature of Energy 3 sessions 1.5 blocks 1. **Distinguish** between kinetic and potential energy. 2. **Calculate** kinetic energy. 3. **Describe** different forms of potential energy. 4. **Calculate** gravitational potential energy.	National Content Standards: UCP.2, UCP.3, UCP.5, A.1, A.2, B.2, B.4		**Science Online,** p. 130 **Applying Math:** Kinetic Energy, p. 130 **MiniLAB:** Interpreting Data from a Slingshot, p. 131 **Integrate Language Arts,** p. 132 **Applying Math:** Gravitational Potential Energy, p. 132 **Lab:** Bouncing Balls, p. 134 Video Lab
Section 2 Conservation of Energy 4 sessions 2 blocks 5. **Describe** how energy can be transformed from one form to another. 6. **Explain** how the mechanical energy of a system is the sum of the kinetic and potential energy. 7. **Discuss** the law of conservation of energy.	National Content Standards: UCP.2, UCP.3, UCP.5, A.1, A.2, B.2, B.4, B.5, G.3		**Visualizing Energy Transformations,** p. 138 **Integrate Environment,** p. 139 **MiniLAB:** Transforming Energy in a Paper Clip, p. 140 **Science Online,** p. 141 **Lab:** Swinging Energy, p. 144–145 **Science and History:** The Impossible Dream, p. 146

StudentWorks Plus

Glencoe Exclusive! TeacherWorks™ All-In-One Planner and Resource Center

Lab Materials	Reproducible Resources	Section Assessment	Technology
Launch Lab: D-cell batteries (2), non-coated paper clips (2), tape, metal tongs, steel wool	**Chapter *Fast File* Resources** Foldables Worksheet, p. 17 Note-taking Worksheets, pp. 31–32	Glencoe's Assessment Advantage	TeacherWorks includes: • Interactive Teacher Edition • Lesson Planner with calendar • Access to all program blacklines • Correlations to standards • Web links
MiniLAB: rubber band, nickel, meterstick **Lab:** tennis ball, rubber ball, balance, meterstick, masking tape, cardboard box	**Chapter *Fast File* Resources** Transparency Activity, p. 42 MiniLAB, p. 3 Enrichment, p. 29 Reinforcement, p. 27 Directed Reading, p. 20 Activity Worksheet, pp. 5–6 Lab Activity, pp. 9–12 Transparency Activity, pp. 45–46 **Reading and Writing Skill Activities,** p. 35	**Portfolio** Curriculum Connection, p. 130 **Performance** MiniLAB, p. 131 Applying Math, p. 132 Applying Math, p. 133 **Content** Section Review, p. 133	Section Focus Transparency Teaching Transparency Interactive Chalkboard CD-ROM StudentWorks Plus Video Lab
MiniLAB: paper clip **Lab:** ring stand, test-tube clamp, support-rod clamp (right angle), 30-cm support rod, 2-hole, medium rubber stopper, 1 m string, metersticks (2) graph paper *Need materials?* Contact Science Kit at 1-800-828-7777 or www.sciencekit.com.	**Chapter *Fast File* Resources** Transparency Activity, p. 43 MiniLAB, p. 4 Enrichment, p. 30 Reinforcement, p. 28 Directed Reading, pp. 21–22 Activity Worksheet, pp. 7–8 Lab Activity, pp. 13–15 **Home and Community Involvement,** p. 36 **Cultural Diversity,** p. 53	**Portfolio** Assessment, p. 143 **Performance** MiniLAB, p. 140 Applying Math, p. 143 **Content** Section Review, p. 143	Section Focus Transparency Virtual Labs CD-ROM Interactive Chalkboard CD-ROM StudentWorks Plus

End of Chapter Assessment

Glencoe's Assessment Advantage

Blackline Masters	Technology	Professional Series
Chapter *Fast File* Resources Chapter Review, pp. 35–36 Chapter Tests, pp. 37–40 **Standardized Test Practice,** pp. 24–27	MindJogger Videoquiz Virtual Labs CD-ROM Exam*View*® Pro Testmaker TeacherWorks CD-ROM Interactive Chalkboard CD-ROM	**Performance Assessment in the Science Classroom (PASC)**

Transparencies

Section Focus

This is a representation of key blackline masters available in the Teacher Classroom Resources. See Resource Manager boxes within the chapter for additional information.

Assessment

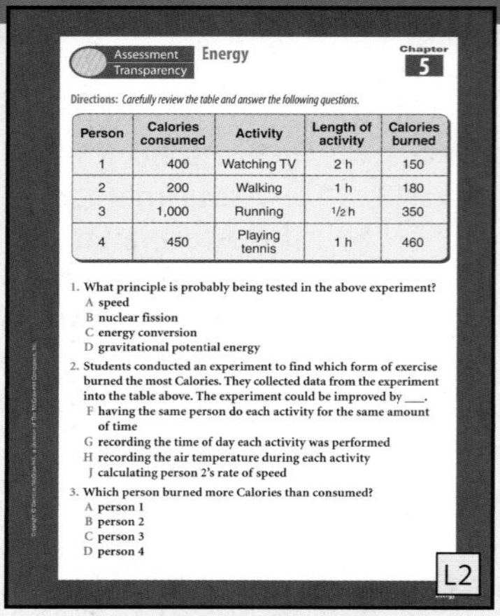

Teaching

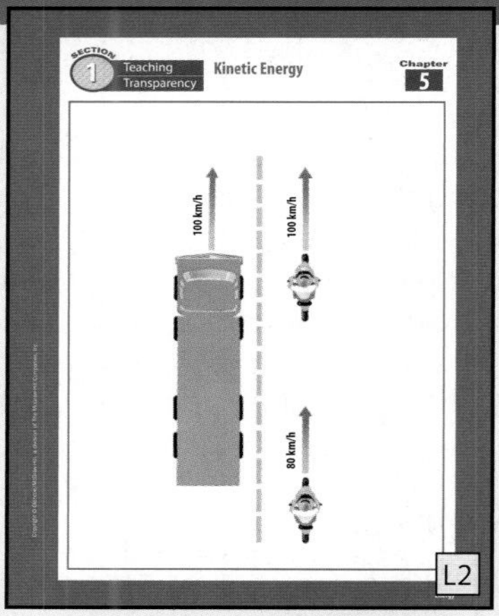

Key to Teaching Strategies

The following designations will help you decide which activities are appropriate for your students.

- L1 Level 1 activities should be appropriate for students with learning difficulties.
- L2 Level 2 activities should be within the ability range of all students.
- L3 Level 3 activities are designed for above-average students.
- ELL ELL activities should be within the ability range of English Language Learners.
- COOP LEARN Cooperative Learning activities are designed for small group work.
- LS Multiple Learning Styles logos, as described on page 12T, are used throughout to indicate strategies that address different learning styles.
- P These strategies represent student products that can be placed into a best-work portfolio.
- PBL Problem-Based Learning activities apply real-world situations to learning.

Hands-on Activities

Student Text Lab Worksheet

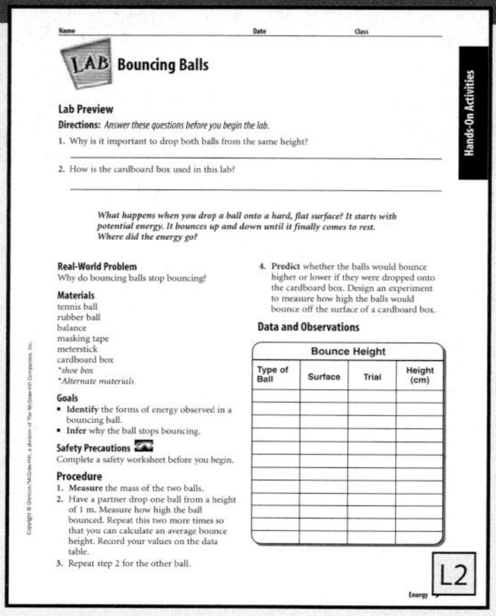

Laboratory Activities

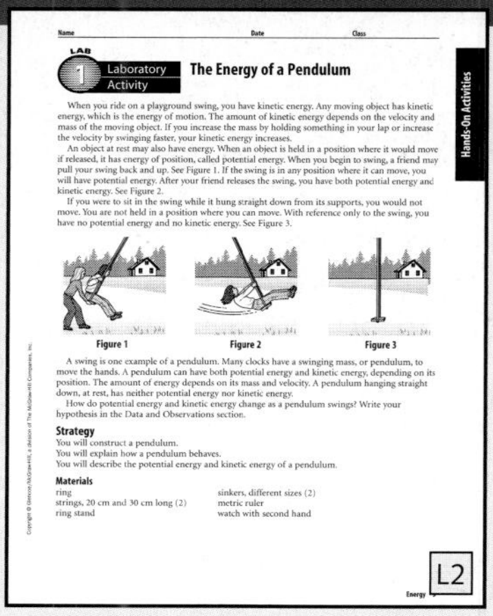

Resource Manager

Meeting Different Ability Levels

Content Outline

Note-taking Worksheet — Energy

Section 1 The Nature of Energy

A. Energy is the ability to cause ______ or do ______.

1. Kinetic energy—energy in the form of ______
   a. The amount of kinetic energy an object has depends on its ______ and its ______.
   b. Kinetic energy = ½ ______ × speed²
   c. ______—the SI unit used to measure energy
2. Potential energy—energy stored in a ______ object, giving it the potential to cause change
3. Elastic potential energy—energy stored by things that ______
4. Chemical potential energy—energy stored in ______ between atoms
5. Gravitational potential energy—energy stored by things that are above ______
   a. The GPE of an object depends on its ______, its acceleration due to ______, and its ______.
   b. GPE = mass in kilograms × 9.8 m/s² × height in ______

Section 2 Conservation of Energy

A. Energy conversions—energy changing from one ______ to another

1. Fuels store energy in the form of ______ energy.
2. ______ energy—the total amount of potential and kinetic energy in a system

B. Law of conservation of energy—energy may change from one form to another, but the ______ of energy never changes.

1. Example: As a swing moves back and forth, its energy continually converts from ______ to ______ and back.
2. If the energy of the swing decreases, then the energy of some other object must ______ by an equal amount.
3. Friction converts some of the mechanical energy into ______ energy.

L2

Reinforcement

Section 1 Reinforcement — The Nature of Energy

Directions: Place a plus (+) to the left of the statements that agree with the textbook. Place a minus (-) to the left of the statements that do not agree with the textbook. Circle the word or words that need to be changed, and change the statement so that it is true.

1. Anything that causes change must have energy.
2. Kinetic energy is energy in the form of motion.
3. The joule is the SI unit of energy.
4. According to the law of conservation of energy, energy can be created or destroyed.
5. Energy may change from one form to another, but the total amount of energy never changes.
6. Mechanical energy is the total amount of potential and kinetic energy in a system.
7. A rock at the edge of a 200-m high cliff has more potential energy than an equal-sized rock at the edge of a 600-m high cliff.
8. The energy stored in foods and fuels is chemical potential energy.

Directions: The chart below compares kinetic energy and gravitational potential energy. Fill in the missing information.

Characteristic	Kinetic Energy	Gravitational Potential Energy
Definition	9.	10.
Units of measure	11.	12.
Quantities in calculation	13.	14.

L2

Enrichment

Section 1 Enrichment — Transferring Kinetic and Potential Energy

In this activity you will build twin pendulums to observe how kinetic and potential energy can be transferred within a system.

Materials

washers or bolts identically sized (2)
ring stands (2)
strong thread

Procedure

1. Try to duplicate the apparatus shown in the figure. To build twin pendulums, place the two ring stands about 50 cm apart. Tie a piece of thread about one-fourth of the way down from the top of one ring stand. Attach the other end of the thread an equal distance from the top of the other ring stand. There should not be any slack in the thread.
2. Cut two 15-cm lengths of thread. Attach a washer to each thread. Tie the other ends of these threads to the horizontal thread, about 5-cm apart. The washers must hang at exactly the same height.
3. Pull one of the washers toward you until it is as high as the horizontal string. Release the washer and observe what happens.

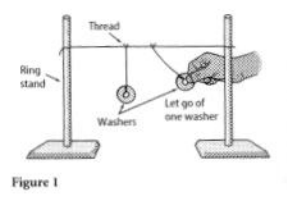

Figure 1

Conclude and Apply

1. Describe what happened to the two pendulums after you released the washer.
2. Explain why the second pendulum was able to move without your touching it.
3. Why did the pendulums eventually stop swinging?

L3

Directed Reading (English/Spanish)

Directed Reading for Content Mastery — Overview — Energy

Directions: Complete the concept map using the terms in the list below.

motion   mechanical energy   potential energy   object

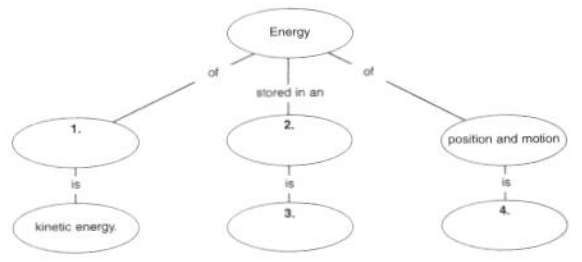

Directions: Three forms of potential energy are gravitational, chemical, and elastic. Write the correct form in the spaces beside the items below. Note that one item has two forms of potential energy.

5. chocolate chip cookie
6. pogo stick on impact
7. gasoline
8. bicycle at the top of a hill
9. stretched rubber band
10. apple in a tree

L1

Study Guide

Section 1 Study Guide — The Nature of Energy — Chapter 5

Directions: Determine whether the italicized term makes each statement true or false. If the statement is true, write true in the blank. If the statement is false, write in the blank the term or terms that make the statement true.

1. *Energy* is done when a force causes an object to move.
2. *Potential* energy is the energy of motion.
3. *Elastic* potential energy is the energy of an object above the surface of Earth.
4. *Thermal* potential energy is the energy stored in chemical bonds between atoms.
5. The *joule* is the unit of energy in the SI system.
6. As the height of an object above the surface of Earth increases, its potential energy *remains the same*.
7. The energy coming from the sun is called *chemical energy*.

Directions: Answer the following questions or complete the sentence by writing the correct letter on the line provided.

8. The kinetic energy of an object moving at a speed of 2 m/s and having a mass of 3 kg is ______.
   a. 6 joules c. 12 joules
   b. 18 joules d. 24 joules
9. The gravitational potential energy of an object with a mass of 1 kg at a height of 2 m above the surface of Earth is approximately ______.
   a. 2 joules c. 2 joules
   b. 10 joules d. 20 joules
10. When a substance burns in oxygen, the amount of chemical energy ______.
   a. increases c. remains the same
   b. decreases d. is not important
11. A car moving at 10 m/s has 400,000 joules kinetic energy. The car's mass is ______.
   a. 4,000 kg c. 8,000 kg
   b. 16,000 kg d. 40,000 kg

L2

Reading Essentials

Chapter 5 Energy

section 1 The Nature of Energy

What You'll Learn
- the different forms of energy
- how energy can be stored

Before You Read

Energy comes in many forms. List as many types of energy as you can think of on the lines below.

Study Coach

State the Main Ideas As you read this section, stop after each paragraph and write the main idea of what you read in your own words.

Read to Learn

What is energy?

Changes are taking place all around you all the time. For example, lightbulbs are heating the air around them, and the wind may be blowing leaves in the trees. Even you are changing as you breathe, blink, or move around at your desk.

All changes involve energy. Imagine a baseball flying through the air. It hits a window and breaks the glass into small pieces. The moving baseball causes the solid pane of glass to change into the small pieces. The moving baseball has energy.

How are energy and work related?

Energy is the ability to do work. Work is done when a force causes something to move. A moving baseball does work on a window. The ball exerts a force on the glass and causes it to break. Energy is also the ability to cause change. When work is done, energy moves from one place to another or changes from one form to another.

Reading Check

1. Define What is energy?

What are some different forms of energy?

Turn on an electric light, and a dark room becomes brighter. Turn on your CD player, and sound comes through the headphones. In both of these cases, energy moves from one place to another. These changes are different from each other. They are also different from the change caused by the baseball hitting the window. Energy has many different forms. Some forms are electrical, chemical, radiant, and thermal.

L1

Assessment

Test Practice Workbook

Chapter Test — Chapter 5 Energy

DIRECTIONS

Choose the best answer choice for each of the following questions.

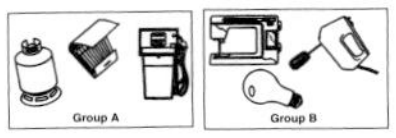

1. The objects in Group A are different from the objects in Group B because only the objects in Group A ______.
   a. are electrical appliances
   b. have chemical potential energy
   c. convert electrical energy to mechanical energy
   d. are fossil fuels

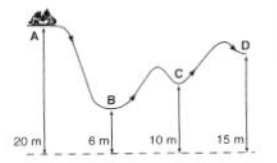

2. In the diagram above, a roller coaster car starts from rest at point A and moves along the track. At which point does the roller coaster car have the greatest kinetic energy?
   f. A
   g. B
   h. C
   j. D

3. Air resistance is a form of friction that makes a moving object slow down. Which of these drawings shows a skier whose shape would allow him or her to move through the air with the LEAST resistance?
   a.
   b.
   c.
   d.

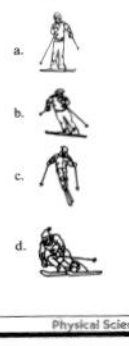

GO ON

L2

Chapter Review

Chapter Review — Energy

Part A. Vocabulary Review

Directions: Match the description in the first column with the term in the second column by writing the correct letter in the space provided.

1. total amount of kinetic and potential energy in a system
2. the ability to cause change
3. stored energy due to position
4. energy in the form of motion
5. energy cannot be created or destroyed
6. unit used to measure energy in food
7. energy stored in food and fuels
8. energy stored by things that stretch or compress
9. energy stored by things that are above earth
10. SI unit of energy
11. causes some mechanical energy to change to thermal energy

a. energy
b. friction
c. kinetic energy
d. law of conservation of energy
e. gravitational potential energy
f. mechanical energy
g. potential energy
h. Calorie
i. elastic potential energy
j. chemical potential energy
k. joule

Part B. Concept Review

Directions: Complete the following sentences using the correct terms.

1. The amount of kinetic energy a moving object has depends on its mass and its ______.
2. The potential energy of an object depends on its ______.
3. The energy stored in foods and fuels is ______ potential energy.
4. The law of ______ states that energy cannot be created or destroyed.
5. Nutritionists use the ______ to measure how much energy we get from foods.
6. The conversion of potential energy to kinetic energy demonstrates the ______.
7. You convert kinetic energy into thermal energy when you rub two sticks together because of ______.

L2

Chapter Tests

Chapter Test — Energy

I. Testing Concepts

Directions: Determine whether each of the following statements is true or false. If the statement is true, write true in the blank. If the statement is false, replace the italicized term with one that makes the statement true.

1. Energy in the form of motion is *potential energy*.
2. As the *mass* of a moving object increases, so does its kinetic energy.
3. A rock at the edge of a cliff has *kinetic* energy because of its position.
4. Friction causes some mechanical energy to change into *thermal* energy.
5. Energy that is stored is *kinetic* energy.
6. *Mass* is measured in joules.
7. Doubling an object's velocity will *double* its kinetic energy.
8. *Chemical potential* energy is energy stored in foods and fuels.
9. *Thermal* energy is energy stored by things that stretch or compress.
10. A book and a feather sitting next to each other on a shelf have *different* potential energies.
11. Two copies of the same book are in a book case. One book is twice as high as the other. They have *the same* potential energy.
12. A toaster uses *chemical* energy to make toast.
13. *Mechanical* energy is the total amount of potential and kinetic energy in a system.
14. When a plant falls from a window its *thermal* energy is transformed into kinetic energy.
15. The *law of conservation of energy* states that although energy can change forms, it can never be created or destroyed.

Directions: In the blanks, write the letter of the term or phrase that correctly answers each question or completes each statement.

16. Which of the following is not used to calculate kinetic energy?
   a. mass c. height
   b. weight d. speed
17. Which of the following is not used to calculate potential energy?
   a. mass c. height
   b. gravitational acceleration d. speed

L2

Science Content Background

section 1 The Nature of Energy

What is energy?

Energy is not matter. Electromagnetic energy can exist independent of matter. Other forms of energy, such as chemical energy, can only exist with matter.

Kinetic Energy

The equation for kinetic energy states that $KE = \frac{1}{2}mv^2$. This means that as an object's velocity doubles its kinetic energy quadruples.

Kinetic comes from a Greek word for movement. The word *cinema*—used to describe moving pictures or movies—shares the same root word.

Potential Energy

Potential energy is energy due to an object's position or condition. A rock on a cliff has potential energy due to its position, while the energy stored in a starch molecule is due to the condition of the bonds between the atoms in that molecule.

Hooke's law describes the relationship between stress and strain in a spring. The amount of force is directly proportional to the compression or extension of the spring. The amount of potential energy depends on the amount of compression or extension and the elasticity of the spring.

Without friction, the work done to lift an object is equal to the object's gain in potential energy. Consider the two equations: *work* = *force* × *distance* and *potential energy* = *mass* × *gravitational acceleration* × *height*. The force needed to lift an object is equivalent to the object's mass multiplied by the acceleration due to gravity. The distance traveled is the height. So in this case, these two equations are equivalent.

If you took a one-kilogram mass to a distance from Earth that corresponds to the distance to the Moon, the mass would have a potential energy relative to Earth of 62,000,000 joules or 62 mega-joules. This is small compared to its potential energy relative to the Sun, which would be 190,000 mega-joules.

Albert Copley/Visuals Unlimited

Teacher to Teacher
Erin Peters, Lead Science Teacher
Williamsburg Middle School
Arlington, Virginia

"This game will show that you trace every type of energy back to the sun. Pick any activity, for example, "doing your homework," then follow it backward. Pushing your pencil is mechanical energy which comes from the chemical energy of eating lunch, which comes from food, which gets its energy from the Sun."

Erin Peters

section 2 Conservation of Energy

Changing Forms of Energy

In our common experiences on Earth, energy is neither created nor destroyed, but is often transformed from one form into another. People use these energy transformations to do work. In most energy transformations, heat is produced.

Energy is not recycled in ecosystems like matter is recycled. Much of the energy that flows through ecosystems is transformed to heat. As energy flows from organism to organism, more and more is transformed as heat. This flow of energy can be visually represented as food chains. The Sun supplies energy to plants, which start almost all food chains.

Conversions Between Kinetic and Potential Energy

As an object falls, its gravitational potential energy is converted into kinetic energy. Therefore, if you know the falling object's initial potential energy, you can calculate the velocity it attains just before it hits the ground using the equation $GPE = mgh$. A 0.06 kg tennis ball dropped from a height of 2.9 m starts with 1.7 J of energy. Solving the kinetic energy equation for v gives 7.54 m/s.

The joule is the SI unit of energy and work. It has the units $kg \cdot m^2/s^2$. In work calculations a joule is sometimes called a newton-meter. Since a newton is composed of the units $kg \cdot m/s^2$, multiplying newtons by meters results in $kg \cdot m^2/s^2$, or joules.

The Law of Conservation of Energy

The law of conservation of energy works for most of our calculations, but Einstein suggested that mass could be converted to energy and energy into mass. Einstein's famous equation, $E = mc^2$, shows the relationship between mass and energy and explains the incredible power unleashed by atomic bombs. So the law of conservation of energy should more accurately be called the law of conservation of energy and mass.

chapter content resources

Internet Resources

For additional content background, visit **gpescience.com** to:

- access your book online
- find references to related articles in popular science magazines
- access Web links with related content background
- access current events with science journal topics

Print Resources

Forces, Motion and Energy Book Two, by Robert Friedhoffer, Franklin Watts Publishers, 1992

Physics for Every Kid, by Janice VanCleave, John Wiley & Sons Publishers, 1991

Great Ideas in Physics, by Alan Lightman, McGraw-Hill, 2000

The Handbook to the Universe, by Richard Paul, Chicago Review Press, 1993

Frank Rossotto/The Stock Market

chapter 5

Chapter Vocabulary

energy, p. 128
kinetic energy, p. 130
joule, p. 130
potential energy, p. 131
elastic potential energy, p. 131
chemical potential energy, p. 131
gravitational potential energy, p. 132
mechanical energy, p. 136
law of conservation of energy, p. 139

Science Journal Walking up stairs and taking the escalator take the same amount of energy as long as the change in elevation is the same. In the first case the energy is provided by the person and in the second it is provided by the escalator.

INTERACTIVE CHALKBOARD with Image Bank

PowerPoint® Presentations

This CD-ROM is an editable Microsoft® PowerPoint® presentation that includes:

- a pre-made presentation for every chapter
- interactive graphics
- animations
- audio clips
- image bank
- all new section and chapter questions
- Standardized Test Practice
- transparencies
- Foldables directions
- links to gpescience.com

chapter 5

Energy

chapter preview

sections

1 The Nature of Energy
Lab Bouncing Balls

2 Conservation of Energy
Lab Swinging Energy

Virtual Lab How is energy converted from one form to another?

A Big Lift

How does this pole vaulter go from standing at the end of a runway to climbing through the air? The answer is energy. During her vault, energy originally stored in her muscles is converted into other forms of energy that enable her to soar.

Science Journal Which takes more energy: walking up stairs, or taking an escalator? Explain your reasoning.

126

Theme Connection

Energy This chapter focuses on different forms of energy and energy conversions. The law of conservation of energy is explained and applied to various systems.

About the Photo

Energy To reach a maximum height, a pole-vaulter must convert as much kinetic energy as possible into potential energy. The bending of the pole transforms kinetic energy into elastic potential energy, then into gravitational potential energy. The vaulting pole is made from carbon fiber and fiberglass composite materials to make it as light as possible, and to minimize the conversion of elastic potential energy into thermal energy as the pole bends.

Start-Up Activities

Launch LAB

Energy Conversions

One of the most useful inventions of the nineteenth century was the electric lightbulb. Being able to light up the dark has enabled people to work and play longer. A lightbulb converts electrical energy to heat energy and light, another form of energy. The following lab shows how electrical energy is converted into other forms of energy.

WARNING: *Steel wool can become hot—connect to battery only for a brief time.*

1. Obtain two D-cell batteries, two non-coated paper clips, tape, metal tongs, and some steel wool. Separate the steel wool into thin strands and straighten the paper clips.
2. Tape the batteries together and then tape one end of each paper clip to the battery terminals.
3. While holding the steel wool with the tongs, briefly complete the circuit by placing the steel wool in contact with both the paper clip ends.
4. **Think Critically** In your Science Journal, describe what happened to the steel wool. What changes did you observe?

Science Online | Preview this chapter's content and activities at gpescience.com

FOLDABLES Study Organizer

Energy Make the following Foldable to help you identify what you already know, what you want to know, and what you learned about energy.

STEP 1 **Fold** a sheet of paper vertically from side to side. Make the front edge about 1 cm shorter than the back edge.

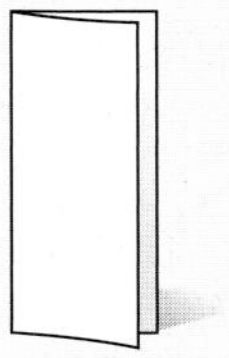

STEP 2 **Turn** lengthwise and **fold** into thirds.

STEP 3 **Unfold and cut** only the top layer along both folds to make three tabs.

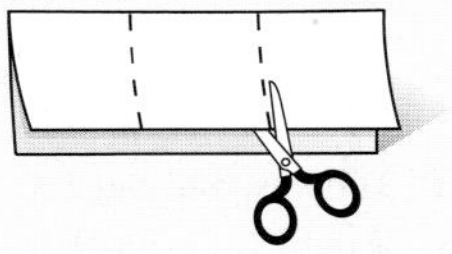

STEP 4 **Label** each tab as shown.

Question Before you read the chapter, write what you already know about energy under the left tab of your Foldable, and write questions about what you'd like to know under the center tab. After you read the chapter, list what you learned under the right tab.

127

Launch LAB

Purpose Use the Launch Lab to introduce students to the conversion of electricity to light and thermal energy. L1 COOP LEARN

LS **Kinesthetic**

Materials 2 D-cell batteries, 2 non-coated paper clips, tape, metal tongs, steel wool

Teaching Strategy Inform students that the steel wool can become quite hot.

Think Critically

When connected to the batteries, the steel wool gives off light and thermal energy.

Assessment

Content Have students investigate how a light bulb works and write a paragraph comparing it with the model they made in this activity. Use **Performance Assessment in the Science Classroom,** p. 159.

FOLDABLES Study Organizer **Dinah Zike Study Fold**

Student preparation materials for this Foldable are available in the **Chapter *Fast File* Resources.**

1 Motivate

An editable Microsoft® PowerPoint® presentation is available on **Interactive Chalkboard** CD-ROM.

Bellringer

Section Focus Transparencies also are available on the Interactive Chalkboard CD-ROM. L2 ELL

Reading Preview

Tie to Prior Knowledge

Common Energy Ask students to describe how the word energy is commonly used. They might mention fuel energy or energy from the Sun. Explain that in this section they will learn the scientific definition of energy.

Activating Background Vocabulary The new vocabulary will be familiar to students in an everyday sense. Have students set up a two-column chart. In the first column, students predict meaning for each word. In the second column, they record the physics definition as found in the text.

section 1

The Nature of Energy

Reading Guide

What You'll Learn

- **Distinguish** between kinetic and potential energy.
- **Calculate** kinetic energy.
- **Describe** different forms of potential energy.
- **Calculate** gravitational potential energy.

Why It's Important

All of the changes that occur around you every day involve the conversion of energy from one form to another.

Review Vocabulary

gravity: the attractive force between any two objects that have mass

New Vocabulary

- energy
- kinetic energy
- joule
- potential energy
- elastic potential energy
- chemical potential energy
- gravitational potential energy

What is energy?

Wherever you are sitting as you read this, changes are taking place—lightbulbs are heating the air around them, the wind might be rustling leaves, or sunlight might be glaring off a nearby window. Even you are changing as you breathe, blink, or shift position in your seat.

Every change that occurs—large or small—involves energy. Imagine a baseball flying through the air. It hits a window, causing the glass to break as shown in **Figure 1.** The window changed from a solid sheet of glass to a number of broken pieces. The moving baseball caused this change—a moving baseball has energy. Even when you comb your hair or walk from one class to another, energy is involved.

Figure 1 The baseball caused changes to occur when it hit the window.
Describe *the changes that are occurring.*

Energy and Work In science, **energy** is defined as the ability to do work. Work is done when a force causes something to move. The ball in **Figure 1** does work on the window when it exerts a force on the glass and causes it to break. Energy also can be defined as the ability to cause change. When work is done, something moves and a change occurs. When work is done and a change occurs, energy moves from place to place or changes from one form to another.

Section 1 Resource Manager

Chapter *Fast File* Resources

- Transparency Activity, p. 42, 45–46
- Note-taking Worksheets, pp. 31–32
- MiniLAB, p. 3
- Directed Reading for Content Mastery, pp. 19–20
- Lab Activity, pp. 9–12
- Enrichment, p. 29
- Reinforcement, p. 7
- Lab Worksheet, pp. 5–6

Reading and Writing Skill Activities, p. 35

Figure 2 Energy can be stored and it can move from place to place.
Infer *which materials are storing chemical energy.*

Different Forms of Energy Turn on an electric light, and a dark room becomes bright. Turn on your CD player, and sound comes through your headphones. In both situations, energy moves from one place to another. These changes are different from each other, and differ from the baseball shattering the window in **Figure 1.** This is because energy has several different forms—electrical, chemical, radiant, and thermal.

Figure 2 shows some examples of everyday situations which involve forms of energy. Is the chemical energy stored in food the same as the energy that comes from the Sun or the energy stored in gasoline? Radiant energy from the Sun travels a vast distance through space to Earth, warming the planet and providing energy that enables green plants to grow. When you make toast in the morning, you are using electrical energy. In short, energy plays a role in every activity that you do.

Reading Check *What are some different forms of energy?*

An Energy Analogy Money can be used in an analogy to help you understand energy. If you have $100, you could store it in a variety of forms—cash in your wallet, a bank account, travelers' checks, or gold or silver coins. You could transfer that money to different forms. You could deposit your cash into a bank account or trade the cash for gold. Regardless of its form, money is money. The same is true for energy. Energy from the Sun that warms you and energy from the food that you eat are only different forms of the same thing.

2 Teach

Caption Answers

Figure 1 The window breaks.

Figure 2 Energy is stored in the gasoline and in the food.

Discussion

Storage and Motion Name some objects that store energy and some examples of energy in motion. Possible answers: stored—springs, muscles in our bodies; motion—bouncing ball, spinning top, baseball flying through the air L1 IS **Linguistic**

Reading Check

Answer thermal energy, chemical energy, radiant energy, and electrical energy

Text Question Answer

Energy stored in food and gasoline is chemical potential energy. Energy from the Sun is in the form of thermal energy and electromagnetic radiation.

Fun Fact

Mitochondria are organelles that convert chemical energy into forms cells can use. This is why they are also known as the powerhouses of living cells.

Differentiated Instruction

English-Language-Learners Have students list ways they can warm up. Possible answers: sit by the fire, sit in the Sun, wrap up in blankets, run in place, rub their hands together. Then have them classify whether they warmed up from kinetic (moving) energy, or by capturing thermal energy.

Science Journal

Different Forms of Energy Have students make a list in their Science Journals of the different types of energy mentioned in the text. Have them list several examples of how they use each form of energy every day. L2 IS **Linguistic**

Use Science Words

Word Origin Have students look up the words *kinetic* and *potential* in the dictionary. *Kinetic* comes from the Greek root *kinein* (to move) and *potential* from the Latin root *potens* (power). Ask a volunteer to state how the words *kinetic* and *potential* reflect the meanings of their roots. Possible answer: Kinetic energy is energy of movement. Potential energy is stored energy due to position, waiting to be unleashed. L1 LS **Linguistic**

Quick Demo

Kinetic Energy

Materials one heavy ball, one light ball, two identical balls and a table top.

Estimated Time five minutes

Procedure

1. Show students two balls; one heavy and one light. Roll them across the table at about the same speed. Ask: Which ball has the greater kinetic energy? If the velocity of both balls is the same, the ball with the greater mass has the greater kinetic energy.

2. Show the students two identical balls. Roll the balls across the table but roll one ball faster than the other. Ask: Which ball has the greater kinetic energy? The ball with the greater speed. L1 LS **Logical-Mathematical**

Applying Math

Math Standards

National: 1, 2, 9

Answers to Practice Problems

1. $KE = \frac{1}{2}(0.15\text{ kg})(40\text{ m/s})^2 = 120\text{ J}$

2. $300{,}000\text{ J} = \frac{1}{2}m(20\text{ m/s})^2$

   $m = 1{,}500\text{ kg}$

3. $v^2 = 2\frac{(4{,}000\text{ J})}{(80\text{ kg})}$

   $v = 10\text{ m/s}$

Science Online

Topic: Glacier Flow

Visit gpescience.com for Web links to information about the speeds at which glaciers flow.

Activity For the five fastest glaciers, calculate the kinetic energy a 1-kg block of ice in each glacier would have.

Kinetic Energy

When you think of energy, you might think of action—or objects in motion—like the baseball that shatters a window. An object in motion does have energy. **Kinetic energy** is the energy a moving object has because of its motion. The kinetic energy of a moving object depends on the object's mass and its speed.

Kinetic Energy Equation

kinetic energy (in joules) $= \frac{1}{2}$ mass (in kg) × [speed (in m/s)]^2

$$KE = \frac{1}{2}mv^2$$

The SI unit of energy is the **joule,** abbreviated J. If you dropped a softball from a height of about 0.5 m, it would have a kinetic energy of about one joule before it hit the floor.

Applying Math **Solve a Simple Equation**

KINETIC ENERGY A jogger whose mass is 60 kg is moving at a speed of 3 m/s. What is the jogger's kinetic energy?

IDENTIFY known values and the unknown value

Identify the known values:

a jogger whose mass is 60 kg → means → $m = 60$ kg

is moving at a speed of 3 m/s → means → $v = 3$ m/s

Identify the unknown value:

What is the jogger's kinetic energy? → means → $KE = ?$ J

SOLVE the problem

Substitute the known values $m = 60$ kg and $v = 3$ m/s into the kinetic energy equation:

$$KE = \frac{1}{2}mv^2 = \frac{1}{2}(60\text{ kg})(3\text{ m/s})^2 = \frac{1}{2}(60)(9)\text{ kg m}^2/\text{s}^2 = 270\text{ J}$$

CHECK your answer

Does your answer seem reasonable? Check your answer by dividing the kinetic energy you calculate by the square of the given velocity, and then multiplying by 2. The result should be the mass given in the problem.

Practice Problems

1. What is the kinetic energy of a baseball moving at a speed of 40 m/s if the baseball has a mass of 0.15 kg?
2. A car moving at a speed of 20 m/s has a kinteic energy of 300,000 J. What is the car's mass?
3. A sprinter has a mass of 80 kg and a kinetic energy of 4,000 J. What is the sprinter's speed?

For more practice problems go to page 879, and visit Math Practice at gpescience.com.

Curriculum Connection

Geography On May 18, 1980, Mount St. Helens in the state of Washington erupted in a devastating volcanic explosion. The tremendous energy of the eruption hurled hot ash and rock more than 16 kilometers. Have students do research to discover other geologic events in history that have involved large amounts of energy. Have each student make a table listing the examples they find and where each event occurred. Possible events: earthquakes in 1964 in Alaska, in 1991 in southern California, in 1995 in Kobe, Japan, and in 2001 in India; and eruptions of the volcanoes Krakatau in 1883 and Mount Vesuvius in 79 A.D. L2 LS **Visual-Spatial** P

Figure 3 As natural gas burns, it combines with oxygen to form carbon dioxide and water. In this chemical reaction, chemical potential energy is released.

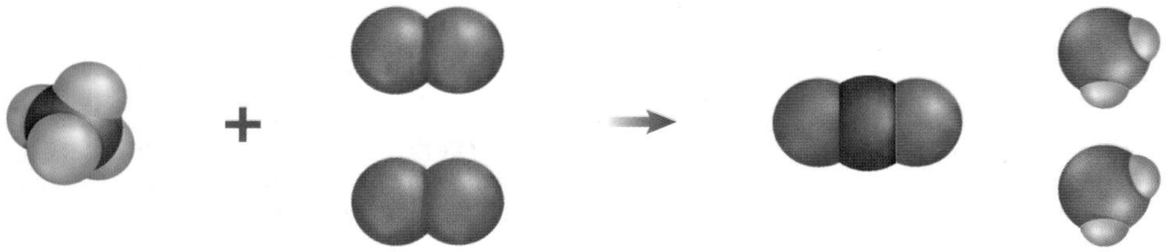

Natural gas + Oxygen → Carbon dioxide and water

Potential Energy

Energy doesn't have to involve motion. Even motionless objects can have energy. This energy is stored in the object. Therefore, the object has potential to cause change. A hanging apple in a tree has stored energy. When the apple falls to the ground, a change occurs. Because the apple has the ability to cause change, it has energy. The hanging apple has energy because of its position above Earth's surface. Stored energy due to position is called **potential energy.** If the apple stays in the tree, it will keep the stored energy due to its height above the ground. If it falls, that stored energy of position is converted to energy of motion.

Elastic Potential Energy Energy can be stored in other ways, too. If you stretch a rubber band and let it go, it sails across the room. As it flies through the air, it has kinetic energy due to its motion. Where did this kinetic energy come from? Just as the apple hanging in the tree had potential energy, the stretched rubber band had energy stored as elastic potential energy. **Elastic potential energy** is energy stored by something that can stretch or compress, such as a rubber band or spring.

Chemical Potential Energy The cereal you eat for breakfast and the sandwich you eat at lunch also contain stored energy. Gasoline stores energy in the same way as food stores energy—in the chemical bonds between atoms. Energy stored in chemical bonds is **chemical potential energy. Figure 3** shows a molecule of natural gas. Energy is stored in the bonds that hold the carbon and hydrogen atoms together and is released when the gas is burned.

Mini LAB

Interpreting Data from a Slingshot

Procedure

1. Using two fingers, carefully stretch a **rubber band** on a table until it has no slack.
2. Place a **nickel** on the table, slightly touching the midpoint of the rubber band.
3. Push the nickel back 0.5 cm into the rubber band and release. Measure the distance the nickel travels.
4. Repeat step 3, each time pushing the nickel back an additional 0.5 cm.

Analysis

1. How did the takeoff speed of the nickel seem to change relative to the distance that you stretched the rubber band?
2. What does this imply about the kinetic energy of the nickel?

Reading Check *How is elastic potential energy different from chemical potential energy?*

Use an Analogy

Saving Money Suggest to students that potential energy is analogous to money in a savings account. The money is not in use now, but it's ready for you to use when needed.

Mini LAB

Purpose Students observe the relationship between the elastic potential energy and kinetic energy of an object. L1 COOP LEARN LS **Kinesthetic**

Materials nickel, rubber band, meterstick

Teaching Strategy Have students work in pairs and take turns making the measurements.

Troubleshooting Be sure students don't pull the rubber band back too far. The nickel can quickly travel a long distance.

Analysis

1. The farther you stretch the band, the faster the nickel moves.
2. The greater the speed of the nickel, the greater its kinetic energy.

Assessment

Process Have students predict how their results would differ on a rough surface. Have them test their hypotheses by repeating the activity on sandpaper. Use **Performance Assessment in the Science Classroom,** p. 93.

Reading Check

Answer Elastic potential energy is energy stored by things that stretch or compress. Chemical potential energy is energy stored in chemical bonds.

Visual Learning

Figure 3 What forms of energy are given off when natural gas burns? light and thermal energy

INTEGRATE Language Arts

The Myth of Sisyphus Sisyphus had to continually provide the rock with gravitational potential energy only to have it turn into kinetic energy again.

Quick Demo
Gravitational Potential Energy

Materials three tennis balls, bookshelf or something with three different heights to put them on

Estimated Time 5 minutes

Procedure Demonstrate the idea of gravitational potential energy by placing the three tennis balls on level surfaces at different heights. Ask: How do the gravitational potential energies of the three balls compare? GPE increases with height. The ball that is highest has the greatest GPE and the ball that is nearest the ground has the lowest GPE. L1

LS **Logical-Mathematical**

Applying Math

Math Standards

National: 1, 2, 9

Answers to Practice Problems

1. $73.5\ \text{J} = (0.15\ \text{kg})\ (9.8\ \text{m/s}^2)\ h$
   $50\ \text{m} = h$
2. $GPE = (0.3\ \text{kg})\ (9.8\ \text{m/s}^2)\ (1\ \text{m})$
   $GPE = 2.94\ \text{J}$
3. $117{,}600\ \text{J} = m\ (9.8\ \text{m/s}^2)\ (200\ \text{m})$
   $60\ \text{kg} = m$

INTEGRATE Language Arts

The Myth of Sisyphus In Greek mythology, a king named Sisyphus angered the gods by attempting to delay death. As punishment, he was doomed for eternity to endlessly roll a huge stone up a hill, only to have it roll back to the bottom again. Explain what caused the potential energy of the stone to change as it moved up and down the hill.

Gravitational Potential Energy Anything that can fall has stored energy called gravitational potential energy. **Gravitational potential energy** (GPE) is energy stored by objects due to their position above Earth's surface. The GPE of an object depends on the object's mass and height above the ground. Gravitational potential energy can be calculated from the following equation.

Gravitational Potential Energy Equation

gravitational potential energy (J) =
mass (kg) × acceleration due to gravity (m/s²) × **height** (m)

$$GPE = mgh$$

On Earth, the acceleration due to gravity is 9.8 m/s² and has the symbol g. Like all forms of energy, gravitational potential energy is measured in joules.

Applying Math — Solve a Simple Equation

GRAVITATIONAL POTENTIAL ENERGY What is the gravitational potential energy of a ceiling fan that has a mass of 7 kg and is 4 m above the ground?

IDENTIFY known values and the unknown value

Identify the known values:

has a mass of 7 kg — means → $m = 7$ kg

is 4 m above the ground — means → $h = 4$ m

Identify the unknown value:

what is the gravitational potential energy — means → $GPE = ?$ J

SOLVE the problem

Substitute the known values $m = 7$ kg, $h = 4$ m, and $g = 9.8$ m/s² into the gravitational potential energy equation:

$$GPE = mgh = (7\ \text{kg})(9.8\ \text{m/s}^2)(4\ \text{m}) = (274)\ \text{kg m}^2/\text{s}^2 = 274\ \text{J}$$

CHECK your answer

Does your answer seem reasonable? Check your answer by dividing the gravitational potential energy you calculate by the given mass, and then divide by 9.8 m/s². The result should be the height given in the problem.

Practice Problems

1. Find the height of a baseball with a mass of 0.15 kg that has a GPE of 73.5 J.
2. Find the GPE of a coffee mug with a mass of 0.3 kg on a 1-m high counter top.
3. What is the mass of a hiker 200 m above the ground if her GPE is 117,600 J?

For more practice problems go to page 879, and visit Math Practice at gpescience.com.

Cultural Diversity

Working with Energy During World War II, O.S. (Ozzie) Williams became the first African American aeronautical engineer hired by Republic Aviation, Inc. Later, his work included the application of solar and wind energy to the needs of Africa. Have students find other scientists who have spent much of their careers working with energy. Ask students to present their findings in oral reports to the class. L2 LS **Interpersonal**

Reading Strategy

Graphic Organizer Have students place the word energy in the middle of a sheet of paper. Ask them to list and describe types of energy in a circular fashion around the central word. The final product should resemble the wheel of a bicycle with the energy descriptions arranged as spokes.

Changing GPE Look at the objects in the bookcase in **Figure 4.** Which of these objects has the most gravitational potential energy? According to the equation for gravitational potential energy, the GPE of an object can be increased by increasing its height above the ground. If two objects are at the same height, then the object with the larger mass has more gravitational potential energy.

In **Figure 4,** suppose the green vase on the lower shelf and the blue vase on the upper shelf have the same mass. Then the blue vase on the upper shelf has more gravitational potential energy because it is higher above the ground.

Imagine what would happen if the two vases were to fall. As they fall and begin moving, they have kinetic energy as well as gravitational potential energy. As the vases get closer to the ground, their gravitational potential energy decreases. At the same time, they are moving faster, so their kinetic energy increases. The vase that was higher above the floor has fallen a greater distance. As a result, the vase that initially had more gravitational potential energy will be moving faster and have more kinetic energy when it hits the floor.

Figure 4 An object's gravitational potential energy increases as its height increases.

section 1 review

Summary

Energy

- Energy is the ability to cause change.
- Forms of energy include electrical, chemical, thermal, and radiant energy.

Kinetic Energy

- Kinetic energy is the energy a moving object has because of its motion.
- The kinetic energy of a moving object can be calculated from this equation:

$$KE = \frac{1}{2}mv^2$$

Potential Energy

- Potential energy is stored energy due to the position of an object.
- Different forms of potential energy include elastic potential energy, chemical potential energy, and gravitational potential energy.
- Gravitational potential energy can be calculated from this equation:

$$GPE = mgh$$

Self Check

1. **Explain** whether an object can have kinetic energy and potential energy at the same time.
2. **Describe** three situations in which the gravitational potential energy of an object changes.
3. **Explain** how the kinetic energy of a truck could be increased without increasing the truck's speed.
4. **Think Critically** The different molecules that make up the air in a room have, on average, the same kinetic energy. How does the speed of the different air molecules depend on their masses?

Applying Math

5. **Calculate Kinetic Energy** Find the kinetic energy of a ball with a mass of 0.06 kg moving at 50 m/s.
6. **Use Ratios** A boulder on top of a cliff has potential energy of 8,800 J and twice the mass of a boulder next to it. What is the GPE of the smaller boulder?
7. **Calculate GPE** An 80-kg diver jumps from a 10-m high platform. What is the gravitational potential energy of the diver halfway down?

More Section Review gpescience.com

Post Reading

Cooperative Project Organize the class into groups of three to four students. Groups will identify everyday examples illustrating kinetic and potential energy, including calculations of each. Groups then will develop creative ways to present their ideas to the class. Encourage groups to consider cartooning, songwriting, or model making.

3 Assess

DAILY INTERVENTION

Check for Understanding

Kinetic Energy Roll a fist-sized piece of soft modeling clay into a ball and drop it on the floor. Ask: Where is the kinetic energy of the clay ball the greatest? What happened to the kinetic energy when the clay ball hit the floor? What other kinds of energy were formed from the kinetic energy of the ball? The kinetic energy is greatest just before the ball hits the floor. It then turned into sound energy and thermal energy.

Reteach

Energy Transformation Perform several tasks, such as clapping your hands, walking across the room, tossing a ball across the room, or turning on a light. Ask students to identify the energy transformations that occur during each task. L1 ELL

LS **Visual-Spatial**

Assessment

Process Tell students that a 5 kg bowling ball is on a rack 1.5 m above the ground. Have them calculate the GPE of the ball. 5 kg $\times$ 9.8 m/s^2 $\times$ 1.5 m = 73.5 J Use **Performance Assessment in the Science Classroom**, p. 101.

section 1 review

1. Yes, an object that is moving above Earth's surface will have kinetic energy and potential energy.
2. An object is raised higher, an object falls to a lower height, and the mass of an object above Earth's surface changes.
3. The kinetic energy could be increased by increasing the truck's mass.
4. Molecules with smaller masses will be moving faster.
5. $KE = \frac{1}{2}mv^2$

   $KE = \frac{1}{2}(0.06\ \text{kg})(50\ \text{m/s})^2$

   $KE = 75\ \text{J}$
6. $\frac{GPE_1}{m_1} = \frac{GPE_2}{m_2}$

   $\frac{8800\ \text{J}}{2x} = \frac{GPE_2}{x}$

   $4400\ \text{J} = GPE$
7. $PE = mgh = 80\ \text{kg} \times 9.8\ \text{m/s}^2 \times 5\ \text{m} = 3900\ \text{J}$

BENCH TESTED

Video Lab available for this Lab.

Real-World Problem

Purpose Students observe how the GPE of a falling ball is converted to kinetic energy and elastic potential energy, enabling the ball to bounce. L2 COOP LEARN **Kinesthetic**

Process Skills observe and infer, predict, compare, recognize cause and effect

Time Required 30 minutes

Procedure

Alternate Materials table tennis ball, book

Safety Precautions Caution students to let the balls drop and not throw them down.

Teaching Strategy Explain that it is only possible to measure the approximate height of the ball's bounce.

Troubleshooting Have students hold a meter stick vertically next to the drop zone and watch closely to estimate bounce heights.

Conclude and Apply

1. Use the formula: $GPE = m\text{ (kg)} \times 9.8\text{ m/s}^2 \times h\text{ (m)}$.
2. Average height = sum of heights ÷ number of trials. Answers will vary.
3. The balls don't bounce as high on the box. Some of the kinetic energy the ball has when it hits the box is transferred to the box, causing the box to vibrate. This energy is then unavailable to help propel the ball up.
4. Some balls store more elastic potential energy than others.

LAB

Bouncing Balls

What happens when you drop a ball onto a hard, flat surface? It starts with potential energy. It bounces up and down until it finally comes to a rest. Where did the energy go?

Real-World Problem

Why do bouncing balls stop bouncing?

Goals

- **Identify** the forms of energy observed in a bouncing ball.
- **Infer** why the ball stops bouncing.

Materials

tennis ball
rubber ball
balance
meterstick
masking tape
cardboard box
**shoe box*

**Alternate materials*

Safety Precautions

Procedure

1. **Measure** the mass of the two balls.
2. Have a partner drop one ball from 1 m. Measure how high the ball bounced. Repeat this two more times so you can calculate an average bounce height. Record your values on the data table.
3. Repeat step 2 for the other ball.
4. **Predict** whether the balls would bounce higher or lower if they were dropped onto the cardboard box. Design an experiment to measure how high the balls would bounce off the surface of a cardboard box.

Bounce Height

Type of Ball	Surface	Trial	Height (cm)
Tennis	Floor	1	36
Tennis	Floor	2	34
Tennis	Floor	3	37
Rubber	Floor	1	54
Rubber	Floor	2	56
Rubber	Floor	3	56
Tennis	Box	1	29

Conclude and Apply

1. **Calculate** the gravitational potential energy of each ball before dropping it.
2. **Calculate** the average bounce height for the three trials under each condition. Describe your observations.
3. **Compare** the bounce heights of the balls dropped on a cardboard box with the bounce heights of the ballls dropped on the floor. *Hint: Did you observe any movement of the box when the balls bounced?*
4. **Explain** why the balls bounced to different heights, using the concept of elastic potential energy.

Communicating Your Data

Meet with three other lab teams and compare average bounce heights for the tennis ball on the floor. Discuss why your results might differ. **For more help, refer to the Science Skill Handbook.**

Assessment

Process Demonstrate how the bounce height of a ball becomes lower and lower each time it bounces. Have students infer why this happens. Each time the ball bounces, part of its energy is converted to other forms of energy, such as thermal energy and sound. Use **Performance Assessment in the Science Classroom,** p. 89.

Communicating Your Data

Students can use a computer graphics program to prepare a display of their activity results. They should be allowed freedom to make their own design, but the picture should clearly show how the balls bounced higher off the floor than off the box.

section 2

Conservation of Energy

Reading Guide

What You'll Learn

- **Describe** how energy can be transformed from one form to another.
- **Explain** how the mechanical energy of a system is the sum of the kinetic and potential energy.
- **Discuss** the law of conservation of energy.

Why It's Important

All the energy transformations that occur inside you and around you obey the law of conservation of energy.

Review Vocabulary

friction: a force that opposes the sliding motion of two surfaces that are touching each other

New Vocabulary

- mechanical energy
- law of conservation of energy

Changing Forms of Energy

Unless you were talking about potential energy, you probably wouldn't think of the book on top of a bookshelf as having much to do with energy—until it fell. You'd be more likely to think of energy as race cars roar past, or as your body uses energy from food to help it move, or as the Sun warms your skin on a summer day. These situations involve energy changing from one form to another form.

Transforming Electrical Energy You use many devices every day that convert one form of energy to other forms. For example, you might be reading this page in a room lit by lightbulbs. The lightbulbs transform electrical energy into light so you can see. The warmth you feel around the bulb is evidence that some of that electrical energy is transformed into thermal energy, as illustrated in **Figure 5.** What other devices have you used today that make use of electrical energy? You might have been awakened by an alarm clock, styled your hair, made toast, listened to music, or played a video game. What form or forms of energy is electrical energy converted to in these examples?

Figure 5 A lightbulb is a device that transforms electrical energy into light energy and thermal energy.
Identify *other devices that convert electrical energy to thermal energy.*

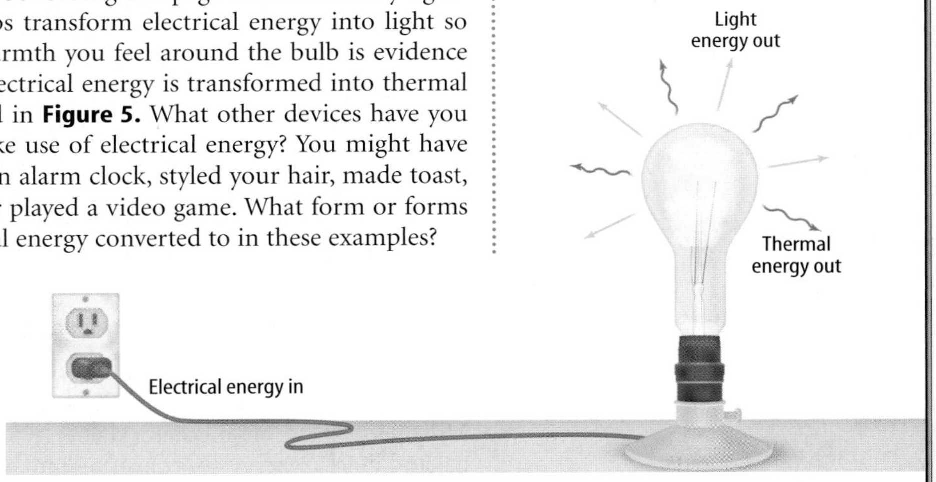

Section 2 Resource Manager

Chapter *FAST FILE* Resources

Transparency Activity, p. 53
Directed Reading for Content Mastery, pp. 21–22
Lab Activity, pp. 13–15
Enrichment, p. 30
MiniLAB, p. 4
Lab Worksheet, pp. 7–8
Reinforcement, p. 28

Cultural Diversity, p. 53
Home and Community Involvement, p. 36
Physical Science Critical Thinking/Problem Solving, p. 17

1 Motivate

INTERACTIVE CHALKBOARD PowerPoint® Presentations An editable Microsoft® PowerPoint® presentation is available on **Interactive Chalkboard** CD-ROM.

Bellringer

Section Focus Transparencies also are available on the Interactive Chalkboard CD-ROM. L2 ELL

Reading Preview

Tie to Prior Knowledge

Skateboarding Discuss the various forms of energy involved in skateboarding.

Word Chart Have students set up a three-column chart. In the first column, students should predict the meaning of the new vocabulary words. In the second column, they should record the actual definition found in the text. Finally, students should make a sketch that illustrates the meaning of the word.

Caption Answer

Figure 5 Possible answers: heater, electric stove, iron, hair dryer

SECTION 2 Conservation of Energy 135

2 Teach

Text Question Answer

alarm clock— sound; hair styler— thermal energy or kinetic; toaster— thermal energy; music— sound; video game— light

Visual Learning

Figure 6 Review the energy conversions at work in an internal combustion engine. Then discuss how a diesel engine works. In a diesel engine, the air in the cylinder is compressed to a high pressure and becomes very hot. When the fuel is sprayed into the cylinder, it ignites in the hot air without the need of a spark plug. What energy conversions take place in a diesel engine? Chemical potential energy is converted to thermal energy and then to kinetic energy. L2 LS **Logical-Mathematical**

Quick Demo
Energy Conversion

Materials rubber "superball"

Estimated Time five minutes

Procedure Demonstrate conversion of gravitational potential energy to kinetic energy and back again by dropping a rubber "superball" from different heights. Point out that the higher the drop, the greater its final velocity and the higher it rebounds. Also, notice the ball never quite bounces to its original height. Ask: Why does the ball not return to its original height each time the ball bounces? Some of the energy is converted to thermal energy each time the ball hits the floor.

Text Question Answer

Mechanical energy is the sum of all potential and kinetic energies. As one transforms into another, the mechanical energy remains constant.

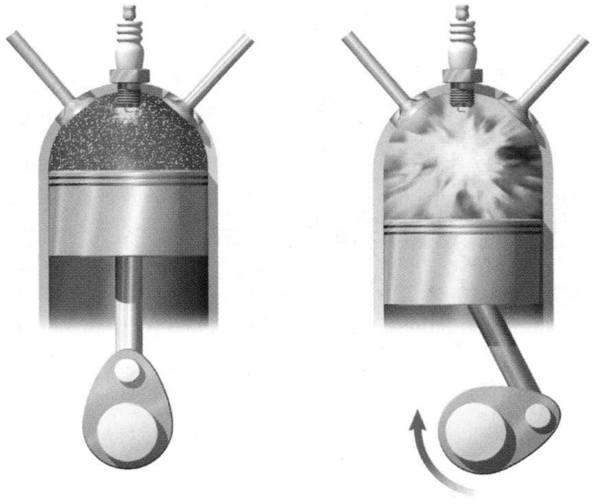

When a spark plug fires in an engine, chemical potential energy is converted into thermal energy.

As the hot gases expand, thermal energy is converted into kinetic energy.

Figure 6 In the engine of a car, several energy conversions occur.

Transforming Chemical Energy Fuel stores energy in the form of chemical potential energy. For example, the car or bus that might have brought you to school this morning probably uses gasoline as a fuel. The engine transforms the chemical potential energy stored in gasoline molecules into the kinetic energy of a moving car or bus. Several energy conversions occur in this process, as shown in **Figure 6.** An electric spark ignites a small amount of fuel. Igniting the fuel changes chemical energy to thermal energy. The thermal energy causes gases to expand and move parts of the engine, producing kinetic energy.

Some energy transformations are less obvious because they do not result in visible motion, sound, heat, or light. Every green plant you see converts light energy from the Sun into energy stored in chemical bonds in the plant. If you eat an ear of corn, the chemical potential energy in the corn is transformed into other forms of energy by your body.

Conversions Between Kinetic and Potential Energy

You have experienced many situations that involve conversions between potential and kinetic energy. Systems such as bicycles, roller coasters, and swings can be described in terms of potential and kinetic energy. Even launching a rubber band or using a bow and arrow involves converting potential energy into kinetic energy. To understand the energy conversions that occur, it is helpful to identify the mechanical energy of a system. **Mechanical energy** is the total amount of potential and kinetic energy in a system and can be expressed by this equation.

$$\text{mechanical energy} = \text{potential energy} + \text{kinetic energy}$$

In other words, mechanical energy is energy due to the position and the motion of an object or the objects in a system. What happens to the mechanical energy of an object as potential and kinetic energy are converted into each other?

Differentiated Instruction

Challenge Remind students that work is the transfer of energy, is measured in the same units as energy, and can be calculated using the formula $W = F \times d$. Provide students the following scenario: The kinetic energy of a hockey puck is 20 J as it moves from ice onto the cement surrounding the rink. By how much is its energy decreased if it stops on the cement? 20 J If the cement causes a frictional force of 10 N on the puck, how far does it slide? $-10\text{ N} \cdot d = -20\text{ J}$, therefore $d = 2.0$ m What happens to this energy? It is converted into thermal energy. L3 LS **Mathematical**

136 CHAPTER 5 Energy

Falling Objects Standing under an apple tree can be hazardous. An apple on a tree, like the one in **Figure 7,** has gravitational potential energy due to Earth pulling down on it. The apple does not have kinetic energy while it hangs from the tree. However, the instant the apple comes loose from the tree, it accelerates due to gravity. As it falls, it loses height so its gravitational potential energy decreases. This potential energy is transformed into kinetic energy as the speed of the apple increases.

Look back at the equation for mechanical energy. If the potential energy is being converted into kinetic energy, then the mechanical energy of the apple doesn't change as it falls. The potential energy that the apple loses is gained back as kinetic energy. The form of energy changes, but the total amount of energy remains the same.

Reading Check *What happens to the mechanical energy of the apple as it falls from the tree?*

Figure 7 Objects that can fall have gravitational potential energy.
Apply *What objects around you have gravitational potential energy?*

Energy Transformations in Projectile Motion Energy transformations also occur during projectile motion when an object moves in a curved path. Look at **Figure 8.** When the ball leaves the bat, it has mostly kinetic energy. As the ball rises, its speed decreases, so its kinetic energy must decrease, too. However, the ball's gravitational potential energy increases as it goes higher. At its highest point, the baseball has the maximum amount of gravitational potential energy. The only kinetic energy it has at this point is due to its forward motion. Then, as the baseball falls, gravitational potential energy decreases while kinetic energy increases as the ball moves faster. However, the mechanical energy of the ball remains constant as it rises and falls.

Figure 8 Kinetic energy and gravitational potential energy are converted into each other as the ball rises and falls.

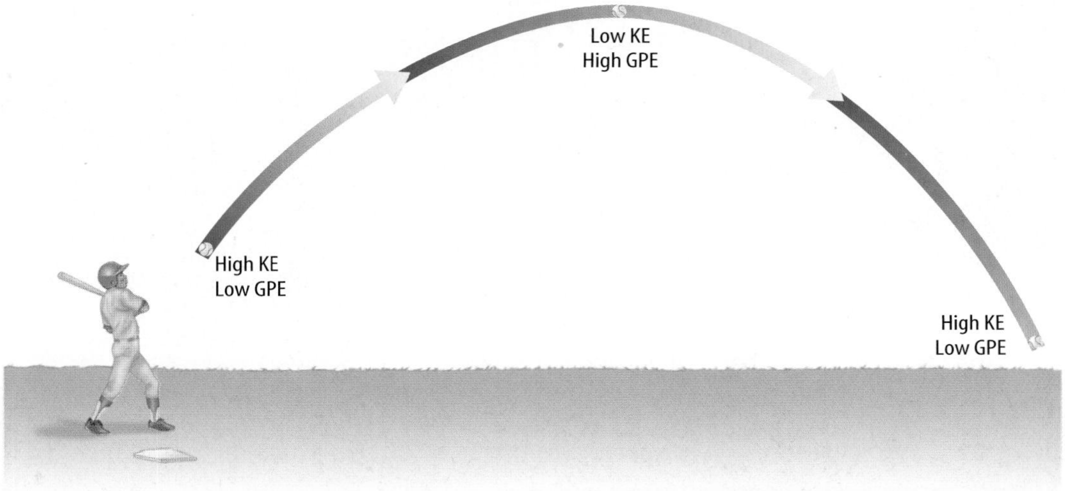

Reading Check

Answer Potential energy decreases; kinetic energy increases; total mechanical energy remains constant.

Caption Answer

Figure 7 Any objects that are elevated have GPE.

Teacher FYI

Free Fall Rate If there is no air resistance, then two objects that start falling at the same time from the same height will hit the ground at the same time. The rate of free fall does not depend on mass. But an object with larger mass has more GPE before it falls and has more kinetic energy when it hits the ground.

IDENTIFYING Misconceptions

Pendulum Swing Some students may not realize that when the bob of a pendulum reaches its maximum height, it momentarily stops, and when it is at its lowest part of its swing, its velocity is highest. Sketch a pendulum on the board and use arrows to show movement. Explain that the bob must briefly stop to change directions. Because it has no velocity, it has no kinetic energy at this point.

Reading Strategy

Clarify Text Have students work with a partner to read Conversions Between Kinetic and Potential Energy, The Law of Conservation of Energy, and The Human Body—Balancing the Energy Equation. For each section, have students take turns restating main ideas as partners listen.

Curriculum Connection

History Students have probably heard the tale of Isaac Newton discovering gravity when an apple fell from a tree onto his head. Have students investigate this story to determine if it is a myth or a true occurrence. Have students share their findings with the class. Newton is purported to have said himself that observing the fall of an apple "occasioned" his "notion of gravitation." L3 IS **Interpersonal**

NATIONAL GEOGRAPHIC

Visualizing Energy Transformations

Have students examine the pictures and read the captions. Then ask the following questions.

As the student goes from point A to B, why is her kinetic energy increasing? because her velocity is increasing

What force accelerates the student as she goes from point A to the lowest point and slows down the student as she goes from the lowest point to point D? gravity

Activity

Model Swings The movement of the swing is similar to the movement of a pendulum. Provide students with a 1-meter piece of string with a large washer tied to the end of it. Ask students to simulate the movement of the swing or a pendulum using the string and washer. Have students experiment to see if the length of the string has any relationship to the time it takes the washer to make one complete period, going from point A on the diagram to point D and back to point A again. Caution students not to swing string and washer strongly or near other students.

NATIONAL GEOGRAPHIC VISUALIZING ENERGY TRANSFORMATIONS

Figure 9

A ride on a swing illustrates how kinetic energy changes to potential energy and back to kinetic energy again. The diagram at right shows four stages of the swing's motion. Although it changes from one form to another, the total energy remains the same.

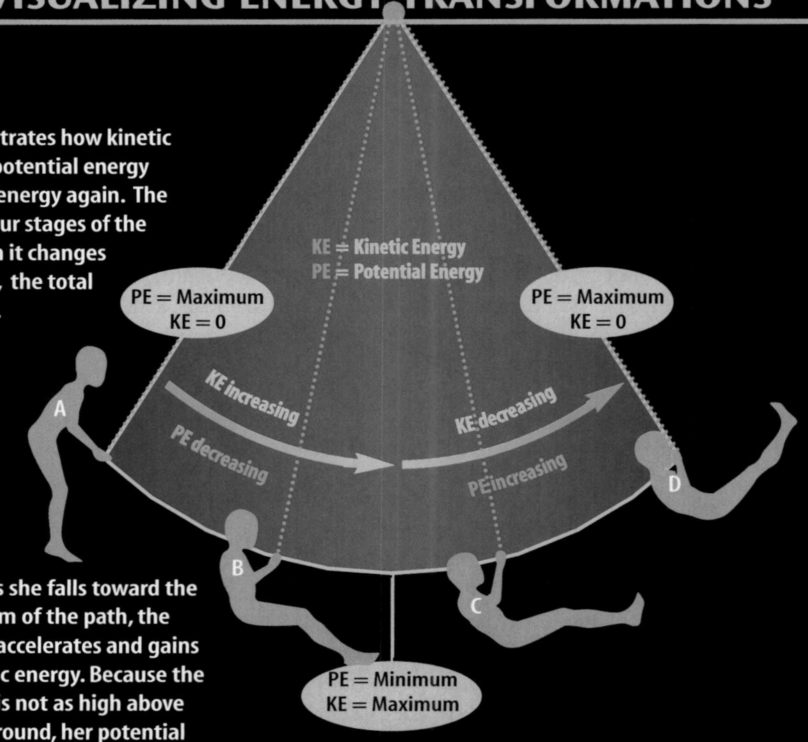

(A) At the rider's highest point, her potential energy is at a maximum and her kinetic energy is zero.

(B) As she falls toward the bottom of the path, the rider accelerates and gains kinetic energy. Because the rider is not as high above the ground, her potential energy decreases.

(C) The rider, rising toward the opposite side, begins to slow down and lose kinetic energy. As she gains height, her potential energy increases.

(D) At the highest point on this side of the swing, her potential energy again is at a maximum, and her kinetic energy is zero.

138

LAB DEMONSTRATION

Purpose to demonstrate the conservation of mechanical energy

Materials 2 m plastic tubing, 2 ring stands with clamps, marble

Preparation Form a U-shaped tunnel by clamping each end of the tubing to a ring stand. The ends should be at identical heights.

Procedure Hold a marble slightly above one end of the tubing. Have students predict the height the marble will reach on the opposite side. Release and discuss the result. Rearrange the tubing to form various shaped tunnels and repeat the activity.

Expected Outcome There should be a slight loss in mechanical energy.

Assessment

How was the mechanical energy affected as the marble traveled along the tubing? Air resistance on a marble inside a plastic tube is negligible. What are possible causes of this? friction from the tubing

Energy Transformations in a Swing When you ride on a swing, like the one shown in **Figure 9,** part of the fun is the feeling of almost falling as you drop from the highest point to the lowest point of the swing's path. Think about energy conservation to analyze such a ride.

The ride starts with a push that gets you moving, giving you kinetic energy. As the swing rises, you lose speed but gain height. In energy terms, kinetic energy changes to gravitational potential energy. At the top of your path, potential energy is at its greatest. Then, as the swing accelerates downward, potential energy changes to kinetic energy. At the bottom of each swing, the kinetic energy is at its greatest and the potential energy is at its minimum. As you swing back and forth, energy continually converts from kinetic to potential and back to kinetic. What happens to your mechanical energy as you swing?

The Law of Conservation of Energy

When a ball is thrown into the air or a swing moves back and forth, kinetic and potential energy are constantly changing as the object speeds up and slows down. However, mechanical energy stays constant. Kinetic and potential energy simply change forms and no energy is destroyed.

This is always true. Energy can change from one form to another, but the total amount of energy never changes. Even when energy changes form from electrical to thermal and other energy forms as in the hair dryer shown in **Figure 10,** energy is never destroyed. Another way to say this is that energy is conserved. This principle is recognized as a law of nature. The **law of conservation of energy** states that energy cannot be created or destroyed. On a large scale, this law means that the total amount of energy in the universe does not change.

Reading Check ***What law states that the total amount of energy never changes?***

Conserving Resources You might have heard about energy conservation or been asked to conserve energy. These ideas are related to reducing the demand for electricity and gasoline, which lowers the consumption of energy resources such as coal and fuel oil. The law of conservation of energy, on the other hand, is a universal principle that describes what happens to energy as it is transferred from one object to another or as it is transformed.

INTEGRATE Environment

Energy and the Food Chain One way energy enters ecosystems is when green plants transform radiant energy from the Sun into chemical potential energy in the form of food. Energy moves through the food chain as animals that eat plants are eaten by other animals. Some energy leaves the food chain, such as when living organisms release thermal energy to the environment. Diagram a simple biological food chain showing energy conservation.

Figure 10 The law of conservation of energy requires that the total amount of energy going into a hair dryer must equal the total amount of energy coming out of the hair dryer.

INTEGRATE Environment

Energy and the Food Chain In a food chain, arrows show the direction in which energy moves from one organism to the next. Possible food chain: grass ⟶ rabbit ⟶ fox

Career Find out how environmental scientists in your area use data on numbers and kinds of plants and animals to evaluate the health of an ecosystem.

Use Science Words

Word Meaning The word *conservation* means to keep from being lost or wasted. Discuss why this is an appropriate word to use for the principle of conservation of energy. Possible answer: It is appropriate because energy is never lost. L2

LS **Linguistic**

Text Question Answer:

Mechanical energy remains constant.

Reading Check

Answer The law of conservation of energy.

Virtual Labs

Energy Conversion *How is energy converted from one form to another?*

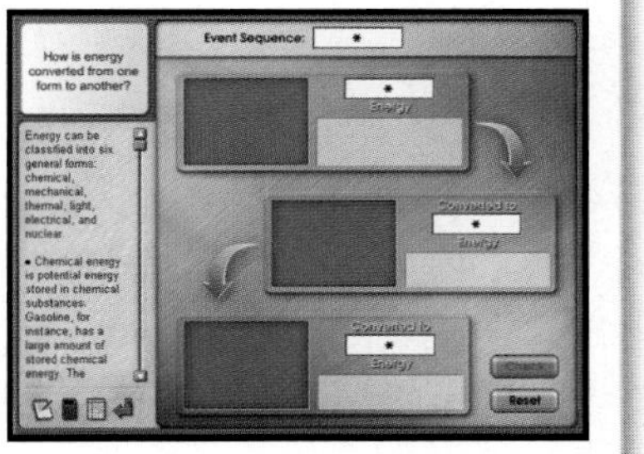

Science Journal

Have students create a flow diagram that traces the conversion of solar energy into different forms of energy on earth. Possible answers: Plants convert solar energy into food for animals who move around. Plants also feed people who use machines and electricity to do work. Thermal energy from the sun causes warm air to rise which causes wind energy, and it fuels the water cycle.

SECTION 2 Conservation of Energy **139**

Mini LAB

Purpose Students observe how kinetic energy can change into thermal energy. L1

LS **Intrapersonal**

Materials paper clip

Teaching Strategy Have students use uncoated clips that are not too thick or brittle to easily bend.

Safety Precaution Students should be careful of the sharp ends of the paper clip when bending it.

Analysis

1. It went up. Some mechanical energy from the paper clip was converted to thermal energy.
2. Chemical energy from the body is converted to kinetic energy that is transferred to the paper clip. Mechanical energy is converted to thermal energy by collisions of the molecules in the paper clip.

Assessment

Oral Have students discuss other examples of the process modeled by this activity. Possible answer: bicycle or car tires heat up as they roll along the road. Use **Performance Assessment in the Science Classroom,** p. 89.

Try at Home

Caption Answer

Figure 11 Both the kinetic and potential energy decrease as friction and air resistance transform the swing's mechanical energy into thermal energy.

Figure 11 In a swing, mechanical energy is transformed into thermal energy because of friction and air resistance.
Infer *how the kinetic and potential energy of the swing change with time.*

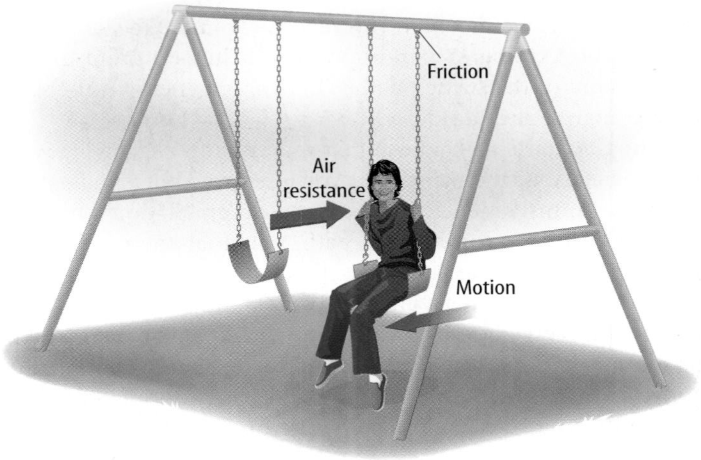

Mini LAB

Transforming Energy in a Paper Clip

Procedure

1. Straighten a **paper clip.** While holding the ends, touch the paper clip to the skin just below your lower lip. Note whether the paper clip feels warm, cool, or about room temperature.
2. Quickly bend the paper clip back and forth five times. Touch it below your lower lip again. Note whether the paper clip feels warmer or cooler than before.

Analysis

1. What happened to the temperature of the paper clip? Why?
2. Describe the energy conversions that take place as you bend the paper clip.

Try at Home

Is energy always conserved? You might be able to think of situations where it seems as though energy is not conserved. For example, while coasting along a flat road on a bicycle, you know that you will eventually stop if you don't pedal. If energy is conserved, why wouldn't your kinetic energy stay constant so that you would coast forever? In many situations, it might seem that energy is destroyed or created. Sometimes it is hard to see the law of conservation of energy at work.

The Effect of Friction You know from experience that if you don't continue to pump a swing or be pushed by somebody else, your arcs will become lower and you eventually will stop swinging. In other words, the mechanical (kinetic and potential) energy of the swing seems to decrease, as if the energy were being destroyed. Is this a violation of the law of conservation of energy?

It can't be—it's the law! If the energy of the swing decreases, then the energy of some other object must increase by an equal amount to keep the total amount of energy the same. What could this other object be that experiences an energy increase? To answer this, you need to think about friction. With every movement, the swing's ropes or chains rub on their hooks and air pushes on the rider, as illustrated in **Figure 11.** Friction and air resistance cause some of the mechanical energy of the swing to change to thermal energy. With every pass of the swing, the temperature of the hooks and the air increases a little, so the mechanical energy of the swing is not destroyed. Rather, it is transformed into thermal energy. The total amount of energy always stays the same.

Fun Fact

Many people have tried to develop a perpetual motion machine, a device which, once set in motion, would forever make more energy than it uses. Conservation of energy means that such a machine is impossible.

Differentiated Instruction

Learning Disabled To help students see how friction affects the velocity and therefore the kinetic energy of objects, have them roll marbles across a smooth table and then across a piece of carpet. Explain that the marbles move more slowly on the carpet and have less kinetic energy because the frictional force opposes their motion. L1 LS **Kinesthetic**

Converting Mass into Energy You might have wondered how the Sun unleashes enough energy to light and warm Earth from so far away. A special kind of energy conversion—nuclear fusion—takes place in the Sun and other stars. During this process a small amount of mass is transformed into a tremendous amount of energy. An example of a nuclear fusion reaction is shown in **Figure 12.** In the reaction shown here, the nuclei of the hydrogen isotopes deuterium and tritium undergo fusion.

Nuclear Fission Another process involving the nuclei of atoms, called nuclear fission, converts a small amount of mass into enormous quantities of energy. In this process, nuclei do not fuse—they are broken apart, as shown in **Figure 12.** In either process, fusion or fission, mass is converted to energy. In processes involving nuclear fission and fusion, the total amount of energy is still conserved if the energy content of the masses involved are included. Then the total energy before the reaction is equal to the total energy after the reaction, as required by the law of conservation of energy. The process of nuclear fission is used by nuclear power plants to generate electrical energy.

Science Online

Topic: Nuclear Fusion

Visit gpescience.com for Web links to information about using nuclear fusion as a source of energy in electric power plants.

Activity Make a table listing the advantages and disadvantages of using nuclear fusion as an energy source.

Figure 12 Mass is converted to energy in the processes of fusion and fission.

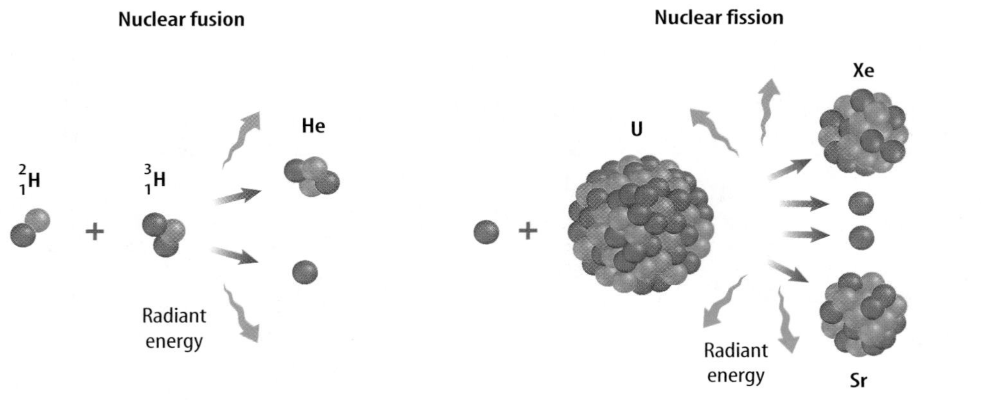

Mass $^2_1$**H** + Mass $^3_1$**H** > Mass **He** +Mass **neutron**

In this fusion reaction, the combined mass of the two hydrogen nuclei is greater than the mass of the helium nucleus, He, and the neutron.

Mass **U** + Mass **neutron** > Mass **Xe** + Mass **Sr** + Mass **neutrons**

In nuclear fission, the mass of the large nucleus on the left is greater than the combined mass of the other two nuclei and the neutrons.

Use Science Words

Word Meaning Have students use a dictionary to look up the words *fusion* and *fission.* Ask them to explain why these are appropriate terms for the nuclear processes discussed in this section. Fusion is combining of things—in nuclear fusion, nuclei combine. Fission is splitting apart of things—in nuclear fission, nuclei split apart. L1 IN **Linguistic**

Inquiry Lab

Calculate Energy

Purpose to calculate elastic potential energy and kinetic energy in a rubber band

Possible Materials rubber band, Newton scale, meterstick, pan balance, stopwatch.

Estimated Time 30 minutes

Procedure Have students devise a method to calculate and a method to check the elastic potential energy of a rubber band using the materials listed. Remind them that velocity can be calculated using the horizontal distance traveled and the time to fall. Have them graph force needed to pull v. distance pulled, and force needed to pull v. velocity.

Safety Precautions Caution students not to shoot rubber bands at each other.

Teaching Strategy

The elastic potential energy can be calculated by multiplying the force needed to pull times one-half the distance pulled. It should nearly equal the kinetic energy which can be calculated from the mass and velocity. The force v. distance graph should be a straight diagonal line because they are directly proportional. Force v. velocity should also be a straight line.

For additional inquiry activities, see *Science Inquiry Lab*.

Cultural Diversity

Energy in Martial Arts Karate, which means "empty hand," originated on Okinawa in the seventeenth century. A trained karateka can break a thin concrete block with his or her hand. Have students research the meanings of the names of other forms of martial arts and where they originated. Possible martial arts include judo, aikido, and tae kwon do. L2 IN **Intrapersonal**

Teacher FYI

Chain Reaction In the process of fission, neutrons are released. They initiate further fission, beginning a chain reaction. For the chain reaction to continue, sufficient fissionable material must be present. The amount of material needed to sustain a chain reaction is known as the critical mass.

IDENTIFYING Misconceptions

Human Conversions Students may confuse energy transformations with changes in matter. Some may state that food is converted into energy in the body. During digestion, chemical compounds in food are converted into compounds that muscle cells use to enable muscles to move.

Use Science Words

Word Origin The word *calorie* originates from the eighteenth-century word *caloric*, which was a hypothetical weightless fluid that scientists thought flowed from hot objects to cold objects. Ask students to find out how caloric theory contributed to the idea of conservation of energy. Benjamin Thompson (1753–1814), working in a German munitions factory noticed that canons became very hot during the boring process even though the canon and the borer were initially cold. He concluded that heat was a form of energy produced by friction. Similar experiments by other scientists confirmed that heat was a form of energy and not a fluid, and that it was energy that was being conserved and not caloric. L2 LS **Linguistic**

Caption Answer

Figure 13 7 to 8 hours depending on body type

INTEGRATE Health **Content Background**

Students may be familiar with the phrase "counting calories" as a synonym for dieting. Counting calories is a way to monitor the amount of energy being consumed in food in hopes of forcing the body to use up its energy reserves stored as unwanted fat.

The Human Body—Balancing the Energy Equation

What forms of energy discussed in this chapter can you find in the human body? With your right hand, reach up and feel your left shoulder. With that simple action, stored potential energy within your body was converted to the kinetic energy of your moving arm. Did your shoulder feel warm to your hand? Some of the chemical potential energy stored in your body is used to maintain a nearly constant internal temperature. A portion of this energy also is converted to the excess heat that your body gives off to its surroundings. Even the people shown standing in **Figure 13** require energy conversions to stand still.

Energy Conversions in Your Body The complex chemical and physical processes going on in your body also obey the law of conservation of energy. Your body stores energy in the form of fat and other chemical compounds. This chemical potential energy is used to fuel the processes that keep you alive, such as making your heart beat and digesting the food you eat. Your body also converts this energy to heat that is transferred to your surroundings, and you use this energy to make your body move. **Table 1** shows the amount of energy used in doing various activities. To maintain a healthy weight, you must have a proper balance between energy contained in the food you eat and the energy your body uses.

Figure 13 The runners convert the energy stored in their bodies more rapidly than the spectators do.
Calculate *Use **Table 1** to calculate how long a person would need to stand to burn as much energy as a runner burns in 1 h.*

Visual Learning

Table 1 Have students think back over the past 24 hours and make a list of the things they did. Have them use the table to find out about how many Calories of energy they used.

Active Reading

Learning Journal Have students draw a vertical line down each page of a Learning Journal and record research notes, lecture notes, or vocabulary terms in the left column. In the right column, they respond to, interpret, question, or analyze the left column entries. Students can write a Learning Journal while reading about conservation of energy.

INTEGRATE Health

Food Energy Your body has been busy breaking down your breakfast into molecules that can be used as fuel. The chemical potential energy in these molecules supplies the cells in your body with the energy they need to function. Your body also can use the chemical potential energy stored in fat for its energy needs. The food Calorie (C) is a unit used by nutritionists to measure how much energy you get from various foods—1 C is equivalent to about 4,184 J. Every gram of fat a person consumes can supply 9 C of energy. Carbohydrates and proteins each supply about 4 C of energy per gram.

Look at the labels on food packages. They provide information about the Calories contained in a serving, as well as the amounts of protein, fat, and carbohydrates.

Table 1 Calories Used in One Hour

Type of Activity	Body Frames		
	Small	Medium	Large
Sleeping	48	56	64
Sitting	72	84	96
Eating	84	98	112
Standing	96	112	123
Walking	180	210	240
Playing tennis	380	420	460
Bicycling (fast)	500	600	700
Running	700	850	1,000

section 2 review

Summary

Energy Transformations

- Energy can be transformed from one form to another.
- Devices such as lightbulbs, hair dryers, and automobile engines convert one form of energy into other forms.
- The mechanical energy of a system is the sum of the kinetic and potential energy in the system:

  mechanical energy = *KE* + *PE*
- In falling, projectile motion, and swings, kinetic and potential energy are transformed into each other and the mechanical energy doesn't change.

The Law of Conservation of Energy

- According to the law of conservation of energy, energy cannot be created or destroyed.
- Friction converts mechanical energy into thermal energy.
- Fission and fusion are nuclear reactions that convert a small amount of mass in a nucleus into an enormous amount of energy.

Self Check

1. **Explain** how friction affects the mechanical energy of a system.
2. **Describe** the energy transformations that occur as you coast down a long hill on a bicycle and apply the brakes, causing the brake pads and bicycle rims to feel warm.
3. **Explain** how energy is conserved when nuclear fission or fusion occurs.
4. **Think Critically** A roller coaster is at the top of a hill and rolls to the top of a lower hill. If mechanical energy is conserved, on the top of which hill is the kinetic energy of the roller coaster larger?

Applying Math

5. **Calculate Kinetic Energy** The potential energy of a swing is 200 J at its highest point and 50 J at its lowest point. If mechanical energy is conserved, what is the kinetic energy of the swing at its lowest point?
6. **Calculate Thermal Energy** The mechanical energy of a bicycle at the top of a hill is 6,000 J. The bicycle stops at the bottom of the hill by applying the brakes. If the potential energy of the bicycle is 2,000 J at the bottom of the hill, how much thermal energy was produced?

More Section Review gpescience.com

Post Reading

Science Journal Compose a written response to the following prompt: Imagine you are pushing a young child on a swing. Describe the role played by the concepts of energy transformation and the law of conservation of energy.

3 Assess

DAILY INTERVENTION

Check for Understanding

Fission v. Fusion Have students use models to demonstrate nuclear fission and nuclear fusion. Students could use marbles for neutrons and protons, with clay to hold them together. L2 **Visual-Spatial**

Reteach

Energy and Calories Show students pictures of people performing various activities, such as those listed in Table 1. Ask students to order the pictures according to how quickly they burn calories. Students should also identify types of energy conversion in each activity. L1 **Visual-Spatial**

Assessment

Process Have students draw diagrams illustrating some of the changing forms of energy involved in bouncing a basketball. Chemical energy from the body changes to kinetic energy to lift the ball. This energy is transferred to the ball as potential energy. As the ball falls, this changes to kinetic energy. As the ball hits the floor, part of the energy changes to sound, part is transferred to the floor, and most is returned to the ball as elastic potential energy, enabling the ball to bounce. Use **PASC**, p. 127. P

section 2 review

1. Friction converts mechanical energy into thermal energy.
2. As you coast down the hill, some of your potential energy is being transformed into kinetic energy. When you apply the brakes, friction between the brake pads and the bicycle rims convert kinetic energy into thermal energy.
3. A small amount of mass is converted into energy.
4. The top of the lower hill; the roller coaster has less potential energy at the top of the lower hill. The difference between the roller coaster's potential energy at the top of the higher hill and lower hill has been converted into kinetic energy.
5. 150 J
6. 4.000 J

BENCH TESTED

Real-World Problem

Purpose Construct a pendulum to compare the exchange of potential and kinetic energy. L2 COOP LEARN IS **Kinesthetic**

Process Skills measure, collect and organize data, observe and infer, communicate, make and use tables, compare and contrast, recognize cause and effect, form a hypothesis, design an experiment, use numbers, separate and control variables

Time Required one class period

Possible Materials Have additional materials available (string, extra ring stands, banner paper, masking tape).

Safety Precautions Students should wear safety goggles when swinging the stoppers.

Form a Hypothesis

Possible Hypothesis Students may suggest that the crossarm's interference halfway up the length of the string will cause the maximum height to decrease by one half. In fact, the shape of the pendulum's path will change, but the height on the opposite end should still be close to the original height.

LAB Design Your Own

Swinging Energy

Goals

- **Construct** a pendulum to compare the exchange of potential and kinetic energy when a swing is interrupted.
- **Measure** the starting and ending heights of the pendulum.

Possible Materials

ring stand
test-tube clamp
support-rod clamp, right angle
30-cm support rod
2-hole, medium rubber stopper
string (1 m)
metersticks (2)
graph paper

Safety Precautions

WARNING: *Be sure the base is heavy enough or well anchored so that the apparatus will not tip over.*

Real-World Problem

Imagine yourself swinging on a swing. What would happen if a friend grabbed the swing's chains as you passed the lowest point? Would you come to a complete stop or continue rising to your previous maximum height? How does the motion and maximum height reached by a swing change if the swing is interrupted?

Form a Hypothesis

Examine the diagram on this page. How is it similar to the situation in the introductory paragraph? An object that is suspended so that it can swing back and forth is called a pendulum. Hypothesize what will happen to the pendulum's motion and final height if its swing is interrupted.

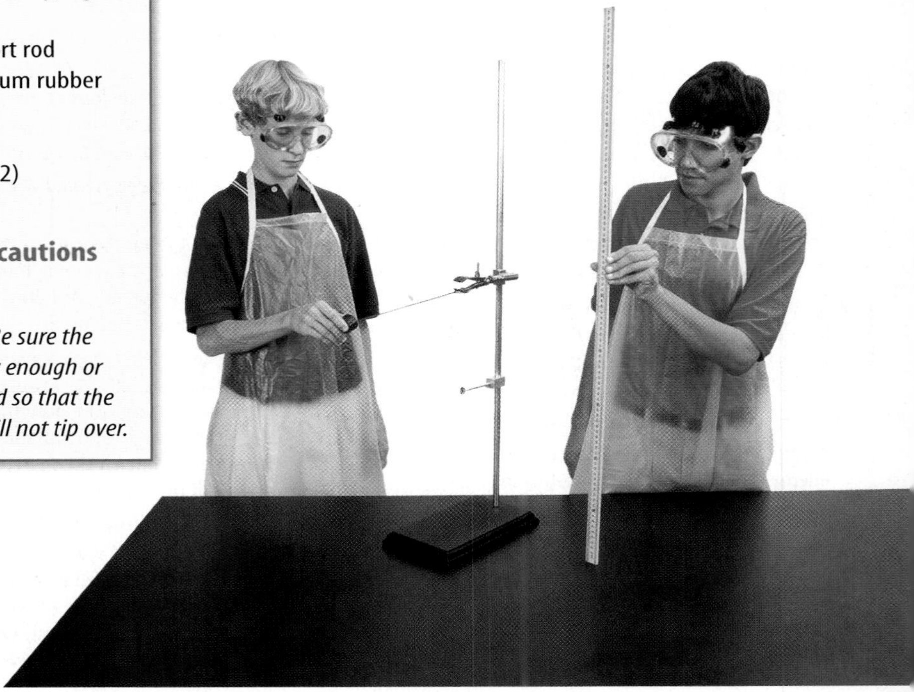

Alternative Inquiry Lab

Energy Loss Have students determine the thermal energy produced by friction after the pendulum has swung 10 times. Have them measure the mass of the stopper, calculate its initial potential energy using its initial height, and calculate its ending potential energy using the height after 10 swings. The difference is the amount of initial potential energy that has been converted into thermal energy by friction. Have them do this exercise both with and without cross-arm interference. L3 IS **Kinesthetic**

Test Your Hypothesis

Make a Plan

1. As a group, write your hypothesis and list the steps that you will take to test it. Be specific. Also list the materials you will need.
2. **Design** a data table and place it in your Science Journal.
3. Set up an apparatus similar to the one shown in the diagram.
4. **Devise** a way to measure the starting and ending heights of the stopper. Record your starting and ending heights in a data table. This will be your control.
5. **Decide** how to release the stopper from the same height each time.
6. Be sure you test your swing, starting it above and below the height of the cross arm. How many times should you repeat each starting point?

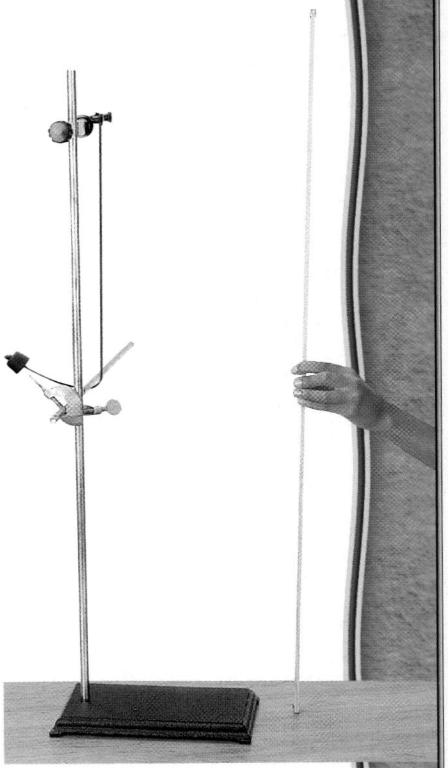

Follow Your Plan

1. Make sure your teacher approves your plan before you start.
2. Carry out the approved experiment as planned.
3. While the experiment is going on, write any observations that you make and complete the data table in your Science Journal.

Analyze Your Data

1. When the stopper is released from the same height as the cross arm, is the ending height of the stopper exactly the same as its starting height? Use your data to support your answer.
2. **Analyze** the energy transfers. At what point along a single swing does the stopper have the greatest kinetic energy? The greatest potential energy?

Conclude and Apply

1. **Explain** Do the results support your hypothesis?
2. **Compare** the starting heights to the ending heights of the stopper. Is there a pattern? Can you account for the observed behavior?
3. **Discuss** Do your results support the law of conservation of energy? Why or why not?
4. **Infer** What happens if the mass of the stopper is increased? Test it.

Communicating Your Data

Compare your conclusions with those of the other lab teams in your class. **For more help, refer to the** Science Skill Handbook.

Test Your Hypothesis

Possible Procedures Set up the pendulum and start it moving. Measure the height at which the stopper was released to start the pendulum. When the pendulum is on the far side of its swing, insert the crossarm. Measure the height to which the pendulum swings after it hits the crossarm.

Teaching Strategy Tape white paper to a wall behind the pendulum for marking stopper height.

Troubleshooting The swing of the pendulum will be irregular if the crossarm inhibits movement of only one side of the pendulum's swing. Suggest students find a way to have the cross arm limit swing in both directions.

Expected Outcome Students will observe that even with the crossarm, the approximate original height is reached.

Analyze Your Data

1. no
2. Kinetic is greatest at the bottom; potential is greatest at the top.

Conclude and Apply

1. Answers will vary with results.
2. Ending heights are lower. Friction slows the stopper and removes some energy from the system.
3. Yes; the apparent loss of energy is due to friction.
4. Kinetic and potential energy increase; the person must pull harder to stop the swing.

Assessment

Process When started from the same height, a pendulum without interference from a crossarm will remain in motion longer than a pendulum with an arm. Ask students to discuss and explain this. Some energy is transferred to the crossarm. Use **Performance Assessment in the Science Classroom,** p. 89. L2 IS **Interpersonal**

Communicating Your Data

Have students use a word processing program to write a short description of their experiment. They may wish to use a computer graphics program to make sketches that help explain the results.

TIME

Content Background

The construction of a perpetual motion machine has been the dream of inventors for centuries. However, the first and second laws of thermodynamics make this impossible. In any real machine, friction causes some of the machine's mechanical energy to be converted to thermal energy that cannot be recovered. As a result, the first law of thermodynamics requires that energy be continually supplied to any machine to keep it moving.

Discussion

Thermodynamics What are the two laws of energy that make perpetual motion machines impossible? 1st Law: Energy cannot be created or destroyed; it only changes form. 2nd Law: Thermal energy flows only from hot to cold.

Historical Significance

Perpetual motion machines have been around at least since Villand de Honnecourt made drawings of one in the 13th century. Between 1635 and 1903, 600 patents were granted for purported free-energy machines. One inventor fooled scientists with a machine that appeared to run on water. He raised five million dollars from investors who later learned that it was actually based on hidden air tubes. In spite of the massive fraud that was found, there are still believers in his "technology" today.

TIME **SCIENCE AND HISTORY** SCIENCE CAN CHANGE THE COURSE OF HISTORY!

The Impossible Dream

A machine that keeps on going? It has been tried for hundreds of years.

Many people have tried throughout history—and failed—to build perpetual-motion machines. In theory, a perpetual-motion machine would run forever and do work without a continual source of energy. You can think of it as a car that you could fill up once with gas, and the car would run forever. Sound impossible? It is!

Science Puts Its Foot Down

For hundreds of years, people have tried to create perpetual-motion machines. But these machines won't work because they violate two of nature's laws. The first law is the law of conservation of energy, which states that energy cannot be created or destroyed. It can change form—say, from mechanical energy to electrical energy—but you always end up with the same amount of energy that you started with.

How does that apply to perpetual-motion machines? When a machine does work on an object, the machine transfers energy to the object. Unless that machine gets more energy from somewhere else, it can't keep doing work. If it did, it would be creating energy.

The second law states that heat by itself always flows from a warm object to a cold object. Heat will only flow from a cold object to a warm object if work is done. In the process, some heat always escapes.

To make up for these energy losses, energy constantly needs to be transferred to the machine. Otherwise, it stops. No perpetual motion. No free electricity. No devices that generate more energy than they use. No engine motors that run forever without refueling. Some laws just can't be broken.

Visitors look at the Keely Motor, the most famous perpetual-motion machine fraud of the late 1800s.

Analyze Using your school or public-library resources, locate a picture or diagram of a perpetual-motion machine. Figure out why it won't run forever. Explain to the class what the problem is.

TIME For more information, visit gpescience.com

Analyze Ask students to think about how perpetual motion machines might be helpful to science and technology if the laws of thermodynamics did not exist. Start a dialogue addressing the thousands of scam artists who have tried in vain to sell their perpetual motion machines.

Resources for Teachers and Students

"Exploiting Zero-Point Energy", by Philip Yam, *Scientific American*, December 1997

Perpetual Motion: The History of An Obsession, by Arthur W.J.G. OrdHume, Barnes and Noble Books, 1998

Reviewing Main Ideas

Section 1 The Nature of Energy

1. Energy is the ability to cause change.
2. Energy can have different forms, including kinetic, potential, and thermal energy.

3. Moving objects have kinetic energy that depends on the object's mass and velocity, and can be calculated from this equation:

$$KE = \frac{1}{2}mv^2$$

4. Potential energy is stored energy. An object can have gravitational potential energy that depends on its mass and its height, and is given by this equation:

$$GPE = mgh$$

Section 2 Conservation of Energy

1. Energy can change from one form to another. Devices you use every day transform one form of energy into other forms that are more useful.
2. Falling, swinging, and projectile motion all involve transformations between kinetic energy and gravitational potential energy.
3. The total amount of kinetic energy and gravitational potential energy in a system is the mechanical energy of the system:

$$\textit{mechanical energy} = KE + GPE$$

4. The law of conservation of energy states that energy never can be created or destroyed. The total amount of energy in the universe is constant.

5. Friction converts mechanical energy into thermal energy, causing the mechanical energy of a system to decrease.
6. Mass is converted into energy in nuclear fission and fusion reactions. Fusion and fission occur in the nuclei of certain atoms, and release tremendous amounts of energy.

FOLDABLES™ Use the Foldable you made at the beginning of this chapter to review what you learned about energy.

chapter 5 Study Guide

Reviewing Main Ideas

Summary statements can be used by students to review the major concepts of the chapter.

Science Online

Visit gpescience.com
More Section Review
Interactive Tutor
Vocabulary PuzzleMaker
More Chapter Review
Standardized Test Practice

Assessment Transparency

For additional assessment questions, use the *Assessment Transparency* located in the transparency book.

Assessment

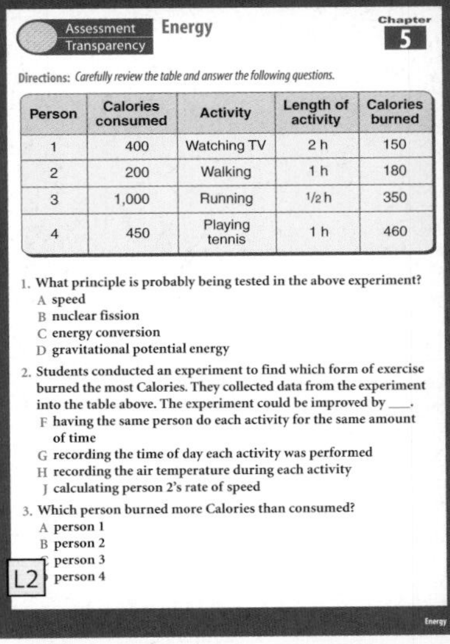

Assessment Transparency — Energy — Chapter 5

Directions: *Carefully review the table and answer the following questions.*

Person	Calories consumed	Activity	Length of activity	Calories burned
1	400	Watching TV	2 h	150
2	200	Walking	1 h	180
3	1,000	Running	1/2 h	350
4	450	Playing tennis	1 h	460

1. What principle is probably being tested in the above experiment?
   A speed
   B nuclear fission
   C energy conversion
   D gravitational potential energy
2. Students conducted an experiment to find which form of exercise burned the most Calories. They collected data from the experiment into the table above. The experiment could be improved by ___.
   F having the same person do each activity for the same amount of time
   G recording the time of day each activity was performed
   H recording the air temperature during each activity
   J calculating person 2's rate of speed
3. Which person burned more Calories than consumed?
   A person 1
   B person 2
   C person 3
   D person 4

L2

Energy

FOLDABLES™ Have students use their Foldables to review the content of the chapter. On the back of the paper, have students write a paragraph about what they learned about energy.

Using Vocabulary

1. mechanical energy
2. elastic potential energy
3. joule
4. potential energy
5. kinetic energy
6. law of conservation of energy

Checking Concepts

7. D
8. B
9. B
10. A
11. D
12. C

Interpreting Graphics

13. See student page.
14. height = 0.50 m, GPE = 0.24 J, KE = 0.24 J; height = 0.75 m, GPE = 0.37 J, KE = 0.37 J; height = 1.0 m, GPE = 0.49 J, KE = 0.49; The GPE and KE are equal.
15. four times, from 400 J to 1,600 J
16. 2,400 J. It will be four times greater than the KE at 25 m/s, which is 600 J.
17. 100 J. It is one fourth the KE at 20 m/s.

chapter 5 Review

Using Vocabulary

chemical potential energy p. 131	joule p. 130
elastic potential energy p. 131	kinetic energy p. 130
energy p. 128	law of conservation of energy p. 139
gravitational potential energy p. 132	mechanical energy p. 136
	potential energy p. 131

Complete each statement using a word(s) from the vocabulary list above.

1. If friction can be ignored, the _________ of a system doesn't change.
2. The energy stored in a compressed spring is _________.
3. The _________ is the SI unit for energy.
4. When a book is moved from a higher shelf to a lower shelf, its _________ changes.
5. The muscles of a runner transform chemical potential energy into _________.
6. According to the _________, the amount of energy in the universe doesn't change.

Checking Concepts

Choose the word or phrase that best answers the question.

7. What occurs when energy is transferred from one object to another?
   A) an explosion
   B) a chemical reaction
   C) nuclear fusion
   D) a change
8. For which of the following is kinetic energy converted into potential energy?
   A) a boulder rolls down a hill
   B) a ball is thrown upward
   C) a swing comes to a stop
   D) a bowling ball rolls horizontally
9. The gravitational potential energy of an object changes when which of the following changes?
   A) the object's speed
   B) the object's mass
   C) the object's temperature
   D) the object's length
10. Friction causes mechanical energy to be transformed into which of these forms?
    A) thermal **C)** kinetic
    B) nuclear **D)** potential
11. The kinetic energy of an object changes when which of the following changes?
    A) the object's chemical potential energy
    B) the object's volume
    C) the object's direction of motion
    D) the object's speed
12. When an energy transformation occurs, which of the following is true?
    A) Mechanical energy doesn't change.
    B) Mechanical energy is lost.
    C) The total energy doesn't change.
    D) Mass is converted into energy.

Interpreting Graphics

13. Copy and complete the following concept map on energy.

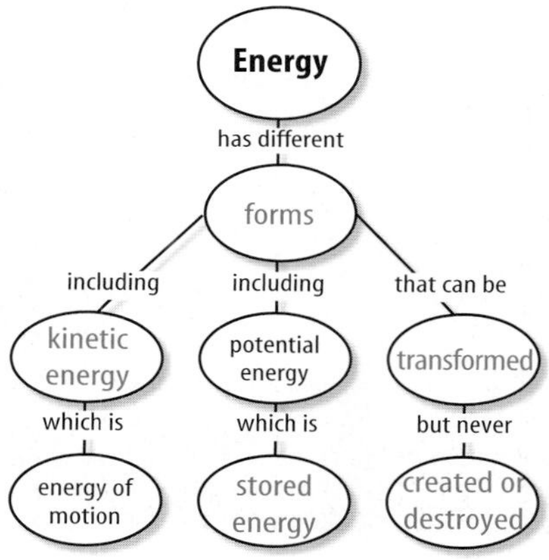

Use the Exam*View*® Pro Testmaker CD-ROM to:

- create multiple versions of tests
- create modified tests with one mouse click for inclusion students
- edit existing questions and add your own questions
- build tests aligned with state standards using built-in State Curriculum Tags
- change English tests to Spanish with one mouse click and vice versa

Use the table below to answer question 14.

Toy Cars Rolling Down Ramps

Ramp Height (m)	Speed at Bottom (m/s)	GPE (J)	KE (J)
0.50	3.13	0.24	0.24
0.75	3.83	0.37	0.37
1.00	4.43	0.49	0.49

14. **Make and Use Tables** Three toy cars, each with a mass of 0.05 kg, roll down ramps with different heights. The height of each ramp and the speed of each car at the bottom of each ramp is given in the table. Copy and complete the table by calculating the GPE of each car at the top of the ramp and the KE for each car at the bottom of the ramp to two decimal places. How do the values of GPE and KE you calculate compare?

Use the graph below to answer questions 15–17.

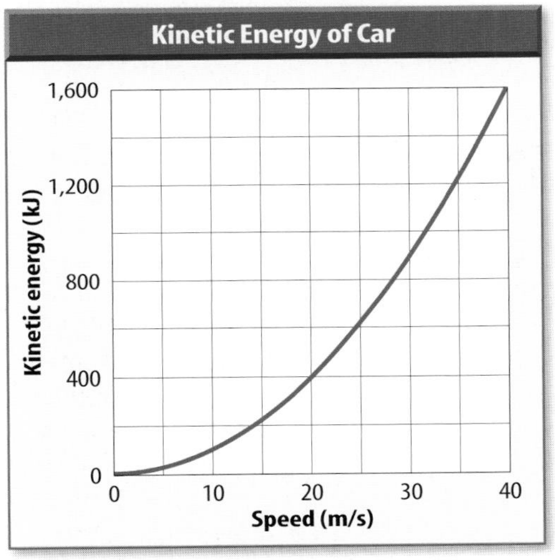

15. When the car's speed doubles from 20 m/s to 40 m/s, by how many times does the car's kinetic energy increase?

16. Using the graph, estimate the car's kinetic energy at a speed of 50 m/s.

17. If the car's kinetic energy at a speed of 20 m/s is 400 kJ, what is the car's kinetic energy at a speed of 10 m/s?

Thinking Critically

18. **Describe** the energy changes that occur in a swing. Explain how energy is conserved as the swing slows down and stops.

19. **Explain** why the law of conservation of energy must also include changes in mass.

20. **Infer** why the tires of a car get hot when the car is driven.

21. **Diagram** On a cold day you rub your hands together to make them warm. Diagram the energy transformations that occur, starting with the chemical potential energy stored in your muscles.

Applying Math

22. **Calculate Kinetic Energy** What is the kinetic energy of a 0.06-kg tennis ball traveling at a speed of 150 m/s?

23. **Calculate Potential Energy** A boulder with a mass of 2,500 kg rests on a ledge 200 m above the ground. What is the boulder's potential energy?

24. **Calculate Mechanical Energy** What is the mechanical energy of a 500-kg roller-coaster car moving with a speed of 3 m/s at the top of hill that is 30 m high?

25. **Calculate Speed** A boulder with a mass of 2,500 kg on a ledge 200 m above the ground falls. If the boulder's mechanical energy is conserved, what is the speed of the boulder just before it hits the ground?

chapter 5 Review

Thinking Critically

18. At the highest point of the swing, the potential energy is a maximum and the kinetic energy is zero. As the swing falls, potential energy is converted into kinetic energy. At the bottom of the swing, the kinetic energy is maximum and the potential energy is a minimum. As the swing moves, friction and air resistance convert the swing's mechanical energy to thermal energy, causing it to slow down and stop.

19. In nuclear fission and nuclear fusion, a small amount of mass is converted into energy.

20. The flexing of the tires as the car is moving coverts elastic potential energy in the tire to thermal energy.

21. Diagram should be: chemical potential energy ⟶ kinetic energy of hands ⟶ thermal energy.

Applying Math

Math Standards

National: 1, 2, 9

22. 1,350 J

23. 4,900,000 J

24. *KE* = 2,250 J, *GPE* = 147,000 J, mechanical energy = 149,250 J

25. *KE* = 4,900,000 J, *v* = 62.6 m/s

Assessment Resources

Reproducible Masters

Chapter *Fast File* Resources
- Chapter Review, pp. 39–40
- Chapter Tests, pp. 41–44
- Assessment Transparency Activity, p. 51

Glencoe Science Web site
- Chapter Review Test
- Standardized Test Practice

Glencoe Technology
- Assessment Transparency
- Exam*View*® Pro Testmaker
- MindJogger Videoquiz
- Interactive Chalkboard

Answer Sheet An answer sheet can be found at **gpescience.com**.

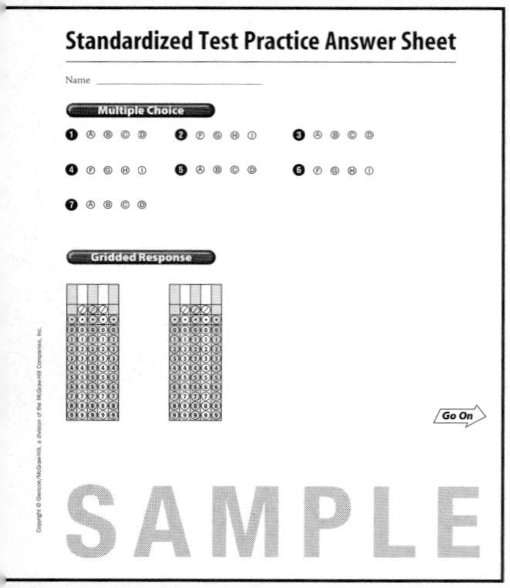

Multiple Choice

1. C
2. B
3. B
4. C
5. D
6. B

Gridded Response

7. 49.5

Short Response

8. The ball's total mechanical energy remains constant. Its value depends on the energy given to it by the batter.
9. Mass changes to energy in nuclear reactions.

Record your answers on the answer sheet provided by your teacher or on a sheet of paper.

Multiple Choice

1. What is the potential energy of a 5.0-kg object located 2.0 m above the ground?

A. 2.5 J

B. 10 J

C. 98 J

D. 196 J

Use the figure below to answer questions 2–4.

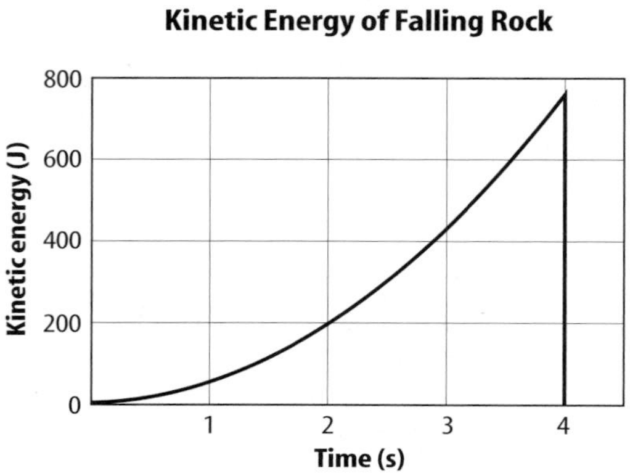

2. According to the graph, which of the following is the best estimate for the kinetic energy of the rock after it has fallen for 1 s?

A. 100 J

B. 50 J

C. 200 J

D. 0 J

3. According to the graph, which of the following is the best estimate for the potential energy of the rock before it fell?

A. 400 J

B. 750 J

C. 200 J

D. 0 J

4. If the rock has a mass of 1 kg, which of the following is the speed of the rock after it has fallen for 2 s?

A. 10 m/s

B. 100 m/s

C. 20 m/s

D. 200 m/s

Use the figure below to answer questions 5 and 6.

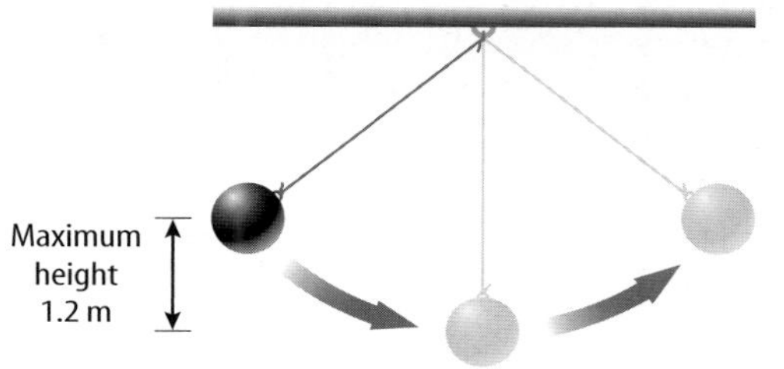

5. At its highest point, the pendulum is 1.2 m above the ground and has a gravitational potential energy of 62 J. If the gravitational potential energy is 10 J at its lowest point, what is the pendulum's kinetic energy at this point?

A. 0 J

B. 31 J

C. 62 J

D. 52 J

Extended Response

Extended Response

10. **Part A** An atom of uranium combines with a neutron. The uranium breaks apart into a xenon atom, a strontium atom, and two neutrons. Radiant energy is released during the process. The original mass of the neutron and the uranium atom is greater than the mass of the xenon atom, the mass of the strontium atom, and the masses of the two neutrons. The remaining mass is converted to energy.

Part B It is less. Some of the mass of the particles before the reaction is converted into energy during the reaction.

6. What is the mass of the pendulum bob?
   - **A.** 2.7 kg
   - **B.** 5.3 kg
   - **C.** 6.3 kg
   - **D.** 52 kg

Gridded Response

7. What is the difference, in J, in the gravitational potential energy of a 7.75 kg book that is 1.50 m above the ground and a 9.53 kg book that is 1.75 m above the ground?

Short Response

Use the figure below to answer question 8.

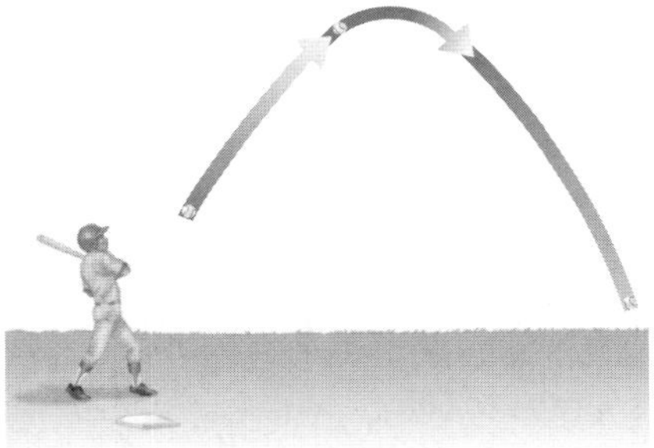

8. How does the mechanical energy of the ball change from the moment just after the batter hits it to the moment just before it touches the ground?

9. Explain why the law of conservation of energy also includes mass when applied to nuclear reactions.

Extended Response

Use the figure below to answer question 10.

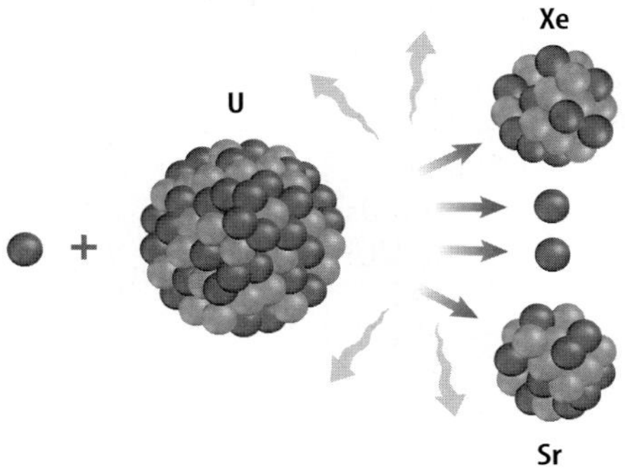

10. The figure shows a nuclear reaction.
    Part A Describe the process and explain how it obeys the law of conservation of energy.
    Part B Describe how the total mass of the particles before the reaction occurs compares to the total mass of the particles produced by the reaction.

11. Describe a process in which energy travels through the environment and changes from one form to another.

Test-Taking Tip

Show All your Work For extended response questions, show all your work and any calculations on your answer sheet.

Question 10 On your answer sheet, list the energy changes that occur during each step.

Rubrics

For more help evaluating Short- and Extended-Response questions, see the rubrics on p. 9T.

11. Possible answer: Radiant energy from the Sun travels to Earth and is absorbed by plants. The plants store this as chemical potential energy. An animal eats the plant and gains energy from it. The animal uses part of the energy for everyday activity and stores part of the energy as chemical potential energy in its body.

chapter 6 Organizer

Section/Objectives	Standards: National	Standards: State/Local	Labs/Features
Chapter Opener	See pp. 16T–17T for a Key to Standards.		**Launch Lab:** Doing Work with a Simple Machine, p. 153 **Foldables,** p. 153
Section 1 Work 2 sessions 1 block 1. **Explain** the meaning of work. 2. **Describe** how work and energy are related. 3. **Calculate** work. 4. **Calculate** power.	National Content Standards: UCP.1-UCP.3, UCP.5, A.1, A.2, B.4, B.6		**Applying Math:** Work, p. 156 **MiniLAB:** Calculating Your Work and Power, p. 157 Video Lab **Applying Math:** Power, p. 158
Section 2 Using Machines 1 session .5 block 5. **Explain** how machines make doing work easier. 6. **Calculate** the mechanical advantage of a machine. 7. **Calculate** the efficiency of a machine.	National Content Standards: UCP.1-UCP.3, UCP.5, A.1, A.2, B.4, B.6		**MiniLAB:** Machines Multiplying Force, p. 162 **Science Online,** p.163 **Integrate Chemistry,** p. 164
Section 3 Simple Machines 3 sessions 1.5 blocks 8. **Describe** the six types of simple machines. 9. **Explain** how the different types of simple machines make doing work easier. 10. **Calculate** the ideal mechanical advantage of the different types of simple machines.	National Content Standards: UCP.1-UCP.3, UCP.5, A.1, A.2, B.4, B.6		**Integrate History,** p. 167 **Visualizing Levers in the Human Body,** p. 168 **Science Online,** p.172 **Lab:** Levers, p. 175 **Lab:** Using Simple Machines, pp. 176–177 **Science and Society:** The Science of Very, Very Small, p. 178

StudentWorks Plus — Glencoe Exclusive! TeacherWorks™ All-In-One Planner and Resource Center

Lab Materials	Reproducible Resources	Section Assessment	Technology
Launch Lab: rope, broom handles (2)	**Chapter *Fast File* Resources** Foldables Worksheet, p. 19 Directed Reading Overview, p. 21 Note-taking Worksheets, pp. 35–37	Glencoe's Assessment Advantage	TeacherWorks includes: • Interactive Teacher Edition • Lesson Planner with calendar • Access to all program blacklines • Correlations to standards • Web links
MiniLAB: stairs, stopwatch, meterstick *Need materials?* Contact Science Kit at 1-800-828-7777 or www.sciencekit.com.	**Chapter *Fast File* Resources** Transparency Activity, p. 46 Enrichment, p. 32 Reinforcement, p. 29 Directed Reading, p. 22 MiniLAB, p. 3 **Cultural Diversity,** p. 63 **Mathematics Skill Activities,** p. 11	**Portfolio** Assessment, p. 159 **Performance** MiniLAB, p. 157 Applying Math, p. 158 Applying Math, p. 159 **Content** Section Review, p. 159	Section Focus Transparency Virtual Labs CD-ROM Interactive Chalkboard CD-ROM StudentWorks Plus Video Lab
MiniLAB: cans of food (2), manual can opener, metric ruler	**Chapter *Fast File* Resources** Transparency Activity, p. 47 Enrichment, p. 33 Reinforcement, p. 30 Directed Reading, p. 22 MiniLAB, p. 4 **Physical Science Critical Thinking/Problem Solving,** p. 3	**Performance** MiniLAB, p. 162 Applying Math, p. 165 **Content** Section Review, p. 165	Section Focus Transparency Interactive Chalkboard CD-ROM StudentWorks Plus
Lab: stiff cardboard, quarter, dime, nickel, balance, metric ruler **Lab:** spring scale, 1-kg mass, double pulley, single pulley, string for pulleys, stand for pulleys, board (40 cm long), support for board (10 cm high)	**Chapter *Fast File* Resources** Transparency Activity, p. 48 Lab Worksheet, pp. 5–6, 7–8 Enrichment, p. 34 Reinforcement, p. 31 Directed Reading, pp. 23, 24 Lab Activity, pp. 9–11, 13–18 Transparency Activity, pp. 49–50 **Home and Community Involvement,** p. 35 **Physical Science Critical Thinking/Problem Solving,** pp. 6–7	**Portfolio** Assessment, p. 165 **Performance** Applying Math, p. 174 **Content** Section Review, p. 174	Section Focus Transparency Teaching Transparency Interactive Chalkboard CD-ROM StudentWorks Plus

End of Chapter Assessment

Glencoe's Assessment Advantage

Blackline Masters	Technology	Professional Series
Chapter *Fast File* Resources Chapter Review, pp. 39–40 Chapter Tests, pp. 41–44 **Standardized Test Practice,** pp. 28–31	MindJogger Videoquiz Virtual Labs CD-ROM Exam*View*® Pro Testmaker TeacherWorks CD-ROM Interactive Chalkboard CD-ROM	**Performance Assessment in the Science Classroom (PASC)**

Transparencies

Section Focus

Section 1 Section Focus Transparency — Onward and Upward — Chapter 6

Backpacking is a lot of fun, but it also can be a lot of work. Whether hoisting the pack onto your back to start the hike or trudging up a long hill, you'll need to exert a good deal of effort to get to the next camp.

1. Compare the effort exerted by a backpacker moving over level ground to that exerted by a backpacker moving uphill.
2. How do you think the weight of the backpack affects the amount of force needed to move it?

L2

Section 2 Section Focus Transparency — A Quiet Glide — Chapter 6

For some people, paddling a canoe is a pleasant diversion. For others, it's work. Out on a lake, the paddle is a big help in moving the canoe. It might even make work fun!

1. How is a person paddling a canoe doing work?
2. If the paddle broke, would it be easier or more difficult to move the canoe? Explain.
3. How does the shape of the canoe make paddling easier?

L2

Section 3 Section Focus Transparency — Moving Day — Chapter 6

Moving can be a chore. Packing boxes, moving them, then unpacking everything can be hard work. But machines can help. Some machines are simple, while others can be very complicated. This mover uses a selection of machines to help make moving day much easier.

1. What do you see in this picture that makes it easier for the mover to do work?
2. How do the ramp and dolly make work easier?

L2

This is a representation of key blackline masters available in the Teacher Classroom Resources. See Resource Manager boxes within the chapter for additional information.

Assessment

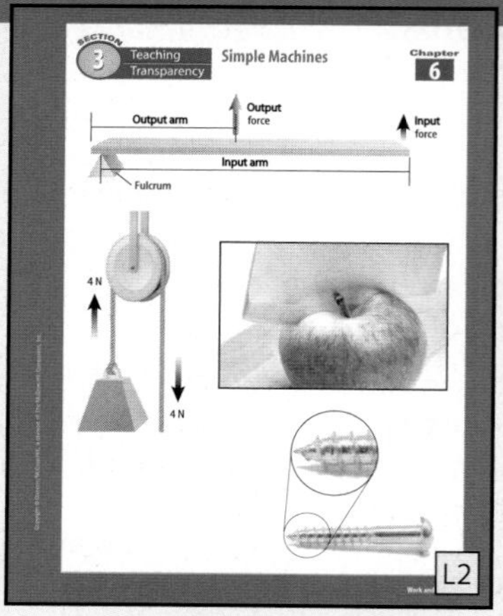
Section 3 Teaching Transparency — Simple Machines — Chapter 6

L2

Teaching

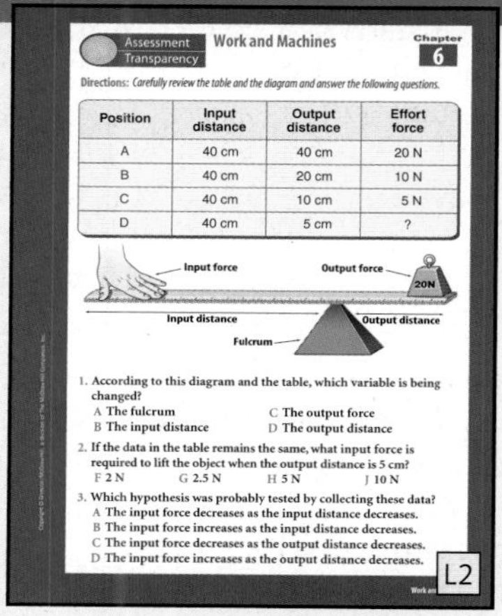
Assessment Transparency — Work and Machines — Chapter 6

Directions: Carefully review the table and the diagram and answer the following questions.

Position	Input distance	Output distance	Effort force
A	40 cm	40 cm	20 N
B	40 cm	20 cm	10 N
C	40 cm	10 cm	5 N
D	40 cm	5 cm	?

1. According to this diagram and the table, which variable is being changed?
A The fulcrum C The output force
B The input distance D The output distance
2. If the data in the table remains the same, what input force is required to lift the object when the output distance is 5 cm?
F 2 N G 2.5 N H 5 N J 10 N
3. Which hypothesis was probably tested by collecting these data?
A The input force decreases as the input distance decreases.
B The input force increases as the input distance decreases.
C The input force decreases as the output distance decreases.
D The input force increases as the output distance decreases.

L2

Key to Teaching Strategies

The following designations will help you decide which activities are appropriate for your students.

- **L1** Level 1 activities should be appropriate for students with learning difficulties.
- **L2** Level 2 activities should be within the ability range of all students.
- **L3** Level 3 activities are designed for above-average students.
- **ELL** ELL activities should be within the ability range of English Language Learners.
- **COOP LEARN** Cooperative Learning activities are designed for small group work.
- **LS** Multiple Learning Styles logos, as described on page 12T, are used throughout to indicate strategies that address different learning styles.
- **P** These strategies represent student products that can be placed into a best-work portfolio.
- **PBL** Problem-Based Learning activities apply real-world situations to learning.

Hands-on Activities

Student Text Lab Worksheet

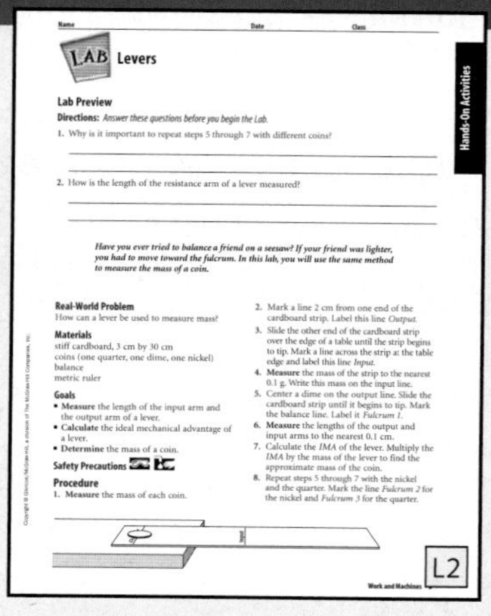
LAB — Levers — Hands-On Activities

Lab Preview

Directions: Answer these questions before you begin the Lab.

1. Why is it important to repeat steps 5 through 7 with different coins?
2. How is the length of the resistance arm of a lever measured?

Have you ever tried to balance a friend on a seesaw? If your friend was lighter, you had to move toward the fulcrum. In this lab, you will use the same method to measure the mass of a coin.

L2

Laboratory Activities

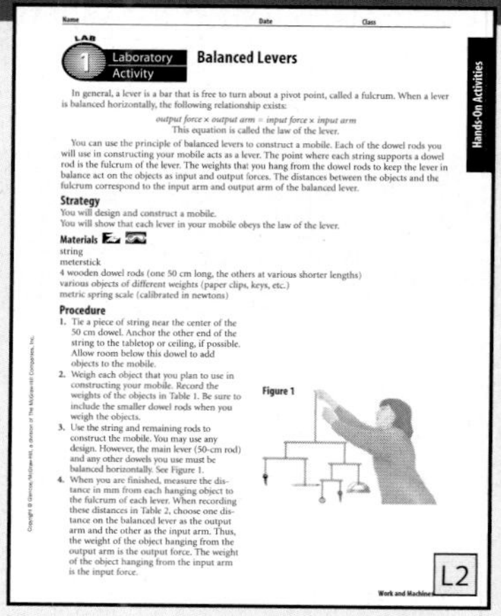
Laboratory Activity 1 — Balanced Levers — Hands-On Activities

Strategy
You will design and construct a mobile.
You will show that each lever in your mobile obeys the law of the lever.

Figure 1

L2

Resource Manager

Meeting Different Ability Levels

Content Outline

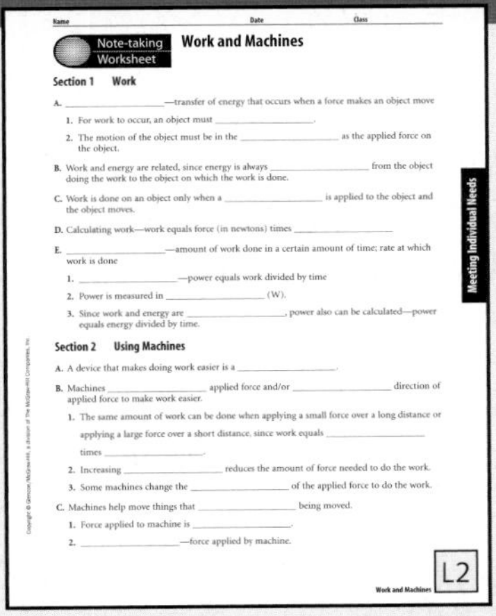
Name Date Class

Note-taking Worksheet — Work and Machines

Section 1 Work

Section 2 Using Machines

L2

Reinforcement

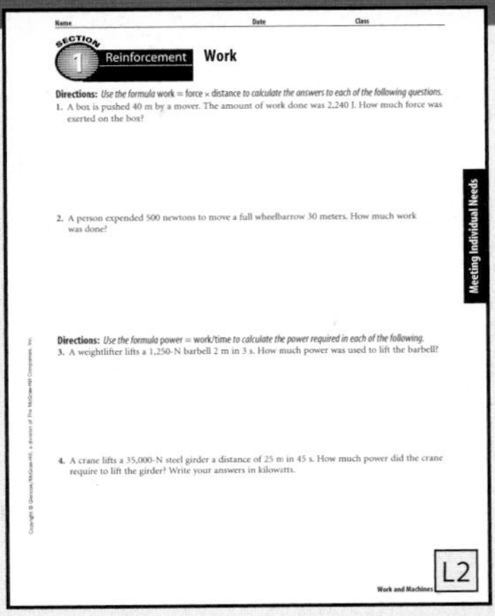
Name Date Class

Section 1 Reinforcement — Work

Directions: Use the formula work = force × distance to calculate the answers to each of the following questions.

Directions: Use the formula power = work/time to calculate the power required in each of the following.

L2

Enrichment

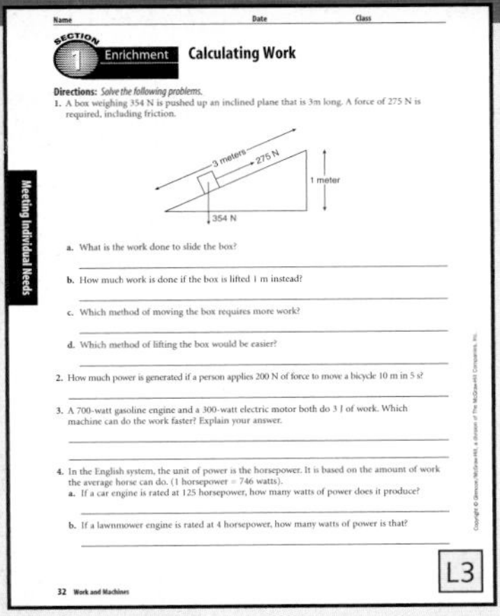
Name Date Class

Section 1 Enrichment — Calculating Work

Directions: Solve the following problems.

L3

Directed Reading (English/Spanish)

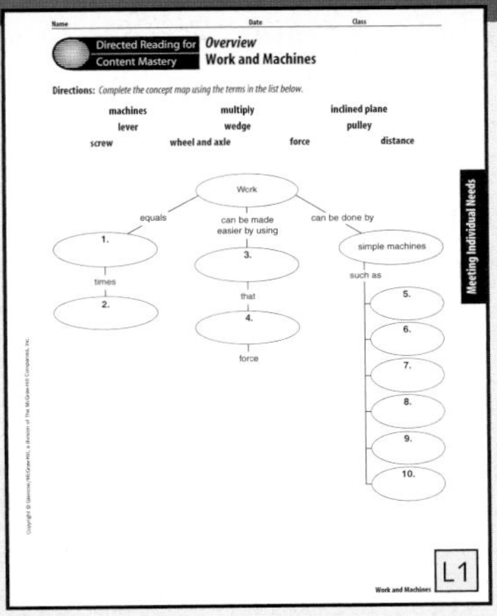
Name Date Class

Directed Reading for Content Mastery — Overview — Work and Machines

Directions: Complete the concept map using the terms in the list below.

machines, multiply, inclined plane, lever, wedge, pulley, screw, wheel and axle, force, distance

L1

Study Guide

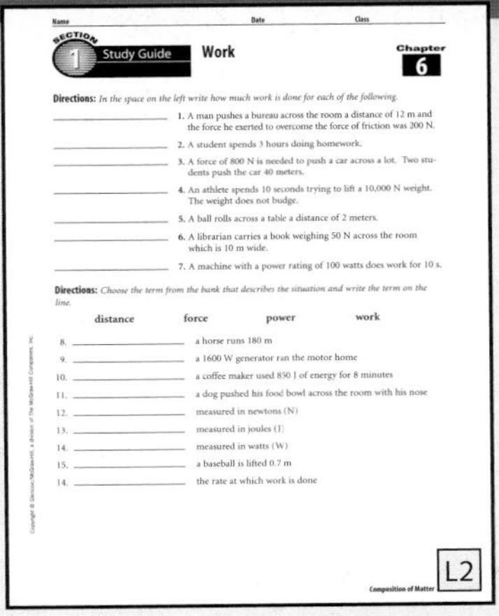
Name Date Class

Section 1 Study Guide — Work — Chapter 6

Directions: In the space on the left write how much work is done for each of the following.

distance, force, power, work

L2

Reading Essentials

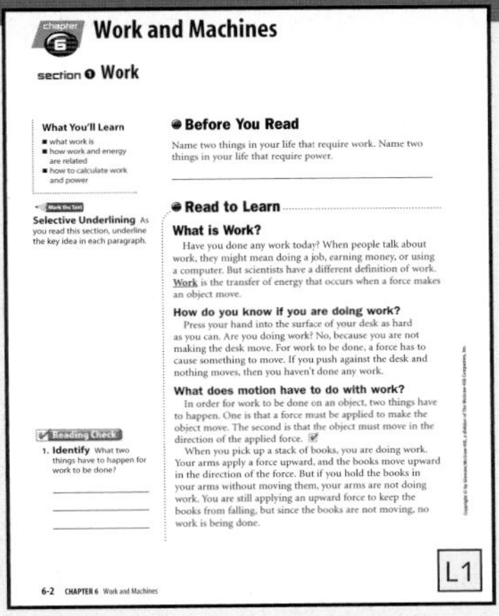
chapter 6 Work and Machines

section 1 Work

What You'll Learn

Before You Read

Read to Learn

What is Work?

How do you know if you are doing work?

What does motion have to do with work?

L1

Assessment

Test Practice Workbook

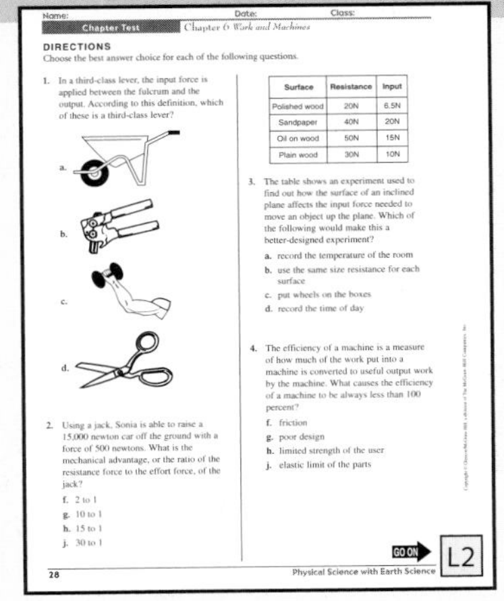
Name: Date: Class:

Chapter Test — Chapter 6 Work and Machines

DIRECTIONS

Choose the best answer choice for each of the following questions.

Surface	Resistance	Input
Polished wood	20N	6.5N
Sandpaper	40N	20N
Oil on wood	50N	15N
Plain wood	30N	10N

L2

Chapter Review

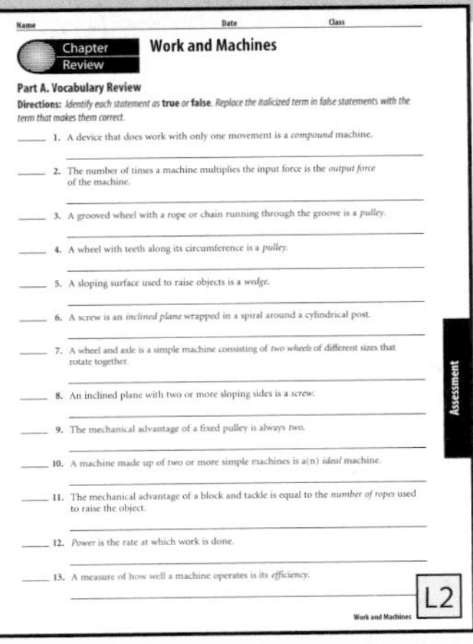
Name Date Class

Chapter Review — Work and Machines

Part A. Vocabulary Review

Directions: Identify each statement as true or false. Replace the italicized term in false statements with the term that makes them correct.

L2

Chapter Tests

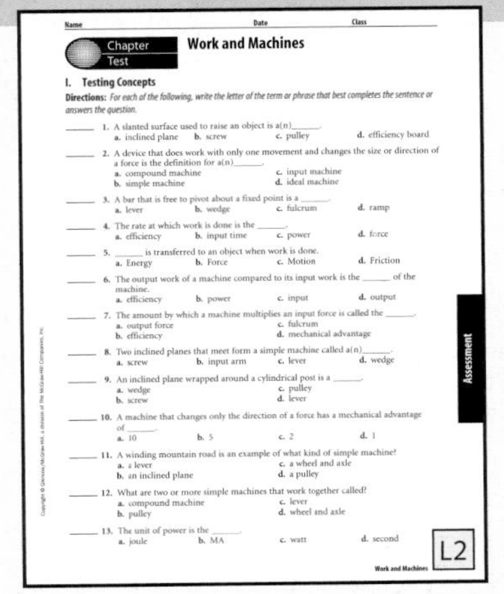
Name Date Class

Chapter Test — Work and Machines

I. Testing Concepts

L2

Science Content Background

section 1 Work

Power

The horsepower is a common, although nonmetric, unit of power. It was originally created by James Watt to compare his steam engines to the power of a horse. It is equivalent to 746 watts.

section 2 Using Machines

Making Work Easier

Many machines allow a person to use less effort to do a job such as lifting an engine or opening a soda bottle. These machines do not reduce the amount of work that must be done. A smaller force must be applied over a greater distance to do the work.

Mechanical Advantage and Efficiency

A machine converts an input force to an output force. The ratio of the output force to the input force is the mechanical advantage of the machine. For a real machine, the output work done by the machine is always less than the input work. Friction always transforms some of the input work into heat. The efficiency of a machine is the output work divided by the input work.

section 3 Simple Machines

Pulleys

The mechanical advantage of a pulley system equals the number of ropes that support the load. Ropes that attach one pulley to another are not counted. The rope that is pulled is counted if the direction of the applied force is in the same direction that the load moves.

Wheel and Axles

The diameter of the wheel is greater than the diameter of the axle. So a force applied on the wheel moves through a greater distance in one revolution than the force applied by the axle. If the amount of work done on the wheel is nearly equal to the amount of work done by the axle, then the force exerted on the wheel must be less than the force applied by the axle.

Wedges

A wedge is useful for two reasons. A downward force applied to a wedge is converted to a horizontal force exerted perpendicular to the sides of the wedge. Also, the wedge is narrower at one end. As a result, the narrow tip of the wedge exerts a higher pressure than the wider edge. This helps the wedge to penetrate materials.

chapter content resources

Internet Resources

For additional content background, visit **gpescience.com** to:

- access your book online
- find references to related articles in popular science magazines
- access Web links with related content background
- access current events with science journal topics

Print Resources

The New Way Things Work, David MacCaulay, Houghton Mifflin Company, 1998

Physics Matters! Vol. 2, John O. E. Clark, Grolier Educational, 2001

Simple Machines Series by David Glover, Rigby Press, 1997

How Things Work, Neil Ardley, Reader's Digest Book, 1995

IDENTIFYING Misconceptions

Find Out What Students Think

Students may think that . . .

A simple machine allows us to do less work.

The term *machine* often makes people think of things such as cars and power tools. By using fuel or electrical energy to do work, these machines do allow people to do less work. This conception of machines may create the misconception that simple machines also allow people to do less work. Additionally, the force used on a simple machine provides an immediate sensation to the worker. Using a simple machine to do a task often requires less effort and so it feels easier than doing the task without the machine, and this may contribute to the idea that less work is being done.

Activity

Ask students to write explanations of why people use simple machines such as the lever, pulley, and inclined plane. Have a few students read their explanations to the class. Then have the class try to decide which is the best explanation. L2

Promote Understanding

Activity

Show students a picture of movers pushing a large object up a ramp into the truck. Why do they use this ramp? Lead the discussion so students debate whether the movers do it to do less work or to use less effort. Have students do the following activity to find the answer. Organize the class into groups and give each group a spring scale, ruler, wooden plank, wood block with hook, and string. Tell them to follow these steps:

- Use the spring scale to lift the block from the floor to a chair, and note the reading from the scale as it rises.
- Measure the height of the chair, and multiply force times distance to obtain the work done lifting the block.
- Rest the plank on the chair so it rises at about a 45° angle from the ground. Pull the block up the plane to the chair, and measure the effort used by reading the scale while the block is moving.
- Measure the distance the block traveled and calculate the amount of work done.
- Compare the amounts of effort used and the amounts of work done in the two situations.

The results show that the simple machine made it easier to lift the load, but the amount of work students did with the ramp was the same or greater than the work done just lifting the block. L2

Assess

After completing the chapter, see *Identifying Misconceptions* in the Study Guide at the end of the chapter.

chapter 6

Chapter Vocabulary

work, p. 154
power, p. 157
machine, p. 160
input force, p. 162
output force, p. 162
mechanical advantage, p. 164
efficiency, p. 164
simple machine, p. 166
lever, p. 166
pulley, p. 169
wheel and axle, p. 171
inclined plane, p. 172
screw, p. 173
wedge, p. 173
compound machine, p. 174

Science Journal Accept all reasonable answers.

INTERACTIVE CHALKBOARD with Image Bank

PowerPoint® Presentations

This CD-ROM is an editable Microsoft® PowerPoint® presentation that includes:

- a pre-made presentation for every chapter
- interactive graphics
- animations
- audio clips
- image bank
- all new section and chapter questions
- Standardized Test Practice
- transparencies
- Foldables directions
- links to gpescience.com

chapter 6

Work and Machines

chapter preview

sections

It Seemed Longer Going Up

Have you ever thought of a mountain bike as a machine? A mountain bike actually is a combination of simple machines. Like all machines, a bicycle makes doing work easier. A mountain bike, for example, gets you uphill and downhill faster than you can travel by walking or running.

Science Journal Diagram a bicycle and identify the parts you think are simple machines.

152

Theme Connection

Systems and Interactions A simple machine is a system that has work done on it. It, in turn, does work on an object or another system. The machine does not lessen the amount of work done; it decreases the effort necessary to do the work.

About the Photo

Compound Machines Riding a mountain bike takes a lot of work, especially over rough terrain. But the gears and levers, wheels and axles help the rider accomplish that work with less effort and with more power. Compound machines like bicycles are excellent examples of how combinations of simple machines make both work and play easier.

Start-Up Activities

Launch LAB

Doing Work with a Simple Machine

Did you know you can lift several times your own weight with the help of a pulley? Before the hydraulic lift was invented, a car mechanic used pulleys to raise a car off the ground. In this lab you'll see how a pulley can increase a force.

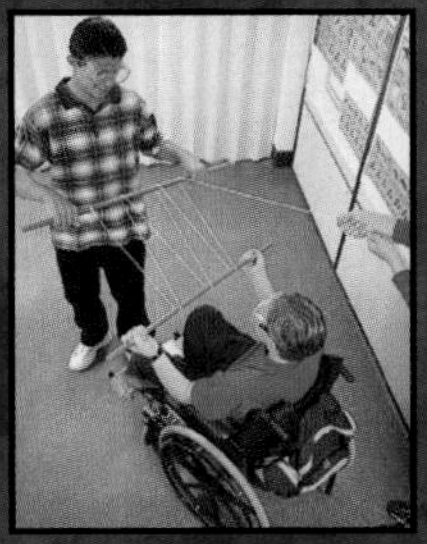

1. Tie a rope several meters in length to the center of a broom handle. Have one student hold both ends of the handle.
2. Have another student hold the ends of a second broom handle and face the first student as shown in the photo.
3. Have a third student loop the free end of the rope around the second handle, making six or seven loops.
4. The third student should stand to the side of one of the handles and pull on the free end of the rope. The two students holding the broom handles should prevent the handles from coming together.
5. **Think Critically** Describe how the applied force was changed. What would happen if the number of rope loops were increased?

FOLDABLES™ Study Organizer

Work and Machines Make the following Foldable to help you understand how machines make doing work easier.

STEP 1 **Fold** a sheet of paper vertically in half from top to bottom.

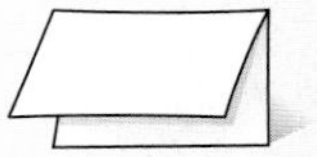

STEP 2 **Fold** in half from side to side with the fold at the top.

STEP 3 **Unfold** the paper once. **Cut** only the fold of the top flap to make two tabs.

STEP 4 **Turn** the paper vertically and **label** the front tabs as shown.

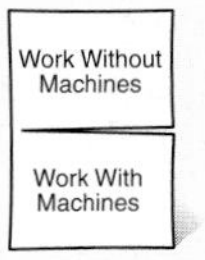

List Before you read the chapter, list five examples of work you do without machines, and five examples of work you do with machines. Next to each example, rate the effort needed to do the work on a scale of 1 (little effort) to 3 (much effort).

Science Online — Preview this chapter's content and activities at gpescience.com

153

Launch LAB

Purpose Use the Launch Lab to introduce students to the force multiplying power of simple machines. L2 IN **Kinesthetic**

Preparation Cut 8-m lengths of rope and collect two broom handles for each group.

Materials broom handles (2), 8-m length of rope

Teaching Strategy Tell the students holding the broom handles that they must keep the handles parallel to each other and they cannot place their hands or fingers on the rope.

Think Critically

The applied force was increased. The third group member easily could pull the broom handles together. Increasing the number of rope loops would increase the applied force even more.

Assessment

Performance Ask each group to predict how the results of the lab would have differed if the rope had been wrapped only twice around the poles. Ask students to test their predictions. The pulley will have far less mechanical advantage, and the student pulling on the rope will not be able to pull the two handles together as easily. Use **Performance Assessment in the Science Classroom,** p. 93.

FOLDABLES™ Study Organizer — Dinah Zike Study Fold

Student preparation materials for this Foldable are available in the Chapter *Fast File* Resources.

1 Motivate

An editable Microsoft® PowerPoint® presentation is available on **Interactive Chalkboard** CD-ROM.

Bellringer

Section Focus Transparencies also are available on the Interactive Chalkboard CD-ROM. L2 ELL

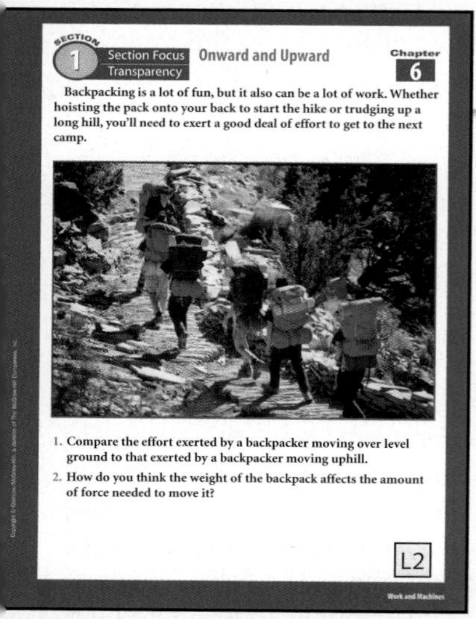
Section 1 Section Focus Transparency — Onward and Upward — Chapter 6

Backpacking is a lot of fun, but it also can be a lot of work. Whether hoisting the pack onto your back to start the hike or trudging up a long hill, you'll need to exert a good deal of effort to get to the next camp.

1. Compare the effort exerted by a backpacker moving over level ground to that exerted by a backpacker moving uphill.
2. How do you think the weight of the backpack affects the amount of force needed to move it?

L2

Work and Machines

Reading Preview

Tie to Prior Knowledge

Student Work Ask students what types of work they do. They might mention cutting grass, taking out garbage, or caring for a younger sibling. In this section they will learn that the scientific definition of work is different from the everyday definition.

Vocabulary Analogy Tell students that work in science can be compared to homework in some ways. A person can devote time to homework by sitting at a table doing nothing. Until the reading, writing, or project required is accomplished, the work is not complete. In science, work is not just exerting a force on an object, but actually moving an object a distance.

section 1

Work

Reading Guide

What You'll Learn
- **Explain** the meaning of work.
- **Describe** how work and energy are related.
- **Calculate** work.
- **Calculate** power.

Why It's Important
Doing work is another way of transferring energy from one place to another.

Review Vocabulary
energy: the ability to cause change

New Vocabulary
- work
- power

What is work?

INTEGRATE Language Arts Have you done any work today? To many people, the word *work* means something they do to earn money. In that sense, work can be anything from filling fast-food orders or loading trucks to teaching or doing word processing on a computer. The word *work* also means exerting a force with your muscles. A person might say he or she does work while pushing as hard as they can against a wall that doesn't move. However, in science the word *work* is used in a different way.

Work Makes Something Move Press your hand against the surface of your desk as hard as you can. Have you done any work? The answer is no, no matter how tired your effort makes you feel. Remember that a force is a push or a pull. For work to be done, a force must make something move. **Work** is the energy transferred when a force makes an object move. If you push against the desk and it doesn't move, then you haven't done any work on the desk.

Doing Work There are two conditions that have to be satisfied for a force to do work on an object. One is that the applied force must make the object move, and the other is that the movement must be in the same direction as the applied force.

For example, if you pick up a pile of books from the floor, as in **Figure 1,** you do work on the books. The books move upward, in the direction of the force you are applying. If you hold the books in your arms without moving the books, you are not doing work on the books. You're still applying an upward force to keep the books from falling, but no movement is taking place.

Figure 1 When you lift a stack of books, your arms apply a force upward and the books move upward. Because the force and distance are in the same direction, your arms have done work on the books.

Section 1 Resource Manager

Chapter *Fast File* Resources
- Transparency Activity, p. 46
- Directed Reading for Content Mastery, pp. 21–22
- Note-taking Worksheets, pp. 35–37
- MiniLAB, p. 3
- Enrichment, p. 32
- Reinforcement, p. 29

Mathematics Skill Activities, p. 11

Cultural Diversity, p. 63

Force and Direction of Motion When you carry books while walking, like the student in **Figure 2,** you might think that your arms are doing work. After all, you are exerting a force on the books with your arms, and the books are moving. Your arms might even feel tired. However, in this case the force exerted by your arms does no work on the books. The force exerted by your arms on the books is upward, but the books are moving horizontally. The force you exert upward is at right angles to the direction the books are moving. As a result, your arms exert no force in the direction the books are moving.

Reading Check ***How are an applied force and an object's motion related when work is done?***

Work and Energy

How are work and energy related? When work is done, a transfer of energy always occurs. This is easier to understand when you think about carrying a heavy box up a flight of stairs. Remember that when the height of an object above Earth's surface increases, the gravitational potential energy of the object increases. As you move up the stairs, you increase the height of the box above Earth's surface. This causes the gravitational potential energy of the box to increase.

You may recall that energy is the ability to cause change. If something has energy, it can transfer energy to another object by doing work on that object. When you do work on an object, you increase its energy. The student carrying the box in **Figure 3** transfers chemical energy in his muscles to the box. Energy is always transferred from the object that is doing the work to the object on which the work is done.

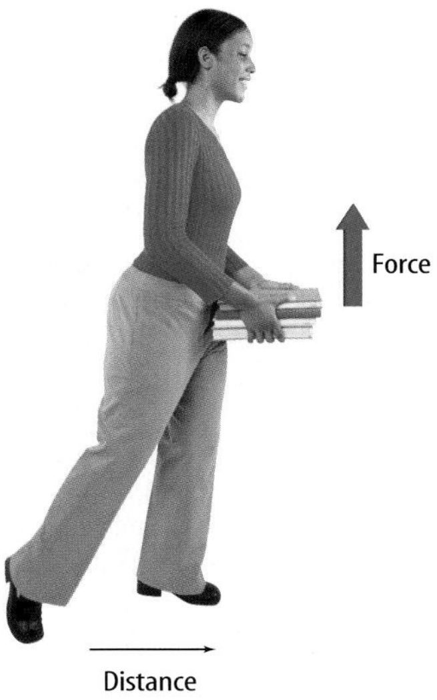

Figure 2 If you hold a stack of books and walk forward, your arms are exerting a force upward. However, the distance the books move is horizontal. Therefore, your arms are not doing work on the books.

Figure 3 By carrying a box up the stairs, you are doing work. You transfer energy to the box. **Explain** *how the energy of the box changes as the student climbs the stairs.*

2 Teach

INTEGRATE Language Arts **Content Background**

Emphasize that although the words *work*, *energy*, and *power* have multiple meanings and are common in everyday speech, in science these words have a specific meaning.

Caption Answer

Figure 3 The potential energy of the box increases as the box is moved up the stairs because the height of the box increases.

Activity

Analyzing Forces Have a volunteer press against the wall. Ask students whether or not the person is doing work on the wall. No, because the wall is not moving in the direction of the applied force. Repeat this demonstration for various other activities, such as raising an object vertically or carrying an object horizontally. If there is more than one force involved, help students analyze which forces are doing work and which are not. L2 LS **Kinesthetic**

Reading Check

Answer The applied force and the object's motion must be in the same direction for work to be done.

Virtual Labs

Work, Force, Distance
What is the relationship between work, force, and distance?

Science Journal

Relating Work and Energy Have students write descriptions in their Science Journals of situations they have seen or been a part of in which work has been done or energy has been transferred. Ask them to include at least one example of a situation in which energy was transferred but no work was done. L2 LS **Linguistic**

Differentiated Instruction

Challenge Have students use the definition of work to define power in terms of velocity. Ask students to relate this to the power of lifting a mass.

$$P = \frac{W}{t} = \frac{(F \times d)}{t} = F \times \left(\frac{d}{t}\right) = F \times v,$$

where v is the constant rate at which the mass is moving vertically L3 LS **Logical-Mathematical**

SECTION 1 Work **155**

Quick Demo
Calculating Work

Materials spring scale, 1-kg mass

Estimated Time 5 minutes

Procedure Hook a spring scale to a 1-kg mass. Using the spring scale, raise the mass 1 m at a constant velocity. Let students read the spring scale, which should read approximately 10 N. Tell them you have just done 10 J of work. Give students the opportunity to repeat your demonstration. L2 LS **Visual-Spatial**

Activity

Joule The unit of work is the joule. Ask students to express a joule in basic SI units. $W = F \times d = m \times a \times d$; therefore, $1\ J = 1\ kg \cdot \frac{m^2}{s^2}$ L2 LS **Logical-Mathematical**

Applying Math

Math Standards

National: 1, 2, 9

Answers to Practice Problems

1. $W = Fd = (75\ N)(5\ m) = 375\ J$
2. $d = \frac{W}{F} = \frac{12{,}000\ J}{80\ N} = 150\ m$
3. $F = \frac{W}{d} = \frac{240{,}000\ J}{50\ m} = 4{,}800\ N$

Discussion

Force and Work Suppose you push a book with a constant force of 25 N for a distance of 20 cm. The book then slides for an additional 80 cm. Did you do 5 J of work or 25 J of work? Explain. You did 5 J of work because you only exerted a force on the book for the first 20 cm of its journey. L2 LS **Logical-Mathematical**

Calculating Work The amount of work done depends on the amount of force exerted and the distance over which the force is applied. When a force is exerted and an object moves in the direction of the force, the amount of work done can be calculated as follows.

Work Equation

work (in joules) = **applied force** (in newtons) × **distance** (in meters)

$$W = Fd$$

In this equation, force is measured in newtons and distance is measured in meters. Work, like energy, is measured in joules. One joule is about the amount of work required to lift a baseball a vertical distance of 0.7 m.

Applying Math — Solve a Simple Equation

WORK You push a refrigerator with a force of 100 N. If you move the refrigerator a distance of 5 m, how much work do you do?

IDENTIFY known values and the unknown value

Identify the known values:

you push a refrigerator with a force of 100 N → means → $F = 100\ N$

you move the refrigerator a distance of 5 m → means → $d = 5\ m$

Identify the unknown value:

how much work you do → means → $W = ?\ J$

SOLVE the problem

Substitute the known values $F = 100\ N$ and $d = 5\ m$ into the work equation.

$$W = Fd = (100\ N)(5\ m) = 500\ Nm = 500\ J$$

CHECK your answer

Does your answer seem reasonable? Check your answer by dividing the work you calculated by the force given in the problem. The result should be the distance given in the problem.

Practice Problems

1. A force of 75 N is exerted on a 45-kg couch, and the couch is moved 5 m. How much work is done in moving the couch?
2. A lawn mower is pushed with a force of 80 N. If 12,000 J of work is done in mowing a lawn, what is the total distance the lawn mower was pushed?
3. The brakes on a car do 240,000 J of work in stopping the car. If the car travels a distance of 50 m while the brakes are being applied, what is the force the brakes exert on the car?

For more practice problems go to page 879, and visit Math Practice at gpescience.com.

Curriculum Connection

History James Prescott Joule was a British scientist who lived from 1818 to 1889. Ask students to find out why the unit of work was named for him. Joule established the relationship between heat and mechanical energy, called the mechanical equivalent of heat. L2 LS **Linguistic**

Teacher FYI

Power The metric unit of power is the watt, or joule/s. The power of heating and cooling units is often given in British thermal units (Btu) per second. One Btu per second is about 1,055 watts. The power of motors and engines is usually given in horsepower. One horsepower is equal to about 746 watts.

156 CHAPTER 6 Work and Machines

Figure 4 A pitcher exerts a force on the ball to throw it to the catcher. After the ball leaves her hand, the pitcher no longer is exerting any force on the ball. She does work on the ball only while it is in her hand.

When is work done? Suppose you give a book a push and it slides along a table for a distance of 1 m before it comes to a stop. The distance you use to calculate the work you did is how far the object moved while the force was being applied. Even though the book moved 1 m, you did work on the book only while your hand was in contact with it. The distance in the formula for work is the distance the book moved while your hand was pushing on the book. As **Figure 4** shows, work is done on an object only when a force is being applied to the object.

Power

Suppose you and another student are pushing boxes of books up a ramp to load them into a truck. To make the job fun, you make a game of it, racing to see who can push a box up the ramp faster. The boxes weigh the same, but your friend is able to push a box a little faster than you can. She moves a box up the ramp in 30 s. It takes you 45 s. You both do the same amount of work on the books because the boxes weigh the same and are moved the same distance. The only difference is the time it takes to do the work.

In this game, your friend has more power than you do. **Power** is the amount of work done in one second. It is a rate, the rate at which work is done.

Reading Check *How is power related to work?*

Mini LAB

Calculating Your Work and Power

Procedure

1. Find a set of **stairs** that you can safely walk and run up. Measure the vertical height of the stairs in meters.
2. Record how many seconds it takes you to walk and then run up the stairs.
3. Calculate the work you did in both walking and running up the stairs. The force is your weight in newtons (your weight in pounds times 4.5). The distance is the vertical height of the stairs.
4. Use the formula $P = W/t$ to calculate the power you needed to both walk and to run up the stairs.

Analysis

1. Is the work you did walking and running up the steps the same?
2. Which required more power, walking or running up the steps? Why?

Mini LAB

Video Lab available.

Purpose Students measure work and power. L2 LS **Kinesthetic**

Materials stairs, stopwatch or clock, meterstick

Teaching Strategy Suggest students work in pairs so one can time while the other climbs the stairs.

Safety Precautions Caution students to choose a set of stairs that they can run up without slipping.

Analysis

1. Yes; the work is independent of speed.
2. More power is used running than walking, because you do the same amount of work in less time.

Assessment

Content Have students work in small groups to write short rhymes to help them remember the relationships among force, distance, work, and power. Use **Performance Assessment in the Science Classroom**, p. 151.

Reading Check

Answer Power is the amount of work done per second.

Reading Strategy

Shared Reading Take time to read the text of this section aloud and pause to discuss the concepts. Restate or paraphrase as needed for students to understand the concepts. Work through the formulas step by step. Allow students to practice comprehending text by asking volunteers to read and explain passages in their own words.

Differentiated Instruction

Physically Challenged Students in wheelchairs can do the MiniLAB by using a ramp instead of stairs. Students can time themselves going up the ramp at a slow rate, and then time themselves going up the ramp quickly. Point out that in order to calculate the force, students will need to know the weight of the wheelchair in newtons. L2

Visual Learning

Figure 4 Point out that work is done by the pitcher only while she still has the ball in her hand. The distance over which she moves her arm to throw the ball and the force with which she throws it determine how much work she does. After she lets go of the ball, work is done by gravity to make it fall. L2

Discussion

Work v. Power Suppose two students are asked to unpack identical cartons of books. One student completes the job in ten minutes, while the other takes twenty minutes. Which student did more work? Both students did the same amount of work. Which student used more power? the one who finished in the least amount of time L2 LS **Logical-Mathematical**

Applying Math

Math Standards

National: 1, 2, 9

Answers to Practice Problems

1. $P = \frac{W}{t} = \frac{50\ \text{J}}{0.5\ \text{s}} = 100\ \text{W}$
2. $W = Pt = \left(\frac{130\ \text{J}}{\text{s}}\right) \times (10\ \text{min}) \times \left(\frac{60\ \text{s}}{1\ \text{min}}\right) = 78{,}000\ \text{J}$
3. $t = \frac{W}{P} = \frac{10{,}000\ \text{J}}{500\ \text{J/s}} = 20\ \text{s}$

Post Reading

Question a Partner Place students in pairs. Have them make flash cards and quiz one another on the definitions and formulas for *work*, *power*, and *power when energy is transferred*. Students also should explain the concepts behind each formula in their own words.

Calculating Power Power is the rate at which work is done. To calculate power, divide the work done by the time that is required to do the work.

Power Equation

$$\text{power (in watts)} = \frac{\text{work (in joules)}}{\text{time (in seconds)}}$$

$$P = \frac{W}{t}$$

The SI unit for power is the watt (W). One watt equals one joule of work done in one second. Because the watt is a small unit, power often is expressed in kilowatts. One kilowatt (kW) equals 1,000 W.

Applying Math — Solve a Simple Equation

POWER You do 900 J of work in pushing a sofa. If it took 5 s to move the sofa, what was your power?

IDENTIFY known values and the unknown value

Identify the known values:

You do 900 J of work — means → $W = 900$ J

it took 5 s to move the sofa — means → $t = 5$ s

Identify the unknown value:

what was your power? — means → $P = ?$ W

SOLVE the problem

Substitute the known values $W = 900$ J and $t = 5$ s into the power equation.

$$P = \frac{W}{t} = \frac{900\ \text{J}}{5\ s} = 180\ \text{J/s} = 180\ \text{W}$$

The symbol for work, *W*, is usually italicized. However, the abbreviation for watt, W, is not italicized.

CHECK your answer

Does your answer seem reasonable? Check your answer by multiplying the power you calculated by the time given in the problem. The result should be the work given in the problem.

Practice Problems

1. To lift a baby from a crib, 50 J of work is done. How much power is needed if the baby is lifted in 0.5 s?
2. If a runner's power is 130 W, how much work is done by the runner in 10 minutes?
3. The power produced by an electric motor is 500 W. How long will it take the motor to do 10,000 J of work?

For more practice problems go to page 879, and visit Math Practice at gpescience.com.

158 CHAPTER 6 Work and Machines

Curriculum Connection

Health Nutritionists recommend a daily diet of about 9,000,000 J (2,100 Cal) to maintain health. Have students calculate the average power that this diet would generate in a 24-hour period. There are 60 × 60 × 24 = 86,400 seconds in 24 hours. Therefore, the amount of power is 9,000,000 J ÷ 86,400 s = 104 watts. L2 LS **Logical-Mathematical**

Fun Fact

One horsepower was the average amount of work a horse could do in one day. Watt underestimated the amount of work his engines could do by about 67 percent so that he would not be accused of exaggeration.

Power and Energy Doing work is a way of transferring energy from one object to another. Just as power is the rate at which work is done, power is also the rate at which energy is transferred. When energy is transferred, the power involved can be calculated by dividing the energy transferred by the time needed for the transfer to occur.

Power Equation for Energy Transfer

$$\text{power (in watts)} = \frac{\text{energy transferred (in joules)}}{\text{time (in seconds)}}$$

$$P = \frac{E}{t}$$

For example, when the lightbulb in **Figure 5** is connected to an electric circuit, energy is transferred from the circuit to the lightbulb filament. The filament converts the electrical energy supplied to the lightbulb into heat and light. The power used by the lightbulb is the amount of electrical energy transferred to the lightbulb each second.

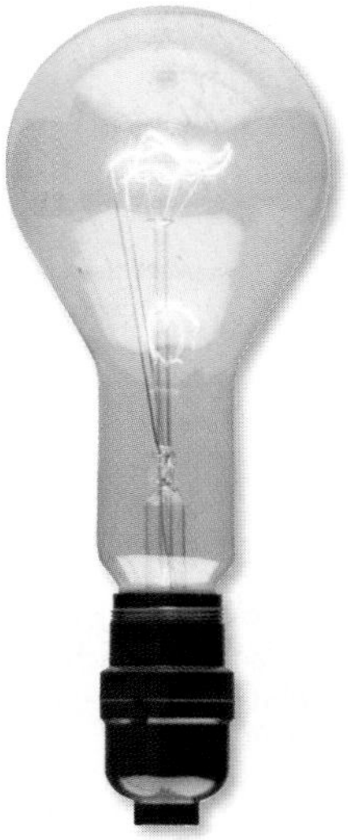

Figure 5 This 100-W lightbulb converts electrical energy into light and heat at a rate of 100 J/s.

section 1 review

Summary

Work and Energy

- Work is done on an object when a force is exerted on the object and it moves in the direction of the force.
- If a force, *F*, is exerted on an object while the object moves a distance, *d*, in the direction of the force, the work done is

$$W = Fd$$

- When work is done on an object, energy is transferred to the object.

Power

- Power is the rate at which work is done or energy is transferred.
- When work is done, power can be calculated from the equation

$$P = \frac{W}{t}$$

- When energy is transferred, power can be calculated from the equation

$$P = \frac{E}{t}$$

Self Check

1. **Explain** how the scientific definition of *work* is different from the everyday meaning.
2. **Describe** a situation in which a force is applied but no work is done.
3. **Explain** how work and energy are related.
4. **Think Critically** In which of the following situations is work being done?
   a. A person shovels snow off a sidewalk.
   b. A worker lifts bricks, one at a time, from the ground to the back of a truck.
   c. A roofer's assistant carries a bundle of shingles across a construction site.

Applying Math

5. **Calculate Force** Find the force a person exerts in pulling a wagon 20 m if 1,500 J of work is done.
6. **Calculate Work** A car's engine produces 100 kW of power. How much work does the engine do in 5 s?
7. **Calculate Energy** A color TV uses 120 W of power. How much energy does the TV use in 1 hour?

More Section Review gpescience.com

3 Assess

DAILY INTERVENTION

Check for Understanding

Logical-Mathematical Have students make a chart that compares the work done and the power it took for each of five students to climb the stairs in the MiniLAB in this section. What one variable determines the different values for work done? student weight What two variables determine the difference in power values? student weight and time L2

Reteach

Work and Power Ask students to name various activities they enjoy. Have the class discuss the work done and the amount of power used while performing each activity. L2 IS **Interpersonal**

Assessment

Portfolio Have students make posters that define the SI units for force, work, and power and illustrate the relationships among them. Use **PASC**, p. 145. L2

section 1 review

1. The scientific definition requires that a force act on an object and that the object move in the direction of that force. The everyday meaning requires that an effort be exerted.
2. Accept any answer in which a force is applied but the object does not move in the direction of the force.
3. Work is the energy transferred when a force makes an object move.
4. **a.** Work is being done when the snow is lifted up by the shovel. Work also is done if the person tosses the snow out of the shovel. **b.** Work is done when the worker lifts the brick off the ground and pushes the brick along the bed of the truck. **c.** The assistant does no work while carrying the shingles.
5. $F = \frac{W}{d} = \frac{1{,}500\ \text{J}}{20\ \text{m}} = 75\ \text{N}$
6. $W = Pt = (100{,}000\ \text{J\s})(5\ \text{s}) = 500{,}000\ \text{J}$
7. $E = Pt = (120\ \text{J\s})(1\ \text{h})\left(\frac{60\ \text{min}}{1\ \text{h}}\right)\left(\frac{60\ \text{s}}{1\ \text{min}}\right) = 20\ \text{J}$

section 2 Using Machines

1 Motivate

INTERACTIVE CHALKBOARD PowerPoint® Presentations An editable Microsoft® PowerPoint® presentation is available on **Interactive Chalkboard** CD-ROM.

Bellringer

Section Focus Transparencies also are available on the Interactive Chalkboard CD-ROM. L2 ELL

SECTION 2 Section Focus Transparency A Quiet Glide Chapter 6

For some people, paddling a canoe is a pleasant diversion. For others, it's work. Out on a lake, the paddle is a big help in moving the canoe. It might even make work fun!

1. How is a person paddling a canoe doing work?
2. If the paddle broke, would it be easier or more difficult to move the canoe? Explain.
3. How does the shape of the canoe make paddling easier?

L2

Work and Machines

Reading Preview

Tie to Prior Knowledge

Easier Work Ask students to name ways that machines make work easier. They might mention that a shovel makes lifting dirt easier, and a hammer makes pushing a nail into wood easier. In this section, students will use the scientific definition of work to learn how machines make work easier.

Facets of Meaning Ask students what would make a person efficient or inefficient. Write "efficient behaviors" and "inefficient behaviors" on the board. Brainstorm ideas and list them under each category. Then ask if a car or machine can be efficient. What would make a car or machine efficient?

Reading Guide

What You'll Learn

- **Explain** how machines make doing work easier.
- **Calculate** the mechanical advantage of a machine.
- **Calculate** the efficiency of a machine.

Why It's Important

Cars, stairs, and teeth are all examples of machines that make your life easier.

Review Vocabulary

force: a push or a pull

New Vocabulary

- machine
- input force
- output force
- mechanical advantage
- efficiency

What is a machine?

A **machine** is a device that makes doing work easier. When you think of a machine, you may picture a device with an engine and many moving parts. However, machines can be simple. Some machines, such as knives, scissors, and doorknobs, are used every day to make doing work easier.

Making Work Easier

Machines can make work easier by increasing the force that can be applied to an object. A screwdriver increases the force you apply to a screw. A second way that machines can make work easier is by increasing the distance over which a force can be applied. A leaf rake is an example of this type of machine. Machines also can make work easier by changing the direction of an applied force. A simple pulley changes a downward force to an upward force.

Increasing Force A car jack, such as the one in **Figure 6,** is an example of a machine that increases an applied force. The upward force exerted by the jack is greater than the downward force you exert on the handle. However, the distance you push the handle downward is greater than the distance the car is pushed upward. Because work is the product of force and distance, the work done by the jack is not greater than the work you do on the jack. The jack increases the applied force, but it doesn't increase the work done.

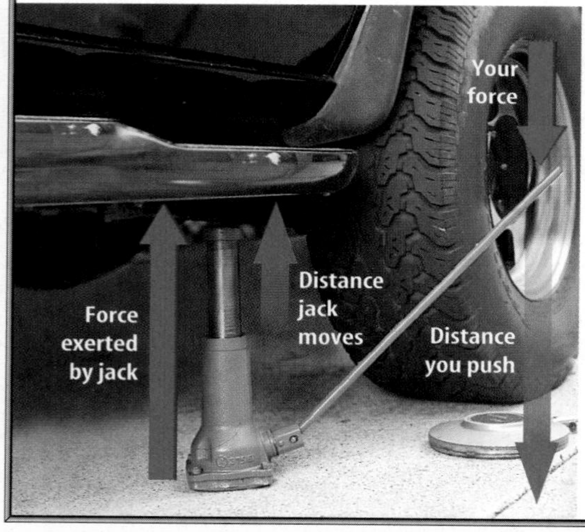

Figure 6 A car jack is an example of a machine that increases an applied force.

Section 2 Resource Manager

Chapter FAST FILE Resources

Transparency Activity, p. 47
Directed Reading for Content Mastery, p. 22
MiniLAB, p. 4
Enrichment, p. 33
Reinforcement, p. 30

Physical Science Critical Thinking/Problem Solving, p. 3

Figure 7 Whether the mover slides the chair up the ramp or lifts it directly into the truck, she will do the same amount of work. Doing the work over a longer distance allows her to use less force.

Force and Distance Why does the mover in **Figure 7** push the heavy furniture up the ramp instead of lifting it into the truck? It is easier because less force is needed to push the furniture up the ramp than is needed to lift it.

The work done in lifting an object depends on the change in height of the object. The same amount of work is done whether the mover pushes the furniture up the long ramp or lifts it straight up. If she uses a ramp to lift the furniture, she moves the furniture a longer distance than if she just raised it straight up. If the work stays the same and the distance is increased, then less force will be needed to do the work.

Reading Check *How does a ramp make lifting an object easier?*

Changing Direction Some machines change the direction of the force you apply. When you use the car jack, you exert a force downward on the jack handle. The force exerted by the jack on the car is upward. The direction of the force you apply is changed from downward to upward. Some machines change the direction of the force that is applied to them in another way. The wedge-shaped blade of an ax is one example. When you use an ax to split wood, you exert a downward force as you swing the ax toward the wood. As **Figure 8** shows, the blade changes the downward force into a horizontal force that splits the wood apart.

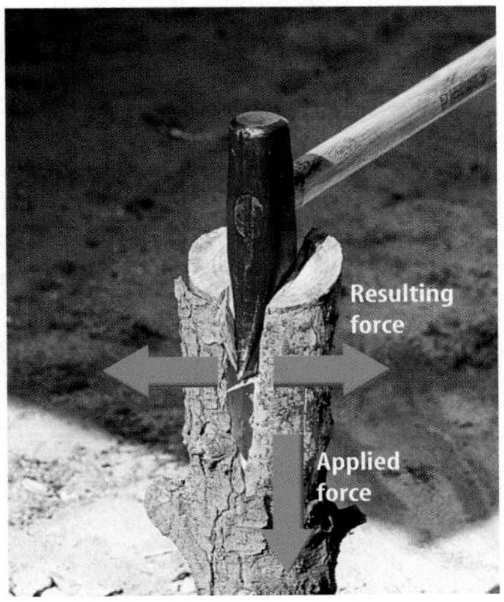

Figure 8 An ax blade changes the direction of the force from vertical to horizontal.

2 Teach

Discussion

Everyday Machines Ask students to name devices that make work easier but aren't normally called machines in everyday conversations. Some examples are a bicycle, a can opener, and a rake. Discuss how each device makes work easier. L1 LS **Linguistic**

Activity

Changing Force Direction Have students experiment with lifting a load using a simple fixed pulley and using a screwdriver to pry the lid off a can. For each activity, have students try to do the job without changing the direction of force. L2 LS **Kinesthetic**

Reading Check

Answer Less force is needed to lift an object when using a ramp.

Reading Strategy

Paired Reading Ask students to read this section in pairs and note statements that use "is equal to" and "is" to abbreviate, define, or explain concepts about machines. Have students take notes using heading titles and writing notes as equations, such as Input Force = F_{in}.

Differentiated Instruction

Learning Disabled Have students push a heavy box up a gentle ramp. Keep the ramp the same height, but make it shorter and therefore steeper. Then ask students to push the box again. Do this several times with increasingly shorter and steeper ramps to help students understand the relationship between the distance the box moves and the force required to move it. L1

Challenge Tell students that some machines have a mechanical advantage that is less than 1. Have them find out why these machines are still useful. In these machines the input force is greater than the output force. These machines can be useful if they increase the distance an object moves or its speed. L3 LS **Logical-Mathematical.**

Mini LAB

Purpose Students observe how machines multiply a person's force of effort. L2

LS **Kinesthetic**

Materials two cans of food, manual can opener, metric ruler

Teaching Strategy Explain to students that the length of the can opener handle is the diameter of the circle or "wheel" that they must turn to be able to move the small circle or "axle" of the cutting blade. The can opener functions as a wheel and axle. To gain force from the cutting blade, they must move the handle a greater distance.

Safety Precaution Caution students not to touch can opener's cutting blades or cut edges of the can's lid.

Analysis

1. Opening the first can was much easier than opening the second can.
2. An input force applied to the can opener's handle is increased so that the output force of the blade is able to cut the can. A longer handle would decrease the input force required to open the can.

Assessment

Process Show students a door handle and ask them to infer how the handle multiplies the force of the person opening the door. Like the can opener, the door handle works as a wheel and axle. The handle is the large "wheel" that easily turns the metal rod or "axle" inserted into the door lock. Use **Performance Assessment in the Science Classroom,** p. 89.

Try at Home

Figure 9 A crowbar increases the force you apply and changes its direction.

Mini LAB

Machines Multiplying Force

Procedure

1. Open a **can of food** using a **manual can opener** that has circular blades. ***WARNING:*** *Do not touch can opener's cutting blades or the cut edges of the cans' lids.*
2. Open another **can of food,** but this time grasp the handle as close as you can to the handle's pivot point.

Analysis

1. Compare how difficult it was to open the first can with how difficult it was to open the second can.
2. Infer why a can opener makes it easier to open a metal can. How would you design a can opener to make opening cans even easier?

Try at Home

The Work Done by Machines

To pry the lid off a wooden crate with a crowbar, you'd slip the end of the crowbar under the edge of the crate lid and push down on the handle. By moving the handle downward, you do work on the crowbar. As the crowbar moves, it does work on the lid, lifting it up. **Figure 9** shows how the crowbar increases the amount of force being applied and changes the direction of the force.

When you use a machine such as a crowbar, you are moving something that resists being moved. For example, if you use a crowbar to pry the lid off a crate, you are working against the friction between the nails in the lid and the crate. You also could use a crowbar to move a large rock. In this case, you would be working against gravity—the weight of the rock.

Input and Output Forces Two forces are involved when a machine is used to do work. You exert a force on the machine, such as a bottle opener, and the machine then exerts a force on the object you are trying to move, such as a bottle cap. The force that is applied to the machine is called the **input force.** F_{in} stands for the input force. The force applied by the machine is called the **output force,** symbolized by F_{out}. When you try to pull a nail out of wood with a hammer, as in **Figure 10,** you apply the input force on the handle. The output force is the force the claw applies to the nail.

Two kinds of work need to be considered when you use a machine: the work done by you on the machine and the work done by the machine. When you use a crowbar, you do work when you apply force to the crowbar handle and make it move. The work done by you on a machine is called the input work and is symbolized by W_{in}. The work done by the machine is called the output work and is abbreviated W_{out}.

Science Journal

Work In and Work Out Have students choose two simple machines that they have used. For each simple machine, write a short paragraph describing the work in and the work out. Describe how the machine simplifies a task. Machines used might include shovel, bicycle, broom, screwdriver, and scissors. L2 LS **Linguistic**

Curriculum Connection

Art Leonardo da Vinci is famous for such well-known paintings as *Mona Lisa* and *The Last Supper.* However, he was also the inventor of an extraordinary collection of machines. Have students research Leonardo da Vinci and prepare a computer presentation showing how his work with mechanical devices inspired much of the technology we use today. L2 LS **Visual-Spatial**

Conserving Energy Remember that energy is always conserved. When you do work on a machine, you transfer energy to the machine. When the machine does work on an object, energy is transferred from the machine to the object. Because energy cannot be created or destroyed, the amount of energy the machine transfers to the object cannot be greater than the amount of energy you transfer to the machine. A machine cannot create energy, so W_{out} is never greater than W_{in}.

However, the machine does not transfer all of the energy it receives to the object. In fact, when a machine is used, some of the input energy changes to thermal energy due to friction. The energy that changes to thermal energy cannot be used to do work, so W_{out} is always smaller than W_{in}.

Ideal Machines Remember that work is calculated by multiplying force by distance. The input work is the product of the input force and the distance over which the input force is exerted. The output work is the product of the output force and the distance over which that force is exerted.

Suppose a perfect machine could be built in which there were no friction. None of the input work or output work would be converted to thermal energy. For such an ideal machine, the input work would equal the output work. For an ideal machine,

$$W_{in} = W_{out}$$

Suppose the ideal machine increases the force applied to it. This means that the output force, F_{out}, is greater than the input force, F_{in}. Recall that work is equal to force times distance. If F_{out} is greater than F_{in}, then W_{in} and W_{out} can be equal only if the input force is applied over a greater distance than the output force.

For example, suppose the hammer claw in **Figure 10** moves a distance of 1 cm to remove a nail. If an output force of 1,500 N is exerted by the claw of the hammer, and you move the handle of the hammer 5 cm, you can find the input force as follows.

$$W_{in} = W_{out}$$
$$F_{in}\, d_{in} = F_{out}\, d_{out}$$
$$F_{in}\,(0.05\text{ m}) = (1{,}500\text{ N})\,(0.01\text{ m})$$
$$F_{in}\,(0.05\text{ m}) = 15\text{ N·m}$$
$$F_{in} = 300\text{ N}$$

Because the distance you move the hammer is longer than the distance the hammer moves the nail, the input force is less than the output force.

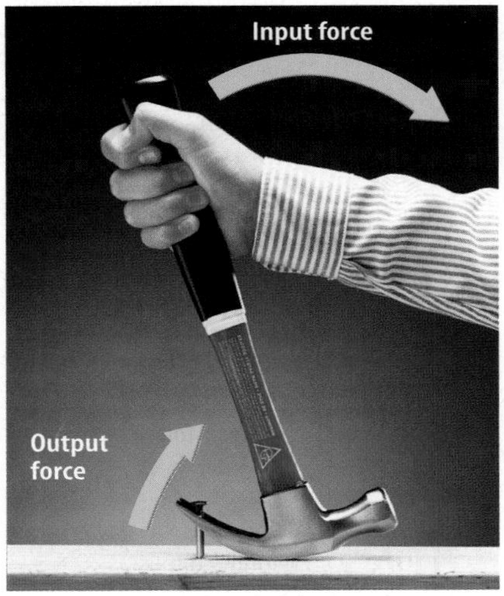

Figure 10 When prying a nail out of a piece of wood with a claw hammer, you exert the input force on the handle of the hammer, and the claw exerts the output force. **Describe** *how the hammer changes the input force.*

Science Online

Topic: Rube Goldberg
Visit gpescience.com for Web links to information about Rube Goldberg devices.

Activity Use the information that you find to sketch a Rube-Goldberg-like device designed to burst a balloon.

Quick Demo
Changing Energy

Materials wood, claw hammer

Estimated Time five minutes

Procedure Bring to class a piece of wood with a nail pounded almost all the way into it. In front of the class, use a claw hammer to pull the nail out of the wood. Invite students to touch the warm nail to show how some of the work was converted to thermal energy. L2 LS **Visual-Kinesthetic**

Caption Answer

Figure 10 The hammer produces an output force that is greater than the input force, but the output force is applied over a shorter distance than the input force.

IDENTIFYING Misconceptions

Always Work Students may think that simple machines allow us to do less work. See page F at the beginning of this chapter for teaching strategies that address this misconception.

Visual Learning

Figure 10 Point out the fact that although this hammer is not an ideal machine, most of the input work is converted to work done on the nail. This means that $W_{in} \approx W_{out}$. Since work = force × distance, if the hammer handle is moved a large distance with a small force, then the claw, which moves a short distance, will exert a large force. Have students draw a diagram to show this relationship. L2 LS **Visual-Spatial**

Activity

Crowbar *MA* Ask students to calculate the mechanical advantage of a crowbar to which you apply 100 N of force to lift a 250-N rock.

$MA = \frac{F_{out}}{F_{in}} = 250\text{ N} \div 100\text{N} = 2.5$

L3 LS **Logical-Mathematical**

Fun Fact

Mechanical advantage also can be determined by dividing the input distance by the output distance.

INTEGRATE Chemistry

Graphite Lubricant Graphite is composed of carbon atoms formed into linked hexagons arranged in weakly bonded layers. Graphite is useful as a lubricant because the layers can slide easily over one another. When graphite is applied to the moving parts of machines, the sliding of the layers reduces the effects of friction.

Research Have students research other types of lubricants such as Teflon, lithium grease, Freon and tungsten oxide that are used in industry to help cut down on wear and tear and heat loss due to friction between moving parts in machines. L2

Reading Check

Answer because some of the input work is converted into thermal energy by friction

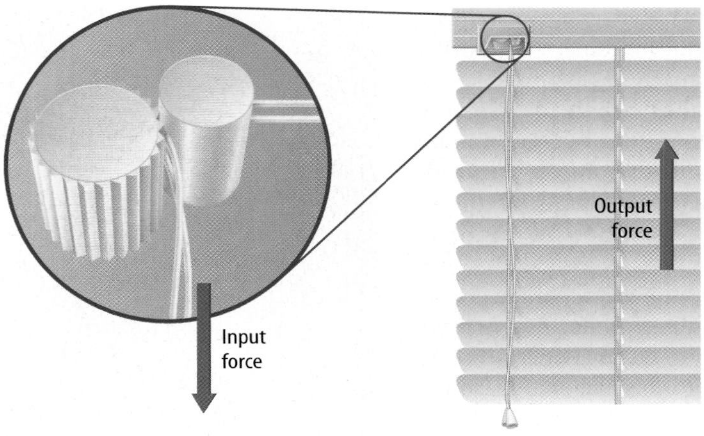

Figure 11 Window blinds use a machine that changes the direction of an input force. A downward pull on the cord is changed to an upward force on the blinds. The input and output forces are equal, so the *MA* is 1.

Mechanical Advantage

Machines such as the car jack, the ramp, the crow bar, and the claw hammer make work easier by making the output force greater than the input force. The ratio of the output force to the input force is the **mechanical advantage** of a machine. The mechanical advantage (*MA*) of a machine can be calculated with the following equation.

Mechanical Advantage Equation

$$\text{mechanical advantage} = \frac{\text{output force (in newtons)}}{\text{input force (in newtons)}}$$

$$MA = \frac{F_{out}}{F_{in}}$$

Figure 11 shows that the mechanical advantage equals one when only the direction of the input force changes.

Ideal Mechanical Advantage The mechanical advantage of a machine without friction is called the ideal mechanical advantage, or *IMA*. The *IMA* can be calculated by dividing the input distance by the output distance. For a real machine, the *IMA* would be the mechanical advantage of the machine if there were no friction.

INTEGRATE Chemistry

Graphite Lubricant
Graphite is a solid that sometimes is used as a lubricant to increase the efficiency of machines. Find out what element graphite is made of and why graphite is a good lubricant.

Efficiency

For real machines, some of the energy put into a machine is always converted to thermal energy by frictional forces. For this reason, the output work of a machine is always less than the work put into the machine.

Efficiency is a measure of how much of the work put into a machine is changed into useful output work by the machine. A machine with high efficiency produces less thermal energy from friction, so more of the input work is changed to useful output work.

Reading Check *Why is the output work always less than the input work for a real machine?*

Teacher FYI

***MA* Information** Mechanical advantage (*MA*) is output force divided input force. If *MA* is less than 1, the input force is greater than the output force. If *MA* equals 1, the machine only changes the direction of the input force. If *MA* is greater than 1, the machine increases the output force.

Calculating Efficiency To calculate the efficiency of a machine, the output work is divided by the input work. Efficiency is usually expressed as a percentage by this equation:

Efficiency Equation

$$\text{efficiency (\%)} = \frac{\text{output work (in joules)}}{\text{input work (in joules)}} \times 100\%$$

$$efficiency = \frac{W_{out}}{W_{in}} \times 100\%$$

In an ideal machine, there is no friction and the output work equals the input work. So the efficiency of an ideal machine is 100 percent. In a real machine, friction causes the output work to always be less than the input work. So the efficiency of a real machine is always less than 100 percent.

Increasing Efficiency Machines can be made more efficient by reducing friction. This usually is done by adding a lubricant, such as oil or grease, to surfaces that rub together, as shown in **Figure 12.** A lubricant fills in the gaps between the surfaces, enabling the surfaces to slide past each other more easily.

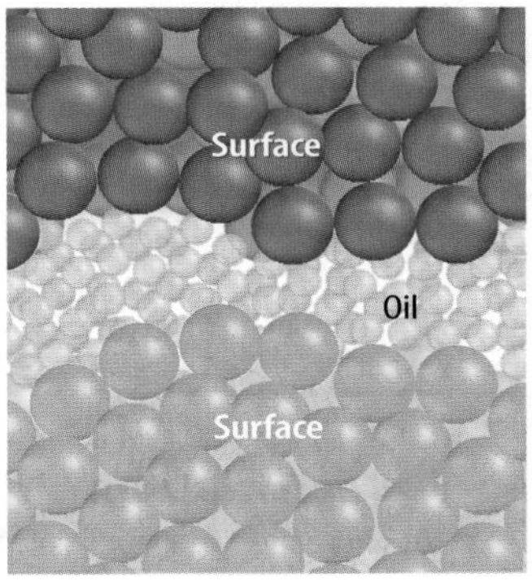

Figure 12 Oil reduces the friction between two surfaces. Oil fills the space between the surfaces so high spots don't rub against each other.

section 2 review

Summary

Work and Machines

- Machines make doing work easier by changing the applied force, changing the distance over which the force is applied, or changing the direction of the applied force.
- Because energy cannot be created or destroyed, the output work cannot be greater than the input work.
- In a real machine, some of the input work is converted into heat by friction.

Mechanical Advantage and Efficiency

- The mechanical advantage of a machine is the output force divided by the input force:
$$MA = \frac{F_{out}}{F_{in}}$$
- The efficiency of a machine is the output work divided by the input work times 100%:
$$efficiency = \frac{W_{out}}{W_{in}} \times 100\%$$

Self Check

1. **Describe** the circumstances for which the output work would equal the input work in a machine.
2. **Infer** how lubricating a machine affects the output force exerted by the machine.
3. **Explain** why, in a real machine, the output work is always less than the input work.
4. **Think Critically** The mechanical advantage of a machine is less than one. Compare the distances over which the input and output forces are applied.

Applying Math

5. **Calculate** the mechanical advantage of a hammer if the input force is 125 N and the output force is 2,000 N.
6. **Calculate Efficiency** Find the efficiency of a machine that does 800 J of work if the input work is 2,400 J.
7. **Calculate Force** Find the force needed to lift a 2,000-N weight using a machine with a mechanical advantage of 15.

Post Reading

Paired Discussion Ask students to review the principles and formulas related to Ideal Machines and Ideal Mechanical Advantage. Allow five minutes for a discussion of the concepts contained within the text. Have students switch partners and continue the discussion.

3 Assess

DAILY INTERVENTION

Check for Understanding

Kinesthetic Set up a wood ramp. Use a spring balance to pull a smooth wood block up the ramp. Measure the force and calculate the work done. Tape sandpaper along the length of the ramp and repeat the procedure. Ask the students which machine was more efficient and why. Ask how they could improve the efficiency of the second ramp without removing the sandpaper. They could put something smooth over the sandpaper. L2

Reteach

Machines Bring in various simple machines for students to examine. For each one, have students decide whether the machine works by increasing force, increasing distance, or changing the direction of the force. L2

LS **Visual-Spatial**

Assessment

Process Have each student choose a machine and prepare a presentation showing different ways to reduce friction in the machine and increase its efficiency. Possible ways of reducing friction include using bearings, wheels, or a lubricant. Use **PASC,** p. 143. L2 P

section 2 review

1. The machine would have to be an ideal machine in which there was no friction.
2. Friction is a force that opposes the motion of two surface sliding past each other. Lubricating a machine increases the output force because it decreases friction.
3. In a real machine, some of the input work is converted into thermal energy by friction.
4. The distance over which the output force is applied is greater than the distance that the input force is applied.
5. $MA = \frac{F_{out}}{F_{in}} = 16$
6. $eff = \frac{W_{out}}{W_{in}} \times 100\% = 33\%$
7. $F_{in} = \frac{F_{out}}{MA} = 133\text{ N}$

1 Motivate

An editable Microsoft® PowerPoint® presentation is available on **Interactive Chalkboard** CD-ROM.

Bellringer

Section Focus Transparencies also are available on the Interactive Chalkboard CD-ROM. L2 ELL

Section 3 Section Focus Transparency — Moving Day — Chapter 6

Moving can be a chore. Packing boxes, moving them, then unpacking everything can be hard work. But machines can help. Some machines are simple, while others can be very complicated. This mover uses a selection of machines to help make moving day much easier.

1. What do you see in this picture that makes it easier for the mover to do work?
2. How do the ramp and dolly make work easier?

L2

Work and Machines

Reading Preview

Tie to Prior Knowledge

Define *MA* Ask students to define mechanical advantage. the number of times a machine multiplies the effort force applied to it Tell them that in this section they will learn how the design of a simple machine affects its mechanical advantage. L2

Activate Background Knowledge Read aloud the vocabulary words and ask students if they have heard these words before. Discuss what they know about the six simple machines. Talk about the concepts of simple and compound and ask them to predict what a compound machine might be.

section 3

Simple Machines

Reading Guide

What You'll Learn

- **Describe** the six types of simple machines.
- **Explain** how the different types of simple machines make doing work easier.
- **Calculate** the ideal mechanical advantage of the different types of simple machines.

Why It's Important

All complex machines, such as cars, are made of simple machines. Even your body contains simple machines.

Review Vocabulary

compound: composed of separate elements or parts

New Vocabulary

- simple machine
- lever
- pulley
- wheel and axle
- inclined plane
- screw
- wedge
- compound machine

Figure 13 There are three classes of levers.

First-Class Lever
The fulcrum is between the input force and the output force.

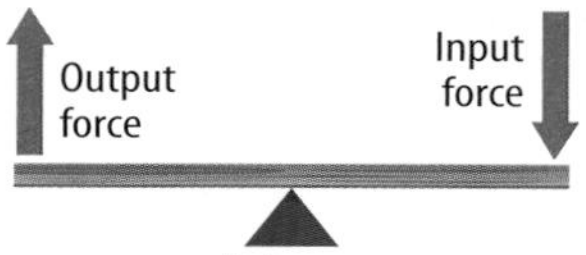

Second-Class Lever
The output force is between the fulcrum and the input force.

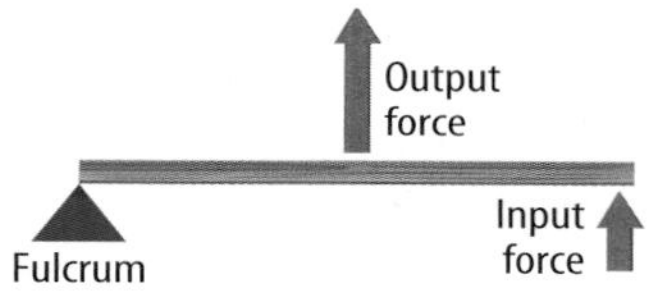

Third-Class Lever
The input force is between the fulcrum and the output force.

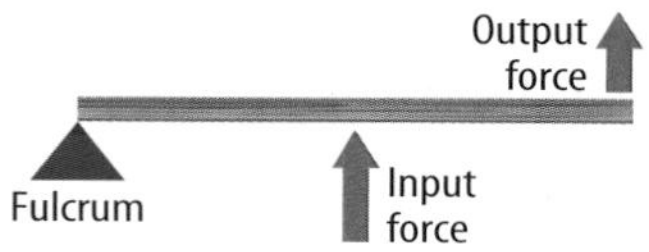

Types of Simple Machines

If you cut your food with a knife, use a screwdriver, or even chew your food, you are using a simple machine. A **simple machine** is a machine that does work with only one movement of the machine. There are six types of simple machines: lever, pulley, wheel and axle, inclined plane, screw, and wedge. The pulley and the wheel and axle are modified levers, and the screw and the wedge are modified inclined planes.

Levers

You've used a lever if you've used a wheelbarrow, a lawn rake, or swung a baseball bat. A **lever** is a bar that is free to pivot or turn around a fixed point. The fixed point the lever pivots on is called the fulcrum. The input arm of the lever is the distance from the fulcrum to the point where the input force is applied. The output arm is the distance from the fulcrum to the point where the output force is exerted by the lever.

The output force produced by a lever depends on the lengths of the input arm and the output arm. If the output arm is longer than the input arm, the law of conservation of energy requires that the output force be less than the input force. If the output arm is shorter than the input arm, then the output force is greater than the input force.

There are three classes of levers, as shown in **Figure 13.** The differences among the three classes of levers depend on the locations of the fulcrum, the input force, and the output force.

Section 3 Resource Manager

Chapter *FAST FILE* Resources

Transparency Activity, p. 48, 49–50
Directed Reading for Content Mastery, pp. 23–24
Lab Activity, pp. 9–11, 13–18
Enrichment, p. 34
Lab Worksheet, pp. 5–6, 7–8
Reinforcement, p. 31

Home and Community Involvement, p. 35

Physical Science Critical Thinking/Problem Solving, pp. 6–7

Figure 14 Levers are classified by the locations of the input force, the output force, and the fulcrum.

A The screwdriver is being used as a first-class lever. The fulcrum is the paint can rim.

B A wheelbarrow is a second-class lever. The fulcrum is the wheel.

C A baseball bat is a third-class lever. The fulcrum here is the batter's left hand.

First-Class Lever The screwdriver used to open the paint can in **Figure 14A** is an example of a first-class lever. For a first-class lever, the fulcrum is located between the input and output forces. The output force is always in the opposite direction to the input force in a first-class lever.

Second-Class Lever For a second-class lever, the output force is located between the input force and the fulcrum. Look at the wheelbarrow in **Figure 14B.** The girl applies an upward input force on the handles, and the wheel is the fulcrum. The output force is exerted between the input force and the fulcrum. For a second-class lever, the output force is always greater than the input force.

Third-Class Lever Many pieces of sports equipment, such as a baseball bat, are third-class levers. For a third-class lever, the input force is applied between the output force and the fulcrum. The right-handed batter in **Figure 14C** applies the input force with the right hand, and the left hand is the fulcrum. The output force is exerted by the bat above the right hand. The output force is always less than the input force in a third-class lever. Instead, the distance over which the output force is applied is increased.

Every lever can be placed in one of these classes. Each class can be found in your body, as shown in **Figure 15** on the next page.

INTEGRATE History

Archimedes and the Lever The Greek mathematician Archimedes (287–212 B.C.) described how a lever could be used to increase force. He also supposedly said "Give me a place to stand and I will move the Earth." Research one of Archimedes' inventions and write a paragraph describing it.

2 Teach

Quick Demo
Classifying Levers

Materials several different kinds of levers, such as crow bars, nut crackers, bottle openers, tweezers, fishing poles

Estimated Time ten minutes

Procedure Display several examples of each of the three classes of levers for students to examine and handle. First-class levers would be pliers, and crowbars. Second-class levers are nutcrackers, wheelbarrows, and bottle openers. Third-class levers are tweezers, baseball bats, and fishing poles. L2 IS **Kinesthetic**

Use Science Words

Word Origin Have students look up the word *fulcrum* in a dictionary to determine its origin. Ask a volunteer to explain how the meaning of the word reflects its root. The word *fulcrum* comes from the Latin root *fulcire*, meaning "to support." A fulcrum acts as a support around which a lever moves. L1 IS **Linguistic**

INTEGRATE History

Archimedes Although the lever had been used long before Archimedes, he was the first to demonstrate how the mechanical advantage of a lever depended on the distances of the input force and output force from the fulcrum. His work on levers led him to claim that if he had a place to stand, he could move the world. After making his famous claim, Archimedes was asked by King Hieron to demonstrate how he easily could move a heavy object. Archimedes devised a pulley system that allowed him to single-handedly drag a large, fully-loaded ship up onto the beach. His mathematical work included the first steps toward integral and differential calculus.

Differentiated Instruction

Challenge Have students create a computer presentation describing the three classes of levers. The description should include the locations of the fulcrum, input force, and output force. If possible, have students create an animated presentation to present to the class. L3

Cultural Diversity

Chinese Wheelbarrow The wheelbarrow, a second-class lever, was invented in China sometime in or before the first century B.C. The Chinese called their wheeled devices such things as wooden goat, wooden sheep, wooden ox, and gliding horse. How does a wheelbarrow give a worker more power? It allows the worker to do more work in a shorter amount of time. L1 IS **Logical-Mathematical**

NATIONAL GEOGRAPHIC

Visualizing Levers in the Human Body

Have students examine the pictures and read the captions. Then ask the following questions.

Newborn babies are not able to support their heads and they must be carefully supported. Why is this? An unborn baby floats in fluid and does not have to support its own head. After birth, these muscles must be strengthened.

Explain why your forearm becomes more muscular when you do curls with a dumbbell. When you increase the output force (the dumbbell), your input force (muscle in your forearm) must also increase. Repeating curls increases the muscle mass in your forearm over time.

Activity

Other Body Levers Find other levers in your body. Make a poster showing the various kinds that you find. For each example, mark the fulcrum, input force, and output force. L2 LS **Visual-Spatial**

NATIONAL GEOGRAPHIC **VISUALIZING LEVERS IN THE HUMAN BODY**

Figure 15

▲ Fulcrum
▼ Input force
▲ Output force

All three types of levers—first-class, second-class, and third-class—are found in the human body. The forces exerted by muscles in your body can be increased by first-class and second-class levers, while third-class levers increase the range of movement of a body part. Examples of how the body uses levers to help it move are shown here.

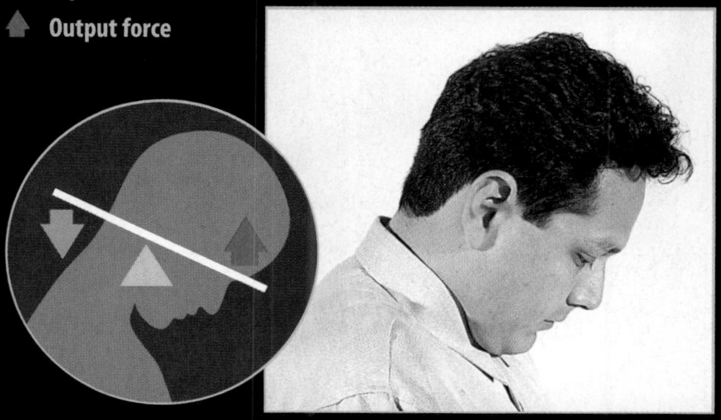

▲ FIRST-CLASS LEVER The fulcrum lies between the input force and the output force. Your head acts like a first-class lever. Your neck muscles provide the input force to support the weight of your head.

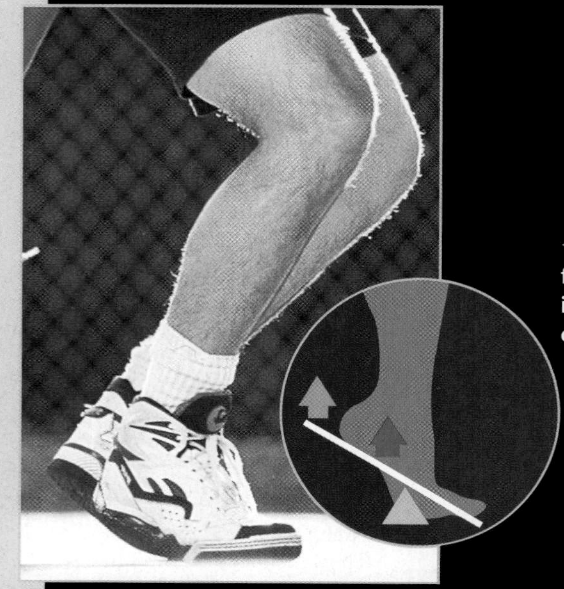

◀ SECOND-CLASS LEVER The output force is between the fulcrum and the input force. Your foot becomes a second-class lever when you stand on your toes.

▶ THIRD-CLASS LEVER The input force is between the fulcrum and the output force. A third-class lever increases the range of motion of the output force. When you do a curl with a dumbbell, your forearm is a third-class lever.

Figure 16 A fixed pulley is another form of the lever.
Infer *the lengths of the input arm and output arm in a pulley.*

Ideal Mechanical Advantage of a Lever The ideal mechanical advantage, or *IMA*, for a lever can be calculated by dividing the length of the input arm by the length of the output arm:

IMA of a Lever

$$\text{ideal mechanical advantage} = \frac{\text{length of input arm (m)}}{\text{length of output arm (m)}}$$

$$IMA = \frac{L_{in}}{L_{out}}$$

Pulleys

A **pulley** is a grooved wheel with a rope, chain, or cable running along the groove. A fixed pulley, as shown in **Figure 16,** is a modified first-class lever. The axle of the pulley acts as the fulcrum. The two sides of the pulley are the input arm and output arm. A pulley can change the direction of the input force or increase the output force, depending on whether the pulley is fixed or movable. A system of pulleys can change the direction of the input force and make the output force larger.

Reading Check *What are the input arm, output arm, and fulcrum of a pulley?*

Fixed Pulleys The cable attached to an elevator passes over a fixed pulley at the top of the elevator shaft. A fixed pulley, such as the one in **Figure 17,** is attached to something that doesn't move, such as a ceiling or wall. Because a fixed pulley changes only the direction of force, the IMA is 1.

Figure 17 A fixed pulley changes only the direction of a force. You need to apply an input force of 4 N to lift the 4-N weight.

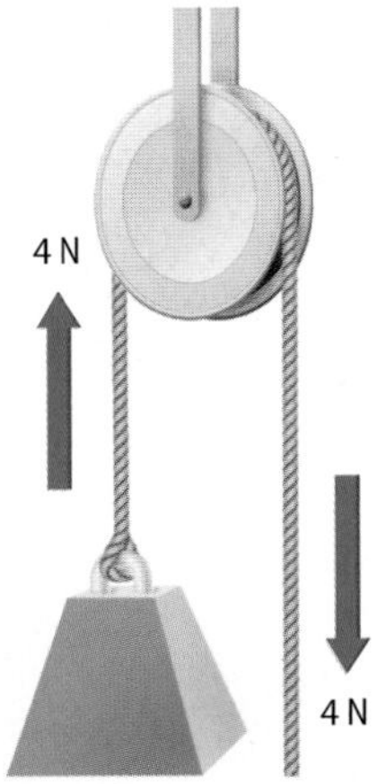

Activity

Calculate *IMA* Ask students to calculate the *IMA* of a lever whose output arm is 1 m long and whose input arm is 80 cm long. What class of lever is this? *IMA* = 0.8 m ÷ 1.0 m = 0.8; this must be a third-class lever. L2 **Logical-Mathematical**

Caption Answer

Figure 16 the radius of the pulley

Make a Model

Belt Pulleys Some pulleys, such as drive pulleys in automobiles, consist of two or more grooved wheels connected by a circular belt. Have students work in pairs to make models of a belt pulley. One student can hold two spools with pencils through the holes. Have students connect the spools with a large rubber band. The other student can turn the spools to show how turning one rotates the other in the same direction. If possible, use one small spool and one large spool. The students can see that the speed of the pulleys is inversely related to their diameter. L3 **Kinesthetic**

Discussion

Fixed Pulleys The *IMA* of a single fixed pulley is 1. What is the benefit of using a fixed pulley? A fixed pulley allows a person to raise objects to high places while the person stays at ground level. L2 **Logical-Mathematical**

Reading Check

Answer The input and output arms are the radius of the pulley: the fulcrum is the axle.

Visual Learning

Figure 16 Point out that a fixed pulley, like that shown in **Figure 16**, is a type of first-class lever because the fulcrum is between the input force and the output force. A movable pulley, like that shown on the next page, is a type of second-class lever. The point where the rope is attached to the ceiling is the fulcrum, and the output force is between the fulcrum and the input force. L3 **Visual-Spatial**

Differentiated Instruction

Challenge Have students design and build a mousetrap using ramps, pulleys, and levers. If supplies are not available, they can draw their design on a poster and present it to the class. L3

Reading Check

Answer by increasing the distance you must pull

Inquiry Lab

Finding Balance

Purpose Students infer how to include the mass of a lever into the input force.

Possible Materials meterstick, string, hanging weights (5 g, 10 g, 50 g, 100 g), vertical support, horizontal bar (to hang meter stick on)

Estimated Time 50 minutes

Procedure

1. Hang a meterstick about 10 cm off center and hang various combinations of weights on the two ends so that the meterstick balances.
2. Derive an equation to determine the exact location for any given combination of weights to make the stick remain balanced.

Teaching Strategy

Students should find that the heavier of the two weights will always be on the short side of the meterstick. They may even find the location for just one weight to balance the meterstick.

The equation is:

$F_{in}d_{in} + W_s d_s = F_{out}d_{out}$

Where W_s = weight of the meterstick and d_s = distance from the center of the meterstick to the fulcrum. L2

For additional inquiry activities, see *Science Inquiry Labs*.

Figure 18 A movable pulley and a pulley system called a block and tackle reduce the force needed to lift a weight.

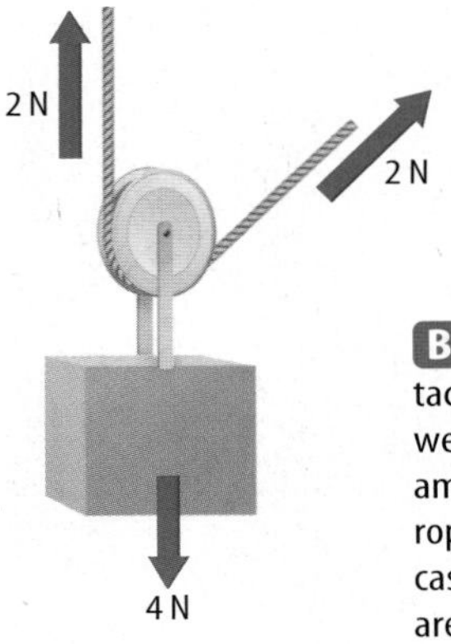

A With a movable pulley, the attached side of the rope supports half of the 4-N weight. You have to apply a 2-N force to lift the weight.

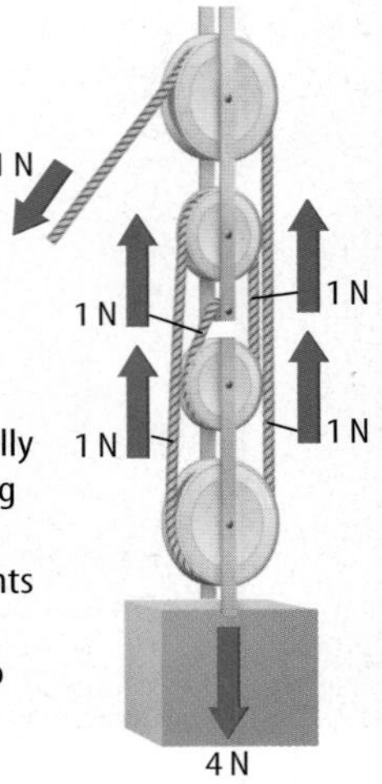

B In a block-and-tackle system, the 4-N weight is divided equally among each supporting rope segment. In this case, four rope segments are supporting the weight. So you have to apply only a 1-N force to lift the weight.

Movable Pulleys A pulley in which one end of the rope is fixed and the wheel is free to move is called a movable pulley. Unlike a fixed pulley, a movable pulley does multiply force. Suppose a 4-N weight is hung from the movable pulley in **Figure 18A.** The ceiling acts like someone helping you to lift the weight. The rope attached to the ceiling will support half of the weight—2 N. You need to exert only the other half of the weight—2 N—to support and lift the weight. The output force exerted on the weight is 4 N, and the applied input force is 2 N. Therefore the *IMA* of the movable pulley is 2.

For a fixed pulley, the distance you pull the rope downward equals the distance the weight moves upward. For a movable pulley, the distance you pull the rope upward is twice the distance the weight moves upward.

Reading Check *How does a movable pulley reduce the input force needed to lift a weight?*

The Block and Tackle A system of pulleys consisting of fixed and movable pulleys is called a block and tackle. **Figure 18B** shows a block and tackle made up of two fixed pulleys and two movable pulleys. If a 4-N weight is suspended from the movable pulley, each rope segment supports one-fourth of the weight, reducing the input force to 1 N. The *IMA* of a pulley system is equal to the number of rope segments that support the weight. The block and tackle shown in **Figure 18B** has an *IMA* of 4. The *IMA* of a block and tackle can be increased by increasing the number of pulleys in the pulley system.

LAB DEMONSTRATION

Purpose to measure the mechanical advantage of various pulley systems

Materials one small, single-sheave pulley; two small, 2-ring tandem pulleys; cord; 1-kg mass; 10-N spring scale

Procedure Use a spring scale to measure the forces required to lift a 1-kg mass using a single fixed pulley, then a single movable pulley, and finally, a block and tackle.

Expected Outcome The *IMA*s are, respectively, 1, 2, and 4.

Assessment

Which system(s) increased force? movable pulley and block and tackle Which system(s) changed direction of the force? single fixed pulley and block and tackle Which system(s) increased force and changed direction? block and tackle L2

Figure 19 The handle on a pencil sharpener is part of a wheel and axle. You apply a force to the handle. This force is made larger by the wheel and axle, making it easy to turn the sharpening mechanism.

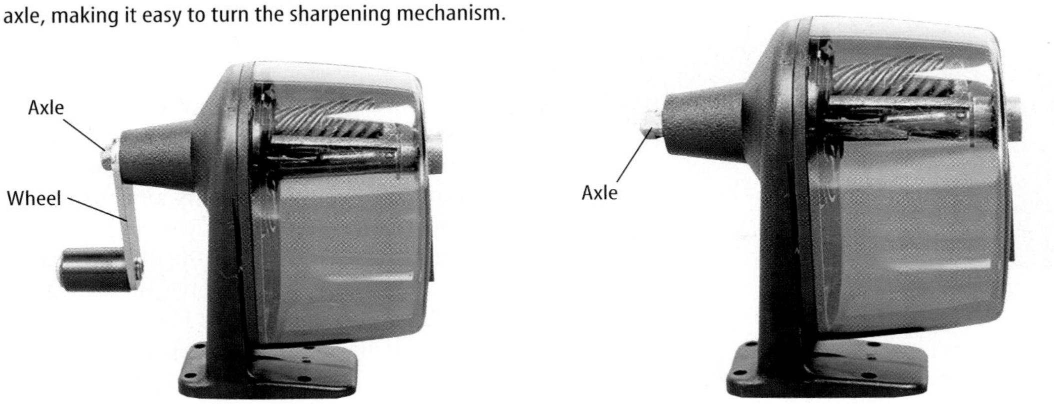

Wheel and Axle

Could you use the pencil sharpener in **Figure 19** if the handle weren't attached? The handle on the pencil sharpener is part of a wheel and axle. A **wheel and axle** is a simple machine consisting of a shaft or axle attached to the center of a larger wheel, so that the wheel and axle rotate together. Doorknobs, screwdrivers, and faucet handles are examples of wheel and axles. Usually, the input force is applied to the wheel, and the output force is exerted by the axle.

Mechanical Advantage of a Wheel and Axle Recall that the mechanical advantage of a lever is the length of the input arm divided by the length of the output arm. A wheel and axle is another modified lever. The center of the axle is the fulcrum. The input force is applied at the rim of the wheel. So the length of the input arm is the radius of the wheel. The output force is exerted at the rim of the axle. So the length of the output arm is the radius of the axle. The *IMA* of a wheel and axle is:

IMA of a Wheel and Axle

$$\text{ideal mechanical advantage} = \frac{\text{radius of wheel (m)}}{\text{radius of axle (m)}}$$

$$IMA = \frac{r_w}{r_a}$$

According to this equation, the *IMA* of a wheel and axle can be increased by increasing the radius of the wheel.

Text Question Answer

No, it would be difficult to turn the axle with your fingers.

Discussion

Lifting a Car A person uses a block and tackle to lift an automobile engine that weighs 1,800 N. The person must exert a force of 300 N to lift the engine. How many ropes support the engine? Explain how you know. Six; the *IMA* is 1,800 N ÷ 300 N = 6, and in a pulley system, the *IMA* equals the number of supporting ropes. L2

IDENTIFYING Misconceptions

Skating The wheel and axle on a skateboard or a pair of in-line skates is not the simple machine known as the wheel and axle. In the simple machine, the wheel and axle rotate together. Usually a small force is applied to the wheel and is translated to a larger force moving over the smaller distance of the axle. The wheels and axles on skateboards and in-line skates are rollers that help the vehicles move with less friction. The axle is fixed and the wheel rotates around the axle.

Reading Strategy

Double-Entry Notes Ask students to draw a line down the middle of their papers. On the left, have them write the name of a simple machine, such as lever, and draw a simple depiction under the name. On the right side, have them write the purpose and advantage of the simple machine. Students should repeat this note-making process for each simple machine.

Curriculum Connection

Math Supply students with several common wheels and axles, such as doorknobs or beaters from an electric mixer. Have them measure the radius of the wheel and the radius of the axle for each item and calculate its *IMA*. L2 LS **Logical-Mathematical**

Differentiated Instruction

English-Language Learners Use visual aids to show students what simple machines look like.Then have students write descriptions of simple machines in their homes. Examples could be a lever, an inclined plane, and a pulley. L2

Activity

Inclined Plane Create an inclined plane by resting a board against a stack of books. Have students measure the input and output distances and calculate the *IMA*. Then ask students to use a spring scale to measure the force required to lift a toy car vertically and the force required to drag it up the ramp. Have them use the numbers they measured for distance and force and calculate the amount of work done pulling the toy car along the ramp and lifting it vertically. Are the two amounts of work the same? Why or why not? The two amounts of work should be close. Any difference is due to inaccurate measurements and loss of energy to friction. L2 ELL IN **Kinesthetic**

Figure 20 If an input force is applied to the larger gear and it rotates clockwise, the smaller gear rotates counterclockwise. The output force exerted by the smaller gear is less than the input force applied to the larger gear.

Gears A gear is a wheel and axle with the wheel having teeth around its rim. When the teeth of two gears interlock, the turning of one gear causes the other gear to turn.

When two gears of different sizes are interlocked, they rotate at different rates. Each rotation of the larger gear causes the smaller gear to make more than one rotation. If the input force is applied to the larger gear, the output force exerted by the smaller gear is less than the input force.

Gears also may change the direction of the force, as shown in **Figure 20.** When the larger gear in is rotated clockwise, the smaller gear rotates counterclockwise.

Inclined Planes

Why do the roads and paths on mountains zigzag? Would it be easier to climb directly up a steep incline or walk a longer path gently sloped around the mountain? An **inclined plane** is a sloping surface, such as a ramp, that reduces the amount of force required to do work.

Mechanical Advantage of an Inclined Plane You do the same work by lifting a box straight up or pushing it up an inclined plane. By pushing the box up an inclined plane, however, the input force is exerted over a longer distance compared to lifting the box straight up. As a result, the input force is less than the force needed to lift the box straight upward. The *IMA* of an inclined plane can be calculated from the following equation:

IMA of an Inclined Plane

$$\text{ideal mechanical advantage} = \frac{\text{length of slope (m)}}{\text{height of slope (m)}}$$

$$IMA = \frac{l}{h}$$

The *IMA* of an inclined plane for a given height is increased by making the plane longer.

When you think of an inclined plane, you might think of moving an object up a ramp—you move and the inclined plane remains stationary. The screw and the wedge, however, are variations of the inclined plane in which the inclined plane moves and the object remains stationary.

Science Online

Topic: Nanobots

Visit gpescience.com for Web links to information about how tiny robots called nanobots might be used as microsurgical instruments.

Activity Use the information you find to make a diagram of a nanobot that might be used to perform surgery.

Visual Learning

Figure 20 Point out that the teeth on the gears must be the same size in order to rotate smoothly. Tell students that the ratio of the number of teeth on the gears determines the speed that the gears turn and the *IMA*. If the small gear has 24 teeth and the large gear has 72 teeth, how much faster will the small gear turn? What is the *IMA*? The large gear will make one-third of a turn for each full turn of the small gear, so the small gear will turn three times faster. The *IMA* is 3. L2 IN **Logical-Mathematical**

Figure 21 A screw has an inclined plane that wraps around the post of the screw.

The thread gets thinner farther from the post. This helps the screw force its way into materials.

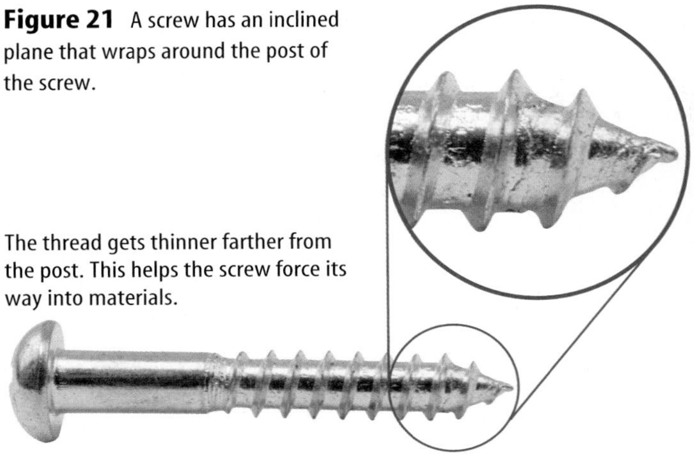

Many lids, such as those on peanut butter jars, also contain threads.

The Screw

A **screw** is an inclined plane wrapped in a spiral around a cylindrical post. If you look closely at the screw in **Figure 21,** you'll see that the threads form a tiny ramp that runs upward from its tip. You apply the input force by turning the screw. The output force is exerted along the threads of the screw. The *IMA* of a screw is related to the spacing of the threads. The *IMA* is larger when the threads are closer together. However, when the *IMA* is larger, more turns of the screw are needed to drive it into a material.

How do you remove the lid from a jar of peanut butter, such as the one in **Figure 21?** If you look closely, you will see threads similar to the ones on the screw in **Figure 21.** Where else can you find examples of a screw?

The Wedge

Like the screw, the wedge is also a simple machine in which the inclined plane moves through an object or material. A **wedge** is an inclined plane with one or two sloping sides. It changes the direction of the input force.

Look closely at the knife in **Figure 22.** One edge is sharp, and it slopes outward at both sides, forming an inclined plane. As it moves through the apple, the downward input force is changed to a horizontal force, forcing the apple apart.

Figure 22 A knife blade is a wedge. As you cut through the apple, the blade pushes the halves of the apple apart.

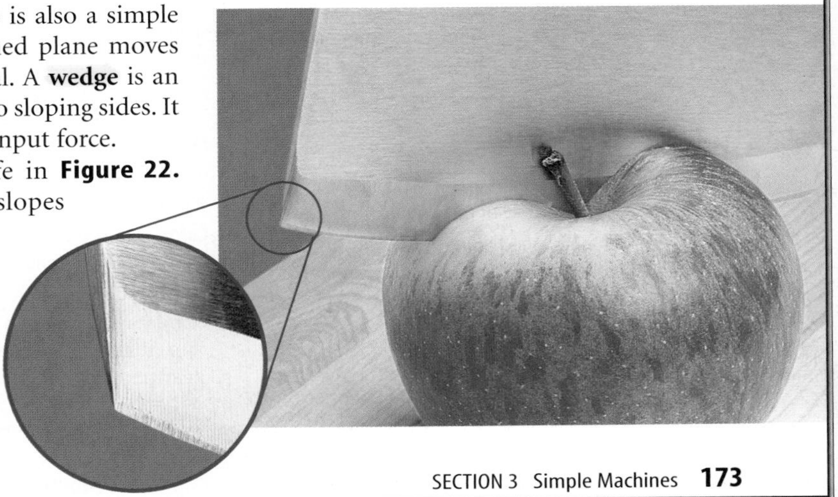

Make a Model

Archimedes Screw An Archimedes' screw is a type of revolving screw used to lift water. This simple device was invented in the third century B.C. by the Greek scientist Archimedes. Have interested students make a model of an Archimedes' screw, using plastic sheeting attached to a dowel. L3

LS **Kinesthetic**

Teacher FYI

Screw Parts The threads of a screw are the windings. The pitch is the distance from a point on one thread to a point directly above it on the next thread. The pitch determines the force you must exert to turn a screw.

Text Question Answer

Other examples of a screw include an auger, a cork screw for opening wine bottles, and a spiral stair case.

Activity

Wedge *IMA* The ideal mechanical advantage of a wedge is calculated by dividing the length of one side of the wedge by the width of the wedge at the thick end. Ask students to calculate the mechanical advantage of a wedge that is 12 cm long and 5 cm wide. $MA = 12\text{ cm} \div 5\text{ cm} = 2.4$

L3 LS **Logical-Mathematical**

Fun Fact

In a compound machine, the output force of one of its simple machines becomes the input force of another. For a compound machine made of two simple machines, $MA = MA_2 \times MA_1$.

Active Reading

Write–Draw–Discuss This strategy encourages students to actively participate in reading and lectures, assimilating content creatively. Have students write about the different simple machines, clarify their ideas, and then make illustrations or drawings of the machines and how they work. Ask students to share responses with the class and display several examples. L2

SECTION 3 Simple Machines 173

Post Reading

Question a Partner Ask students to review what they have learned about simple machines. Then, have them question each other about a machine's purpose and advantages, as well as providing an example. Remind students to refer to their drawings and notes to form or answer questions.

3 Assess

DAILY INTERVENTION

Check for Understanding

Logical-Mathematical Have students brainstorm how to organize information about the six kinds of simple machines into a table. Include the type of machine, an example of each type, and a brief description of how it works. You may want to include other information such as mechanical advantage and efficiency. L2

Reteach

Arrows From construction paper, cut three arrows, about 10, 20, and 30 cm long. Make a similar set in another color. Label the first set of arrows F_{in} and the second set F_{out}. Collect examples of simple machines. Ask volunteers to choose a machine and use the arrows to show the direction and relative sizes of F_{in} and F_{out}. L2 ELL IN **Visual-Spatial**

Assessment

Process Ask students to compare and contrast pulleys and gears. Both use wheels. Gears have teeth, but pulleys don't. Pulleys use a cord to move the wheels. Gears are pulled by interlocking teeth or a chain. L2

Figure 23 A compound machine, such as a can opener, is made up of simple machines.

Compound Machines

Some of the machines you use every day are made up of several simple machines. Two or more simple machines that operate together form a **compound machine.**

Look at the can opener in **Figure 23.** To open the can, you first squeeze the handles together. The handles act as levers and increase the force applied on a wedge, which then pierces the can. You then turn the handle, a wheel and axle, to open the can.

A car is also a compound machine. Burning fuel in the cylinders of the engine causes the pistons to move up and down. This up-and-down motion makes the crankshaft rotate. The force exerted by the rotating crankshaft is transmitted to the wheels through other parts of the car, such as the transmission and the differential. Both of these parts contain gears which can change the rate at which the wheels rotate, the force exerted by the wheels, and even reverse the direction of rotation.

section 3 review

Summary

The Lever Family

- A lever is a bar that is free to pivot about a fixed point called the fulcrum.
- There are three classes of levers based on the relative locations of the input force, the output force, and the fulcrum.
- A pulley is a grooved wheel with a rope, chain, or cable placed in the groove and is a modified form of a lever.
- The *IMA* of a lever is the length of the input arm divided by the length of the output arm.
- A wheel and axle consists of a shaft or axle attached to the center of a larger wheel.

The Inclined Plane Family

- An inclined plane is a ramp or sloping surface that reduces the force needed to do work.
- The *IMA* of an inclined plane is the length of the plane divided by the height of the plane.
- A screw consists of an inclined plane wrapped around a shaft.
- A wedge is an inclined plane that moves and can have one or two sloping surfaces.

Self Check

1. **Classify** a screwdriver being used to turn a screw as one of the six types of simple machines. Explain how the *IMA* of a screwdriver could be increased.
2. **Determine** for which class of lever the output force is always greater than the input force. For which class is the output force always less than the input force?
3. **Make a diagram** of a bicycle and label the parts of a bicycle that are simple machines.
4. **Think Critically** Use the law of conservation of energy to explain why, in a second-class lever, the distance over which the input force is applied is always greater than the distance over which the output force is applied.

Applying Math

5. **Calculate *IMA*** What is the *IMA* of a car's steering wheel if the wheel has a diameter of 40 cm and the shaft it's attached to has a diameter of 4 cm?
6. **Calculate Output Arm Length** A lever has an *IMA* of 4. If the length of the input arm is 1.0 m, what is the length of the output arm?
7. **Calculate *IMA*** A 6.0-m ramp runs from a sidewalk to a porch that is 2.0 m above the sidewalk. What is the ideal mechanical advantage of this ramp?

More Section Review gpescience.com

section 3 review

1. wheel and axle; by increasing the radius of the handle of the screwdriver
2. second-class lever; third-class lever
3. Check students' diagrams.
4. The input work cannot be greater than the output work. The input force is always less than the output force, so the input distance must be greater than the output distance.
5. $IMA = \frac{r_w}{r_a} = \frac{(40\text{ cm})}{(4\text{ cm})} = 10$
6. $L_{out} = \frac{(1.0\text{ m})}{4} = 0.25\text{ m}$
7. $IMA = \frac{1}{h} = \frac{(6.0\text{ m})}{(2.0\text{ m})} = 3$

LAB

Levers

Have you ever tried to balance a friend on a seesaw? If your friend was lighter, you had to move toward the fulcrum. In this lab, you will use the same method to measure the mass of a coin.

Real-World Problem

How can a lever be used to measure mass?

Goals

- **Measure** the lengths of the input arm and output arm of a lever.
- **Calculate** the ideal mechanical advantage of a lever.
- **Determine** the mass of a coin.

Materials

stiff cardboard, 3 cm by 30 cm
coins (one quarter, one dime, one nickel)
balance
metric ruler

Safety Precautions

Procedure

1. **Measure** the mass of each coin.
2. Mark a line 2 cm from one end of the cardboard strip. Label this line *Output.*
3. Slide the other end of the cardboard strip over the edge of a table until the strip begins to tip. Mark a line across the strip at the table edge and label this line *Input.*
4. **Measure** the mass of the strip to the nearest 0.1 g. Write this mass on the input line.
5. Center a dime on the output line. Slide the cardboard strip until it begins to tip. Mark the balance line. Label it *Fulcrum 1.*

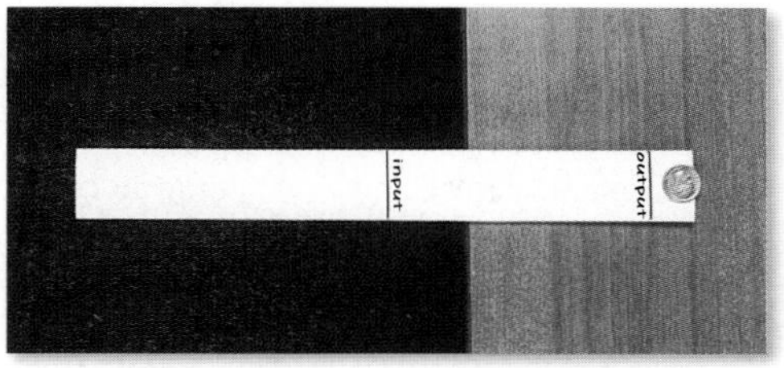

6. **Measure** the lengths of the output and input arms to the nearest 0.1 cm.
7. Calculate the *IMA* of the lever. Multiply the *IMA* by the mass of the lever to find the approximate mass of the coin.
8. Repeat steps 5 through 7 with the nickel and the quarter. Mark the fulcrum line *Fulcrum 2* for the nickel and *Fulcrum 3* for the quarter.

Conclude and Apply

1. **Explain** why there might be a difference between the mass of each coin measured by the balance and the mass measured using the lever.
2. **Explain** what provides the input and output forces for the lever.
3. **Explain** why the *IMA* of the lever changes as the mass of the coin changes.

Communicating Your Data

Compare your results with those of other students in your class. **For more help, refer to the Science Skill Handbook.**

BENCH TESTED

Real-World Problem

Purpose Students calculate the mechanical advantage of levers. L1 LS **Logical-Mathematical**

Process Skills measure, use numbers, interpret data, classify, observe and infer, compare and contrast, recognize cause and effect, form operational definitions, interpret scientific illustrations

Time Required 40 minutes

Procedure

Teaching Strategies

- Be sure students understand how to use a balance to accurately get a mass of their coin.
- Some students may need help labeling their strips of cardboard.

Conclude and Apply

1. There will be some experimental error in this process.
2. The input force is the weight of the coin. The output force is the weight of the cardboard extended over the edge of the table.
3. because the input force changes with the changes in the weights of the coins

Communicating Your Data

Have students use graphics software to draw diagrams that explain the lab and illustrate their results.

Assessment

Oral Evaluate student understanding of the lever design by having them explain to the class how they performed the calculations. Use **Performance Assessment in the Science Classroom,** p. 101.

BENCH TESTED

Real-World Problem

Purpose Students will make models of different simple machines to lift a weight and compare the forces used. L2 COOP LEARN LS **Kinesthetic**

Process Skills observe, use numbers, communicate, measure, infer, compare and contrast, recognize cause and effect, interpret data, formulate models, make and use tables

Time Required one class period

Materials The block and tackle can be difficult to set up unless the pulleys and string sizes are matched. The pulleys should be made for block and tackle use. The small pulleys typically available from hardware stores will work, but can be difficult to handle as they don't usually have the needed fastening points on both top and bottom. Be sure to arrange the double pulley and single pulley as illustrated.

Safety Precautions Be sure students wear eye protection for this lab.

LAB **Model and Invent**

Using Simple Machines

Goals

- **Model** lifting devices based on a block and tackle and on an inclined plane.
- **Calculate** the output work that will be accomplished.
- **Measure** the force needed by each machine to lift a weight.
- **Calculate** the input work and efficiency for each model machine.
- **Select** the best machine for your job based on the force required.

Possible Materials

spring scale, 0–10 N range
9.8-N weight (1-kg mass)
double pulley
single pulley
string for the pulleys
stand or support for the pulleys
wooden board, 40 cm long
support for board, 10 cm high

Safety Precautions

Real-World Problem

Suppose that you are the contractor on a one-story building with a large air conditioner. How can you get the air conditioner to the roof? How can you minimize the force needed to lift an object? What machines could you use? Consider a fixed pulley, a block and tackle system of pulleys, and an inclined plane. How can you find the efficiency of machines?

Make a Model

1. Work in teams of at least two. **Collect** all the needed equipment.
2. Sketch a model for each lifting machine. Include a control in which the weight is lifted while being suspended directly from the spring scale. **Model** the inclined plane with a board 40-cm long and raised 10 cm at one end.
3. Make a data table like the one below.
4. Is the pulley support high enough that the block and tackle can lift a weight 10 cm?
5. Obtain your teacher's approval of your sketches and data table before proceeding.

Problem Data

	Control	Inclined Plane	Block and Tackle
Ideal Mechanical Advantage, *IMA*	1	4	3
Input force, F_{in}, N	Will vary	Will vary	Will vary
Input distance, d_{in}, m	0.10	0.40	0.30
Output force, F_{out}, N	9.8	9.8	9.8
Output distance, d_{out}, m	0.10	0.10	0.10
$Work_{in} = F_{in}\, d_{in}$, Joules	Will vary	Will vary	Will vary
$Work_{out} = F_{out}\, d_{out}$, Joules	0.98	0.98	0.98
$Efficiency = (Work_{out}/Work_{in}) \times 100\%$	Will vary	Will vary	Will vary

Using Scientific Methods

Test Your Model

1. Tie the weight to the spring scale and measure the force required to lift it. Record the input force in your data table under *Control,* along with the 10-cm input distance.
2. Assemble the inclined plane so that the weight can be pulled up the ramp at a constant rate. The 40-cm board should be supported so that one end is 10 cm higher than the other end.
3. Tie the string to the spring scale and measure the force required to move the weight up the ramp at a constant speed. Record this input force under *Inclined Plane* in your data table. Record 40 cm as the input distance for the inclined plane.
4. Assemble the block and tackle using one fixed double pulley and one movable single pulley.
5. Tie the weight to the single pulley and tie the spring scale to the string at the top of the upper double pulley.
6. **Measure** the force required to lift the weight with the block and tackle. Record this input force.
7. **Measure** the length of string that must be pulled to raise the weight 10 cm. Record this input distance.

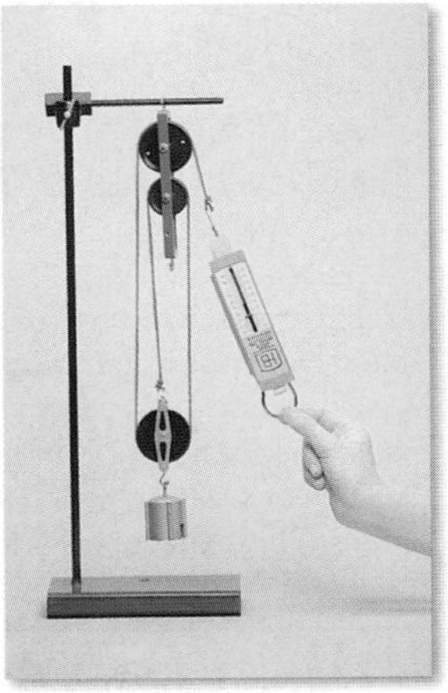

Analyze Your Data

1. **Calculate** the output work for all three methods of lifting the 9.8-N weight a distance of 10 cm.
2. **Calculate** the input work and the efficiency for the control, the inclined plane, and the block and tackle.
3. **Compare** the efficiencies of each of the three methods of lifting.

Conclude and Apply

1. **Explain** how you might improve the efficiency of the machine in each case.
2. **Infer** what types of situations would require the use of a ramp over a pulley to help lift something.
3. **Infer** which machines would be most likely to be affected by friction.

Communicating Your Data

Make a poster showing how the best machine would be used to lift the air conditioner to the roof of the building.

Make a Model

Possible Procedures If you don't have double pulleys, you can tie the string on the single pulley, as shown, and loop the string over a horizontal bar, then around the moveable pulley and then around the bar again instead.

Teaching Strategy Teams of two will be required to simplify assembly of apparatus and measurements.

Troubleshooting When students pull on the weight using the spring scale, make sure they pull slowly, smoothly, and at constant speed. Jerky pulling will lead to the use of unnecessarily large forces.

Test Your Model

Expected Outcome Students will build models of three simple machines and use them to model lifting an air conditioner to a roof. L2

Analyze Your Data

1. Output work is the same for all three, 0.98 J.
2. Answers will vary.
3. The block and tackle require the lowest force. The reason for the efficiency difference is probably the difference in the friction between the ramp and the block and tackle.

Conclude and Apply

1. You could improve both by lubricating the ramp and the pulleys.
2. Answers will vary.
3. Answers will vary. A slick ramp will be less affected by friction than a rusty pulley. A well-oiled pulley will work better than a rough-surfaced ramp.

Assessment

Process Have students make bar graphs of the different amounts of force used and work done using each machine. Use **Performance Assessment in the Science Classroom,** p. 111. L2

Communicating Your Data

Have students compare their posters. Did they all agree on the best machine? Display student posters in the classroom. L2

TIME

Content Background

The current vision of nanotechnology and its possible uses was discussed in a book by Dr. K. Eric Drexler in 1986. He envisioned the precise construction of advanced materials from chemically pure ingredients, eliminating the toxic byproducts of conventional manufacturing. The long-term goals for molecular manufacturing range from ultra-small computers and space construction to the alleviation of disease, hunger and pollution. As developments increase at a rapid pace, many questions arise concerning the possible use and misuse of the new technology.

Discussion

Nanobots What would be the advantage of having nanobots perform medical tasks now done by drugs or surgery? Possible answer: By acting on a cell-by-cell basis nanobots can avoid damaging healthy cells and reduce recovery time. L2 LS **Logical-Mathematical**

Activity

Precision drawing Divide the class into groups of three or four. Assign a word to each group. Each group will use four different ways to spell out the word using sand on black paper, each time making the word as small as possible. The first time students put on gloves, the second time they will use their bare fingers to move the sand. For the third time, have them use an implement such as a craft stick to move the sand to make the word, and finally, provide students with tweezers and a magnifying glass. Ask students to compare their smallest word with 500 nanometers. L2 LS **Kinesthetic**

TIME SCIENCE AND Society

SCIENCE ISSUES THAT AFFECT YOU!

The Science of very, very small

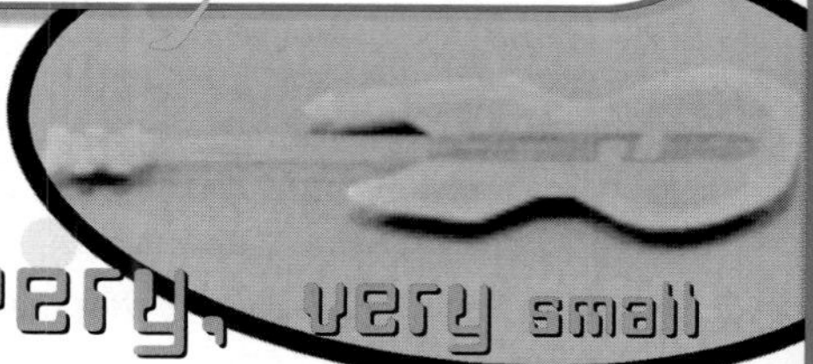

This is the smallest guitar in the world. It is about as big as a human white blood cell. Each of its six silicon strings is 100 atoms wide. You can see the guitar only with an electron microscope.

Imagine an army of tiny robots, each no bigger than a bacterium swimming through your bloodstream.

Welcome to the world of nanotechnology, the science of creating molecular-sized machines. These machines are called nanobots.

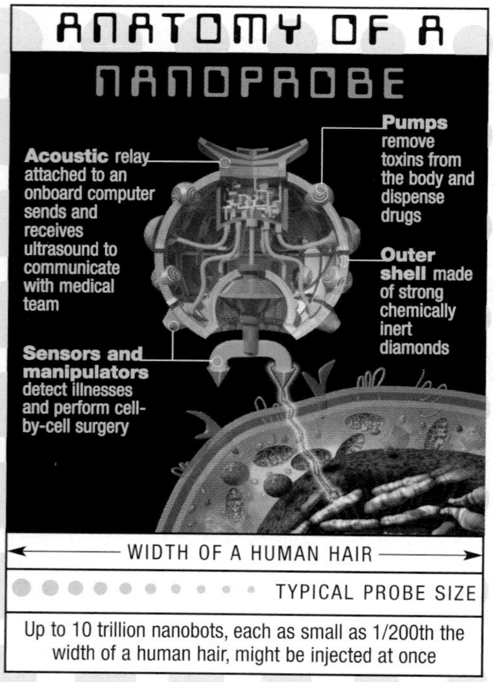

Up to 10 trillion nanobots, each as small as 1/200th the width of a human hair, might be injected at once

The smallest of these machines are only billionths of a meter in size. They are so tiny that they can do work on the molecular scale.

Small, Smaller, Smallest

Nanotechnologists are predicting that within a few decades they will be creating nanobots that can do just about anything, as long as it's small. Already, nanotechnologists have built gears 10,000 times thinner than a human hair. They've also built tiny molecular "motors" only 50 atoms long. At Cornell University, nanotechnologists created the world's smallest guitar. It is appoximately the size of a white blood cell and it even has six strings.

In the future, nanobots might transmit your internal vital signs to a nanocomputer implanted under your skin. There the data could be analyzed for signs of disease. Other nanomachines then could be sent to scrub your arteries clean of dangerous blockages, or mop up cancer cells, or even vaporize blood clots with tiny lasers. These are just some of the possibilities in the imaginations of those studying the new science of nanotechnology.

Design **Think up a very small simple or complex machine that could go inside the body and do something. What would the machine do? Where would it go? Share your diagram or design with your classmates.**

TIME
For more information, visit gpescience.com

Design Provide time for students to give short presentations of their designs to the class. Ask each student to describe why the tiny machine would do the job better than current technology.

Resources for Teachers and Students

Engines of Creation by K. Eric Drexler, Garden City, N.Y.: Anchor Press/Doubleday, 1986

Nanotechnology: A Gentle Introduction to the Next Big Idea by Mark Ratner, Prentice Hall PTR, 2003

Reviewing Main Ideas

Section 1 Work

1. Work is the energy transferred when a force makes an object move.
2. Work is done only when a force produces motion in the direction of the force.
3. Power is the amount of work, or the amount of energy transferred, in a certain amount of time.

Section 2 Using Machines

1. A machine makes work easier by changing the size of the force applied, by increasing the distance an object is moved, or by changing the direction of the applied force.

2. The number of times a machine multiplies the force applied to it is the mechanical advantage of the machine. The actual mechanical advantage is always less than the ideal mechanical advantage.
3. The efficiency of a machine equals the output work divided by the input work.
4. Friction always causes the output work to be less than the input work, so no real machine can be 100 percent efficient.

Section 3 Simple Machines

1. A simple machine is a machine that can do work with a single movement.
2. A simple machine can increase an applied force, change its direction, or both.
3. A lever is a bar that is free to pivot about a fixed point called a fulcrum. A pulley is a grooved wheel with a rope running along the groove. A wheel and axle consists of two different-sized wheels that rotate together. An inclined plane is a sloping surface used to raise objects. The screw and the wedge are special types of inclined planes.
4. A combination of two or more simple machines is called a compound machine.

FOLDABLES Use the Foldable that you made at the beginning of this chapter to help you review how machines make doing work easier.

chapter 6 Study Guide

Reviewing Main Ideas

Summary statements can be used by students to review the major concepts of the chapter.

Science Online

Visit gpescience.com
More Section Review
Interactive Tutor
Vocabulary PuzzleMaker
More Chapter Review
Standardized Test Practice

Assessment Transparency

For additional assessment questions, use the *Assessment Transparency* located in the transparency book.

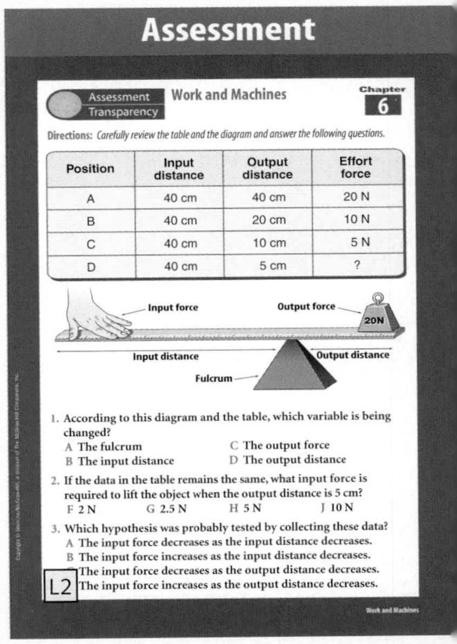

Assessment

Assessment Transparency — Work and Machines — Chapter 6

Directions: *Carefully review the table and the diagram and answer the following questions.*

Position	Input distance	Output distance	Effort force
A	40 cm	40 cm	20 N
B	40 cm	20 cm	10 N
C	40 cm	10 cm	5 N
D	40 cm	5 cm	?

1. According to this diagram and the table, which variable is being changed?
   A The fulcrum
   B The input distance
   C The output force
   D The output distance
2. If the data in the table remains the same, what input force is required to lift the object when the output distance is 5 cm?
   F 2 N G 2.5 N H 5 N J 10 N
3. Which hypothesis was probably tested by collecting these data?
   A The input force decreases as the input distance decreases.
   B The input force increases as the input distance decreases.
   C The input force decreases as the output distance decreases.
   D The input force increases as the output distance decreases.

L2

Work and Machines

Identifying Misconceptions

Assess

After students have done the activity on page F and completed the chapter, have them answer the following question.

Julio lifted a box onto a desk. Joshua pushed an identical box up an inclined plane onto the desk. Friction on the inclined plane opposes Joshua's push. Which boy probably used more force in lifting the boxes? Julio Which boy did more work? They did about the same amount of work.

Expected Outcome Students will see that simple machines may reduce the amount of force exerted; but not the work done. L2

FOLDABLES Have students use their Foldables to review the content of the chapter. Ask them to think of ways to improve the efficiency of the work they do without machines.

Using Vocabulary

1. compound machine
2. inclined plane
3. mechanical advantage
4. pulley
5. output force
6. work
7. Power

Checking Concepts

8. B
9. B
10. A
11. D
12. C
13. A
14. B
15. D

Interpreting Graphics

16. See student page.
17. B
18. $F_{out} = 1.3 \times 50\ \text{N} = 65\ \text{N}$

Using Vocabulary

compound machine p. 174
efficiency p. 164
inclined plane p. 172
input force p. 162
lever p. 166
machine p. 160
mechanical advantage p. 164
output force p. 162
power p. 157
pulley p. 169
screw p. 173
simple machine p. 166
wedge p. 173
wheel and axle p. 171
work p. 154

Complete each statement using a word(s) from the vocabulary list above.

1. A combination of two or more simple machines is a(n) _________.
2. A wedge is another form of a(n) _________.
3. The ratio of the output force to the input force is the _________ of a machine.
4. A(n) _________ is a grooved wheel with a rope, chain, or cable in the groove.
5. The force exerted by a machine is the _________.
6. Energy is transferred when _________ is done.
7. _________ is the rate at which work is done or energy is transferred.

Checking Concepts

Choose the word or phrase that best answers the question.

8. Which of these is not done by a machine?
   A) multiply force
   B) multiply energy
   C) change direction of a force
   D) work
9. Which of the following increases as the efficiency of a machine increases?
   A) work input
   B) work output
   C) friction
   D) *IMA*
10. In an ideal machine, which of the following is true?
    A) Work input is equal to work output.
    B) Work input is greater than work output.
    C) Work input is less than work output.
    D) The *IMA* is always equal to one.

Use the picture below to answer question 11.

11. What simple machines make up a pair of scissors?
    A) lever and pulley
    B) pulley and wheel and axle
    C) wedge and pulley
    D) wedge and lever
12. What term indicates the number of times a machine multiplies the input force?
    A) efficiency
    B) power
    C) mechanical advantage
    D) resistance
13. How could you increase the *IMA* of an inclined plane?
    A) increase its length
    B) increase its height
    C) decrease its length
    D) make its surface smoother
14. What is the *IMA* of a screwdriver with a shaft radius of 3 mm and a handle radius of 10 mm?
    A) 0.3
    B) 3.3
    C) 30
    D) 13
15. What is the *IMA* of an inclined plane that is 2.1 m long and 0.7 m high?
    A) 0.3
    B) 2.8
    C) 1.5
    D) 3.0

Vocabulary PuzzleMaker gpescience.com

Interpreting Graphics

16. Copy and complete the concept map of simple machines using the following terms: *compound machines, mechanical advantage, output force, work.*

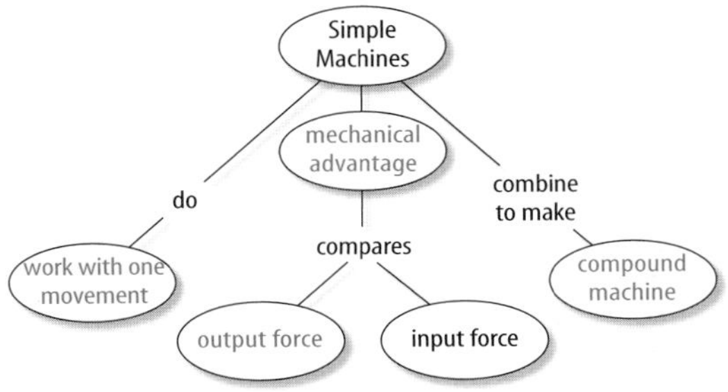

Use the table below to answer questions 17 and 18.

Lever Input and Output Arms

Lever	Input Arm (cm)	Output Arm (cm)
A	25	75
B	53	42
C	36	36
D	32	99
E	10	30

17. Determine which of the levers listed in the table above has the largest *IMA*.

18. Calculate An input force of 50 N is applied to lever B. If the lever is 100 percent efficient, what is the output force?

Thinking Critically

19. Describe how the input force, output force, and fulcrum should be arranged so that a child can lift an adult using his own body weight on a seesaw.

20. Determine what arrangement of movable and fixed pulleys would give a mechanical advantage of 3.

21. Explain which would give the best mechanical advantage for driving a screw down into a board: a screwdriver with a long, thin handle, or a screwdriver with a short, thick handle.

Applying Math

22. Calculate Work Find the work needed to lift a 20.0-N book 2.0 m.

23. Calculate Axle Radius A doorknob has an *IMA* equal to 8.5. If the diameter of the doorknob is 8.0 cm, what is the radius of the shaft the doorknob is connected to?

24. Calculate Input Work A machine has an efficiency of 61 percent. Find the input work if the output work is 140 J.

25. Calculate Efficiency Using a ramp 6 m long, workers apply an input force of 1,250 N to move a 2,000-N crate onto a platform 2 m high. What is the efficiency of the ramp?

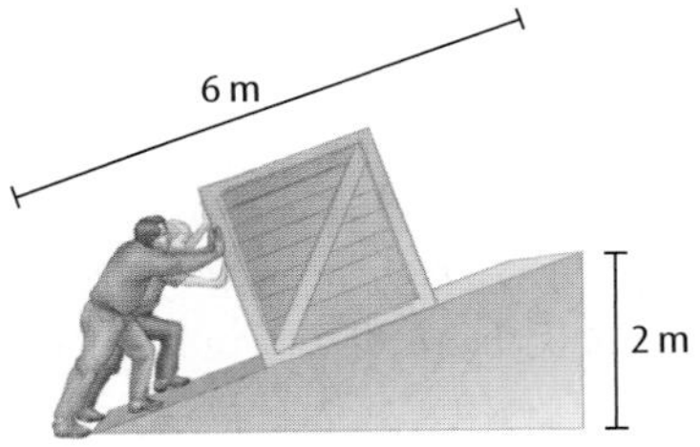

26. Calculate Power A person weighing 500 N climbs 3 m. How much power is needed to make the climb in 5 s?

Thinking Critically

19. The fulcrum should be moved toward the adult to increase the length of the input arm of the child's lever. This will multiply the input force exerted by the child.

20. A fixed double pulley with a moveable single will give $MA = 3$. Tie the string to the moveable pulley and loop it first through the lower pulley on the fixed double pulley, then through the single, moveable, and finally over the top double pulley. This gives three supporting strings.

21. The one with the fat handle; the screwdriver is being used as a wheel and axle, with the handle acting as the wheel. The screwdriver with the fat handle will therefore have a greater *MA*. The length does not matter.

Applying Math

Math Standards

National: 1, 2, 9

22. 40 J
23. 0.47 cm
24. 230 J
25. 53%
26. 300 W

Assessment Resources

Reproducible Masters

Chapter *Fast File* Resources
Chapter Review, pp. 39–40
Chapter Tests, pp. 41–44
Assessment Transparency Activity, p. 51

Glencoe Science Web site
Chapter Review Test
Standardized Test Practice

Glencoe Technology

Assessment Transparency
Exam*View*® Pro Testmaker
MindJogger Videoquiz
Interactive Chalkboard

Answer Sheet An answer sheet can be found at **gpescience.com**.

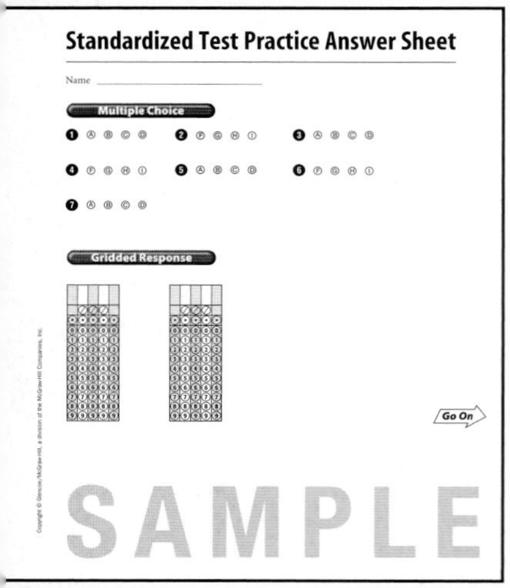

Multiple Choice

1. B
2. B
3. C
4. D
5. D
6. C

Gridded Response

7. 23N
8. 1.9 J

chapter 6 Standardized Test Practice

Record your answers on the answer sheet provided by your teacher or on a sheet of paper.

Multiple Choice

Use the figure below to answer questions 1 and 2.

1. The figure above shows a doorknob with a radius of 4.8 cm and a mechanical advantage of 4.0. What is the radius of the inner rod that connects the knob to the door?

A. 0.6 cm
B. 1.2 cm
C. 1.8 cm
D. 2.4 cm

2. What would happen to the mechanical advantage if the radius of the doorknob were doubled?

A. It would be multiplied by 4.
B. It would be multiplied by 2.
C. It would be divided by 4.
D. It would be divided by 2.

3. A ramp is 2.8 m long and 1.2 m high. How much power is needed to push a box up the ramp in 4.6 s with a force of 96 N?

A. 21 W
B. 25 W
C. 58 W
D. 270 W

4. How much work is done in lifting a 9.10-kg box onto a shelf 1.80 m high?

A. 5.06 J
B. 16.4 J
C. 49.5 J
D. 161 J

5. An input force of 80 N is used to lift an object weighing 240 N with a system of pulleys. How far down must the rope around the pulleys be pulled to lift the object a distance of 1.4 m?

A. 0.47 m
B. 1.4 m
C. 2.8 m
D. 4.2 m

Use the figure below to answer questions 6 and 7.

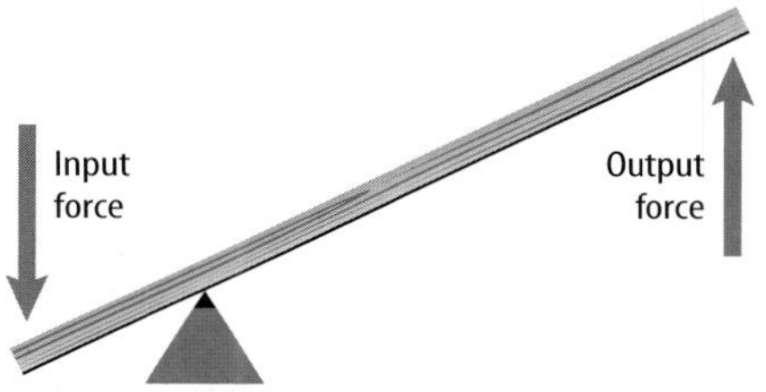

6. If a lever's input arm is 8 cm and its output arm is 24 cm, what is the ideal mechanical advantage of the lever?

A. 4
B. 3
C. 0.33
D. 0.25

Short Response

9. 4
10. 5 N

Gridded Response

7. How much more work is done to push a box 2.5 m with a force of 30 N than to push a box 2.0 m with a force of 26 N?

8. As you throw a ball, you exert a force of 4.2 N on the ball. You exert this force on the ball while the ball moves a distance of 0.45 m. The ball leaves your hand and travels a horizontal distance of 8.5 m to your friend. How much work have you done on the ball?

Short Response

Use the illustration below to answer questions 9 and 10.

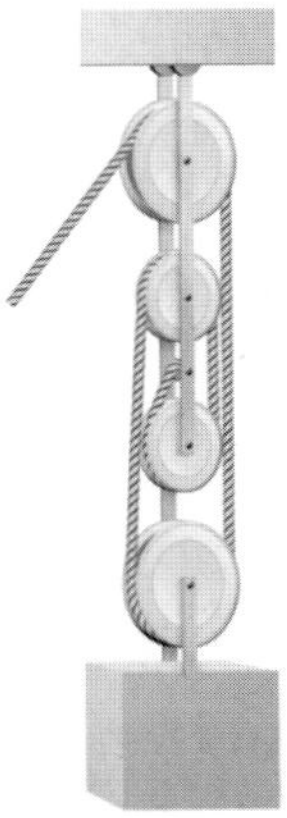

9. What is the ideal mechanical advantage of the pulley system shown in the figure above?

10. If the block supported by the pulley system has a weight of 20 N, what is the input force on the rope?

Extended Response

11. Use the law of conservation of energy to explain why it is impossible for the output work of a machine to be greater than the machine's input work.

Use the illustration below to answer question 12.

12. The boy in the figure below is carrying a box to the top of the stairs.

PART A Describe how the work that the boy does on the box is related to the energy transfer that occurs. How does the energy of the box change form as the boy carries the box up the stairs?

PART B Explain how the work, power, and energy would change if the boy walked faster. How would the work, power, and energy change if the steps were the same height but steeper?

Test-Taking Tip

Don't Panic Stay calm during the test. If you feel yourself getting nervous, close your eyes and take five slow, deep breaths.

11. When work is done on the machine, energy is transferred to the machine. When the machine does work, energy is transferred from the machine. If energy cannot be created, then the output work cannot be greater than the input work.

12. Part A. The chemical energy from the boy's muscles is converted to potential energy of the box. The potential energy of the box increases as the boy increases the height of the box.

12. Part B. Work would be the same. Power would increase because the time required to do the work decreased. The energy change of the box would be the same.

Rubrics

For more help evaluating Short- and Extended-Response questions, see the rubrics on p. 9T.

Section/Objectives	Standards		Lab/Features
	National	State/Local	
Chapter Opener	See pp. 16T–17T for a Key to Standards.		**Launch Lab:** Relative Sizes of Earth, the Moon, and the Sun, p. 185 **Foldables,** p. 185
Section 1 Earth in Space 1 session .5 block 1. **Compare and contrast** Earth's physical characteristics with those of other planets. 2. **Explain** Earth's magnetic field. 3. **Describe** Earth's movement in space and how eclipses occur.	National Content Standards: UCP.1-3, UCP.5, A.1, A.2, D.1, D.3		**Science Online,** p.187 **Integrate Physics,** p. 188
Section 2 Time and Seasons 2 sessions 1 block 4. **Calculate** the time and date in different time zones. 5. **Differentiate** between revolution and rotation. 6. **Discuss** what causes seasons to change.	National Content Standards: UCP.1-3, UCP.5, A.1, A.2		**MiniLAB:** Modeling the Sun's Rays at Solstice, p. 195 **Lab:** Comparing the Angle of Sunlight to Intensity, p. 196
Section 3 Earth's Moon 3 sessions 1.5 blocks 7. **Describe** how tides on Earth are caused by the Moon. 8. **Explain** how the Moon's phases depend on the relative positions of the Sun, the Moon, and Earth. 9. **Compare and contrast** solor and lunar eclipses. 10. **Analyze** what surface features of the Moon reveal about its history.	National Content Standards: UCP.1-5, A.1, A.2, D.3, D.4		**Applying Math,** Tides, p. 198 **MiniLAB:** Modeling Phases and Eclipses, p. 200 Video Lab **Integrate History,** p. 201 **Science Online,** p. 204 **Visualizing Water on the Moon,** p. 205 **Lab:** Identifying the Moon's Surface Features and *Apollo* Landing Sites, pp. 208–209 **Oops! Accidents in Science:** Even Great Scientists Make Mistakes,p. 210

Lab Materials	Reproducible Resources	Section Assessment	Technology
Launch Lab: chalk, meterstick	**Chapter *Fast File* Resources** Foldables Worksheet, p. 17 Note-taking Worksheets, pp. 33–35 Directed Reading Overview, p. 19	Glencoe's Assessment Advantage	TeacherWorks includes: • Interactive Teacher Edition • Lesson Planner with calendar • Access to all program blacklines • Correlations to standards • Web links
Need materials? Contact Science Kit at 1-800-828-7777 or www.sciencekit.com.	**Chapter *Fast File* Resources** Transparency Activity, p. 44 Enrichment, p. 30 Reinforcement, p. 27 Directed Reading, p. 20 Lab Activity, pp. 9–11 **Home and Community Involvement,** p. 36	Portfolio Check for Understanding, p. 189 Performance Applying Math, p. 189 Content Section Review, p. 189	Section Focus Transparency Interactive Chalkboard CD-ROM StudentWorks Plus
MiniLAB: globe, flashlight or gooseneck lamp **Lab:** 75-W gooseneck lamp, alcohol thermometers (2), two sheets of a single color of construction paper, protractor	**Chapter *Fast File* Resources** Transparency Activity, p. 45 MiniLAB, p. 3 Enrichment, p. 31 Reinforcement, p. 28 Directed Reading, p. 20 Lab Worksheet, pp. 5–6 **Cultural Diversity,** p. 29	Portfolio Check for Understanding, p. 195 Performance Applying Math, p. 195 Content Section Review, p. 195	Section Focus Transparency Interactive Chalkboard CD-ROM StudentWorks Plus
MiniLAB: lamp with no shade; small, white, plastic-foam ball; pencil **Lab:** large-scale maps or globes of the Moon; individual, smaller maps of the Moon	**Chapter *Fast File* Resources** Transparency Activity, p. 46 MiniLAB, p. 4 Enrichment, p. 32 Reinforcement, p. 29 Directed Reading, pp. 21–22 Transparency Activity, pp. 47–48 Lab Worksheet, pp. 7–8 Lab Activity, pp. 13–15 **Laboratory Management and Safety,** p. 66	Performance Applying Math, p. 198 MiniLAB, p. 200 Applying Math, p. 207 Content Section Review, p. 207	Section Focus Transparency Teaching Transparency Interactive Chalkboard CD-ROM StudentWorks Plus Video Lab

End of Chapter Assessment

Glencoe's Assessment Advantage

Blackline Masters	Technology	Professional Series
Chapter *Fast File* Resources Chapter Review, pp. 37–38 Chapter Test, pp. 39–42 **Standardized Test Practice,** pp. 32–35	MindJogger Videoquiz Exam*View*® Pro Testmaker TeacherWorks CD-ROM Interactive Chalkboard CD-ROM	**Performance Assessment in the Science Classroom (PASC)**

The Earth-Moon-Sun System

Transparencies

Section Focus

SECTION 1 Section Focus Transparency **Aurora B. Moves South** Chapter 7

Most of the time, the aurora borealis, shown below, can only be seen by people located close to or within the Arctic Circle. Occasionally, people located further south can experience these curtains or ribbons of lights. The lights are created when charged particles that are spiraling along the Earth's magnetic field lines (see inset) bump into particles in the Earth's atmosphere, emitting various colors of light.

1. When do you think the aurora borealis can be seen by people located south of the Arctic Circle?
2. What would happen to solar winds if Earth did not have a magnetic field around it?

L2

SECTION 2 Section Focus Transparency **Sunny Side Up** Chapter 7

To take advantage of the nonstop energy provided by the Sun, some utility companies have developed solar power plants, like the one shown below. These plants rely on solar panels that are precisely oriented to capture as much of the Sun's energy as possible at any given time of the year.

1. In which direction would the panels need to face if located in the northern hemisphere? The southern hemisphere?
2. How would panels in the northern hemisphere need to be adjusted during the year to capture as much of the Sun's energy as possible?

L2

SECTION 3 Section Focus Transparency **High Highs and Low Lows** Chapter 7

Boaters all over the world must pay attention to the tides to safety navigate into and out of harbors and around dangerous underwater rocks and sandbars, among other hazards. They particularly need to pay attention to the positions of the Sun and the Moon in relation to Earth, which create more extreme tidal levels.

1. What is a spring tide and how do meteorologists know one will occur?
2. What is a neap tide and when does it occur?

L2

This is a representation of key blackline masters available in the Teacher Classroom Resources. See Resource Manager boxes within the chapter for additional information.

Assessment

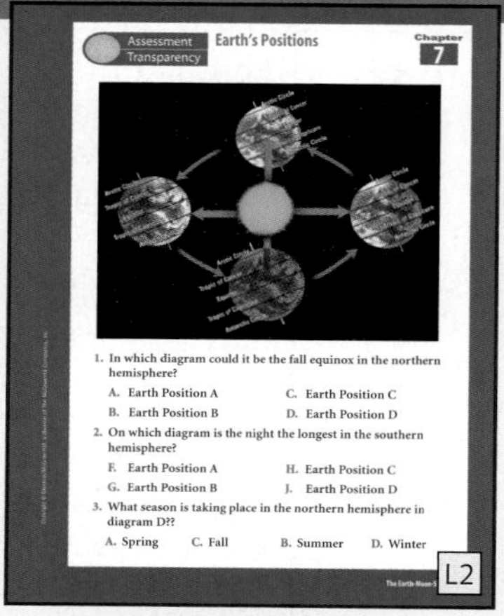
Assessment Transparency **Earth's Positions** Chapter 7

1. In which diagram could it be the fall equinox in the northern hemisphere?
   A. Earth Position A C. Earth Position C
   B. Earth Position B D. Earth Position D
2. On which diagram is the night the longest in the southern hemisphere?
   F. Earth Position A H. Earth Position C
   G. Earth Position B J. Earth Position D
3. What season is taking place in the northern hemisphere in diagram D??
   A. Spring C. Fall B. Summer D. Winter

L2

Teaching

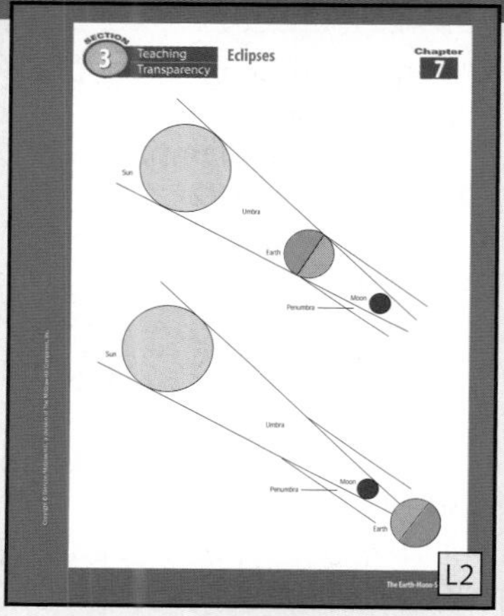
SECTION 3 Teaching Transparency **Eclipses** Chapter 7

L2

Key to Teaching Strategies

The following designations will help you decide which activities are appropriate for your students.

- L1 Level 1 activities should be appropriate for students with learning difficulties.
- L2 Level 2 activities should be within the ability range of all students.
- L3 Level 3 activities are designed for above-average students.
- ELL ELL activities should be within the ability range of English Language Learners.
- COOP LEARN Cooperative Learning activities are designed for small group work.
- LS Multiple Learning Styles logos, as described on page 12T, are used throughout to indicate strategies that address different learning styles.
- P These strategies represent student products that can be placed into a best-work portfolio.
- PBL Problem-Based Learning activities apply real-world situations to learning.

Hands-on Activities

Student Text Lab Worksheet

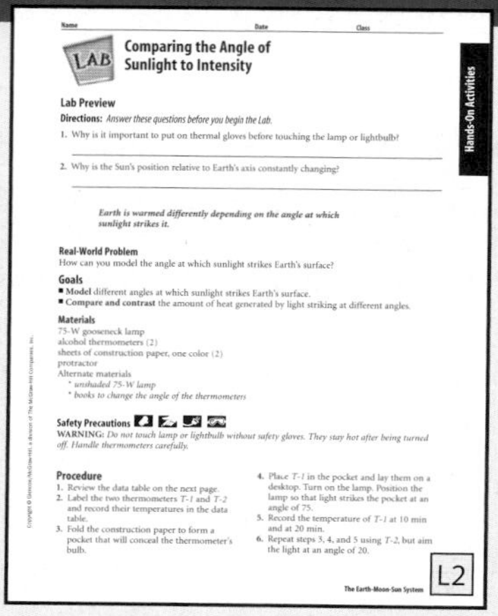
Name Date Class

LAB **Comparing the Angle of Sunlight to Intensity**

Hands-On Activities

Lab Preview

Directions: *Answer these questions before you begin the Lab.*

1. Why is it important to put on thermal gloves before touching the lamp or lightbulb?
2. Why is the Sun's position relative to Earth's axis constantly changing?

Earth is warmed differently depending on the angle at which sunlight strikes it.

Real-World Problem
How can you model the angle at which sunlight strikes Earth's surface?

Goals
- **Model** different angles at which sunlight strikes Earth's surface.
- **Compare and contrast** the amount of heat generated by light striking at different angles.

Materials
75-W gooseneck lamp
alcohol thermometers (2)
sheets of construction paper, one color (2)
protractor
Alternate materials
* *unshaded 75-W lamp*
* *books to change the angle of the thermometers*

Safety Precautions
WARNING: *Do not touch lamp or lightbulb without safety gloves. They stay hot after being turned off. Handle thermometers carefully.*

Procedure
1. Review the data table on the next page.
2. Label the two thermometers *T-1* and *T-2* and record their temperatures in the data table.
3. Fold the construction paper to form a pocket that will conceal the thermometer's bulb.
4. Place *T-1* in the pocket and lay them on a desktop. Turn on the lamp. Position the lamp so that light strikes the pocket at an angle of 75.
5. Record the temperature of *T-1* at 10 min and at 20 min.
6. Repeat steps 3, 4, and 5 using *T-2*, but aim the light at an angle of 20.

The Earth-Moon-Sun System L2

Laboratory Activities

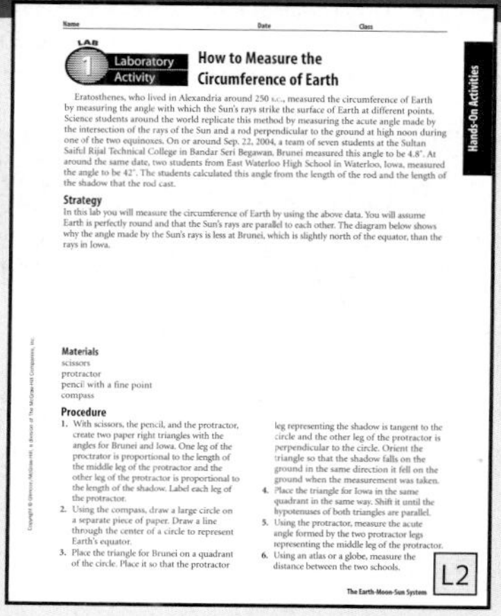
Name Date Class

LAB 1 Laboratory Activity **How to Measure the Circumference of Earth**

Hands-On Activities

Eratosthenes, who lived in Alexandria around 250 B.C., measured the circumference of Earth by measuring the angle with which the Sun's rays strike the surface of Earth at different points. Science students around the world replicate this method by measuring the acute angle made by the intersection of the rays of the Sun and a rod perpendicular to the ground at high noon during one of the two equinoxes. On or around Sep. 22, 2004, a team of seven students at the Sultan Saiful Rijal Technical College in Bandar Seri Begawan, Brunei measured this angle to be 4.8°. At around the same date, two students from East Waterloo High School in Waterloo, Iowa, measured the angle to be 42°. The students calculated this angle from the length of the rod and the length of the shadow that the rod cast.

Strategy
In this lab you will measure the circumference of Earth by using the above data. You will assume Earth is perfectly round and that the Sun's rays are parallel to each other. The diagram below shows why the angle made by the Sun's rays is less at Brunei, which is slightly north of the equator, than the rays in Iowa.

Materials
scissors
protractor
pencil with a fine point
compass

Procedure
1. With scissors, the pencil, and the protractor, create two paper right triangles with the angles for Brunei and Iowa. One leg of the proctrator is proportional to the length of the middle leg of the protractor and the other leg of the protractor is proportional to the length of the shadow. Label each leg of the protractor.
2. Using the compass, draw a large circle on a separate piece of paper. Draw a line through the center of a circle to represent Earth's equator.
3. Place the triangle for Brunei on a quadrant of the circle. Place it so that the protractor leg representing the shadow is tangent to the circle and the other leg of the protractor is perpendicular to the circle. Orient the triangle so that the shadow falls on the ground in the same direction it fell on the ground when the measurement was taken.
4. Place the triangle for Iowa in the same quadrant in the same way. Shift it until the hypotenuses of both triangles are parallel.
5. Using the protractor, measure the acute angle formed by the two protractor legs representing the middle leg of the protractor.
6. Using an atlas or a globe, measure the distance between the two schools.

The Earth-Moon-Sun System L2

Meeting Different Ability Levels

Content Outline

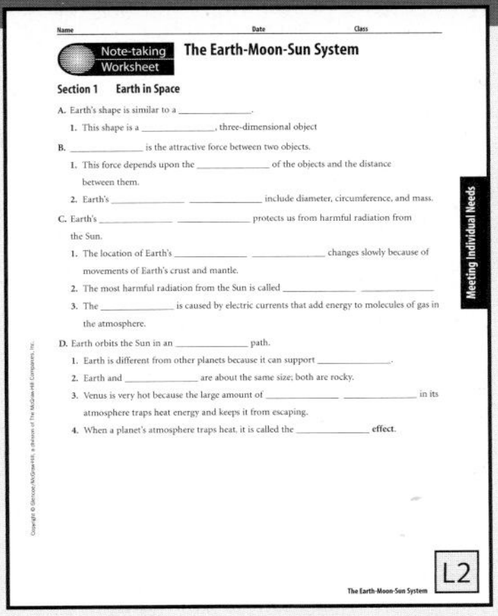
Name Date Class

Note-taking Worksheet — The Earth-Moon-Sun System

Section 1 Earth in Space

A. Earth's shape is similar to a ______________.
1. This shape is a ______________, three-dimensional object
B. ______________ is the attractive force between two objects.
1. This force depends upon the ______________ of the objects and the distance between them.
2. Earth's ______________ ______________ include diameter, circumference, and mass.
C. Earth's ______________ ______________ protects us from harmful radiation from the Sun.
1. The location of Earth's ______________ ______________ changes slowly because of movements of Earth's crust and mantle.
2. The most harmful radiation from the Sun is called ______________ ______________
3. The ______________ is caused by electric currents that add energy to molecules of gas in the atmosphere.
D. Earth orbits the Sun in an ______________ path.
1. Earth is different from other planets because it can support ______________.
2. Earth and ______________ are about the same size; both are rocky.
3. Venus is very hot because the large amount of ______________ ______________ in its atmosphere traps heat energy and keeps it from escaping.
4. When a planet's atmosphere traps heat, it is called the ______________ effect.

Meeting Individual Needs

The Earth-Moon-Sun System

L2

Reinforcement

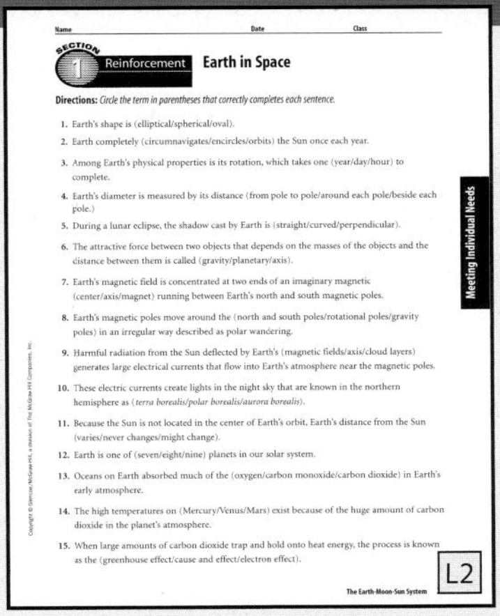
Name Date Class

Section 1 Reinforcement — Earth in Space

Directions: Circle the term in parentheses that correctly completes each sentence.

1. Earth's shape is (elliptical/spherical/oval).
2. Earth completely (circumnavigates/encircles/orbits) the Sun once each year.
3. Among Earth's physical properties is its rotation, which takes one (year/day/hour) to complete.
4. Earth's diameter is measured by its distance (from pole to pole/around each pole/beside each pole.)
5. During a lunar eclipse, the shadow cast by Earth is (straight/curved/perpendicular).
6. The attractive force between two objects that depends on the masses of the objects and the distance between them is called (gravity/planetary/axis).
7. Earth's magnetic field is concentrated at two ends of an imaginary magnetic (center/axis/magnet) running between Earth's north and south magnetic poles.
8. Earth's magnetic poles move around the (north and south poles/rotational poles/gravity poles) in an irregular way described as polar wandering.
9. Harmful radiation from the Sun deflected by Earth's (magnetic fields/axis/cloud layers) generates large electrical currents that flow into Earth's atmosphere near the magnetic poles.
10. These electric currents create lights in the night sky that are known in the northern hemisphere as (*terra borealis/polar borealis/aurora borealis*).
11. Because the Sun is not located in the center of Earth's orbit, Earth's distance from the Sun (varies/never changes/might change).
12. Earth is one of (seven/eight/nine) planets in our solar system.
13. Oceans on Earth absorbed much of the (oxygen/carbon monoxide/carbon dioxide) in Earth's early atmosphere.
14. The high temperatures on (Mercury/Venus/Mars) exist because of the huge amount of carbon dioxide in the planet's atmosphere.
15. When large amounts of carbon dioxide trap and hold onto heat energy, the process is known as the (greenhouse effect/cause and effect/electron effect).

Meeting Individual Needs

The Earth-Moon-Sun System

L2

Enrichment

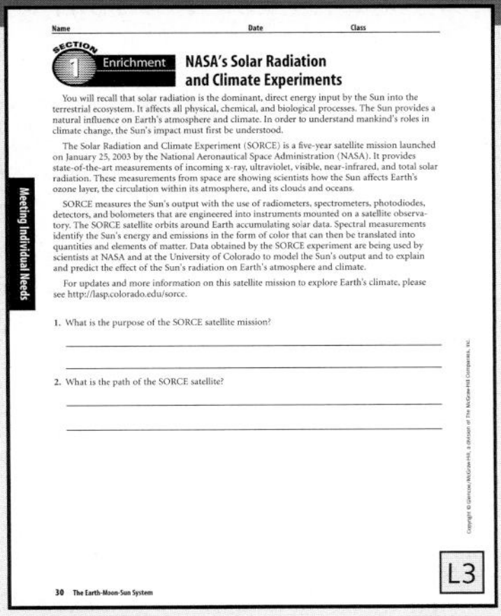
Name Date Class

Section 1 Enrichment — NASA's Solar Radiation and Climate Experiments

You will recall that solar radiation is the dominant, direct energy input by the Sun into the terrestrial ecosystem. It affects all physical, chemical, and biological processes. The Sun provides a natural influence on Earth's atmosphere and climate. In order to understand mankind's roles in climate change, the Sun's impact must first be understood.

The Solar Radiation and Climate Experiment (SORCE) is a five-year satellite mission launched on January 25, 2003 by the National Aeronautical Space Administration (NASA). It provides state-of-the-art measurements of incoming x-ray, ultraviolet, visible, near-infrared, and total solar radiation. These measurements from space are showing scientists how the Sun affects Earth's ozone layer, the circulation within its atmosphere, and its clouds and oceans.

SORCE measures the Sun's output with the use of radiometers, spectrometers, photodiodes, detectors, and bolometers that are engineered into instruments mounted on a satellite observatory. The SORCE satellite orbits around Earth accumulating solar data. Spectral measurements identify the Sun's energy and emissions in the form of color that can then be translated into quantities and elements of matter. Data obtained by the SORCE experiment are being used by scientists at NASA and at the University of Colorado to model the Sun's output and to explain and predict the effect of the Sun's radiation on Earth's atmosphere and climate.

For updates and more information on this satellite mission to explore Earth's climate, please see http://lasp.colorado.edu/sorce.

1. What is the purpose of the SORCE satellite mission?
2. What is the path of the SORCE satellite?

Meeting Individual Needs

30 The Earth-Moon-Sun System

L3

Directed Reading (English/Spanish)

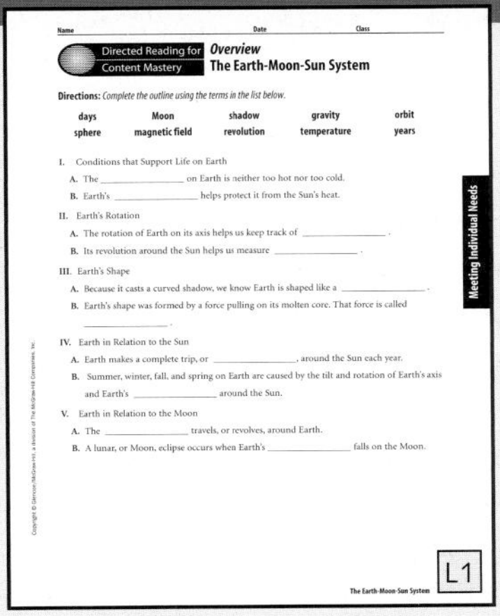
Name Date Class

Directed Reading for Content Mastery — *Overview* The Earth-Moon-Sun System

Directions: Complete the outline using the terms in the list below.

days	Moon	shadow	gravity	orbit
sphere	magnetic field	revolution	temperature	years

I. Conditions that Support Life on Earth
A. The ______________ on Earth is neither too hot nor too cold.
B. Earth's ______________ helps protect it from the Sun's heat.
II. Earth's Rotation
A. The rotation of Earth on its axis helps us keep track of ______________.
B. Its revolution around the Sun helps us measure ______________.
III. Earth's Shape
A. Because it casts a curved shadow, we know Earth is shaped like a ______________.
B. Earth's shape was formed by a force pulling on its molten core. That force is called ______________.
IV. Earth in Relation to the Sun
A. Earth makes a complete trip, or ______________, around the Sun each year.
B. Summer, winter, fall, and spring on Earth are caused by the tilt and rotation of Earth's axis and Earth's ______________ around the Sun.
V. Earth in Relation to the Moon
A. The ______________ travels, or revolves, around Earth.
B. A lunar, or Moon, eclipse occurs when Earth's ______________ falls on the Moon.

Meeting Individual Needs

The Earth-Moon-Sun System

L1

Study Guide

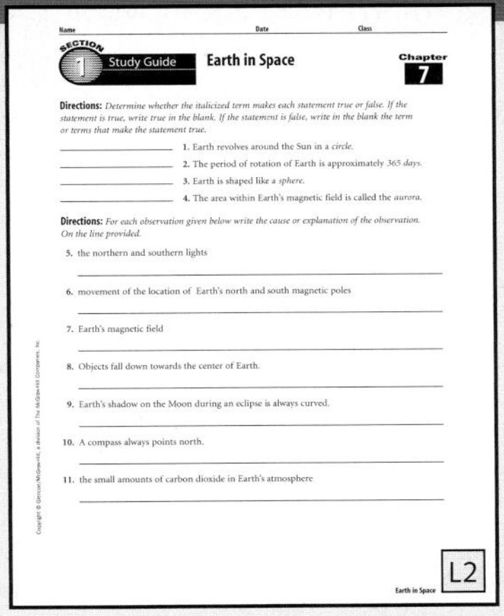
Name Date Class

Section 1 Study Guide — Earth in Space — Chapter 7

Directions: Determine whether the italicized term makes each statement true or false. If the statement is true, write true in the blank. If the statement is false, write in the blank the term or terms that make the statement true.

1. Earth revolves around the Sun in a *circle*.
2. The period of rotation of Earth is approximately *365 days*.
3. Earth is shaped like a *sphere*.
4. The area within Earth's magnetic field is called the *aurora*.

Directions: For each observation given below write the cause or explanation of the observation. On the line provided.

5. the northern and southern lights
6. movement of the location of Earth's north and south magnetic poles
7. Earth's magnetic field
8. Objects fall down towards the center of Earth.
9. Earth's shadow on the Moon during an eclipse is always curved.
10. A compass always points north.
11. the small amounts of carbon dioxide in Earth's atmosphere

Earth in Space

L2

Reading Essentials

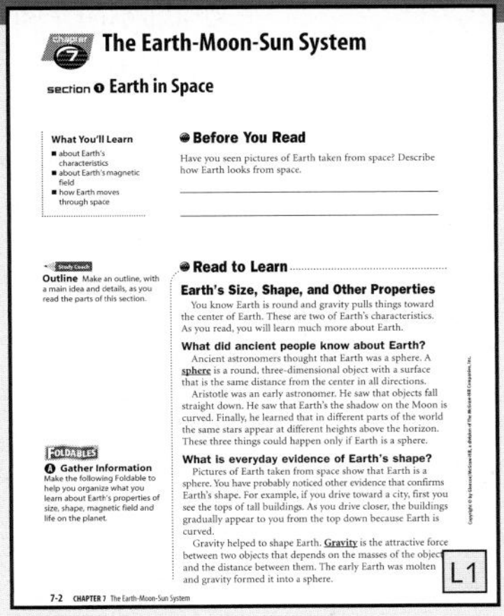
chapter 7 — The Earth-Moon-Sun System

section 1 Earth in Space

What You'll Learn
- about Earth's characteristics
- about Earth's magnetic field
- how Earth moves through space

Before You Read

Have you seen pictures of Earth taken from space? Describe how Earth looks from space.

Study Coach

Outline Make an outline, with a main idea and details, as you read the parts of this section.

Read to Learn

Earth's Size, Shape, and Other Properties

You know Earth is round and gravity pulls things toward the center of Earth. These are two of Earth's characteristics. As you read, you will learn much more about Earth.

What did ancient people know about Earth?

Ancient astronomers thought that Earth was a sphere. A **sphere** is a round, three-dimensional object with a surface that is the same distance from the center in all directions.

Aristotle was an early astronomer. He saw that objects fall straight down. He saw that Earth's shadow on the Moon is curved. Finally, he learned that in different parts of the world the same stars appear at different heights above the horizon. These three things could happen only if Earth is a sphere.

FOLDABLES

A Gather Information Make the following Foldable to help you organize what you learn about Earth's properties of size, shape, magnetic field and life on the planet.

What is everyday evidence of Earth's shape?

Pictures of Earth taken from space show that Earth is a sphere. You have probably noticed other evidence that confirms Earth's shape. For example, if you drive toward a city, first you see the tops of tall buildings. As you drive closer, the buildings gradually appear to you from the top down because Earth is curved.

Gravity helped to shape Earth. **Gravity** is the attractive force between two objects that depends on the masses of the objects and the distance between them. The early Earth was molten and gravity formed it into a sphere.

7-2 CHAPTER 7 The Earth-Moon-Sun System

L1

Assessment

Test Practice Workbook

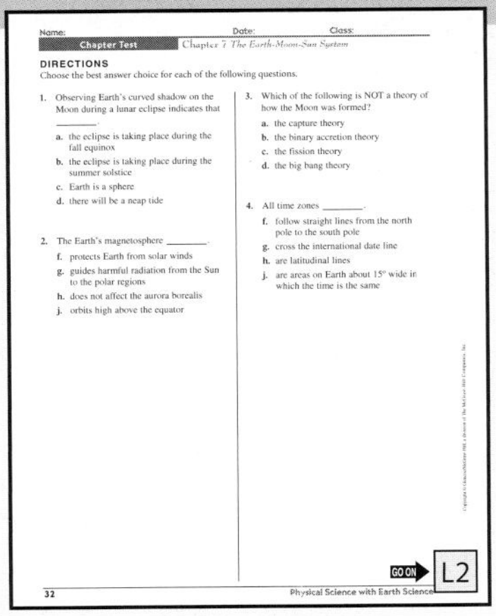
Name: Date: Class:

Chapter Test — Chapter 7 The Earth-Moon-Sun System

DIRECTIONS

Choose the best answer choice for each of the following questions.

1. Observing Earth's curved shadow on the Moon during a lunar eclipse indicates that ______.
a. the eclipse is taking place during the fall equinox
b. the eclipse is taking place during the summer solstice
c. Earth is a sphere
d. there will be a neap tide

2. The Earth's magnetosphere ______.
f. protects Earth from solar winds
g. guides harmful radiation from the Sun to the polar regions
h. does not affect the aurora borealis
j. orbits high above the equator

3. Which of the following is NOT a theory of how the Moon was formed?
a. the capture theory
b. the binary accretion theory
c. the fission theory
d. the big bang theory

4. All time zones ______.
f. follow straight lines from the north pole to the south pole
g. cross the international date line
h. are latitudinal lines
j. are areas on Earth about 15° wide in which the time is the same

32 Physical Science with Earth Science

GO ON

L2

Chapter Review

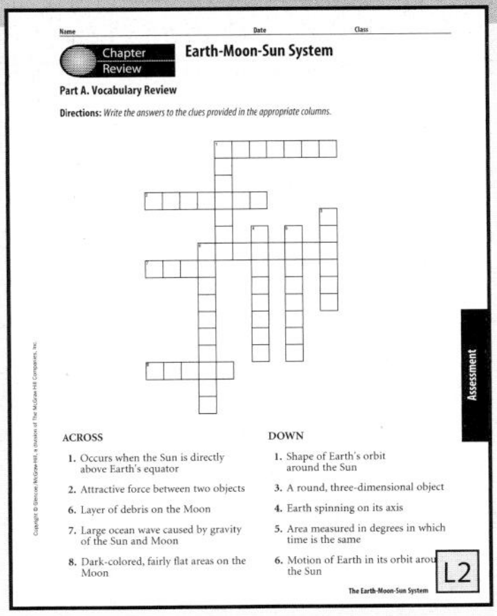
Name Date Class

Chapter Review — Earth-Moon-Sun System

Part A. Vocabulary Review

Directions: Write the answers to the clues provided in the appropriate columns.

ACROSS
1. Occurs when the Sun is directly above Earth's equator
2. Attractive force between two objects
6. Layer of debris on the Moon
7. Large ocean wave caused by gravity of the Sun and Moon
8. Dark-colored, fairly flat areas on the Moon

DOWN
1. Shape of Earth's orbit around the Sun
3. A round, three-dimensional object
4. Earth spinning on its axis
5. Area measured in degrees in which time is the same
6. Motion of Earth in its orbit around the Sun

Assessment

The Earth-Moon-Sun System

L2

Chapter Tests

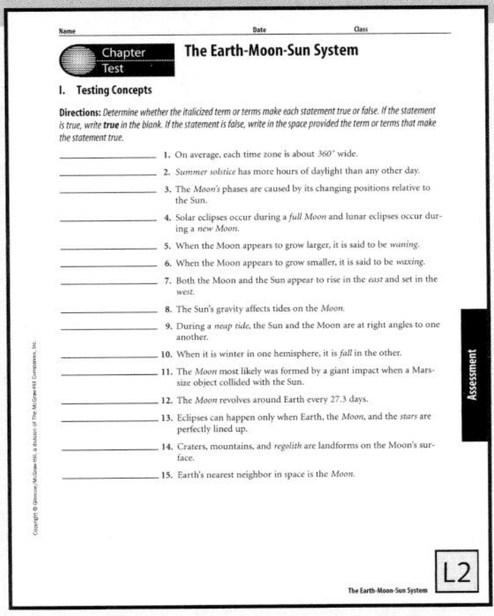
Name Date Class

Chapter Test — The Earth-Moon-Sun System

I. Testing Concepts

Directions: Determine whether the italicized term or terms make each statement true or false. If the statement is true, write true in the blank. If the statement is false, write in the space provided the term or terms that make the statement true.

1. On average, each time zone is about *360°* wide.
2. *Summer solstice* has more hours of daylight than any other day.
3. The *Moon's* phases are caused by its changing positions relative to the Sun.
4. Solar eclipses occur during a *full Moon* and lunar eclipses occur during a new *Moon*.
5. When the Moon appears to grow larger, it is said to be *waning*.
6. When the Moon appears to grow smaller, it is said to be *waxing*.
7. Both the Moon and the Sun appear to rise in the *east* and set in the west.
8. The Sun's gravity affects tides on the *Moon*.
9. During a *neap tide*, the Sun and the Moon are at right angles to one another.
10. When it is winter in one hemisphere, it is *fall* in the other.
11. The *Moon* most likely was formed by a giant impact when a Mars-size object collided with the Sun.
12. The *Moon* revolves around Earth every 27.3 days.
13. Eclipses can happen only when Earth, the *Moon*, and the *stars* are perfectly lined up.
14. Craters, mountains, and *regolith* are landforms on the Moon's surface.
15. Earth's nearest neighbor in space is the *Moon*.

Assessment

The Earth-Moon-Sun System

L2

Science Content Background

section 1 Earth in Space

Earth's Magnetic Field

Convection currents of molten iron deep in Earth's core, along with Earth's rotation, produce huge electrical currents. These electrical currents cause Earth's magnetic field.

The orientation of the direction of Earth's magnetic field changes periodically over time. In the past, the direction of Earth's magnetic field has been north-south, as it is now. At other times, the direction has been south-north. This is one bit of evidence supporting the theories of sea-floor spreading and plate tectonics.

Recent evidence suggests that Earth's inner, solid core is rotating slightly faster than the rest of the planet. The rate of increase is such that the inner core completes one extra quarter turn in 100 years. In fact, the orientation of Earth's solid inner core has shifted about 20 km during the past 30 years, equivalent to a motion that is a million times faster than the motion of continents at Earth's surface due to plate tectonics.

A better understanding of the outer core-inner core boundary will help scientists understand how the inner core is growing as Earth cools, how the outer core continues to solidify, and how the interaction of these two layers helps to produce Earth's magnetic field.

section 2 Time and Seasons

Why do seasons change?

Earth's seasons result from the fact that Earth always tilts in the same direction as it revolves around the Sun. This constant tilt of 23.5 degrees means that sunlight strikes different locations on Earth at different angles throughout the year, and that there are more hours of daylight in some areas, and fewer hours of daylight in others.

section 3 Earth's Moon

Craters, Maria, and Mountains

About 3.9 billion years ago, large meteorites created huge impact basins on the Moon's surface. By 3.2 billion years ago, lava flows had filled in these impact basins forming the large, relatively flat, dark maria seen today. Craters have formed on the maria and other areas of the Moon's surface since, but its surface looks much as it did 3.2 billion years ago. Fewer maria formed on the Moon's far side because the crust is thicker on that side, making it harder for lava to reach the surface.

chapter content resources

Internet Resources

For additional content background, visit **gpescience.com** to:

- access online college-level textbooks
- find references to related articles in popular science magazines
- access Web links with related content background
- access current events with science journal topics

Print Resources

A+ Projects in Astronomy, Janice VanCleave, John Wiley & sons, 2002.

Astronomy—Journey to the Cosmic Frontier, John D. Fix, McGraw-Hill Companies, 2004.

Foundations of Astronomy, Michael A. Seeds, Brooks/Cole—Thomson Learning Inc., 2005

IDENTIFYING Misconceptions

Find Out What Students Think

Students may think that...

- **Sunlight strikes Earth indirectly at some times during the year, causing seasonal changes.**

A common misconception is that the sunlight that falls on Earth during the summer is more direct than the sunlight that falls on Earth during other seasons. In reality, the Sun's rays that strike Earth are always direct, no matter what season it is. This misconception comes about because of the misuse of the word *direct*.

Discussion

Organize the class into groups, and have them work together to define the words *direct* and *indirect* as they are used in other subjects. Possible answer: When the bus takes the most direct route to school, it travels on only one street. However, when it takes an indirect route, it travels down several side streets on its way to school. Similarly, the Sun's rays follow a straight line.

Promote Understanding

Demonstration

Have two students help with the demonstration. Provide each student with a meterstick and chalk.

- Shine light from the overhead projector perpendicularly on the chalkboard. Have one student measure the length and width of the lighted square and ask students to calculate the area of the lighted square.
- Shine light from the overhead projector so that it strikes the chalkboard at 45°. Have another student measure the length and width of this rectangular area of light. Have students calculate the area of the lighted rectangle.
- Ask students to compare the areas of the two lighted areas. Emphasize that light from the projector covered more area when striking the chalkboard at the lower angle. Relate this to the fact that light from the Sun covers a larger area when striking Earth's surface at angles other than vertical. Thus, Earth's surface receives less light and heat per unit area.

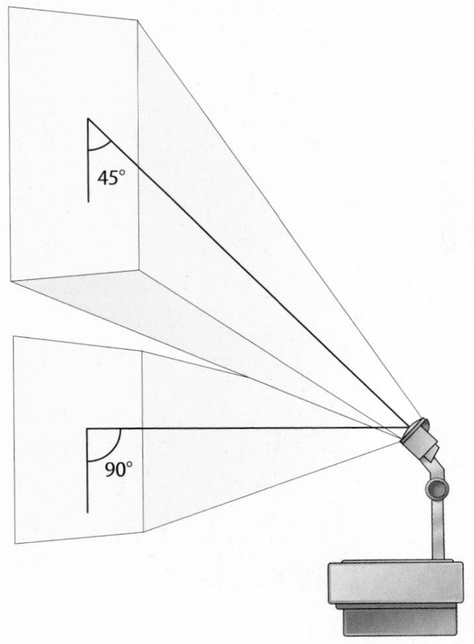

Assess

After completing the chapter, see *Identifying Misconceptions* in the Study Guide at the end of the chapter.

chapter 7

Chapter Vocabulary

sphere, p. 186
gravity, p. 187
ellipse, p. 188
time zone, p. 190
rotation, p. 192
revolution, p. 192
ecliptic, p. 192
equinox, p. 195
solstice, p. 195
tide, p. 199
moon phase, p. 199
solar eclipse, p. 201
lunar eclipse, p. 202
maria, p. 203
regolith, p. 203

Science Journal The Moon's influence on tides is well-known. Some scientists also suspect that the Moon's gravity might influence a slight flexing of tectonic plates and trigger some earthquakes.

INTERACTIVE CHALKBOARD with Image Bank

PowerPoint® Presentations

This CD-ROM is an editable Microsoft® PowerPoint® presentation that includes:

- a pre-made presentation for every chapter
- interactive graphics
- animations
- audio clips
- image bank
- all new section and chapter questions
- Standardized Test Practice
- transparencies
- Foldables directions
- links to gpescience.com

chapter 7

The Earth-Moon-Sun System

chapter preview

sections

Are there tides in a desert?

Did you know the Moon exerts gravitational force on Earth? On Earth, the Moon's gravitational attraction is evidenced as tides in oceans and seas. Even in the desert, the Moon's gravity influences the flexing of tectonic plates.

Science Journal Research to discover what landforms or events are affected by the Moon's gravitational force on Earth.

Theme Connection

Systems and Interactions The day-night cycle on Earth and its seasons are caused by Earth's rotation and revolution. Interactions among the Earth-Moon-Sun system set up conditions that produce the different phases of the Moon and eclipses of the Sun and the Moon. Tides on Earth also are produced by interactions among the Earth-Moon-Sun system.

About the Photo

Swaying Cactus? You can watch tides come and go under swaying palms along the beach. But, this saguaro cactus stands motionless under a crescent moon in Kofa National Wildlife Refuge in Arizona. Scientists study the Earth-Moon-Sun system to discover possible effects on plate tectonics. It is unknown whether the Moon's gravitational influence triggers some earthquakes.

Start-Up Activities

Launch LAB

Relative Sizes of Earth, the Moon, and the Sun

Can you picture the relative sizes of Earth, the Moon, and the Sun? Earth is about four times larger than the Moon in diameter, but the Sun is much larger than either. The Sun's diameter is about 100 times that of Earth and about 400 times that of the Moon. In this Lab, you'll investigate the relative sizes of all three objects.

1. Get permission to draw some circles on a sidewalk or paved area with chalk. You could also use a stick to draw circles on a dirt playing field.
2. Select a scale that will enable you to draw circles that will represent each object. *Hint: Using 1 cm for the Moon's diameter is a good start.*
3. Use a meterstick to draw a circle with a 1-cm diameter for the Moon.
4. Now draw two more circles to represent Earth and the Sun.
5. **Think Critically** In your Science Journal, explain how the Moon and the Sun can appear to be about the same size in the sky. Think about how things look smaller the farther they are from you.

FOLDABLES™ Study Organizer

Earth, Sun, and Moon Make the following Foldable to help organize what you learn about the Earth-Moon-Sun system.

STEP 1 **Fold** a sheet of paper vertically from side to side. Make the front edge about $\frac{1}{2}$ inch longer than the back edge.

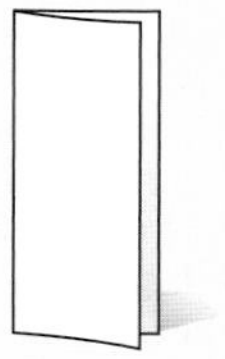

STEP 2 **Turn** lengthwise and fold into thirds.

STEP 3 **Unfold** and cut only the top layer along both folds to make three tabs.

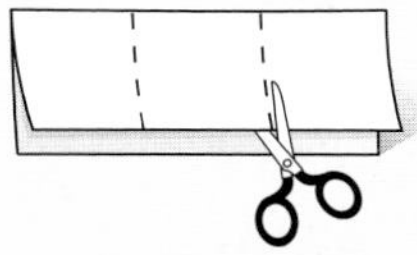

STEP 4 **Label** each tab.

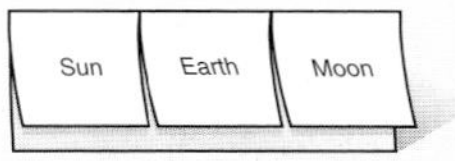

Questions As you read the chapter, write what you learn about each body under the correct tab of your Foldable. After you read the chapter, note the many ways that the three affect each other.

Science Online | Preview this chapter's content and activities at gpescience.com

Launch LAB

Purpose Use this Launch Lab to introduce students to the relative sizes of Earth, the Moon, and the Sun. Students will model the relative sizes of these bodies. L2

Preparation Locate a sidewalk or other paved area for the lab and obtain permission to draw on it with chalk.

Materials chalk, meterstick, metric ruler

Alternate Materials stick

Teaching Strategy Encourage students to select a size for the Moon. If no one does, or if the size selected is too large, suggest a 1-cm radius for the Moon.

Troubleshooting Draw the representative circles ahead of time to be sure all will fit on the section of sidewalk that is selected.

Safety Precautions

- Select a site near the school that is away from traffic.
- Caution students to be on the lookout for cars that might cross the sidewalk.

Think Critically

The Moon can appear the same size as the Sun because it is much closer. Tell students that the Sun is about 400 times farther from Earth than the Moon. Ask them how much larger the Sun must be. about 400 times

Assessment

Process Students can model the relative positions and sizes of the Moon and Sun by closing one eye and using their thumbs to block their view of a classmate. The thumb can completely block the view of a classmate if it is held close enough.

FOLDABLES™ Study Organizer **Dinah Zike Study Fold**

Student preparation materials for this Foldable are available in the **Chapter *Fast File* Resources.**

section 1

Earth in Space

Reading Guide

What You'll Learn

- **Compare and contrast** Earth's physical characteristics with those of other planets.
- **Explain** Earth's magnetic field.
- **Describe** Earth's movement in space and how eclipses occur.

Why It's Important

Gravity from the Earth-Moon-Sun system directly affects what it's like to live here on Earth.

Review Vocabulary

orbit: curved path of one object, such as the Moon, around another object, such as Earth

New Vocabulary

- sphere
- ellipse
- gravity

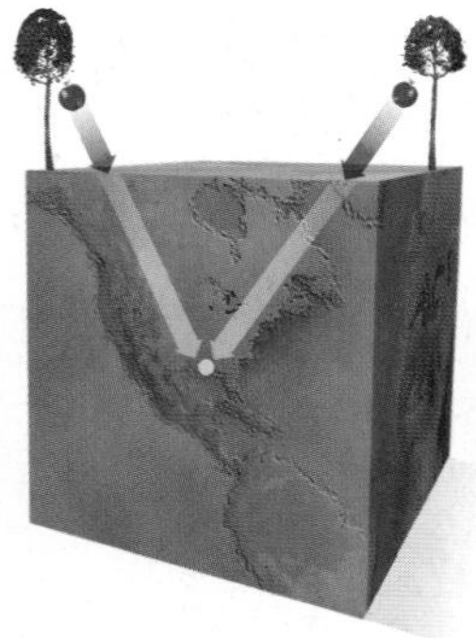

Figure 1 Objects fall toward Earth's center.
Infer *How would apples fall from trees if Earth were shaped like a cube?*

Earth's Size and Shape

Like most people, you are aware that Earth is round like a ball. But can you prove that this is true? If you jump up, you know that you'll come back down, but why is this so? What is the force that brings you down? You may have used a compass to tell directions, but do you know how a compass works? You will learn the answers to these questions and also about many physical characteristics of Earth in this section.

Ancient Measurements Earth's shape is similar to a sphere. A **sphere** is a round, three-dimensional object, the surface of which is the same distance from the center in all directions. Even ancient astronomers knew that Earth is spherical in shape. We have pictures of Earth from space that show us that it is spherical, but how could astronomers from long ago have learned this? They used evidence from observations.

Aristotle was one of these early astronomers. He made three different observations that indicated that Earth's shape is spherical. First, as shown in **Figure 1,** no matter where you are on Earth, objects fall straight down to the surface, as if they are falling toward the center of a sphere. Second, Earth's shadow on the Moon during a lunar eclipse is always curved. If Earth weren't spherical, this might not always be the case. For example, a flat disk casts a straight-edged shadow sometimes. Finally, people in different parts of the world see different stars above their horizons. More specifically, the pole star Polaris is lower in the sky at some locations on Earth than at others.

1 Motivate

An editable Microsoft® PowerPoint® presentation is available on **Interactive Chalkboard** CD-ROM.

Bellringer

Section Focus Transparencies also are available on the Interactive Chalkboard CD-ROM. L2 ELL

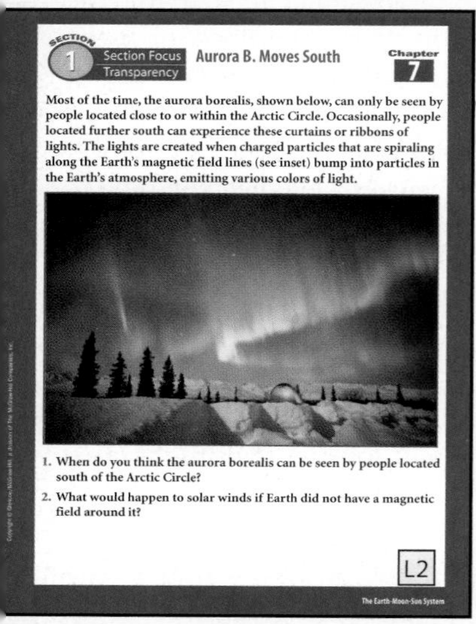

SECTION 1 Section Focus Transparency — Aurora B. Moves South — Chapter 7

Most of the time, the aurora borealis, shown below, can only be seen by people located close to or within the Arctic Circle. Occasionally, people located further south can experience these curtains or ribbons of lights. The lights are created when charged particles that are spiraling along the Earth's magnetic field lines (see inset) bump into particles in the Earth's atmosphere, emitting various colors of light.

1. When do you think the aurora borealis can be seen by people located south of the Arctic Circle?
2. What would happen to solar winds if Earth did not have a magnetic field around it?

L2

The Earth-Moon-Sun System

Reading Preview

Tie to Prior Knowledge
Earth's Unique Properties Tell students that every planet in the solar system has unique physical properties. Ask students to brainstorm about unique properties of Earth that make it possible for life to exist. Start them out by writing, "Earth has oceans" on the board. Accept other student responses. L2

Predict The new vocabulary words for this section may be familiar to students in an everyday sense. Ask students to share what they know about each word with a partner. Then have students seek out the physics definition in the text.

Section 1 Resource Manager

Chapter *Fast File* Resources

Note-taking Worksheet, pp. 33–35
Transparency Activity, p. 44
Enrichment, p. 30
Reinforcement, p 27
Directed Reading for Content Mastery, pp. 19, 20
Lab Activity, pp. 9–11

Home and Community Involvement, p. 36

Reading and Writing Skills Activities, pp. 11–12

Everyday Evidence of Earth's Shape What have you seen, other than pictures from space, that indicates Earth's shape? Think about walking toward someone over a hill. First, you see the top of the person's head, and then you can see more and more of that person. Similarly, if you sail toward a lighthouse, you first see the top of the lighthouse and then see more and more of it as you move over Earth's curved surface.

You can see other evidence, too. Just like ancient astronomers, you can see for yourself that objects always fall straight down. Today, however, we know more about gravity. **Gravity** is the attractive force between two objects that depends on the masses of the objects and the distance between them. Astronomers think Earth formed by the accumulation of infalling objects toward a central mass. Energy released in the impacts kept the growing Earth molten. Gravity caused it to form into the most stable shape, a sphere. In this shape, the pull of gravity toward the center of the planet is the same in all directions. If a planet is massive enough, the pull of gravity could be so strong that even tall mountains would collapse under their own weight. **Table 1** lists some of Earth's other properties.

Reading Check *How does the pull of gravity indicate that Earth's shape is spherical?*

Science Online

Topic: Comparing Earth to Other Planets

Visit gpescience.com for Web links to information about how Earth is similar to and different from other planets in the solar system.

Activity Make a table that lists the similarities and differences of Mercury, Venus, Earth, and Mars.

Table 1 Earth's Physical Properties

Diameter (pole to pole)	12,714 km
Diameter (through equator)	12,756 km
Circumference (poles)	40,008 km
Circumference (equator)	40,075 km
Mass	5.98×10^{24} kg
Average density	5.52 g/cm^3
Average distance to the Sun	149,600,000 km
Average distance to the Moon	384,400 km
Period of rotation	23 h, 56 min
Period of revolution	365 days, 6 h, 9 min

2 Teach

Caption Answer

Figure 1 at an angle

Reading Check

Answer All objects affected by Earth's gravity tend to fall toward the center of the planet.

Quick Demo

Earth's Shadow is Round

Materials Earth globe, jar lid, 2 flashlights

Estimated Time 5 minutes

Procedure Have one student hold a globe or large ball about 3 m from the wall. Have another student hold the jar lid at the same distance. Shine the flashlights on both the Earth globe and on the jar lid so the shadows fall on the wall. Have the students slowly rotate the globe and the jar lid. Which object always casts a round shadow, no matter how it is held? the globe

Visual Learning

Table 1 Ask students to explain how they can tell Earth is not a perfect sphere from the information presented in **Table 1.** Students should note that measurements of Earth's diameter and circumference are different if measured at the poles or at the equator. They should explain that a perfect sphere would have the same measurements in each direction.

Reading Strategy

Causal Relationships Have students identify cause and effect relationships for concepts in this section. For instance, gravity may have caused objects in space to pull together and eventually form the spherical shape that earth possesses. Another idea might involve earth's magnetic field causing the auroras.

Cultural Diversity

Arab Astronomers After about 620 A.D. the Islamic religion spread from Arabia into Egypt, Mesopotamia (Iraq), and Syria. In this religion, it is necessary to have accurate readings of time and direction to follow the Koran concerning daily prayer and worship. Astronomy was crucial to the teachings of Islam. A very useful handbook of astronomical tables, called the *Zij*, was developed in Baghdad, and this city became the first major center of Islamic science. Persian poet Omar Khayyam was also an astronomer and mathematician who corrected the Islamic calendar. Have students research the history and importance of contributions of Arab astronomers to the study of astronomy during the Renaissance. When Constantinople fell, eastern scholars headed to Europe carrying knowledge that helped begin the European Renaissance after the Dark Ages.

INTEGRATE Physics

Van Allen Belts Earth's magnetosphere traps charged particles of the solar wind from the Sun, thus protecting Earth's surface. The magnetosphere contains two belts of high-energy, charged particles, the Van Allen belts—one lies about 3,000 km and the other about 20,000 km above Earth's surface.

Research Are the Van Allen belts hazardous to humans? Possible answer: The highly charged particles in the Van Allen belts are hazardous to humans and must be shielded to protect astronauts. Without shielding, living organisms and delicate instruments would be subjected to high energy discharge if they come in contact with the charged particles. For this reason, the *International Space Station* is located below the Van Allen belts.

Caption Answer

Figure 2 The shapes follow Earth's magnetic field lines.

Discussion

Planet Earth Remind students that Earth has many forms of life. **What characteristics of Earth make it possible for life to exist?** Possible answer: Earth's atmosphere moderates temperatures and provides oxygen to breathe. L2

INTEGRATE Physics

Van Allen Belts The magnetosphere lies above the outer layers of Earth's atmosphere. Within this magnetosphere are belts of charged particles known as the Van Allen belts. They contain thin plasma composed of protons (inner belt) and electrons (outer belt) that are trapped by Earth's magnetic field. Research how the magnetosphere protects Earth from the solar wind and why the Van Allen belts are hazardous to astronauts and satellites. Report your findings to the class.

Earth's Magnetic Field

Earth has a magnetic field that protects us from harmful radiation from the Sun. Scientists hypothesize that Earth's rotation and movement of matter in the core set up a strong magnetic field in and around Earth. This field resembles that surrounding a bar magnet, shown in **Figure 2.** Earth's magnetic field is concentrated at two ends of an imaginary magnetic axis running from Earth's north magnetic pole to its south magnetic pole. This axis is tilted about 11.5° from Earth's geographic axis of rotation.

Wandering Poles The locations of Earth's magnetic poles change slowly over time. Large-scale movements, called polar wandering, are thought to be caused by movements in Earth's crust and upper mantle. The magnetic north pole is carefully remapped periodically to pinpoint its location.

The Aurora An area within Earth's magnetic field, called the magnetosphere, deflects harmful radiation coming from the Sun, a stream of particles called solar wind. Some of these ejected particles from the Sun produce other charged particles in Earth's outer atmosphere. These charged particles spiral along Earth's magnetic field lines toward Earth's magnetic poles. There they collide with atoms in the atmosphere. These collisions cause the atoms to emit light. This light is called the aurora borealis (northern lights) in the northern hemisphere and the aurora australis (southern lights) in the southern hemisphere.

Figure 2 Like a common bar magnet, Earth also has north and south magnetic poles. The inner and outer gold shells respectively represent the positive and negative Van Allen Belts.
Explain *why the Van Allen Belts are shaped as they are.*

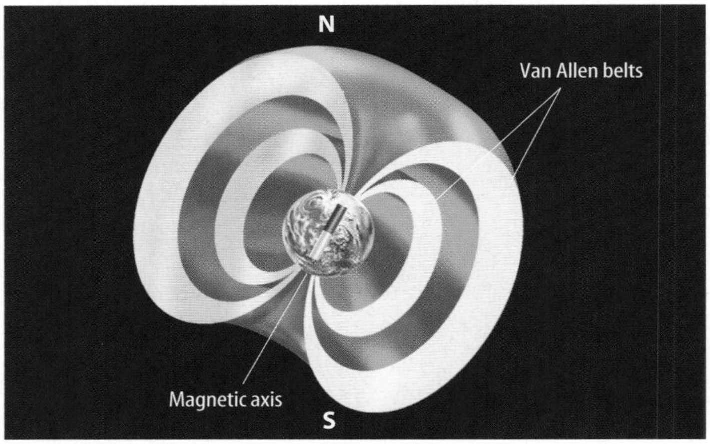

Earth Orbits the Sun

Earth orbits the Sun at an average distance of 149,600,000 km. Its orbit, like those of all the planets, moons, asteroids, and many comets, is shaped like an ellipse. An **ellipse** is an elongated, closed curve with two foci. The Sun is not located at the center of the ellipse, but at one of its two foci. This means the distance from Earth to the Sun varies during the year. Earth is closest to the Sun—about 147 million km away—around January 3 and is farthest from the Sun—about 152 million km away—around July 4 of each year.

Curriculum Connection

Geography Show students a map that includes the directions of geographic (rotational) and magnetic north. This is called the declination of the map. Ask them to determine the number of degrees east or west they would have to measure from magnetic north in order to find the geographic North Pole. If magnetic north is east, they must subtract that number of degrees, if it is west, they must add. L2 ELL LS **Visual-Spatial**

Differentiated Instruction

Learning Disabled To help students understand how to use the two north directions on a map, have the student look at a desk forward but to their right and then to the front of the room. Ask them how far they have to turn their heads in order for to look at the front of the room again. Relate this to the difference between the two norths. L2 ELL LS **Visual-Spatial**

Earth as a Planet Earth is a planet, just as Venus, Mars, and Jupiter are planets. However, Earth is the only planet whose characteristics make it possible for life as we know it to survive.

Earth resembles Venus more than any other planet. Earth and Venus are nearly the same size, and both have atmospheres that contain carbon dioxide, although in greatly different amounts. Earth's oceans, shown in **Figure 3,** absorbed much of the carbon dioxide in Earth's early atmosphere. Also, Venus's atmosphere is much denser than Earth's, with pressures as high as those encountered by submarines in Earth's oceans at depth of 900 m.

Another difference is the surface temperatures. On Earth, you can walk outside and feel how cold or warm it is. However, temperature on Venus is over 450°C. This high temperature is caused by the large amount of carbon dioxide in Venus's atmosphere, which traps heat energy and prevents it from escaping. Think about what life on Earth might be like with more carbon dioxide in the atmosphere.

Reading Check *What feature of Earth's surface has led to such a difference between Earth and Venus?*

Although Mars is almost half the size of Earth, its surface gravitational pull is less than two-fifths that of Earth's. Yet conditions there are more like those on Earth than any other planet in the solar system. Mars may even have frozen water near its surface. Mercury is very different from Earth; it has no atmosphere, and is cratered like Earth's moon.

Figure 3 By absorbing carbon dioxide, oceans protect Earth from experiencing a greenhouse effect like that on Venus.

section 1 review

Summary

Earth's Size and Shape

- Earth has a spherical shape.
- Gravity causes very large objects in space to form spheres.

Earth's Magnetic Field

- Earth's magnetic field protects life on Earth's surface from harmful radiation.
- Interaction of the solar wind with Earth's magnetic field produces the aurora.

Earth Orbits the Sun

- Earth orbits the Sun in an elliptical orbit.
- Earth and Venus are similar in size, and both have atmospheres that contain carbon dioxide.

Self Check

1. **Identify** two pieces of evidence that prove Earth's spherical shape.
2. **Define** the term *gravity.*
3. **Explain** what produces Earth's magnetic field.
4. **Describe** how Venus and Earth are similar.
5. **Think Critically** Evidence indicates that Mars once had liquid water on its surface. Discuss some possible reasons why it has none today.

Applying Math

6. **Calculate Speed** Earth's circumference at the equator is 40,075 km. If it spins once each day, what is the speed of spinning in km/h?

More Section Review gpescience.com

Reading Check

Answer oceans

Post Reading

Illustration Ask students to create an illustration that incorporates the major ideas found in this section. Remind students to include detailed information about Earth's shape, magnetic field, orbit, and atmosphere. Share the illustrations in a class booklet.

3 Assess

DAILY INTERVENTION

Check for Understanding

Visual-Spatial Have students draw a diagram of Earth orbiting the Sun. Have them add the orbits of Mercury, Venus, and Mars to their drawings. L1 ELL P

Reteach

Planet Surfaces Show students photographs of the surfaces of Mercury and Earth's moon. Ask them to list ways in which the two objects are similar. Possible answer: both are covered with craters and both lack color. L1 ELL

Assessment

Performance Provide students with 3 × 5 cards and ask them to make flash cards for the terrestrial planets. The name of the planet should be written on one side and important characteristics on the other side. Have them quiz each other on the planet characteristics using the completed cards. L2 ELL

section 1 review

1. curved shadow on the Moon; photos from space, appearance of objects as they approach over the horizon
2. the attractive force between two objects that depends on the masses of the two objects and the distance between them
3. Earth's rotation and movement of matter in its core
4. they have about the same size, density, and rocky nature
5. Water on Mars may be frozen in its rocks and at its poles.
6. 1,670 km/h

Time and Seasons

Reading Guide

What You'll Learn

- **Calculate** the time and date in different time zones.
- **Differentiate** between revolution and rotation.
- **Discuss** what causes seasons to change.

Why It's Important

Days and years are measurements of Earth's movements.

Review Vocabulary

latitude: angular distance north or south of Earth's equator

New Vocabulary

- time zone
- rotation
- revolution
- ecliptic
- equinox
- solstice

Measuring Time on Earth

People can determine the approximate time of day by determining where the Sun is in the sky. If the Sun is near an imaginary line drawn from due north to due south, it is about 12:00 noon. Humans have used movements of Earth, the Moon, and the Sun to measure time for thousands of years.

Around 3000 B.C., the Babylonians devised a method of timekeeping using their counting methods, which were based on 60. They noticed that the Sun appeared to take a circular path through the sky. Because their counting methods were based on 60, they divided a circle into 360 parts called degrees. The symbol for degree (°) was taken from their symbol for the Sun.

Earth Movements Measure Time Earth spins and makes one complete turn in about 24 hours, as shown in **Figure 4.** This spinning causes the Sun to appear to move across the sky from east to west. It takes 24 hours from when the Sun is highest in the sky (noon) until it is highest in the sky again (noon the next day).

Figure 4 The sunlit side of Earth is day; the shadow side is night.

If Earth spins approximately 360° in 24 hours, then it spins through 15° in one hour. This led to the setting up of time zones on Earth that have the same time in minutes but vary in hours. A **time zone** is an area 15° wide in which the time is the same. **Figure 5** shows the time zones in the U.S. Ideally, time zones should be equal in size and follow lines drawn from the north pole to the south pole. However, for convenience, time zones are modified to fit around city, state, and country borders, and other key sites.

Reading Check *How many degrees does Earth spin in one hour?*

Section 2 Resource Manager

Chapter *FAST FILE* Resources

Transparency Activity, p. 45
MiniLAB, p. 3
Enrichment, p. 31
Reinforcement, p. 28
Directed Reading for Content Mastery, p. 20
Lab Worksheet, pp. 5–6

Home and Community Involvement, p. 45

Cultural Diversity, p. 29

Reading and Writing Skills Activities, pp. 45–46

1 Motivate

INTERACTIVE CHALKBOARD An editable Microsoft® PowerPoint® presentation is available on **Interactive Chalkboard** CD-ROM.

Bellringer

Section Focus Transparencies also are available on the Interactive Chalkboard CD-ROM. L2 ELL

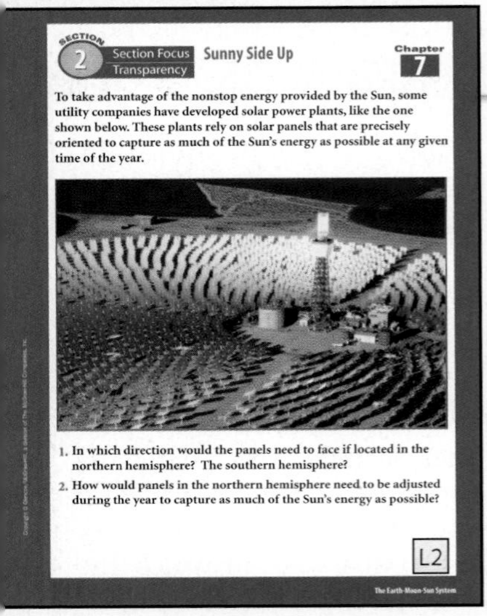

Section 2 Section Focus Transparency — Sunny Side Up — Chapter 7

To take advantage of the nonstop energy provided by the Sun, some utility companies have developed solar power plants, like the one shown below. These plants rely on solar panels that are precisely oriented to capture as much of the Sun's energy as possible at any given time of the year.

1. **In which direction would the panels need to face if located in the northern hemisphere? The southern hemisphere?**
2. **How would panels in the northern hemisphere need to be adjusted during the year to capture as much of the Sun's energy as possible?**

L2

The Earth-Moon-Sun System

Reading Preview

Tie to Prior Knowledge

Seasons Ask students to think about the different seasons. Ask them to list at least one positive and one negative comment about each season. Then ask each student to select his or her favorite season and to write a brief paragraph explaining the choice.

Word Wall Post new vocabulary words in a prominent place in the classroom. Before reading, have students practice pronouncing the words. Ask them to predict meaning. After reading, ask students to use the terms in sentences, either orally or in written form.

The Date Line You can see that a problem would quickly arise if you just kept dropping back an hour earlier for each 15°. Eventually, you would come around Earth and it would be 24 hours earlier. It cannot be two different days at the same spot, so a day is added to the time at the International Date Line. If it is Monday to the east of the date line, then it is the same hour on Tuesday to the west of the date line. This line is drawn down through the Pacific Ocean (around islands, such as New Zealand) directly opposite the Prime Meridian, the starting point for this worldwide system of measuring time. The Prime Meridian is an imaginary line drawn on Earth that passes through Greenwich, England. Time based on this method is called Coordinated Universal Time (UTC). In some areas, this time is modified in summer so that there are more hours of daylight in the evening. This is referred to as Daylight Saving Time (DST). Some areas apply local modifications to this system as well.

Figure 5 The globe is divided into 24 time zones. Lines of longitude roughly determine the locations of time zone boundaries. Notice that each successive time zone to the west is one hour earlier.
Think Critically *If you leave Russia at 12:30 A.M. on Tuesday and fly east for one hour across the Bering Strait, what time and day will you arrive in Alaska?*

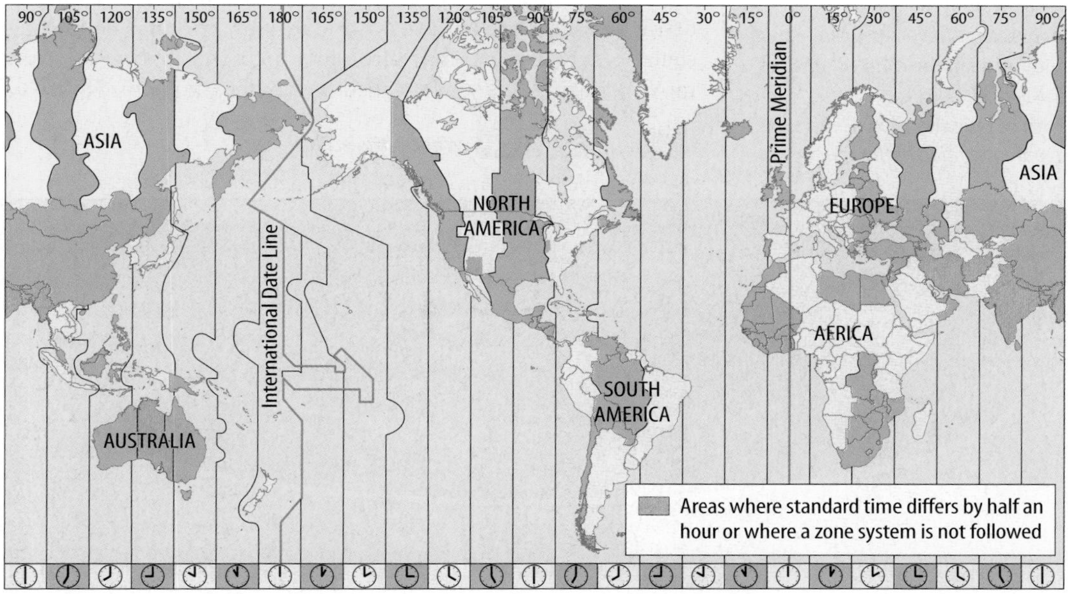

2 Teach

Reading Check

Answer fifteen degrees

Discussion

Sunset Ask students to consider whether the Sun sets at the same time everywhere within a time zone. Would the Sun set at the same time in Wilmington, NC and Pittsburgh, PA? Possible answer: No, because it is farther east, the Sun sets earlier in Wilmington, NC. L2

Caption Answer

Figure 5 4:30 A.M., Monday (observe convergence of time zones near the Bering Strait on the map)

Teacher FYI

Earth's Rotation Using atomic clocks, scientists have found that each successive day on Earth is getting longer. Apparently, Earth's rotation has been slowing down for millions of years. Studies of ancient corals, which produce a growth line for each day-night cycle, show more growth lines per year than do present-day corals. By studying the growth lines on 500-million-year-old corals, scientists have determined that there were nearly 400 deposits per year. The year was the same length, but there were more days in a year when these corals were growing. Scientists hypothesize that Earth is being slowed by the gravitational attraction of the Moon. As this slowing continues, the length of a day will increase. The length of a year will not be affected. This means that the number of days in a year will continue to decrease, but the length of a year will not change.

Differentiated Instruction

English-Language Learners Use an Earth globe and a light source to show students how the length of the day varies at different places on Earth. Tilt the globe so the Northern Hemisphere is pointing toward the light source. Show how areas farther north receive more hours of daylight than areas farther south. Reverse the tilt and show students how the opposite is true.

Reading Strategy

Double-Entry Notes Ask students to divide a sheet of paper into two columns. In the left column, students should record specific notes from the text. The right column is reserved for student responses to the reading, such as comments, reflections, and opinions.

Fun Fact

Inform students that each year, they have ridden Earth one more time around the Sun.

Use an Analogy

Walking Around the Room Explain to students that the Sun appearing to move around Earth in reference to the stars is like one of them walking around the room. Students sitting in their seats see the person's position change with reference to objects on the wall. The person doing the walking sees his or her classmates seem to move with respect to the same objects. L2 ELL IS **Visual-Spatial**

Use Science Words

Word Meaning Students often have difficulty with describing the difference between rotation and revolution. Have one student stand in front of the class and start to slowly spin around. Ask students to say whether the moving student is rotating or revolving. Possible answer: rotating Then ask students to explain what the moving student should do to demonstrate revolution. Possible answer: The moving student should walk around the outer edge of the room, thus revolving around the other students. L1 ELL IS **Visual-Spatial**

Reading Check

Answer the plane of Earth's orbit around the Sun

Caption Answer

Figure 6 Earth's revolution around the Sun

Rotation Measures Days The spinning motion of Earth enables you to measure the passing hours of the day. **Rotation** is the spinning of Earth on its axis, an imaginary line drawn through Earth from its rotational north pole to its rotational south pole.

The apparent movement of the Sun from noon one day until noon the next day is called a solar day. This period is a bit longer than the time it takes Earth to rotate on its axis, however. This is because while Earth rotates, it also moves in orbit around the Sun and must rotate a bit more each day to make the Sun reach noon. However, if you measure time based on when a certain star rises above the horizon until it rises again, you will see a slightly shorter time period (23 h 56 m 4 s). This is called a sidereal day and is the true measure of the time it takes for Earth to rotate once on its axis.

Revolution Measures Years The motion of Earth around the Sun enables you to measure the passing of years. **Revolution** is the motion of Earth in its orbit around the Sun. **Figure 6** shows Earth's orbit around the Sun. As Earth revolves in its orbit, the Sun appears to move through the skies compared to the seemingly fixed positions of the stars.

The time it takes for the Sun to make one complete trip through the sky in reference to the background of stars is the same amount of time it takes for Earth to complete one trip around the Sun, or one sidereal year. The apparent path of the Sun during this year is called the ecliptic. Also, the **ecliptic** is defined as the plane of Earth's orbit around the Sun. The 12 constellations (star patterns) through which we observe the Sun moving during this year is called the zodiac, shown in **Figure 6.**

Reading Check *What is the ecliptic?*

Figure 6 If the Sun were as faint as the stars at night, then you would see it travel along an annual path through the constellations of the Zodiac.
Think Critically *What causes this apparent motion of the Sun?*

Science Journal

The Time of Year Have students write a brief paragraph in their Science Journals describing differences they have noticed about the area near their homes or school as an entire year passes. L2 IS **Linguistic**

Why do seasons change?

Recall that Earth's orbit around the Sun is an ellipse. This means that Earth is closer to the Sun at one time than it is at other times. Is this the cause of seasonal changes on Earth? Because Earth is closest to the Sun in January, you would expect this to be the warmest month. However, you know this isn't true in the northern hemisphere; something else must be causing the change. These seasonal changes are caused by Earth's rotation, its revolution, and the tilt of its axis.

Seasons change on Earth because the number of hours of daylight each day varies and also because the angle at which sunlight strikes Earth's surface varies at different times of the year. Earth's axis is tilted 23.5° from a line drawn perpendicular to the plane of its orbit, or ecliptic. Because of this tilt, Earth's north geographic pole points toward Polaris throughout the year. Later, you will learn how this tilt, along with Earth's revolution, causes the seasons.

Changing Angle of Sunlight During the summer, the Sun is higher in the sky, and sunlight hits Earth's surface at a higher angle. As the year progresses, the Sun is lower and lower in the sky, and sunlight strikes Earth's surface at lower angles. When striking Earth's surface at higher angles, approaching 90°, sunlight is more intense and warms Earth's surface more than when it strikes the surface at lower angles. Because Earth remains tilted in the same direction as it revolves, different hemispheres are tilted toward the Sun at different times of the year. As shown in **Figure 7,** the hemisphere tilted toward the Sun receives sunlight at higher angles than the hemisphere tilted away from the Sun. The greater intensity of sunlight is one reason why summer is warmer than winter, but it is not the only reason. Another factor is involved.

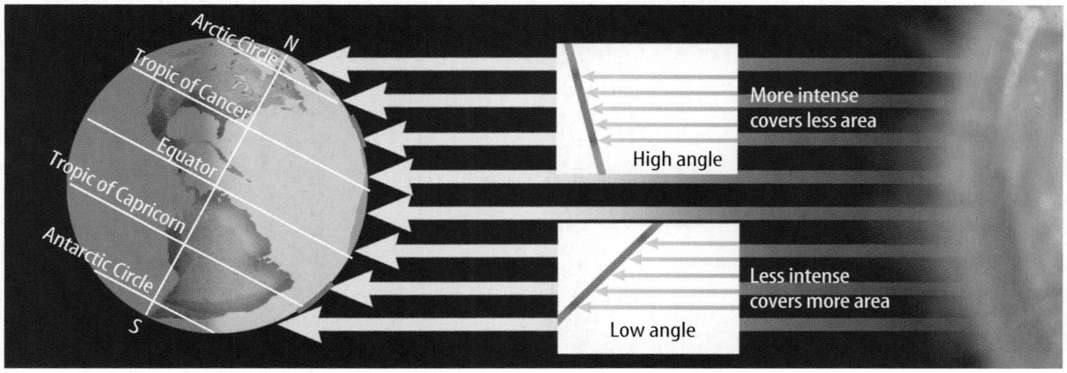

Figure 7 The Sun's rays strike Earth's surface at higher angles in the northern hemisphere when the north pole is tilted toward the Sun.

IDENTIFYING Misconceptions

Seasons Many people, including many of your students, think that one cause of seasons is that the Sun's rays hit Earth directly at some times and indirectly at other times. All rays from the Sun are direct; the true explanation is that sometimes the rays hit at higher angles compared to other times.

Activity

Intensity of Sunlight Provide students with flashlights. Have them turn the flashlights on and hold them vertically above their desks so the light falls straight down on their desks. Then have them hold the flashlights at an angle with the surface of their desks. Discuss how the angle at which sunlight strikes Earth determines how intense or how spread out it is. Possible answer: The light from the flashlight, like that from the Sun, is spread out more when it strikes at an angle. L2 ELL LS **Visual-Spatial**

LAB DEMONSTRATION

Purpose Students will see how area covered affects the intensity of sunlight.

Materials empty paper towel roll

Preparation Cut one end of the empty towel roll at a 45° angle.

Procedure Have students hold each end of the towel roll against a sheet of paper and draw around it with a pencil.

Expected Outcome Students should have drawn a circle around the flat end and an ellipse around the slanted end of the empty paper towel roll.

Assessment

Which drawing, the circle or the ellipse covers a greater area? Possible answer: the ellipse How does this relate to the intensity of sunlight striking Earth? Possible answer: If the same rays from the Sun cover a larger area, the intensity of the light must be lower. L2

Teacher FYI

A 12-hour day There are 12 hours of daylight and 12 hours of night all over Earth on only two days—the first day of spring and the first day of autumn.

Quick Demo
Hours of Daylight

Materials two thermometers, 75-watt goose-neck lamp

Estimated Time 15 minutes

Procedure Place a thermometer flat on a desk. Turn on the goose-neck lamp and direct its light on the thermometer for 4 min. Record the temperature. Shine the goose-neck lamp on the other thermometer for 8 min. and record this temperature. What is observed about the temperature readings on the two thermometers? Possible answer: The temperature on the thermometer under the light for 8 min will be higher. How does this relate to the number of hours of daylight? Possible answer: More hours of daylight result in higher temperatures on Earth's surface. L2 ELL LS **Visual-Spatial**

Reading Check

Answer June

Post Reading

Science Journal Immediately following the reading, have students write what they learned from the following sections: Measuring Time on Earth and Why Do Seasons Change? Respond to students' comments without assigning a grade.

More Hours of Daylight in Summer During the summer, the Sun is above the horizon for more hours than it is when school begins in the fall. As the year progresses, the number of hours of daylight each day becomes fewer and fewer until it reaches a minimum around December 21 for the northern hemisphere. When do you think the number of hours of daylight would be at a maximum in the northern hemisphere? This happens six months later, around June 21. As shown in **Figure 8,** the hemisphere of Earth that is tilted toward the Sun receives more hours of daylight each day than the hemisphere tilted away from the Sun. This longer period of daylight is the second reason why summer is warmer than winter.

Reading Check *During which month does Earth's northern hemisphere experience more hours of daylight?*

Figure 8 During the winter solstice for the northern hemisphere, the Sun's rays strike Earth perpendicular at the Tropic of Capricorn, while the area within the arctic circle remains in darkness. During the summer solstice, the Sun's rays are perpendicular to Earth at the Tropic of Cancer, while the area within the arctic circle remains in sunlight.

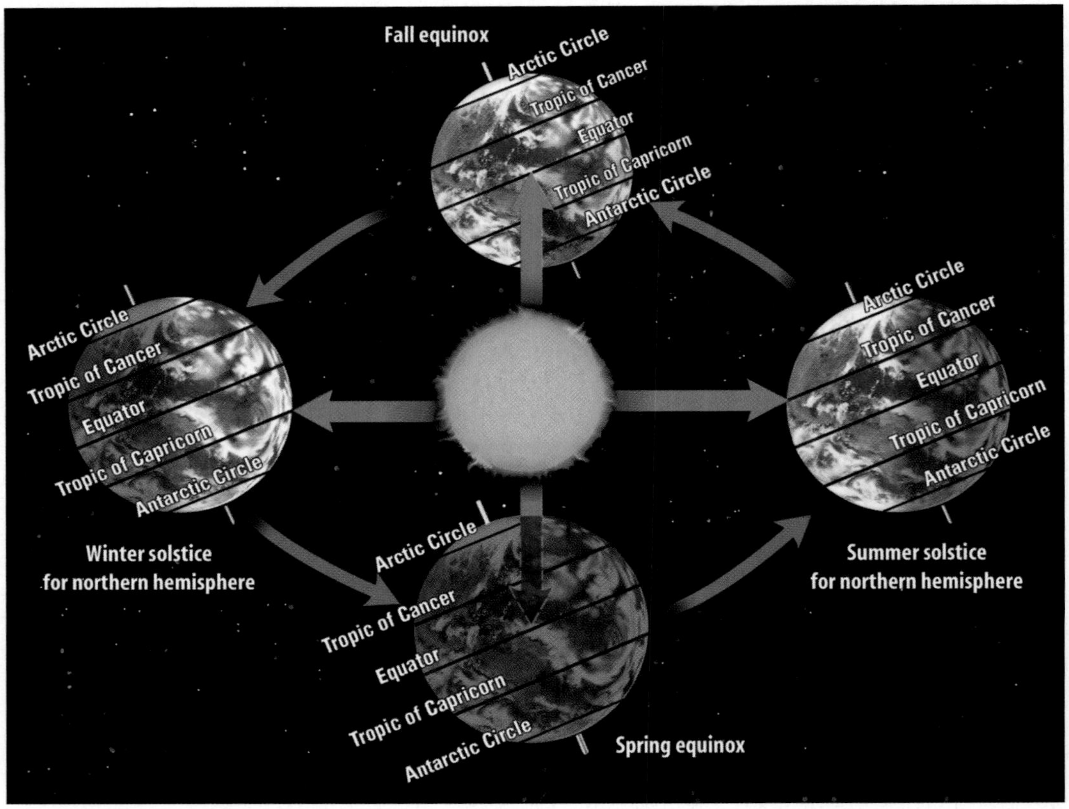

Visual Learning

Figure 8 Help students understand the information shown in **Figure 8.** As you read the description, emphasize that the hemisphere of Earth tilted toward the Sun experiences more hours of daylight each day. Also help students understand that the farther north you are on Earth when the northern hemisphere is tilted toward the Sun, the more hours of daylight you will experience. The farther south you are when the southern hemisphere is tilted toward the Sun, the more hours of daylight you will experience. L2 ELL

Equinoxes and Solstices Because of the tilt of Earth's axis, the Sun's position relative to Earth's equator constantly changes. Most of the time, the Sun is north or south of the equator, but two times during the year, the Sun is directly over the equator. **Figure 8** shows that the Sun reaches an **equinox** when it is directly above Earth's equator, and the number of daylight hours equals the number of nighttime hours all over the world. The term *equinox* is derived from two words meaning "equal" and "night." At that time, neither the northern nor the southern hemisphere is tilted toward the Sun. In the northern hemisphere, the Sun reaches the spring equinox on March 20 or 21, and the fall equinox on September 22 or 23. In the southern hemisphere, the equinoxes are reversed.

The **solstice** is the point at which the Sun reaches its greatest distance north or south of the equator the Tropic of Cancer and Tropic of Capricorn, respectively. The term *solstice* is derived from the Sun's name, *Sol*, and a Latin word meaning "standing"; that is, it appears to stand, or stop moving, north or south in the sky. In the northern hemisphere, the Sun reaches the summer solstice on June 21 or 22, and it reaches the winter solstice on December 21 or 22. Just the opposite is true for the southern hemisphere. When the Sun is at the summer solstice, there are more hours of daylight than during any other day of the year, and the Sun's rays strike at a higher angle. When it's at the winter solstice, on the shortest day of the year, the most nighttime hours occur and the Sun's rays strike at the lowest angle.

Mini LAB

Modeling the Sun's Rays at Solstice

Procedure

1. Use a **globe** with the equator, the Tropic of Cancer, and the Tropic of Capricorn indicated.
2. Set up a light source, such as a **flashlight or gooseneck lamp,** so light shines vertically at Earth's equator.
3. Tilt the globe 23.5° from vertical so that first the northern and then the southern hemisphere is tilted toward the light.

Analysis

1. When the globe was tilted 23.5° toward and away from the light, what latitudes received vertical rays?
2. What areas of Earth never received vertical rays?

section 2 review

Summary

Measuring Time on Earth

- Humans use movements of Earth, the Moon, and the Sun to measure time.
- Earth's rotation is used to measure days.
- Earth's revolution is used to measure years.
- The ecliptic is the Sun's apparent yearly path through the zodiac.

Why do seasons change?

- Earth's seasonal changes are caused by its tilt, rotation, and revolution.
- Equinoxes occur when the Sun is directly over Earth's equator. Solstices occur when the Sun reaches it greatest distance north or south of the equator.

Self-Check

1. **Determine** how long it takes Earth to make one complete turn on its axis.
2. **Explain** why each time zone contains 15° of longitude. If it is 4:15 P.M. in one time zone, what is the time two time zones to the west?
3. **Explain** how a solar day differs from a sidereal day.
4. **Compare and contrast** rotation and revolution.
5. **Think Critically** Why does Earth's surface become warmer in summer than it does in winter?

Applying Math

6. **Use Decimals** It takes Earth about 365.25 days to make one trip around the Sun. As it does this, Earth travels 360° in its orbit. On average, how many degrees does Earth travel each day?

More Section Review gpescience.com

Mini LAB

Purpose Students model the Sun's rays **Kinesthetic**

Materials Earth globe, flashlight or goose-neck lamp

Teaching Strategy Anchor the light source so students only need to move the globe.

Safety Precautions Caution students that the lamp is hot.

Troubleshooting Mark the location of the Tropics of Cancer and Capricorn on the globe.

Analysis

1. 23.5° N and 23.5° S
2. north of 23.5° N and south of 23.5° S

Assessment

Oral Which season begins in the Northern Hemisphere when the Sun's rays strike the Tropic of Capricorn vertically? winter L2

3 Assess

DAILY INTERVENTION

Check for Understanding

Linguistic Have students write a short narrative explaining two causes of Earth's seasonal changes. P

Reteach

Equinox or Solstice Ask students whether an equinox or a solstice occurs when the Sun is at its farthest point south of the equator.

section 2 review

1. 24 hours; one day
2. If Earth rotates once in 24 hours, then it rotates 360° in 24 hours or 15° per hour; 2:15 P.M.
3. A solar day is measured from noon on one day until noon the next day. A sidereal day is Earth's period of rotation based on the position of a star. As Earth revolves around the Sun, the Sun appears to move slightly each day, making the solar day slightly longer than the sidereal day.
4. Both are movements of Earth. Rotation is the spinning of Earth on its axis; revolution is Earth's movement around the Sun.
5. The Sun's rays strike Earth's surface at a higher angle for more time each day during the summer.
6. 0.99° or about 1°

Assessment

Oral How much is light intensity decreased, if the same amount of light is spread over an area three times larger? by one-third L2

BENCH TESTED

Real-World Problem

Purpose Students will model the intensity of light as it strikes Earth's surface at different angles. **Kinesthetic**

Process Skills model, compare and contrast, measure, observe, recognize cause and effect, make and use tables

Time Required 40 minutes

Alternate Materials unshaded 75-W lamp, books, small envelopes

Safety Precautions Caution students that the lamp will be hot. Ask students to carefully handle thermometers.

Procedure

Teaching Strategies
- Practice setting the goose-neck lamp at different angles or using books to change angles.

Troubleshooting
- Check bulbs in lamps, and have extras available.

Conclude and Apply

1. Temperature readings both increase. However, T-1 increases faster and reaches higher temperature.
2. 75° = summer; 20° = winter
3. The angle at which sunlight strikes Earth's surface changes, the intensity of light changes and the surface is heated to a different amount.

Assessment

Process Infer how placing the goose-neck lamp at 90° would affect temperature. It should rise more quickly and reach a higher final reading. Use **PASC**, p. 89. L2

LAB

Comparing the Angle of Sunlight to Intensity

Earth is warmed differently depending on the angle at which sunlight strikes it.

Real-World Problem

How can you a model the angle at which sunlight strikes Earth's surface?

Goals

- **Model** different angles at which sunlight strikes Earth's surface.
- **Compare and contrast** the amount of heat generated by light striking at different angles.

Materials

75-W bulb in a gooseneck lamp
alcohol thermometers (2)
sheets of construction paper, one color (2)
protractor
** unshaded 75-W lamp*
** books to change the angle of the thermometers*
**Alternate materials*

Safety Precautions

WARNING: *Do not touch lamp or lightbulb without safety gloves. They stay hot after being turned off. Handle thermometers carefully.*

Procedure

1. Copy the data table shown on this page.
2. Label the thermometers *T-1* and *T-2* and record their temperatures in the data table.
3. Fold the construction paper to form a pocket that will conceal the thermometer's bulb.
4. Place *T-1* in the pocket and lay them on a desktop. Turn on the lamp. Position the lamp so that light strikes the pocket at an angle of 75°.
5. Record the temperature of *T-1* at 10 min and at 20 min.
6. Repeat steps 3, 4, and 5 using *T-2*, but aim the lamp at an angle of 20°.

Conclude and Apply

1. **Compare and contrast** the temperature readings of each thermometer.
2. **Infer** which angle models the Sun's position during the summer and during the winter.
3. **Explain** how changes in the angle at which sunlight strikes Earth's surface are one cause of Earth's changing seasons.

Data Table

Thermometer	Original Temperature	Temperature at 10 min	Temperature at 20 min
T-1			
T-2			

Communicating Your Data

Compile your classmates' data. Find the average temperatures—original, at 10 min, and at 20 min—for *T-1* and *T-2*. Compare and contrast your results with the class averages.

Communicating Your Data

Students should prepare a drawing of sunlight falling on a round Earth. It should show how light hitting Earth at different latitudes strikes the surface at different angles. Temperatures should be higher where angles of sunlight are higher.

Differentiated Instruction

Visually Impaired Have visually impaired students watch while you show them how much light is concentrated when an overhead projector is held directly in front of the wall and then how it spreads over a larger area when held at an angle to the wall. L2

196 CHAPTER 7 The Earth-Moon-Sun System

section 3

Earth's Moon

Reading Guide

What You'll Learn

- **Describe** how tides on Earth are caused by the Moon.
- **Explain** how the Moon's phases depend on the relative positions of the Sun, the Moon, and Earth.
- **Compare and contrast** solar and lunar eclipses.
- **Analyze** what surface features of the Moon reveal about its history.

Why It's Important

The Moon is our nearest neighbor in space and affects Earth in many ways.

Review Vocabulary

lava: molten rock

New Vocabulary

- tide
- moon phase
- solar eclipse
- lunar eclipse
- maria
- regolith

Movement of the Moon

You have seen the Moon move across the sky from east to west, just like the Sun. This is an apparent movement like the Sun's, caused by Earth's rotation. But, the Moon actually does move in another way. If you look at the Moon each day at the same time over a period of a few days, you will see that it moves toward the east.

Rotation and Revolution This eastward movement of the Moon is an actual movement that is caused by the Moon's revolution in its orbit. It takes 27.3 days (a sidereal month) for the Moon to revolve once around Earth and line up with the same star again. Because Earth also revolves around the Sun, it takes more than two more days for the Moon to line up with Earth and the Sun again. This means that a complete lunar phase cycle takes 29.5 days, known as a synodic month.

Many people think the Moon does not rotate because it always keeps the same side facing Earth. This is not true. As shown in **Figure 9,** the Moon keeps the same side facing Earth because it takes 27.3 days to rotate once on its axis—the same amount of time that it takes to revolve once around Earth. You can observe this by having a friend move the ball around you while keeping the same side of it facing you. You will see only one side.

Figure 9 The face of the "man in the moon" is always facing Earth. **Explain** *why the same side of the Moon always faces Earth.*

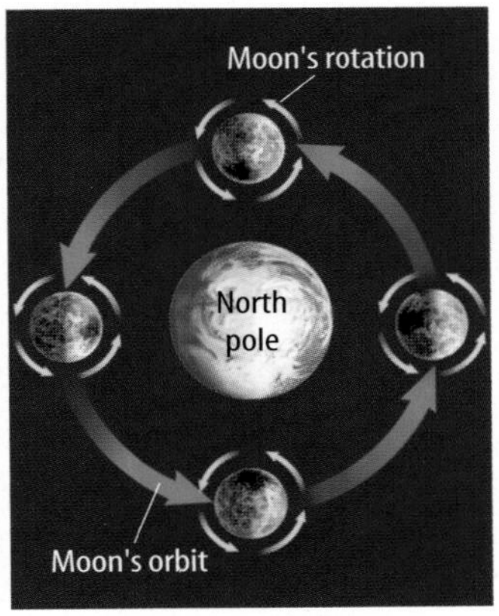

Section 3 Resource Manager

Chapter *FAST FILE* Resources

Transparency Activity, pp. 46, 47–48
MiniLAB, p. 4
Enrichment, p. 32
Reinforcement, p. 29
Directed Reading for Content Mastery, p. 21–22
Lab Worksheet, pp. 7–8
Lab Activity, pp. 13–15
Critical Thinking/Problem Solving–Earth Science, p. 23
Laboratory Management and Safety, p. 66
Mathematics Skill Activities, pp. 39–40
Cultural Diversity, p. 71–72

1 Motivate

INTERACTIVE CHALKBOARD PowerPoint® Presentations An editable Microsoft® PowerPoint® presentation is available on **Interactive Chalkboard** CD-ROM.

Bellringer

Section Focus Transparencies also are available on the Interactive Chalkboard CD-ROM. L2 ELL

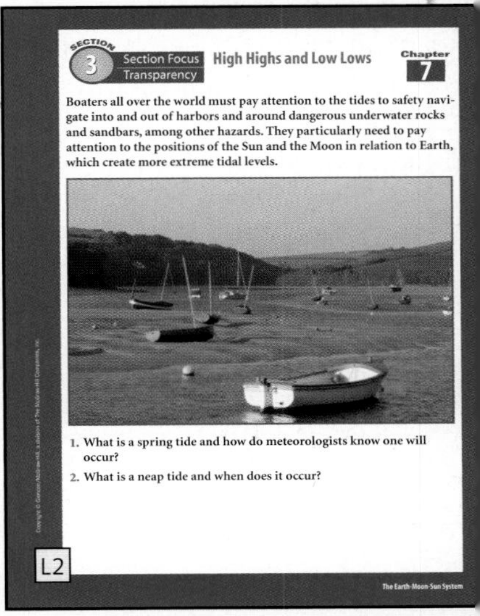
SECTION 3 Section Focus Transparency **High Highs and Low Lows** Chapter 7

Boaters all over the world must pay attention to the tides to safety navigate into and out of harbors and around dangerous underwater rocks and sandbars, among other hazards. They particularly need to pay attention to the positions of the Sun and the Moon in relation to Earth, which create more extreme tidal levels.

1. What is a spring tide and how do meteorologists know one will occur?
2. What is a neap tide and when does it occur?

L2

The Earth-Moon-Sun System

Reading Preview

Tie to Prior Knowledge

When do we see the Moon? Ask students to draw the shape of the Moon they see during the day. Students may have seen crescent, quarter, and gibbous phases. Explain that the only phase that is visible only at night is the full moon and that the new moon is not seen during the day or the night.

Skim Explain that skimming involves reading quickly to get the essence of text. Ask students to skim a few lines before and after each vocabulary term then record the meaning of the term in their own words.

2 Teach

Caption Answer

Figure 9 The Moon's period of revolution and period of rotation are the same.

IDENTIFYING Misconceptions

The Moon's Rotation Some students may think that the Moon does not rotate because it keeps the same side facing Earth. Explain that since the Moon revolves around Earth we would see all sides if it did not rotate. Ask students to hold their right hand at the side of their faces edge-on, so that they see the palms. Tell them to move their hands to the left side of their faces without rotating it. They should now see the backs of their hands.

Applying Math

Math Standards

National: 1, 2, 9

Teaching Strategy

- Explain that because the Moon revolves around Earth in a counterclockwise direction as Earth revolves around the Sun, it rises 52.7 minutes later each day.
- The Moon travels around Earth (360°) in 27.3 days or 13.2° per day. Earth spins through 360° in one day and 13.2° is equal to 52.7 minutes.

Answers

1. 2:38 PM

How does the Moon affect Earth?

The Moon affects Earth in many ways, some obvious and others less so. If you have ever been to a beach for vacation, you realized that the water is not always at the same location on the beach. Sometimes the water comes farther up the beach than at other times. Have you ever placed your towel on the beach and come back later to find it wet because the tide came in? You also may have noticed that the Moon doesn't look the same each evening. Sometimes you can see all of the side facing Earth, while at other times, you can barely see any of it. Let's take a look at these and some other effects of the Moon on Earth.

Applying Math — Solve a Simple Equation

TIDES The Moon rises an average of 52.7 min later each day. If the time of high tide is known for one day, this formula can be used to determine when high tide will occur on the next day or any successive day.

$$T_N = T_0 + N \times 52.7 \text{ min}$$

In this formula, T_0 is the original time of high tide on a given day and T_N is the time of high tide on any successive day. N is the number of days later for which you wish to determine the time of high tide. If the tide is high at 1:00 P.M., find out what time it will be high in 7 days.

IDENTIFY known values and unknown values

Identify the known values:

T_0 = original time of high tide = 1:00 P.M.

N = the number of days later for which you wish to determine high tide = 7

52.7 min = how much later the Moon rises each day

Identify the unknown value:

T_N = the time of high tide on N number of days

SOLVE the problem

Substitute the known values into the equation for time.

T_N = 1:00 P.M. + 7 × 52.7 min = 1:00 P.M. + 369 min

T_N = 1:00 P.M. + 6 h 09 min = 7:09 P.M.

Practice Problem

Low tide is the best time to hunt for seashells. If you see that the tide is low at noon on Thursday, when during the day will it be low on the following Sunday?

For more practice problems, go to page 879 and visit Math Practice at gpescience.com.

Reading Strategy

Infer Inferring involves using prior knowledge to make a logical prediction based on evidence. Use a statement, such as the following, to model: The Earth's surface passes through a high tide and a low tide. Students might infer that the closest coastal area to their home would experience a high tide and a low tide daily.

Tides Think again of the beach and how the level of the sea rose and fell during the day. This rise and fall in sea level is called a **tide**. A tide on Earth is caused by a giant wave produced by the gravitational pulls of the Sun and the Moon. This wave has a wave height of only 1 or 2 m, but it has a wavelength of thousands of kilometers. As the crest of this large wave approaches the shore, the level of the water in the ocean rises. This rise of sea level is called high tide. About six hours later, as the trough of the wave approaches, sea level drops, causing a low tide.

Earth and the Moon both revolve around their common center of mass located about 1,700 km below Earth's surface. Because Earth is much more massive, the Moon does most of the moving, and it seems to us as though the Moon were revolving around Earth. This center of mass, in turn, revolves around the Sun. This is why Earth, Moon, Sun are considered as a three-body system.

As Earth rotates and the Moon revolves, different locations on Earth's surface pass through the high and low tides. Although the Sun is much more massive than the Moon, it also is much farther away. Because of this, the Moon has a greater effect on Earth's tides than does the Sun. However, the Sun does affect Earth's tides: it can strengthen or weaken the tidal effect. When the Moon and the Sun pull together, when they are lined up, high tides are much higher and low tides are much lower. This is called a spring tide, as shown in **Figure 10.** However, when the two are at right angles to each other, the high tide is not as high and the low tide not as low, producing a neap tide.

Reading Check *What happens to the sea level at spring tide?*

Figure 10 Earth's tides are an example of how the Sun, Moon, and Earth pull on each other and operate as a three-body system. **A** The Sun, Earth, and Moon are in alignment during spring tide. **B** The Sun, Earth, and Moon form a right angle during neap tide. **Identify** *whether high tide is higher during spring tide or neap tide.*

A

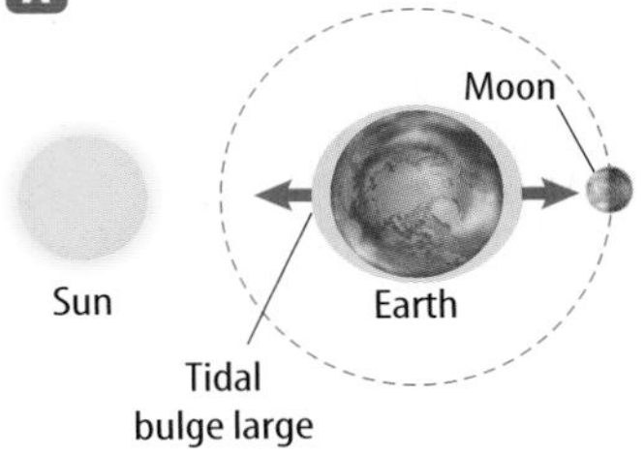

B

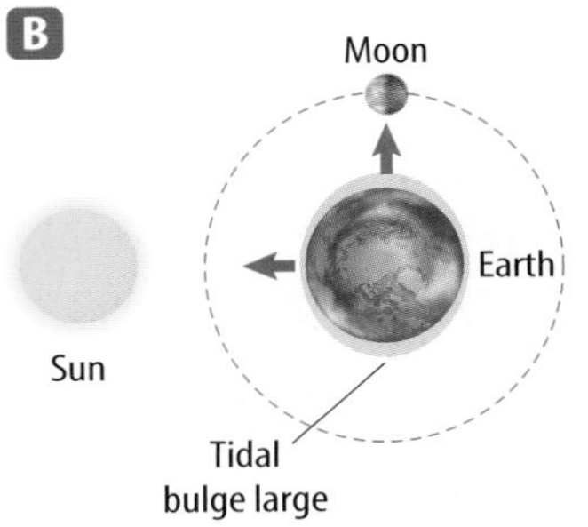

Moonlight

The Moon shines because it reflects sunlight from its surface. Just as half of Earth experiences day as the other half experiences night, half of the Moon is lighted while the other half is dark. As the Moon revolves around Earth, different portions of the side facing Earth are lighted, causing the Moon's appearance to change. **Moon phases** are the changing appearances of the Moon as seen from Earth. The phase you see depends on the relative positions of the Moon, Earth, and the Sun.

Phases of the Moon A new moon occurs when the Moon is between Earth and the Sun. During a new moon, the side of the Moon facing away from Earth is lighted and the side of the Moon facing Earth receives no light from the Sun. The Moon is in the sky, but it cannot be seen, except for a special alignment you will learn about later.

Teacher FYI

Tides Just as the Moon produces tides on Earth and its oceans, Earth has a similar effect on the Moon. Earth's pull on the Moon is why the Moon keeps one side facing Earth. It has become tidally locked into a synchronous orbit in which its rotation matches its revolution.

Reading Check

Answer High tides are higher and low tides are lower.

Caption Answer

Figure 10 neap tide

Discussion

Phases of the Moon Remind students that when standing on Earth, they can see phases of the Moon. If they were on the Moon, would they see Earth go through phases? Possible answer: Yes, Earth would go through all of the phases, except that Earth would stay in one position in the lunar sky. This occurs because the Moon keeps one side always facing Earth. L2

Use Science Words

Word Usage The words *waxing* and *waning* are used to describe Moon phases. Have students research the meanings of these words and use them in sentences. Possible answer: Waxing phases occur as the Moon appears to grow larger. Waning phases occur as the Moon appears to get smaller. L2 IN **Linguistic**

Activity

Moon Phases Have students face south and observe a first quarter moon in the southwestern sky shortly after sunset. Have them sketch what they see. Student sketches should show that the right side of the moon was lighted. Ask students if people living south of the equator would see the same thing. Possible answer: No, they would see the Moon in their northwestern sky and would see it in reverse, with the left side of the Moon lighted. L2 ELL IN **Visual-Spatial**

Teacher FYI

Proxigean Spring Tide Just as Earth's orbit around the Sun is elliptical, the Moon's orbit around Earth is also elliptical. This means that the Moon is closer to Earth at some times compared to others. The closest point in its orbit is called perigee. In the case of the Moon, orbits vary, and some perigees are closer than others. The closest perigee is called proxigee. When this occurs at a new moon or a full moon, the high spring tides are unusually high and the low spring tides are unusually low.

Mini LAB

Purpose Students will model the interactions among Earth, the Moon, and the Sun that cause phases and eclipses to occur.

Materials unshaded lamp, pencil, small white-plastic foam ball

Teaching Strategy Prior to doing the lab, ask students to brainstorm about what they think causes eclipses and lunar phases.

Safety Precaution Warn students that the lightbulb will be hot.

Analysis

1. More or less of the side of the ball facing the student was lighted. New moon—the ball was between the student and the light. The other phases followed in order.
2. During new moon, the ball blocked the light. During full moon, the ball was in the shadow of the student.

Assessment

Performance Ask students to use their models to demonstrate various phases of the Moon or an eclipse to members of their families or a fellow student.

Try at Home

INTEGRATE History

Content Background

In 1504, Columbus and his crew were stranded in what is now Jamaica while they repaired their ship. They faced starvation when the native people refused to sell them food. But Columbus knew exactly when a lunar eclipse would occur and told them that he would darken the Moon if they did not supply food. At first they laughed, but were terrified as the Moon started to disappear. Although they probably had seen eclipses before, they could not imagine a man causing one to happen. Columbus got his food.

Mini LAB

Modeling Phases and Eclipses

Procedure

1. Turn on a **lamp with no shade** and place a **small, white, plastic-foam ball** on the end of a **pencil.**
2. Stand facing the lamp and hold the white plastic-foam ball between your head and the lamp.
3. Slowly move the ball counterclockwise around your head and observe how much of the side of the ball facing you is lighted at different positions.
4. Note positions where the ball blocks light from the lamp—or moves into the shadow cast by your head.

Analysis

1. Describe what happened to the ball as it was moved around your head, and identify the moon phases at various positions.
2. At which positions (phases) was the ball blocking the light or falling into shadow? At which phase(s) can eclipses occur?

Try at Home

Waxing Phases After a new moon, the moon's phases are said to be waxing—the lighted portion that we see appears larger each night. The first phase we see after a new moon is called the waxing crescent. About a week after a new moon, we see one-half of the Moon's lighted side, or one-quarter of the Moon's surface. This phase is the first-quarter.

The moon is in the waxing gibbous phase from the first quarter up until full moon. A full moon occurs when we see all of the Moon's lighted side. At this time, the Moon is on the side of Earth opposite from the Sun.

Waning Phases After a full moon, the lighted portion that we see begins to appear smaller. The phases are said to be waning. When only half of the side of the Moon facing Earth is lighted, the third-quarter phase occurs. The waning crescent occurs before another new moon. Only a small slice of the side of the Moon facing Earth is lighted.

The word *month* is derived from the same root word as *Moon.* The complete cycle of the Moon's phases, shown in **Figure 11,** takes about 29.5 days, or one synodic month. Recall that it takes about 27.3 days for the Moon to revolve around Earth. The discrepancy between these two numbers is due to Earth's revolution around the Sun. It takes the Moon a little over two days to "catch up" with Earth's advancement around the Sun.

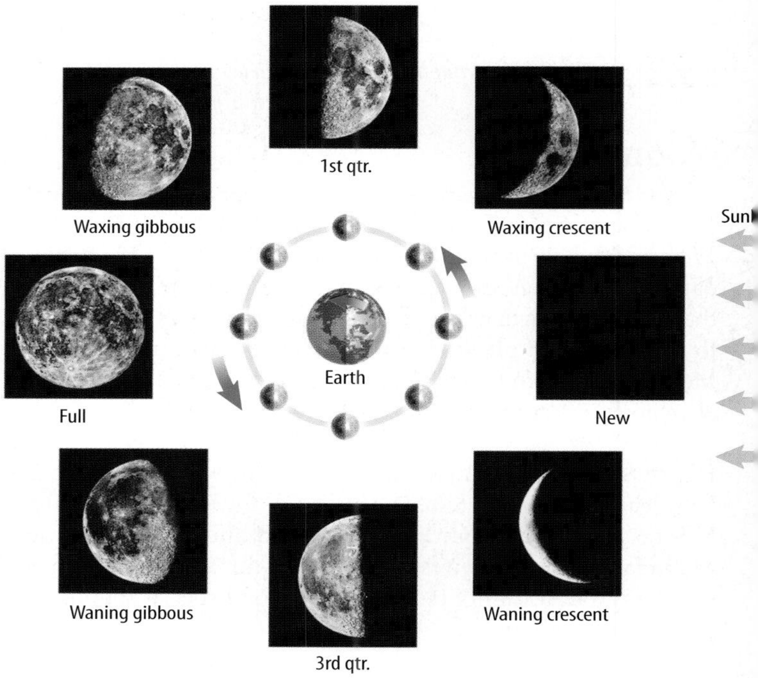

Figure 11 When viewed from Earth's north pole, the Moon has a counterclockwise orbit.
Infer *In this figure, the Sun's rays are coming from the right. Why are the Moon's waning phases showing sunlight on the left?*

Differentiated Instruction

Learning Disabled Help your learning-disabled students to understand how a smaller Moon can block out a larger Sun. Have them hold one hand in front of their faces and then move it until their hand (much smaller) can block out your desk (much larger). Tell students to compare the distances between their faces and their hands and their faces and the desk. L1 ELL

Visual Learning

Figure 11 Help students understand the information presented in **Figure 11.** The Moon's cycle of phases begins with new moon. From new moon to full moon the phases are waxing or growing in size. After full moon, the phases are waning or getting smaller. A full moon is on the opposite side of Earth from the Sun, so it rises as the Sun sets and sets as the Sun rises. A new moon rises and sets with the Sun. L2 ELL

Eclipses

INTEGRATE History

If you knew nothing about what the Sun is or why it produces so much light and heat, wouldn't you be concerned if suddenly it darkened? Think of how humans from long ago must have reacted when the Moon passed in front of the Sun and the source of light and heat was blocked, as it is during an eclipse.

In the year 585 B.C., a battle was raging between the armies of the Lydians and the Persians when suddenly, the Sun was eclipsed by the Moon. The two armies were so stunned by the event that they put down their weapons and stopped fighting.

Now we understand what causes eclipses of both the Sun and the Moon. We know that for the Moon to block out the Sun, it must appear to be the same size. In fact, both the Sun and the Moon have apparent diameters that are almost the same, about 0.5°. If it weren't for this, a total eclipse of the Sun might never happen. Because the Sun is about 400 times larger than the Moon, it also must be about 400 times farther from Earth for a total solar eclipse to occur.

Eclipses occur when Earth or the Moon temporarily blocks sunlight from reaching the other object. Sometimes, during a new moon, a shadow cast by the Moon falls on Earth, causing a solar eclipse. During a full moon, a shadow of Earth can be cast on the Moon, resulting in a lunar eclipse. Eclipses can occur only when the Sun, the Moon, and Earth are lined up perfectly. Because the Moon's orbit is tilted about 5° from the plane of Earth's orbit around the Sun, eclipses happen only a few times each year.

Solar Eclipses A **solar eclipse** occurs when the Moon moves directly between the Sun and Earth and casts a shadow on part of Earth. The darkest portion of the Moon's shadow is called the umbra. A person standing within the umbra experiences a total solar eclipse. As shown in **Figure 12,** the only portion of the Sun that is visible during a total eclipse is part of its atmosphere, which appears as a pearly white glow around the edge of the eclipsing Moon. This is the only time the entire disk of the new moon phase can be photographed—it appears black against the Sun.

As shown in **Figure 13,** surrounding the umbra is a lighter shadow on Earth's surface called the penumbra. Persons standing in the penumbra experience a partial solar eclipse. **WARNING:** *Regardless of where you are standing, never look directly at a solar eclipse. The light can permanently damage your eyes.*

Reading Check ***How are Earth, the Moon, and the Sun aligned during a solar eclipse?***

Figure 12 The solar corona can be seen as a pale glow around the lunar disk. Sunlight shining through lunar valleys produces a diamond-ring effect.

INTEGRATE History

Early Civilizations
Celestial objects were studied by early civilizations. Some hypotheses proposed by the Babylonians and the early Greeks were close to reality, but other ideas were wrong. Research how some early civilizations explained eclipses and other astronomical observations and report your findings to your class using drawings and diagrams.

Figure 13 A total solar eclipse appears only within the Moon's umbra.

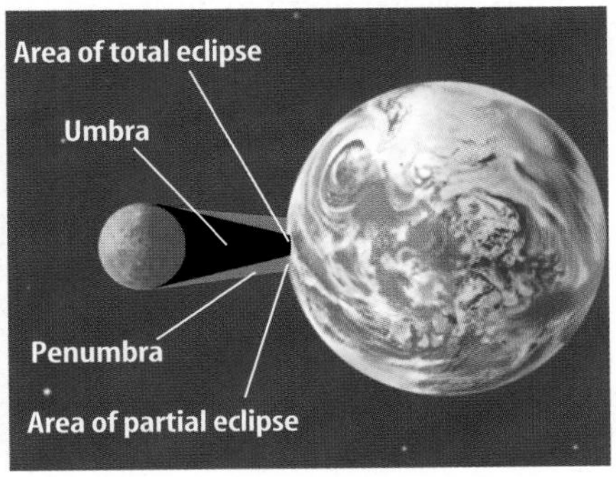

Science Journal

Solar Eclipse Have students write a brief description of factors that must be true in order for a solar eclipse to occur. Possible answer: The Moon must line up directly between Earth and the Sun. This can occur during new moon. Then ask them why a solar eclipse doesn't occur every new moon. Possible answer: The Moon's orbit is tilted such that it can sometimes be above or below the Sun during a new moon. L2 **Linguistic**

Caption Answer

Figure 11 The photos show the Moon as seen from Earth position.

INTEGRATE History

Early Civilizations It is said that Thales predicted a soloar eclipse in 585 B.C. By 430 B.C., Athenian Meton described the 19-year cycle of eclipses. Aristotle claimed that Earth was the center of the universe. He thought that if it wasn't, we should see parallax among the stars. Since no parallax could be observed, either Earth was in the center or the stars were very far away. He believed stars were fairly close, thus he concluded that Earth was in the middle of the universe.

Make a Model

A Sun-Moon Model Have students cut out a circle 200 cm (2 m) in diameter from yellow paper that has been pieced together. Have them cut another circle from a piece of gray paper that is 0.5 cm in diameter. Tell students that they have cut out circles that represent the comparative diameters of the Sun and Moon. Have one student hold the small paper circle up to his or her eye. Have other students carry the large circle away from the first student until he or she says that the small circle can block out the large one. Students now have a model of the Moon eclipsing the Sun. Ask students to explain how the Moon can block out the Sun. Possible answer: the Sun is about 400 times farther from Earth then is the Moon. L1 ELL

Reading Check

Answer The Moon is directly between Earth and the Sun.

Reading Check

Answer The Moon is on the opposite side of Earth from the Sun.

Inquiry Lab

Lunar Eclipses

Question Why don't lunar eclipses occur every time the Moon is full?

Possible Materials flashlight, small light source, plastic foam balls, large pieces of cardboard or hard plastic, cardboard circles or plastic hoops

Estimated Time 30 minutes

Teaching Strategies

- Encourage students to develop models that demonstrate a full moon can occur without a lunar eclipse.
- Remind students that the Moon's orbit varies about 5° above and below the ecliptic and that for a total lunar eclipse to occur, the Sun, Earth, and the Moon must be perfectly aligned—that is, they must be on the same plane.
- Guide students to see how two planes can intersect, but do not have to be in the same plane.
- If students ask, tell them that the diameter of Earth is about four times that of the Moon and that the distance from Earth to the Moon is about 30 Earth diameters.
- Suggest that students use their model to demonstrate partial lunar eclipses.

For additional inquiry activities, see *Science Inquiry Lab Manual*.

Caption Answer

Figure 15 small shadow

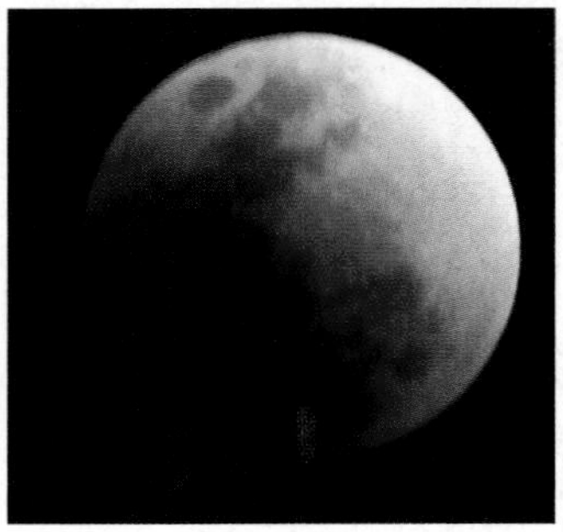

Figure 14 Sometimes during a partial lunar eclipse, Earth's curvature can be seen silhouetted on the Moon. The red coloration is caused by the refraction of sunlight passing through Earth's atmosphere before reaching the Moon's surface.

Lunar Eclipses When Earth's shadow falls on the Moon, a **lunar eclipse** occurs. A lunar eclipse begins when the Moon moves into Earth's penumbra. As the Moon continues to move, it enters Earth's umbra, and you see a curved shadow on the Moon's surface, as shown in **Figure 14.** It was this shadow that led Aristotle to conclude that Earth is spherical. When the Moon moves completely into Earth's umbra, a total lunar eclipse occurs, as shown in **Figure 15.** The Moon sometimes becomes red during an eclipse because light from the Sun is scattered and refracted by Earth's atmosphere. Longer wavelength red light is affected less than shorter wavelengths, so more red light falls on the Moon.

A partial lunar eclipse occurs when only a portion of the Moon moves into Earth's umbra. The remainder of the Moon is in Earth's penumbra and, therefore, receives some direct sunlight. A partial lunar eclipse also occurs when the Moon is partially or totally within Earth's penumbra. However, this can be difficult to see because some direct sunlight falls on the Moon, making it appear only slightly dimmer than usual.

A total solar eclipse can occur as often as twice a year, yet most people live their entire lives without witnessing one. You may never see a total solar eclipse, but it is almost certain you will have a chance to see a total lunar eclipse. The reason why it is so rare to view a total solar eclipse is that only those people in the small region where the Moon's umbra strikes Earth can see one and, even then, there must be clear skies. In contrast, the opportunities to witness lunar eclipses are much more frequent, and anyone on the night side of Earth can see them.

Reading Check *How are Earth, the Moon, and the Sun aligned during a lunar eclipse?*

Figure 15 A total lunar eclipse occurs when the Moon is entirely within Earth's umbra. *Umbra* is the Latin word for "shadow." Just as a peninsula is almost an island, a penumbra is almost a shadow.
Research *What does* umbrella *mean?*

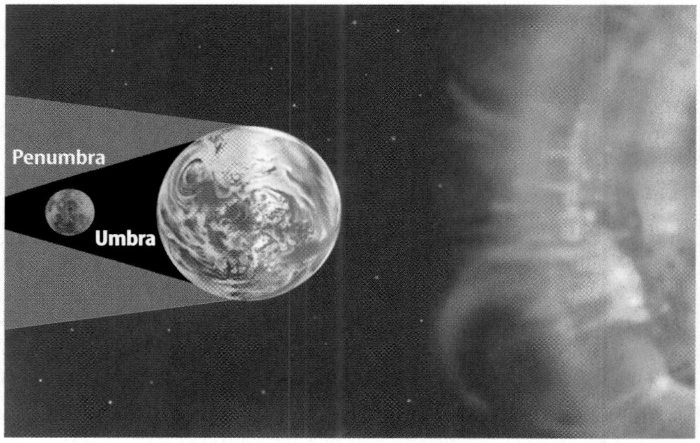

Science Journal

Lunar Eclipse Have students write a brief description of factors that must be true in order for a lunar eclipse to occur. Possible answer: The Moon must line up directly on the opposite side of Earth from the Sun. This can occur during full moon. Then ask them why a lunar eclipse can be seen by more people than a solar eclipse. Possible answer: Since the Moon is passing into Earth's shadow, all people on the night side of Earth can see a lunar eclipse. L2 **Linguistic**

202 CHAPTER 7 The Earth-Moon-Sun System

Caption Answer

Figure 16 maria; rays

Fun Fact

The Moon is covered in dust, called regolith, to an average depth of about 20 m. The regolith has the consistency of fine powder, similar to ready-mix dry mortar. It has formed from billions of years of meteorite impacts.

Quick Demo

Moon Surface Features

Materials moon map or globe

Estimated Time 10 minutes

Procedure Show students a map of the Moon (near side and far side) or a globe. Show how the far side has many more craters than the near side. Ask students why this might be true. Possible answer: Earth protects the near side of the Moon. Many meteorites that would have hit the Moon's near side were pulled toward Earth. Point out key features on the near side of the Moon (craters, maria, mountains). Ask students how maria may have formed. Possible answer: When meteorites impacted on the Moon's surface, they formed depressions and cracks in the crust. Magma flowed through the cracks onto the Moon's surface, filling the depressions. L2 ELL

LS **Visual-Spatial**

The Moon's Surface

When you look at the Moon, as shown in **Figure 16,** you can see many of its larger surface features. Craters, rays, mountains, and maria can easily be seen through a small telescope or a pair of binoculars. What are these different features, how did they form, and what do they tell us about the Moon's history and interior?

Figure 16 Notice the light-colored material radiating outward from the large crater near the base of the Moon.

Identify *What are the flat, dark-colored regions called? What are the light-colored areas radiating from the craters called?*

Craters, Maria, and Mountains Many depressions on the Moon were formed by meteorites, asteroids, and comets, which strike the surfaces of planets and their satellites. These depressions, which are called craters, formed early in the Moon's history. Surrounding many craters are ray patterns produced by lighter-colored material from just below the lunar surface that was blasted out on impact and settled on top of the darker surface material around the craters. During the impact, when these large basins formed, cracks may have formed in the Moon's crust, allowing lava from the still-molten interior to reach the surface and fill in the basins, forming maria.

Maria are the dark-colored, relatively flat regions on the Moon's surface, shown in **Figure 16.** The igneous rocks of the maria are 3 to 4 billion years old. They are the youngest rocks found on the Moon so far. This indicates that the craters formed after the Moon's surface originally cooled. However, the maria formed early enough in the Moon's history that molten rock material still remained in the Moon's interior.

Surrounding the large depressions that later filled with lava are areas that were thrown upward in the original collision and formed mountains. The largest mountain ranges on the Moon surround the large, flat, dark-colored maria.

Regolith When NASA scientists started to plan for crewed spacecraft to land on the Moon, they were concerned about whether the lunar surface would be able to support the craft? To find out, unmanned *Surveyor* spacecraft were landed on its surface. One *Surveyor* craft actually bounced a few times as it landed on the side of a crater. What was this material that the spacecraft had landed on?

Impacts on the Moon thoughout its history led to the accumulation of debris known as **regolith.** On some areas of the Moon, this regolith is almost 40 m thick, while in other locations, it is only a few centimeters thick. Some regolith is coarse, but some is a fine dust. If you watch astronauts walking on the Moon, you will notice that they often kick up a lot of dust.

Visual Learning

Figure 16 Help students understand the information presented in **Figure 16.** Show students that rays of lighter material radiate outward from craters. Explain that when the meteorites struck the Moon, light material of the crust was ejected out over the darker surrounding rock. L2 ELL

LS **Visual-Spatial**

Caption Answer

Figure 17 Earth's gravitational attraction is stronger between Earth and the Moon's greater-density core than between Earth and the Moon's less-dense crust.

Content Background

The Moon's Interior Discuss with students that seismographs were left behind on the Moon. They detected moonquakes and this data has enabled NASA scientists to model the Moon's interior.

Data shows that the Moon's interior is differentiated. Although it is thought that the Moon has an iron core, it is not as large as Earth's. This may be a result of the giant impact that formed the Moon. Most of the iron cores of the two colliding bodies fell back to the reforming Earth.

As the Moon began to cool, Earth's gravity affected different parts of the Moon's structure differently. The thinner crust on the side of the Moon facing Earth was caused by the tidal influence of gravity pulling more on the mantle material than on the crustal material.

Reading Check

Answer on the side facing away from Earth

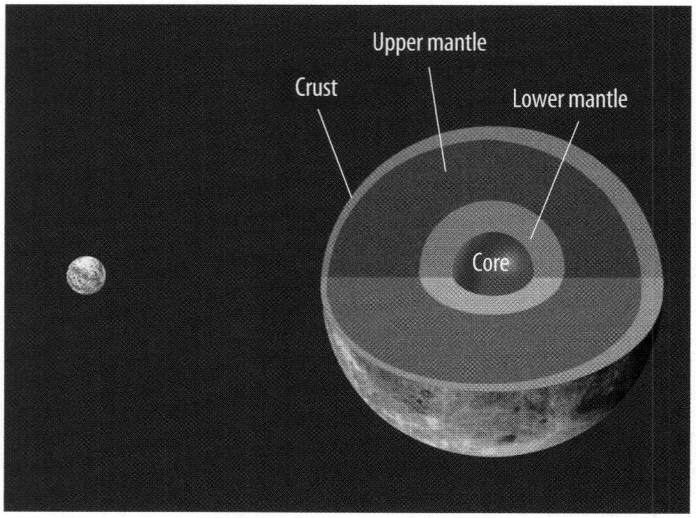

Figure 17 The Moon's crust is thinnest on the side nearest to Earth.
Infer *Why is the Moon's crust thinnest on the side facing Earth?*

The Moon's Interior

The presence of maria on the Moon's surface tells us something about its interior. If cracks did form when the large depressions were produced by impacts, and lava did flow onto the lunar surface, then the interior of the Moon just below its surface must have been molten at that time. It is believed that this was the case and that before the Moon cooled to what it is like today, its interior separated into layers.

Other information about the Moon's interior comes from seismographs left on the Moon by *Apollo* astronauts. Just as the study of earthquakes allows scientists to map Earth's interior, the study of moonquakes helps them study the Moon's interior and has led to the model shown in **Figure 17.** This model shows that the Moon's crust is about 60 km thick on the side facing Earth and about 150 km thick on the side facing away. Below the crust, a solid mantle may extend to a depth of 1,000 km. A partly molten zone of the mantle extends farther down. Below this is an iron-rich, solid core.

Reading Check *Where is the Moon's crust thickest?*

Exploring the Moon

More than 20 years after the *Apollo* program ended, the *Clementine* spacecraft was placed in lunar orbit. *Clementine* compiled a detailed map of the Moon's surface, including the South Pole-Aitken Basin. This is the oldest identifiable impact feature on the Moon's surface. It is also the largest and deepest impact basin or depression found so far anywhere in the solar system, measuring 12 km in depth and 2,500 km in diameter. Because the angle of sunlight is always low near the poles, much of this depression remains in shadow throughout the Moon's rotation. This location provides a cold area where ice deposits from impacting comets may have collected. The *Clementine* spacecraft, and later the *Lunar Prospector*, both collected evidence that supports the hypothesis that water-ice has accumulated in South Pole-Aitken Basin. See **Figure 18** to learn more about this.

Science Online

Topic: *Clementine* and *Lunar Prospector* Missions
Visit gpescience.com for Web links to information about the missions of the *Clementine* and *Lunar Prospector* spacecraft.

Activity Make a table that lists the major goals of each mission and whether or not it succeeded.

Teacher FYI

Water on the Moon The water that may exist at the Moon's poles was not found directly. Its presence is hypothesized from the detection of neutrons by the *Lunar Prospector* spacecraft. Scientists believe that cosmic rays continually bombard the Moon's surface interact with the hydrogen in the water and release neutrons that were detected by the spacecraft. The water could be used by humans in the everyday operation of a nearby moon base or could be separated into oxygen and hydrogen to be used for rocket fuel. The anticipated cost of transporting water to the Moon is thousands of dollars per kg. This led one scientist to state that the water-ice deposits could become the most valuable real estate in the solar system.

NATIONAL GEOGRAPHIC **VISUALIZING WATER ON THE MOON**

Figure 18

Astronomers long believed that the Moon was a cold, dry place without atmosphere. But a few scientists hypothesized that water could exist on the Moon under certain conditions. This hypothesis was proven correct in the late 1990s by data from the spacecrafts *Clementine* and *Lunar Prospector*.

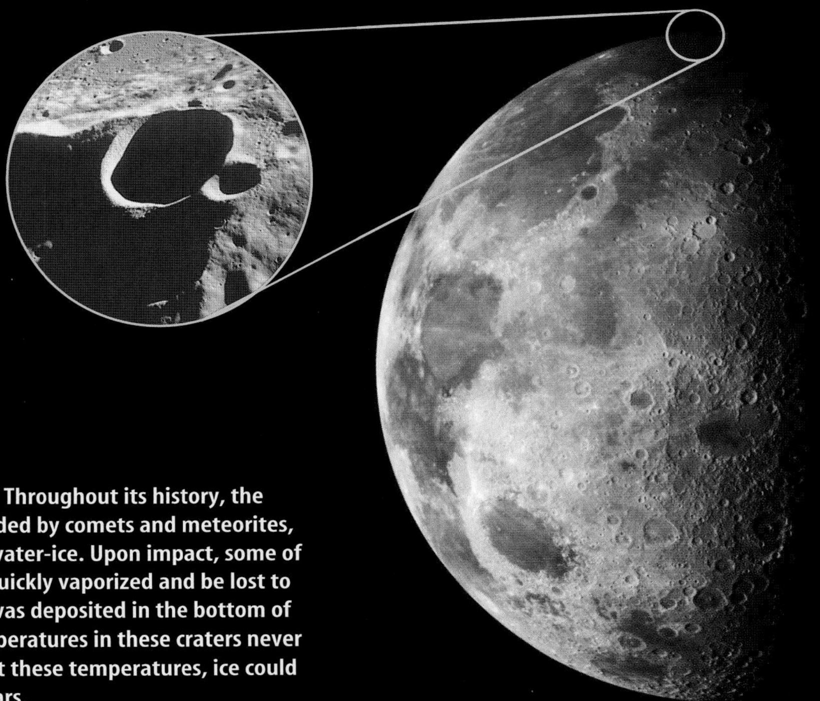

HOW DID IT GET THERE? **Throughout its history, the Moon has been bombarded by comets and meteorites, most of which contain water-ice. Upon impact, some of the water would have quickly vaporized and be lost to space. However, some was deposited in the bottom of deep polar craters. Temperatures in these craters never exceed about −173°C. At these temperatures, ice could persist for billions of years.**

HOW MUCH IS THERE? **Estimates of how much water-ice exists vary, but some estimates are as high as 6 trillion kg. Ice might be buried several meters below the surface, either in solid blocks or as ice crystals mixed with lunar regolith. Water is important for many reasons. It would be needed for the survival of humans at any future lunar bases. Also, it could be split using solar power into hydrogen and oxygen to make rocket fuel.**

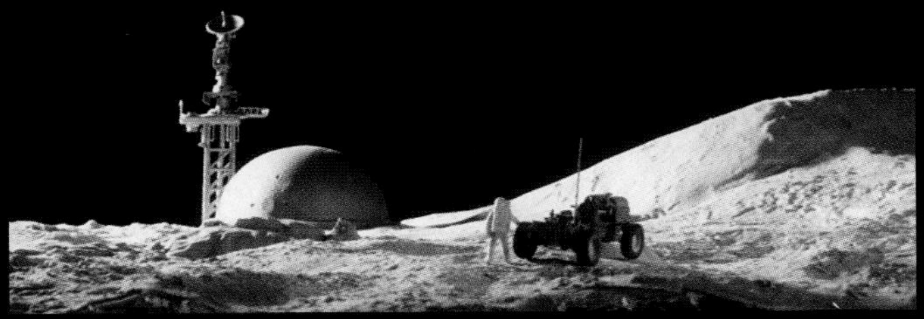

NATIONAL GEOGRAPHIC

Visualizing Water on the Moon

Have students examine the pictures and read the captions. Then ask the following questions.

What made some scientists think that water might exist on the Moon? The fact that the Moon has many craters caused by impacts with comets and meteorites that are known to contain water-ice.

How and where has water been detected on the Moon? It was detected by orbiting spacecraft using an instrument called a neutron spectrometer near the Moon's poles.

Why might a source of water on the Moon be important for future space exploration? Any future Moon base or colony could use the water for life support or as a source of rocket fuel.

Activity

Devise a model or use a common object to show how the bottoms of craters at the Moon's poles are not struck by sunlight. Possible solutions: Use a more or less spherical object with an indentation on one or both ends. Then shine light so that it strikes the object at right angles. Objects could include an apple, a clay sphere with large craters at the top and bottom, or plastic-foam balls having craters carved in them.

Differentiated Instruction

Challenge Ask students to research the topic and find out more why the water is found primarily in craters at the poles and more specifically in craters in the Aitken Basin. Prepare a diagram showing how parts of this area are particularly suited to preserving water-ice and present it to your class. L3

Activity

Crater Formation Provide students with a flat pan in which you have placed a 2.5–cm layer of flour covered by a 0.5-cm layer of dark gray ready-mix mortar. Have them drop various-sized objects into the pan from different heights. Have students write a brief description of their observations in their Science Journals. Possible answer: As an object impacted on the gray powder, a crater formed and lighter material from just under the surface was ejected and fell back onto the surrounding gray material. Deeper and larger craters were formed by larger objects. L2 ELL LS **Visual-Spatial**

Reading Check

Answer Mascons are concentrations of mass under the Moon's surface. They could be what are left of the meteorites that formed the impact basins.

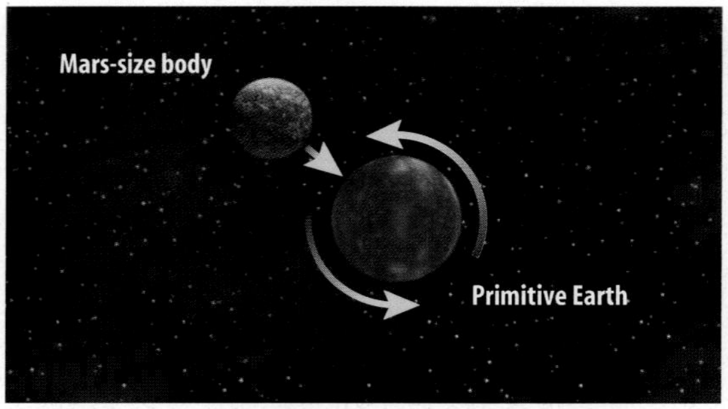

A large, Mars-sized body collided with primitive Earth approximately 4.6 billion years ago.

The violent collision melted and vaporized some of Earth's crust and mantle and hurled it into space.

Figure 19 According to the giant impact theory, the Moon formed after Earth was struck a glancing blow by a body that was more massive than Mars. For millions of years after the Moon's birth, stray rock fragments ejected by the original impact continued to pelt its surface, creating the craters that now blanket the Moon.

Clementine and Lunar Prospector Data from *Clementine* confirmed that the crust on the side facing Earth is much thinner than on the far side. Data also found that the crust thins under impact basins and showed the location of mascons, concentrations of mass that are located under impact basins. What do you think they might be? *Clementine* also provided information on the mineral content of Moon rocks. In fact, this part of its mission explains the spacecraft's name. Clementine was the daughter of a miner in the ballad "My Darlin' Clementine."

Reading Check *What are mascons?*

In 1998, the *Lunar Prospector* spacecraft orbited the Moon, taking photographs of the lunar surface. Maps made using these photographs confirmed the *Clementine* data. Also, data from *Lunar Prospector* confirmed that the Moon has a small, iron-rich core about 600 km in diameter. *Lunar Prospector* also conducted a detailed study of the Moon's surface searching for clues as to its origin and structure.

Origin of the Moon

Prior to the data obtained from the Apollo space missions, there were three theories about the Moon's origin. The first was that the Moon was captured by Earth's gravity (the capture theory). It had formed elsewhere and wandered near Earth. The second theory was that the Moon condensed from the same loose material that Earth formed from during the early formation of the solar system (the binary accretion theory). The third theory was that a glob of molten material was ejected from Earth while Earth was still molten (the fission theory). Ironically, the goal of one Apollo mission was to help determine which of these theories was correct. Instead, the mission showed that none of the three theories can explain the Moon's composition.

Differentiated Instruction

Behaviorally Disordered Have teams of students make illustrated posters, each showing one stage in the formation of the Moon. Display posters in the correct order to show all the stages in the formation of the Moon according to the giant impact theory. L2 LS **Visual-Spatial**

Visual Learning

Figure 19 Help students understand the theory being presented in **Figure 19.** A Mars-sized body impacted a young Earth at a glancing angle. The cores of the two bodies and most of the other material merged to form a new Earth. Material that was thrown far enough away from Earth later condensed to form the Moon. L2

Some material fell back to Earth, some escaped into interplanetary space, and some orbited Earth as a ring of hot gas and debris.

Solid particles eventually condensed from the cooling gas and the Moon began to accumulate.

Giant Impact Theory Data gathered by the *Apollo* missions led many scientists to form a new giant impact theory, which has gained wide acceptance among astronomers. According to this theory, the Moon formed about 4.6 billion years ago when a Mars-sized object collided with Earth. After colliding, the cores of the two bodies combined and settled toward the center of the larger object. Gas and other debris were thrown into orbit. Some fell back to Earth, but the remainder condensed into a large mass, forming the Moon. This sequence is shown in **Figure 19.** This theory helps to explain how the Moon and Earth are similar, yet not similar enough to have formed from the same condensing mass. If the core of the Mars-sized body was added to the core of Earth, this explains why the Moon's composition is like Earth's mantle and why the Moon has a much smaller central core than expected.

section 3 review

Summary

How does the Moon affect Earth?

- The Moon and the Sun affect Earth's tides.
- As the Moon revolves, different amounts of the side facing Earth are lighted by the Sun, causing the changing phases.
- The alignment of Earth, the Moon, and the Sun produces eclipses.

The Moon's Surface and Interior

- The Moon's surface has craters, mountains, and maria.
- Maria are the dark-colored, relatively flat regions on the Moon.
- The *Clementine* and *Lunar Prospector* found evidence of water-ice on the Moon.

Self Check

1. **Compare and contrast** solar and lunar eclipses.
2. **Explain** tides in Earth's oceans.
3. **Diagram** the positions of Earth, the Moon, and the Sun during a full moon.
4. **Describe** how lunar maria might have formed.
5. **Think Critically** Why is it so important to future space exploration if the Moon has water-ice near its surface?

Applying Math

6. **Calculate** An estimate of the amount of water frozen at the Moon's south pole is 100,000 m^3. If this deposit was spread over an area measuring 160 m by 125 m, how many meters deep would the deposit be?

section 3 review

1. Both are eclipses involving Earth, the Moon, and the Sun. A solar eclipse occurs when the Moon's shadow falls on Earth. A lunar eclipse occurs when the Moon moves into Earth's shadow.
2. Tides are one large water wave in Earth's oceans caused by the gravities of the Moon and the Sun.
3. Student diagrams should show the Moon on the opposite side of Earth from the Sun.
4. Large meteorites struck the Moon, forming large depressions and cracking its surface. Magma from inside the Moon flowed onto the surface and filled the large depressions.
5. The water-ice could be used by a lunar base, and rocket fuel (oxygen and hydrogen) could be obtained from the water-ice.
6. 5 m deep

Post Reading

Reflection Ask students to respond to the following prompts: How have lunar explorations broadened our understanding of the Moon's physical characteristics? How does the Moon affect Earth? In your opinion, should future explorations to the Moon and other parts of space be pursued?

3 Assess

DAILY INTERVENTION

Check for Understanding

Visual-Spatial Divide students into small groups. Have each group of students devise a way to show what happens to cause a solar eclipse or a lunar eclipse. L2 ELL IS **Linguistic**

Reteach

Tides Ask students to hypothesize about how tides on Earth would be affected if we had no Moon. Possible answer: High and low tides would still occur because of the Sun's gravity. The tidal range between high tide and low tide would be less and there would be no spring or neap tides. L2

Assessment

Oral Have students discuss why the pull of the Moon's gravity causes higher and lower tides on Earth than does the pull of the Sun's gravity. Possible answer: Although the Moon is much smaller than the Sun, it is much closer to Earth. L2

BENCH TESTED

Real-World Problem

Purpose Students will use a map of the Moon to locate specific features and Apollo landing sites on the Moon.

Process Skills use a map, identify, interpret scientific illustrations, draw and label, trace

Time Required 40 minutes

Alternate Materials tracing paper

Procedure

Teaching Strategies

- Place a large map of the Moon with features labeled in front of the class.
- Prior to beginning this lab, show students the differences among various lunar features (craters, maria, mountains, and rays)

Tie to Prior Knowledge Ask students if they have ever used their imagination to try to find the 'man in the Moon.' Tell them that the dark-colored maria can look like the eyes of a face in the full moon. Mention that other cultures have found a woman, a rabbit, and an ant in the features of the Moon.

Troubleshooting Have students trace an illustration of the full moon. They can then label the features and Apollo landing sites on their tracings.

LAB

Identifying the Moon's Surface Features and *APOLLO* Landing Sites

Goals

- **Identify** prominent surface features on the Moon.
- **Determine** the relative ages of features on the Moon's surface.
- **Locate** the *Apollo* landing sites on the Moon.

Materials

large-scale maps or globes of the Moon

individual, smaller maps of the Moon

Real-World Problem

When you look at a full moon in the night sky, you can see light and dark areas. When you look through binoculars or a small telescope, you can see many craters and the large, dark-colored maria. Many craters are named after great philosophers and scientists. The maria are named for what early scientists thought they saw there; for example, *Oceanus Procellarum* means "ocean of storms." Can you tell the difference between an old crater and one that has formed more recently? If craters are seen on a maria, which of the features is older? If one crater partially covers another, which one formed first?

Procedure

1. Obtain a large-scale map or globe of the Moon.
2. Familiarize yourself with some of the more prominent surface features of the Moon.

Alternative Inquiry Lab

Modeling the Moon Students could construct a 3-D model of a section of the Moon's surface to extend the investigation of specific features and *Apollo* landing sites on the Moon's surface. They could place a thin layer of modeling clay that covers a spherical ball. Craters and maria could be impressions on the surface with mountains being areas where additional clay is placed. Students could use a Moon map or globe to determine the scale to be used on their models. They might want to concentrate on just one of the landing sites and include as much as possible about the lunar topography around the specific landing site. For example, *Apollo 15* would enable students to show the relative altitude of mountains on the Moon.

3. Look for examples of younger craters (those with sharp sides and peaks in the center) and examples of older craters (those whose sides are worn down or missing).
4. Using a large-scale, labeled map or globe of the Moon, locate, identify, and label the following prominent surface features of the Moon and *Apollo* landing sites on a copy of the Moon's surface. (If an unlabeled Moon map is not available, draw one and illustrate and label the features listed below.)

Features on the Moon

Maria	Craters	Mountain Ranges	Apollo Landing Sites
Mare Crisium	Alphonsus	Alps	11-Mare Tranquillitatus
Mare Frigoris	Aristarchus	Apennine	12-Oceanus Procellarum
Mare Imbrium	Clavius	Caucasus	14-Fra Mauro
Mare Serenitatis	Copernicus	Jura	15-Mt. Hadley
Mare Tranquillitatus	Fra Mauro	Mt. Hadley	16-Descartes
Oceanus Procellarum	Grimaldi		17-Taurus Littrow
	Kepler		
	Plato		
	Tycho		

Analyze Your Data

1. **Describe** the specific lunar features you studied and what you learned from them.
2. **Identify** one specific observation that helped you decide which of two features formed first.

Conclude and Apply

1. **Infer** from your study of the large-scale map or globe whether Copernicus Crater or Grimaldi Crater is older. Do the same for Fra Mauro Crater and Tycho Crater. **Explain** your answers.
2. **Research** the *Apollo* missions and **explain** why there is no landing site for *Apollo 13*.

Communicating Your Data

Compare your map of the Moon with the maps labeled by other students in your class. **Discuss** why individual maps may be labeled differently or why map illustrations might look different.

Communicating Your Data

Instruct students to view the Moon through a pair of binoculars or a small telescope. Ask them to locate as many of the features they have written on their maps, as they can see. Have students share what they observed on the Moon with other classmates.

Differentiated Instruction

Learning Disabled Provide small or book-sized maps for your students who have learning disabilities. Trace a copy of a map of the full moon and provide a copy of the tracing for your students to use. L1 ELL **Visual-Spatial**

Analyze Your Data

Expected Outcome Students will draw and label a map (or a tracing of a map) of the Moon. Students will find all features and Apollo landing sites listed in this lab.

Answers to Questions

1. Answers will vary. Students may mention differences among craters or interest in Apollo landing sites.
2. Again, answers will vary but should mention differences in crater appearance (sharp or worn sides) and superimposed craters.

Error Analysis Possible sources of error are students not realizing that maria are colored darker than highland areas of the Moon and that craters can form on maria and on top of other craters. Ask students where on their maps they located Tycho crater. This crater has bright rays radiating out from it over long distances on the Moon's surface.

Conclude and Apply

1. Copernicus crater is younger than Grimaldi crater. Tycho crater is younger than Fra Mauro. Younger craters have steep sides and often show central peaks. Older craters have been weathered by continued impacts.
2. *Apollo 13* experienced a failure on route to the Moon. One of its fuel tanks exploded and the fuel that remained in the Command Module and Lunar Excursion Module was used to power the spacecraft around the Moon and its return trip to Earth.

Assessment

Process Ask students to use a map of the Moon to locate Ptolemaeus crater and Mare Humorum. L2 ELL IS **Visual-Spatial**

Content Background

Newton worked with optics from 1670 to 1672. He was the first to realize that the colors produced when light passes through a prism are inherent in the light. Before this, it was believed that the colors of the sprectrum were added by the prism.

In Newton's time, the borders between science and alchemy were not sharply defined. Newton himself believed in the existence of an ether that transmits forces between particles and in what was then the "occult idea" of action at a distance. Such erroneous beliefs possibly aided him in developing his ideas of gravity. Because of his contributions in mechanics, optics, and mathematics, Newton is often ranked foremost among scientists.

Analyze the Event

Today we know that refraction and dispersion occur because the light passes though substances of different density. What examples of this have you seen in everyday life and what are substances involved. Possible Answers: Students may mention seeing rainbows, either in the sky or in the spray of a garden hose, seeing colors as light passed through hanging glass pieces on lamps, seeing colors in a puddle covered by an oil slick.

Discussion

Ask students how a person like Newton who discovered so many basic scientific principles could have considered alchemical or occult ideas. Help them to see Newton in the context of his time and to see that even great scientists can make mistakes.

Oops! Accidents in SCIENCE

SOMETIMES GREAT DISCOVERIES HAPPEN BY ACCIDENT!

Even Great Scientists Make Mistakes

"If I have been able to see further, it was only because I stood on the shoulders of giants."
—Sir Isaac Newton

Today, scientists know that sometimes light behaves like a wave and at other times it behaves like a particle. However, early scientists believed it had to be one way or the other. Sir Isaac Newton, 1642–1727, believed in the particle nature of light. Based on his observations and a few erroneous assumptions, he eventually invented what is now called the Newtonian reflecting telescope.

Where did Newton go wrong?

One erroneous assumption involved the behavior of light as it passes through matter such as glass, a property known as chromatic aberration. White light is composed of many different wavelengths that can disperse when refracted. This also happens with telescopes because lenses act like a combination of many prisms and disperse white light into the colors of the rainbow. We now know that the larger the lens, the less of a problem this dispersal of light causes. Newton thought the opposite was true. He tried to eliminate chromatic aberration by changing or adding lenses and using prisms, but was unable to correct the problem.

Another mistake made by Newton was that he assumed light particles begin to refract before they contact matter. Because of these assumptions, he concluded that there was no way to fix the problem. So, he gave up on refracting telescopes and used a curved mirror to focus light. This worked, because light does not disperse when it is reflected. His incorrect assumptions led to the invention of the most-used instrument in astronomy, the reflecting telescope.

Sometimes the greatest discoveries in science are based on incorrect assumptions. But, that's okay—it is called science.

Newtonian Telescope

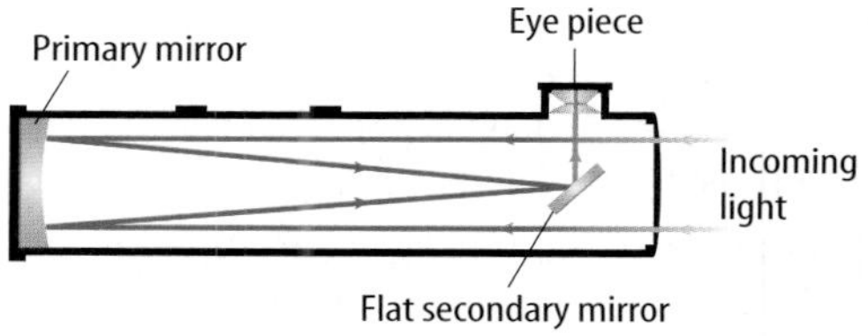

Try it yourself **Experiment with shining light through a prism and reflecting it from a mirror. Try using several different prisms with different angles.**

Oops! For more information, visit gpescience.com

Try it Yourself Students should be able to disperse light using prisms or any angular pieces of glass or plastic. The light refracted by prisms will produce colors; the light reflected by mirrors will not.

Resources for Teachers and Students

The Life of Isaac Newton, Richard S. Westfall, Cambridge University Press, 1999

Isaac Newton:The Last Sorcerer, Michael White, Helix Books, 1997

Newton's Gift , David Berlinski, Touchstone, 2000

Isaac Newton, by James Gleick, Vintage Books, 2003

Reviewing Main Ideas

Section 1 Earth in Space

1. The fact that Earth always casts a curved shadow, as shown here, is evidence of its spherical shape.
2. When Earth was molten, the force of gravity pulling equally in all directions caused Earth to form into a spherical shape.

3. Earth's rotation and movement of matter in its core cause Earth's magnetic field.
4. Earth is different than other planets. These differences enable life to flourish on Earth.

Section 2 Time and Seasons

1. Earth's rotation and revolution are used to measure time in days and years.
2. During the year, the Sun appears to move on the ecliptic through a background of constellations called the zodiac.
3. Earth experiences changing seasons because locations on Earth receive sunlight for varying amounts of time each day and at varying angles throughout the year, as shown here.

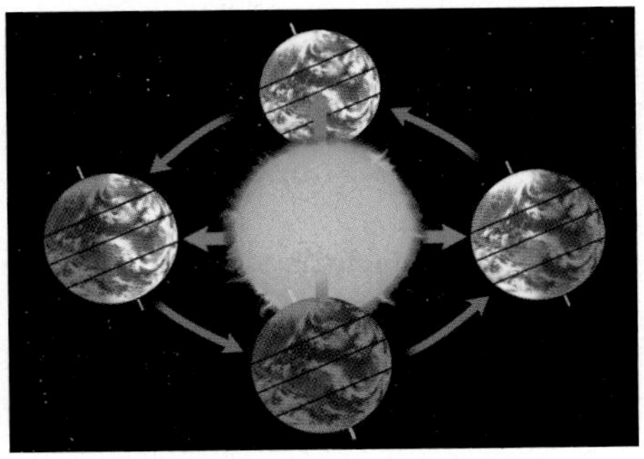

4. The Sun reaches its greatest distance north of the equator on the summer solstice for the northern hemisphere and on the winter solstice for the southern hemisphere.

Section 3 Earth's Moon

1. Tides in Earth's oceans are affected by the gravity of the Moon and the Sun. The Moon's gravity has a greater effect because the Moon is much closer to Earth.
2. Changing positions of the Moon in relation to the Sun cause it to go through a lunar phase cycle every 29.5 days.
3. Solar eclipses occur during a new moon, and lunar eclipses occur during a full moon.
4. Craters, like this one, are depressions on the Moon's surface. Some large depressions may have filled with lava, forming maria.

FOLDABLES™ Use the foldable that you made at the beginning of this chapter to review the Earth-Moon-Sun system.

Identifying Misconceptions

Assess

Demonstration Use this assessment as a follow-up to page F at the beginning of the chapter after students have completed the chapter.

Materials flashlight

Procedure Demonstrate that light from the flashlight that falls on the wall, no matter from what angle, are direct; all light falls directly on the wall. Show that light falling perpendicularly strikes the wall with more intensity than light from the flashlight that falls on the wall from an angle other than vertical.

Expected Outcome Students will understand that the more vertical the rays are from the Sun, the more intense the light and heat from the Sun is. Students will realize that all rays from the Sun, whether vertical or slanted are direct rays.

Reviewing Main Ideas

Summary statements can be used by students to review the major concepts of the chapter.

Science Online

Visit gpescience.com
More Section Review
Interactive Tutor
Vocabulary PuzzleMaker
More Chapter Review
Standardized Test Practice

Assessment Transparency

For additional assessment questions, use the *Assessment Transparency* located in the transparency book.

Assessment

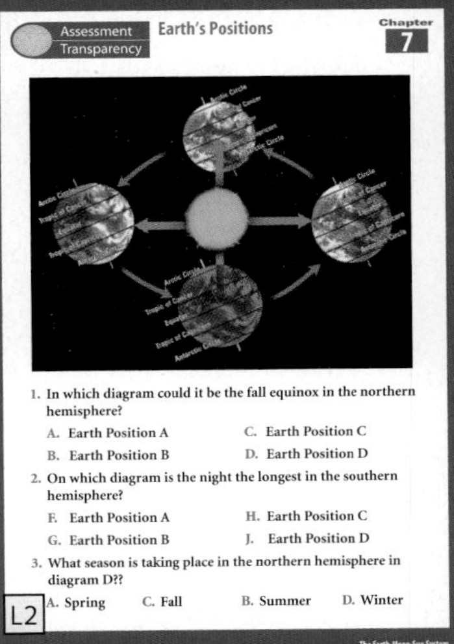

Assessment Transparency — Earth's Positions — Chapter 7

1. In which diagram could it be the fall equinox in the northern hemisphere?
   A. Earth Position A C. Earth Position C
   B. Earth Position B D. Earth Position D
2. On which diagram is the night the longest in the southern hemisphere?
   F. Earth Position A H. Earth Position C
   G. Earth Position B J. Earth Position D
3. What season is taking place in the northern hemisphere in diagram D??
   A. Spring C. Fall B. Summer D. Winter

L2

The Earth-Moon-Sun System

FOLDABLES™ Have students use their Foldables to review the Earth-Moon-Sun system.

Using Vocabulary

1. maria
2. rotation
3. tide
4. sphere
5. revolution
6. solar eclipse
7. time zone
8. equinox
9. gravity
10. ecliptic

Checking Concepts

11. C	16. D
12. D	17. B
13. C	18. C
14. D	19. B
15. B	20. A

chapter 7 Review

Using Vocabulary

ecliptic p. 192
ellipse p. 188
equinox p. 195
gravity p. 187
lunar eclipse p. 202
maria p. 203
moon phase p. 199
regolith p. 203
revolution p. 192
rotation p. 192
solar eclipse p. 201
solstice p. 195
sphere p. 186
tide p. 199
time zone p. 190

Match the correct vocabulary word or phrase with each definition given below.

1. dark-colored, relatively flat areas on the Moon
2. Earth spinning on its axis
3. a large wave in Earth's oceans caused by the gravity of the Moon and the Sun
4. a round, three-dimensional object, the surface of which is the same distance from the center in all directions
5. Earth moving in orbit around the Sun
6. eclipse that occurs during a new moon
7. 15°-wide area on Earth's surface in which the time is the same
8. occurs when the Sun is directly above Earth's equator
9. attractive force between two objects
10. yearly path of Earth around the Sun

Checking Concepts

Choose the word or phrase that best answers each question.

11. How long is a month of lunar phases?
A) 14 days
B) 27.3 days
C) 29.5 days
D) 365 days

12. During winter solstice in the northern hemisphere, the Sun is directly over which part of Earth?
A) equator
B) pole
C) Tropic of Cancer
D) Tropic of Capricorn

13. Which movement causes lunar phases?
A) Earth's revolution
B) Earth's rotation
C) the Moon's revolution
D) the Moon's rotation

14. Which eclipse do you experience if you are standing in the Moon's umbra?
A) partial lunar **C)** total lunar
B) partial solar **D)** total solar

15. Which phase occurs when the Moon is on the opposite side of Earth from the Sun?
A) **B)** **C)** **D)**

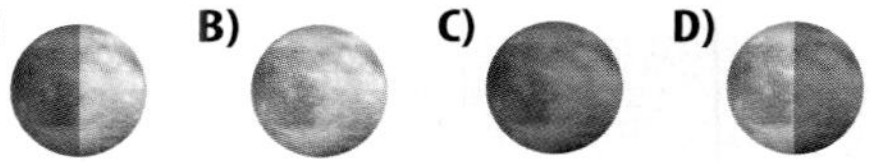

16. Which material may have been found on the Moon by the *Clementine* spacecraft?
A) atmosphere
B) dark-colored rocks
C) light-colored rocks
D) water-ice

17. On average, how many degrees of longitude are contained in one time zone?
A) 0.5° **C)** 23.5°
B) 15° **D)** 30°

18. Which occurs a few days after a full moon?
A) waning crescent
B) waxing crescent
C) waning gibbous
D) waxing gibbous

Vocabulary PuzzleMaker gpescience.com

Use the ExamView® Pro Test Bank CD-ROM to:
- create multiple versions of tests
- create modified tests with one mouse click for inclusion students
- edit existing questions and add your own questions
- build tests aligned with state standards using built-in State Curriculum Tags
- change English tests to Spanish with one mouse click and vice versa

19. Which season begins around December 21 in Australia?
A) spring
B) summer
C) fall
D) winter

20. Which forms when small meteorites crash into the Moon?
A) craters
B) maria
C) mountains
D) cracks

Interpreting Graphics

21. **Make an illustration** showing how magnetic force lines surrounding Earth are similar to those surrounding a bar magnet.

Use the data in the table below to answer question 22.

Earth's Physical Properties	
Diameter (pole to pole)	12,714 km
Diameter (through equator)	12,756 km
Circumference (poles)	40,008 km
Circumference (equator)	40,075 km
Average distance to the Sun	149,600,000 km
Average distance to the Moon	384,400 km

22. What is the difference between the diameter of Earth through the poles compared to the equator? How many times farther from Earth is the Sun, compared to the Moon?

Thinking Critically

23. **Infer** why more craters are present on the Moon's surface than on Earth's. *Hint: Consider gravity and the presence of an atmosphere.*

24. **Infer** how seasons would be affected if Earth had no tilt instead of the 23.5° tilt that it has.

25. **Explain** why a lunar base would best be built on a plateau that is always in sunlight.

26. **Form a hypothesis** about why during crescent phases we can often see a dim image of the rest of that side of the Moon. *Hint: Recall the arrangement of Earth, the Moon, and the Sun during crescent phases.*

27. **Form a hypothesis** about how the thickness of the Moon's crust might play a part in the fact that the side of the Moon facing Earth has more maria than the side facing away.

Applying Math

Use the illustration below to answer questions 28–29.

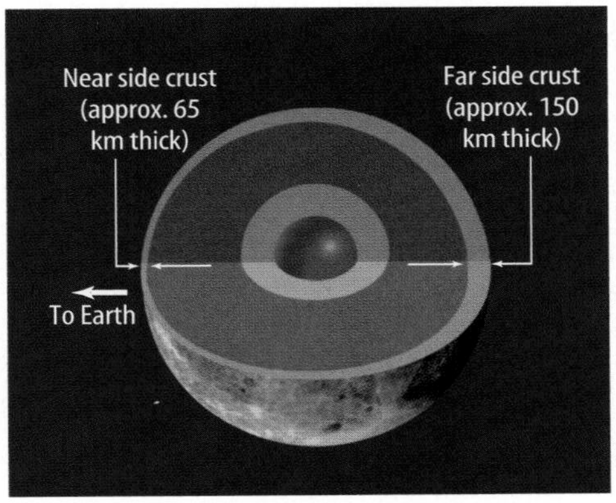

28. **Model to Scale** If you are making a scale model of the Moon (diameter approx. 3,500 km), what scale should you use to obtain a model that is about 35 cm in diameter?

29. **Calculate** Using your scale, what would the thicknesses be, in centimeters, for the near-side crust and the far-side crust?

chapter 7 Review

Interpreting Graphics

21. Student illustrations should show a spherical Earth with magnetic force lines drawn around the planet between the North and South Poles.

22. Earth's diameter through the equator is 42 km more than through the poles. The Sun is 389 times farther than Moon.

Thinking Critically

23. Although Earth's higher gravity would have pulled more meteorites toward it, its atmosphere would have burned many of them up. Also, some fell into oceans and some on land, making craters that eroded or remain covered by vegetation.

24. Weather conditions would vary at different locations on Earth, but there would be no changing seasons.

25. The Sun's rays could be used to produce power.

26. Sunlight reflecting off of Earth lights up the dark portion of the Moon facing Earth. This is called earthlight.

27. Since the Moon's crust is thinner on the side facing Earth, cracks formed more readily allowing lava to seep up.

Applying Math

Math Standards
National: 1, 4, 9

28. 1 cm = 100 km
29. 0.65 cm; 1.5 cm

Assessment Resources

Reproducible Masters

Chapter *Fast File* Resources
Chapter Review, pp. 37–38
Chapter Tests, pp. 39–42
Assessment Transparency Activity, p. 49

Glencoe Science Web site
Chapter Review Test
Standardized Test Practice

Glencoe Technology
Assessment Transparency
Exam*View*® Pro Testmaker
MindJogger Videoquiz
Interactive Chalkboard

Answer Sheet An answer sheet can be found at **gpescience.com**.

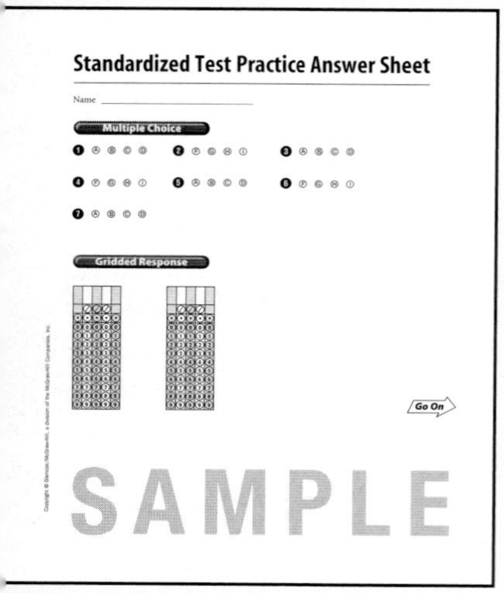
Standardized Test Practice Answer Sheet

Name

Multiple Choice

Gridded Response

Go On

SAMPLE

Multiple Choice

1. D
2. B
3. B
4. C
5. D
6. C
7. C

Gridded Response

8. 29.5 – 27.3 = 2.2 days
9. 6:00 AM

chapter 7 Standardized Test Practice

Record your answers on the answer sheet provided by your teacher or on a sheet of paper.

Multiple Choice

Use the illustration below to answer question 1.

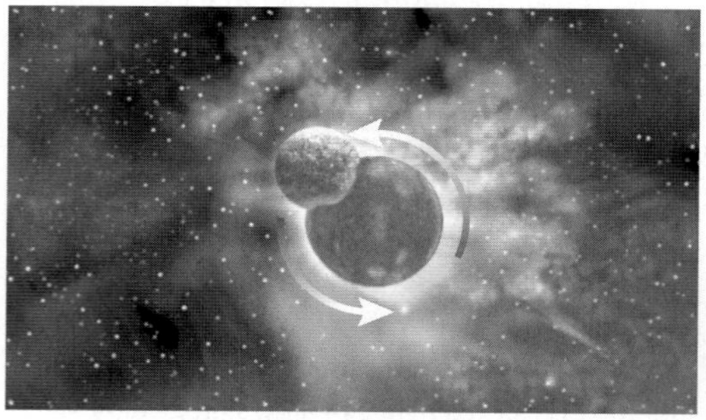

1. Which theory explaining the Moon's origin is widely accepted by astronomers?

A. binary accretion theory
B. capture theory
C. fission theory
D. giant impact theory

2. How far is Earth's magnetic axis tilted from its geographic axis?

A. 5°
B. 11.5°
C. 15°
D. 23.5°

3. On which number did the Babylonians base their counting methods?

A. 10
B. 60
C. 100
D. 360

4. Which is a way that Venus and Earth are similar?

A. atmospheric density
B. liquid water oceans
C. rocky nature
D. surface temperature

Use the illustration below to answer question 5.

5. Which is a group of constellations through which the Sun appears to move?

A. ecliptic
B. equinox
C. solstice
D. zodiac

6. Which contains bands of charged particles known as the Van Allen belts?

A. exosphere
B. ionosphere
C. magnetosphere
D. stratosphere

Test-Taking Tip

Caution Read each question carefully for full understanding.

Short Response

10. Most of the material from the cores of the two objects fell back to Earth and formed one iron core inside Earth.

11. Oceans on Earth may have absorbed much of the CO2 in Earth's early atmosphere.

12. The interaction of solar wind with Earth's magnetosphere generates large electrical currents which add energy to molecules of gas in Earth's atmosphere. When the molecules return to a lower energy state, light is produced.

7. During which month of the year is Earth farthest from the Sun?

A. January

B. April

C. July

D. September

Gridded Response

8. If a synodic month is 29.5 days long and a sidereal month is 27.3 days long, how much longer is a synodic month?

Use the illustration below to answer question 9.

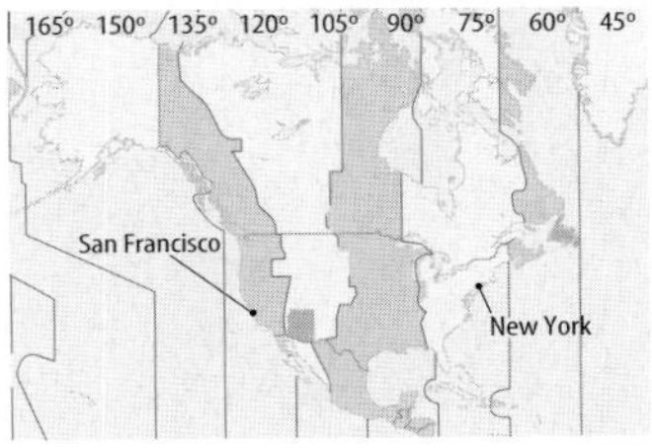

9. If it is 9:00 A.M. in New York city, what time is it in San Francisco?

10. If the collision of two planetary-sized objects (Earth and another object) formed the Moon, why is the Moon's iron core so small compared to Earth's?

Short Response

11. What may have caused the great difference in the percentage of CO_2 found in Earth's atmosphere compared to those of Venus and Mars?

12. What causes the auroras?

Extended Response

Use the illustration below to answer question 13.

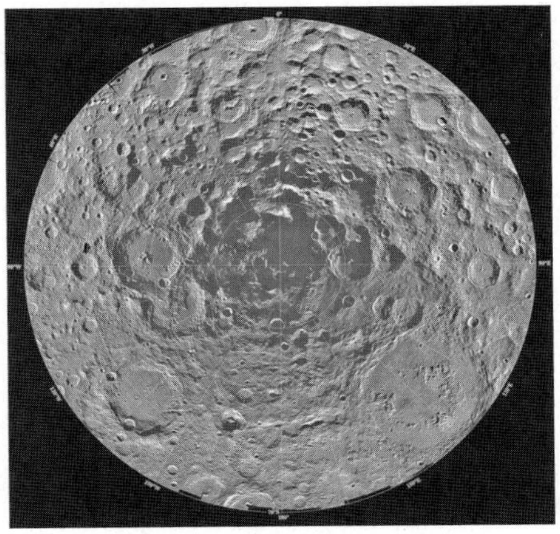

13. **PART A** The *Lunar Prospector* discovered possible concentrations of water-ice in the area of the South Pole-Aitken Basin on the Moon. How does location and geographic terrain affect the possibility of finding water there?

PART B How might this discovery affect the future of spaceflight?

Rubrics

For more help evaluating Short- and Extended-Response questions, see the rubrics on p. 9T.

Extended Response

13. **Part A:** The location of possible sources of water have been found in some of the Moon's crater's. Some craters located near the poles, such as the South Pole-Aitken Basin, do not receive direct sunlight at their bottoms. These locations maintain very cold temperatures that might allow water-ice to remain buried below the surface without melting or evaporating.

Part B: It could supply the water needs of a Moon base or could be used to extract hydrogen and oxygen for rocket fuel, possibly making flight to other planets more economical and easier.

chapter 8 Organizer

Section/Objectives	Standards		Lab/Features
	National	**State/Local**	
Chapter Opener	See pp. 16T-17T for a Key to Standards.		**Launch Lab:** The Size of the Solar System, p. 217 **Foldables,** p. 217
Section 1 Planet Motion 2 sessions 1 block 1. **Compare and contrast** geocentric and heliocentric models of the solar system. 2. **Describe** each planet's position in orbit around the Sun. 3. **Classify** planets by location and characteristics.	National Content Standards: UPC. 1-5, A.1, A.2, B.4, D.3, D.4, G.3		**MiniLab:** Plotting Retrograde Motion, p. 219 **Applying Math:** Heliocentric Longitude, p. 220 **Integrate Physics,** p. 220
Section 2 The Inner Planets 2 sessions 1 block 4. **Compare and contrast** other inner planets with Earth. 5. **Describe** important characteristics for each inner planet. 6. **Evaluate** the success of various missions to Mars.	National Content Standards: UCP. 1-5, A.1, A.2, D.3, G.3		**Science Online,** p. 227 **Integrate Chemistry,** p. 228 **Lab:** Interpreting Features of Mars's Surface, p. 230 Video Lab
Section 3 The Outer Planets 2 sessions 1 block 7. **Compare and contrast** the outer planets. 8. **Describe** important characteristics for each outer planet. 9. **Evaluate** the success of NASA missions Galileo and Cassini.	National Content Standards: UCP. 1-5, A.1, A.2, B.4, D.3, D.4, G.3		**Integrate Language Arts,** p. 232 **What Galileo Saw,** p. 233 **Science Online,** p.234 **MiniLab:** Comparing Sizes of Outer and Inner Planets, p. 235
Section 4 Life in the Solar System 2 sessions 1 block 10. **Evaluate** other planets in the solar system for the possibility of containing life. 11. **Examine** life forms that exist in exotic locations on Earth. 12. **Discuss** locations in which life might exist on other planets.	National Content Standards: UCP. 1-5, A.1, A.2, C.3, C.5, C.6, D.3, D.4		**Lab:** Testing Unknown Soil Samples for Life, pp. 242–243 **Science Stats:** Night Sky Wonders, p. 244

Glencoe Exclusive! StudentWorks Plus | TeacherWorks™ All-In-One Planner and Resource Center

Lab Materials	Reproducible Resources	Section Assessment	Technology
Launch Lab: adding-machine tape, meterstick, metric ruler	**Chapter *Fast File* Resources** Foldables Worksheet, p. 17 Directed Reading Overview, p. 19 Note-taking Worksheets, pp. 35–37	Glencoe's Assessment Advantage	TeacherWorks includes: • Interactive Teacher Edition • Lesson Planner with calendar • Access to all program blacklines • Correlations to standards • Web links
MiniLab: graph paper Need materials? Contact Science Kit at 1-800-828-7777 or www.sciencekit.com.	**Chapter *Fast File* Resources** Transparency Activity, p. 46 MiniLAB, p. 3 Enrichment, p. 31 Reinforcement, p. 27 Directed Reading, p. 20 **Lab Management and Safety,** p. 69	**Portfolio** Assessment, p. 222 **Performance** MiniLab, p. 219 Applying Math, p. 222 **Content** Section Review, p. 222	Section Focus Transparency Interactive Chalkboard CD-ROM StudentWorks Plus
Lab: scissors, erasable marker, transparent removable tape, photograph of the Martian surface, clear-plastic sheet	**Chapter *Fast File* Resources** Transparency Activity, p. 47 Enrichment, p. 32 Reinforcement, p. 28 Directed Reading, p. 20 Lab Worksheets, pp. 5–6 Lab Activity, pp. 9–11	**Portfolio** Activity, p. 225 **Performance** Lab, p. 230 Applying Math, p. 229 **Content** Section Review, p. 229	Section Focus Transparency Interactive Chalkboard CD-ROM StudentWorks Plus Video Lab
MiniLab: drawing paper, colored pencils, drawing compasses	**Chapter *Fast File* Resources** Transparency Activity, p. 48 MiniLAB, p. 4 Enrichment, p. 33 Reinforcement, p. 29 Directed Reading, p. 21 Lab Activity, pp. 13–15	**Portfolio** Activity, p. 233 Assessment, p. 237 **Performance** MiniLab, p. 235 Applying Math, p. 237 **Content** Section Review, p. 237	Section Focus Transparency Interactive Chalkboard CD-ROM StudentWorks Plus
Lab: clear-plastic cups, sand or soil, warm water, magnifying glass, thermometer	**Chapter *Fast File* Resources** Transparency Activity, pp. 49, 51–52 Enrichment, p. 34 Reinforcement, p. 30 Directed Reading, pp. 21 Lab Worksheets, pp. 7–8	**Portfolio** Assessment, p. 243 **Performance** Lab, pp. 242–243 Applying Math, p. 241 **Content** Section Review, p. 241	Section Focus Transparency Teaching Transparency Interactive Chalkboard CD-ROM StudentWorks Plus

End of Chapter Assessment

Glencoe's Assessment Advantage

Blackline Masters	Technology	Professional Series
Chapter *Fast File* Resources Chapter Review, pp. 39–40 Chapter Tests, pp. 43–44 **Standardized Test Practice,** pp. 36–39	MindJogger Videoquiz Exam*View*® Pro Testmaker TeacherWorks CD-ROM Interactive Chalkboard CD-ROM	**Performance Assessment in the Science Classroom (PASC)**

Transparencies

Section Focus

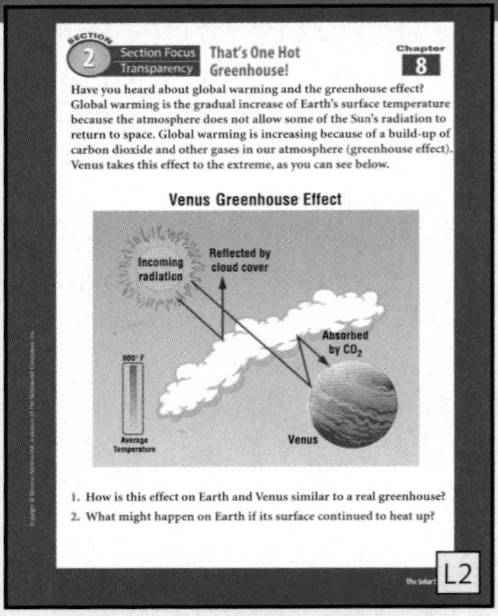
Section 2 Section Focus Transparency — That's One Hot Greenhouse! — Chapter 8

Have you heard about global warming and the greenhouse effect? Global warming is the gradual increase of Earth's surface temperature because the atmosphere does not allow some of the Sun's radiation to return to space. Global warming is increasing because of a build-up of carbon dioxide and other gases in our atmosphere (greenhouse effect). Venus takes this effect to the extreme, as you can see below.

Venus Greenhouse Effect

1. How is this effect on Earth and Venus similar to a real greenhouse?
2. What might happen on Earth if its surface continued to heat up?

L2

Section 3 Section Focus Transparency — Holy Comet! That's Halley's comet. — Chapter 8

Records indicate that about every 76 years since 240 B.C., people have viewed Halley's comet. Although some sightings have been more spectacular than others, probably none has been as striking as the photographs taken by modern spacecraft. One of these photos is shown below.

1. In what year would you be able to see Halley's comet if it were last visible early in 1986? How old will you be?
2. Why did scientists say that people were able to see bits and pieces of this comet in 1998?

L2

Section 4 Section Focus Transparency — 40,000 Years Old and Going Strong! — Chapter 8

Could you live here? Maybe not. But a type of moss was found that had survived in an environment like this. Scientists estimated that it had been lying dormant for 40,000 years. Could life, then, survive on other worlds with similar conditions?

1. Name several other types of extreme environments in which life exists on Earth.
2. How do you think the moss was able to survive for so long?

L2

This is a representation of key blackline masters available in the Teacher Classroom Resources. See Resource Manager boxes within the chapter for additional information.

Assessment

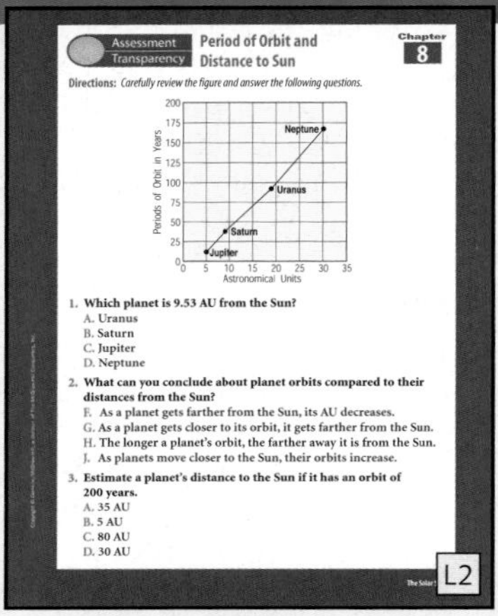
Assessment Transparency — Period of Orbit and Distance to Sun — Chapter 8

Directions: *Carefully review the figure and answer the following questions.*

1. Which planet is 9.53 AU from the Sun?
   A. Uranus
   B. Saturn
   C. Jupiter
   D. Neptune
2. What can you conclude about planet orbits compared to their distances from the Sun?
   F. As a planet gets farther from the Sun, its AU decreases.
   G. As a planet gets closer to its orbit, it gets farther from the Sun.
   H. The longer a planet's orbit, the farther away it is from the Sun.
   J. As planets move closer to the Sun, their orbits increase.
3. Estimate a planet's distance to the Sun if it has an orbit of 200 years.
   A. 35 AU
   B. 5 AU
   C. 80 AU
   D. 30 AU

L2

Teaching

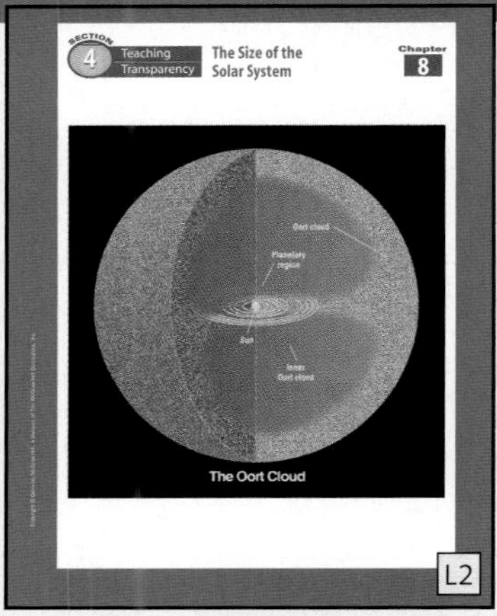
Section 4 Teaching Transparency — The Size of the Solar System — Chapter 8

The Oort Cloud

L2

Key to Teaching Strategies

The following designations will help you decide which activities are appropriate for your students.

- L1 Level 1 activities should be appropriate for students with learning difficulties.
- L2 Level 2 activities should be within the ability range of all students.
- L3 Level 3 activities are designed for above-average students.
- ELL ELL activities should be within the ability range of English Language Learners.
- COOP LEARN Cooperative Learning activities are designed for small group work.
- LS Multiple Learning Styles logos, as described on page 12T, are used throughout to indicate strategies that address different learning styles.
- P These strategies represent student products that can be placed into a best-work portfolio.
- PBL Problem-Based Learning activities apply real-world situations to learning.

Hands-on Activities

Student Text Lab Worksheet

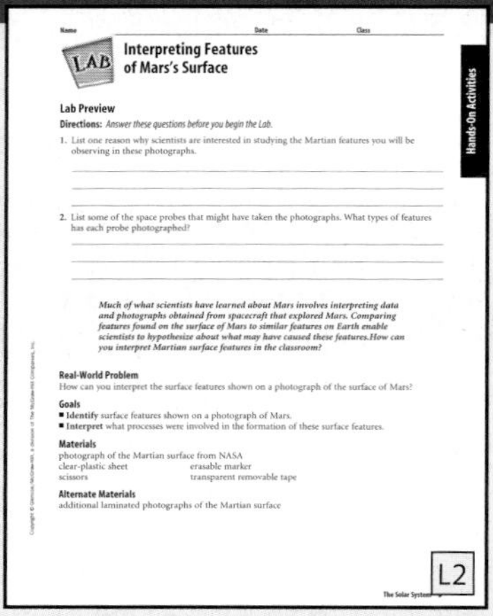
Name Date Class

LAB Interpreting Features of Mars's Surface

Hands-On Activities

Lab Preview

Directions: *Answer these questions before you begin the Lab.*

1. List one reason why scientists are interested in studying the Martian features you will be observing in these photographs.
2. List some of the space probes that might have taken the photographs. What types of features has each probe photographed?

Much of what scientists have learned about Mars involves interpreting data and photographs obtained from spacecraft that explored Mars. Comparing features found on the surface of Mars to similar features on Earth enable scientists to hypothesize about what may have caused these features.How can you interpret Martian surface features in the classroom?

Real-World Problem
How can you interpret the surface features shown on a photograph of the surface of Mars?

Goals
- **Identify** surface features shown on a photograph of Mars.
- **Interpret** what processes were involved in the formation of these surface features.

Materials
photograph of the Martian surface from NASA
clear-plastic sheet
erasable marker
scissors
transparent removable tape

Alternate Materials
additional laminated photographs of the Martian surface

L2

The Solar System

Laboratory Activities

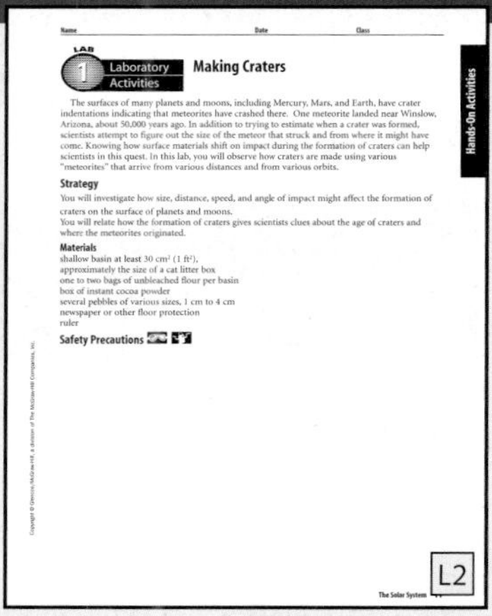
Name Date Class

LAB 1 Laboratory Activities — Making Craters

Hands-On Activities

The surfaces of many planets and moons, including Mercury, Mars, and Earth, have crater indentations indicating that meteorites have crashed there. One meteorite landed near Winslow, Arizona, about 50,000 years ago. In addition to trying to estimate when a crater was formed, scientists attempt to figure out the size of the meteor that struck and from where it might have come. Knowing how surface materials shift on impact during the formation of craters can help scientists in this quest. In this lab, you will observe how craters are made using various "meteorites" that arrive from various distances and from various orbits.

Strategy
You will investigate how size, distance, speed, and angle of impact might affect the formation of craters on the surface of planets and moons.
You will relate how the formation of craters gives scientists clues about the age of craters and where the meteorites originated.

Materials
shallow basin at least 30 cm^2 (1 ft^2),
approximately the size of a cat litter box
one to two bags of unbleached flour per basin
box of instant cocoa powder
several pebbles of various sizes, 1 cm to 4 cm
newspaper or other floor protection
ruler

Safety Precautions

L2

The Solar System

Meeting Different Ability Levels

Content Outline

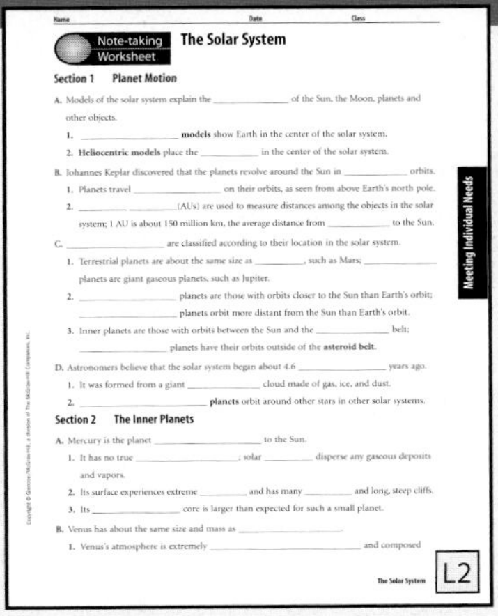
Note-taking Worksheet — The Solar System

Section 1 Planet Motion

Section 2 The Inner Planets

The Solar System L2

Reinforcement

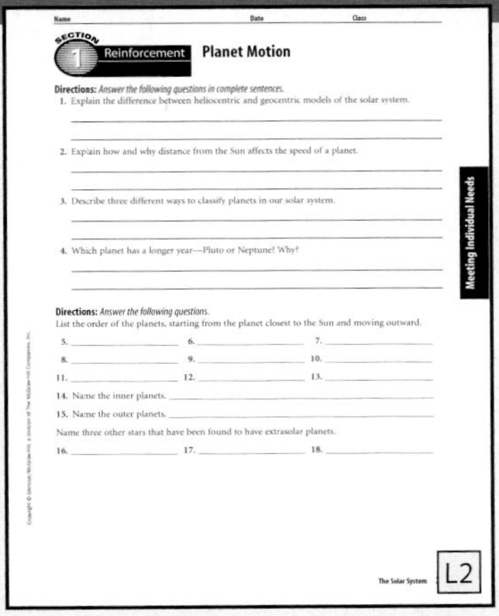
Section 1 Reinforcement — Planet Motion

The Solar System L2

Enrichment

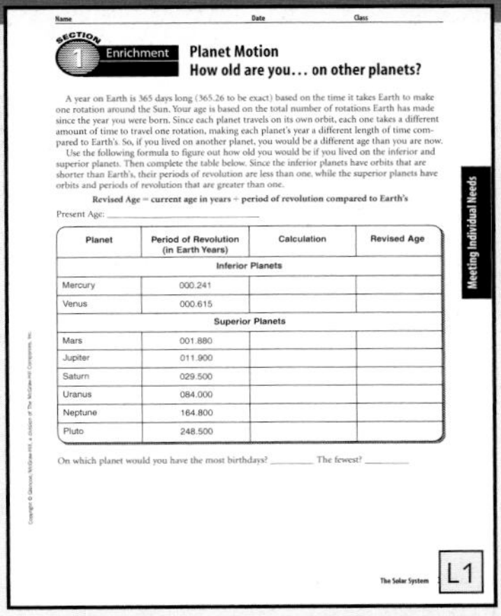
Section 1 Enrichment — Planet Motion

How old are you . . . on other planets?

The Solar System L1

Directed Reading (English/Spanish)

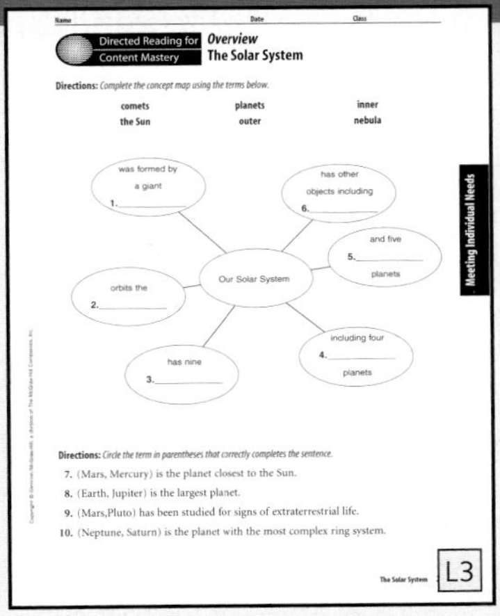
Directed Reading for Content Mastery — Overview — The Solar System

The Solar System L3

Study Guide

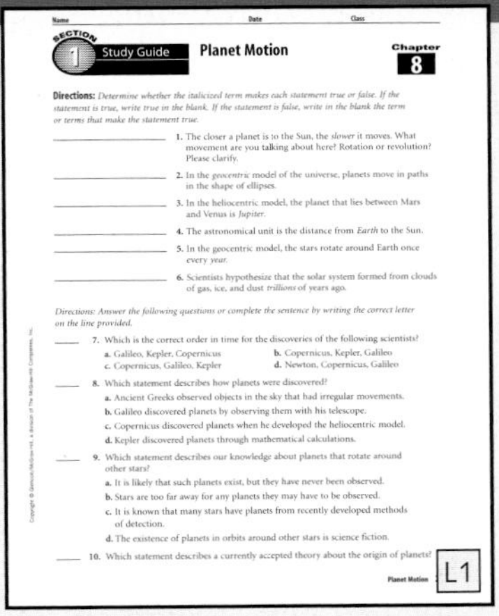
Section 1 Study Guide — Planet Motion — Chapter 8

Planet Motion L1

Reading Essentials

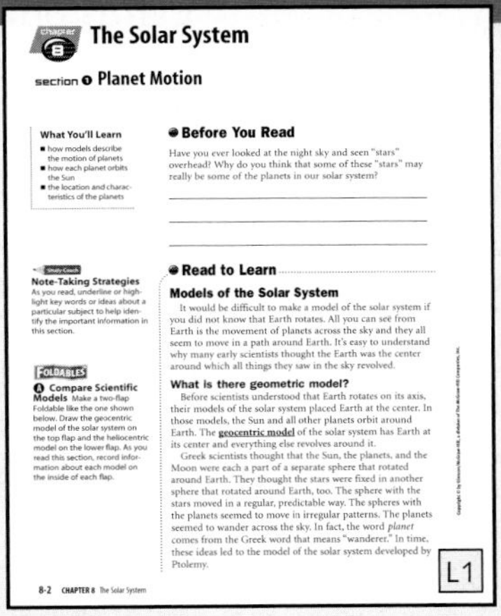
Chapter 8 The Solar System

section 1 Planet Motion

8-2 CHAPTER 8 The Solar System L1

Assessment

Test Practice Workbook

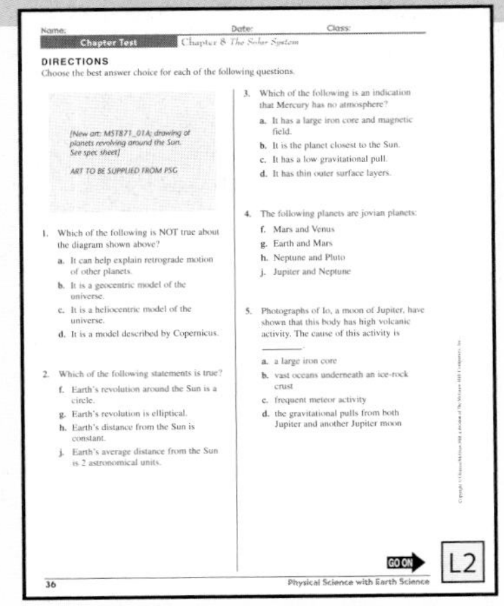
Chapter Test — Chapter 8 The Solar System

Physical Science with Earth Science L2

Chapter Review

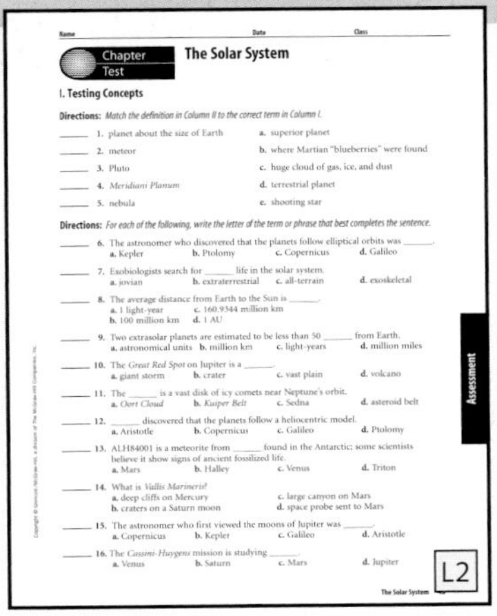
Chapter Test — The Solar System

I. Testing Concepts

The Solar System L2

Chapter Tests

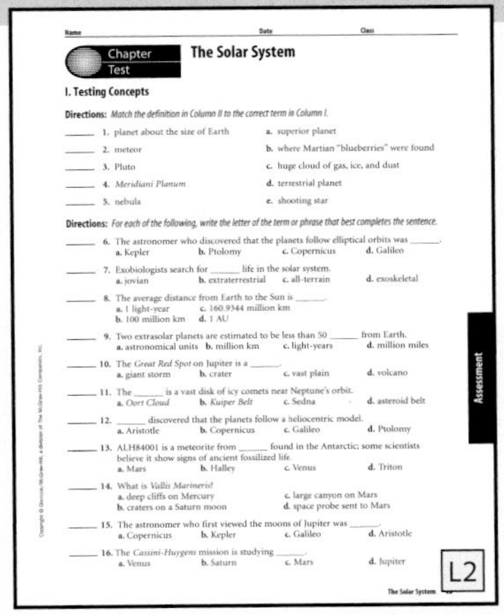
Chapter Test — The Solar System

I. Testing Concepts

The Solar System L2

Science Content Background

section 1

Planet Motion

Heliocentric Model

Most objects in the solar system rotate and revolve in a counterclockwise direction as viewed from above the north pole of the Sun. From Earth, objects appear to move from west to east. Any apparent motion different from this counterclockwise motion is called retrograde motion. Retrograde motion of Mars was one piece of evidence Copernicus used to support his Sun-centered, heliocentric model of the solar system. Any planet in an orbit farther from the Sun than Earth's orbit will occasionally display retrograde motion because Earth travels more rapidly in its orbit than the superior planets.

Origin of the Solar System

One hypothesis on the formation of our solar system, as well as formation of Sun and other stars, suggests that a nearby star might have exploded, sending shock waves through the nebula from which the solar system eventually formed. The shock waves from the explosion caused the particles in the cloud to condense, leading to gravitational instability that caused the cloud to fragment into smaller and smaller pieces. One of these fragments eventually formed into the solar system. Whether this shock was the cause or not, scientists agree that something had to initiate the process within the nebula that eventually formed the Sun and most likely several other stars. Perhaps the movement of one of the arms of the Milky Way through the nebula started the formation process.

section 2

The Inner Planets

Venus, Earth, and Mars

When secondary atmospheres formed, temperatures on Mars were low enough that H_2O most likely condensed as ice, thus no greenhouse effect could develop on Mars. However, Earth's temperatures were warm enough to allow H_2O to condense as liquid water.

Carbon dioxide (CO_2) dissolves in water; therefore, much of the CO_2 in Earth's atmosphere has been removed by rain. If no liquid water existed on Earth, the amount of CO_2 in the air would probably be similar to that in Venus's atmosphere.

On Venus, the high temperatures caused H_2O to evaporate and no liquid water remained to dissolve the CO_2 in the atmosphere. The combination of H_2O vapor and CO_2 caused a runaway greenhouse effect.

If Earth were just 5 percent closer to the Sun, it would have evolved like Venus—something to consider when searching for life elsewhere.

chapter content resources

Internet Resources

For additional content background, visit **gpescience.com** to:

- access your book online
- find references to related articles in popular science magazines
- access Web links with related content background
- access current events with science journal topics

Print Resources

A+ Projects in Astronomy, by Janice VanCleave, John Wiley & Sons, 2002

Astronomy—Journey to the Cosmic Frontier, by John D. Fix, McGraw—Hill Companies, 2004

Moons & Planets, by William K. Hartmann, Brooks/Cole—Thompson Learning, Inc., 2005

section 3 The Outer Planets

Jupiter, Saturn, and Uranus

The atmospheres of Jupiter and Saturn contain three distinct layers. The upper layer is composed of ammonia ice; just below this is a layer of ammonium hydrosulfide ice, and the lowest cloud layer is composed mostly of water ice.

Unlike the other jovian planets, Uranus doesn't appear to have an internal heat source. Some scientists believe a collision with another object may have turned Uranus on its side and destroyed its heat source.

Other Objects in the Solar System

Comets appear to orbit the Sun in the Oort comet cloud some 50,000 AU from the Sun. Some comets take more than one million years to complete one orbit. The Oort comet cloud is most likely where long-period comets originate. Short-period comets (those taking fewer than 200 years to orbit the Sun) are thought to originate in the Kuiper Belt beyond the orbit of Neptune.

The Kuiper Belt is thought to extend about 30 AU outward from the orbit of Neptune to about a distance of 100 AU from the Sun. Some scientists believe that the retrograde revolution of Neptune's moon, Triton, indicates that it was captured by the gravity of Neptune and could once have been a planet like Pluto. In fact, Pluto and Charon might have been members of the Kuiper Belt. One Kuiper Belt object, 28,978 Ixion is about 1,000 km across and has the same type of orbit as Pluto. Its closest approach to the Sun is 29.8 AU (Pluto's is 29.7 AU) and its farthest distance is 49 AU (Pluto's is 49.3 AU).

Another group of objects from which comets could originate is known as the Centaurs. These objects have elliptical orbits and are located in the region extending from Saturn to Neptune.

section 4 Life in the Solar System

Europa

Europa's crust of ice is cracked but smoother than expected, and has hardly any large craters. Some areas of Europa's crust appear to have floated around like icebergs. Photographs show ice flows and systems of ridges. It is thought that gravitational pulling and pushing between Jupiter and its larger moons generated the heat to melt Europa's interior, smooth Europa's crust, and possibly supply energy needed for life to begin and survive on Europa. For life as we know it on Earth to form on Europa, the oceans would have to contain molecules with C, H, O, and N.

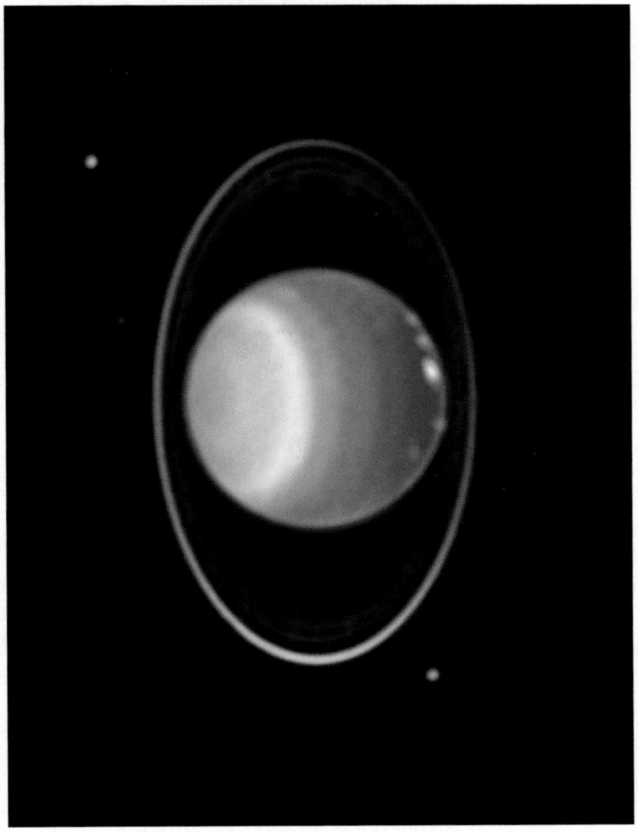

Goddard Space Flight Center/NASA

chapter 8

Chapter Vocabulary

geocentric model, p. 218
heliocentric model, p. 219
astronomical unit, p. 220
extrasolar planet, p. 222
Mercury, p. 223
Venus, p. 224
Earth, p. 225
Mars, p. 225
Jupiter, p. 231
Saturn, p. 234
Uranus, p. 235
Neptune, p. 235
Pluto, p. 236
comet, p. 236
asteroid, p. 236
meteoroid, p. 236
Sedna, p. 237
extraterrestrial life, p. 239

Science Journal A quartz crystal grows, but is a quartz crystal living? Students are encouraged to explore what is meant by *life* and what conditions might be required to support life.

INTERACTIVE CHALKBOARD with Image Bank

PowerPoint® Presentations

This CD-ROM is an editable Microsoft® PowerPoint® presentation that includes:

- a pre-made presentation for every chapter
- interactive graphics
- animations
- audio clips
- image bank
- all new section and chapter questions gpescience.com
- Standardized Test Practice
- transparencies
- Foldables directions
- links to

chapter 8

The Solar System

chapter preview

sections

Home Sweet Home

Nestled within one of the great spiral arms of the Milky Way lies our solar system. As large as the solar system is, it is still only a tiny fraction of our galaxy!

Science Journal In your Science Journal, write a hypothesis about whether life might exist beyond Earth, or even beyond the solar system, and how you would test for it.

216

Theme Connection

Scale and Structure The solar system has an overall structure, with smaller inner planets and generally larger outer planets. The entire solar system lies within a large cloud of comets that completely surrounds the Sun, the planets, the asteroids, and many other objects. The theme of scale is emphasized when comparing the inner with the outer planets.

About the Photo

Imaginary View From Afar This page shows an illustration of our solar system because a photograph cannot show the entire solar system. The Sun, Mercury, Venus, Earth, and Mars are surrounded by a broad asteroid belt. Jupiter and Saturn are in the foreground, Uranus and Neptune are in the background, and Pluto and Charon are in the upper left.

Start-Up Activities

Launch Lab

The Size of the Solar System

Even if you consider only the planets, the solar system is enormous compared to things you see in your daily life. You may be better able to understand the size of the solar system by using a scale model. Distances between the orbits of the nine planets usually are measured in astronomical units (AUs). One AU equals 150 million km, the average distance between Earth and the Sun. Using a scale of 1 AU = 10 cm and the data from the table below, draw a model of the solar system.

Planet	Distance to Sun (AU)
Mercury	0.39
Venus	0.72
Earth	1.00
Mars	1.52
Jupiter	5.20
Saturn	9.54
Uranus	19.19
Neptune	30.07
Pluto	39.48

1. Obtain a roll of adding-machine tape at least 4 m long. Place a symbol for the Sun on one end of the tape.
2. Using the scale above, measure and place the name of each planet at its proper distance from the Sun.
3. **Think Critically** In your Science Journal, explain how a scale model helped you to visualize the size of the solar system.

Foldables Study Organizer

The Solar System Make the following Foldable to help you organize information about the planets.

STEP 1 **Collect** five sheets of paper and layer them about $\frac{1}{2}$ inch apart vertically. Keep the edge level.

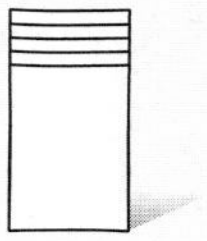

STEP 2 **Fold** up the bottom edges of the paper to form ten equal tabs.

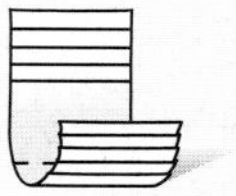

STEP 3 **Fold** the papers and crease well to hold the tabs in place. Staple along the fold. **Label** each tab with the names of the nine planets and Sedna.

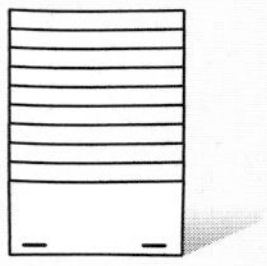

Organize As you read the chapter, write information about each planet on its sheet.

Science Online — Preview this chapter's content and activities at gpescience.com

Launch Lab

Purpose Use this Launch Lab to introduce students to the size of the solar system. L2

Preparation Cut 4.5-m sections from a roll of adding machine tape.

Materials adding machine tape, meterstick, metric ruler

Teaching Strategy Have students work in pairs.

Think Critically

Possible answer: The solar system is very large. A scale model is needed to show the relative positions of all planets. To do this, at least 40 m of tape are needed.

Assessment

Oral Could you use the same scale if you wanted to add the planets to your model? Explain. Possible answer: No, the planets would all be very small on the scale used in this lab. L2

Foldables Study Organizer — Dinah Zike Study Fold

Student preparation materials for this Foldable are available in the **Chapter *Fast File* Resources.**

section 1 Planet Motion

1 Motivate

An editable Microsoft® PowerPoint® presentation is available on **Interactive Chalkboard** CD-ROM.

Bellringer

Section Focus Transparencies also are available on the Interactive Chalkboard CD-ROM. L2 ELL

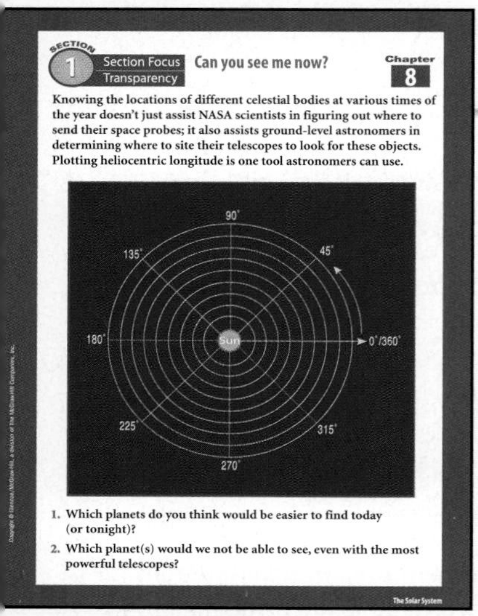
Section 1 Section Focus Transparency — Can you see me now? — Chapter 8

Knowing the locations of different celestial bodies at various times of the year doesn't just assist NASA scientists in figuring out where to send their space probes; it also assists ground-level astronomers in determining where to site their telescopes to look for these objects. Plotting heliocentric longitude is one tool astronomers can use.

1. **Which planets do you think would be easier to find today (or tonight)?**
2. **Which planet(s) would we not be able to see, even with the most powerful telescopes?**

The Solar System

Reading Preview

Tie to Prior Knowledge

Planet Movement Have students think about how stars, planets, the Moon, and the Sun appear to move across the sky. Discuss why people thought Earth was in the center of the universe. Possible answer: Seeing all objects move across the sky made people think they all moved around Earth. L2

Morphological Word Analysis Write *geocentric* and *heliocentric* on the board. Tell students that the prefix *geo-* means "Earth", *helio-* means "Sun", and *centric-* means "centered upon". In this section, they will read about two early theories of the solar system—geocentric and heliocentric. Have students infer what the theories might be. L2

Reading Guide

What You'll Learn

- **Compare and contrast** geocentric and heliocentric models of the solar system.
- **Describe** each planet's position in orbit around the Sun.
- **Classify** planets by location and characteristics.

Why It's Important

Understanding the solar system helps you understand Earth's position in space.

Review Vocabulary

ellipse: an oblong, closed curve drawn around two foci

New Vocabulary

- geocentric model
- heliocentric model
- astronomical unit
- extrasolar planet

Models of the Solar System

Think how difficult it would be to construct a model of the solar system if you didn't know that Earth is a rotating planet. All you can see is the nightly movement of planets across the sky and they all appear to move in a path around Earth. You can understand why many early scientists thought that Earth was the center around which everything they saw in the sky revolved.

Figure 1 Ptolemy presented his geocentric model of the solar system in 140 A.D.

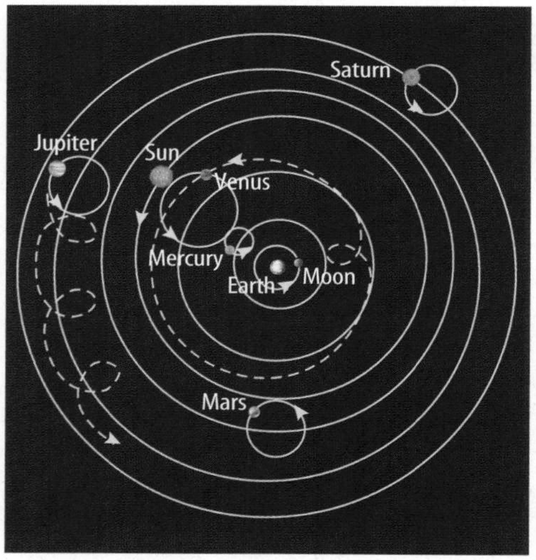

INTEGRATE History

Geocentric Model In the **geocentric model** of the solar system, Earth is considered the center and everything else revolves around it. You have seen why ancient scientists thought this. Many early Greek scientists explained this by saying that the planets, the Sun, and the Moon were embedded in separate crystal spheres that rotated around Earth. They thought that the stars were imbedded in another sphere that also rotated around Earth. The sphere bearing the stars moved in a regular, predictable way, but those bearing the planets seemed often to move erratically against this background. For this reason, they were called *planasthai*, a Greek word that means "to wander." Our word *planet* comes from this. These ideas led to the model of the solar system devised by Ptolemy, shown in **Figure 1.**

Section 1 Resource Manager

Chapter *FAST FILE* Resources

- Transparency Activity, p. 46
- Directed Reading for Content Mastery, pp. 19, 20
- Note-taking Worksheets, pp. 35–37
- MiniLAB, p. 3
- Enrichment, p. 31
- Reinforcement, p. 27

Lab Management and Safety, p. 69

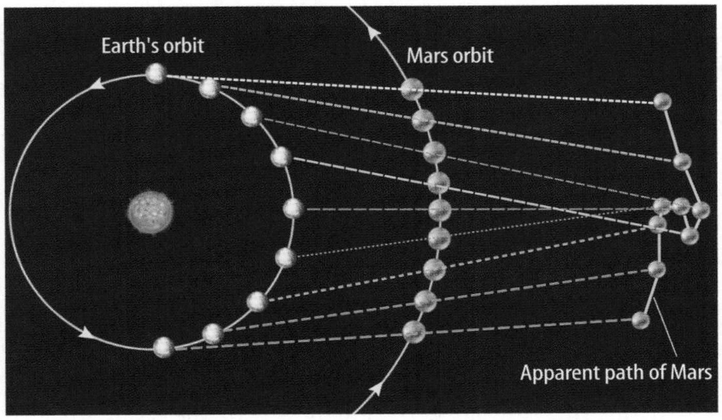

Figure 2 As Earth catches up and passes Mars, Mars appears to move backward, or retrograde.

Geocentric Modifications Although the Ptolemaic model of the solar system was accepted and used for centuries, there were many problems with it. One problem was the fact that planets periodically appear to move in a retrograde, or backward, direction when viewed against a background of stars, as shown in **Figure 2.** Modifications helped, but eventually the model grew very complex.

Heliocentric Model In spite of its complexity, the Earth-centered model held until 1543 when Polish astronomer Nicholas Copernicus published a different view. Using an idea proposed by an early Greek scholar, Copernicus stated that the Moon revolves around Earth, which is a planet, and that Earth and the other planets revolve around the Sun. He also stated that the apparent motion of the planets, the stars, and the Sun is due to Earth's rotation. This is the **heliocentric model,** or Sun-centered model of the solar system, shown in **Figure 3.**

Galileo Using his telescope, Italian astronomer Galileo Galilei found evidence that supported the ideas of Copernicus. He observed that Venus went through phases like the Moon's. These phases could be explained only if Venus orbited the Sun and passed between Earth and the Sun on each orbit. He also saw moons in orbit around Jupiter. These observations convinced him that everything didn't move around Earth, and he concluded that Earth and Venus revolve around the Sun and that the Sun is the center of the solar system.

Mini LAB

Plotting Retrograde Motion

Procedure

1. Using **graph paper,** draw and label the following: *x*-axis, Right ascension, from 12 hours to ten hours; *y*-axis, Declination, from 0° to 20°.
2. Plot and label these positions of Jupiter:
   Oct. 1, 2003 (10h 38m, 10°);
   Jan. 1, 2004 (11h 21m, 6°);
   April 1, 2004 (10h 51m, 9°);
   May 1, 2004 (10h 44m, 9°);
   Aug. 1, 2004 (11h 20m, 6°).
3. Connect the plotted positions in chronological order with a solid line.

Analysis

1. What do you notice about Jupiter's direction of motion?
2. Using a heliocentric model of the solar system, explain why Jupiter appears to move as it does.

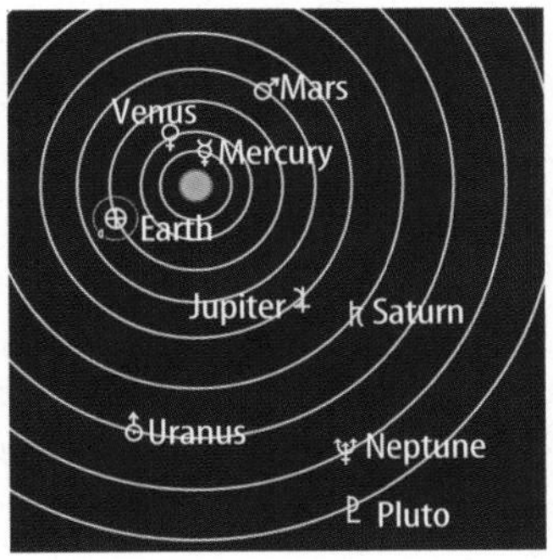

Figure 3 The heliocentric model of the solar system states that Earth and the other planets revolve around the Sun.

INTEGRATE History — Content Background

In order to understand what we now know to be true about planet positions and movement, students should understand why a geocentric universe was considered to be correct for so long.

2 Teach

Mini LAB

Purpose Students will recognize the cause and effect of planetary motion in their orbits around the Sun.

Materials graph paper

Teaching Strategy Use a transparency to show students how to mark the axes. Right ascension is divided into hours and minutes and declination.

Troubleshooting Show students how to locate a place on an Earth globe using longitude and latitude. Compare this to locating objects in the sky using right ascension and declination.

Analysis

1. The direction of Jupiter started to the east, backed up to the west, and then moved east again.
2. Jupiter appears to do this because Earth moves past it in the solar system. When Earth catches and passes Jupiter, the planet seems to move in the opposite direction.

Assessment

Process Have students plot the current positions of Mars, Jupiter, and Saturn on a star chart of the complete sky. Current positions are given in astronomy magazines and observer's handbooks. L2 ELL

Reading Strategy

Clarify Text Have groups of three students model the process described in **Figure 2** by demonstrating the movement of Earth, Mars, and the Sun. Remind them that Earth travels faster than Mars, causing the retrograde effect. L2 ELL

Differentiated Instruction

Visually Impaired Provide a tracing of **Figure 2** on which key stars have been marked with fingernail polish drops and the lines for right ascension and declination have been marked with wax-coated yarn. L2 ELL

SECTION 1 Planet Motion 219

INTEGRATE Physics

Planet Motion If p = the planet's period in years, and d = the planet's distance in AUs the equation then becomes: $p^2 = d^3$.

Jupiter: $d = 5.2$ AU

$p^2 = (5.2)^3 = 140.6$

$p = 11.86$ years

Applying Math

Math Standards

National: 1, 5, 9, 10

Teaching Strategies

- Inform students that the arrow in the diagram points toward the point on the celestial equator where the Sun is on March 21.
- Explain to students that H.L. is the angle between the planet and the position of vernal equinox (first day of spring) in the northern hemisphere.
- Obtain H.L. values for another day from astronomy magazines or an observer's handbook or make up values of H.L. to give students the opportunity to practice.

Answers to Practice Problems

Answers will depend on the values given to the student.

INTEGRATE Physics

Planet Motion Johannes Kepler devised a system of equations that determine a planet's motion based on its position in the solar system. Use this equation to calculate the orbital period (in years) for Jupiter, which is 5.2 AU from the Sun.

(planet's distance in AUs)^3 = (planet's period in years)^2

Check your result against the known value.

Understanding the Solar System

Copernicus and Galileo led the way, but many scientists contributed to our understanding of the solar system. Foremost among them is German mathematician Johannes Kepler. In the early 1600s, Kepler discovered that the planets travel around the Sun in ellipses, not circles, as Copernicus had believed. Kepler also learned that the planets travel at different speeds in their orbits. The closer a planet is to the Sun, the faster it travels. This means that the outer planets take more time to orbit than the inner planets. Mercury takes just 88 days to complete one orbit, or period, but Pluto takes over 248 years to complete an orbital period.

To measure the large distances within the solar system, astronomers use a different unit. This is the **astronomical unit** (AU), which equals the average distance from Earth to the Sun, about 150 million km.

Applying Math — Use Geometry

HELIOCENTRIC LONGITUDE (H.L.) This is the position of a planet on any day of any year. It is plotted by measuring the angle between a line of the spring equinox in the northern hemisphere and the position of the planet on its orbit. This measurement is done counterclockwise because that is how planets appear to move when viewed from above the north pole of Earth. Plot the heliocentric longitudes given below.

IDENTIFY known values and the unknown value

Identify known values:

H.L. on March 4, 2004 for Mercury, Venus, Earth, Mars, and Jupiter are 344°, 103°, 164°, 84°, and 164° respectively.

Identify unknown values:

the position of each planet marked below

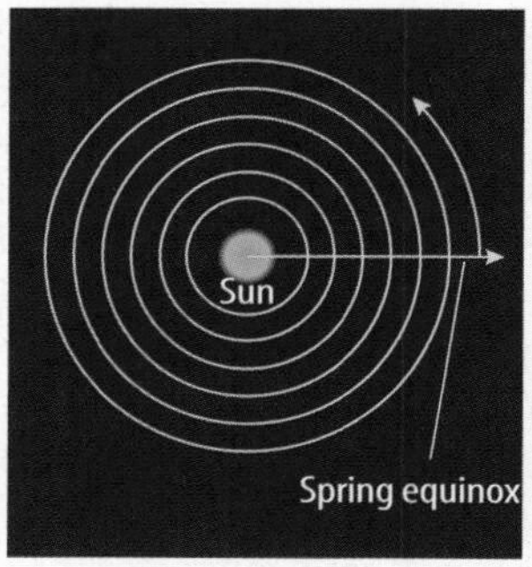

SOLVE the problem

Using this diagram as a model, make a larger drawing on a piece of paper. Use a protractor to measure the H.L. angles and mark the position of each planet on its orbit in the diagram and label it with its name or planet symbol: Mercury ☿, Venus ♀, Earth ⊕, Mars ♂, and Jupiter ♃

CHECK the answers

Switch papers with another student and use a protractor to check each other's plots.

Practice Problems

For more practice problems, go to p. 879 and visit Math Practice at gpescience.com.

Teacher FYI

Planet Positions Heliocentric longitude (H.L.) is the position of a planet with respect to 0 hours of right ascension. If a superior planet has the same H.L. as Earth, it is positioned on the opposite side of Earth from the Sun. This is known as opposition. Because inferior planets (Mercury and Venus) can never be opposite from the Sun, they are said to be in inferior conjunction when they have the same H.L. as Earth. Planets with a H.L. that is 180° removed from the H.L. of Earth are said to be in conjunction if they are superior planets and in superior conjunction if inferior planets.

Classifying Planets The nine planets can be classified in several ways. One system uses size and other characteristics. Those similar to Earth are called terrestrial planets, and the giant planets are jovian planets. Pluto is sometimes called terrestrial, but does not perfectly fit either category.

Two other systems classify planets by location. The system used most often classifies planets whose orbits are between the Sun and the asteroid belt as inner planets and those beyond the asteroid belt as outer planets. The other system classifies planets whose orbits are between Earth's orbit and the Sun as inferior planets, and those whose orbits are beyond Earth's orbit as superior planets.

Reading Check *What separates the inner planets from the outer planets?*

Origin of the Solar System Evidence suggests that the Sun probably formed as part of a multiple star system or star cluster. Scientists hypothesize that a huge cloud of gas, ice, and dust began forming into the present solar system about 4.6 billion years ago. This cloud, called a nebula, might have been as large as a million billion kilometers across. When something in nearby space produced an immense shock wave, the nebula began to condense and fragment because of gravitational instability.

Eventually fragmentation stopped, but contraction continued. The cloud fragment from which our Sun formed was about the size of the entire solar system and was slowly rotating in space. As it continued to contract, the matter in the cloud fragment condensed into less space. As its density became greater, gravity pulled more gas, ice, and dust toward the center. This caused the cloud fragment to rotate faster, which in turn caused it to flatten into a disk with a dense center, as shown in **Figure 4.**

Temperature inside the cloud fragment increased. When it reached about ten million degrees Celsius, hydrogen fused into helium, and the Sun was born. Viewed from above the north pole of the Sun, the nebular disk rotated in a counterclockwise direction. Leftover mass in the outer portions of the disk condensed and formed planets and other objects that continue to revolve around the Sun in a counterclockwise direction.

Figure 4 Our solar system formed from one fragment of a giant nebula in a sequence of contractions and condensations.

Visual Learning

Figure 4 Help students understand the information presented in **Figure 4**. The nebula fragment was slowly turning in space. As the material in the cloud condensed, it began to flatten into a disk. The center of the disk became hotter and hotter until deep inside the center of the disk, hydrogen fused into helium. Once fusion began and the energy released began to radiate into space, this fragment was a star, the Sun. The remainder of the disk condensed to form the planets and other objects. L2 ELL

Discussion

Classifying Earth All planets can be classified in three ways, except Earth. Have students discuss why Earth is only classified in two ways. What two ways is Earth classified? Why is it not classified in the third way? Possible answers: Earth is an inner planet and a terrestrial planet. Earth is not classified as an inferior or superior planet because it is the basis for this classification. L2 ELL IS **Linguistic**

Reading Check

Answer the asteroid belt

Quick Demo
Extrasolar Planets

Materials yellow softball, small, plastic-foam ball

Estimated Time 5 minutes

Procedure Hold the softball in one hand and the plastic foam ball in the other. Move both objects as if they were in orbit around each other. Move the smaller ball more than the larger one. While doing this, gradually move the two object system across the student's line of sight. Explain how this models the movement of a planet around another star. Ask students to explain how they would know the smaller object is there if it was too close to the larger object to be seen. Possible answer: The movement of the larger object back and forth as it moved across our line of sight indicates that another object (possibly a planet) is in orbit around the larger object (a star). L2 ELL IS **Visual-Spatial**

Activity

Classifying Planets Provide students with plastic foam models of two of the planets (Mars and Saturn). Be sure the models conform to the same scale. Have students classify the model planets according their positions relative to Earth (inferior/superior), their size (terrestrial/jovian), and their position relative to the asteroid belt (inner/outer). L1 ELL IS **Visual-Spatial**

Reading Check

Answer planet orbiting another star

Post Reading

Check Comprehension Have students check their comprehension of Origin of the Solar System by retelling the theory to a partner. Encourage them to refer to the text if needed or use simple drawings in their explanation.

3 Assess

DAILY INTERVENTION

Check for Understanding

Visual-Spatial Show students slides of Mars, Earth, Jupiter, and Saturn. Ask students to classify these planets as terrestrial or jovian. The terrestrial planets would be Earth and any planets close to Earth's size (Mars). The jovian planets would be larger, like Saturn. L2 ELL

Reteach

Planet Movement Ask students what was the direction of spin of the original cloud that formed the solar system. Since all planets move around the Sun in a counterclockwise direction—as seen from above, the original cloud was spinning counterclockwise. L2

Assessment

Performance Have students draw an illustration of how the cloud from which the solar system formed was moving. The cloud was moving counterclockwise, as viewed from above, and the inner part of the cloud was moving faster than the outer part of the cloud. Use **PASC,** p. 127. L2 P

Figure 5 The planetary system around Upsilon Andromedae is shown below. This star is barely visible to the unaided eye.

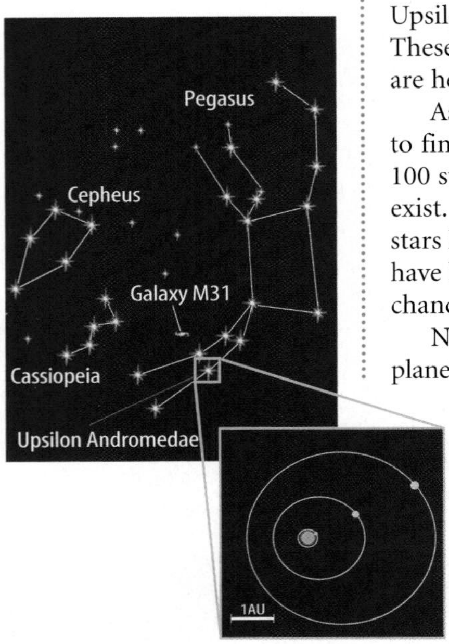

Other Solar Systems

Until recently, our solar system was the only one known. Now we know that many other stars also have planets around them. **Figure 5** shows the orbits of three planets around the star Upsilon Andromedae, a yellow star about 44 light-years away. These **extrasolar planets**—planets in orbit around other stars—are helping astronomers learn how planetary systems form.

Astronomers have devised new techniques and instruments to find planets around other stars. So far, they have found over 100 stars that have planetary systems, and many more probably exist. Some of these planetary systems have been found around stars like the Sun, but so far only giant planets similar to Jupiter have been detected. If these large planets exist, scientists say the chances are good that planets of lower mass exist also.

New instruments developed by NASA will look for Earthlike planets around other stars. It is difficult because the low mass of planets like Earth make them harder to find than giant planets. Even so, some of the planets found so far are comparatively low in mass and a few of these have a mass very similar to Neptune's. Scientists hypothesize this indicates that many more planets of even lower mass will be found.

Reading Check *What is an extrasolar planet?*

section 1 review

Summary

Models of the Solar System

- Geocentric models of the solar system place Earth in the center.
- Heliocentric models of the solar system place the Sun in the center.

Understanding the Solar System

- Planet orbits are ellipses.
- Planets are classified by their positions in the solar system and by their characteristics.
- Planets move around the Sun in a counterclockwise direction.

Other Solar Systems

- Extrasolar planetary systems have been discovered.

Self Check

1. **Compare and contrast** the geocentric and heliocentric models of the solar system.
2. **Explain** how heliocentric longitude is used to show the position of planets in orbit around the Sun.
3. **Classify** planets two ways using their positions in the solar system.
4. **Define** terrestrial planets.
5. **Think Critically** Would a year on Venus be longer or shorter than an Earth year? Explain.

Applying Math

6. **Using Equations** Use the equation (planet's period in years)^2 = (planet's distance in AUs)^3 to find the orbital period of a planet that is 19.2 AU from the Sun.

More Section Review gpescience.com

section 1 review

1. Both are models of the solar system. In the geocentric model, Earth is in the center; whereas in the heliocentric model, the Sun is in the center.
2. Measurements of heliocentric longitude show the angular position of a planet in its orbit around the Sun.
3. Planets can be inferior or superior (based on the position of Earth's orbit) or inner or outer (based on the location of the asteroid belt).
4. planets that are about 16,000 km in diameter (Earth-sized) and Earth-like
5. A year on Venus would be shorter because its orbit lies closer to the Sun and it takes less time to complete an orbit. Being closer to the Sun, Venus also travels around the Sun at a faster rate.
6. 84 years

222 CHAPTER 8 The Solar System

section 2

The Inner Planets

Reading Guide

What You'll Learn

- **Compare and contrast** other inner planets with Earth.
- **Describe** important characteristics for each inner planet.
- **Evaluate** the success of various missions to Mars.

Why It's Important

Answering questions about life on other planets helps you better appreciate the unique qualities of Earth.

Review Vocabulary

robot lander: part of a spacecraft that lands on another planet or other object

New Vocabulary

- Mercury
- Venus
- Earth
- Mars

Planets Near the Sun

Recall that not all the gas, ice, and dust in the nebula fragment that formed the Sun was drawn into its core. Remaining gas, ice, and dust particles collided and stuck together, forming solid objects that in turn attracted more particles because of the stronger pull of gravity. Close to the Sun, high temperatures vaporized lighter elements so they could not condense. This explains why light elements are scarcer in planets closer to the Sun than in those that formed farther away. Also, any lighter elements surviving were probably driven from the surface by the solar wind. As a result, small, rocky planets with iron cores formed in the inner solar system.

Mercury

The second-smallest and closest planet to the Sun is **Mercury.** *Mariner 10* was the first American space probe sent to Mercury. During 1974 and 1975, it flew by the planet and sent pictures back to Earth, but only 45 percent of Mercury's surface was photographed. What we can see of its surface looks very much like our Moon's. Mercury is covered by craters, some of which have double rings, as shown in **Figure 6.** Scientists do not yet understand why this is true.

The magnetic field around Mercury, discovered by *Mariner 10*, indicates that Mercury has a much larger iron core than would be expected and is missing some lighter materials you would expect to find in its mantle. One theory is that two similarly sized bodies collided. Their cores merged to form one large iron core, and some of the lighter material vaporized and was lost to space.

Figure 6 The outer ring of this double-ringed crater on Mercury is 170 km across.

1 Motivate

INTERACTIVE CHALKBOARD An editable Microsoft® PowerPoint® presentation is available on **Interactive Chalkboard** CD-ROM.

Bellringer

Section Focus Transparencies also are available on the Interactive Chalkboard CD-ROM. L2 ELL

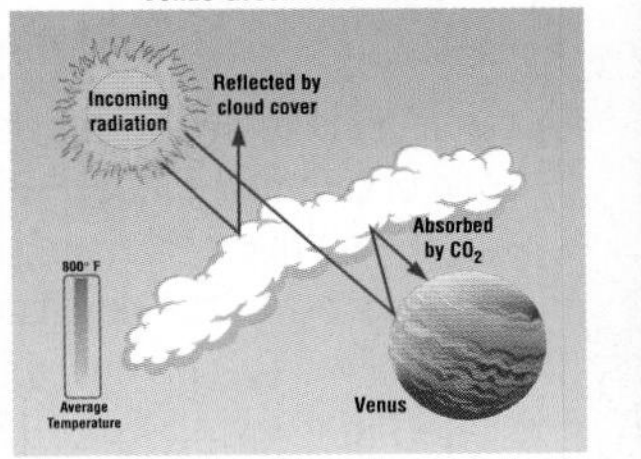

SECTION 2 Section Focus Transparency **That's One Hot Greenhouse!** Chapter 8

Have you heard about global warming and the greenhouse effect? Global warming is the gradual increase of Earth's surface temperature because the atmosphere does not allow some of the Sun's radiation to return to space. Global warming is increasing because of a build-up of carbon dioxide and other gases in our atmosphere (greenhouse effect). Venus takes this effect to the extreme, as you can see below.

Venus Greenhouse Effect

1. How is this effect on Earth and Venus similar to a real greenhouse?
2. What might happen on Earth if its surface continued to heat up?

The Solar System

Reading Preview

Tie to Prior Knowledge

Inner Planets Help students recall information about the inner planets. Ask them to write the names of the terrestrial planets in their Science Journals and list one fact about each. Possible answer: Mercury—cratered, Venus—greenhouse effect, Earth—liquid water, Mars—red color L1 ELL

Activate Vocabulary Knowledge Ask students why the vocabulary words are capitalized. Tell them that these are planets in our solar system. The words *Sun* and *Moon* also are capitalized. Remind them that the use of capital letters references a named planet, moon, or star. L1 ELL

Section 2 Resource Manager

Chapter *FAST FILE* Resources

- Transparency Activity, p. 47
- Enrichment, p. 32
- Reinforcement, p. 28
- Directed Reading for Content Mastery, p. 20
- Lab Worksheets, pp. 5–6
- Lab Activity, pp. 9–11

Critical Thinking/Problem Solving-Earth Science, p. 8

Lab Management and Safety, p. 71

Reading and Writing Skills Activities, pp. 11–12

2 Teach

Discussion

Messenger In August 2004, NASA sent the first spacecraft toward Mercury since *Mariner* 10 flew by the planet in 1975. Have students research and discuss the method that will be employed by NASA to place the *Messenger* spacecraft into orbit around Mercury in 2011. Possible answer: To save fuel that would be needed to slow the spacecraft down and go into orbit, NASA will send Messenger past Earth, Venus, and Mercury several times so that the gravity of those planets will slow the craft enough to enter an orbit around Mercury L3

Fun Fact

Mercury is named for the Roman god of commerce, travel, and thievery. It was given this name because it moves across the sky so quickly. Ironically, its year is only 88 days long, but its day lasts for 176 Earth days.

Reading Check

Answer Venus's clouds produce an intense greenhouse effect

Figure 7 Thick clouds obscure the surface of Venus. This view of the surface was assembled from radar data of *Magellan* and *Pioneer Venus Orbiter* and then colorized.

Mercury's Surface Mercury's relatively large core and thin outer layers resulted in some extreme differences in its surface terrain. Mercury's large, solid core shrank much more rapidly than its thin outer layers. As the outer layers adjusted, they wrinkled, forming dramatic cliffs as high as 3 km. This is similar to what happens when an apple dries and shrivels up.

Is there an atmosphere around Mercury? Mercury is small, has a comparatively low gravitational pull, and its surface experiences extremes in temperature. These conditions indicate that the planet has no atmosphere. *Mariner 10* and Earth-based observations did find traces of what was thought to be an atmosphere, but turned out to be gases that remain for a while and then leak into space. They are thought to be hydrogen and helium deposited by the solar wind and sodium and potassium vapors that diffuse upward through the crust. Mercury has no true atmosphere. This, along with its closeness to the Sun, causes surface temperatures that vary from 427°C to –170°C.

Venus

Venus, shown in **Figure 7,** is the second planet from the Sun. Venus and Earth are similar in some respects; their sizes and masses are almost the same. However, one major difference is that the entire surface of Venus is blanketed by a dense atmosphere. The atmosphere of Venus, which has 92 times the surface pressure of Earth's at sea level, is mostly carbon dioxide. The clouds in the atmosphere also contain droplets of sulfuric acid, which gives them a slightly yellow color.

Clouds on Venus are so dense that only about two percent of sunlight reaches the planet's surface. However, the solar energy that reaches warms Venus's surface. Then, heat radiated from Venus's surface is absorbed by the carbon dioxide gas, causing what is called a greenhouse effect. Due to this intense greenhouse effect, temperatures on the surface of Venus are between 450°C and 475°C.

Reading Check *Why is Venus's surface temperature so high?*

In the 1970s, the former Soviet Union sent the *Venera* lander probes to Venus. One photographed and mapped the surface before landing, but after about an hour, was destroyed by the intense heat. In 1995, the U. S. *Magellan* probe sent back radar images that revealed features of Venus, as shown in **Figure 8.**

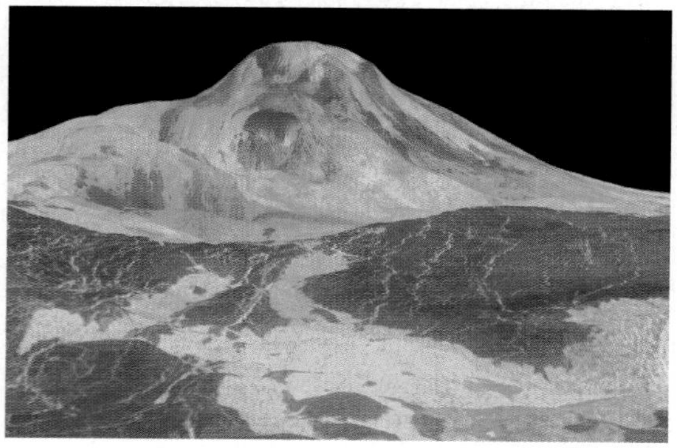

Figure 8 Radar images of volcanoes with visible lava flows on Venus were captured by the *Magellan* space probe.

Science Journal

Water on Mercury Have students write a brief paragraph in their Science Journals about how a planet as hot as Mercury could have deposits of water-ice on it. Possible answer: Radar studies of Mercury indicate the presence of a highly reflective material in craters at its poles. Since Mercury is tilted very little, the Sun is never very high in the sky at the poles and some craters remain in darkness all the time. L2 LS **Linguistic**

Visual Learning

Figure 7 Help students understand the information shown in **Figure 7.** The surface of Venus is constantly covered by thick clouds. Explain to students that the only way to get 'pictures' of the surface of the planet is to use radar images. This photograph is a mosaic of radar images pieced together to show the surface of the planet as if it had no clouds. L2 ELL

Earth

The third planet from the Sun is **Earth,** shown in **Figure 9.** Unlike other planets, surface temperatures on Earth allow water to exist as a solid, a liquid, and a gas. Earth's atmosphere causes most meteors to burn up before they reach the surface. Ozone in Earth's atmosphere also protects life from the Sun's intense radiation. Life exists all over the planet. Life has been found on Earth in extreme conditions of temperature and pressure in which scientists would never have guessed it could survive. These finds are encouraging for the possibility of life existing elsewhere in the solar system. You will learn more about this in Section 4.

Figure 9 Seen from space, Earth's white clouds and blue oceans testify to the abundant water that makes life possible.

Mars

The fourth planet from the Sun, **Mars,** is called the red planet because iron oxide in some of the weathered rocks on its surface gives it a reddish color, as shown in **Figure 10.** Other Martian features visible from Earth are the polar ice caps and changes in the coloring of Mars's surface.

Mars is tilted 25° on its axis, which is very close to Earth's tilt. Because of this, Mars goes through seasons as it orbits the Sun, just like Earth does. The polar ice caps, which are made of frozen carbon dioxide and frozen water, get larger during the Martian winter and shrink during the summer. The color of Mars's surface changes according to its seasons.

In fact, both the changing sizes of the ice caps and changes in Mars's surface coloration were observed from Earth long before we ever sent a probe to the planet. Some people saw these changes and thought that life forms such as lichens might exist on Mars and grew more during the summer, thus making the area look darker. We know now that what actually causes this seasonal change in coloration of the Martian surface is wind, not the cyclic nature of plant life. As the seasons change during the Martian year, winds blow the dust around on the planet's surface. When the wind blows dust off one area, it may appear darker.

Figure 10 The dark region below Mars's polar cap in this *Hubble* photograph is composed of pulverized volcanic rock. A swirling storm of water-ice is visible to the left of the polar cap.

Make a Model

Terrestrial Planets Provide students with various-sized balls. Have them select different balls to represent the four inner planets and explain their choices. Possible answer: If a softball is used as a model of Earth, then Venus is a softball, Mercury is a ping-pong ball, and Mars is a 5-cm rubber ball (a golf ball will work, but it is slightly small). L2 ELL IN **Visual-Spatial**

Activity

Colorful Planets Explain to students that a planets color is dependent on the composition of its surface or atmosphere. Have them draw Earth, Venus, and Mars to scale in their Science Journals and then find out what causes each planet's distinctive color. Have them color their drawings. L2 P

Fun Fact

Mercury's iron core appears to make up about 65% of the planet's mass.

Reading Strategy

Question the Text Tell students that good readers ask questions as they read to make certain they understand. Have them write questions that come to mind as they read Earth. For example: What is the range of temperature on Earth? Is there Life at the South Pole? Discuss the role of questions in understanding text. L2 ELL

Curriculum Connection

Literature Invite students to read a classic work of fiction dealing with Martians or Mars. Examples would be *War of the Worlds* by H.G. Wells, originally published in 1898, *The Martian Chronicles* by Ray Bradbury, originally published in 1946, and the *Red Mars, Green Mars, Blue Mars* trilogy by Kim Stanley Robinson, published in 1993, 1994, and 1996. Encourage students to discuss in class what they read. Have them concentrate on how the authors pictured Mars and its possible inhabitants. Have them compare what the authors thought Mars would be like with what we now know it to be. Another discussion could center on the possibility of changing Mars into a more Earthlike planet. L2 IN **Linguistic**

IDENTIFYING Misconceptions

Air on Mars Because of science fiction books, television shows, and movies, some students might think the Martian atmosphere is breathable. Help students realize that Mars's atmosphere is too thin for humans to survive without a special suit and portable air supply. The density of air at the surface of Mars is about the same as 32 km above Earth's, 3.6 times higher than Mt. Everest. It is about 1 percent of Earth's surface atmosphere.

Visual Learning

Figure 11 Help students understand the information presented in **Figure 11.** The so-called blueberries were discovered on Mars by the *Opportunity* robot rover. Although they are not berries or blue, analysis indicates they are concretions of the mineral hematite. Emphasize the importance of this discovery. On Earth, this type of hematite deposit is usually formed in the presence of standing water. L2

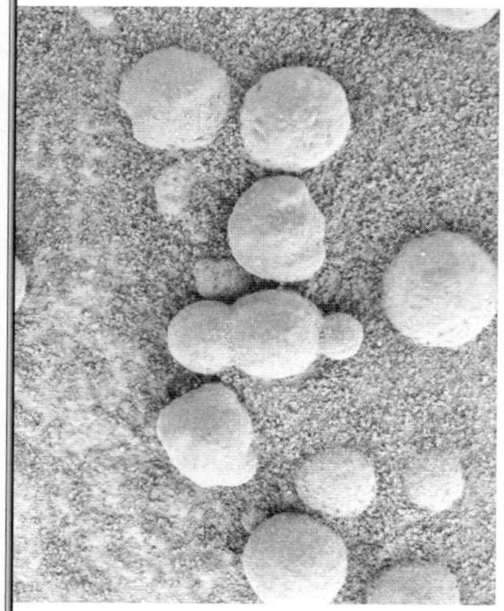

Figure 11 These spherical concretions found on Mars provide evidence of Mar's wet past.

Mars's Atmosphere The Martian atmosphere is much thinner than Earth's and is composed mostly of carbon dioxide with some nitrogen and argon. The thin atmosphere does not filter out harmful rays from the Sun as Earth's atmosphere does. Surface temperatures range from 37°C to −123°C. This temperature difference sets up strong winds on the planet, which can cause global dust storms.

Martian Moons Mars has two small, heavily cratered moons called Phobos and Deimos. Phobos is slowly spiraling inward toward Mars, and is expected to hit the Martian surface in about 50 million years. Deimos, which is smaller, orbits about 23,500 km above the surface.

Was Mars once wet? Currently, Mars appears to be a very dry world, but has it always been dry? Does it have any water now? The *Spirit* and *Opportunity* probes sent to Mars seem to indicate that liquid water was once on the planet and may still be there. **Figure 11,** a photo from *Opportunity*, shows deposits on Mars that have been labeled "blueberries" because of their round shape. These are concretions, most likely composed of hematite. Similar concretions form on Earth in the presence of water. **Figure 12** shows photographs taken in 2000 by the *Mars Global Surveyor* spacecraft. You can see the layering and gullies that look as if they were made by running water. Wind might have formed the layering of sediment and gullies, but more and more evidence indicates that water was once present on Mars. Other formations at the edges of craters suggest that frozen water in Mars's surface may flow outward from time to time, forming the channels. NASA has sent many spacecraft to Mars to find out if Mars is or was once wet.

Figure 12 These photographs taken by *Mars Global Surveyor* show gullies and channels inside the Newton Basin.

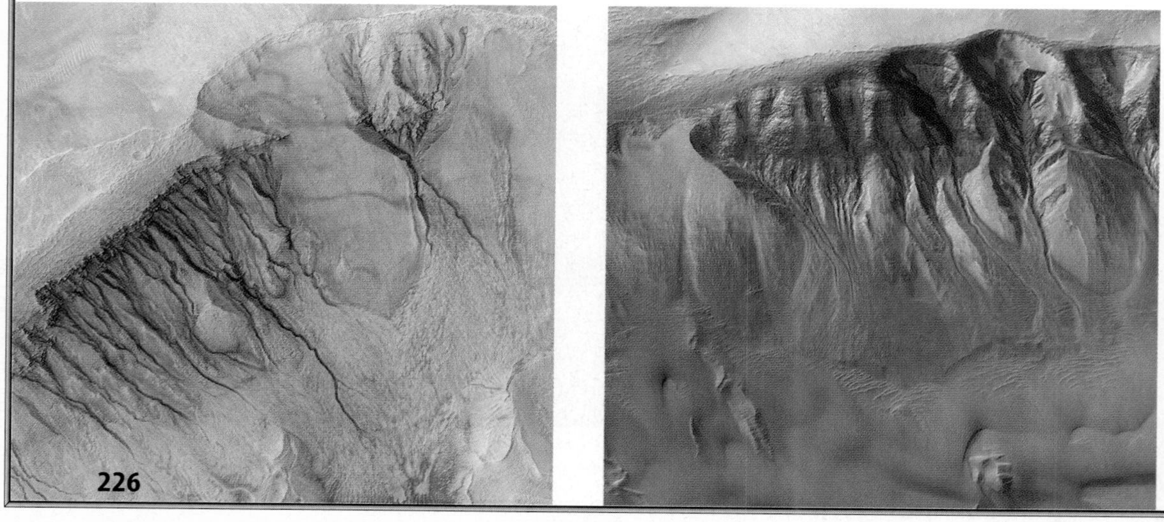

LAB DEMONSTRATION

Purpose to demonstrate how water-carved channels formed on Mars

Materials large, flat pan; fine-grained sand, plastic beaker, water

Alternate Materials stream table

Preparation Place enough fine-grained sand to completely cover the bottom of the flat pan.

Procedure Tilt the flat pan slightly by placing two books under one end. Gradually pour water from the plastic beaker onto the elevated end of the pan.

Expected Outcome The flowing water will erode a channel and produce an apron of sediment in the flat pan.

Assessment

What did the flowing water do to the sand in the flat pan? What formed where the water stopped flowing? Possible answers: a water-carved channel; a delta or apron of sediment L2

NASA on Mars

Mars has been a major focal point of NASA planetary exploration for many years. Although not all missions to Mars have been successful, several missions have returned a great amount of data about our reddish-colored neighbor. One of the earliest missions to Mars was the *Mariner 9* space probe that orbited Mars in 1971–1972. It revealed long channels on the planet that may have been carved by flowing water. *Valles Marineris* (the valley of the Mariners), shown in **Figure 13,** is a large canyon that was discovered by this early mission. It is so large that, if it were on Earth, this canyon would reach from San Francisco to New York City. It probably formed when Mars was still geologically active. *Mariner 9* also found large, extinct volcanoes. One of these, Olympus Mons, is the largest volcano found in the solar system.

Reading Check *What is* Valles Marineris?

Until 2003, most of the information about Mars came from the *Mariner 9, Viking probes, Mars Global Surveyor, Mars Pathfinder,* and *Odyssey.* The most recent data come from the *Mars Exploration Rover Mission* and its two landers, *Spirit* and *Opportunity.*

The Viking Probes In 1976, the *Viking 1* and *Viking 2* probes landed on Mars at the locations shown in **Figure 13.** Each spacecraft consisted of an orbiter and a lander. The *Viking 1* and *Viking 2* orbiters photographed the entire surface of Mars from orbit, while their landers conducted meteorological, chemical, and biological experiments on the planet's surface. Although initial results of the biological tests provided data that seemed to indicate the presence of life, scientists soon realized that the same data also could indicate chemical reactions. The biological experiments found no conclusive evidence of life in the soil.

The *Viking* landers also sent back pictures of Mars's reddish-colored, barren, rocky, and windswept surface.

Science Online

Topic: NASA Missions to Mars
Visit gpescience.com for Web links to information from recent studies of missions to Mars.

Activity List new information you learned about Mars and write about the significance of each discovery in your Science Journal.

Figure 13 Mars's *Valles Marineris* is six to seven times deeper than Earth's Grand Canyon.

Teacher FYI

Dust Storms on Mars Winds on Mars can reach speeds of hundreds of kilometers per hour. These winds can pick up loose dust from the Martian surface and produce dust storms that can block out the entire surface. This happened in 1971 when Mariner 9 went into orbit around the planet. Scientists had to wait for the storm to subside before beginning a detailed study of the planet's surface.

Reading Check

Answer a large canyon on Mars

Use Science Words

Word Meaning Have students research the meaning of *Valles Marineris.* Why was this feature on Mars given this name? Possible answers: Valley of the Mariners; It was first seen by the Mariner spacecraft. L1 ELL

Visual Learning

Figure 13 Help students understand the information presented in **Figure 13.** This photograph of Mars shows *Valles Marineris* and the landing sites of *Pathfinder* and *Viking 1. Valles Marineris* is the largest canyon in the solar system. Although its origin remains unknown, a leading hypothesis suggests that it started as a crack billions of years ago as the planet cooled. L2 ELL

INTEGRATE Chemistry

Martian Minerals Deposits of salt could have been left behind by evaporating water. Sulfates also could have been in solution and deposited as the water evaporated. Deposits of salt and sulfates have been found on Earth that were formed by the evaporation of a body of water. Hematite concretions can form on Earth in the presence of standing water. Vugs are openings in rocks in which sulfates, such as gypsum, were deposited as they evaporated from water. Once the sulfates were weathered and eroded away, the openings were left behind.

Research Find examples where vugs were formed on Earth.

Quick Demo

Terrestrial/Jovian Planets

Materials soccer ball, large marble

Estimated Time 5 minutes

Procedure Walk around the room holding a large marble and a soccer ball. Ask students if they know what you are demonstrating. Possible answer: The relative sizes of terrestrial versus jovian planets. The large marble represents a terrestrial planet; the soccer ball represents a jovian planet. L2 ELL LS **Visual-Spatial**

INTEGRATE Chemistry

Martian Minerals In addition to "blueberries," *Opportunity* discovered evidence that water once existed on Mars. It found deposits of salts and high concentrations of sulfur. It also found holes in Martian deposits left behind when a mineral is eroded. Research evidence that indicates water was in *Meridiani Planum.* Write about it in your Science Journal.

Global Surveyor, Pathfinder,* and *Odyssey Cameras on board *Global Surveyor* showed that the walls of *Valles Marineris,* shown in **Figure 13,** have distinct layers similar to those of the Grand Canyon. They also showed that a vast flat region, resembling a dried-up seabed or mudflat, covers a large area of Mars's northern hemisphere. Many believe the water is now frozen into Mars's crust at the poles or has soaked into the ground. In fact, a more recent probe, *Mars Odyssey,* provided evidence for water as frost beneath a thin layer of soil in the far northern and southern parts of Mars.

The *Mars Pathfinder* and its rover, *Sojourner,* gathered data that indicated that iron in Mar's crust may have been leached out by groundwater.

***Mars Exploration Rover* Mission** Recall the round concretions, called "blueberries," that indicate water may once have existed on the surface of Mars. These were discovered by the *Opportunity* rover in *Meridiani Planum.* The rover confirmed that the concretions were hematite deposits. The fact that the hematite was deposited on top of other features suggests that it was deposited in a standing body of water. Other deposits of hematite have been found by the *Spirit* rover in *Gusev Crater.* The *Mars Exploration Rover* mission that placed these two landers on Mars provided a great deal of evidence that water existed on Mars in the past. Photographs of the Martian surface taken by the two landers *Spirit* and *Opportunity* are shown in **Figure 14.**

Figure 14 The top photograph of light-colored volcanic rocks and fine-grained soils was taken by *Spirit* in Gusev Crater. The bottom photograph shows *Opportunity's* landing site on the Meridiani Planum and a rock outcrop about 8 meters away.

Teacher FYI

Mars Mars' axis is tilted 25° degrees from the orbital plane. This means that Mars experiences seasons as Earth does. However, Mars's orbit is more elliptical causing summer in the southern hemisphere to be much warmer than summer in the northern hemisphere.

Fun Fact

Each Mars rover (*Spirit* and *Opportunity*) is equipped with 9 cameras or imagers; four Hazcams (engineering hazard avoidance cameras), two Navcams (Navigation cameras), two Pancams (panoramic cameras), and one Science Microscopic Imager.

Martian Meteorites Space probes sent to Mars are not the only way we have learned about our planetary neighbor. Meteorites have been found on Earth that are believed to have been blasted into space from Mars. An interesting discovery was reported in 1996 that caused a lot of debate over the possibility of life on Mars. A meteorite from Mars (ALH84001) that had been found in the Antarctic in 1984 was studied by a group of scientists. They found long, egg-shaped microscopic structures that they thought were fossilized evidence of ancient life on Mars. The meteorite, shown in **Figure 15,** is thought to have been ejected by an impact on Mars about 16 million years ago.

Figure 15 This meteorite fragment found in Antarctica is believed to have been dislodged from Mars by a huge impact about 16 million years ago.

Reading Check *How was a meteorite that originated on Mars found on Earth?*

A debate began in which many scientists suggested other possible reasons for the egg-shaped structures. They pointed out that processes not related to life might have formed these structures. Although no firm conclusions can be drawn from this evidence, research will continue until data are found to determine whether life exists, or may once have existed, on Mars.

section 2 review

Summary

Mercury
- Mercury has an extreme range of temperatures, many craters, and long, steep cliffs.

Venus
- The sizes and masses of Venus and Earth are similar.
- The carbon dioxide in Venus's atmosphere has caused an extreme greenhouse effect, creating high surface temperatures.

Earth
- Surface temperatures on Earth allow water to exist as a solid, a liquid, and a gas.
- Earth is the only planet definitely known to support life.

Mars
- Mars has ice caps and surface coloring that experience seasonal changes.
- There is much evidence of water on Mars in both past and present.

Self Check

1. **Compare and contrast** Mercury, Venus, Earth, and Mars.
2. **Describe** the atmosphere of Venus.
3. **Explain** why scientists believe Mars was once a wetter planet.
4. **Explain** why the *Mars Exploration Rover* mission is considered a success.
5. **Think Critically** Explain why Mars is a more likely planet for humans to visit than Venus.

Applying Math

6. **Using Percentages** If the diameter of Mars is 53.3 percent of Earth's diameter (12,756 km), find its diameter in kilometers.
7. **Converting Units** If Earth takes 365.26 days to orbit the Sun and Mars takes 686.98 days, how many Earth years does Mars take to orbit once around the Sun?

More Section Review gpescience.com

section 2 review

1. All are terrestrial planets. Mercury has essentially no atmosphere and like Venus, is very hot. Mars is much colder than the others because of its distance from the Sun and lack of a thick atmosphere.
2. Venus's atmosphere is composed mostly of carbon dioxide. It has an atmospheric pressure 92 times that of Earth at sea level. Clouds contain droplets of sulfuric acid.
3. Hematite and other deposits have been discovered which often form on Earth in the presence of water.
4. It has discovered evidence that could mean water once existed on Mars. This was one of its major goals.
5. Mars has a thin atmosphere and temperatures more like Earth's. Venus has a very dense atmosphere and surface temperatures of 450°C to 475°C.
6. 6,799 km
7. 1.88 Earth years

Reading Check

Answer It was blasted off Mars about 16 million years ago, traveled through space, and eventually fell to Earth.

Post Reading

Time-Line Project Have students begin a time-line of space probes that shows what was learned from each mission. It may be helpful for students to write information for each space probe on separate note cards and then arrange them in proper sequence. L2 ELL LS **Visual-Spatial**

3 Assess

DAILY INTERVENTION

Check for Understanding

Visual-Spatial Have students review the photographs of the Martian surface in this section. What is true about the Martian surface that helps explain the pink color of its atmosphere? Possible answer: There is so much red dust in the lower atmosphere that it reflects its color and the sky is pink. L2 ELL

Reteach

"Planet Jeopardy" Provide students with answers about each of the terrestrial planets. Have them form questions to go with each answer. L1 ELL

Assessment

Oral Why does the Martian surface have more craters than are on Earth? Possible answer: Meteorites do not burn up in the thin Martian atmosphere like they do in Earth's. Also, much of Earth is covered by ocean, and many meteorites might have landed there. Also, Earth's plate tectonics could have destroyed many craters formed in its early history and vegetation on Earth might conceal meteorite craters. L2

Video Lab available for this Lab.

Real-World Problem

Purpose Students will identify Martian features and interpret formation processes.

Process Skills identify, infer, interpret scientific illustrations, make and use tables, observe, recognize cause and effect

Time Required 40 minutes

Safety Precaution Caution students to use scissors with care.

Procedure

Teaching Strategy A high quality photo of Mars's surface for this activity is available at gpescience.com. Also at this site is a link to an Exploring Mars Project, that may interest advanced students. Show photographs of features on Earth that are similar to the ones the students will be looking at on Mars photographs.

Troubleshooting Point out one key surface feature to show students what they are expected to do.

Conclude and Apply

1. Table should resemble the one given in the lab.
2. and **3.** Refer to data table.
4. Flowing water or lava formed the flow structures. Channel flow is from NE to SW; Lava flows, NW to SE.
5. from the east

LAB: Interpreting Features of Mars's Surface

Much of what scientists have learned about Mars involves interpreting data and photographs obtained from spacecraft that explored Mars. Comparing features found on the surface of Mars to similar features on Earth enables scientists to hypothesize about what may have caused these features. How can you interpret Martian surface features in the classroom?

Real-World Problem

How can you interpret the surface features shown on a photograph of the surface of Mars?

Goals

- **Identify** surface features shown on a photograph of Mars.
- **Interpret** what processes were involved in the formation of these surface features.

Materials

photograph of the Martian surface from NASA
clear-plastic sheet
erasable marker
scissors
transparent removable tape

Alternate Materials

additional laminated photographs of the Martian surface

Safety Precautions

Procedure

1. Cut the clear-plastic sheet to fit, and tape it over the photograph.
2. Use the erasable marker to mark, trace, or circle the features you can recognize, such as craters, lava flows, flow structures (channels), terraces, and sediment layering.
3. Indicate the direction that a flow of lava or water may have traveled.

Conclude and Apply

1. **Make a table** to show the data you will obtain in this Lab.
2. **List** in your table the features you were able to recognize in the photograph.
3. **Identify** and **list** in your table a process that might have formed each feature.

NASA Photograph MOC2-102

Surface Feature	Formation Process
terraces	water erosion or lava flows
craters	meteorite impact
lava flows	volcanic eruptions
flow structures	water or lava flow
sediment layering	deposition by water or wind
possible volcano	volcanic eruptions

4. **Recognize cause and effect** for the flow structures you identified. Record possible flow material and the direction for flow.
5. **Infer** from which direction sunlight was shining on the Martian surface when this photograph was taken.

Communicating Your Data

Explain to friends, classmates, or your family that this is what NASA scientists do with data obtained from spacecraft.

Assessment

Content Have students work in groups of three to write a poem about the processes that may have formed the features observed in the Mars photograph. Poems may rhyme or not. Use **Performance Assessment in the Science Classroom**, p. 169. L2 ELL LS **Linguistic**

Communicating Your Data

Have students discuss with one another any differences in their interpretations of features or the processes that may have formed them. Have them list possible reasons for these different interpretations.

230 CHAPTER 8 The Solar System

section 3

The Outer Planets

Reading Guide

What You'll Learn

- **Compare and contrast** the outer planets.
- **Describe** important characteristics for each outer planet.
- **Evaluate** the success of NASA missions *Galileo* and *Cassini.*

Why It's Important

Studying the outer planets helps scientists to understand the formation of planets orbiting other stars.

Review Vocabulary

space probe: an instrument that is sent to space to gather information

New Vocabulary

- Jupiter
- Saturn
- Uranus
- Neptune
- Pluto
- comet
- asteroid
- meteoroid
- Sedna

Why are the outer planets so different?

Recall how the small, rocky inner planets formed. High temperatures near the Sun prevented the lighter elements from condensing readily, so these elements are scarcer in the planets closer to the Sun. Things were different in the outer portion of the cloud fragment that formed our solar system. There, lighter elements condensed, collided, and stuck together. The growing masses collected still more particles because of the stronger pull of gravity. This produced the giant planets found in the outer part of our solar system. Only Pluto does not fit this description.

Jupiter

The largest and fifth planet from the Sun is **Jupiter.** It is composed mostly of hydrogen and helium, with some ammonia, methane, and water vapor. Scientists theorize that the atmosphere of hydrogen and helium gradually changes to a planetwide ocean of liquid metallic hydrogen toward the middle of the planet. Below this liquid layer may be a solid rocky core much larger than Earth. However, the extreme pressure (about 50 million Earth atmospheres) and temperature (40,000°C), make the core different from any rock on Earth.

You've probably seen pictures of Jupiter's colorful clouds. Its atmosphere has bands of white, red, tan, and brown clouds, as shown in **Figure 16.** Continuous storms of swirling, high-pressure gas have been observed on Jupiter. The Great Red Spot is the most spectacular of these storms. Lightning also has been observed within Jupiter's clouds.

Figure 16 The Great Red Spot on Jupiter in the lower right is a storm that has raged for more than 300 years.

Section 3 Resource Manager

Chapter *FAST FILE* Resources

Transparency Activity, p. 48

MiniLAB, p.4

Enrichment, p. 33

Reinforcement, p. 29

Directed Reading for Content Mastery, p. 21

Lab Activity, pp. 13–15

Home and Community Involvement, p. 27

Mathematics Skill Activities, pp. 1–2

Lab Management and Safety, p. 70

1 Motivate

INTERACTIVE CHALKBOARD PowerPoint® Presentations An editable Microsoft® PowerPoint® presentation is available on **Interactive Chalkboard** CD-ROM.

Bellringer

Section Focus Transparencies also are available on the Interactive Chalkboard CD-ROM. L2 ELL

SECTION 3 Section Focus Transparency **Holy Comet! That's Halley's comet.** Chapter 8

Records indicate that about every 76 years since 240 B.C., people have viewed Halley's comet. Although some sightings have been more spectacular than others, probably none has been as striking as the photographs taken by modern spacecraft. One of these photos is shown below.

1. In what year would you be able to see Halley's comet if it were last visible early in 1986? How old will you be?
2. Why did scientists say that people were able to see bits and pieces of this comet in 1998?

The Solar System

Reading Preview

Tie to Prior Knowledge

Outer Planets Ask students to recall what they know about the outer planets. Ask if any students have seen Saturn's rings through a telescope. Some students will recall Jupiter's Great Red Spot. L2

K-W-L Ask students to make a three-column K-W-L chart. Have them write three things they already know about each vocabulary word in the know column. Then have them write three things they want to learn in the middle column. As they read, have them complete the learned column. L1 ELL

2 Teach

Activity

Classifying Planets Have pairs of students make flash cards of the three ways to classify planets. Students should write a planet classification on one side and the planets in the classification on the reverse of the card. Students should quiz each other on planet classification. L1 ELL **Visual-Spatial**

Reading Check

Answer water may exist under the icy surface

Use Science Words

Word Origin Help students recall that planets can be classified as terrestrial or jovian. Ask students to research the origin of these words and explain their use. Possible answers: terrestrial—of Earth of its inhabitants, from *terra* (Earth); jovian—of Jove (Roman god, Jupiter or planet Jupiter); Planets that are Earth-like are terrestrial; those that are Jupiter-like are jovian. L1 ELL

INTEGRATE Language Arts

Naming Moons The names of the four Galilean moons refer to characters in myths about Jupiter, and the names of the moons of Uranus come from works by Shakespeare or Pope. The names of Mar's moons Deimos and Phobos mean panic and fear, respectively.

Figure 17 Jupiter's gravity holds more than sixty moons in orbit. Two of them are shown above.

Space Probes to Jupiter

In 1979, *Voyager 1* and *Voyager 2* flew past Jupiter, and the *Galileo* space probe reached Jupiter in 1995. The major discoveries of these probes include information about the composition and motion of Jupiter's atmosphere, characteristics of some of its moons (including volcanoes on one of them), and the discovery of new moons. The *Voyager* probes also discovered that Jupiter has faint dust rings around it.

Jupiter's Moons Jupiter has more than 60 moons. You can see some of them orbiting the planet in **Figure 17.** Many of these are small, rocky bodies that may be captured asteroids. However, four are large enough to be considered small planets. Galileo was the first to discover these moons when he looked through his telescope and he drew a picture of what he saw. These Galilean moons of Jupiter are Io, Europa, Ganymede, and Callisto, and are described in more detail in **Figure 18.** One of these, Ganymede, is larger than the planet Mercury and is the largest moon in the solar system.

Io is under a constant tug-of-war between the gravities of Jupiter and Europa. This heats up the interior of Io and causes it to be the most volcanically active body in the solar system. The volcanoes on Io were first seen in photographs from the *Voyager* probes.

The most recent interpretation of the data sent back by the *Galileo* space probe about the other three Galilean moons is that they all most likely have an ocean of water underneath an ice-rock crust. Some scientists speculate that Europa's ocean is very large and could possibly harbor some kind of life. Using gravity and magnetic field measurements, NASA scientists generated a model that shows the existence of water beneath Europa, Ganymede, and Callisto. When *Galileo's* mission ended, NASA chose to send the probe into Jupiter's atmosphere, where it was crushed and destroyed. They didn't want to risk having it crash on Europa and contaminate any life that might exist there.

Reading Check ***Why do scientists think Europa is a good candidate for supporting life?***

INTEGRATE Language Arts

Naming Moons You may know that the names of all the planets except Earth come from names of Greek and Roman gods. But did you realize that many of the names chosen for moons come from either mythology or literature? For example, Charon was the name of the boatman who erried the dead to the underworld kingdom of Pluto. Research the moons of Mars and find out why their names are appropriate.

Reading Strategy

Question the Author Tell students that good readers ask questions of the author as they read. Model this strategy after reading Jupiter's Moons by asking: How does the tug of war of gravity between Jupiter and Europa cause Io to heat? Have students develop a question they would like to ask the author. L2 ELL

232 CHAPTER 8 The Solar System

NATIONAL GEOGRAPHIC **VISUALIZING WHAT GALILEO SAW**

Figure 18

Galileo Galilei, 1564–1642 In 1610, Italian scientist Galileo Galilei did something revolutionary for his time. Galileo used a telescope to look at the planet Jupiter and saw four objects revolving around it. This and other observations convinced him that our solar system is heliocentric.

Like its namesake, the *Galileo* spacecraft changed our understanding of the solar system. *Galileo* launched a probe into Jupiter's atmosphere, which gathered data about cloud layers, chemical composition, and lightning.

Ganymede, the largest moon in the solar system, is larger than the planet Mercury. It has grooves covering its surface that indicate a violent past. These grooves most likely resurfaced over time through volcanic activity.

Callisto is marked by one giant crater called Valhalla, which was formed by an impact over four billion years ago. Callisto has a thin atmosphere of carbon dioxide and most likely has an ocean of salty water surrounding its interior of ice and rock.

Io is caught between Jupiter's tremendous gravitational force and the gravity of neighbor Europa. It is the most volcanically active object in the solar system.

Europa is mostly rock with a thick, cracked but smooth crust of ice.

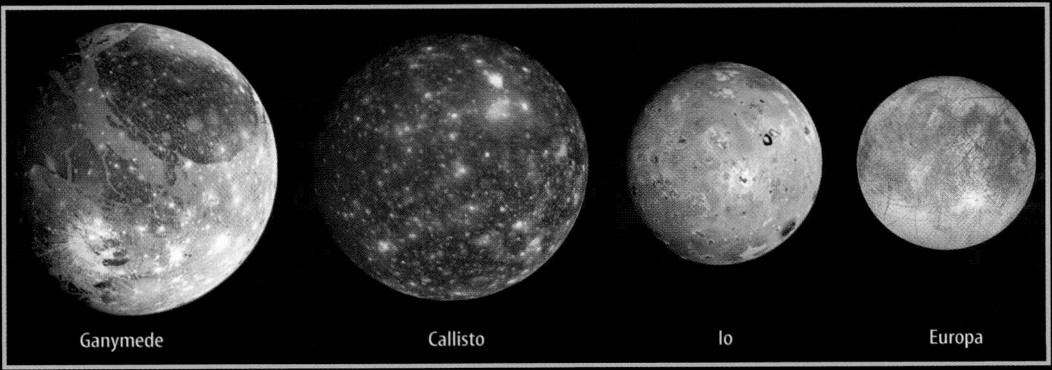

NATIONAL GEOGRAPHIC

Visualizing Jupiter's Galilean Moons

Have students compare what Galileo, the man, saw compared to what *Galileo*, the spacecraft saw by examining the pictures and reading the captions. Then ask the following questions.

What is true about the number of craters seen on the four Galilean moons? Possible answer: The farther a moon is from Jupiter, the more craters it has.

Which moon is the most geologically active? Possible answer: Io

Which moon shows cracks on its surface that may have been caused by tidal pulls from Jupiter on an ocean underneath? Possible answer: Europa

Have students examine the pictures and read the captions. Then ask the following question.

Explain how Galileo's discovery of these satellites provided evidence for the Copernican theory? Possible answer: Copernicus believed all solar system bodies revolved around the Sun, rather than the Earth. Galileo's discovery demonstrated that at least four solar system bodies did not revolve around the Earth.

Activity

What *Galileo* Achieved The *Galileo* mission increased scientific understanding of Jupiter and its moons. Have students research the mission and create a poster, booklet, or multimedia presentation describing some of *Galileo's* major findings. L2 P

Differentiated Instruction

Visually Impaired Have a student helper read the text about Galileo and about each moon described. Have the helper show enlarged images of those in this feature to the other student. Encourage the helper to discuss what is shown in each image with the other student. For example, the helper can point out the fact that active volcanoes are evident on Io. This can help the visually-impaired student "see" the image. L2 ELL

Discussion

Saturn's Rings Tell students that the Roche Limit is a critical distance from a planet below which gravitational forces of the large planet overcome a moon's internal gravity and the moon is torn apart. Smaller moons (less than 10 km) can exist inside a planet's Roche Limit because they are held together by interatomic forces, not gravity. Ask students to explain whether they believe Saturn's Roche Limit lies inside or outside its ring system. Possible answer: Inside the Roche Limit, moons larger than 10 km in diameter were pulled apart by Saturn's gravity and the pieces formed rings around the planet. Thus Saturn's ring system lies inside the Roche Limit. L3

Fun Fact

The *Cassini-Huygens* spacecraft began a four-year study of Saturn and its moons on July 1, 2004. The *Cassini-Huygens* Mission is an international program. It involves NASA, the European Space Agency, and the Italian Space Agency.

Activity

Planet Flash Cards Have students make flash cards of the nine planets. On one side of the card, they should draw the planet and name it. On the reverse of the card, they should list three or four facts about the planet. Have students work in teams of two to quiz each other on planet characteristics. L2 ELL LS **Visual-Spatial**

Figure 19 *Cassini-Huygens* provided detailed views of Saturn and its rings.

Science Online

Topic: Discoveries of *Cassini-Huygens*

Visit gpescience.com for Web links to information about discoveries made by the *Cassini* and *Huygens* probes at Saturn.

Activity Write a paragraph describing new discoveries made by *Cassini* space probe about Saturn.

Saturn

NASA began a new study of Saturn when the *Cassini-Huygens* spacecraft reached Saturn in July 2004. The spacecraft's arrival, insertion into orbit, and initial operation went flawlessly. Many data about Saturn, its rings, and its moons were collected during its approach. **Saturn,** shown in **Figure 19,** is the sixth planet from the Sun and is known as the ringed planet. It is not the only ringed planet, but it has the largest and most complex ring system. Based on *Cassini-Huygens* data, Saturn could have at least 34 moons. Although Saturn is the second-largest planet in the solar system, it has the lowest density. This is because Saturn's gravitational pull is weaker than Jupiter's—Saturn's cloud layers are not squeezed as close together as cloud layers in Jupiter's atmosphere are.

Like Jupiter, Saturn is a large planet with a thick outer atmosphere composed mostly of hydrogen and helium with some ammonia, methane, and water vapor. As you go deeper into Saturn's atmosphere, the gases gradually change to liquid hydrogen and helium. Below its atmosphere and liquid ocean, Saturn may have a small rocky core, but no rocky surface like Earth's. When compared to Earth, the pressures and temperatures at the core must be tremendous.

Saturn's Rings Saturn's rings are composed of countless ice and rock particles ranging in size from a speck of dust to tens of meters across. The rings appear as several broad bands, each of which is composed of thousands of thin ringlets.

As *Cassini-Huygens* entered its orbit around Saturn, it took close-up pictures of these rings that showed a density wave, just as had been predicted by physicists, as shown in **Figure 20.** Also shown in this figure, are areas where the ring material bends up and down. Other *Cassini-Huygens* photographs showed that the gravity of Saturn's moons affects its rings and the presence of a new ring associated with the moon, Atlas.

Figure 20 *Cassini* produced this image by filtering starlight through Saturn's rings. The bands of color represent changes in ring density as rings are affected by the gravity of two of Saturn's moons.

***Cassini-Huygens* at Saturn** *Cassini-Huygens* is actually two spacecraft in one. *Cassini* was programmed to orbit Saturn for over four years and to release a probe named *Huygens* when it passed Saturn's moon Titan. *Huygens* was designed to descend through the thick atmosphere of Titan and land on its surface. You will learn more about Titan later.

Teacher FYI

Uranus If you know exactly where to look on a dark night, Uranus is visible to the unaided eye. Even in large Earth-based telescopes, it appears as just a tiny greenish disk. Because its rotational axis is tilted 98°, the poles of Uranus alternately point in the direction of the Sun.

Uranus

After touring Saturn, *Voyager 2* flew by Uranus in 1986. **Uranus,** shown in **Figure 21,** is the seventh planet from the Sun and wasn't discovered until 1781. It is a large planet with 27 moons.

Uranus's axis of rotation is tilted on its side, so that it is nearly perpendicular to the plane of its orbit. This may have happened as the result of a collision with another object. *Voyager* also revealed numerous thin rings, and detected that the planet's magnetic field is tilted 55 degrees from its rotational poles.

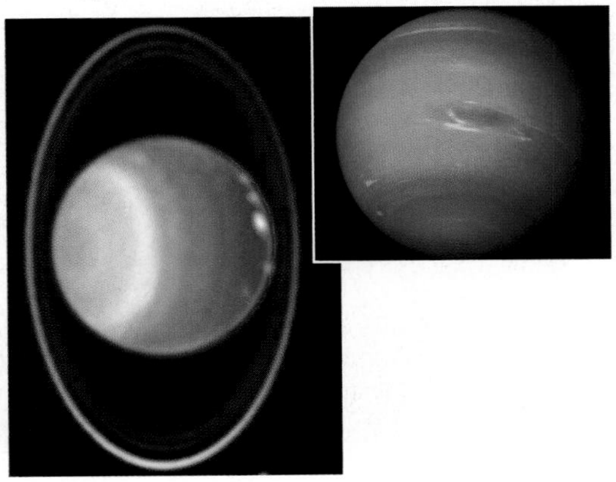

Figure 21 Uranus, left, and Neptune, right, are about the same size. Uranus has faint cloud bands and a ring system that are visible only in false color.

The atmosphere of Uranus contains hydrogen, helium, and about two percent methane. The methane gives the planet its blue-green color because methane absorbs red and yellow light, and the clouds reflect green and blue light. No cloud bands and few storm systems are seen on Uranus because of its cold upper atmosphere. This lack of bands and storms may be connected to the fact that Uranus has less internal heat than Neptune. Evidence suggests that under its atmosphere, Uranus has a mantle of liquid water, methane, and ammonia surrounding a rocky core.

Reading Check *What causes Uranus to have a blue-green color?*

Neptune

From Uranus, *Voyager 2* traveled on to Neptune. **Neptune,** another large planet similar in size to Uranus, is the eighth planet from the Sun. Neptune, also shown in **Figure 21,** was discovered in 1846 when studies of Uranus's orbit indicated that the gravity of another unseen planet must be pulling on it. Under its atmosphere, Neptune is thought to have liquid water, methane, and ammonia covering a rocky core. *Voyager* also detected that Neptune has rings that are thin in some places and thick in others.

Neptune's atmosphere is similar to that of Uranus, but has a little more methane—about three percent—causing it to look bluer. Neptune's atmosphere has dark spots similar to the Great Red Spot on Jupiter. With its dynamic atmosphere, Neptune's internal heat must be greater than Uranus's.

Neptune has at least 13 moons. Triton, the largest, has a diameter of 2,700 km and a thin atmosphere composed mostly of nitrogen. Some methane is also present; *Voyager* detected methane geysers erupting on Triton.

Mini LAB

Comparing Sizes of Outer and Inner Planets

Procedure

1. Research the planets to find their diameters in kilometers.
2. Select a scale to draw the planets. The scale must be such that the small planets can be seen and the larger planets can fit your paper.
3. Using your scale, draw a circle with the diameter of the smallest planet.
4. Using the same scale, draw circles representing each of the other planets.

Analysis

1. How do the model sizes of the inner planets compare to those of the outer planets?
2. Which planet is smallest? Largest?

Try at Home

Mini LAB

Purpose Students will compare the relative sizes of the planets.

Materials drawing paper, colored pencils, drawing compasses

Teaching Strategies

- Show students how to use a drawing compass.
- Provide students with the diameters of the nine planets.
- Encourage students to color their planets.

Safety Precaution If drawing compasses are used, caution students to handle them carefully and to place a pad under their drawing paper.

Troubleshooting Try some scales ahead of time to see what size best fits the paper being used.

Analysis

1. Inner planets are smaller than outer planets (except Pluto).
2. Pluto; Jupiter

Assessment

Oral Based on the relative sizes of the planets, does Pluto seem to fit the inner or the outer planets better? Pluto's size fits better with the inner planets. L2

Try at Home

Reading Check

Answer methane in its atmosphere

Quick Demo
Comets

Materials crushed ice, dirt, small rocks (pebbles)

Estimated Time 10 minutes

Procedure Mix ice, dirt, and pebbles in a pan. Make a dirty snowball that consists of about half ice and half dirt and rock. Explain that comets often are described as dirty snowballs. L2

Active Reading

Think-Pair-Share Getting students involved as active participants is key to helping them learn. The Think-Pair-Share strategy allows students to think about a topic and brainstorm what they know about it, pair up to discuss what they know, and finally, get involved in a whole-class share session. Have students use this strategy on a Think Critically question in a Section Review in this chapter.

Differentiated Instruction

Visually Impaired Help your visually impaired students gain understanding from the MiniLAB. Have your visually impaired students work with other students who are using brightly colored pieces of wax-covered yarn to make 3-D drawings of the planets' comparative sizes. Encourage visually impaired students to help build the 3-D models. L2 ELL

Inquiry Lab

Speeding Baseballs and Meteoroids

Question How do the speeds of a thrown ball and a meteoroid compare?

Possible Materials stopwatch, tennis ball, baseball, softball, racquetball, meterstick, calculator.

Estimated Time 30 minutes

Teaching Strategies

- Students should use a tennis ball or racquetball when possible. Students should never throw balls near other students, cars, buildings, or streets.
- Students can measure a 10-m distance and use stopwatches to determine the time it takes for a thrown ball to travel the distance.
- Using the formula for speed, students can calculate the speed of the ball in meters per second. They can derive the mathematical equation for converting m/s to km/s or simply divide their value for speed by 1,000. After converting the ball's speed to km/s, they can compare their value with the range of meteoroid speeds.
- Encourage students to research the orbital velocities for the planets and compare the speed of their ball to these values.

For additional inquiry activities, see *Science Inquiry Lab Manual*.

Figure 22 Pluto's moon, Charon, is about half the size of Pluto.

Pluto

The smallest planet in our solar system and the one we know the least about is Pluto. Because **Pluto** is farther from the Sun than Neptune during most of its orbit, it is considered the ninth planet from the Sun. Although Pluto comes closer to the Sun than Neptune for part of its orbit, the two planets will never collide because Pluto's orbit is inclined farther from the ecliptic plane. Because of this angle, the two orbits cannot intersect.

Pluto is unlike the other outer planets. It has a thin atmosphere and is the only outer planet with a solid, ice-rock surface. Pluto's only moon, Charon, is large compared to Pluto and orbits close to Pluto, as shown in **Figure 22.**

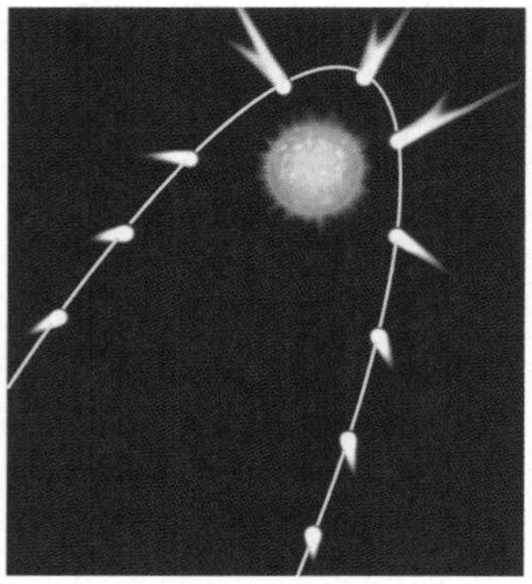

Figure 23 Comets often have two tails—one made of dust and one made of ions.

Comets and Other Objects

A **comet** is composed of dust and rock particles mixed with frozen water, methane, and ammonia. As a comet approaches the Sun, it begins to vaporize because of heat from the Sun. The released dust and gases form a bright cloud called a coma around the nucleus, the solid part of the comet. The solar wind pushes on the vaporized coma, forming a tail that always points away from the Sun, as shown in **Figure 23.**

Most comets come from two places—a vast disk of icy comets called the Kuiper Belt near Neptune's orbit and the Oort Cloud, which completely surrounds the solar system. Gravity from the Sun or from passing stars may periodically disturb these areas, sending comets on long journeys toward the Sun. Once in orbit around the Sun, comets reappear at predictable times. One of the most famous of these is Halley's comet, which returns every 76 years.

Figure 24 Asteroid 433 Eros has an irregular shape and is 23 km long. Spacecraft *NEAR-Shoemaker* landed on its surface in 2001.

Asteroids Rocky objects formed from material similar to that of the planets are called **asteroids.** One of these is shown in **Figure 24.** Most asteroids are found in a belt between the orbits of Mars and Jupiter. Asteroids range in size from tiny particles to objects 940 km in diameter.

Meteoroids Other rocky objects orbiting within the solar system are **meteoroids.** They may have formed when asteroids collided or when comets passed close to the Sun, leaving a trail of debris. When Earth passes through these trails, meteoroids may enter the atmosphere. Most burn up completely and we see them as meteors or "shooting stars." Others do not burn completely and strike Earth. These are called meteorites.

Teacher FYI

NEAR-Shoemaker On February 14, 2000, the *NEAR-Shoemaker* spacecraft went into orbit around asteroid 433 Eros. It showed that Eros was composed of solid rock, probably primitive, solar system material. The *NEAR-Shoemaker* spacecraft later successfully survived a low-velocity landing on the asteroid and sent radio signals to Earth for 16 days.

Cultural Diversity

Japan in Space Japan launched two spacecraft that studied Halley's Comet in 1986. The spacecraft were the *Sakigake* spacecraft which studied Halley's Comet from a distance of 6.88 million km and the *Suisei* which conducted a flyby at a distance of 151,520 km. Have students research current space missions conducted by the Japan Aerospace Exploration Agency.

Sedna Another object in the solar system that has puzzled astronomers is Sedna, shown in **Figure 25. Sedna** has been labeled a distant planetoid and with a diameter of 1,200 to 1,700 km, it is smaller than Pluto, but larger than comets in the Kuiper Belt. Also, it has a very elliptical orbit. Sedna comes as close as 76 AU from the Sun, but travels to a distance of 950 AU—far beyond the Kuiper Belt, but much closer than the Oort Cloud.

Some suggest that the Sedna's orbit was severely affected by a passing star less than 100 million years after the Sun formed. This supports the idea that our Sun formed as part of a star cluster. A close encounter with another star so soon after the Sun's formation and so nearby (800 AU) could be explained if the Sun formed within a cluster.

Another puzzle is Sedna's apparent rate of rotation of 40 days. This is best explained if the object had another object in orbit around it. Even if Sedna has no companion, there may be other similar objects, some even larger than Pluto, out there. At present, objects this far away and having orbits this elliptical can be detected only when they are closest to the Sun.

Figure 25 Sedna is larger than an asteroid or comet, but smaller than a planet.

section 3 review

Summary

Jupiter
- Jupiter is the largest planet in the solar system.
- The four largest moons of Jupiter are Io, Europa, Ganymede, and Callisto.

Saturn
- Saturn has the most complex system of rings.

Uranus, Neptune, and Pluto
- Uranus's axis of rotation is tilted on its side.
- Neptune's atmosphere has storms similar to those on Jupiter.
- Pluto has a solid, icy-rock surface.

Comets, Asteroids, and Meteoroids
- The asteroid belt lies between the orbits of Mars and Jupiter.
- Meteoroids form from pieces of comets and asteroids.

Self Check

1. **Compare and contrast** Jupiter, Saturn, Uranus, Neptune, and Pluto.
2. **Explain** what Saturn's rings are composed of.
3. **List** three things scientists learned about Jupiter and its moons from the *Galileo* space probe.
4. **Think Critically** Explain what would happen to the density of Saturn if its atmospheric layers squeezed inward toward the center of the planet.

Applying Math

5. **Use Numbers** If the diameters of Earth and Jupiter are 12,756 km and 142,984 km, respectively, how many Earths could fit across Jupiter's equator?
6. **Use Decimals** On average, if Earth is 150 million km, or 1 AU, from the Sun and Venus is 0.71 AU from the Sun, what is the distance to Venus in kilometers?

More Section Review gpescience.com

section 3 review

1. All are outer planets. All except Pluto are gas giant planets. The gas giants have differently colored clouds.
2. Pieces of rock and ice ranging from fractions of millimeters to tens of meters. Most are the size of snowballs.
3. discovery of new moons, volcanic activity on Io, possible ocean under the ice crust of Europa, new data about Jupiter's atmosphere
4. If the atmospheric layers of Saturn squeezed inward toward the center of the planet, the density would increase.
5. slightly over 11
6. 106.5 million km

Post Reading

Discussion Have students share their questions and answers from their K-W-L Charts. Are there any unanswered questions? Discuss how to do further reading or research to answer these questions. Challenge students to use research materials to gain knowledge about a topic of interest.

3 Assess

DAILY INTERVENTION

Check for Understanding

Visual-Spatial Show students pictures of each of the outer planets. Have them identify the planet shown and write at least one fact about each planet. Write comments from students on the board under the name of each planet. Have students check comments on the board for correctness. L1 ELL

Reteach

Planet Sizes Have students write the names of the outer planets in order of size from the largest to the smallest. Possible answer: Jupiter, Saturn, Uranus, Neptune, and Pluto L1

Assessment

Content Have students draw a comet as it would appear when approaching the Sun. Possible answer: Student drawings should include a nucleus, a coma, and a tail. Students might show more than one tail; one of ions and one of dust. Use **Performance Assessment in the Science Classroom,** p. 127. P L2 ELL IS **Visual-Spatial**

1 Motivate

INTERACTIVE CHALKBOARD — An editable Microsoft® PowerPoint® presentation is available on **Interactive Chalkboard** CD-ROM.

Bellringer

Section Focus Transparencies also are available on the Interactive Chalkboard CD-ROM. L2 ELL

Section 4 Section Focus Transparency — **40,000 Years Old and Going Strong!** — Chapter 8

Could you live here? Maybe not. But a type of moss was found that had survived in an environment like this. Scientists estimated that it had been lying dormant for 40,000 years. Could life, then, survive on other worlds with similar conditions?

1. Name several other types of extreme environments in which life exists on Earth.
2. How do you think the moss was able to survive for so long?

The Solar System

Reading Preview

Tie to Prior Knowledge

Life on Other Worlds NASA considers it possible that Mars, Europa, and Titan could have or once did have life on them. Remind students of the ocean under the icy crust of Europa. L2

Morphological Word Analysis
Tell students that *extra-* means "beyond" and *terre–* means "Earth". Something that is *extraterrestrial* is from beyond Earth. Ask them to describe how *terrarium, terrian, terrace, territory, terrazzo,* and *terrier* are related to the word *earth.* L2

section 4

Life in the Solar System

Reading Guide

***What* You'll Learn**
- **Evaluate** other planets in the solar system for the possibility of containing life.
- **Examine** life forms that exist in exotic locations on Earth.
- **Discuss** locations in which life might exist on other planets.

***Why* It's Important**
The lack of evidence showing that life exists elsewhere helps you realize how important it is to take care of Earth.

Review Vocabulary
fossil: remains, imprints, or traces of past life

New Vocabulary
- extraterrestrial life

Life As We Know It

We know life exists in our solar system. It's all around us; in the air, on rocks, and in the sea, as shown in **Figure 26.** It thrives even in harsh environments on Earth, but does it exist anywhere else in the solar system and, if so, where? What does life need to survive? Life on Earth is carbon-based and requires water to survive. Does water exist elsewhere in sufficient quantities to make life possible?

Think about what you consider to be life. You might think of yourself, your friends, your pet, and maybe birds flying by the window. There is so much diversity to life on Earth. There is life we easily can see, such as grass, trees, and animals, but there is also a multitude of life that we cannot see. For example, microorganisms are so small you need a microscope to see them. When we define life, we might forget about microorganisms but they are very important to us.

Figure 26 Tube worms and mussels at this hydrocarbon seep on the floor of the Gulf of Mexico get their energy from bacteria that consume methane. Predators, such as crabs feed on the community.

If you were asked to check a sample of soil to see if there was or ever had been life in it, what would you do? You might look for moving things, but motion doesn't always mean something is alive. You might look for residues or traces of life that once lived in the soil, such as fossils. You know that you release gases as you breathe. You might check to see if gases are being emitted from the soil. Think about what type of tests you could perform on Martian soil to check for life, and remember that these tests would have to be done by a robot lander.

Section 4 Resource Manager

Chapter *FAST FILE* Resources
Transparency Activity, pp. 49, 51–52
Enrichment, p. 34
Reinforcement, p. 30
Directed Reading for Content Mastery, pp. 21
Lab Worksheet, pp. 7–8
Critical Thinking/ Problem Solving-Earth Science, p. 4
Reading and Writing Skills Activities, pp. 9–10

Exotic Life on Earth Before we rule out the possibility of life on other worlds, we should take a closer look at life on Earth. Some of the exotic life-forms that exist on Earth are strange, indeed.

In the 1970s, a research submarine, the *Alvin*, found some interesting life-forms while exploring hot, volcanic vents on the ocean floor at depths where light could not penetrate. A variety of life was living where scientists didn't think it could. Life-forms found included crabs, clams, and tubeworms. They were living and thriving in a dark environment under tremendous pressures. *Alvin* also discovered colonies of bacteria living off the extremely hot material spewing from volcanic vents. These organisms use thermal and chemical energy to survive and are the basis of food webs there.

A surprising amount of life has been found elsewhere on Earth in extreme conditions—scalding heat, freezing cold, salt, lye, and darkness. For example, a moss shown in **Figure 27** was dormant for 40,000 years in permafrost in northeastern Siberia. Three forms of bacteria thrive in the mud of Mono Lake, California, where the environment is dark, lacks oxygen, and contains a large amount of salt and lye. What does this tell us about the ability of life to exist in the harsh environments of other planets?

Figure 27 The moss shown to the left is growing again after being dormant for 40,000 years. The photograph above shows a researcher collecting mud samples from Mono Lake, California. One bacteria in this mud obtains energy from chemicals rather than sunlight.

Can life exist on other worlds?

Think about what you have learned about Earth compared to other planets. None of the planets you have studied has characteristics so close to Earth's that you could definitely say life as we know it could exist there. But can you say for certain that life cannot exist on other planets in the solar system?

The high temperatures found on Mercury and Venus and the lack of a surface on Jupiter and the other gaseous giants make finding life as we know it unlikely. But such facts do not rule out the possibility of some form of **extraterrestrial life,** that is, life on other worlds. Let's take a look at some places where scientists are searching for extraterrestrial life.

Reading Check *What is extraterrestrial life?*

2 Teach

Text Question Answer

It is possible.

Discussion

Life in Extreme Environments Remind students that even though NASA is looking for life as we know it (similar to life on Earth) on other worlds, there are many environments on Earth where scientists have found life where it was least expected. Where do life-forms that exist in the darkest parts of Earth's oceans, get the energy needed for life processes? Possible answer: thermal and chemical energy L2

Activity

Creature Feature Have students choose one of the other planets or moons in our solar system. Ask them to research the conditions on the surface or in the atmosphere of the place they selected. Have them write a one-page description in their Science Journals that explains how a life-form might have developed and survived on their chosen world. Students will need to answer the following questions: How and what does the creature breathe, eat, and drink? How does the creature reproduce? How is the creature protected from the enviroment? Does it move? If so, how does it move? Have then draw an illustration of the life–form L2 LS **Linguistic**

Reading Check

Answer life beyond Earth, on other worlds

Visual Learning

Figure 27 Explain to students that the moss shown here was discovered by scientists in an extreme environment on Earth and had survived thousands of years in a dormant state. Also tell them other life forms have been found on Earth living in environments that are usually not conducive to the survival of life. L2 ELL

Differentiated Instruction

English-Language Learners Help your English-language learners with their Creature Feature activity. Provide illustrations of life-forms that could possibly exist beyond Earth. For example, some scientists have proposed large life-forms filled with gas that could possibly live in the atmospheres of the jovian planets. The life-form they choose could be one-celled organisms.

SECTION 4 Life in the Solar System **239**

Quick Demo
Ocean Under Ice

Materials crushed ice, clear-plastic container, water

Estimated Time 10 minutes

Procedure Place crushed ice into the plastic container until it covers the bottom of the pan and is about 2 cm thick. Pour cold water into the pan until all of the ice is floating. Place a thermometer into the water and explain that an icy crust completely covering the water would help to maintain some warmth in the water. Explain that the ice covering the Arctic Ocean is similar to the ice that is believed to cover the oceans on Europa. L2 ELL LS **Visual-Spatial**

Reading Strategy

Make Connections As students read the section about Mars and the caption for **Figure 28**, ask them what the words *splish*, *splash*, and *splosh* bring to mind. Scientists speculate that "splosh" craters on Mars might have been made when a space object struck a water-soaked area. Remind students to make connections with the text to help them remember information. L2 ELL

Figure 28 This crater on Mars is called a splosh crater. It is hypothesized that a splosh crater forms from the impact of an object on a water-soaked surface.

Mars During most of Earth's history, one-celled organisms were the major form of life on Earth. Could such life-forms be present on Mars today or could they have existed on Mars in the past when the planet was wetter? Evidence from space probes has shown that Mars probably had large amounts of water on its surface, as shown in **Figure 28.** If life existed and left evidence, future astronauts will find it. Such a discovery would be almost as exciting as finding living life-forms.

Actually, searches for life on Mars already have been done. *Viking* landers on Mars performed some tests designed to detect life. The first tests showed positive results, but additional study showed that these results could be explained just as well by chemical reactions that did not require life. Ultimately, the *Viking* experiments found no evidence of life. However, the tests used only would detect life similar to that which exists on Earth. What if life on Mars is totally different from life on Earth?

Europa Data from the *Galileo* probe of Jupiter and its moons indicate that three Galilean moons have ice-covered oceans. The oceans under the ice of Ganymede and Callisto might be partially frozen. However, data related to surface cracking, as shown in **Figure 29,** tidal bulges, and movement of the surface over some lubricating substance below, support the idea of a liquid ocean about 25 km deep in Europa. Europa's ocean could hold more than twice the amount of water that Earth's oceans hold.

Some scientists speculate there is a chance that Europa's ocean could harbor life. One reason is that it might be deep and long-lasting, possibly even liquid water that is warmed by Jupiter's gravitational pull on Europa.

On Earth, we find life everywhere there is water. If life can exist in extremely hot liquid flowing from volcanic vents on Earth's ocean floor, could it not exist in a similar environment if it exists on Europa? In fact, ocean currents have been detected on Europa. Today, some scientists consider Europa to be the most promising location to look for extraterrestrial life.

Figure 29 Surface cracking on Europa may indicate that a liquid ocean lies beneath.

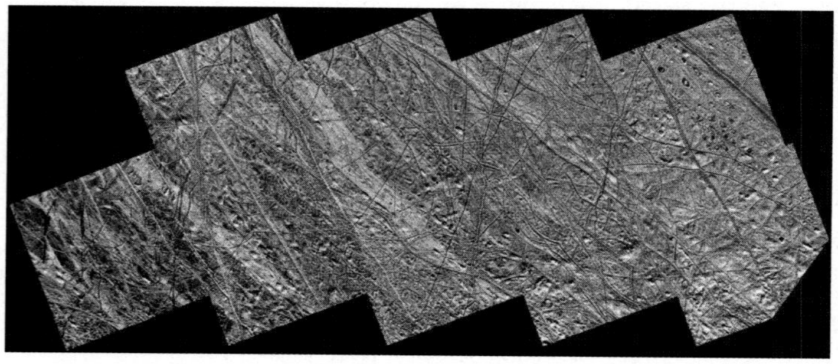

Teacher FYI

Europa Europa's surface does not have many craters. This indicates a geologically active surface. One explanation is the presence of a liquid-water ocean under the crust. Data from the *Galileo* spacecraft indicate that cracks form on Europa's surface because of the tidal influence of Jupiter on the ocean.

Visual Learning

Figure 29 This photograph mosaic of Europa, Jupiter's fourth largest moon, shows some double ridges on the moon's surface. These double ridges are thought to be frozen remnants of water eruptions onto the surface that indicate the presence of liquid oceans under the frozen crust. L2

240 CHAPTER 8 The Solar System

Titan Saturn's moon, Titan, shown in **Figure 30,** is larger than Mercury and has an atmosphere composed mostly of nitrogen, with some argon and methane. Certain features on Titan's surface indicate this moon has a long-term, interesting geologic history. Some darker areas contain relatively pure water-ice, while other, brighter areas are composed of hydrocarbons, organic compounds containing hydrogen and carbon. Recall that life on Earth is carbon-based. A bright cloud of the hydrocarbon methane is visible near the south pole. Large particles in this area indicate that a dynamically active atmosphere exists there.

The presence of hydrocarbons on the surface of Titan interests exobiologists, scientists who search for evidence of life on other worlds. Also, the apparent absence of large impact craters indicates that Titan has experienced internal geologic activity. This activity could provide the energy needed for organic molecules to develop into the building blocks of life.

A more detailed study of Titan is programmed for the *Huygens* probe. Data obtained from the *Huygens* probe might help solve the mystery of whether life exists or may have existed on Titan.

Figure 30 This image of Titan taken by *Cassini* shows two thin layers of hazy atmosphere that are thought to contain nitrogen and methane.

Reading Check *What fact about Titan particularly interests exobiologists?*

section 4 review

Summary

Life As We Know It

- Life as we know it is carbon-based and needs liquid water to survive.

Exotic Life On Earth

- Life exists in extreme environments on Earth.
- Life can remain dormant for long periods of time and still survive.

Mars

- *Viking's* tests for life on Mars were inconclusive.

Europa

- There is strong evidence for a warm, liquid ocean on Europa.
- Europa is considered the most promising location to look for extraterrestrial life.

Titan

- Organic compounds exist on Titan.

Self Check

1. **Define** extraterrestrial life.
2. **Describe** how finding life in extreme environments on Earth supports the idea that life may exist elsewhere.
3. **Explain** how hot fluids from volcanic vents on Earth's ocean floor support energy for life.
4. **Discuss** other locations in the solar system where life may once have existed.
5. **Think Critically** Explain why scientists consider Europa to be a good place to search for extraterrestrial life.

Applying Math

6. **Use Numbers** Atmospheric pressure at the surface of Venus is 92 times Earth's at sea level. If atmospheric pressure on Earth at sea level is 101.3 kPa, find the atmospheric pressure on the surface of Venus in kPa.
7. **Use Percentages** The average composition of Mars's atmosphere is 95% CO_2, 3% N, and 2% Ar. Approximately what fraction of Mars's atmosphere is nitrogen?

More Section Review gpescience.com

Reading Check

Answer the presence of hydrocarbons and absence of large impact craters, which indicate internal geological activity

Post Reading

Reflection Ask students to imagine that they are scientists who must design the next space probe and decide where it should be sent. Have them write a brief paragraph that includes the name of the space probe, why they named it as they did, the destination, and purpose of the probe. How will this space probe benefit the people on Earth? L2

3 Assess

DAILY INTERVENTION

Check for Understanding

Linguistic Have students write a poem or song about the likelihood that life will be found on another world in our solar system. Possible answer: Hey, hey, Mars is red. Could it be we've found a bed? For life to use when tired. Life not of Earth, I've said. L2

Reteach

Needs of Life Ask students to consider what primitive life on Earth needs to develop. Possible answer: water and warmth Then ask them where conditions like these may exist other than on Earth. Possible answer: Europa L2

section 4 review

1. life that developed on other worlds
2. If life can withstand, and even thrive, in extreme environments on Earth, then life could exist in the extreme environments found on other planets.
3. Organisms use thermal and chemical energy instead of sunlight to produce food that supplies the energy for life.
4. Mars was once a wetter planet and could have supported life. Europa may have an ocean under its ice that could or may have supported life.
5. Evidence suggests that ocean currents, perhaps caused by volcanoes, are present under Europa's icy crust. This could supply energy for life processes.
6. 9,320 kPa
7. 3/100

Assessment

Oral Why do scientists want to find out if Mars had liquid water on its surface sometime in the past? Possible answer: If Mars had oceans or large seas when it had a warmer environment, life may have begun. Fossils might provide evidence of this possible early life. L2

BENCH TESTED

Real-World Problem

Purpose Identify evidence that might indicate that life exists in soil from another world.

Process Skills form a hypothesis, design an experiment, separate and control variables, interpret data, observe, infer, compare and contrast, recognize cause and effect, communicate

Time Required 30 minutes to plan the experiment and 40 minutes to conduct the experiment, observe results, and draw conclusions

Materials Provide three containers of sand/soil mixture; one containing finely crushed antacid tablets, one containing dry yeast (about 1/2 tsp per 3 T), and one with nothing added.

Alternate Materials baking soda (however, the reaction is not as great as it is for antacid tablets)

Safety Precautions

- Students should wear protective clothing and eye protection in case of spills.
- Caution students to wash hands thoroughly after the experiment

Form a Hypothesis

- The sample of soil or sand containing life will release gas.
- The sample of soil or sand containing life will release gas and produce heat.
- The sample of soil or sand containing life will release gas, produce heat, and release odors.

LAB Design Your Own

Testing Unknown Soil Samples for Life

Goals

- **Identify** several things that you might see if life existed in an unknown sand or soil sample.
- **Demonstrate** processes you could use to search for life in the unknown sample.
- **Illustrate** evidence of life that you observe in each of your samples.
- **Compare and contrast** observations that may or may not indicate that life exists in your samples.

Possible Materials

clear plastic cups (3)
sand or soil
warm tap water
magnifying glass
thermometer

Safety Precautions

Real-World Problem

What is life? You know that life needs water, air, and food to survive. The type of food depends on the life form. You eat certain foods to provide you with the energy to live. Other forms of life need different foods for energy. You know that many plants make their own food using photosynthesis, and you have learned about life-forms on Earth that obtain their energy from chemical reactions. How might you find out if life is present in an unknown sample? Perhaps you might look for evidence that an organism was taking in one gas and expelling others. Perhaps you might look for energy being produced. How could you determine if an unknown sample of sand or soil contained life?

Form a Hypothesis

Form a hypothesis about what evidence might indicate that a sand or soil sample contained life. Have your teacher approve your hypothesis before you begin your experiment.

Test Your Hypothesis

Make a Plan

1. As a group, agree upon the hypothesis and decide how to test it. Identify which results will confirm your hypothesis.
2. **List** the steps you will need to test your hypothesis. Be sure to include a control run. Describe exactly what you will do in each step.

Data Table

Comparison of Soil or Sand Samples	
Sample number	**Observations**
Cup 1	No observed reactions.
Cup 2	Gas escapes
Cup 3	Gas escapes; heat and odor are produced.

Alternative Inquiry Lab

Hypothesize and Research Students imagine a life form and describe conditions that will support it. Remind them of conditions such as temperature, pressure, gravity, chemical composition, and energy sources. Students then will research whether a planet provides the necessary conditions to support their hypothesize life form.

Using Scientific Methods

3. **List** the materials you will need to perform the experiment. Determine who will prepare your unknown samples from your materials.
4. **Prepare** an illustration in your Science Journal where you will record your observations.
5. **Read** the entire experiment to make sure all steps will be performed in a logical order.
6. **Identify** all constants, variables, and controls of the experiment. Keep in mind that the person who prepares your unknowns must follow your instructions carefully and not divulge which sample(s) contain life.

Follow Your Plan

1. Make sure your teacher approves your plan and oversees the preparation of your unknown samples before you start.
2. Carry out your experiment as planned.
3. While doing the experiment, record your observations in your illustration in your Science Journal.

Analyze Your Data

1. **Illustrate** your visual observations of unknown sand or soil samples.
2. Label your drawings with other observations that you make, such as production of heat or change in odor.

Conclude and Apply

1. **Examine** Do the illustrations show the observations you expected to make? Describe any unexpected observations noted.
2. **Determine** Do any of your observations indicate that life exists in any of your unknown samples? Describe any inconclusive observations.
3. **Draw Conclusions** Did your results support your hypothesis? Explain why or why not.

Communicating Your Data

Compare your data with those of other students. Discuss how your experiments may have differed, and how this could have changed the observations.

Test Your Hypothesis

Possible Procedures One student from each group obtains warm water from the tap and adds just enough to completely cover the material in each cup.

Teaching Strategy Encourage students to measure equal amounts of soil or sand mixtures and to add the same amount of water into each cup.

Tie to Prior Knowledge Help students recall that life processes can produce gas, heat, and odors.

Troubleshooting Before beginning the lab, provide three containers with properly mixed material.

Expected Outcome Students should note gas being released from two of the mixtures. Increased heat and odors may be present.

Analyze Your Data

1. Illustrations should show gas being emitted from two of the samples.
2. Illustrations might show an increase in temperature and odors may be present.

Error Analysis Ask students to compare their results with others and discuss possible differences in conclusions drawn.

Conclude and Apply

1. Gas is released from two mixtures. Answers will vary.
2. Released gas and production of heat indicate life may be present. Released gas alone is inconclusive.
3. Answers will depend on student hypotheses.

Assessment

Portfolio Have groups of students prepare a mission description of an experiment to search for evidence of life on Mars that could be done by a robot rover. Possible answer: A robotic arm scoops up soil from the Martian surface and retracts it into a container where various solutions are introduced into the sample. Use **Performance Assessment in the Science Classroom**, p. 169. P L2

Communicating Your Data

Have students use graphics software to prepare a poster explaining their experiment and the results. Posters should contain the illustrations and data table produced during the experiment, as well as any conclusions they have reached.

SCIENCE Stats

Content Background

Many planets are easily visible with the unaided eye. Venus appears as the brightest object in the night or morning sky, with the exception of the Moon. Jupiter is also bright, and resembles a cream-colored star. Mars looks like a bright, orange-yellow star, while Saturn appears as a gold-colored star. Mercury is the most difficult planet to spot, because its location usually keeps it within the Sun's glare. Often the weather page of a newspaper says which planets are visible. You can also check astronomy guidebooks and internet sites. L2 ELL

Discussion

What do you think? Some people believe that planetary alignments can cause natural disasters, such as floods, earthquakes, and hurricanes. Do you think these phenomena are related? Possible answer: Scientists know that all planets, even those closest to Earth, are too far away to have any noticeable gravitational effect on Earth processes, the oceans, or the atmosphere. L2

Teaching Strategies

- Make sure students use the correct units to express the answer to question 2.
- Review with students how to best establish ratios to answer question 3.
- Remind students to measure angles in a counterclockwise direction.

SCIENCE Stats

Night Sky Wonders

Did You Know...

. . . Five of the nine planets can be seen from Earth without the aid of a telescope or binoculars. Mars, Venus, Mercury, Jupiter, and Saturn can be seen at various times throughout the year in the night or early morning sky. Mercury is visible for only a few days, but the other planets are often clearly visible, such as Mars and Venus shown here.

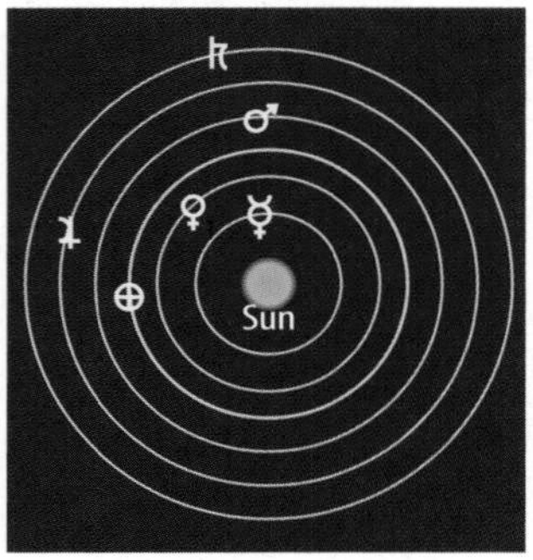

. . . All five planets were visible as a group in the evening sky in the spring of 2004. All five planets were briefly positioned on the same side of the Sun at the same time. This stunning sight will not be seen in the evening skies again until 2036. Because they orbit the Sun at different rates, it is rare for all five visible planets to be as close together in the sky as they were in 2004.

Applying Math

1. How old will you be when the next planetary alignment like the one that was visible in 2004 can be seen from Earth again?
2. The reflected light we see when observing planets travels through space at 300,000 km/s. If Jupiter is 588.5 million km from Earth at its closest approach, what is the minimum amount of time required for light to reach Earth from Jupiter?
3. Using the heliocentric longitude diagram you made in the Applying Math feature, plot the positions of the planets using the following longitudes: Mercury 96°, Venus 135°, Earth 184°, Mars 94°, Jupiter 165°, and Saturn 103°.

244 CHAPTER 8 The Solar Sytem

Applying Math

Answers

1. Answers will vary. Have students subtract the current year from 2036, then add the remainder to their age.
2. 1,962 s or 32.7 minutes
3. Check diagrams

Activity

Study the sky. Have students research which planets are currently visible in your area. Ask students to locate these planets in the nighttime or early morning sky. Students should record their observations for at least one week, describing any trends they notice. L3

Reviewing Main Ideas

Section 1 Planet Motion

1. In the geocentric model of the solar system, Earth is in the center. In the heliocentric model, the Sun is in the center.
2. The position of a planet in orbit around the Sun can be shown by heliocentric longitude.
3. Inner planets have orbits closer to the Sun than the asteroid belt; outer planets have orbits beyond the asteroid belt.
4. A large nebula, like the one shown below, fragmented into smaller ones, one of which later condensed and flattened to form the solar system.

Section 2 The Inner Planets

1. Mercury has a larger iron core than expected for a planet its size.
2. The carbon dioxide in Venus's dense atmosphere has caused a strong greenhouse effect that produces very high surface temperatures.
3. Mars landers like the one shown in the next column have provided evidence that Mars, once had more water on its surface than it does today.

Section 3 The Outer Planets

1. Jupiter is the largest planet in the solar system and has the most moons. Four of these moons were first seen by Galileo.
2. Saturn has the most developed ring system of all outer planets.
3. The green-blue color of Uranus and the blue color of Neptune are caused by methane in their atmospheres.
4. Pluto is the smallest planet, and unlike other outer planets, it has a thin atmosphere and an icy rock surface.

Section 4 Life in the Solar System

1. Life exists in extreme environments on Earth and may be able to survive in extreme environments on other planets.
2. Europa is considered the most promising location in the solar system to look for extraterrestrial life.

FOLDABLES™ Use the Foldable that you made at the beginning of this chapter to help you review details about each of the planets.

chapter 8 Study Guide

Reviewing Main Ideas

Summary statements can be used by students to review the major concepts of the chapter.

Science Online

Visit gpescience.com
More Section Review
Interactive Tutor
Vocabulary PuzzleMaker
More Chapter Review
Standardized Test Practice

Assessment Transparency

For additional assessment questions, use the *Assessment Transparency* located in the transparency book.

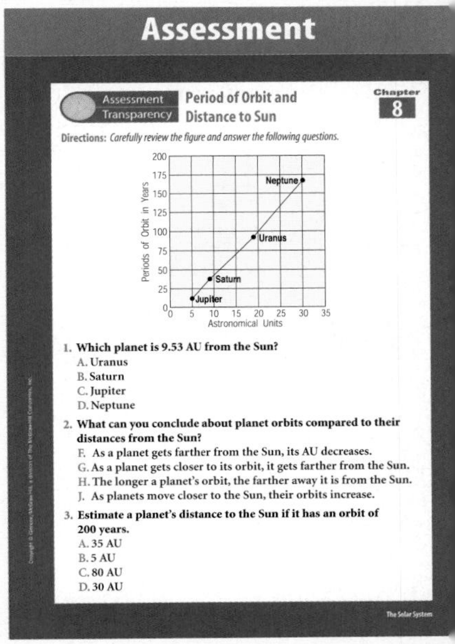

Assessment

Assessment Transparency **Period of Orbit and Distance to Sun** Chapter 8

Directions: *Carefully review the figure and answer the following questions.*

1. **Which planet is 9.53 AU from the Sun?**
   A. Uranus
   B. Saturn
   C. Jupiter
   D. Neptune
2. **What can you conclude about planet orbits compared to their distances from the Sun?**
   F. As a planet gets farther from the Sun, its AU decreases.
   G. As a planet gets closer to its orbit, it gets farther from the Sun.
   H. The longer a planet's orbit, the farther away it is from the Sun.
   J. As planets move closer to the Sun, their orbits increase.
3. **Estimate a planet's distance to the Sun if it has an orbit of 200 years.**
   A. 35 AU
   B. 5 AU
   C. 80 AU
   D. 30 AU

The Solar System

FOLDABLES™ Have students use their Foldables to review the content of the chapter.

chapter 8 Review

Using Vocabulary

1. Neptune has slightly more methane in its atmosphere. Both are jovian (gas giant) planets.
2. Extraterrestrial life might be found on extrasolar planets. Both are beyond Earth.
3. Pluto is a planet; Sedna is a planetoid. Both are icy worlds far from the Sun.
4. Venus is much hotter and has a denser atmosphere. Both are about the same size.
5. Mercury is an inner planet; Jupiter is an outer planet. Both are planets.
6. Asteroids are located between Mars and Jupiter; Sedna lies far beyond Pluto. Both are small rocky bodies.
7. Earth is at the center of the geocentric model; the Sun lies at the center of the heliocentric model. Both are models of the solar system.
8. An astronomical unit is a measure of distance; Earth is a planet. Earth is one astronomical unit from the Sun.
9. Jupiter is larger and denser than Saturn; Both are jovian (gas giant) planets.
10. Earth has oceans; Mars may once have had water on its surface. Both are terrestrial and inner planets.

Checking Concepts

11. A	**16.** C
12. C	**17.** D
13. B	**18.** A
14. B	**19.** D
15. D	**20.** D

chapter 8 Review

Using Vocabulary

asteroid p. 236	Mars p. 225
astronomical unit p. 220	Mercury p. 223
comet p. 236	meteoroid p. 236
Earth p. 225	Neptune p. 235
extrasolar planet p. 222	Pluto p. 236
extraterrestrial life p. 239	Saturn p. 234
geocentric model p. 218	Sedna p. 237
heliocentric model p. 219	Uranus p. 235
Jupiter p. 231	Venus p. 224

Use what you know about the vocabulary terms to explain the differences in the following sets of words. Then explain how they are related.

1. Uranus—Neptune
2. extrasolar planet—extraterrestrial life
3. Pluto—Sedna
4. Venus—Earth
5. Mercury—Jupiter
6. asteroid—Sedna
7. geocentric model—heliocentric model
8. astronomical unit—Earth
9. Jupiter—Saturn
10. Earth—Mars

Checking Concepts

Choose the word or phrase that best answers the question.

11. Who proposed the heliocentric model of the solar system?
A) Copernicus **C)** Kepler
B) Galileo **D)** Ptolemy

12. Which planet has the most complex ring system?
A) Jupiter **C)** Saturn
B) Neptune **D)** Uranus

13. Which planet is the red planet?
A) Jupiter **C)** Neptune
B) Mars **D)** Venus

14. Which chemical or gas produces a green-blue to blue color in Uranus and Neptune?
A) carbon dioxide **C)** oxygen
B) methane **D)** sulfur dioxide

15. Which planet has the highest surface temperature?
A) Earth **C)** Mercury
B) Mars **D)** Venus

16. Which fact is true of superior planets?
A) Earth-sized
B) Jupiter-sized
C) lie beyond Earth's orbit
D) lie beyond the asteroid belt

17. Which Galilean satellite has active volcanoes?
A) Callisto **C)** Ganymede
B) Europa **D)** Io

Use the illustration below to answer question 18.

18. Which planet is shown?
A) Jupiter
B) Mars
C) Saturn
D) Venus

19. Which part of a comet is on the opposite side of a comet from the Sun?
A) coma **C)** nucleus
B) head **D)** tail

20. What is a reason Europa might be a good place to look for extraterrestrial life?
A) liquid methane
B) presence of organic molecules
C) rust-colored rocks
D) water ocean and tidal energy

Vocabulary PuzzleMaker gpescience.com

Use the ExamView® Pro Test Bank CD-ROM to:
- create multiple versions of tests
- create modified tests with one mouse click for inclusion students
- edit existing questions and add your own questions
- build tests aligned with state standards using built-in State Curriculum Tags
- change English tests to Spanish with one mouse click and vice versa

Interpreting Graphics

21. **Make a table** summarizing the gases contained in the atmospheres of the nine planets.

22. **Make a model** of how you think the geocentric model of the solar system was organized.

Use the data in the table below to answer questions 23–25.

Planet Orbits

Planet	Distance to the Sun (AU)
Mercury	0.39
Venus	0.72
Earth	1.00
Mars	1.52
Jupiter	5.20
Saturn	9.54
Uranus	19.19
Neptune	30.07
Pluto	39.48

23. Which planet is a little over nine times farther from the Sun than Earth?

24. How far is the orbit of Mars from that of Jupiter in AU's?

25. How much closer to Earth is Venus than is Mars?

Thinking Critically

26. **Explain** why Venus has a higher surface temperature than Mercury even though Mercury is closer to the Sun.

27. **Form a hypothesis** about where the oxygen that combined with the iron in rocks on Mars came from.

28. **Classify** a newly discovered planet, by using three classification systems, with the following characteristics: 10,000 km in diameter, rocky surface, an orbit beyond Pluto's.

29. **Explain** why Mars, Europa, and Titan are of interest to scientists searching for extraterrestrial life.

30. **Explain** several reasons why Earth is the only planet in the solar system that appears capable of supporting life as we know it.

Applying Math

31. **Use Angles** How far around in its orbit would a planet be if its heliocentric longitude was 90 degrees?

32. **Calculate** Jupiter's distance from the Sun is 5.2 AUs. Use the equation (planet's distancein AUs)^3 = (planet's period in years)^2 to calculate Jupiter's period of revolution.

Use the diagram below to answer No. 33.

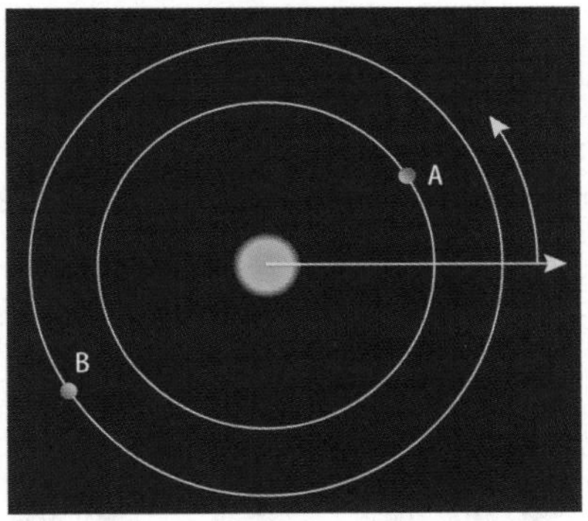

33. **Use Angles** If the Heliocentric Longitude (H. L.) of planet A is 33 degrees, what is the approximate H.L. of planet B?

34. **Using Equations** Use the equation $V = \frac{4}{3}(\pi r^3)$ to determine the volume of Venus, which has a radius of 6052 km.

Assessment Resources

Reproducible Masters

Chapter *Fast File* Resources
- Chapter Review, pp. 39–40
- Chapter Tests, pp. 43–44
- Assessment Transparency Activity, p. 53

Glencoe Science Web site
- Chapter Review Test
- Standardized Test Practice

Glencoe Technology
- Assessment Transparency
- Exam*View*® Pro Testmaker
- MindJogger Videoquiz
- Interactive Chalkboard

Interpreting Graphics

21.

Gases in the Planet Atmospheres	
Mercury	none
Venus	mostly carbon dioxide
Earth	nitrogen, oxygen, other
Mars	mostly carbon dioxide
Jupiter	helium, water, methane, hydrogen, ammonia
Saturn	water, helium methane, ammonia, hydrogen
Uranus	hydrogen, helium, methane
Neptune	hydrogen, helium, methane
Pluto	very thin

22. Earth, then Moon, Mercury, Venus, Sun, Mars, Jupiter, and Saturn.
23. Saturn
24. 3.68 AU
25. 0.24 AU closer

Thinking Critically

26. Venus has a thick cloud cover that causes a greenhouse effect.
27. Oxygen was once in the Martian atmosphere or in water.
28. terrestrial; outer; superior
29. Mars and Europa may have, Titan might have seas of methane.
30. Water exists as a solid, a liquid, and a gas on Earth. Ozone protects life from intense solar radiation.

Applying Math

Math Standards

National: 1, 4, 9

31. $\frac{1}{4}$ of the way
32. 11.9
33. 213°
34. 928 billion km^3

Answer Sheet An answer sheet can be found at **gpescience.com**.

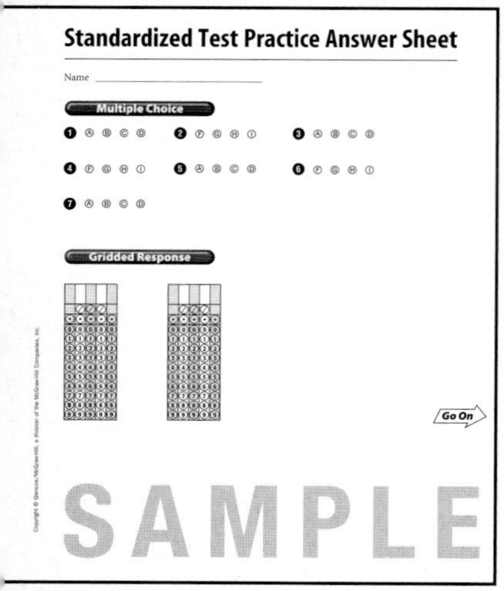
Standardized Test Practice Answer Sheet

Name

Multiple Choice

Gridded Response

Go On

SAMPLE

Multiple Choice

1. B
2. B
3. A
4. C
5. B
6. B

Record your answers on the answer sheet provided by your teacher or on a sheet of paper.

Multiple Choice

Use the illustration below to answer question 1.

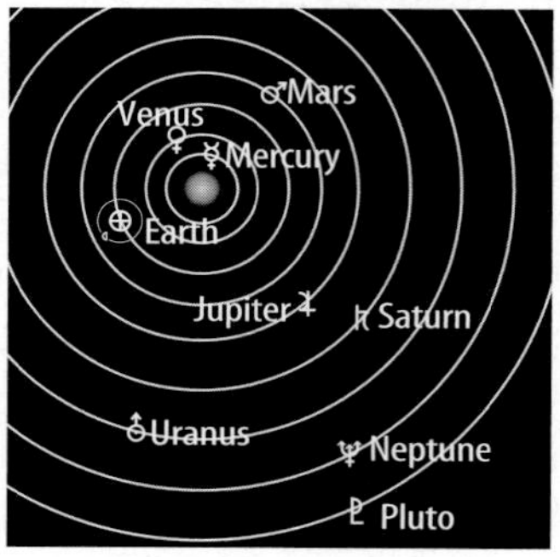

1. As seen from above their north poles, in which direction do planets move around the Sun?

A. clockwise
B. counterclockwise
C. geocentric
D. heliocentric

2. Which model of the solar system places the Sun in the center?

A. geocentric
B. heliocentric
C. inferior
D. superior

Test-Taking Tip

Practice Remember that test-taking skills can improve with practice. If possible, take at least one practice test and familiarize yourself with the test format and instructions.

3. What did Galileo observe about Venus?

A. It goes through phases.
B. It has two moons.
C. It is covered by clouds.
D. Its surface temperature is over 450°C.

4. Who determined that planets orbit the Sun in elliptical orbits?

A. Brahe
B. Copernicus
C. Kepler
D. Ptolemy

Use the photo below to answer question 5.

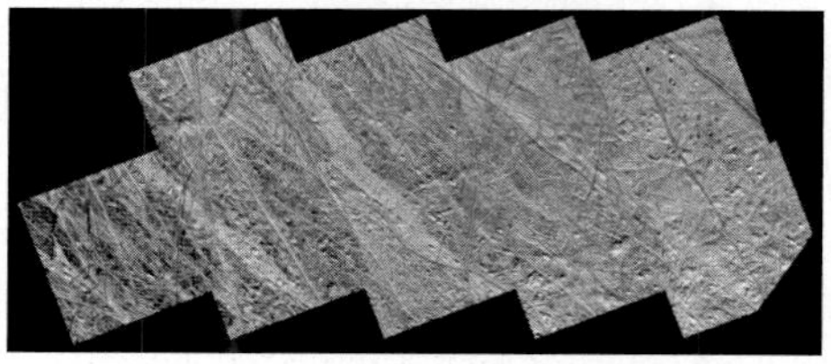

5. Which moon of Jupiter, pictured here, is most likely to have liquid water under its ice crust?

A. Callisto
B. Europa
C. Ganymede
D. Io

6. Which is composed of dust and rock particles mixed in with frozen water, methane, and ammonia?
   A. asteroid
   B. comet
   C. meteoroid
   D. meteorite

Gridded Response

7. Saturn travels 360° around the Sun for 29.5 years to complete one orbit. How many years will it take Saturn to complete 195° of its orbit?
8. If the orbital radius of Jupiter is 5.2 AU, what fraction of that distance is Earth's orbital radius?

Short Response

Use the illustration below to answer question 9.

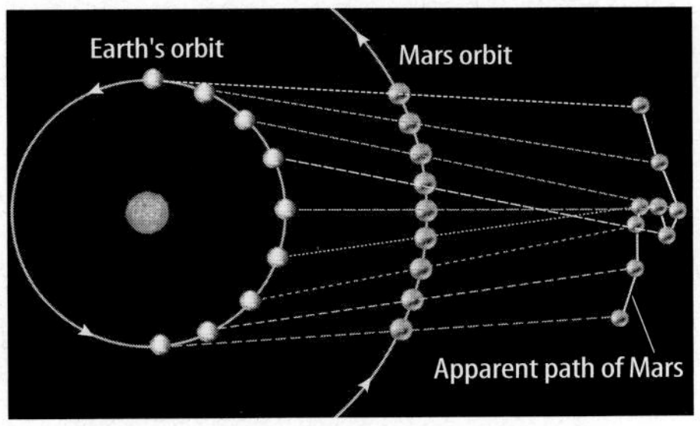

9. How does retrograde motion of planets, such as Mars shown in the illustration, provide support for the heliocentric model of the solar system?
10. What causes Mars to have a reddish-orange color?
11. Why was the *Galileo* spacecraft given this name?
12. What is generally true of all jovian planets?
13. Compare and contrast Venus to Earth. Why does it appear unlikely that Venus is capable of supporting life as we know it?
14. Compare and contrast Jupiter to Earth. Why does it appear unlikely that Jupiter is capable of supporting life as we know it?
15. Why would the discovery of oceans existing under the surface ice of Europa be so interesting to astronomers?

Extended Response

Use the photo below to answer question 16.

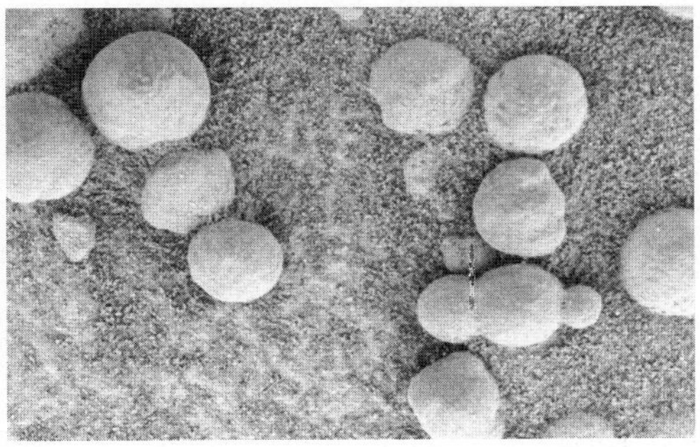

16. **PART A** What, shown in the photograph, did the NASA spacecraft, *Opportunity*, discover on Mars?
    PART B Why is this discovery so important?

chapter 8 Standardized Test Practice

Gridded Response

7. about 16 years
8. about one-fifth

Short Response

9. As Earth moves in orbit around the Sun, it overtakes and then passes the position of Mars, or other superior planets. Mars, or other superior planets, seem to move backward compared to their earlier movement.
10. Mars's surface is composed of weathered rocks containing iron oxide.
11. Galileo recognized that four objects were orbiting Jupiter, which were named the Galilean moons of Jupiter.
12. Jovian planets are gaseous giant planets, similar in size and characteristics to Jupiter. They have diameters greater than 10,000 km, the visible surface being thick cloud layers that gradually change to denser layers deep inside the planets.
13. Both are rocky inner planets. Liquid water, which is needed for life, cannot exist on Venus because its surface temperature is too great.
14. Jupiter's gravity, chemical composition, temperature, pressure, storms, and lack of a well-defined surface are not conditions that support life.
15. If liquid-water existed on Europa under its icy crust, temperatures might have been high enough to that life could exist, especially if volcanic vents provided the chemical energy needed for life processes.

Extended Response

16. **Part A:** The *Opportunity* spacecraft discovered blueberries, concretion deposits of hematite.
    Part B: Deposits of hematite of this nature form in the presence of standing water on Earth. This indicates that Mars was once wetter than it is today. If Mars were once wetter than today, perhaps life could have existed on ancient Mars.

Rubrics

For more help evaluating Short- and Extended-Response questions, see the rubrics on p. 9T.

Unit Contents

WebQuest ***Created Gemstones: The Real Thing?*** is a real-life scenario. Given the task of purchasing a natural or synthetic gemstone, students research to discover how natural gems form, what their chemical, physical, and optical properties are, as well as how their flaws are corrected and their colors enhanced. Students will compare the laboratory processes used to create gems, their prices, and properties, and decide if they are the same as their natural counterparts. Students will choose between a simulated or a naturally created gemstone as a gift for someone. They must be able to give their reasons and justify the amount of money they will spend.

unit 3

Energy in Motion

How Are Glassblowing & X Rays Connected?

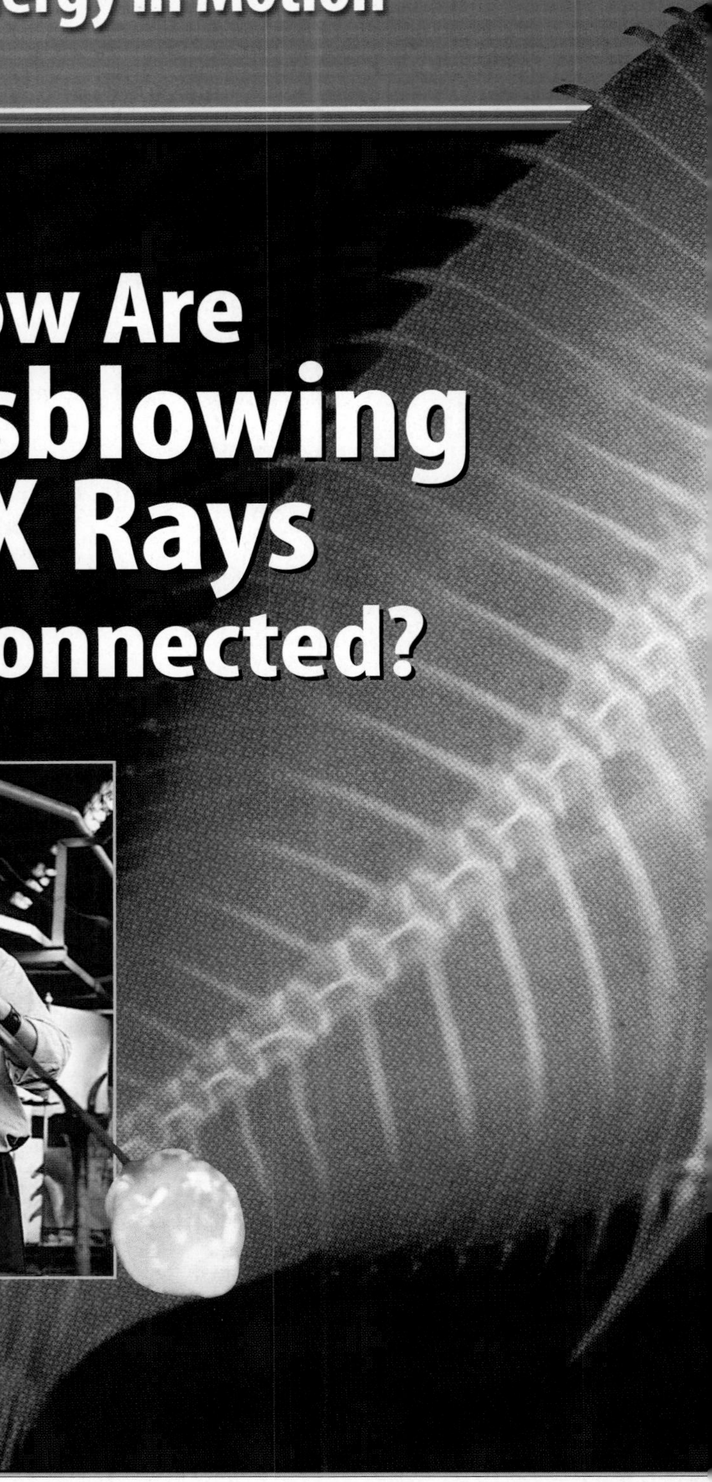

250

PROJECT CRISS[SM]

Study Skills

Vocabulary Students expand their knowledge to extend beyond a strict definition. Students use a definition map in this unit to better understand essential vocabulary. The center box of the map might contain the word "wave." One arm would answer the question, "What is it?" Another arm would answer, "What are the types of waves?" Cooperative teams would continue the map until they have reached a full definition of the word.

NATIONAL GEOGRAPHIC

Glassblowing (far left) is an art in which air is blown through a tube to shape melted glass. In the mid-1800s, a glassblower created a glass tube, sealed metal electrodes into the ends, and removed most of the air from inside. When electricity was passed through the tube, it glowed. The glow aroused the curiosity of scientists, who began experimenting with similar tubes. In order to observe the glow more closely, one physicist surrounded a tube with black cardboard and darkened the laboratory. When the electric current was turned on, the tube glowed—but so did an object across the room! Apparently the tube was emitting some kind of radiation that could pass through cardboard. The mysterious radiation became known as X rays. Scientists eventually learned that X rays are a form of electromagnetic radiation, similar to visible light but with shorter wavelengths and higher energy. Because X rays pass through many substances, they have become important in medicine and science, making it possible to "see" structures inside the bodies of people—and also fish.

unit projects

Visit unit projects at gpescience.com to find project ideas and resources. Projects include:

- **History** Adopt a landform to research and record its geological and environmental changes throughout history.
- **Technology** Research medical procedures that use waves, sound, light, or heat to form diagnostic images.
- **Model** Design and construct your own creative musical instrument. Participate in a class orchestra of homemade instruments.

WebQuest *Created Gemstones: The Real Thing* offers an opportunity to evaluate the process and value of manufactured gems.

NATIONAL GEOGRAPHIC How Are Glassblowing & X Rays Connected?

- Tell students that X rays can be used on things that are not living. For example, they are helpful in locating cracks and overstressed areas in buildings and other structures.
- Ask students to brainstorm as many examples of energy on the move as they can. In addition to X rays and other types of electromagnetic radiation, such as visible light, lists might include transfer of heat from one place to another or the movement of an object, such as a bouncing ball.

unit projects

History Ask students to "adopt" a specific volcano, earthquake fault, mountain range, or geological region of the world and study its history. Patterns of activity, intensity of movement, and how these changes have affected the surrounding environment, as well as plant and animal populations should be considered. Students can prepare a journal, time line, or technology presentation to display the change in their land form and its populations over time.

Technology Working in small groups, have students research medical procedures that use waves, sound, or light to form diagnostic images. Procedures may include MRI, CAT scan, X rays, thermal imaging, or ultrasound. Have students create an advertisement or news broadcast about their particular procedure to demonstrate how their image is formed, its benefits and limitations, and any related health risks.

Model Ask students to design their own creative musical instrument. Instruments should demonstrate a full scale and be able to be tuned to the proper pitch. Applying appropriate physics terms, students should be able to explain how their instrument produces a variety of sounds. Using a simple musical score ("Twinkle, Twinkle Little Star," for example) have students participate in an all-class orchestra with their physics musical instruments.

Additional Resources Visit unit projects at gpescience.com for more information, resources, and assessment rubrics.

chapter 9 Organizer

Section/Objectives	Standards: National	Standards: State/Local	Labs/Features
Chapter Opener	See pp. 16T–17T for a Key to Standards.		**Launch Lab:** Expansion of a Gas, p. 253 **Foldables,** p. 253
Section 1 Temperature and Thermal Energy 2 sessions 1 block 1. **Define** temperature. 2. **Explain** how thermal energy and temperature are related. 3. **Calculate** the change in thermal energy of an object due to a temperature change.	National Content Standards: UCP.1–3, UCP.5, A.1, A.2, B.2, B.4, B.5, B.6		**Applying Math:** Converting to Celsius, p. 255 **Science Online,** p. 256 **Integrate Earth Science,** p. 258 **Applying Math:** Change in Thermal Energy, p. 258
Section 2 States of Matter 2 sessions 1 block 4. **Describe** the differences in the four states of matter. 5. **Explain** how the motion of particles in a material changes at the material's melting point and boiling point. 6. **Explain** why thermal expansion occurs.	National Content Standards: UCP.1–3, UCP.5, A.1, A.2, B.2, B.5, B.6, G.3		**Science Online,** p. 261 **MiniLAB:** Comparing States of Water, p. 262
Section 3 Transferring Thermal Energy 2 sessions 1 block 7. **Compare and contrast** the transfer of thermal energy by conduction, convection, and radiation. 8. **Compare and contrast** thermal conductors and insulators. 9. **Explain** how insulators are used to control the transfer of thermal energy.	National Content Standards: UCP.1–3, UCP.5, A.1, A.2, B.2, B.4, B.6		**MiniLAB:** Comparing Thermal Conductors, p. 267 **Visualizing Convection Currents,** p. 268 **Lab:** Convection in Gases and Liquids, p. 271
Section 4 Using Thermal Energy 3 sessions 2 blocks 10. **Describe** the first and second laws of thermodynamics. 11. **Explain** how an internal combustion engine converts thermal energy to mechanical energy. 12. **Describe** how the entropy of the universe changes when any event occurs.	National Content Standards: UCP.1–3, UCP.5, A.1, A.2, B.2, B.4, B.5		**Integrate History,** p. 273 **Science Online,** p. 274 **Lab:** Conduction in Gases, pp. 278–279 Video Lab **Science Stats:** Surprising Thermal Energy, p. 280

Glencoe Exclusive!

StudentWorks Plus

TeacherWorks™ All-In-One Planner and Resource Center

Lab Materials	Reproducible Resources	Section Assessment	Technology
Launch Lab: balloon, hot plate, tape measure, large beaker, water	**Chapter *Fast File* Resources** Foldables Worksheet, p. 17 Directed Reading Overview, p. 19 Note-taking Worksheets, pp. 35–37	Glencoe's Assessment Advantage	TeacherWorks includes: • Interactive Teacher Edition • Lesson Planner with calendar • Access to all program blacklines • Correlations to standards • Web links
Need materials? Contact Science Kit at 1-800-828-7777 or www.sciencekit.com.	**Chapter *Fast File* Resources** Transparency Activity, p. 46 Enrichment, p. 31 Reinforcement, p. 27 Directed Reading, p. 20 **Lab Management and Safety,** p. 66	**Portfolio** Sciene Journal, p. 257 **Performance** Applying Math, p. 255 Applying Math, p. 258 Applying Math, p. 259 **Content** Section Review, p. 259	Section Focus Transparency Teaching Transparency Interactive Chalkboard CD-ROM StudentWorks Plus
MiniLAB: plastic bowl or ice tray, water marker or masking tape	**Chapter *Fast File* Resources** Transparency Activity, pp. 47, 51–52 MiniLAB, p.3 Lab Activity, pp. 9–12 Enrichment, p. 32 Reinforcement, p. 28 Directed Reading, p. 20	**Portfolio** MiniLAB Assessment, p. 262 **Performance** Applying Math, p. 265 **Content** Section Review, p. 265	Section Focus Transparency Interactive Chalkboard CD-ROM StudentWorks Plus
MiniLAB: metallic spoon, plastic spoon, wooden spoon, small plastic beads (3), butter, water, beaker **Lab:** hot plate, water, candle, 500-mL beaker, black pepper	**Chapter *Fast File* Resources** Transparency Activity, p. 48 MiniLAB, p.4 Lab Activity, pp. 13–15 Enrichment, p. 33 Reinforcement, p. 29 Directed Reading, p. 21 Lab Worksheets, pp. 5–6	**Portfolio** MiniLAB Assessment, p. 267 **Performance** Applying Math, p. 270 **Content** Section Review, p. 270	Section Focus Transparency Virtual Labs CD-ROM Interactive Chalkboard CD-ROM StudentWorks Plus
Lab: thermometers (3), foam cups (2), 400-mL beaker (2), hot plate or burner, paring knife, thermal mitts	**Chapter *Fast File* Resources** Transparency Activity, p. 49 Enrichment, p. 34 Reinforcement, p. 30 Directed Reading, pp. 22–23 Assessment Transparency Activity, p. 53 Lab Worksheets, pp. 7–8	**Portfolio** Assessment p. 277 **Performance** Applying Math, p. 277 **Content** Section Review, p. 277	Section Focus Transparency Interactive Chalkboard CD-ROM StudentWorks Plus Video Lab

End of Chapter Assessment

Glencoe's Assessment Advantage

Blackline Masters	Technology	Professional Series
Chapter *Fast File* Resources Chapter Review, pp. 39–40 Chapter Tests, pp. 41–44 **Standardized Test Practice,** pp. 40–43	MindJogger Videoquiz Virtual Labs CD-ROM Exam*View*® Pro Testmaker TeacherWorks CD-ROM Interactive Chalkboard CD-ROM	**Performance Assessment in the Science Classroom (PASC)**

Transparencies

Section Focus

Section 1 Section Focus Transparency — A Spectacular Reentry — Chapter 9

In 1968, *Apollo 8* became the first piloted vehicle to orbit the Moon. Below you see *Apollo 8* as it reenters Earth's atmosphere. Friction between the atmosphere and the hurdling spacecraft created temperatures of up to 3,000°C! The craft and the astronauts inside needed special protection in order to survive these inferno-like temperatures.

1. Why is it a concern that the exterior of a spacecraft experiences very high temperatures upon reentry?
2. If a metal pan with a metal handle sits on a lit burner for a long time, what happens to the handle?
3. When it's cold out, why does a jacket help you stay nice and warm?

L2

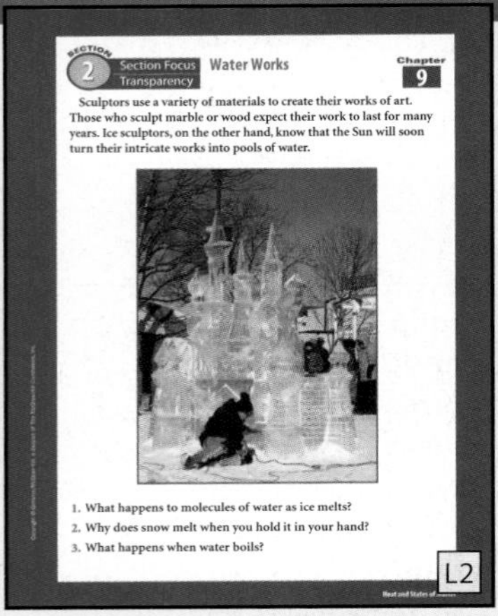
Section 2 Section Focus Transparency — Water Works — Chapter 9

Sculptors use a variety of materials to create their works of art. Those who sculpt marble or wood expect their work to last for many years. Ice sculptors, on the other hand, know that the Sun will soon turn their intricate works into pools of water.

1. What happens to molecules of water as ice melts?
2. Why does snow melt when you hold it in your hand?
3. What happens when water boils?

L2

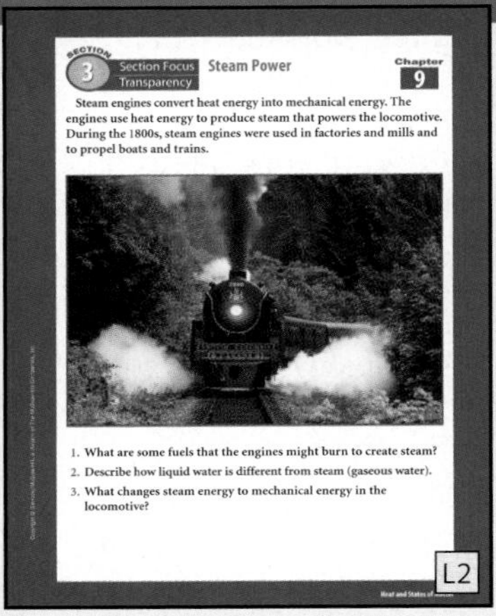
Section 3 Section Focus Transparency — Steam Power — Chapter 9

Steam engines convert heat energy into mechanical energy. The engines use heat energy to produce steam that powers the locomotive. During the 1800s, steam engines were used in factories and mills and to propel boats and trains.

1. What are some fuels that the engines might burn to create steam?
2. Describe how liquid water is different from steam (gaseous water).
3. What changes steam energy to mechanical energy in the locomotive?

L2

Section 4 Section Focus Transparency — One Small Step — Chapter 9

From a farm in Massachusetts, Robert Goddard launched the first liquid-powered rocket in 1926. Using liquid oxygen and gasoline as propellants, the small rocket rose to 41 feet, arched over, and landed in a cabbage patch. The flight lasted only 2.5 seconds, yet it was the beginning of the rocket age.

1. When you heat a liquid, what happens?
2. When you heat a gas, what will it do?
3. Why do you think gases are cooled to a liquid state for use in rocket fuel?

L2

This is a representation of key blackline masters available in the Teacher Classroom Resources. See Resource Manager boxes within the chapter for additional information.

Assessment

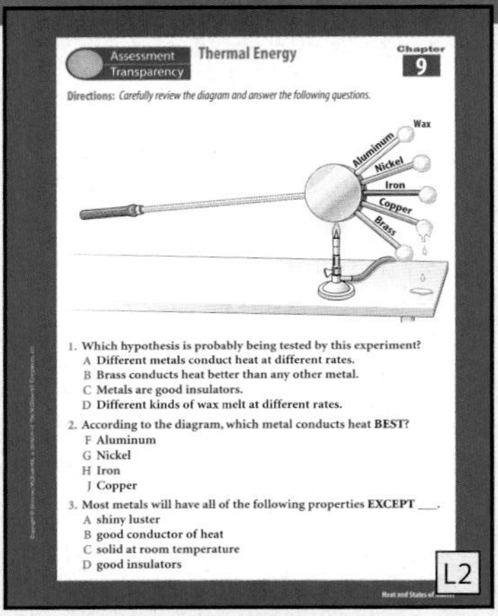
Assessment Transparency — Thermal Energy — Chapter 9

Directions: *Carefully review the diagram and answer the following questions.*

1. Which hypothesis is probably being tested by this experiment?
   A Different metals conduct heat at different rates.
   B Brass conducts heat better than any other metal.
   C Metals are good insulators.
   D Different kinds of wax melt at different rates.
2. According to the diagram, which metal conducts heat BEST?
   F Aluminum
   G Nickel
   H Iron
   J Copper
3. Most metals will have all of the following properties EXCEPT ___.
   A shiny luster
   B good conductor of heat
   C solid at room temperature
   D good insulators

L2

Teaching

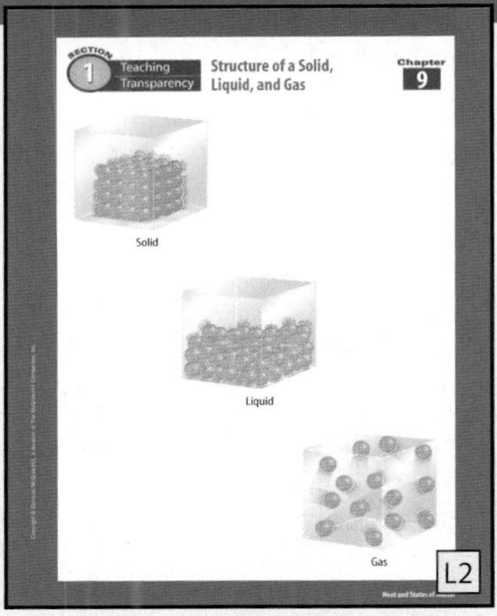
Section 1 Teaching Transparency — Structure of a Solid, Liquid, and Gas — Chapter 9

L2

Key to Teaching Strategies

The following designations will help you decide which activities are appropriate for your students.

- L1 Level 1 activities should be appropriate for students with learning difficulties.
- L2 Level 2 activities should be within the ability range of all students.
- L3 Level 3 activities are designed for above-average students.
- ELL ELL activities should be within the ability range of English Language Learners.
- COOP LEARN Cooperative Learning activities are designed for small group work.
- LS Multiple Learning Styles logos, as described on page 12T, are used throughout to indicate strategies that address different learning styles.
- P These strategies represent student products that can be placed into a best-work portfolio.
- PBL Problem-Based Learning activities apply real-world situations to learning.

Hands-on Activities

Student Text Lab Worksheet

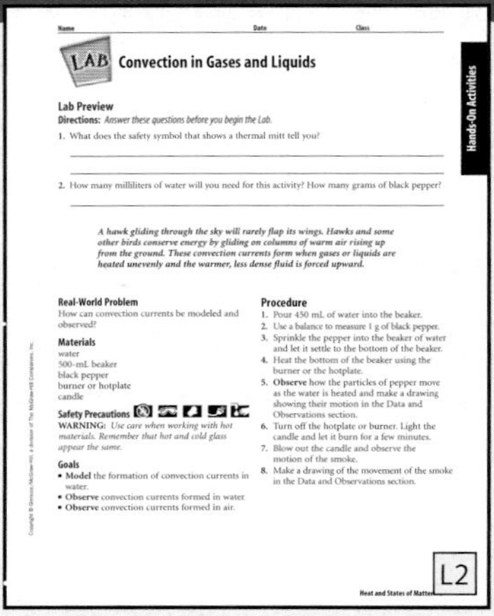
LAB — Convection in Gases and Liquids

Lab Preview

Directions: *Answer these questions before you begin the Lab.*

1. What does the safety symbol that shows a thermal mitt tell you?
2. How many milliliters of water will you need for this activity? How many grams of black pepper?

A hawk gliding through the sky will rarely flap its wings. Hawks and some other birds conserve energy by gliding on columns of warm air rising up from the ground. These convection currents form when gases or liquids are heated unevenly and the warmer, less dense fluid is forced upward.

L2

Laboratory Activities

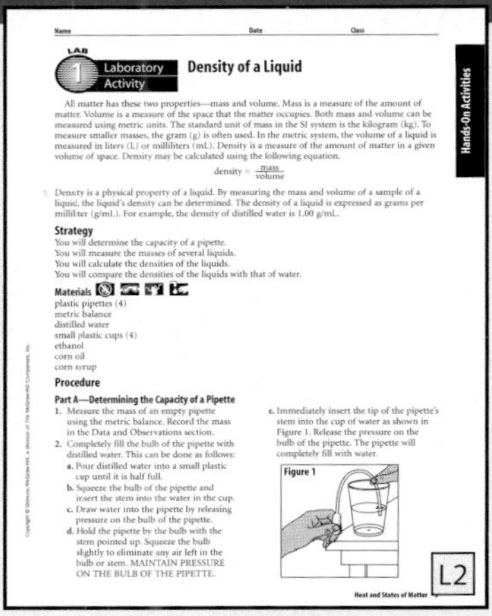
Laboratory Activity 1 — Density of a Liquid

L2

Resource Manager

Meeting Different Ability Levels

Content Outline

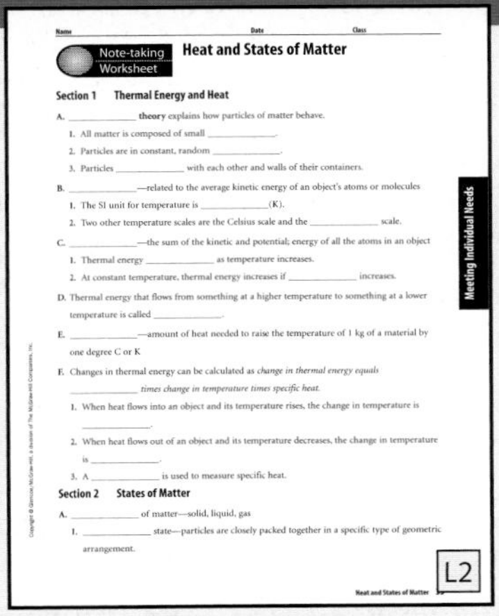

Reinforcement

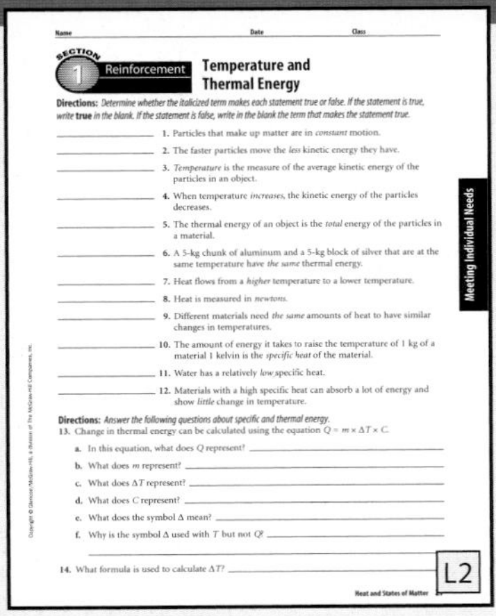

Enrichment

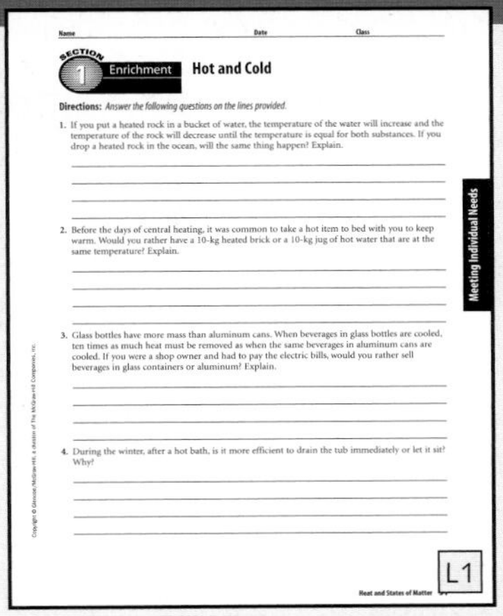

Directed Reading (English/Spanish)

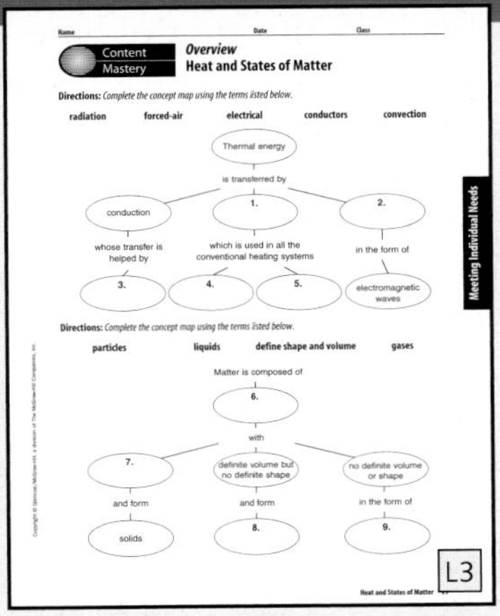

Study Guide

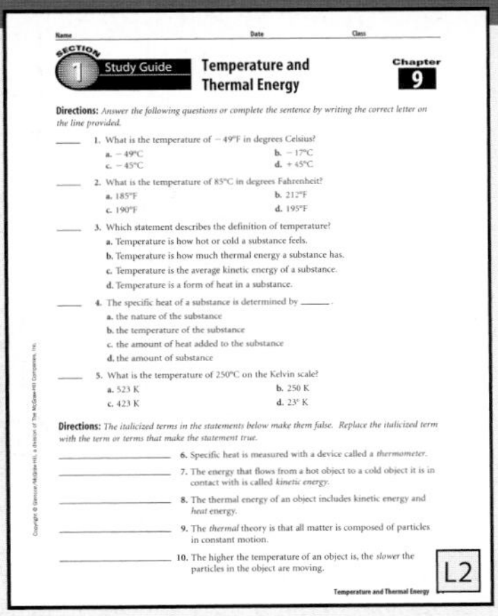

Reading Essentials

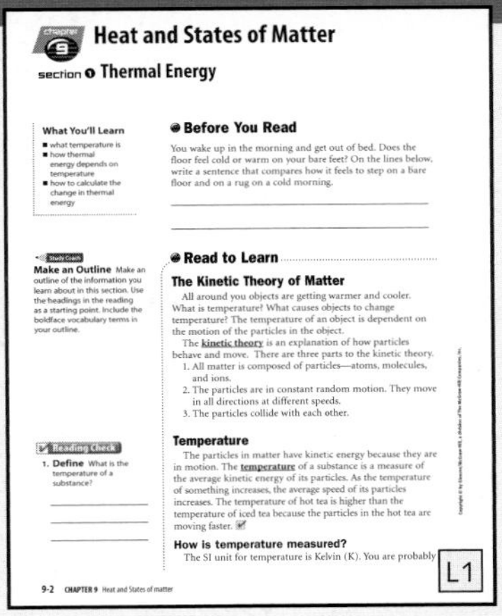

Assessment

Test Practice Workbook

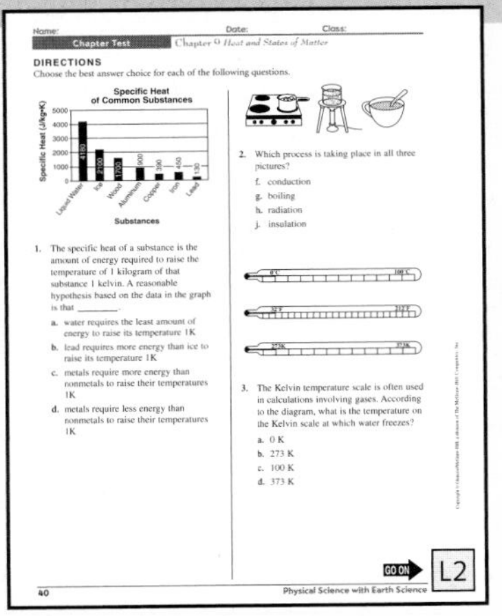

Chapter Review

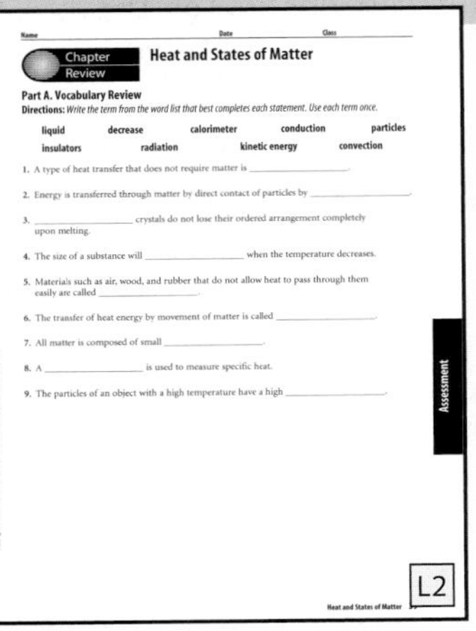

Chapter Tests

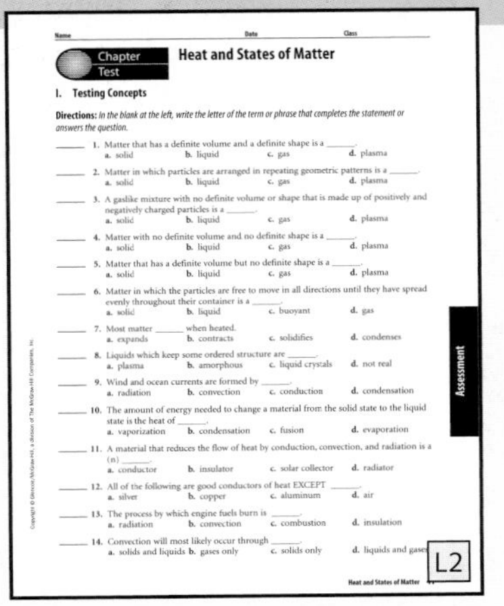

Science Content Background

section 1 Temperature and Thermal Energy

Temperature

It is important to differentiate between temperature and thermal energy. A small nail at 100°C has less thermal energy than a large hammer at 90°C.

The common thermometer is a tube filled with colored alcohol or mercury, which expands with increasing thermal energy to give a reading of the temperature. Digital thermometers rely on the increase in electrical resistance with higher temperature to ascertain temperature.

Three temperature scales are commonly used. The Celsius scale is used by most of the world and in most scientific work. The oldest, the Fahrenheit scale, is used in the United States. The Kelvin is the official SI unit for temperature. This scale, used by scientists, is based on absolute zero—the lowest possible temperature. 0 K is a theoretical value not yet observed.

Thermal Energy

Which contains more thermal energy, liquid water at 100°C or steam at 100°C? Anyone who has been burned by steam knows the correct answer—steam! Thermal energy is the sum of both kinetic and potential energy. The steam, although at the same temperature as the liquid water, has more potential energy. This is the energy it absorbed in the phase change from a liquid to a gas.

Properties of materials can change as they gain or lose thermal energy. For example, most substances expand when they are heated, resistance in wire increases with rises in temperature, the color of some materials is influenced by temperature, and materials can change phase as they gain or lose thermal energy.

Heat

The SI unit of thermal energy is the joule. Calorie is another unit frequently used. One calorie, equal to 4.184 joules, is the amount of thermal energy needed to raise the temperature of one gram of water 1° C. This amount is so small that food energy is measured in kilocalories. Kilocalories are also called Calories. So, if a food label says the food contains 150 Calories, it really has 150,000 calories, or 627,600 joules, of energy.

Specific Heat

Water has a very high specific heat. If you have 1 g of water and 1 g of aluminum and you add one calorie of thermal energy to each, the water will increase in temperature by about one degree and the aluminum's temperature will increase by about five degrees. The high specific heat of water has important influences on climate. Large bodies of water tend to maintain their temperatures longer than smaller bodies of water, so areas near the ocean often have milder summers and winters.

section 2 States of Matter

Matter at 0 K has the lowest possible amount of thermal energy. The freezing point of water on the Celsius scale is 0 degrees; the freezing point of water on the Kelvin scale is 273 K. The average kinetic energy of the particles that make up a substance is directly proportional to the Kelvin temperature.

Matter is made of tiny particles separated by distances with nothing between the particles. The particles are in motion. In gases, the separation of the particles is the greatest because these particles are moving the fastest. The amount of space between the particles varies with temperature, volume, and pressure.

section 3 Transferring Thermal Energy

Thermal energy can move from one place to another in three ways: conduction, convection, and radiation.

In any material, atoms and molecules are in constant random motion, continually colliding with one another. These collisions cause energy to be transferred between particles.

Conduction

Heat transfer by conduction is the most effective way of transferring heat in a solid. Particles vibrate about a fixed position in a solid, and are not free to move from place to place. Collisions between vibrating particles cause thermal energy to be transferred from higher-energy to lower-energy particles. Conduction occurs when thermal energy moves in a material without any net movement of the material itself. Conduction can also occur in liquids and gases, but thermal energy is transferred more slowly than in solids.

Convection

Particles can move more freely in liquids and gases than in solids. As a result, thermal energy is transferred when particles in a material move from regions of higher temperature to regions of lower temperature. Convection occurs when thermal energy is transferred by the movement of matter from place to place. Thermal energy usually is transferred more rapidly by convection than conduction.

Radiation

Thermal energy can be transferred most rapidly by radiation. The vibrations of charged particles in any material cause the material to emit electromagnetic waves. These waves travel at the speed of light from one place to another. Like all waves, electromagnetic waves transfer energy. The transfer of thermal energy by radiation occurs when electromagnetic waves strike a material, and energy is transferred to the material. This causes particles in the material to move faster, increasing the material's temperature and thermal energy.

section 4 Using Thermal Energy

Thermodynamics

Thermodynamics is the study of the relationship between thermal energy and work. Scientists in the early nineteenth century began developing thermodynamics as a result of their interest in improving the efficiency of the steam engine.

The work of Count Rumford, James Joule, and others showed that work could be converted into an equivalent amount of thermal energy. According to the first law of thermodynamics, the increase in the thermal energy of a system equals the thermal energy added to the system plus the work done on the system.

According to the second law of thermodynamics, only processes that cause the entropy of the universe to increase can occur. The entropy of a system can be defined as a measure of the amount of energy of the system that cannot be converted into usable energy. The second law of thermodynamics means that the amount of usable energy is always decreasing.

chapter content resources

Internet Resources

For additional content background, visit gpescience.com to:

- access your book online
- find references to related articles in popular science magazines
- access Web links with related content background
- access current events with science journal topics

Print Resources

Thermal Physics: Entropy and Free energies, by Joon Chang Lee, World Scientific Publishing Company, Inc., 2002

Fundamentals of Thermodynamics, by Richard E. Sonntag, Claus Borgnakke, and Gordon J. Van Wylen, John Wiley & Sons, 2002

Fundamentals of Heat and Mass Transfer, by Frank P. Incropera and David P. DeWitt, John Wiley & Sons, 2001

Experiments with Solids, Liquids, and Gases, Salvatore Tocci, Children's Book Press, 2002

chapter 9

Chapter Vocabulary

kinetic theory, p. 254
temperature, p. 255
Kelvin, p. 255
thermal energy, p. 256
heat, p. 257
specific heat, p. 257
plasma, p. 261
heat of fusion, p. 262
heat of vaporization, p. 262
conduction, p. 266
convection, p. 267
radiation, p. 268
thermal insulator, p. 270
first law of thermodynamics, p. 274
second law of thermodynamics, p. 274
entropy, p. 276

Science Journal Student answers will vary. Accept al reasonable responses.

INTERACTIVE CHALKBOARD with Image Bank

PowerPoint® Presentations

This CD-ROM is an editable Microsoft® PowerPoint® presentation that includes:

- a pre-made presentation for every chapter
- interactive graphics
- animations
- audio clips
- image bank
- all new section and chapter questions
- Standardized Test Practice
- transparencies
- Foldables directions
- links to gpescience.com

chapter 9

Heat and States of Matter

chapter preview

sections

1 Temperature and Thermal Energy
2 States of Matter
3 Transferring Thermal Energy
Lab Convection in Gases and Liquids
4 Using Thermal Energy
Lab Conduction in Gases
Virtual Labs How do the insulation properties of various materials compare?

Hot Stuff

This hot, glowing liquid will become solid steel when it cools. The difference between liquid and solid steel is energy—thermal energy. Increasing the thermal energy of solid steel can cause it to melt and change into a fiery liquid.

Science Journal Describe things you do to make yourself feel warmer or cooler.

252

Theme Connection

Energy Thermal energy is the kinetic and potential energy of the molecules, ions, and atoms that make up matter. The kinetic energy of the particles in a substance plays a major role in determining whether the substance is in the solid, liquid, or gas state. Thermal energy can be transferred by conduction, convection, and radiation, and can be converted into mechanical energy to do work.

About the Photo

Molten Steel Steel is an alloy of iron and carbon. The carbon content of steel ranges up to 2% carbon. Alloys with higher carbon content are classified as cast iron. Steel is widely used to manufacture a wide range of products, from skyscrapers to rail cars. It is used extensively because it is relatively inexpensive to process; the raw materials are available in abundance, and because of its desirable properties.

Start-Up Activities

Launch LAB

Expansion of a Gas

Why does mercury in a thermometer rise? Why do sidewalks, streets, and bridges have cracks? Many substances expand when heated and contract when cooled, as you will see during this lab.

1. Blow up a balloon until it is half filled. Use a tape measure to measure the circumference of the balloon.
2. Pour water into a large beaker until it is half full. Place the beaker on a hot plate and wait for the water to boil.
3. Set the balloon on the mouth of the beaker and observe for 5 min. Be careful not to allow the balloon to touch the hot plate. Again measure the circumference of the balloon.
4. **Think Critically** Write a paragraph in your Science Journal describing the changing size of the balloon's circumference. Infer why the balloon's circumference changed.

FOLDABLES™ Study Organizer

Thermal Energy and States of Matter Make the following Foldable to help you understand thermal energy and states of matter.

STEP 1 **Fold** a vertical sheet of paper in half from top to bottom.

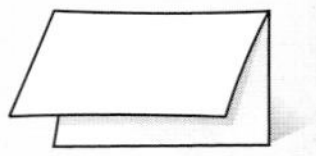

STEP 2 **Fold** in half from side to side with the fold at the top.

STEP 3 **Unfold** the paper once. **Cut** only the fold of the top flap to make two tabs.

STEP 4 **Turn** the paper vertically and **label** the front tabs as shown.

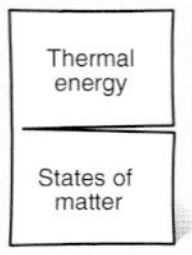

Find Main Ideas As you read the chapter, write the main ideas you find about thermal energy and states of matter under the appropriate tab.

Science Online | Preview this chapter's content and activities at gpescience.com

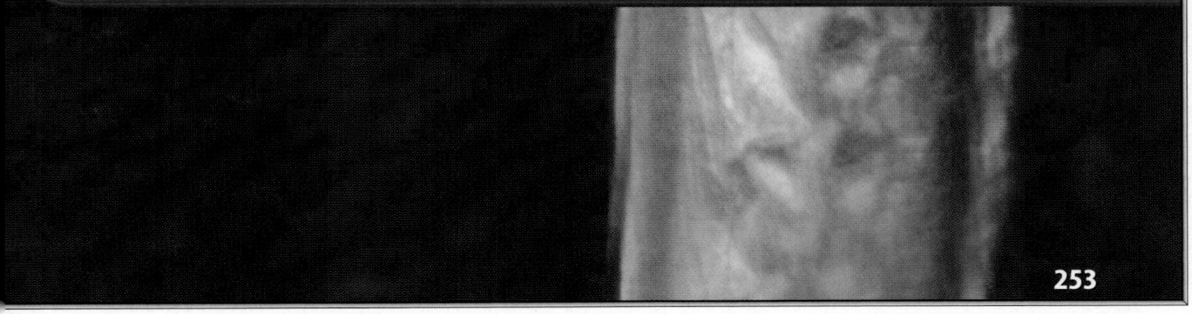

Launch LAB

Purpose Use the Launch Lab to introduce students to the fact that matter changes as temperature changes.

Preparation Before students do this activity, obtain metric tape measures.

Materials balloon, tape measure, large beaker, hot plate, water

Teaching Strategy Help students set up data tables in which to record their measurements.

Think Critically

The circumference of the balloon increased as the temperature of the air in the balloon increased. The balloon's size would decrease if it were cooled.

Assessment

Process Ask the students how the results of this activity would have been different if they had put water in the balloon instead of air. The balloon would not have expanded much when it was heated. Use **Performance Assessment in the Science Classroom**, p. 89.

FOLDABLES™ Study Organizer — Dinah Zike Study Fold

Student preparation materials for this Foldable are available in the **Chapter *Fast File* Resources.**

section 1

Temperature and Thermal Energy

Reading Guide

What You'll Learn
- **Define** temperature.
- **Explain** how thermal energy and temperature are related.
- **Calculate** the change in thermal energy of an object due to a temperature change.

Why It's Important

Cars, buses, trucks, and airplanes could not operate without thermal energy.

Review Vocabulary

kinetic energy: energy an object has due to its motion

New Vocabulary
- kinetic theory
- Kelvin
- temperature
- thermal energy
- heat
- specific heat

Kinetic Theory of Matter

All around you objects are warming and cooling. What is temperature and what causes the temperature of an object to change? The temperature of an object is related to the motion of the particles in that object. The motion of the particles in matter is described by the **kinetic theory** of matter.

According to the kinetic theory, matter is composed of particles that are atoms, molecules, or ions that always are in random motion. This means that the particles in matter are moving at different speeds in all directions. Because these particles are in motion, they have kinetic energy. These particles also can collide and kinetic energy can be transferred from one particle to another particle.

Reading Check *How do the particles in matter move?*

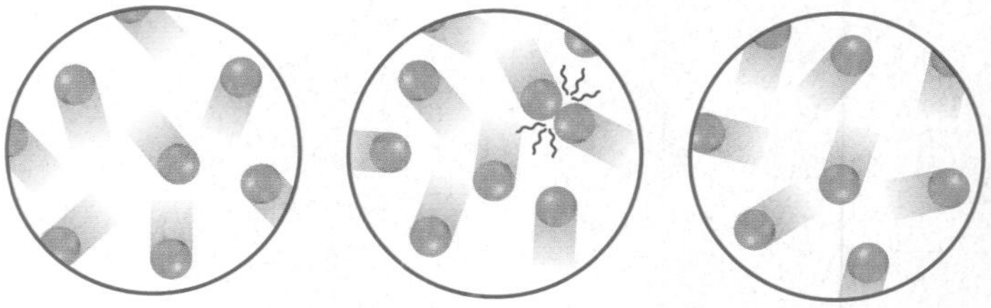

Figure 1 When particles collide, kinetic energy can be transferred from one particle to another and the direction of particle motion changes.

1 Motivate

INTERACTIVE CHALKBOARD An editable Microsoft® PowerPoint® presentation is available on **Interactive Chalkboard** CD-ROM.

Bellringer

Section Focus Transparencies also are available on the Interactive Chalkboard CD-ROM. L2 ELL

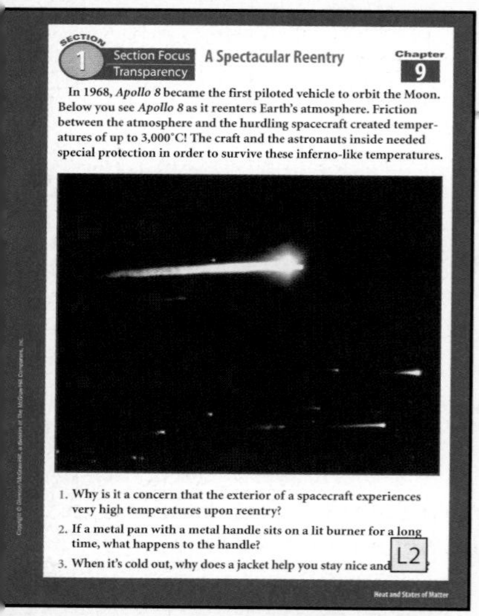

SECTION 1 Section Focus Transparency **A Spectacular Reentry** Chapter 9

In 1968, *Apollo 8* became the first piloted vehicle to orbit the Moon. Below you see *Apollo 8* as it reenters Earth's atmosphere. Friction between the atmosphere and the hurdling spacecraft created temperatures of up to 3,000°C! The craft and the astronauts inside needed special protection in order to survive these inferno-like temperatures.

1. Why is it a concern that the exterior of a spacecraft experiences very high temperatures upon reentry?
2. If a metal pan with a metal handle sits on a lit burner for a long time, what happens to the handle?
3. When it's cold out, why does a jacket help you stay nice and L2

Heat and States of Matter

Reading Preview

Tie to Prior Knowledge

Specific Heat Ask students whether they have ever noticed that some materials heat up faster than others. Tell students that the amount of thermal energy it takes to make a substance warm up is called its specific heat, one of the things they will learn about in this section.

Activate Background Knowledge Ask students what they know about the new vocabulary words. Point out that each word is connected to a complex concept. Have students find passages that contain the words and explain the words to a partner, using context clues within the text. Have the class share their word conversations.

Section 1 Resource Manager

Chapter *FAST FILE* Resources
- Transparency Activity, p. 46,
- Enrichment, p. 31
- Reinforcement, p. 27
- Directed Reading for Content Mastery, pp. 19–20
- Note-taking Worksheets, pp. 35–37

Earth Science Critical Thinking/Problem Solving, p. 1

Lab Management and Safety, p. 66

Reading and Writing Skills Activities, pp. 35–36

Mathmatics Skill Activities, pp. 19–20

Temperature

The particles in matter are moving at various speeds and have a range of kinetic energies. The **temperature** of a substance is a measure of the average kinetic energy of its particles. As the average speed of the particles in random motion increases, the temperature of the substance increases. For example, the particles in hot tea move faster on average than those in iced tea.

Temperature Scales The SI unit for temperature is the **Kelvin** (K). More commonly used temperature scales are the Celsius scale and the Fahrenheit scale. Subtracting 273 from a temperature in Kelvin converts the temperature to degrees Celsius. Temperatures measured on the Celsius and Fahrenheit scales can be converted into one another using these equations:

Celsius-Fahrenheit Conversion Equations

To convert temperature in °F to °C: $°C = \frac{5}{9}(°F - 32)$

To convert temperature in °C to °F: $°F = \frac{9}{5}°C + 32$

Applying Math — Solve a Simple Equation

CONVERTING TO CELSIUS What is a temperature of 86°F on the Celsius scale?

IDENTIFY known values and the unknown value

Identify the known values:

the temperature is 86°F → means → $°F = 86$

Identify the unknown values:

What is this temperature on the Celsius scale? → means → $°C = ?$

SOLVE the problem

Substitute the temperature 86°F into the equation that converts °F to °C:

$$°C = \frac{5}{9}(°F - 32) = \frac{5}{9}(54) = 30°C$$

CHECK your answer

Does your answer seem reasonable? Multiply your answer by $\frac{9}{5}$ and add 32. The result should be the given Fahrenheit temperature.

Practice Problems

1. What is –40°F in degrees Celsius?
2. What is a temperature of 22°C in degrees Fahrenheit?

For more practice problems, go to page 879 and visit Math Practice at gpescience.com.

2 Teach

Reading Check

Answer in all directions with various speeds

Activity

Temperature Conversions Ask students how they might test to see if the temperature conversion equations are correct. Lead them to suggest that they can check the equations by inserting the correct numbers for the boiling and/or freezing points of water and making sure that the two sides are equal.

Applying Math

Math Standards

National: 1, 4, 9

Answers to Practice Problems

1. $°C = (5/9)(-40 - 32) = -40°C$
2. $°F = (9/5)(22) + 32 = 72°F$

Teacher FYI

Shivering One way the human body maintains its internal temperature is through the rapid movement known as shivering.

Fun Fact

Water is a unique substance. Unlike most materials that expand when heated, water at temperatures of 1, 2, or 3°C contracts when heated. Water is most dense at 4°C. This property allows ice to float in your glass of water and keeps ponds from freezing from the bottom up.

Reading Check

Answer potential energy

Caption Answer

Figure 2 Increasing the temperature increases the kinetic energy of the particles.

IDENTIFYING Misconceptions

Maintaining Thermal Energy During cold weather, people often close doors and windows "to keep the cold out." Since cold is the absence of thermal energy, they are actually attempting to keep the thermal energy inside, not keep the cold out.

Reading Strategy

Note Taking Have students read Thermal Energy and ask them to write a formula for thermal energy as a way of summarizing and note taking. Thermal Energy = Kinetic Energy + Potential Energy

Science Online

Topic: Weather Satellites
Visit gpescience.com for Web links to information about how weather satellites use thermal energy to acquire weather data.

Activity Draw a diagram showing how a satellite uses thermal energy to produce images.

Thermal Energy

According to the kinetic theory, atoms and molecules that make up matter are in constant motion. However, not only do these particles have kinetic energy due to their motion, they also have potential energy. This is because atoms and molecules exert attractive electric forces on each other. Recall that Earth exerts an attractive gravitational force on a ball. When the ball is above the ground, the ball and Earth are separated, and the ball has potential energy. In the same way, particles that exert attractive forces on each other have potential energy that increases as they get farther apart. The sum of the kinetic and potential energies of all the particles in an object is the **thermal energy** of the object. **Figure 2** shows how thermal energy depends on the kinetic and potential energies of the particles in a material.

Reading Check *What type of energy results from the attractive forces between particles?*

Thermal Energy of a Moving Object You've learned that the faster an object moves, the greater its kinetic energy. A ball rolling across the floor has greater kinetic energy than if it were sitting still. Does this mean that the rolling ball also has greater thermal energy? At first, the answer might seem to be yes, but in fact, the thermal energy is the same for both of the balls, if they are at the same temperature. Thermal energy is the sum of the kinetic energy and potential energy of the particles that make up the ball, not of the ball itself. The increase in the ball's speed doesn't affect the random motion of its particles, so it doesn't affect its thermal energy.

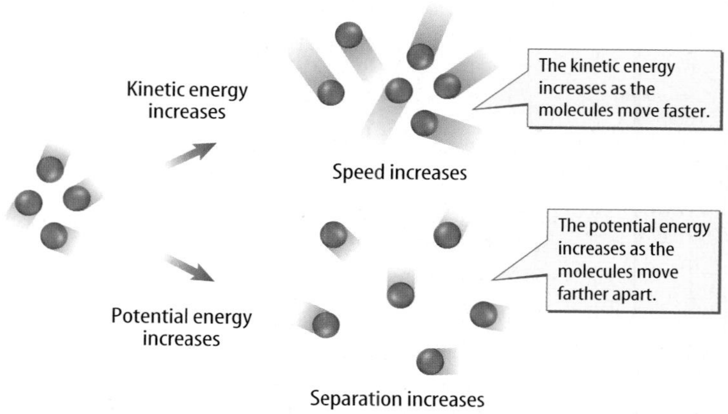

Figure 2 The thermal energy of a substance is the sum of the kinetic and potential energies of its molecules.
Infer *why increasing the temperature of an object increases its thermal energy.*

Active Reading

Quickwrites This strategy, sometimes called freewrite, lets students use spontaneous writing to discover what they already know. Have students write a list of ideas about thermal energy and then share these ideas with the class. Next, have students write about these ideas freely without worrying about punctuation, spelling, or grammar. Have students use a quickwrite to share ideas about thermal energy and heat. L2 LS **Linguistic**

Heat

Can you tell if someone has been sitting in your chair? Perhaps you've noticed that your chair felt warm, and maybe you concluded that someone was sitting in it recently. The chair felt warmer because thermal energy from the person's body flowed to the chair, increasing the chair's temperature.

Heat is thermal energy that flows from something at a higher temperature to something at a lower temperature. Heat is a form of energy, so it is measured in joules. Thermal energy always flows from a warmer to a cooler material. How did the ice cream in **Figure 3** become cold? Thermal energy flowed from the warmer liquid ingredients to the cooler ice-and-salt mixture. The liquid ingredients lost enough thermal energy to become cold enough to freeze. Meanwhile, the ice-and-salt solution absorbed thermal energy, causing some of the ice to melt.

Figure 3 Thermal energy flows from the warmer ingredients inside the container to the ice-and-salt mixture around it.

Reading Check *How are heat and thermal energy related?*

Specific Heat

If you are at the beach in the summer, you might notice that the ocean seems cooler than the air or sand. Even though energy from the Sun goes to the air, sand, and water at the same rate, the water's temperature changes less than that of the air or sand.

As a substance is heated, its temperature change depends both on the amount of thermal energy added and the nature of the substance. For an equal mass of water and sand, about six times as much thermal energy is needed to raise the temperature of the water than the sand by 1°C. It's not surprising, then, that the sand feels much warmer than the ocean. The amount of thermal energy needed to raise the temperature of 1 kg of some material by 1°C is called the **specific heat** of the material. Specific heat is measured in joules per kilogram per degree Celsius, which is written as J/(kg °C). **Table 1** shows the specific heats of some familiar materials.

Table 1 Specific Heat of Some Common Materials

Substance	Specific Heat [J/(kg°C)]
Water	4,184
Ice	2,110
Asphalt	920
Glass	800
Iron	450

Reading Check *What is the specific heat of a material?*

Visual Learning

Figure 3 Why is it necessary to stir the ice cream while it is freezing? Stirring allows the ice cream mix to cool evenly and more quickly. L2 LS **Logical-Mathematical**

Reading Check

Answer Heat is thermal energy that flows from something with a higher temperature to something with a lower temperature.

Answer the amount of thermal energy that is needed to raise the temperature of 1 kg of the material by 1°C

Discussion

Specific Heat Why is water often used in cooling systems? The specific heat of water is higher than that of most materials. This means that water will warm more slowly than other materials as thermal energy is added to it.

Use Science Words

Word Origin Have students use their dictionaries to identify the origin of the word *thermal*. The word *thermal* comes from the Greek word *therme,* meaning "heat." Many English words derive from this, including thermos.

Curriculum Connection

History Have a group of students report on the experiments of James Joule that quantitatively related thermal energy and work. Joule used falling weights to turn paddles that stirred water and raised its temperature. He calculated the mechanical energy of the falling weights and the thermal energy from the increase in temperature of the water. L2 LS **Linguistic**

Science Journal

Body Heat Have students describe in their Science Journals how thermal energy flows when an oral thermometer is used to take someone's temperature. The thermometer usually has a temperature lower than that of a human body, 37°C (98.6°F). In the mouth, thermal energy moves from the body to the thermometer, raising the temperature of the material in the thermometer. L2 LS **Logical-Mathematical** P

INTEGRATE Earth Science

Coastal Climates A narrow band of land that runs along coastal areas experiences little temperature difference throughout the year. The proximity to the water moderates the temperature.

Quick Demo
Comparing Specific Heat

Materials large beaker, crushed ice, water, three test tubes, sand (or table salt), iron filings, starch-based packing peanuts

Estimated Time 15 minutes

Procedure Partially fill a large beaker with crushed ice. Add water to fill voids in the ice. Place a thermometer in each test tube. Partially fill each test tube with sand, iron filings, or packing peanuts. Break up the packing peanuts, if needed. Make sure the thermometers don't touch the bottoms of the test tubes. They should be completely surrounded by the other material. Place the test tubes in the beaker of ice water. Record the temperature of each test tube every minute for 5 min. To remove the packing peanuts from the test tube, add water to the test tube to dissolve the peanuts.

Applying Math

Math Standards

National: 1, 4, 9

Answer to Practice Problem

$Q = m \times (T_{final} - T_{initial}) \times C$
$= (72\text{ kg})(25°C - 20°C)(1{,}010\text{ J/kg °C}) = 363{,}600\text{ J}$

INTEGRATE Earth Science

Coastal Climates The high specific heat of water causes large bodies of water to heat up and cool down more slowly than land masses. As a result, the temperature changes in coastal areas tend to be less extreme than they are farther inland.

Changes in Thermal Energy The thermal energy of an object changes when its temperature changes. If Q is the change in thermal energy and C is the specific heat, the change in thermal energy can be calculated from the following equation:

Thermal Energy Equation

change in thermal energy (J) =
mass (kg) × change in temperature (°C) × specific heat $\left(\frac{\text{J}}{\text{kg°C}}\right)$

$$Q = m(T_f - T_i)C$$

Applying Math — Solve a Simple Equation

CHANGE IN THERMAL ENERGY Find the change in thermal energy of a 20-kg wooden chair that warms from 15°C to 25°C if the specific heat of wood is 1,700 J/(kg °C).

IDENTIFY known values and the unknown value

Identify the known values:

A wooden chair with a mass of 20 kg → means → $m = 20$ kg

warms from 15°C to 25°C → means → $T_i = 15°C$ and $T_f = 25°C$

the specific heat of wood is 1,700 J/(kg °C) → means → $C = 1{,}700$ J/(kg °C)

Identify the unknown value:

What is the change in thermal energy → means → $Q = ?$ J

SOLVE the problem

Substitute the known values into the thermal energy equation:

$$Q = m(T_f - T_i)C = (20\text{ kg})(25°C - 15°C)(1{,}700\ \frac{\text{J}}{\text{kg °C}})$$
$$= (20\text{ kg})(10°C)(1{,}700\ \frac{\text{J}}{\text{kg °C}}) = 340{,}000\text{ kg °C}\ \frac{\text{J}}{\text{kg °C}} = 340{,}000\text{ J}$$

CHECK your answer

Does your answer seem reasonable? Check your answer by dividing the change in thermal energy you calculated by the mass and the specific heat given in the problem. The result should be the difference in temperature given in the problem.

Practice Problems

The air in a living room has a mass of 72 kg and a specific heat of 1,010 J/(kg °C). What is the change in thermal energy of the air when it warms from 20°C to 25°C?

For more practice problems, go to page 879 and visit Math Practice at gpescience.com.

Differentiated Instruction

Learning Disabled To help students calculate changes in thermal energy, make sure they know what each variable in the formula means, and show the places where numerical values are put in. Be sure to show them how to calculate the change in temperature. L2 LS **Logical-Mathematical**

Post Reading

Chart Text In their Science Journals, have students summarize the characteristics of thermal energy, kinetic energy, potential energy, and heat. Then, in groups, have students create a graphic that demonstrates how each type of energy is related to the other.

Measuring Specific Heat

The specific heat of a material can be measured using a device called a calorimeter, shown in **Figure 4.** The specific heat of a material can be determined if the mass of the material, its change in temperature, and the amount of thermal energy absorbed or released are known. In a calorimeter, a heated sample transfers thermal energy to a known mass of water. The energy absorbed by the water can be calculated by measuring the water's temperature change. The thermal energy released by the sample is equal to the thermal energy absorbed by the water.

Using a Calorimeter To measure the specific heat of a material, the mass of a sample of the material is measured, as is the initial temperature of the water in the calorimeter. The material then is heated, its temperature is measured, and the sample is placed in the water in the inner chamber of the calorimeter. The sample cools as thermal energy is transferred to the water, and the temperature of the water increases. The transfer continues until the sample and the water are at the same temperature. Then the initial and final temperatures of the water are known, and the thermal energy gained by the water can be calculated.

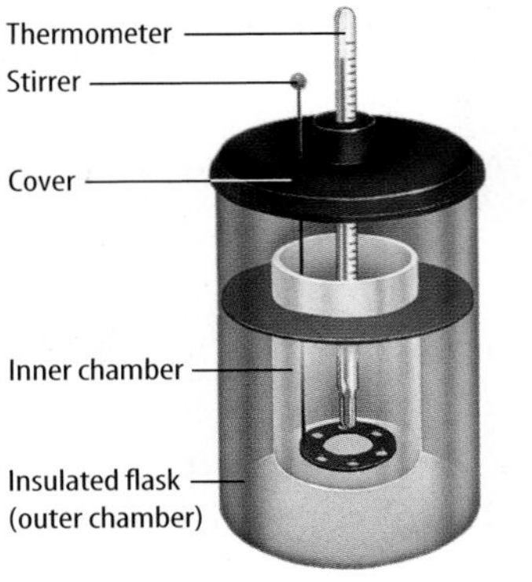

Figure 4 A calorimeter can be used to measure the specific heat of materials. The sample is placed in the inner chamber.

section 1 review

Summary

Temperature

- The kinetic theory is a description of how the particles in a material are moving.
- The temperature of an object is a measure of the average kinetic energy of the particles that make up the object.

Thermal Energy and Heat

- Thermal energy is the sum of the kinetic and potential energies of the particles in an object.
- Heat is thermal energy that is transferred from an object at a higher temperature to an object at a lower temperature.

Specific Heat

- The specific heat of a material is the amount of thermal energy needed to raise the temperature of 1 kg of the material by 1°C.
- The change in thermal energy of an object can be calculated from this equation:

$$Q = m(T_f - T_i)C$$

Self Check

1. **Explain** how energy moves when you touch a block of ice with your hand.
2. **Describe** how the thermal energy of an object changes when the object's temperature changes.
3. **Infer** When thermal energy flows between two objects, does the temperature increase of one object always equal the temperature decrease of the other? Explain.
4. **Describe** how the particles in matter move, using the assumptions of the kinetic theory.
5. **Think Critically** Explain whether or not the following statement is true: For any two objects, the one with the higher temperature always has more thermal energy.

Applying Math

6. **Calculate** the change in thermal energy of the water in a pond with a mass of 1,000 kg and a specific heat of 4,184 J/(kg °C) if the water cools by 1°C.
7. **Calculate** the specific heat of a metal if 0.5 kg absorbs 9,000 J of thermal energy as it warms by 10°C.

More Section Review gpescience.com

3 Assess

DAILY INTERVENTION

Check for Understanding

Linguistic Have students write three sample test questions about the information in this section, then have students exchange papers. Have students write a complete answer to the sample questions they now have. Ask students to return the papers to the original owner to check the answers. Answer any questions that students may have. L2 LS

Reteach

Temperature, Thermal Energy, and Heat Have students form small groups and draw concept maps that connect the following quantities: temperature, thermal energy, molecular motion, heat, mass, and specific heat. Students should use short phrases to label the links on their concept maps. L2 LS COOP LEARN **Visial-Spatial**

Assessment

Process Ask students to imagine that equal masses of water and alcohol are put into identical pans and heated for ten minutes. At the end of ten minutes, the alcohol has a higher temperature. What does this tell you about the specific heat of alcohol? The alcohol must have a lower specific heat since its temperature rose more with the same amount of thermal energy added. Use **Performance Assessment in the Science Classroom,** p. 89.

section 1 review

1. Thermal energy transfers from your hand to the block of ice as the particles in your hand strike the particles of ice where your hand touches the ice.
2. Temperature is the average kinetic energy of the particles in the object. Kinetic energy is one of the components of thermal energy—as kinetic energy changes, thermal energy changes.
3. No. The temperature change depends on the specific heat of each material.
4. The particles in matter are constantly moving and colliding with other particles.
5. It is false. Thermal energy depends on the amount of material and the potential energy of the particles in the objects.
6. −4,184,000 J
7. 1,800 J/(kg°C)

section 2

States of Matter

Reading Guide

What You'll Learn
- **Describe** the differences in the four states of matter.
- **Explain** how the motion of particles in a material changes at the material's melting point and boiling point.
- **Explain** why thermal expansion occurs.

Why It's Important

You can use energy that is lost or gained when a substance changes from one state to another.

Review Vocabulary

force: a push or a pull that one object exerts on another

New Vocabulary
- plasma
- heat of fusion
- heat of vaporization

Four States of Matter

Every day you encounter different states of matter. Your lunch probably includes a solid and a liquid, such as pizza and a drink. The air you breathe is a gas. The Sun, lightning, and fluorescent lights contain a fourth state of matter called plasma. The differences between solids, liquids and gases are due to differences in the attraction between particles.

Solid State The spacing between particles is different for solids, liquids, and gases, as shown in **Figure 5.** The particles of a solid are packed closely together and are constantly vibrating in place. Because the attractions between particles are strong, solids have a fixed volume and shape.

Figure 5 In solids, strong attractive forces hold particles in place. Particles in liquids and gases do not have fixed arrangements. Particles are farther apart in gases than in solids and liquids.

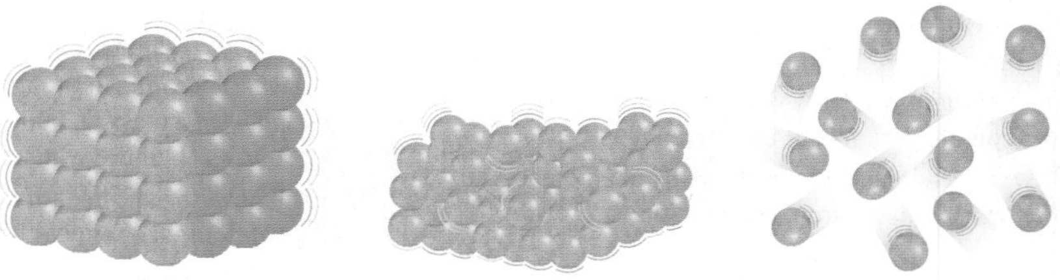

1 Motivate

INTERACTIVE CHALKBOARD An editable Microsoft® PowerPoint® presentation is available on **Interactive Chalkboard** CD-ROM.

Bellringer

Section Focus Transparencies also are available on the Interactive Chalkboard CD-ROM. L2 ELL

Section 2 Section Focus Transparency — Water Works — Chapter 9

Sculptors use a variety of materials to create their works of art. Those who sculpt marble or wood expect their work to last for many years. Ice sculptors, on the other hand, know that the Sun will soon turn their intricate works into pools of water.

1. What happens to molecules of water as ice melts?
2. Why does snow melt when you hold it in your hand?
3. What happens when water boils?

L2

Heat and States of Matter

Reading Preview

Tie to Prior Knowledge

Temperature and Fuel Ask students if they have ever heard of fuel line freeze-up or vapor lock. In summer, fuel can vaporize at a hot spot, partially filling a fuel line with vapor. In winter, water from condensation in the gasoline tank can freeze and block the fuel line. Discuss how temperature affects the state of matter of the fuel.

Activate Background Knowledge Ask students if they have heard of plasma television sets and discuss what may be special about them. Tell them that the terms *plasma*, *heat of fusion*, and *heat of vaporization* have very narrow and exact meanings in science. Have students find these words in the text and read the definitions to a partner.

Section 2 Resource Manager

Chapter *Fast File* Resources
- MiniLAB, p. 3
- Lab Activity, pp. 9–12
- Enrichment, p. 32
- Reinforcement, p. 28
- Directed Reading for Content Mastery, p. 20
- Transparency Activity, pp. 47, 51–52

Physical Science Critical Thinking/Problem Solving, p. 3

Cultural Diversity, pp. 27–28

Liquid State In a liquid the attractive forces between particles are weaker than in a solid. The particles can slide past each other, allowing liquids to flow and take the shape of their container. However, the attractive forces are strong enough to cause particles to cling together. As a result, liquids have a definite volume, but not a definite shape.

Reading Check *Why do liquids flow?*

Gas State In a gas, the particles are much farther apart than in a liquid or a solid. Because the particles are so far apart, the attractive forces between them are weak. In a gas the forces between particles are so weak that the particles no longer cling together. As a result, gases do not have a definite shape or volume.

Because the particles in a gas are so far apart, a gas contains mostly empty space. This means that the density of gases is much less than the density of solids and liquids. Also, the particles in a gas will spread throughout a given volume until they are distributed evenly. This process is called diffusion. Diffusion also occurs in solids and liquids, but occurs much more rapidly in gases.

INTEGRATE Astronomy

Plasma State The most common state of matter in the universe is the plasma state. **Plasma** is matter consisting of positively and negatively charged particles and does not have a definite shape or volume. It results from collisions between particles moving at such high speeds that electrons are knocked from the atoms, leaving only charged particles. All of the observed stars, including the Sun shown in **Figure 6,** contain plasma. Lightning bolts, neon and fluorescent tubes, and auroras also contain plasmas.

Changing States

If you hold an ice cube in your hand, you can see it change from a solid to a liquid. A liquid changes to a gas when a puddle of water disappears after a rain on a hot day. Adding thermal energy caused the solid ice to change to a liquid and the liquid water to become a gas. Changes in the thermal energy of a material can cause it to change from one state to another.

Science Online
Topic: States of Matter
Visit gpescience.com for Web links to information about states of matter.

Activity Create a slide presentation about the states of matter using computer presentation software.

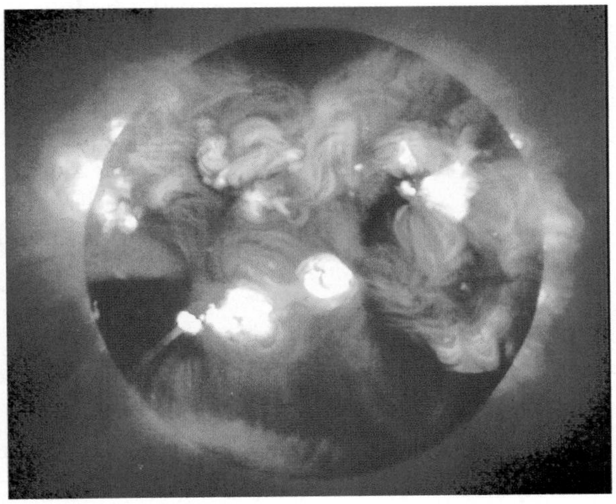

Figure 6 The Sun and other stars contain matter that is in the plasma state. Plasma usually exists where the temperature is extremely high.
Describe *the plasma state.*

2 Teach

Reading Check

Answer The particles have gained enough kinetic energy to partially escape the attractive forces in the solid.

Quick Demo
Observing Salt Crystals

Materials salt crystals, microscope or magnifying lens

Estimated Time 10 minutes

Procedure Have students observe the regular, cubic shape of salt crystals under a microscope or with a magnifying lens.

Caption Answer
Figure 6 matter consisting of positively and negatively charged particles

INTEGRATE Astronomy **Content Background**

Plasma Over 99% of the visible universe is composed of plasma, found mostly in interstellar space and stars. Here on Earth, small amounts of plasma are used in the production of microchips and semiconductors. The challenge of controlling a large quantity of plasma is the main stumbling block in the development of a nuclear fusion reactor.

LAB DEMONSTRATION

Purpose to demonstrate the movement of gas particles

Materials balloon, vanilla flavoring, dropper

Procedure Use a dropper to put five drops of vanilla into a balloon. Close the bottle of vanilla flavoring so that a minimum amout of vanilla odor is released. Blow up the balloon, tie it closed, then smell near the surface of the balloon.

Expected Outcome Students will detect the aroma of vanilla as it evaporates inside the balloon.

Assessment
Ask the students why they can smell the vanilla near the surface of the balloon. The moving particles of vanilla passed between the molecules of the stretched balloon.

Use an Analogy

Sporting Event States of matter are like the crowd at a sporting event. When seated, people are like particles in a solid. They can move in place but don't go anywhere. The people in the aisles are like particles in a liquid. They move past each other but aren't free to move far apart. Upon reaching the parking lot, the people are free to disperse, as are particles in a gas.

Activity

Altitude and Cooking Have students examine the labels of foods such as cake mixes. On Earth, air pressure decreases as altitude increases. Have students determine the effect of altitude on cooking time and temperature for these items. L2 LS **Linguistic**

Mini LAB

Purpose Students observe changes in volume due to change in state. L2 ELL LS **Kinesthetic**

Materials plastic bowl or ice tray, marker or masking tape

Teaching Strategies Warn the students to not fill the bowl or ice tray completely full.

Analysis

1. The level of the ice is higher than the level of the water.
2. Particles in the solid state of water have more space between them than particles in liquid water.

Assessment

Process Have each student write up the procedure used and results obtained for this MiniLAB in a lab report. Use **PASC**, p. 119 P

Try at Home

Mini LAB

Comparing States of Water

Procedure

1. Fill a **plastic bowl or ice tray** with **water**. Mark the level of the top surface of the water with a **marker** or piece of **masking tape**.
2. Place the container in a freezer overnight.
3. Remove the container from the freezer and observe the level of the ice that has formed.

Analysis

1. How does the level of ice compare with the level of water that you placed in the container?
2. Explain why the level of ice is different from the level of the water.

Try at Home

Melting What causes an ice cube to melt into liquid water? As the temperature of the ice increases, its particles move faster, and the attractive forces between them aren't strong enough to keep them in place. The particles can slip out of their ordered arrangement, and the ice melts. The temperature at which a solid begins to melt is its melting point. Energy is required for the particles to slip out of the ordered arrangement. The amount of energy required to change 1 kg of a substance from a solid to a liquid at its melting point is known as the **heat of fusion.**

Freezing The heat of fusion is also the energy released when a liquid freezes, or changes to a solid. If you lower a liquid's temperature, you decrease its particles' average kinetic energy, and they move slower. The attractive forces then are strong enough that the particles form an ordered arrangement.

Vaporization As the temperature of a liquid increases, the particles in the liquid move faster. As the particles move faster and become farther apart, the forces between them can become so weak that the particles no longer cling together. Then vaporization occurs as liquid changes into a gas. Vaporization can occur within the liquid or at the surface of the liquid. Vaporization that occurs at the surface of a liquid is called evaporation. Particles that enter the gas state have more energy than the particles left in the liquid. Evaporation causes the temperature of the liquid to decrease.

Boiling A second way that a liquid can vaporize is by boiling, shown in **Figure 7.** Unlike evaporation, boiling occurs throughout a liquid. It occurs only at a certain temperature depending on the pressure on the surface of the liquid. The boiling point of a liquid is the temperature at which the pressure of the vapor in the liquid is equal to the external pressure acting on its surface. This external pressure is a force pushing down upon a liquid, keeping particles from escaping. The **heat of vaporization** is the amount of energy required for 1 kg of the liquid at its boiling point to become a gas.

Figure 7 Boiling occurs throughout a liquid when the pressure of the pockets of gas forming in the liquid equals the pressure of the vapor at the surface of the liquid.
Explain *the difference between boiling and evaporation.*

Differentiated Instruction

English-Language Learners Have students make vocabulary study cards out of index cards. Have students write a vocabulary word in both languages on one side of the card. On the other side, write the definition of the word in both languages. Make a card for each vocabulary word in the chapter. Use the cards to study for quizzes and tests.

Caption Answer

Figure 7 Evaporation is vaporization that occurs at the surface of a liquid. It can occur at temperatures below the liquid's boiling point. Boiling is vaporization that occurs throughout the liquid at a specific temperature depending on the pressure at the surface of the liquid.

262 CHAPTER 9 Heat and States of Matter

Condensation The heat of vaporization is also the amount of energy released during condensation, when a gas changes into a liquid. You've probably seen condensation form on the sides of a glass of ice water on a hot day. The cold glass reduced the temperature of nearby water vapor. The average kinetic energy of the water particles decreased, and the water vapor changed to a liquid. As shown in **Figure 8,** dew also is the result of condensation.

Reading Check *What change of state occurs during condensation?*

Heating Curve of a Substance A graph representing water being heated from –20°C to 120°C is shown in **Figure 9.** This graph is called a heating curve because it shows the temperature change of water as thermal energy is added. There are two areas on the graph where the temperature does not change. One is at 0°C, where ice is melting. All of the energy absorbed by the ice at this temperature increases the potential energy of the water molecules. This causes water molecules to move farther apart and weakens the forces between molecules. However, the average kinetic energy of the water molecules doesn't change. As a result, the temperature remains constant during melting.

After the ice melts completely, adding additional energy causes the water molecules to move faster so that the temperature of the water increases. At 100°C, the water changes from a liquid to a gas. As the water absorbs energy, only the potential energy of the water molecules increases and the temperature of the water doesn't change. After the liquid water has changed completely into a gas, the temperature of the gas increases as energy is added.

Figure 8 The formation of dew is an example of condensation. Dew forms when the air around matter, such as spider webs, cools enough so that water vapor in the air changes to a liquid.
Identify *the change in state that occurs when dew evaporates.*

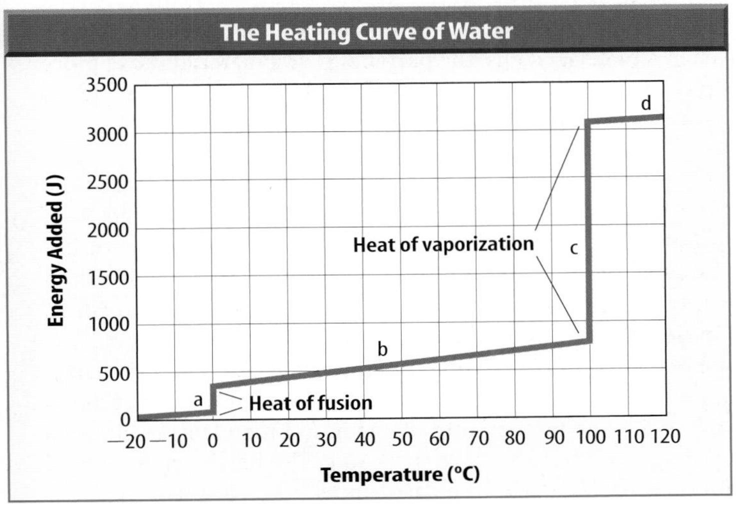

Figure 9 This graph shows the heating curve of one gram of water from –20°C to 120°C. At **a** and **c,** the energy absorbed causes water molecules to move faster and so the temperature increases. At **b** and **d,** the water changes from one state to another. The added energy increases the potential energy of the water molecules, but not the kinetic energy, so the temperature doesn't change.

Teacher FYI

Effects of Pressure At 1 atm, water freezes at 0°C and boils at 100°C. At different pressures, water goes through these changes at different temperatures. In fact, when the pressure is 0.61 kPA and the temperature is 0.01°C, water can exist as a solid, a liquid, and a gas. This is called the triple point for water.

Reading Check

Answer the gas state to the liquid state

Visual Learning

Figure 9 Ask a volunteer to read aloud the section of the SE text that describes the graph while the rest of the students follow the graph with their fingers. Discuss with students the effect of adding heat to water at different temperatures. L1 ELL
LS **Auditory-Musical**

Identifying Misconceptions

Steam Students may think that steam is water in the gaseous state. Actually, steam is made of liquid water droplets that have condensed from gaseous water vapor in the air.

Caption Answer

Figure 8 the liquid state to the gas state

Cultural Diversity

Sharing Languages In English-speaking countries, the three states of water are called *ice, water,* and *water vapor.* In Spanish-speaking countries the words are *bielo, aqua,* and *vapor.* If you have students in your class that speak other languages, ask them to share the terms they know with the class.

Reading Strategy

Use Graphs Ask students to look at the graph in **Figure 9** as they are reading Heating Curve of a Substance. Have them read the labels on both axis and the range of numbers on the scales. Ask them to notice the temperatures at which there are two "jumps" or "spikes" in the curve. What occurs at 0° and 100° centigrade?

SECTION 2 States of Matter 263

Discussion

States of Matter Around Us Ask students to think about shopping malls and how different states of matter are used to decorate the mall and make shopping more pleasant. Items may include fountains (liquid), helium-filled balloons (gas), marble floors (solid), and fluorescent and neon lighting (plasmas).

IDENTIFYING Misconceptions

Sweating and Evaporation If you ask students whether sweating is a heating or cooling process, many may initially say it's a heating process, thinking of the fact that they sweat when they feel warm. Lead them to understand that being warm causes the body to sweat in an effort to cool down; therefore, evaporation must be a cooling process.

Figure 10 This expansion joint enables the road surface on this bridge to expand without causing the road surface to crack or buckle.

Thermal Expansion

When you have gone over a highway bridge in a car, you might have noticed the gaps between sections of the bridge, such as the gap shown in **Figure 10.** This gap is called an expansion joint. The materials that make up the bridge and the road surface expand when they get warmer. Expansion joints provide space for these materials to expand on hot days without causing the materials to become warped or cracked.

The Thermal Expansion of Matter The kinetic theory explains why an object expands when its temperature increases. According to the kinetic theory, the particles in an object are in constant motion. The speed of these particles increases as the temperature of the object increases. As the particles move faster, the attractive forces between them become weaker and the distance between particles increases. The increased separation between the particles results in the expansion of the object and the size of the object increases. When a material cools, the particles in the material move more slowly and become closer together. As a result, the material contracts and its dimensions decrease.

Figure 11 The liquid in the thermometer tube expands as its temperature increases. Because the tube expands much less than the liquid, the height of the liquid column increases as the temperature increases.

Thermal Expansion of Liquids The forces between the particles in liquids are usually weaker than the forces between the particles in a solid. As a result, the same temperature increase usually causes liquids to expand much more than solids. For example, the liquid in the thermometer shown in **Figure 11** expands as its temperature increases. However, the dimensions of the glass tube containing the liquid hardly change at all. This causes the height of the liquid column in the tube to increase as the temperature of the liquid increases. If the glass tube expanded as much as the liquid, the height of the liquid column wouldn't change as the temperature changed.

Differentiated Instruction

Challenge Find out what the concept of absolute zero means. How do real and ideal gases behave at absolute zero? Which two widely used temperature scales are absolute temperature scales? Prepare a report of your research findings about absolute zero and share it with your class. Kelvin and Rankine are absolute temperature scales. L3

264 CHAPTER 9 Heat and States of Matter

Thermal Expansion of Gases In a gas, the forces between particles are much weaker than they are in liquids. As a result, gases expand even more than liquids for the same increase in temperature. When thermal expansion occurs, the volume of the material increases. Recall that the density of an object is the mass of the object divided by its volume. Because the material's volume has increased, but its mass hasn't changed, the material becomes less dense as it expands.

Reading Check *How does the density of a material change when the material expands?*

The decrease in density caused by thermal expansion enables the hot-air balloon in **Figure 12** to rise. The air inside the balloon is heated by a burner. The hot air in the balloon expands and becomes less dense than the cooler air outside the balloon. As a result, the hot-air balloon is pushed upward by the denser, cooler air around it.

Figure 12 The air inside the hot-air balloon expands as it is heated. Its density decreases and the balloon rises.

section 2 review

Summary

Four States of Matter

- In solids, particles are held in place by strong attractive forces. Solids have a definite volume and shape.
- In liquids, the attractive forces are weaker and particles can move past each other. Liquids have a definite volume, but no definite shape.
- In gases, the attractive forces between particles are weakest. Gases have neither a definite volume nor shape.
- A plasma is made of electrically charged particles.

Changing States

- The heat of fusion is the amount of energy needed to change 1 kg of a material at its melting point from a solid to a liquid.
- The heat of vaporization is the amount of energy needed to change 1 kg of material at its boiling point from a liquid to a gas.

Self Check

1. **Compare and contrast** solids, liquids, gases, and plasma.
2. **Explain** whether the temperature of a substance must increase when thermal energy is added to the substance.
3. **Explain** how the forces between water molecules in an ice cube change when the ice cube melts.
4. **Think Critically** The atmospheric pressure on a mountain peak is lower than the atmospheric pressure at sea level. Compare the boiling point of water at sea level to its boiling point on the mountain peak.

Applying Math

5. **Calculate** the amount of thermal energy required to change a 0.45-kg block of ice at 0°C to water at 0°C if the heat of fusion of water is 334,000 J/kg.
6. **Calculate** The heat of vaporization for water is 2.26×10^6 J/kg. What mass of liquid water at 100°C can be changed to water vapor at 100°C by adding 1.0×10^6 J of thermal energy to the liquid water?

More Section Review gpescience.com

Reading Check

Answer it decreases

Post Reading

Essays Explain to students the concept of comparison and contrast. Then, have them write an essay comparing and contrasting the effects of thermal expansion in solids, liquids, and gases. Model the format by showing them how they can write about each in a separate paragraph. Encourage them to support their points with everyday examples of thermal expansion.

3 Assess

DAILY INTERVENTION

Check for Understanding

Visual-Spatial Have students make an illustration showing how solid, liquid, and gas particles behave and interact.

Reteach

Demonstrating the States of Matter Have students make a snow globe to model the behavior of solids, liquids, and gases. Have students use a small jar with a lid as the container. Fill the jar with enough glitter to cover the bottom of the jar to a depth of 1 cm. Fill the jar with water, mineral oil, or baby oil. The particles will move slower in oil. Have students use their snow globe to model the behavior of solids, liquids, and gases.

section 2 review

1. As the temperature increases, particles move faster on average and become farther apart. The volume occupied by the particles increases but the mass of the particles doesn't change. As a result, the density decreases.
2. When a substance is undergoing a phase change, the temperature doesn't change as thermal energy is added to the substance.
3. When the ice cube melts, the forces between molecules become weaker.
4. The boiling point at sea level is higher.
5. (0.45 kg) (334,000 J/kg) = 150,000 J
6. $(1.0 \times 10^6 \text{ J}) / (2.26 \times 10^6 \text{ J/kg}) = 0.44$ kg

Assessment

Process Ask students to draw diagrams illustrating what determines the boiling point of a liquid. At the boiling point, the pressure from molecules leaving the liquid to become gas is equal to the atmospheric pressure above them. Use **PASC,** p. 127.

1 Motivate

An editable Microsoft® PowerPoint® presentation is available on **Interactive Chalkboard** CD-ROM.

Bellringer

Section Focus Transparencies also are available on the Interactive Chalkboard CD-ROM. L2 ELL

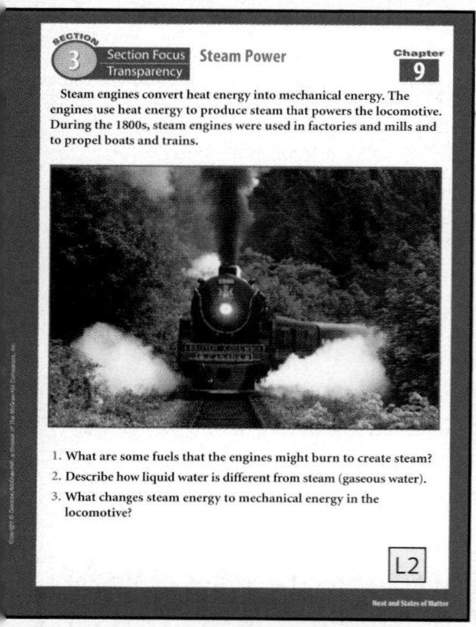
Section Focus Transparency — Steam Power — Chapter 9

Steam engines convert heat energy into mechanical energy. The engines use heat energy to produce steam that powers the locomotive. During the 1800s, steam engines were used in factories and mills and to propel boats and trains.

1. What are some fuels that the engines might burn to create steam?
2. Describe how liquid water is different from steam (gaseous water).
3. What changes steam energy to mechanical energy in the locomotive?

L2

Heat and States of Matter

Reading Preview

Tie to Prior Knowledge

Conductors Ask students if they have ever been burned by touching a hot object. What type of material was the object made of? It probably was made of a good conductor that transferred its thermal energy to the student's hand by conduction.

Make Connections Tell students that thermal energy is common in our lives. On a stove, a pan gets hot by contacting a hot burner. This is conduction. In an oven, a red-hot coil cooks food by radiation. A convection oven cooks food by using a fan to move hot air around the oven.

section 3

Transferring Thermal Energy

Reading Guide

What You'll Learn

- **Compare and contrast** the transfer of thermal energy by conduction, convection, and radiation.
- **Compare and contrast** thermal conductors and insulators.
- **Explain** how thermal insulators are used to control the transfer of thermal energy.

Why It's Important

You must be able to control the flow of thermal energy to keep from being too hot or too cold.

Review Vocabulary

density: the mass per unit volume of a substance

New Vocabulary

- conduction
- convection
- radiation
- thermal insulator

Ways to Transfer Thermal Energy

When water is heated on a stove or when a hot slice of pizza becomes cool enough to eat, thermal energy is transferred from one place to another. Thermal energy can be transferred from one place to another by conduction, convection, or radiation.

Conduction

According to the kinetic theory, particles in matter are always in random motion. Thermal energy can be transferred when particles collide. This transfer of thermal energy between colliding particles is **conduction. Figure 13** shows a metal pot being heated over a fire. The metal atoms nearest the fire absorb the most thermal energy, causing their kinetic energy to increase. Kinetic energy is transferred when these faster-moving atoms collide with slower-moving particles. As these collisions continue, thermal energy is transferred throughout the pot. When thermal energy is transferred by conduction, it is transferred by the collisions between particles, not by the movement of matter.

Figure 13 Conduction occurs within the metal of this pot as faster-moving particles transfer thermal energy when they collide with slower-moving particles.

266 CHAPTER 9 Heat and States of Matter

Section 3 Resource Manager

Chapter *Fast File* Resources

Transparency Activity, p. 48
MiniLAB, p. 4
Lab Activity, pp. 13–15
Enrichment, p. 33
Reinforcement, p. 29
Directed Reading for Content Mastery, p. 21
Lab Worksheets, pp. 5–6
Life Science Critical Thinking/Problem Solving, p. 14

Thermal Conductors Thermal energy can be transferred by conduction in all materials. However, the rate at which thermal energy is transferred depends on the material. A material in which thermal energy is transferred easily is called a thermal conductor. The conduction of thermal energy in solids and liquids is faster than in gases. Particles in gases are farther apart than in solids or liquids and collide less frequently. Therefore, gases are poorer thermal conductors than solids or liquids. Solids usually are better thermal conductors than liquids or gases. The best thermal conductors are metals.

Convection

Unlike solids, liquids and gases can flow and are classified as fluids. In fluids, thermal energy can be transferred by convection. **Convection** is the transfer of thermal energy in a fluid by the movement of fluid from place to place. When convection occurs, particles with more energy transfer energy to other particles in the fluid as they move from place to place.

As the particles move faster, they tend to be farther apart. As a result, a fluid expands as its temperature increases. Recall that density is the mass of a material divided by its volume. When a fluid expands, its volume increases, but its mass doesn't change. The density of the fluid therefore decreases. The same is true for parts of a fluid that have been heated. The density of the warmer fluid is less than that of the surrounding cooler fluid.

Convection Currents The difference in densities between warmer and cooler fluids can cause convection currents to occur. **Figure 14** shows the formation of convection currents in a beaker of water that is being heated from the bottom. Warm water at the bottom of the beaker is less dense than the cooler water above it. Because the warmer water is less dense, it is forced upward by the sinking cooler water. As it rises, the warm water transfers thermal energy to the cooler water around it. When the warm water cools, it becomes denser than the surrounding warmer water and sinks to the bottom of the beaker. The rising and sinking water forms a convection current. In this way, convection currents transfer thermal energy by the movement of water from place to place.

Mini LAB

Comparing Thermal Conductors

Procedure

1. Obtain a **plastic spoon,** a **metal spoon,** and a **wooden spoon** with similar lengths.
2. Stick a small **plastic bead** to the handle of each spoon with a dab of **butter or wax.** Each bead should be the same distance from the tip of the spoon.
3. Stand the spoons in a **beaker,** with the beads hanging over the edge of the beaker.
4. Carefully pour about 5 cm of **boiling water** in the beaker holding the spoons.

Analysis

1. Describe how heat was transferred from the water to the beads.
2. Rank the spoons in their ability to conduct heat.

Figure 14 Convection currents result when heated fluid rises and cooler fluid sinks.

2 Teach

Use an Analogy

Kicking a Soccer Ball Explain that transferring energy to a soccer ball by kicking it is similar to transferring energy by conduction. A collision with a person's foot causes energy to be transferred to the soccer ball.

Mini LAB

Purpose Students observe the thermal conductivity of a metallic alloy, plastic, and wood. L2 ELL IS **Kinesthetic**

Materials Each group will need: metallic, plastic, and wooden spoons (similar length), three small plastic beads, three small dabs of butter, beaker, and boiling water

Teaching Strategies Have students place their beakers on paper towels to catch butter drips.

Safety Precautions Students should be careful when handling boiling water.

Analysis

1. by conduction through the spoons and the butter
2. metal, plastic, then wood

Assessment

Process Have students draw cartoons explaining why items in the kitchen are made of insulators or conductors. Use **PASC,** p. 133. P

Visual Learning

Figure 13 Using the figure as a guide, have several students explain how heat travels from the bottom of the frying pan up to and through the handle.

NATIONAL GEOGRAPHIC

Visualizing Convection Currents

Have students examine the pictures and read the captions. Then ask the following questions.

Why does the air lose its moisture as it rises and cools at the equator? The water vapor in the air condenses as the air cools.

Why does the dry air create a cone of deserts at the tropics? The dry air causes moisture to evaporate out of the ground. Since there is a continuous stream of hot, dry air that blows across the land, any water on the ground is vaporized and carried away. In addition to this drying process, there is insufficient rainfall to replenish the moisture.

Activity

World Map Have students obtain or draw a world map. Ask students to locate and mark the equator and both tropics. Have them find the major rain forests and deserts of the world and mark them on their maps. L2 ELL LS **Visual-Spatial**

Quick Demo

Heat and Convection

Materials three 250-mL beakers, one 600-mL beaker, food coloring, dropper, hot plate, ice

Estimated Time 10 minutes

Procedure Fill the 600-mL beaker two-thirds full of ice. Put water in the small beakers. Using the dropper, gently place a drop of food coloring in the bottom of each beaker. Place one beaker on a hot plate, one on the ice, and one in your hand. Since heat causes convection to occur more rapidly, the food coloring will disperse more rapidly in the warmer beakers.

NATIONAL GEOGRAPHIC **VISUALIZING CONVECTION CURRENTS**

Figure 15

When the Sun beats down on the equator, warm, moist air begins to rise. As it rises, the air cools and loses its moisture as rain that sustains rain forests near the equator. Convection currents carry the now dry air farther north and south. Some of this dry air descends at the tropics, where it creates a zone of deserts.

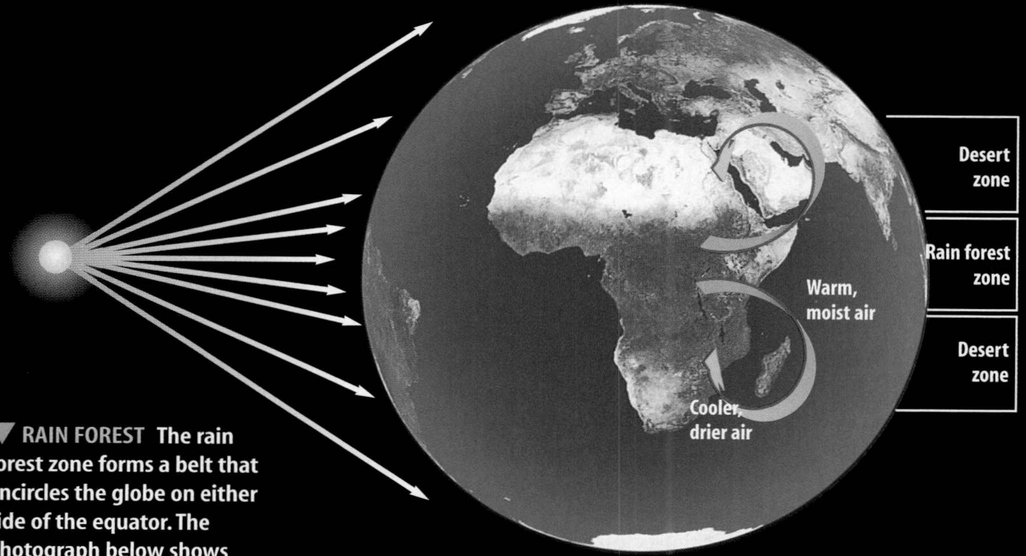

▼ RAIN FOREST The rain forest zone forms a belt that encircles the globe on either side of the equator. The photograph below shows a rain forest near the Congo River in central Africa.

▲ DESERT Like many of the great desert regions of the world, the Sahara, in northern Africa, is largely a result of atmospheric convection currents. Here, a group of nomads gather near a dried-up river in Mali.

Differentiated Instruction

Challenge Have students research the living conditions of the people in the desert areas discussed in this feature. Students should find out how they obtain food, shelter, and how they cope with their harsh conditions. Ask students to give an oral report of their findings to their class. L2 LS **Auditory-Musical**

Reading Strategy

Reciprocal Teaching Have students read Visualizing Convection Currents. Ask them to study this global weather pattern until they can explain it in their own words to a partner.

Deserts and Rain Forests Earth's atmosphere is made of various gases and is a fluid. The atmosphere is warmer at the equator than it is at the north and south poles. Also, the atmosphere is warmer at Earth's surface than at higher altitudes. These temperature differences create convection currents that transfer thermal energy to cooler regions. **Figure 15** shows how these currents create rain forests and deserts in different regions.

Radiation

Earth is warmed by energy from the Sun, but how does that energy travel through space? Almost no matter exists in the space between Earth and the Sun, so thermal energy cannot be transferred by conduction or convection. Instead, the Sun's energy reaches Earth by radiation.

Radiation is the transfer of energy by electromagnetic waves. These waves travel through space even when no matter is present. Energy transferred by radiation often is called radiant energy. When you stand near a fire, much of the warmth you feel is caused by radiation transferring thermal energy to your skin. Radiation can pass through solids, liquids, and gases, but the transfer of energy by radiation is most important in gases.

Radiant Energy and Matter When radiation strikes a material, some energy is absorbed, some is reflected, and some may be transmitted through the material. The amount of energy that does each depends on the material. Light-colored materials reflect more radiant energy, while dark-colored materials are more absorbent. When a material absorbs radiant energy, its thermal energy increases. **Figure 16** shows what happens to radiant energy from the Sun as it reaches Earth.

For example, when a car sits out in the Sun, some of the Sun's radiation passes through the car windows. Materials inside the car absorb some of this radiation and become hot.

The Flow of Thermal Energy

You do a number of things every day to control the flow of thermal energy. When it's cold outside you wear a coat. You use an oven mitt when handling a hot dish. In each case, you use an insulating material to help reduce the flow of thermal energy. Your coat keeps you warm by reducing the flow of thermal energy from your body to the surrounding air. The oven mitt keeps your hand from being burned by reducing the flow of thermal energy from the hot dish to your hand.

Figure 16 Not all of the Sun's radiant energy reaches Earth's surface. Some of it is reflected or absorbed by the atmosphere. Even some of the radiation that reaches Earth's surface is reflected.

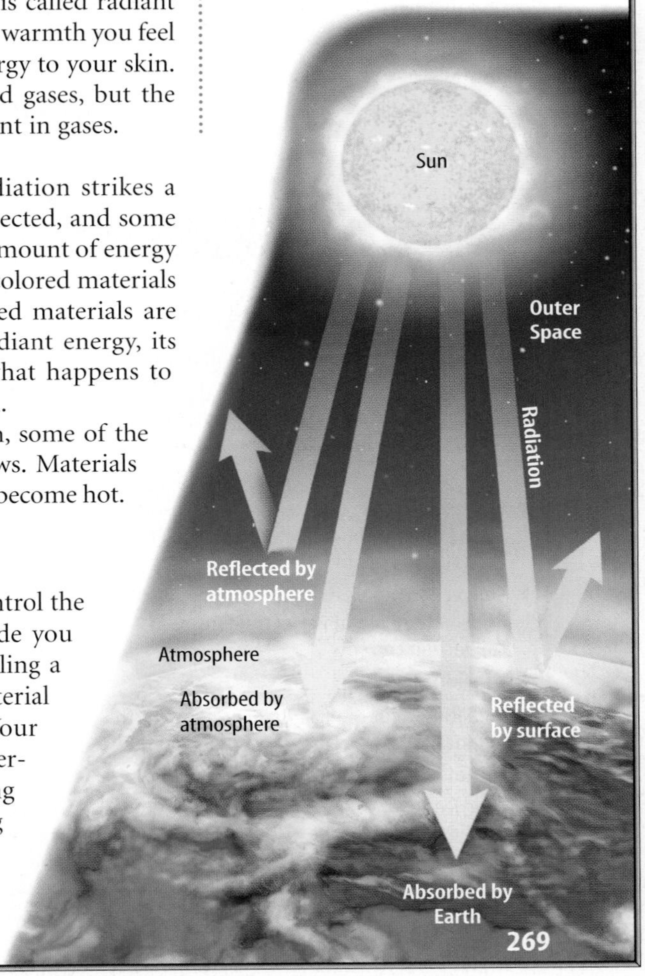

Use Science Words

Word Origins Have students look up the origins of the words *conduction*, *convection*, and *radiation* in a dictionary. Students should find that the words come from the Latin roots *conducere* (to lead), *convehere* (to bring together), and *radius* (ray), respectively. Ask volunteers to connect the meaning of each word with its root. L2 ELL LS **Linguistic**

IDENTIFYING Misconceptions

Radiation Students may confuse radiation as a form of thermal energy transfer with nuclear radiation or radioactivity. Both types of radiation involve the sending of energy as waves or particles. In nuclear radiation, radioactive nuclei of atoms break down and emit particles and electromagnetic waves. In thermal radiation, matter emits electromagnetic waves of much lower frequency.

Virtual Labs

Insulation *How do the insulation properties of various materials compare?*

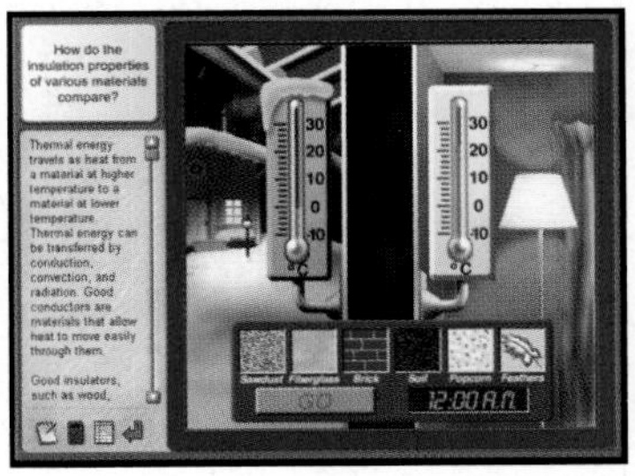

Differentiated Instruction

Learning Disabled Obtain samples of insulation materials for students to observe. Point out the air pockets in the insulation samples for students to see. Materials may include fiber fill, fleece, and building insulation. If fiberglass is used, put the sample in a plastic bag to protect the students. Do not allow students to remove the material from the bag. L2 ELL LS **Visual-Spatial**

Reading Check

Answer Air is a good insulator. It reduces the rate at which thermal energy is transferred to the colder outside.

Post Reading

Chart Text Allow students to work in groups to create charts that compare the action of particles and states of matter in conduction, convection, and radiation. Instruct students that each chart should contain a variety of methods of presenting the information, such as direct quotes from the text, paraphrases, or illustrations.

3 Assess

DAILY INTERVENTION

Check for Understanding

Interpersonal Have students quiz one another on the three means by which thermal energy is transferred. conduction, convection, radiation L2 LS

Reteach

Heat Transfer Have students brainstorm about which method of thermal energy transfer would most concern an astronaut floating in space. Thermal energy radiated between the suit and outer space would be of serious concern. L3 LS **Logical-Mathematical**

Assessment

Oral Have students describe the forms of thermal energy transfer they might experience when they go to a beach or pool on a hot day. How might they use insulation to increase their comfort? Answers might include conduction from hot sand or concrete, convection while in the water, and radiation from the Sun. Insulators could include sandals and a towel. Use **PASC**, p. 89.

Figure 17 The fibers of this insulating material contain air spaces that are good thermal insulators. They reduce the rate at which thermal energy flows in the material.

Thermal Insulators

A jacket and an oven mitt are examples of thermal insulators. A material in which thermal energy moves slowly is a **thermal insulator.** Examples of materials that are thermal insulators are wood, some plastics, fiberglass, and air. Materials that are good conductors of thermal energy, such as metals, are poor thermal insulators.

Gases, such as air, are usually much better thermal insulators than solids or liquids. Some types of insulating material contain many pockets of trapped air. These air pockets are poor conductors of thermal energy and also keep convection currents from forming. Winter jackets often are made of insulating materials consisting of fibers, like the ones shown in **Figure 17,** that trap air and hold it next to you. This trapped air slows the flow of your body heat to the colder air outside the jacket. Gradually, the air trapped by the material is warmed by your body heat. Underneath the jacket you are wrapped in a blanket of warm air.

Reading Check *Why is a material that traps air a good insulator?*

section 3 review

Summary

Conduction

- Conduction is the transfer of thermal energy by collisions between particles.
- Conduction occurs in solids, liquids, and gases. Metals are the best conductors of heat.

Convection

- Convection is the transfer of thermal energy by the movement of warmer and cooler material.
- Convection occurs in fluids. Rising of warmer fluid and sinking of cooler fluid forms a convection current.

Radiation

- Radiation is the transfer of energy by electromagnetic waves.

Thermal Insulators

- Thermal energy moves slowly in thermal insulators. Thermal insulators are used to control the flow of thermal energy.

Self Check

1. **Explain** why convection can occur in fluids but not in solids.
2. **Explain** why the air temperature near the ceiling of a room tends to be warmer than near the floor.
3. **Predict** whether plastic foam, which contains pockets of air, would be a good conductor or a good insulator.
4. **Describe** how a convection current occurs.
5. **Think Critically** Several days after a snowfall, the roofs of some homes on a street have almost no snow on them, while the roofs of other houses are still snow covered. Describe what would cause this difference.

Applying Math

6. **Calculate Solar Radiation** Averaged over a year in the central United States, radiation from the Sun transfers about 200 W to each square meter of Earth's surface. If a house is 10 m long by 10 m wide, how much solar energy falls on the house each second?

More Section Review gpescience.com

section 3 review

1. In solids, particles are held in place by strong forces and vibrate about a fixed position. The particles in a fluid can move throughout the fluid.
2. In warm air particles are farther apart, making the warm air less dense than the cool air.
3. It would be a good insulator, because thermal energy would move slowly through the air pockets.
4. If the fluid is heated from below, the warmer fluid rises. Cooler fluid sinks to the bottom where it is heated, and then rises. The process continues until all the fluid is at the same temperature.
5. The snow-covered houses are better insulated. Not enough thermal energy escaped to melt the snow.
6. $(200\ W) / (1\ m^2) = x / (100\ m^2)$; $x = 20{,}000\ W$

LAB

Convection in Gases and Liquids

A hawk gliding through the sky will rarely flap its wings. Hawks and some other birds conserve energy by gliding on columns of warm air rising up from the ground. These convection currents form when gases or liquids are heated unevenly and the warmer, less dense fluid is forced upward.

Real-World Problem

How can convection currents be modeled and observed?

Goals

- **Model** the formation of convection currents in water.
- **Observe** convection currents formed in water.
- **Observe** convection currents formed in air.

Materials

burner or hot plate
water
candle
500-mL beaker
black pepper

Safety Precautions

WARNING: *Use care when working with hot materials. Remember that hot and cold glass appear the same.*

Procedure

1. Pour 450 mL of water into the beaker.
2. Use a balance to measure 1 g of black pepper.
3. Sprinkle the pepper into the beaker of water and let it settle to the bottom of the beaker.
4. Heat the bottom of the beaker using the burner or the hotplate.
5. **Observe** how the particles of pepper move as the water is heated and make a drawing showing their motion in your Science Journal.
6. Turn off the hot plate or burner. Light the candle and let it burn for a few minutes.
7. Blow out the candle and observe the motion of the smoke.
8. Make a drawing of the movement of the smoke in your Science Journal.

Conclude and Apply

1. **Describe** how the particles of pepper moved as the water became hotter.
2. **Explain** how the motion of the pepper particles is related to the motion of the water.
3. **Explain** how a convection current formed in the beaker.
4. **Explain** why the motion of the pepper changed when the heat was turned off.
5. **Predict** how the pepper would move if the water were heated from the top.
6. **Describe** how the smoke particles moved when the candle was blown out.
7. **Explain** why the smoke moved as it did.

Communicating Your Data

Compare your conclusions with other students in your class.

BENCH TESTED

Real-World Problem

Purpose Students will model and observe convection currents. L2 ELL IN Kinesthetic

Process Skills make models, observe, record data, predict

Time Required one class period

Alternate Materials Other fine-grained spices that are insoluble in water can replace the black pepper.

Safety Precautions Caution students never to taste foods during science class. Caution them not to touch the hot plate when it is on.

Procedure

Teaching Strategy Ask students to bring insoluable particles from home to be used during their experiments.

Conclude and Apply

1. The particles swirled upward.
2. As the water heated, the convection currents in the water carried the black pepper upward.
3. The water was hotter in the bottom of the beaker because it was nearer the heat source. The hot water rose in the beaker and the cold water sank.
4. There was no longer a temperature gradient in the beaker, so convection stopped.
5. The pepper would stay on the top because hot water is less dense than cold water.
6. The smoke rose as long as there was a heat source. The rise of the smoke became slower as the wick cooled.
7. Smoke particles were carried upward by the convection currents in air.

Assessment

Process Ask each student to make an events chain for each of the convection currents observed. Use **Performance Assessment in the Science Classroom,** p. 163. L2 ELL IN **Visual-Spatial**

Communicating Your Data

Have each group observe the convection current patterns created by the experiments of other groups. Ask students to explain any differences in results.

section 4

Using Thermal Energy

Reading Guide

***What* You'll Learn**

- **Describe** the first and second laws of thermodynamics.
- **Explain** how an internal combustion engine converts thermal energy to mechanical energy.
- **Describe** how the entropy of the universe changes when any event occurs.

***Why* It's Important**

Imagine your life without heating systems, cooling systems, or cars.

Review Vocabulary

work: the product of the force exerted on an object and the distance the object moves in the direction of the force

New Vocabulary

- first law of thermodynamics
- second law of thermodynamics
- entropy

How is thermal energy used?

If you've ever lit a campfire to keep warm or turned on a stove to boil water, you've used thermal energy. Heating a house and using a gasoline engine to mow a lawn are other ways that thermal energy is used. Sometimes thermal energy is transferred to an object to heat it, as when water is boiled or a room is heated. Sometimes thermal energy is converted into work.

Heating Systems

Almost everywhere in the United States a heating system is needed to make indoor temperatures comfortable on cold days. Heating systems add thermal energy to the interiors of rooms. The best heating system for a building depends on the local climate and how the building is constructed.

Forced-Air Systems The most common type of heating system in use today is the forced-air system, as shown in **Figure 18.** In this system, fuel is burned in a furnace and heats a volume of air. A fan blows the heated air through a series of large pipes called ducts. The ducts lead to openings called vents in each room. Cool air is returned through additional vents to the furnace, where it is reheated.

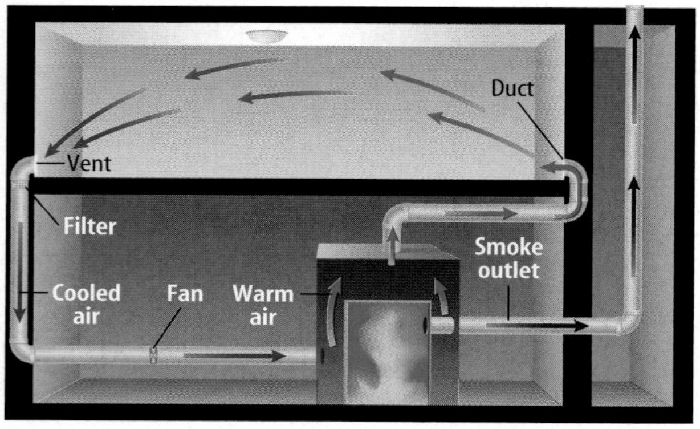

Figure 18 In a forced-air system, heated air is blown through ducts that lead to rooms in the building.

1 Motivate

An editable Microsoft® PowerPoint® presentation is available on **Interactive Chalkboard** CD-ROM.

Bellringer

Section Focus Transparencies also are available on the Interactive Chalkboard CD-ROM. L2 ELL

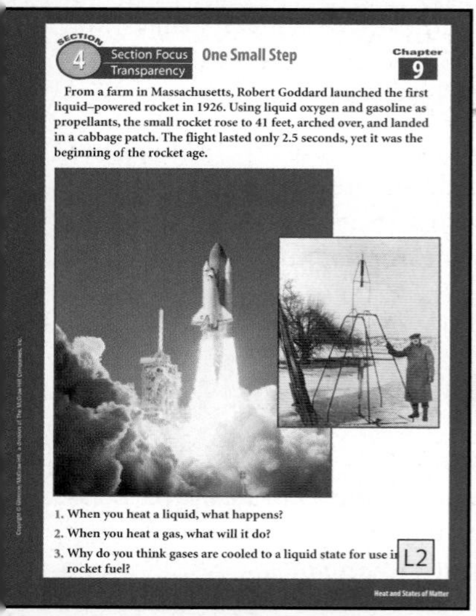
Section 4 Section Focus Transparency **One Small Step** Chapter 9

From a farm in Massachusetts, Robert Goddard launched the first liquid–powered rocket in 1926. Using liquid oxygen and gasoline as propellants, the small rocket rose to 41 feet, arched over, and landed in a cabbage patch. The flight lasted only 2.5 seconds, yet it was the beginning of the rocket age.

1. When you heat a liquid, what happens?
2. When you heat a gas, what will it do?
3. Why do you think gases are cooled to a liquid state for use in rocket fuel? L2

Heat and States of Matter

Reading Preview

Tie to Prior Knowledge

Energy Sources Have students identify the energy sources and the types of energy used in their home heating systems. From a class poll, rank the energy sources from most used to least used. Compare and contrast some of the common energy sources mentioned.

Structural Word Analysis Explain the parts of the word *thermodynamics*. *Thermo-* means "heat" and *dynamics* means "continuous changes." Laws of thermodynamics are universal rules about the continuous process of heat transfer in matter.

Section 4 Resource Manager

Chapter *FAST FILE* Resources

Enrichment, p. 34
Reinforcement, p. 30
Directed Reading for Content Mastery, pp. 22–23
Transparency Activity, p. 49
Lab Worksheets, pp. 7–8

Home and Community Involvement, p. 25

Radiator Systems Before forced-air systems were widely used, many homes and buildings were heated by radiators. A radiator is a closed metal container that contains hot water or steam. The thermal energy contained in the hot water or steam is transferred to the air surrounding the radiator by conduction. This warm air then moves through the room by convection.

In radiator heating systems, fuel burned in a central furnace heats a tank of water. A system of pipes carries the hot water to radiators in the rooms of the building. After the water cools, it flows through the pipes back to the water tank, and is reheated.

Electric Heating Systems Unlike forced-air and radiator systems, electric heaters, like the one in **Figure 19,** convert electrical energy to thermal energy. In an electric heating system, electrically heated coils placed in floors and in walls heat the surrounding air by conduction and convection. Electric heating systems are not as widely used as forced-air systems. However, in warmer climates the walls and floors of some buildings may not be thick enough to contain pipes and ducts. Then an electric heating system might be the only practical way to provide heat.

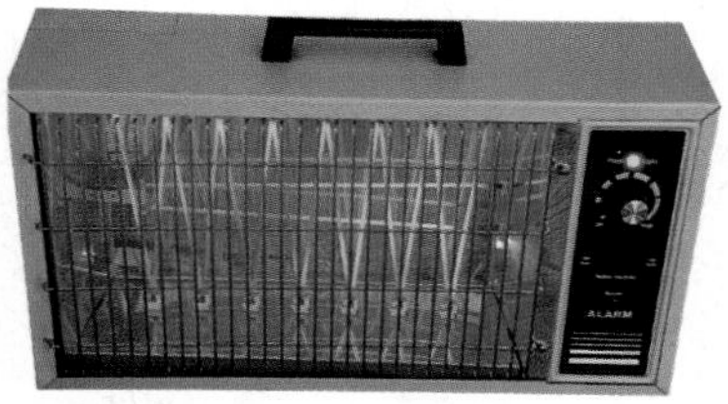

Figure 19 Electric heaters convert electrical energy to thermal energy. Thermal energy is transferred to the room mainly by radiation and convection.

Thermodynamics

There is another way to increase the thermal energy of an object besides heating it. Have you ever rubbed your hands together to warm them on a cold day? Your hands get warmer and their thermal energy and temperature increase. You did work on your hands by rubbing them together. The work you did caused the thermal energy of your hands to increase. Thermal energy, heat, and work are related. The study of the relationship among thermal energy, heat, and work is thermodynamics.

Heating and Work Increase Thermal Energy You can warm your hands by placing them near a fire. Thermal energy is added to your hands by radiation. You can make your hands even warmer by rubbing them together and holding them near a fire. Both the work you do and energy from the fire increase the thermal energy of your hands.

In the example above, your hands can be considered as a system. A system can be a group of objects, such as a galaxy or a car's engine, or something as simple as a ball. In fact, a system is anything you can draw a boundary around. The energy transferred to a system is the amount of energy flowing into the system across the boundary. Heating a system transfers energy to the system. The work done on a system is the work done by something outside the system's boundary.

INTEGRATE History

Thermodynamics and the Steam Engine By the end of the eighteenth century, the steam engine was being used in manufacturing and transportation, leading to a wide-spread change in society called the industrial revolution. A young French engineer named Sadi Carnot (1796–1832) studied how the efficiency of steam engines could be improved. His work provided the basis for the development of thermodynamics by others in the nineteenth century. Research the life of Sadi Carnot and write a paragraph describing the results of his studies.

2 Teach

Discussion

Heating Water Why is water rather than other fluids used in home heating systems? The specific heat of water is high compared with that of other fluids. Thus, it carries more thermal energy per unit of mass and loses it more slowly, keeping the room warm longer. L2 LS **Logical-Mathematical**

Quick Demo

Observe Radiant Heating

Materials electric space heater

Estimated Time five minutes

Procedure Bring a small electric space heater to class. Plug the heater in and have students put their hands near the heater to feel the thermal energy. Explain to students that the wires become hot because of their electrical resistance. Thermal energy is transferred to the room by radiation. A small fan in some heaters helps transfer the thermal energy into the room.

INTEGRATE History

Thermodynamics and the Steam Engine Carnot's great contribution that gave birth to thermodynamics was the idea that the efficiency of any engine, such as a steam engine, that relies on the transfer of thermal energy to do work is limited by the temperature difference between the "hot" input and "cold" output. The greater the ratio of input to output temperatures (measured on the Kelvin scale), the greater the engine's ideal efficiency. However, no engine can convert 100% of its input thermal energy to useful work. To do so would require that the cold output temperature be 0K, or absolute zero.

Cultural Diversity

Home Heating Have students find out how the Inuit use convection currents to regulate temperature inside igloos. The Inuit make the entranceways to their igloos lower than the inside. Because cold air is denser than warm air, the coldest air in the igloo sinks into the entranceway, leaving the warmer air inside the igloo. L3 LS **Logical-Mathematical**

Science Journal

Heating Systems Have students investigate the types of heating that are common in your area and why they are common. Find information about initial cost, efficiency, and maintenance requirements of different systems. Have students write their findings in their Science Journals. L2 LS **Linguistic**

Inquiry Lab

Passive Solar Heating

Purpose To research, explore, and observe passive solar heating, have students design and construct box models of buildings that include design elements for passive solar heating. L2 ELL LS **Kinesthetic**

Possible Materials small boxes such as shoe boxes, cardboard, assorted sheets of colored paper, clear sheeting such as overhead transparencies, insulating materials, resources to research passive solar heating

Estimated Time two weeks outside class time

Teaching Strategies

- Compass orientation of the building can maximize Sun exposure.
- Students should have windows exposed to the Sun to collect solar energy.
- Buildings should be insulated to retain thermal energy.
- Windows should have provisions for blocking the Sun during the summer to maintain comfort in the building.
- The color and type of flooring materials should be considered for thermal energy absorption.
- Students may provide a way to test their design. Have students take temperature measurements to show that a comfortable temperature is maintained.
- Students may find other design elements that should be included during their research.

For additional inquiry activities, see Science Inquiry Lab Manual.

Reading Check

Answer According to the first law of thermodynamics, the increase in thermal energy of the cool object equals the decrease of thermal energy of the warm object.

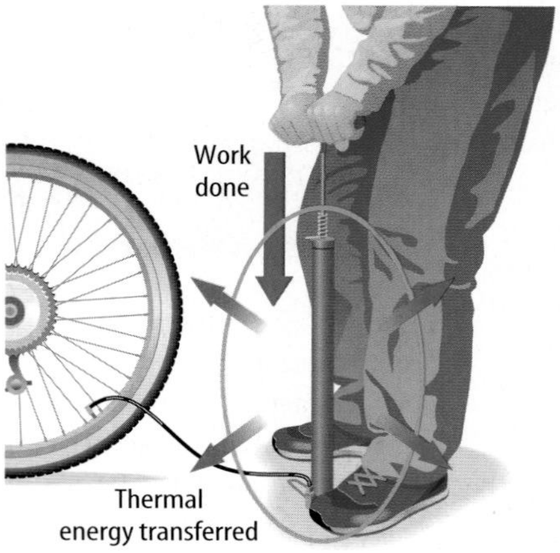

Figure 20 A bicycle air pump can be a system. Work is done on the system by pushing down on the handle. This causes the pump to become warm and thermal energy is transferred from the system to the air around it.
Infer *if the air pump is an open or a closed system.*

The First Law of Thermodynamics According to the **first law of thermodynamics,** the increase in thermal energy of a system equals the work done on the system plus the thermal energy transferred to the system. Doing work on a system is a way of adding energy to a system, as shown in **Figure 20.** As a result, the temperature of a system can be increased by heating the system, doing work on the system, or both. The first law of thermodynamics is another way of stating the law of conservation of energy. The increase in energy of a system equals the energy added to the system.

Closed and Open Systems A system is an open system if thermal energy flows across the boundary or if work is done across the boundary. The energy of an open system can change. If no thermal energy flows across the boundary and no outside work is done, the system is a closed system. According to the first law of thermodynamics, the thermal energy of a closed system doesn't change. Energy might change form within the system, but the total energy of the system doesn't change.

The Second Law of Thermodynamics When thermal energy flows from a warm object to a cool object, the first law of thermodynamics is satisfied. The increase in thermal energy of the cool object equals the decrease in thermal energy of the warm object. Energy is neither created or destroyed.

Reading Check ***How does the flow of thermal energy from a warm object to a cool object satisfy the first law of thermodynamics?***

Can thermal energy flow spontaneously from a cool object to a warm object? This never happens, but it doesn't violate the first law of thermodynamics. The first law requires only that energy be conserved. The first law would be satisfied if the decrease in thermal energy of the cool object equaled the increase in thermal energy of the warm object.

However, the flow of thermal energy spontaneously from a cool object to a warm object never happens because it violates another law—the second law of thermodynamics. One way to state the **second law of thermodynamics** is that it is impossible for thermal energy to flow from a cool object to a warmer object unless work is done. For example, if you hold an ice cube in your hand, no work is done. As a result, thermal energy flows only from your warmer hand to the colder ice.

Science Online

Topic: Solar Heating
Visit gpescience.com for Web links to information about heating systems that use solar energy to heat buildings.

Activity Draw a diagram showing how an active solar heating system is used to heat a home.

Differentiated Instruction

Challenge The statement that thermal energy can be made to flow from the cool refrigerator to the warm room only if work is done is one way to state the second law of thermodynamics. Have students find out who first stated the second law of thermodynamics and how he stated it. Have students write a brief report. The second law of thermodynamics was first stated by Rudolph Clausius and Lord Kelvin and was based on work done by Sadi Carnot. Clausius' version of the second law says it is impossible for any self-acting machine unaided by external agency to convey heat from a body at one temperature to another at a higher temperature. L2 LS **Linguistic**

274 CHAPTER 9 Heat and States of Matter

Converting Thermal Energy to Work

If you give a book sitting on a table a push, the book slides for a while and then stops. Friction between the book and the table converts all of the work you did on the book into thermal energy. Is it possible to convert thermal energy completely into work? Even though this process wouldn't violate the first law of thermodynamics, it violates the second law of thermodynamics. No device or process can convert thermal energy completely into work.

Heat Engines A device that converts thermal energy into work is called a heat engine. A car's engine is a heat engine. It converts some of the thermal energy produced by burning fuel into work that causes the car to move. However, only about 25 percent of the thermal energy in the burning fuel is converted into work. The rest of the thermal energy is transferred to the air surrounding the engine. When thermal energy is converted into work, some thermal energy always is transferred to the surroundings.

Internal Combustion Engines The heat engine in a car is an internal combustion engine, in which fuel is burned inside the engine in chambers or cylinders. Each cylinder contains a piston that moves up and down. Each up or down movement of the piston is called a stroke. Automobile and diesel engines make four different strokes, as shown in **Figure 21.**

Figure 21 The up-and-down movement of a piston in an automobile engine consists of four separate strokes. The four strokes form a cycle that is repeated many times each second by each piston.

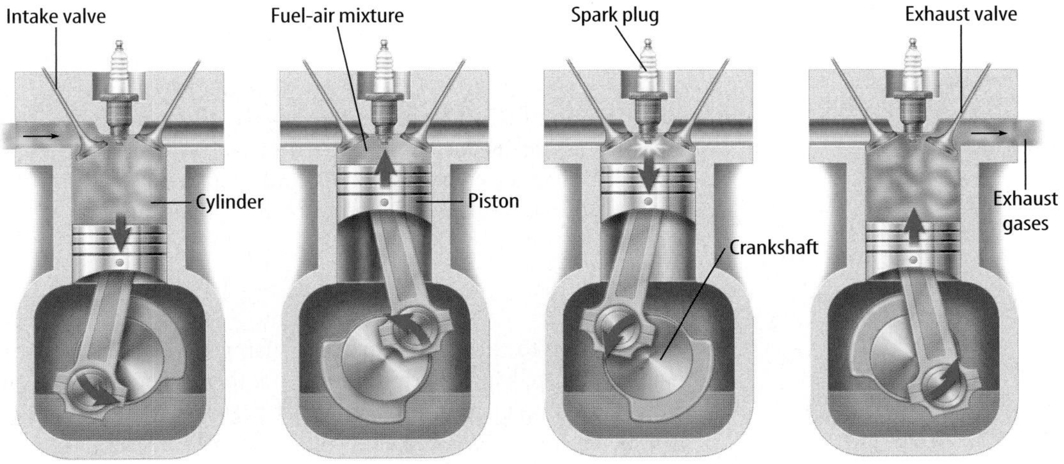

Intake stroke
The intake valve opens as the piston moves downward, drawing gasoline and air into the cylinder.

Compression stroke
The intake valve closes as the piston moves upward, compressing the fuel-air mixture.

Power stroke
A spark plug ignites the fuel-air mixture. The hot gases expand, pushing the piston down.

Exhaust stroke
As the piston moves up, the exhaust valve opens, and the hot gases are pushed out of the cylinder.

Fun Fact

In engines with several cylinders, the piston in each cylinder goes through a four-stroke cycle. However, at any given time, the pistons in the various cylinders are in different positions.

Discussion

Types of Engines Would you prefer to own a car with a four-cylinder, six-cylinder, or eight-cylinder engine? Why? Answers will vary and may include concerns about fuel use, acceleration, and power going uphill. L2 LS **Logical-Mathematical**

Activity

Invention's Impact Have students write short paragraphs in their Science Journals about the impact of the internal combustion engine on everyday life. Afterward, have the class generate a list of all the applications of this technology they wrote about. The list could include cars, tractors, lawn mowers, cement tracks, moving vans, and airplanes. L2 LS **Linguistic**

Visual Learning

Figure 21 Read aloud the descriptions of each of the cycles in a four-cycle engine. Ask students to trace on the diagram each process as you read it. L2 LS **Auditory-Musical**

Fun Fact

The maximum efficiency possible for any heat engine is called the ideal efficiency and depends only on the highest and lowest temperatures in the engine cycle. The ideal efficiency of a four-cycle gasoline engine, such as those used in cars, is between 40 and 50%. This means that regardless of the engine's design, it can never be more efficient than this.

Teacher FYI

Blood Flow To regulate body temperature, blood flow to the skin is automatically adjusted. When the environment is too cold, blood is drawn away from the skin and sent to more vital organs. When the environment is hot, more blood is sent to the skin so that its thermal energy can be exchanged with the environment.

Make a Model

Heat Pumps Have students work in small groups to look up heat pumps and then draw two diagrams: one showing how a heat pump cools during warm weather, and the second showing how a heat pump warms during cool weather. L2 LS **Visual-Spatial** COOP LEARN

Reading Strategy

Sequence Have students read the passage Refrigerators and then write the sequence of coolant flowing through the parts of a refrigerator. Tell students that sequenced text sometimes has signal words, such as *first*, *second*, *third*, *next*, *then*, and *finally*. Have students write the steps of the cooling cycle using appropriate sequencing words.

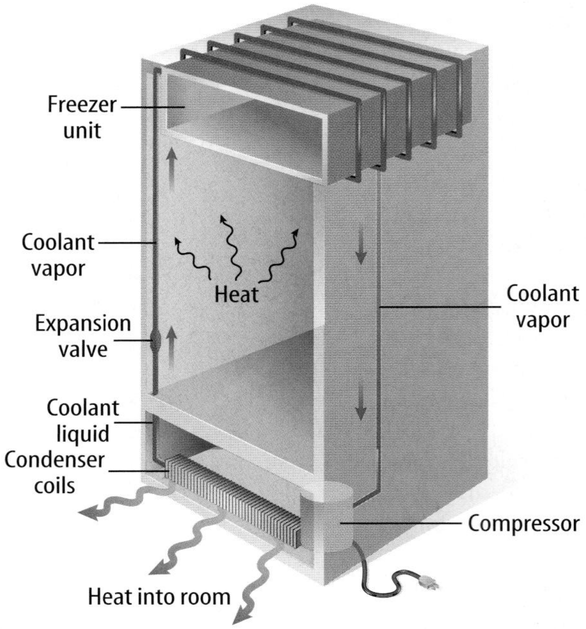

Figure 22 A refrigerator does work on the coolant in order to transfer thermal energy from inside the refrigerator to the warmer air outside. Work is done when the compressor compresses the coolant, causing its temperature to increase.

Moving Thermal Energy

How do refrigerators stay cold? The second law of thermodynamics prevents thermal energy from spontaneously flowing from inside the refrigerator to the warmer room. However, the second law of thermodynamics allows thermal energy to be moved from a cold area to a warmer area if work is done in the process. A refrigerator does work as it moves thermal energy from inside the refrigerator to the warmer room. The energy to do the work comes from the electrical energy the refrigerator obtains from an electric outlet.

Refrigerators A refrigerator contains a coolant that is pumped through pipes in the refrigerator. The coolant is a special substance that evaporates at a low temperature. **Figure 22** shows how a refrigerator operates. Liquid coolant is pumped through an expansion valve and changes into a gas. When the coolant changes to a gas, it cools. The cold gas is pumped through pipes inside the refrigerator. The coolant absorbs thermal energy and the inside of the refrigerator cools.

The gas then is pumped to a compressor that does work by compressing the gas. This makes the coolant gas warmer than the room. The warm gas then flows through condenser coils. There thermal energy flows from the gas to the air in the room. Some of this thermal energy is the thermal energy the coolant gas absorbed from inside the refrigerator. As the gas gives off thermal energy, it cools and changes into a liquid. Then liquid coolant is changed back into a gas, and the cycle is repeated.

Entropy

According to the laws of thermodynamics, work can be converted completely into thermal energy, but thermal energy can't be converted completely into work. What prevents thermal energy from being converted completely into work? The answer has to do with entropy. **Entropy** is a measure of how spread out, or dispersed, energy is. Entropy increases when energy becomes more spread out and less concentrated. Converting thermal energy completely into work causes energy to become less spread out and more concentrated. As a result, entropy decreases.

Differentiated Instruction

English-Language Learners To help students understand the refrigeration cycle, have them construct a simple diagram or schematic of the process. Students should identify where heat transfers occur. L2 ELL LS **Visual-Spatial**

Post Reading

Cooperative Groups Have students form groups of four or five. Ask for volunteers who feel they understand the Internal Combustion Engines passage to lead their group in a discussion or explanation of the internal combustion engine. Ask them to talk about why some cars have four, six or eight cylinders.

Entropy Always Increases All events that occur, such as the production of work in an automobile engine, must obey the entropy principle. According to the entropy principle, all events that occur cause the entropy of the universe to increase. This means that all events cause energy to spread out and become less concentrated. **Figure 23** shows how the potential energy stored in a ball becomes less concentrated when the ball is dropped and hits the ground.

How does an automobile engine cause entropy to increase? The energy source in an automobile engine is the chemical potential energy concentrated in the gasoline in the fuel tank. When gasoline is burned in the cylinders, 75 percent of the thermal energy produced is not converted into work, but spreads out into the air surrounding the car. Because energy becomes more spread out, entropy increases. However, the energy that becomes spread out is no longer useable. Any event that occurs causes the amount of useable energy to decrease.

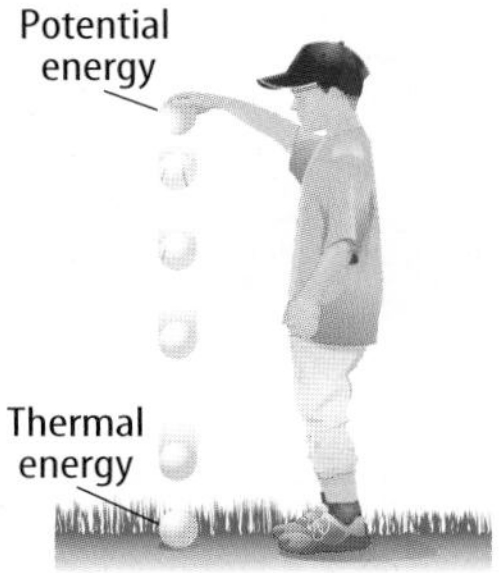

Figure 23 When the ball hits the ground, the potential energy it initially had is converted into thermal energy. This thermal energy spreads out and becomes less concentrated. This causes entropy to increase.

section 4 review

Summary

Heating Systems

- A forced-air heating system uses a fan to force air heated by a furnace through a system of ducts.
- Heating systems transfer thermal energy to rooms by conduction and convection.

Thermodynamics

- The first law of thermodynamics states that the increase in thermal energy of a system equals the work done on the system plus the thermal energy added to the system.
- One way to state the second law of thermodynamics is that thermal energy will not flow from a hot to a cold object unless work is done.

Converting Thermal Energy to Work

- The second law of thermodynamics states that thermal energy cannot be converted completely into work.
- Entropy is a measure of how spread out or dispersed energy is. Entropy increases when thermal energy is produced in an energy transformation.
- According to the entropy principle, all events that occur cause the entropy of the universe to increase. As a result, the amount of usable energy decreases.

Self Check

1. **Explain** how the thermal energy of a closed system changes with time.
2. **Compare and contrast** a forced-air heating system with a radiator system.
3. **Explain** whether or not a heat engine could be made 100 percent efficient by eliminating friction.
4. **Explain** Use the entropy principle to explain why thermal energy can never be converted completely into work.
5. **Think Critically** Suppose you vigorously shake a bottle of fruit juice. Predict how the temperature of the juice will change. Explain your reasoning.

Applying Math

6. **Calculate Change in Thermal Energy** You push down on the handle of a bicycle pump with a force of 20 N. The handle moves 0.3 m, and the pump does not absorb or release any thermal energy. What is the change in thermal energy of the bicycle pump as a result of the work you did on it?
7. **Calculate Work** The thermal energy released when a gallon of gasoline is burned in a car's engine is 140 million J. If the engine is 25 percent efficient, how much work does it do when one gallon of gasoline is burned?

3 Assess

DAILY INTERVENTION

Check for Understanding

Logical-Mathematical Have students work in small groups to think of as many ways as they can to keep a house warmer in the winter and then categorize those ways according to energy source. L2 IS COOP LEARN

Reteach

Four-Stroke Engine Have students make flash cards with the names of the strokes of the four-stroke cycle of an internal combustion engine. On the reverse side of the card, have them write descriptions of that stroke. Partners can then test each other by shuffling the cards and sequencing them by both name and description. L2 IS **Linguistic** COOP LEARN

Assessment

Portfolio Have students make posters or drawings showing thermal energy flow in any of the heating or cooling systems or engines studied. Some may be simpler than others, but all should show areas of high and low temperature and direction of thermal energy flow. Use **Performance Assessment in the Science Classroom**, p. 177. L2 IS **Visual-Spatial**

section 4 review

1. In a closed system, no thermal energy flows across the boundary and no work is done across the boundary. The thermal energy stays constant.
2. Both systems rely on fuel as the source of energy. In a forced air system, the burning fuel heats the air directly which is then blown to the areas to be heated. In a radiator system, the fuel heats water that is pumped to the heated areas, which then heats the air in the room.
3. The second law of thermodynamics states that it is impossible to build a device that is 100% efficient. Increasing the temperature of the burning gases can increase the efficiency, but the engine will never be 100% efficient.
4. Complete conversion of thermal energy to work would concentrate energy rather than spreading it out, a violation of the fact that entropy, or the diffuseness of energy, always increases.
5. The temperature of the juice will increase because you do work on the juice as you shake it.
6. $W = Fd = (20\ N)(0.3\ m) = 6\ N\ m = 6\ J$
7. $(0.25)(140{,}000{,}000\ J) = 35{,}000{,}000\ J$

BENCH TESTED

Video Lab available for this Lab.

Real-World Problem

Purpose Students will observe how thermal energy is transferred by conduction in liquids and gases L2 LS **Kinesthetic**

Process Skills collect data, measure, make and use tables, record data, make and use graphs, interpret data

Time Required 80 minutes

Alternate Materials The knife used for cutting the foam cup should have a thin blade. A kitchen paring knife works well, but scissors are an acceptable substitute.

Safety Precautions Students should be careful while handling hot liquids. Caution them to use care while cutting with the knife. Number the knives and collect them before the end of class.

Procedure

Teaching Strategies

- Have students work in small groups for this lab. Two students can call out the temperature readings as another student records them.
- Remind students that thermal energy transfer by conduction occurs by touch. The particles have to touch in order for conduction to occur.

LAB

Conduction in Gases

Goals
- **Measure** temperature changes in air near a heat source.
- **Observe** conduction of heat in air.

Materials
thermometers (3)
foam cups (2)
400-mL beakers (2)
burner or hot plate
paring knife
thermal mitts (2)

Safety Precautions

WARNING: *Use care when handling hot water. Pour hot water using both hands.*

Real-World Problem

Does smog occur where you live? If so, you may have experienced a temperature inversion. Usually the Sun warms the ground and the air above it. When the air near the ground is warmer than the air above, convection occurs. This convection also carries smoke and other gases emitted by cars, chimneys, and smokestacks upward into the atmosphere. If the air near the ground is colder than the air above, convection does not occur. Then smoke and other pollutants can be trapped near the ground, sometimes forming smog. How do the insulating properties of air cause a temperature inversion to occur?

Procedure

1. Using the paring knife, carefully cut the bottom from one foam cup.
2. Use a pencil or pen to poke holes about 2 cm from the top and bottom of each foam cup, as shown in the photo.
3. Turn both cups upside down, and poke the ends of the thermometers through the upper holes and lower holes, so both thermometers are supported horizontally. The bulb end of each thermometer should extend into the middle of the bottomless cup.

Alternative Inquiry Lab

Weather Research To extend this lab into an Inquiry Lab, have students research the effects of convection of energy on weather patterns. Topics to research may include explaining typical local weather patterns, tornados, hurricanes, Chinook winds, trade winds, ocean currents, weather in relation to geographic features (such as mountains or plains), the ocean's effect on weather, hail storms, cloud formations, or any other suitable topic. Have students explain the phenomenon using an experiment, poster, model, or computer-generated presentation and written or oral descriptions.

4. Heat about 350 mL of water to about 80°C in one of the beakers.
5. Place an empty 400-mL beaker on top of the bottomless cup. Record the temperatures of the two thermometers in a data table like the one shown here.
6. Add about 100 mL of hot water to the empty beaker. After one minute, record the temperatures of the thermometers in your data table.
7. Continue to record the temperatures every minute for 10 min. Add hot water as needed to keep the temperature of the water at about 80°C.

Air Temperatures in Foam Cup

Time (min)	Upper Thermometer (°C)	Lower Thermometer (°C)
0		
1		
2	Measured temperatures will vary.	
3		
4		
5		

Analyze Your Data

1. **Graph** the temperatures measured by the upper and lower thermometers on the same graph. Make the vertical axis the temperature and the horizontal axis the time.
2. **Calculate** the total temperature change for each thermometer by subtracting the initial temperature from the final temperature.
3. **Calculate** the average rate of temperature change for each thermometer by dividing the total temperature change by 10 min.

Conclude and Apply

1. **Explain** whether convection can occur in the foam cup if it's being heated from the top.
2. **Describe** how heat was transferred through the air in the foam cup.
3. **Explain** why the average rates of temperature change were different for the two thermometers.

Communicating Your Data

Compare your results with other students in your class. **Identify** the factors that caused the average rate of temperature change to be different for different groups.

Analyze Your Data

Expected Outcome The heat source is at the top of the container. Thermal energy transfer by convection cannot occur, therefore the thermal energy transfer must occur by conduction.

Answers to Questions

1. Check students' graphs.
2. Answers will vary. Check students' work.
3. Answers will vary. Check students' work.

Error Analysis Have each group compare its results with those of another group. If the data disagree, have students list reasons for the discrepancy.

Conclude and Apply

1. No; if the cup is heated from the top, the air at the top becomes warmer and less dense than the air below. As a result, this air does not sink and transfer thermal energy to the cooler air below.
2. Because convection could not occur, thermal energy was transferred by conduction in the air.
3. The thermometer at the top was closer to the hot water, so it took less time for thermal energy to be transferred to the air around it. Thermal energy had to be transferred by conduction to the lower thermometer. Because thermal energy moves slowly through air, it took more time for thermal energy to reach this thermometer and the temperature change of this thermometer occurred more slowly.

Assessment

Oral Ask students to use the kinetic theory to explain why thermal energy transfers in the following order: from fastest to slowest solids, liquids, and gases. Use **Performance Assessment in the Science Classroom,** p. 143.

Communicating Your Data

Have students compare results with other groups and discuss differences noted. Why might these differences have occurred?

Content Background

The energy in the Sun is generated by the fusion of hydrogen atoms to form helium. Since the Sun is composed primarily of hydrogen atoms, the fuel for this reaction is readily available. The energy radiated from the Sun provides Earth with an environment that can support life as we know it. The Sun provides energy for photosynthesis to occur, which provides a food source for many organisms. It provides thermal energy, which combined with our atmosphere and water sources, provides a moderate temperature range that supports life. Despite all of these uses of solar energy, a large portion of the energy that arrives on Earth's surface is not used. Scientists are developing technology to enable people to use more of the Sun's energy.

Activity

Solar Energy Have students research the various ways people use solar energy. Students should make oral presentations to share their information with their class. L2 IN **Auditory-Musical**

Differentiated Instruction

Challenge Solar energy from the Sun travels at a speed of 299,274 km/s. Express this number in scientific notation using three significant digits. 3.00×10^5 km/s Express this number in m/s using three significant digits and scientific notation. 3.00×10^8 m/s L3

SCIENCE Stats

Surprising Thermal Energy

Did you know...

. . . The average amount of solar energy that reaches the United States each year is about 600 times greater than the nation's annual energy demands.

. . . When a space shuttle reenters Earth's atmosphere at more than 28,000 km/h, its outer surface is heated by friction to nearly 1,650°C. This temperature is high enough to melt steel.

. . . A lightning bolt heats the air in its path to temperatures of about 25,000°C. That's about 4 times hotter than the average temperature on the surface of the Sun.

Applying Math

1. The highest recorded temperature on Earth is 58°C and the lowest is −89°C. What is the range between the highest and lowest recorded temperatures?
2. What is the average temperature of the surface of the Sun? Draw a bar graph comparing the temperature of a lightning bolt to the temperature of the surface of the Sun.
3. The Sun is almost 150 million km from Earth. How long does it take solar energy to reach Earth if the energy travels at 300,000 km/s?

Applying Math

Teaching Strategies

- Review with students how to find range for question 1.
- Discuss which units should be used to mark the *y*–axis on the bar graph for question 2.
- Provide graph paper to assist the students with question 2.

Answers

1. 147°C
2. 6,250°C; Check students' graphs.
3. 500 s = 8 min, 20 s

Reviewing Main Ideas

Section 1 Temperature and Thermal Energy

1. According to the kinetic theory, all matter is made of constantly moving particles that collide without losing energy.
2. The temperature of a material is a measure of the average kinetic energy of the particles in the material.
3. The thermal energy of an object is the total kinetic and potential energies of the particles in the object.
4. Heat is thermal energy that flows from a higher to a lower temperature.
5. The specific heat is the amount of energy needed to raise the temperature of 1 kg of a substance by 1°C.

Section 2 States of Matter

1. The states of matter are solid, liquid, gas, and plasma.
2. Changes of state can be interpreted in terms of the kinetic theory of matter.
3. Most matter expands when heated and contracts when cooled. An expansion joint allows concrete to expand and contract without damage.

Section 3 Transferring Thermal Energy

1. Conduction occurs when thermal energy is transferred by collisions between particles. Matter is not transferred.
2. Convection occurs in a fluid as warmer and cooler fluid move from place to place.
3. Radiation is the transfer of energy by electromagnetic waves. Radiation can transfer energy through empty space.
4. Thermal energy flows more quickly in materials that are conductors than in insulators.
5. Some insulating materials contain pockets of air that reduce the flow of thermal energy.

Section 4 Using Thermal Energy

1. According to the first law of thermodynamics, the increase in the thermal energy of a system equals the work done and the amount of thermal energy added to the system.

2. The second law of thermodynamics states that thermal energy cannot flow from a colder to a hotter temperature unless work is done.
3. Any event that occurs decreases the amount of usable energy and increases the entropy of the universe.

FOLDABLES™ Use the Foldable that you made at the beginning of this chapter to help you review thermal energy.

chapter 9 Study Guide

Reviewing Main Ideas

Summary statements can be used by students to review the major concepts of the chapter.

Science Online

Visit gpescience.com
More Section Review
Interactive Tutor
Vocabulary PuzzleMaker
More Chapter Review
Standardized Test Practice

Assessment Transparency

For additional assessment questions, use the *Assessment Transparency* located in the transparency book.

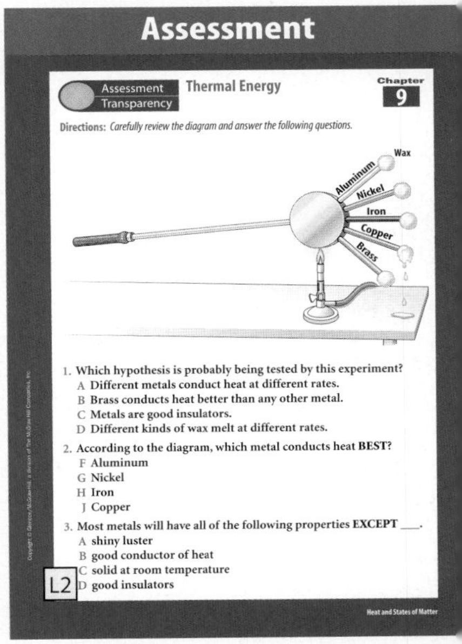

Assessment

Assessment Transparency — Thermal Energy — Chapter 9

Directions: *Carefully review the diagram and answer the following questions.*

1. Which hypothesis is probably being tested by this experiment?
   A Different metals conduct heat at different rates.
   B Brass conducts heat better than any other metal.
   C Metals are good insulators.
   D Different kinds of wax melt at different rates.
2. According to the diagram, which metal conducts heat BEST?
   F Aluminum
   G Nickel
   H Iron
   J Copper
3. Most metals will have all of the following properties EXCEPT ___.
   A shiny luster
   B good conductor of heat
   C solid at room temperature
   D good insulators

L2

Heat and States of Matter

FOLDABLES™ Have students use their Foldables to review the content of the chapter. On the back of the paper, have students write a paragraph comparing and contrasting temperature and thermal energy.

Using Vocabulary

1. heat
2. Temperature
3. specific heat
4. conduction
5. Kinetic theory
6. radiation

Checking Concepts

7. D
8. C
9. B
10. C
11. C
12. D
13. D
14. A
15. B

Interpreting Graphics

16. See student page.

chapter 9 Review

Using Vocabulary

conduction p. 266	kinetic theory p. 254
convection p. 267	plasma p. 261
entropy p. 276	radiation p. 269
first law of thermodynamics p. 274	second law of thermodynamics p. 274
heat p. 257	specific heat p. 257
heat of fusion p. 262	temperature p. 255
heat of vaporization p. 262	thermal energy p. 256
Kelvin p. 255	thermal insulator p. 270

Complete each statement using a word or phrase from the vocabulary list above.

1. Thermal energy that is transferred from warmer to cooler materials is ________.
2. ________ is a measure of the average kinetic energy of the particles in a material.
3. The energy required to raise the temperature of 1 kg of a material 1°C is a material's ________.
4. In ________, thermal energy is transferred by the collisions between particles, not by the transfer of matter.
5. ________ is the theory used to explain the behavior of particles in matter.
6. The transfer of energy by electromagnetic waves is ________.

Checking Concepts

Choose the word or phrase that best answers the question.

7. Which is NOT a method of heat transfer?
   A) conduction
   B) convection
   C) radiation
   D) specific heat
8. Which state of matter is made of electrically charged particles?
   A) gas
   B) liquid
   C) plasma
   D) solid
9. During which phase of a four-stroke engine are waste gases removed?
   A) combustion stroke
   B) exhaust stroke
   C) intake stroke
   D) power stroke

Use the table below to answer question 10.

Latent Heats

Substance	Heat of Fusion (J/g)	Heat of Vaporization (J/g)
Ethanol	109	838
Water	334	2,258
Aluminum	397	10,900
Propane	61	387

10. Which material would require the least amount of energy to change 1 kg from a solid to a liquid?
    A) aluminum
    B) ethanol
    C) propane
    D) water
11. Which of the following is a measure of the average kinetic energy of the particles in an object?
    A) potential energy
    B) specific heat
    C) temperature
    D) thermal energy
12. Which of these is NOT used to calculate change in thermal energy?
    A) mass
    B) specific heat
    C) temperature change
    D) volume
13. Which of the following processes does NOT require the presence of particles of matter?
    A) combustion
    B) conduction
    C) convection
    D) radiation

Vocabulary PuzzleMaker gpescience.com

Use the ExamView® Pro Test Bank CD-ROM to:

- create multiple versions of tests
- create modified tests with one mouse click for inclusion students
- edit existing questions and add your own questions
- build tests aligned with state standards using built-in State Curriculum Tags
- change English tests to Spanish with one mouse click and vice versa

14. Which of the following is the name for thermal energy that is transferred only from a higher temperature to a lower temperature?
A) heat
B) kinetic energy
C) potential energy
D) solar energy

15. According to the entropy principle, any event that occurs in the universe must cause which of the following to happen?
A) energy to become more concentrated
B) energy to become less concentrated
C) total amount of energy to increase
D) total amount of energy to decrease

Interpreting Graphics

16. Copy and complete this concept map.

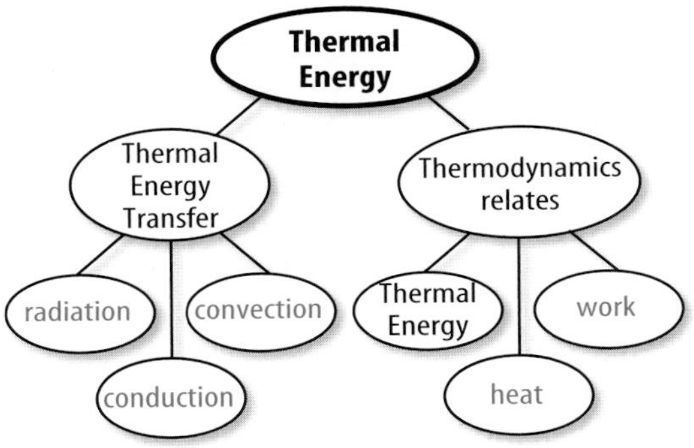

Thinking Critically

17. **Explain** On a hot day a friend suggests that you can make your kitchen cooler by leaving the refrigerator door open. Explain whether leaving the refrigerator door open would cause the air temperature in the kitchen to decrease.

18. **Explain** Which has the greater amount of thermal energy, one liter of water at 50°C or two liters of water at 50°C?

19. **Explain** whether or not the following statement is true: If the thermal energy of an object increases, the temperature of the object must also increase.

20. **Predict** Suppose a beaker of water is heated from the top. Explain which is more likely to occur in the water—thermal energy transfer by conduction or convection.

21. **Classify** Order the events that occur in the removal of thermal energy from an object by a refrigerator. Draw the complete cycle, from the placing of a warm object in the refrigerator to the changes in the coolant.

Applying Math

Use the table below to answer questions 22 to 24.

Specific Heat of Materials

Material	Specific Heat (J/kg°C)
Water	4,184
Copper	385
Silver	235
Graphite	710
Iron	450

22. **Calculate Thermal Energy** How much thermal energy is needed to raise the temperature of 4.0 kg of water from 25°C to 75°C?

23. **Calculate Temperature Change** How does the temperature of 33.0 g of graphite change when it absorbs 350 J of thermal energy?

24. **Calculate Mass** A certain mass of water gains 1,673 J of thermal energy when its temperature increases by 2.0°C. What is the mass of the water?

chapter 9 Review

Thinking Critically

17. It would not cool the kitchen. The thermal energy from the kitchen that is transferred to the refrigerator coolant would be transferred back to the kitchen from the condenser coils.

18. Thermal energy is the sum of the kinetic and potential energy of the water molecules. Doubling the amount of water will double the amount of thermal energy.

19. It is not true. The increase in thermal energy may increase the potential energy so that the temperature remains unchanged.

20. If the water is heated from the top, conduction will occur instead of convection. The warm water on the top is less dense than the cooler water below and will not sink.

21. Thermal energy transferred from the warm object to the coolant in the refrigerator, coolant is compressed and the temperature rises, thermal energy transferred from the warm coolant to the outside air, the coolant expands as it passes through expansion valve and cools.

Applying Math

Math Standards

National: 2, 9

22. $Q = m(T_{final} - T_{initial})C$
$= (4.0\ kg)(50°C)(4{,}184 J/kg°C)$
$= 836{,}800\ J$

23. increases by 14.9°C

24. $1{,}673\ J = m(2°C)(4.184\ J/kg°C)$
$m = 0.20\ kg$

✓ Assessment Resources

Reproducible Masters

Chapter *Fast File* Resources
Chapter Review, pp. 39–40
Chapter Tests, pp. 41–44
Assessment Transparency Activity, p. 53

Glencoe Science Web site
Chapter Review Test
Standardized Test Practice

Glencoe Technology
Assessment Transparency
Exam*View*® Pro Testmaker
MindJogger Videoquiz
Interactive Chalkboard

Answer Sheet An answer sheet can be found at **gpescience.com**.

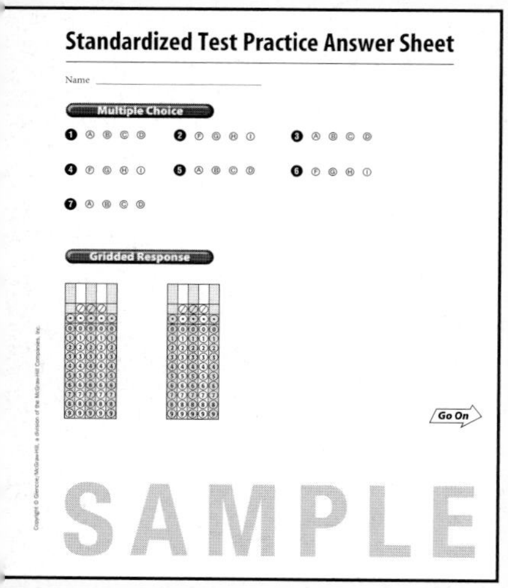
Standardized Test Practice Answer Sheet

Name

Multiple Choice

Gridded Response

Go On

SAMPLE

Multiple Choice

1. C
2. B
3. A
4. A
5. A
6. A

chapter 9 Standardized Test Practice

Record your answers on the answer sheet provided by your teacher or on a sheet of paper.

Multiple Choice

Use the graph below to answer questions 1 and 2.

State Changes of Water

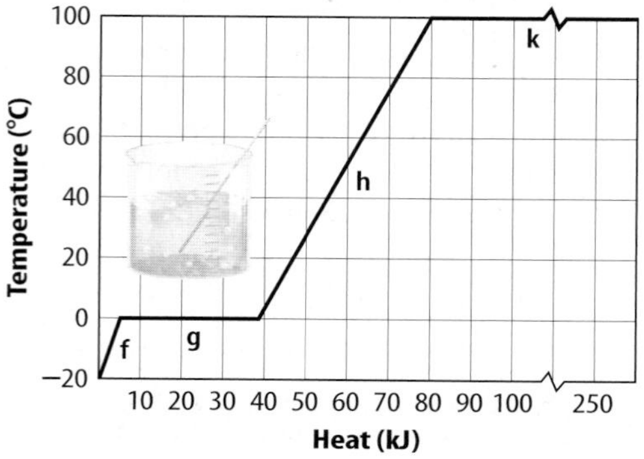

1. At which points on the graph is the average kinetic energy of the water molecules increasing?

A. F and G

B. G and K

C. F and H

D. H and K

2. At which points on the graph is the potential energy of the water molecules increasing, but the average kinetic energy is not?

A. F and G

B. G and K

C. F and H

D. H and K

Test-Taking Tip

Read Carefully Read all choices before answering the question.

3. Which is the term for the amount of energy required for 1 kg of a liquid at its boiling point to become a gas?

A. heat of vaporization

B. diffusion

C. heat of fusion

D. thermal energy

Use the table below to answer questions 4 and 5.

Material	Specific Heat [J/(kg °C)]
Copper	385
Gold	449
Lead	129
Tin	228
Zinc	388

4. According to the table above, a 2-kg block of which of the following materials would require 898 J of heat to increase its temperature by 1°C?

A. gold

B. lead

C. tin

D. zinc

5. Which of the following materials would require the most heat to raise a 5-kg sample of the material from 10°C to 50°C?

A. gold

B. lead

C. tin

D. zinc

Use the figure below to answer question 6.

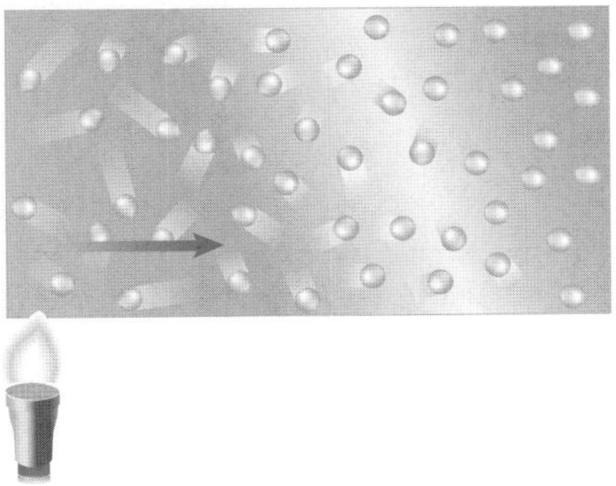

6. The illustration above shows the particles in a material being heated at one end. Thermal energy is transferred from the warmer part of the material to the cooler part. What heat transfer process is occurring in the material?

A. conduction

B. convection

C. radiation

D. entropy

Gridded Response

7. The temperature of a 24.5-g block of aluminum decreases from 30.0°C to 21.5°C. If aluminum has a specific heat of 897 J/(kg °C), what is the change in thermal energy, measured in joules, of the block of aluminum?

8. The difference between the boiling point and the freezing point of potassium is 695.72 K. What is this difference in degrees on the Celsius temperature scale?

Short Response

9. Explain how the temperature and thermal energy of an object are related.

10. What property of water makes it useful as a coolant?

Extended Response

Use the figure below to answer question 11.

11. The figure shows a calorimeter that is used to measure the specific heat of materials.

PART A Explain why it is necessary to measure the temperature change of the water when using a calorimeter to measure the specific heat of a material.

PART B Explain why the calorimeter must be insulated from its surroundings.

12. Explain how changes in a fluid's density enable convection currents to occur.

Gridded Response

7. Q = (0.0245 kg) (21.5°C − 30.0°C)(897 J/(kg °C)) = -187 J

8. 695.72

Short Response

9. Temperature is a measure of the average kinetic energy of particles in a substance. Thermal energy is the combined kinetic and potential energies due to the random motion of the particles in a substance.

10. It has a high specific heat, meaning it can absorb thermal energy without a large change in temperature.

Extended Response

11. **Part A:** Measuring the temperature change and mass of the water allows the calculation of the amount of thermal energy transferred between the sample and the water. The thermal energy transferred to the water equals the thermal energy transferred from the sample.

Part B: Insulating the calorimeter minimizes the thermal energy lost to the surrounding air. Lost thermal energy would lower the measured temperature change in the water and lead to a low value for the sample's specific heat.

12. Convection is the transfer of energy in a fluid by the movement of the heated particles. When a fluid is heated, the particles move faster. As the particles move faster, they tend to be farther apart. The fluid expands as its temperature increases. The volume of the fluid increases, but its mass remains unchanged. The result is that the density of the fluid decreases. Convection occurs when the warmer, less-dense fluid rises above the cooler, denser fluid. This fluid then cools and sinks when it becomes denser than the surrounding fluid.

Rubrics

For more help evaluating Short- and Extended-Response questions, see the rubrics on p. 9T.

chapter 10 Organizer

Section/Objectives	Standards: National	Standards: State/Local	Labs/Features
Chapter Opener	See pp. 16T–17T for a Key to Standards.		**Launch LAB:** How do waves transfer energy?, p. 287 **Foldables,** p. 287
Section 1 The Nature of Waves 1 session .5 block 1. **Recognize** that waves transfer energy but not matter. 2. **Define** mechanical waves. 3. **Compare and contrast** transverse waves and compressional waves.	National Content Standards: UCP.1–3, UCP.5, A.1, A.2, B.2, B.4, B.5, B.6		**Visualizing Formation of Ocean Waves,** p. 292 **Science Online,** p. 293
Section 2 Wave Properties 2 sessions 1 block 4. **Define** wavelength, frequency, period, and amplitude. 5. **Describe** the relationship between frequency and wavelength. 6. **Explain** how a wave's energy and amplitude are related. 7. **Calculate** wave speed.	National Content Standards: UCP.1–3, UCP.5, A.1, A.2, B.2, B.4, B.6		**MiniLAB:** Observing Wavelength, p. 295 **Integrate Social Studies,** p. 297 **Applying Math:** The Speed of Sound, p. 297 **Lab:** Wave, Speed and Tension, p. 300
Section 3 The Behavior of Waves 3 sessions 1.5 blocks 8. **State** the law of reflection. 9. **Explain** why waves change direction when they travel from one material to another. 10. **Compare and contrast** refraction and diffraction. 11. **Describe** how waves interfere with each other.	National Content Standards: UCP.1–3, UCP.5, A.1, A.2, B.2, B.4, B.5, B.6, G.3		**Science Online,** p.305 **Integrate Health,** p. 307 **MiniLAB:** Experimenting with Resonance, p. 309 **Lab:** Measuring Wave Properties, pp. 310–311 Video Lab **Science and History:** Making Waves, p. 312

Glencoe Exclusive! StudentWorks Plus TeacherWorks™ All-In-One Planner and Resource Center

Lab Materials	Reproducible Resources	Section Assessment	Technology
Launch Lab: 4 marbles, textbook, pen or pencil	**Chapter *Fast File* Resources** Foldables Worksheet, p. 17 Directed Reading Overview, p. 19 Note-taking Worksheets, pp. 33–35	Glencoe's Assessment Advantage	TeacherWorks includes: • Interactive Teacher Edition • Lesson Planner with calendar • Access to all program blacklines • Correlations to standards • Web links
Need materials? Contact Science Kit at 1-800-828-7777 or www.sciencekit.com.	**Chapter *Fast File* Resources** Transparency Activity, p. 44 Enrichment, p. 30 Reinforcement, p. 27 Directed Reading, p. 20 **Cultural Diversity,** p. 43 **Science Inquiry Labs,** pp. 25–26 **Reading and Writing Skill Activities,** p. 7	Portfolio Assessment, p. 293 Performance Applying Math, p. 293 Content Section Review, p. 293	Section Focus Transparency Interactive Chalkboard CD-ROM StudentWorks Plus
MiniLAB: pie plate, water **Lab:** coiled-spring toys, stopwatch, meterstick	**Chapter *Fast File* Resources** Transparency Activity, p. 45 MiniLAB, p. 3 Enrichment, p. 31 Reinforcement, p. 28 Directed Reading, p. 20 Lab Worksheet, pp. 5–6 Lab Activity, pp. 9–11 Transparency Activity, pp. 47–48 **Mathematics Skill Activities,** p. 9	Portfolio Make a Model, p. 298 Performance MiniLAB, p. 295 Applying Math, p. 297 Applying Math, p. 299 Content Section Review, p. 299	Section Focus Transparency Teaching Transparency Virtual Lab CD-ROM Interactive Chalkboard CD-ROM StudentWorks Plus
MiniLAB: 3 tuning forks, mallet **Lab:** long spring, rope or hose, meterstick, stopwatch	**Chapter *Fast File* Resources** Transparency Activity, p. 46 MiniLAB, p. 4 Enrichment, p. 32 Reinforcement, p. 29 Directed Reading, pp. 21, 22 Lab Worksheet, p. 7–8 Lab Activity, pp. 13–16 **Reading and Writing Skill Activities,** p. 33	Portfolio Differentiated Instruction, p. 303 Curriculum Connection, p. 305 Performance MiniLAB, p. 309 Applying Math, p. 309 Content Section Review, p. 309	Section Focus Transparency Interactive Chalkboard CD-ROM StudentWorks Plus Video Lab

End of Chapter Assessment

Glencoe's Assessment Advantage

Blackline Masters	Technology	Professional Series
Chapter *Fast File* Resources Chapter Review, pp. 37–38 Chapter Tests, pp. 39–42 **Standardized Test Practice,** pp. 44–47	MindJogger Videoquiz Virtual Lab CD-ROM Exam*View*® Pro Testmaker TeacherWorks CD-ROM Interactive Chalkboard CD-ROM	**Performance Assessment in the Science Classroom (PASC)**

Transparencies

Section Focus

SECTION 1 Section Focus Transparency **Wave to the Camera**

How many waves can you pick out in this scene? Is light described as a wave? If you were there when this photograph was taken, you might also mention sound waves.

1. Describe the different waves in this picture.
2. If you are swimming underwater, can you still hear the noises around you? What does this tell you about sound waves?
3. What does light travel through as it goes from the Sun to the eyes of an underwater swimmer?

L2

SECTION 2 Section Focus Transparency **Big Fiddle, Little Fiddle**

Have you ever heard the instruments below played? If you have, you probably noticed that the bass produces a much lower sound than the violin. The difference in the sounds is related to differences in the waves each instrument produces.

1. Name some muscial instruments. How are the instruments you named played?
2. A cello is bigger than a violin but smaller than a bass. How do you think the sound made by a cello compares to the sounds made by violins and basses?

L2

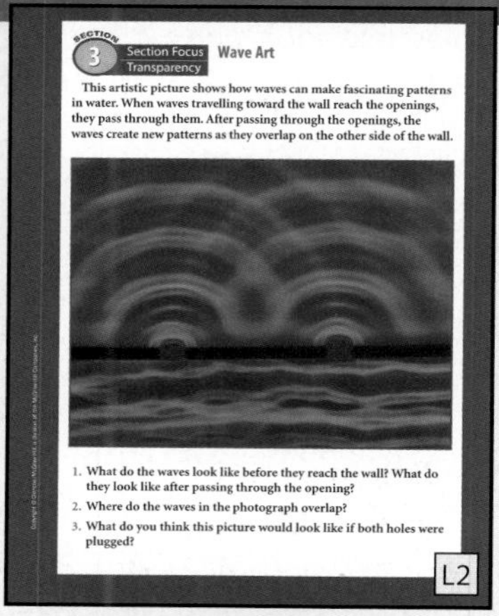
SECTION 3 Section Focus Transparency **Wave Art**

This artistic picture shows how waves can make fascinating patterns in water. When waves travelling toward the wall reach the openings, they pass through them. After passing through the openings, the waves create new patterns as they overlap on the other side of the wall.

1. What do the waves look like before they reach the wall? What do they look like after passing through the opening?
2. Where do the waves in the photograph overlap?
3. What do you think this picture would look like if both holes were plugged?

L2

This is a representation of key blackline masters available in the Teacher Classroom Resources. See Resource Manager boxes within the chapter for additional information.

Assessment

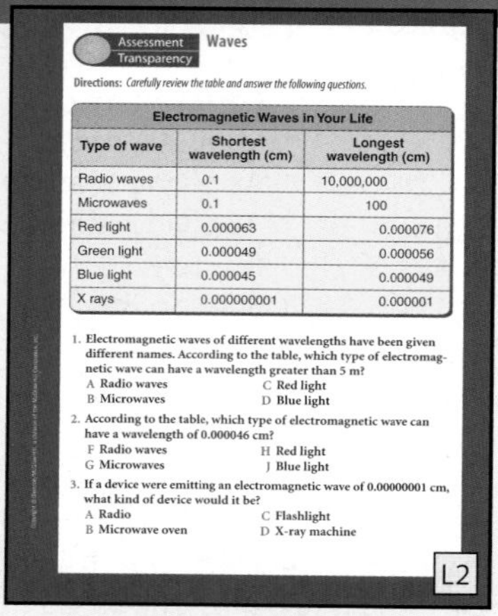
Assessment Transparency **Waves**

Directions: *Carefully review the table and answer the following questions.*

Electromagnetic Waves in Your Life		
Type of wave	Shortest wavelength (cm)	Longest wavelength (cm)
Radio waves	0.1	10,000,000
Microwaves	0.1	100
Red light	0.000063	0.000076
Green light	0.000049	0.000056
Blue light	0.000045	0.000049
X rays	0.000000001	0.000001

1. Electromagnetic waves of different wavelengths have been given different names. According to the table, which type of electromagnetic wave can have a wavelength greater than 5 m?
   A Radio waves C Red light
   B Microwaves D Blue light
2. According to the table, which type of electromagnetic wave can have a wavelength of 0.000046 cm?
   F Radio waves H Red light
   G Microwaves J Blue light
3. If a device were emitting an electromagnetic wave of 0.00000001 cm, what kind of device would it be?
   A Radio C Flashlight
   B Microwave oven D X-ray machine

L2

Teaching

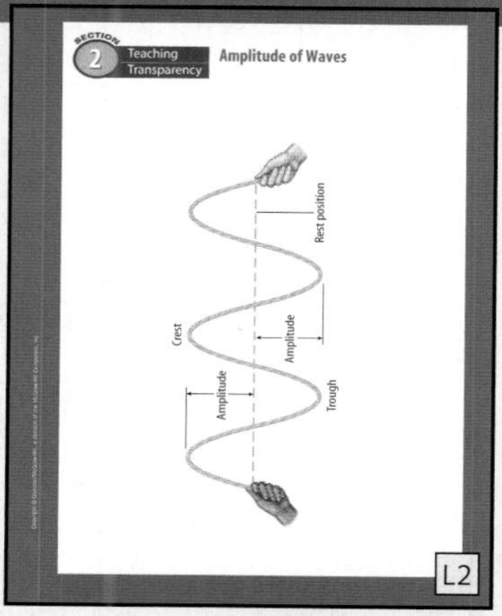
SECTION 2 Teaching Transparency **Amplitude of Waves**

L2

Key to Teaching Strategies

The following designations will help you decide which activities are appropriate for your students.

L1 Level 1 activities should be appropriate for students with learning difficulties.

L2 Level 2 activities should be within the ability range of all students.

L3 Level 3 activities are designed for above-average students.

ELL ELL activities should be within the ability range of English Language Learners.

COOP LEARN Cooperative Learning activities are designed for small group work.

LS Multiple Learning Styles logos, as described on page 12T, are used throughout to indicate strategies that address different learning styles.

P These strategies represent student products that can be placed into a best-work portfolio.

PBL Problem-Based Learning activities apply real-world situations to learning.

Hands-on Activities

Student Text Lab Worksheet

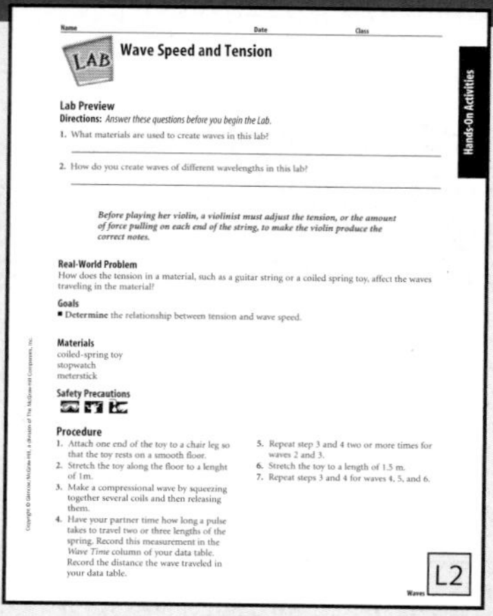
Name Date Class

LAB **Wave Speed and Tension**

Hands-On Activities

Lab Preview
Directions: *Answer these questions before you begin the Lab.*
1. What materials are used to create waves in this lab?
2. How do you create waves of different wavelengths in this lab?

Before playing her violin, a violinist must adjust the tension, or the amount of force pulling on each end of the string, to make the violin produce the correct notes.

Real-World Problem
How does the tension in a material, such as a guitar string or a coiled spring toy, affect the waves traveling in the material?

Goals
- **Determine** the relationship between tension and wave speed.

Materials
coiled-spring toy
stopwatch
meterstick

Safety Precautions

Procedure
1. Attach one end of the toy to a chair leg so that the toy rests on a smooth floor.
2. Stretch the toy along the floor to a lenght of 1m.
3. Make a compressional wave by squeezing together several coils and then releasing them.
4. Have your partner time how long a pulse takes to travel two or three lengths of the spring. Record this measurement in the *Wave Time* column of your data table. Record the distance the wave traveled in your data table.
5. Repeat step 3 and 4 two or more times for waves 2 and 3.
6. Stretch the toy to a length of 1.5 m.
7. Repeat steps 3 and 4 for waves 4, 5, and 6.

Waves L2

Laboratory Activities

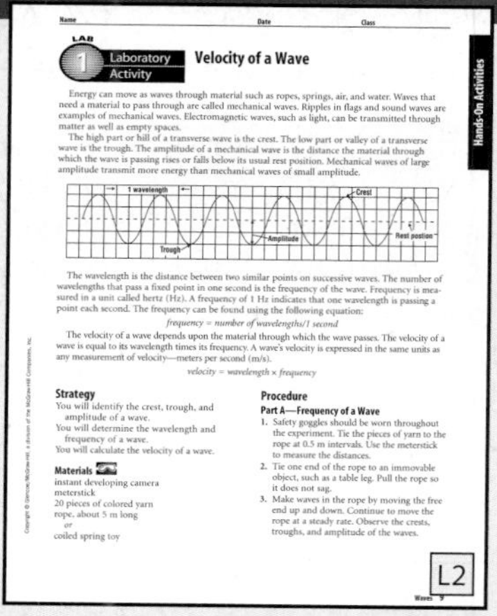
Name Date Class

LAB 1 Laboratory Activity **Velocity of a Wave**

Hands-On Activities

Energy can move as waves through material such as ropes, springs, air, and water. Waves that need a material to pass through are called mechanical waves. Ripples in flags and sound waves are examples of mechanical waves. Electromagnetic waves, such as light, can be transmitted through matter as well as empty spaces.

The high part or hill of a transverse wave is the crest. The low part or valley of a transverse wave is the trough. The amplitude of a mechanical wave is the distance the material through which the wave is passing rises or falls below its usual rest position. Mechanical waves of large amplitude transmit more energy than mechanical waves of small amplitude.

The wavelength is the distance between two similar points on successive waves. The number of wavelengths that pass a fixed point in one second is the frequency of the wave. Frequency is measured in a unit called hertz (Hz). A frequency of 1 Hz indicates that one wavelength is passing a point each second. The frequency can be found using the following equation:

frequency = number of wavelengths/1 second

The velocity of a wave depends upon the material through which the wave passes. The velocity of a wave is equal to its wavelength times its frequency. A wave's velocity is expressed in the same units as any measurement of velocity—meters per second (m/s).

velocity = wavelength × frequency

Strategy
You will identify the crest, trough, and amplitude of a wave.
You will determine the wavelength and frequency of a wave.
You will calculate the velocity of a wave.

Materials
instant developing camera
meterstick
20 pieces of colored yarn
rope, about 5 m long
or
coiled spring toy

Procedure
Part A—Frequency of a Wave
1. Safety goggles should be worn throughout the experiment. Tie the pieces of yarn to the rope at 0.5 m intervals. Use the meterstick to measure the distances.
2. Tie one end of the rope to an immovable object, such as a table leg. Pull the rope so it does not sag.
3. Make waves in the rope by moving the free end up and down. Continue to move the rope at a steady rate. Observe the crests, troughs, and amplitude of the waves.

L2 Waves 9

Meeting Different Ability Levels

Content Outline

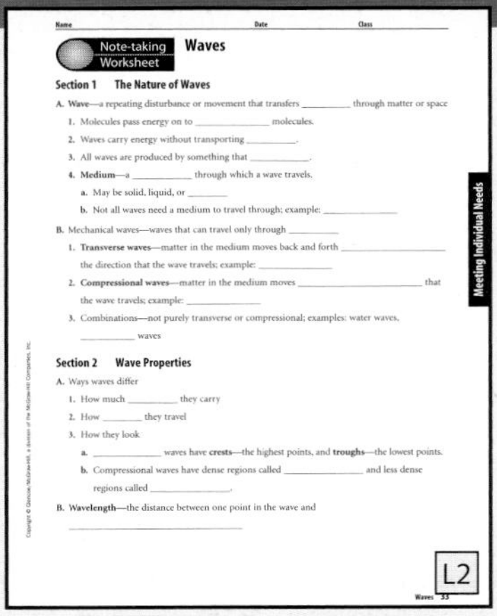

Reinforcement

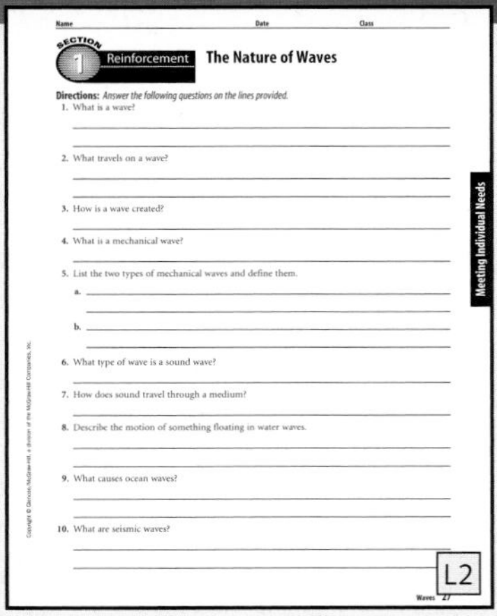

Enrichment

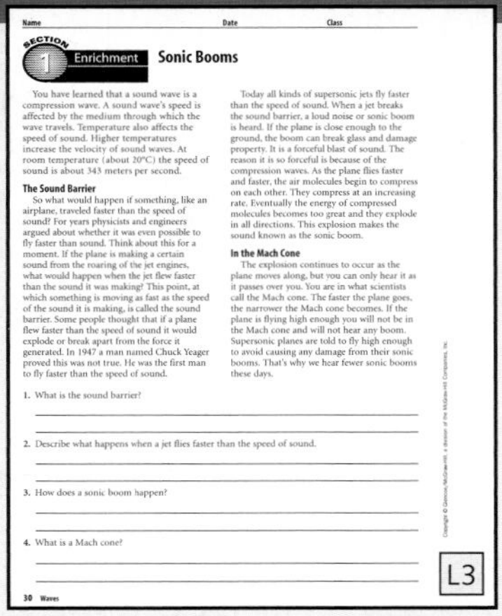

Directed Reading (English/Spanish)

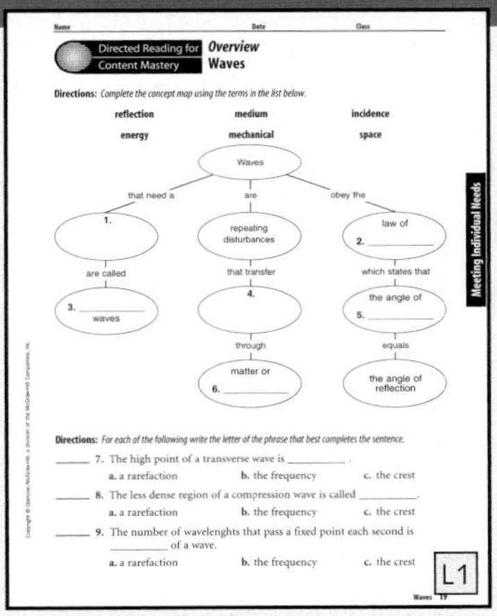

Study Guide

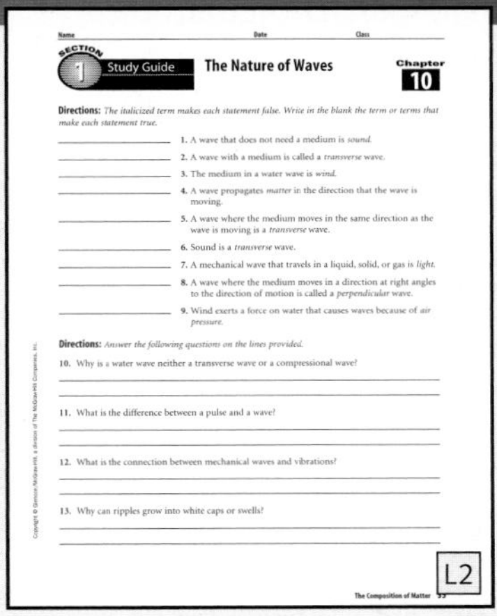

Reading Essentials

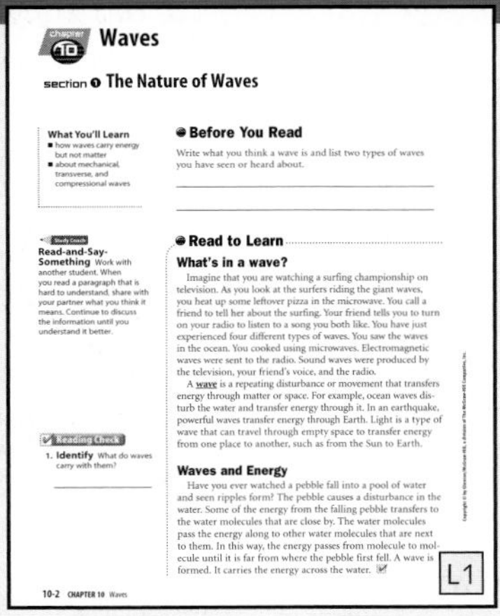

Assessment

Test Practice Workbook

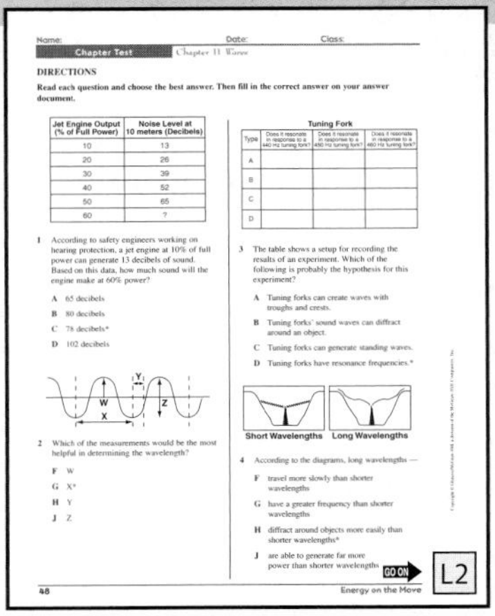

Chapter Review

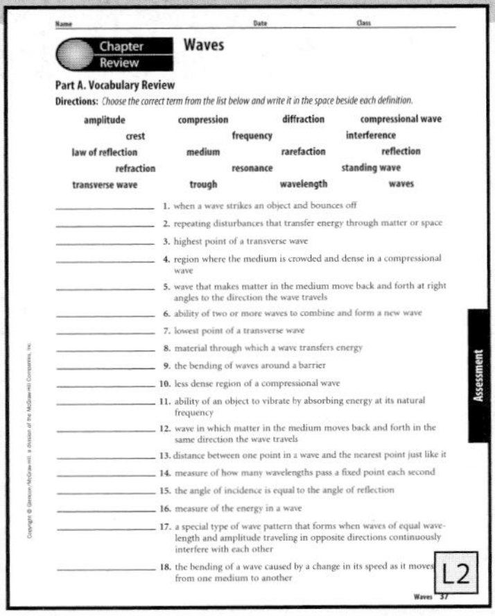

Chapter Tests

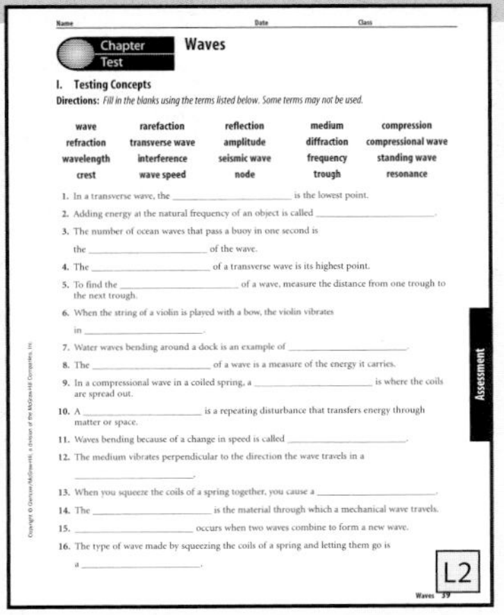

Science Content Background

section 1 The Nature of Waves

What's in a wave?

From radio waves to light waves to sound waves, we are immersed in a world of waves.

Waves transfer energy from one place to another. Mechanical waves such as sound and water need a medium to travel through. These waves create disturbances in the medium as they travel. The particles of the medium, however, do not move with the wave as it travels.

Waves can be transverse waves or compressional waves. In a transverse wave, the particles in the medium are displaced perpendicular to the direction of the wave motion. In a compressional wave, the particles move back and forth in the same direction as the wave moves. Transverse waves cannot travel through fluids. Earthquakes produce both transverse waves (S waves) and compressional waves (P waves).

section 2 Wave Properties

Wavelength

A great deal of variation exists in the wavelengths of electromagnetic waves. Electromagnetic waves with wavelengths greater than about 1 mm are radio waves. These waves have the longest wavelengths. Light wavelengths range from about 400 to 700 nanometers. One nanometer is 0.000000001 m or 10^{-9} m.

Frequency

Frequency and period are related. Frequency is how often something happens in a given time. Period is the time for something to happen. Thus for a wave, frequency is equal to the reciprocal of the period. Frequency is expressed as cycles per second, and period is seconds per cycle.

Amplitude and Energy

The amplitude of a wave is the maximum displacement of the particles in the medium from their resting position. Attractive forces between the particles in the medium act like springs that pull the particles back to their original position when the wave passes.

The energy transferred by a wave is proportional to the square of the amplitude. Thus, higher ocean waves produce more damage. Doubling the height of the wave makes the energy transferred four times greater.

section 3 The Behavior of Waves

Refraction and Diffraction

Waves do not always travel in a straight line. Refraction and diffraction cause waves to change direction. Refraction occurs when waves change speed as they pass from one material into another. Diffraction occurs when a wave strikes an obstacle or an opening.

chapter content resources

Internet Resources

For additional content background, visit gpescience.com to:

- access your book online
- find references to related articles in popular science magazines
- access Web links with related content background
- access current events with science journal topics

Print Resources

Basic Physics: A Self-Teaching Guide, by Karl F. Kuhn, John Wiley and Sons, 1996

Waves in the Ocean and Atmosphere: Introduction to Wave Dynamics, by Joseph Pedlosky, Springer Verlag, 2003

Wave Motion, by J. Billingham and A.C. King, Cambridge University Press, 2001

IDENTIFYING Misconceptions

Find Out What Students Think

Students may think that . . .

When a wave travels through a medium, particles of the medium travel along with the wave.
Students have probably seen water waves hit land and flow up the beach. They may even have felt the force of an ocean wave pushing them towards the beach. Because these waves encounter the shore, they move differently from normal waves. But they do form lasting impressions. Thus, it is understandable that students would think that the medium travels with the wave.

Demonstration
Draw the figure below on the board. Tell students to imagine a rock is dropped into the water at Point A. Ask students to predict where each of the floating bobs will end up after ten waves go by the bobs.

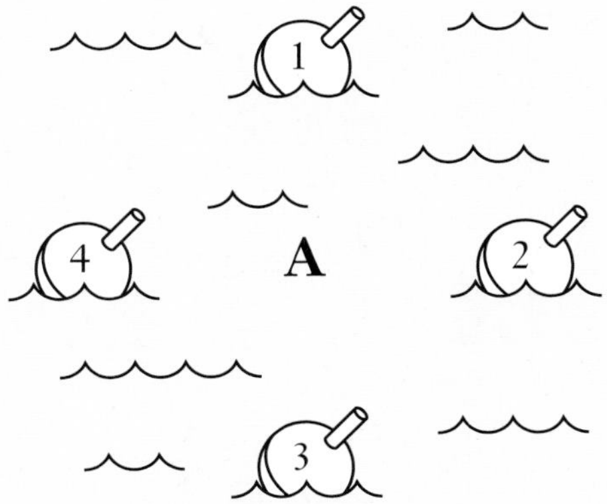

Promote Understanding

Activity
Students make two models of waves—one that is incorrrect and one that is correct.
Model 1 (incorrect): Place on the floor alternating strips of green and red tape 2 m apart so they form the outline of a large circle. Have students walk slowly around the circle. Tell them to duck down when they get to a strip of green tape and to walk on their toes when they get to a strip of red tape. Students move up and down as they walk around the room.
Model 2 (correct): This resembles the "wave" done by fans at sporting events. Have students stand in a circle and not leave their positions. Start the wave by having a student reach up high, pause, duck down low, pause, and return to normal standing. After the first person rises, the second person rises and does the same thing. Each person in turn passes the wave around the circle.

Ask students to analyze the two models of waves and write which one they think is the better model and why.

Assess
After completing the chapter, see *Identifying Misconceptions* in the Study Guide at the end of the chapter.

chapter 10

Chapter Vocabulary

wave, p. 288
medium, p. 289
transverse wave, p. 290
compressional wave, p. 290
crest, p. 294
trough, p. 294
rarefaction, p. 294
wavelength, p. 295
frequency, p. 295
period, p. 295
amplitude, p. 298
refraction, p. 302
diffraction, p. 304
interference, p. 306
standing wave, p. 308
resonance, p. 309

Science Journal Student responses will vary, but may include that they know waves occur in different materials, that they take different forms, even that they involve energy and motion. Students may want to learn about their causes and effects.

INTERACTIVE CHALKBOARD with Image Bank

PowerPoint® Presentations

This CD-ROM is an editable Microsoft® PowerPoint® presentation that includes:

- a pre-made presentation for every chapter
- interactive graphics
- animations
- audio clips
- image bank
- all new section and chapter questions
- Standardized Test Practice
- transparencies
- Foldables directions
- links to gpescience.com

chapter 10

Waves

chapter preview

sections

Waves, anyone?

This surfer in Hawaii is surrounded by an ocean wave that forms a huge wall of water. You are surrounded by waves, too. Everything you see or hear is brought to you by waves. Easy to see—like this ocean wave—or invisible, all waves transfer energy.

Science Journal Write down three things you already know about waves and one thing you would like to learn about waves.

Theme Connection

Energy Waves are rhythmic disturbances that transfer energy. As the amplitude of a wave increases, the energy it transfers also increases.

About the Photo

Ocean Waves The area in Hawaii where this photo was taken is known for huge ocean waves. Thousands of miles of open ocean separate this region from the place where the waves originate. Distant storms in the north Pacific supply the energy for gigantic waves that are legendary among surfers.

Start-Up Activities

Launch LAB

How do waves transfer energy?

Light enters your eyes and sound strikes your ears, enabling you to sense the world around you. Light and sound are waves that transfer energy from one place to another. Do waves transfer anything else along with their energy? Does a wave transfer matter, too? In this activity, you'll observe one way that waves can transfer energy.

1. Place your textbook flat on your desk. Line up four marbles on the groove at the edge of the textbook so that the marbles are touching each other.
2. Hold the first three marbles in place using three fingers of one hand.
3. Use your other hand to tap the first marble with a pen or pencil.
4. Observe the behavior of the fourth marble.
5. **Think Critically** Write a paragraph explaining how the fourth marble reacted to the pen tap. Draw a diagram showing how energy was transferred through the marbles.

Science Online | Preview this chapter's content and activities at gpescience.com

FOLDABLES™ Study Organizer

Types of Waves Make the following Foldable to compare and contrast two types of waves.

STEP 1 **Fold** one sheet of paper lengthwise.

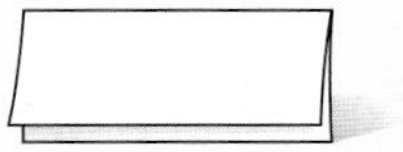

STEP 2 **Fold** into thirds.

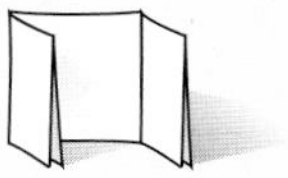

STEP 3 **Unfold and draw** overlapping ovals. Cut the top sheet along the folds.

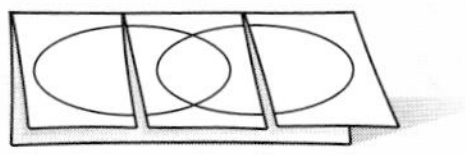

STEP 4 **Label** the ovals as shown.

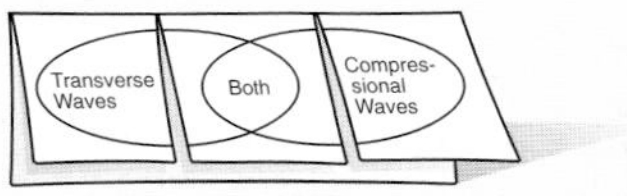

Construct a Venn Diagram As you read this chapter, list properties and characteristics unique to transverse waves under the left tab, those unique to compressional waves under the right tab, and those common to both under the middle tab.

Launch LAB

Purpose Use the Launch Lab to illustrate for students energy moving through matter. L2

LS **Kinesthetic**

Preparation Obtain enough marbles of the same size so that each student can have four.

Materials marbles, textbook, pen

Teaching Strategy Instruct students to make sure books are on a flat surface. Make sure students hold the marbles so they are touching one another.

Think Critically

Students should notice that the fourth marble moved even though the first three marbles stayed in place. This shows that energy transferred through the first three marbles, which caused the fourth marble to move without matter being transferred.

Assessment

Performance Have students write short paragraphs explaining what happens if the marbles are held in place without touching each other. After the first marble hits the second marble nothing happens. This is because the energy of the first marble is transferred to the air, which transfers very little energy to the next marble. Use **Performance Assessment in the Science Classroom,** p. 157.

FOLDABLES™ Study Organizer — Dinah Zike Study Fold

Student preparation materials for this Foldable are available in the **Chapter *Fast File* Resources.**

1 Motivate

INTERACTIVE CHALKBOARD An editable Microsoft® PowerPoint® presentation is available on **Interactive Chalkboard** CD-ROM.

Bellringer

Section Focus Transparencies also are available on the Interactive Chalkboard CD-ROM. L2 ELL

SECTION 1 Section Focus Transparency **Wave to the Camera**

How many waves can you pick out in this scene? Is light described as a wave? If you were there when this photograph was taken, you might also mention sound waves.

1. Describe the different waves in this picture.
2. If you are swimming underwater, can you still hear the noises around you? What does this tell you about sound waves?
3. What does light travel through as it goes from the Sun to the eyes of an underwater swimmer?

L2

Waves

Reading Preview

Tie to Prior Knowledge

Energy Review the idea of energy and have students give examples of waves. Emphasize to students that waves transfer energy but not matter.

Structural Analysis Have students look for smaller words within the new vocabulary words. Point out *compress* in the word *compressional* and ask them to brainstorm meanings. Help students make connections by asking how *compress* relates to a household sponge. They may say squeezing a sponge is like compression.

section 1

The Nature of Waves

Reading Guide

What You'll Learn

- **Recognize** that waves transfer energy but not matter.
- **Define** mechanical waves.
- **Compare and contrast** transverse waves and compressional waves.

Why It's Important

You can see and hear the world around you because of the energy transferred by waves.

Review Vocabulary

energy: the ability to do work

New Vocabulary

- wave
- medium
- transverse wave
- compressional wave

What's in a wave?

A surfer bobs in the ocean waiting for the perfect wave, microwaves warm up your leftover pizza, and sound waves from your CD player bring music to your ears. Do these and other types of waves have anything in common with one another?

A **wave** is a repeating disturbance or movement that transfers energy through matter or space. For example, ocean waves disturb the water and transfer energy through it. During earthquakes, energy is transferred in powerful waves that travel through Earth. Light is a type of wave that can travel through empty space to transfer energy from one place to another, such as from the Sun to Earth.

Figure 1 Falling pebbles transfer their kinetic energy to the particles of water in a pond, forming waves.

Waves and Energy

Kerplop! A pebble falls into a pool of water and ripples form. As **Figure 1** shows, the pebble causes a disturbance that moves outward in the form of a wave. Because it is moving, the falling pebble has energy. As it splashes into the pool, the pebble transfers some of its energy to nearby water molecules, causing them to move. These molecules then pass the energy along to neighboring water molecules, which, in turn, transfer it to their neighbors. The energy moves farther and farther from the source of the disturbance. What you see is energy traveling in the form of a wave on the surface of the water.

Section 1 Resource Manager

Chapter *FAST FILE* Resources
Transparency Activity, p. 44
Directed Reading for Content Mastery, pp. 19–20
Note-taking Worksheets, pp. 33–35
Enrichment, p. 30
Reinforcement, p. 27

Cultural Diversity, p. 43
Science Inquiry Labs, pp. 25–26
Reading and Writing Skill Activities, p. 7
Earth Science Critical Thinking/Problem Solving, p. 9

Waves and Matter Imagine that you're in a boat on a lake. Approaching waves bump against your boat, but they don't carry it along with them as they pass. The boat does move up and down and maybe even a short distance back and forth because the waves transfer some of their energy to it. However, after the waves have moved on, the boat is still in nearly the same place. The waves don't even carry the water along with them. Only the energy transferred by the waves moves forward. All waves have this property—they transfer energy without transporting matter from place to place.

Reading Check *What do waves transfer?*

Making Waves A wave will travel only as long as it has energy to transfer. For example, when you drop a pebble into a puddle, the ripples soon die out and the surface of the water becomes still again.

Suppose you are holding a rope at one end, and you give it a shake. You would create a pulse that would travel along the rope to the other end, and then the rope would be still again, as **Figure 2** shows. Now suppose you shake your end of the rope up and down for a while. You would make a wave that would travel along the rope. When you stop shaking your hand up and down, the rope will be still again. It is the up-and-down motion of your hand that creates the wave.

Anything that moves up and down or back and forth in a rhythmic way is vibrating. The vibrating movement of your hand at the end of the rope created the wave. In fact, all waves are produced by something that vibrates.

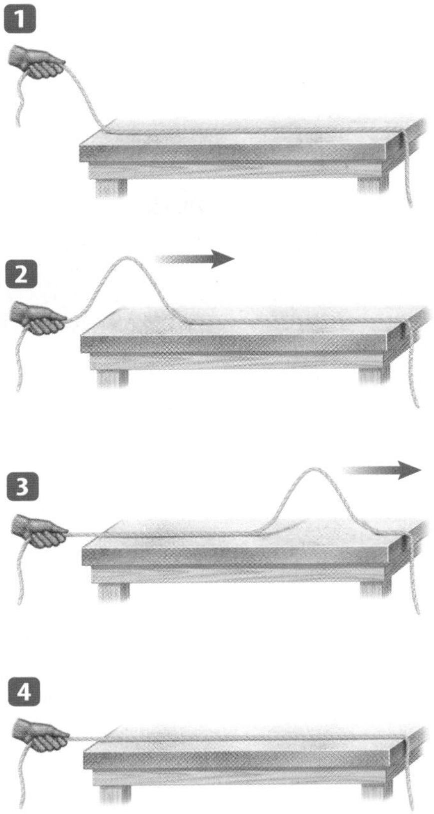

Figure 2 A wave will exist only as long as it has energy to transfer. **Explain** *what happened to the energy that was transferred by the wave in this rope.*

Mechanical Waves

Sound waves travel through the air to reach your ears. Ocean waves move through water to reach the shore. In both cases, the matter the waves travel through is called a **medium.** A medium can be a solid, a liquid, a gas, or a combination of these. For sound waves, the medium is air, and for ocean waves, the medium is water. Not all waves need a medium. Some waves, such as light and radio waves, can travel through space. Waves that can travel only through matter are called mechanical waves. The two types of mechanical waves are transverse waves and compressional waves.

2 Teach

Caption Answer

Figure 2 It was transferred to the end of the rope and then to the surrounding air.

Quick Demo
Wave Motion

Materials table-tennis ball, wide pan of water, small rock

Estimated Time five minutes

Procedure Place the table-tennis ball in the pan about halfway between the center and the edge of the pan. When the water is still, drop the rock into the pan. The ball moves up and down, but not horizontally in the direction in which the wave moves. L2 LS **Visual-Spatial**

Reading Check

Answer energy

IDENTIFYING Misconceptions

Wave Motion Students may think that when a wave travels through a medium, particles of the medium travel along with the wave. See the beginning of this chapter for teaching strategies that address this misconception.

LAB DEMONSTRATION

Purpose to demonstrate the movement of a wave through matter

Materials rope, broom

Preparation Tie the end of a rope to the handle of a broom.

Procedure Rest the broom upright in the corner of the room. Send a wave through the rope.

Expected Outcome Students will see the wave travel through the rope and cause the broom to shake or fall down.

Assessment

Where did the energy that caused the broom to shake or fall come from? from the hand moving the rope How did the energy get to the broom? It traveled along the rope in a wave. L2

Use Science Words

Word Meaning Tell students that the word *transverse* means "acting, lying, or being across; set crosswise." What makes a transverse wave transverse? When a transverse wave travels through a medium, the particles of the medium move crosswise to the direction in which the wave moves. L2 IS **Linguistic**

Activity

Wave Types Have students use a coiled spring toy to make both transverse and compressional waves. Have them compare and contrast how the waves look and the different things they did to make the two different types of waves. L1 ELL IS **Kinesthetic**

Teacher FYI

Wave Names Another name for a compressional wave is longitudinal wave. Sound waves are examples of this type of wave.

Caption Answer

Figure 4 Possible answer: sound wave

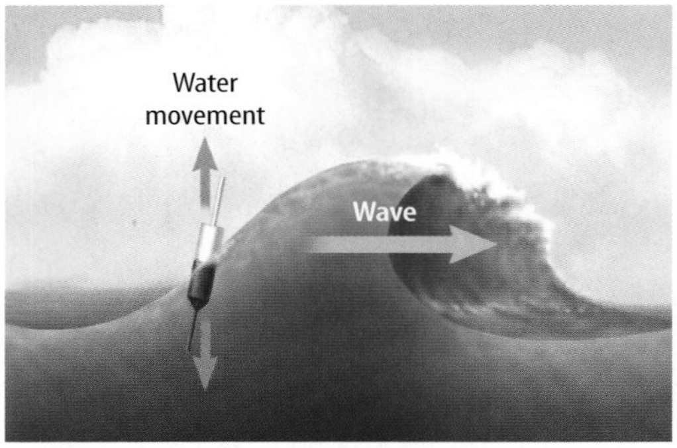

Figure 3 A water wave travels horizontally as the water moves vertically up and down.

Transverse Waves In a **transverse wave,** matter in the medium moves back and forth at right angles to the direction that the wave travels. For example, **Figure 3** shows how a wave in the ocean moves horizontally, but the water that the wave passes through moves up and down. When you shake one end of a rope while your friend holds the other end, you are making transverse waves. The wave and its energy travel from you to your friend as the rope moves up and down.

Compressional Waves In a **compressional wave,** matter in the medium moves back and forth along the same direction that the wave travels. You can model compressional waves with a coiled-spring toy, as shown in **Figure 4.** Squeeze several coils together at one end of the spring. Then let go of the coils, still holding onto coils at both ends of the spring. A wave will travel along the spring. As the wave moves, it looks as if the whole spring is moving toward one end. Suppose you watched the coil with yarn tied to it, as in **Figure 4.** You would see that the yarn moves back and forth as the wave passes, and then it stops moving after the wave has passed. The wave transfers energy, but not matter, forward along the spring. Compressional waves also are called longitudinal waves.

Sound Waves Sound waves are compressional waves. When a noise is made, such as when a locker door slams shut and vibrates, nearby air molecules are pushed together by the vibrations. The air molecules are squeezed together like the coils in a coiled-spring toy are when you make a compressional wave with it. The compressions travel through the air to make a wave.

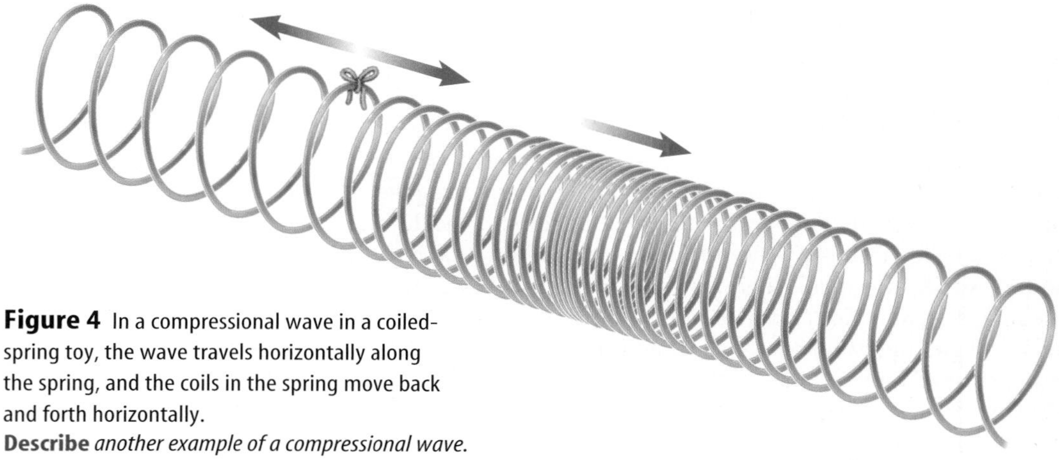

Figure 4 In a compressional wave in a coiled-spring toy, the wave travels horizontally along the spring, and the coils in the spring move back and forth horizontally.
Describe *another example of a compressional wave.*

Differentiated Instruction

Visually Impaired Have each visually impaired student place a hand on a section of a rope or spring toy. Make waves in the rope or spring toy. Ask each student to describe how the section he or she is touching moves. Does it move up or down, backwards or forwards? Does it travel from one place to another? L1 ELL COOP LEARN IS **Kinesthetic**

Challenge Have students hypothesize how transverse waves will travel in different kinds of ropes. Then, have students test their hypotheses using different ropes. Ask them to write a single summary sentence that describes the relationship between the wave and type of rope used. Students will find that thick ropes will carry waves, but might require more energy to start wave action than do thin ropes. L3

Sound in Other Materials Sound waves also can travel through other mediums, such as water and wood. Particles in these mediums also are pushed together and move apart as the sound waves travel through them. When a sound wave reaches your ear, it causes your eardrum to vibrate. Your inner ear then sends signals to your brain, and your brain interprets the signals as sound.

Reading Check *How do sound waves travel in solids?*

Water Waves Water waves are not purely transverse waves. The water moves up and down as the waves go by. However, the water also moves a short distance back and forth along the direction the wave is moving. This movement happens because the low part of the wave can be formed only by pushing water forward or backward toward the high part of the wave, as in **Figure 5A.** Then, as the wave passes, the water that was pushed aside moves back to its initial position, as in **Figure 5B.** In fact, if you looked closely, you would see that the combination of this up-and-down and back-and-forth motion causes water to move in circles. Anything floating on the surface of the water absorbs some of the waves' energy and bobs in a circular motion.

Ocean waves are formed most often by wind blowing across the ocean surface. As the wind blows faster and slower, the changing wind speed is like a vibration. The size of the waves that are formed depends on the wind speed, the distance over which the wind blows, and how long the wind blows. **Figure 6** on the next page shows how ocean waves are formed.

Figure 5 A water wave causes water to move back and forth, as well as up and down. Water is pushed back and forth to form the crests and troughs.

A The low point of a water wave is formed when water is pushed aside and up to the high point of the wave.

B The water that is pushed aside returns to its initial position.

Reading Check

Answer Particles in the solid are pushed together and move apart as sound waves travel through them.

Discussion

Beach Breakers Why do waves break where they meet beaches? As waves of water move into the increasingly shallow area near the shore, the particles of water are forced to move in shallower and shallower ellipses. The wave breaks when it hits the ground as it tries to complete its elliptical path. The energy of the wave dissipates as the water moves up the beach and then falls back into the ocean. L2

Science Journal

Wave Diary Have students list in their Science Journals the kinds of waves they see in a typical day, classifying each wave as transverse or compressional. Have them identify the effects each wave's energy produces. L2 LS **Linguistic**

Visual Learning

Figure 5 When you throw a stone into the water, how does it start the motion of the wave? When the stone hits the water, it pushes down on the water. Why does the wave spread out as it moves? It spreads because the energy moves in all directions from the point of origin. L2 LS **Visual-Spatial**

NATIONAL GEOGRAPHIC

Visualizing Formation of Ocean Waves

Have students examine the pictures and read the captions. Then ask the following questions.

What happens to the surface area of water exposed to the wind as waves build up? The surface area increases. How does this affect the waves? The greater surface area means that there is more contact area between the air and water, providing an increased area to which energy may be transferred.

Activity

Observe Waves Use a wave tank or large flat pan such as a cake pan partially filled with water to observe waves. Students can blow across the surface or a fan can be provided to simulate the wind. Students should try to duplicate the four types of seas presented. L2 LS **Kinesthetic**

INTEGRATE Earth Science **Content Background**

Earthquakes produce three types of waves, all of which move out in concentric circles from the focus of the earthquake. Primary waves, known as P waves, are compressional waves that travel deep inside Earth. These waves travel the fastest. Secondary waves, called S waves, are transverse waves that can travel only through solids. They also travel deep inside Earth. Most of the damage from earthquakes is caused by surface waves that spread out from the epicenter, the point on Earth's surface above the focus. Surface waves cause both transverse and compressional movement of the ground.

NATIONAL GEOGRAPHIC **VISUALIZING FORMATION OF OCEAN WAVES**

Figure 6

When wind blows across an ocean, friction between the moving air and the water causes the water to move. As a result, energy is transferred from the wind to the surface of the water. The waves that are produced depend on the length of time and the distance over which the wind blows, as well as the wind speed.

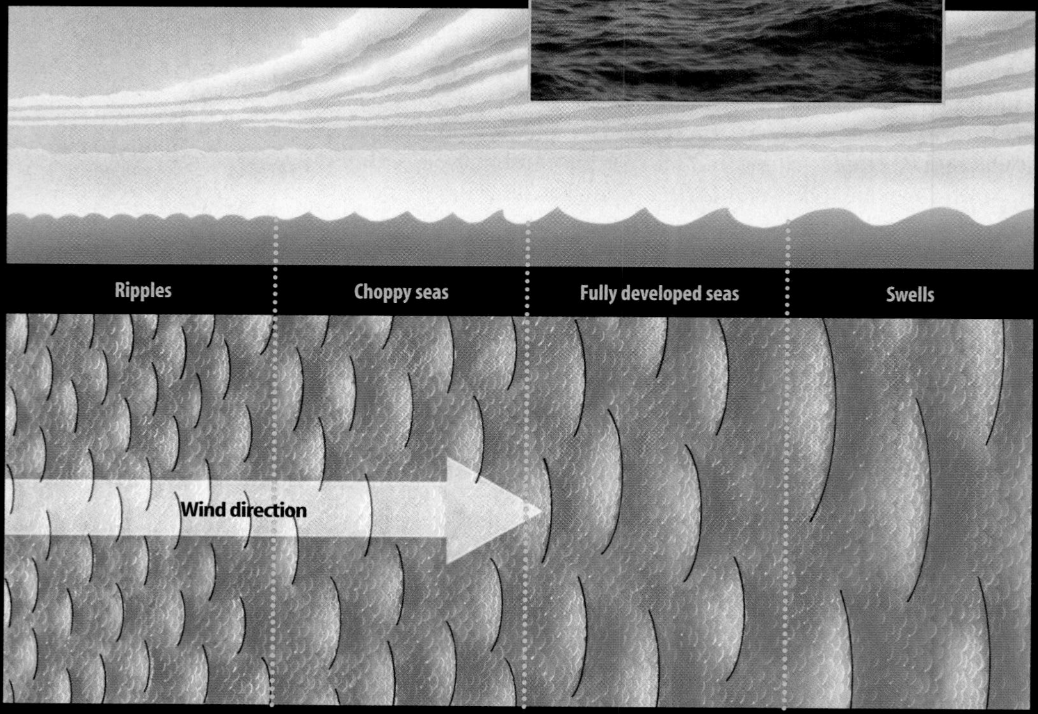

▲ Wind causes ripples to form on the surface of the water. As ripples form, they provide an even larger surface area for the wind to strike, and the ripples increase in size.

▲ Waves that are higher and have longer wavelengths grow faster as the wind continues to blow, but the steepest waves break up, forming whitecaps. The surface is said to be choppy.

▲ The shortest-wavelength waves break up, while the longest-wavelength waves continue to grow. When these waves have reached their maximum height, they form fully developed seas.

▲ After the wind dies down, the waves lose energy and become lower and smoother. These smooth, long-wavelength ocean waves are called swells.

Differentiated Instruction

Challenge Ask students to research the impact to the shoreline when ocean waves repeatedly strike the shore. Have them find what measures are being taken to keep the shoreline unchanged. L3

Reading Strategy

Cooperative Learning Scaffold students' understanding of **Figure 6,** Visualizing Formation of Ocean Waves, by allowing students to engage in a discussion. Have one student read the text on ripples and another explain the drawings, adding any prior knowledge about the term. Continue for the text on choppy seas, fully developed seas, and swells.

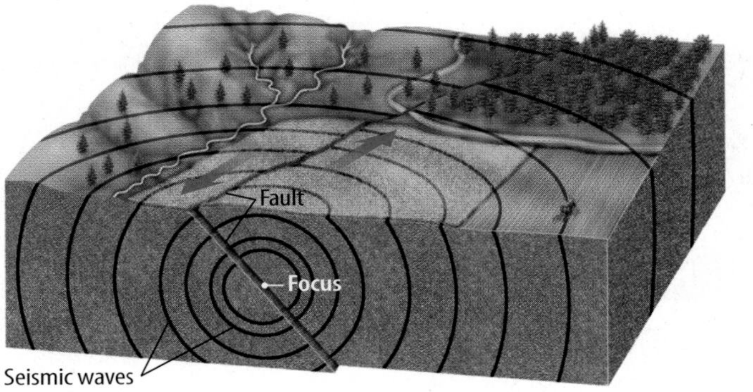

Figure 7 When Earth's crust shifts or breaks, the energy that is released is transmitted outward, causing an earthquake.
Explain *why earthquakes are mechanical waves.*

INTEGRATE Earth Science

Seismic Waves A guitar string makes a sound when it breaks. The string vibrates for a short time after it breaks and produces sound waves. In a similar way, forces in Earth's crust can cause regions of the crust to shift, bend, or even break. The breaking crust vibrates, creating seismic waves that transfer energy outward, as shown in **Figure 7.** Seismic waves are a combination of compressional and transverse waves. They can travel through Earth and along Earth's surface. When objects on Earth's surface absorb some of the energy transferred by seismic waves, they move and shake. The more the crust moves during an earthquake, the more energy is released.

Science Online
Topic: Seismic Waves
Visit gpescience.com for Web links to information about seismic waves.
Activity Write a summary of how seismic waves are used to map Earth's interior.

section 1 review

Summary

Waves and Energy
- A wave is a repeating disturbance or movement that transfers energy through matter or space.
- Waves transfer energy without transporting matter.
- Waves are produced by something that is vibrating.

Mechanical Waves
- Mechanical waves must travel in matter.
- Mechanical waves can be transverse waves or compressional waves.
- In a transverse wave, matter in the medium moves at right angles to the wave motion.
- In a compressional wave, matter in the medium moves back and forth along the direction of the wave motion.

Self Check

1. **Compare and contrast** a transverse wave and a compressional wave. Give an example of each type.
2. **Describe** the motion of a buoy when a water wave passes. Does it move the buoy forward?
3. **Explain** how you could model a compressional wave using a coiled-spring toy.
4. **List** the characteristics of a mechanical wave.
5. **Think Critically** Why do boats need anchors if ocean waves do not carry matter forward?

Applying Math

6. **Calculate Time** The average speed of sound in water is 1,500 m/s. How long would it take a sound wave to travel 9,000 m?

Caption Answer

Figure 7 Because they require a medium through which to travel.

Post Reading

Extended Research Project Students may be aware of the tsunami that occurred in the Indian Ocean in December 2004. Have them research news and magazine articles that describe how energy from the underwater earthquake caused the tsunami.

3 Assess

DAILY INTERVENTION

Check for Understanding

Logical-Mathematical With a partner, have each student draw a diagram of both a transverse wave and a compressional wave. Ask them to label peaks and troughs; compressions and rarefactions, as well as the direction of energy transfer for each wave. L2

Reteach

Comparing Waves Pair students and give each pair a coiled spring toy. Tie a piece of colored string or yarn around one of the coils. Have students make transverse and then compressional waves in the toy. Ask them to identify what is the same and what is different about the motion of the string with each wave. L2

Assessment

Process Have students do research on earthquakes. Have them find out how the waves form and why they form in the places they do. Have students make events chains of their findings. Use **PASC**, p. 163. P L2

section 1 review

1. Possible answers include that transverse waves move at right angles to the direction the waves travel, while compressional waves move back and forth in the same direction as the waves travel. Water waves are partly transverse waves. Sound waves are compressional waves.
2. A buoy moves up and down when a wave passes. The wave does not move the buoy forward.
3. Pull the ends of the toy apart and anchor them firmly at both ends. Then, squeeze several coils together at one end and release them.
4. Mechanical waves are either transverse or compressional, but always require a medium to travel through.
5. The tide and its related currents will move unanchored boats.
6. 6 s

section 2

Wave Properties

Reading Guide

What You'll Learn

- **Define** wavelength, frequency, period, and amplitude.
- **Describe** the relationship between frequency and wavelength.
- **Explain** how a wave's energy and amplitude are related.
- **Calculate** wave speed.

Why It's Important

Waves with different properties can be used in different ways.

Review Vocabulary

vibration: a back and forth movement

New Vocabulary

- crest
- trough
- rarefaction
- wavelength
- frequency
- period
- amplitude

The Parts of a Wave

What makes sound waves, water waves, and seismic waves different from each other? Waves can differ in how much energy they transfer and in how fast they travel. Waves also have other characteristics that make them different from each other.

Suppose you shake the end of a rope and make a transverse wave. The transverse wave in **Figure 8** has alternating high points, called **crests,** and low points, called **troughs.**

On the other hand, a compressional wave has no crests and troughs. When a compressional wave passes through a medium, it creates regions where the medium becomes crowded together and more dense, as in **Figure 8.** These regions are compressions. When you make compressional waves in a coiled spring, the compressions are regions where the coils are close together. **Figure 8** also shows that the coils in the regions next to a compression are spread apart, or less dense. These less-dense regions of a compressional wave are called **rarefactions.**

Figure 8 Transverse and compressional waves have different features that travel through a medium and form the wave.

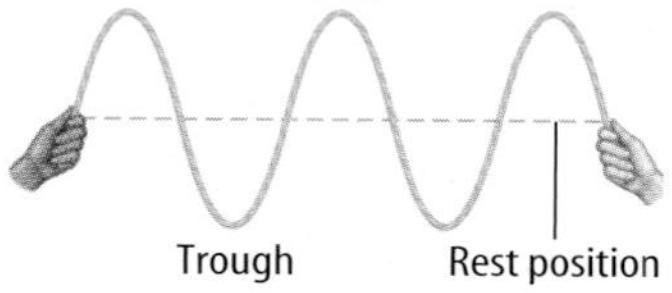

A transverse wave is made of crests and troughs that travel through the medium.

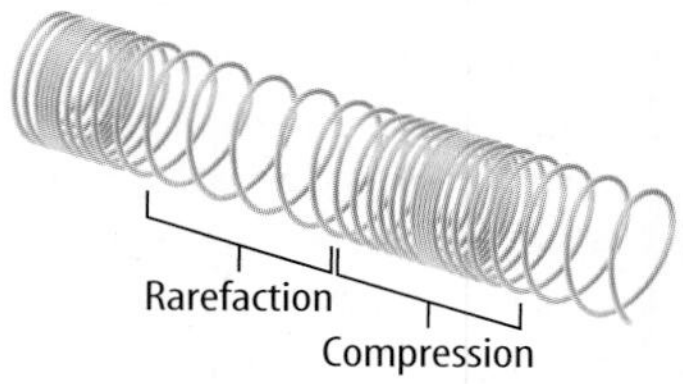

A compressional wave is made of compressions and rarefactions that travel through the medium.

1 Motivate

An editable Microsoft® PowerPoint® presentation is available on **Interactive Chalkboard** CD-ROM.

Bellringer

Section Focus Transparencies also are available on the Interactive Chalkboard CD-ROM. L2 ELL

Section 2 Section Focus Transparency **Big Fiddle, Little Fiddle**

Have you ever heard the instruments below played? If you have, you probably noticed that the bass produces a much lower sound than the violin. The difference in the sounds is related to differences in the waves each instrument produces.

1. Name some muscial instruments. How are the instruments you named played?
2. A cello is bigger than a violin but smaller than a bass. How do you think the sound made by a cello compares to the sounds made by violins and basses? L2

Waves

Reading Preview

Tie to Prior Knowledge

Comparing Waves Have students compare common examples of waves and ask them whether they can identify any similarities among all waves. Tell students that they will learn about the different parts of waves and how these parts determine the amount of energy a wave transfers. L2

Preview and Predict Ask students to explain the saying, "A picture is worth a thousand words." After discussing the meaning of the saying, have volunteers make up definitions for each vocabulary term based on **Figures 8** and **9.** Remind them to use the illustrations to make sense of text concepts and terms.

Section 2 Resource Manager

Chapter *Fast File* Resources

Transparency Activity, pp. 45, 47–48
Directed Reading for Content Mastery, p. 20
MiniLAB, p. 3
Enrichment, p. 31
Lab Activity, pp. 9–11
Reinforcement, p. 28
Lab Worksheet, pp. 5–6
Mathematics Skill Activities, p. 9

294 CHAPTER 10 Waves

Figure 9 One wavelength starts at any point on a wave and ends at the nearest point just like it.

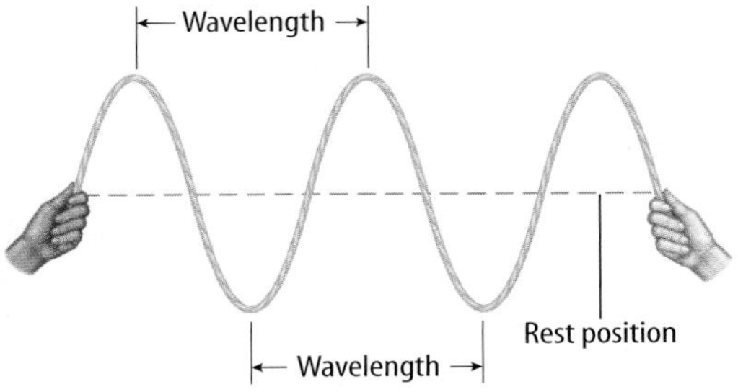

For transverse waves, a wavelength can be measured from crest to crest or trough to trough.

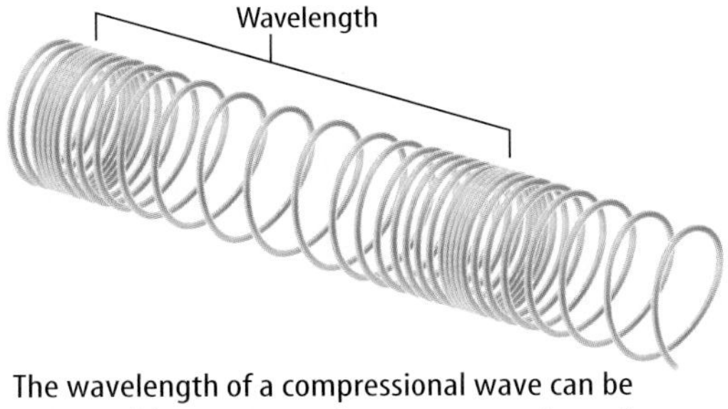

The wavelength of a compressional wave can be measured from compression to compression or from rarefaction to rarefaction.

Wavelength

Waves also have a property called wavelength. A **wavelength** is the distance between one point on a wave and the nearest point just like it. **Figure 9** shows that for transverse waves, the wavelength is the distance from crest to crest or trough to trough.

A wavelength in a compressional wave is the distance between two neighboring compressions or two neighboring rarefactions, as shown in **Figure 9.** You can measure from the start of one compression to the start of the next compression or from the start of one rarefaction to the start of the next rarefaction. The wavelengths of sound waves that you can hear range from a few centimeters for the highest-pitched sounds to about 15 m for the deepest sounds.

Reading Check *How is wavelength measured in transverse and compressional waves?*

Frequency and Period

When you tune your radio to a station, you are choosing radio waves of a certain frequency. The **frequency** of a wave is the number of wavelengths that pass a fixed point each second. You can find the frequency of a transverse wave by counting the number of crests or troughs that pass by a point each second. The frequency of a compressional wave is the number of compressions or rarefactions that pass a point every second. Frequency is expressed in hertz (Hz). A frequency of 1 Hz means that one wavelength passes by in 1 s. In SI units, 1 Hz is the same as 1/s. The **period** of a wave is the amount of time it takes one wavelength to pass a point. As the frequency of a wave increases, the period decreases. Periods are measured in units of seconds.

Mini LAB

Observing Wavelength

Procedure

1. Fill a **pie plate or other wide pan** with **water** about 2 cm deep.
2. Lightly tap your finger once per second on the surface of the water and observe the spacing of the water waves.
3. Increase the rate of your tapping, and observe the spacing of the water waves.

Analysis

1. How is the spacing of the water waves related to their wavelength?
2. How does the spacing of the water waves change when the rate of tapping increases?

Try at Home

2 Teach

Reading Check

Answer transverse wave—crest to crest or trough to trough; compressional wave—compression to compression or rarefaction to rarefaction

Mini LAB

Purpose to observe the relationship between the wavelength and frequency of a wave L2

ELL IS Kinesthetic

Materials pie plate, water

Teaching Strategy Suggest students use a watch to measure the rate of tapping.

Analysis

1. The closer the waves, the shorter their wavelength.
2. As the rate of tapping increases, the spacing of the waves decreases.

Assessment

Process Have students draw diagrams of the water waves they formed by tapping at two different rates. Ask students to label the wavelength on their diagrams. Use **Performance Assessment in the Science Classroom,** p. 127.

Try at Home

Activity

Compressional Waves Use a metal spring toy to create waves of differing wavelengths, then of differing frequency. Have your students describe how they accomplished each. L2

Teacher FYI

Heinrich Hertz The hertz is named for the German physicist Heinrich Hertz. Hertz showed that radio waves are electromagnetic waves, as is light. He produced electromagnetic waves in his laboratory, and he pioneered broadcasting and receiving radio waves.

Differentiated Instruction

English-Language Learners Have students create an illustrated glossary of new terms. Have students write the term on one side of an index card and the definition and an illustration showing what the term means on the other side of the card.

Quick Demo
Measuring Wavelength

Materials meterstick; overhead transparency, projector and pen

Estimated Time five minutes

Procedure Draw transverse waves on the board or on the overhead transparency. Be sure the wavelengths are of equal size. With a meterstick, measure the wavelength of the waves at several heights. Show students that, no matter which two points are chosen to measure wavelength, if the points correspond, the answer is always the same. L2

LS **Visual-Spatial**

Use Science Words

Word Usage Have students use the word *frequency* to refer to something other than waves. Possible answer: He looked at his watch with great frequency, glancing at it three times in one minute. Have students explain how the everyday use of the word frequency relates to its use in describing waves. When something has a greater frequency, it occurs more often within a given time period. When waves have a greater frequency, more of them pass a particular point within a given time period. L2

LS **Linguistic**

Discussion

Traveling Sound Why does sound travel faster in solids than in gases? The particles in solids are close together, and they bump into each other more often than do the particles in a gas. Why does sound travel faster in warm air than it does in cold air? Gas particles travel faster in warm air than they do in cold air, and they bump into each other more often. L3

LS **Logical-Mathematical**

Reading Check

Answer As frequency increases, wavelength decreases.

Wavelength Is Related to Frequency If you make transverse waves with a rope, you increase the frequency by moving the rope up and down faster. Moving the rope faster also makes the wavelength shorter. This relationship is always true: as frequency increases, wavelength decreases. **Figure 10** compares the wavelengths and frequencies of two different waves.

The frequency of a wave is always equal to the rate of vibration of the source that creates it. If you move the rope up, down, and back up in 1 s, the frequency of the wave you generate is 1 Hz. If you move the rope up, down, and back up five times in 1 s, the resulting wave has a frequency of 5 Hz.

Reading Check *How are the wavelength and frequency of a wave related?*

Wave Speed

You're at a large stadium watching a baseball game, but you're high up in the bleachers, far from the action. The batter swings and you see the ball rise. An instant later, you hear the crack of the bat hitting the ball. You see the impact before you hear it because light waves travel much faster than sound waves. Therefore, the light waves reflected from the flying ball reach your eyes before the sound waves created by the crack of the bat reach your ears.

The speed of a wave depends on the medium it is traveling through. Sound waves usually travel faster in liquids and solids than they do in gases. However, light waves travel more slowly in liquids and solids than they do in gases or in empty space. Also, sound waves usually travel faster in a material when the temperature of the material is increased. For example, sound waves travel faster in air at 20°C than in air at 0°C.

Figure 10 The wavelength of a wave decreases as the frequency increases.

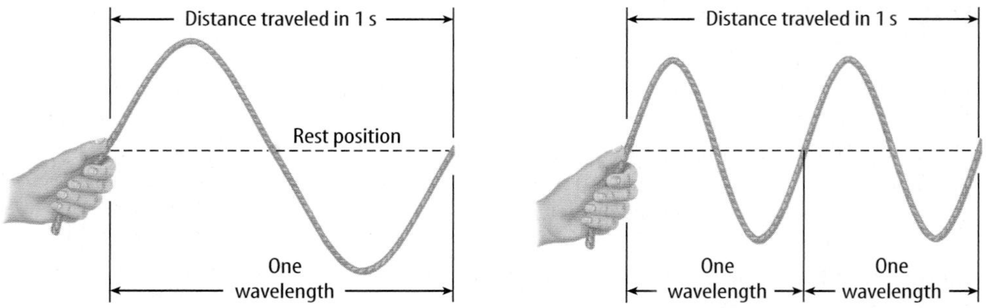

The rope is moved down, up, and down again one time in 1 s. One wavelength is created on the rope.

The rope is shaken down, up, and down again twice in 1 s. Two wavelengths are created on the rope.

Visual Learning

Figure 10 Why might it be more difficult to measure the exact wavelength of a compressional wave than that of a transverse wave? It's difficult to determine where compressions begin and where they end. L2 LS **Logical-Mathematical**

Teacher FYI

Speed of Light The first widely accepted value for the speed of light was calculated by Ole Rømer in 1676. He realized that the periods of the orbits of Jupiter's moons appeared shorter when Earth approached Jupiter and longer when Earth receded from Jupiter. His value for the speed of light was about two-thirds the modern value.

Calculating Wave Speed You can calculate the speed of a wave, represented by v, by multiplying its frequency times its wavelength. Wavelength is represented by the Greek letter *lambda* (λ), and frequency is represented by f.

Wave Speed Equation

speed (in m/s) = frequency (in Hz) × wavelength (in m)

$$v = f\lambda$$

Why does multiplying the frequency unit Hz by the distance unit m give the unit for speed, m/s? Recall that the SI unit Hz is the same as 1/s. Multiplying m × Hz equals m × 1/s, which equals m/s.

INTEGRATE Social Studies

Deadly Ocean Waves Tsunamis can cause serious damage when they hit land. These waves can measure up to 30 m tall and can travel faster than 700 km/h. Research which areas of the world are most vulnerable to tsunamis. Describe the effects of a tsunami that has occurred in these areas.

Applying Math — Solve a Simple Equation

THE SPEED OF SOUND What is the speed of a sound wave that has a wavelength of 2.00 m and a frequency of 170.5 Hz?

IDENTIFY known values and the unknown value

Identify the known values:

wavelength of 2.0 m → means → $\lambda = 2.00$ m

frequency of 170.5 Hz → means → $f = 170.5$ Hz

Identify the unknown value:

the speed of a sound wave → means → $v = ?$ m/s

SOLVE the problem

Substitute the known values $\lambda = 2.00$ m and $f = 170.5$ Hz into the wave speed equation:

$$v = f\lambda = (170.5\ \text{Hz})\ (2.00\ \text{m}) = 341\ \text{m/s}$$

CHECK the answer

Does your answer seem reasonable? Check your answer by dividing the wave speed you calculated by the wavelength given in the problem. The result should be the frequency given in the problem.

Practice Problems

1. A wave traveling in water has a frequency of 500.0 Hz and a wavelength of 3.0 m. What is the speed of the wave?
2. The lowest-pitched sounds humans can hear have a frequency of 20.0 Hz. What is the wavelength of these sound waves if their wave speed is 340.0 m/s?
3. The highest-pitched sound humans can hear have a wavelength of 0.017 m in air. What is the frequency of these sound waves if their wave speed is 340.0 m/s?

For more practice problems go to page 879, and visit Math Practice at gpescience.com.

INTEGRATE Social Studies

Deadly Ocean Waves all coastal areas of the Pacific Ocean; loss of life, property and land

IDENTIFYING Misconceptions

Tsunamis Tsunamis are sometimes mistakenly called *tidal waves*, which may cause students to think they are related to tides. A tsunami is set off by an underwater geological disturbance; tides are the result of gravitational interactions between Earth, the Moon, and the Sun. Ordinary waves are stirred up by wind. Point out to students that this is a good example of the wide range of disturbances that can transfer energy by waves.

Applying Math

Math Standards

National: 1, 2, 9

Answers to Practice Problems

1. $v = 3.0\ \text{m} \times 500\ \text{Hz} =$ 1,500 m/s.
2. $\lambda = \dfrac{340\ \text{m/s}}{20\ \text{Hz}} = 17\ \text{m}$
3. $f = \dfrac{340\ \text{m/s}}{0.017\ \text{m}} = 20{,}000\ \text{Hz}$

Reading Strategy

Illustrations Working in pairs, have students make their own illustrations that show the concepts of wavelength, frequency and period, wave speed, and amplitude of transverse and compressional waves. Have students read, illustrate, and reread to check their comprehension as captured by their illustrations.

Curriculum Connection

Math Tell students that as frequency decreases, the wavelength increases if the speed of the wave is constant. Ask students what the relationship between wavelength and frequency is called when the wave speed is constant. They are inversely proportional. L3 LS **Linguistic**

Visual Learning

Figure 11 Point out to students the areas of compression and rarefaction in each of the waves in **Figure 11**. Which wave has denser compressions? the top wave Which has the less dense rarefactions? also the top wave L2
LS **Visual-Spatial**

Make a Model

Penny Compressions Have students use pennies and 11 × 17 paper to make models of compression waves. Have students divide the paper into twelve equal sections from left to right. Label the sections *R* (for rarefaction), *T* (for transition), and *C* (for compression). The twelve sections in order should be labeled *R, T, C, T, R, T, C, T, R, T, C, T*. Tell students to fill the areas with pennies to model a compressional wave. The areas of compression should have the most pennies and the areas of rarefaction should have the fewest pennies. Ask students how they would need to move the pennies to increase the amplitude of the wave. Move pennies out of the rarefaction section and put them in the compression section. L2
P LS **Visual-Spatial**

Caption Answer

Figure 12 Move the rope only a small distance up and down for smaller amplitude, and a larger distance up and down for greater amplitude.

Post Reading

Reciprocal Teaching Have the class count off as ones and twos. Assign ones to become experts in transverse waves and twos to become experts in compressional waves. Have students work in small groups as they study their own assignments. Then, have ones and twos pair off for reciprocal teaching.

Amplitude and Energy

Why do some earthquakes cause terrible damage, while others are hardly felt? This is because the amount of energy a wave transfers can vary. **Amplitude** is related to the energy transferred by a wave. The greater the wave's amplitude, the more energy the wave transfers. Amplitude is measured differently for compressional and transverse waves.

Amplitude of Compressional Waves The amplitude of a compressional wave is related to how tightly the medium is pushed together at the compressions. The denser the medium is at the compressions, the larger its amplitude is and the more energy the wave transfers. For example, it takes more energy to push the coils in a coiled-spring toy tightly together than to barely move them. The closer the coils are in a compression, the farther apart they are in a rarefaction. So, the less dense the medium is at the rarefactions, the more energy the wave transfers. **Figure 11** shows compressional waves with different amplitudes.

Figure 11 The amplitude of a compressional wave depends on the density of the medium in the compressions and rarefactions.

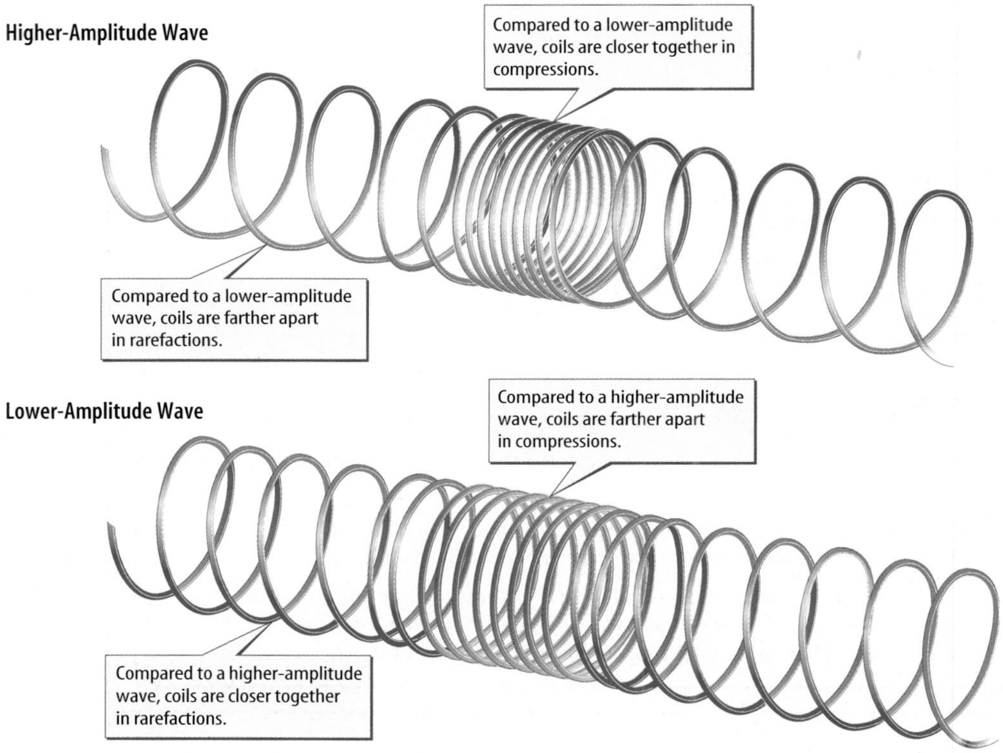

Differentiated Instruction

Challenge Tell students that AM stands for "amplitude modulation" and that FM stands for "frequency modulation." Explain that to modulate means to vary the frequency or amplitude. Have students research and report on AM and FM radio technology. In AM signals, the amplitude is varied to convey the message; in FM signals, the frequency is varied. L3 LS **Linguistic**

Curriculum Connection

Music Play a recording of a piece of music for students. Make sure the music includes soft sections and loud sections. Ask students to identify the portions of the music in which the sound waves have a large amplitude and those where the sound waves have a lower amplitude. The loud sections have high amplitude waves and the soft sections have low amplitude waves. L2 LS **Auditory-Musical**

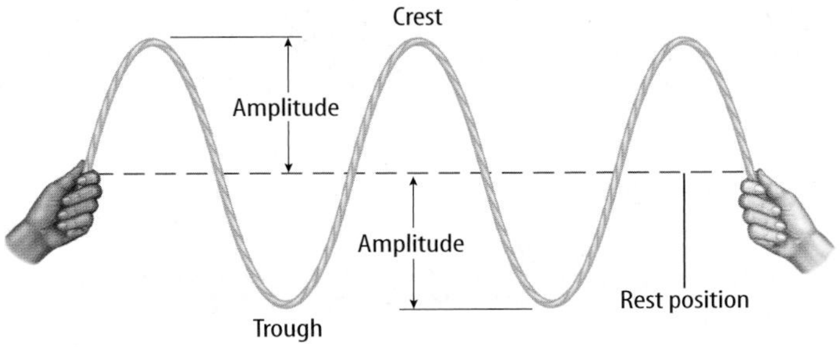

Figure 12 The amplitude of a transverse wave is the distance between a crest or a trough and the position of the medium at rest. **Describe** *how you could create waves with different amplitudes in a piece of rope.*

Amplitude of Transverse Waves If you've ever been knocked over by an ocean wave, you know that the higher the wave, the more energy it transfers. Remember that the amplitude of a wave increases as the energy transferred by the wave increases. So a tall ocean wave has a greater amplitude than a short ocean wave does. The amplitude of any transverse wave is the distance from the crest or trough of the wave to the rest position of the medium, as shown in **Figure 12.**

section 2 review

Summary

The Parts of a Wave

- Transverse waves have repeating high points called crests and low points called troughs.
- Compressional waves have repeating high-density regions called compressions, and low-density regions called rarefactions.

Wavelength, Frequency, and Period

- Wavelength is the distance between a point on a wave and the nearest point just like it.
- A wave's frequency is the number of wavelengths passing a fixed point each second.
- A wave's period is the amount of time it takes one wavelength to pass a fixed point.

Wave Speed and Amplitude

- The speed of a wave depends on the material it is traveling in, and on the temperature.
- The speed of a wave is the product of its frequency and its wavelength:

$$v = f\lambda$$

- As the amplitude of a wave increases, the energy transferred by the wave increases.

Self Check

1. **Describe** the difference between a compressional wave with a large amplitude and one with a small amplitude.
2. **Describe** how the wavelength of a wave changes when the wave slows down but its frequency doesn't change.
3. **Explain** how the frequency of a wave changes when the period of the wave increases.
4. **Form a hypothesis** to explain why a sound wave travels faster in a solid than in a gas.
5. **Think Critically** You make a transverse wave by shaking the end of a long rope up and down. Explain how you would shake the end of the rope to make the wavelength shorter. How would you shake the end of the rope to increase the energy transferred by the wave?

Applying Math

6. **Calculate** the frequency of a water wave that has a wavelength of 0.5 m and a speed of 4.0 m/s.
7. **Calculate Wavelength** An FM radio station broadcasts radio waves with a frequency of 100,000,000 Hz. What is the wavelength of these radio waves if they travel at a speed of 300,000 km/s?

section 2 review

1. A compressional wave with a larger amplitude has particles of the medium closer together in the compressions and farther apart in the rarefactions.
2. The wavelength decreases.
3. As the period increases, the frequency decreases.
4. The particles in a solid are more closely spaced, so that collisions between particles occur more frequently than in a gas, where particles are farther apart.
5. To make the wavelength shorter, increase the frequency of the wave by shaking the end of the rope up and down more rapidly. To increase the amplitude, increase the distance that the end of the rope is moved up and down.
6. $f = \frac{v}{\lambda} = \frac{(4.0 \text{ m/s})}{(0.5 \text{ m})} = 8.0 \text{ Hz}$
7. $\lambda = \frac{v}{f} = \frac{(300{,}000{,}000 \text{ m/s})}{(100{,}000{,}000 \text{ Hz})} = 3.0 \text{ m}$

3 Assess

DAILY INTERVENTION

Check for Understanding

Visual-Spatial Have students draw a diagram of a transverse wave and compressional wave. Have students label the following parts of the waves: trough, crest, rest position, rarefaction, compression, and wavelength.

Reteach

Transverse Waves Give students a piece of string about 60 cm long. Instruct them to work in pairs to shake the string to form a transverse wave. Have students count the number of waves and measure the average wavelength. Suggest that they change the wave so it has a greater amplitude, then change it again so it has shorter wavelengths. What happens to the frequency? It increases with shorter wavelengths, but it should not change with change in amplitude. L2 ELL COOP LEARN

LS **Kinesthetic**

Assessment

Performance Have students shake a coiled spring toy to form a transverse wave, and then determine which variable (amplitude, wavelength, or frequency) cannot be controlled. Wavelength can be controlled only indirectly by changing frequency. Use **PASC,** p. 89. L2

Virtual Labs

Waves *What are some charateristics of waves?*

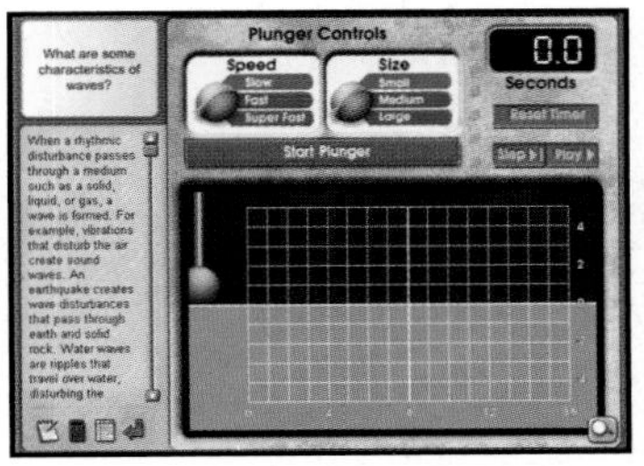

BENCH TESTED

Real-World Problem

Purpose Students will investigate the relationship between wave speed and tension. L2 ELL COOP LEARN

Process Skills observe, compare and contrast, interpret data, infer

Time Required 30 minutes

Alternate Materials Telephone cord can be used to demonstrate the behavior of coiled material.

Safety Precautions eye protection, laboratory aprons

Procedure

Teaching Strategy Caution students before they collect their materials to be careful with the spring toys. They should not be overstretched. If the lengths suggested in the text of the lab will overstretch the toys available, designate new lengths to the students.

Troubleshooting If students have difficulty timing the pulses, have them count the wavelengths instead.

Analyze Your Data

Expected Outcome Wave speed should be greater in waves 4 through 6.

Answers to Questions

1. Answers will vary.
2. Answers will vary.
3. Answers will vary.

Conclude and Apply

1. As the length increased, the tension increased.
2. As the tension increased, the wave speed increased; by stretching the toy more.

LAB

Wave Speed and Tension

Before playing her violin, a violinist must adjust the tension, or the amount of force pulling on each end of the string, to make the violin produce the correct notes.

Real-World Problem

How does the tension in a material affect the waves traveling in the material?

Goal

- **Determine** the relationship between tension and wave speed.

Materials

coiled-spring toy
stopwatch
meterstick

Safety Precautions

Procedure

1. Attach one end of the spring to a chair leg so that the spring rests on a smooth floor.
2. Stretch the spring along the floor to a length of 1 m.
3. Make a compressional wave by squeezing together several coils and then releasing them.
4. Have your partner time how long a pulse takes to travel two or three lengths of the spring. Record this measurement in the *Wave Time* column of your data table. Record the distance the wave traveled in your data table.
5. Repeat steps 3 and 4 two more times for waves 2 and 3.
6. Stretch the spring to a length of 1.5 m.
7. Repeat steps 3 and 4 for waves 4, 5, and 6.

Data Table

	Distance (m)	Wave Time (s)	Wave Speed (m/s)
Wave 1			
Wave 2			
Wave 3			
Wave 4			
Wave 5			
Wave 6			

Analyze Your Data

1. **Calculate** the wave speed for each wave using the formula:

   speed = distance/time

2. Calculate the average speed of the waves on the spring with a length of 1.0 m by adding the measured wave speeds and dividing by 3.
3. Calculate the average speed of the waves on the spring with a length of 1.5 m.

Conclude and Apply

1. How did the tension in the spring change as the length of the spring increased?
2. How did the wave speed depend on the tension? How could you make the waves travel even faster? Test your prediction.

Communicating Your Data

Compare your results with those of other students in your class. Discuss why results might be different.

Communicating Your Data

After allowing the students to discuss their results in small groups, list on the board all groups' average wave speeds. If there are significant differences, lead the discussion to an investigation of the toys to see if the medium could be the cause of the differing results. L2

Assessment

Process Provide students with a coiled-spring toy whose stiffness differs considerably from the ones used in lab. Ask them to predict the wave speed in this toy compared to the spring used in the lab. Give students an opportunity to test their predictions. Use **Performance Assessment in the Science Classroom,** p. 93. L2

section 3 The Behavior of Waves

Reading Guide

What You'll Learn
- **State** the law of reflection.
- **Explain** why waves change direction when they travel from one material to another.
- **Compare and contrast** refraction and diffraction.
- **Describe** how waves interfere with each other.

Why It's Important

You can hear an echo, see shadows, and check your reflection in a mirror because of how waves behave.

Review Vocabulary

perpendicular: a line that forms a 90-degree angle with another line

New Vocabulary
- refraction
- diffraction
- interference
- standing wave
- resonance

Reflection

If you are one of the last people to leave your school building at the end of the day, you'll probably find the hallways quiet and empty. When you close your locker door, the sound echoes down the empty hall. Your footsteps also make a hollow sound. Thinking you're alone, you may be startled by your own reflection in a classroom window. The echoes and your image looking back at you from the window are caused by wave reflection.

Reflection occurs when a wave strikes an object and bounces off it. All types of waves—including sound, water, and light waves—can be reflected. How does the reflection of light allow the boy in **Figure 13** to see himself in the mirror? It happens in two steps. First, light strikes his face and bounces off. Then, the light reflected off his face strikes the mirror and is reflected into his eyes.

Echoes A similar thing happens to sound waves when your footsteps echo. Sound waves form when your foot hits the floor and the waves travel through the air to both your ears and other objects. Sometimes, when the sound waves hit another object, they reflect off it and come back to you. Your ears hear the sound again, a few seconds after you first heard your footstep.

Bats and dolphins use echoes to learn about their surroundings. A dolphin makes a clicking sound and listens to the echoes. These echoes enable the dolphin to locate nearby objects.

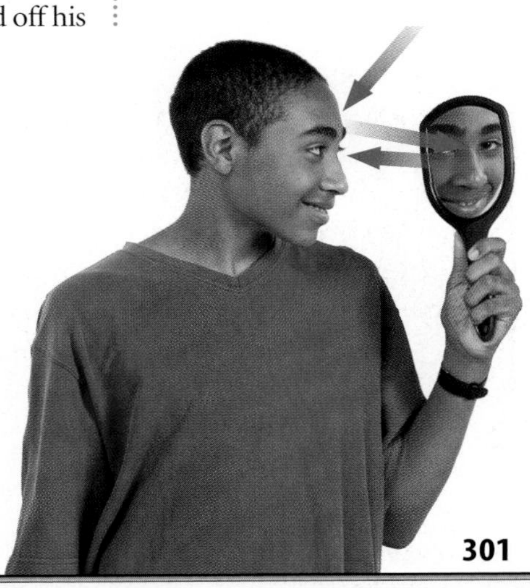

Figure 13 The light that strikes the boy's face is reflected into the mirror. The light then reflects off the mirror into his eyes.
List *examples of waves that can be reflected.*

Section 3 Resource Manager

Chapter *Fast File* Resources
- Transparency Activity, p. 46
- Directed Reading for Content Mastery, pp. 21–22
- Enrichment, p. 32
- Lab Activity, pp. 13–16
- Reinforcement, p. 29
- Lab Worksheet, pp. 7–8
- MiniLAB, p. 4

Reading and Writing Skill Activities, p. 33
Home and Community Involvement, p. 38
Performance Assessment in the Science Classroom, p. 52
Cultural Diversity, p. 61

1 Motivate

INTERACTIVE CHALKBOARD PowerPoint® Presentations An editable Microsoft® PowerPoint® presentation is available on **Interactive Chalkboard** CD-ROM.

Bellringer

Section Focus Transparencies also are available on the Interactive Chalkboard CD-ROM. L2 ELL

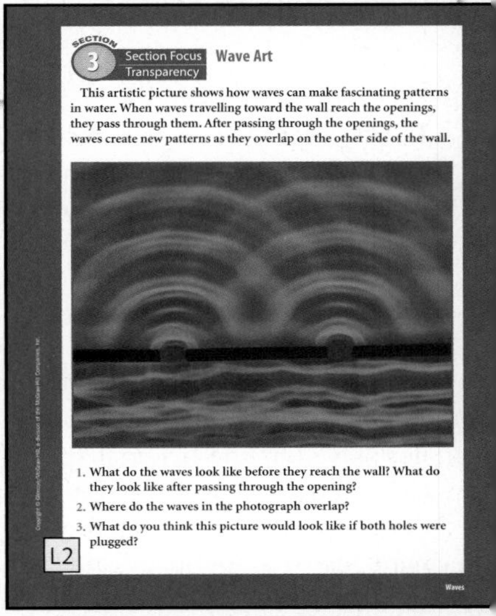
Section 3 Section Focus Transparency **Wave Art**

This artistic picture shows how waves can make fascinating patterns in water. When waves travelling toward the wall reach the openings, they pass through them. After passing through the openings, the waves create new patterns as they overlap on the other side of the wall.

1. What do the waves look like before they reach the wall? What do they look like after passing through the opening?
2. Where do the waves in the photograph overlap?
3. What do you think this picture would look like if both holes were plugged?

L2

Waves

Reading Preview

Tie to Prior Knowledge

Waves Ask students to contrast the movement of a ball in air and in water. Tell students that they will learn how a wave travels through different media.

K-W-L Have students create a Know-Want-Learn chart. Students should tell what they know about the vocabulary words. Ask them to think of what they want to know about light, sound, and music. Have them find answers as they read.

Caption Answer

Figure 13 Possible answers: water waves, sound waves, light waves.

2 Teach

Activity

Tennis Ball Angles Have students sit on the floor and roll a tennis ball against a wall. Have them first roll the ball directly toward the wall and then at increasing angles to the normal. Ask them what they notice about how the ball bounces off the wall as the angle to the normal is increased. The greater the angle between the normal and the ball's path to the wall, the greater the angle to the normal the ball's path away from the wall. L1 ELL LS **Kinesthetic**

Use an Analogy

Turning Sleds Ask students whether they've ever ridden on a sled that's moved from snow to ice or mud. If the sled hit the ice or mud at an angle, one of its runners hit the ice or mud before the other. That runner then started moving more quickly or more slowly while the other runner stayed at the original speed, causing the sled to turn. Tell students that this is similar to what happens to a sound, seismic, or light wave when it moves from one medium to another. L2

Reading Check

Answer when a wave changes speed as it moves from one medium to another at an angle

Use Science Words

Word Origins Have students look up the word *refraction* or *refract* in a dictionary and find the Latin word from which it is derived. Ask students why this word is appropriate to use to describe refraction. The word *refract* comes from the Latin word *refringere,* which means "to break up or break open." When you look at the pencil through water, it looks as if it's broken. L2 LS **Linguistic**

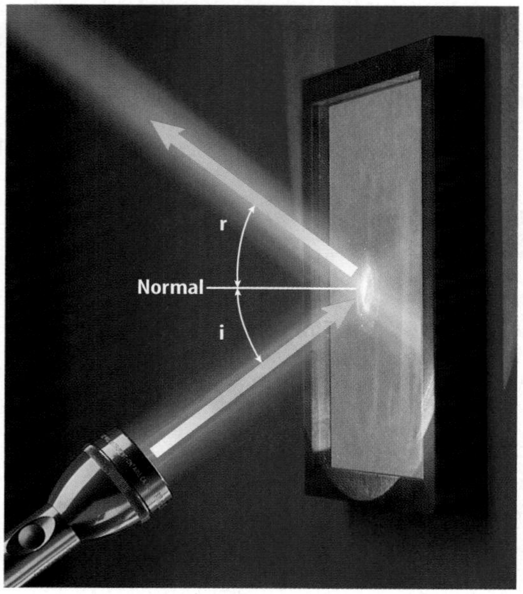

Figure 14 A flashlight beam is made of light waves. When any wave is reflected, the angle of incidence, *i*, equals the angle of reflection, *r*.

The Law of Reflection Look at the two light beams in **Figure 14.** The beam striking the mirror is called the incident beam. The beam that bounces off the mirror is called the reflected beam. The line drawn perpendicular to the surface of the mirror is called the normal. The angle formed by the incident beam and the normal is the angle of incidence, labeled *i.* The angle formed by the reflected beam and the normal is the angle of reflection, labeled *r.* According to the law of reflection, the angle of incidence is equal to the angle of reflection. All reflected waves obey this law. Objects that bounce from a surface sometimes behave like waves that are reflected from a surface. For example, suppose you throw a bounce pass while playing basketball. The angle between the ball's direction and the normal to the floor is the same before and after it bounces.

Refraction

Do you notice anything unusual in **Figure 15?** The pencil looks as if it is broken into two pieces. But if you pulled the pencil out of the water, you would see that it is unbroken. This illusion is caused by refraction. How does it work?

Remember that a wave's speed depends on the medium it is moving through. When a wave passes from one medium to another—such as when a light wave passes from air to water—it changes speed. If the wave is traveling at an angle when it passes from one medium to another, it changes direction, or bends, as it changes speed. **Refraction** is the bending of a wave caused by a change in its speed as it moves from one medium to another. The greater the change in speed is, the more the wave bends.

Reading Check *When does refraction occur?*

Figure 16A on the next page shows what happens when a wave passes into a material in which it slows down. The wave is refracted (bent) toward the normal. **Figure 16B** shows what happens when a wave passes into a medium in which it speeds up. Then the wave is refracted away from the normal.

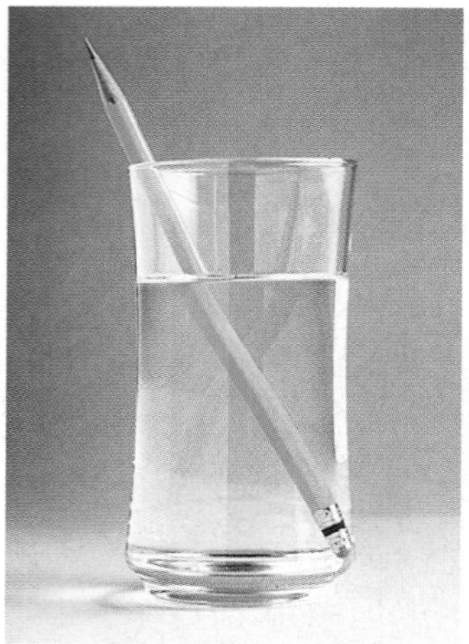

Figure 15 The pencil looks like it is broken at the surface of the water because of refraction.

Science Journal

Ray Diagrams Have students trace into their Science Journals **Figure 14** and **Figure 16**. Then ask them to use the tracings to construct ray diagrams of the reflection and refraction shown in each one. Tell them to be sure to include the line normal to the surface in each diagram and to measure and label the angles. L2 LS **Visual-Spatial**

Figure 16 Light waves travel more slowly in water than in air. This causes light waves to change direction when they move from water to air or air to water.
Predict *how the beam would bend if the speed were the same in both air and water.*

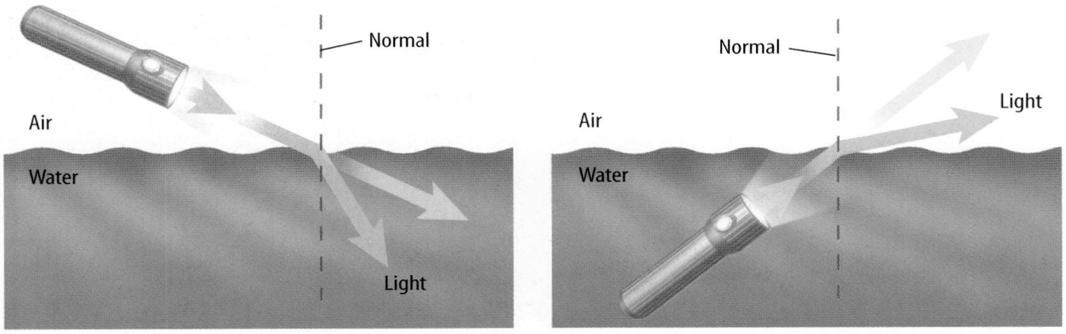

A When light waves travel from air to water, they slow down and bend toward the normal.

B When light waves travel from water to air, they speed up and bend away from the normal.

Refraction of Light in Water You may have noticed that objects that are under water seem closer to the surface than they really are. **Figure 17** shows how refraction causes this illusion. In the figure, the light waves reflected from the boy's foot are refracted away from the normal and enter your eyes. However, your brain assumes that all light waves have traveled in a straight line. The light waves that enter your eyes seem to have come from a foot that was higher in the water. This is also why the pencil in **Figure 15** seems broken. The light waves coming from the part of the pencil that is under water are refracted, but your brain interprets them as if they have traveled in a straight line. However, the light waves coming from the part of the pencil above the water are not refracted. So, the part of the pencil that is under water looks as if it has shifted.

Figure 17 Light waves from the boy's foot bend away from the normal as they pass from water to air. This makes his foot look closer to the surface than it really is.
Infer *whether the boy's knee would seem closer to the surface than it is.*

Caption Answers

Figure 16 The beam wouldn't bend at all. It's the difference in speed that makes the light bend.

Figure 17 Yes, for the same reasons.

Differentiated Instruction

Challenge Light travels at a different speed through glass than it does through air. Ask students to find out whether light travels faster or slower in glass than it does in air. slower Have students research to discover how refraction of light waves through glass is made useful in optometry. Ask them to depict their findings on an informational poster. L3 LS **Logical-Mathematical** P

Teacher FYI

Medium Refraction How much a wave will be refracted when passing from one medium to another depends on the media involved, the angle of the wave, and sometimes its frequency. Some waves with higher frequencies are refracted more than those with lower frequencies in some media.

Quick Demo
Observing Diffraction

Materials petri dish, water, pen or pencil, overhead projector, scissors, small pieces of cardboard

Estimated Time 10 minutes

Procedure Place the water-filled petri dish on the overhead projector. Use the pen or pencil to make waves in the water. Cut the cardboard pieces into several different shapes, and place them into the dish, one at a time and in different combinations. Have students observe how each piece or combination of pieces causes a different diffraction pattern. L2 ELL IS Visual-Spatial

Reading Check

Answer Refraction occurs when waves change direction as they change speed; diffraction occurs when waves bend around an object.

Make a Model

Slit Diffraction Have students use rectangular glass baking dishes and flat pieces of metal or plastic to make a model of the diffraction of water waves through a slit. Have students tape two flat pieces of metal or plastic so they stand vertically across the width of the baking dish. Be sure they leave an open slit between the two pieces. Then have students fill the baking dish with water, use pencils to generate waves, and observe the diffraction. Suggest that students experiment with slit widths until they find the one that diffracts the water waves the most. L2 IS Kinesthetic

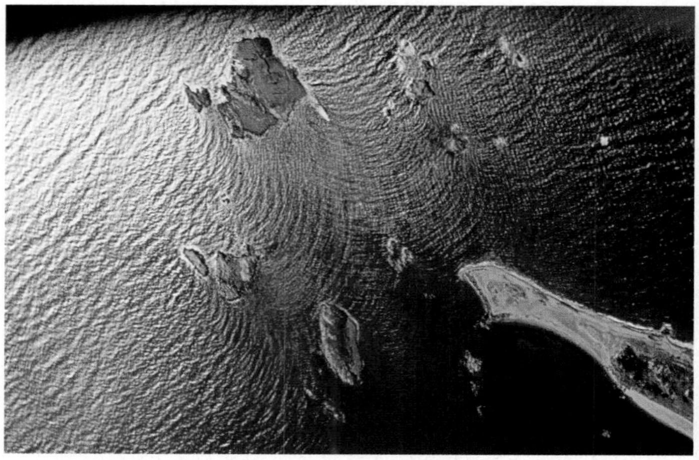

Figure 18 Diffraction causes ocean waves to change direction as they pass a group of islands.

Diffraction

When waves strike an object, several things can happen. Some of the wave's energy can be absorbed by the object. The waves can also be reflected. If the object is transparent, light waves can be refracted as they pass through it. Sometimes, the waves may be both reflected and refracted. If you look into a glass window, sometimes you can see your reflection in the window, as well as objects behind it.

Waves also can behave another way when they strike an object. The waves can bend around the object. **Figure 18** shows how ocean waves change direction and bend after they strike an island. **Diffraction** occurs when an object causes a wave to change direction and bend around it. Diffraction and refraction both cause waves to bend. The difference is that refraction occurs when waves pass through an object, while diffraction occurs when waves pass around an object.

Reading Check *How do diffraction and refraction differ?*

Waves also can be diffracted when they pass through a narrow opening, as shown in **Figure 19.** After they pass through the opening, the waves spread out. In this case, the waves are bending around the corners of the opening.

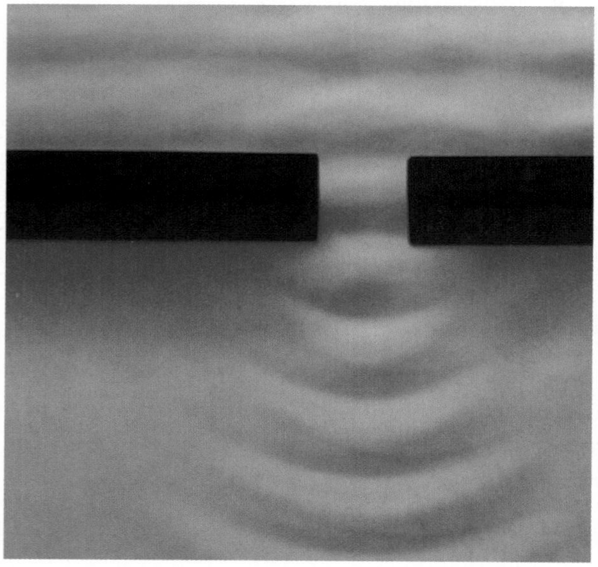

Figure 19 When water waves pass through a small opening in a barrier, they diffract and spread out after they pass through the hole.

Reading Strategy

Paired Reading Have students read this section in pairs. Ask them to stop after each topic and talk about what they learned. Then, they should formulate a sentence or two that explains the main idea and supporting details to add to their K-W-L charts.

Diffraction and Wavelength How much does a wave bend when it strikes an object or an opening? The amount of diffraction that occurs depends on how big the obstacle or opening is compared to the wavelength, as shown in **Figure 20.** When an obstacle is smaller than the wavelength, the waves bend around it. But if the obstacle is larger than the wavelength, the waves do not diffract as much. In fact, if the obstacle is much larger than the wavelength, almost no diffraction occurs. The obstacle casts a shadow because almost no waves bend around it.

Hearing Around Corners For example, suppose that you're walking down a hallway and hear sounds coming from the lunchroom before you reach the open lunchroom door. However, you can't see into the room until you reach the doorway. Why can you hear the sound waves but not see the light waves while you're still in the hallway? The wavelengths of sound waves are similar in size to a door opening. Sound waves diffract around the door and spread out down the hallway. Light waves have a much shorter wavelength. They are hardly diffracted at all by the door. This is why you can't see into the room until you get close to the door.

Diffraction of Radio Waves Diffraction also affects your radio's reception. AM radio waves have longer wavelengths than FM radio waves do. Because of their longer wavelengths, AM radio waves diffract around obstacles such as buildings and mountains. The FM waves with their short wavelengths do not diffract as much. As a result, AM radio reception is often better than FM reception around tall buildings and natural barriers such as hills.

Science Online

Topic: Diffraction
Visit gpescience.com for Web links to information about diffraction.

Activity Research the wave lengths of several types of waves. For each wave type, give an example of an object that could cause diffraction to occur.

Figure 20 The diffraction of waves around an obstacle depends on the wavelength and the size of the obstacle.

More diffraction occurs when the wavelength is the same size as the obstacle.

Less diffraction occurs when the wavelength is smaller than the obstacle.

Teacher FYI

X Rays Because the wavelengths of X rays are about the same size as the distances between atoms in crystals, X rays are diffracted by crystals. This phenomenon is exploited in X-ray crystallography, in which crystals are bombarded from different angles by X rays, and the crystal structure is determined by the diffraction of the X rays. This method has been used to determine the structure of thousands of organic, inorganic, organometallic, and biological compounds.

Discussion

Television Reception TV reception from antennas tends to be poor in mountainous regions. Based on what you read here, what type of radio waves would you guess delivers television signals? Why? FM waves. Due to their short wavelengths, they do not bend around natural obstacles like mountains. L2

Curriculum Connection

Art Have students use reflection, refraction, and diffraction to create artwork. The art could be as simple as sketching how refraction distorts objects viewed through water or as involved as photographing the diffraction patterns of light waves. Students may wish to research and experiment with how the surface of a CD diffracts light. Have students explain the phenomenon at work in their art. L2 ELL P LS **Visual-Spatial**

Interference

Suppose two waves are traveling toward each other on a long rope, as in **Figure 21A.** What will happen when the two waves meet? If you did this experiment, you would find that the two waves pass right through each other, and each one continues to travel in its original direction, as shown in **Figure 21B** and **Figure 21C.** If you look closely at the waves when they meet each other in **Figure 21B,** you will see a wave that looks different from either of the two original waves. When the two waves arrive at the same place at the same time, they combine to form a new wave. When two or more waves overlap and combine to form a new wave, the process is called **interference.** This new wave exists only while the two original waves continue to overlap. The two ways that the waves can combine are called constructive interference and destructive interference.

Figure 21 Interference occurs while two waves are overlapping. Then the waves combine to form a new wave. Two waves traveling on a rope can interfere with each other.

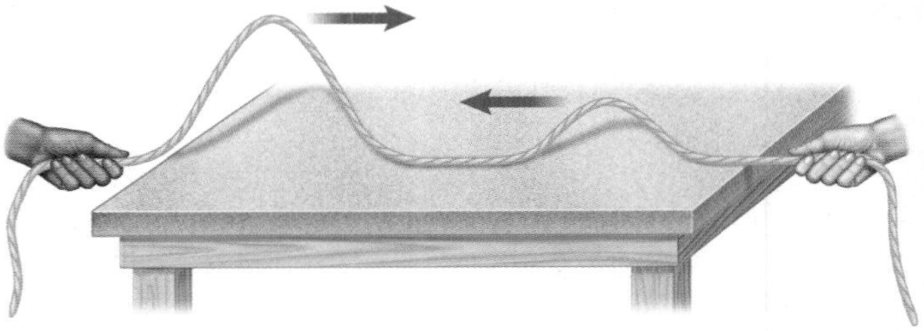

A Two waves move toward each other on a rope.

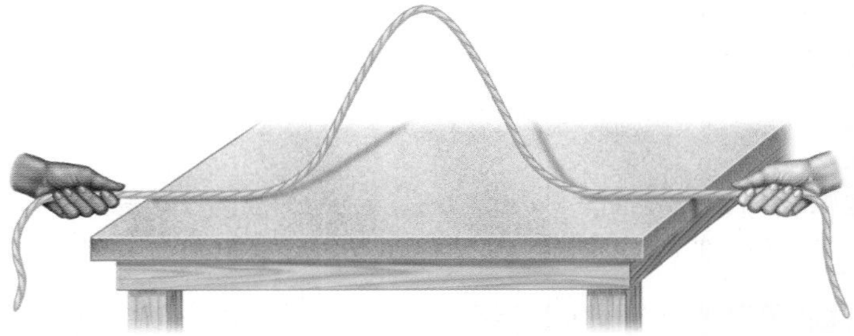

B As the waves overlap, they interfere to form a new wave. **Identify** *What is the amplitude of the new wave?*

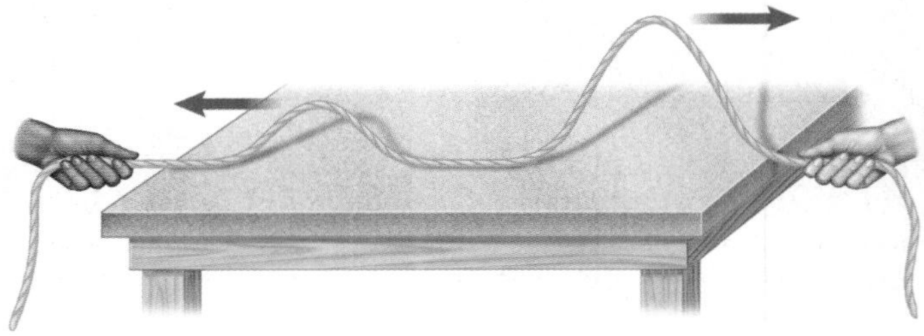

C While the two waves overlap, they continue to move right through each other. Afterward, they continue moving unchanged, as if they had never met.

Caption Answer

Figure 21 The sum of the amplitudes of the original waves.

Inquiry Lab

Addition of Waves

Purpose to model interfering waves

Possible Materials translucent straws, sheet of cardboard or poster paper, marker, tape

Estimated Time one class session

Teaching Strategies

- Make a 2 × 4 grid on a vertical piece of paper with each cell the same size. Use the top half as one set of x and y axes to draw a sine wave. Draw a sine wave of three times the frequency on the x and y axes formed in the bottom half.
- Cover the top with straws (resting on the halfway line) and tape the straws down. Use the marker to trace the sine wave onto the straws. Number the straws on their bottom ends from left to right. Now remove the tape and cut out the sine wave from the tops of the straws.
- Place the bottoms of the straws along the bottom wave. The tops of the straws now show the wave formed by the addition of these two waves.
- You can also try this on a graphing calculator. Graph $y = \sin(x)$, $y = \sin(3x)$, then $y = \sin(x) + \sin(3x)$.
- Extend this lab to other wave additions. Allow students to explore other questions about waves.

For additional inquiry activities, see Science Inquiry Lab Manual.

Cultural Diversity

Mayan Echoes If you clap your hands in the Mayan temple of Kukulkan at Chichén Itzá in Mexico, you're greeted with a piercing echo. Many believe this echo sounds like the call of a quetzal bird. The bird is native to the region and prized for its bright colors and long tail. Archaeologists are studying the architecture of the temple to determine whether the Maya built it with this effect in mind. The shrieking, birdlike echo is produced by sound waves being diffracted by the gaps in the steps of one of the large staircases. The sound's amplification comes from waves interfering at just the right places.

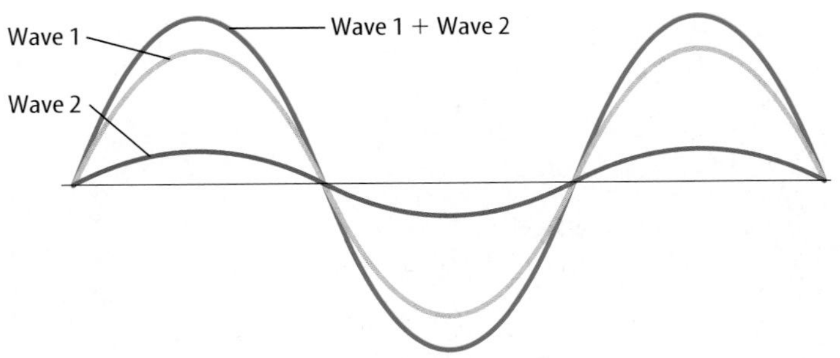

Constructive Interference

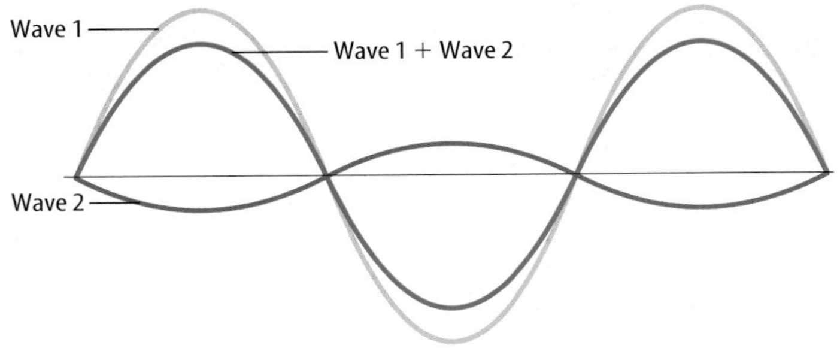

Destructive Interference

A If Wave 1 and Wave 2 overlap, they constructively interfere and form the green wave. Wave 1 and Wave 2 are in phase.

B If Wave 1 and Wave 2 overlap, they destructively interfere and form the green wave. Wave 1 and Wave 2 are out of phase.

Figure 22 When waves interfere with each other, constructive and destructive interference can occur. **Infer** *how the energy transferred by each wave changes when interference occurs.*

Constructive Interference In constructive interference, shown in **Figure 22A,** the waves add together. This happens when the crests of two or more transverse waves arrive at the same place at the same time and overlap. The amplitude of the new wave that forms is equal to the sum of the amplitudes of the original waves. Constructive interference also occurs when the compressions of different compressional waves overlap. If the waves are sound waves, for example, constructive interference produces a louder sound. Waves undergoing constructive interference are said to be in phase.

Destructive Interference In destructive interference, the waves subtract from each other as they overlap. This happens when the crests of one transverse wave meet the troughs of another transverse wave, as shown in **Figure 22B.** The amplitude of the new wave is the difference between the amplitudes of the waves that overlapped. With compressional waves, destructive interference occurs when the compression of one wave overlaps with the rarefaction of another wave. The compressions and rarefactions combine and form a wave with reduced amplitude. When destructive interference happens with sound waves, it causes a decrease in loudness. Waves undergoing destructive interference are said to be out of phase.

INTEGRATE Health

Noise Damage People who are exposed to constant loud noises, such as those made by airplane engines, can suffer hearing damage. Special ear protectors have been developed that use destructive interference to cancel damaging noise. With a classmate, list all the jobs you can think of that require ear protectors.

Activity

Creating Interference Position a student at each end of a jump rope, and have them make different interference patterns in the rope. Challenge the students to create both constructive and destructive interference. L2 ELL

COOP LEARN LS **Kinesthetic**

Quick Demo

Interference Effects

Materials two or more musical instruments

Estimated Time 10 minutes

Procedure Ask students who play instruments to bring them in and demonstrate what happens when two notes that have almost the same pitch are played at the same time. Students should be able to hear the beats produced by the interference between the two notes. These pulses of sound disappear when the pitches become equal, so they are used by musicians as they tune their instruments. L2 LS **Auditory-Musical**

INTEGRATE Health

Noise Damage The use of destructive interference to cancel out noise is called active noise control. In active noise control, sounds are generated that exactly cancel out the unwanted sounds. Jobs requiring ear protection include rock concert sound mixer, airport runway worker, and factory worker.

Research Have students research the various types of hearing-protection devices that are available. Have students give a brief oral report to the class describing the various types.

Caption Answer

Figure 22 Destructive interference results in less energy transferred; constructive interference results in more energy transferred than each wave transferred independently.

Fun Fact

When we listen to an orchestra, the sound waves that reach our ears have the amplitude and frequency that result from adding together all of the waves produced by the individual instruments.

Curriculum Connection

History Scientists first knew that light had wave properties when it could be shown that it produced interference patterns when passed through a slit. Have students find out whose experiments first showed this, and when. Thomas Young in 1801 L3 LS **Linguistic**

Caption Answer

Figure 23 The nodes of a standing wave form where the waves traveling in opposite directions cancel out.

Mini LAB

Purpose Students observe resonance and the conditions under which it can occur. L2 ELL

LS **Auditory-Musical**

Materials three tuning forks, two of which are at the same frequency, mallet

Teaching Strategy Demonstrate for students the best way to set a tuning fork vibrating. You don't have to hit it hard, but you do have to hit it sharply.

Analysis

The second tuning fork started vibrating, but the third one did not. The natural frequency of the second tuning fork is the same as the frequency of the waves that were hitting it from the first tuning fork, so it resonated. The natural frequency of the third tuning fork is different, so it did not resonate.

Assessment

Process Have students take the tuning forks to different areas of the classroom and see if they can find anything else that resonates with them. Use **Performance Assessment in the Science Classroom,** p. 97.

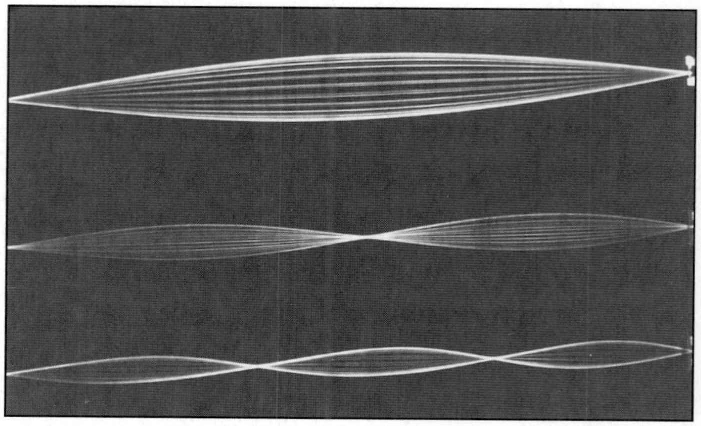

Figure 23 Standing waves form a wave pattern that seems to stay in the same place.
Explain *how nodes form in a standing wave.*

Standing Waves

When you make transverse waves with a rope, you might shake one end while your friend holds the other end still. What would happen if you both shook the rope continuously to create identical waves moving toward each other? As the two waves travel in opposite directions down the rope, they continually pass through each other. Interference takes place as the waves from each end overlap along the rope. At any point where a crest meets a crest, a new wave with a larger amplitude forms. However, at points where crests meet troughs, the waves cancel each other and no motion occurs.

The interference of the two identical waves makes the rope vibrate in a special way, as shown in **Figure 23.** The waves create a pattern of crests and troughs that do not seem to be moving. Because the wave pattern stays in one place, it is called a standing wave. A **standing wave** is a special type of wave pattern that forms when waves equal in wavelength and amplitude, but traveling in opposite directions, continuously interfere with each other. The places where the two waves always cancel are called nodes. The nodes always stay in the same place on the rope. Meanwhile, the wave pattern vibrates between the nodes.

Standing Waves in Music When the string of a violin is played with a bow, it vibrates and creates standing waves. The standing waves in the string help produce a rich, musical tone. Other instruments also rely on standing waves to produce music. Some instruments, such as flutes, create standing waves in a column of air. In other instruments, such as drums, a tightly stretched piece of material vibrates in a special way to create standing waves. As the material in a drum vibrates, nodes are created on the surface of the drum.

Visual Learning

Figure 23 Provide pairs of students with jump ropes, and ask them to create standing waves similar to those shown in **Figure 23.** L2
LS **Kinesthetic**

Resonance

You might have noticed that bells of different sizes and shapes create different notes. When you strike a bell, the bell vibrates at certain frequencies called the natural frequencies. All objects have their own natural frequencies of vibration, which depend on the object's size, shape, and the material it is made from.

There is another way to make something vibrate at its natural frequencies. Suppose you have a tuning fork that has a single natural frequency of 440 Hz. Imagine that a sound wave of the same frequency strikes the tuning fork. Because the sound wave has the same frequency as the natural frequency of the tuning fork, the tuning fork will vibrate. The process by which an object is made to vibrate by absorbing energy at its natural frequencies is called **resonance.**

Sometimes, resonance can cause an object to absorb a large amount of energy. Recall that the amplitude of a wave increases as the energy it transfers increases. In the same way, an object vibrates more strongly as it continues to absorb energy at its natural frequencies. If enough energy is absorbed, the object can vibrate so strongly that it breaks apart.

Mini LAB

Experimenting with Resonance

Procedure

1. Strike a **tuning fork** with a **mallet.**
2. Hold the vibrating tuning fork 1 cm from a **second tuning fork** that has the same frequency.
3. Strike the tuning fork again. Hold it 1 cm from a **third tuning fork** that has a different frequency.

Analysis

What happened when you held the vibrating tuning fork near each of the other two? Explain.

section 3 review

Summary

Reflection and Refraction

- When reflection of a wave occurs, the angle of incidence equals the angle of reflection.
- Refraction occurs when a wave changes direction as it moves from one medium to another.

Diffraction

- Diffraction occurs when a wave changes direction by bending around an obstacle.
- The effects of diffraction are greatest when the wavelength is nearly the obstacle's size.

Interference and Resonance

- Interference occurs when two or more waves overlap and form a new wave.
- Interference between two waves with the same wavelength and amplitude, but moving in opposite directions, produces a standing wave.
- Resonance occurs when an object is made to vibrate by absorbing energy from vibrations at its natural frequencies.

Self Check

1. **Compare** the loudness of sound waves that are in phase when they interfere with the loudness of sound waves that are out of phase when they interfere.
2. **Describe** how the reflection of light waves enables you to see your image in a mirror.
3. **Describe** the energy transformations that occur when one tuning fork makes another tuning fork resonate.
4. **Think Critically** Suppose the speed of light were greater in water than in air. Draw a diagram to show whether an object under water would seem deeper or closer to the surface than it really is.

Applying Math

5. **Use Percentages** You aim a flashlight at a window. The radiant energy in the reflected beam is two-fifths of the energy in the incident beam. What percentage of the incident beam energy passed through the window?
6. **Calculate Angle of Incidence** The angle between a flashlight beam that strikes a mirror and the reflected beam is 80°. What is the angle of incidence?

More Section Review gpescience.com

Post Reading

Discussion Have students report the answers to questions generated in their K-W-L charts about light and sound waves. Students may find it interesting to make connections between their lives and science by exploring electronically synthesized music and laser light shows.

3 Assess

DAILY INTERVENTION

Check for Understanding

Visual-Spatial Have students create illustrated diagrams of the following wave behaviors: reflection, refraction, diffraction, interference, and standing wave. Have students label each drawing using the correct term.

Reteach

Wave Patterns Give pairs of students pieces of yarn and construction paper. Ask them to glue the yarn to the paper to show wave patterns. Students should identify the amplitude, wavelength, and frequency of the waves and point out any nodes. L2 COOP LEARN IS **Kinesthetic**

Assessment

Performance Have students make up songs describing the reflection, refraction, diffraction, and interference of waves. Use **Performance Assessment in the Science Classroom,** p. 151. L1

section 3 review

1. Sound waves that are in phase will be louder than the two waves are individually. Sound waves that are out of phase will be softer.
2. The light strikes your face and bounces off. The reflected light off your face strikes the mirror and is reflected into your eyes.
3. tuning fork vibrates forming a sound wave—mechanical energy to sound energy; sound waves strike tuning fork and make it vibrate—sound energy to mechanical energy
4. Students' drawings should show objects deeper than they actually are.
5. 60 percent
6. 40°

BENCH TESTED

Video Lab available for this Lab.

Real-World Problem

Purpose Students will generate transverse waves with a long spring and measure the speed and frequency of the waves. L2

Process Skills Observe, measure, recognize cause and effect, make and use tables, interpret data.

Time Required 45 minutes

Safety Precautions Caution students to keep a firm hold on the spring so it doesn't fly off and hit someone.

Procedure

Teaching Strategy Suggest to students that they practice the procedures for making and counting waves described in steps 2, 3, and 6 several times before they make their measurements.

Troubleshooting Make sure the spring has no kinks or rough places in it, as this will make it difficult for students to produce consistent waves.

Differentiated Instruction

Learning Disabled Have these students work in groups with students proficient in the lab. As students do the activity, have them take turns illustrating for each other the wavelength, frequency, and amplitude of waves they generate. Ask them to also create compressional waves, and compare and contrast them with transverse waves. L1 LS **Linguistic**

LAB

Measuring Wave Properties

Goals

- **Measure** the speed of a transverse wave.
- **Create** waves with different amplitudes.
- **Measure** the wavelength of a transverse wave.

Materials

long spring, rope, or hose
meterstick
stopwatch

Safety Precautions

Real-World Problem

Some waves travel through space; others pass through a medium such as air, water, or earth. Each wave has a wavelength, speed, frequency, and amplitude. How can the speed of a wave be measured? How can the wavelength be determined from the frequency?

Procedure

1. With a partner, stretch your spring across an open floor and measure the length of the spring. Record this measurement in the data table. Make sure the spring is stretched to the same length for each step.
2. Have your partner hold one end of the spring. Create a single wave pulse by shaking the other end of the spring back and forth.
3. Have a third person use a stopwatch to measure the time needed for the pulse to travel the length of the spring. Record this measurement in the *Wave Time* column of your data table.
4. Repeat steps 2 and 3 two more times.
5. **Calculate** the speed of waves 1, 2, and 3 in your data table by using the formula speed = distance/time. Average the speeds of waves 1, 2, and 3 to find the speed of waves on your spring.
6. **Create** a wave with several wavelengths. You make one wavelength when your hand moves left, right, and left again. Count the number of wavelengths that you generate in 10 s. Record this measurement for wave 4 in the *Wavelength Count* column in your data table.
7. **Repeat** step 6 two more times. Each time, create a wave with a different wavelength by shaking the spring faster or slower.

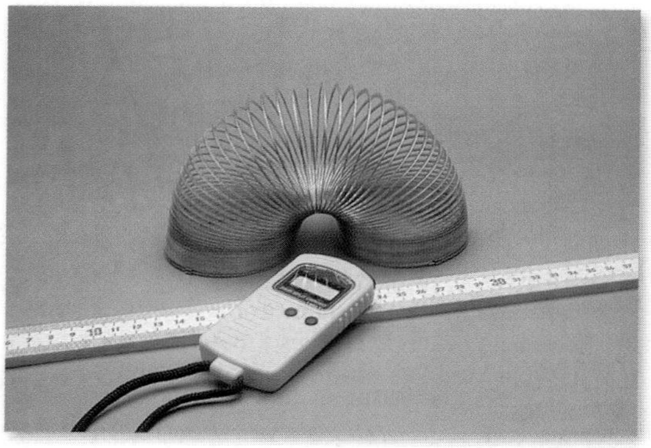

Alternative Inquiry Lab

Waves and Boundaries To extend this Lab into an Inquiry Lab, have students observe wave behavior at a boundary. To simulate waves traveling between two media, attach a hose and a rope, or two other materials, end to end and create a pulse. Try starting the pulse from the other end. Compare transmitted pulse to reflected pulse. Interested students can research coated optics (such as antiglare coating on glasses and camera lenses) or other uses for these wave properties.

Using Scientific Methods

Analyze Your Data

1. **Calculate** the frequency of waves 4, 5, and 6 by dividing the number of wavelengths by 10 s.
2. Calculate the wavelength of waves 4, 5, and 6 using the formula wavelength = wave speed/frequency. Use the average speed calculated in step 5 for the wave speed.

Wave Property Measurement

	Spring Length	Wave Time	Wave Speed
Wave 1	Results will vary depending on the springs used.		
Wave 2			
Wave 3			
	Wavelength Count	**Frequency**	**Wavelength**
Wave 4	Results will vary depending on the springs used.		
Wave 5			
Wave 6			

Conclude and Apply

1. Was the wave speed different for the three different pulses you created? Why or why not?
2. Why would you average the speeds of the three different pulses to calculate the speed of waves on your spring?
3. How did the wavelength of the waves you created depend on the frequency of the waves?

Communicating Your Data

Ask your teacher to set up a contest between the groups in your class. Have each group compete to determine who can create waves with the longest wavelength, the highest frequency, and the largest wave speed. Record the measurements of each group's efforts on the board.

Analyze Your Data

Expected Outcome Wave times measured in steps 3 and 4 should be similar.

Answers to Questions

1. Answers will vary.
2. Answers will vary.

Error Analysis Have groups compare their data with other students and discuss possible reasons for errors. As they compare their data, make sure students understand that wave times and wave speeds will be different for different springs.

Conclude and Apply

1. Accept all reasonable responses. Wave speed probably varies because it would be difficult to shake the spring exactly the same way each time.
2. to compensate for errors in measurement
3. Wavelength decreased as frequency increased. Wavelength = wave speed/frequency

Assessment

Performance Ask students to repeat the activity, but this time to generate compressional waves. Use **Performance Assessment in the Science Classroom,** p. 97.

Active Reading

Reflective Journal Have students divide pieces of paper into several columns. Have them record their thoughts under headings such as *What I did*, *What I learned*, *Questions I have*, and *Surprises I experienced.* Have students write a Reflective Journal entry for this activity. L2

Communicating Your Data

Help students analyze the data on the board to determine whether there was any relationship between the amplitude, frequency, wavelength, and wave speed of the winning waves.

TIME

Content Background

The speed of sound in water was first calculated in 1822. Unlike light or radio waves, sound waves can travel long distances underwater.

Piezoelectric crystals discovered in the late 1800s made modern sonar feasible. When compressed, they produce an electrical charge. This enabled the development of transducers that could change the mechanical energy of sound waves into electrical signals.

Sonar enables the detection of silent objects by bouncing a sound wave from the object and listening for the echo. Today, sonar is used to inspect metals for flaws, monitor oceanic temperatures, and determine the health of unborn babies.

Historical Significance

The development of sonar tremendously increased the safety of shipping. Sonic fathometers allow deep drafted vessels to safely navigate previously hazardous channels. The ability to detect icebergs lengthens the shipping season in the high latitudes. In wartime sonar was a key element in the protection of commercial convoys.

Sonar and related technologies have improved the search for oil, made it possible to locate sunken objects, and have improved the quality of medical diagnostics and the integrity of structural materials.

TIME SCIENCE AND HISTORY

SCIENCE CAN CHANGE THE COURSE OF HISTORY!

MAKING WAVES

Sonar Helps Create Deep-Sea Pictures and Save Lives

This machine houses side-scan sonar. It was used to help locate the wreck of the *Titanic*.

What is sonar?

Sonar is a device that uses sound waves to locate and measure the distance to underwater objects. Its name is a shortened version of SOund NAvigation and Ranging.

How does sonar work?

Sonar sends out a ping sound that reflects back when it hits an underwater object. Because sound travels through water at a known speed (about 1,500 m/s), scientists measure how long the sound takes to return, then they calculate the distance.

Why was it invented?

Sonar was developed by scientists in the early twentieth century as a way to detect icebergs and prevent boating disasters. Its technical advancement was hurried by the Allies' need to detect German submarines in World War I. By 1918, the United States and Great Britain had developed an active sonar system placed in submarines sent to attack other subs.

By World War II, sonar allowed ships to defend themselves effectively from enemy subs. The strategy was to use sonar to find subs and then fire depth charges at them from a safe distance. After the war, sonar-absorbing hulls and quiet engines and machinery ensured that subs could partly shield themselves from sonar.

Sonar is now used to help find schools of fish. Oceanographers also use it to map ocean and lake floors. Sonar has been vital, too, in the discovery of sunken airplanes and ships.

In 1985, a French and American team used a new type of sonar device called side-scan sonar to locate the *Titanic*, the passenger liner that sank in 1912. This kind of sonar projects a tight beam of sound to create detailed images of the sea bed. Members of the expedition towed this sonar device about 170 m above the seabed across a section of the Atlantic Ocean where the *Titanic* went down. Weeks later, video cameras finally spotted the wreck.

The *Titanic* was found thanks to sonar.

Report Research how sonar was used by navies in World War I and World War II. Did sonar affect each war's outcome? How did it save lives? What uses can you think of for sonar if it could be used in everyday life?

TIME For more information, visit gpescience.com

Report Have students research the modern uses of acoustic technology and make a "Family Tree" chart of all the products and equipment they can discover that perform their primary function through the use or detection of sounds, both audible and inaudible. Through class discussion, determine which are directly related to sonar and its basic principles. L2

Resources for Teachers and Students

Center for Bioacoustics, Texas A&M University-Corpus Christi, Natural Resources Center 3404, 6300 Ocean Drive, Corpus Christi, Texas 78412

National Sonar Association, 40414 Yardley Court, Temecula, CA 92591

Reviewing Main Ideas

Section 1 The Nature of Waves

1. Waves are rhythmic disturbances that transfer energy through matter or space.
2. Waves transfer only energy, not matter.

3. Mechanical waves need matter to travel through. Mechanical waves can be compressional or transverse.
4. When a transverse wave travels in a medium, matter in the medium moves at right angles to the direction the wave travels.
5. When a compressional wave travels in a medium, matter moves back and forth along the same direction that the wave travels.

Section 2 Wave Properties

1. The movement of high points in a medium, called crests, and low points, called troughs, forms a transverse wave.
2. The movement of more-dense regions, called compressions, and less-dense regions, called rarefactions, forms a compressional wave.
3. Transverse and compressional waves can be described by their wavelengths, frequencies, periods, and amplitudes. As frequency increases, wavelength always decreases.
4. The greater a wave's amplitude is, the more energy it transfers.

5. A wave's velocity can be calculated by multiplying its frequency times its wavelength.

Section 3 The Behavior of Waves

1. For all waves, the angle of incidence equals the angle of reflection.
2. A wave is bent, or refracted, when it changes speed as it enters a new medium.

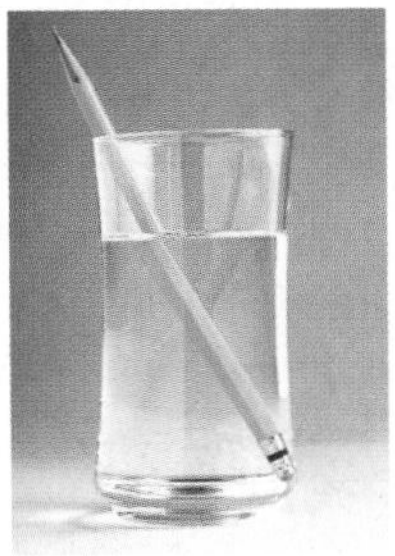

3. When two or more waves overlap, they combine to form a new wave. This process is called interference.

FOLDABLES™ Use the Foldable that you made at the beginning of this chapter to help you review waves.

Reviewing Main Ideas

Summary statements can be used by students to review the major concepts of the chapter.

Science Online

Visit gpescience.com
More Section Review
Interactive Tutor
Vocabulary PuzzleMaker
More Chapter Review
Standardized Test Practice

Assessment Transparency

For additional assessment questions, use the *Assessment Transparency* located in the transparency book.

Assessment

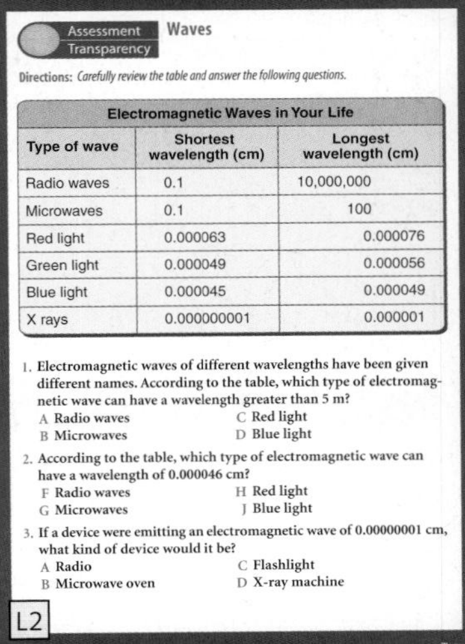

Assessment Transparency **Waves**

Directions: *Carefully review the table and answer the following questions.*

Electromagnetic Waves in Your Life		
Type of wave	Shortest wavelength (cm)	Longest wavelength (cm)
Radio waves	0.1	10,000,000
Microwaves	0.1	100
Red light	0.000063	0.000076
Green light	0.000049	0.000056
Blue light	0.000045	0.000049
X rays	0.000000001	0.000001

1. Electromagnetic waves of different wavelengths have been given different names. According to the table, which type of electromagnetic wave can have a wavelength greater than 5 m?
   A Radio waves C Red light
   B Microwaves D Blue light
2. According to the table, which type of electromagnetic wave can have a wavelength of 0.000046 cm?
   F Radio waves H Red light
   G Microwaves J Blue light
3. If a device were emitting an electromagnetic wave of 0.00000001 cm, what kind of device would it be?
   A Radio C Flashlight
   B Microwave oven D X-ray machine

L2

Waves

Identifying Misconceptions

Assess

After students have done the activity at the beginning of this chapter, have them perform this activity.

Materials corks, pan of water, eyedropper

Procedure Have students work in groups and use the materials provided to design an experiment to see how water waves move corks. Use the dropper to create the waves.

Expected Outcome Students will realize that the corks are not displaced by the waves. Students should realize that the medium does not travel with the waves. L2

FOLDABLES™ Have students use their Foldables to review the content of the chapter. How would the differences between light waves and sound waves become apparent if you were visiting the Moon? Explain. L2

Using Vocabulary

1. Reflection and refraction both involve waves contacting a surface and changing direction. In reflection, waves bounce off a surface, whereas refraction occurs when waves enter a new medium at an angle, change speed, and are bent.
2. Standing waves have nodes that do not move.
3. The rarefaction of a compressional wave has the lowest density.
4. Refraction and diffraction describe the bending of a wave.
5. When waves overlap, they interfere and form a new wave.
6. The amplitude of any transverse wave is the distance from the crest or trough to the rest position of the medium.
7. Frequency measures how many wavelengths pass a fixed point each second.
8. A mechanical wave always travels through a medium.

Checking Concepts

9. B
10. A
11. D
12. A
13. B
14. A
15. C
16. D
17. D

Interpreting Graphics

18. See student page.

chapter 10 Review

Using Vocabulary

amplitude p. 288	rarefaction p. 294
compressional wave p.290	refraction p. 302
crest p. 294	resonance p. 309
diffraction p. 304	standing wave p. 308
frequency p. 295	transverse wave p. 290
interference p. 306	trough p. 294
medium p. 289	wave p. 298
period p. 295	wavelength p. 295

Answer the following questions using complete sentences.

1. Compare and contrast reflection and refraction.
2. Which type of wave has points called nodes that do not move?
3. Which part of a compressional wave has the lowest density?
4. Find two words in the vocabulary list that describe the bending of a wave.
5. What occurs when waves overlap?
6. What is the relationship among amplitude, crest, and trough?
7. What does frequency measure?
8. What does a mechanical wave always travel through?

Checking Concepts

Choose the word or phrase that best answers each question.

9. Which of the following do waves transfer?
   A) matter **C)** matter and energy
   B) energy **D)** the medium
10. What is the formula for calculating wave speed?
   A) $v = \lambda f$ **C)** $v = \lambda / f$
   B) $v = f - \lambda$ **D)** $v = \lambda + f$
11. When a compressional wave travels through a medium, which way does matter in the medium move?
   A) backward
   B) forward
   C) perpendicular to the rest position
   D) along the same direction the wave travels
12. What is the highest point of a transverse wave called?
   A) crest **C)** wavelength
   B) compression **D)** trough
13. If the frequency of the waves produced by a vibrating object increases, how does the wavelength of the waves produced change?
   A) It stays the same. **C)** It vibrates.
   B) It decreases. **D)** It increases.
14. If the amplitude of a wave changes, which of the following changes?
   A) wave energy **C)** wave speed
   B) frequency **D)** refraction
15. Which term describes the bending of a wave around an object?
   A) resonance **C)** diffraction
   B) interference **D)** reflection
16. What is equal to the angle of reflection?
   A) refraction angle **C)** bouncing angle
   B) normal angle **D)** angle of incidence

Use the table below to answer question 17.

Speed of Sound in Air

Temperature (°C)	Sound Speed (m/s)
0	331.4
10	337.4
20	343.4

17. Based on the data in the table above, which of the following would be the speed of sound in air at 30°C?
   A) 340.4 m/s **C)** 353.4 m/s
   B) 346.4 m/s **D)** 349.4 m/s

Vocabulary PuzzleMaker gpescience.com

Use the Exam*View*® Pro Testmaker CD-ROM to:

- create multiple versions of tests
- create modified tests with one mouse click for inclusion students
- edit existing questions and add your own questions
- build tests aligned with state standards using built-in State Curriculum Tags
- change English tests to Spanish with one mouse click and vice versa

Interpreting Graphics

18. Copy and complete the following concept map.

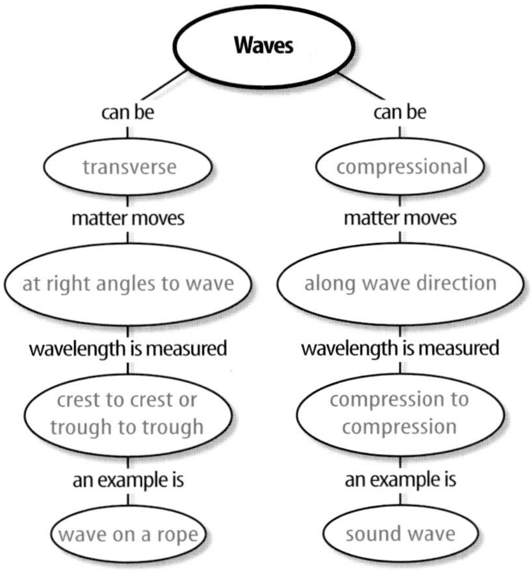

Thinking Critically

19. Explain An earthquake on the ocean floor produces a tsunami that hits a remote island. Is the water that hits the island the same water that was above the earthquake on the ocean floor?

20. Compare Suppose waves with different amplitudes are produced by a vibrating object. How do the frequencies of the waves with different amplitudes compare?

21. Explain Use the law of reflection to explain why you see only a portion of the area behind you when you look in a mirror.

22. Explain why you can hear a fire engine coming around a street corner before you can see it.

23. Describe the objects or materials that vibrated to produce three of the sounds you've heard today.

24. Form a Hypothesis In 1981, people dancing on the balconies of a Kansas City, Missouri, hotel caused the balconies to collapse. Use what have you learned about wave behavior to form a hypothesis that explains why this happened.

25. Make and Use Tables Find information in newspaper articles or magazines describing five recent earthquakes. Construct a table that shows for each earthquake the date, location, magnitude, and whether the damage caused by the earthquake was light, moderate, or heavy.

26. Concept Map Design a concept map that shows the characteristics of transverse waves. Include the terms *crest, trough, medium, wavelength, frequency, period,* and *amplitude.*

Applying Math

27. Calculate Wavelength Calculate the wavelength of a wave traveling on a spring if the wave moves at 0.2 m/s and has a period of 0.5 s.

28. Calculate Wavespeed The microwaves produced inside a microwave oven have a wavelength of 12.0 cm and a frequency of 2,500,000,000 Hz. At what speed do the microwaves travel in units of m/s?

29. Calculate Frequency Water waves on a lake travel toward a dock with a speed of 2.0 m/s and a wavelength of 0.5 m. How many wave crests strike the dock each second?

Assessment Resources

Reproducible Masters

Chapter *Fast File* Resources
Chapter Review, pp. 37–38
Chapter Tests, pp. 39–42
Assessment Transparency Activity, p. 51

Glencoe Science Web site
Chapter Review Test
Standardized Test Practice

Glencoe Technology
Assessment Transparency
Exam*View*® Pro Testmaker
MindJogger Videoquiz
Interactive Chalkboard

Thinking Critically

19. No; the water that hits the island is water that already was near the island. Through the wave, it has received energy from the earthquake miles away.

20. frequency is independent of amplitude

21. In a mirror, you can see only objects located at an angle such that their reflected beam bounces toward your eyes.

22. Sound waves have a longer wavelength than light waves. They can diffract around the street corner, but light waves cannot.

23. Possible answers: vocal cords, bell, car engine

24. The dancers created vibrations at the resonant frequency of the balcony. The vibrations of the balcony increased as it absorbed energy at its resonant frequency until its amplitude of vibration was large enough to cause the balcony to break.

25. Check students' work. Make sure magnitude is given in the same scale for all earthquakes.

26. Check students' work.

Applying Math

Math Standards

National: 1, 2, 9

27. $f = \frac{1}{\text{period}}; = \frac{1}{0.5_s} = 2\ \text{Hz};$

$\lambda = \frac{v}{f} = \frac{(0.2\ \text{m/s})}{2\ \text{Hz}}$

$= 0.1\ \text{m}$

28. $v = \lambda f$

$= (0.12\ \text{m})(2.5 \times 10^9\ \text{Hz})$

$= 3.0 \times 10^8\ \text{m/s}$

29. $f = \frac{v}{\lambda} = \frac{(2.0\ \text{m/s})}{(0.5\ \text{m})} = 4\ \text{Hz};$

4 wave crests

Answer Sheet An answer sheet can be found at **gpescience.com**.

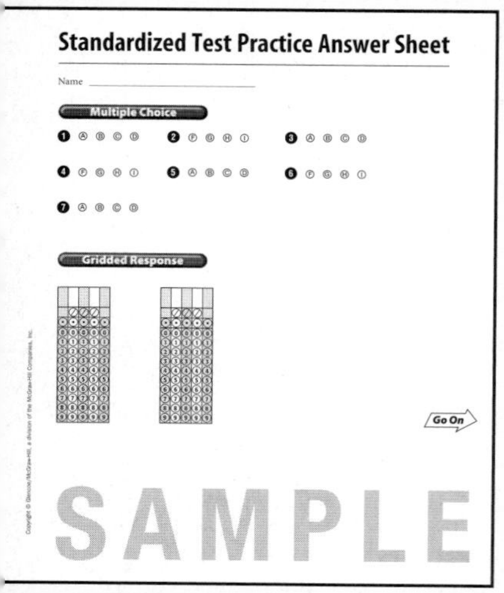

Multiple Choice

1. C
2. A
3. D
4. B
5. A
6. C
7. A

chapter 10 Standardized Test Practice

Record your answers on the answer sheet provided by your teacher or on a sheet of paper.

Multiple Choice

1. When a transverse wave travels through a medium, which way does matter in the medium move?

A. backward

B. in all directions

C. at right angles to the direction the wave travels

D. in the same direction the wave travels

Use the illustration below to answer questions 2 and 3.

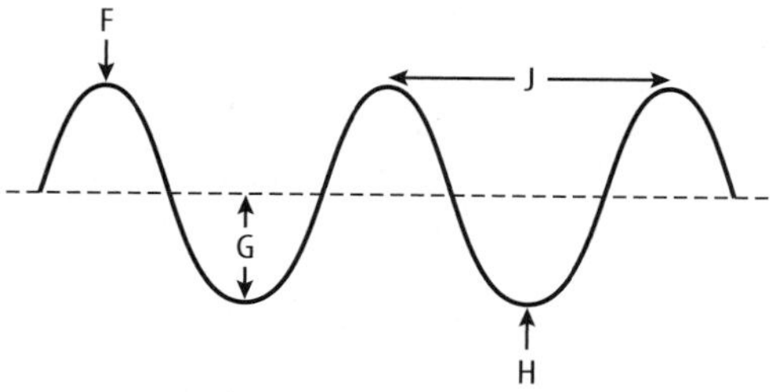

2. What wave property is shown at G?

A. amplitude

B. wavelength

C. crest

D. trough

3. What property of the wave is shown at H?

A. amplitude

B. wavelength

C. crest

D. trough

Use the illustration below to answer questions 4 and 5.

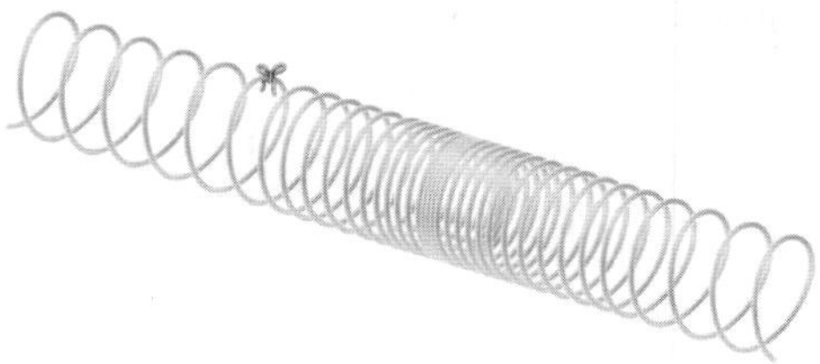

4. What kind of wave is shown?

A. mechanical

B. compressional

C. transverse

D. both A and B

5. What happens to the yarn tied to the coil?

A. It moves back and forth as the wave passes.

B. It moves up and down as the wave passes.

C. It does not move as the wave passes.

D. It moves to the next coil as the wave passes.

6. What kind of waves are the seismic waves produced during an earthquake?

A. transverse

B. compressional

C. combination of transverse and compressional

D. electromagnetic

7. What is the bending of a wave as it enters a new material called?

A. refraction

B. diffraction

C. reflection

D. interference

Gridded Response

8. A tuning fork vibrates at a frequency of 256 Hz. The wavelength of the sound produced by the tuning fork is 1.32 m. What is the speed of the wave in m/s?

9. A wave has a speed of 345 m/s and its frequency is 2050 Hz. What is its wavelength in m?

Short Response

Use the illustration below to answer questions 10 and 11.

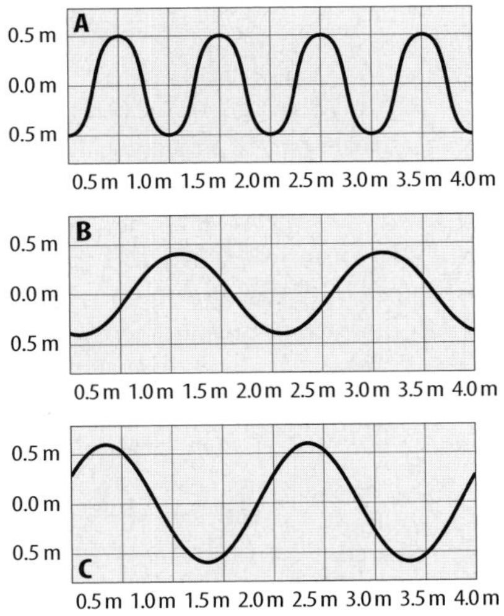

10. Determine the amplitudes and the wavelengths of each of the three waves.

11. If the length of the x-axis on each diagram represents 2 s of time, what is the frequency of each wave?

Extended Response

12. In a science fiction movie, a huge explosion occurs on the surface of a planet. People in a spaceship heading toward the planet see and hear the explosion. Is this realistic? Explain.

Use the illustrations below to answer question 13.

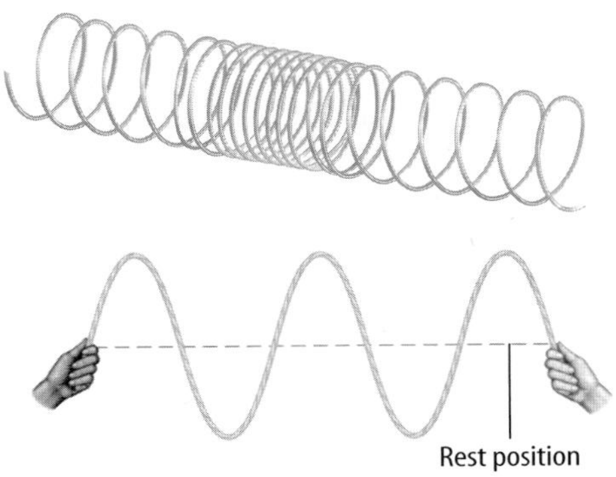

13. The illustrations show two mechanical waves.

Part A Describe how the amplitude of each of the two waves shown is defined.

Part B Describe how you would change both drawings to show waves that transfer more energy.

Test-Taking Tip

Answer Every Question Never leave any open-ended answer blank. Answer each question as best you can. You can receive partial credit for partially correct answers.

Question 12 Before you answer the question, list what you know about light waves and sound waves.

Gridded Response

8. 338
9. 0.168

Short Response

10. A: Amp. = 0.5 m; λ = 1.0 m;
B: Amp. = 0.4 m; λ = 2.0 m;
C: Amp. = 0.6 m; λ = 2.0 m;

11. A, 2 Hz; B, 1 Hz; C, 1 Hz

Extended Response

12. No, sound waves must have a medium to travel through. Sound waves would not travel through outer space. They would see the explosion because light waves do not require a medium to travel.

PART A: The wavelength of the compressional wave is the distance from compression to compression or rarefaction to rarefaction. The wavelength of the transverse wave is the distance from crest to crest or trough to trough.

PART B: For the compressional wave, make the spring coil farther apart in the rarefactions and closer together in the compressions. For the transverse wave, make the crests higher and the troughs deeper.

Rubrics

For more help evaluating Short- and Extended-Response questions, see the rubrics on p. 9T.

Section/Objectives	Standards		Lab/Features
	National	State/Local	
Chapter Opener	See pp. 16T–17T for a Key to Standards.		**Launch Lab:** What sound does a ruler make? p. 319 **Foldables,** p. 319
Section 1 Sound 2 sessions .5 block 1. **Explain** how sound travels through different mediums. 2. **Explain** different properties of sound. 3. **Discuss** the Doppler effect. 4. **Identify** ways sound can be used.	National Content Standards: UCP.1–3, UCP. 5, A.1, A.2, F.1		**MiniLAB:** Comparing Intensity, p. 323 **Integrate Astronomy,** p. 324 **Science Online,** p. 325 **Applying Math:** Using Sonar, p. 325
Section 2 Reflection and Refraction of Light 1 session .5 block 5. **Describe** how light waves interact with matter. 6. **Explain** the difference between regular and diffuse reflection. 7. **Define** the index of refraction of a material. 8. **Explain** why a prism separates white light into different colors.	National Content Standards: UCP.1–3, UCP. 5, A.1, A.2, B.2, B.6		
Section 3 Mirrors, Lenses, and the Eye 2 sessions 1 block 9. **Describe** how images are formed by three types of mirrors. 10. **Explain** how convex and concave lenses form images. 11. **Explain** how the human eye enables you to see. 12. **Describe** how lenses are used to correct vision problems.	National Content Standards: UCP.1–3, UCP. 5, A.1, A.2, B.2		**Visualizing Images Formed by a Convex Lens,** p. 334 **Integrate Career,** p. 335 **MiniLAB:** Experimenting with Focal Lengths, p. 336 Video Lab **Lab:** Reflections of Reflections, p. 338
Section 4 Light and Color 2 sessions 1.5 blocks 13. **Explain** how you see color. 14. **Describe** the difference between light color and pigment color. 15. **Predict** what happens when different colors are mixed.	National Content Standards: UCP.1–3, UCP. 5, A.1, A.2, B.2, B.6, C.6		**Science Online,** p. 340 **Integrate Life Science,** p. 342 **Lab:** Blocking Noise Pollution, pp. 344–345 **Science and Language Arts:** A Haiku Garden, p. 346

StudentWorks Plus | Glencoe Exclusive! TeacherWorks™ All-In-One Planner and Resource Center

Lab Materials	Reproducible Resources	Section Assessment	Technology
Launch Lab: plastic rulers	**Chapter *FAST FILE* Resources** Foldables, p. 17 Directed Reading Overview, p. 19 Note-taking Worksheets, pp. 35–37	Glencoe's Assessment Advantage	TeacherWorks includes: • Interactive Teacher Edition • Lesson Planner with calendar • Access to all program blacklines • Correlations to standards • Web links
MiniLAB: metal object such as a spoon, 1.5 m of string, chair or table	**Chapter *FAST FILE* Resources** Transparency Activity, p. 46 MiniLAB, p. 3 Lab Activity, pp. 9–12 Enrichment, p. 31 Reinforcement, p. 27 Directed Reading, p. 20	**Portfolio** Active Reading, p. 322 **Performance** MiniLAB, p. 323 Applying Math, p. 325 Applying Math, p. 326 **Content** Section Review, p. 326	Section Focus Transparency Interactive Chalkboard CD-ROM StudentWorks Plus
Need materials? Contact Science Kit at 1-800-828-7777 or www.sciencekit.com.	**Chapter *FAST FILE* Resources** Transparency Activity, p. 47 Lab Activity, pp. 13–16 Enrichment, p. 32 Reinforcement, p. 28 Directed Reading, p. 20 **Cultural Diversity,** pp. 57–58	**Performance** Applying Math, p. 330 **Content** Section Review, p. 330	Section Focus Transparency Interactive Chalkboard CD-ROM StudentWorks Plus
MiniLAB: glass test tube with stopper, water, paper **Lab:** plane mirrors (2), masking tape, protractor, paper clip	**Chapter *FAST FILE* Resources** Transparency Activity, pp. 48, 51–52 MiniLAB, p. 4 Enrichment, p. 33 Reinforcement, p. 29 Directed Reading, p. 21 Lab Worksheets, pp. 5–6 **Lab Management and Safety,** pp. 67–68	**Portfolio** Curriculum Connection, p. 336 **Performance** MiniLAB, p. 336 Applying Math, p. 337 **Content** Section Review, p. 337	Section Focus Transparency Teaching Transparency Interactive Chalkboard CD-ROM StudentWorks Plus Video Lab
Lab: loud noise source, sound meter, meterstick or metric tape measure	**Chapter *FAST FILE* Resources** Transparency Activity, p. 49 Enrichment, p. 34 Reinforcement, p. 30 Directed Reading, p. 21, 22 Lab Worksheets, pp. 7–8	**Portfolio** Activity, p. 342 **Performance** Applying Math, p. 343 **Content** Section Review, p. 343	Section Focus Transparency Virtual Labs CD-ROM Interactive Chalkboard CD-ROM StudentWorks Plus

End of Chapter Assessment

Glencoe's Assessment Advantage

Blackline Masters	Technology	Professional Series
Chapter *FAST FILE* Resources Chapter Review, pp. 39–40 Chapter Tests, pp. 41–44 **Standardized Test Practice,** pp. 48–51	MindJogger Videoquiz Virtual Labs CD-ROM Exam*View*® Pro Testmaker TeacherWorks CD-ROM Interactive Chalkboard CD-	ROM**Performance Assessment in the Science Classroom (PASC)**

Transparencies

Section Focus

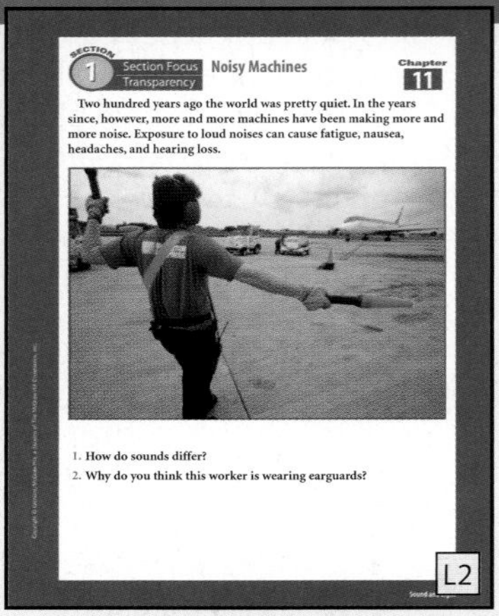
SECTION 1 Section Focus Transparency **Noisy Machines** Chapter 11

Two hundred years ago the world was pretty quiet. In the years since, however, more and more machines have been making more and more noise. Exposure to loud noises can cause fatigue, nausea, headaches, and hearing loss.

1. How do sounds differ?
2. Why do you think this worker is wearing earguards?

L2

SECTION 2 Section Focus Transparency **Knight Light** Chapter 11

The colors of stained glass are metallic oxides (combinations of different metals and oxygen), but the beautiful colors you see aren't due solely to the coloring in the glass. It's the light passing through the glass that reaches your eyes. The natural light changes from morning to night, even from moment to moment. Our perception of stained glass changes with the light.

1. Where can you see totally through this window?
2. Where can you see light but not what's on the other side of the window?
3. What do you think causes these differences?

L2

SECTION 3 Section Focus Transparency **Fun-House Mirrors** Chapter 11

If you've ever been to an amusement park or fair, you may have seen mirrors like this one. These full-length mirrors provide distorted images of the viewer. They're often found in the fun-house along with other amusing exhibits.

1. How does the image made by a fun-house mirror differ from that of an ordinary mirror? How are they the same?
2. Why does a fun-house mirror provide such a different image from an ordinary mirror?

L2

This is a representation of key blackline masters available in the Teacher Classroom Resources. See Resource Manager boxes within the chapter for additional information.

Assessment

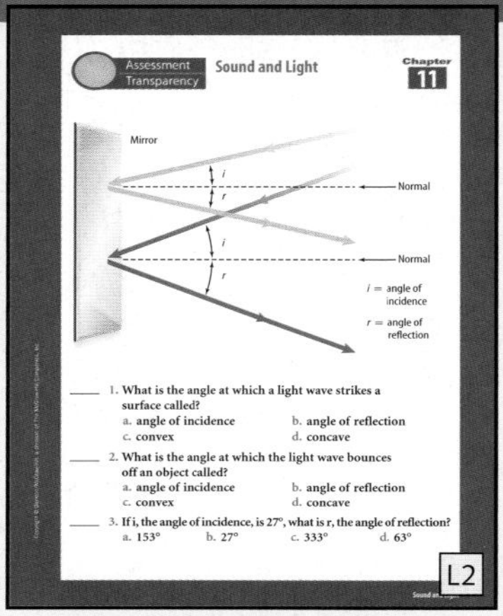
Assessment Transparency **Sound and Light** Chapter 11

____ 1. What is the angle at which a light wave strikes a surface called?
a. angle of incidence b. angle of reflection
c. convex d. concave

____ 2. What is the angle at which the light wave bounces off an object called?
a. angle of incidence b. angle of reflection
c. convex d. concave

____ 3. If i, the angle of incidence, is 27°, what is r, the angle of reflection?
a. 153° b. 27° c. 333° d. 63°

L2

Teaching

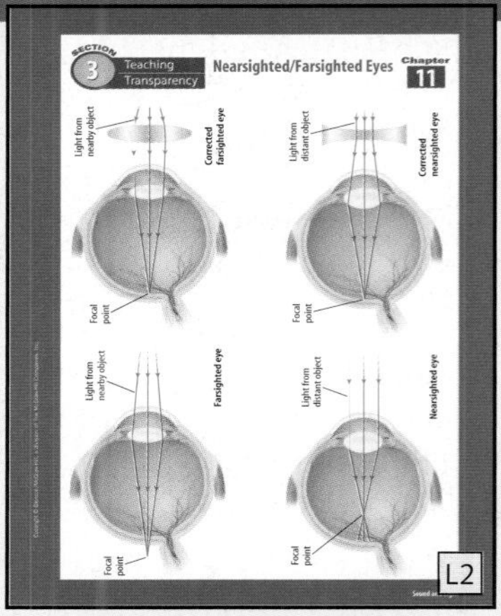
SECTION 3 Teaching Transparency **Nearsighted/Farsighted Eyes** Chapter 11

L2

Key to Teaching Strategies

The following designations will help you decide which activities are appropriate for your students.

L1 Level 1 activities should be appropriate for students with learning difficulties.

L2 Level 2 activities should be within the ability range of all students.

L3 Level 3 activities are designed for above-average students.

ELL ELL activities should be within the ability range of English Language Learners.

COOP LEARN Cooperative Learning activities are designed for small group work.

LS Multiple Learning Styles logos, as described on page 12T, are used throughout to indicate strategies that address different learning styles.

P These strategies represent student products that can be placed into a best-work portfolio.

PBL Problem-Based Learning activities apply real-world situations to learning.

Hands-on Activities

Lab Worksheets

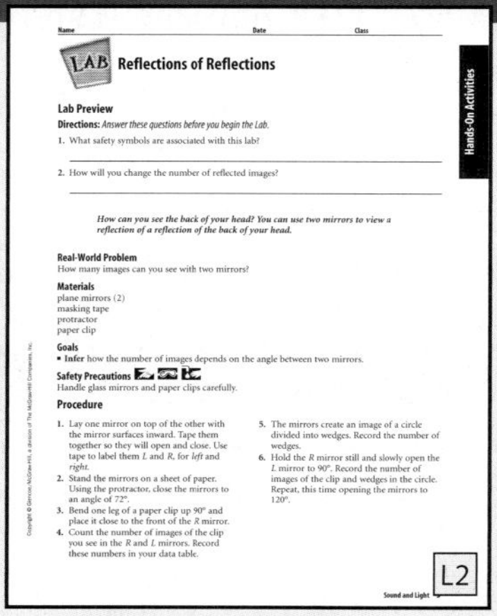
Name Date Class

LAB **Reflections of Reflections**

Hands-On Activities

Lab Preview

Directions: *Answer these questions before you begin the Lab.*

1. What safety symbols are associated with this lab?
2. How will you change the number of reflected images?

How can you see the back of your head? You can use two mirrors to view a reflection of a reflection of the back of your head.

Real-World Problem
How many images can you see with two mirrors?

Materials
plane mirrors (2)
masking tape
protractor
paper clip

Goals
- **Infer** how the number of images depends on the angle between two mirrors.

Safety Precautions
Handle glass mirrors and paper clips carefully.

Procedure

1. Lay one mirror on top of the other with the mirror surfaces inward. Tape them together so they will open and close. Use tape to label them *L* and *R*, for *left* and *right*.
2. Stand the mirrors on a sheet of paper. Using the protractor, close the mirrors to an angle of 72°.
3. Bend one leg of a paper clip up 90° and place it close to the front of the *R* mirror.
4. Count the number of images of the clip you see in the *R* and *L* mirrors. Record these numbers in your data table.
5. The mirrors create an image of a circle divided into wedges. Record the number of wedges.
6. Hold the *R* mirror still and slowly open the *L* mirror to 90°. Record the number of images of the clip and wedges in the circle. Repeat, this time opening the mirrors to 120°.

Sound and Light L2

Laboratory Activities

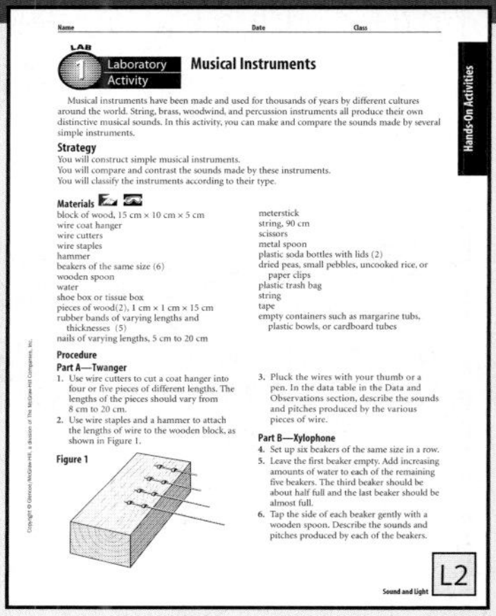
Name Date Class

LAB 1 Laboratory Activity **Musical Instruments**

Hands-On Activities

Musical instruments have been made and used for thousands of years by different cultures around the world. String, brass, woodwind, and percussion instruments all produce their own distinctive musical sounds. In this activity, you can make and compare the sounds made by several simple instruments.

Strategy
You will construct simple musical instruments.
You will compare and contrast the sounds made by these instruments.
You will classify the instruments according to their type.

Materials
block of wood, 15 cm × 10 cm × 5 cm
wire coat hanger
wire cutters
wire staples
hammer
beakers of the same size (6)
wooden spoon
water
shoe box or tissue box
pieces of wood(2), 1 cm × 1 cm × 15 cm
rubber bands of varying lengths and thicknesses (5)
nails of varying lengths, 5 cm to 20 cm
meterstick
string, 90 cm
scissors
metal spoon
plastic soda bottles with lids (2)
dried peas, small pebbles, uncooked rice, or paper clips
plastic trash bag
string
tape
empty containers such as margarine tubs, plastic bowls, or cardboard tubes

Procedure

Part A—Twanger

1. Use wire cutters to cut a coat hanger into four or five pieces of different lengths. The lengths of the pieces should vary from 8 cm to 20 cm.
2. Use wire staples and a hammer to attach the lengths of wire to the wooden block, as shown in Figure 1.

Figure 1

3. Pluck the wires with your thumb or a pen. In the data table in the Data and Observations section, describe the sounds and pitches produced by the various pieces of wire.

Part B—Xylophone

4. Set up six beakers of the same size in a row.
5. Leave the first beaker empty. Add increasing amounts of water to each of the remaining five beakers. The third beaker should be about half full and the last beaker should be almost full.
6. Tap the side of each beaker gently with a wooden spoon. Describe the sounds and pitches produced by each of the beakers.

Sound and Light L2

Resource Manager

Meeting Different Ability Levels

Content Outline

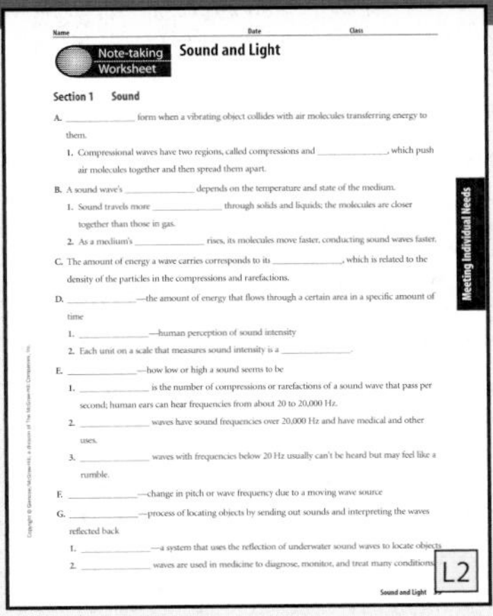
Note-taking Worksheet — Sound and Light
Section 1 Sound
L2

Reinforcement

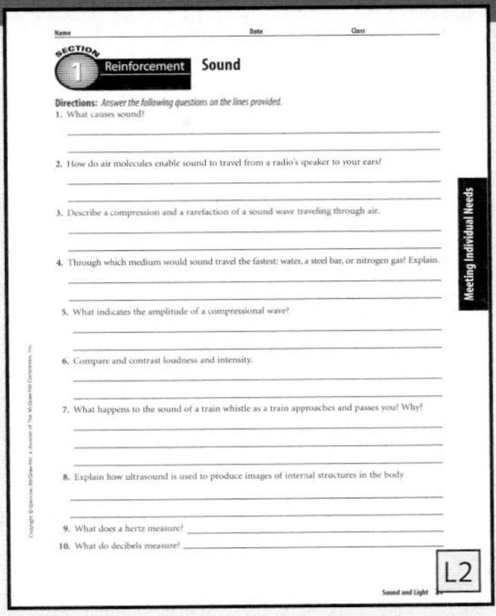
Section 1 Reinforcement — Sound
L2

Enrichment

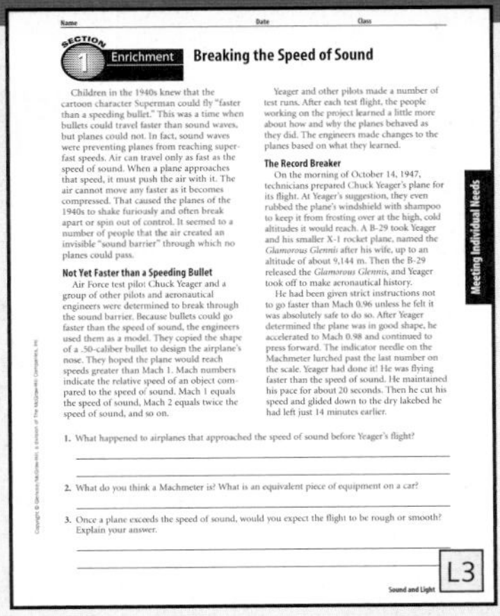
Section 1 Enrichment — Breaking the Speed of Sound
L3

Directed Reading (English/Spanish)

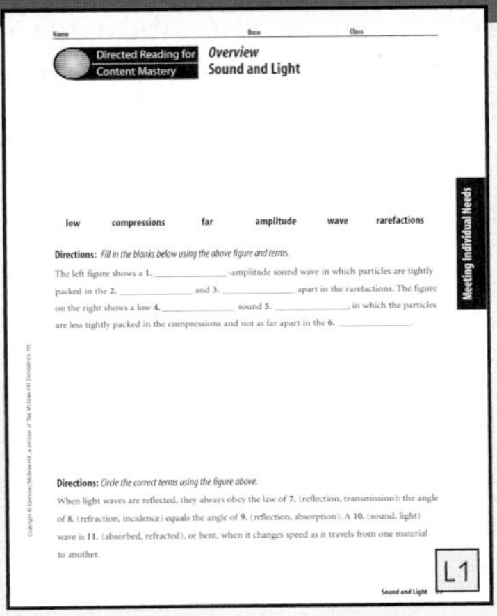
Directed Reading for Content Mastery — Overview: Sound and Light
L1

Study Guide

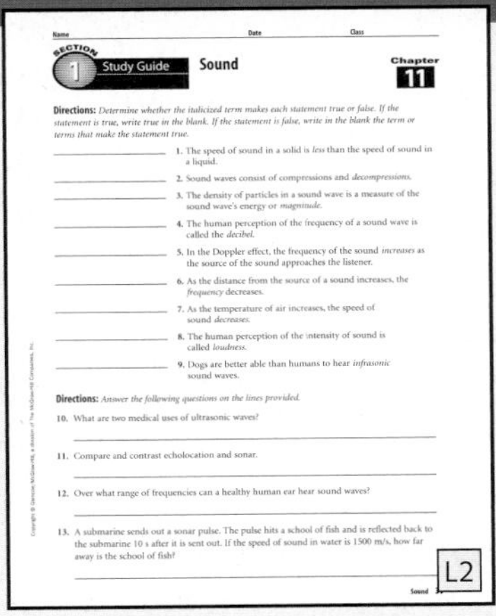
Section 1 Study Guide — Sound — Chapter 11
L2

Reading Essentials

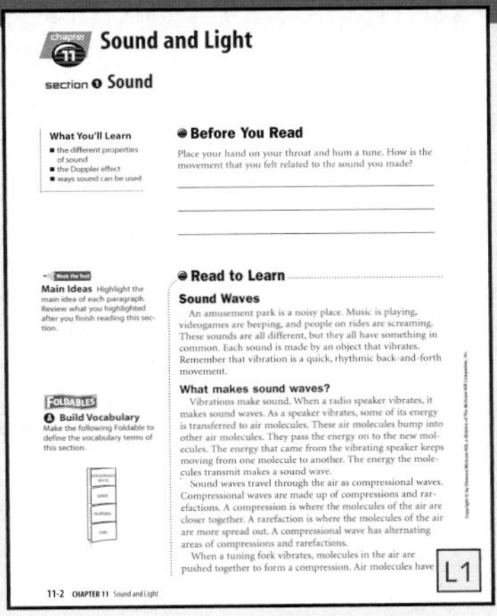
Chapter 11 Sound and Light
Section 1 Sound
L1

Assessment

Test Practice Workbook

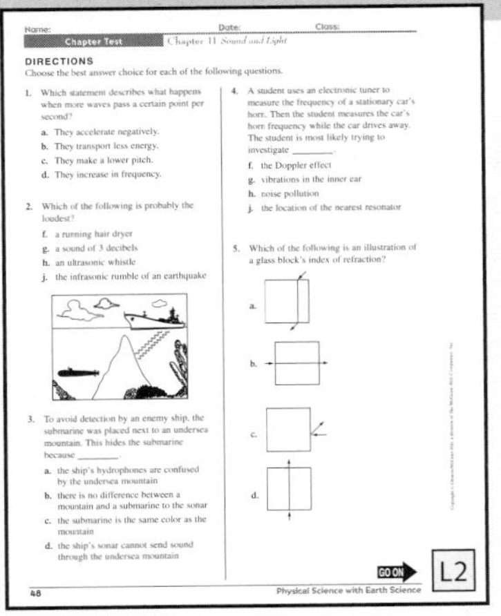
L2

Chapter Review

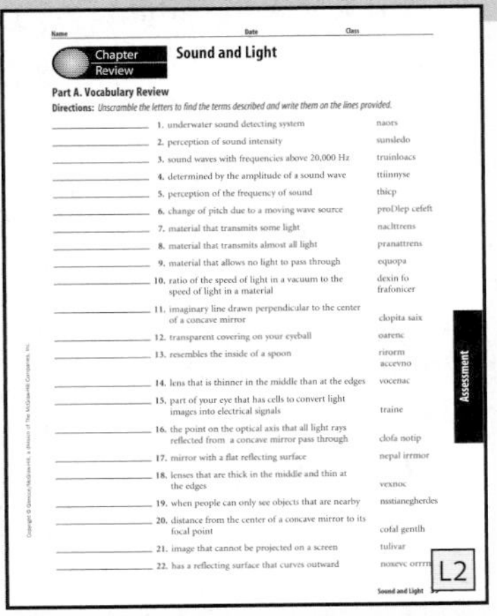
Chapter Review — Sound and Light
L2

Chapter Tests

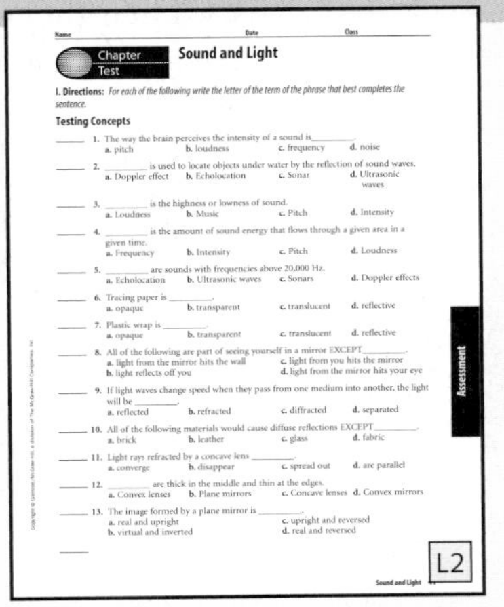
Chapter Test — Sound and Light
L2

Science Content Background

section 1 Sound

Sound

A sound wave is a type of mechanical wave called a compressional or longitudinal wave. The compressions and rarefactions produced cause temporary changes in the pressure of the medium through which the waves travel. Our ears respond to this changing pressure and interpret it as sound.

Intensity and Loudness

Sound intensity is the amount of energy that passes through a given area in a given amount of time. Because sound waves spread out as they travel, the intensity of a sound decreases as it travels and is proportional to the inverse square of the distance from the source. This means that if the distance from the source doubles, the intensity of sound is one-fourth as large. Humans can detect very low levels of sound. This threshold is defined as 0 dB. A sound of 0 dB will move our eardrums as little as one-billionth of a centimeter, but we can still hear it.

The Doppler Effect

When an airplane going faster than the speed of sound passes over us, it produces a very loud noise called a sonic boom. This is an example of the Doppler effect. The sound waves are pushed closer together as the high-speed airplane continues to produce sound waves. The plane goes so fast that the waves pile up on each other. Then the wave energy reaches the listener all at once, producing a loud noise.

section 2 Reflection and Refraction of Light

Reflection of Light

The reason we can see objects is that they either emit or reflect light. Most materials don't produce their own light, so almost everything we see is reflected light. The reflected light travels to the retinas of our eyes, where an image is received and sent to the brain.

Transparency

Materials that are transparent to visible light are not necessarily transparent to other wavelengths. For example, clear glass transmits long-wavelength ultraviolet rays but blocks most short-wavelength ultraviolet rays. This is why you are not likely to get a sunburn through a window.

Refraction of Light

For refraction to occur, light must pass at an angle other than 90° from one material into another with a different index of refraction. When light slows down as it moves from one material to another, it is refracted toward the normal. When it speeds up, it is refracted away from the normal.

When most people swim underwater without goggles, their vision is not as good. Normally light is refracted when it goes from air into the eye, and this is necessary in order to see clearly. Because water has a higher index of refraction than air, light is not refracted enough by water. Wearing goggles puts air in front of the eye and restores normal vision.

Teacher to Teacher
Erin Peters
Lead Science Teacher
Williamsburg Middle School
Arlington, VA

"I use a wind-up music box apparatus to demonstrate how sound waves travel through different mediums. Hold the apparatus in the air, wind the arm, and listen to the sound that it makes. The sound should be very quiet. Now wind the arm and put the apparatus on the desk. It should sound like the music box. Sound waves travel better when the vibrating particles are closer together."

Erin Peters

section 3 Mirrors, Lenses, and the Eye

Mirrors

The law of reflection applies whenever light is reflected. The angle of incidence is equal to the angle of reflection. To determine these angles, an imaginary reference line called the normal line is drawn perpendicular to the reflecting surface. The angle between the incident ray and the normal is the angle of incidence. The angle between the reflected ray and the normal is the angle of reflection. The law of reflection applies to plane mirrors as well as convex and concave mirrors.

Lenses

A lens is a curved, transparent device that bends light that passes through it. The bending, or refraction, of light requires two conditions: (a) Light must pass from one material through another that has a different optical density; (b) the light must enter the lens at an angle other than perpendicular.

Concave lenses and convex mirrors both cause light rays to diverge. When light rays are made to diverge, the image that is formed is virtual. The image seems to be located where the diverging light rays would converge if they were extended backward. As a result, no light rays actually pass through the location of a virtual image. Convex lenses and concave mirrors also cause light rays to diverge and form virtual images when the object is located less than one focal length from the lens or mirror. For all other object locations, convex lenses and concave mirrors form real images.

The Human Eye

Eyes focus by a process called accommodation. In this process, muscles attached to the eye lens make the lens thinner or thicker to form a sharp image on the retina. Most people with glasses or contact lenses wear concave lenses to correct myopia, or nearsightedness. This condition has various causes. For instance, a person may genetically have an eyeball that is too long, causing a sharp image to be formed in front of, instead of on, the retina.

section 4 Light and Color

Mixing Colors

Three types of color dots—red, blue, and green—are repeated throughout the screen of a color television. By varying the intensity of the light emitted by each, all colors can be displayed.

Each primary pigment color results when one of the primary colors of light is absorbed. Magenta corresponds to the absorption of green, cyan to the absorption of red, and yellow to the absorption of blue.

chapter content resources

Internet Resources

For additional content background, visit **gpescience.com** to:

- access your book online
- find references to related articles in popular science magazines
- access Web links with related content background
- access current events with science journal topics

Print Resources

Hands-On Physics Activities with Real-Life Applications: Easy-to-Use Labs and Demonstrations for Grades 8-12, by James Cunningham and Norman Herr, Jossey-Bass, 2002

Visual Perception, by Steven H. Schwartz, McGraw-Hill/Appleton and Lange, 1998

Geometric, Physical, and Visual Optics, by Michael Keating, Butterworth-Heinemann, 2002

chapter 11

Chapter Vocabulary

intensity, p. 322
loudness, p. 322
decibel, p. 322
pitch, p. 323
Doppler effect, p. 323
opaque, p. 327
translucent, p. 327
transparent, p. 327
index of refraction, p. 329
plane mirror, p. 331
concave mirror, p. 332
convex mirror, p. 333
convex lens, p. 333
concave lens, p. 335
pigment, p. 342

Science Journal Student responses will vary. Students might want to know the wave types, how fast they travel, and how they might harm hearing.

INTERACTIVE CHALKBOARD with Image Bank

PowerPoint® Presentations

This CD-ROM is an editable Microsoft® PowerPoint® presentation that includes:

- a pre-made presentation for every chapter
- interactive graphics
- animations
- audio clips
- image bank
- all new section and chapter questions
- Standardized Test Practice
- transparencies
- Foldables directions
- links to gpescience.com

chapter 11

Sound and Light

chapter preview

sections

Cracking the Sound Barrier

Have you ever heard a sonic boom? A plane moving faster than the speed of sound makes a sonic boom. The sound waves from the plane add together to form a cone-shaped shock wave. Behind the cone are low-pressure regions that can cause water vapor to condense, forming the cloud you see here.

Science Journal Write three things that you would like to learn about sound.

Theme Connection

Energy Sound and light are waves that transfer energy. Sound is a mechanical, compressional wave that transfers energy by the collisions of molecules. Light transfers energy by electromagnetic radiation. The amount of energy transferred by a wave determines the intensity of sound or light.

About the Photo

Sonic Boom This airplane is producing a sonic boom as it moves faster than the speed of sound. As the plane approaches the speed of sound, the Doppler effect causes the sound waves emitted by the plane to pile up in front of it. These wave fronts form a cone-shaped shock wave when they overlap as the plane reaches the speed of sound. Observers on the ground hear a loud boom or crack when the shock wave passes them.

Start-Up Activities

Launch LAB

What sound does a ruler make?

Think of the musical instruments you've seen and heard. Some have strings, some have hollow tubes, and others have keys or pedals. Musical instruments come in many shapes and sizes and are played with various techniques. These differences give each instrument a unique sound. What would an instrument made from a ruler sound like?

1. Firmly hold one end of a thin ruler lying flat on a desk, allowing the free end to extend beyond the edge of the desk.
2. Gently pull up on and release the end of the ruler. What do you see and hear?
3. Vary the length of the overhanging portion and repeat the experiment several times.
4. **Think Critically** In your Science Journal, write instructions for playing a song with the ruler. Explain how the length of the overhanging part of the ruler affects the sound.

FOLDABLES™ Study Organizer

Sound and Light Make the following Foldable to help you identify ways in which sound and light are different and alike.

STEP 1 **Fold** one sheet of paper lengthwise.

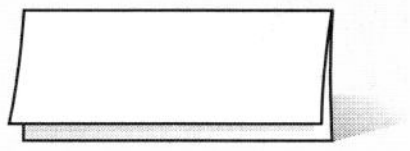

STEP 2 **Fold** into thirds.

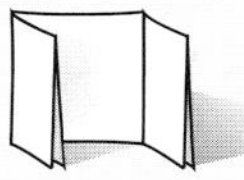

STEP 3 **Unfold and draw** overlapping ovals. **Cut** the top sheet along the folds.

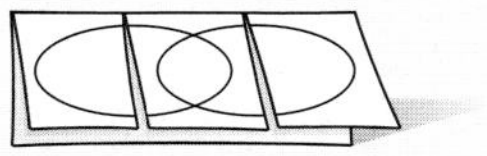

STEP 4 **Label** the ovals as shown.

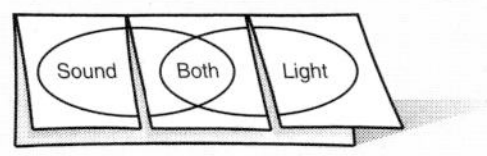

Constructing a Venn Diagram As you read the chapter, list the characteristics unique to sound under the left tab, the characteristics unique to light under the right tab, and those common to both under the middle tab.

Science Online | Preview this chapter's content and activities at gpescience.com

319

Launch LAB

Purpose Use the Launch Lab to introduce students to musical pitches. Explain that one of the things they will learn in this chapter is what sound is and what makes sounds different. L1 ELL IS **Auditory-Musical**

Preparation Test the rulers that you plan to have students use to be sure that they are flexible enough for the activity.

Materials thin rulers

Teaching Strategy Suggest that students work in pairs. Have one student describe and record the sounds heard while the other student adjusts and plays the ruler.

Think Critically

The longer the extending segment of the ruler, the deeper the pitch.

Assessment

Content Have students listen to the tones that occur at different lengths and then try to play a simple song.

FOLDABLES™ Study Organizer **Dinah Zike Study Fold**

Student preparation materials for this Foldable are available in the Chapter *Fast File* Resources.

1 Motivate

An editable Microsoft® PowerPoint® presentation is available on **Interactive Chalkboard** CD-ROM.

Bellringer

Section Focus Transparencies also are available on the Interactive Chalkboard CD-ROM. L2 ELL

Reading Preview

Tie to Prior Knowledge

Sounds Ask students to name sounds they have heard today. Can they identify what made each sound? Tell them that sounds are made by vibrating objects. Human speech is caused by the vibration of vocal cords in the larynx.

Text Structure Have students study the structure of this section. How are topics introduced? headings What technique is used to highlight vocabulary words? boldface type Tell students that text structure can help them see, at a glance, what a section covers.

section 1

Sound

Reading Guide

What You'll Learn

- **Explain** how sound travels through different mediums.
- **Explain** different properties of sound.
- **Discuss** the Doppler effect.
- **Identify** ways sound can be used.

Why It's Important

Sounds are one way that you learn about the world around you.

Review Vocabulary

vibration: rhythmic back-and-forth motion

New Vocabulary

- intensity
- loudness
- decibel
- pitch
- Doppler effect

Sound Waves

An amusement park can be a noisy place. With all the racket of carousel music and booming loudspeakers, it can be hard to hear what your friends say. The many sounds you hear every day are different, but they do have something in common—each sound is produced by an object that vibrates.

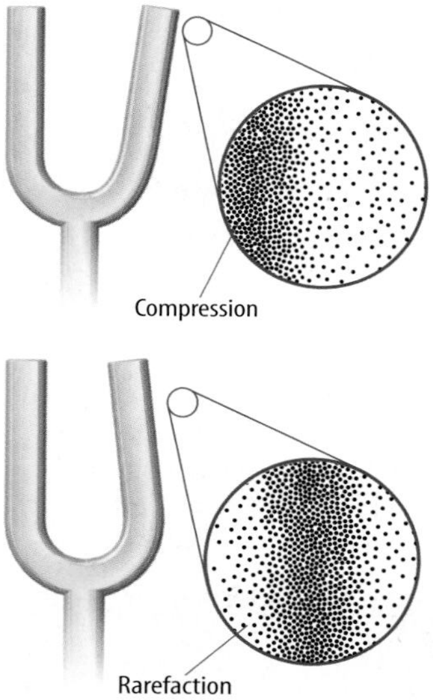

Figure 1 A vibrating tuning fork produces compressions and rarefactions that travel outward from the tuning fork. These compressions and rarefactions form a sound wave.

Making Sound Waves When an object like the tuning fork in **Figure 1** vibrates, it creates sound waves. Sound waves are compressional waves. Recall that a compressional wave is made of compressions and rarefactions. When an end of the tuning fork moves outward, it forms a compression on that side by pushing the molecules in air together. The compression moves away from the tuning fork as these molecules collide with other molecules in air. When the end of the tuning fork moves back, a rarefaction is formed where the molecules are farther apart. As the tuning fork vibrates, it produces a series of compressions and rarefactions that travels outward. This series of compressions and rarefactions is the sound wave that you hear.

The Speed of Sound

A sound wave moves in air as collisions between the molecules in air transfer energy from place to place. Sound waves also can move in other materials. The material in which a sound wave moves is called a medium. Just as in air, sound waves travel in solids, liquids, and other gases as a vibrating object transfers energy to the particles in the material. However, sound waves cannot travel in empty space where there are no particles.

Section 1 Resource Manager

Chapter *FAST FILE* Resources

Transparency Activity, p. 46
Note-taking Worksheets, pp. 35–37
MiniLAB, p. 3
Lab Activity, pp. 9–12
Enrichment, p. 31
Reinforcement, p. 27
Directed Reading for Content Mastery, pp. 19–20
Earth Science Critical Thinking/Problem Solving, p. 21
Reading and Writing Skills Activities, pp. 7–8

The Speed of Sound in Different Materials The speed of a sound wave in a medium depends on the type of substance and whether it is a solid, liquid, or gas. For example, **Table 1** shows the speed of sound in different mediums at room temperature. In general, sound travels slowest in gases and fastest in solids.

Temperature and the Speed of Sound The speed of sound waves also depends on the temperature of the medium. As the temperature of a substance increases, its atoms and molecules move faster. At a higher temperature, atoms and molecules collide with each other more frequently. As a result, sound waves move faster. For example, in air at a temperature of 0°C, sound travels at a speed of 331 m/s, but in air at a temperature of 20°C, sound travels at 343 m/s.

Table 1 Speed of Sound in Different Mediums

Medium	Speed of Sound (m/s)
Air (20°C)	343
Cork	500
Water	1,498
Brick	3,650
Aluminum	5,000

Amplitude and Energy of Sound Waves

Think about the differences among sounds you hear. Some are loud; others are soft. The flute plays high notes, whereas the tuba is much lower. What properties of sound waves cause these differences in the sounds you hear?

Recall that the amount of energy a wave carries corresponds to its amplitude. For a compressional wave, amplitude is related to the density of the particles in the compressions and rarefactions. A vibrating object makes a wave by transferring energy to the medium. More energy is transferred to the medium when the particles of the medium are forced closer together in the compressions and spread farther apart in the rarefactions. Look at **Figure 2.** A sound wave has a higher amplitude and carries more energy when particles in the medium are closer together in the compressions and more spread out in the rarefactions.

Figure 2 The amplitude of a sound wave depends on the density of the particles in the compressions and rarefactions.

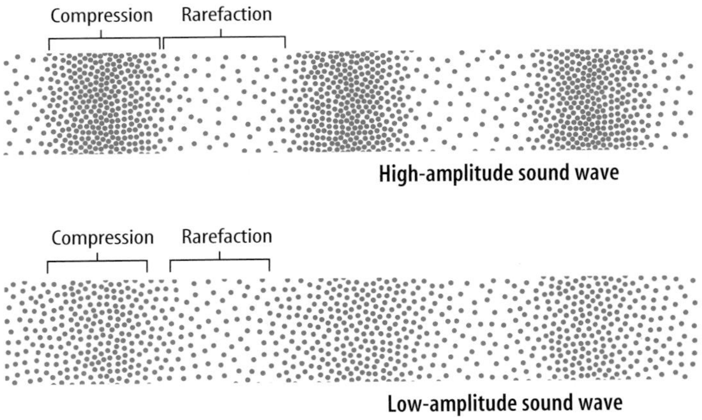

In a high-amplitude sound wave, particles are tightly packed in the compressions and far apart in the rarefactions.

In a low-amplitude sound wave, particles are less tightly packed in the compressions and not as far apart in the rarefactions.

2 Teach

Activity

Vocal Cords Have students place their hands on their throats while talking to feel the vibrations caused by their vocal cords. L2 ELL IN **Kinesthetic**

IDENTIFYING Misconceptions

Moving Molecules When looking at the pictures of compressions and rarefactions of sound waves, students might think that the molecules travel away from the sound source. Explain that the molecules push on their neighbors and then return to their original positions. Only the energy is transported.

Activity

Ranking Volume Have students bring in various whistles. Have them blow the whistles and rank them from loudest to softest. Afterward, have the students examine the whistles to find out what produced the vibration and what feature caused one whistle to be louder than another. L2 ELL IN **Auditory-Musical**

Reading Strategy

Shared Reading Have students read together in small groups as they study Amplitude and Energy of Sound Waves. Many of the terms in this passage, such as amplitude and energy, build upon prior knowledge. Encourage students to help one another recall previous vocabulary terms.

Differentiated Instruction

Hearing Impaired For many of the activities in this section, an alternative way to learn how sound is produced is by feeling the vibrations. When students do the MiniLAB, have them feel the vibrations transmitted through the string to their fingers. Using different types of string and metal objects, they can feel how the vibrations differ for various materials. IN **Kinesthetic** L1

Teacher FYI

Sound Speed The speed of sound in a material depends on the material's elasticity and density. Elasticity is the ability of the material to resume its previous shape after being acted on by a force. For example, steel has high elasticity, so sound travels quickly through steel.

SECTION 1 Sound 321

Inquiry Lab

Build a Muffler

Purpose to explore sound reduction

Possible Materials shoe box, packing material, corks, waxed paper, cardboard dividers, aluminum foil, sound meter, radio or stereo

Estimated Time two class periods

Teaching Strategies

- Students should make a hole in each end of a shoebox. Noise goes in one end and is measured at the other end.
- Encourage students to test different materials and muffler designs. Students can find muffler designs online. They might try a mazelike passage for the sound waves. Allow students to bring extra materials from home.
- Encourage competition by having a contest to see which group can build the most effective muffler.

For additional inquiry activities, see Science Inquiry Lab Manual.

Reading Check

Answer Intensity is the amount of energy that flows through an area in a specific amount of time. Loudness is the human perception of this intensity.

Fun Fact

A decibel is one-tenth of a bel, named in honor of Alexander Graham Bell.

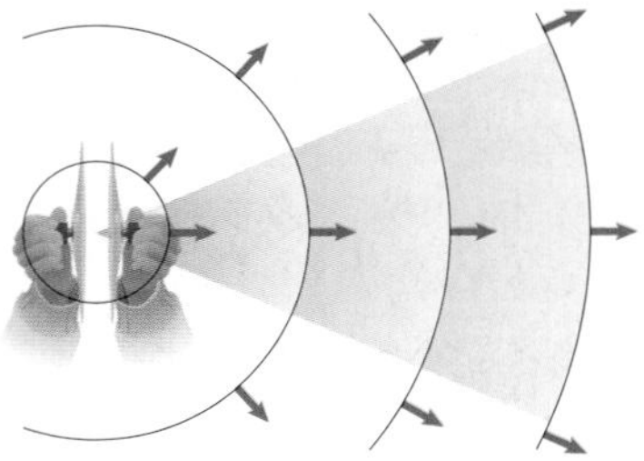

Figure 3 The intensity of a sound wave decreases as the wave spreads out from the source of the sound. The energy of the wave is spread over a larger area as the wave spreads out.

Intensity and Loudness

Imagine you are listening to music from your CD player. Sound waves produced by the CD player travel through the air and transfer energy from the CD player to your ears. The energy that reaches your ears depends not only on the amplitude of the sound waves, but also on how close you are to the CD player. **Figure 3** shows that as you get farther from a source of sound, the energy of the sound waves is spread over a greater area. The amount of energy transferred by a sound wave through a certain area each second is the **intensity** of the sound wave. As sound waves travel away from the source of the sound, the intensity of the waves decreases as the waves spread out. This means that as you get farther from the source, less energy reaches your ears each second.

Loudness When you hear different sounds, you do not need special equipment to know which sounds have greater intensity. Your ears and brain can tell the difference. **Loudness** is the human perception of sound intensity. As the intensity of a sound wave increases, the loudness of the sound also increases.

Reading Check *How are intensity and loudness related?*

A Scale for Sound Intensity The intensity of sound can be described using a measurement scale. Each unit on the scale for sound intensity is called a **decibel,** abbreviated dB. On this scale, the faintest sound that most people can hear is 0 dB. Sounds with intensity levels above 120 dB may cause pain and permanent hearing loss. During some rock concerts, sounds reach this damaging intensity level. Wearing ear protection, such as earplugs, around loud sounds can help protect against hearing loss. **Figure 4** shows some sounds and their intensity levels in decibels.

Figure 4 The decibel scale measures the intensity of sound. **Identify** *where a normal speaking voice would fall on the scale.*

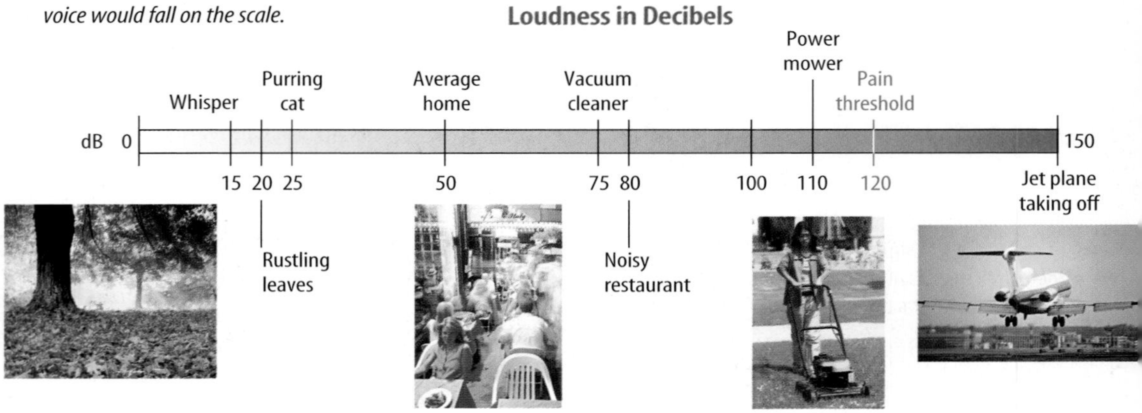

Caption Answer

Figure 4 Between an average home and a vacuum cleaner; people normally speak at about 60 dB.

Active Reading

Bubble Map Using a bubble map helps students start ideas flowing about a given topic. Words are clustered to describe a topic or idea that is studied. Students can use a bubble map to generate ideas for a prewriting or before writing in their journals, or to review for a test. Have students design a bubble map for the concepts about sound discussed in this section. L2 P

Teacher FYI

Sound Intensity The intensity of sound decreases as it travels away from a source not only because the waves transfer energy to matter, but also because they radiate out from the source. Sound intensity decreases as $1/r^2$, where r is the distance from the source.

322 CHAPTER 11 Sound and Light

Pitch and Frequency

You might be familiar with the music scale do, re, mi, fa, sol, la, ti, do shown in **Figure 5.** If you were to sing this scale, you would hear the pitch of your voice get higher. **Pitch** is the human perception of the frequency of sound waves. Pitch gets higher as the frequency of the sound waves increases.

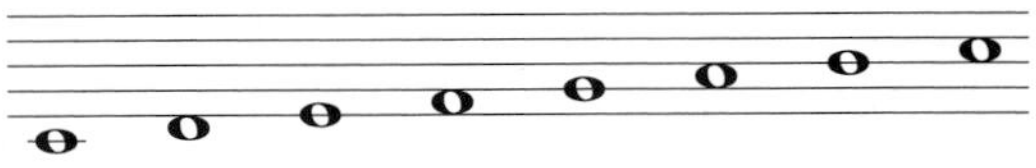

C	D	E	F	G	A	B	C
do	re	mi	fa	sol	la	ti	do
262 Hz	294 Hz	330 Hz	349 Hz	392 Hz	440 Hz	494 Hz	523 Hz

Figure 5 Every note has a different frequency, which gives it a distinct pitch.
Describe *how pitch changes when frequency increases.*

Frequency Frequency is a measure of how many wavelengths pass a particular point each second. For a compressional wave, such as sound, the frequency is the number of compressions or the number of rarefactions that pass by each second. Frequency is measured in hertz (Hz). A frequency of 1 Hz means that one complete wavelength passes by in 1 s.

A healthy human ear can hear sound waves with frequencies from about 20 Hz to 20,000 Hz. The human ear is most sensitive to sounds in the range of 440 Hz to about 7,000 Hz. In this range, most people can hear much fainter sounds than they can at higher or lower frequencies.

Ultrasonic and Infrasonic Waves Most people can't hear sound frequencies above 20,000 Hz, which are called ultrasonic waves. Dogs can hear sounds with frequencies up to about 35,000 Hz, and bats can detect frequencies higher than 100,000 Hz. Even though humans can't hear ultrasonic waves, they have a number of uses. For example, ultrasonic waves directed into the human body are used in medical diagnosis and treatment. Ultrasonic waves are reflected by objects underwater, and can be used to determine the size, shape, and depth of underwater objects.

Infrasonic, or subsonic, waves have frequencies below 20 Hz—too low for most people to hear. These waves are produced by sources that vibrate slowly, such as wind, heavy machinery, and earthquakes. Although you can't hear infrasonic waves, you might feel them as a rumble inside your body.

The Doppler Effect

Imagine that you are standing at the side of a racetrack with race cars zooming past. As they move toward you, the pitches of their engines become higher. As they move away, the pitches become lower. The change in pitch or frequency due to the relative motion of a wave source is called the **Doppler effect.**

Mini LAB

Comparing Intensity

Procedure
1. Tie the middle of a 50-cm length of **string** to a metal object such as a **spoon.**
2. Wrap each end of the string around a finger on each hand. Place one of these fingers in each ear.
3. Swing the object so it bumps against a **table** or a **chair.** Note the sound.
4. Take your fingers out of your ears and repeat step 3.

Analysis
1. Compare the sounds you heard in both trials.
2. Compare the intensity of the sound waves that reached your ears in both trials.

Try at Home

Caption Answer

Figure 5 As frequency increases, pitch becomes higher.

Discussion

Changing Pitch Ask students to describe times when they have heard a sound's pitch change because of the Doppler effect. Some examples are a moving police or fire engine siren, a school bell when they are moving toward or away from it quickly, and a train's whistle. Encourage students to listen for other examples of the Doppler effect over the next few weeks and to describe them to the class.

Mini LAB

Purpose Students listen to sounds through different mediums. L1 ELL LS **Auditory-Musical**

Materials metal objects such as a spoon, 1.5 m of string, chair or table

Teaching Strategy Suggest students try a variety of metal objects to obtain different sounds.

Analysis
1. Possible answer: the sound is louder and more muffled when your fingers are in your ears.
2. The intensity is greater with fingers in your ears.

Assessment

Content How would the intensity of the sound that travels through the string depend on the length of the string? The intensity would decrease as the string became longer. Use **PASC,** p. 89.

Try at Home

Science Journal

Feeling Pitch Have students place their hands gently over their necks and sing the musical scale "do re mi fa so la ti do." Have them write their observations in their Science Journals. They should be able to tell that their vocal cords vibrate differently as they go up the scale. L2 LS **Kinesthetic**

Differentiated Instruction

English-Language Learners Use the musical scale to help students understand the relationship between frequency and pitch. Have someone play the notes on a guitar or other musical instrument as you point them out on the staff lines. Be sure students understand that as the notes go up the scale, the frequency and pitch increase.

Visual Learning

Figure 6 Remind students that the sound waves emitted by the car in the figure don't change. It is only the frequency at which they reach the flagger that changes. The car's driver hears no change in pitch at all. Have students draw circles representing sound waves to show how the Doppler effect increases if the speed of the sound source increases. L2 LS **Visual-Spatial**

Quick Demo
The Doppler Effect

Materials sponge ball, small electric buzzer, battery, tape

Estimated Time 15 minutes

Procedure Cut a small opening in the side of the sponge ball. Place the small electric buzzer connected to the battery inside the opening and tape the opening shut. Throw the ball from the front to the back of the room. The increased and decreased pitches caused by the Doppler effect should be audible.

INTEGRATE Astronomy

Red Shift The light from most galaxies is shifted toward the red end of the spectrum because, as these galaxies are moving away from Earth, their light waves become "stretched out." This is known as the red shift. The stretching of the light waves is caused by the Doppler effect.

Reading Check

Answer The pitch decreases.

Figure 6 The Doppler effect occurs when the source of a sound wave is moving relative to a listener.

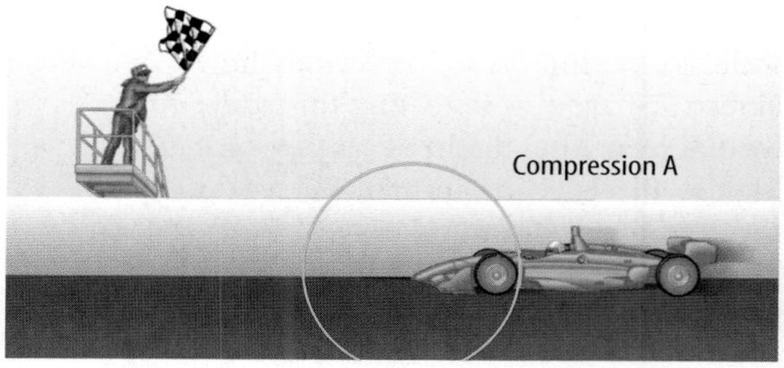

A The race car creates compression A, which spreads through the air in all directions from the point where it was created.

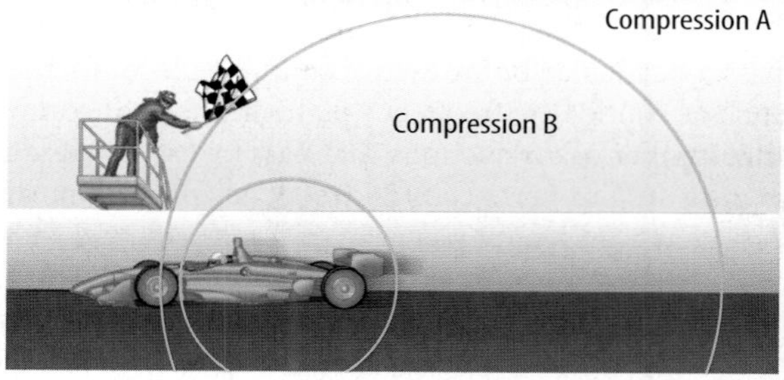

B The car is closer to the flagger when it creates compression B. Compressions A and B are closer together in front of the car, so the flagger hears a higher-pitched sound.

A Moving Source of Sound As a race car moves, it produces sound waves in the form of compressions and rarefactions. In **Figure 6A,** the race car creates a compression, labeled A. Compression A moves through the air toward the flagger. By the time compression B leaves the race car in **Figure 6B,** the car has moved forward. Because the car has moved since the time it created compression A, compressions A and B are closer together in front of the car than they would be if the car had stayed still. Because the compressions are closer together, more compressions pass by the flagger each second than if the car had been at rest. As a result, the flagger hears a higher pitch. **Figure 6B** also shows that the compressions behind the moving car are farther apart, resulting in a lower frequency. The flagger hears a lower pitch after the car passes.

A Moving Listener You also can hear the Doppler effect when you are moving past a sound source that is standing still. Suppose you were riding in a school bus and passed a building with a ringing bell. The pitch would become higher as you approached the building and lower as you rode away from it. The Doppler effect happens any time the source of a sound is changing position relative to the listener. It occurs no matter whether it is the sound source or the listener that is moving. The faster the change in position, the greater the change in frequency and pitch.

INTEGRATE Astronomy

Red Shift The Doppler effect can also be observed in light waves emanating from moving sources—although the sources must be moving at tremendous speeds. Astronomers have learned that the universe is expanding by observing the Doppler effect in light waves. Research the phenomenon known as red shift and explain in your Science Journal how it relates to the Doppler effect.

Reading Check *How does pitch change if you are moving away from a sound source?*

Curriculum Connection

History When a jet travels faster than the speed of sound, the sound waves it produces trail behind as a cone of pressure disturbances in the air. This Mach cone might be heard as a loud sonic boom as the jet passes. Have students research the first human-made sonic boom. Test pilot Chuck Yeager was the first person to break the sound barrier in an airplane and cause a sonic boom. He did this on October 14, 1947. L2

324 CHAPTER 11 Sound and Light

Using Sound

When sound waves strike an object, they can be absorbed by the object, transmitted through the object, or reflected from the object. By detecting the sound waves reflected from an object, the size, shape, and location of an object can be determined.

Echolocation and Sonar Some species of bats, as well as dolphins, whales, and other animals, use sound waves to detect their prey. Echolocation is the process of locating objects by emitting sounds and detecting the sound waves that reflect back.

Sonar is a system that uses the reflection of underwater sound waves to detect objects. First, a sound pulse is emitted underwater. The sound waves travel in the water and are reflected when they strike an object, such as a fish or a ship. An underwater microphone detects the reflected waves. Because the speed of sound in water is known, the distance to the object can be calculated by measuring how much time passes between when the sound pulse is emitted and when the reflected signal is received.

Science Online

Topic: Sonar
Visit gpescience.com for Web links to information about ways sonar is used.

Activity Research to find out the different types of sonar. Make a poster that describes active and passive sonar.

Applying Math — Solve a Simple Equation

USING SONAR A sonar pulse returns in 3.00 s from a sunken ship that is directly below. Find the depth of the ship if the speed of the pulse is 1,500 m/s. *Hint:* The sonar pulse travels a distance equal to twice the depth of the ship, so use the equation $d = st/2$ to find the depth.

IDENTIFY known values and the unknown value

Identify the known values:

speed of sound in water → means → $s = 1{,}500$ m/s

time for round trip → means → $t = 3.00$ s

Identify the unknown value:

depth of the ship → means → $d = ?$ m

SOLVE the problem

Substitute the known values $s = 1{,}500$ m/s and $t = 3.00$ s into the equation for depth:

$$d = \frac{st}{2} = \frac{(1{,}500 \text{ m/s})(3.00 \text{ s})}{2} = \frac{1}{2}(4{,}500 \text{ m}) = 2{,}250 \text{ m}$$

CHECK your answer

Check your answer by dividing the distance by the time and multiplying by 2. The result should be the speed of sound given in the problem.

Practice Problems

Find the speed of a sonar pulse that returns in 2.0 s from a ship at a depth of 1,500 m.

For more practice problems go to page 879, and visit Math Practice at gpescience.com.

Use Science Words

Word Origin Have students find what the letters of the word sonar stand for and explain why this is an accurate description. Sonar stands for sound navigation and ranging. This is accurate because sonar is the use of sound to navigate and determine the distance or range to objects. L2

Reading Check

Answer by emitting a sound pulse and measuring the time for the pulse to travel to the object and return

Applying Math

Math Standards

National: 1, 2, 9

Teaching Strategy

Be sure students understand that the reason the equation is divided by 2 is that the distance to the object is one-half the distance that the sound travels, because the sound must travel to the object and back.

Answers to Practice Problem

1,500 m/s

Teacher FYI

There are three types of sonar systems. An active sonar system sends sound waves toward a target and analyzes the reflected waves. A passive sonar system doesn't emit sound waves; it simply detects and analyzes sounds made by a target. Sonar systems can also be used for communication, as is done by naval and oceanography ships, for example.

Differentiated Instruction

Learning Disabled Go through the Applying Math feature step by step. Make sure the student understands the reason for each step in the problem. Watch to be sure the student is performing the calculations correctly.

Post Reading

Extended Research Have students research how the Doppler effect is used to predict storms. What advantage does Doppler radar have over conventional radar? Invite a meteorologist to provide a more thorough explanation to the class.

3 Assess

DAILY INTERVENTION

Check for Understanding

Kinesthetic Have students use their hands to demonstrate the motion of particles when sound waves pass through them. Ask students to show the movement of sound waves through air and then through aluminum. L2

Reteach

Sound Wave Properties Place a clear, shallow container of water on top of an overhead projector to demonstrate various properties of waves. For example, touch the water with vibrating tuning forks to show low and high frequencies. Move a vibrating tuning fork along the surface to show the Doppler effect. L2

Assessment

Process Strike a tuning fork and place its handle against various surfaces, such as a wooden desk, a book, a metal surface, and a wall. For each surface, have students explain why the amplified sound is loud or soft. Sounds will be louder for larger, denser, and stiffer surfaces. Use **Performance Assessment in the Science Classroom,** p. 89 L2

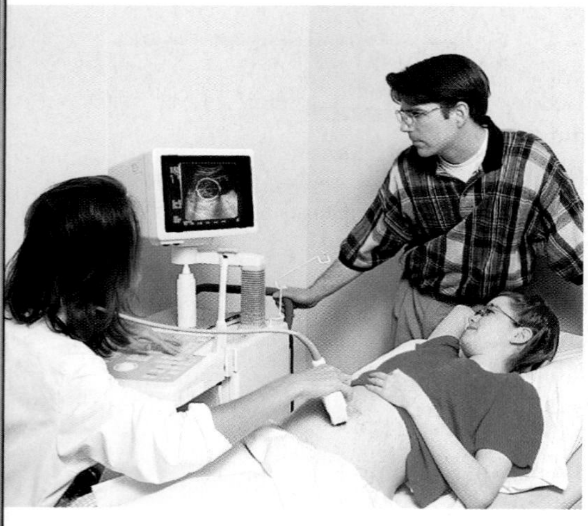

Figure 7 Ultrasonic waves are directed into a pregnant woman's uterus to form images of her fetus.

Ultrasound in Medicine High-frequency sound waves can also be used to remove dirt buildup on jewelry and glassware. One of the most important uses of ultrasonic waves, though, is in medicine. Using special instruments, medical professionals can send ultrasonic waves into a specific part of a patient's body. Reflected ultrasonic waves are used to examine different body parts and to detect and monitor certain types of heart disease and cancer. Ultrasound imaging also is used to monitor the development of a fetus, as shown in **Figure 7.** However, ultrasound does not produce good images of the bones and lungs, because hard tissues and air absorb the ultrasonic waves instead of reflecting them.

High-frequency sound waves can be used to treat certain medical problems. For example, sometimes small, hard deposits of calcium compounds or other minerals form in the kidneys, making kidney stones. In the past, physicians had to perform surgery to remove kidney stones. Now ultrasonic treatments are commonly used to break them up instead. Bursts of ultrasound create vibrations that cause the stones to break into small pieces that can easily pass out of the body with the urine. A similar treatment is available for gallstones.

section 1 review

Summary

Sound Waves

- Sound waves are compressional waves that are produced by vibrating objects.
- Sound usually travels fastest in solids and slowest in gases.
- Sound travels faster as the temperature of the medium increases.

Properties of Sound

- The amplitude of sound waves increases as the density of particles increases in the compressions and decreases in rarefactions
- Loudness is the human perception of the intensity of sound waves. Pitch is the human perception of the frequency of sound waves.
- The Doppler effect is the change in the frequency of a sound wave when the source of the sound is moving relative to a listener.

Self Check

1. **Explain** how sound travels from your vocal cords to your friend's ears when you talk.
2. **Explain** how the loudness of a sound wave depends on the intensity of the sound wave.
3. **Draw and label** a diagram that explains the Doppler effect.
4. **Describe** at least three uses of ultrasonic technology in medicine.
5. **Think Critically** How could sonar technology be used to locate deposits of oil and minerals?

Applying Math

6. **Calculate Time** How long would it take a sound wave from a car alarm to travel 1.0 km in air if the air temperature were 0°C?
7. **Calculate Distance** If sound travels in the ocean with a speed of 1,500 m/s, how far will a sonar pulse travel in 45 s?

More Section Review gpescience.com

section 1 review

1. Your vocal cords create compressions and rarefactions in air molecules that travel out in all directions.
2. Loudness is related to how the human ear and brain interpret intensity. As a sound wave's intensity increases so does the loudness.
3. Check students' work.
4. Possible answers: producing sonograms of a developing fetus, breaking up kidney stones, breaking up gall stones.
5. Sonar waves could be transmitted through the ground and reflected from oil deposits. They also would travel with a different speed in oil and mineral deposits than in the surrounding ground.
6. 1,000 m/(331 m/s) = 3.02 s
7. 1,500 m/s × 45 s = 37,500 m = 37.5 km

Reflection and Refraction of Light

Reading Guide

What You'll Learn

- **Describe** how light waves interact with matter.
- **Explain** the difference between regular and diffuse reflection.
- **Define** the index of refraction of a material.
- **Explain** why a prism separates white light into different colors.

Why It's Important

The images you see every day are due to the behavior of light waves.

Review Vocabulary

visible light: an electromagnetic wave with wavelengths between about 400 and 700 billionths of a meter

New Vocabulary

- opaque
- translucent
- transparent
- index of refraction

The Interaction of Light and Matter

Look around your darkened room at night. You know that some of the objects are brightly colored, but they look gray or black in the dim light. Turn on the light, and you can see all the objects in the room clearly, including their colors. What you see depends on the amount of light in the room and the color of the objects. For you to see an object, it must reflect or emit some light that reaches your eyes.

Absorption, Transmission, and Reflection Objects can absorb light, reflect light, and transmit light—allow light to pass through them. The type of matter in an object determines the amount of light it absorbs, reflects, and transmits. For example, the **opaque** material in the top candleholder in **Figure 8** only absorbs and reflects light—no light passes through it. As a result, you cannot see the candle inside. Materials that allow some light to pass through them, like the material of the middle candleholder in **Figure 8,** are described as **translucent.** You cannot see clearly through translucent materials.

Transparent materials, such as the bottom candleholder in **Figure 8,** transmit almost all the light striking them, so you can see objects clearly through them. Only a small amount of light is absorbed and reflected by transparent materials.

Figure 8 These candleholders interact with light differently.

A Opaque

B Translucent

C Transparent

Section 2 Resource Manager

Chapter *FAST FILE* Resources

Transparency Activity, p. 47

Lab Activity, pp. 13–16

Enrichment, p. 32

Reinforcement, p. 28

Directed Reading for Content Mastery, p. 20

Performance Assessment in the Science Classroom, pp. 55–56

Mathematical Skills Activities, pp. 17–18

Cultural Diveristy, pp. 57–58

1 Motivate

INTERACTIVE CHALKBOARD PowerPoint® Presentations An editable Microsoft® PowerPoint® presentation is available on **Interactive Chalkboard** CD-ROM.

Bellringer

Section Focus Transparencies also are available on the Interactive Chalkboard CD-ROM. L2 ELL

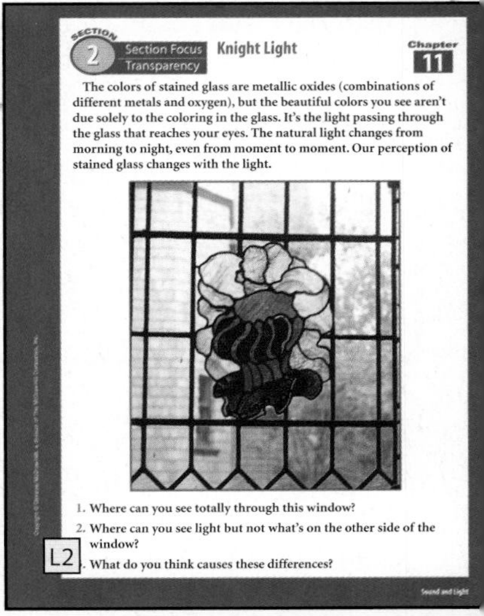

Section 2 Section Focus Transparency **Knight Light** Chapter 11

The colors of stained glass are metallic oxides (combinations of different metals and oxygen), but the beautiful colors you see aren't due solely to the coloring in the glass. It's the light passing through the glass that reaches your eyes. The natural light changes from morning to night, even from moment to moment. Our perception of stained glass changes with the light.

1. Where can you see totally through this window?
2. Where can you see light but not what's on the other side of the window?
3. What do you think causes these differences?

L2

Sound and Light

Reading Preview

Tie to Prior Knowledge

Water Distortion Ask how students' feet appear if they stand in a swimming pool with their heads above the water. The feet look distorted because the speed of light in water is different from the speed of light in air. This causes light to change direction when it enters water at an angle.

Make Connections Pour some water in a translucent glass and a transparent glass. Ask students which glass is easier to see through. transparent glass Explain that some objects transmit more light than others. Which glass allows the most light to pass through? transparent glass

Make a Model

Law of Reflection Have students roll a ball at an angle toward a wall to model light striking a surface. The ball, like light, obeys the law of reflection. The incident and reflected angles are the same.

IDENTIFYING Misconceptions

Reflecting Light Some students may think that only special materials, such as mirrors and shiny metals, reflect light. To correct this misconception, darken the room and have students shine a flashlight on the wall, a mirror, a book, a desk, and other surfaces. They should realize that all of the surfaces reflect light.

Activity

Reflective Foil Distribute two pieces of aluminum foil to small groups of students. Be careful not to wrinkle the foil. Have students crumple and then flatten one of their foil pieces. Ask which piece has a more regular reflection and why. The unwrinkled foil; its surface is smoother, so the normal is pointing in about the same direction at all points, meaning that the angles of incidence and reflection will be about the same everywhere for parallel light waves. L1

Reading Check

Answer light waves reflecting in many directions after striking a rough surface or being deflected by small particles

Caption Answer

Figure 10 Light rays obey the law of reflection at each point on the surface, but because the rough surface is sloped in different directions at each location, the parallel light rays that strike the rough surface are reflected in different directions.

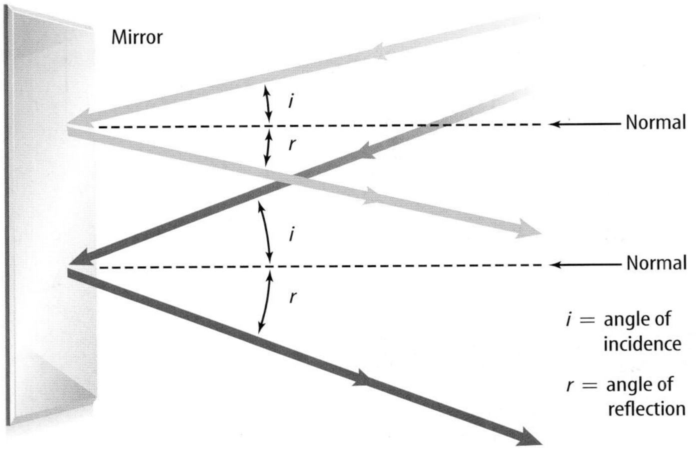

Figure 9 According to the law of reflection, light is reflected so that the angle of incidence always equals the angle of reflection.

Reflection of Light

Have you glanced in a mirror today? You see your reflection in the mirror when light is reflected off you, strikes the mirror, and is reflected off the mirror into your eye. Because light behaves as a wave, it obeys the law of reflection, as shown in **Figure 9.** Recall that, according to the law of reflection, the angle at which a light wave strikes a surface is the same as the angle at which it is reflected. Light reflected from any surface—a mirror or a sheet of paper—obeys this law.

Regular and Diffuse Reflection Why can you see your reflection in a store window but not in a sheet of paper? The answer has to do with the smoothness of the surfaces. A smooth, even surface such as a pane of glass produces a sharp image by reflecting parallel light waves in only one direction. Reflection of light waves from a smooth surface is regular reflection. To cause a regular reflection, the roughness of a surface must be less than the wavelengths it reflects. A sheet of paper has an uneven surface that causes incoming parallel light waves to be reflected in many directions, as shown in **Figure 10.** Reflection of light from a rough surface is diffuse reflection.

Scattering Diffuse reflection is a type of scattering that occurs when light waves traveling in one direction are made to travel in many different directions. Scattering also occurs when light waves traveling through the air reflect off small particles. An example is light scattering off the small water droplets that make up a cloud. Scattering causes the cloud to appear white, even though the droplets are transparent.

Reading Check *What is scattering of light?*

Figure 10 A sheet of paper has an uneven surface that produces a diffuse reflection.
Explain *Use the law of reflection to explain why a rough surface causes parallel light waves to be reflected in many directions.*

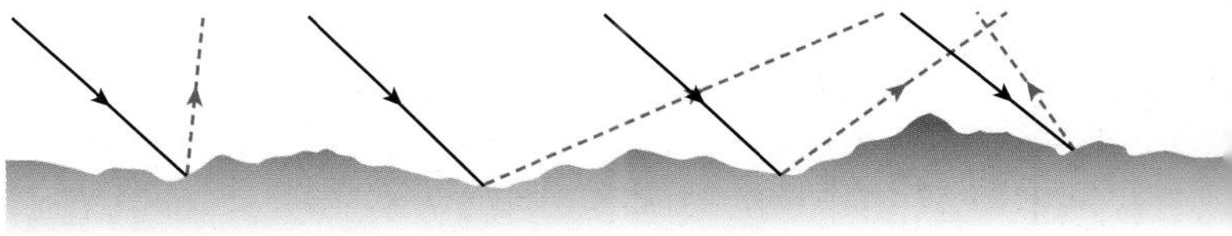

Differentiated Instruction

Visually Impaired Allow students to feel different grades of sandpaper. Explain that unless the light is absorbed, light reflects more evenly off the smoother surfaces. Students should realize that even surfaces that seem smooth can have microscopic roughness that prevents them from being good reflectors.

Teacher FYI

Index of Refraction The index of refraction of a material is the ratio of the speed of light in a vacuum to the speed of light in the material. The indices of refraction (n) in some common materials are: water, $n = 1.33$; glass, $n = 1.52$; diamond, $n = 2.42$. LS **Logical-Mathematical**

Refraction of Light

What occurs when a light wave passes from one material to another—from air to water, for example? Recall that refraction is caused by a change in the speed of a wave when it passes from one material to another. If the light wave is traveling at an angle to the boundary between the materials and the speed of light is different in the two materials, the wave will be bent, or refracted.

Reading Check *Why does refraction occur?*

The Index of Refraction The amount of bending that takes place depends on the speeds of light in both materials. The greater the change in speed, the more the light will be bent as it passes at an angle from one material to the other. **Figure 11** shows an example of refraction. Every material has an **index of refraction** which is the ratio of the speed of light in a vacuum to the speed of light in the material. The index of refraction indicates how much the speed of light is reduced in the material compared to its speed in empty space.

The larger the index of refraction, the more light is slowed down in the material. For example, because glass has a larger index of refraction than air, light moves more slowly in glass than air. The index of refraction is usually largest for solids and smallest for gases.

Figure 11 The spoon looks broken because light waves are refracted as they change speed when they pass from the water to the air.

Prisms A sparkling glass prism hangs in a sunny window, refracting the sunlight and projecting a colorful pattern onto the walls of the room. How does the refraction of light create these colors? The spectrum of colors is produced because the speed of light in a material also depends on the wavelength of the light. In a glass prism, light waves with longer wavelengths, such as red light waves, are slowed less than light waves with shorter wavelengths, such as blue light waves.

Figure 12 shows what occurs when white light passes through a prism. White light, such as sunlight, is made up of light waves with range of wavelengths from red to blue. The triangular prism refracts the light twice—once when it enters the prism and again when it leaves the prism and reenters the air. Because the longer wavelengths of light are slowed less than the shorter wavelengths are, red light is bent the least. As a result of these different amounts of bending, the different colors are separated when they emerge from the prism.

Figure 12 Refraction causes a prism to separate a beam of white light into different colors.

Reading Check

Answer Refraction occurs when a light wave changes speed as it passes at an angle from one material to another.

Discussion

Index Matching Ask students to imagine light traveling at an angle from one material into another with no refraction. What would this imply? The materials have the same index of refraction.

Use an Analogy

Bouncing Ball Tell students that reflecting light is similar to a ball bouncing off a wall. If you roll the ball directly toward the wall, it will bounce back straight toward you. If you roll it at an angle, it will bounce so that the angle between the incoming ball and the wall equals the angle between the outgoing ball and the wall. Allow the students to roll a ball at a wall from different angles. L2 ELL IN **Kinesthetic**

Fun Fact

Rainbows are formed when sunlight is refracted by water droplets in the air. If light traveled at the same speed in water and air, there would be no rainbows.

Visual Learning

Figure 11 Emphasize that the spoon appears to be broken because of the different paths the light takes. Light from the top of the spoon travels straight through the air. Light from the bottom of the spoon is bent when it passes from the water to the air. Have students sketch the paths the light takes in this picture. L2 ELL IN **Visual-Spatial**

Reading Strategy

Cooperative Groups Have students recreate the activity shown in **Figure 11.** Place students in groups of four, and give each group a beaker of water and a spoon. Have one student read the directions, one student perform the experiment, one student take notes, and one student explain to the class what the group learned about refraction.

Post Reading

Summarize Have students summarize the law of reflection and the index of refraction in their Science Journals. Ask students to apply each concept to an everyday situation, such as light reflecting off a mirror.

3 Assess

DAILY INTERVENTION

Check for Understanding

Visual-Spatial Draw different surfaces on the board and light rays approaching them. Make some rough and some smooth. Have the students copy the surfaces and draw light diagrams for them.

Reteach

Ray Diagrams Ask students to draw ray diagrams showing light coming from a flashlight, being refracted as it moves from air to water, being reflected off an object in the water, being refracted as it moves from the water to air, and then hitting an observer's eye.

Assessment

Process Show the class various materials and have students classify them as opaque, transparent, or translucent.

Figure 13 Mirages result when air near the ground is much warmer or cooler than the air above. This causes light waves reflected from an object to refract, creating one or more additional images.

Mirages When you're traveling in a car, you might see what looks like a pool of water on the road ahead. As you get closer, the water seems to disappear. You've seen a mirage—an image of a distant object produced by the refraction of light through air layers of different densities. Mirages result when the air at ground level is much warmer or cooler than the air above, as shown in **Figure 13.** The density of air increases as air cools and light waves move slower in cooler air than in warmer air. As a result, light waves are refracted as they pass through air layers with different temperatures.

section 2 review

Summary

Light and Matter

- The amount of light that is absorbed, reflected, or transmitted depends on the material making up the object.

Reflection of Light

- Light waves always obey the law of reflection: the angle of incidence equals the angle of reflection.
- Regular reflection causes parallel light waves to be reflected in only one direction.
- Diffuse reflection causes parallel light waves to be reflected in many directions.
- Scattering occurs when light waves are reflected and travel in many different directions.

Refraction of Light

- Refraction occurs when a light wave changes speed in moving from one material to another.
- The index of refraction of a material indicates how much light slows down in the material.

Self Check

1. **Compare and contrast** opaque, transparent, and translucent materials. Give one example of each.
2. **Discuss** why you can see your reflection in a smooth piece of aluminum foil but not in a crumpled ball of foil.
3. **Infer** what happens to light waves that are reflected off dust particles in the air.
4. **Explain** what happens to white light when it passes through a prism.
5. **Think Critically** Suppose a material has the same index of refraction as water. How would a light wave change direction as it traveled from water into this material?

Applying Math

6. **Find an Angle** A light wave strikes a mirror at an angle of 42° from the surface of the mirror. What angle does the reflected wave make with the normal?
7. **Find an Angle** A light wave reflects from a mirror at 27° from the normal. What was the angle between the mirror and the incident wave?

More Section Review gpscience.com

section 2 review

1. Transparent materials (clear glass) transmit almost all visible light, opaque materials (a wall) transmit no visible light, and translucent materials (waxed paper) transmit some visible light.
2. Smooth surfaces reflect parallel rays in one direction, but rough surfaces reflect parallel rays in many directions.
3. Light strikes the dust particles at different angles, causing the light to scatter in many directions.
4. The different wavelengths of light that pass through the prism are bent by different amounts, causing a rainbow effect.
5. There would be no change in direction.
6. An incident angle of 42° to the surface corresponds to an angle of 48° to the normal. The reflected angle, then, will also be 48° to the normal.
7. 63°

Section 3: Mirrors, Lenses, and the Eye

Reading Guide

What You'll Learn
- **Describe** how images are formed by three types of mirrors.
- **Explain** how convex and concave lenses form images.
- **Explain** how the human eye enables you to see.
- **Describe** how lenses are used to correct vision problems.

Why It's Important
Mirrors and lenses are used in optical instruments such as cameras and telescopes.

Review Vocabulary
reflection: the process of changing direction after striking a surface

New Vocabulary
- plane mirror
- concave mirror
- convex mirror
- convex lens
- concave lens

Light Rays

Light sources send out light waves in all directions. These waves spread out like ripples on the surface of water spread out from the point of impact of a pebble. You can think of the light coming from the source as being many narrow beams of light traveling in all directions. Each narrow light beam is called a light ray.

Mirrors

A mirror is any surface that produces a regular reflection. A pool of still water, a metal pan, and even the back of a shiny spoon can be mirrors. Mirrors can be flat, curved inward, or curved outward.

Plane Mirrors A flat, smooth mirror is a **plane mirror.** When you look in a plane mirror, your image appears upright. If you stand 1 m from the mirror, your image appears 1 m behind the mirror, or 2 m from you. In fact, your image is what a friend standing 2 m from you would see. **Figure 14** shows how your image is formed. First, light rays from a light source strike you. Every point that is struck by the light rays reflects these rays so they travel outward in all directions. If your friend were looking at you, these reflected light rays coming from you would enter her eyes so she could see you. However, if a mirror is placed between you and your friend, light rays are reflected from the mirror back to your eyes.

Figure 14 Seeing an image of yourself in a mirror involves two sets of reflections: light rays are reflected from you and then are reflected by the mirror.

Section 3 Resource Manager

Chapter *FAST FILE* Resources
- Transparency Activity, pp. 48, 51–52
- MiniLAB, p. 4
- Enrichment, p. 33
- Reinforcement, p. 29
- Directed Reading for Content Mastery, p. 21
- Lab Worksheets, pp. 5–6

Home and Community Involvement, p. 34

Lab Management and Safety, pp. 67–68

1 Motivate

INTERACTIVE CHALKBOARD An editable Microsoft® PowerPoint® presentation is available on **Interactive Chalkboard** CD-ROM.

Bellringer

Section Focus Transparencies also are available on the Interactive Chalkboard CD-ROM. L2 ELL

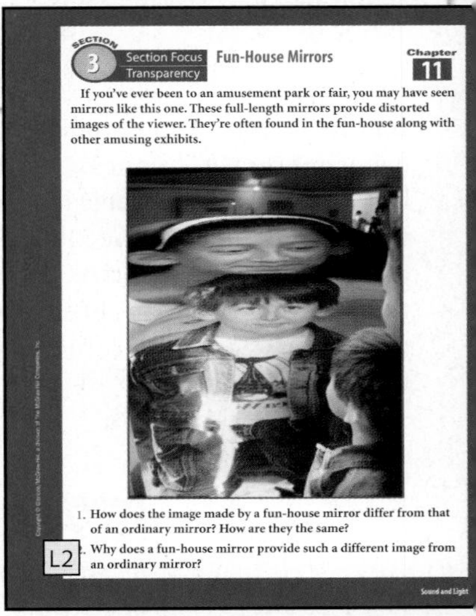

Section 3 Section Focus Transparency — Fun-House Mirrors — Chapter 11

If you've ever been to an amusement park or fair, you may have seen mirrors like this one. These full-length mirrors provide distorted images of the viewer. They're often found in the fun-house along with other amusing exhibits.

1. How does the image made by a fun-house mirror differ from that of an ordinary mirror? How are they the same?
2. Why does a fun-house mirror provide such a different image from an ordinary mirror?

L2

Sound and Light

Reading Preview

Tie to Prior Knowledge

Reflection Distortion Ask students if they have ever noticed a distorted reflection in a shiny, rounded surface, such as a doorknob. In this section, students will learn how the shape of a mirror determines the type of reflection they see.

Concept Maps Have students make concept maps about the different types of mirrors discussed in this section. The first, center oval should be labeled *Mirror*. The second row of ovals should be labeled *Plane Mirror*, *Concave Mirror* and *Convex Mirror*. The third row of ovals should contain characteristics of each type of mirror.

2 Teach

Use Science Words

Word Meaning Have students explain why a flat mirror is called a plane mirror. In mathematics, the word plane refers to a flat surface that extends infinitely in all directions, so the word plane is frequently used as a synonym for flat.

Caption Answers

Figure 15 The farther you are from the mirror, the smaller your image will appear.

Figure 16 Check students' answers.

Activity

Concave Mirrors Allow students to experiment with concave mirrors to observe how focusing the image depends on the object's distance from the mirror. Have them also observe how the image varies as they move the mirror from side to side. L2 ELL LS **Visual-Spatial**

Teacher FYI

Spherical Aberration Spherical mirrors can't produce perfectly focused images because rays from their outer edges focus slightly closer to the mirror than rays from the middle. To avoid this effect, large mirrors typically have a parabolic shape, which allows all of the rays to converge at the same point.

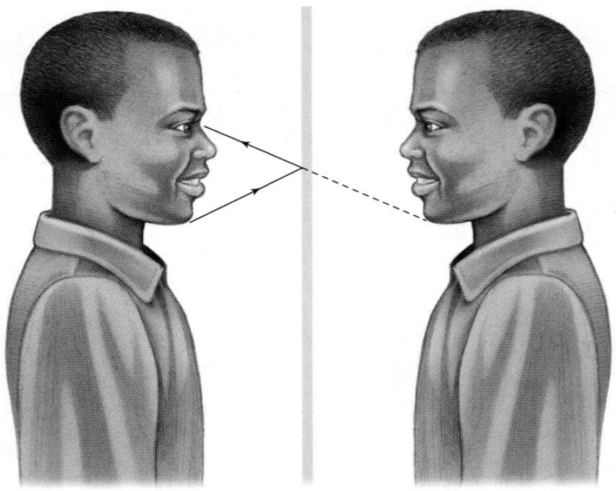

Figure 15 Your brain interprets the light rays reflected by the mirror as coming from a point behind the mirror.
Infer *how the size of your image in a plane mirror depends on your distance from the mirror.*

Virtual and Real Images The formation of an image by a plane mirror is shown in **Figure 15.** Your brain assumes that light rays travel in a straight line. As a result, rays that enter your eyes seem to come from behind the mirror. This makes the image seem to be behind the mirror. However, no light rays actually pass through the place where the image seems to be located. This type of image is called a virtual image. Plane mirrors always form virtual images. If light rays from an object pass through the location of the image, the image is called a real image. Curved mirrors can form both real and virtual images.

Concave Mirrors If the surface of a mirror is curved inward, it is called a **concave mirror,** as shown in **Figure 16.** The optical axis is an imaginary straight line drawn perpendicular to the surface of the mirror at its center. Every light ray traveling parallel to the optical axis is reflected through a point on the optical axis called the focal point. The distance from the center of the mirror to the focal point is called the focal length.

The image formed by a concave mirror depends on the location of the object relative to the focal point. **Figure 16** shows a candle located more than twice the focal length from the mirror. Although many light rays come from each point on the candle, only two rays from the same point are shown. Ray A passes through the focal point and then reflects off the mirror moving parallel to the optical axis. Ray B travels parallel to the optical axis before reflecting off the mirror and passing through the focal point. The point where the two rays meet is the location of the image of the original point on the candle. The image formed is a real image because light rays from the candle pass through the place where the image is located.

Figure 16 Rays A and B start from the same place on the candle, travel in different directions, and meet again on the reflected image.
Diagram *how two other points on the image of the candle are formed.*

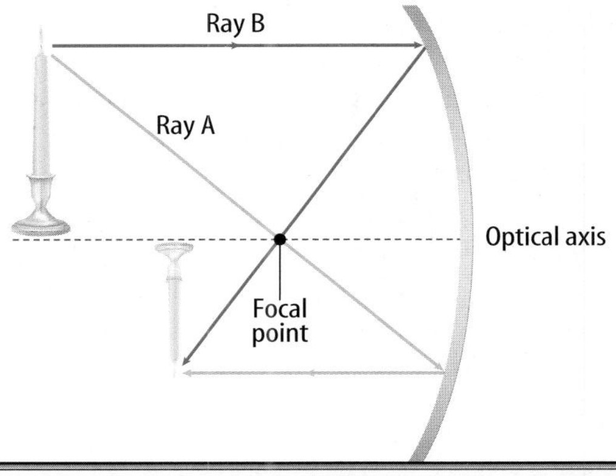

Visual Learning

Figure 16 Although only two rays are shown in the figure, students should realize that rays are reflected in all directions. Have students work in pairs and discuss how rays from all parts of the candle are reflected off the concave mirror to form an image. L1 ELL LS **Visual-Spatial**

Active Reading

Write-Draw-Discuss This strategy encourages students to participate actively in reading and lectures, assimilating content creatively. Have students write about an idea, clarify it and then make an illustration or drawing. Ask students to share responses with the class and display several examples. Have students Write-Draw-Discuss about convex and concave mirors.

Images Produced by a Concave Mirror When an object is between one and two focal lengths from a concave mirror, the image is real, inverted, and larger than the object. An object closer than one focal length from a concave mirror produces a virtual image that is upright and larger than the object. No image is produced if the object is located at the focal point.

Convex Mirrors When you are in a store, look up toward one of the back corners or at the end of an aisle to see if a large, rounded mirror is mounted there. You can see a large area of the store in such a mirror. A mirror that curves outward like the back of a spoon is called a **convex mirror.** Light rays that hit a convex mirror diverge, or spread apart, after they are reflected. **Figure 17** shows how the rays from an object are reflected by a convex mirror to form an image. The reflected rays diverge and never meet, so a convex mirror forms only a virtual image. The image also is upright and smaller than the actual object is.

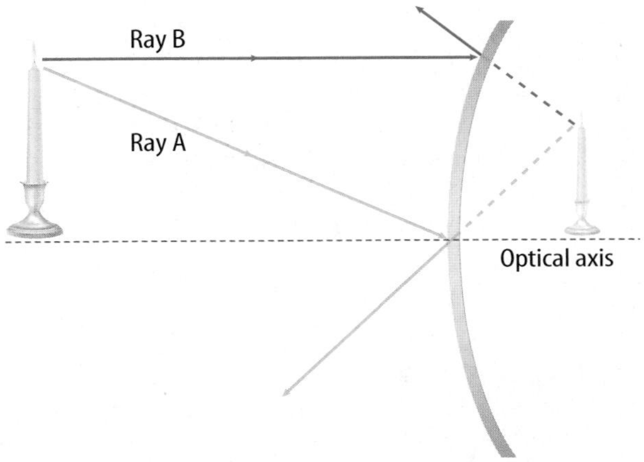

Figure 17 A convex mirror forms a reduced, upright, virtual image.

Reading Check *Describe the image formed by a convex mirror.*

Lenses

What do your eyes have in common with cameras, eyeglasses, and microscopes? Each of these contains at least one lens. A lens is a transparent object with at least one curved surface that causes light rays to refract. The image that a lens forms depends on the shape of the lens. Like curved mirrors, lenses can be convex or concave.

Convex Lenses A **convex lens** is thicker in the middle than at the edges. Its optical axis is an imaginary straight line that is perpendicular to the surface of the lens at its thickest point. When light rays approach a convex lens traveling parallel to its optical axis, the rays are refracted toward the center of the lens, as in **Figure 18.** Light rays traveling along the optical axis are not bent at all. All light rays traveling parallel to the optical axis are refracted so they pass through a single point, which is the focal point of the lens. The less curved the sides of the lens, the less light rays are bent. As a result, lenses with flatter sides have longer focal lengths. **Figure 19** on the next page shows that convex lenses can form either real or virtual images.

Figure 18 Convex lenses are thicker in the middle than at the edges. Light rays that are parallel to the optical axis are refracted so that they pass through the focal point. A light ray that passes through the center of the lens is not refracted.

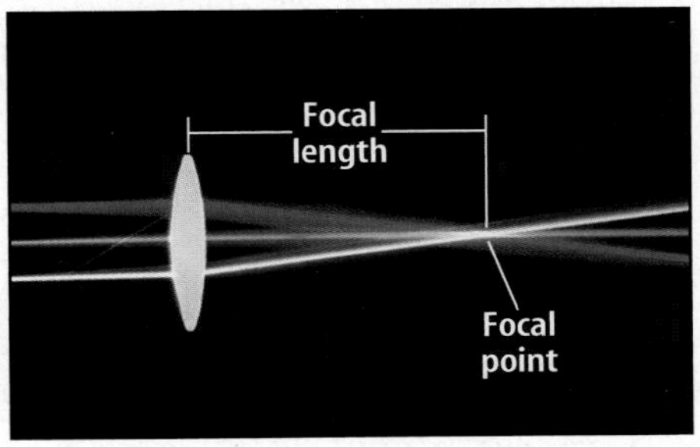

Quick Demo
Mirror Reflections

Materials laser pointer; plane, concave, and convex mirrors

Estimated Time five minutes

Purpose Use the laser pointer to show light reflecting from a plane mirror, a concave mirror, and a convex mirror. Students should notice the difference in reflections from the three mirrors. Remind them that the law of reflection applies to each mirror. **WARNING:** *Never direct a laser pointer toward someone's eyes. Be sure the reflected light does not point toward someone's eyes.* L2 ELL IS **Visual-Spatial**

Reading Check

Answer upright, smaller, and virtual

Discussion

Lenses v. Mirrors What is the primary difference between lenses and mirrors? Mirrors reflect light, whereas lenses transmit light.

Activity

Convex Lenses Distribute to your class some convex lenses of varying focal lengths. Show students how to find the focal length of a lens by focusing the clearest possible image of an overhead light on a white piece of paper (held by a partner) and measuring the distance from the paper to the lens. L2 IS **Visual-Spatial**

LAB DEMONSTRATION

Purpose to observe images with convex and concave lenses

Materials concave and convex lenses, optical bench and lens holders, tape, pencil

Preparation Place a convex lens in a holder on the bench. Using tape, mark one and two focal lengths.

Procedure Hold a pencil more than two focal lengths from the lens, between one and two focal lengths from the lens, and less than one focal length from the lens. At each position, have students look through the lens. Repeat using a concave lens.

Expected Outcome The convex lens diverges light. Light through a concave lens depends on image distance.

Assessment

Ask why the image flips when the pencil moves closer than one focal length to the convex lens. The light rays no longer converge.

SECTION 3 Mirrors, Lenses, and the Eye 333

NATIONAL GEOGRAPHIC

Visualizing Images Formed by a Convex Lens

Have students examine the pictures and read the captions. Then ask the following questions.

To which type of mirror is a convex lens most similar? Describe the similarities. Concave mirror; both cause light rays to converge and form different types of images depending on the position of the object relative to the focal point.

How does the position of the focal point change as the lens becomes more curved? It moves closer to the lens. Less curved? It moves away from the lens.

Activity

Have students create tables describing the images formed by lenses. The columns should be labeled *Lens Shape*, *Location of Object*, *Type of Image*, including the three subheadings *Virtual/Real*, *Upright/Inverted*, and *Size*. For example, one row for convex lenses would include the entries: convex, object beyond 2 focal lengths from the lens, real, inverted, and smaller than object, respectively.

NATIONAL GEOGRAPHIC **VISUALIZING IMAGES FORMED BY A CONVEX LENS**

Figure 19

A convex lens can form images that are real or virtual, enlarged or reduced, and upright or inverted. Just as for a concave mirror, the type of image formed by a convex lens depends on the location of the object relative to the focal point of the lens.

If the object is more than two focal lengths from the lens, the image formed is real, inverted, and smaller than the object. As the object moves farther from the lens, the image becomes smaller.

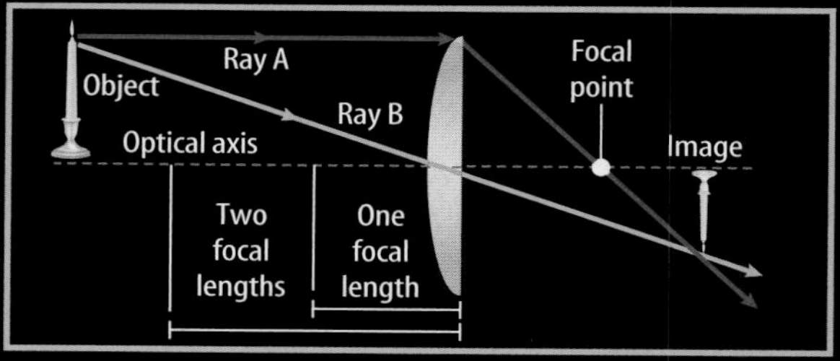

If the object is between one and two focal lengths from the lens, the image formed is real, inverted, and larger than the object. As the object moves closer to the focal point, the image becomes larger.

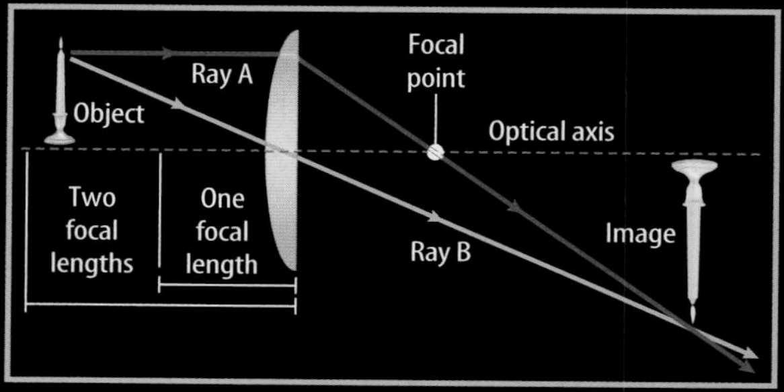

If the object is less than one focal length from the lens, the image is virtual, upright, and larger than the object. The image is virtual because the light rays from the object diverge after they pass through the lens. The image becomes smaller as the object moves closer to the lens.

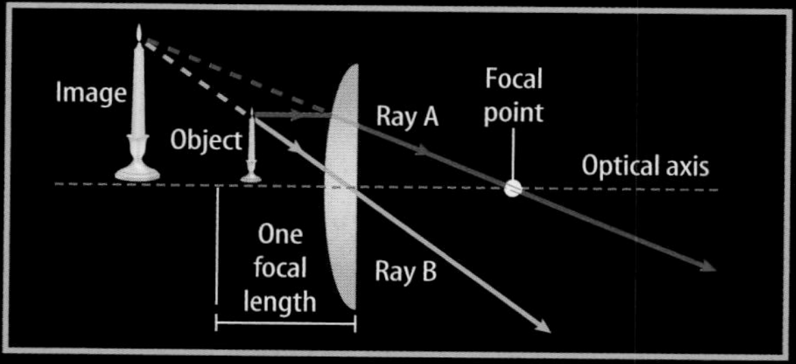

Reading Strategy

Clarify Illustrations As you read aloud the captions in **Figure 19,** have students use their fingers to trace the path of light from the object to the image. Ask them to raise their hands if any step along the path is unclear. Pause and clarify the concept for students.

Concave Lenses A **concave lens** is thinner in the middle and thicker at the edges. As shown in **Figure 20,** light rays that pass through a concave lens bend away from the optical axis. The rays spread out and never meet, so a real image is never formed. The image is always virtual, upright, and smaller than the object is. Concave lenses are used in some types of eyeglasses and some telescopes. Concave lenses usually are used in combination with other lenses.

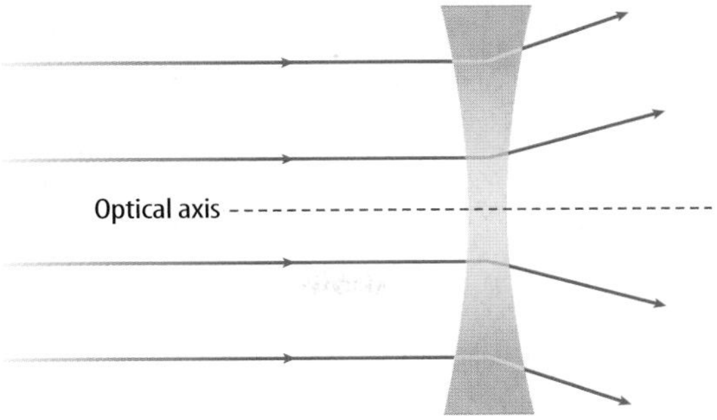

Figure 20 A concave lens refracts light rays so they spread out away from the optical axis.
Classify *Is a concave lens most like a concave mirror or a convex mirror?*

Reading Check *What type of image is formed by a concave lens?*

The Human Eye

What determines how well you can see the words on this page? If you don't need eyeglasses, the structure of your eye gives you the ability to focus on these words and other objects around you. Look at **Figure 21.** Light enters your eye through a transparent covering on your eyeball called the cornea. The cornea causes light rays to bend so that they converge. The light then passes through an opening called the pupil. Behind the pupil is a flexible convex lens. Muscles attached to the lens change its shape to help focus light, forming a sharp image on your retina.

The retina is the inner lining of your eye. The retina contains light-sensitive cells that convert an image into electrical signals. These signals then are carried along the optic nerve to your brain to be interpreted. With this complex structure, the human eye is capable of seeing clearly in bright and dim conditions, focusing on both near and far objects, and also detecting colors.

INTEGRATE Career

Eye Doctors Optometrists and ophthalmologists treat many different eye problems. They often use advanced technology to diagnose and correct malfunctioning parts of the eye. Research an eye problem and how it is treated. Write a paragraph describing what parts of the eye are affected by the problem and how doctors correct it.

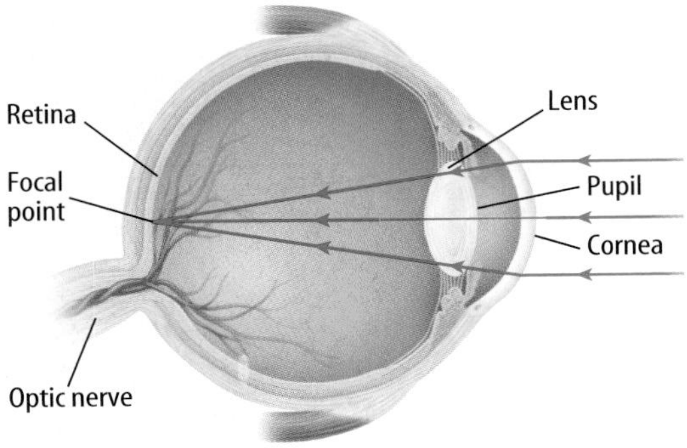

Figure 21 The cornea and lens in your eye bend light rays so that a sharp image is formed on the retina.

Reading Check

Answer virtual, upright, smaller than the object

Caption Answer

Figure 20 Convex mirror; both cause light to diverge and produce virtual images.

INTEGRATE Career

Eye Doctors A main distinction between the two professions is that ophthalmologists perform eye surgery while optometrists do not. Possible student topics include: keratoconus (deformed cornea, treated with glasses and contacts or cornea transplant), cataracts (cloudy lens, treated by implanting artificial lens), macular degeneration (affects the retina, often treated with laser surgery)

Quick Demo
Exploring an Eye

Materials model of a human eye

Estimated Time 30 minutes

Procedure Allow students to explore the model and observe the cornea, lens, and retina. Have students explain how light enters through the cornea and is refracted onto the retina. Point out the muscles that adjust the size of the lens, and note the optic nerve, which carries information about images to the brain. L2 **Visual-Spatial**

Use Science Words

Word Origin Lenses were named because of the resemblance of an eye's lens to a small legume called a lentil. The Latin word for lentil is *lenticula*.Bring lentils to class so students can see the resemblance in shape. L2 **Visual-Spatial**

Differentiated Instruction

Learning Disabled If students have trouble remembering which type of curved surface is concave and which is convex, tell them to remember that a concave surface is curved inward like a cave. To practice using this mnemonic, have them name some curved surfaces and identify them as concave or convex.

Teacher FYI

Animal Eyes Vertebrates, cephalopods, and some spiders have camera-like eyes with variable focusing. Worms, mollusks, and some crustaceans and insects have simple eyes that can distinguish light and dark. Most arthropods have compound eyes, with many separate lenses, each of which forms its own image.

Mini LAB

Video Lab available.

Purpose to observe how an object's distance from a convex lens affects its image L1 ELL

IS **Visual-Spatial**

Materials glass test tube with stopper, water, paper

Teaching Strategy Print the words in capital letters.

Analysis

1. When the tube is on the paper, the words are slightly magnified. About 1 cm away, beyond the focal point, SULFUR is inverted, but DIOXIDE seems unchanged because it is symmetrical.
2. The upright image is virtual. The inverted image is real.

Assessment

Content Ask whether a magnifying lens could invert images. Yes, if it is far enough away from the object.

Mini LAB

Experimenting with Focal Lengths

Procedure

1. Fill a glass **test tube** with **water** and seal it with a **lid or stopper.**
2. Type or print *SULFUR DIOXIDE* in capital letters on a piece of **paper.**
3. Set the test tube horizontally over the words. Record your observations.
4. Hold the tube at several heights above the words. Record your observations.

Analysis

1. Describe how the words changed as the height of the test tube increased.
2. Classify the image at each height as real or virtual.

Brightness and Intensity The human eye can adjust to the brightness of the light that strikes it. If you step outside on a sunny day, you may have to shade your eyes against the intensity of the sunlight. Light intensity is the amount of light energy that strikes a certain area each second. Brightness is the human perception of light intensity. Sunlight seems bright because a large amount of light energy strikes your retina each second. Your eyes respond to bright light by decreasing the size of your pupil. This reduces the amount of light that enters your eye and strikes the retina.

Intensity depends on your distance from a light source. If you move away from a bare lightbulb, you can see how the intensity of the light rapidly decreases. Because light rays spread out from the source, less light energy strikes your retina the farther away you are from the bulb.

Correcting Vision Problems

If you have good vision, you should be able to see objects clearly when they are 25 cm or farther away from your eyes. A sharp image of an object should be formed on your retina. However, for many people, the image is blurry or formed in the wrong place, causing vision problems.

Farsightedness If you can see distant objects clearly but can't bring nearby objects into focus, then you are farsighted. In this case, the eyeball might be too short or the lens isn't curved enough to form a sharp image of nearby objects on the retina, as shown in **Figure 22.** To correct the problem, convex lenses can be used to bend incoming light rays so they converge before they enter the eye.

Figure 22 Farsightedness can be corrected by convex lenses.

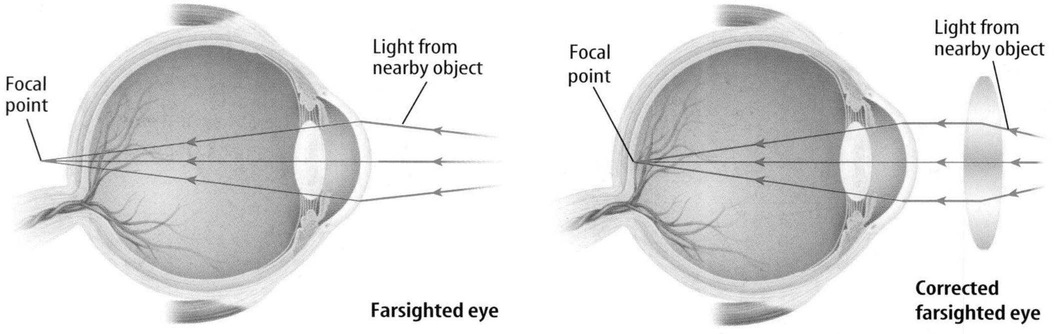

The focal length of a farsighted eye is too long to form a sharp image of nearby objects on the retina.

A convex lens in front of a farsighted eye enables a sharp image of nearby objects to be formed on the retina.

Visual Learning

Figure 22 Be sure students understand that the light rays in the image are shown extending past the eyeball only to show where the focal point is located. In reality, the rays are blocked by the retina before they can focus. Also point out the shape of the lens of the eye. Although the cornea is mostly responsible for refracting the light, the lens is able to change shape. This enables a person to slightly change the amount of refraction so that light from both near and far objects can be focused.

Fun Fact

Eyeglasses were used as early as the thirteenth century, and some crystals were used even earlier as natural magnifying glasses by the Greeks and Arabs.

Cultural Diversity

Arabian Lights One of the greatest early physicists was an Arabian scientist named Abu Ali al-Hasan ibn al-Haytham, better known in the West as Alhazen. Among Alhazen's contributions was the theory that vision is based on light coming from a source and being reflected from an object.

Curriculum Connection

Language Arts The manufacture of convex and concave lenses for eyeglasses and optical instruments requires high-precision measurements and the use of high-quality glass. Have students write a paper about this process. Students might mention cutting the glass, shaping the convex or concave surface, polishing, and grinding edges so that physical and optical centers match. L2 P IS **Linguistic**

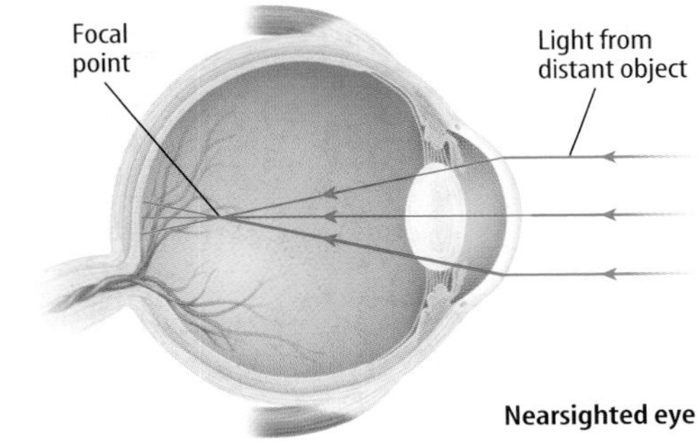

When a nearsighted person looks at distant objects, a sharp image is formed in front of the retina.

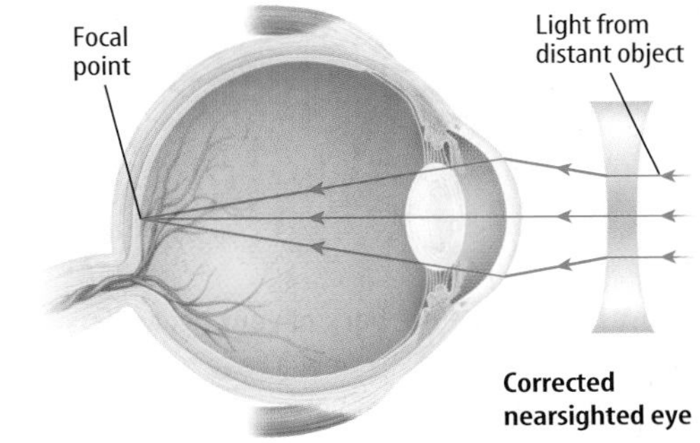

A concave lens in front of a nearsighted eye makes light rays diverge so a sharp image is formed on the retina.

Figure 23 Nearsightedness can be corrected with concave lenses.

Nearsightedness If you have nearsighted friends, you know that they can see only nearby objects clearly. Their eyes cannot form a sharp image on the retina of an object that is far away. Instead, the image is formed in front of the retina, as shown in **Figure 23.** To correct this problem, a nearsighted person can wear concave lenses. **Figure 23** shows how a concave lens causes incoming light rays from distant objects to diverge before they reach the eye. Then the rays can be focused by the eye to form a sharp image on the retina.

section 3 review

Summary

Mirrors

- A plane mirror forms upright, virtual images.
- The image formed by a concave mirror depends on the location of the object relative to the focal point.
- Convex mirrors always produce virtual, upright images that are smaller than the object.

Lenses

- The image formed by a convex lens depends on the distance of the object from the lens.
- Concave lenses always form virtual, upright images that are smaller than the object.

The Eye and Vision

- The eye contains a lens that changes shape to produce sharp images on the retina.
- Farsightedness occurs when the eye cannot form a sharp image of nearby objects. Nearsightedness occurs when the eye cannot form sharp images of distant objects.

Self Check

1. **Diagram** how light rays from an object are reflected by a convex mirror to form an image.
2. **Infer** how the size of the image changes if an object that is less than one focal length from a concave mirror moves closer to the mirror.
3. **Explain** how the focal length of a convex lens changes as the sides of the lens become less curved.
4. **Compare** the image of an object less than one focal length from a convex lens with the image of an object more than two focal lengths from the lens.
5. **Think Critically** Describe the image formed by a light source placed at the focal point of a convex lens.

Applying Math

6. **Calculate Object Distance** If you looked through a convex lens with a focal length of 15 cm and saw a real, inverted, enlarged image, what is the maximum distance between the lens and the object?

More Section Review gpescience.com

Post Reading

Reflection Tell students to imagine they are a ray of light from a distant object. Ask them to write a description of their journey through the human eye.

3 Assess

DAILY INTERVENTION

Check for Understanding

Kinesthetic Place flashlights and various plane, convex, and concave mirrors on a table. Allow students to experiment with the different mirrors and the flashlights in a darkened room. Have the students write down an observation about how each mirror affected the beams of light.

Reteach

Eyeglass Exploration Compare eyeglasses that correct nearsightedness and farsightedness. Have students examine near and far objects through each type of lens, identify whether each lens is concave or convex, and explain how each lens corrects vision problems. L2 ELL IN **Visual-Spatial**

Assessment

Process Ask students to explain why the image you see with a magnifying glass is blurry if you hold the glass too far from the object. The object is more than one focal length from the lens, so the image formed is real. To see the image clearly, the eye must be at the image's location. Use **Performance Assessment in the Science Classroom,** p. 89

section 3 review

1. Sketches should show light rays from a single point on the object diverging after being reflected from the mirror and an upright, smaller, virtual image being formed on the other side of the mirror.
2. The image gets smaller.
3. The focal length increases as the sides of the lens become less curved.
4. The image of an object positioned less than one focal length from the lens is enlarged, upright, and virtual. The image of an object positioned more than two focal lengths from the lens is reduced, inverted, and real.
5. Light rays from the light source will be refracted by the lens so they travel parallel to the optical axis. A beam of light will be formed.
6. 30 cm (two focal lengths)

BENCH TESTED

Real-World Problem

Purpose Students will observe image formation by plane mirrors. L1 COOP LEARN LS **Visual-Spatial**

Process Skills measure, infer, recognize cause and effect, compare and contrast, form operational definitions

Time Required 45 minutes

Procedure

Teaching Strategies

- Use rectangular mirrors at least 5 cm across. Mirror tiles from a hardware store can be cut to size, but sharp edges must be ground or taped.
- Photocopy a protractor to make worksheets for measuring angles.

Conclude and Apply

1. The number of paper clip images is one less than the number of wedges.
2. The angle producing six wedges is $\frac{360}{6} = 60°$. Five images will be produced.

Assessment

Performance Ask students to open the mirrors to an angle of 45° to each other. How many images of your face do you see? eight What about smaller angles? more images Larger angles? fewer images Explain. The number of images is 360° divided by the angle in degrees minus 1. Use **Performance Assessment in the Science Classroom,** p. 89

LAB

Reflections of Reflections

How can you see the back of your head? You can use two mirrors to view a reflection of a reflection of the back of your head.

Real-World Problem

How many images can you see with two mirrors?

Goal

- **Infer** how the number of images depends on the angle between two mirrors.

Materials

plane mirrors (2)
protractor
masking tape
paper clip

Safety Precautions

Handle glass mirrors and paper clips carefully.

Procedure

1. Lay one mirror on top of the other with the mirror surfaces inward. Tape them together so they will open and close. Use tape to label them *L* and *R* for *left* and *right.*
2. Stand the mirrors on a sheet of paper. Using the protractor, close the mirrors to an angle of 72°.

Images and Wedges Seen in the Mirrors

Angle of Mirrors	Number of Paper Clip Images		Number of Wedges
	R	L	
72°	2	2	5
90°	2	1	4
120°	1	1	3

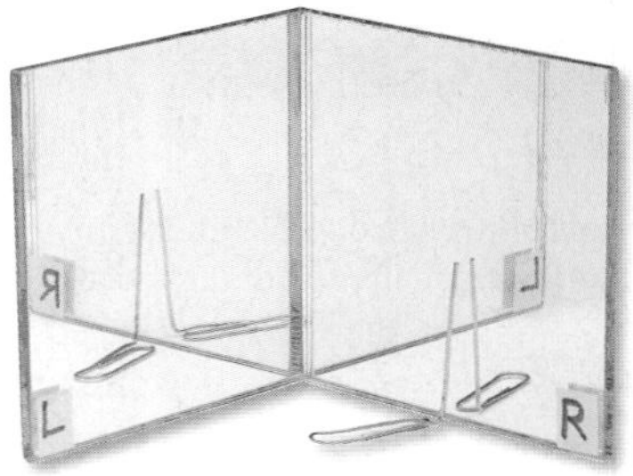

3. Bend one leg of a paper clip up 90° and place it close to the front of the *R* mirror.
4. Count the number of images of the paper clip you see in the *R* and *L* mirrors. Record these numbers in your data table.
5. The mirrors create an image of a circle divided into wedges. Record the number of wedges.
6. Hold the *R* mirror still and slowly open the *L* mirror to 90°. Record the numbers of images of the clip and wedges in the circle. Repeat, this time opening the mirrors to 120°.

Conclude and Apply

1. **Infer** the relationship between the number of wedges and paper clip images.
2. **Determine** the angle that would divide a circle into six wedges. Hypothesize how many images would be produced. Test your hypothesis.

Communicating Your Data

Demonstrate for younger students the relationship between the angle of the mirrors and the number of reflections.

Communicating Your Data

Have students draw circles divided into thirds (120°), quarters (90°), fifths (72°), and sixths (60°) and use the circles in their demonstrations to position the mirrors. Have them show younger students how the number of wedges seen relates to the angle between the mirrors.

section 4

Light and Color

Reading Guide

What You'll Learn

- **Explain** how you see color.
- **Describe** the difference between light color and pigment color.
- **Predict** what happens when different colors are mixed.

Why It's Important

From traffic lights to great works of art, color is an important part of your world.

Review Vocabulary

retina: inner layer of the eye containing cells that convert light images into electrical signals

New Vocabulary

- pigment

Why Objects Have Color

Why do some apples appear red, while others look green or yellow? An object's color depends on the wavelengths of light it reflects. Recall that white light is a blend of all colors of visible light. When a red apple is struck by white light, it reflects red light back to your eyes and absorbs all of the other colors. **Figure 24** shows white light striking a green leaf. Only the wavelengths corresponding to green light are reflected to your eyes.

Although some objects appear to be black, black isn't a color. Black is the absence of visible light. Objects that appear black absorb all colors of light and reflect little or no light back to your eyes. White objects appear to be white because they reflect all colors of visible light.

Reading Check *Why does a white object appear white?*

Figure 24 This leaf absorbs all wavelengths of visible light except the wavelengths you see as green.

Colored Filters Wearing tinted glasses changes the color of almost everything you see. If the lenses are yellow, the world takes on a golden glow. If they are rose colored, everything looks rosy. Something similar would occur if you placed a colored, clear plastic sheet over this white page. The paper would appear to be the same color as the plastic. The plastic sheet and the tinted lenses are filters. A filter is a transparent material that transmits one or more colors of light but absorbs all others. The color of a filter is the color of the light that it transmits.

Section 4 Resource Manager

Chapter *FAST FILE* Resources

Transparency Activity, p. 49

Enrichment, p. 34

Reinforcement, p. 30

Directed Reading for Content Mastery, pp. 21–22

Lab Worksheets, pp. 7–8

Earth Science Critical Thinking/Problem Solving, p. 22

Life Science Critical Thinking/Problem Solving, p. 4

1 Motivate

INTERACTIVE CHALKBOARD PowerPoint® Presentations An editable Microsoft® PowerPoint® presentation is available on **Interactive Chalkboard** CD-ROM.

Bellringer

Section Focus Transparencies also are available on the Interactive Chalkboard CD-ROM. L2 ELL

SECTION 4 Section Focus Transparency **The Wild Ones** Chapter 11

In the early 1900s, a group of painters began to emphasize intense colors and forms. This group, called the fauves, included Henri Matisse, André Derain, and Raoul Dufy. This picture is Matisse's "Harmoney in Red" (1908).

1. **What colors can you identify in this painting?**
2. **How do you feel when you look at a painting done with bright colors?**

L2

Sound and Light

Reading Preview

Tie to Prior Knowledge

Object Color Ask students to find something in the classroom that is red. Do this for orange, yellow, green, blue, and violet also. Tell students that in this section they will learn that the color of an object depends on how it absorbs or reflects light.

Activate Background Knowledge Ask students if they have ever used paints to create a picture. Explain that paints are made with pigments. Pigments are colored materials that change the color of other substances.

2 Teach

Reading Check

Answer It reflects all colors of visible light.

IDENTIFYING Misconceptions

Individual Colors Students might assume that red, green, and blue are individual wavelengths of light. Explain that each of these is a range of wavelengths that has its strongest reflection at a certain wavelength.

Discussion

Black Pupils Why do the pupils of your eyes appear black? Almost all of the light that enters your eyes through the pupils is absorbed by the retina. LS **Logical-Mathematical**

Quick Demo

Colored Filters

Materials colored filters and a multicolored object

Estimated Time five minutes

Procedure Use colored filters to demonstrate the effects shown in **Figure 25** with a colorful object in the classroom. LS **Visual-Spatial**

Reading Check

Answer The object absorbs red light, so no color is reflected back to your eyes.

Discussion

Colors in the Dark Are objects still colored in a dark room? Some students may say no because color results from light reflection. Others may say yes, because the property that makes the object a certain color is still present whether or not the lights are on. L2 LS **Logical-Mathematical**

Figure 25 The color of this cooler changes when viewed through different color filters.

Looking Through Colored Filters **Figure 25** shows how the color of an object can change when you look at it through various colored filters. The cooler looks blue under white light because it reflects only the wavelengths of blue light that strike it. If you look at the cooler through a blue filter, the cooler still looks blue because the blue filter transmits the reflected blue light. However, if you look at the cooler through a red filter, the cooler seems black because the red filter blocks the blue light reflected by the cooler.

Reading Check *Why does a blue object appear black when viewed through a red filter?*

Seeing Color

As you approach a busy intersection, the color of the traffic light changes from green to yellow to red. On the cross street, the color changes from red to green. At a busy intersection, traffic safety depends on your ability to detect color changes rapidly. How do you see colors?

Light and the Eye In a healthy eye, light enters the eye through the cornea, is focused by the lens, and finally forms an image on the retina. The retina is made up of two types of cells that absorb light, as shown in **Figure 26.** When these cells absorb light energy, chemical reactions convert light energy into nerve impulses that are transmitted to the brain. One type of cell in the retina, called a cone, enables you to distinguish colors and detailed shapes of objects. Cones need bright light to generate nerve impulses, so they do not operate in dim light. As a result, even brightly colored objects might look gray or black in dim light.

Science Online

Topic: Color Blindness

Visit gpescience.com for Web links to information about the causes of color blindness.

Activity Research the causes and types of color blindness. Find out how cones are related to the ability to distinguish colors.

Differentiated Instruction

Learning Disabled If students have trouble remembering which type of nerve cells of the retina interpret color and which interpret black and white, tell them to remember that the word *cone* starts with the same letter as the word *color*. To practice using this mnemonic, name some different things they might see and have them identify which type of retinal nerve cells would be used.

Cultural Diversity

Names of Colors It might seem obvious to say that the sky is blue and grass is green, but the Mayan people of Mexico have no words that clearly define these two colors. Many other cultures distinguish between colors differently as well. Even in English, differences in colors are often difficult to define. Have students bring samples of such colors to class.

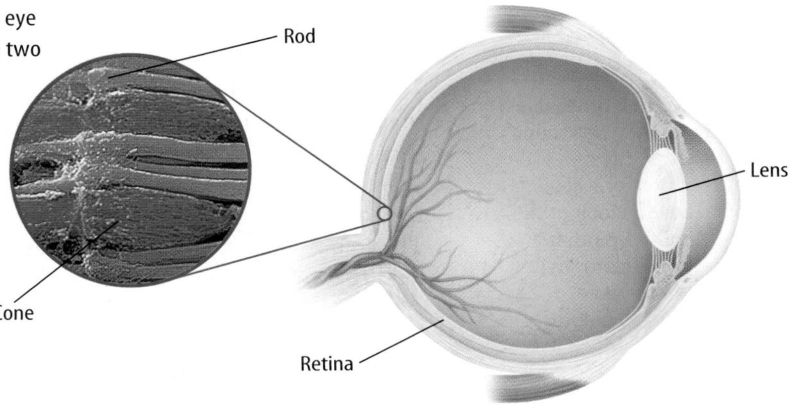

Figure 26 Light enters the eye and focuses on the retina. The two types of light-detecting cells that make up the retina are called rods and cones.

Cones and Rods Your eyes have three types of cones, each of which responds to a different range of wavelengths. Red cones respond to mostly red and yellow light. Green cones respond to mostly yellow and green light. Blue cones respond to mostly blue and violet light. The second type of cell in the retina, called a rod, is sensitive to dim light and enables you to see at night. However, rod cells do not enable you to see colors.

INTEGRATE Life Science

Interpreting Color Why does a banana look yellow? The light reflected by the banana causes the cone cells that are sensitive to red and green light to send signals to your brain. Your brain could get the same signal if a mixture of red light and green light reached your eyes. This mixture also would cause your red and green cones to respond, and you would see the color yellow. As a result, light with wavelengths corresponding to yellow light and light that is a mixture of red and green light both cause the color yellow to be seen. What happens when you look at a white shirt? You see white when all wavelengths of visible light enters your eyes. Then all three sets of cones cells send signals to the brain. The combination of these signals cause you to see the shirt as white.

Color Blindness If one or more of your sets of cone cells do not function properly, you might not be able to distinguish certain colors. This condition is called color blindness or color deficiency. About eight percent of men and one-half percent of women have some form of color blindness. The most common form of color blindness makes it difficult to distinguish between red and green. **Figure 27** shows an image that is used in a test for red–green color blindness. Because red and green are used in traffic signals, drivers and pedestrians must be able to identify them.

Figure 27 Color blindness is an inherited sex-linked condition in which certain sets of cones in the retina do not function properly. **Identify** *the number that you see in the dots.*

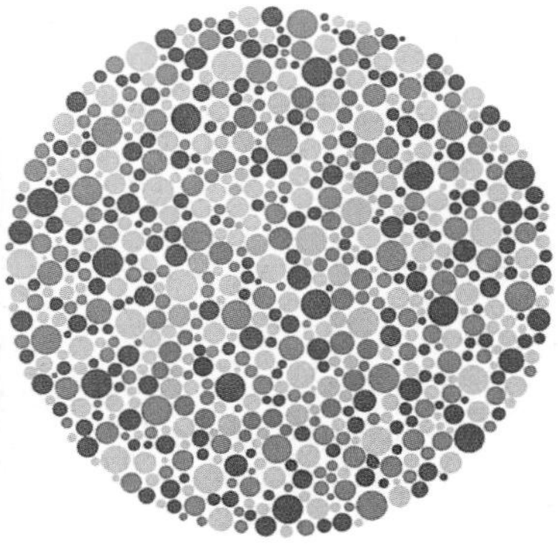

Visual Learning

Figure 26 Point out the position of the retina. Behind the retina is the optic nerve, which takes information from the rods and cones and sends it to the brain. Humans have many more rod cells than cone cells. Ask students to infer the number of rods in the eyes of nocturnal animals. They have far more rod cells than humans so they can see well at night.

INTEGRATE Life Science

Content Background

Although there are infinitely many color combinations, most people can distinguish about one million different color mixtures. While the basic function of the rods and cones is generally understood, the brain's interpretation of color signals is an active field of research. Current research into the eye-brain interface may lead to new treatments for visual impairments as well as artificial vision systems for use in many different fields, from industry to robotic space exploration.

Caption Answer

Figure 27 Students who are not red-green deficient will see the number 8.

Fun Fact

Have you ever noticed that brown is not in the rainbow? Brown is actually dark yellow.

Teacher FYI

Section of Spectrum Visible light is a tiny part of the EM spectrum. Imagine the distance between Earth and the Sun compared to the width of your thumb. Your thumb is a much larger percentage of the Earth–Sun distance than the percentage of the EM spectrum that is visible light.

Differentiated Instruction

Challenge Have students stare at a red object for 20 seconds and then look at a white wall. They should see a faint blue/green afterimage of the object on the wall. Ask them to explain why they think this happens based on how our eyes see color. Their red cones lose sensitivity. When they look at the white wall, the part of their retinas that stared at the red object have only blue and green cones that are sensitive. L3

Reading Strategy

Metacognitive Strategies Ask students: What is blue? What is yellow? How would you describe these colors? Do you find it easier to describe something that you can feel and touch, such as a desk? Do you find it difficult to comprehend text when you are reading about something that is not tangible?

INTEGRATE Life Science

Color for Photosynthesis Carotenoids, yellow and orange pigments that include xanthophyll, are always present in green plants. These pigments absorb light in the blue and green wavelengths, which helps plants, especially those growing in low-light conditions, to absorb enough light to make food.

Research Have students research to learn the primary pigment responsible for blue, lavender, and purple flowers. anthocyanins

Activity

Filter Combinations Provide groups of students with red, green, and blue color filters (or colored transparency film) and an overhead projector. Have them use different combinations of filters to produce the colors yellow, magenta, and cyan. Ask them to write down the combination of filters they used to produce each color. Red and green produce yellow. Red and blue produce magenta. Green and blue produce cyan.

L2 ELL LS Visual-Spatial P

Reading Check

Answer red, green, and blue

Virtual Labs

Colors *How are colors created?*

INTEGRATE Life Science

Color for Photosynthesis Plant pigments determine the wavelengths of light for photosynthesis. Leaves usually look green because of the pigment chlorophyll. Chlorophyll absorbs most wavelengths of visible light except green, which it reflects. However, not all plants are green. Research different plant pigments to find out how they allow plant species to survive in diverse habitats.

Mixing Colors

If you have ever browsed through a paint store, you have probably seen displays where customers can select paint samples of almost every imaginable color. The colors are a result of mixtures of pigments. For example, you might have mixed blue and yellow paint to produce green paint. A **pigment** is a colored material that is used to change the color of other substances. The color of a pigment results from the different wavelengths of light that the pigment reflects.

Mixing Colored Lights From the glowing orange of a sunset to the deep blue of a mountain lake, all the colors you see can be made by mixing three colors of light. These three colors—red, green, and blue—are the primary colors of light. They correspond to the three different types of cones in the retina of your eye. When mixed together in equal amounts, they produce white light, as **Figure 28** shows. Mixing the primary colors in different proportions can produce the colors you see.

Reading Check *What are the primary colors of light?*

Paint Pigments If you were to mix equal amounts of red, green, and blue paint, would you get white paint? If mixing colors of paint were like mixing colors of light, you would, but mixing paint is different. Paints are made with pigments. Pigments produce color as a result of the wavelengths of light they reflect. Paint pigments usually are made of chemical compounds such as titanium oxide, a bright white pigment, and lead chromate, which is used for painting yellow lines on highways.

Figure 28 White light is produced when the three primary colors of light are mixed in equal amounts.

Active Reading

Cause-and-Effect Chart This strategy is used to focus on cause-effect relationships. Have students write *Mixing Colors.* On the left, instruct them to write combinations of the primary colors of light, followed by combinations of the primary pigments. On the right side, have students record the color that will result from each combination.

Mixing Pigments You can make any pigment color by mixing different amounts of the three primary pigments—magenta (bluish red), cyan (greenish blue), and yellow. In fact, color printers use these pigments, as well as black ink, to make full-color prints like the pages in this book. A primary pigment's color depends on the wavelengths of the light that it reflects. Actually, pigments both absorb and reflect a range of colors in sending a single color message to your eye. For example, in white light, yellow pigment appears yellow because it reflects red and green light but absorbs the other wavelengths of visible light. The color of a mixture of two primary pigments is determined by the primary colors of light that both pigments reflect.

Look at **Figure 29.** The area in the center where the colors all overlap appears to be black because the three blended primary pigments absorb all the primary colors of light. Recall that the primary colors of light combine to produce white light. They are called additive colors. However, when the primary pigment colors are combined, they absorb all wavelengths of visible light and produce black. Because black results from the absence of reflected light, the primary pigments are called subtractive colors.

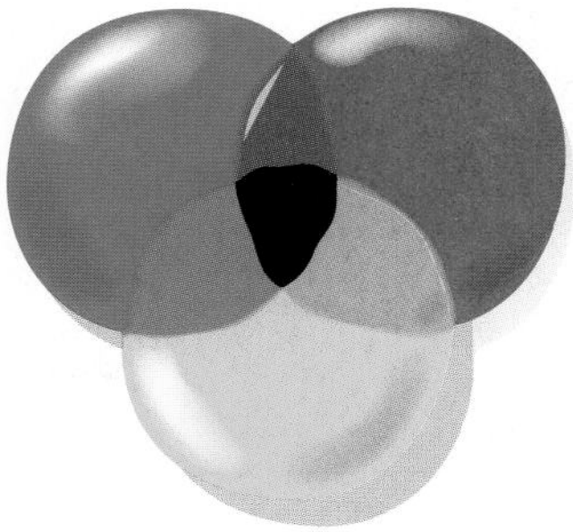

Figure 29 The three primary pigment colors appear to be black when they are mixed.
Describe *how the primary pigment colors are similar to the primary colors of light.*

Caption Answer

Figure 29 Primary pigment and light colors can each be mixed in different amounts to form all colors.

Post Reading

Lab Notes Give small groups of students red, blue, and yellow fingerpaints. Students should wear lab aprons as they experiment with mixing the colors. Have them take lab notes as they work, describing the color combinations they produce.

section 4 review

Summary

Why Objects Have Color
- The color of an object is determined by the wavelengths of light it reflects.
- The color of a filter is the color of the light the filter transmits.

Seeing Color
- Rod and cone cells are light-sensitive cells found in the retina of the human eye.
- Rod cells are sensitive to dim light. Cone cells enable colors to be seen.
- There are three types of cone cells. One type responds to red light, another to green light, and another to blue light.

Mixing Colors
- Red, green, and blue are the primary light colors. Any color of light can be created by mixing these primary light colors.
- Any pigment color can be formed by mixing the primary pigment colors—magenta, cyan, and yellow.

Self Check

1. **Identity** what colors are reflected and what colors are absorbed if a white light shines on a red shirt.
2. **Discuss** how the primary colors of light differ from the primary pigment colors.
3. **Explain** why a red apple would appear black if you looked at it through a blue filter.
4. **Determine** why a white fence appears to be white instead of multicolored if all colors are present in white light.
5. **Think Critically** Light reflected from an object passes through a green filter, then a red filter, and finally a blue filter. What color will the object seem to be?

Applying Math

6. **Use Percentages** In the human eye there are about 120,000,000 rods. If 90,000,000 rods trigger at once, what percentage of the total number of rods triggered?
7. **Convert Units** The wavelengths of light are measured in nanometers (nm) which equals 0.000001 mm. Find the wavelength in mm of a light wave that has a wavelength of 690 nm.

More Section Review gpescience.com

3 Assess

DAILY INTERVENTION

Check for Understanding

Kinesthetic Create some color samples with combinations of magenta, cyan, and yellow paints. Provide students with sets of magenta, cyan, and yellow paint. Have students match the color samples with the paint you have provided.

Reteach

Pigments Have students work in groups to combine small amounts of various primary pigment paints to make other colors. For each color, have them describe which colors are reflected and which are absorbed. Be sure they mix all three primary pigments to produce black. Point out that black pigment absorbs almost all light and reflects almost none. L2 ELL COOP LEARN IN **Kinesthetic**

section 4 review

1. Red is reflected and all others are absorbed.
2. The primary colors of light are red, green, and blue. The primary pigment colors are magenta, cyan, and yellow. The primary colors of light transmit the color you see, whereas the primary pigment colors reflect the color you see.
3. Red light from the apple would be absorbed by the filter.
4. The fence reflects all colors of visible light. Because all the cones in your eyes are stimulated, you see white.
5. It will appear black.
6. 75%
7. 0.00069 mm

Assessment

Oral Assess students' understanding of colors by asking them to explain why black and white are not true colors. Black is a lack of color that occurs when all light is absorbed. White occurs when all colors are reflected. Use **PASC,** p. 89.

BENCH TESTED

Real-World Problem

Purpose Students will test various sound barriers for effectiveness. L2 IN **Auditory-Musical**

Process Skills form a hypothesis, predict, test a hypothesis, identify and manipulate variables, collect data, interpret data

Time Required 2 weeks outside of class time

Materials Many of these barriers are not normally located around a school. Students may need to be provided with a sound meter and a meterstick or metric tape measure to perform this lab outside of class.

Safety Precautions Students should have some adult supervision when collecting their data.

Form a Hypothesis

Possible Hypothesis Students may hypothesize that thick concrete walls or thick stone walls are the best sound barriers and hanging laundry is the least effective.

Test Your Hypothesis

Possible Procedures Students should choose a sound that will remain constant for each sound barrier tested, such as a recording of a sound at a constant volume. At the location of the sound barrier, students should record the level of the sound using the sound meter at the same distance from the source to the meter both behind the sound barrier and bypassing the sound barrier. These conditions will provide a test with only one variable.

LAB **Design Your Own**

Blocking Noise Pollution

Goals

- **Design** an experiment that tests the effectiveness of various types of barriers and materials for blocking out noise pollution.
- **Test** different types of materials and barriers to determine the best noise blocks.

Possible Materials

radio, CD player, horn, drum, or other loud noise source
shrubs, trees, concrete walls, brick walls, stone walls, wooden fences, parked cars, or hanging laundry
sound meter
meterstick or metric tape measure

Real-World Problem

What loud noises do you enjoy, and which ones do you find annoying? Most people enjoy a music concert performed by their favorite artist, booming displays of fireworks on the Fourth of July, and the roar of a crowd when their team scores a goal or makes a touchdown. Although these are loud noises, most people enjoy them for short periods of time. Most people find certain other loud noises, such as traffic, sirens, and loud talking, annoying. Constant, annoying noises are called noise pollution. What can be done to reduce noise pollution? What types of barriers best block out loud noises? What types of barriers will best block out noise pollution?

Form a Hypothesis

Based on your experiences with loud noises, form a hypothesis that predicts the effectiveness of different types of barriers at blocking out noise pollution.

Test Your Hypothesis

Make a Plan

1. **Decide** what type of barriers or materials you will test.
2. **Describe** exactly how you will use these materials.

344

Alternative Inquiry Lab

Real-World Connection To extend this lab, have students research various sound barriers and sound control strategies in their own municipality and in other municipalities nationally and worldwide. Which areas of the world have the most noise pollution? What causes the noise pollution? What effects does noise pollution have on human and animal health? Other topics of research include the use of destructive wave strategies through headphones to reduce noise for helicopter pilots and for factory workers. Encourage students to test noise-reduction materials and methods that can be used.

Using Scientific Methods

3. **Identify** the controls and variables you will use in your experiment.
4. **List** the steps you will use and describe each step precisely.
5. **Prepare** a data table in your Science Journal to record your measurements.
6. **Organize** the steps of your experiment in logical order.

Follow Your Plan

1. Ask your teacher to approve your plan and data table before you start.
2. **Conduct** your experiment as planned.
3. **Test** each barrier two or three times.
4. **Record** the results from each test in your data table in your Science Journal.

Analyze Your Data

1. **Identify** the barriers that most effectively reduced noise pollution.
2. **Identify** the barriers that least effectively reduced noise pollution.
3. **Compare** the effective barriers and identify common characteristics that might explain why they reduced noise pollution.
4. **Compare** the natural barriers you tested with the artificial barriers. Which type of barrier best reduced noise pollution?
5. **Compare** the different types of materials the barriers were made of. Which type of material best reduced noise pollution?

Conclude and Apply

1. **Evaluate** whether your results support your hypothesis.
2. **Predict** how your results would differ if you used a louder source of noise such as a siren.
3. **Infer** from your results how people living near a busy street could reduce noise pollution.
4. **Identify** major sources of noise pollution in or near your home. How could they be reduced?
5. **Research** how noise pollution can be unhealthy.

Communicating Your Data

Draw a poster illustrating how builders and landscapers could use certain materials to better insulate a home or office from excess noise pollution.

Teaching Strategy Remind students that it is important for the sound barriers to be tested using the same distance from the sound source to the sound meter in each test.

Expected Outcome Most results will show that thick concrete walls or thick stone walls are the best sound barriers.

Analyze Your Data

Answers to Questions

1. Answers will vary but may include concrete and stone walls.
2. Answers will vary but may be similar to hanging laundry.
3. The effective barriers are thick and dense structures.
4. Answers will vary.
5. Answers will vary.

Error Analysis Have students compare their results and their hypotheses and explain why differences occurred.

Conclude and Apply

1. Answers will vary.
2. The ranking of sound barriers would be the same.
3. People could build some type of sound barrier between the house and the street.
4. Answers will vary.
5. Reported findings should include eardrum damage.

Assessment

Process Have students describe their procedures and their results for this activity in lab reports. Suggest that they include diagrams or photographs of their setups. Use **Performance Assessment in the Science Classroom,** p.119 L2

Communicating Your Data

A gardening book from your local library will be helpful in choosing plants to use in the landscape design.

Understanding Literature

Japanese Haiku Because haiku uses few words, the reader must use his or her imagination to complete the picture or message.

Respond to the Reading

1. Possible answer: It helps the reader picture the season.
2. Possible answer: Lingering indicates that the Sun remains longer in the sky each day during spring.
3. **Linking Science and Writing** Suggest that students pay attention to the mood they want to convey with their poems, and use color and properties of light appropriately.

INTEGRATE Physics **Color** The perception of color can affect the human body. For example, the color red can cause physiological changes in the body. Some studies have shown that seeing red can be correlated with increasing blood pressure, more rapid breathing, increased taste bud sensitivity, and heightened sense of smell. Seeing the color blue has been linked to the opposite effects: slowing of the pulse, lowering of the body temperature, and reduction of the appetite.

Yellow is usually the first color a person notices when he or she looks at something. Studies have suggested that yellow prepares a person for flight or fight, that children are more apt to cry in a yellow room, and that allergies flare up more frequently in yellow surroundings. Green, on the other hand, has been found to help decrease allergic reactions in some people.

Science and Language Arts

A Haiku Garden:

The Four Seasons in Poems and Prints

by Stephen Addiss with Fumiko and Akira Yamamoto

Withered by winter
the sound of the wind—
one-color world
Basho

Lingering
in every pool of water—
spring sunlight
Issa

Understanding Literature

Japanese Haiku A haiku is a verse that consists of three lines and 17 syllables in the Japanese language. The first and third lines have five syllables each, and the middle line has seven syllables. Why is imagination important in reading haiku?

Respond to the Reading

1. How do the illustrations help the reader better understand the poems?
2. What do you think is meant by the word *lingering* in the Haiku about spring sunlight?
3. **Linking Science and Writing** Write one haiku about summer and another about fall. In one poem, use color to help you describe the season. In the other, use light or some property of light to help describe the season.

INTEGRATE Physics Research has determined that there is a connection between color and mood. Warm colors have longer wavelengths and can be more stimulating. Cool colors, which have shorter wavelengths, tend to have a calming or soothing effect on people. Light and color have long been used as literary symbols. Does the use of color change what you imagine when you read the haiku?

Resources for Teachers and Students

The Essential Haiku, ed. and trans. Robert Hass, The Ecco Press, 1994

The Power of Color, Dr. Morton Walker, Avery Publishing Group, 1991

Reviewing Main Ideas

Section 1 Sound

1. Sound waves are compressional waves that travel only in matter.
2. The speed of sound in a material depends on the type of material as well as its temperature.
3. Loudness depends on a sound wave's intensity. Pitch depends on a sound wave's frequency.
4. Sound waves are used in echolocation, sonar, and medical imaging.

Section 2 Reflection and Refraction of Light

1. Light can be absorbed, reflected, or transmitted by a material.
2. When light waves are reflected, they obey the law of reflection—the angle of incidence equals the angle of reflection.

3. A light wave is refracted, or bent, when it changes speed as it travels at an angle from one material to another.

Section 3 Mirrors, Lenses, and the Eye

1. Plane mirrors form upright, virtual images.
2. Images formed by concave mirrors and convex lenses depend on the location of the object relative to the focal point.
3. Convex mirrors and concave lenses form virtual, upright images that are smaller than the object.
4. The lens in the human eye changes shape to produce a sharp image on the retina.

Section 4 Light and Color

1. You see color when light is reflected off objects and into your eyes.
2. Cone cells in the retina are light-sensitive cells that enable you to distinguish colors.
3. Red, blue, and green are the three primary colors of light and can be mixed to form all other colors.
4. The primary pigment colors are magenta, cyan, and yellow.

FOLDABLES™ Use the Foldable you made at the beginning of the chapter to help you review sound and light.

chapter 11 Study Guide

Reviewing Main Ideas

Summary statements can be used by students to review the major concepts of the chapter.

Science Online

Visit gpescience.com
More Section Review
Interactive Tutor
Vocabulary PuzzleMaker
More Chapter Review
Standardized Test Practice

Assessment Transparency

For additional assessment questions, use the *Assessment Transparency* located in the transparency book.

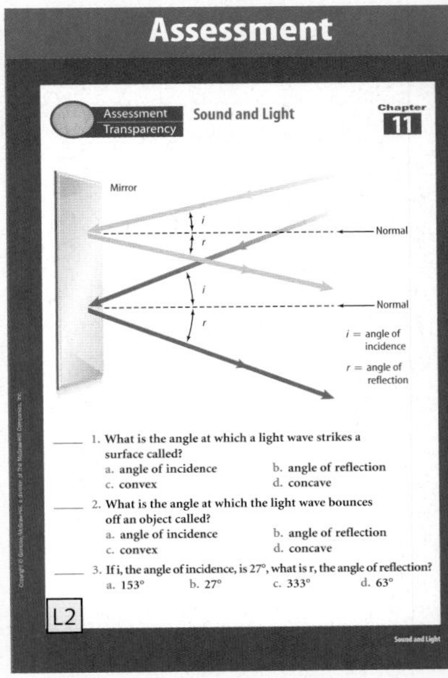

Assessment

Assessment Transparency — Sound and Light — Chapter 11

____ 1. What is the angle at which a light wave strikes a surface called?
a. angle of incidence b. angle of reflection
c. convex d. concave

____ 2. What is the angle at which the light wave bounces off an object called?
a. angle of incidence b. angle of reflection
c. convex d. concave

____ 3. If i, the angle of incidence, is 27°, what is r, the angle of reflection?
a. 153° b. 27° c. 333° d. 63°

L2

Sound and Light

FOLDABLES™ Have students use their Foldables to review the content of the chapter. Have the students make similar Foldables comparing and contrasting convex and concave mirrors and convex and concave lens.

Using Vocabulary

1. Doppler effect
2. plane mirror
3. transparent
4. index of refraction
5. pigment
6. convex mirror
7. loudness

Checking Concepts

8. D
9. B
10. C
11. C
12. B
13. C
14. C

Interpreting Graphics

15. The candle moved away from the lens.

Thinking Critically

16. Possible answer: The room would eliminate any sound reflections except those coming directly from the bat's food.
17. The glass absorbs all colors except green, and it transmits green light. The shirt absorbs all colors except green, and it reflects green light.

chapter 11 Review

Using Vocabulary

concave lens p. 335	loudness p. 322
concave mirror p. 332	opaque p. 327
convex lens p. 333	pigment p. 342
convex mirror p. 333	pitch p. 323
decibel p. 322	plane mirror p. 331
Doppler effect p. 323	translucent p. 327
index of refraction p. 329	transparent p. 327
intensity p. 322	

Complete each statement with the correct vocabulary word or phrase.

1. A change in frequency due to a moving sound source is due to the ______.
2. A flat, smooth surface that reflects light and forms an image is a(n) ______.
3. An object is ______ if you can see through it clearly.
4. The ______ of a material indicates how much the speed of light in the material changes as light passes through.
5. You can change the color of white paint by adding a(n) ______ to it.
6. A(n) ______ is a reflecting surface that curves outward like the back of a spoon.
7. The human perception of the intensity of a sound wave is ______.

Checking Concepts

Choose the word or phrase that best answers each question.

8. Which of the following best describes image formation by a plane mirror?
   A) A real image is formed in front of the mirror.
   B) A real image is formed behind the mirror.
   C) A virtual image is formed in front of the mirror.
   D) A virtual image is formed behind the mirror.

9. For a sound with low pitch, what else is also always low?
   A) amplitude **C)** wavelength
   B) frequency **D)** wave velocity

10. Which of the following occurs when a sound source moves away from you?
    A) The sound's velocity decreases.
    B) The sound's loudness increases.
    C) The sound's frequency decreases.
    D) The sound's frequency increases.

Use the table below to answer question 11.

Speed of Sound in Air

Temperature (°C)	Sound Speed (m/s)
0	331.4
10	337.4
20	343.4

11. Based on the data in the table above, which of the following would be the speed of sound in air at 30°C?
    A) 340.4 m/s **C)** 349.4 m/s
    B) 346.4 m/s **D)** 353.4 m/s

12. What happens to a light ray traveling parallel to the optical axis of a convex lens that passes through the lens?
    A) It travels parallel to the optical axis.
    B) It passes through the focal point.
    C) It is bent away from the optical axis.
    D) It forms a virtual image.

13. Light waves of which color are bent most when passing through a prism?
    A) blue **C)** violet
    B) red **D)** yellow

14. Which way does a concave lens bend light?
    A) toward its optical axis
    B) toward its center
    C) toward its edges
    D) toward its focal point

Vocabulary PuzzleMaker gpescience.com

Use the Exam*View*® Pro Test Bank CD-ROM to:

- create multiple versions of tests
- create modified tests with one mouse click for inclusion students
- edit existing questions and add your own questions
- build tests aligned with state standards using built-in State Curriculum Tags
- change English tests to Spanish with one mouse click and vice versa

Interpreting Graphics

Use the illustration below to answer question 15.

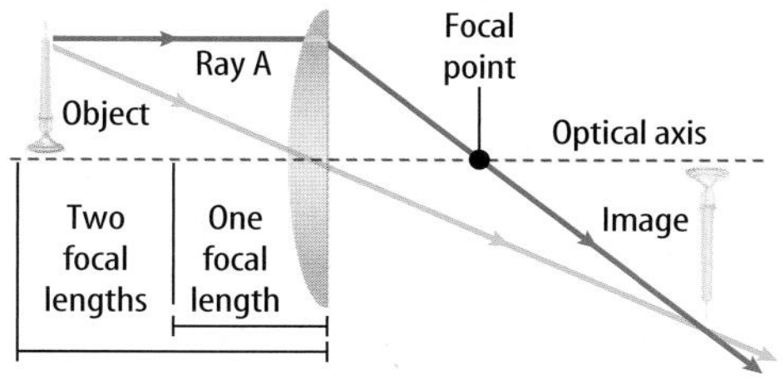

15. **Describe** how the position of the candle changed if the image of the candle moved away from the focal point.

Thinking Critically

16. **Apply** Acoustic scientists sometimes do research in rooms that absorb all sound waves. How could such a room be used to study how bats find their food?
17. **Compare** White light passes through a translucent pane of glass and shines on a shirt. Both the translucent glass and the shirt appear green. Compare the colors of light that are absorbed and transmitted by the glass and the shirt.
18. **Infer** Most mammals, including dogs and cats, can't see colors. Infer how the retina of a cat's eye might be different from the retina of a human eye.
19. **Determine** whether a convex lens could form an image that is enlarged, real, and upright.
20. **Infer** A car comes to a railroad crossing. The driver hears a train's whistle and its pitch becomes lower. What can be assumed about how the train is moving?
21. **Compare and contrast** the reflection of light from a white wall with a rough surface with the reflection of light from a mirror.
22. **Infer** why a convex mirror and a concave lens can never produce a real image.
23. **Predict** what color a white shirt would appear to be if the light reflected from the shirt passed through a red filter and then through a green filter.
24. **Explain** why windows might begin to rattle when an airplane flies overhead.
25. **Communicate** Some people enjoy using snowmobiles. Others object to the noise that they make. Write a proposal for a policy that seems fair to both groups for the use of snowmobiles in a state park.

Applying Math

Use the wave speed equation, $v = f\lambda$, to answer questions 26 and 27.

26. **Calculate Frequency** A sonar pulse has a wavelength of 3.0 cm and a speed in water of 1,500 m/s. Find its frequency.
27. **Calculate Wavelength** What is the wavelength of a sound wave with a frequency of 440 Hz if the speed of sound in air is 340 m/s?
28. **Calculate Angle of Incidence** A light ray is reflected from a mirror. If the angle between the incident ray and the reflected ray is 136°, what is the angle of incidence.
29. **Determine Object Distance** You hold an object in front of a concave mirror with a focal length of 30 cm. If you do not see a reflected image, how far from the mirror is the object?
30. **Calculate Speed** The speed of light in a vacuum is 300,000 km/s. If the index of refraction of water is 1.33, what is the speed of light in water?

Assessment Resources

Reproducible Masters

Chapter *Fast File* Resources
- Chapter Review, pp. 39–40
- Chapter Tests, pp. 41–44
- Assessment Transparency Activity, p. 53

Glencoe Science Web site
- Chapter Review Test
- Standardized Test Practice

Glencoe Technology
- Assessment Transparency
- Exam*View*® Pro Testmaker
- MindJogger Videoquiz
- Interactive Chalkboard

chapter Review 11

Thinking Critically

18. Possible answer: A cat's retina does not have the cone nerve cells that a human's retina does.
19. No; a convex lens forms an enlarged, upright image that is virtual when the object is less than one focal length from the lens and an enlarged, real image that is inverted when the object is between one and two focal lengths from the lens. An object more than two focal lengths from the lens forms a real, upright, smaller image.
20. The train is moving away from the crossing.
21. Both reflect all the colors of light that hit them. Reflection from a rough white wall is diffuse, whereas reflection from a mirror is regular.
22. Both a convex mirror and a concave lens cause light rays that strike them always to diverge.
23. The red filter transmits only the red light reflected from the shirt. This light would be absorbed completely by the green filter, and no light would be transmitted. The shirt would appear black.
24. The airplane produces sound waves that vibrate the glass.
25. Proposals might suggest limiting the use of snowmobiles to certain times of the day or to certain areas that are more isolated.

Applying Math

Math Standards

National: 1, 4, 9

26. 50,000 Hz (50 kHz)
27. 0.77 m
28. 68°
29. 30 cm
30. 225,000 km/s

Answer Sheet An answer sheet can be found at **gpescience.com**.

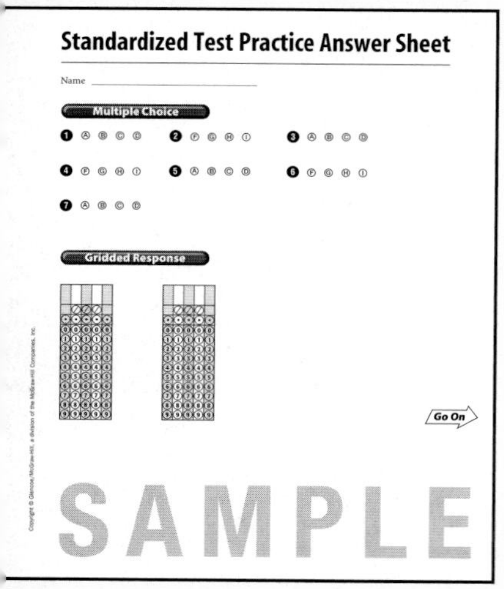

Multiple Choice

1. D
2. A
3. A
4. D
5. D
6. D
7. A

Record your answers on the answer sheet provided by your teacher or on a sheet of paper.

Multiple Choice

1. Which of the following describes the image formed by a convex mirror?

A. enlarged

B. inverted

C. real

D. virtual

Use the figure below to answer question 2.

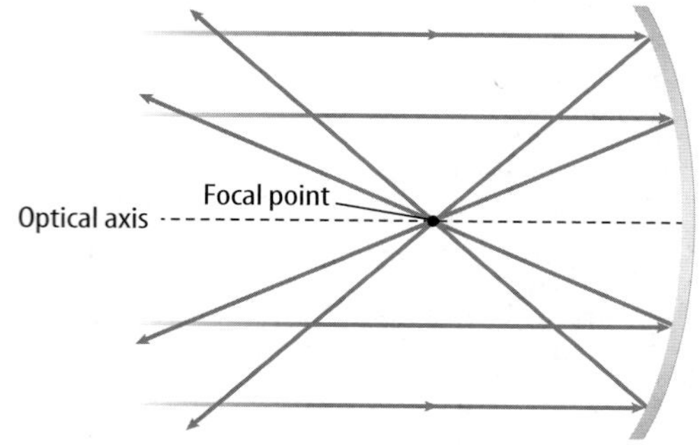

2. Which of the following describes a light ray that passes through the focal point and then is reflected by the mirror?

A. It travels parallel to the optical axis.

B. It forms a real image.

C. It is reflected back through the focal point.

D. It forms a virtual image.

3. Why does an apple look red?

A. It reflects red light.

B. It absorbs red light.

C. It reflects green and blue light.

D. It reflects all colors of light except red.

Use the figure below to answer questions 4 and 5.

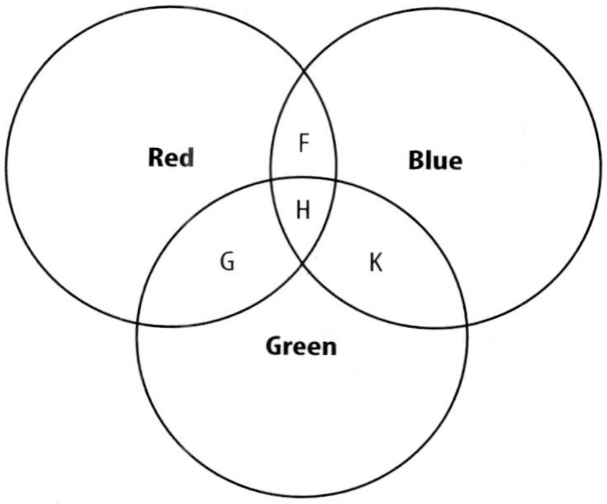

4. When the primary colors of light are added together, what color appears in area H?

A. cyan

B. magenta

C. white

D. yellow

5. When the primary colors of light are added together, what color appears in area G?

A. cyan

B. magenta

C. white

D. yellow

6. Which of the following increases as the frequency of a sound increases?

A. amplitude

B. intensity

C. loudness

D. pitch

7. Which of the following parts of the eye enable you to see colors in bright light?
   A. cone cells
   B. cornea
   C. lens
   D. rod cells

Gridded Response

Use the graph below to answer questions 8 and 9.

Image Distance for a Convex Lens

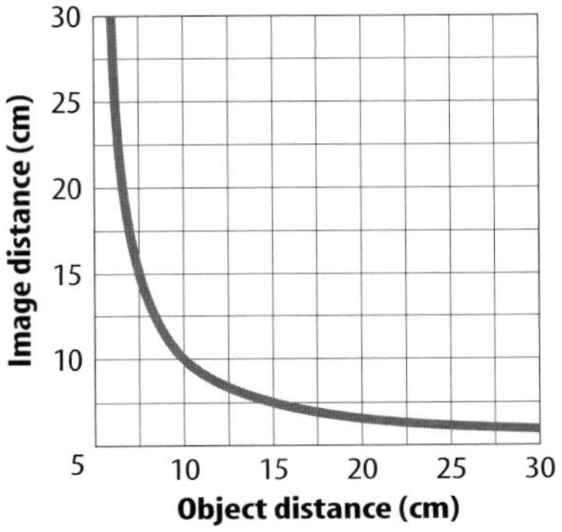

8. Determine how far, in centimeters, the image is from the lens when the object is 15 centimeters from the lens.
9. How far, in centimeters, is the object from the lens when the image distance and object distance are equal?

Test-Taking Tip

Note Units Read carefully and make note of the units used in any measurement.

Short Response

10. A shirt has stripes that are black and white in white light. If green light shines on this shirt, what colors will the black and white stripes be?
11. If you are on a moving train, what happens to the pitch of a crossing bell as you approach the crossing and then move away from the crossing?

Extended Response

Use the figure below to answer question 12.

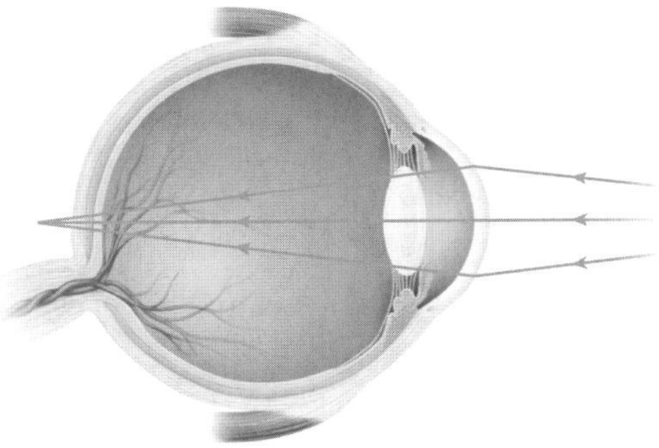

12. Describe the vision problem show by the figure and explain how this vision problem can be corrected.
13. Explain why the human eye can see colors better in bright light than in dim light.

Gridded Response

8. 7.5 cm
9. 10 cm

Short Response

10. The black stripes will still appear black, and the white stripes will appear green.
11. The pitch is higher as you approach the signal and lower as you move away.

Extended Response

12. This problem is farsightedness, which is the inability to focus on nearby objects. A convex lens in front of the eye converges light rays so the lens in the eye is able to focus on nearby objects.
13. In bright light, cone cells in the retina are stimulated by visible light and produce the sensation of color. In dim light, these cells are not stimulated.

Rubrics

For more help evaluating Short– and Extended-Response questions, see the rubic on p. 9T.

chapter 12 Organizer

Section/Objectives	Standards: National	Standards: State/Local	Lab/Features
Chapter Opener	See pp. 16T–17T for a Key to Standards.		**Launch Lab:** Global Jigsaw Puzzle, p. 353 **Foldables,** p. 353
Section 1 Evolution of Earth's Crust 1 session .5 block 1. **Explain** supporting evidence for the continental drift hypothesis. 2. **Discuss** the failings of the continental drift hypothesis.	National Content Standards: UCP.1-3, UCP. 5, A.1, A.2, D.1		**Applying Math:** Spreading Distances, p. 357 **Integrate Physics,** p. 358 **Science Online,** p. 359
Section 2 Earthquakes 2 sessions 1 block 3. **Describe** the causes and characteristics of earthquakes. 4. **Explain** how seismic waves affect Earth's surface. 5. **Describe** how seismic waves are used to infer Earth's internal structure.	National Content Standards: UCP.1-5, A.1, A.2, B.4, D.1, D.3, E.1, F.5, F.6		**MiniLAB:** Demonstrating Four Types of Stress, p. 364 **Visualizing Earthquake-Proof Buildings,** p. 368
Section 3 Earth's Interior 1 session .5 block 6. **Explain** how geologists infer the structure of Earth's deep interior. 7. **Describe** Earth's internal structure and composition.	National Content Standards: UCP.1-5, A.1, A.2, B.6, D.1, D.3		
Section 4 Volcanoes 3 sessions 1.5 blocks 8. **Describe** the types and causes of different types of volcanic eruptions. 9. **Explain** the pattern of occurrence of volcanoes and its link to plate tectonics.	National Content Standards: UCP.1-5, A.1, A.2, B.6, D.1, D.2, D.3, F.5		**Science Online,** p. 374 **MiniLAB:** Modeling Lava Viscosity, p. 375 Video Lab **Science Online,** p. 376 **Integrate History,** p. 377 **Lab:** A Case for Pacific Plate Motion, p. 379 **Lab:** Earthquake! Earthquake! Where's the earthquake?, pp. 380–381 **Science and History:** Volcano Weather, p. 382

StudentWorks Plus

Glencoe Exclusive! TeacherWorks™ All-In-One Planner and Resource Center

Lab Materials	Reproducible Resources	Section Assessment	Technology
Launch Lab: copies of a world map	**Chapter *Fast File* Resources** Foldables Worksheet, p. 15 Directed Reading Overview, p. 17 Note-taking Worksheets, pp. 33–35	Glencoe's Assessment Advantage	TeacherWorks includes: • Interactive Teacher Edition • Lesson Planner with calendar • Access to all program blacklines • Correlations to standards • Web links
Need materials? Contact Science Kit at 1-800-828-7777 or www.sciencekit.com.	**Chapter *Fast File* Resources** Transparency Activity, p. 44 Enrichment, p. 29 Reinforcement, p. 25 Directed Reading, p. 18 **Cultural Diversity,** pp. 47–48	Performance Applying Math, p. 357 Applying Math, p. 361 Content Section Review, p. 361	Section Focus Transparency Interactive Chalkboard CD-ROM StudentWorks Plus
MiniLAB: bar of taffy	**Chapter *Fast File* Resources** Transparency Activity, pp. 45, 49–50 MiniLAB, p. 3 Lab Activity, pp. 11–12,13–4 Enrichment, p. 30 Reinforcement, p. 26 Directed Reading, p. 18	Performance MiniLAB, p. 364 Applying Math, p. 369 Content Section Review, p. 369	Section Focus Transparency Teaching Transparency Interactive Chalkboard CD-ROM StudentWorks Plus
	Chapter *Fast File* Resources Transparency Activity, p. 46 Enrichment, p. 31 Reinforcement, p. 27 Directed Reading, p. 19	Performance Applying Math, p. 372 Content Section Review, p. 372	Section Focus Transparency Interactive Chalkboard CD-ROM StudentWorks Plus
MiniLAB: pancake mix, bowl, milk, small funnel, watch with a second hand, small frying pan, hot plate **Lab:** ruler, calculator, scale map of the Hawaiian Islands **Lab:** ruler, plain white paper, graph paper, compass	**Chapter *Fast File* Resources** Transparency Activity, p. 47 MiniLAB, p. 4 Enrichment, p. 32 Reinforcement, p. 28 Directed Reading, pp. 19, 20 Lab Worksheets, pp. 5–6, 7–9 **Reading and Writing Skills Activities,** pp. 14–15	Portfolio Science Journal, p.374 Performance MiniLAB, p. 375 Applying Math, p. 378 Content Section Review, p. 378	Section Focus Transparency Interactive Chalkboard CD-ROM StudentWorks Plus Video Lab

End of Chapter Assessment

Blackline Masters	Technology	Professional Series
Chapter *Fast File* Resources Chapter Review, pp. 37–38 Chapter Tests, pp. 39–42 **Standardized Test Practice,** pp. 52–55	MindJogger Videoquiz Exam*View*® Pro Testmaker TeacherWorks CD-ROM Interactive Chalkboard CD-ROM	**Performance Assessment in the Science Classroom (PASC)**

Transparencies

Section Focus

Section 1 Section Focus Transparency — A Man with a Vision — Chapter 12

Alfred Wegener once wrote, "Scientists still do not... understand sufficiently that all earth sciences must contribute evidence toward unveiling the state of our planet in earlier times…It is only by combing the information… that we can hope…to find the picture that sets out all the known facts in the best arrangement and that therefore has the highest degree of probability. Further, we have to be prepared always for the possibility that each new discovery, no matter what science furnishes it, may modify the conclusions we draw."

1. Why was Wegener's belief that all branches of science must work together considered radical during his lifetime?
2. Have commonly accepted ideas about scientific research changed since then?
3. Do you agree with Wegener's statement? Why or why not?

L2

Section 2 Section Focus Transparency — Earthquake Hazards — Chapter 12

During earthquakes, buildings and bridges can collapse, roads can be twisted and underground utilities such as electrical, water, and natural gas lines can be broken. Even after the earthquake is over, damaged structures still pose a risk of falling and exposed electrical and gas sources can still be dangerous.

1. How do you think earthquakes affect physical structures?
2. Where are earthquakes most likely to occur?
3. Where do you think would be the safest place to be during an earthquake?

L2

Section 3 Section Focus Transparency — A Hollow Earth? — Chapter 12

The French author Jules Verne wrote one of the greatest science fiction books of all time called A Journey to the Center of the Earth. In the book, the professor does indeed find the entrance to the hollow Earth. The professor and his companions walk on the underside of Earth's crust and gaze at the inner Earth's sun. They sail the inner sea, traverse immense dense forests, and even encounter beings much like ourselves.

1. Do you believe Earth could be hollow?
2. How could living beings survive inside a hollow Earth?
3. Does modern science disprove the possibility that Earth is hollow? How?

L2

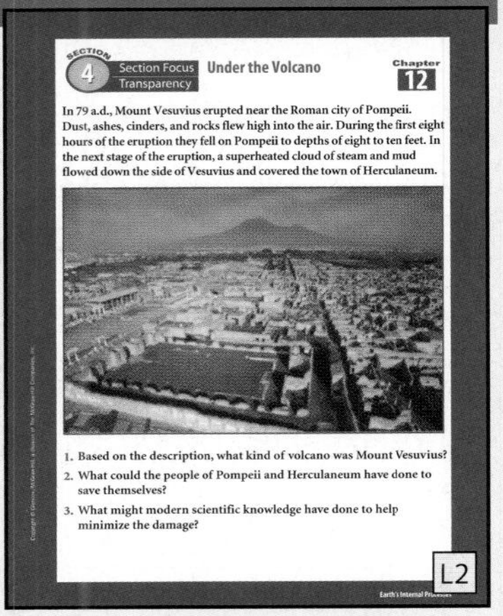
Section 4 Section Focus Transparency — Under the Volcano — Chapter 12

In 79 A.D., Mount Vesuvius erupted near the Roman city of Pompeii. Dust, ashes, cinders, and rocks flew high into the air. During the first eight hours of the eruption they fell on Pompeii to depths of eight to ten feet. In the next stage of the eruption, a superheated cloud of steam and mud flowed down the side of Vesuvius and covered the town of Herculaneum.

1. Based on the description, what kind of volcano was Mount Vesuvius?
2. What could the people of Pompeii and Herculaneum have done to save themselves?
3. What might modern scientific knowledge have done to help minimize the damage?

L2

This is a representation of key blackline masters available in the Teacher Classroom Resources. See Resource Manager boxes within the chapter for additional information.

Assessment

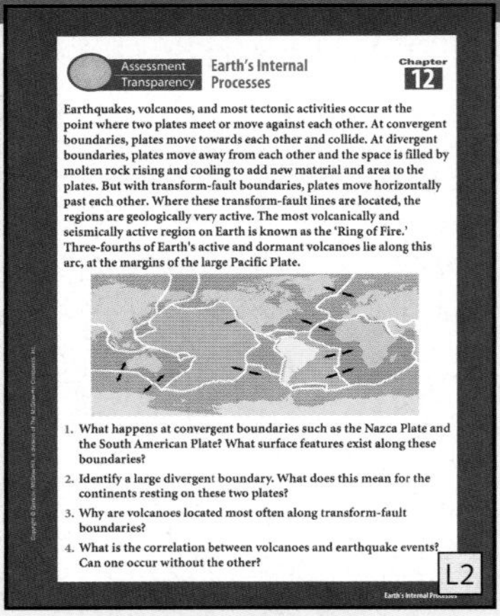
Assessment Transparency — Earth's Internal Processes — Chapter 12

Earthquakes, volcanoes, and most tectonic activities occur at the point where two plates meet or move against each other. At convergent boundaries, plates move towards each other and collide. At divergent boundaries, plates move away from each other and the space is filled by molten rock rising and cooling to add new material and area to the plates. But with transform-fault boundaries, plates move horizontally past each other. Where these transform-fault lines are located, the regions are geologically very active. The most volcanically and seismically active region on Earth is known as the 'Ring of Fire.' Three-fourths of Earth's active and dormant volcanoes lie along this arc, at the margins of the large Pacific Plate.

1. What happens at convergent boundaries such as the Nazca Plate and the South American Plate? What surface features exist along these boundaries?
2. Identify a large divergent boundary. What does this mean for the continents resting on these two plates?
3. Why are volcanoes located most often along transform-fault boundaries?
4. What is the correlation between volcanoes and earthquake events? Can one occur without the other?

L2

Teaching

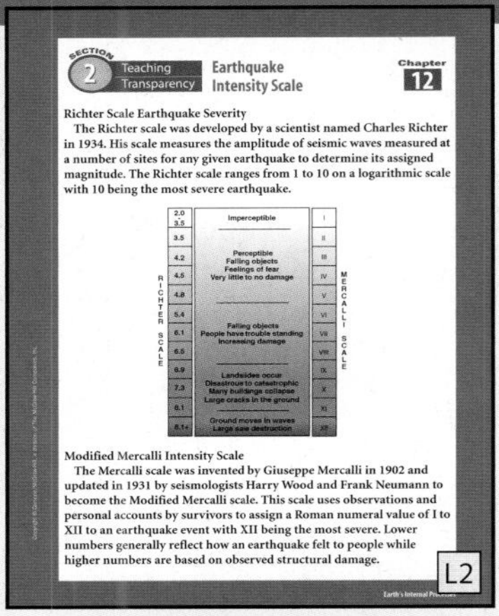
Section 2 Teaching Transparency — Earthquake Intensity Scale — Chapter 12

Richter Scale Earthquake Severity

The Richter scale was developed by a scientist named Charles Richter in 1934. His scale measures the amplitude of seismic waves measured at a number of sites for any given earthquake to determine its assigned magnitude. The Richter scale ranges from 1 to 10 on a logarithmic scale with 10 being the most severe earthquake.

Modified Mercalli Intensity Scale

The Mercalli scale was invented by Giuseppe Mercalli in 1902 and updated in 1931 by seismologists Harry Wood and Frank Neumann to become the Modified Mercalli scale. This scale uses observations and personal accounts by survivors to assign a Roman numeral value of I to XII to an earthquake event with XII being the most severe. Lower numbers generally reflect how an earthquake felt to people while higher numbers are based on observed structural damage.

L2

Key to Teaching Strategies

The following designations will help you decide which activities are appropriate for your students.

- L1 Level 1 activities should be appropriate for students with learning difficulties.
- L2 Level 2 activities should be within the ability range of all students.
- L3 Level 3 activities are designed for above-average students.
- ELL ELL activities should be within the ability range of English Language Learners.
- COOP LEARN Cooperative Learning activities are designed for small group work.
- LS Multiple Learning Styles logos, as described on page 12T, are used throughout to indicate strategies that address different learning styles.
- P These strategies represent student products that can be placed into a best-work portfolio.
- PBL Problem-Based Learning activities apply real-world situations to learning.

Hands-on Activities

Student Text Lab Worksheet

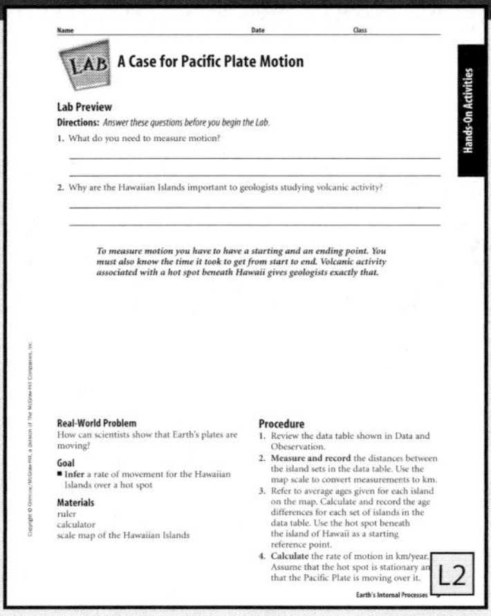
LAB A Case for Pacific Plate Motion

Lab Preview

L2

Laboratory Activities

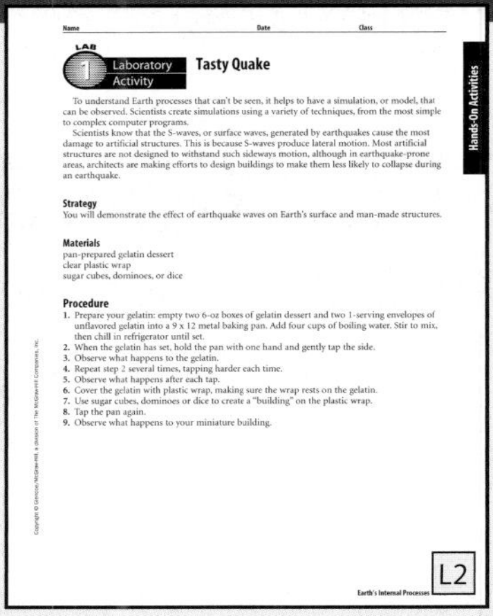
Laboratory Activity 1 — Tasty Quake

L2

Resource Manager

Meeting Different Ability Levels

Content Outline

L2

Reinforcement

L2

Enrichment

L1

Directed Reading (English/Spanish)

L1

Study Guide

L2

Reading Essentials

L1

Assessment

Test Practice Workbook

L2

Chapter Review

L2

Chapter Tests

L2

chapter 12 Earth's Internal Processes

Science Content Background

section 1 Evolution of Earth's Crust

Continental Drift

The theory of plate tectonics has its roots in Alfred Wegener's hypothesis of continental drift. Key ideas are:

- that the theory is "new", barely a century old.
- Wegener was unable to explain a mechanism for his hypothesis. The hypothesis was not accepted.
- World events helped to develop the technology needed to support the theory.

Seafloor Spreading Hypothesis

Dr. Harry Hess revived the notion of moving plates. He added several important revisions:

- Earth's crust is divided into interconnected plates.
- Plates may consist of continental crust, oceanic crust, or both.
- Oceanic crust is forming along the mid-ocean ridge system, which is coincident with divergent zones.

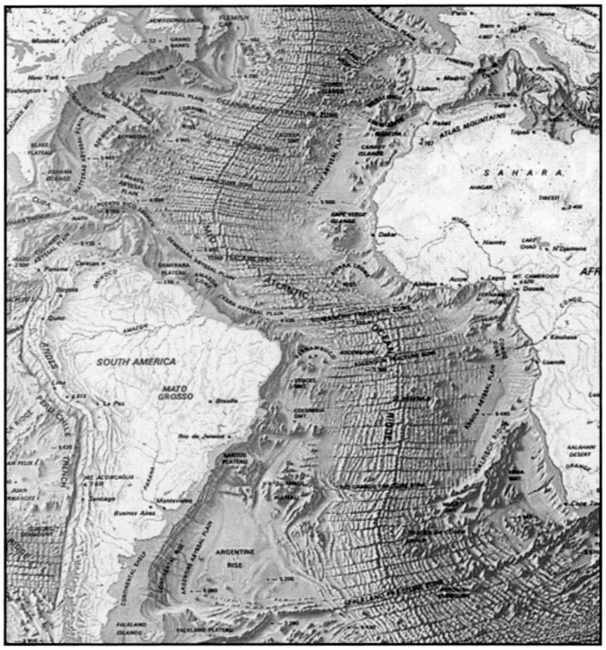

- Growth of Earth's crust is counteracted by destruction of crust at other locations.

The seafloor spreading hypothesis supports plate tectonic theory.

- Convection beneath the crust is hypothesized to be the driving mechanism.
- Convection drives both divergent and convergent zones; it creates tensional stress beneath continental crust, which results in formation of rift valleys.
- It facilitates the collision and destruction of crust at plate boundaries.
- Collision zones are locations of many earthquakes and formation of volcanic mountain chains either at sea (island arcs) or along continental margins (volcanic arcs).
- The mid-ocean ridge seafloor spreading zone experiences shallow volcanic activity.

section 2 Earthquakes

Predicting Earthquakes

Earthquakes are a subsurface phenomena that originate at a point of weakness in the rock structure. Faults are breaks or cracks in rock along which movement has occurred. Energy radiates spherically outward in all directions from the focus. Energy travels in three different seismic wave patterns: primary, secondary, and surface. The different patterns are critical to the behavior of surface materials and their destructive effects. These waves can break the integral structure of buildings, allowing them to collapse under their own weight. Attempts to precisely predict earthquakes have been unsuccessful to date. Efforts center around: (1) measuring stresses and strain across known faults, (2) monitoring suspected precursor factors, such as changes in water table levels or release of gases into the fault zone, or (3) monitoring surface deformation using laser surveying technology.

section 3 Earth's Interior

Density Differentiation

Earth's layered structure was created through density differentiation. During its formational stages, Earth was bombarded by meteors and asteroids (planetesimals). Impact of planetesimals caused melting of primordial Earth. The molten matter then separated or differentiated according to density and either sank toward the planetary center or solidified on the surface. Millions of years of this process have allowed the densest matter to accumulate in the core and grade toward a less dense crust.

The physical state of these layers is dependent on the interaction of temperature and pressure. The outer core is a liquid. This is believed to be because the pressure of the overlying matter is insufficient to overcome the effect of temperature created by heat release from radioactive material in the core.

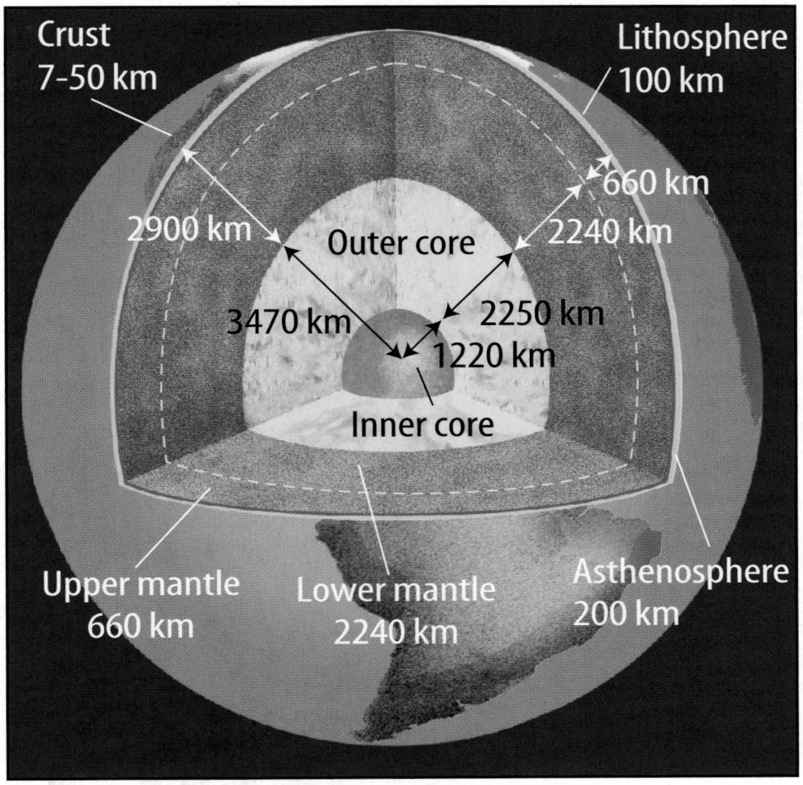

section 4 Volcanoes

Differences in Magma

Volcanic eruptions are controlled by temperature, gas content, and composition of the magma. The interplay of these variables produces a variety of eruption styles and resulting landforms. As a rule, temperature is most important and is directly linked to composition. High temperature magmas tend to be low in silica (basaltic) and have a low viscosity. This facilitates rapid flow and low profile landforms. In contrast, low temperature magmas are high in silica (granitic) and are resistant to flow. This creates high profile landforms. Magmas can change composition and viscosity as they move up to the surface or as they flow across the surface.

Bowen's reaction series is critical to an understanding of the order of crystallization of various magma compositions.

chapter content resources

Internet Resources

For additional content background, visit **gpescience.com** to:

- access your book online
- find references to related articles in popular science magazines
- access Web links with related content background
- access current events with science journal topics

Print Resources

Physical Geology, Fifth Edition, by Charles C. Plummer and David McGeary, Wm. C. Brown Publishers, 1991

Petrology, by Loren A. Raymond, Wm. C. Brown Publishers, 1995

chapter 12

Chapter Vocabulary

mid-ocean ridge, p. 356
rift valley, p. 356
divergent boundary, p. 358
convergent boundary, p. 359
subduction, p. 359
transform boundary, p. 360
fault, p. 364
elastic rebound, p. 364
focus, p. 364
epicenter, p. 364
discontinuity, p. 371
shadow zone, p. 371
asthenosphere, p. 372
viscosity, p. 375
cinder cone volcano, p. 377
shield volcano, p. 377
composite volcano, p. 378

Science Journal The most recent activity was in February 2004, with the eruption of ash clouds. This follows a series of eruptions which occurred from October 2002 through January 2003.

INTERACTIVE CHALKBOARD with Image Bank

PowerPoint® Presentations

This CD-ROM is an editable Microsoft® PowerPoint® presentation that includes:

- a pre-made presentation for every chapter
- interactive graphics
- animations
- audio clips
- image bank
- all new section and chapter questions
- Standardized Test Practice
- transparencies
- Foldables directions
- links to gpescience.com

chapter 12

Earth's Internal Processes

chapter preview

sections

Italian Fireworks

Sicily's Mt. Etna is the largest volcano in Europe. Molten rock from deep in Earth rose through a weak spot in the crust and erupted many times onto Earth's surface. Some of the exposed lava at the base of Mount Etna is nearly 300,000 years old.

Science Journal Research the most recent eruption and write a report about how it affected the surrounding environment.

352

Theme Connection

Stability and Change An expanding sphere will grow in diameter and its surface material will thin, much like an inflating balloon. An expanding Earth should do the same; however, it does not. This is because even though in some places Earth appears to be expanding (divergent boundaries), in others it appears to be contracting (convergent boundaries).

About the Photo

Get Ready Mt. Etna is located on the island of Sicily and is one of Earth's most active volcanoes. The photo shows a pyroclastic mixture of gas and lava erupting from the cone. Scientists predict that this is the beginning of more frequent eruptions due to increased earthquake activity associated with a recent, large intrusion of magma.

Start-Up Activities

Launch LAB

Global Jigsaw Puzzle

Alfred Wegener, a German scientist, noticed that the shapes of continental coastlines appeared as though they could match up. He suggested that the continents once were together as one giant landmass. Use a map of the world to test this idea. Can you see what he saw?

1. Cut out continents from a copy of a world map provided by your teacher.
2. Try to arrange continents so that they fit together.
3. Infer why the fit might not be perfect.
4. **Think Critically** What changes in procedure might demonstrate a better fit for the continents?

Science Online | Preview this chapter's content and activities at gpescience.com

FOLDABLES™ Study Organizer

Systems Make the following Foldable to help you organize information about types of plate boundaries.

STEP 1 **Fold** one piece of paper lengthwise into thirds.

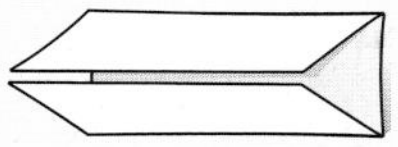

STEP 2 **Fold** the paper widthwise into fourths.

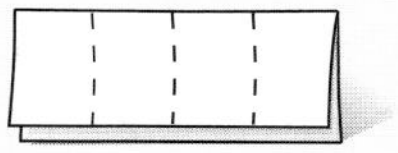

STEP 3 **Unfold,** lay the paper lengthwise, and draw lines along the folds. **Label** your table as shown.

Plate Boundary Type	Description	Illustration
Divergent		
Convergent		
Transform		

Making a Table As you read the chapter, complete the table describing and illustrating divergent, convergent, and transform plate boundaries.

353

Launch LAB

Purpose Use this Launch Lab to introduce students to Wegener's concept of continental drift. L2 LS **Kinesthetic**

Preparation Make copies of a world map. Be careful to use a modern conic or Robinson projection. Use a different map projection to stimulate class critical thinking.

Materials copies of a world map, scissors

Teaching Strategy Be open ended. Allow students to be creative.

Troubleshooting Discuss what a continent is and how to locate its edges.

Think Critically

Answers may vary, but the map projection used will be most important. Using something other than continental edges for positioning land masses should be discussed.

Assessment

Oral Have students speculate why this idea was not thought of sooner. Technology of map making and knowledge of longitude was lacking.

FOLDABLES™ Study Organizer **Dinah Zike Study Fold**

Student preparation materials for this Foldable are available in the **Chapter *Fast File* Resources.**

1 Motivate

An editable Microsoft® PowerPoint® presentation is available on **Interactive Chalkboard** CD-ROM.

Bellringer

Section Focus Transparency also are available on the Interactive Chalkboard CD-ROM. L2 ELL

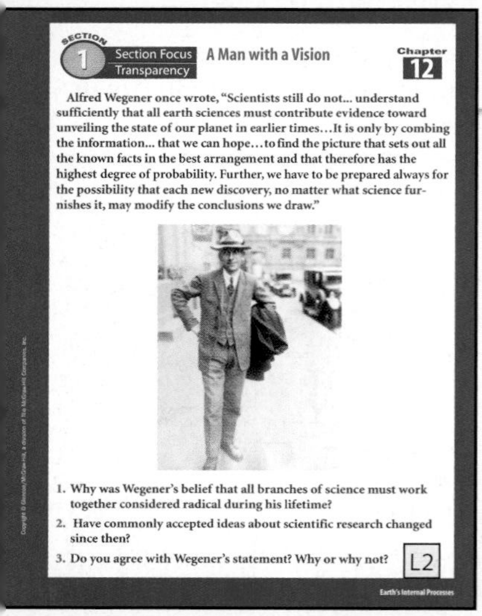
Section 1 Section Focus Transparency — A Man with a Vision — Chapter 12

Alfred Wegener once wrote, "Scientists still do not... understand sufficiently that all earth sciences must contribute evidence toward unveiling the state of our planet in earlier times…It is only by combing the information... that we can hope…to find the picture that sets out all the known facts in the best arrangement and that therefore has the highest degree of probability. Further, we have to be prepared always for the possibility that each new discovery, no matter what science furnishes it, may modify the conclusions we draw."

1. Why was Wegener's belief that all branches of science must work together considered radical during his lifetime?
2. Have commonly accepted ideas about scientific research changed since then?
3. Do you agree with Wegener's statement? Why or why not? L2

Earth's Internal Processes

Reading Preview

Tie to Prior Knowledge

Change in Shape When a mass is heated it expands; an expanding solid will stretch or crack. L2

Word Chart Have students make a four-column chart and write new vocabulary terms in the first column. In the second column, ask them to define each term without reading the text. As they read, students should record word definitions in the third column. In the last column, have students make a drawing related to the word.

section 1

Evolution of Earth's Crust

Reading Guide

What You'll Learn

- **Explain** supporting evidence for the continental drift hypothesis.
- **Discuss** the failings of the continental drift hypothesis.

Why It's Important

Wegner's continental drift hypothesis led to a unifying theory of Earth sciences known as plate tectonics.

Review Vocabulary

hypothesis: statement proposed to explain an observation or answer a question

New Vocabulary

- mid-ocean ridge
- rift valley
- divergent boundary
- convergent boundary
- subduction
- transform boundary

Continental Drift

In the early twentieth century, there was no single theory of how Earth processes interrelated. Much geologic study was done locally because transportation and communication were expensive. Based upon their observations, geologists developed theories that emphasized vertical changes, for example, an erosion process that leveled high places, and a mountain-building process that lifted them up again.

Then in 1915, Alfred Wegener (VEG nur) proposed a hypothesis that suggested that Earth's continents once were part of a large super-continent, shown in **Figure 1,** called Pangaea (pan GEE uh). Then, about 200 million years ago, the super-continent broke into pieces that drifted over the surface of Earth like rafts on water. This revolutionary idea of horizontal movement met with great resistance among his peers. He was unable to find the force capable of moving continents. It wasn't until after his death in 1930, that scientific advances finally justified his hypothesis.

Figure 1 This illustration is an artist's conception of what Pangaea may have looked like 200 million years ago.

Section 1 Resource Manager

Chapter *Fast File* Resources

Transparency Activity, p. 44
Note-taking Worksheets, pp. 33–35
Enrichment, p. 29
Reinforcement, p. 25
Directed Reading for Content Mastery, pp. 17, 18

Physical Science Critical Thinking/Problem Solving, p. 9
Performance Assessment in the Science Classroom, p. 42
Cultural Diversity, pp. 47–48
Mathematics Skill Activities, pp. 29–30

354 CHAPTER 12 Earth's Internal Processes

Matching Coastlines The most apparent match of continents is the eastern coastline of South America with the western coastline of Africa. If you use your imagination, you can see that the coastline of northwestern Africa fits nicely with that of the eastern United States. When South America and Africa are joined together, their southern tips fit very well into the Weddell Sea of Antarctica.

Figure 2 Weathering of the continental edges does not affect the continental shelves (light blue).

Wegener had to show that the continents were actually joined. He used the analogy of a torn newspaper being repaired. Not only did you have to match the shapes, but also join the lines of print. And the print had to match in terms of its content as well. What kind of content could this refer to in coastal regions of the continents? Wegener argued that you could match rock types, fossils, erosion features, and mountain ranges. If you found similar formations and structures on each continent then the continents could have been joined together in that place.

Wegener's opponents pointed out that the coastlines are constantly wearing away due to wave action. How could someone compare the present coastlines? Years later, during the revival of the hypothesis, oceanographers were able to show, using sonar, that the edges of the continental shelves matched very well, as shown in **Figure 2.**

Matching Fossils Wegener could not use the remains of just any ancient living thing to support the existence of Pangaea. For instance, animals that could fly or swim could appear in the fossil record in widely separated places due to their mobility, not because the places were necessarily joined. Large land animals provided better evidence because they could not have crossed oceans. Animals such as *Lystrosaurus* or *Cynognathus,* large animals that preceded the dinosaurs, supported a contiguous landmass. *Glossopteris,* a large fern with large, heavy spores also supported the idea of Pangaea. You can see in **Figure 3** that these living things were widely distributed.

Figure 3 Wegener chose fossils of animals that could not swim or fly to prove Pangaea's existence. **Explain** *Why would being able to fly or swim eliminate a fossil organism from Wegener's proof?*

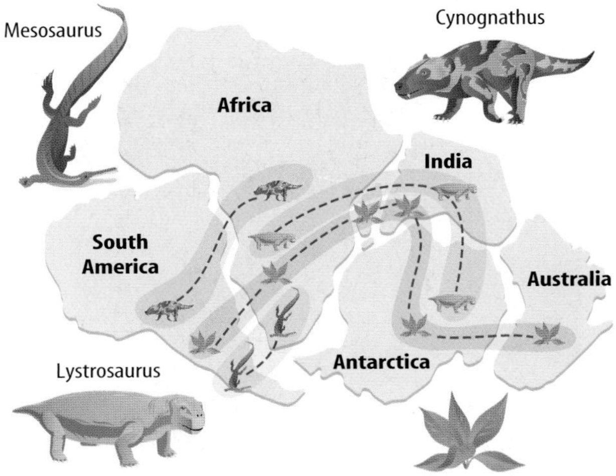

2 Teach

IDENTIFYING Misconceptions

Continental Boundaries Wegener's misconception was that the continents alone were drifting through the ocean basins. Students can easily have the same view. Stress that plate edges often are not the same as continental edges and that the whole plate is moving.

Make a Model

Continents Have students use construction paper or cardboard to trace the shapes of the continents and carefully cut them out. Add geographical features. Students may matchup the edges of the continents to illustrate Wegener's hypothesis. L1 ELL

LS **Visual-Spatial**

Activity

Continental Reconstruction Replicate Wegener's argument about torn newspaper. Randomly tear an entire section of newspaper into strips. Jumble all the page strips. Give different groups different strips and clear tape. Have the groups reconstruct what they can and then collaborate with other groups to reassemble the whole section.

Caption Answer

Figure 3 Mobile animals could overcome gaps between continents.

Discussion

Animal Evidence Challenge the students to list animals that would not have been useful to Wegener in his proof of continental drift, and why. Students should list saltwater swimmers and fliers because they can move from continent to continent freely. L3

SECTION 1 Evolution of Earth's Crust 355

IDENTIFYING Misconceptions

Subduction Inform students that most rocks sink. This is how one plate can subduct beneath another. It is heavier and denser than the material below it.

Reading Check

Answer Wegener couldn't explain the force or mechanism that moved the continents.

Visual Learning

Figure 4 Ask students to examine a world map and note the position of mountain ranges. Then have them look at the figure and locate these mountain ranges. Ask them if these mountain ranges could once have been positioned at plate boundaries. Yes, many mountain ranges were formed through plate tectonic activity. This shows how plate boundaries have changed over time. L2 ELL IS **Linguistic**

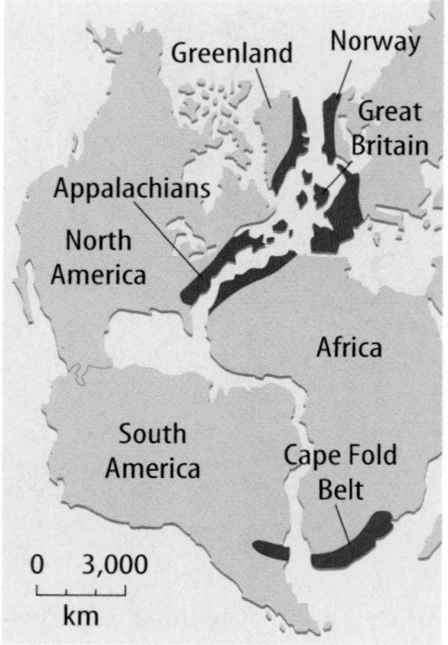

Figure 4 Wegener's hypothesis showed mountains on several continents were once part of the same range.

Matching Rocks and Mountains Mountain ranges were shown to be continuous in Pangaea, as shown in **Figure 4.** Once Pangaea broke apart, the mountain ranges became separated. For decades, geologists studied and attempted to explain the origin of these mountains as separate ranges; Wegener showed them to be one mountain range. Wegener was able to show that continents that were joined shared unique rocks and minerals.

Wegener's hypothesis was not accepted by his contemporaries because he was unable to conceive of a force or mechanism that could drive continents apart. Wegener reasoned that Earth's rotation, the gravitational pull of the Sun and the Moon, and centrifugal force could move continents. Physicists quickly showed that even combining these forces would not be sufficient.

Reading Check *Why didn't Wegener's contemporaries accept his hypothesis?*

Wegener used the analogy of continents moving over Earth's surface as ships moving through water. Skeptics argued that this ship would push a wall of water ahead of it and leave a wake. The continents didn't leave a wake. Instead of the continents pushing up a wall of water, they were deformed. How could this be if they were thicker and stronger?

Seafloor Spreading Hypothesis

After World War II, Dr. Harry Hess revived Wegener's ideas. He used sonar, intended to detect submarines, to obtain accurate maps of the seafloor. Using sonar data, astonishing three-dimensional seafloor models were created in 1960. Soon it was apparent that a **mid-ocean ridge** system, or MOR, was continuous and wrapped around Earth. A MOR is shown in **Figure 5.**

Hess proposed a hypothesis of seafloor spreading, or divergence. He suggested that magma from the mantle is forced upward because of its low density. This causes the crust to crack (fault) and move apart. The faulting causes twin mountain ranges with a down-dropped **rift valley** between. This continuous process allows new rock to form as magma fills in from below. See **Figure 6.**

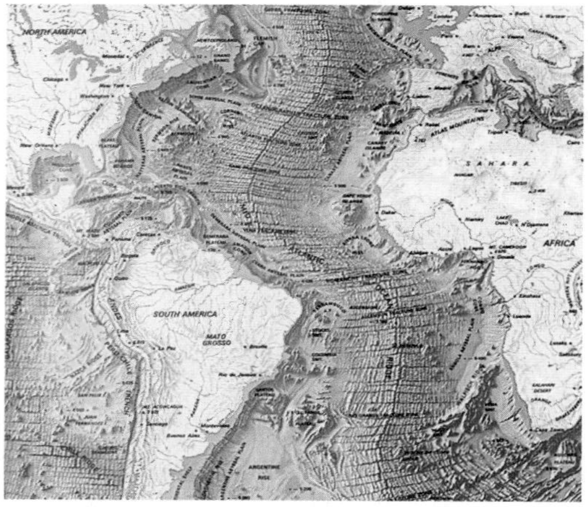

Figure 5 Discovery of a mid-ocean ridge led Hess to hypothesize seafloor spreading.

Differentiated Instruction

Visually Impaired Use a large, raised-relief world map or maps that denote different intervals of elevation with color. Even better, have students work together to develop their own maps. Visually impaired students can work with materials that circumvent their disabilities. For example: red-green color blind students might use blue-yellow colors. L2 IS **Visual-Spatial**

Ages of Sediment and Rocks In the early 1960s, massive programs for drilling into the seafloor began. Extracted cores of seafloor showed that sediments are thicker on top of seafloor basalt near the continents. MOR sediments, however, are thin. Cores of both sediments found that near the continents the oldest sediments are at the bottom and young sediments are at the top. MOR sediments are all of recent age. When the ages of rocks are measured, the continental rocks are billions of years old, while seafloor rocks are less than 200 million years of age. Rocks of the oceanic crust increase in age as their location extends from the MOR, and at the MOR they are new.

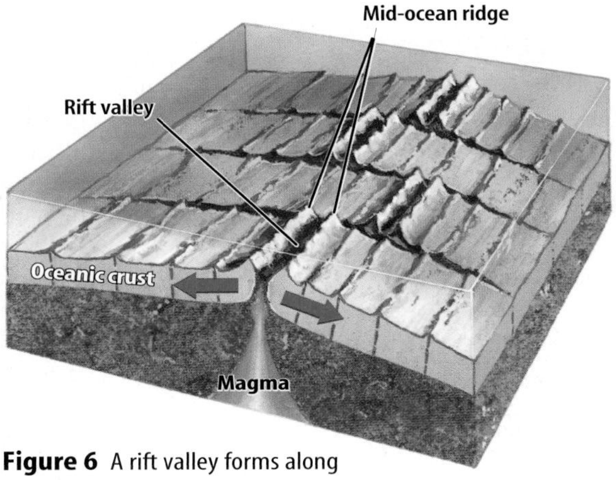

Figure 6 A rift valley forms along the mid-ocean ridge as plates diverge.

Applying Math — Solve One-Step Equations

SPREADING DISTANCES The spreading rate along the mid-ocean ridge varies. In the Atlantic Ocean, it averages about 2.5 cm/year. About how far, in kilometers, would the Atlantic seafloor have widened after 100 million years?

IDENTIFY known values and unknown values

Identify the known values:

time = 100,000,000 years

spreading rate = 2.5 cm/year

Identify the unknown values:

spreading distance

SOLVE the problem

Substitute the known values into the equation:

distance = rate × time

distance = 2.5 cm/year × 100,000,000 years = 250,000,000 cm

1 km/100,000 cm × 250,000,000 cm = 2,500 km

CHECK the answer

Does your answer seem reasonable? How wide is the Atlantic Ocean?

Practice Problems

If the East Pacific Rise spreads at 12 cm/year, how wide will it be in 10 million years?

For more practice problems, go to page 879 and visit Math Practice at gpescience.com.

Use an Analogy

Displacement and Distortion Masses moving through a fluid displace and distort the fluid. When riding a bike, your body pushes against the air. The air moves aside, and your body is not distorted. In Wegener's model, he envisioned the continents getting distorted as they moved, while the oceans and the oceanic crust remained the same. This is actually backward and did not help his argument. L2

Applying Math

Math Standards

National: 1, 2, 9

Teaching Strategy

Remind students of the velocity formula, $v = d/t$.

Answer to Practice Problem

1,200 km

Active Reading

Write-Draw-Discuss This strategy encourages students to actively participate in reading and lectures, assimilating content creatively. Students write about an idea, clarify it, and then make an illustration or drawing. They share responses with the class and display several examples. Have students Write-Draw-Discuss as they read about seafloor spreading.

INTEGRATE Physics

Sonar In the process of refining sonar's capabilities, discoveries were made that had peacetime benefits. For example, sonar often is equipped on boats to locate schools of fish. A related technique called ultrasound is used in medicine. Use print and online resources to research current uses and applications of sonar and ultrasound. The speed of sound in water is about 1,500 m/sec. If a sonar pulse takes 2 s to reach the sea floor and return to the ship, how deep is the water? Remember that $d = rt$. The depth is 1,500 m; remind students to take into account the roundtrip time of 2 s.

INTEGRATE Physics

Sonar In the process of refining sonar's capabilities, discoveries were made that had peacetime benefits. For example, sonar often is equipped on boats to locate schools of fish. A related technique called ultrasound is used in medicine. Research current uses and applications of sonar and ultrasound.

Magnetic Polarity of Rocks Studies show that Earth's magnetic field repeatedly reverses itself, meaning that the magnetic north pole becomes the south pole. Vine, Matthews, Wilson, et al discovered bands of reversed polarity in the seafloor rocks similar to those found on the continents. As magma crystals form, they take on the polarity of Earth at the time they form. The pattern is identical on both sides of the MOR.

Theory of Plate Tectonics

Originating in the 1960s, the theory of plate tectonics is relatively new. After seafloor spreading demonstrated that Earth's crust moved horizontally on a global scale, many investigators were determined to understand such a whole-Earth system of movement. This system consists of about a dozen major plates and many minor ones. Plates are composed of a rigid layer of uppermost mantle and a layer of either oceanic or continental crust above. Some plates are composed only of oceanic crust, and some are composed of part oceanic and part continental crust. J. T. Wilson is credited with describing the cycle of repeated opening and closing of ocean basins through Earth's history.

There are three main kinds of plate motions. These are best visualized by considering how plates interact along plate boundaries, where they meet. Plates can move apart, move together, or slide past one another. Although often visualized as narrow boundaries, scientists now consider many boundaries to be wide zones of interaction.

Divergent Plate Boundaries You learned that at a mid-ocean ridge (MOR), magma rises along a faulted rift valley, spreads, and cools to form new oceanic crust. This spreading apart is what happens at **divergent boundaries.** An MOR represents divergence that is well-developed and that has resulted in the production of major ocean basins. In some locations on Earth today, divergent boundaries exist as rift valleys, where no mature ocean basins exist yet, such as in East Africa, shown in **Figure 7.**

Figure 7 Large lakes and volcanic mountains are characteristics of a continental rift valley.

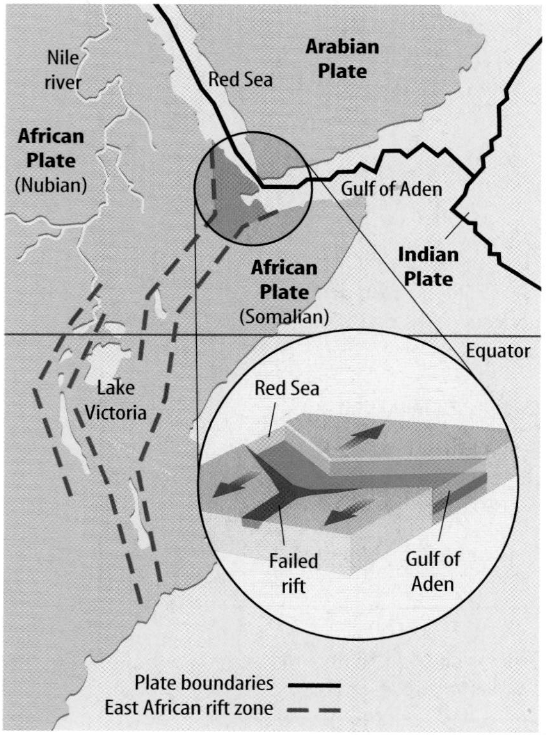

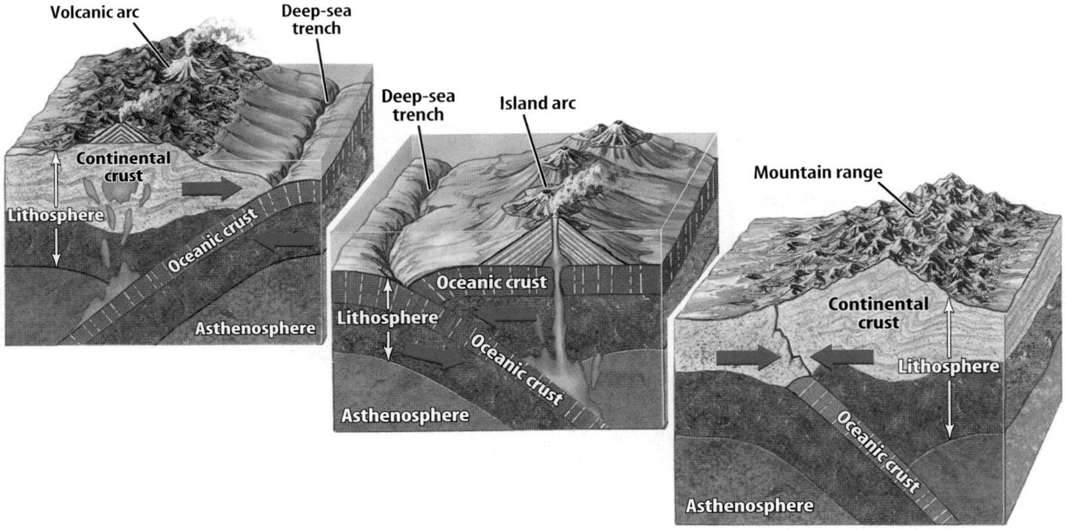

Figure 8 When plates collide, the more dense plate is subducted. The resulting features include volcanoes, mountains, and deep trenches.

Convergent Plate Boundaries Where plates collide, they come together to form **convergent boundaries.** In some cases, less-dense, thick continental lithosphere moves toward denser, thin oceanic lithosphere. This results in the oceanic side bending and being forced downward beneath the continental slab in a process called **subduction.** Heat along a subduction zone partially melts rock at depth and produces magma, which rises toward the surface. This magma feeds a volcanic arc that parallels this zone, shown in **Figure 8.** The region of collision also has a deep-sea trench that parallels the zone. The Andes mountain range in South America is an example.

Convergent plate boundaries also exist between two slabs of oceanic lithosphere. In this case, the oceanic lithosphere that is colder, and therefore denser, subducts. Magma erupted here produces chains of volcanic islands called island arcs. Japan is an example of an ocean-ocean convergent boundary, also shown in **Figure 8.** As plates converge, stress builds, which could be released as tsunami-causing earthquakes.

Along some convergent plate boundaries, two continental slabs of low density collide and tend not to subduct. Because of this resistance to subduction, the plates collide and buckle upward to form a high range of folded mountains. Volcanic activity is noticeably absent and there is no trench. The Himalaya of Asia are an example of folded mountains that occur where continental lithosphere collides.

Reading Check *What is formed when two continental plates converge?*

Science Online

Topic: Tsunamis

Visit gpescience.com for Web links to information about tsunamis.

Activity Research the most recent tsunami and its destruction. Record the epicenter and magnitude of the earthquake that caused the tsunami and post these data on a world map. Write a short report that describes the tsunami's impact on humans and the environment.

Using Science Words

Word Origin Introduce the prefixes used in the vocabulary words from this chapter:

litho = stone

astheno = weak

seismo = shake

epi = upon

Have the students choose two prefixes and list other words with the same prefix. Have them explain how they are related. Litho = lithography, lithograph—the process of, or writing or engraving on stone L2 IS **Linguistic**

Reading Check

Answer folded mountains

Teacher FYI

Compare and contrast the different types of plate boundaries. Some students easily get them confused. Use of overheads and other media may be helpful. Stress the fact that each boundary type has at least one characteristic that differentiates it from the others.

Quick Demo
Mantle Convection

Materials lava lamp

Estimated Time 30 minutes

Procedure Leave the lamp on long enough for convection to become well-developed. Explain that convection currents cannot happen in solids. The presence of these currents is based on an assumption that the layer beneath the crust is not rock solid. The rising and falling blobs of wax in a lava lamp demonstrate mantle convection. Students will learn more about this idea later in the chapter. L2

ELL LS **Visual-Spatial**

Reading Strategy

Causal Relationships Have students determine the causes of each of the following: sea-floor spreading, divergent plate boundaries, convergent plate boundaries, and transform plate boundaries. Encourage students to make sketches to help clarify cause and effect relationships.

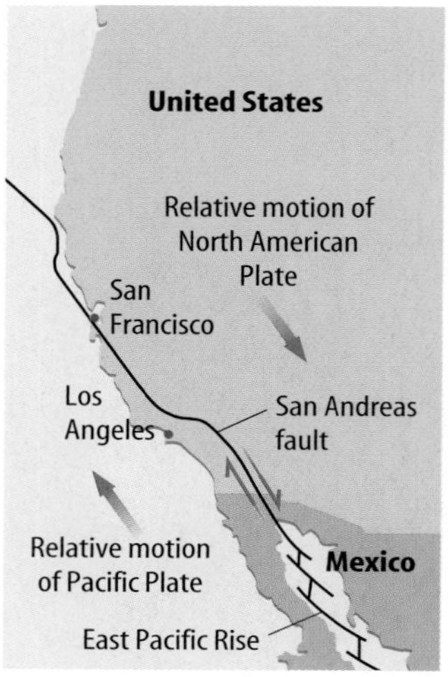

Figure 9 Friction between plates moving side by side causes cracks and breaks in the edges of the plates. This is the site of brief, but rapid energy release called an earthquake.

Transform Plate Boundaries Some boundaries among plates exist as large faults, or cracks, along which mostly horizontal movement is taking place, as shown in **Figure 9.** In this case, no new lithosphere is forming, as along a divergent boundary. In addition, old lithosphere is not being recycled, as along a subduction zone. The main result of **transform boundaries** is horizontal motion of lithosphere.

Transform faults are extremely important where they cut perpendicular to the MOR. These fault systems allow movement away from ridge crests to occur, as shown in **Figure 10.** If you observe arrows that indicate net motion along these transform faults, you will notice that this net motion trends away from the MOR.

What drives the plates?

Research indicates that plates are driven by a combination of forces. One such force is ridge push at the MOR. Because divergent boundaries are higher at the center of the ridge, gravity forces material down the slopes of the MOR.

When a plate subducts back into Earth at some convergent boundaries, the process of slab pull is thought to operate. You probably have experienced an analogy to slab pull when you found your bed covers on the floor in the morning. During the night, as you tossed and turned, the covers began to move off of the bed. Eventually, enough of the covers were over the side that gravity took over and pulled the rest of the covers to the floor. Subducting plates may act in much the same way, as portions of descending plates are pulling the rest of a plate down with them.

Figure 10 A transform fault cuts through the MOR, offsetting the mountain range.

Post Reading

Time-Line Project Ask students to research the following: continental drift, sea floor spreading, and the theory of plate tectonics. Have students develop a timeline that illustrates the evolution of ideas regarding the movement of Earth's crust.

Teacher FYI

Driving Forces The convection below the surface causes conveyor-belt-like motion at the surface. At the MOR, rising magma causes *ridge push*, friction below the plate causes *plate drag*, and subduction in convergent zones promotes *slab pull.* Treat these as an integrated system driven by internal heating and convection in the mantle.

Friction between a plate and mantle material below the plate probably is of major importance in relative plate motion. For example, plates that drag continental material along with them are noticeably slower than are purely oceanic plates. Scientists think that continental lithosphere has deep roots that cause more frictional force than would be expected at the base of oceanic lithosphere.

Reading Check *What role does friction play in plate motion?*

Thermal Energy Internal convection of mantle material is the driving force for all mechanisms of plate motion. In turn, the main source of thermal energy that keeps Earth materials convecting comes from the decay of radioactive elements in Earth. Increased temperature due to pressure and frictional heating produced as part of the mechanism itself probably are important. Conversion of secondary earthquake waves in the outer core may yet be another source of energy.

section 1 review

Summary

Continental Drift

- Wegener proposed that former supercontinent Pangaea broke up into pieces, which drifted to their present positions.
- Evidence favoring continental drift includes matching shorelines of continents and correlating rocks, fossils, and mountain ranges of those continents.

Seafloor Spreading Hypothesis

- Hess suggested that seafloor was created and spread apart at the mid-ocean ridge.
- Moving away from the MOR, rocks are older and sediments are thicker.
- Magnetic reversals preserved in seafloor rocks are symmetrically distributed on either side of the MOR.

Theory of Plate Tectonics

- Earth's rigid, outermost layers are composed of a dozen or so major plates and many smaller ones.
- New lithosphere is created at the MOR and recycled at convergent boundaries. Convective flow within the mantle drives the plates.

Self-Check

1. **Explain** the processes of convergence and divergence.
2. **Describe** the key features of a divergent boundary.
3. **Compare and contrast** the three types of convergent plate boundaries.
4. **Describe** the possible driving mechanisms in the plate tectonic theory.
5. **Think Critically** Predict what would happen if Earth's plates stopped moving.
6. **Think Critically** What would have to occur to stop Earth's plate movement?

Applying Math

7. If two plates diverge at a rate of 1.3 cm/year, how much farther apart will the plates be after 200 million years?
8. How many times faster are plates moving at 7.3 cm/year than those moving at 1.3 cm/year?
9. The average distance across an ocean is 16,000 km. Two continents on either side of the ocean are converging at a rate of 10 cm/year. How long will it take for them to collide?

More Section Review gpescience.com

Reading Check

Answer Continental lithosphere has deep roots which cause friction and slows their movement.

3 Assess

DAILY INTERVENTION

Check for Understanding

Kinesthetic Using thin (oceanic) and thick (continental) blocks of foam rubber, have students model the movements that take place at plate tectonic boundaries. L2 ELL

Reteach

Density Differences Using sponges, wood blocks, ceramic tiles, and water, have students model what happens when objects of different densities come into contact with each other. L1 ELL IS **Visual-Spatial**

Assessment

Process Have students correctly label sketches of different plate tectonic boundaries. L2 ELL **Visual-Spatial**

Create Have each student prepare a quiz-show answer for the category Plate Tectonics. Critique each answer and save the best for a game at the end of the chapter. L2

section 1 review

1. During convergence, plates collide and one subducts under the other; during divergence, plates move apart and create a rift valley.
2. mid-ocean ridge in some places, rift valley from which magma flows, new ocean crust forms
3. There is collision at all convergent plate boundaries. Continental-ocean boundaries have volcanic arcs, ocean-ocean have volcanic island arcs, continental-continental generally lack volcanic activity and develop high mountains.
4. All are the result of convection currents in the upper mantle; *ridge push,* divergence due to magma injection; *plate drag,* due to friction between plate and asthenosphere; *slab pull,* due to gravitational pull during subduction in convergent zones
5. Earthquakes and volcanic activity would cease. Erosion would wear down continents to sea level.
6. Earth's core would have to cool.
7. 2,600 km
8. 5.6 times faster
9. 8×10^7 years

1 Motivate

INTERACTIVE CHALKBOARD An editable Microsoft® PowerPoint® presentation is available on **Interactive Chalkboard** CD-ROM.

Bellringer

Section Focus Transparencies also are available on the Interactive Chalkboard CD-ROM. L2 ELL

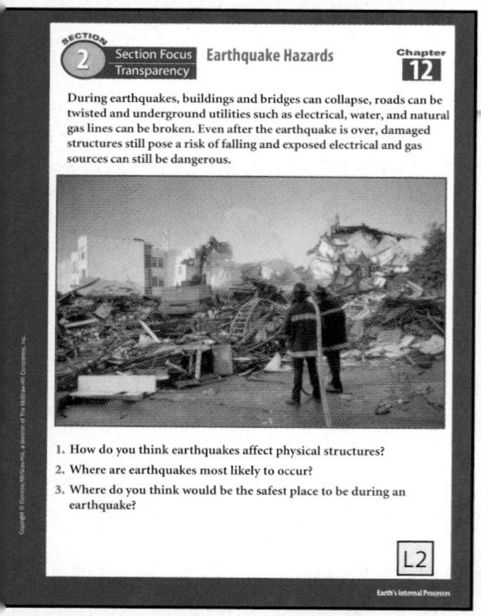

Section 2 Section Focus Transparency **Earthquake Hazards** Chapter 12

During earthquakes, buildings and bridges can collapse, roads can be twisted and underground utilities such as electrical, water, and natural gas lines can be broken. Even after the earthquake is over, damaged structures still pose a risk of falling and exposed electrical and gas sources can still be dangerous.

1. How do you think earthquakes affect physical structures?
2. Where are earthquakes most likely to occur?
3. Where do you think would be the safest place to be during an earthquake?

L2

Earth's Internal Processes

Reading Preview

Tie to Prior Knowledge

Wave Description Waves are identified by their wavelength, amplitude, and frequency. L2

Facets of Meaning For each new vocabulary word, ask students to identify common meanings. For the word *focus*, students might say, "an area of interest." Have them scan the text to find word definitions that specifically relate to earthquakes. Have students record all facets of meaning and compare notes with a partner.

section 2

Earthquakes

Reading Guide

What You'll Learn

- **Describe** the causes and characteristics of earthquakes.
- **Explain** how seismic waves affect Earth's surface.
- **Describe** how seismic waves are used to infer Earth's internal structure.

Why It's Important

Earthquakes kill people and destroy property. Understanding earthquakes may help minimize their effects.

Review Vocabulary

friction: force that opposes the sliding motion between two touching surfaces

New Vocabulary

- fault
- elastic rebound
- focus
- epicenter

Global Earthquake Distribution

For decades, scientists have known that earthquakes are not distributed randomly, but rather, they occur in well-defined zones. These zones coincide with the edges of lithospheric plates. In fact, seismic data originating from earthquakes helped to decipher the structure of Earth's ocean floor and to infer the structure and motion of Earth's plates. **Figure 11** shows the distribution of large earthquakes.

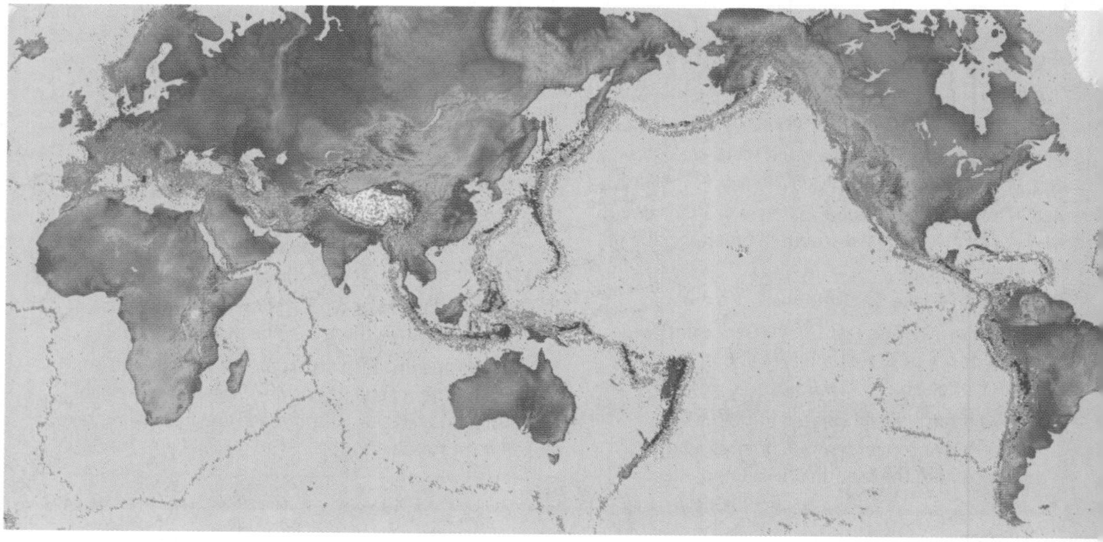

Figure 11 Most earthquakes occur along the edges of plates. **Identify** *some other places earthquakes occur.*

Section 2 Resource Manager

Chapter *FAST FILE* Resources

Transparency Activity, pp. 45, 49–50
MiniLAB, p. 3
Lab Activity, pp. 11–12, 13–14
Enrichment, p. 30
Reinforcement, p. 26
Directed Reading for Content Overview, p. 18

Home and Community Involvement, p. 31

Life Science Critical Thinking/Problem Solving, p. 10

Depth of Focus Patterns develop when data about the focus depths of earthquakes are plotted on a world map. Recall that divergent boundaries are associated with transform faulting that allows plates to move in opposite directions. All of this faulting creates a narrow band of numerous, shallow earthquakes. In contrast, convergent boundaries have broad zones of earthquakes with the shallowest foci near the surface at the point of convergence, and the deepest foci located under volcanoes or mountains created in the collision area, as shown in **Figure 12.**

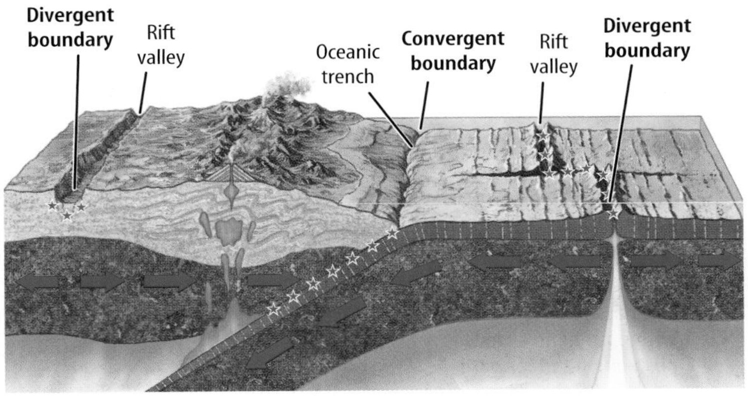

Figure 12 The depth of the earthquake focus (indicated by the stars) is related to the activity causing the earthquake.

Causes of Earthquakes

An earthquake is any seismic vibration of Earth caused by the rapid release of energy. Earthquake events can be either natural or human-caused. Passing trains or large trucks and explosions can cause Earth to vibrate. As shown in **Figure 13,** sudden, virtually unpredictable, natural earthquakes that result in major destruction are greatly feared.

Deformation Earth's crust is composed of rigid, rocky material. Engineers would describe it as brittle. When a stress is applied to a brittle material it shows little sign of strain, or deformation, until it suddenly breaks. A strain is the manner of deformation in response to a stress. Stress is the force per unit area that acts on a material. Stresses can be of four types: (1) compressive stress, in which a mass is squeezed or shortened, (2) a tension stress, in which the mass is stretched or lengthened, (3) a shear stress, in which different parts of a mass are moved in opposite directions along a plane, or (4) torsion stress, in which a mass is subjected to twisting.

Figure 13 This damage was caused when the buildings were shaken off their foundations.
Explain *How might this damage have been prevented?*

2 Teach

Caption Answer

Figure 11 near artificial disturbances, such as bomb blasts

Teacher FYI

Nukes v. Earthquakes There is no real difference between the wave patterns of nuclear bombs and earthquakes. Seismic studies advanced during the cold war because the U.S. thought that it could monitor Soviet bomb testing through seismic monitoring. It didn't work.

Discussion

Earthquake or not? Use photographs of destruction from earthquakes and bomb blasts. Ask students if they can tell the difference. Earthquake patterns show response to gravity alone—vertically collapsed building or tilted structures. Bomb blasts show an outward, "radial" pattern. L2 ELL LS **Visual-Spatial**

Fun Fact

Both the U.S. and the former Soviet Union placed their nuclear testing facilities in remote areas that had plenty of natural earthquakes so that their testing would be cloaked.

Caption Answer

Figure 13 The building could be anchored to the foundation; the foundation should be on solid ground.

Visual Learning

Figure 13 Have students examine the types of buildings and their construction in the picture, and not the damage. Ask them what might have been done to avoid such damage. Students might suggest changes to improve building structure, construction farther away from earthquake prone areas, etc.

Fun Fact

Meteorologists now use the same pattern identification idea to distinguish between tornado damage and microburst damage. Microburst debris is scattered outward like the spokes of a wheel from a point; tornado debris tends to be scattered along the sides of a "lane" of destruction and may show a hop-and-skip type pattern.

Reading Strategy

Think Aloud Model this strategy by reading aloud a section of text. Share how you absorb the text. You might say, "I don't understand this paragraph. I need to slow down and reread." Have students brainstorm other ways of comprehending challenging text.

Mini LAB

Purpose Students will model four types of stress and their resulting deformations.

Materials taffy bars

Teaching Strategy Have students keep their palms facing down and hands in constant contact with each other during the entire procedure.

Analysis

1. Step 1: shear;
   Step 2: torsion;
   Step 3: tension;
   Step 4: compression
2. Compression: smooshed, squeezed, folded, compressed, crushed, condensed; Tension: stretched, pulled apart, broken, pulled thin, snapped, drawn out; Shear: shaved off, sliced, split, ground up, scraped, peeled, abrasion; Torsion: twisted, wrenched, wound up, coiled, curled, entwined, spiraled, corkscrewed, turned, torque

Assessment

Oral Have students describe some examples of items they have observed that have been deformed by each of the four types of stress. Use **Performance Assessment in the Science Classroom**, p. 123. L2

Mini LAB

Demonstrating Four Types of Stress

Procedure

1. With palms facing down at all times and your hands in contact with each other, clasp a **large bar of taffy** with both hands. First, push one hand forward 2 cm while simultaneously pulling the other backward 2 cm. Return your hands to the original position.
2. Still holding your hands in contact, twist your hands in opposite directions and return them to the original position.
3. Next move your hands about 4 cm apart.
4. Finally push your hands back together to the original position.

Analysis

1. Which type of stress did you demonstrate in each of steps 1–4?
2. Describe the kinds of deformation you would expect to result from each of the four stresses.

Elastic Deformation Elastic deformation occurs when a material deforms as a stress is applied, but snaps back to its origin shape when the stress is removed. Plastic deformation occurs when a material deforms, or changes shape, as a stress is applied and remains in the new shape when the stress is released. Modeling clay behaves plastically. You would expect all rocks to show brittle deformation, which means breaking in response to stress. But rocks at depth, where temperatures are high enough, display plastic behavior. For example, you can break off an edge of a wax candle when it is cold and brittle, but the wax bends more under stress—without breaking—when it warms up.

Energy Release Strain energy builds up along cracks in Earth's crust in response to stress. When this strain energy is released suddenly, it causes rock to lurch to a new position. A **fault** is a crack along which movement has taken place. If no movement takes place, the crack is a fracture. Earthquake-producing faults occur in broad zones in which rock is deformed in a brittle manner during the fault movements. These zones can be tens of meters wide. The sudden energy release that goes with fault movement is called **elastic rebound.** Elastic rebound causes seismic vibrations, or earthquakes, like when you drag a table across the floor and the legs catch and release making a rumbling sound.

Earthquake Waves

Earthquake waves travel out in all directions from a point where strain energy is released. This point is the **focus,** or point of origin, of an earthquake. The point on Earth's surface directly above the focus is the **epicenter.** When you throw a stone into water you see concentric rings of waves move out across the surface from the point of impact. Earthquake waves are much the same, except they move out from the focus in all directions, like a sphere of waves. These ideas are shown in **Figure 14.**

Earthquake waves can be sorted broadly into two major types. Body waves travel through Earth. Surface waves travel across Earth's surface.

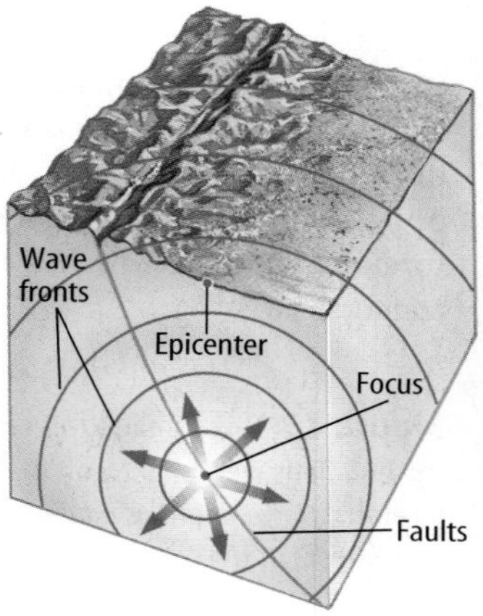

Figure 14 Waves moving out from the focus may travel through the mantle. These may be picked up by seismographs on the opposite side of Earth.

364 CHAPTER 12 Earth's Internal Processes

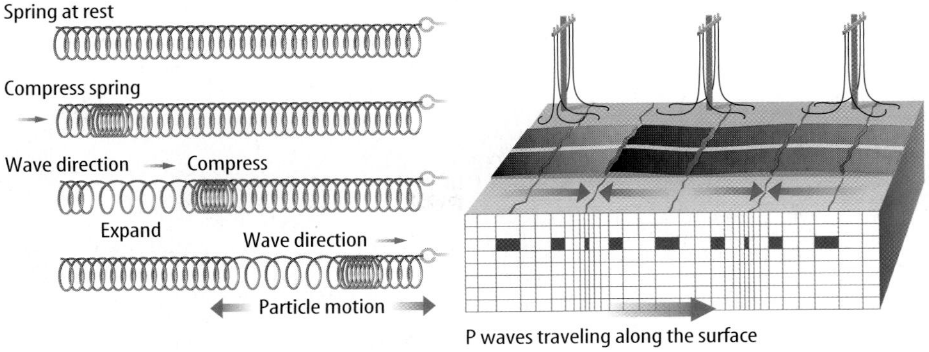

Body Waves One type of body wave is called a primary wave. Primary waves, also called P-waves, cause particles in a material to undergo a push-pull type motion as shown in **Figure 15.** Because this motion is in the direction of wave travel, the wave energy is transferred very quickly. The particles do not permanently change location. If there is matter around where particles can bump into each other, then primary waves can move through it. Much like sound waves, P-waves travel through all kinds of matter.

Secondary waves (S-waves) are body waves that travel more slowly than primary waves. They are sometimes called shear waves, because of the relative motion of particles as energy is transferred. S-waves cause particles to move perpendicular to the direction of wave travel. The farther body waves travel from an earthquake focus, the farther behind the S-waves get. It is this lag in time between the arrival of the first P-waves and the first S-waves that is important in locating epicenters.

S-waves only can travel through solids. When one particle moves, it moves its neighbors along with it. In gases and liquids the bonds are weak, or there are no bonds, so particles can move independently. The motions of S-waves are shown in **Figure 16.**

Figure 15 P-waves are compressional waves like those moving in a coiled spring.
Describe *How are P-waves like sound waves?*

Figure 16 S-waves cause the earth to undulate creating surface damage.

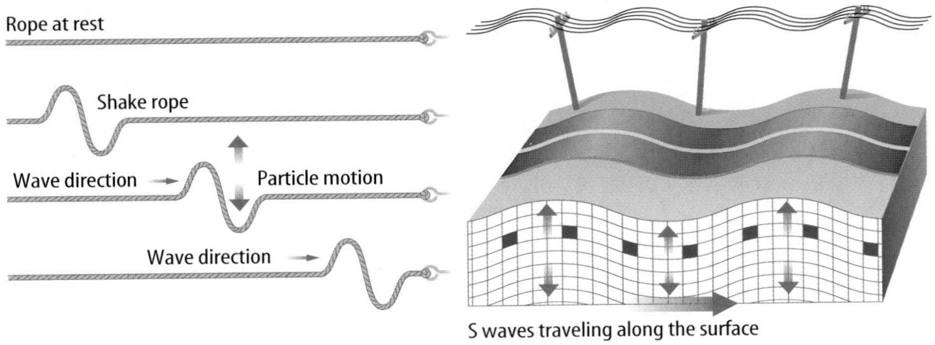

Quick Demo
Wave Motion

Materials toy spring

Estimated Time 10 minutes

Procedure Demonstrate the action of P-waves and S-waves. This is best done on the floor or a long table. A rope tied to a doorknob can be used to model S-wave movement.

Activity

Turn the Quick Demo into an activity. Provide groups with toy springs or ropes and have them investigate how the waves change with different energy inputs or different lengths of input movement, i.e. short v. long push-pull movement to make P-waves, or short and long side-to-side movement for S-waves. L2 ELL IN
Visual-Spatial

Caption Answer

Figure 15 Both waves are compressional and both need particles that can bump into one another.

SECTION 2 Earthquakes **365**

Fun Fact

There are thousands of earthquakes every day—most are too small to even report. Show students a world map plotting the distribution of different magnitude earthquakes.

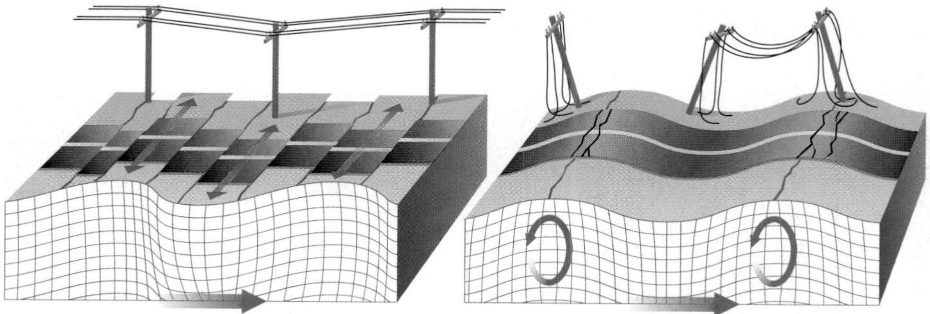

Figure 17 During an earthquake the surface can roll like the ocean and shift side to side at the same time.

Surface Waves Surface waves move in a more complex manner, often causing a rolling motion much like ocean waves. As surface waves travel through material, they can exhibit an up and down rolling motion, and also a side-to-side motion that parallels Earth's surface. Foundations of human-built structures often are susceptible to the side-to-side rocking that might result from surface waves. These surface wave motions are illustrated in **Figure 17.**

Table 1 Estimates of Earthquake Magnitude and Frequency

Richter Magnitude Range	Description Index	Estimated Occurrence per Year
< 2.0	recorded, but not generally felt	600,000
2.0–2.9	potentially felt	300,000
3.0–3.9	felt by some	49,000
4.0–4.9	felt by most	6200
5.0–5.9	damaging	800
6.0–6.9	destructive in densely populated areas	266
7.0–7.9	potential to inflict major damage	18
8.0 and above	potential to destroy communities near epicenter	1.4

Cultural Diversity

Stories from Home Have students from another culture describe their culture's beliefs and attitudes toward earthquakes, particularly if the student comes from a place that has frequent earthquakes.

Earthquake Measurement

Two measurement schemes that have been used to characterize earthquakes are the Modified Mercalli intensity scale and the Richter magnitude scale. Intensity is a measure of ground shaking and the damage that it causes. The Modified Mercalli scale, **Table 2,** ranks earthquakes in a range from I–XII, XII being the worst, and uses eyewitness observations and post-earthquake assessments to assign an intensity value. The Richter magnitude scale, Richter scale for short, uses the amplitude of the largest earthquake wave. Richter magnitude is intended to give a measure of the energy released during the earthquake. **Figure 18** shows a seismogram and how it is used to determine a Richter value. **Table 1** shows the global frequency of different magnitude earthquakes.

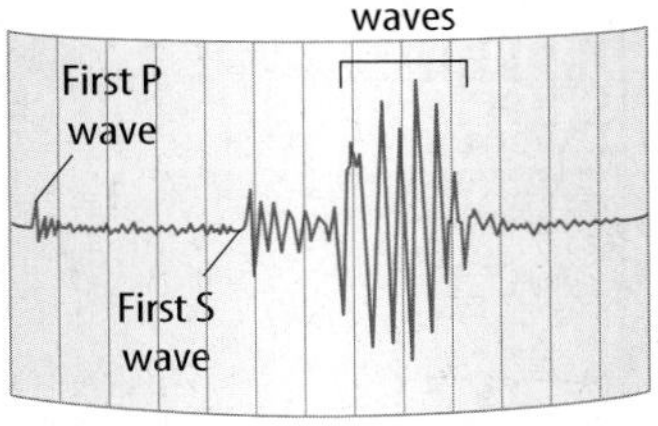

Figure 18 A seismograph is an instrument used to measure earthquake waves. A seismogram is a tracing of the seismograph's pen.

Table 2 The Mercalli Scale of Earthquake Intensity

Level	Description
I	Rarely felt by people.
II	Felt by resting people indoors; some hanging objects may swing.
III	Felt indoors by several. Vibration like passing of a light truck.
IV	Felt indoors by many. Vibration like passing of a heavy truck. Standing autos rock. Windows, dishes and doors rattle. Walls and frames may creak.
V	Felt by nearly everyone indoors and outdoors. Small unstable objects upset. Some dishes and glassware broken. Swaying of tall objects noticed.
VI	Felt by all. Walking is unsteady, many run outdoors. Windows, dishes, and glassware broken. Furniture overturned and plaster may crack.
VII	Difficult to stand. Noticed by drivers of autos. Furniture and chimneys broken. Well built buildings hardly damaged. Poor structures considerable damage.
VIII	People frightened. Ordinary buildings slightly damaged. Driving of autos affected. Tree limbs fractured. Damage to tall objects. Cracks in wet ground.
IX	General panic. Damage great in substantial buildings. Some houses thrown off foundations. Underground pipes broken. Serious ground cracks.
X	Most masonry and frame structures destroyed. Serious damage to dams, dikes, embankments. Water splashed out of rivers, canals, lakes. Rails bent.
XI	Few structures remain standing. Bridges destroyed. Broad fissures in the ground. Slumps and landslides. Rails bent generally.
XII	Damage nearly total. Waves seen on ground surfaces. Lines of sight and level distorted. Objects thrown into the air. Large rock masses displaced.

Discussion

Shaky Earth Ask the students for ways that Earth might be vibrated other than fault movement. Stress that scale makes a difference. bomb blasts (nuclear), pounding of surf, heavy trucks, railroad trains, people walking/running, etc; All are detectable by modern seismic equipment. L2

Inquiry Lab

Earthquake Magnitude Scale

Question How can you design a model of an earthquake magnitude scale?

Possible Materials pennies, nickels, foreign coins, metric ruler, meterstick, magazines, paperback books, heavy books.

Estimated Time 30 minutes

Teaching Strategies

- Students can stand coins on their ends and drop different-sized books from uniform heights and distances to measure the "earthquake" size produced by each item. Students can experiment with placing different-sized coins and different numbers of coins on a flat surface to establish a magnitude scale and to measure the vibrations of different-sized books. They also can fine-tune their measurement systems by placing the coins at different angles with respect to the falling books.
- Encourage students to experiment with the magnitude of vibrations passing through different surfaces such as tile, carpet, and wood.

For additional inquiry activities, see *Science Inquiry Lab Manual*.

NATIONAL GEOGRAPHIC

Visualizing Earthquake-Proof Buildings

Have students read the information and examine the pictures. Then ask the following questions: Why do some parts of the world experience more earthquakes than others? Locations that are close to plate boundaries often experience more earthquakes. Why do earthquakes of the same magnitude destroy buildings in some parts of the world, but not in others? Different localities have different regulations and building codes. Why do similar buildings within a city collapse, while others remain standing? The nature of the soil and rock material under some buildings can magnify vibrations. Buildings located on wet soil, loose sediment, and land-filled areas often experience more damage.

Activity

Earthquake Proofing Have students use wooden blocks to build structures on a table. Vibrate the table until the structure collapses. Have students devise methods of reinforcing their structures to withstand the vibrations. Test their new structures after they have been reinforced.

NATIONAL GEOGRAPHIC **VISUALIZING EARTHQUAKE PROOF BUILDINGS**

Figure 19

Because the most severe damage from an earthquake is not caused when a structure shakes, but when it falls down, engineers are developing ways to make buildings safer. Their job is to prevent the energy of an earthquake from damaging a building's structure.

What happens when the ground moves back and forth under a building? The first floor moves back and forth, but the energy is not transferred to the whole building. The result is that the bottom of the structure collapses.

One way to keep the building stable is to design a system that allows the whole structure to move as a unit. Base isolation systems use bearings that separate the building from the ground. These bearings can be made of large rubber pads or giant metal springs and are placed between the ground and the building support beams. The stretchy rubber or metal spring absorbs the earthquake energy.

Another way to protect buildings in an earthquake is active damping. Large blocks of metal or concrete, weighing many tons slide back and forth as the building sways. The pendulum motion of the damper absorbs the energy of the earthquake, and reduces the movement of the building.

Buildings also can be protected by using structures that can bend. These diagonal braces, called unbonded braces, are made of steel and concrete. The steel beam is shaped so that it can bend back and forth without breaking. The building moves but it does not collapse.

Differentiated Instruction

Challenge The gigantic steel ball, shown above in the third photograph, is called a tuned mass damper. It is situated on the 89th floor in the tallest building in the world—the Taipei 101 Building, in Taipei, Taiwan. Have students research this object to discover how it is intended to avert or mitigate earthquake damage. Students can share their discoveries with the class by preparing demonstration models or posters and performing a class presentation.

Levels of Destruction The level of destruction by earthquakes is extremely variable. Research has shown that poor building methods are the largest contributors to earthquake damage and loss of life. In countries where there are poorly constructed buildings, it is not uncommon for tens of thousands of people to die in a single earthquake event. It is possible to use high-technology building methods to make structures earthquake resistant, but not earthquake proof. A large proportion of earthquake damage is secondary, such as damage by landslides, fires, and tsunamis. Active earthquake zones are well established, but predicting precise times for earthquakes in those zones is not yet possible.

Earthquake Proofing Although no building can be made entirely earthquake proof, scientists and engineers are finding ways to reduce the damage to structures during mild or moderate earthquakes. Much damage occurs when older structures are shaken off their foundations, so securing a building to its foundation is important. Large masses that can move with the earthquake absorb energy to make a building more secure. **Figure 19** shows some other possible methods for reducing the effects of earthquakes and making buildings safer.

section 2 review

Summary

Global Earthquake Distribution

- The majority of earthquakes occur at varying depths, and in zones that define the locations of plate boundaries.

Causes of Earthquakes

- Earthquake waves are the result of elastic rebound in faults.

Earthquake Waves

- Body waves move throughout Earth.
- Surface waves move along Earth's surface. Their motions cause the majority of earthquake damage.

Earthquake Measurement

- The Modified Mercalli scale is a subjective damage scale that indicates earthquake intensity.
- The Richter magnitude scale measures amplitudes of waves generated by an earthquake. Energy released by an earthquake are estimated from amplitude data.

Self Check

1. **Describe** the elastic rebound process.
2. **Contrast** primary and secondary seismic waves.
3. **Compare and contrast** the Richter scale with the Mercalli scale.
4. **Summarize** the patterns of global earthquake distribution.
5. **Think Critically** Why couldn't you use the Mercalli scale to measure an undersea earthquake?

Applying Math

6. **Calculate** If a primary earthquake wave travels at a rate of about 6 km/s through continental crust, how long will it take it to reach a seismic station located 1,200 km away?
7. **Calculate** If the secondary wave travels at 10 km/s to the same station in question 6, how much longer will it take for the secondary wave to arrive after the primary wave?

More Section Review gpescience.com

Post Reading

Extended Research Have students research a particular earthquake. Ask them to develop a poster or paper that describes the fault movement, wave generation, and effects of the quake. Students can present their poster to the class.

3 Assess

DAILY INTERVENTION

Check for Understanding

Auditory-Musical Because earthquake waves and sound waves have different frequencies, have students write lyrics and an appropriate rhythm pattern for different-frequency P and S waves. Sound does not produce S waves except in solids. L2 ELL

Reteach

Mold a block of plasticene into a rectangle about 3 cm thick. Demonstrate plastic deformation by steadily pulling the block apart. Then demonstrate brittle deformation by quickly pulling the block apart. It should snap apart. Compare how much of the block is deformed in both instances. L1 ELL **Visual-Spatial**

Assessment

Create Have each student prepare a quiz-show answer for the category Earthquakes. Critique each answer and save the best for a game at the end of the chapter. L2 PBL

section 2 review

1. Stress builds up along a fault. When the rock can no longer resist the stress, rock on either side of the fault snaps to a new position, releasing energy.
2. Primary waves are waves of compression, have high velocities, and cause matter to move in the direction of wave motion. They can travel through all matter. Secondary waves are waves of translation, have low velocities, and cause matter to move at right angles to the direction of wave motion. They can only travel through solid matter.
3. difference in arrival time of primary and secondary waves, velocity graph for both P and S waves, and location of at least three cities that have a record of the earthquake
4. Most earthquakes occur at plate margins.
5. The time difference between P- and S- wave arrival at the epicenter allows for calculation of focus depth. San Andreas Fault is a transform fault and foci are usually shallow.
6. 200 seconds or 3.33 minutes
7. 80 seconds or 1.33 minutes

section 3 Earth's Interior

1 Motivate

An editable Microsoft® PowerPoint® presentation is available on **Interactive Chalkboard** CD-ROM.

Bellringer

Section Focus Transparencies also are available on the Interactive Chalkboard CD-ROM. L2 ELL

Section 3 Section Focus Transparency — A Hollow Earth? — Chapter 12

The French author Jules Verne wrote one of the greatest science fiction books of all time called A Journey to the Center of the Earth. In the book, the professor does indeed find the entrance to the hollow Earth. The professor and his companions walk on the underside of Earth's crust and gaze at the inner Earth's sun. They sail the inner sea, traverse immense dense forests, and even encounter beings much like ourselves.

1. Do you believe Earth could be hollow?
2. How could living beings survive inside a hollow Earth?
3. Does modern science disprove the possibility that Earth is hollow? How?

L2

Earth's Internal Processes

Reading Preview

Tie to Prior Knowledge

Density Given three liquids of different densities, the densest will move through the other two due to gravity. The liquid of lightest density will float on the liquid of middle density. L2

Context Clues Have students scan the text for new vocabulary terms. Ask them to read the sentence containing the word. From the context of the sentence, students should predict word meaning. Have them write the definitions in their own words and share with the class. Chart words and meanings to assess understanding.

Reading Guide

What You'll Learn

- **Explain** how geologists infer the structure of Earth's deep interior.
- **Describe** Earth's internal structure and composition.

Why It's Important

Using waves to indirectly determine the internal structure of an object has many applications in the sciences and engineering.

Review Vocabulary

refraction: the bending of a wave as it changes speed in moving from one medium to another

New Vocabulary

- discontinuity
- shadow zone
- asthenosphere

What's inside?

How is it possible to know anything about the interior of Earth? In 1961 scientists drilled a 200 m deep hole into the oceanic crust trying to reach the Mohorovicic discontinuity. The project was discontinued after Phase I. It is 6,371 km to the center of Earth. By human standards, this attempt was barely a scratch on Earth's surface. Imagine adding this feature to the diagram in **Figure 20.**

Seismologists, geologists who use seismic earthquake waves to interpret characteristics of Earth, conceived of the idea to use these waves to gather data. It is similar to a doctor using sound waves to see inside a human body. As energy passes through matter it is scattered, absorbed, or unaffected. Observation of seismic waves allows scientists to infer images of Earth's interior.

Figure 20 Also known as the Moho layer, the red line below was the target of the 1961 Mohole Project.
Infer *why they attempted to drill through oceanic crust instead of continental crust.*

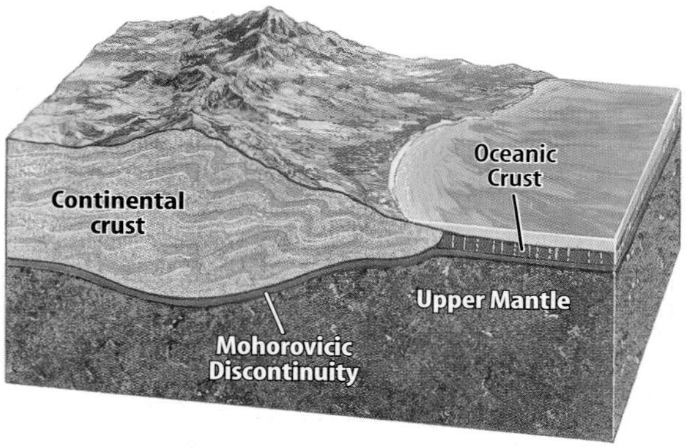

Uniform Earth? If Earth was uniform in structure and composition, and you knew how fast earthquake waves traveled through its material, then it would be easy to calculate when earthquake waves should be detected on its opposite side. Observations show that seismic waves arrive at different times than expected. In order for seismic waves to change speed, Earth must not be uniform throughout. If Earth is not uniform, then is there a pattern to its interior structure?

Section 3 Resource Manager

Chapter *Fast File* Resources

Transparency Activity, p. 46
Enrichment, p. 31
Reinforcement, p. 27
Directed Reading for Content Overview, p. 19
Lab Management and Safety, p. 70

Earthquake Observations

As seismic wave recording stations began to spread over Earth, new discoveries were made as seismic wave data from earthquakes were interpreted. Observations of refracted waves show that the waves do indeed bend as they encounter sharp changes in density. A boundary that marks a density change between layers is called a **discontinuity.** One such discontinuity separates the crust from uppermost mantle, and is known as the Mohorovicic (moh huh ROH vee chihch) discontinuity, or Moho, illustrated in **Figure 20.**

Shadow Zones Observations show that, from a given epicenter, P-waves and S-waves travel through Earth for 105 degrees of arc in all directions. Between 105 and 140 degrees from the epicenter, nothing is recorded. This "dead zone" is termed the **shadow zone.** From 140 degrees to 180 degrees (directly opposite the epicenter), only P-waves are recorded.

Shadow zones reveal two interesting facts about Earth's interior. Because S-waves seem not to appear on seismographs located beyond 105 degrees from an epicenter, scientists think that there is a layer of Earth that is absorbing them. In fact, these waves are thought to be converted to P-like waves in the outer core. Recall that S-waves only travel through solids. This suggests that the outer core is in a liquid state. See **Figure 21.**

If you move an energy source all around an object, you would eventually be able to compile many different views and describe the three-dimensional shape of the object. This process is called tomography and is the way Magnetic Resonance Imaging (MRI) can show doctors the inside images of the human body. With earthquakes happening all over the globe, seismologists have thousands of point sources of energy, and can construct a tomographic view of the core.

Solid Inner Core The fact that P-waves pass through the core, but are refracted along the way, indicates that the inner core is denser than the outer core and solid. The state of a particular material depends on both pressure caused by the weight of overlying material and temperature. When pressure dominates, atoms are squeezed together tightly and exist in the solid state. If temperatures are high enough, atoms move apart enough to exist in the liquid state, even at extreme pressures.

Figure 21 S-waves only travel through solids so they cannot penetrate the liquid outer core, creating shadow zones.

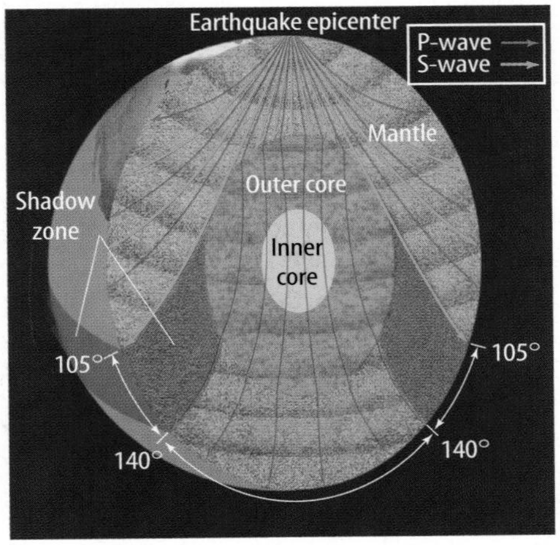

2 Teach

Text Question Answer
Yes, Earth appears to have a layered structure.

Caption Answer
Figure 20 Oceanic crust is thinner.

Quick Demo
Earth's Layers

Materials clay, clear straw, plastic knife

Estimated Time 15 minutes

Procedure Construct a 20-cm model of Earth using concentric layers of clay. Use a clear straw to drill into the sphere and extract a core that shows layering. Slice a wedge out of model to show layering. Ask students if this is how we know that the Earth has a layered structure. Possible answers: No, earthquake wave patterns are used to infer layered structure Drilling and mining don't go deep enough. L2 ELL IN **Visual-Spatial**

Discussion
Seeing Earth's Layer's Ask students what methods, other than drilling and mining, might be used to visualize Earth's interior. Possible Answers: X-rays, lasers, or ultrasound (won't penetrate rock), sonar or radar (reflected). Low frequency waves from blasts or natural earthquake waves will penetrate and refract or reflect to reveal interior. L2

Activity
Calculate Use your school's football field to model a cross section of Earth. Have one goal line be the center of Earth and one be the surface of Earth. Have students calculate on what yard line the inner core would end, outer core, etc. Have students stand on these boundaries. center = goal line; inner core = 19.2 yards; outer core = 54.5 yards; lower mantle = 89.5 yards; asthenosphere = 96.9 to 98.5 yards; upper mantle = 99.6 yards; surface = 100 yards L2 ELL IN **Logical-Mathmatical**

Reading Strategy
Question a Partner Before reading, ask students to develop questions based these topics: shadow zones, Earth's interior structure, and the composition of Earth's layers. After reading, have students work in pairs to ask and answer questions.

Differentiated Instruction
Learning Disabled Have these students be the field crew for the football field Earth activity in this Section. Have them count off the yards and place the markers. Colored flags might be used to represent the boundary of each layer. For example: white = center; light yellow = inner core; goldenrod = outer core; tan = lower mantle; red = asthenosphere; orange = upper mantle; brown = surface

Post Reading

Science Journal Ask students to write a response to the following prompt: What do scientists know about Earth's interior? How do they know this? Have students share their thoughts with a partner or with the class.

Visual Learning

Figure 22 Display cross-sectional drawings of all nine planets in our solar system. Remove any identifying labels. Ask students to identify Earth and explain their choice. Ask what all the planets seem to have in common. Then refer students to the figure to confirm their selection. Be prepared to give clues about Earth's layer composition. All the planets are alike in that their layers increase in density toward the center. L2

3 Assess

DAILY INTERVENTION

Check for Understanding

Visual-Spatial Have students identify the various layers of Earth's interior, their compositions, and states of matter. Ask how we know the thickness and the state of matter of these layers. L2

Reteach

Seismic Wave Movement Using **Figure 24,** discuss the relationship between P and S waves and their movement through Earth. Point out the liquid layers and explain that S waves do not travel through the outer core. L1 ELL

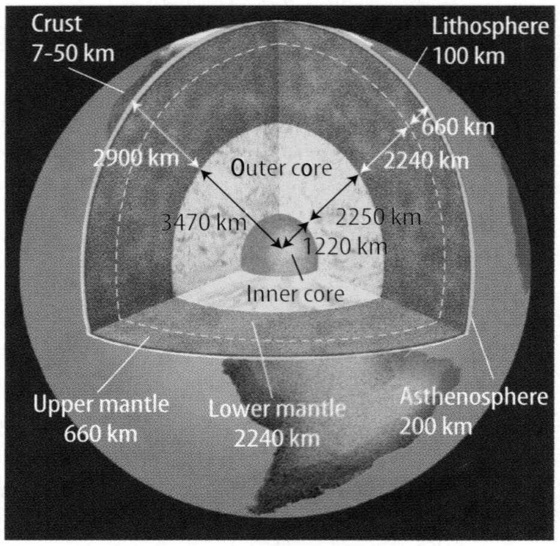

Figure 22 Layering of Earth is caused by heat and pressure. The most dense materials are at the center and the less dense materials are near the crust.

Composition of Earth's Layers

Earth's internal layers, illustrated in **Figure 22,** generally become denser with depth. The crust and uppermost mantle, which together form the lithosphere, are made of rocky material—mostly silicates. The **asthenosphere** is a weaker, plasticlike layer upon which Earth's lithospheric plates move. Much like the lithosphere, mantle below the asthenosphere also is composed of silicates, but the minerals present have different structures in response to conditions of higher pressure. The cores are made mostly of metallic material, such as iron and nickel with noticeable amounts of oxygen and sulfur also present. The core apparently has a composition similar to some iron meteorites that have struck Earth throughout its history.

Astronomers hypothesize that early Earth may have formed from meteorite-like material that was forced together by gravity and heated to melting. Some of the material then was able to migrate toward the core. Over billions of years, Earth's matter has melted and differentiated. The densest materials settled toward the core, and relatively low-density materials floated toward the surface. This differentiation due to gravity is thought to have taken place in all of the planets.

section 3 review

Summary

What's inside?

- Earthquake-generated seismic waves provide information about Earth's deep interior.

Earthquake Observations

- Earth's interior has a layered structure.
- Earth's layers become denser with depth.
- Changes in density occur at layer boundaries called discontinuities.

Composition of Earth's Layers

- Layers of crust and mantle are rocky, and composed mainly of silicates.
- The cores have a high density, metallic composition.
- Composition of Earth closely resembles the composition of meteorites.

Self Check

1. **Describe** the evidence used for subdividing Earth's interior into layers.
2. **Explain** the following points, using seismic evidence for your argument:
   a. Earth has a non-uniform density.
   b. Earth has a layered structure.
   c. Earth has a liquid outer core.
3. **Compare and contrast** the inner and outer cores of Earth.
4. **Think Critically** Explain why it is impossible to ever really know what materials compose Earth's interior.

Applying Math

5. **Calculate** What percent of the mantle are the upper mantle, lower mantle, and the asthenosphere?

More Section Review gpescience.com

section 3 review

1. refraction of P and S waves; seismic waves arriving at different times; and absorption of S waves
2. a. Seismic waves arrive sooner than expected if all of Earth had a density equal to the crust, the conclusion is that density must increase toward the core.
   b. Seismic waves arrive sooner and arrive in a path that suggests they have been refracted, creation of a shadow zone.
   c. S-waves fail to arrive on opposite side of Earth; creation of P & S shadow zone.
3. Both have a metallic composition; outer core is liquid, inner core is solid.
4. It is impossible to extract actual samples.
5. Upper mantle 21%
   Lower mantle 72%
   Asthenosphere 7%

Assessment

Create Have each student prepare a quiz-show answer about Earth's interior. Critique answers and save the best for a game at the end of the chapter.

section 4

Volcanoes

Reading Guide

What You'll Learn
- **Describe** the types and causes of different types of volcanic eruptions.
- **Explain** the pattern of occurrence of volcanoes and its link to plate tectonics.

Why It's Important
Volcanic eruptions have an impact on the composition of the atmosphere and on climate.

Review Vocabulary
melting point: temperature at which a solid begins to liquefy

New Vocabulary
- viscosity
- cinder cone volcano
- shield volcano
- composite volcano

Origin of Magma

Recall that faults are weaknesses in Earth's crust along which movement takes place. This movement results in a local decrease in pressure, called decompression. With less pressure, the melting point of rock material decreases, but the temperature can remain the same. Hot, nearly molten rock in Earth's asthenosphere, considered an important source for molten rock material, can change to a liquid by decompression melting. Rising magma can become more fluid as it decompresses, particularly if its gas content is high.

Any molten rock material has a lower density than that of its solid counterpart. Because of this density difference, a buoyant force acts on magma that forms from rock surrounding it. Rising magma may reach Earth's surface if pressure conditions allow and the rock has conduits through which it can flow.

Imagine hot magma rising through the crust, creating brittle deformation near the surface in the form of fractures or faults. The cracks in turn cause a drop in pressure, and more paths are available through which magma can move toward the surface, as shown in **Figure 23.** This causes more deformation until magma reaches Earth's surface as a volcanic eruption.

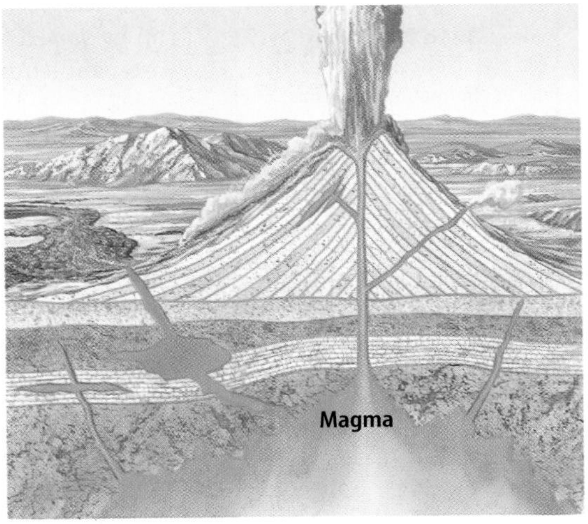

Figure 23 Less dense, liquid rock rises to the surface through cracks and fissures creating a volcano.

Section 4 Resource Manager

Chapter *FAST FILE* Resources
- Transparency Activity, p. 47
- MiniLAB, p. 4
- Enrichment, p. 32
- Reinforcement, p. 28
- Directed Reading for Content Overview, pp. 19–20
- Lab Worksheets, pp. 5–6, 7–9

Earth Science Critical Thinking/Problem Solving p. 1

Reading and Writing Skills Activities, pp. 14–15

1 Motivate

INTERACTIVE CHALKBOARD An editable Microsoft® PowerPoint® presentation is available on **Interactive Chalkboard** CD-ROM.

Bellringer

Section Focus Transparencies also are available on the Interactive Chalkboard CD-ROM. L2 ELL

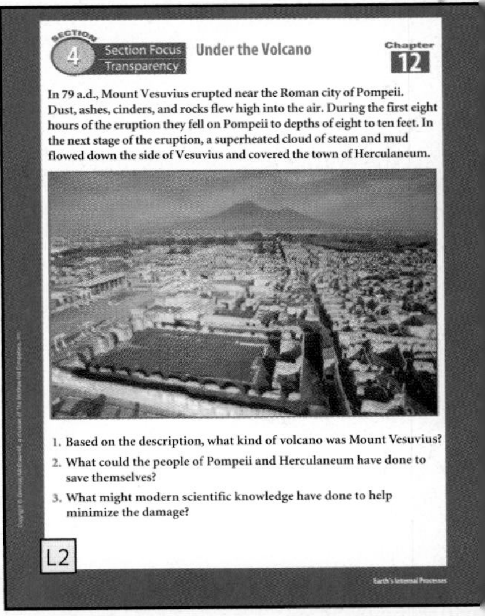

Section 4 Section Focus Transparency **Under the Volcano** Chapter 12

In 79 a.d., Mount Vesuvius erupted near the Roman city of Pompeii. Dust, ashes, cinders, and rocks flew high into the air. During the first eight hours of the eruption they fell on Pompeii to depths of eight to ten feet. In the next stage of the eruption, a superheated cloud of steam and mud flowed down the side of Vesuvius and covered the town of Herculaneum.

1. Based on the description, what kind of volcano was Mount Vesuvius?
2. What could the people of Pompeii and Herculaneum have done to save themselves?
3. What might modern scientific knowledge have done to help minimize the damage?

L2

Earth's Internal Processes

Reading Preview

Tie to Prior Knowledge

Melting/Freezing Point Most materials have a temperature above which they exist in nature as a liquid; and below it as a solid. L2

Word Associations Have students scan the text to find images and ideas that are associated with the new vocabulary terms. For example, while thinking of the word *viscosity*, students might consider the analogy of cold and warm flowing syrup. Using either phrases or sketches, students should record word associations.

2 Teach

Quick Demo
Dissolved Gases

Materials tap water, carbonated water, mixture of tap and carbonated water, clear bottles with lids (3)

Estimated Time 15 minutes

Procedure Provide students with the three solutions in clear, capped plastic bottles. Shake each bottle vigorously, uncap, and observe the reactions.

Ask them to estimate the amount of dissolved gas in each container. Ask how this would relate to a volcanic eruption. The tap water is like magma that has little dissolved gas and is a quiet eruption; the mixture is like a lava that is not very thick, has some dissolved gas and is somewhat explosive; the carbonated water is like thick lava that has a lot of dissolved gas and is explosive. L2

ELL IN **Visual-Spatial**

Teacher FYI

Gas Composition Magmatic gases are usually composed of water vapor or carbon dioxide. Smoke seen coming from erupting volcanoes is usually a mix of volcanic ash and condensed water vapor.

Figure 24 Volcanoes are common in subduction zones. Friction, conduction, and convection may all play a role in creating fissures through which a volcano may erupt.

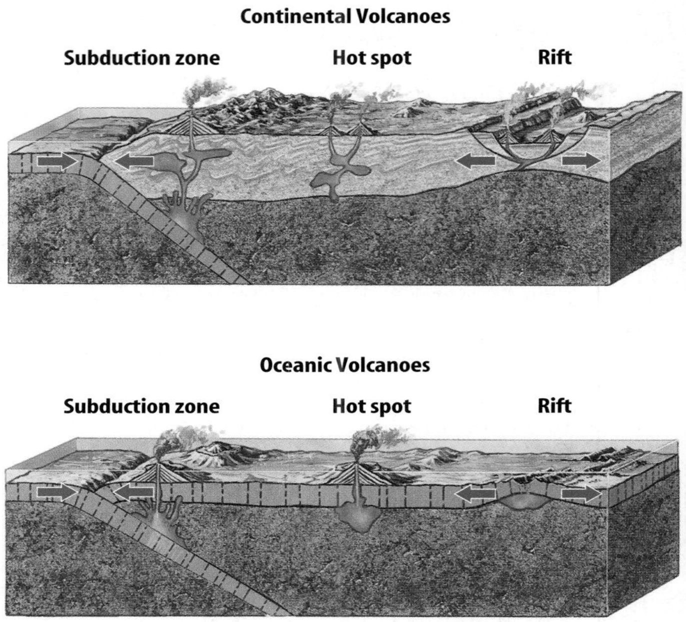

Magma on the Surface Two major physical settings on Earth produce most lava flows at the surface. Eruptions most commonly are found near boundaries that separate tectonic plates, above mantle plumes or hot spots on continents or in the ocean basins. **Figure 24** illustrates these volcanic settings.

Eruptive Products

Volcanoes expel a wide variety of materials. These materials can be sorted first by their state of matter. Volcanoes erupt lava, gases, and chunks of solid material.

Solids All solid materials expelled by a volcano are collectively called pyroclasts. Often, lava is ejected into the air as globules. These globules cool and solidify as they fall to Earth. The smallest particles cool very quickly and form volcanic ash. Larger globules form streamlined, volcanic bombs. In addition to chunks that cool as they fall, there often are chunks of already solid material ripped away from the conduit of the volcano as material travels through it. These chunks of rock are termed volcanic blocks. The larger the size of a pyroclastic particle, the closer it will fall to the volcano. Blocks fall back to ground on a volcano's flanks. Ash can be picked up by wind and blown hundreds or even thousands of kilometers away.

Science Online

Topic: Huge Eruptions
Visit gpescience.com for Web links to information about the world's most powerful volcanic eruptions.

Activity In your Science Journal, list information, including dates and locations, of ten of the world's most powerful volcanic eruptions. On a copy of a world map, plot the locations of these events. Is there a pattern to their occurrence in place or in time?

Science Journal

Internal Activity Have students keep a current events page for all of the volcanic and earthquake activity that takes place worldwide during the time you spend on the chapter. Encourage them to look for government internet sources that report daily Earth activity. L2 P

374 CHAPTER 12 Earth's Internal Processes

Gases Volcanoes release a broad variety of superheated gases, the most common of which is water vapor. In addition carbon dioxide and gases composed of sulfur compounds are expelled high into the atmosphere. There is strong evidence that volcanoes are major contributors of greenhouse gases that can affect climate long after an eruption is over.

Liquids Magma from a volcano or fissure may remain a liquid, at least initially, and flow across the Earth's surface as lava. Lavas can vary considerably in composition, which in turn affects their physical properties.

Viscosity is a measure of the resistance of a fluid to flow. The temperature of molten rock material influences its viscosity. You have experience with temperature control on viscosity when you try to pour cold pancake syrup. It has a high viscosity when it first comes out of the refrigerator. But, let it warm up and it flows more easily because its viscosity decreases. Other factors that affect viscosity and flow are gas content and composition.

Low-viscosity lavas are generally basaltic in composition. Basaltic lavas are low in silica (SiO_2) content, and high in certain chemical elements such as calcium, magnesium, and iron. Basaltic lavas flow from fissures—such as along the MOR and zones of continental rifting, and also from hot spot volcanoes. They tend to flow easily and form huge volcanic forms such as shield volcanoes and flood basalts, both of which cover large areas on Earth's surface.

If lavas have large quantities of gas dissolved in them, then the viscosity is lowered. High gas quantities allow magma to forcefully migrate through rock, sometimes spewing out explosively as a lava fountain that behaves much like a geyser!

Eruptive Styles

Volcanoes can erupt in many different ways, depending on viscosity. Thick, sticky, high-silica magmas are so viscous that they tend not to erupt, causing internal pressure within a volcano to rise. When Earth's crust fails under such high pressure conditions, a violently explosive eruption occurs. This style of eruption is characterized by abundant pyroclasts. In contrast, the runny, low-silica, high-temperature basaltic lavas are so low in viscosity that they erupt quite easily and often produce quiet eruptions of freely flowing lava. Eruptive style is strongly linked to temperature and composition, factors that are hard to measure until after an eruption. Temperature and composition of a magma that ultimately erupts as lava can be linked to the type of plate boundary associated with it.

Mini LAB

Modeling Lava Viscosity

Procedure

1. Mix a small batch of batter from **pancake mix** according to directions.
2. Mix a second small batch, but use 25% more **milk.**
3. Hold your finger under a **small funnel** and fill the funnel with the first batch of batter.
4. Have a partner hold a **watch with a second hand.** Remove your finger and time how long it takes the funnel to empty. Record your data.
5. Clean the funnel and repeat step 4 using the second batch of batter.
6. Gently heat a **small pan** on a **hot plate.**
7. Pour part of the first batch of batter on the pan and observe.
8. Repeat step 7 using the second batch of batter.

Analysis

1. Which batter made the flattest pancakes? Explain why.
2. Compare and contrast the properties of the batters.
3. Which batter modeled low-silica lava?

Try at Home

Mini LAB

Video Lab available.

Purpose Students will model viscosity.

Materials pancake mix, water, spoon or whisk, plastic spatula, plastic measuring cup with pouring lip, small funnel, watch with second hand, non-stick pan, hot plate, oil (optional)

Teaching Strategies Stress careful measurement so that batters have noticeably different textures.

Safety Precautions

Analysis

1. 25% more water; has a lower viscosity
2. both have similar ingredients; one has more water and is runnier
3. the runny batter is more like low-silica (basaltic) lava

Assessment

Oral Ask students to give other examples of viscosity differences. road tar or syrup at different temperatures; flour or corn starch added to foods as a thickener L2

Try at Home

Discussion

Additional Dangers Have students list the ancillary events that might occur during and after a volcanic eruption. earthquakes, collapsed structures from weight of ash, thunderstorms, forest fires; if volcanoes are ice-capped, then flooding, and mudflows L3

Caption Answer

Figure 26 Pinatubo, Fujiyama, Mt. St. Helens, Paricutin

Activity

Identify Display a variety of rocks, some of which are volcanic (extrusive igneous rocks). Ask the students to select those that are volcanic and justify their choices. Recall volcanic rock may have gas bubble holes (vesicular), will be fine grained or glassy. L2 ELL IS **Visual-Spatial**

Reading Strategy

Discussion Groups Form groups of three or four students. Assign a facilitator and recorder in each group. Ask students to hold a discussion using the following questions as prompts: Where does magna form and how does it move to the surface? What happens during a volcanic eruption? Where are volcanoes commonly found?

Figure 25 Many volcanoes occur on Earth along plate boundaries, over hot spots, or in rift valleys.

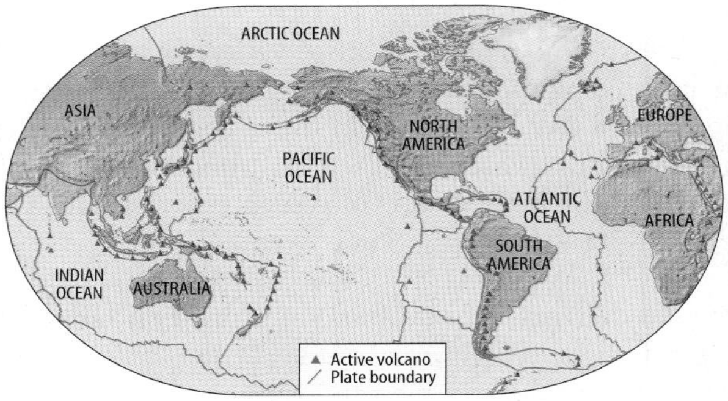

Plate Boundary Setting Look at **Figure 25.** Most of Earth's volcanoes are located along the Ring of Fire, which rims the Pacific Ocean. They lie in subduction zones where continental and oceanic materials are being mixed and partially melted. This plate motion and the associated melting create a wide variety of magma types that can potentially erupt. Large earthquakes and violent volcanic eruptions often are located along these ocean-continent and ocean-ocean convergent boundaries.

Divergent plate boundaries also are volcanically active, but most of the activity is underwater, along the MOR, and goes unnoticed by most people. There are places were divergence takes place on land and you could witness its associated volcanic activity. Iceland and the East African Rift Valley are examples of land areas that are part of divergent boundaries. Lava erupted in these settings is generally low-viscosity and basaltic in composition.

Hot Spots Hot spots are volcanically active sites that arise in places where large quantities of magma move to the surface in large, column-like plumes. Scientists think that plumes are positioned according to internal convection patterns within the mantle, and some may originate at the core-mantle boundary. It seems that hot spots do not move much, but the plates move over them. When a hot spot occurs under an oceanic plate, this stable source of hot magma forms volcanic island chains. The Hawaiian islands are such a chain. Yellowstone National Park is an example of a hot spot under a continental plate. When a volcano moves off the hot spot it becomes inactive.

Hot spot volcanic eruptions produce lava somewhat similar to that formed along divergent boundaries, but they are not an exact match. These lavas tend to contain greater abundances of alkali metals such as potassium and sodium. Like MOR lavas, hot spots, which can occur far from a plate boundary, tend to generate fluid, basaltic lavas. But their compositions can change as magmas penetrate rock material of changing composition, like in continental crust.

Science Online

Topic: Mt. Pinatubo

Visit gpescience.com for Web links to information the 1991 eruption of Mt. Pinatubo in the Philippines.

Activity Construct a time line for this eruption. Begin with precursors, which are events that indicate volcanic activity is imminent, and end with long-term effects after the eruption.

LAB DEMONSTRATION

Purpose Demonstrate the effect of silica content on lava viscocity

Materials 250-mL beaker, graduated cylinder, stirring rod, table salt, liquid hand soap

Procedure Pour 120 mL of hand soap into a 250-mL beaker. Stir the liquid with a stirring rod. Describe the viscocity. Add 30 g of NaCl (table salt) to the liquid. Stir well. Describe what happens. Repeat the procedure three more times by adding 30 g of NaCl, stirring, and observing. Describe what happens.

Expected Outcome The liquid will become thicker with each addition of the salt.

Assessment

Ask the students what the liquid and the salt represent in terms of volcanoes. What is the relationship between the salt and soap and lava and silica? The soap represents lava and the salt represents silica. Just as the salt thickens the soap, silica thickens lava. L2

Types of Volcanoes

Volcanoes are classified according to their size, shape, and the materials that compose them. Recall that eruptive materials that form a volcano are related to the physical properties of its magma source. The temperature, composition, and gas content of magma are important controls on the type of volcanic structure that forms during an eruption. **Table 3** summarizes the characteristics of main types of volcanoes.

Cinder Cone Volcanoes When eruption of gas-rich magma takes place, eruptive products often are spewed into the air explosively as large chunks. These large pyroclastic materials may pile up near the exit hole, or vent. When the primary eruptive products are large fragments of solid material, **cinder cone volcanoes** form. They tend to be small, with most cones having heights in the hundreds of meters range. When cinder cones occur on the flanks of larger volcanoes, they are called parasitic cones. An example of a volcano with parasitic cones is Mount Kilimanjaro in the African rift valley.

Reading Check *What are the characteristics of cinder cones?*

Shield Volcanoes Because they form from high-temperature, fluid, basaltic lava, **shield volcanoes** erupt with abundant lava flows that can move for kilometers over Earth's surface before stopping. Shield volcanoes are broad, flat structures made up of layer upon layer of lava. Think of pancake batter. If the batter is cold or thick, it piles up and you get thick pancakes. Add more milk and make a runny batter, and it flows easily across the skillet and makes thin pancakes. Volcanism in Hawaii produces shield volcanoes.

INTEGRATE History

Volcano Eruptions
Volcanic eruptions can throw tons of ash into the atmosphere where winds carry the ash around the world. The ash blocks sunlight and affects plant growth. Scientists measure fossilized tree rings to infer the affect ancient volcanoes had on Earth. Research the amount of ash produced by Mount Pinatubo and how quickly it circled the globe.

Table 3 Comparison of Melt Properties

Composition	Silica Content	Gas Content	Viscosity	Volcano Type
Basaltic	lowest	least (1-2%)	lowest	shield, fissure eruptions (such as MOR)
Andesitic	intermediate	intermediate (3-4%)	intermediate	composite
Rhyolitic	highest	highest (4-6%)	highest	volcanic dome

Reading Check

Answer small, made up of cinders and pyroclastic materials, heights in the hundreds of meters range

Post Reading

Create a Chart Have students develop a chart to describe characteristics of volcano types, including cinder cones, sheild volcanoes and composite volcanoes. Remind them to include information regarding magma composition, shape of the volcano, and locations around the world.

Differentiated Instruction

Learning Disabled Have students use modeling clay to make and label models of the three principle forms of volcanoes. Help them to recognize the relationship between the height and width ratios and overall size. L1 ELL IS **Visual-Spatial**

Curriculum Connection

Geography The spatial content of this chapter can be summarized on a world map with earthquake zones, volcanic zones, and plate tectonic boundaries plotted on it. Decide how much data to provide on the map and how much is to be added by the students. Once the map is completed have students use a world atlas to identify countries with particular connection to these geologically hazardous zones. L2 ELL IS **Visual-Spatial**

Visual Learning

Figure 26 Display slides or photos of volcanoes. Ask students to compare these to the illustration and classify each one as to type. Most photos will be of composite volcanoes—Fuji, Kilimanjaro, Mt. St.Helens, etc. Cinder cones will be small and noticeably devoid of vegetation, and Hawaiian volcanoes are all shield volcanoes. L2 ELL LS **Visual-Spatial**

3 Assess

DAILY INTERVENTION

Check for Understanding

Visual-Spatial Use a world map with several major volcanoes plotted on it. Ask the students to identify the type of volcano and type of plate tectonic boundary associated with each point. Be sure to include Hawaii, which has an unusual plate tectonic connection. Also include islands found along the MOR as examples of divergent boundary volcanoes. L2 ELL

Reteach

Volcano Shape Lead a discussion in which students compare how fluid the lava is and the resulting volcano shape. L1 ELL

Assessment

Create Have each student prepare a quiz-show answer for the category Volcanoes. Critique each answer and save the best for a game at the end of the chapter. L2

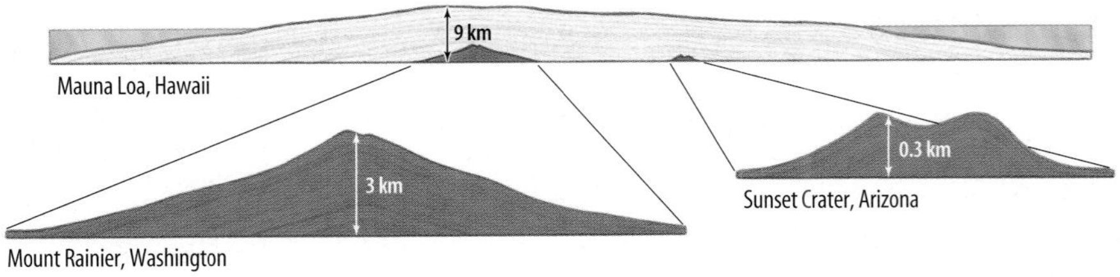

Figure 26 Shield volcanoes, like Mauna Loa, have created some of the largest mountains on Earth. Cinder cones, like Sunset Crater, are the smallest. Some of the famous volcanoes are the composites, like Mount Rainier.

Composite Volcanoes When volcanoes occur along convergent plate boundaries, they tend to have magmas that are richer in silica content than those formed at hot spots or divergent boundaries. This is because as subduction takes place, water and sediment are forced down to regions of higher temperature. Partial melting of materials, in which the silica-rich portion of rock and sediment melts first, produces viscous magma. This produces volcanoes formed from alternating explosive events that produce pyroclastic materials, and lava flows. These **composite volcanoes,** composed of alternating layers, are large, often thousands of meters high and tens of kilometers across the base. **Figure 26** shows all three types.

section 4 review

Summary

Origin of Magma

- Magma originates as molten rock material below the surface and erupts at Earth's surface as lava.
- When the density of magma is lower than surrounding solid rock, it is forced toward Earth's surface.

Eruptive Products

- Eruptive products can be solids, liquids, or gases.

Eruptive Styles

- The style of eruption, whether quiet or explosive, is related to its plate tectonic setting.

Types of Volcanoes

- Cinder cones are small, but they erupt violently.
- Shield volcanoes are very large and mostly expel free-flowing lava quietly.
- Composite volcanoes are large and tend to erupt violently.

Self Check

1. **Explain** why most volcanoes are found at plate boundaries.
2. **Compare and contrast** the physical settings for composite volcanoes, cinder cones, and shield volcanoes.
3. **Describe** causes for variation in eruptive style for volcanoes.
4. **Explain** how magma that originates at depth can erupt as lava at the surface.
5. **Describe** how island chains form over a hot spot.
6. **Think Critically** List some possible consequences if volcanic activity on Earth were to slow down or stop.

Applying Math

7. If a cinder cone is 540 m high and has a base diameter of 3 km, what is the volume of the volcanic cone in cubic meters? Use the formula $V_{cone} = (r^2 h \pi)/3$.
8. The dome in the caldera of the volcano has a height of 12 meters and a diameter of 50 m. What is its volume?

More Section Review gpescience.com

section 4 review

1. Plate boundaries contain numerous faults along which decompression melting occurs. The fractured crust here allows magma to reach the surface easily.
2. All are landforms created by eruption of magma; cinder cones are small and composed mostly of pyroclastics; composite volcanoes are intermediate in size and composed of layers of pyroclastics and lava flows; shield volcanoes are largest and composed mostly of lava flows.
3. Eruptive style is controlled by silica (quartz) content, gas content, and temperature.
4. Molten rock material has a lower density than the solid rock around it so it is forced upwards.
5. The hot spot remains at a fixed location in the mantle while the overlying plate passes over it. Magma erupts through the plate at new locations forming a chain.
6. Slowing of volcanic activity might cause changes in atmospheric composition; volcanic mountains in divergent zones to stop growing; volcanic mountains in convergent zones to stop growing.
7. 1.27×10^9 m^3
8. 7,850 m^3

378 CHAPTER 12 Earth's Internal Processes

LAB

A Case for Pacific Plate Motion

To measure motion you have to have a starting and an ending point. You must also know the time it took to get from start to end. Volcanic activity associated with a hot spot beneath Hawaii gives geologists exactly that.

Real-World Problem

How can scientists show that Earth's plates are moving?

Goal

- **Infer** a rate of movement for the Hawaiian Islands over a hot spot

Materials

ruler
calculator
scale map of the Hawaiian Islands

Procedure

1. Make a data table like the one shown below.
2. **Measure and record** the distances between the island sets in the data table. Use the map scale to convert measurements to km.
3. Refer to average ages given for each island on the map. Calculate and record the age differences for each set of islands in the data table. Use the hot spot beneath the island of Hawaii as a starting reference point.
4. **Calculate** the rate of motion in km/year. Assume that the hot spot is stationary and that the Pacific plate is moving over it.

Distance/Time Data for Hawaiian Islands

From/To	Distance (km)	Time (years)	Rate (km/year)
Hawaii to Maui	161		
Maui to Molokai			
Molokai to Oahu			
Oahu to Kauai			

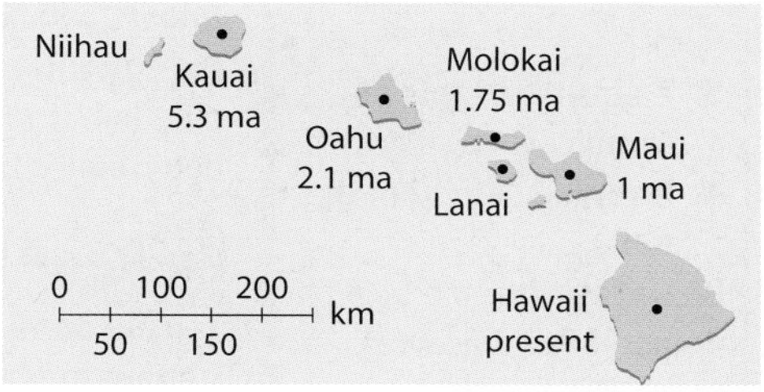

Conclude and Apply

1. **Evaluate** how meaningful your calculated rate numbers are. Determine a better rate unit and convert your km/year rates to these new units.
2. **Infer** why the rates are not consistent using what you know about plate movement.
3. **Describe** the overall motion of the Pacific Plate based on your data.
4. **Observe** a map of the Pacific Ocean and infer the location of a divergent zone that could be "pushing" the Pacific plate.

Communicating Your Data

Share your findings with the class and discuss alternative interpretations.

LAB 379

BENCH TESTED

Real-World Problem

Purpose Students will determine if scientists can prove that Earth's plates are moving.

Process Skills measure, infer, record, calculate

Time Required 40 minutes

Procedure

Teaching Strategy Students must measure very carefully between dots on each island.

From/To	Distance (km)	Time (years)	Rate (km/yr)
H-M	161	10^6	1.61×10^{-4}
M-M	80	7.5×10^5	1.06×10^{-4}
M-O	116	3.5×10^5	3.31×10^{-4}
O-K	186	3.2×10^6	5.8×10^{-5}

Conclude and Apply

1. The numbers are very small; use cm/yr; 16.1, 10.6, 33.1, 5.8
2. Plates move at different rates over time.
3. The Pacific plate appears to be moving WNW to NW at an average rate of 10.2 cm/yr.
4. East Pacific Rise

Communicating Your Data

Class discussion Select a plate and identify the ridge push and slab pull regions. Pacific Plate; push—East Pacific Rise, pull – Aleutian, Kuril, Japan Trenches.

Assessment

Process Using a world map showing plate boundaries, have students infer various directions of plate motion and the divergent zones assisting that motion. L2

ELL LS **Visual-Spatial**

BENCH TESTED

Real-World Problem

How do you determine the location of an earthquake epicenter?

Purpose Demonstrate the method used to locate earthquake epicenters.

Process Skills measure, make and use graphs, record, infer, interpret data

Time Required 70 minutes

Procedure

Teaching Strategies

- Do the lab in two stages. Check students' graphs for accuracy before they use them to find an epicenter.
- Caution students that it is the time difference between the curves that is used.
- Graph is non-standard in that time is a *y*-axis variable.

Table 3 Answers

Time Diff.	Distance to Epicenter	Distance On Map
3m 0 sec	1500 km	7.5 cm
7m 30 sec	2100 km	10.5 cm
2m 30 sec	1200 km	6.0 cm

LAB

Earthquake! Earthquake! Where's the earthquake?

Goals

- **Examine** a table of seismic wave velocities.
- **Analyze** data from the table.
- **Determine** the location of an epicenter.

Possible Materials

plain white paper
graph paper
compass
metric ruler

Safety Precaution

Understanding earthquakes begins with locating them. To determine the epicenter of an earthquake, scientists use a method called triangulation. If you know the locations of three points on a map, you can determine a fourth point **Diagram 1** shows how triangulation works.

Real-World Problem

You are on vacation in City A and experience an earthquake. The radio stations are broadcasting information about the earthquake. Your home is in City B. Is your home near the epicenter?

Procedure

1. Draw a 20-cm × 15-cm rectangle on a piece of plain white paper. Orient the rectangle so that the 20-cm edge is vertical. This rectangle will serve as your map.
2. Using a scale of 1 cm = 200 km, draw a distance scale just below the rectangle on the white paper. Place an arrow parallel to one of the 20-cm vertical edges and label it *North*.
3. Within the rectangle, place City A 400 km from the north edge and 400 km from the west edge. Locate City B 800 km from the north edge and 800 km from the east edge; and City C 1,200 km from the south edge and 1,200 km from the west edge of the rectangle. Your map will look similar to **Diagram 2.**
4. The earthquake happened at 08:37:00 PST. Copy and complete **Table A** on your own paper. Subtract the P-wave and S-wave arrival times to find the time differences for cities B and C. Use the travel time graph and the time differences to complete the last two columns.

Table A Earthquake Arrival Time Data for Cities A, B, and C

City	P-wave Arrival	S-wave Arrival	Time Difference (min/sec)	Distance to Epicenter	Distance on Map
A	08:40:00	08:43:00	3 min/0 sec		
B	08:41:15	08:45:00			
C	08:39:40	08:42:10			

Using Scientific Methods

5. **Estimate** the distance from each city from Table B below.
6. Use the Distance on Map measurement for City A to set the compass width, and then draw the distance circle around City A on your map. Your circle may go off the map, but don't worry. The epicenter is somewhere on the arc you can draw on the map. Repeat this process for City B and City C.

Table B Seismic Wave Arrival Times

Point	Time difference between P-waves and S-waves (min)	Distance (km) traveled by waves
M	1.3	500
O	2.2	1,000
P	3.6	2,000
Q	4.5	3,000
R	5.4	4,000

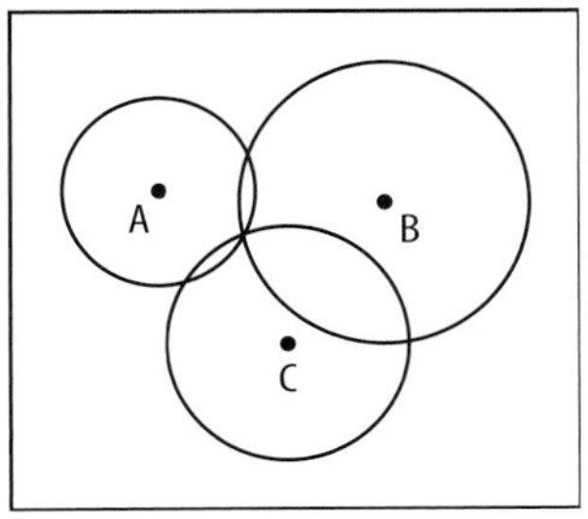

Diagram 1

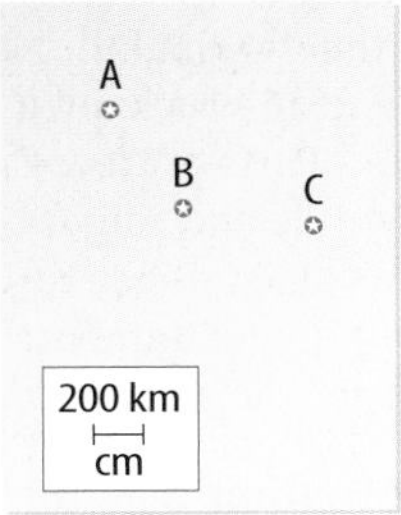

Diagram 2

Analyze Your Data

1. **Estimate** the time difference for P-waves and S-waves coming from 2,500 km.
2. **Estimate** the distance for a P-wave and S-wave pair that measure a time difference of 3.3 minutes.
3. **Determine** how much closer to the epicenter City A is than City B. City A received waves 3.0 minutes apart. City B received waves 4.2 minutes apart.

Conclude and Apply

1. **Explain** the relationship between body wave travel time differences and the distance to an earthquake epicenter.
2. **Evaluate** the potential danger to your home City B. How far is your city from the epicenter?
3. **Infer** the arrival time difference for S-waves and P-waves at or very close to the epicenter.
4. **List** the possible sources of error in the methods you used to determine an epicenter. How can you minimize errors?

Communicating Your Data

Describe the location of the epicenter in terms of distances from a reference point on your map. **Compare** your descriptions with others.

Analyze Your Data

Expected Outcome Slight variations in answers are expected due to plotting and estimation. Students should be able to explain that as seismic waves travel farther, the difference in arrival times between them increases.

Answers to Questions

1. 4.5 sec
2. 8.3 sec
3. 3,450-3,500 km

Error Analysis

Ask students to identify the sources of any errors in this procedure.

Conclude and Apply

1. distance to epicenter increases as time difference increases
2. 2,100 km; Because it is farther away, damage should be less than other cities. Damage is dependent on magnitude, which is not established by the graph.
3. arrival time difference should be near zero. There should be a slight difference due to the depth of the focus. If the epicenter and focus are at the surface, the answer is zero.
4. plotting, measuring, calculation; responses will vary.

Communicating Your Data

Have students use their data to deliver a newscast which informs the public of what effects the earthquake had.

Assessment

Process Show students seismic wave graphs with less slope or greater slope—flatter or more upright and ask what this implies about the seismic waves. flatter = faster; upright = slower L2 ELL LS **Visual-Spatial**

TIME

Content Background

Current theories are that the cooling effect of volcanoes is mostly due to aerosols—very small droplets—of sulfuric acid in the stratosphere. Stratospheric effects only occur during very large volcanic eruptions. Because it is so high in the atmosphere, the material is not quickly removed by rain. By reflecting and absorbing sunlight, these aerosols significantly reduce surface temperatures. A drop of several degrees has a major effect on growing season and crop productivity. In addition to less light and lower temperatures, the cooling causes more clouds and rainfall. Even a small change in average temperature can have a major effect on wind patterns.

Not all of the effects of volcanic eruptions are negative. In addition to ash and sulfuric acid, volcanoes bring up air and water from deep inside Earth. Much of the cloud above a volcano consists of steam. Some theories attribute the water of the oceans to ancient volcanic activity.

Historical Significance

Strothers' research demonstrates the value of historic records to current scientific research. In a paper published in 1999, he reported that the seven largest volcanoes of the last 2000 years were all followed by plague epidemics. This is a strong enough correlation to suggest a connection. Shortages of food and cold, wet weather tend to weaken disease resistance within a population. The cool and moist conditions are also favorable for the microorganisms that cause plague.

TIME **SCIENCE** AND HISTORY

SCIENCE CAN CHANGE THE COURSE OF HISTORY!

Volcano Weather

In 1815, people worldwide noticed unusually brightly colored sunsets. Then in 1816, the weather in many parts of the world was colder than normal. In North America and Europe, 1816 was known as "the year without a summer." Parts of New England had damaging frosts in July and August. The fantastic sunsets and the cold summer resulted from the massive eruption of Tambora, a volcano in Indonesia.

Giant Weather Makers

Communication was slow in the early nineteenth century, so scientists immediately did not connect Tambora's eruption to weather change. Today, many researchers study the effects of volcanic eruptions on weather. When Mount Pinatubo in the Philippines erupted in June 1991, weather stations around the world—and even in space—recorded its effects.

Mt. Pinatubo's eruption was smaller than Tambora's but was the second largest eruption in over 100 years. It blew ash and gases into the stratosphere, where they were carried by wind around the world. Because the suspended particles and droplets absorbed and reflected sunlight, average temperatures temporarily dropped by about 0.5°C in many places. Other weather-related affects included the increased strength of hurricanes in the Atlantic and Pacific Oceans and as well as flooding rains in the U.S. Midwest.

Looking Back at Volcanoes

The effect of volcanoes on climate is so important that some scientists even study volcanic eruptions from thousands of years ago. They compare the dates of these ancient eruptions with records of unusual weather. It has been found that crop failures and disease epidemics often occurred soon after large eruptions. Because changes in weather can affect the growth of trees, the growth rings of ancient trees also are evidence that support the data from written records. These ancient records help scientist predict the weather impacts of future volcanic eruptions.

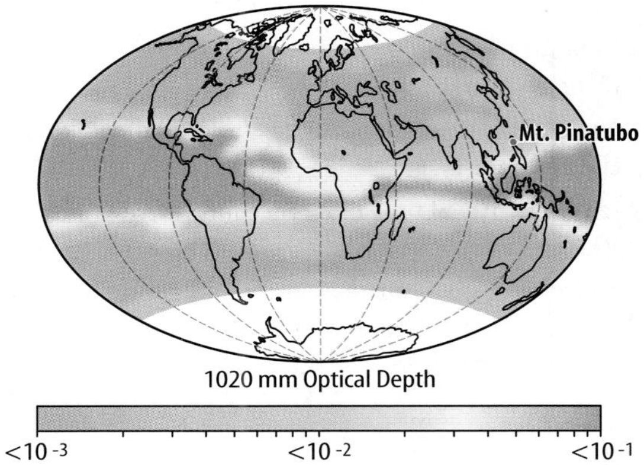

Experiment **Lay two sheets of black construction paper on a sunny windowsill and place a thermometer on each sheet. Tape a large piece of gauze or cheesecloth to the window so that it shades one of the sheets. Record the change in temperature for one half hour.**

TIME

For more information, visit gpescience.com

Experiment Students should observe a significant temperature difference between the two sheets of paper. Be sure that conditions other than shading by the screening material are identical. If a sunny windowsill is not available, an incandescent lamp can be used.

Resources for Teachers and Students

Encyclopedia of Volcanoes, Haraldur Sigurdsson, ed, Academic Press 2000

Krakatoa, The Day the World Exploded by Simon Winchester, HarperCollins, 2003

Volcanoe Weather: The Story of The Year Without a Summer 1816, by Henry Stommel & Elizabeth Stommel, Seven Seas Press 1983

Reviewing Main Ideas

Section 1 Evolution of Earth's Crust

1. Earth's crust and uppermost mantle, together called the lithosphere, consist of about seven large and numerous smaller plates.
2. Plate motion over the asthenosphere is influenced by forces that include ridge push, frictional drag, and slab pull.
3. Mantle convection drives the system of plates. Thermal energy sources for convection include heat left over from Earth's formation, and decay of radioactive isotopes.

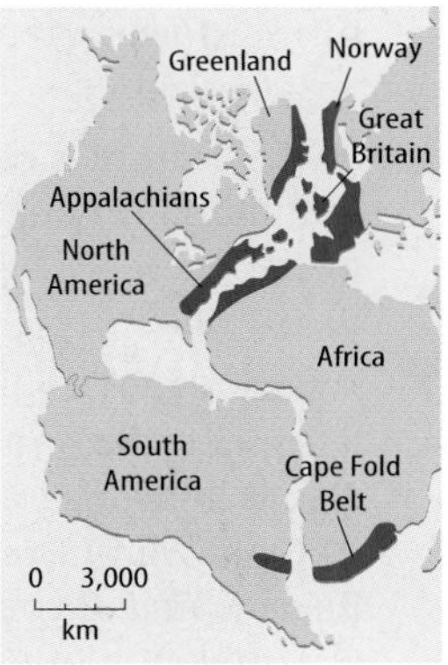

4. Plates meet along divergent, convergent, and transform boundaries.

Section 2 Earthquakes

1. Earthquakes are vibrations in Earth caused by the sudden release of energy.
2. During an earthquake caused by movement along a fault, strain energy is released in the form of seismic waves.
3. Most earthquake activity is confined to regions near plate boundaries.
4. Short-term prediction of earthquakes is not yet possible, but earthquakes can be rated by their intensities and magnitudes.

Section 3 Earth's Interior

1. The interior of Earth consists of four main layers: crust, mantle, inner and outer core.
2. The crust and mantle are largely composed of solid silicates. The asthenosphere is a layer of mantle in a semi-solid state.
3. The two innermost layers, the inner and outer core, are mainly composed of iron, nickel, oxygen and sulfur. The outer core is in a liquid state, and the inner core is solid.
4. The crust is the thinnest layer, while the mantle is the thickest.

Section 4 Volcanoes

1. Most volcanic activity on Earth occurs in the vicinity of plate boundaries or above mantle plumes.
2. The viscosity of the magma feeding volcanoes controls the volcanoes' eruptive characteristics.

3. Major controls on magma viscosity are: temperature, chemical composition, and gas content.
4. Cinder cones, shield volcanoes, and composite volcanoes are three principle volcanic landforms.

FOLDABLES Use the Foldable that you made at the beginning of this chapter to help you review Earth's internal process.

Reviewing Main Ideas

Summary statements can be used by students to review the major concepts of the chapter.

Science Online

Visit gpescience.com
More Section Review
Interactive Tutor
Vocabulary PuzzleMaker
More Chapter Review
Standardized Test Practice

Assessment Transparency

For additional assessment questions, use the *Assessment Transparency* located in the transparency book.

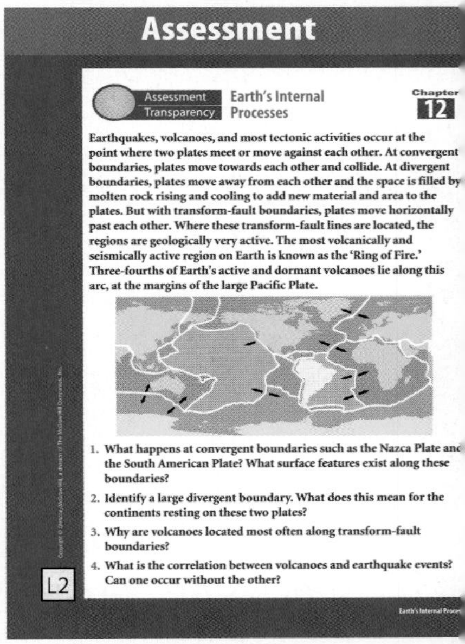
Assessment

Assessment Transparency Earth's Internal Processes — Chapter 12

Earthquakes, volcanoes, and most tectonic activities occur at the point where two plates meet or move against each other. At convergent boundaries, plates move towards each other and collide. At divergent boundaries, plates move away from each other and the space is filled by molten rock rising and cooling to add new material and area to the plates. But with transform-fault boundaries, plates move horizontally past each other. Where these transform-fault lines are located, the regions are geologically very active. The most volcanically and seismically active region on Earth is known as the 'Ring of Fire.' Three-fourths of Earth's active and dormant volcanoes lie along this arc, at the margins of the large Pacific Plate.

1. What happens at convergent boundaries such as the Nazca Plate and the South American Plate? What surface features exist along these boundaries?
2. Identify a large divergent boundary. What does this mean for the continents resting on these two plates?
3. Why are volcanoes located most often along transform-fault boundaries?
4. What is the correlation between volcanoes and earthquake events? Can one occur without the other?

L2

Earth's Internal Processes

FOLDABLES Have students use their Foldables to review divergent, convergent, and transform plate boundaries.

Using Vocabulary

1. focus
2. fault
3. rift valley
4. cinder cone
5. discontinuity

Checking Concepts

6. D
7. C
8. C
9. A
10. B
11. A
12. B
13. C

chapter 12 Review

Using Vocabulary

asthenosphere p. 372	fault p. 364
cinder cone volcano p. 377	focus p. 364
composite volcano p. 378	mid-ocean ridge p. 356
convergent boundary p. 359	rift valley p. 356
discontinuity p. 371	shadow zone p. 371
divergent boundary p. 358	shield volcano p. 377
elastic rebound p. 364	subduction p. 359
epicenter p. 364	transform boundary p. 360
	viscosity p. 375

Complete each sentence with the correct vocabulary word or words.

1. The ________ is the point of origin of an earthquake.
2. A zone of cracking in Earth's crust along which movement takes place is a ________.
3. A long, linear feature within a divergent plate boundary is a(n) ________.
4. A feature consisting of a relatively small pile of pyroclastic materials is a(n) ________.
5. A boundary marking an abrupt change in density is a(n) ________.

Checking Concepts

Choose the word or phrase that best answers the question.

6. What process causes a material to break due to excess stress?
   A) plastic deformation.
   B) elastic rebound.
   C) elastic deformation.
   D) brittle deformation.
7. Which best identifies a shield volcano?
   A) sticky, silica-rich magmas
   B) great height compared to width
   C) forms above hot spots
   D) found mostly on continents
8. What characteristic was first used to identify Earth's layers?
   A) temperature.
   B) composition.
   C) density.
   D) thickness.
9. Which pair of plate tectonic boundaries is best characterized by mostly shallow-focus earthquakes?
   A) divergent and transform
   B) divergent and continent-ocean convergent
   C) continent-continent and continent-ocean convergent
   D) transform and ocean-ocean convergent zones
10. Which feature is common to and only found in diverging regions?
    A) trenches
    B) rift valleys
    C) volcanic arcs
    D) island arcs
11. Which is **NOT** evidence used by Wegener to support the continental drift hypothesis?
    A) matching magnetic patterns symmetrical to the Mid-Ocean Ridge
    B) matching of continental margins
    C) correlation of fossils among the continents
    D) mountain-range matching among the continents

Use the illustration below to answer question 12.

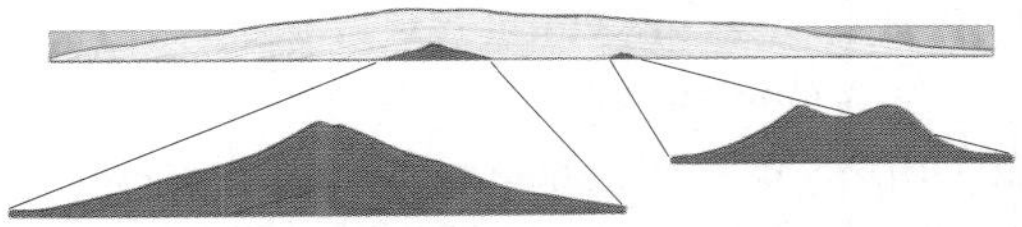

12. Which volcano type has small height, small diameter and consists mostly of pyroclasts?
    A) Hawaiian volcano
    B) cinder cone volcano
    C) composite volcano
    D) shield volcano

Vocabulary PuzzleMaker gpescience.com

Use the ExamView® Pro Test Bank CD-ROM to:
- create multiple versions of tests
- create modified tests with one mouse click for inclusion students
- edit existing questions and add your own questions
- build tests aligned with state standards using built-in State Curriculum Tags
- change English tests to Spanish with one mouse click and vice versa

13. Which earthquake waves travel through matter with a push-pull motion?
A) secondary waves
B) surface waves
C) primary waves
D) body waves

Interpreting Graphics

14. Copy and complete the concept map below summarizing characteristics of divergent, convergent and transform plate boundaries.

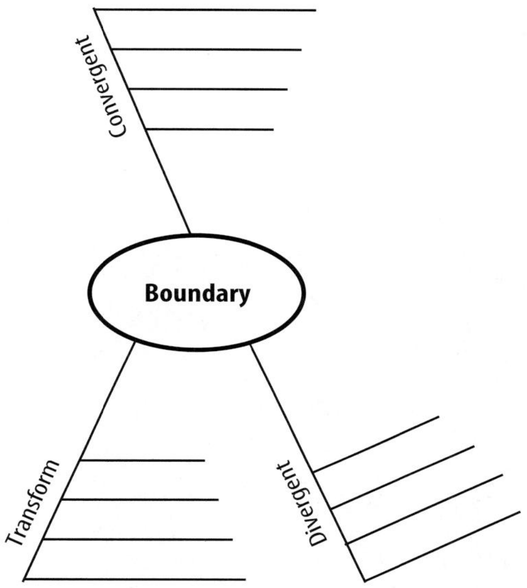

15. Copy and complete the table summarizing three types of volcanoes.

Magma Properties and Volcano Types

General Composition	Relative silica (SiO_2) Content	Relative Viscosity	Volcano Type
Basaltic	lowest	lowest	shield
Andesitic	intermediate	intermediate	composite
Rhyolitic	highest	highest	Lava Dome

Thinking Critically

16. **Explain** why the island of Kauai, often referred to as the "Garden Isle," has thicker soils and is better able to sustain agriculture than other Hawaiian Islands.

17. **Infer** what general depth of focus earthquakes are likely to occur in the Himalaya.

18. **Explain** how the processes associated with plate tectonics maintain Earth's recycling of materials.

Applying Math

19. **Calculating Lava Thickness** Suppose that hot spot volcanism produces an average of 76,000 m^3 of lava per day and does so for 340 days. This lava flows across a region that has an area of 10 km^2. How thick will the resulting lava flow be?

20. Located on the island of Hawaii, Mauna Loa is the largest volcano on Earth and rises 17 km above its base. Using the thickness you found in question 19 as the annual thickness, how many years did it take for Mauna Loa to build from the sea bed?

21. Mauna Loa rises 4 km above sea level. How many years did it take to grow from sea level to its present height?

22. An active volcano called Loihi lies just off the coast of the island of Hawaii. It is called a seamount because it still lies below the surface. If it grows at the same rate you used in question 21 and lies 1250 m below the surface, how long will it take for Loihi to break the ocean surface?

Interpreting Graphics

14. See student page.
15. See student page.

Thinking Critically

16. It is older and has had a longer time for rock to weather and produce a soil.
17. Himalayas are in a continent-continent convergence zone, which results in deep focus earthquakes.
18. At convergent boundaries sediment and rock is subducted, metamorphosed and eventually melted. The resulting magma returns to the surface during volcanic eruptions to be weathered to sediments again.

Applying Math

Math Standards

National: 1, 2, 9

19. 0.26
20. 65,000
21. 15,000
22. 4,800

Assessment Resources

Reproducible Masters

Chapter *Fast File* Resources
Chapter Review, pp. 39–40
Chapter Tests, pp. 41–44
Assessment Transparency Activity, p. 51

Glencoe Science Web site
Chapter Review Test
Standardized Test Practice

Glencoe Technology

Assessment Transparency
Exam*View*® Pro Testmaker
MindJogger Videoquiz
Interactive Chalkboard

chapter 12 Standardized Test Practice

Answer Sheet An answer sheet can be found at **gpescience.com**.

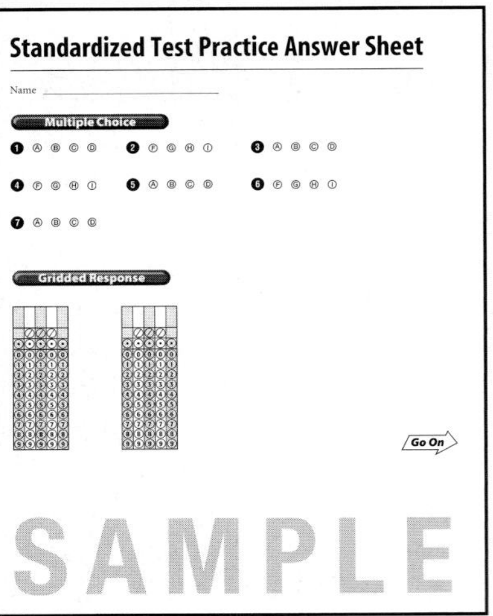

Multiple Choice

1. C
2. B
3. A
4. C
5. C

Gridded Response

6. 5.75 meters
7. 6 times farther (34.5 m/5.75 m)

Short Response

8. The magnetic polarity of Earth has reversed many times during geologic history. This reversal is reflected in symmetrical bands of igneous rocks that are located on either side of the MOR. This indicates that the new ocean floor moves horizontally away from the MOR and in opposite directions.

9. Tectonic plates can converge, diverge, or move past each other.

10. When two continental plates converge, they build up mountain ranges as Earth's crust is compressed and folded. When two oceanic plates converge, the denser one subducts under the less dense one. When an oceanic plate converges with a continental plate, the denser oceanic plate subducts under the less dense continental plate.

11. He was using sonar to search for and detect submarines. While doing this, he also determined the distance from the ocean surface to the ocean floor, enabling him to map the ocean floor.

12. Upwelling magma causes cracks to form in the overlying crust. As the cracks develop, movement of the magma causes crust on either side of the cracks to move away from each other. Faulting then causes a down-dropped valley between two parallel mountain ranges.

13. Sediments are thinner near the mid-ocean ridge and thicker as you approach the continents. Also, sediments near the MOR are recent in age, whereas sediments near the continents are recent on top, but older near the bottom. This

chapter 12 Standardized Test Practice

Record your answers on the answer sheet provided by your teacher or on a sheet of paper.

Multiple Choice

1. Who first proposed the hypothesis of continental drift?

A. Matthews
B. Vine
C. Wegener
D. Wilson

Use the image below to answer question 2.

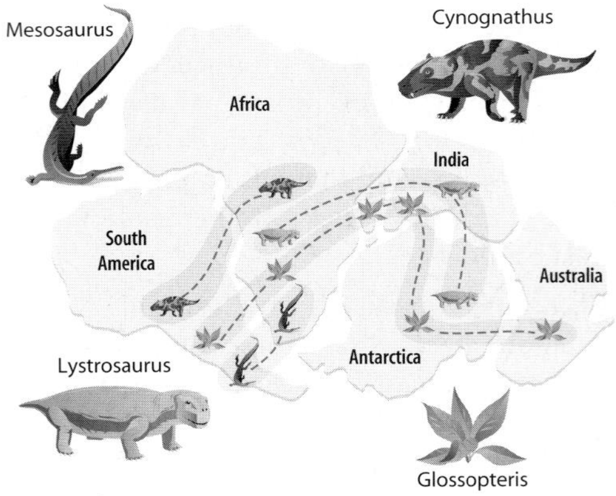

2. Which is the fern, pictured above, that provided support for Pangaea?

A. Antarctica
B. Glossopteris
C. Mesosaurus
D. Lystrosaurus

Test-Taking Tip

For each question, double-check that you are filling in the correct answer bubble for the question number you are completing.

3. What did oceanographers show, using sonar, which helped revive continental drift?

A. edges of the continental shelves matched
B. edges of the continents matched
C. fossils match similar fossils
D. rocks match similar rocks

4. Which forms when a less-dense plate converges on a denser plate?

A. mid-ocean ridge
B. rift valley
C. subduction zone
D. transform boundary

Use the image below to answer question 5.

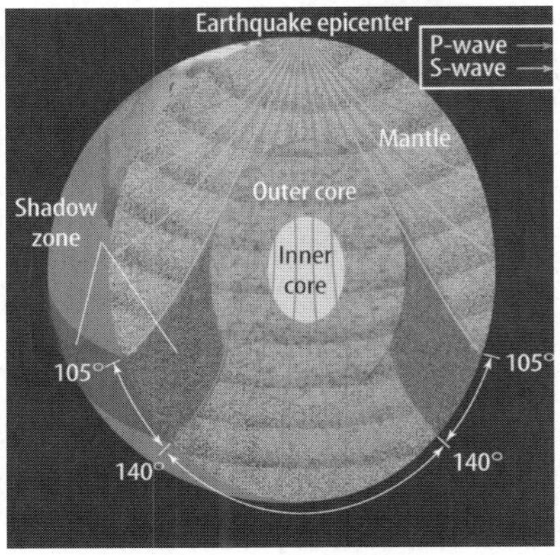

5. The shadow zone, illustrated above, is caused by which layer of Earth?

A. crust
B. mantle
C. outer core
D. inner core

Gridded Response

6. If a divergent boundary separates at a rate of 2.5 cm/year, how much farther apart would the two plates be after 230 years?

7. Compared to the two plates in question 7, how much farther apart would two plates be after 230 years if the divergent boundary between them separated at 15 cm/year?

Short Response

Use the illustration below to answer question 8.

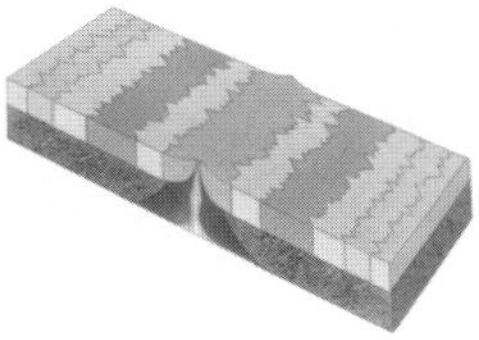

8. The illustration shows reverse polarity bands on the seafloor. How does magnetic polarity of rocks support seafloor spreading?

9. What are the three different ways in which tectonic plates can move?

10. What is different about what happens to plate edges at the different types of convergent boundaries?

11. How did Dr. Harry Hess obtain detailed maps of the ocean floor?

12. What causes a rift valley to form at divergent boundaries?

13. What is true about the thickness and age of sediments at different locations on the ocean floor that supports seafloor spreading?

14. What is the driving force for all mechanisms of tectonic plate movement?

15. What is the difference between a crack in Earth's crust and a fault?

16. What causes the energy of an earthquake?

17. How are the focus and epicenter of an earthquake related?

Extended Response

Use the image below to answer question 18.

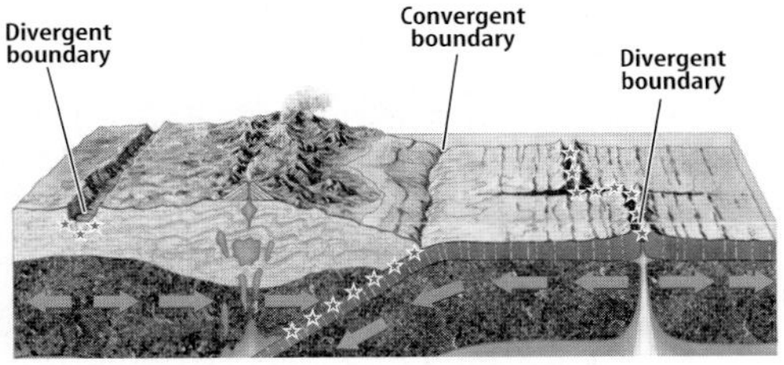

18. **Part A** What is true about the depth of earthquake foci and the location of tectonic plate boundaries?

Part B Why are deep-focus earthquakes noted only at ocean-ocean convergent boundaries and ocean-continental convergent boundaries?

Short Response

indicates that sediments on the ocean floor near the MOR are too recent to have accumulated into thick deposits such as are found nearer the continents.

14. Internal convection of mantle material inside Earth.
15. A fault is a crack in Earth's crust along which there has been movement.
16. Elastic rebound, the sudden energy release that occurs when brittle rocks move along a fault, provides the energy to cause vibrations (earthquakes) in the rock layers.
17. The point inside Earth where energy is released to cause an earthquake is the focus, the point on Earth's surface directly above the focus is the epicenter of the earthquake.

18. **Part A** Shallow focus earthquakes occur along divergent and transform boundaries. Both shallow and deep focus earthquake occur at convergent boundaries.
Part B Deep focus earthquakes occur at ocean-continent and ocean-ocean convergent boundaries where subduction forces one plate down and under a less dense plate. As the one plate subducts under the other, earthquakes are generated near Earth's surface and deep inside Earth along the subducting plate.

Rubrics

For more help evaluating Short- and Extended-Response questions, see the rubrics on p. 9T.

Unit Contents

WebQuest ***Maglev Trains: Floating Locomotives*** is an investigation of magnets and how they work. Using online resources, students study different types of magnetic levitation, design and build a maglev train, then test and refine their models. Class presentations reflect student designs, procedures, refinements, and results.

unit 4

Forms of Energy

How Are Clouds & Toasters Connected?

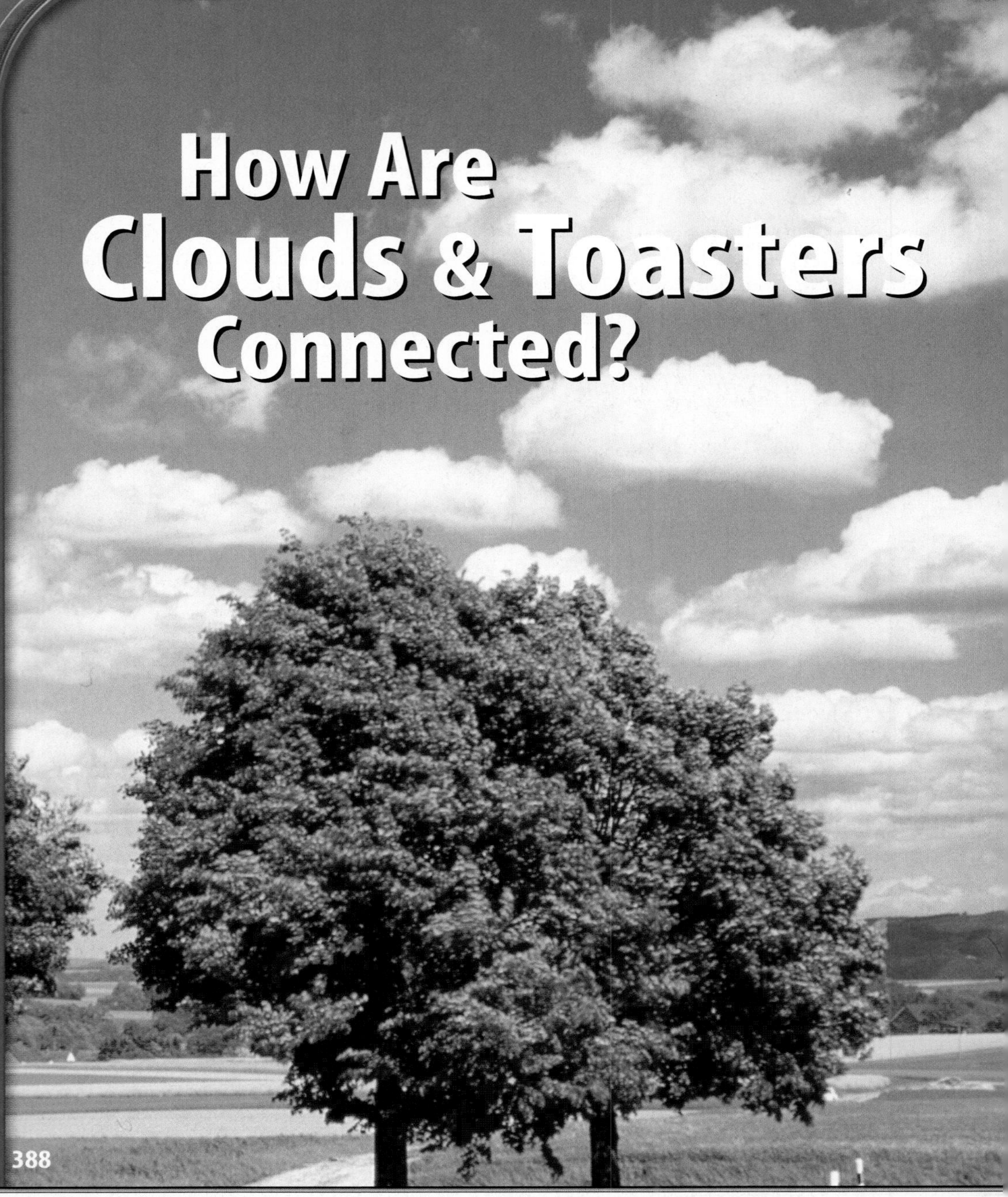

388

PROJECT CRISS℠

Study Skills

Discussion Provide students with sticky notes. Have students read through one or more chapters in the unit, either at home or as an in-class assignment. As they read, they should use the sticky notes to mark topics or examples they find especially interesting or difficult. They may use the notes for short descriptions or questions they may have, or to mark uses for electricity, magnetism, or nuclear energy that they find interesting.

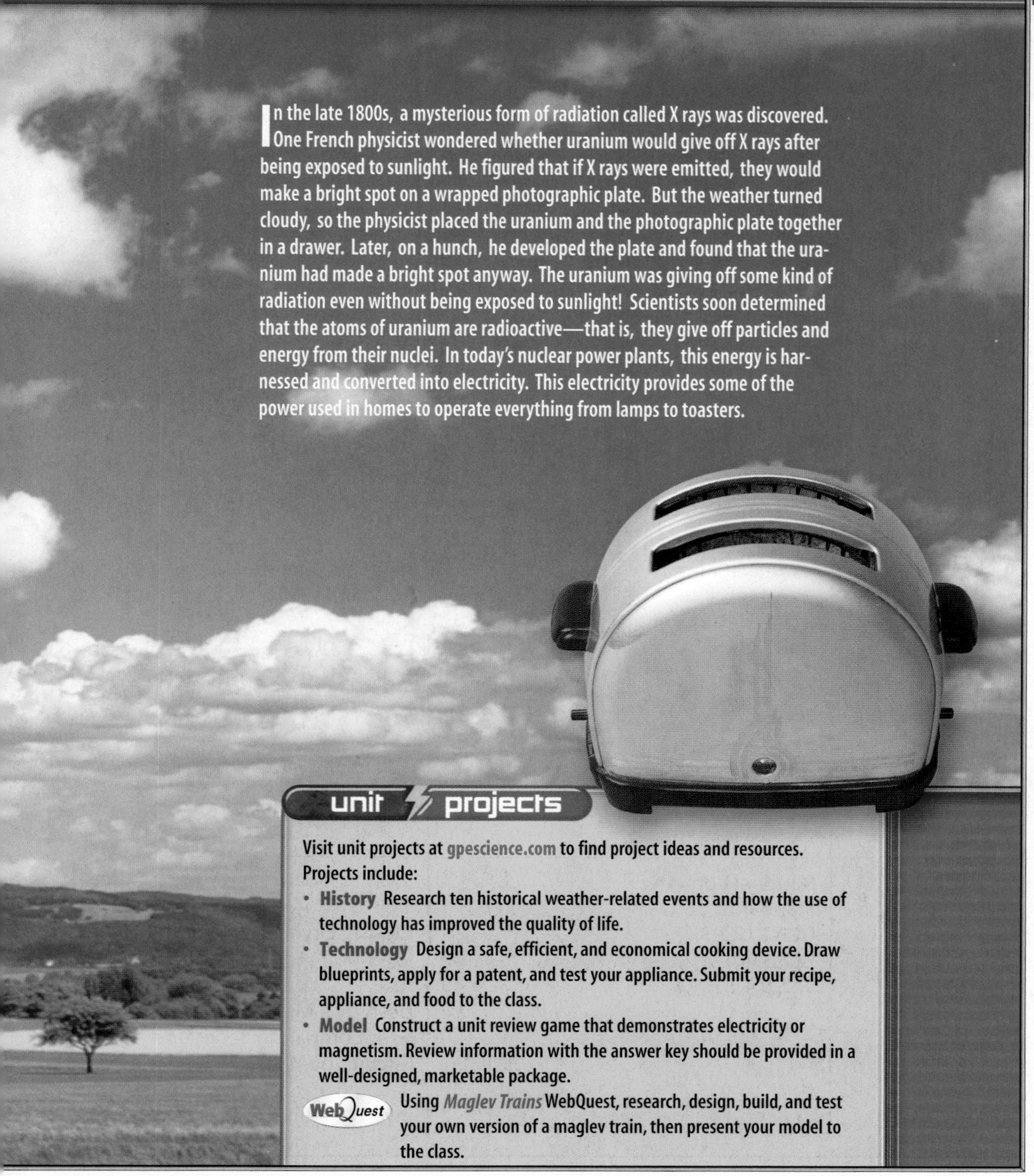

In the late 1800s, a mysterious form of radiation called X rays was discovered. One French physicist wondered whether uranium would give off X rays after being exposed to sunlight. He figured that if X rays were emitted, they would make a bright spot on a wrapped photographic plate. But the weather turned cloudy, so the physicist placed the uranium and the photographic plate together in a drawer. Later, on a hunch, he developed the plate and found that the uranium had made a bright spot anyway. The uranium was giving off some kind of radiation even without being exposed to sunlight! Scientists soon determined that the atoms of uranium are radioactive—that is, they give off particles and energy from their nuclei. In today's nuclear power plants, this energy is harnessed and converted into electricity. This electricity provides some of the power used in homes to operate everything from lamps to toasters.

unit projects

Visit unit projects at gpescience.com to find project ideas and resources.
Projects include:

- **History** Research ten historical weather-related events and how the use of technology has improved the quality of life.
- **Technology** Design a safe, efficient, and economical cooking device. Draw blueprints, apply for a patent, and test your appliance. Submit your recipe, appliance, and food to the class.
- **Model** Construct a unit review game that demonstrates electricity or magnetism. Review information with the answer key should be provided in a well-designed, marketable package.

WebQuest Using *Maglev Trains* WebQuest, research, design, build, and test your own version of a maglev train, then present your model to the class.

unit projects

History Have students research ten historical weather-related events. Students prepare a brief summary of these events, how they relate to geographical features, and how technology and weather forecasting have improved everyday lives.

Technology Ask students to design a safe, efficient, and economical cooking device that uses energy other than fossil fuels. Have students draw blueprints, apply to the teacher for a "patent" on their original device, test their appliance with a recipe, and then submit the recipe, appliance, and cooked food for teacher and peer evaluation.

Model Have students design and construct a unit review game or toy that demonstrates electricity or magnetism as one of its characteristics. The completed model should contain directions for use, an ample amount of unit review information with answer guide, and be contained in a well-designed box, ready for the game-store market. Display each creative, quality product for class review, as well as evaluation by peers and teachers for educational review value, electric and magnetic modeling, construction quality, safety, and enjoyment.

Additional Resources Visit unit projects at gpescience.com for more information, resources, and assessment rubrics.

NATIONAL GEOGRAPHIC **How Are Clouds & Toasters Connected?**

- Ask students to list the connections between clouds and toasters. You might want them to use a concept map to relate one step to another.
- Students might start this activity with negative ideas about nuclear energy. Have them make a two-column table they can use to list the positive and negative aspects of nuclear energy as they learn more about it.
- Ask students to brainstorm what geographic areas might most likely use nuclear power to produce electricity and why. Most nuclear power plants are in regions of the country with the highest populations, where there is the greatest need.

Organizer

Section/Objectives	Standards: National	Standards: State/Local	Labs/Features
Chapter Opener	See pp. 16T–17T for a Key to Standards.		**Launch Lab:** Electric Circuits, p. 391 **Foldables,** p. 391
Section 1 Electric Charge 2 sessions 1 block 1. **Describe** how electric charges exert forces on each other. 2. **Compare** the strengths of electric and gravitational forces. 3. **Distinguish** between conductors and insulators. 4. **Explain** how objects become electrically charged.	National Content Standards: UCP.2, UCP.3, UCP.5, A.1, A.2, B.2, B.4		**Science Online,** p. 396 **Visualizing Lightning,** p. 397 **MiniLAB:** Investigating Charged Objects, p. 398
Section 2 Electric Current 3 sessions 1.5 blocks 5. **Describe** how voltage difference causes current to flow. 6. **Explain** how batteries produce a voltage difference in a circuit. 7. **List** the factors that affect an object's electrical resistance. 8. **Define** Ohm's law.	National Content Standards: UCP.2, UCP.3, UCP.5, A.1, A.2, B.2, B.4		**MiniLAB:** Investigating Battery Addition, p. 402 **Integrate Health,** p. 405 **Lab:** Identifying Conductors and Insulators, p. 406 Video Lab
Section 3 Electrical Energy 3 sessions 1.5 blocks 9. **Describe** the difference between series and parallel circuits. 10. **Recognize** the function of circuit breakers and fuses. 11. **Calculate** electrical power. 12. **Calculate** the electrical energy used by a device.	National Content Standards: UCP.2, UCP.3, UCP.5, A.1, A.2, B.2, B.4, B.6, F.6		**Integrate Career,** p. 408 **Applying Math:** Power Used by a Clothes Dryer, p. 411 **Science Online,** p. 412 **Applying Math:** Electrical Energy Used by a Microwave Oven, p. 412 **Lab:** Comparing Series and Parallel Circuits, pp. 414–415 **Science and Language Arts:** Invisible Man, p. 416

StudentWorks Plus | Glencoe Exclusive! TeacherWorks™ All-In-One Planner and Resource Center

Lab Materials	Reproducible Resources	Section Assessment	Technology
Launch Lab: battery, flashlight bulb, insulated wire, electrical tape or battery holder	**Chapter *Fast File* Resources** Foldables Worksheet, p. 15 Note-taking Worksheets, pp. 31–33 Directed Reading Overview, p. 17	Glencoe's Assessment Advantage	TeacherWorks includes: • Interactive Teacher Edition • Lesson Planner with calendar • Access to all program blacklines • Correlations to standards • Web links
MiniLAB: transparent tape Need materials? Contact Science Kit at 1-800-828-7777 or www.sciencekit.com.	**Chapter *Fast File* Resources** Transparency Activity, p. 42 MiniLAB, p. 3 Enrichment, p. 28 Reinforcement, p. 25 Directed Reading, p. 18	**Portfolio** Differentiated Instruction, p. 395 **Performance** Applying Math, p. 399 **Content** Section Review, p. 399	Section Focus Transparency Interactive Chalkboard CD-ROM StudentWorks Plus
MiniLAB: D-cell batteries (2), 3-volt bulbs and sockets (2), insulated wire **Lab:** battery, flashlight bulb, bulb holder, insulated wire	**Chapter *Fast File* Resources** Transparency Activity, p. 43 MiniLAB, p. 4 Enrichment, p. 29 Reinforcement, p. 26 Directed Reading, p. 19 Lab Worksheet, pp. 5–6 Lab Activity, pp. 9–12	**Portfolio** Assessment, p. 405 **Performance** MiniLAB, p. 402 Applying Math, p. 405 **Content** Section Review, p. 405	Section Focus Transparency Virtual Labs CD-ROM Interactive Chalkboard CD-ROM StudentWorks Plus Video Lab
Lab: 6-V dry-cell battery, small lights with sockets (3), aluminum foil, paper clips, tape, scissors, paper	**Chapter *Fast File* Resources** Transparency Activity, p. 44 Enrichment, p. 30 Reinforcement, p. 27 Directed Reading, pp. 19, 20 Transparency Activity, pp. 45–46 Lab Activity, pp. 13–14 Lab Worksheet, pp. 7–8 **Mathematics Skill Activities,** p. 9	**Portfolio** Assessment , p. 413 **Performance** Applying Math, pp. 411–412 Applying Math, p. 413 **Content** Section Review, p. 413	Section Focus Transparency Teaching Transparency Interactive Chalkboard CD-ROM StudentWorks Plus

End of Chapter Assessment

Glencoe's Assessment Advantage

Blackline Masters	Technology	Professional Series
Chapter *Fast File* Resources Chapter Review, pp. 35–36 Chapter Tests, pp. 37–40 **Standardized Test Practice,** pp. 56–59	MindJogger Videoquiz Virtual Labs CD-ROM Exam*View*® Pro Testmaker TeacherWorks CD-ROM Interactive Chalkboard CD-ROM	**Performance Assessment in the Science Classroom (PASC)**

chapter 13 Electricity

Transparencies

Section Focus

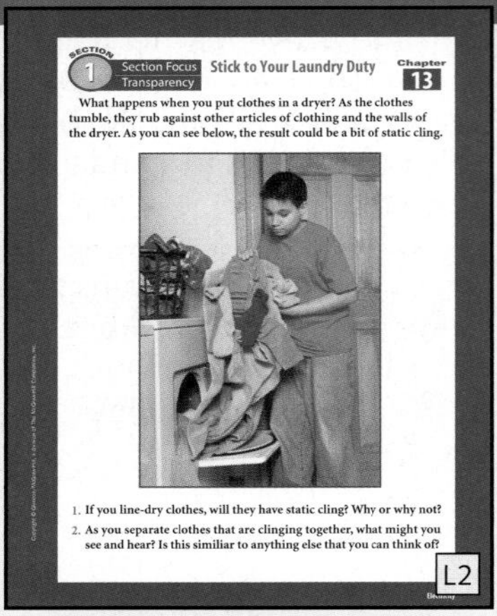
Section 1 Section Focus Transparency — Stick to Your Laundry Duty — Chapter 13

What happens when you put clothes in a dryer? As the clothes tumble, they rub against other articles of clothing and the walls of the dryer. As you can see below, the result could be a bit of static cling.

1. If you line-dry clothes, will they have static cling? Why or why not?
2. As you separate clothes that are clinging together, what might you see and hear? Is this similiar to anything else that you can think of?

L2

Section 2 Section Focus Transparency — Go with the Flow — Chapter 13

Do you see how the water flows down the cliff? Water takes the path of least resistance—it flows where it's easiest for water to go. Electric currents flow and experience resistance, too.

1. Which do you think has more energy, the waterfall in the picture or Niagara Falls which are higher and have more water flowing over? Explain your answer.
2. How do people use the energy in water currents?

L2

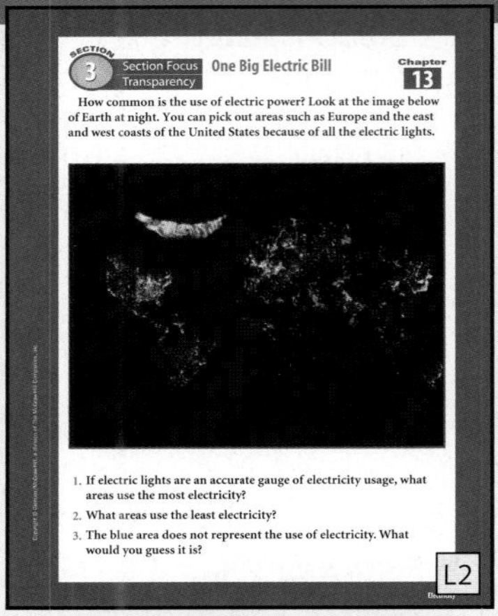
Section 3 Section Focus Transparency — One Big Electric Bill — Chapter 13

How common is the use of electric power? Look at the image below of Earth at night. You can pick out areas such as Europe and the east and west coasts of the United States because of all the electric lights.

1. If electric lights are an accurate gauge of electricity usage, what areas use the most electricity?
2. What areas use the least electricity?
3. The blue area does not represent the use of electricity. What would you guess it is?

L2

This is a representation of key blackline masters available in the Teacher Classroom Resources. See Resource Manager boxes within the chapter for additional information.

Assessment

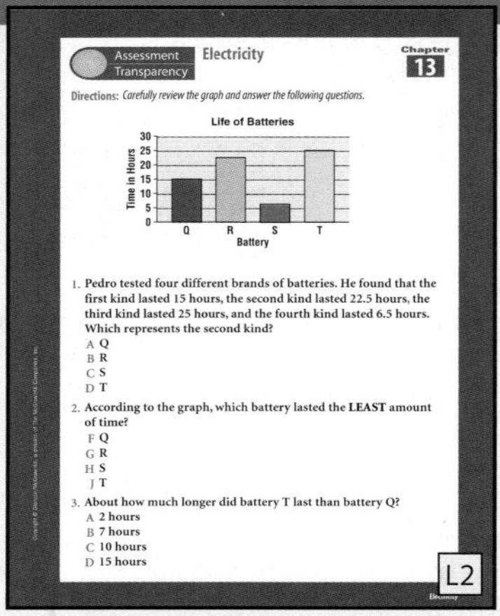
Assessment Transparency — Electricity — Chapter 13

Directions: *Carefully review the graph and answer the following questions.*

1. Pedro tested four different brands of batteries. He found that the first kind lasted 15 hours, the second kind lasted 22.5 hours, the third kind lasted 25 hours, and the fourth kind lasted 6.5 hours. Which represents the second kind?
A Q
B R
C S
D T
2. According to the graph, which battery lasted the **LEAST** amount of time?
F Q
G R
H S
J T
3. About how much longer did battery T last than battery Q?
A 2 hours
B 7 hours
C 10 hours
D 15 hours

L2

Teaching

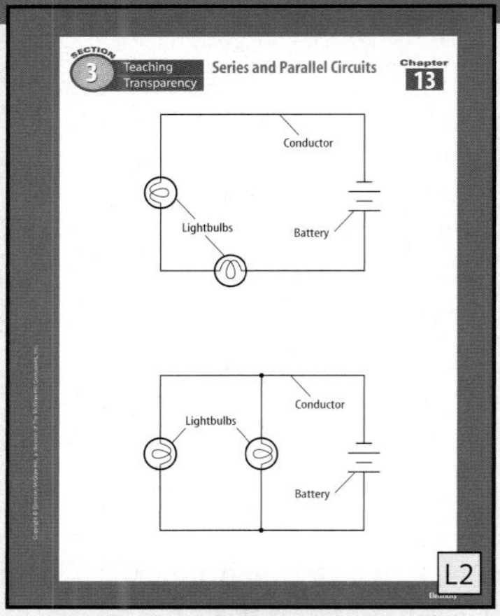
Section 3 Teaching Transparency — Series and Parallel Circuits — Chapter 13

L2

Key to Teaching Strategies

The following designations will help you decide which activities are appropriate for your students.

- L1 Level 1 activities should be appropriate for students with learning difficulties.
- L2 Level 2 activities should be within the ability range of all students.
- L3 Level 3 activities are designed for above-average students.
- ELL ELL activities should be within the ability range of English Language Learners.
- COOP LEARN Cooperative Learning activities are designed for small group work.
- LS Multiple Learning Styles logos, as described on page 12T, are used throughout to indicate strategies that address different learning styles.
- P These strategies represent student products that can be placed into a best-work portfolio.
- PBL Problem-Based Learning activities apply real-world situations to learning.

Hands-on Activities

Student Text Lab Worksheet

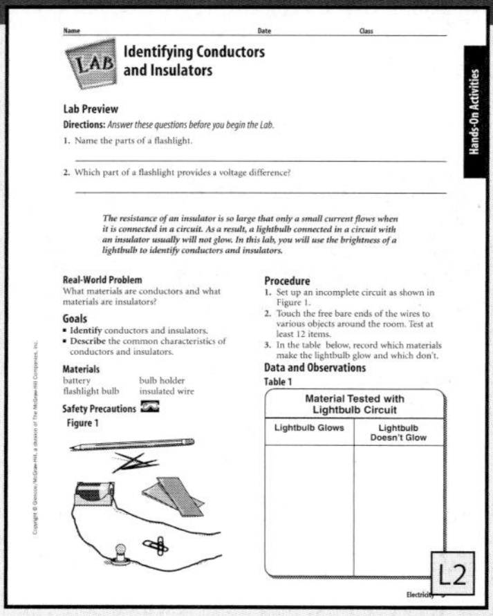
Name Date Class

LAB Identifying Conductors and Insulators

Hands-On Activities

Lab Preview

Directions: *Answer these questions before you begin the Lab.*

1. Name the parts of a flashlight.
2. Which part of a flashlight provides a voltage difference?

The resistance of an insulator is so large that only a small current flows when it is connected in a circuit. As a result, a lightbulb connected in a circuit with an insulator usually will not glow. In this lab, you will use the brightness of a lightbulb to identify conductors and insulators.

Real-World Problem

What materials are conductors and what materials are insulators?

Goals

- Identify conductors and insulators.
- Describe the common characteristics of conductors and insulators.

Materials

battery, flashlight bulb, bulb holder, insulated wire

Safety Precautions

Figure 1

Procedure

1. Set up an incomplete circuit as shown in Figure 1.
2. Touch the free bare ends of the wires to various objects around the room. Test at least 12 items.
3. In the table below, record which materials make the lightbulb glow and which don't.

Data and Observations

Table 1

Material Tested with Lightbulb Circuit	
Lightbulb Glows	Lightbulb Doesn't Glow

L2

Laboratory Activities

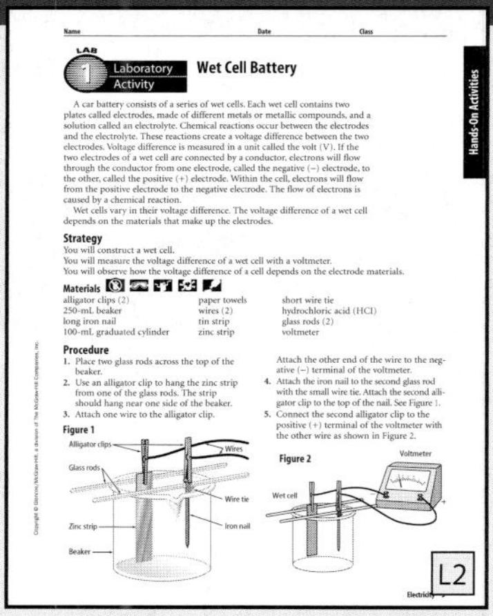
Name Date Class

LAB 1 Laboratory Activity — Wet Cell Battery

Hands-On Activities

A car battery consists of a series of wet cells. Each wet cell contains two plates called electrodes, made of different metals or metallic compounds, and a solution called an electrolyte. Chemical reactions occur between the electrodes and the electrolyte. These reactions create a voltage difference between the two electrodes. Voltage difference is measured in a unit called the volt (V). If the two electrodes of a wet cell are connected by a conductor, electrons will flow through the conductor from one electrode, called the negative (−) electrode, to the other, called the positive (+) electrode. Within the cell, electrons will flow from the positive electrode to the negative electrode. The flow of electrons is caused by a chemical reaction.

Wet cells vary in their voltage difference. The voltage difference of a wet cell depends on the materials that make up the electrodes.

Strategy

You will construct a wet cell.
You will measure the voltage difference of a wet cell with a voltmeter.
You will observe how the voltage difference of a cell depends on the electrode materials.

Materials

alligator clips (2), 250-mL beaker, long iron nail, 100-mL graduated cylinder, paper towels, wires (2), tin strip, zinc strip, short wire tie, hydrochloric acid (HCl), glass rods (2), voltmeter

Procedure

1. Place two glass rods across the top of the beaker.
2. Use an alligator clip to hang the zinc strip from one of the glass rods. The strip should hang near one side of the beaker.
3. Attach one wire to the alligator clip.
4. Attach the iron nail to the second glass rod with the small wire tie. Attach the second alligator clip to the top of the nail. See Figure 1.
5. Connect the second alligator clip to the positive (+) terminal of the voltmeter with the other wire as shown in Figure 2.

Figure 1

Figure 2

L2

Meeting Different Ability Levels

Content Outline

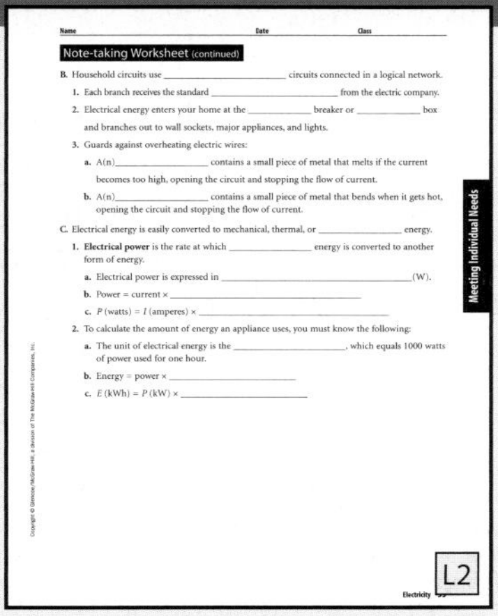
Note-taking Worksheet (continued)

L2

Reinforcement

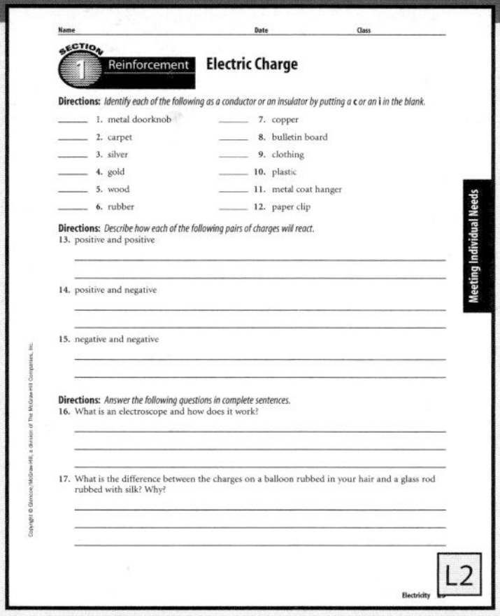
Section 1 Reinforcement Electric Charge

L2

Enrichment

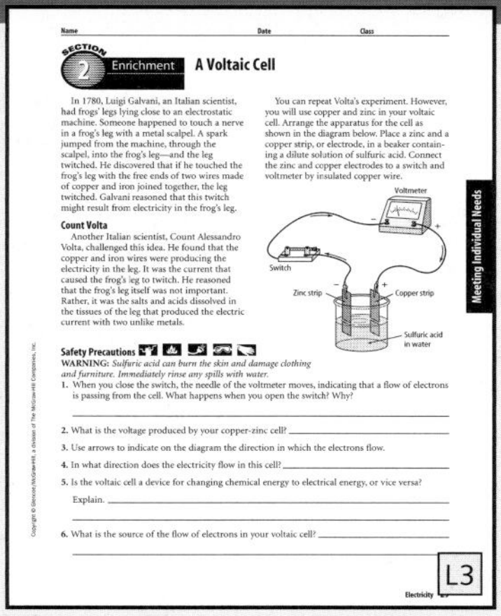
Section 2 Enrichment A Voltaic Cell

L3

Directed Reading (English/Spanish)

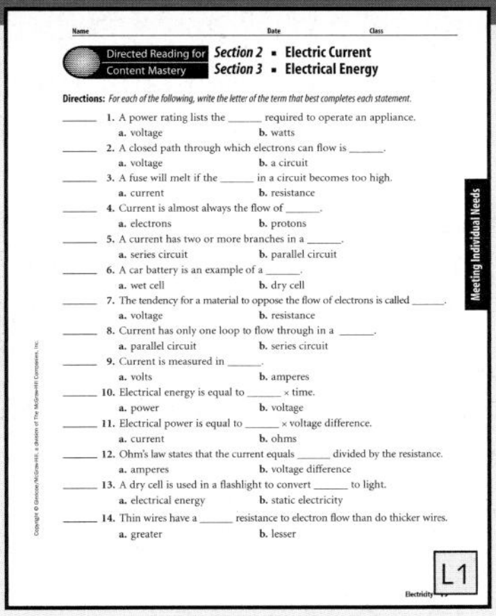
Directed Reading for Content Mastery Section 2 ▪ Electric Current Section 3 ▪ Electrical Energy

L1

Study Guide

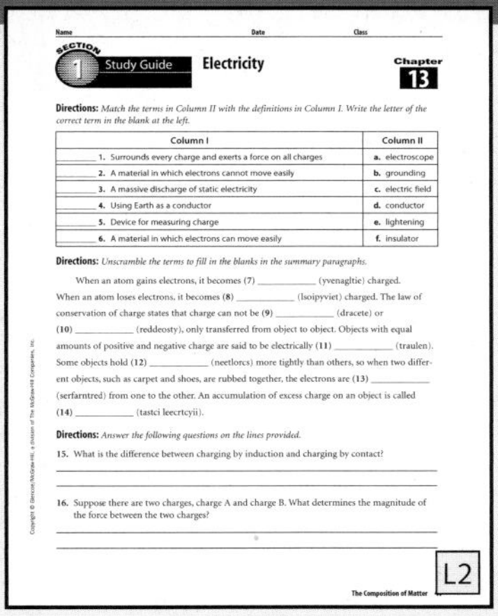
Section 1 Study Guide Electricity Chapter 13

L2

Reading Essentials

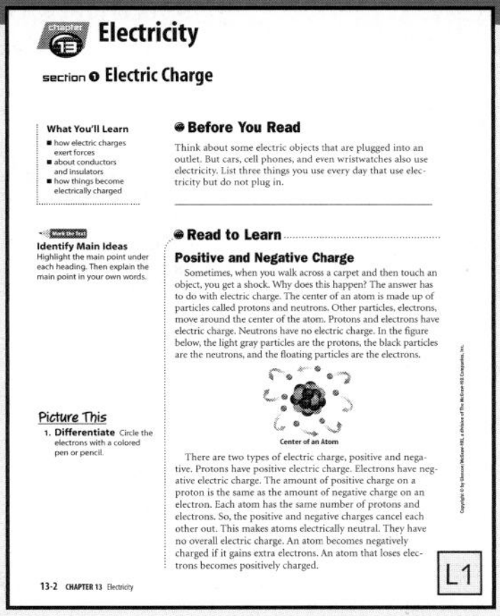
Chapter 13 Electricity

Section 1 Electric Charge

L1

Assessment

Test Practice Workbook

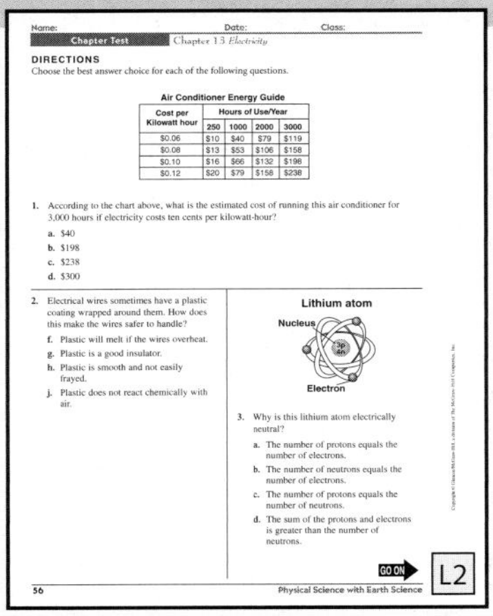
Chapter Test Chapter 13 Electricity

L2

Chapter Review

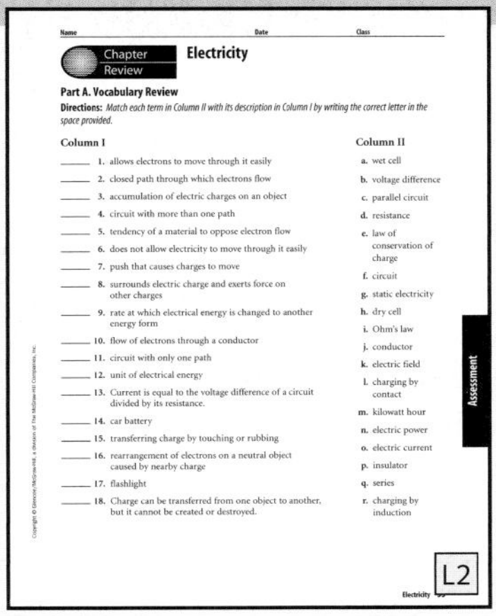
Chapter Review Electricity

L2

Chapter Tests

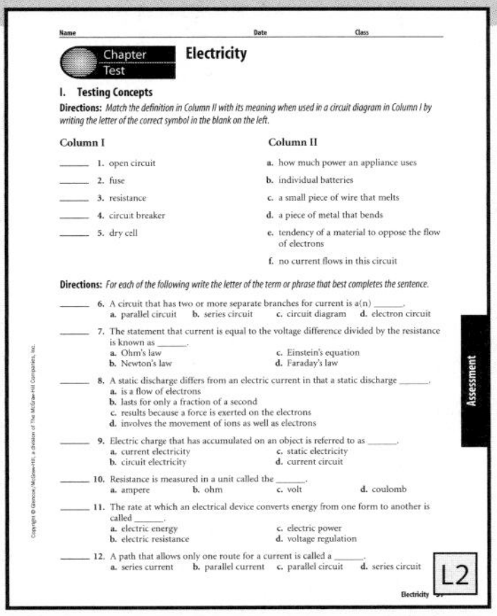
Chapter Test Electricity

L2

Science Content Background

section 1 Electric Charge

Positive and Negative Charge

Waterfalls produce airborne negative charges. Some people believe these charges make us feel happy and healthy. Ion machines were created to produce negative charges in houses and offices.

Transferring Charge

Benjamin Franklin invented the lightning rod to protect homes by transferring charge. It was a metal rod that was grounded through a wire. The top of the rod was sharpened to a point. Recently scientists discovered that the rods actually work better if they are not sharpened at the top.

section 2 Electric Current

Current and Voltage Difference

Electric current flows from a region of high electric potential energy to low electric potential energy. Electric charge loses electric potential energy as it flows through a circuit just as a ball loses gravitational potential energy when it falls. The electric potential energy lost by a coulomb of charge from one point to another is the voltage difference between the two points. This energy can be used to do useful tasks, such as run electric motors. A battery increases the electrical potential energy of charges, just as lifting a ball increases the ball's gravitational potential energy. All circuits contain electric resistance that converts some electric potential energy to thermal energy as charges move through the circuit.

Electric current has the unit of the ampere, which is defined as one coulomb per second. One coulomb is equivalent to the charge of 6.25×10^{18} electrons.

section 3 Electrical Energy

Series and Parellel Circuits

We pay the electric company for our use of electrical energy. The electrons that transfer electrical energy are not used up in the process; they keep flowing.

In a series circuit with three different resistors, the current at all points in the circuit is the same but the voltage difference across each resistor is different. In a parallel circuit with three different resistors, the voltage difference across the resistors is the same but the current is different.

Electric Power

Electric power is found by multiplying current (coulombs/second) times voltage (joules/coulomb), giving units of joules/second, which is equivalent to a watt.

chapter content resources

Internet Resources

For additional content background, visit gpescience.com to:

- access your book online
- find references to related articles in popular science magazines
- access Web links with related content background
- access current events with science journal topics

Print Resources

Electricity, by Wendy Baker, Alexandra Parsons, Andrew Haslam, Two-Can Publishing, 2000

Electricity, by John Farndon, Benchmark Books, 2000

Electricity (Discovery Channel School Science), by Richie Chevat, Jacqueline A. Ball, Joellyn M. Ausanka, Steve Grey, Gareth Stevens Publishing, May 2003

IDENTIFYING Misconceptions

Find Out What Students Think

Students may think that . . .

Voltage is the same at different places in a circuit and it exists only when current flows. Because electrons and the flow of charge that make up electricity cannot be seen directly, electricity can be difficult to understand and terms such as voltage, current, power, and energy can be confusing. Of all these terms, voltage is the most abstract and can be the most difficult to grasp. Because of the omnipresence of batteries, students are probably familiar with the volt as a unit of measure. This may conceal their misconceptions about voltage. They may confuse the relationship between voltage and current and may come to the wrong conclusion that voltage is a consequence of current and not the cause of it. They also may have inaccurate conceptions of how voltages in a circuit vary.

Activity

Draw the circuit shown in the figure below on the board, and ask students to predict and write what the voltages will be between the points A–B, B–C, C–D, B–D, and A–E.

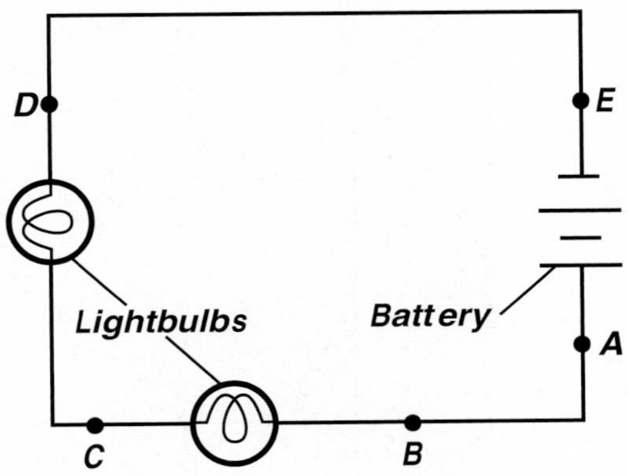

Promote Understanding

Activity

Give each group of students four wires, two flashlight bulbs in sockets, a D battery in a battery holder, and a voltmeter. Ask students to make a series circuit using the battery, bulbs, and four wires. Caution students not to touch a hot bulb.

- Instruct them in the use of the voltmeter. Then have them refer to the figure above and record the voltages between points A–B, A–E, B–C, B–D, and C–D.
- The experimental results should show a voltage of approximately 1.5 volts across points A–E, and B–D, an approximate voltage of 0.75 volts across B–C and C–D, and zero across A–B.
- Have them compare their experimental results with the predictions they made in the previous activity.
- Remove the lightbulb at points B–C from the circuit to leave a gap in the circuit.
- Ask students what they think the voltage across points B–C will now be. Have them share their thoughts and then test their ideas.
- The voltage across the gap should be approximately 1.5 volts.

Assess

After completing the chapter, see *Identifying Misconceptions* in the Study Guide at the end of the chapter.

chapter 13

Chapter Vocabulary

static electricity, p. 392
law of conservation of charge, p. 393
conductor, p. 395
insulator, p. 395
charging by contact, p. 395
charging by induction, p. 396
electric current, p. 400
voltage difference, p. 400
circuit, p. 401
resistance, p. 403
Ohm's law, p. 405
series circuit, p. 407
parallel circuit, p. 408
electric power, p. 410

Science Journal Possible answers: lamp–light energy and thermal energy; hair dryer–thermal energy and kinetic energy; toaster–thermal energy, TV–light energy and sound; CD player–sound.

INTERACTIVE CHALKBOARD with Image Bank
PowerPoint® Presentations

This CD-ROM is an editable Microsoft® PowerPoint® presentation that includes:

- a pre-made presentation for every chapter
- interactive graphics
- animations
- audio clips
- image bank
- all new section and chapter questions
- Standardized Test Practice
- transparencies
- Foldables directions
- links to gpescience.com

chapter 13

Electricity

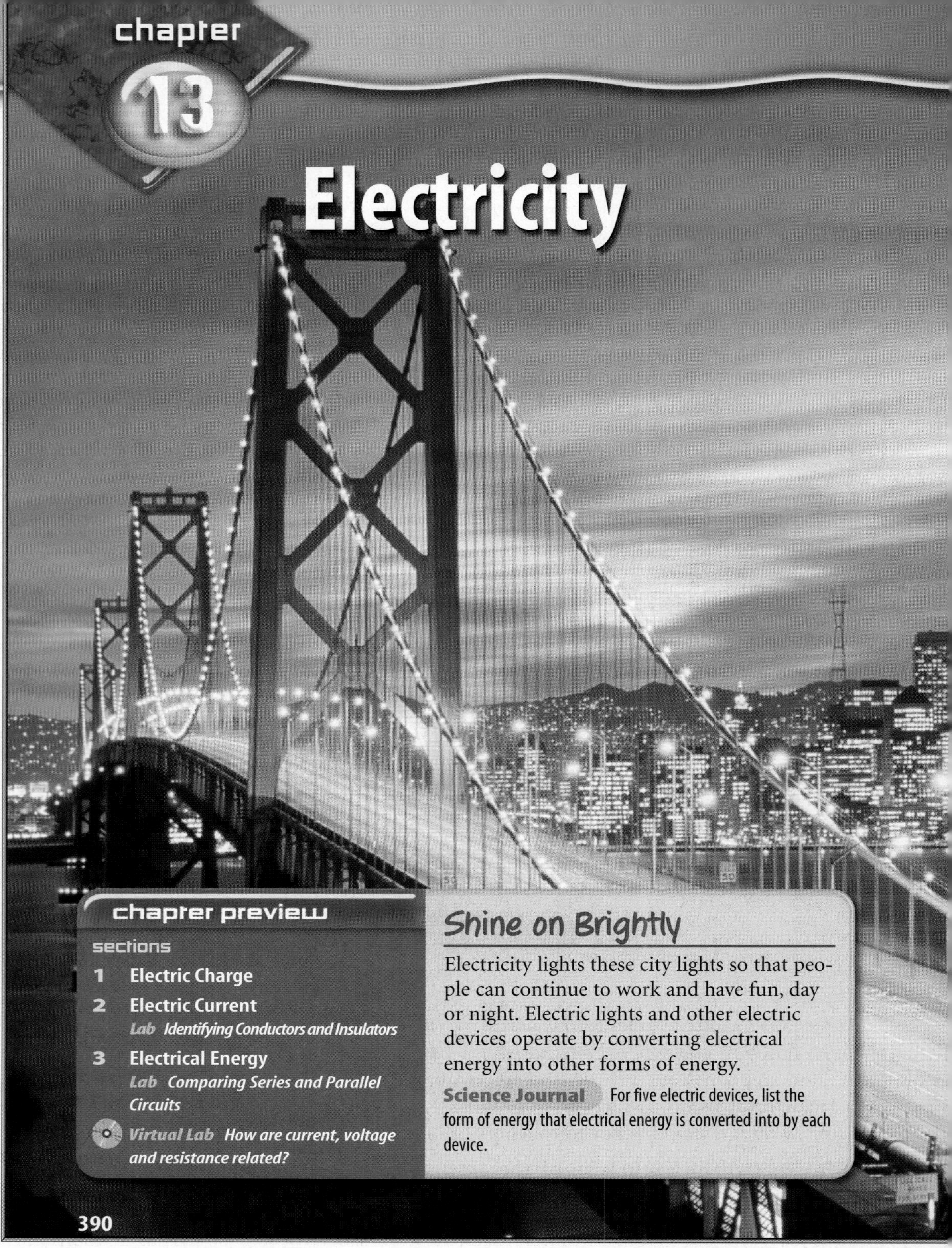

chapter preview

sections

Shine on Brightly

Electricity lights these city lights so that people can continue to work and have fun, day or night. Electric lights and other electric devices operate by converting electrical energy into other forms of energy.

Science Journal For five electric devices, list the form of energy that electrical energy is converted into by each device.

390

Theme Connection

Energy This chapter explores the fundamental nature of electrical energy—how it is produced, measured, transmitted, and transformed into other forms of energy.

About the Photo

Keeping the Lights On Cities are connected to large power distribution grids, or networks. Energy is transmitted through big power lines from generating plants, which are often hundreds of miles away. In the city the power lines usually run through underground tunnels to each of the buildings. Regional control centers use computers to regulate the flow of energy within and between power grids.

Start-Up Activities

Launch LAB

Electric Circuits

No lights! No CD players! No computers, video games or TVs! Without electricity, many of the things that make your life enjoyable wouldn't exist. For these devices to operate, electric current must flow in the electric circuits that are part of the device. Under what conditions does electric current flow in an electric circuit?

1. Obtain a battery, a flashlight bulb, and some wire.
2. Connect the materials so that the lightbulb lights.
3. Draw diagrams of all the ways that you were able to light the bulb.
4. Record a few of the ways that didn't work.
5. Can you light the bulb using only one wire and the battery?
6. **Think Critically** Write a paragraph describing the requirements to light the bulb. Write out a procedure for lighting the bulb and have a classmate follow your procedure.

FOLDABLES™ Study Organizer

Electricity Make the following Foldable to help you organize information about electricity.

STEP 1 **Fold** a sheet of paper vertically from top to bottom. Make the top edge about 2 cm shorter than the bottom edge.

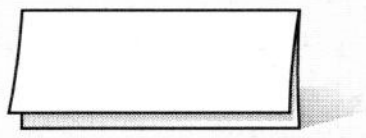

STEP 2 **Turn** lengthwise and fold into thirds.

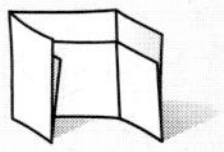

STEP 3 **Unfold and cut** only the top layer along both folds to make three tabs.

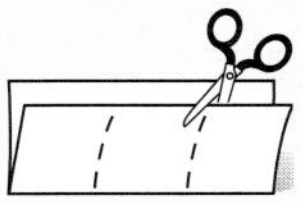

STEP 4 **Label** the Foldable as shown.

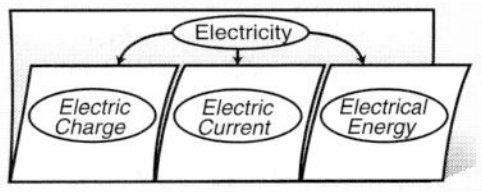

Organize Information As you read the chapter, organize the information you find about electric charge, electric current, and electrical energy under the appropriate tab.

Science Online Preview this chapter's content and activities at gpescience.com

Launch LAB

Purpose Students explore how electric light circuits work.

L2 ELL IN **Kinesthetic**

Preparation Strip insulation off the ends of the wires.

Materials battery, flashlight bulb, insulated wire, electrical tape or battery holder

Teaching Strategy If battery holders are used, demonstrate how to attach the wires to the clips. If not, show students how to tape the stripped ends of the wires to the battery.

Think Critically

In order to light the bulb, a continuous path must be made from the battery, through a wire, to the bottom of the bulb. The path must then lead from the side of the bulb, through another wire, and back to the battery.

Assessment

Process Have students make a list of configurations that did NOT light the bulb. Have them infer what was wrong in each. Use **Performance Assessment in the Science Classroom,** p. 89. L2 IN **Logical-Mathematical**

FOLDABLES™ Study Organizer **Dinah Zike Study Fold**

Student preparation materials for this Foldable are available in the **Chapter *Fast File* Resources.**

1 Motivate

INTERACTIVE CHALKBOARD An editable Microsoft® PowerPoint® presentation is available on **Interactive Chalkboard** CD-ROM.

Bellringer

Section Focus Transparencies also are available on the Interactive Chalkboard CD-ROM. L2 ELL

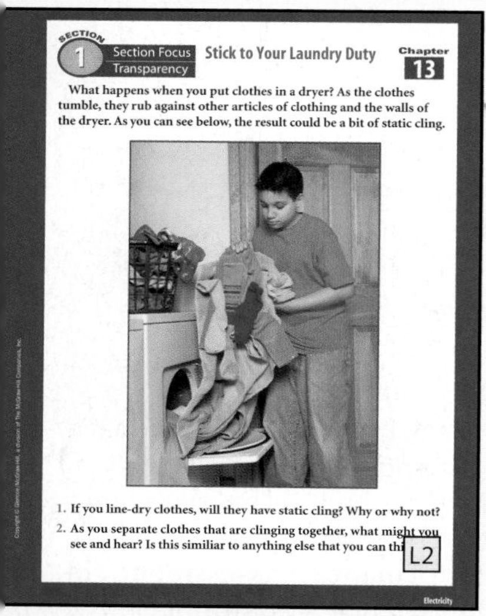
SECTION 1 Section Focus Transparency **Stick to Your Laundry Duty** Chapter 13

What happens when you put clothes in a dryer? As the clothes tumble, they rub against other articles of clothing and the walls of the dryer. As you can see below, the result could be a bit of static cling.

1. If you line-dry clothes, will they have static cling? Why or why not?
2. As you separate clothes that are clinging together, what might you see and hear? Is this similiar to anything else that you can thi L2

Electricity

Reading Preview

Tie to Prior Knowledge

Static Cling Ask students whether they have ever noticed clothes sticking together when they are taken out of the dryer. Explain that this is caused by static electricity, the topic of this section.

Predict Ask students what they think *charging by contact* and *charging by induction* might mean in a study of electricity. Some will surmise that contact means touching and induction means not touching. Have students preview the text to see if their predictions are correct.

section 1

Electric Charge

Reading Guide

What You'll Learn

- **Describe** how electric charges exert forces on each other.
- **Compare** the strengths of electric and gravitational forces.
- **Distinguish** between conductors and insulators
- **Explain** how objects become electrically charged.

Why It's Important

The electrical energy that all electrical devices use comes from the forces that electric charges exert on each other.

Review Vocabulary

atom: the smallest particle of an element

New Vocabulary

- static electricity
- law of conservation of charge
- conductor
- insulator
- charging by contact
- charging by induction

Positive and Negative Charge

Why does walking across a carpeted floor and then touching something sometimes result in a shock? The answer has to do with electric charge. Atoms contain particles called protons, neutrons, and electrons, as shown in **Figure 1.** Protons and electrons have electric charge, and neutrons have no electric charge.

There are two types of electric charge. Protons have positive electric charge and electrons have negative electric charge. The amount of positive charge on a proton equals the amount of negative charge on an electron. If an atom contains equal numbers of protons and electrons, the positive and negative charges cancel out and the atom has no net electric charge. Objects with no net charge are said to be electrically neutral.

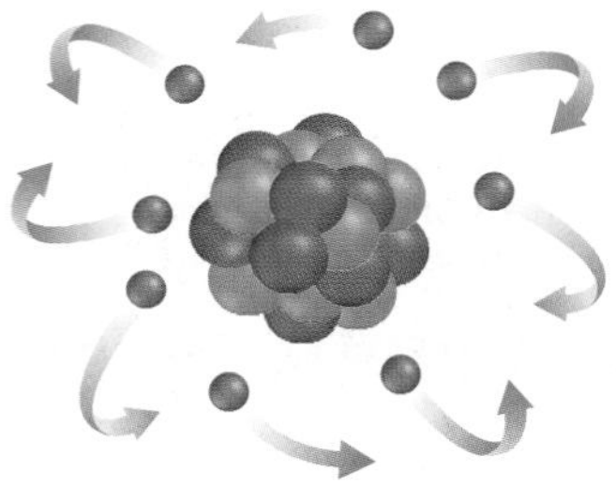

Figure 1 The center of an atom contains protons (orange) and neutrons (blue). Electrons (red) swarm around the atom's center.

Transferring Charge Electrons are bound more tightly to some atoms and molecules. For example, compared to the electrons in atoms in the carpet, electrons are bound more tightly to the atoms in the soles of your shoes. **Figure 2** shows that when you walk on carpet, electrons are transferred from the carpet to the soles of your shoes. The soles of your shoes have an excess of electrons and become negatively charged. The carpet has lost electrons and has an excess of positive charge. The carpet has become positively charged. The accumulation of excess electric charge on an object is called **static electricity.**

Section 1 Resource Manager

Chapter FAST FILE Resources

- Transparency Activity, p.42
- Note-taking Worksheets, pp. 31–33
- Directed Reading for Content Mastery, pp. 17–18
- Enrichment, p. 28
- MiniLAB, p. 3
- Reinforcement, p. 25

Before the shoe scuffs against the carpet, both the sole of the shoe and the carpet are electrically neutral.

As the shoe scuffs against the carpet, electrons are transferred from the carpet to the sole of the shoe.

Figure 2 Atoms in the shoe's sole hold their electrons more tightly than atoms in the carpet hold their electrons.
Explain *how the sole gained charge even though charge can't be created or destroyed.*

Conservation of Charge When an object becomes charged, charge is neither created nor destroyed. Usually it is electrons that have moved from one object to another. According to the **law of conservation of charge,** charge can be transferred from object to object, but it cannot be created or destroyed. Whenever an object becomes charged, electric charges have moved from one place to another.

Reading Check *How does an object become charged?*

Charges Exert Forces Have you noticed how clothes sometimes cling together when removed from the dryer? These clothes cling together because of the forces electric charges exert on each other. **Figure 3** shows that unlike charges attract each other and like charges repel each other. The force between electric charges also depends on the distance between charges. The force decreases as the charges get farther apart.

Just as for two electric charges, the force between any two objects that are electrically charged decreases as the objects get farther apart. This force also depends on the amount of charge on each object. As the amount of charge on either object increases, the electrical force also increases.

As clothes tumble in a dryer, the atoms in some clothes gain electrons and become negatively charged. Meanwhile the atoms in other clothes lose electrons and become positively charged. Clothes that are oppositely charged attract each other and stick together.

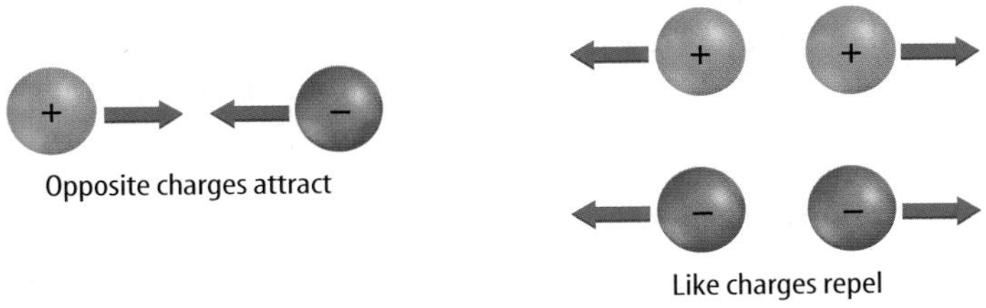

Figure 3 Positive and negative charges exert forces on each other.

2 Teach

Activity

Changes Have students use balloons, glass rods, polystyrene, puffed cereal, and pieces of silk and wool cloth to explore the ideas of positive and negative charge and the law of conservation of charge. L2 ELL
LS **Kinesthetic**

Caption Answer

Figure 2 Charge was transferred from the carpet to the shoe.

Use an Analogy

Swarming Bees Reinforce the idea that electrons, not atoms, move to cause static electricity by describing an atom as being like a swarm of bees (the electrons) around honey (the tightly held protons and neutrons). L1
LS **Visual-Spatial**

Reading Check

Answer Electrons move from one object to another. The object that gains electrons becomes negatively charged. The one that loses electrons becomes positively charged.

Reading Strategy

Double-Entry Notes Ask students to divide their papers into two columns and label the left column *Main Ideas* and the right column *Important Details*. Have them use topic headings and bold print words as entries on the left side. In the right column, have students add important details related to the main ideas.

Science Journal

Flyaway Hair Have students write a paragraph in their journals in which they use conservation of charge to explain why hair combed on a dry day may become "flyaway hair." Before combing, both the comb and hair have equal numbers of positive and negative charges. Combing causes hair to lose electrons to the comb. The hairs then have like charges on them and repel one another. This makes them "fly away." L2 LS **Linguistic, Logical-Mathematical, Intrapersonal**

Discussion

Conductivity Explain that, when substances are categorized as conductors, semiconductors, and insulators, they are being ranked according to the ease with which electrons move around in them (their conductivity). Then have students explain, in terms of electrons, the two extreme limits of conductivity; that is, what would zero conductivity mean and what would the maximum possible conductivity mean? Zero conductivity means that no electrons can move. Maximum conductivity means that electrons move freely; there is no resistance to electron movement. L2 LS **Logical-Mathematical**

Use Science Words

Word Meaning Students may have heard the word *semiconductor*. A semiconductor is a material, such as silicon or germanium, that is neither a good insulator nor a good conductor on its own, but becomes a good conductor when a tiny impurity is added to it. Have students find what semiconductors are used for. Semiconductors are used in computer chips and to make electronic components such as transistors and diodes. L3 LS **Linguistic**

Reading Check

Answer The electric force between protons and electrons is greater than the gravitational force between the particles.

Quick Demo
Static Shock

Materials pieces of wool carpeting, metal objects (doorknob, ring stand, etc.)

Estimated Time 5 minutes

Procedure Scuff your feet across the carpet several times and then touch the metal object, producing a spark as in **Figure 5**. Darkening the room may make the spark visible; works best on a dry day. Invite the students to try the demo.

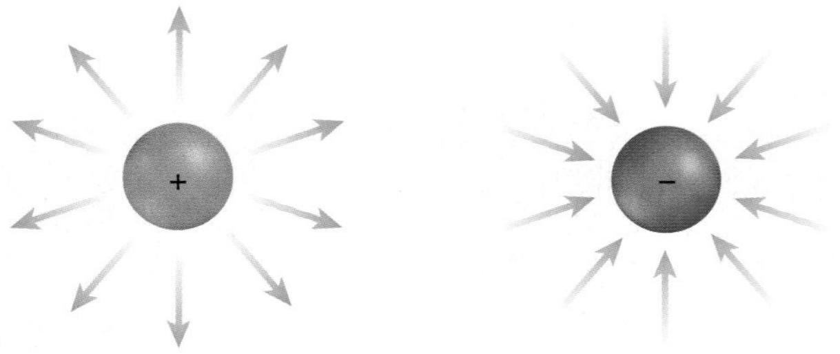

Figure 4 Surrounding every electric charge is an electric field that exerts forces on other electric charges. The arrows point in the direction a positive charge would move.

Figure 5 As you walk across a carpeted floor, excess electrons can accumulate on your body. When you reach for a metal doorknob, electrons flow from your hand to the doorknob and you see a spark.

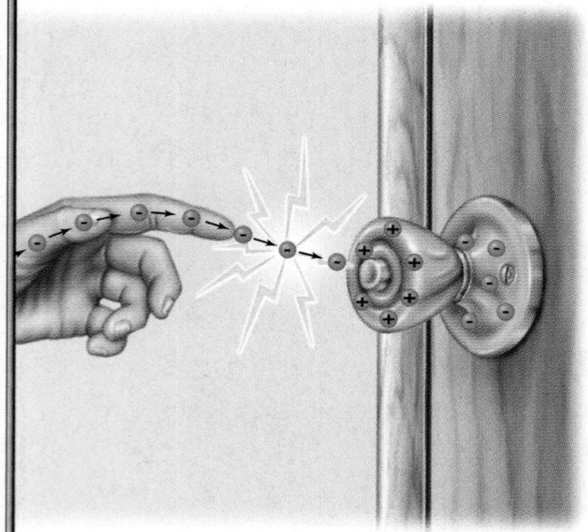

Electric Fields You might have seen bits of paper fly up and stick to a charged balloon. The bits of paper do not need to touch the charged balloon for an electric force to act on them. If the balloon and the paper are not touching, what causes the paper to move?

An electric field surrounds every electric charge, as shown in **Figure 4,** and exerts the force that causes other electric charges to be attracted or repelled. Any charge that is placed in an electric field will be pushed or pulled by the field. Electric fields are represented by arrows that show how the electric field would make a positive charge move.

The Strength of Electric Forces The force of gravity between you and Earth seems to be strong. Yet, compared with electric forces, the force of gravity is much weaker. For example, the attractive electric force between a proton and an electron in a hydrogen atom is about a thousand trillion trillion trillion times larger, or 10^{39} times larger, than the attractive gravitational force between the two particles.

In fact, all atoms are held together by electric forces between protons and electrons that are tremendously larger than the gravitational forces between the same particles. The chemical bonds that form between atoms in molecules also are due to the electric forces between the atoms. These electric forces are much larger than the gravitational forces between the atoms.

Reading Check *Compare the strength of electric and gravitational forces between protons and electrons.*

Some Observable Forces are due to Electric Forces Many of the forces that act on objects are due to the electric forces between atoms and molecules. All atoms contain electrically charged electrons and protons. When atoms or molecules get close enough, they can exert electric forces on each other that can be attractive or repulsive. For example, when you push on a door, the atoms on the surface of your hand get close to the atoms on the surface of the door. These atoms are close enough that they exert electric forces on each other. The electric forces the atoms in your hand exert on the atoms in the door cause the door to move. The frictional force between two surfaces in contact is due to the attractive electric forces between the atoms on the two surfaces. These forces cause the surfaces to stick together.

Curriculum Connection

Ancient Greeks and Electricity Have students research what ancient Greeks knew about electricity. Ancient people knew that if amber was rubbed, it would become charged. *Elektron* is Greek for "amber." L2 LS **Linguistic, Intrapersonal**

394 CHAPTER 13 Electricity

Conductors and Insulators

If you reach for a metal doorknob after walking across a carpet, you might see a spark. The spark is caused by electrons moving from your hand to the doorknob, as shown in **Figure 5.** Recall that electrons were transferred from the carpet to your shoes. How did these electrons move from your shoes to your hand?

Conductors A material in which electrons are able to move easily is a **conductor.** Electrons on your shoes repel each other and some are pushed onto your skin. Because your skin is a better conductor than your shoes, the electrons spread over your skin, including your hand.

The best electrical conductors are metals. The atoms in metals have electrons that are able to move easily through the material. Electric wires usually are made of copper because copper metal is one of the best conductors.

Insulators A material in which electrons are not able to move easily is an **insulator.** Electrons are held tightly to atoms in insulators. Most plastics are insulators. The plastic coating around electric wires, such as the one shown in **Figure 6,** prevents a dangerous electric shock when you touch the wire. Other good insulators are wood, rubber, and glass.

Charging Objects

You might have noticed socks clinging to each other after they have been tumbling in a clothes dryer. Rubbing two materials together can result in a transfer of electrons. Then one material is left with a positive charge and the other with an equal amount of negative charge. The process of transferring charge by touching or rubbing is called **charging by contact.**

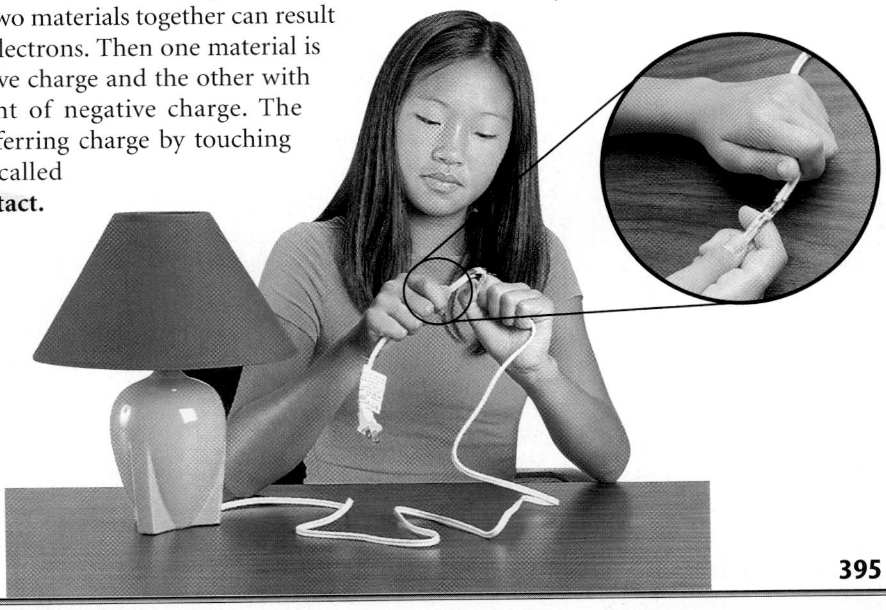

Figure 6 The plastic coating around wires is an insulator. A damaged electrical cord is hazardous when the conducting wire is exposed.
Explain *how the coating on a wire prevents an electric shock.*

Fun Fact

The process of charging by contact is known as *triboelectricity.* The triboelectric properties of materials are of significant interest to scientists working on missions to Mars. The dry, windy conditions on Mars provide an ideal environment for triboelectric charging.

Teacher FYI

Charging by Friction The process of charge transfer by rubbing is often called *charging by friction.* This term can be misleading because the process requires only light contact, not heating. The rubbing increases the area of contact, thereby enhancing the charge transfer.

Caption Answer

Figure 6 Electrons cannot travel easily through the insulator. The coating prevents the electrons in the wire from traveling into you body as an electric shock.

Active Reading

Cause-and-Effect Chart Have students design a cause-and-effect chart for static electricity. In the center, students write the topic, in this case, static electricity. To the left, they write the apparent causes of static electricity. On the right, they write the apparent effects of static electricity. L2 IN **Linguistic, Logical-Mathematical, Visual-Spatial**

Differentiated Instruction

Challenge Have students investigate various conductors and insulators. Suggest that they design and make a circuit to test these objects. They also should make a chart to show which items are conductors and which are insulators. L3 IN P **Kinesthetic**

Caption Answer

Figure 7 from the balloon to the sweater

Discussion

Winter Shocks Why are you more likely to get shocked when you touch a door handle in the winter than in the summer? In winter, the air in homes and buildings is often dry. Dry air is an insulator and doesn't easily discharge the excess charge on your body. The charge is therefore more likely to remain until your hand nears a door handle. L2 LS **Logical-Mathematical**

Use Science Words

Word Meaning Ask students to look up the word *static* and tell one reason why this word is appropriate for the term *static electricity* and one reason why the word is misleading. The word static means "not moving." It is true that static electricity is not in continual motion like current electricity. However, a static discharge is far from motionless; it is a very rapid, though noncontinuous, transfer of charge. L2 LS **Linguistic**

IDENTIFYING Misconceptions

Franklin's Kite Students may have heard the tale of Benjamin Franklin's kite being struck by lightning. Fortunately, the kite was *not* struck by lightning, but a negative charge from the air collected on a wire attached to the kite and traveled down the wet string. The sparks Franklin observed enabled him to show (as French scientists had done a month before) the relation between lightning and electricity.

Figure 7 The balloon on the left is neutral. The balloon on the right is negatively charged. It produces a positively charged area on the sleeve by repelling electrons. **Determine** *the direction of the electric force acting on the balloon.*

Charging at a Distance

Because electrical forces act at a distance, charged objects brought near a neutral object will cause electrons to rearrange their positions on the neutral object. Suppose you charge a balloon by rubbing it with a cloth. If you bring the negatively charged balloon near your sleeve, the extra electrons on the balloon repel the electrons in the sleeve. The electrons near the sleeve's surface move away from the balloon, leaving a positively charged area on the surface of the sleeve, as shown in **Figure 7.** As a result, the negatively charged balloon attracts the positively charged area of the sleeve. The rearrangement of electrons on a neutral object caused by a nearby charged object is called **charging by induction.** The sweater was charged by induction. The balloon will now cling to the sweater, being held there by an electrical force.

Lightning Have you ever seen lightning strike Earth? Lightning is a large static discharge. A static discharge is a transfer of charge between two objects because of a buildup of static electricity. A thundercloud is a mighty generator of static electricity. As air masses move and swirl in the cloud, areas of positive and negative charge build up. Eventually, enough charge builds up to cause a static discharge between the cloud and the ground. As the electric charges move through air, they collide with atoms and molecules. These collisions cause the atoms and molecules in air to emit light. You see this light as a spark, as shown in **Figure 8.**

Thunder Not only does lightning produce a brilliant flash of light, it also generates powerful sound waves. The electrical energy in a lightning bolt rips electrons off atoms in the air and produces great amounts of thermal energy. The surrounding air temperature can rise to about 25,000°C—several times hotter than the Sun's surface. The hot air in the lightning bolt's path expands rapidly, producing sound waves that you hear as thunder.

The sudden discharge of so much energy can be dangerous. It is estimated that Earth is struck by lightning about 100 times every second. Lightning strikes can cause power outages, injury, loss of life, and fires.

Science Online

Topic: Lightning
Visit gpescience.com for Web links to information about lightning strikes.

Activity Make a table listing tips on how people can protect themselves from lightning.

Science Journal

Thunderstorm Safety You often hear the warning, "Don't stand near a tree during a thunderstorm." Ask students to explain the reasoning behind this warning based on what they have learned in this section. Trees are more susceptible to lightning strikes because they are often the tallest objects around. L2 LS **Logical-Mathematical**

NATIONAL GEOGRAPHIC VISUALIZING LIGHTNING

Figure 8

Storm clouds can form when humid, Sun-warmed air rises to meet a colder air layer. As these air masses churn together, the stage is set for the explosive electrical display we call lightning. Lightning strikes when negative charges at the bottom of a storm cloud are attracted to positive charges on the ground.

A Convection currents in the storm cloud cause charge separation. The top of the cloud becomes positively charged, the bottom negatively charged.

B Negative charges on the bottom of the cloud induce a positive charge on the ground below the cloud by repelling negative charges in the ground.

C When the bottom of the cloud has accumulated enough negative charges, the attraction of the positive charges below causes electrons in the bottom of the cloud to move toward the ground.

D When the electrons get close to the ground, they attract positive charges that surge upward, completing the connection between cloud and ground. This is the spark you see as a lightning flash.

INTRACLOUD LIGHTNING never strikes Earth and can occur ten times more often in a storm than cloud-to-ground lightning.

NATIONAL GEOGRAPHIC

Visualizing Lightning

Have students examine the pictures and read the captions. Then ask the following questions.

When the warm humid air rises to meet the cold air, what causes the air masses to churn together? convection currents

What electric property causes the negative charges in the cloud to be attracted to the positive charges in the ground? like charges repel and unlike charges attract

Why does the ground below a cloud have a concentration of positive charges? because the negative charges in the bottom of the cloud repel the negative charges in the ground and attract the positive charges L2 LS **Visual-Spatial, Logical Mathematical**

Activity

Lightning Posters Have students research the different types of lightning and have them make posters illustrating them. If possible, students also could include statistical data involving the number of strikes that occur per year in their area. L2 LS **Visual-Spatial, Linguistic, Logical-Mathematical**

Differentiated Instruction

Challenge Have students find out more about storm chasers. These professionals intentionally go to areas where tornadoes, hurricanes, typhoons, etc. are occurring to study them. Students should report to the class what they learn. L3 LS **Visual-Spatial**

Text Question Answer

Possible answers: faucet (if plumbing is metal), electrical outlet ground

Mini LAB

Purpose Students analyze how charged objects interact with each other. L1 ELL IN **Logical-Mathematical,** IN **Kinesthetic**

Materials transparent tape

Teaching Strategy Cellophane tape often works, but transparent tape is better.

Analysis

1. The tapes attracted each other because they had opposite charges. When pulled apart, one became positively charged and one became negatively charged.
2. The pieces of tape repelled each other because they had like charges. Pulling both strips off the surface charged each the same way.

Assessment

Process Have students write up the procedures and results for this MiniLAB as lab reports. Use **Performance Assessment in the Science Classroom,** p. 119. L2 IN **Linguistic**

Try at Home

Figure 9 A lightning rod directs the charge from a lightning bolt safely to the ground.

Mini LAB

Investigating Charged Objects

Procedure

1. Fold over about 1 cm on the end of a **roll of transparent tape** to make a handle. Tear off a strip of tape about 10 cm long.
2. Stick the strip to a clean, dry, smooth surface, such as a countertop. Make another identical strip and stick it directly on top of the first.
3. Pull both pieces off the counter together and pull them apart. Then bring the nonsticky sides of both tapes together. What happens?
4. Now stick the two strips of tape side by side on the smooth surface. Pull them off and bring the nonsticky sides near each other again.

Analysis

1. What happened when you brought the pieces close together the first time? Were they charged alike or opposite? What might have caused this?
2. What did you observe when you brought the pieces together the second time? How were they charged? What did you do differently that might have changed the behavior?

Try at Home

Grounding The sensitive electronics in a computer can be harmed by large static discharges. A discharge can occur any time that charge builds up in one area. Providing a path for charge to reach Earth prevents any charge from building up. Earth is a large, neutral object that is also a conductor of charge. Any object connected to Earth by a good conductor will transfer any excess electric charge to Earth. Connecting an object to Earth with a conductor is called grounding. For example, to prevent damage by lightning, buildings often have a metal lightning rod that provides a conducting path from the highest point on the building to the ground, as shown in **Figure 9.**

Plumbing fixtures, such as metal faucets, sinks, and pipes, often provide a convenient ground connection. Look around. Do you see anything that might act as a path to the ground?

Detecting Electric Charge

The presence of electric charges can be detected by an electroscope. One kind of electroscope is made of two thin, metal leaves attached to a metal rod with a knob at the top. The leaves are allowed to hang freely from the metal rod. When the device is not charged, the leaves hang straight down, as shown in **Figure 10A.**

Suppose a negatively charged rod touches the knob. Because the metal is a good conductor, electrons travel down the rod into the leaves. Both leaves become negatively charged as they gain electrons, as shown in **Figure 10B.** Because the leaves have similar charges, they repel each other.

If a glass rod is rubbed with silk, electrons move away from the atoms in the glass rod and build up on the silk. The glass rod becomes positively charged.

Visual Learning

Figure 9 The lightning rod's long, narrow shape causes charges induced into it to bunch together and produce a strong electric field. This electric field causes nearby air molecules to be ionized, enabling charges to travel from the storm cloud to the lightning rod. This reduces the likelihood of a lightning strike elsewhere. Look for lightning rods on buildings in your area. L2 IN **Visual-Spatial**

Post Reading

Question A Partner Put students in pairs and ask them to review the contents of the chapter by using their notes. Have them form three questions that are central to the learning in this section. They should then take turns asking the class their questions and monitoring responses for accuracy and completeness.

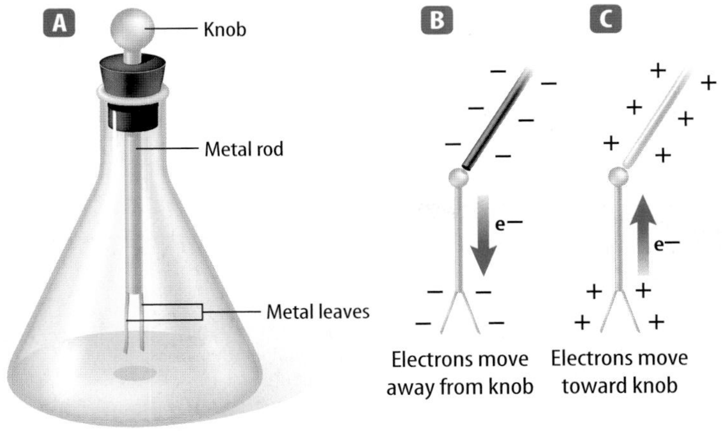

Figure 10 Notice the position of the leaves on the electroscope when they are **A** uncharged, **B** negatively charged, and **C** positively charged.
Infer *How can you tell whether an electroscope is positively or negatively charged?*

When the positively charged glass rod is brought into contact with the metal knob of an uncharged electroscope, electrons flow out of the metal leaves and onto the rod. The leaves repel each other because each leaf becomes positively charged as it loses electrons, as shown in **Figure 10C.**

section 1 review

Summary

Positive and Negative Charge

- There are two types of electric charge: positive charge and negative charge.
- Electric charges can be transferred between objects but cannot be created or destroyed.
- Like charges repel and unlike charges attract.
- An electric charge is surrounded by an electric field that exerts forces on other charges.

Electrical Conductors and Insulators

- A conductor contains electrons that can move easily. The best conductors are metals.
- The electrons in an electrical insulator do not move easily. Rubber, glass, and most plastics are examples of insulators.

Charging Objects

- Electric charge can be transferred between objects by bringing them into contact.
- Charging by induction occurs when the electric field around a charged object rearranges electrons in a nearby neutral object.

Self Check

1. **Define** static electricity.
2. **Describe** how lightning is produced.
3. **Explain** why electrically neutral objects can become electrically charged even though charge cannot be created or destroyed.
4. **Predict** what would happen if you touched the knob of a positively charged electroscope with another positively charged object.
5. **Think Critically** Humid air is a better electrical conductor than dry air. Explain why you're more likely to receive a shock after walking across a carpet when the air is dry than when the air is humid.

Applying Math

6. **Determine Lightning Strikes** Earth is struck by lightning 100 times each second. How many times is Earth struck by lightning in one day?
7. **Calculate Electric Force** A balloon with a mass of 0.020 kg is charged by rubbing and then is stuck to the ceiling. If the acceleration of gravity is 9.8 m/s^2, what is the electrical force on the balloon?

Caption Answer

Figure 10 A rod with an opposite charge will cause the leaves to fall.

3 Assess

DAILY INTERVENTION

Check for Understanding

Kinesthetic/ Interpersonal Pair up students and have one pair (one of which has long fine hair) come to the front of the class. Give the pair an inflated balloon. Have one student rub the balloon on his clothing then bring it near the other's long fine hair. Observe the attraction of the hair to the balloon. Have pairs of students confer and write down the answers to these questions: What causes the hair to be attracted to the balloon? What kind of transfer of electric charge occurs? How does the charge on the balloon compare to that on the hair? Discuss the students' answers. L2 IS **Linguistic, Logical-Mathematical**

Reteach

Detecting Electric Charge Use an electroscope to touch various objects, some of which are charged. Have students discuss the results based on what they have learned. L1 ELL IS **Visual-Spatial, Kinesthetic, Logical-Mathematical**

Assessment

Content Have students create posters showing the different methods of transferring electric charge. Use **PASC,** p. 145. L2 IS **Visual Spatial**

section 1 review

1. Static electricity is the accumulation of excess electric charge on an object.
2. Lightning occurs when excess negative charge in clouds discharges to regions of positive charge on the ground or in other clouds.
3. Electrically neutral objects can become charged when they gain or lose electric charges.
4. The leaves of the electroscope would remain apart.
5. Excess electric charge remains on an object in dry air, which is an insulator. Humid air is a better conductor and allows any excess electric charge to drain away into the air.
6. 8,640,000 times/day
7. 0.20 N

section 2 Electric Current

1 Motivate

INTERACTIVE CHALKBOARD PowerPoint® Presentations An editable Microsoft® PowerPoint® presentation is available on **Interactive Chalkboard** CD-ROM.

Bellringer

Section Focus Transparencies also are available on the Interactive Chalkboard CD-ROM.
L2 ELL

SECTION 2 Section Focus Transparency — Go with the Flow — Chapter 13

Do you see how the water flows down the cliff? Water takes the path of least resistance—it flows where it's easiest for water to go. Electric currents flow and experience resistance, too.

1. Which do you think has more energy, the waterfall in the picture or Niagara Falls which are higher and have more water flowing over? Explain your answer.
2. How do people use the energy in water currents?

L2

Electricity

Reading Preview

Tie to Prior Knowledge

Battery Trouble Ask students if they know what happens when a battery dies in a CD player. Explain that the battery is no longer able to cause enough electric current to operate the CD player. Tell students they will learn what an electric current is and how it is produced.
L2 LS **Logical-Mathematical**

Set a Purpose Before reading, ask students to scan the text noticing figures and bold print. Provide prompts such as the following to spark interest and set a purpose: Why did the author include a water system illustration in a chapter on electricity?

Reading Guide

What You'll Learn

- **Describe** how voltage difference causes current to flow.
- **Explain** how batteries produce a voltage difference in a circuit.
- **List** the factors that affect an object's electrical resistance.
- **Define** Ohm's law.

Why It's Important

You control electric current every time you change the volume on a TV, stereo, or CD player.

Review Vocabulary

pressure: amount of force exerted per unit area

New Vocabulary

- electric current
- voltage difference
- circuit
- resistance
- Ohm's law

Figure 11 Electric forces in a material cause electric current to flow, just as forces in the water cause water to flow.

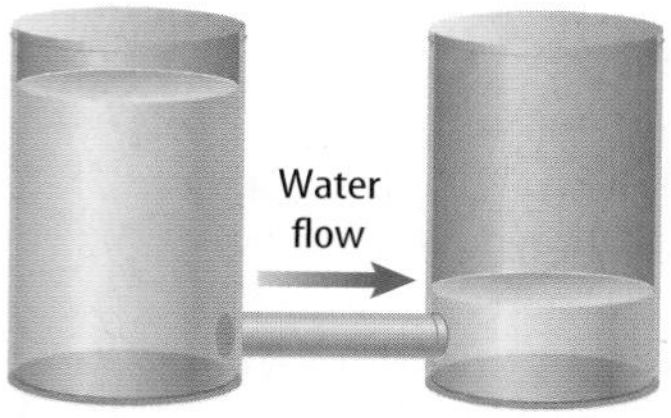

The force that causes water to flow is related to a pressure difference.

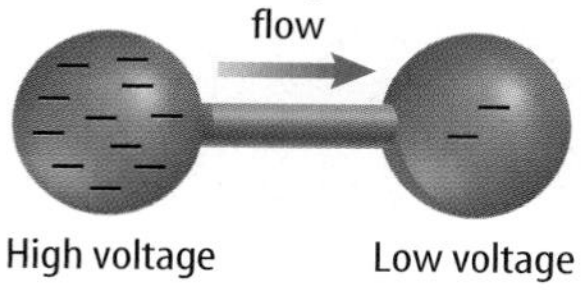

The force that causes a current to flow is related to a voltage difference.

Current and Voltage Difference

When a spark jumps between your hand and a metal doorknob, electric charges move quickly from one place to another. The net movement of electric charges in a single direction is an **electric current.** In a metal wire, or any material, electrons are in constant motion in all directions. As a result, there is no net movement of electrons in one direction. However, when an electric current flows, electrons continue their random movement, but they also drift in the direction that the electron current flows.

Electric current is measured in amperes. One ampere is equal to 6,250 million billion electrons flowing past a point every second.

Reading Check *What is electric current?*

Voltage Difference The movement of an electron in an electric current is similar to a ball bouncing down a flight of stairs. Even though the ball changes direction when it strikes a stair, the net motion of the ball is downward. The downward motion of the ball is caused by the force of gravity. When a current flows, the net movement of electric charges is caused by an electric force acting on the charges.

In some ways, the electric force that causes charges to flow is similar to the force acting on the water in a pipe. Water flows from higher pressure to lower pressure, as shown in **Figure 11.** In a similar way, electric charge flows when there is a voltage difference. A **voltage difference** is related to the force that causes electric charges to flow. Voltage difference is measured in volts.

Section 2 Resource Manager

Chapter *FAST FILE* Resources

- Transparency Activity, p. 43
- Directed Reading for Content Mastery, p. 19
- MiniLAB, p. 4
- Enrichment, p. 29
- Lab Activity, pp. 9–12
- Reinforcement, p. 26
- Lab Worksheet, pp. 5–6

Home and Community Involvement, p. 25

Mathematics Skill Activities, p. 3

Figure 12 Water or electric current will flow continually only through a closed loop. If any part of the loop is broken or disconnected, the flow stops.

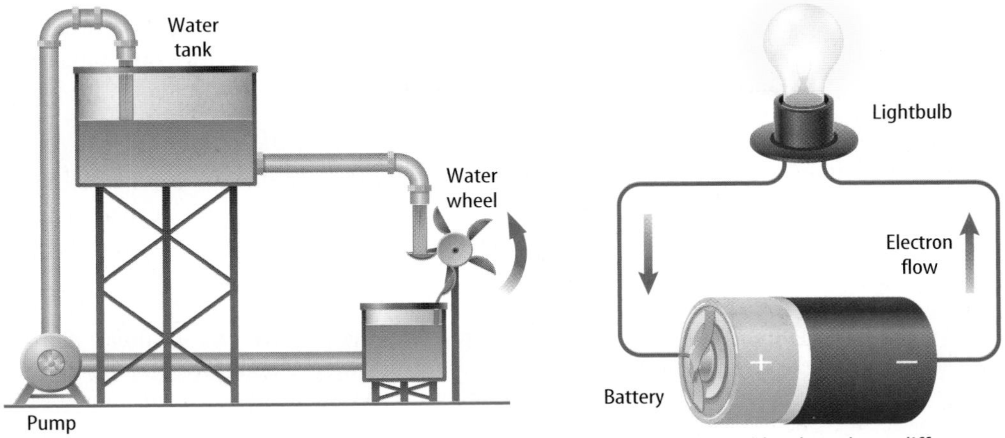

A pump provides the pressure difference that keeps water flowing.

A battery provides the voltage difference that keeps electric current flowing.

Electric Circuits One way to have flowing water perform work is shown in **Figure 12.** Water flows out of the tank and falls on a paddle wheel, causing it to rotate. A pump then provides a pressure difference that lifts the water back up into the tank. The constant flow of water would stop if the pump stopped working. The flow of water also would stop if one of the pipes broke. Then water no longer could flow in a closed loop, and the paddle wheel would stop rotating.

Figure 12 also shows an electric current doing work by lighting a lightbulb. Just as the water current stops flowing if there is no longer a closed loop to flow through, the electric current stops if there is no longer a closed path to follow. A closed path that electric current follows is a **circuit.** If the circuit in **Figure 12** is broken by removing the battery, the lightbulb, or one of the wires, current will not flow.

Batteries

To keep water flowing continually in the water circuit in **Figure 12,** a pump is used to provide a pressure difference. In a similar way, to keep an electric current continually flowing in the electric circuit in **Figure 12,** a voltage difference needs to be maintained in the circuit. A battery can provide the voltage difference that is needed to keep current flowing in a circuit. Current flows as long as there is a closed path that connects one battery terminal to the other battery terminal.

Visual Learning

Figure 12 Use the figure to have students identify the corresponding parts of the water flow to electric current analogy. pipes-wires; pump-battery; water wheel-lightbulb L2 IN Visual-Spatial

Teacher FYI

Battery Makeup A 9-volt battery is actually composed of six small 1.5-volt batteries connected in series. A 12-volt car battery is a series of six 2-volt batteries.

2 Teach

Reading Check

Answer the net movement of electric charge in a single direction

Identifying Misconceptions

Current Early researchers established the convention that current flows from the positive terminal to the negative terminal of a battery. After the discovery of the electron, researchers realized that the electrons actually move from the negative terminal to the positive terminal. Today, we talk about conventional current, which is the direction of the hypothetical flow of positive charges. However, it is negatively-charged electrons that flow in a wire. It is important for students to learn these distinctions and to realize that positive charges do not flow through the wire.

Quick Demo
Simple Cells

Materials small glass or plastic container about three-fourths full of acid solution (lemon juice, tomato juice, or vinegar), strip of copper, strip of zinc or silver, two wires with alligator clips, sensitive voltmeter (0-1 VDC)

Estimated Time five minutes

Procedure Clip one end of a wire to one metal strip and the other end to the voltmeter. Repeat for the second metal strip and wire. Place the metal strips in the acid solution, taking care that the strips do not touch each other. Have a student read the voltage difference that the cell produces between the two electrodes.

Mini LAB

Purpose Students discover the effect of adding an additional battery to a circuit. COOP LEARN

L2 **Kinesthetic, Visual-Spatial,** LS **Logical-Mathematical**

Materials D-cell batteries (2), 3-volt bulbs and sockets (3), insulated wire

Teaching Strategy Tell students to leave the bulbs burning only long enough to make observations. Caution them to not touch a hot bulb.

Troubleshooting Connecting more than two batteries per lamp in series will shorten the bulb's life or cause it to burn out.

Analysis

1. 1.5 volts, 3.0 volts
2. As the voltage difference increases across the lamp, the charge flowing through it increases.

Assessment

Performance Have students design and label several possible arrangements showing how to light a bulb at different levels of brightness. Have them demonstrate each method. Use **PASC,** p. 127. L2 LS **Kinesthetic, Visual-Spatial**

INTEGRATE Chemistry **Content Background**

Each cell of a battery has an *electrolyte* (a chemical that conducts charge) and two *electrodes* (terminals). One electrode provides electrons to the electrolyte. The other electrode takes electrons from the electrolyte. In dry cells the electrolyte is a paste, and in wet cells it is a liquid.

Mini LAB

Investigating Battery Addition

Procedure

1. Make a circuit by using wire to link two **bulbs** and one **D-cell battery** in a loop. Observe the brightness of the bulbs.
2. Assemble a new circuit by linking two bulbs and two D-cell batteries in a loop. Observe the brightness of the bulbs.

Analysis

1. What is the voltage difference of each D cell? Add them together to find the total voltage difference for the circuit you tested in step 2.
2. Assuming that a brighter bulb indicates a greater current, what can you conclude about the relationship between the voltage difference and current?

Dry-Cell Batteries You probably are most familiar with dry-cell batteries. A cell consists of two electrodes surrounded by a material called an electrolyte. The electrolyte enables charges to move from one electrode to the other. Look at the dry cell shown in **Figure 13.** One electrode is the carbon rod, and the other is the zinc container. The electrolyte is a moist paste containing several chemicals. The cell is called a dry cell because the electrolyte is a moist paste, not a liquid solution.

INTEGRATE Chemistry When the two terminals of a dry-cell battery are connected in a circuit, such as in a flashlight, a reaction involving zinc and several chemicals in the paste occurs. Electrons are transferred between some of the compounds in this chemical reaction. As a result, the carbon rod becomes positive, forming the positive (+) terminal. Electrons accumulate on the zinc, making it the negative (−) terminal.

The voltage difference between these two terminals causes current to flow through a closed circuit. You make a battery when you connect two or more cells together to produce a higher voltage difference.

Wet-Cell Batteries Another commonly used type of battery is the wet-cell battery. A wet cell, like the one shown in **Figure 13,** contains two connected plates made of different metals or metallic compounds in a conducting solution. A wet-cell battery contains several wet cells connected together.

Figure 13 Chemical reactions in batteries produce a voltage difference between the positive and negative terminals. **Identify** *when these chemical reactions occur.*

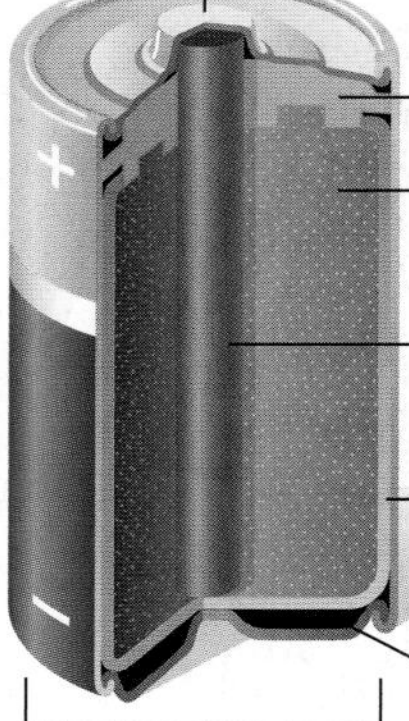

In this dry cell, chemical reactions in the moist paste transfer electrons to the zinc container.

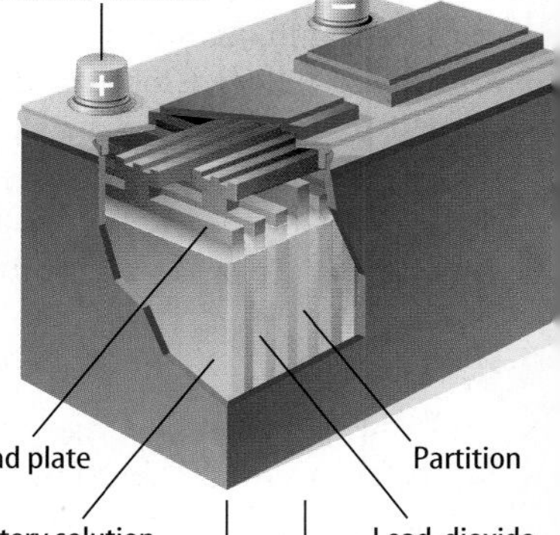

In this wet cell, chemical reactions transfer electrons from the lead plates to the lead-dioxide plates.

Caption Answer

Figure 13 The chemical reactions occur when the battery is connected in a circuit.

Differentiated Instruction

Learning Disabled To emphasize the usefulness of batteries, ask students to list as many things as they can think of that use batteries. Encourage them to think of many different size batteries, from watch batteries to car batteries.

Lead-Acid Batteries Most car batteries are lead-acid batteries, like the wet-cell battery shown in **Figure 13.** A lead-acid battery contains a series of six wet cells made up of lead and lead dioxide plates in a sulfuric acid solution. The chemical reaction in each cell provides a voltage difference of about 2 V, giving a total voltage difference of 12 V. As a car is driven, the alternator recharges the battery by sending current through the battery in the opposite direction to reverse the chemical reaction.

A voltage difference is provided at electrical outlets, such as a wall socket. This voltage difference usually is higher than the voltage difference provided by batteries. Most types of household devices are designed to use the voltage difference supplied by a wall socket. In the United States, the voltage difference across the two holes in a wall socket is usually 120 V. Some wall sockets supply 240 V, which is required by appliances such as electric ranges and electric clothes dryers.

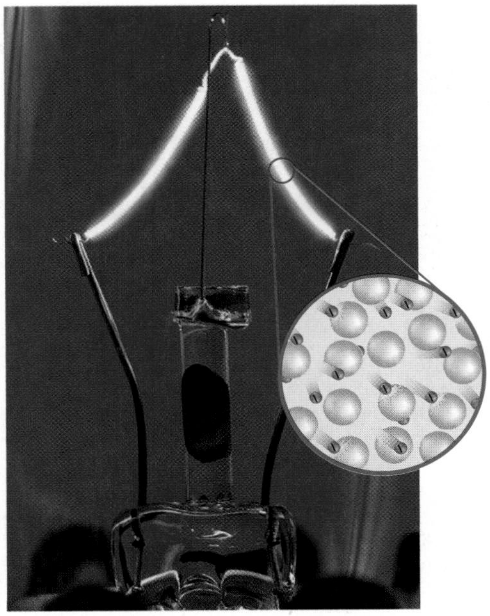

Figure 14 As electrons move through the filament in a lightbulb, they bump into metal atoms. Due to the collisions, the metal heats up and starts to glow.
Describe *the energy conversions that occur in a lightbulb filament.*

Resistance

Flashlights use dry-cell batteries to provide the electric current that lights a lightbulb. What makes a lightbulb glow? Look at the lightbulb in **Figure 14.** Part of the circuit through the bulb is a thin wire called a filament. As the electrons flow through the filament, they bump into the metal atoms that make up the filament. In these collisions, some of the electrical energy of the electrons is converted into thermal energy. Eventually, the metal filament becomes hot enough to glow, producing radiant energy that can light up a dark room.

Resisting the Flow of Current Electric current loses energy as it moves through the filament because the filament resists the flow of electrons. **Resistance** is the tendency of a material to oppose the flow of electrons, changing electrical energy into thermal energy and light. With the exception of some substances that become superconductors at low temperatures, all materials have some electrical resistance. Electrical conductors have much less resistance than insulators. Resistance is measured in ohms (Ω).

Copper is an excellent conductor and has low resistance to the flow of electrons. Copper is used in household wiring because only a small amount of electrical energy is converted to thermal energy as current flows in copper wires.

IDENTIFYING Misconceptions

Voltage Students sometimes think that voltage is the same at different places in a circuit and it exists only when current flows. See page 192F for teaching strategies that address this misconception.

Use an Analogy

Water Flow You can describe resistance by building on the analogy of charge flow being similar to water flow. Suppose a jug of water has a large hole in one side and a small hole in the other side. More water will flow out of the large hole. Similarly, a wire with a large diameter has less resistance and therefore carries greater current than a smaller-diameter wire.

Discussion

Making Thermal Energy Should the heating elements on a stove top be made of high-resistance or low-resistance material? high-resistance L2 LS **Logical-Mathematical**

Caption Answer

Figure 14 Electrical energy is converted into thermal energy and radiant energy.

Activity

An Electron's Story Have the students write a short story describing an electron's journey through a simple circuit from the point of view of the electron. The circuit should include a battery, some wire, and a lightbulb. L2 **Linguistic**

Reading Strategy

Context Clues Assign a new vocabulary word to each student. Have students look up the words in the chapter. Then, have them create a sentence using the word in a way that will allow a partner to predict its meaning. Clarify meanings as needed.

Curriculum Connection

Math In a car battery, the following chemical reaction occurs: $Pb + PbO_2 + H_2SO_4 \rightarrow PbSO_4 + H_2O$. Use coefficients to balance this equation. $Pb + PbO_2 + 2H_2SO_4 \rightarrow 2PbSO_4 + 2H_2O$

SECTION 2 Electric Current 403

Reading Check

Answer The resistance increases as the length of the wire increases and as its thickness decreases.

IDENTIFYING Misconceptions

Static Danger When it comes to electricity and our bodies, it often is true that high voltages are dangerous and low voltages are safer. Students frequently are not aware of a common situation where this is not true. In many static electricity situations, such as walking across a carpet, sparks of 1,500 volts or higher are generated. No damage occurs to our bodies because there is little actual current flow.

Virtual Labs

Electric Charges *How are current, voltage, and resistance related?*

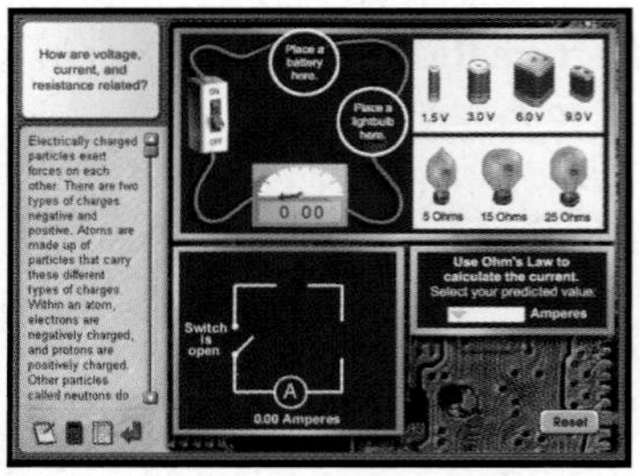

Post Reading

Compare and Contrast Ask students to write a brief summary of a wet cell, a dry cell, and lead-acid batteries by using comparison/contrast words such as *both*, *in comparison*, *the difference between*, *more*, *less*, or *about the same*. For example, Both wet cell and lead-acid batteries use lead as a component, but dry cells do not.

Temperature, Length, and Thickness The electric resistance of most materials usually increases as the temperature of the material increases. The resistance of an object such as a wire also depends on the length and diameter of the wire. The resistance of a wire, or any conductor, increases as the wire becomes longer. The resistance also increases as the wire becomes thinner.

In a 60-W lightbulb, the filament is a piece of tungsten wire made into a short coil a few centimeters long. The uncoiled wire is about 2 m long and only about 0.25 mm thick. Even though tungsten metal is a good conductor, by making the wire thin and long, the resistance of the filament is made large enough to cause the bulb to glow.

Reading Check *How does changing the length and thickness of a wire affect its resistance?*

The Current in a Simple Circuit

A simple electric circuit contains a source of voltage difference, such as a battery, a device that has resistance, such as a lightbulb, and conductors that connect the device to the battery terminals. When the wires are connected to the battery terminals, current flows in the closed path. An example of a simple circuit is shown in **Figure 15.**

The voltage difference, current, and resistance in a circuit are related. If the voltage difference doesn't change, decreasing the resistance increases the current in the circuit, as shown in **Figure 15.** Also, if the resistance doesn't change, increasing the voltage difference increases the current.

Figure 15 The amount of current flowing through a circuit is related to the amount of resistance in the circuit.

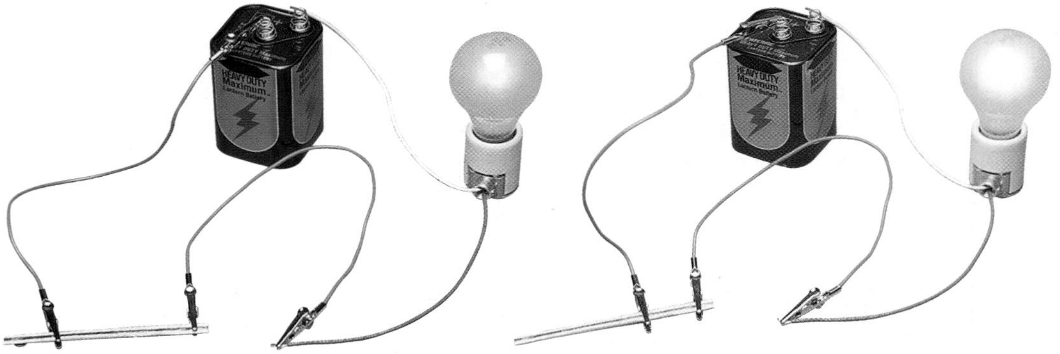

When the clips on the graphite rod are farther apart, the resistance of the rod in the circuit is larger. As a result, less current flows in the circuit and the lightbulb is dim.

When the clips on the graphite rod are closer together, the resistance of the rod in the circuit is less. As a result, more current flows in the circuit and the lightbulb is brighter.

Teacher FYI

High-Temperature Conductivity Conductivity depends on temperature. A higher temperature causes more movement of atoms and generally results in lower conductivity. However, the increased movement of atoms in some substances, such as carbon and semiconductors, frees electrons so that higher temperatures for these substances results in higher conductivity.

Ohm's Law The relationship among voltage difference, current, and resistance in a circuit is known as Ohm's law. According to **Ohm's law,** the current in a circuit equals the voltage difference divided by the resistance. Ohm's law can be written as the following equation, where *I* stands for electric current.

Ohm's Law

$$\text{current (in amperes)} = \frac{\text{voltage difference (in volts)}}{\text{resistance (in ohms)}}$$

$$I = \frac{V}{R}$$

Ohm's law provides a way to measure the resistance of objects and materials. First, the equation above is written as:

$$R = \frac{V}{I}$$

An object is connected to a source of voltage difference and the current flowing in the circuit is measured. The object's resistance then equals the voltage difference divided by the measured current.

INTEGRATE Health

Current and the Human Body When an electric shock occurs, an electric current moves through some part of the body. The damage caused by an electric shock depends on how large the current is. Research the effects of current on the human body. Make a table showing the effects on the body at different amounts of current.

section 2 review

Summary

Current and Voltage Difference

- Electric current is the net movement of electric charge in a single direction.
- A voltage difference is related to the force that causes charges to flow.
- A circuit is a closed, conducting path.

Batteries

- Chemical reactions in a battery produce a voltage difference between the positive and negative battery terminals.
- Two commonly used types of batteries are dry-cell batteries and wet-cell batteries.

Resistance and Ohm's Law

- Resistance is the tendency of a material to oppose the flow of electrons.
- Ohm's law relates the current, I, resistance, R, and voltage difference, V, in a circuit:

$$I = \frac{V}{R}$$

Self Check

1. **Compare and contrast** a current traveling through a circuit with a static discharge.
2. **Explain** how a carbon-zinc dry cell produces a voltage difference between the positive and negative terminals.
3. **Identify** two ways to increase the current in a simple circuit.
4. **Compare and contrast** the flow of water in a pipe and the flow of electrons in a wire.
5. **Think Critically** Explain how the resistance of a lightbulb filament changes after the light has been turned on.

Applying Math

6. **Calculate** the voltage difference in a circuit with a resistance of 25 ohms if the current is 0.5 A.
7. **Calculate Resistance** A current of 0.5 A flows in a 60-W lightbulb when the voltage difference between the ends of the filament is 120 V. What is the resistance of the filament?

More Section Review gpescience.com

INTEGRATE Health

Current and the Human Body Currents of about 0.5 mA can cause a slight shock to a person. Higher currents cause increasing degrees of pain and loss of muscle control. Currents higher than about 150 mA will likely result in death.

3 Assess

DAILY INTERVENTION

Check for Understanding

Visual-Logical Without students seeing, reverse one battery in a flashlight. Show students that the flashlight does not work. Ask them to suggest possible reasons why an electric circuit may not work. L2 LS **Logical-Mathematical, Visual-Spatial**

Reteach

Ohm's Law Use the diagram below to help students remember how to rearrange Ohm's law. When the desired variable is covered, the other two variables are in proper mathematical order. L2 LS **Visual-Spatial**

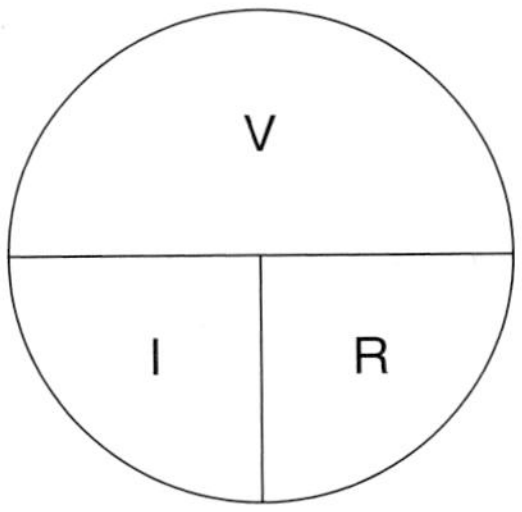

section 2 review

1. Both are a movement of electrons from the negative to the positive charge. A circuit has a continuous current provided by a voltage source. A static discharge is a very rapid, non-continuous transfer of charge.
2. A chemical reaction causes a negative charge on the zinc container and a positive charge on the carbon rod.
3. Increasing the voltage difference or decreasing the resistance will increase the current.
4. Water flow is the movement of molecules, not just electrons. The larger the diameter of pipe or wire, the greater the flow of water or electrons.
5. A lightbulb filament heats up as an electic current flows through it, causing an increase in the wire's resistance. According to Ohm's Law, the highter resistance results in a lower current.
6. 12.5 volts
7. 240 ohms

Assessment

Process Show the students a flashlight and ask them to draw its electric circuit. Have them calculate the current that flows if the resistance of the bulb is 20 ohms. Circuit should show battery, wires, bulb, and possibly a switch. The current will depend on voltage of batteries. L2 P

LS **Visual-Spatial, Logical-Mathematical**

BENCH TESTED

Video Lab available for this Lab.

Real-World Problem

Purpose Students will compare the conductivity of various materials. L2 LS **Kinesthetic, Visual-Spatial**

Process collect data, make and use tables, record observations, draw conclusions

Time Required 40 minutes

Procedure

Teaching Strategy Have a collection of items ready for students to test, but let students offer additional items to be tested.

Troubleshooting Make sure all connections in the circuit have good contact.

Conclude and Apply

1. Answers will vary. Students should realize that metallic items will conduct electricity.
2. They are metallic.
3. They are nonmetallic.
4. Materials that allow the lightbulb to glow have metallic bonding. Materials that do not allow the lightbulb to glow are nonmetallic.
5. Metallic materials will conduct electricity; bad connections will prevent the lightbulb from lighting.
6. Answers will vary.

LAB

Identifying Conductors and Insulators

The resistance of an insulator is so large that only a small current flows when it is connected in a circuit. As a result, a lightbulb connected in a circuit with an insulator usually will not glow. In this lab, you will use the brightness of a lightbulb to identify conductors and insulators.

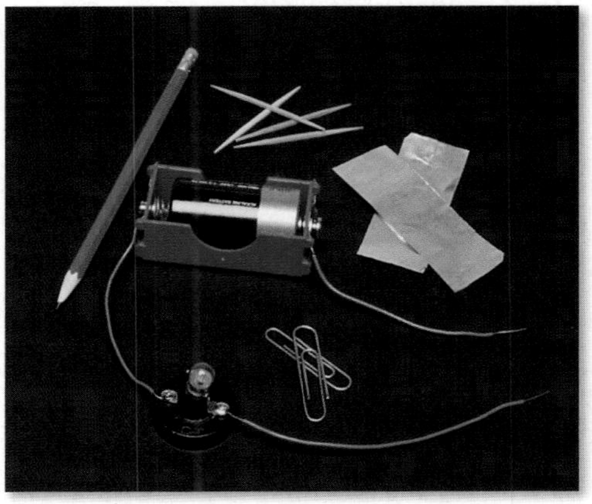

Real-World Problem

What materials are conductors and what materials are insulators?

Goals

- **Identify** conductors and insulators.
- **Describe** the common characteristics of conductors and insulators.

Materials

battery	bulb holder
flashlight bulb	insulated wire

Safety Precautions

Procedure

1. Set up an incomplete circuit as pictured in the photograph.
2. Touch the free bare ends of the wires to various objects around the room. Test at least 12 items.
3. Copy the table below. In your table, record which materials make the lightbulb glow and which don't.

Material Tested with Lightbulb Circuit	
Lightbulb Glows	Lightbulb Doesn't Glow
Results will vary	Results will vary

Conclude and Apply

1. Is there a pattern to your data?
2. Do all or most of the materials that light the lightbulb have something in common?
3. Do all or most of the materials that don't light the lightbulb have something in common?
4. **Explain** why one material might allow the lightbulb to light and another might prevent the lightbulb from lighting.
5. **Predict** what other materials will allow the lightbulb to light and what will prevent the lightbulb from lighting.
6. **Classify** all the materials you have tested as conductors or insulators.

Communicating Your Data

Compare your conclusions with those of other students in your class. **For more help, refer to the Science Skill Handbook.**

Assessment

Process Silicon is an element that is nonconductive. Have students make posters illustrating how scientists treat silicon to alter its conductivity and how the altered silicon is used. Use **Performance Assessment in the Science Classroom,** p. 145 L2 LS **Visual-Spatial, Logical-Mathematical**

Communicating Your Data

Students should discuss why their conclusions did or did not agree. They can cite references to support their arguments. L3 LS **Linguistic, Logical-Mathematical**

section 3

Electrical Energy

Reading Guide

What You'll Learn

- **Describe** the difference between series and parallel circuits.
- **Recognize** the function of circuit breakers and fuses.
- **Calculate** electrical power.
- **Calculate** the electrical energy used by a device.

Why It's Important

When you use an electric appliance, such as a hair dryer or a toaster oven, you pay for the electrical energy you use.

Review Vocabulary

energy: the ability to cause change

New Vocabulary

- series circuit
- parallel circuit
- electrical power

Series and Parallel Circuits

Look around. How many electrical devices such as lights, clocks, stereos, and televisions do you see that are plugged into electrical outlets? Circuits usually include three components. One is a source of voltage difference that can be provided by a battery or an electrical outlet. Another is one or more devices that use electrical energy. Circuits also include conductors such as wires that connect the devices to the source of voltage difference to form a closed path.

Think about using a hair dryer. The dryer must be plugged into an electrical outlet to operate. A generator at a power plant produces a voltage difference across the outlet, causing charges to move when the circuit is complete. The dryer and the circuit in the house contain conducting wires to carry current. The hair dryer turns the electrical energy into thermal energy and mechanical energy. When you unplug the hair dryer or turn off its switch, you open the circuit and break the path of the current. To use electrical energy, a complete circuit must be made. There are two kinds of circuits.

Series Circuits One kind of circuit is called a series circuit. In a **series circuit,** the current has only one loop to flow through, as shown in **Figure 16.** Series circuits are used in flashlights and some holiday lights.

Reading Check *How many loops are in a series circuit?*

Figure 16 A series circuit provides only one path for the current to follow.
Infer *What happens to the brightness of each bulb as more bulbs are added?*

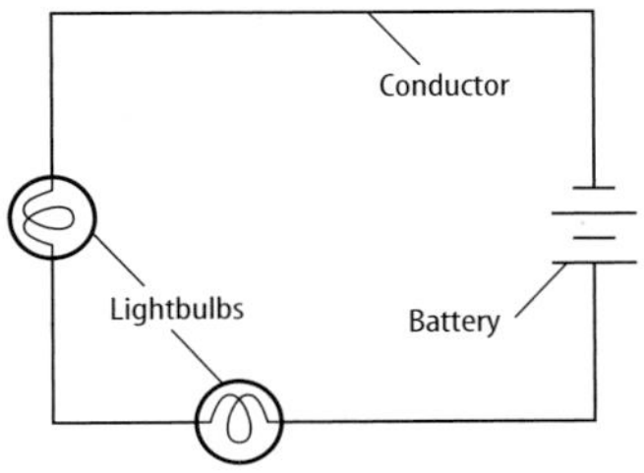

Section 3 Resource Manager

Chapter *FAST FILE* Resources

- Transparency Activity, pp. 44, 45–46
- Enrichment, p. 30
- Directed Reading for Content Mastery, pp. 19–20
- Lab Activity, pp. 13–14
- Lab Worksheet, pp. 7–8
- Reinforcement, p. 27
- **Mathematics Skill Activities,** p. 9

1 Motivate

INTERACTIVE CHALKBOARD PowerPoint® Presentations An editable Microsoft® PowerPoint® presentation is available on **Interactive Chalkboard** CD-ROM.

Bellringer

Section Focus Transparencies also are available on the Interactive Chalkboard CD-ROM. L2 ELL

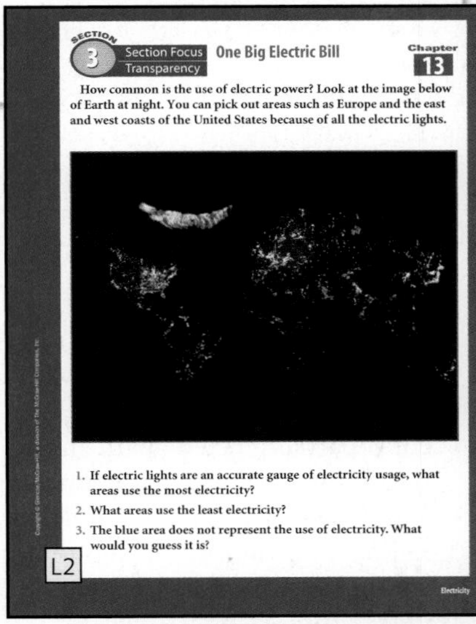
SECTION 3 Section Focus Transparency **One Big Electric Bill** Chapter 13

How common is the use of electric power? Look at the image below of Earth at night. You can pick out areas such as Europe and the east and west coasts of the United States because of all the electric lights.

1. If electric lights are an accurate gauge of electricity usage, what areas use the most electricity?
2. What areas use the least electricity?
3. The blue area does not represent the use of electricity. What would you guess it is?

L2

Electricity

Reading Preview

Tie to Prior Knowledge

Real Circuits Discuss with students what they learned in the last section about how resistance, voltage, and current are related. L2 LS **Auditory**

Make Connections Ask students to discuss what the word *series* means. Have them do the same for the word *parallel.* Ask them to predict the difference between a series circuit and a parallel circuit. Have them look at **Figures 16** and **17** to see how the drawings show the difference.

Reading Check

Answer one

Caption Answer

Figure 16 The brightness decreases.

2 Teach

INTEGRATE Career

Electrician Electricians must have good reading and comprehension skills to interpret and apply building code requirements and to use wiring diagrams. Electricians also must have basic math skills to calculate the materials required for a job and to calculate costs.

Research Have students research the requirements to become a licensed electrician in your state.

Activity

Examine Circuits Have several small devices with electric circuits, partially taken apart, in the room for students to examine. Possible displays include a small radio, a flashlight, a telephone, and a light fixture with two or more bulbs. L3 ELL LS **Kinesthetic**

Caption Answer

Figure 17 It is the same.

INTEGRATE Career

Electrician The installation of electrical wiring in any building usually requires an electrician. Electricians must have a thorough understanding of electricity. They also must constantly be aware of the safety issues involved in working with electricity. Write a paragraph describing other skills that electricians must have.

Open Circuits If you have ever decorated a window or a tree with a string of lights, you might have had the frustrating experience of trying to find one burned-out bulb. How can one faulty bulb cause the whole string to go out? Because the parts of a series circuit are wired one after another, the amount of current is the same through every part. When any part of a series circuit is disconnected, no current flows through the circuit. This is called an open circuit. The burned-out bulb causes an open circuit in the string of lights.

Parallel Circuits What would happen if your home were wired in a series circuit and you turned off one light? This would cause an open circuit, and all the other lights and appliances in your home would go out, too. This is why houses are wired with parallel circuits. **Parallel circuits** contain two or more branches for current to move through. Look at the parallel circuit in **Figure 17.** The current can flow through both or either of the branches. Because all branches connect the same two points of the circuit, the voltage difference is the same in each branch. Then, according to Ohm's law, more current flows through the branches that have lower resistance.

Parallel circuits have several advantages. When one branch of the circuit is opened, such as when you turn a light off, the current continues to flow through the other branches. Houses, automobiles, and most electrical systems use parallel wiring so individual parts can be turned off without affecting the entire circuit.

Figure 17 In parallel circuits, the current follows more than one path. **Describe** *how the voltage difference will compare in each branch.*

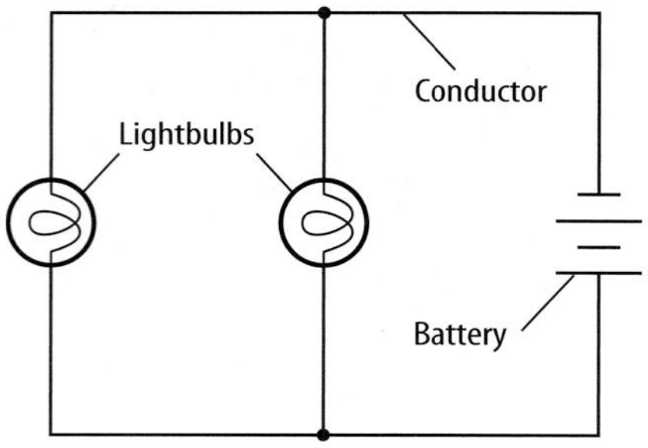

LAB DEMONSTRATION

Purpose to demonstrate series and parallel circuits

Materials battery, small lightbulbs (2), ammeters (2), wire

Procedure Set up a series circuit with the two lightbulbs. Include ammeters in two places in the circuit. Disconnect one lamp so the circuit is broken. Do the same for a parallel circuit.

Expected Outcome In the series circuit, the entire circuit is broken when the lamp is disconnected. For the parallel circuit, the circuit is only broken in the branch with the disconnected lamp.

Assessment

Why do results differ for the two circuits? Series-current has only one path so it is the same everywhere; parallel-current has two paths, so it is split between the paths. L2 LS **Logical-Mathematical, Visual-Spatial**

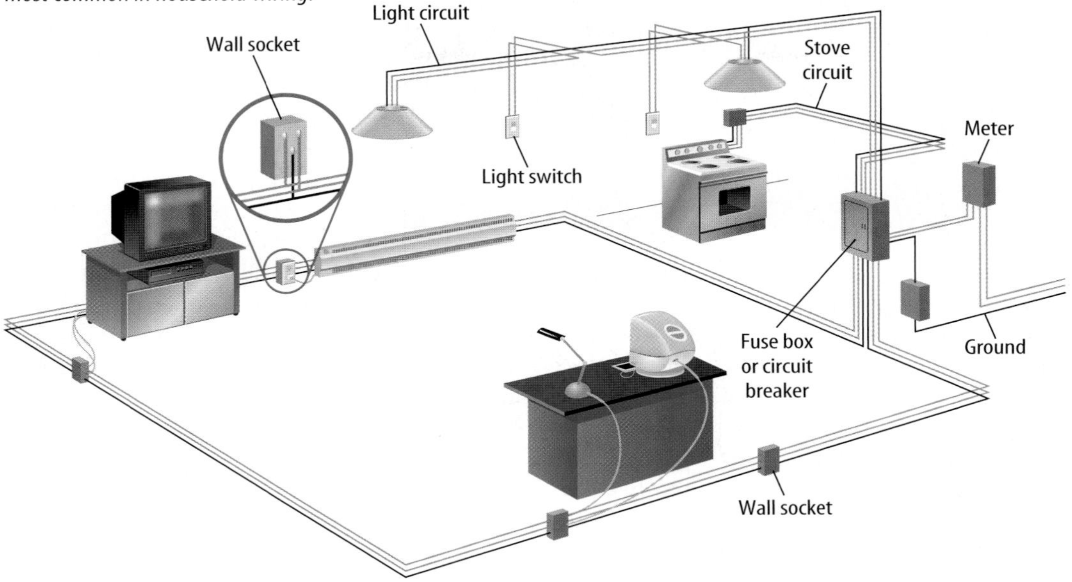

Figure 18 The wiring in a house must allow for the individual use of various appliances and fixtures. **Identify** *the type of circuit that is most common in household wiring.*

Household Circuits

Count how many different things in your home require electrical energy. You don't see the wires because most of them are hidden behind the walls, ceilings, and floors. This wiring is mostly a combination of parallel circuits connected in an organized and logical network. **Figure 18** shows how electrical energy enters a home and is distributed. In the United States, the voltage difference in most of the branches is 120 V. In some branches that are used for electric stoves or electric clothes dryers, the voltage difference is 240 V. The main switch and circuit breaker or fuse box serve as an electrical headquarters for your home. Parallel circuits branch out from the breaker or fuse box to wall sockets, major appliances, and lights.

In a house, many appliances draw current from the same circuit. If more appliances are connected, more current will flow through the wires. As the amount of current increases, so does the amount of heat produced in the wires. If the wires get too hot, the insulation can melt and the bare wires can cause a fire. To protect against overheating of the wires, all household circuits contain either a fuse or a circuit breaker.

Activity

Circuit Diagrams Draw several circuit diagrams on the board and have students identify them either as series circuits or as parallel circuits. At this point, avoid combination series/parallel circuits. L2 LS **Visual-Spatial**

Caption Answer

Figure 18 parallel circuit

Quick Demo

Series or Parallel Circuit?

Materials string of minature lights (should be three-wire type)

Estimated Time 10 minutes

Procedure Hang the string of lights across the front of the classroom and plug them in. Have students predict whether the circuit is series or parallel. Remove one bulb from the first half of the string. One section of the lights should go out. Discuss why one section went out but not the other. Have a student draw a possible circuit diagram on the board. L2

LS **Visual-Spatial, Logical-Mathematical, Kinesthetic**

Teacher FYI

Resistance In a series circuit, total resistance is equal to the sum of the individual resistances: $R_{total} = R_1 + R_2 + \ldots$ In a parallel circuit, the total resistance is calculated as follows: $1/R_{total} = 1/R_1 + 1/R_2 + \ldots$ The total resistance is less than any single resistance in a parallel circuit.

Visual Learning

Figure 18 Students should notice that all wiring in the house first runs through the fuse box or circuit breaker for protection. Why are three lines shown in the wiring? One line is ground; the other two are for the closed-current path. L2 LS **Visual-Spatial, Logical-Mathematical**

Caption Answer

Figure 19 A circuit breaker, because it can be easily reset, whereas a fuse must be replaced.

Make a Model

Fuses Students can learn about the behavior of fuses by constructing a simple circuit containing a battery and a lightbulb. To model a fuse, include as part of the circuit's wiring a strip of aluminum foil about 3 cm long. The strip should have a thin middle section that is about 1 mm wide. When the circuit is completed, the thin part of the foil will quickly melt, opening the circuit, and the light will go out, as occurs when a real fuse blows. L2 LS **Kinesthetic, Visual-Spatial**

Reading Check

Answer to protect against overheating and possible fire if the current in a wire becomes too high

Discussion

Blowing a Fuse Why is "blowing a fuse" an appropriate phrase to mean losing one's temper? Possible answer: too much current through a circuit causes a fuse to blow just as too many maddening incidents cause you to lose control of your temper. **Linguistic**

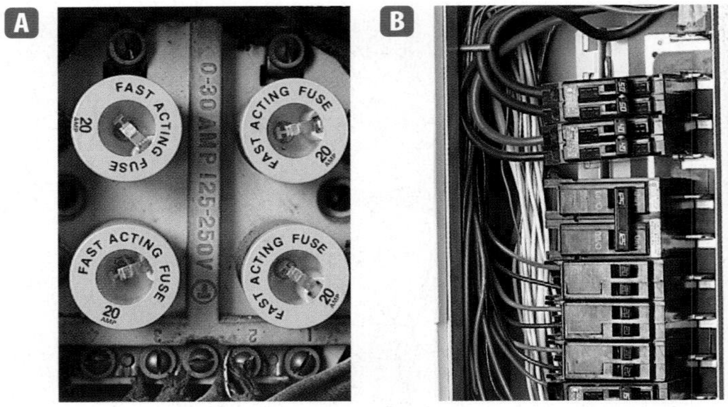

Figure 19 Two useful devices to prevent electric circuits from overheating are **A** fuses and **B** circuit breakers.
Evaluate *which device, a fuse or a circuit breaker, would be more convenient to have in the home.*

Fuses When you hear that somebody has "blown a fuse," it means that the person has lost his or her temper. This expression comes from the function of an electrical fuse, shown in **Figure 19A,** which contains a small piece of metal that melts if the current becomes too high. When it melts, it causes a break in the circuit, stopping the flow of current through the overloaded circuit. To enable current to flow again in the circuit, you must replace the blown fuse with a new one. However, before you replace the blown fuse, you should turn off or unplug some of the appliances. Too many appliances in use at the same time is the most likely cause of the overheating of the circuit.

Circuit Breaker A circuit breaker, shown in **Figure 19B,** is another device that prevents a circuit from overheating and causing a fire. A circuit breaker contains a piece of metal that bends when the current in it is so large that it gets hot. The bending causes a switch to flip and open the circuit, stopping the flow of current. Circuit breakers usually can be reset by pushing the switch to its "on" position. Again, before you reset a circuit breaker, you should turn off or unplug some of the appliances from the overloaded circuit. Otherwise, the circuit breaker will switch off again.

Reading Check ***What is the purpose of fuses and circuit breakers in household circuits?***

Electrical Power

The reason why electricity is so useful is that electrical energy is converted easily to other types of energy. For example, electrical energy is converted to mechanical energy as the blades of a fan rotate to cool you. Electrical energy is converted to light energy in lightbulbs. A hair dryer changes electrical energy into thermal energy. The rate at which electrical energy is converted to another form of energy is the **electrical power.**

The electrical power used by appliances varies. Appliances often are labeled with a power rating that describes how much power the appliance uses, as shown in **Figure 20.** Appliances that have electric heating elements, such as ovens and hair dryers, usually use more electrical power than other appliances.

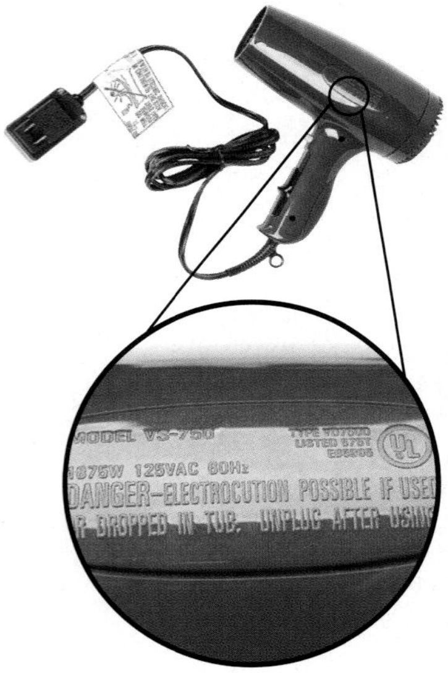

Figure 20 All appliances come with a power rating.

Cultural Diversity

Electric Lighting Lewis H. Latimer, the son of a former slave, taught himself to be a draftsman when he was a teenager. In 1880, Latimer was hired by the United States Electric Lighting Company, where he invented the first carbon-filament electric lamp and an inexpensive way to produce the filaments. In 1883, he joined Thomas Edison, and in 1890, he published the first textbook on electric lighting—*Incandescent Electric Lighting*. In 1918, the Edison Pioneers organization was formed to honor some of the people who worked with Thomas Edison as the "creators of the electric industry." One member was Lewis H. Latimer.

Calculating Electrical Power The electrical power used depends on the voltage difference and the current. Electrical power can be calculated from the following equation.

Electrical Power Equation

electrical power (in watts) = current (in amperes) × voltage difference (in volts)

$$P = IV$$

The unit for power is the watt (W). Because the watt is a small unit of power, electrical power is often expressed in kilowatts (kW). One kilowatt equals 1,000 watts.

Applying Math — Solve a Simple Equation

POWER USED BY A CLOTHES DRYER The current in an electric clothes dryer is 15 A when it is plugged into a 240-V outlet. How much power does the clothes dryer use?

IDENTIFY known values and the unknown value

Identify the known values:

current in the clothes dryer is 15 A —means→ $I = 15$ A

plugged into a 240-V outlet —means→ $V = 240$ V

Identify the unknown value:

how much power does the clothes dryer use —means→ $P = ?$ W

SOLVE the problem

Substitute the known values $I = 15$ A and $V = 240$ V into the electrical power equation:

$$P = IV = (15\text{ A})(240\text{ V}) = 3{,}600\text{ W} = 3.6\text{ kW}$$

CHECK the answer

Does your answer seem reasonable? Check your answer by dividing the power you calculated by the current given in the problem. The result should be the voltage difference given in the problem.

Practice Problems

1. A toaster oven is plugged into an outlet that provides a voltage difference of 120 V. What power does the oven use if the current is 10 A?
2. A VCR that is not playing still uses 10.0 W of power. What is the current if the VCR is plugged into a 120-V electrical outlet?
3. A flashlight bulb uses 2.4 W of power when the current in the bulb is 0.8 A. What is the voltage difference?

For more practice problems go to page 879, and visit Math Practice at gpescience.com.

Use Science Words

Word Origin Many units of measurement in science are named for people who did related research. Have students investigate the origins of the words *ampere*, *watt*, and *volt*. The ampere is named after André Marie Ampère, who proposed the relationship between electricity and magnetism. The watt is named after James Watt, who created the first efficient steam engine and first used the word horsepower. The volt is named after Alessandro Volta, who observed that a conducting liquid produced a continuous transfer of electrons, a phenomenon later called electric current. L2 LS **Linguistic**

Applying Math

National Math Standards

National: 1, 2, 9

Answers to Practice Problems

1. $P = (10\text{ A})(120\text{ V}) = 1200\text{ W}$
2. $I = \frac{P}{V} = \frac{10.0\ W}{120\ V} = 0.833\text{ A}$
3. $V = \frac{P}{I} = \frac{2.4\ W}{0.8\ A} = 3\text{ V}$

Reading Strategy

Fix-Up Strategy Choose a challenging piece of text, such as the Applying Math section, and read it aloud while interjecting questions and strategies to aid comprehension. Show students how to use the related equations to aid in comprehension. Then have students try the next Applying Math section as they work in pairs.

Science Journal

Power, Voltage, Current, and Resistance Remind students that they have been given Ohm's law and the formula for electric power. Have them write both formulas in their Science Journals and combine them to relate power to resistance. $I = V/R$; $P = IV$; therefore $P = V/R \times V = V^2/R$; also, $V = IR$, so $P = I \times IR = I^2 R$. L2 LS **Linguistic, Logical-Mathematical**

Fun Fact

Benjamin Franklin was first to use the terms *positive* and *negative* to describe charged objects. He also invented the lightning rod.

Applying Math

National Math Standards

National: 1, 2, 9

Answers to Practice Problems

1. $E = Pt$, $E = (0.7\ \text{kW})(10.0\ \text{h}) = 7\ \text{kWh}$

2. $t = \frac{E}{P}$ $t = \frac{(0.8\ \text{kWh})}{(0.2\ \text{kW})} = 4\ \text{h}$

Science Online

Topic: Energy

Visit gpescience.com for Web links to information about the cost of electrical energy around the country.

Activity Using a blank map of the United States, create a key showing the relative energy costs in different states in different colors. With a partner, color in the states to create a visual map of energy costs. Give your map a title.

Electrical Energy Using electrical power costs money. However, electric companies charge by the amount of electrical energy used rather than by the electrical power used. Electrical energy usually is measured in units of kilowatt-hours (kWh) and can be calculated from this equation:

Electrical Energy Equation

electrical energy (in kWh) = electrical power (in kW) × time (in hours)

$$E = Pt$$

In the above equation, electrical power is in units of kW and the time is the number of hours that the electrical power is used.

Applying Math — Solve a Simple Equation

ELECTRICAL ENERGY USED BY A MICROWAVE OVEN A microwave oven with a power rating of 1,200 W is used for 0.25 h. How much electrical energy is used by the microwave oven?

IDENTIFY known values and the unknown value

Identify the known values:

power rating of 1,200 W means $P = 1{,}200\ \text{W} = 1.2\ \text{kW}$

is used for 0.25 h means $t = 0.25\ \text{h}$

Identify the unknown value:

how much electrical energy is used means $E = ?\ \text{kWh}$

SOLVE the problem

Substitute the known values $p = 1.2$ kW and $t = 0.25$ h into the electrical energy equation:

$$E = Pt = (1.2\ \text{kW})(0.25\ \text{h}) = 0.30\ \text{kWh}$$

CHECK your answer

Does your answer seem reasonable? Check your answer by dividing the electrical energy you calculated by the power given in the problem. The results should be the time given in the problem.

Practice Problems

1. A refrigerator operates on average for 10.0 h a day. If the power rating of the refrigerator is 700 W, how much electrical energy does the refrigerator use in one day?
2. A TV with a power rating of 200 W uses 0.8 kWh in one day. For how many hours was the TV on during this day?

For more practice problems go to page 879, and visit Math Practice at gpescience.com.

Differentiated Instruction

Challenge Have students work in pairs to research and build a Leyden jar, a device used to store electric energy. **WARNING:** *Warn students not to use any flammable materials in their construction.* L3 LS **Visual-Spatial, Kinesthetic** COOP LEARN

Teacher FYI

Horsepower In the United States, the power of car engines is rated using the British unit horsepower (hp). One horsepower is equal to 746 watts.

The Cost of Using Electrical Energy

The cost of using an appliance can be computed by multiplying the electrical energy used by the amount the power company charges for each kWh. For example, if a 100-W lightbulb is left on for 5 h, the amount of electrical energy used is

$$E = Pt = (0.1\ \text{kW})(5\ \text{h}) = 0.5\ \text{kWh}$$

If the power company charges $0.10 per kWh, the cost of using the bulb for 5 h is

$$\text{cost} = (\text{kWh used})(\text{cost per kWh})$$
$$= (0.5\ \text{kWh})(\$0.10/\text{kWh}) = \$0.05$$

The cost of using some household appliances is given in **Table 1,** where the cost per kWh is assumed to be $0.09/kWh.

Table 1 Cost of Using Home Appliances

Appliance	Hair Dryer	Stereo	Color Television
Power rating	1,000	100	200
Hours used daily	0.25	2.0	4.0
kWh used monthly	7.5	6.0	24.0
Cost per kWh	$0.09	$0.09	$0.09
Monthly cost	$0.68	$0.54	$2.16

section 3 review

Summary

Series and Parallel Circuits

- A series circuit has only one path that current can follow. A parallel circuit has two or more branches that current can follow.
- Household wiring usually consists of a number of connected parallel circuits.
- Fuses and circuit breakers are used to prevent wires from overheating when the current in the wires becomes too large.

Electrical Power

- Electrical power is the rate at which electrical energy is converted into other forms of energy.
- Electrical power can be calculated by multiplying the current by the voltage difference:

$$P = IV$$

Electrical Energy

- The electrical energy used can be calculated by multiplying the power by the time:

$$E = Pt$$

- Electric power companies charge customers for the amount of electrical energy they use.

Self Check

1. **Explain** how electrical power and electrical energy are related.
2. **Discuss** why fuses and circuit breakers are used in household circuits.
3. **Explain** what determines the current in each branch of a parallel circuit.
4. **Explain** whether or not a fuse or circuit breaker should be connected in parallel to the circuit it is protecting.
5. **Think Critically** A parallel circuit consisting of four branches is connected to a battery. Explain how the amount of current that flows out of the battery is related to the amount of current in the branches of the circuit.

Applying Math

6. **Calculate** the current flowing into a desktop computer plugged into a 120-V outlet if the power used is 180 W.
7. **Calculate Electrical Power** A circuit breaker is tripped when the current in the circuit is greater than 15 A. If the voltage difference is 120 V, what is the power being used when the circuit breaker is tripped?
8. **Calculate** the monthly cost of using a 700-W refrigerator that runs for 10 h a day if the cost per kWh is $0.09.

More Section Review gpescience.com

section 3 review

1. Power is the rate at which electrical energy is converted to another form of energy. The amount of electrical energy used is the power times the time the power is used.
2. Fuse and circuit breakers stop the flow of current in a circuit when the circuit becomes overloaded. This prevents the wires from becoming so hot they melt or start a fire.
3. The current is determined by the resistance of each branch. The voltage differences across each branch are the same.
4. A fuse or circuit breaker must be connected in series, not parallel, to the circuit it is protecting in order to stop the flow of current.
5. The current flowing out of the battery is equal to the sum of the currents in the four branches.
6. 1.5 A
7. The power is greater than 1.8 kW.
8. $18.90 (30 days)

Post Reading

Discussion Have students discuss what they have learned about electricity in small groups. Ask one student to facilitate the discussion, another to record the comments, and a third to report to the class. Provide the following prompts: How does the measurement system for electricity work? What causes static electricity? How do products reduce it in clothing?

3 Assess

DAILY INTERVENTION

Check for Understanding

Visual-Spatial Have students work in pairs to draw a model of the lights, switches, and wall outlets that are in the classroom. The drawing should be similar to that shown in Figure 18 and show that switches are wired in series while outlets and some lights are wired in parallel. L2 LS **Interpersonal, Visual-Spatial**

Reteach

Process Bring in an energy rating label from a new appliance. Have students use the voltage and current specifications of the appliance to determine its power, the energy it will use, and the cost of operation. L2 LS **Visual-Spatial, Logical-Mathematical**

Assessment

Process Ask students to write paragraphs that compare and contrast series and parallel circuits. Charge flows through both types of circuits. A series circuit has only one loop through which charge can flow; a parallel circuit has more than one. Use **PASC**, p. 157. L2 LS **Linguistic,** P **Logical-Mathematical**

BENCH TESTED

Real-World Problem

Purpose Students will design and test parallel and series circuits. L1 COOP LEARN

LS Logical-Mathematical

Process Skills observe, communicate, classify, compare and contrast, recognize cause and effect, interpret data, use numbers, experiment, hypothesize

Time Required one class period

Materials The lightbulb voltage requirements should closely match the battery voltage so bulbs don't burn out quickly.

Alternate Materials Obtain economical low-voltage lightbulbs by cutting apart a string of Christmas minilights. Insulated wire may be used instead of foil.

Safety Precautions To avoid overheating the wire, students should hook up the battery only long enough to make observations.

Form a Hypothesis

Possible Hypothesis If a bulb is removed from a series circuit, all lights will go out. In a parallel circuit, the remaining bulbs will stay lit. Lights shine brightest in the parallel circuit.

Test Your Hypothesis

Possible Procedures Series circuits should have a single path with lights in a chain. Parallel circuits should have the lights on three separate paths.

LAB Design Your Own

Comparing Series and Parallel Circuits

Goals
- **Design** and construct series and parallel circuits.
- **Compare** and contrast the behaviors of series and parallel circuits.

Possible Materials
6-V dry-cell battery
small lights with sockets (3)
aluminum foil
paper clips
tape
scissors
paper

Safety Precautions

Some parts of circuits can become hot. Do not leave the battery connected or the circuit closed for more than a few seconds at a time. Never connect the positive and negative terminals of the dry-cell battery directly without including at least one bulb in the circuit.

Real-World Problem

Imagine what a bedroom might be like if it were wired in series. For an alarm clock to keep time and wake you in the morning, your lights and anything else that uses electricity would have to be on. Fortunately, most outlets in homes are wired in parallel circuits on separate branches of the main circuit. How do the behaviors of series and parallel circuits compare?

Form a Hypothesis

Predict what will happen to the other bulbs when one bulb is unscrewed from a series circuit and from a parallel circuit. Explain your prediction. Also, form a hypothesis to explain in which circuit the lights shine the brightest.

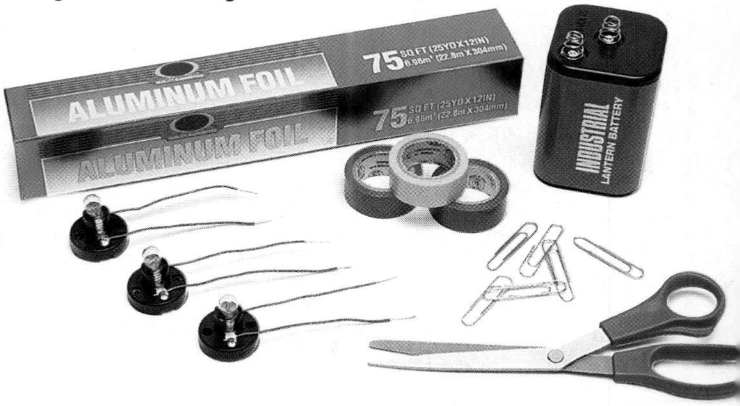

Differentiated Instruction

Visually Impaired Instead of using lamps, this activity can be performed using buzzers in the circuits. A visually impaired student could be paired with a sighted student to aid in circuit construction. L2 LS COOP LEARN **Kinesthetic, Visual-Spatial**

Alternative Inquiry Lab

Test a Hypothesis To extend this Lab into an Inquiry Lab, have students hypothesize how $V = IR$ applies to parallel circuits, and experiment to test those hypotheses. For this experiment, supply light bulbs with different power ratings. Have students use Ohm's law to calculate the current through each lightbulb. Then have them compare the results of their calculations with their observations.

414 CHAPTER 13 Electricity

Using Scientific Methods

Test Your Hypothesis

Make a Plan

1. As a group, agree upon and write the hypothesis statement.
2. Work together to determine and write the steps you will take to test your hypothesis. Include a list of the materials you will need.
3. How will your circuits be arranged? On a piece of paper, draw a large parallel circuit of three lights and the dry-cell battery as shown. On the other side, draw another circuit with the three bulbs arranged in series.
4. Make conducting wires by taping a piece of transparent tape to a sheet of aluminum foil and folding the foil over twice to cover the tape. Cut these to any length that works in your design.

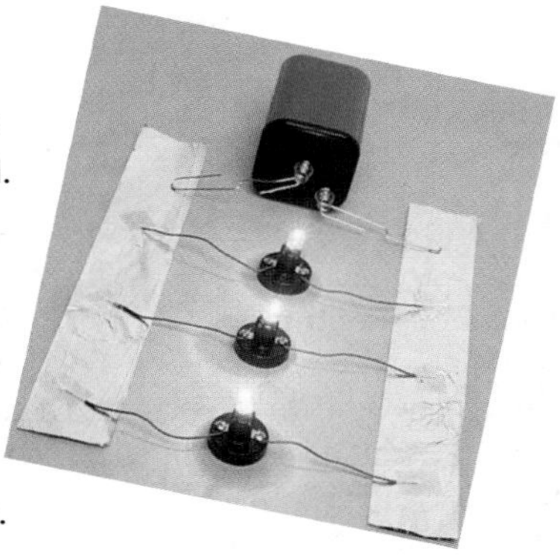

Follow Your Plan

1. Make sure your teacher approves your plan before you start.
2. Carry out the experiment. **WARNING:** *Leave the circuit on for only a few seconds at a time to avoid overheating.*
3. As you do the experiment, record your predictions and your observations in your Science Journal.

Analyze Your Data

1. **Predict** what will happen in the series circuit when a bulb is unscrewed at one end. What will happen in the parallel circuit?
2. **Compare** the brightness of the lights in the different circuits. Explain.
3. **Predict** what will happen to the brightness of the bulbs in the series circuit if you complete it with two bulbs instead of three bulbs. Test your prediction. How do the results demonstrate Ohm's law?

Conclude and Apply

1. Did the results support your hypothesis? Explain by using your observations.
2. Where in the parallel circuit would you place a switch to control all three lights? Where would you place a switch to control only one light? Test your predictions.

Communicating Your Data

Prepare a poster to highlight the differences between a parallel and a series circuit. Include possible practical applications of both types of circuits. **For more help, refer to the Science Skill Handbook.**

Troubleshooting Students may design a circuit having two lightbulbs in parallel that are wired in series with the third light. Although interesting, this will not help students completely explore the behavior of each of the circuits independently. L2 LS **Visual-Spatial, Kinesthetic**

Expected Outcome When a light in series is removed, all the lights go out. In a parallel circuit, when a light is removed, others remain lit.

Analyze Your Data

Answers to Questions

1. In series, the current will stop and all bulbs will go out. In parallel, the charge will flow through other branches and the other bulbs will remain lit.
2. The lights are brighter in parallel because more current flows through each loop than the loop with three bulbs in a series circuit.
3. It will be brighter because of less resistance in the circuit.

Error Analysis Have students analyze their circuits for possible sources of errors. dead batteries, burned-out bulbs, poor connections with the aluminum foil

Conclude and Apply

1. Answers depend on student hypotheses.
2. between the battery and a wire leading to one side of the lights; along the wire that goes to only one of the lights

Assessment

Oral Ask students to discuss why houses and buildings are wired in parallel and not in series. In a series circuit, all lights and appliances would have to be on at the same time; if one is off or burned out, no charge flows anywhere in the circuit. L2 LS **Logical-Mathematical**

Communicating Your Data

Have students use a computer graphics program to draw sketches of circuits for their posters. They can also use the computer to write any explanations they wish to include on their posters. L3 LS **Visual-Spatial, Logical-Mathematical**

Science and Language Arts

Invisible Man

by Ralph Ellison

I am an invisible man. No, I am not a spook like those who haunted Edgar Allan Poe; nor am I one of your Hollywood-movie ectoplasms.[1] I am a man of substance, of flesh and bone, fiber and liquids—and I might even be said to possess a mind. I am invisible, understand, simply because people refuse to see me. . . . Nor is my invisibility exactly a matter of biochemical accident to my epidermis.[2] That invisibility to which I refer occurs because of a peculiar disposition . . . of those with whom I come in contact. . . .

. . . . Now don't jump to the conclusion that because I call my home a "hole" it is damp and cold like a grave. . . . Mine is a warm hole.

My hole is warm and full of light. Yes, *full* of light. I doubt if there is a brighter spot in all New York than this hole of mine. . . . Perhaps you'll think it strange that an invisible man should need light, desire light, love light. Because maybe it is exactly because I *am invisible.* Light confirms my reality, gives birth to my form. . . . I myself, after existing some twenty years, did not become alive until I discovered my invisibility.

. . . In my hole in the basement there are exactly 1,369 lights. I've wired the entire ceiling, every inch of it. . . . Though invisible, I am in the great American tradition of tinkers. That makes me kin to Ford, Edison and Franklin.

1 The outer layer of a part of the cell.

2 The outer layer of skin.

Ralph Ellison

Understanding Literature

Prologue A prologue is an introduction to a novel, play, or other work of literature. Often a prologue contains useful information about events to come in the story. Foreshadowing is the use of clues by the author to prepare readers for future events or recurring themes.

Respond to the Reading

1. What clues does the narrator give that he is not really invisible?
2. Why does the narrator believe he is in the "great American tradition of tinkers"?
3. **Linking Science and Writing** Write a prologue to a fictional book describing Edison's invention of the lightbulb. Recall that a prologue is not a summary of the book. Rather, it can state general themes that the work of literature will address or set the stage or describe the setting of the story.

INTEGRATE Physics

If all 1,369 light-bulbs were wired together in a series circuit, the electrical resistance in the circuit would be high. According to Ohm's law, the current in the circuit would be low and the bulbs wouldn't glow. If all the bulbs were wired in a parallel circuit, so much current would flow in the circuit that the connecting wires would melt. For the bulbs to light, the narrator must have wired them in many independent circuits.

Understanding Literature

Pre-Reading Activity Ask students to do a clustering of terms that define who they are. Each student should put his or her name in the center of a cluster that includes elements that define his or her identity such as ethnic heritage, extracurricular activities, and family members. L2 LS **Linguistic**

Respond to the Reading

Connect Ask students if they can remember a time they were unfairly judged or misunderstood simply because their outward appearance was different from others around them.

Respond Tell students to be aware of their responses as they read about the invisible man. His description of himself might make them think that anyone who is judged by others is an outsider. Ask students how the text conveys that it is important for a person to have a positive view of himself or herself. L2 LS **Linguistic, Logical-Mathematical**

Answers to Questions

1. The narrator says he is "a man of substance, of flesh and bone, fiber and liquids."
2. because he has wired his ceiling with 1,369 lights
3. Check students' work.

INTEGRATE Physics

Resistance The total electrical resistance of a series circuit is the sum of the resistance of each resistor in the circuit. However, the total resistance of a parallel circuit decreases, and the current flowing into the circuit increases, as more resistors are added to the circuit.

Resources for Teachers and Students

Juneteenth, by Ralph Ellison, Random House, 1999

The African American Century, by Henry Louis Gates, Jr. and Cornel West, The Free Press, 2000

Reviewing Main Ideas

Section 1 Electric Charge

1. There are two types of electric charge: positive charge and negative charge.
2. Electric charges exert forces on each other. Like charges repel and unlike charges attract.
3. Electric charges can be transferred from one object to another but cannot be created or destroyed.
4. Electrons can move easily in an electrical conductor. Electrons do not move easily in an insulator.
5. Objects can be charged by contact or by induction. Charging by induction occurs when a charged object is brought near an electrically neutral object.

Section 2 Electric Current

1. Electric current is the net movement of electric charges in a single direction. A voltage difference causes an electric current to flow.
2. A circuit is a closed path along which charges can move. Current will flow continually only along a circuit that is unbroken.
3. Chemical reactions in a battery produce a voltage difference between the positive and negative terminals of the battery.
4. Electrical resistance is the tendency of a material to oppose the flow of electric current.
5. In an electric circuit, the voltage difference, current, and resistance are related by Ohm's law:

$$I = \frac{V}{R}$$

Section 3 Electrical Energy

1. Current has only one path in a series circuit and more than one path in a parallel circuit.
2. Circuit breakers and fuses prevent excessive current from flowing in a circuit.
3. Electrical power is the rate at which electrical energy is used and can be calculated with $P = IV$.
4. The electrical energy used by a device can be calculated with the equation $E = Pt$.

FOLDABLES Use the Foldable you made at the beginning of the chapter to help you review electric charge, electric current, and electrical energy.

Identifying Misconceptions

Assess

Materials D-battery (1), flashlight (1), bulb in socket (1), switch (1), wires (5), voltmeter (1)

Procedure Have each group set up a circuit. Ask students to predict the voltage between the two sides of the switch when it is open and when it is closed. Students can use voltmeters to test their predictions.

Expected Outcome Voltage varies across different points in a circuit and can exist without current flow. A voltage exists across the two sides of the switch when it is open. The voltage approaches zero when it is closed. L2 COOP LEARN

LS Logical-Mathematical, Kinesthetic, Visual-Spatial

Reviewing Main Ideas

Summary statements can be used by students to review the major concepts of the chapter.

Science Online

Visit gpescience.com
- More Section Review
- Interactive Tutor
- Vocabulary PuzzleMaker
- More Chapter Review
- Standardized Test Practice

Assessment Transparency

For additional assessment questions, use the *Assessment Transparency* located in the transparency book.

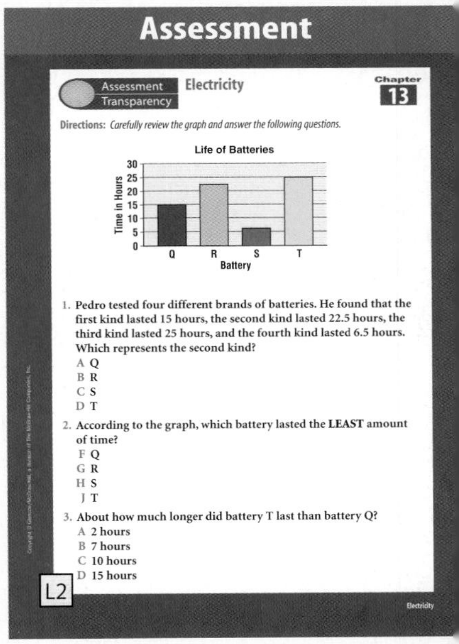

Assessment

Assessment Transparency — Electricity — Chapter 13

Directions: *Carefully review the graph and answer the following questions.*

1. Pedro tested four different brands of batteries. He found that the first kind lasted 15 hours, the second kind lasted 22.5 hours, the third kind lasted 25 hours, and the fourth kind lasted 6.5 hours. Which represents the second kind?
   A Q
   B R
   C S
   D T
2. According to the graph, which battery lasted the **LEAST** amount of time?
   F Q
   G R
   H S
   J T
3. About how much longer did battery T last than battery Q?
   A 2 hours
   B 7 hours
   C 10 hours
   D 15 hours

L2

Electricity

FOLDABLES Have students use their Foldables to review the content of the chapter. On the back of the paper, have students write a paragraph about the nature of the forces between magnets.

Using Vocabulary

1. series circuit
2. static electricity
3. voltage difference
4. the law of conservation of charge
5. Resistance
6. charging by contact

Checking Concepts

7. C
8. C
9. C
10. A
11. B
12. A
13. A

Interpreting Graphics

14. circuit A—2.6 Ω; circuit B—10 Ω; circuit C—30 Ω; circuit D—3.3 Ω The line is curved, descending from left to right. As the resistance becomes larger, the current decreases toward zero. As the resistance approaches zero, the current approaches infinity.
15. See student page.

Using Vocabulary

Complete each statement using a word(s) from the vocabulary list above.

1. A(n) _________ is a circuit with only one path for current to follow.
2. An accumulation of excess electric charge is _________.
3. The electric force that makes current flow in a circuit is related to the _________.
4. According to _________, electric charge cannot be created or destroyed.
5. _________ is the result of electrons colliding with atoms as current flows in a material.
6. Charging a balloon by rubbing it on wool is an example of _________.

Checking Concepts

Choose the word or phrase that best answers the question.

7. Which of the following is a conductor?
   A) glass **C)** tungsten
   B) wood **D)** plastic
8. Resistance in wires causes electrical energy to be converted into which form of energy?
   A) chemical energy
   B) nuclear energy
   C) thermal energy
   D) sound
9. The electric force between two charged objects depends on which of the following?
   A) their masses and their separation
   B) their speeds
   C) their charge and their separation
   D) their masses and their charge
10. An object becomes positively charged when which of the following occurs?
   A) loses electrons **C)** gains electrons
   B) loses protons **D)** gains neutrons
11. Which of the following does NOT provide a voltage difference in a circuit?
   A) wet cell **C)** electrical outlet
   B) wires **D)** dry cell
12. A commonly used unit for electrical energy is which of the following?
   A) kilowatt-hour **C)** ohm
   B) ampere **D)** newton
13. Which of the following is the rate at which appliances use electrical energy?
   A) power **C)** resistance
   B) current **D)** speed

Interpreting Graphics

Use the table below to answer question 14.

Current in Electric Circuits

Circuit	Current (A)
A	2.3
B	0.6
C	0.2
D	1.8

14. The table shows the current in circuits that were each connected to a 6-V dry cell. Calculate the resistance of each circuit. Graph the current versus the resistance of each circuit. Describe the shape of the line on your graph.

Vocabulary PuzzleMaker gpescience.com

Use the ExamView® Pro Testmaker CD-ROM to:
- create multiple versions of tests
- create modified tests with one mouse click for inclusion students
- edit existing questions and add your own questions
- build tests aligned with state standards using built-in State Curriculum Tags
- change English tests to Spanish with one mouse click and vice versa

15. Copy and complete the following concept map on electric current.

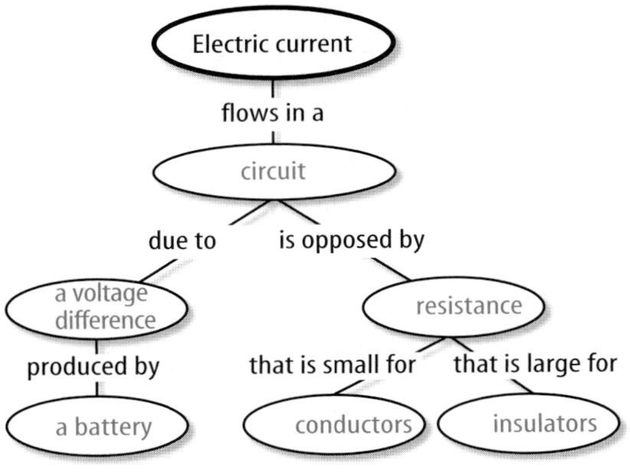

Thinking Critically

16. **Identify and Manipulate Variables** Design an experiment to test the effect on current and voltage differences in a circuit when two identical batteries are connected in series. What is your hypothesis? What are the variables and controls?

17. **Explain** A metal rod is charged by induction when a negatively charged plastic rod is brought nearby. Explain how the net charge on the metal rod has changed.

18. **Predict** You walk across a carpet on a dry day and touch a glass doorknob. Predict whether or not you would receive an electric shock. Explain your reasoning.

19. **Explain** The electric force between electric charges is much larger than the gravitational force between the charges. Why, then, is the gravitational force between Earth and the Moon much larger than the electric force between Earth and the Moon?

20. **Diagram** Draw a circuit diagram showing how a stereo, a TV, and a computer can be connected to a single source of voltage difference, such that turning off one appliance does not turn off all the others. Include a circuit breaker in your diagram that will protect all the appliances.

Applying Math

21. **Calculate Current** Using the information in the circuit diagram below, compute the current flowing in the circuit.

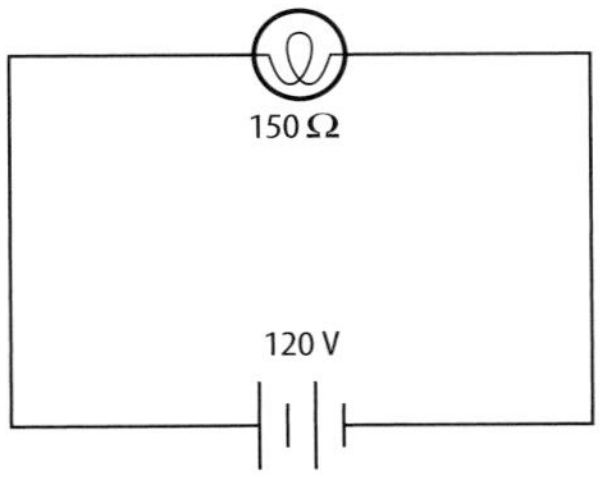

22. **Calculate Current** A toy car with a resistance of 20 Ω is connected to a 3-V battery. How much current flows in the car?

23. **Calculate Electrical Energy** The current flowing in an appliance connected to a 120-V source is 2 A. How many kilowatt-hours of electrical energy does the appliance use in 4 h?

24. **Calculate Electrical Energy Cost** A self-cleaning oven uses 5,400 W when cleaning itself. If it takes 1.5 h to clean, how many kilowatt-hours of electricity are used? At a cost of $0.09 per kWh, what does it cost to clean the oven?

25. **Calculate Power** A calculator uses a 9-V battery and draws 0.1 A of current. How much power does it use?

chapter Review 13

Thinking Critically

16. The hypothesis should include the voltage doubling and the current doubling. Variables should include the voltage of the second battery. Controls should include testing the voltage of the second battery.

17. The net charge does not change since electrons are not lost nor gained, only displaced.

18. No, the glass doorknob is an insulator and resists being charged inductively.

19. The net charge on Earth or the Moon is nearly zero. So the electric force is very small.

20. Drawings will vary but should show the appliances in parallel branches with a circuit breaker in series with the voltage source.

Applying Math

National Math Standards

National: 1, 2, 9

21. 0.8 V
22. 0.15 V
23. 0.96 k W h
24. 8.1 k W h, $.73
25. 0.9 W

Assessment Resources

Reproducible Masters

Chapter *Fast File* Resources
Chapter Review, pp. 39–40
Chapter Tests, pp. 41–44
Assessment Transparency Activity, p. 51

Glencoe Science Web site
Chapter Review Test
Standardized Test Practice

Glencoe Technology
Assessment Transparency
Exam*View*® Pro Testmaker
MindJogger Videoquiz
Interactive Chalkboard

Answer Sheet An answer sheet can be found at **gpescience.com**.

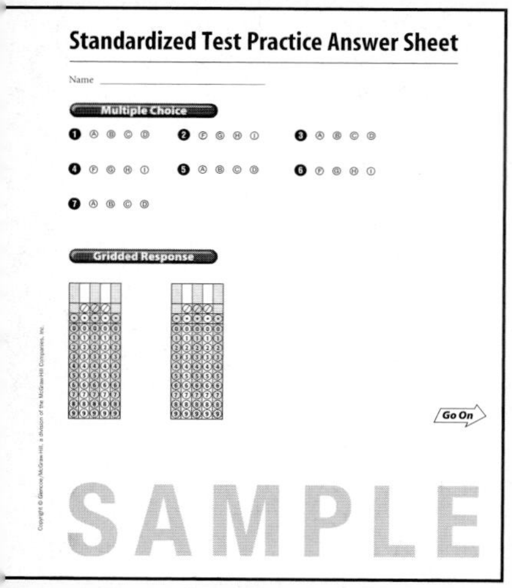

Multiple Choice

1. C
2. B
3. A
4. C
5. B
6. C
7. B

chapter 13 Standardized Test Practice

Record your answers on the answer sheet provided by your teacher or on a sheet of paper.

Multiple Choice

1. Which of the following is true about two adjacent electric charges?
   - **A.** If both are positive, they attract.
   - **B.** If both are negative, they attract.
   - **C.** If one is positive and one is negative, they attract.
   - **D.** If one is positive and one is negative, they repel.

The figure below shows a negatively charged electroscope. Use the figure to answer questions 2 and 3.

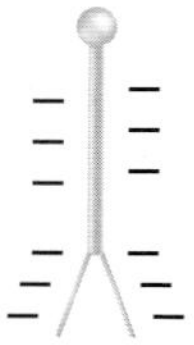

2. If a negatively charged rod is brought close to, but not touching, the knob, the two leaves will
   - **A.** move closer together.
   - **B.** move farther apart.
   - **C.** not move at all.
   - **D.** become positively charged.

3. If a positively charged rod touches the knob, the two leaves will
   - **A.** move closer together.
   - **B.** move farther apart.
   - **C.** not move at all.
   - **D.** become positively charged.

4. When an object becomes charged by induction, which of the following best describes the net charge on the object?
   - **A.** The net charge increases.
   - **B.** The net charge decreases.
   - **C.** The net charge doesn't change.
   - **D.** The net charge is negative.

Use the figure below to answer questions 5, 6, and 7.

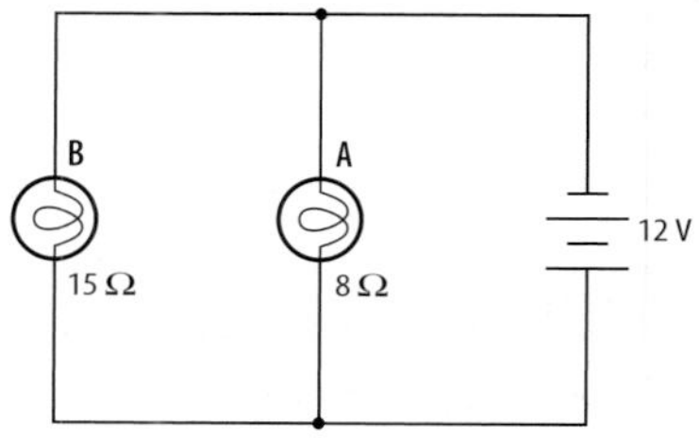

5. Which of the following is the same for each lightbulb?
   - **A.** current in the filament
   - **B.** voltage difference
   - **C.** electric resistance
   - **D.** charging by induction

6. Which of the following is the current that flows through lightbulb B?
   - **A.** 1.25 A
   - **B.** 0.67 A
   - **C.** 0.8 A
   - **D.** 1.5 A

7. Which of the following is the electrical power used by lightbulb A?

A. 8 W

B. 18 W

C. 12 W

D. 15 W

Gridded Response

Use the figure below to answer questions 8 and 9.

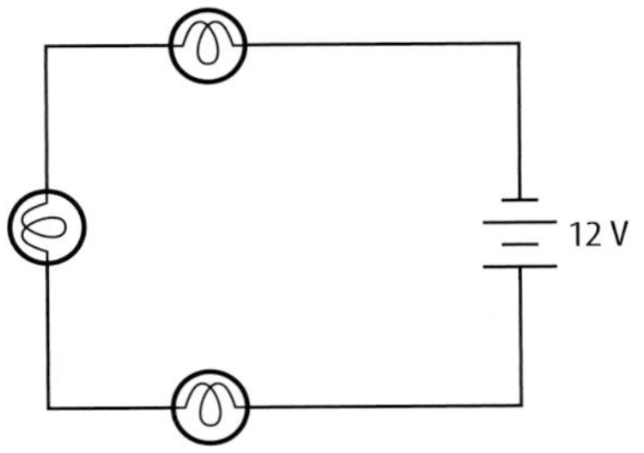

8. If the current in the circuit is 1.0 A, what is the total resistance of the circuit in ohms?

9. If the current in the circuit is 1.0 A, how much electrical energy, in kWh, is used by the circuit in 2.5 h?

Short Response

10. Two balloons are rubbed with a piece of wool. Describe what happens as the balloons are brought close together.

11. The current flowing through a lightbulb is 2.5 A. The lamp is connected to a battery supplying a voltage difference of 12 V. What is the power used by the lightbulb?

Extended Response

Use the table below to answer question 12.

Resistance of Copper Wire	
Length (m)	**Resistance (Ω)**
10	0.8
20	1.6
25	2.0
30	2.4

12. Suppose you were asked to estimate the resistance of a 5-m length of wire based on data in the table. What additional information would be needed to make your estimate more accurate?

13. The filament in a 75-W lightbulb has a smaller electric resistance than the filament in a 40-W lightbulb. Describe two ways the filament in the 75-W bulb could be different from the filament in the 40-W lightbulb.

Test-Taking Tip

Be sure you understand all symbols on a table or graph before attempting to answer any questions about the table or graph.

Gridded Response

8. 12
9. 30

Short Response

10. They repel each other because they have the same charge.
11. P = IV 2.5 A × 12 V = 30 W

Extended Response

12. The temperature, material, and diameter of the 5 m wire must be the same as the wire in the table.
13. The 75-W bulb filament could be shorter or have a larger diameter than the 40-W light bulb.

Rubrics

For more help evaluating Short- and Extended-Response questions, see the rubrics on p. 9T.

chapter 14 Organizer

Section/Objectives	Standards		Labs/Features
	National	State/Local	
Chapter Opener	See pp. 16T–17T for a Key to Standards.		**Launch Lab:** The Strength of Magnets, p. 423 **Foldables,** p. 423
Section 1 Magnetism 2 sessions 1 block 1. **Explain** how a magnet exerts a force. 2. **Describe** the properties of temporary and permanent magnets. 3. **Explain** why some materials are magnetic and some are not. 4. **Model** magnetic behavior using magnetic domains.	National Content Standards: UCP.1, UCP.2, UCP.3, UCP.5, A.1, A.2, B.2, B.4, D.1, D.3		**MiniLAB:** Observing Magnetic Interference, p. 427 **Integrate Life Science,** p. 428 **Applying Science:** How can magnetic parts of a junk car be salvaged?, p. 428 **MiniLAB:** Making Your Own Compass, p. 429
Section 2 Electricity and Magnetism 3 sessions 1.5 blocks 5. **Describe** the magnetic field produced by an electric current. 6. **Explain** how an electromagnet produces a magnetic field. 7. **Describe** how electromagnets are used. 8. **Explain** how an electric motor operates.	National Content Standards: UCP.1, UCP.2, UCP.3, UCP.5, A.1, A.2, B.2, B.4, G.3		**Science Online,** p. 437
Section 3 Producing Electric Current 3 sessions 1.5 blocks 9. **Define** electromagnetic induction. 10. **Describe** how a generator produces an electric current. 11. **Distinguish** between alternating current and direct current. 12. **Explain** how a transformer can change the voltage of an alternating current.	National Content Standards: UCP.1, UCP.2, UCP.3, UCP.5, A.1, A.2, B.2, B.4, G.3		**Integrate Career,** p. 440 **Visualizing Motors and Generators,** p. 441 **Science Online,** p. 442 **Lab:** Electricity and Magnetism, p. 445 Video Lab **Lab:** Controlling Electromagnets, pp. 446–447 **Science and History:** Body Art, p. 448

StudentWorks Plus

Glencoe Exclusive! TeacherWorks™ All-In-One Planner and Resource Center

Lab Materials	Reproducible Resources	Section Assessment	Technology
Launch Lab: bar magnet, paper clips	**Chapter *FAST FILE* Resources** Foldables Worksheet, p. 17 Note-taking Worksheets, pp. 33–35 Directed Reading Overview, p. 19	Glencoe's Assessment Advantage	TeacherWorks includes: • Interactive Teacher Edition • Lesson Planner with calendar • Access to all program blacklines • Correlations to standards • Web links
MiniLAB: bar magnet, ring stand, thread, paper clip, book, paper, aluminum foil, fabric, butter knife **MiniLAB:** plastic foam cup, magnet, sewing needle, tape, plate, water	**Chapter *FAST FILE* Resources** Transparency Activity, p. 44 MiniLAB, pp. 3, 4 Enrichment, p. 30 Reinforcement, p. 27 Directed Reading, p. 20 Lab Activity, pp. 9–12 **Mathematics Skill Activities,** p. 47	Portfolio Curriculum Connection, p. 427 Performance MiniLAB, p. 427 Applying Science, p. 428 MiniLAB, p. 429 Applying Math, p. 430 Content Section Review, p. 430	Section Focus Transparency Interactive Chalkboard CD-ROM StudentWorks Plus
Need materials? Contact Science Kit at 1-800-828-7777 or www.sciencekit.com.	**Chapter *FAST FILE* Resources** Transparency Activity, p. 45 Enrichment, p. 31 Reinforcement, p. 28 Directed Reading, p. 21 Lab Activity, pp. 13–16 **Physical Science Critical Thinking/Problem Solving,** p. 17	Portfolio Curriculum Connection, p. 435 Performance Applying Math, p. 437 Content Section Review, p. 437	Section Focus Transparency Interactive Chalkboard CD-ROM StudentWorks Plus
Lab: cardboard tube; scissors; bar magnet; thin, flexible, insulated wire; galvanometer or ammeter **Lab:** 22–gauge insulated wire, 16–penny iron nail, aluminum rod or nail, 6-V DC power supply, 1.5-V D-cell batteries (3), steel paper clips, magnetic compass, duct tape	**Chapter *FAST FILE* Resources** Transparency Activity, p. 46 Enrichment, p. 32 Reinforcement, p. 29 Directed Reading, pp. 21, 22 Transparency Activity, pp. 47–48 Lab Worksheet, pp. 5–6, 7–8 **Cultural Diversity,** p. 53 **Home and Community Involvement,** p. 37 **Performance Assessment in the Science Classroom,** p. 53	Portfolio Curriculum Connection, p. 440 Performance Applying Math, p. 444 Content Section Review, p. 444	Section Focus Transparency Teaching Transparency Virtual Labs CD-ROM Interactive Chalkboard CD-ROM StudentWorks Plus Video Lab

End of Chapter Assessment

Glencoe's Assessment Advantage

Blackline Masters	Technology	Professional Series
Chapter *FAST FILE* Resources Chapter Review, pp. 37–38 Chapter Tests, pp. 39–42 **Standardized Test Practice,** pp. 60–63	MindJogger Videoquiz Virtual Labs CD-ROM Exam*View*® Pro Testmaker TeacherWorks CD-ROM Interactive Chalkboard CD-ROM	**Performance Assessment in the Science Classroom (PASC)**

Transparencies

Section Focus

SECTION 1 Section Focus Transparency **Magnetic Appeal** Chapter 14

You might think of magicians when you hear the word levitation, but scientists can levitate, too! This photo shows a magnet levitating over a ceramic plate. Magnetic levitation has applications ranging from advertising displays to high-speed trains.

1. **What happens as you move a magnet closer to a refrigerator door?**
2. **How do people use magnets in their daily lives?**

L2

SECTION 2 Section Focus Transparency **It Was an Age of Small Appliances** Chapter 14

Many common household items contain small motors. Some examples are fans, vacuums, and hair dryers. What other appliances are pictured below?

1. **Which items use electricity? Which items have motors?**
2. **Name some ways you have used electric current today.**

L2

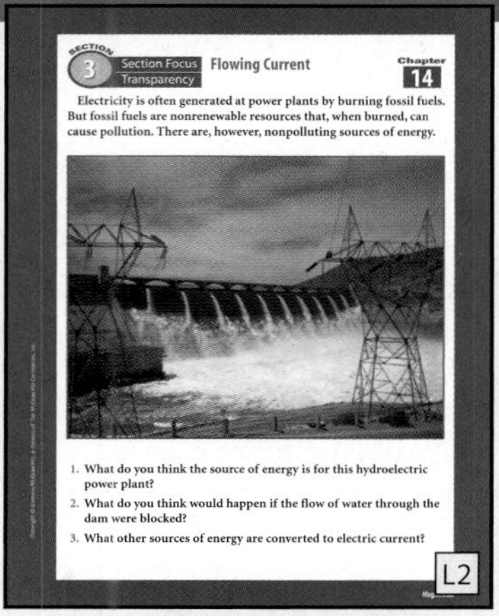
SECTION 3 Section Focus Transparency **Flowing Current** Chapter 14

Electricity is often generated at power plants by burning fossil fuels. But fossil fuels are nonrenewable resources that, when burned, can cause pollution. There are, however, nonpolluting sources of energy.

1. **What do you think the source of energy is for this hydroelectric power plant?**
2. **What do you think would happen if the flow of water through the dam were blocked?**
3. **What other sources of energy are converted to electric current?**

L2

This is a representation of key blackline masters available in the Teacher Classroom Resources. See Resource Manager boxes within the chapter for additional information.

Assessment

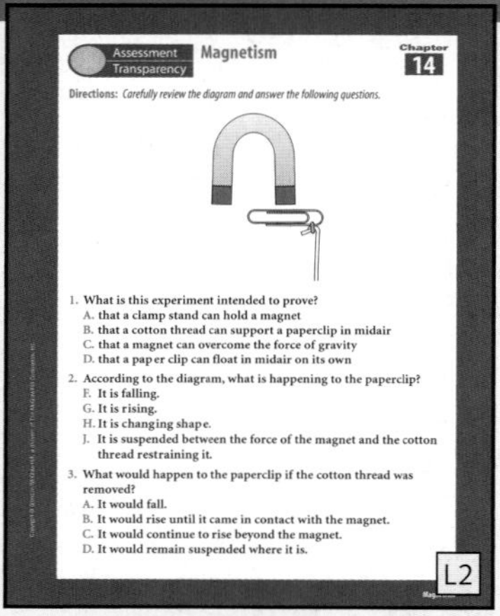
Assessment Transparency **Magnetism** Chapter 14

Directions: *Carefully review the diagram and answer the following questions.*

1. **What is this experiment intended to prove?**
   A. **that a clamp stand can hold a magnet**
   B. **that a cotton thread can support a paperclip in midair**
   C. **that a magnet can overcome the force of gravity**
   D. **that a pap er clip can float in midair on its own**
2. **According to the diagram, what is happening to the paperclip?**
   F. **It is falling.**
   G. **It is rising.**
   H. **It is changing shap e.**
   J. **It is suspended between the force of the magnet and the cotton thread restraining it.**
3. **What would happen to the paperclip if the cotton thread was removed?**
   A. **It would fall.**
   B. **It would rise until it came in contact with the magnet.**
   C. **It would continue to rise beyond the magnet.**
   D. **It would remain suspended where it is.**

L2

Teaching

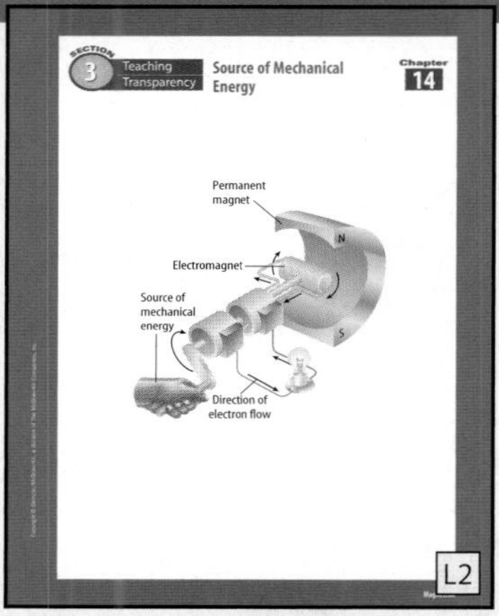
SECTION 3 Teaching Transparency **Source of Mechanical Energy** Chapter 14

L2

Key to Teaching Strategies

The following designations will help you decide which activities are appropriate for your students.

- L1 Level 1 activities should be appropriate for students with learning difficulties.
- L2 Level 2 activities should be within the ability range of all students.
- L3 Level 3 activities are designed for above-average students.
- ELL ELL activities should be within the ability range of English Language Learners.
- COOP LEARN Cooperative Learning activities are designed for small group work.
- LS Multiple Learning Styles logos, as described on page 12T, are used throughout to indicate strategies that address different learning styles.
- P These strategies represent student products that can be placed into a best-work portfolio.
- PBL Problem-Based Learning activities apply real-world situations to learning.

Hands-on Activities

Student Text Lab Worksheet

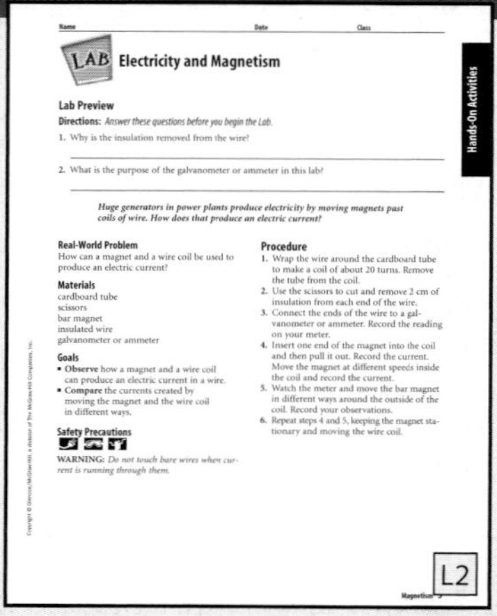
Name Date Class

LAB **Electricity and Magnetism**

Hands-On Activities

Lab Preview

Directions: *Answer these questions before you begin the Lab.*

1. Why is the insulation removed from the wire?
2. What is the purpose of the galvanometer or ammeter in this lab?

Huge generators in power plants produce electricity by moving magnets past coils of wire. How does that produce an electric current?

Real-World Problem
How can a magnet and a wire coil be used to produce an electric current?

Materials
cardboard tube
scissors
bar magnet
insulated wire
galvanometer or ammeter

Goals
- **Observe** how a magnet and a wire coil can produce an electric current in a wire.
- **Compare** the currents created by moving the magnet and the wire coil in different ways.

Safety Precautions

WARNING: *Do not touch bare wires when current is running through them.*

Procedure
1. Wrap the wire around the cardboard tube to make a coil of about 20 turns. Remove the tube from the coil.
2. Use the scissors to cut and remove 2 cm of insulation from each end of the wire.
3. Connect the ends of the wire to a galvanometer or ammeter. Record the reading on your meter.
4. Insert one end of the magnet into the coil and then pull it out. Record the current. Move the magnet at different speeds inside the coil and record the current.
5. Watch the meter and move the bar magnet in different ways around the outside of the coil. Record your observations.
6. Repeat steps 4 and 5, keeping the magnet stationary and moving the wire coil.

L2

Laboratory Activities

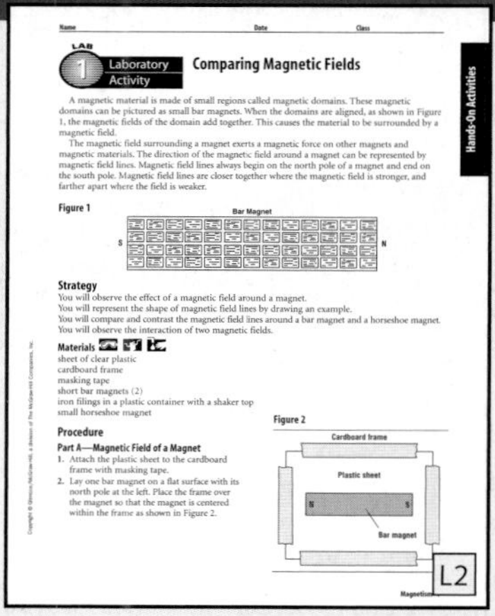
Name Date Class

LAB 1 Laboratory Activity **Comparing Magnetic Fields**

Hands-On Activities

A magnetic material is made of small regions called magnetic domains. These magnetic domains can be pictured as small bar magnets. When the domains are aligned, as shown in Figure 1, the magnetic fields of the domain add together. This causes the material to be surrounded by a magnetic field.

The magnetic field surrounding a magnet exerts a magnetic force on other magnets and magnetic materials. The direction of the magnetic field around a magnet can be represented by magnetic field lines. Magnetic field lines always begin on the north pole of a magnet and end on the south pole. Magnetic field lines are closer together where the magnetic field is stronger, and farther apart where the field is weaker.

Figure 1

Strategy
You will observe the effect of a magnetic field around a magnet.
You will represent the shape of magnetic field lines by drawing an example.
You will compare and contrast the magnetic field lines around a bar magnet and a horseshoe magnet.
You will observe the interaction of two magnetic fields.

Materials
sheet of clear plastic
cardboard frame
masking tape
short bar magnets (2)
iron filings in a plastic container with a shaker top
small horseshoe magnet

Procedure

Part A—Magnetic Field of a Magnet
1. Attach the plastic sheet to the cardboard frame with masking tape.
2. Lay one bar magnet on a flat surface with its north pole at the left. Place the frame over the magnet so that the magnet is centered within the frame as shown in Figure 2.

Figure 2

L2

Meeting Different Ability Levels

Content Outline

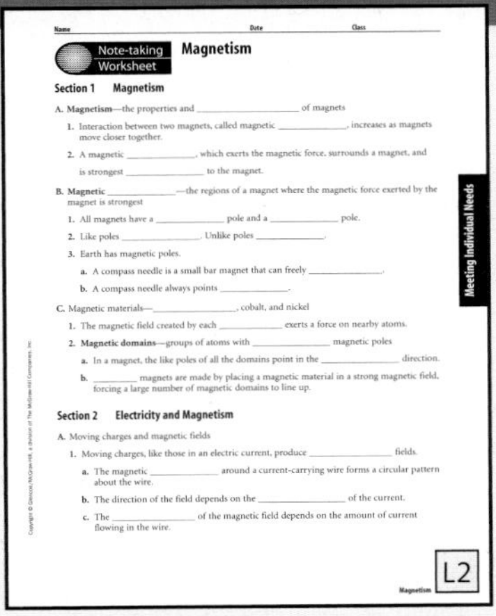
Note-taking Worksheet — Magnetism

L2

Reinforcement

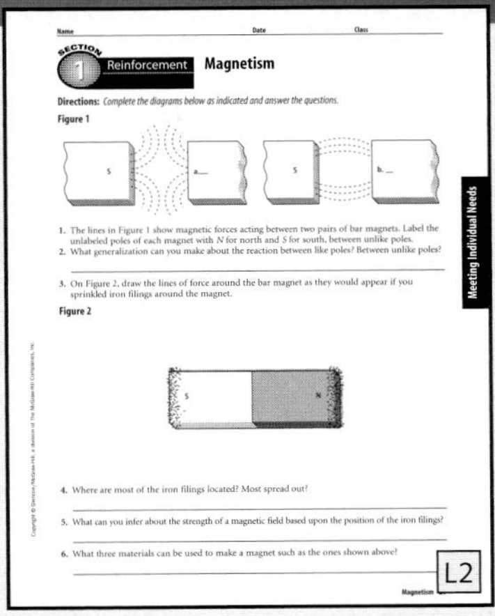
Section 1 Reinforcement — Magnetism

L2

Enrichment

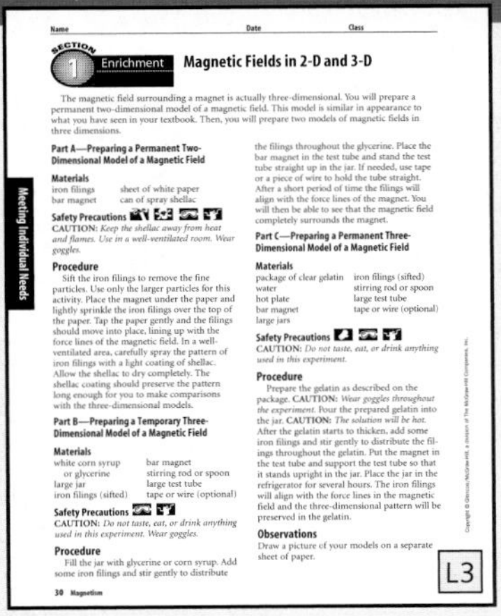
Section 1 Enrichment — Magnetic Fields in 2-D and 3-D

L3

Directed Reading (English/Spanish)

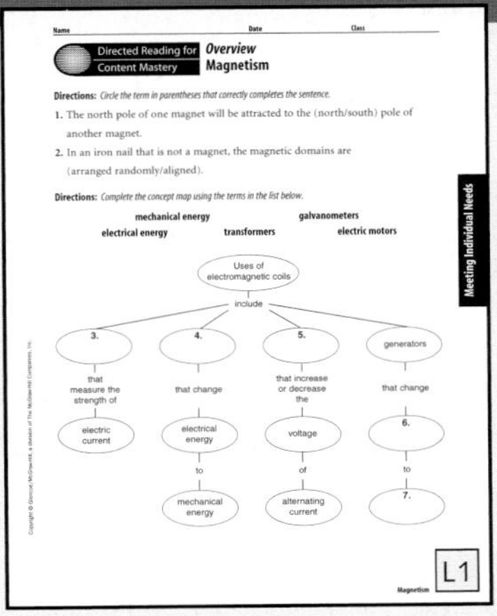
Directed Reading for Content Mastery — Overview Magnetism

L1

Study Guide

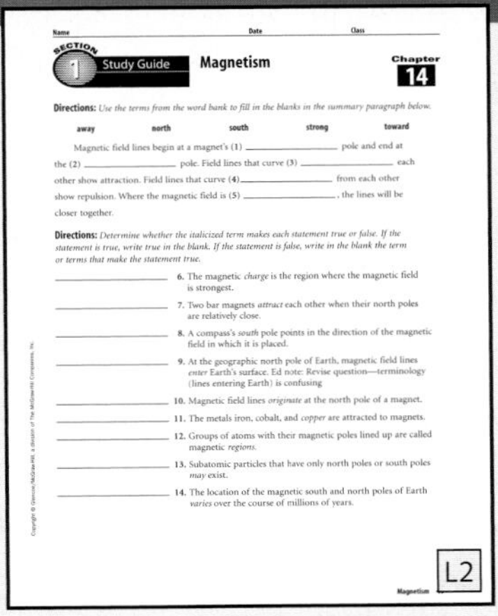
Section 1 Study Guide — Magnetism

L2

Reading Essentials

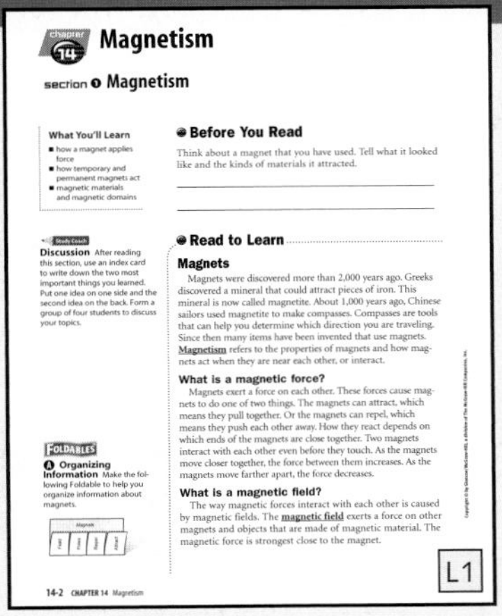
Chapter 14 Magnetism — section 1 Magnetism

L1

Assessment

Test Practice Workbook

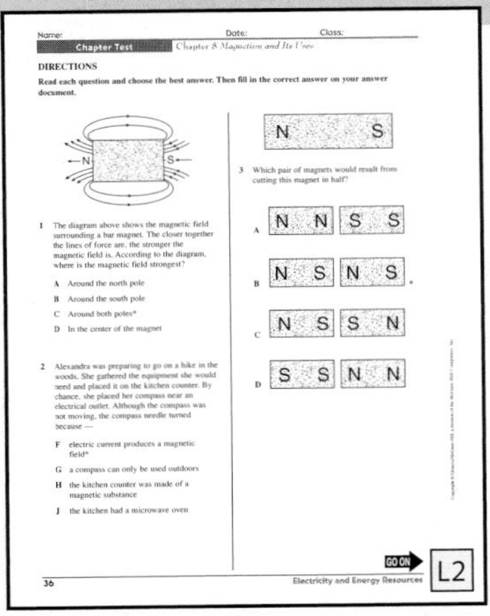
L2

Chapter Review

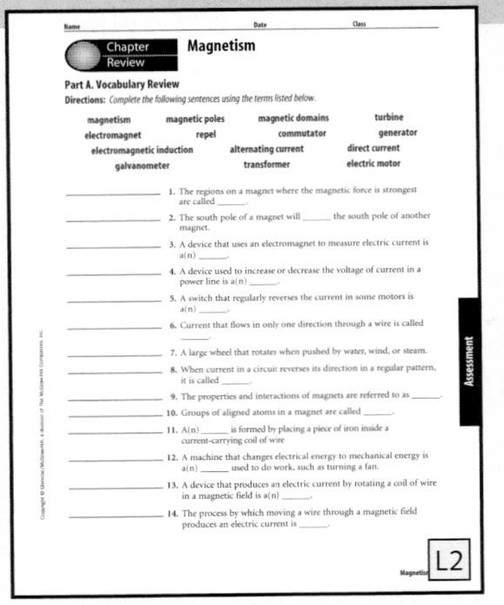
Chapter Review — Magnetism

L2

Chapter Tests

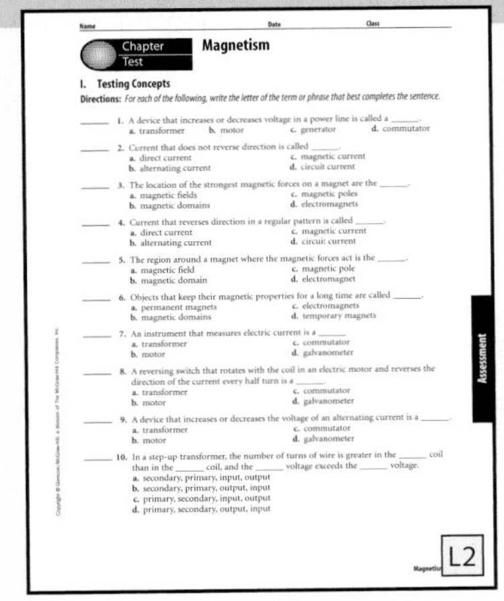
Chapter Test — Magnetism

L2

Science Content Background

section 1 Magnetism

Magnets

In 1269 Petrus Peregrinus published an article describing the properties of lodestone. He reported that if it is hung freely, lodestone orients in a north-south plane but does not point exactly to true North. He also noted that like poles repel and unlike poles attract, and that iron can be magnetized by contact with it.

Magnetic Materials

A common definition of magnetism is the ability to attract iron. Steel is composed of iron and carbon molecules that form a strong material used in many common products. Steel is magnetic because it contains iron. This property allows cars to be lifted by electromagnets in junkyards and soup can lids to be held by the magnet on a can opener. Cobalt and nickel are also attracted to magnets. Iron, nickel, and cobalt are called ferromagnetic materials.

section 2 Electricity and Magnetism

Electric Current and Magnetism

Frictional forces usually act in the opposite direction to the motion of an object. For example, air resistance on a car traveling north acts toward the south. The magnetic field produced by an electric current acts at right angles to the direction of the current. The right-hand rule shows the direction of the magnetic field in a wire. The thumb points in the direction of the conventional current, or the way a positive charge would flow in a wire. The fingers then show the direction of the magnetic field.

section 3 Producing Electric Current

From Mechanical to Electrical Energy

Niagara Falls generates significant tourism and electricity. In order to keep the tourism industry vibrant, only about 55 percent of the water that goes over the falls is diverted into turbines in the daytime; at night this amount is increased to 75 percent.

Transformers

The ability of alternating current (AC) to be transformed into higher and lower voltages gives it an advantage over direct current (DC) in electrical power distribution. Increasing the voltage does not create energy because current decreases as voltage increases. This increase does, however, result in more efficient transmission. This efficiency becomes significant as electricity travels through miles of wire.

chapter content resources

Internet Resources

For additional content background, visit **gpescience.com** to:

- access your book online
- find references to related articles in popular science magazines
- access Web links with related content background
- access current events with science journal topics

Print Resources

Magnetic Materials: Fundamentals and Device Applications, by Nicola A. Spaldin, Cambridge University Press, 2003

Modern Magnetic Materials: Principles and Applications, by Robert C. O'Handley, Wiley InterScience, 1999

Electricity, Magnetism, and Light, by Wayne Saslow, Academic Press, 2002

Waves: Principles of Light, Electricity, and Magnetism (Secrets of the Universe), by Paul Fleisher, Lerner Publications Company, 2001

IDENTIFYING Misconceptions

Find Out What Students Think

Students may think that . . .

All metals are magnetic.
Students are aware of common properties of metals such as the fact that they are good conductors of electricity and heat. It is natural for students to extend these similarities to magnetism and think that all metals can be attracted by a magnet. Lack of first-hand experience with magnets and metals makes this misconception common, even in adults. In addition, iron alloys are omnipresent, so people's limited experiences with magnets may lead them to believe that all metals are magnetic.

Activity

Ask students to draw two columns on their papers and label one *Attracted to a Magnet* and the other *Not Attracted to a Magnet.* Then ask that they place the following words into the appropriate columns: *iron*, *lead*, *plastic*, *copper*, *steel*, *aluminum*, *nickel*, *cobalt*, *oxygen*, and *wood.* Have students form groups and discuss any differences in opinion about which items belong in each column. The iron, steel, nickel, and cobalt are attracted to a magnet, and the lead, plastic, copper, aluminum, oxygen and wood are not. L2

Promote Understanding

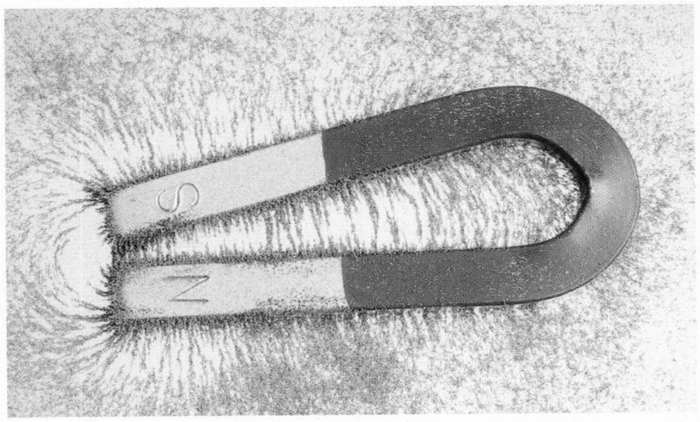

Dallas and John Heaton/Corbis

Activity

Provide students with different metals and nonmetals and with magnets with which to test them. The materials should include easily obtainable ferromagnetic materials such as iron and steel as well as nonferromagnetic metals such as aluminum and copper. Make sure to include nonmetals, even though most students will realize that these are not magnetic.

- Have students use the magnets to test for attraction and sort materials that are and are not magnetic.
- On the board, make a class list of the results.
- Help students realize that iron (Fe) is a magnetic material, so things made from iron, including steel, are attracted to magnets.
- Explain that cobalt (Co) and nickel (Ni) are also magnetic materials.
- Have students locate iron, cobalt, and nickel on a periodic table of the elements. Point out that on the periodic table, these metals are in the same row and are next to each other. L2

Assess

After completing the chapter, see *Identifying Misconceptions* in the Study Guide at the end of the chapter.

chapter 14

Chapter Vocabulary

magnetism, p. 424
magnetic field, p. 425
magnetic pole, p. 425
magnetic domain, p. 429
electromagnet, p. 432
solenoid, p.432
galvanometer, p. 434
electric motor, p. 435
electromagnetic induction, p. 438
generator, p. 438
turbine, p. 440
direct current (DC), p. 442
alternating current (AC), p. 442
transformer, p. 443

Science Journal Student responses will vary, but may include magnets attract some metals, likes repel, and opposites attract.

INTERACTIVE CHALKBOARD with Image Bank

PowerPoint® Presentations

This CD-ROM is an editable Microsoft® PowerPoint® presentation that includes:

- a pre-made presentation for every chapter
- interactive graphics
- animations
- audio clips
- image bank
- all new section and chapter questions
- Standardized Test Practice
- transparencies
- Foldables directions
- links to gpescience.com

chapter 14

Magnetism

chapter preview

sections

1 Magnetism
2 Electricity and Magnetism
3 Producing Electric Current
Lab *Electricity and Magnetism*
Lab *Controlling Electromagnets*
Virtual Lab *How does a generator work?*

A Natural Light Show

Have you ever seen an aurora? This light display occurs when blasts of charged particles from the Sun are captured by Earth's magnetic field. Atoms in the upper atmosphere emit the aurora light when they collide with charged particles that result from the Sun's blasts.

Science Journal List three things you know about magnets.

422

Theme Connection

Systems and Interactions Electricity and magnetism are related. Electrical flow causes magnetic effects, and moving magnets are used to produce electrical energy.

About the Photo

Aurora These colorful light displays occur primarily in the upper latitudes of the Northern and Southern Hemispheres. Auroras that occur in the Northern Hemisphere are called aurora borealis or northern lights and those in the Southern Hemisphere are called aurora australis or southern lights.

Start-Up Activities

Launch LAB

The Strength of Magnets

Did you know that magnets are used in TV sets, computers, stereo speakers, electric motors, and many other devices? Magnets also help create images of the inside of the human body. Even Earth acts like a giant bar magnet. How do magnets work?

1. Hold a bar magnet horizontally and put a paper clip on one end. Touch a second paper clip to the end of the first one. Continue adding paper clips until none will stick to one end of the chain. Copy the data table below and record the number of paper clips the magnet holds. Remove the paper clips from the magnet.
2. Repeat step 1 three more times. First, start the chain about 2 cm from the end of the magnet. Second, start the chain near the center of the magnet. Third, start the chain at the other end of the magnet.
3. **Think Critically** Infer which part of the magnet exerts the strongest attraction. Compare the attraction at the center of the magnet with the attraction at the ends.

Magnet and Paper Clip Data

	Paper Clip Chain (number of clips)
Trial 1 (end)	
Trial 2 (2 cm)	
Trial 3 (center)	
Trial 4 (other end)	

FOLDABLES™ Study Organizer

Using Magnets Many devices you use contain magnets that help convert one form of energy to another. Make the following Foldable to help you understand how magnets are used to transform electrical and mechanical energy.

STEP 1 **Fold** a sheet of paper in half lengthwise.

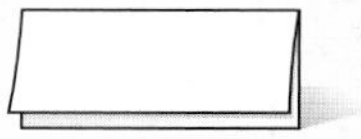

STEP 2 **Fold** the paper down about 2 cm from the top.

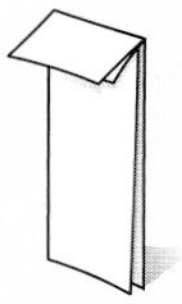

STEP 3 **Open and draw** lines along the top fold. **Label** as shown.

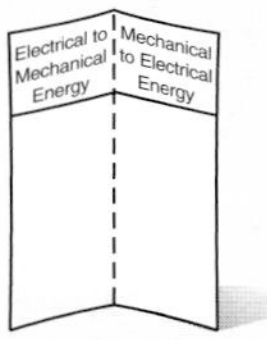

Summarize As you read the chapter, summarize how magnets are used to convert electrical energy to mechanical energy in the left column, and how magnets are used to convert mechanical energy to electrical energy in the right column.

Science Online | Preview this chapter's content and activities at gpescience.com

Launch LAB

Purpose Use the Launch Lab to illustrate the fact that the strength of a magnetic field varies over the length of a bar magnet. L2 ELL LS **Kinesthetic**

Preparation Test the bar magnets to see approximately how many paper clips each team will need. Small clips make it easier to observe differences in field strength.

Materials bar magnet, many small paper clips of the same size

Teaching Strategy If you have a variety of bar magnets, have the class compare results after finishing the activity. Ask students why the paper clips need to be the same size. so you can compare the numbers picked up

Think Critically

The two ends of the magnet exert the strongest attraction. The middle exerts a weaker attraction. Some magnets will not hold any clips there.

Assessment

Process Have students sketch a graph showing how the strength of the magnetic field changes over the length of the magnet. Use **Performance Assessment in the Science Classroom**, p. 127.

FOLDABLES™ Study Organizer **Dinah Zike Study Fold**

Student preparation materials for this Foldable are available in the **Chapter *Fast File* Resources.**

section 1

Magnetism

Reading Guide

What You'll Learn

- **Explain** how a magnet exerts a force.
- **Describe** the properties of temporary and permanent magnets.
- **Explain** why some materials are magnetic and some are not.
- **Model** magnetic behavior using magnetic domains.

Why It's Important

Without the forces exerted by magnets, you could not use televisions, computers, CD players, or even refrigerators.

Review Vocabulary

electric field: surrounds an electric charge and exerts a force on other electric charges

New Vocabulary

- magnetism
- magnetic field
- magnetic pole
- magnetic domain

Magnets

More than 2,000 years ago, Greeks discovered deposits of a mineral that was a natural magnet. They noticed that chunks of this mineral could attract pieces of iron. This mineral was found in a region of Turkey that then was known as Magnesia, so the Greeks called the mineral magnetic. The mineral is now called magnetite. In the twelfth century, Chinese sailors used magnetite to make compasses that improved navigation. Since then, many devices have been developed that rely on magnets to operate. Today, the word **magnetism** refers to the properties and interactions of magnets. **Figure 1** shows a device you might be familiar with that uses magnets and magnetism.

Figure 1 Magnets can be found in many devices you use every day, such as TVs, video games, and telephones. Headphones and CD players also contain magnets.

Magnetic Force You probably have played with magnets and noticed that two magnets exert a force on each other. Depending on which ends of the magnets are close together, magnets either repel or attract each other. You might have noticed that the interaction between two magnets can be felt even before the magnets touch. The strength of the force between two magnets increases as magnets move closer together and decreases as the the magnets move farther apart.

Reading Check *What does the force between two magnets depend on?*

1 Motivate

INTERACTIVE CHALKBOARD An editable Microsoft® PowerPoint® presentation is available on **Interactive Chalkboard** CD-ROM.

Bellringer

Section Focus Transparencies also are available on the Interactive Chalkboard CD-ROM. L2 ELL

Section 1 Section Focus Transparency — **Magnetic Appeal** — Chapter 14

You might think of magicians when you hear the word levitation, but scientists can levitate, too! This photo shows a magnet levitating over a ceramic plate. Magnetic levitation has applications ranging from advertising displays to high-speed trains.

1. What happens as you move a magnet closer to a refrigerator door?
2. How do people use magnets in their daily lives?

L2

Magnetism

Reading Preview

Tie to Prior Knowledge

Magnets Discuss with students places where they have used magnets. Most have used magnets on refrigerator doors. Explain that magnets are also used in such items as stereo speakers, televisions, and floppy disks.

Word Map Post the new vocabulary words in a prominent place in the classroom. Give students a sentence using each term. Ask them to determine the meaning of the word from the context of the sentence. Have students verify their ideas using the definitions in the text.

Section 1 Resource Manager

Chapter *FAST FILE* Resources

- Transparency Activity, p. 44
- Directed Reading for Content Mastery, pp. 19–20
- Note-taking Worksheets, pp. 33–35
- MiniLAB, pp. 3–4
- Enrichment, p. 30
- Lab Activity, pp. 9–12
- Reinforcement, p. 27
- **Mathematics Skill Activities**, p. 47

424 CHAPTER 14 Magnetism

Figure 2 A magnet is surounded by a magnetic field.

A magnet's magnetic field is represented by magnetic field lines.

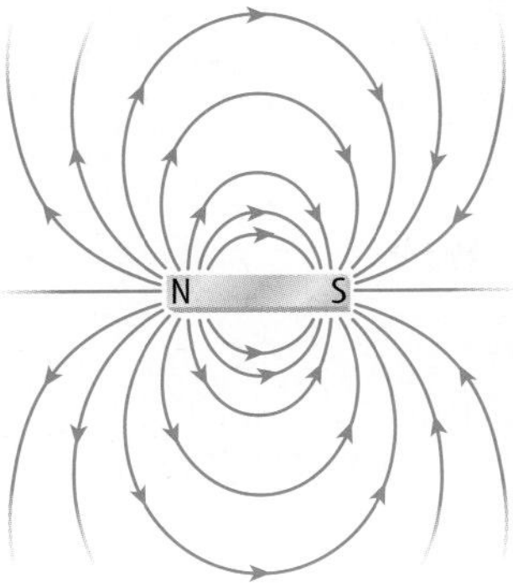

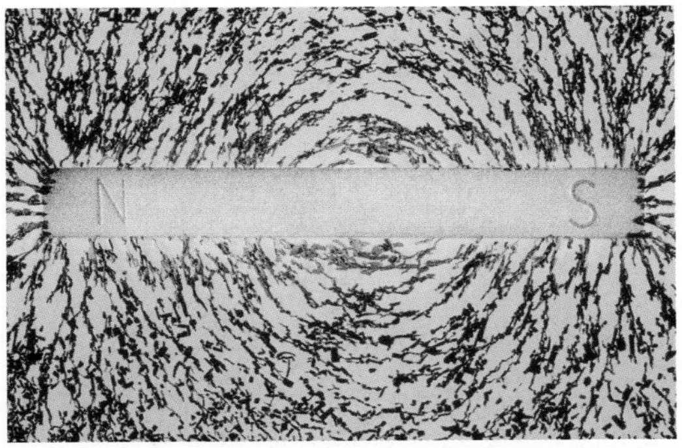

Iron filings sprinkled around a magnet line up along the magnetic field lines.

Magnetic Field A magnet is surrounded by a magnetic field. A **magnetic field** exerts a force on other magnets and objects made of magnetic materials. The magnetic field is strongest close to the magnet and weaker farther away. The magnetic field can be represented by lines of force, or magnetic field lines. **Figure 2** shows the magnetic field lines surrounding a bar magnet. A magnetic field also has a direction. The direction of the magnetic field around a bar magnet is shown by the arrows on the left side of **Figure 2.**

Magnetic Poles Look again at **Figure 2.** Do you notice that the magnetic field lines are closest together at the ends of the bar magnet? These regions, called the **magnetic poles,** are where the magnetic force exerted by the magnet is strongest. All magnets have a north pole and a south pole. For a bar magnet, the north and south poles are at the opposite ends.

Figure 3 shows the north and south poles of magnets with more complicated shapes. The two ends of a horseshoe-shaped magnet are the north and south poles. A magnet shaped like a disk has opposite poles on the top and bottom of the disk. Magnetic field lines always connect the north pole and the south pole of a magnet.

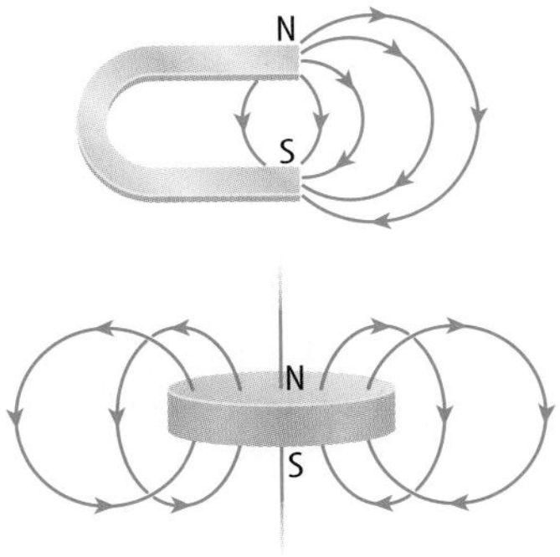

Figure 3 The magnetic field lines around horseshoe and disk magnets begin at each magnet's north pole and end at the south pole.
Identify *where the magnetic field is strongest.*

2 Teach

Reading Check

Answer the distance between the two magnets

Use an Analogy

Earth's Attraction A magnet's field, like a gravitational field, affects objects without touching them, even at a great distance. The faraway north magnetic pole attracts a compass needle, like the distant Sun holds Earth in orbit.

Use Science Words

Word Meaning Have students find out what *field* means in physics. A field is a region of space with a physical property (such as gravitational force, fluid pressure, etc.) that has a definite value at every point in the region. Compare and contrast this with other meanings of *field.* Other meanings also refer to areas, such as a meadow, a playing field, a background region, or even an area of interest. L3 LS **Linguistic**

Activity

Magnets Divide the class into small groups and provide each group with a set of magnets. Allow students to observe the properties and behaviors of the magnets. L1

Caption Answer

Figure 3 at the magnetic poles

Reading Strategy

Brainstorm Give students a statement that summarizes the content of each section and ask them to brainstorm words related to the statement. For example, provide the summary statement, "A magnetic field exerts a force on objects made of magnetic materials." Have students read the section and add to the brainstorming list.

Differentiated Instruction

Visually Impaired For students who cannot see the field lines in the illustrations and demonstrations, provide an opportunity to experiment with strong magnets. Make sure these students can feel the forces of attraction and repulsion between the magnets. L1 LS **Kinesthetic**

Quick Demo
Magnetic Fields

Materials overhead projector, iron filings or an iron nail and file, petri dish or 2 overhead sheets, several different magnets

Estimated Time 15 minutes

Procedure Show magnetic fields on the overhead projector. Make iron filings by rubbing a metal file on an iron nail. Place the iron filings in a covered petri dish or between two overhead sheets. Place different magnets on top of the filings on the projector. Then show the fields between attracting and repelling poles, and how the fields change as you move the magnets slowly toward or away from each other. This demonstrates how field strength diminishes with distance. L2

ELL LS **Visual-Spatial**

Reading Check

Answer Like poles repel each other; unlike poles attract.

INTEGRATE Earth Science — Content Background

Earth's magnetic poles do not perfectly align with Earth's geographic poles, the endpoints of the axis about which Earth rotates. Also, Earth's magnetic field is not fixed. The north magnetic pole has traveled about 10 km/year over the past century, and, many times in the past, magnetic north and south have switched places.

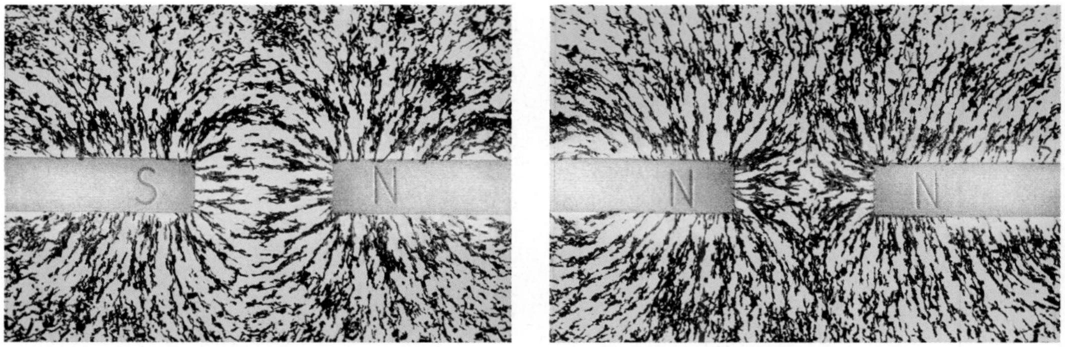

Unlike poles closest together — Like poles closest together

Figure 4 Two magnets can attract or repel each other, depending on which poles are closest together.

How Magnets Interact Two magnets can either attract or repel each other. Two north poles or two south poles of two magnets repel each other. However, north poles and south poles always attract each other. Like magnetic poles repel each other and unlike poles attract each other. When two magnets are brought close to each other, their magnetic fields combine to produce a new magnetic field. **Figure 4** shows the magnetic field that results when like poles and unlike poles of bar magnets are brought close to each other.

Reading Check *How do magnetic poles interact with each other?*

Magnetic Field Direction When a compass is brought near a bar magnet, the compass needle rotates. The compass needle is a small bar magnet with a north pole and a south pole. The force exerted on the compass needle by the magnetic field causes the needle to rotate. The compass needle rotates until it lines up with the magnetic field lines, as shown in **Figure 5.** The north pole of a compass points in the direction of the magnetic field. This direction is always away from a north magnetic pole and toward a south magnetic pole.

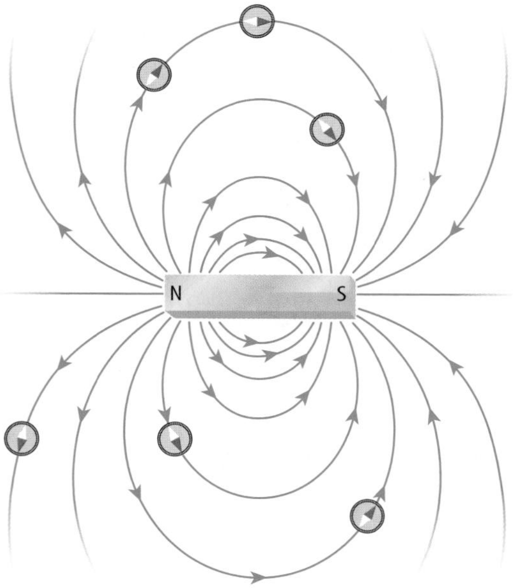

Figure 5 Compass needles placed around a bar magnet line up along magnetic field lines. The north poles of the compass needles are shaded red.

Visual Learning

Figure 4 What do you think happens to the magnetic force in the gaps between the lines? The force is still there even though the lines don't show it. L2

Cultural Diversity

Compasses Compasses were invented in China. By the ninth century A.D., the Chinese had discovered that magnetic north does not exactly coincide with geographic north. The compass was used for navigation at sea starting about 1,000 years ago (850–1050 A.D.). Before that they were used for a type of divination based on geographic features.

INTEGRATE Earth Science

Earth's Magnetic Field A compass can help determine direction because the north pole of the compass needle points north. This is because Earth acts like a giant bar magnet and is surrounded by a magnetic field that extends into space. Just as with a bar magnet, the compass needle aligns with Earth's magnetic field lines, as shown in **Figure 6.**

Earth's Magnetic Poles The north pole of a magnet is defined as the end of the magnet that points toward the geographic north. Sometimes the north pole and south pole of a magnet are called the north-seeking pole and the south-seeking pole. Because opposite magnetic poles attract, the north pole of a compass is being attracted by a south magnetic pole. Earth is like a bar magnet with its south magnetic pole near its geographic north pole.

Currently, Earth's south magnetic pole is located in northern Canada, about 1,500 km from the geographic north pole. However, Earth's magnetic poles move slowly with time. Sometimes Earth's magnetic poles switch places so that Earth's south magnetic pole is in the southern hemisphere near the geographic south pole. Measurements of magnetism in rocks show that Earth's magnetic poles have changed places over 150 times in the past 70 million years.

No one is sure what produces Earth's magnetic field. Earth's inner core is made of a solid ball of iron and nickel, surrounded by a liquid layer of molten iron and nickel. According to one theory, circulation of the molten iron and nickel in Earth's outer core produces Earth's magnetic field.

Figure 6 A compass needle aligns with the magnetic field lines of Earth's magnetic field.
Predict *Which way would a compass needle point if Earth's magnetic poles switched places?*

Mini LAB

Observing Magnetic Interference

Procedure

1. Clamp a **bar magnet** to a **ring stand.** Tie a **thread** around one end of a **paper clip** and stick the paper clip to one pole of the magnet.
2. Anchor the other end of the thread under a **book** on the table. Slowly pull the thread until the paper clip is suspended below the magnet but not touching it.
3. Without touching the paper clip, slip a piece of paper between the magnet and the paper clip. Does the paper clip fall?
4. Try other materials, such as **aluminum foil, fabric,** and a **butter knife.**

Analysis

1. Which materials caused the paper clip to fall? Why do you think these materials interfered with the magnetic field?
2. Which materials did not cause the paper clip to fall? Why do you think these materials did not interfere with the magnetic field?

Mini LAB

Purpose Students observe that magnetic fields extend beyond the magnet and through barriers, and that some materials can affect the field. L2 ELL IS **Kinesthetic**

Materials bar magnet, ring stand, 50 cm of thread, paper clip, tape, book, paper, aluminum foil, fabric, butter knife

Teaching Strategy Have students compare magnetic force to gravitational force. Remind students that gravitational force also acts through barriers.

Analysis

1. Some metals cause the paper clip to fall. These metals can be magnetized, so they affect the magnetic field.
2. Paper, glass, and plastic do not affect the field. The magnetic force is not affected by materials that cannot be magnetized.

Assessment

Process Have students examine the refrigerator door at home. Does it appear to be metal, or another material? Relate this to the lab. The plastic coating on some refrigerator doors does not interfere with the attraction between a magnet and the underlying metal. Use **Performance Assessment in the Science Classroom,** p. 89.

Caption Answer

Figure 6 toward the south magnetic pole in the southern hemisphere

Discussion

North Star What natural body has been used for centuries in the northern hemisphere to find the north-south direction? the star Polaris.

Fun Fact

Earth's magnetic field lines are not parallel to the surface. A carefully balanced magnetized needle can be used to measure the dip of the magnetic field, as well as its direction.

Curriculum Connection

History The compass was an important invention for navigation at sea. Have students research and write reports about some of the sea routes used before and after the invention of the compass. Most European exploration occurred after the adoption of the compass. Polynesian islanders and Vikings managed long sea voyages without the compass, depending on knowledge of the skies and the sea to find their way. L2 P IS **Kinesthetic**

INTEGRATE Life Science

Magnets in Organisms Animals may perceive Earth's magnetic field by mechanical effects, where the magnetite is deflected like a compass needle. They may also sense field variations that cause electrical induction within the animal.

Applying Science

Answers

1. A magnet will attract about 65% of the total mass of the car. Other metals (such as aluminum and copper) are not magnetic and will not be attracted.
2. 525 kg
3. 9.75×10^9 kg

IDENTIFYING Misconceptions

Magnetic Metals Students may think that all metals are magnetic. See p. 422F for teaching strategies that address this misconception.

INTEGRATE Life Science

Magnets in Organisms
Some organisms may use Earth's magnetic field to help them find their way around. Some species of birds, insects, and bacteria have been shown to contain small amounts of the mineral magnetite. Research how one species uses Earth's magnetic field, and report your findings to your class.

Magnetic Materials

You might have noticed that a magnet will not attract all metal objects. For example, a magnet will not attract pieces of aluminum foil. Only a few metals, such as iron, cobalt, and nickel, are attracted to magnets or can be made into permanent magnets. What makes these elements magnetic? Remember that every atom contains electrons. Electrons have magnetic properties. In the atoms of most elements, the magnetic properties of the electrons cancel out. However, in the atoms of iron, cobalt, and nickel, these magnetic properties don't cancel out. Each atom in these elements behaves like a small magnet and has its own magnetic field.

Even though these atoms have their own magnetic fields, objects made from these metals are not always magnets. For example, if you hold an iron nail close to a refrigerator door and let go, it falls to the floor. However, you can make the nail behave like a magnet temporarily.

Applying Science

How can magnetic parts of a junk car be salvaged?

Every year over 10 million cars containing plastics, glass, rubber, and various metals are scrapped. Magnets are often used to help retrieve some of these materials from scrapped cars. The materials can then be reused, saving both natural resources and energy. Once the junk car has been fed into a shredder, large magnets can easily separate many of its metal parts from its nonmetal parts. How much of the car does a magnet actually help separate? Use your ability to interpret a circle graph to find out.

Percentage Weight of Materials in a Car

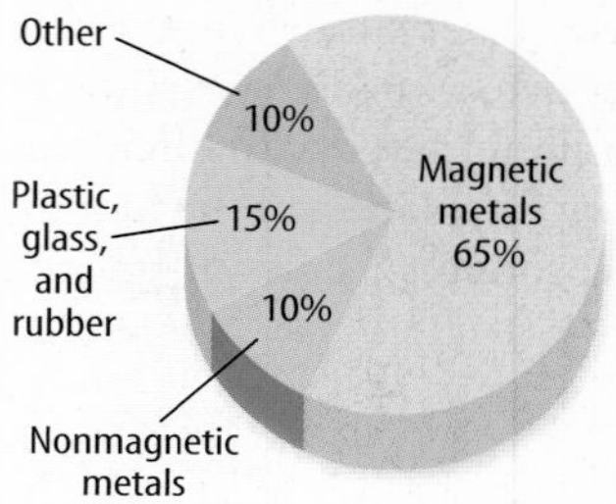

Identifying the Problem

The graph at the right shows the average percent by weight of the different materials in a car. Included in the magnetic metals are steel and iron. The nonmagnetic metals refer to aluminum, copper, lead, zinc, and magnesium. According to the graph, how much of the car can a magnet separate for recycling?

Solving the Problem

1. What percent of the car's weight will a magnet recover?
2. A certain scrapped car has a mass of 1,500 kg. What is the mass of the materials in this car that cannot be recovered using a magnet?
3. If the average mass of a scrapped car is 1,500 kg and 10 million cars are scrapped each year, what is the total mass of iron and steel that could be recovered from scrapped cars each year?

LAB DEMONSTRATION

Purpose to show how a hard blow can magnetize a steel rod aligned with Earth's magnetic field

Materials compass, steel rod, hammer, paper clips, protractor

Preparation Use the compass to mark a line on the ground running north–south.

Procedure Position the rod along the north-south line as shown. Sharply rap the south end of the rod with a hammer.

Expected Outcome The rod becomes magnetized and will pick up a few clips. Repeat if needed, as this effect depends on hitting the rod just right.

Assessment

What happened to the magnetic domains in the steel rod when it was struck with the hammer? They were jolted and could realign. Enough of the magnetic domains realigned along Earth's field lines to make a magnet. L2

428 CHAPTER 14 Magnetism

Magnetic Domains—A Model for Magnetism In iron, cobalt, nickel, and some other magnetic materials, the magnetic field created by each atom exerts a force on the other nearby atoms. Because of these forces, large groups of atoms align their magnetic poles so that almost all like poles point in the same direction. The groups of atoms with aligned magnetic poles are called **magnetic domains.** Each domain contains an enormous number of atoms, yet the domains are too small to be seen with the unaided eye. Because the magnetic poles of the individual atoms in a domain are aligned, the domain itself behaves like a magnet with a north pole and a south pole.

Lining Up Domains An iron nail contains an enormous number of these magnetic domains, so why doesn't the nail behave like a magnet? Even though each domain behaves like a magnet, the poles of the domains are arranged randomly and point in different directions, as shown in **Figure 7.** As a result, the magnetic fields from all the domains cancel each other out.

If you place a magnet against the same nail, the atoms in the domains orient themselves in the direction of the nearby magnetic field, as shown on the right in **Figure 7.** The like poles of the domains point in the same direction and no longer cancel each other out. The nail itself now acts as a magnet. However, when the external magnetic field is removed, the constant motion and vibration of the atoms bump the magnetic domains out of their alignment. The magnetic domains in the nail return to a random arrangement. For this reason, the nail is only a temporary magnet. Paper clips and other objects containing iron also can become temporary magnets.

Mini LAB

Making Your Own Compass

Procedure

WARNING: *Use care when handling sharp objects.*

1. Cut off the bottom of a **plastic foam cup** to make a polystyrene disk.
2. Magnetize a **sewing needle** by continuously stroking the needle in the same direction with a magnet for 1 min.
3. **Tape** the needle to the center of the foam disk.
4. Fill a **plate** with **water** and float the disk, needle-side up, in the water.
5. Bring the magnet close to the foam disk.

Analysis

1. How did the needle and disk move when you placed them in the water? Explain.
2. How did the needle and disk move when the magnet was brought near? Explain.

Try at Home

Figure 7 Magnetic materials contain magnetic domains.

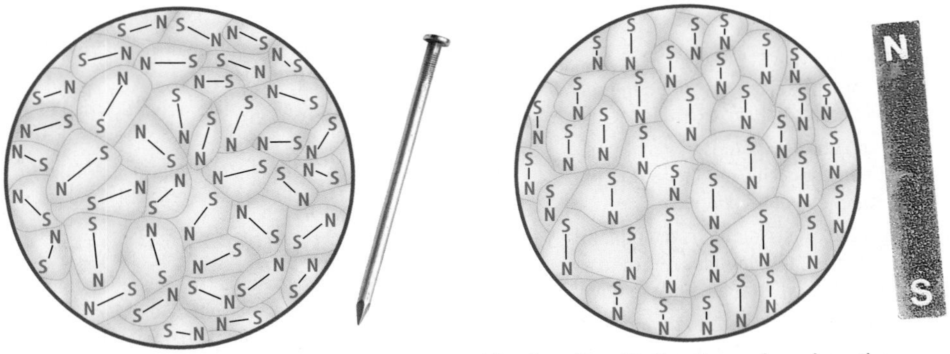

A normal iron nail is made up of microscopic domains that are arranged randomly.

The domains will align themselves along the magnetic field lines of a nearby magnet.

Use an Analogy

Rope Pulling Lining up magnetic domains is like getting a group of people to pull together on one end of a rope. If each person pulls the rope in a different direction, the pulls cancel each other and nothing happens. If they all pull together in one direction, the individual forces add together.

Mini LAB

Purpose Students will make a compass. L2 IN **Kinesthetic**

Materials plastic foam cup, magnet, sewing needle, tape, plate, water

Teaching Strategy Remind students that the sewing needle contains, or is made of, iron.

Safety Precautions Caution students to handle the needle with care.

Analysis

1. The needle aligned with Earth's magnetic field lines.
2. The needle swung around to point toward the magnet. The magnet's field is stronger than Earth's at that distance, so the needle aligns with the magnet's magnetic field.

Assessment

Oral What causes the needle to become magnetic when you stroke it with the magnet? The magnet rearranges the domains in the needle so that they line up and make the needle magnetic. Use **Performance Assessment in the Science Classroom,** p. 89.

Try at Home

Teacher FYI

Rock Minerals Iron minerals in some rocks (such as basalt) align themselves with Earth's magnetic field if the rock forms under the right conditions. This provides a record of Earth's changing magnetic field, which is studied by geologists and those hoping to determine Earth's past climates.

Post Reading

Cooperative Learning Project Have students work in groups to research an application of magnetism. For example, students might investigate MRI machines or magnetic recording. Encourage students to develop a ten-minute oral presentation augmented by a visual aide.

3 Assess

DAILY INTERVENTION

Check for Understanding

Visual-Spatial Have students use **Figure 4** to make illustrations of the magnetic field of two bar magnets with like poles near each other and with unlike poles near each other. Have students clearly label the poles on the illustrations. L2

Reteach

Magnetizing a Nail Hang a nail, by the flat head, from the end of a bar magnet. Next, place the nail and a compass on the overhead to show that the nail has N and S poles. LS **Visual-Spatial** L2

Assessment

Performance Ask students to use a compass to map the magnetic field of a large horseshoe magnet. Use **Performance Assessment in the Science Classroom,** p. 97. L2

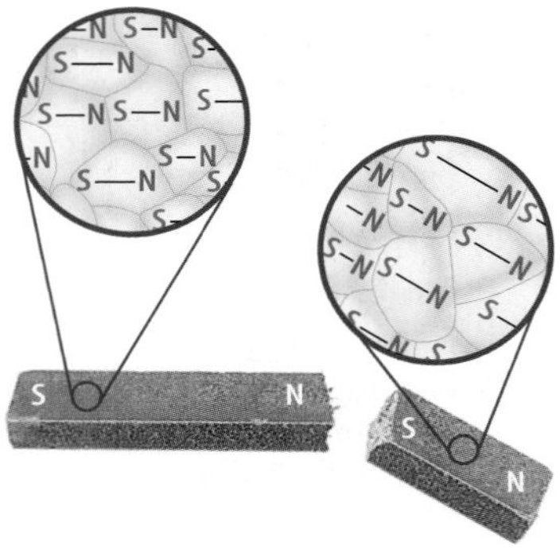

Figure 8 Each piece of a broken magnet still has a north and a south pole.

Permanent Magnets A permanent magnet can be made by placing a magnetic material, such as iron, in a strong magnetic field. The strong magnetic field causes the magnetic domains in the material to line up. The magnetic fields of these aligned domains combine and create a strong magnetic field inside the material. This field prevents the constant motion of the atoms from bumping the domains out of alignment. The material is then a permanent magnet.

Even permanent magnets can lose their magnetic behavior if they are heated. Heating causes atoms in a magnet to move faster. If a permanent magnet is heated enough, its atoms may be moving fast enough to jostle the domains out of alignment. Then the permanent magnet loses its magnetic field and is no longer a magnet.

Can a pole be isolated? What happens when a magnet is broken in two? Can one piece be a north pole and one piece be a south pole? Look at the domain model of the broken magnet in **Figure 8.** Recall that even individual atoms of magnetic materials act as tiny magnets. Because every magnet is made of many aligned smaller magnets, even the smallest pieces have both a north pole and a south pole.

section 1 review

Summary

Magnets

- A magnet is surrounded by a magnetic field that exerts a force on magnetic materials.
- A magnet has a north pole and a south pole.
- Like magnetic poles repel and unlike poles attract.

Magnetic Materials

- Iron, cobalt, and nickel are magnetic elements because their atoms behave like magnets.
- Magnetic domains are regions in a material that contain an enormous number of atoms with their magnetic poles aligned.
- A magnetic field causes domains to align. In a temporary magnet, the domains return to a random alignment when the field is removed.
- In a permanent magnet, a stong magnetic field aligns domains, and they remain aligned when the field is removed.

Self Check

1. **Describe** what happens when you move two unlike magnetic poles closer together. Draw a diagram to illustrate your answer.
2. **Describe** how a compass needle moves when it is placed in a magnetic field.
3. **Explain** why only certain materials are magnetic.
4. **Predict** how the properties of a bar magnet would change if it were broken in half.
5. **Explain** how heating a bar magnet would change its magnetic field.
6. **Think Critically** Use the magnetic domain model to explain why a magnet sticks to a refrigerator door.

Applying Math

7. **Calculate Number of Domains** The magnetic domains in a magnet have an average volume of 0.0001 mm^3. If the magnet has dimensions of 50 mm by 10 mm by 4 mm, how many domains does the magnet contain?

More Section Review gpescience.com

section 1 review

1. The poles attract one another.
2. It aligns itself along the field lines.
3. The atoms of magnetic materials are themselves individual magnets. They form magnetic domains containing large numbers of atoms. Each domain is a magnet. A magnet brought nearby causes domains to align so they are attracted to the nearest pole of the magnet.
4. Each piece still would contain large numbers of domains and have a north pole and a south pole. Because each piece contains few domains, the magnetic field of each piece would be weaker.
5. When the magnet is heated, the atoms in the magnet move faster. If the atoms are moving fast enough, collisions with other atoms may cause atoms in domains to become unaligned. This would reduce the magnetic field.
6. If the metal in the door contains a magnetic material, the magnetic domains align when the magnet is brought close so the opposite poles of the domains attract the closest pole of the magnet.
7. $(50\text{ mm})(10\text{ mm})(4\text{ mm})/0.0001\text{ mm}^3 = 2.0 \times 10^7$

section 2

Electricity and Magnetism

Reading Guide

What You'll Learn

- **Describe** the magnetic field produced by an electric current.
- **Explain** how an electromagnet produces a magnetic field.
- **Describe** how electromagnets are used.
- **Explain** how an electric motor operates.

Why It's Important

Electric motors contained in many of the devices you use every day operate because electric currents produce magnetic fields.

Review Vocabulary

electric current: the flow of electric charges in a wire or any conductor

New Vocabulary

- electromagnet
- solenoid
- galvanometer
- electric motor

Electric Current and Magnetism

In 1820, Hans Christian Oersted, a Danish physics teacher, found that electricity and magnetism are related. While doing a demonstration involving electric current, he happened to have a compass near an electric circuit. He noticed that the flow of the electric current affected the direction the compass needle pointed. Oersted hypothesized that the electric current must have produced a magnetic field around the wire, and that the direction of the field changed with the direction of the current.

Moving Charges and Magnetic Fields Oersted's hypothesis that an electric current creates a magnetic field was correct. Moving charges, such as those in an electric current, produce magnetic fields. Around a current-carrying wire the magnetic field lines form circles, as shown in **Figure 9.** The direction of the magnetic field around the wire reverses when the direction of the current in the wire reverses. As the current in the wire increases, the strength of the magnetic field increases. As the distance from the wire increases, the strength of the magnetic field decreases.

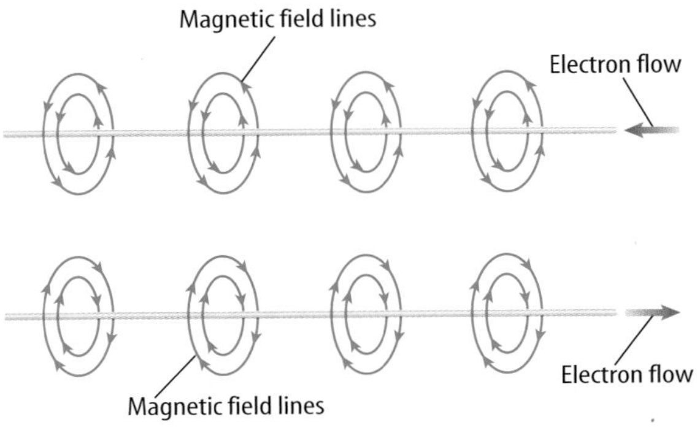

Figure 9 When electric current flows through a wire, a magnetic field forms around the wire. The direction of the magnetic field depends on the direction of the current in the wire.

Section 2 Resource Manager

Chapter *FAST FILE* Resources

Transparency Activity, p. 45
Directed Reading for Content Mastery, p. 21
Lab Activity, pp. 13–16
Enrichment, p. 31
Reinforcement, p. 28
Physical Science Critical Thinking/Problem Solving, p. 17

1 Motivate

INTERACTIVE CHALKBOARD An editable Microsoft® PowerPoint® presentation is available on **Interactive Chalkboard** CD-ROM.

Bellringer

Section Focus Transparencies also are available on the Interactive Chalkboard CD-ROM. L2 ELL

Reading Preview

Tie to Prior Knowledge

Electric Motors Ask students to name some items that run by electric motors. Possible answers: fan, CD player, tape player Explain that this section describes how electricity and magnetism work together in electric motors.

Vocabulary Visualization Have students scan the text to find new vocabulary terms. Ask them to visualize these definitions and then sketch pictures in their minds. For *electromagnet*, a student might visualize a coil of wire with a long piece of iron in the middle.

2 Teach

Fun Fact

The source of Earth's magnetic field is still not well understood. One hypothesis is that convection currents of molten rock deep in Earth's core generate electric currents, which in turn generate a magnetic field, just like the current in a wire.

Discussion

Crane's Magnet Explain that a crane can have a grabbing end to pick up an object, or it can use an electromagnet. Compare the two cranes. Possible responses: the electromagnet will only work on certain types of metals, while the mechanical crane can lift anything it can grab. The strength of the mechanical crane depends on the materials it is made from and how they are attached; the strength of the electromagnet crane depends on these factors plus the number of turns in the coil and the strength of the current running through it. L2 **Logical-Mathematical**

Caption Answer

Figure 10B The direction of the magnetic field would be reversed.

Reading Strategy

Paraphrase Ask students to paraphrase sections of the text. Be sure students know that paraphrasing involves putting text material into their own words. The paraphrase, a condensed version of the text, is shorter than the original section. Have students paraphrase the text orally to a partner or in writing.

Electromagnets

The magnetic field that surrounds a current-carrying wire can be made much stronger in an electromagnet. An **electromagnet** is a temporary magnet made by wrapping a wire coil carrying a current around an iron core. When a current flows through a wire loop, such as the one shown in **Figure 10A,** the magnetic field inside the loop is stronger than the field around a straight wire. A single wire wrapped into a cylindrical wire coil is called a **solenoid.** The magnetic field inside a solenoid is stronger than the field in a single loop. The magnetic field around each loop in the solenoid combines to form the field shown in **Figure 10B.**

If the solenoid is wrapped around an iron core, an electromagnet is formed, as shown in **Figure 10C.** The solenoid's magnetic field magnetizes the iron core. As a result, the field inside the solenoid with the iron core can be more than 1,000 times greater than the field inside the solenoid without the iron core.

Properties of Electromagnets Electromagnets are temporary magnets because a magnetic field is present only when current is flowing in the solenoid. The strength of the magnetic field can be increased by adding more turns of wire to the solenoid or by increasing the current passing through the wire.

An electromagnet behaves like any other magnet when current flows through the solenoid. One end of the electromagnet is a north pole and the other end is a south pole. If it is placed in a magnetic field, an electromagnet will align itself along the magnetic field lines, just as a compass needle will. An electromagnet also will attract magnetic materials and be attracted or repelled by other magnets. What makes an electromagnet so useful is that its magnetic properties can be controlled by changing the electric current flowing through the solenoid.

When current flows in an electromagnet and it moves toward or away from another magnet, electric energy is converted into mechanical energy to do work. Electromagnets do work in various devices, such as stereo speakers and electric motors.

Figure 10 An electromagnet is made from a current-carrying wire.

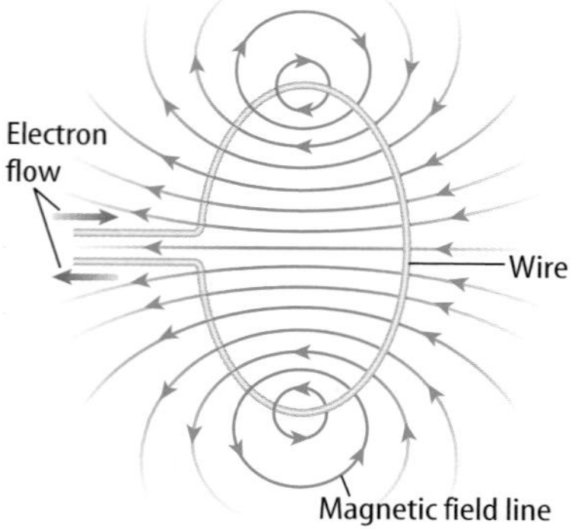

A The magnetic fields around different parts of the wire loop combine to form the field inside the loop.

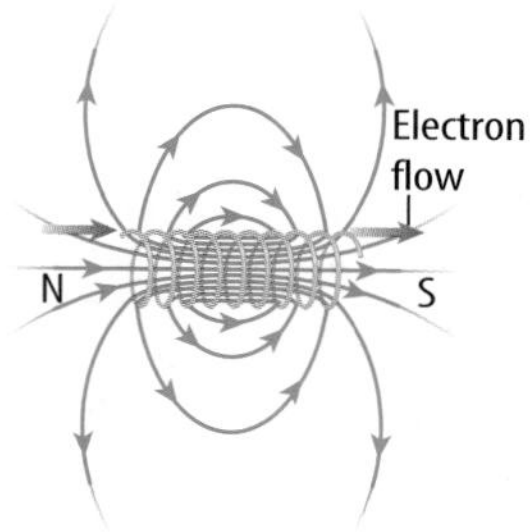

B When many loops of current-carrying wire are formed into a solenoid, the magnetic field is increased inside the solenoid. The solenoid has a north pole and a south pole.
Predict *how the field would change if the current reversed direction.*

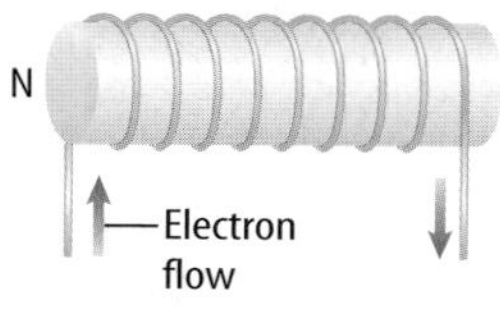

C A solenoid wrapped around an iron core forms an electromagnet.

Differentiated Instruction

English-Language Learners For students who have difficulty following diagrams and complex descriptions, focus on the basic definitions—for example, that a motor converts electricity into motion. Provide a chance for students to observe, handle, and take apart a simple motor or generator. L1 IS **Kinesthetic**

Teacher FYI

Electrons Each electron in an atom acts like a tiny electromagnet—the electron orbiting the nucleus is a loop of electric current, just like electrons moving in a wire. An electron also has "spin,"—a quantum physics characteristic that contributes to the magnetic field generated by the electron.

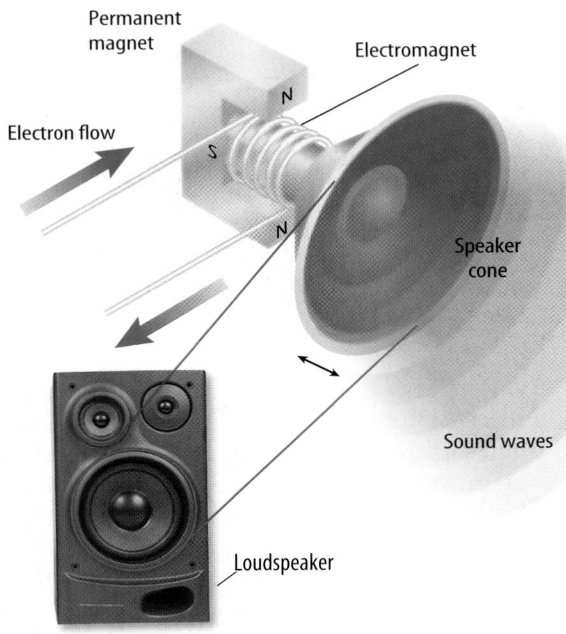

Figure 11 The electromagnet in a speaker converts electrical energy into mechanical energy to produce sound.
Explain *why a speaker needs a permanent magnet to produce sound.*

Using Electromagnets to Make Sound How does musical information stored on a CD become sound you can hear? The sound is produced by a loudspeaker that contains an electromagnet connected to a flexible speaker cone that is usually made from paper, plastic, or metal. The electromagnet changes electrical energy to mechanical energy that vibrates the speaker cone to produce sound, as shown on **Figure 11.**

Reading Check *How does a stereo speaker use an electromagnet to produce sound?*

When you listen to a CD, the CD player produces a voltage that changes according to the musical information on the CD. This varying voltage produces a varying electric current in the electromagnet connected to the speaker cone. Both the amount and the direction of the electric current change, depending on the information on the CD. The varying electric current causes both the strength and the direction of the magnetic field in the electromagnet to change. The electromagnet is surrounded by a permanent, fixed magnet. The changing direction of the magnetic field in the electromagnet causes the electromagnet to be attracted to or repelled by the permanent magnet. This makes the electromagnet move back and forth, causing the speaker cone to vibrate and reproduce the sound that was recorded on the CD.

Quick Demo
Electromagnets

Materials large nail, battery, battery holder, wire

Estimated Time 15 minutes

Procedure Make an electromagnet by connecting a battery to a wire coiled 20 times around a large nail. Demonstrate that the nail picks up no paper clips before the wire is connected and several when it is connected. When the wire again is disconnected, the paper clips should fall. However, the nail will still be slightly magnetized and may pick up one or two paper clips after the current is turned off. **WARNING:** *The wire will heat up if it is left connected, so disconnect the battery as soon as you are done.*
L2 IS **Visual-Spatial**

Caption Answer

Figure 11 The permanent magnet attracts and repels the electromagnet, causing the speaker cone to vibrate and produce sound.

Visual Learning

Figure 11 Have students analyze the diagram of the speaker. Review step by step the process in which electrical energy is converted to sound energy. Make sure students understand that the changing electrical signal causes a changing magnetic field in the electromagnet, and that the interaction of that magnetic field with the magnetic field of the permanent magnet causes the electromagnet to move.

Curriculum Connection

History Have students find out how Alexander Graham Bell used an electromagnet in the first telephone and present their findings to the class.
L2 IS **Linguistic**

Reading Check

Answer The electromagnet changes electrical energy to mechanical energy that vibrates parts of the speaker to produce sound.

Inquiry Lab

Observing an Electric Motor

Purpose To construct and observe a simple electric motor.

Possible Materials pliable copper wire, stiff bare copper wire, D-cell battery, D-cell battery holder, wire cutters or pliers, permanent magnet, tape

Estimated Time one class period

Teaching Strategies

- Students can brainstorm about how they will construct a simple electric motor by creating a coil of wire suspended above a permanent magnet.
- The battery can be used to create a flow of current in the wire coil.
- Students can observe the principles of an electric motor.
- Allow students to explore other questions that arise.

For additional inquiry activities, see *Science Inquiry Labs*.

Reading Check

Answer When current flows in the solenoid, like poles of the electromagnet are repelled by and attracted to the poles of the permanent magnet. This causes the electromagnet to rotate.

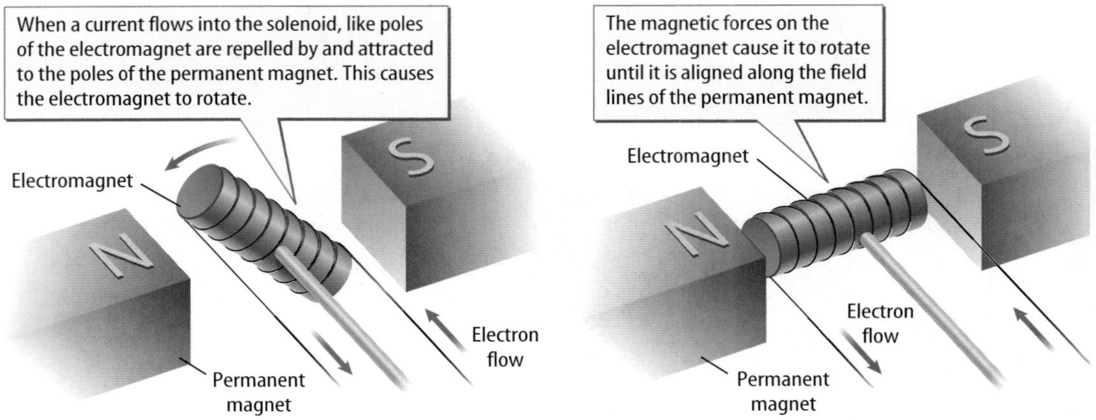

Figure 12 An electromagnet can be made to rotate in a magnetic field.

Making an Electromagnet Rotate The forces exerted on an electromagnet by another magnet can be used to make the electromagnet rotate. **Figure 12** shows an electromagnet suspended between the poles of a permanent magnet. The poles of the electromagnet are repelled by the like poles and attracted by the unlike poles of the permanent magnet. When the electromagnet is in the position shown on the left side of **Figure 12,** there is a downward force on the left side and an upward force on the right side of the electromagnet forces. These forces cause the electromagnet to rotate as shown.

Reading Check *How can a permanent magnet cause an electromagnet to rotate?*

The electromagnet continues to rotate until its poles are next to the opposite poles of the permanent magnet, as shown on the right side of **Figure 12.** In this position, the forces on the north and south poles of the electromagnet are in opposite directions. The net force on the electromagnet is now zero, and the electromagnet stops rotating.

One way to change the forces that make the electromagnet rotate is to change the current in the electromagnet. Increasing the current increases the strength of the forces that the two magnets exert on each other.

Galvanometers You've probably noticed the gauges in the dashboard of a car. One gauge shows the amount of gasoline left in the tank, and another shows the engine temperature. How does a change in the amount of gasoline in a tank or the water temperature in the engine make a needle move in a gauge on the dashboard? These gauges are **galvanometers,** which are devices that use an electromagnet to measure electric current.

Cultural Diversity

China The first dial and pointer devices were made in China, using compass needles. Modern dials and pointers, including galvanometers, descend from these early Chinese devices.

434 CHAPTER 14 Magnetism

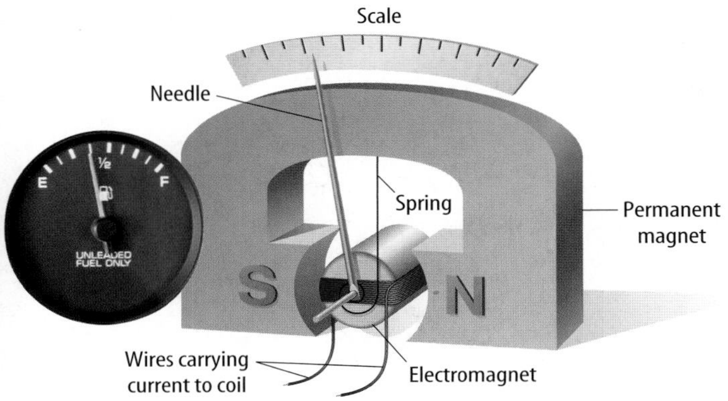

Figure 13 The rotation of the needle in a galvanometer depends on the amount of current flowing in the electromagnet. The current flowing into the galvanometer in a car's fuel gauge changes as the amount of fuel changes.

Using Galvanometers An example of a galvanometer is shown in **Figure 13.** In a galvanometer, the electromagnet is connected to a small spring. The electromagnet rotates until the force exerted by the spring is balanced by the magnetic forces on the electromagnet. Changing the current in the electromagnet causes the needle to rotate to different positions on the scale.

For example, a car's fuel gauge uses a galvanometer. A float in the fuel tank is attached to a sensor that sends a current to the fuel-gauge galvanometer. As the level of the float in the tank changes, the current sent by the sensor changes. The changing current in the galvanometer causes the needle to rotate by different amounts. The gauge is calibrated so that the current sent when the tank is full causes the needle to rotate to the full mark on the scale.

Electric Motors

On sizzling summer days, do you ever use an electric fan to keep cool? A fan uses an **electric motor,** which is a device that changes electrical energy into mechanical energy. The motor in a fan turns the fan blades, moving air past your skin to make you feel cooler.

Electric motors are used in all types of industry, agriculture, and transportation, including airplanes and automobiles. If you were to look carefully, you probably could find electric motors in every room of your home. Almost every appliance in which something moves contains an electric motor. Electric motors are used in devices such as VCRs, CD players, and computers, and appliances such as those shown in **Figure 14.**

Figure 14 All the devices shown here contain electric motors.
List *three additional devices that contain electric motors.*

Use Science Words

Word Origin Have students use a dictionary to find the origin of the word *motor.* It is derived from the Latin word for move. L2 LS **Linguistic**

Activity

Hobby Motors Bring a set of direct current hobby motors to class. Have students take them apart and identify the different parts. L2

Discussion

Galvanometers Have students describe all the dials with pointers they can find in their homes, school, cars, etc. Which ones are galvanometers? Possible answer: Older voltmeters and ammeters contain galvanometers. Some gauges in a car are galvanometers. A clock is an example of a motorized measuring device that is not a galvanometer. L3 LS **Logical-Mathematical**

Caption Answer

Figure 14 Answers will vary.

Curriculum Connection

History Have students research the history of the development of electric motors. Have them present their findings in the form of a newspaper article. The first commercially useful electric motor was a reversible DC electrical generator built in the early 1870s by Zénobe-Théophile Gramme. The first practical AC motor was built in 1888 by Nikola Tesla. L2 P LS **Linguistic**

SECTION 2 Electricity and Magnetism **435**

Use an Analogy

Waterwheel An electric motor is like a waterwheel. A force (running water, magnetism) applied to a wheel (paddle of wheel, end of magnet) turns an axle. In either case, things can be attached to the axle to use the mechanical energy produced.

Make a Model

Simple Electric Motors Have students use **Figure 15** as a guide to make models of simple electric motors. L3 LS **Kinesthetic**

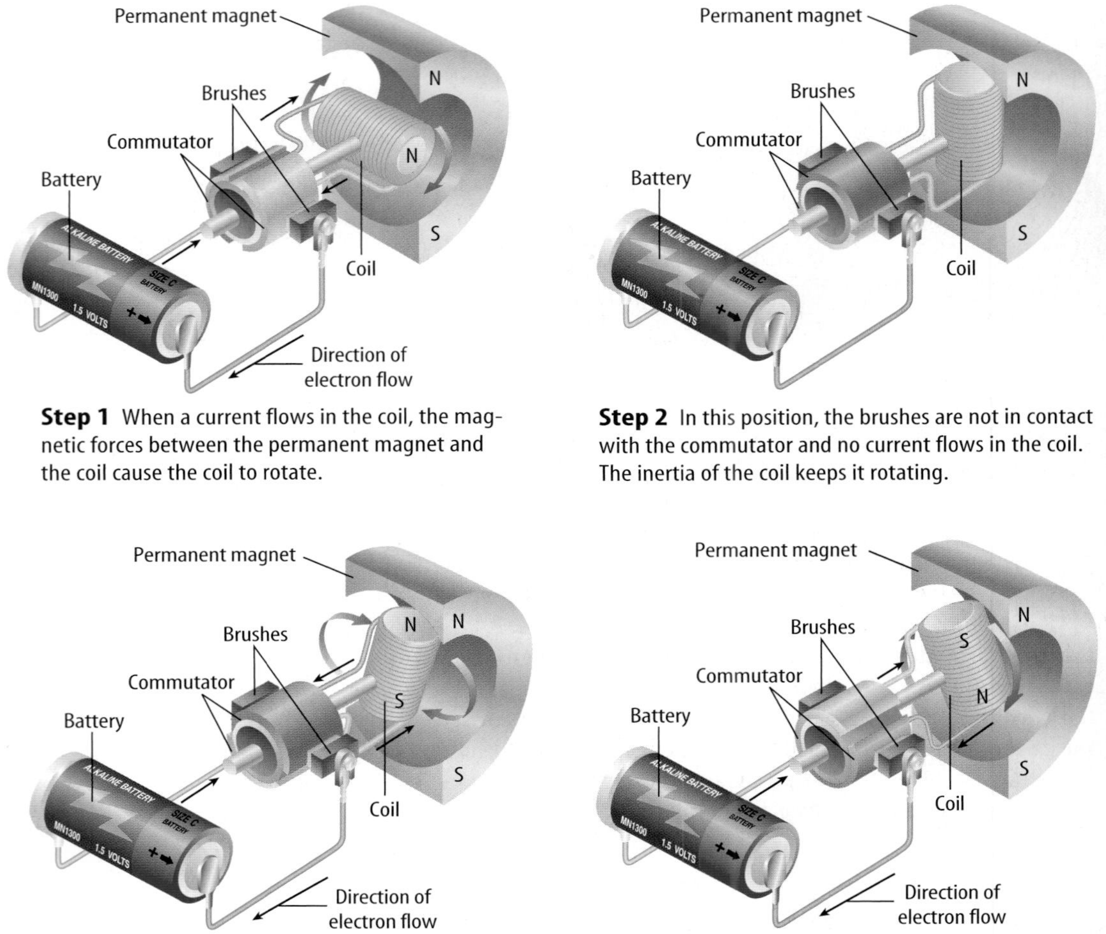

Step 1 When a current flows in the coil, the magnetic forces between the permanent magnet and the coil cause the coil to rotate.

Step 2 In this position, the brushes are not in contact with the commutator and no current flows in the coil. The inertia of the coil keeps it rotating.

Step 3 The commutator reverses the direction of the current in the coil. This flips the north and south poles of the magnetic field around the coil.

Step 4 The coil rotates until its poles are opposite the poles of the permanent magnet. The commutator reverses the current, and the coil keeps rotating.

Figure 15 In a simple electric motor, a coil rotates between the poles of a permanent magnet. To keep the coil rotating, the current must change direction twice during each rotation.

A Simple Electric Motor A diagram of the simplest type of electric motor is shown in **Figure 15.** The main parts of a simple electric motor include a wire coil, a permanent magnet, and a source of electric current, such as a battery. The battery produces the current that makes the coil an electromagnet. A simple electric motor also includes components called brushes and a commutator. The brushes are conducting pads connected to the battery. The brushes make contact with the commutator, which is a conducting metal ring that is split. Each half of the commutator is connected to one end of the coil so that the commutator rotates with the coil. The brushes and the commutator form a closed electric circuit between the battery and the coil.

Differentiated Instruction

Challenge Have students find out more about how the commutator in an electric motor works. Have students prepare an oral presentation to present to the class. The commutator rotates with the electromagnet and alternately contacts the positive and negative terminals of the power source. The reversing current causes the poles of the rotating electromagnet to switch and rotate toward the opposite pole of the permanent magnet. L3 LS **Logical-Mathematical**

Making the Motor Spin When current flows in the coil, the forces between the coil and the permanent magnet cause the coil to rotate, as shown in step 1 of **Figure 15.** The coil continues to rotate until it reaches the position shown in step 2. Then, the brushes no longer make contact with the commutator, and no current flows in the coil. As a result, there are no magnetic forces exerted on the coil. However, the inertia of the coil causes it to continue rotating.

In step 3, the coil has rotated so that the brushes again are in contact with the commutator. However, the halves of the commutator that are in contact with the positive and negative battery terminals have switched. This causes the current in the commutator to reverse direction. Now the top of the electromagnet is a north magnetic pole and the bottom is a south pole. These poles are repelled by the nearby like poles of the permanent magnet, and the magnet continues to rotate.

In step 4, the coil rotates until its poles are next to the opposite poles of the permanent magnet. Then the commutator again reverses the direction of the current, enabling the coil to keep rotating. In this way, the coil is kept rotating as long as the battery remains connected to the commutator.

Science Online

Topic: Electric Motors
Visit gpescience.com for Web links to information about electric motors.

Activity Using the information provided at these links, construct a simple electric motor.

section 2 review

Summary

Electric Current and Magnetic Fields

- A magnetic field surrounds a moving electric charge.
- The strength of the magnetic field surrounding a current-carrying wire depends on the amount of current.

Electromagnets

- An electromagnet is a temporary magnet consisting of a current-carrying wire wrapped around an iron core.
- The magnetic properties of an electromagnet can be controlled by changing the current in the coil.
- A galvanometer uses an electromagnet to measure electric current.

Electric Motors

- In a simple electric motor, an electromagnet rotates between the poles of a permanent magnet.

Self Check

1. **Explain** why, if the same current flows in a wire coil and a single wire loop, the magnetic field inside the coil is stronger than the field inside the loop.
2. **Describe** two ways you could change the strength of the magnetic field produced by an electromagnet.
3. **Predict** how the magnetic field produced by an electromagnet would change if the iron core were replaced by an aluminum core.
4. **Explain** why it is necessary to continually reverse the direction of current flow in the coil of an electric motor.
5. **Think Critically** A bar magnet is repelled when an electromagnet is brought close to it. Describe how the bar magnet would have moved if the current in the electromagnet had been reversed.

Applying Math

6. **Use a Ratio** The magnetic field strength around a wire at a distance of 1 cm is twice as large as at a distance of 2 cm. How does the field strength at 0.5 cm compare to the field strength at 1 cm?

More Section Review gpescience.com

Post Reading

Illustrations Have students research uses of motors and make an illustration of a motor and the device that uses it. Students should label the parts of the motor and describe the function of the device. Have students display the illustrations for the class to view.

3 Assess

DAILY INTERVENTION

Check for Understanding

Kinesthetic Divide the class into groups. Provide each group with D-cell batteries, a few meters of insulated wire, and iron bolts. Ask the groups to construct electromagnets. **WARNING:** The bolt cores will become hot if the current is left connected. Make sure students disconnect the wire from the battery when they are not using the electromagnet. L2 ELL COOP LEARN

LS **Kinesthetic**

Reteach

Electromagnets Make two electromagnets from iron nails wrapped in wire. Wrap the first one with only a few coils, the second one with many coils. Have students compare the strength of the two electromagnets as you attempt to pick up a number of paper clips. L2

LS **Visual-Spatial**

Assessment

Oral Demonstrate the different speeds on a fan or mixer. Ask students how they think the speed is varied. To make the appliance rotate faster, the amount of current passing through the coil of the electric motor is increased. To slow down the appliance, the amount of current is decreased. Use **PASC,** p. 89. L2

section 2 review

1. The magnetic field around each bit of wire has the same strength, but when the wire is looped, the fields combine, making a stronger field.
2. by varying the electric current passing through it or by changing the number of loops
3. The magnetic field would be weaker because aluminum is not a magnetic material. The only magnetic field would be that created by the looped wire.
4. When an end of the coil moves past a pole of the permanent magnet, reversing the current causes the end of the coil to be attracted to the other pole of the permanent magnet. Repeating this process keeps the coil continually rotating in the same direction.
5. The bar magnet would have been attracted to the electromagnet because the pole would have been opposite to what it was.
6. It would be twice as large as the strength at 1 cm and four times the strength at 2 cm.

1 Motivate

INTERACTIVE CHALKBOARD PowerPoint® Presentations An editable Microsoft® PowerPoint® presentation is available on **Interactive Chalkboard** CD-ROM.

Bellringer

Section Focus Transparencies also are available on the Interactive Chalkboard CD-ROM. L2 ELL

Section 3 Section Focus Transparency **Flowing Current** Chapter 14

Electricity is often generated at power plants by burning fossil fuels. But fossil fuels are nonrenewable resources that, when burned, can cause pollution. There are, however, nonpolluting sources of energy.

1. What do you think the source of energy is for this hydroelectric power plant?
2. What do you think would happen if the flow of water through the dam were blocked?
3. What other sources of energy are converted to electric current?

L2

Magnetism

Reading Preview

Tie to Prior Knowledge

Windmills Ask students if they have ever seen a windmill. Refer them to **Figure 19** and have them describe the motion of the blades and what the force of the wind is doing to the generators that they are connected to. L2

Activate Background Knowledge Have students create sentences using the new vocabulary words based on their prior knowledge of the words. Write the sentences on the board. Ask students to read the section. After reading, have students discuss the accuracy of the sentences.

section 3

Producing Electric Current

Reading Guide

What You'll Learn

- **Define** electromagnetic induction.
- **Describe** how a generator produces an electric current.
- **Distinguish** between alternating current and direct current.
- **Explain** how a transformer can change the voltage of an alternating current.

Why It's Important

Electromagnetic induction enables power plants to generate the electric current an appliance uses when you plug it into an electric outlet.

Review Vocabulary

voltage difference: a measure of the electrical energy provided by charges as they flow in a circuit

New Vocabulary

- electromagnetic induction
- generator
- turbine
- direct current (DC)
- alternating current (AC)
- transformer

From Mechanical to Electrical Energy

Working independently in 1831, Michael Faraday in Great Britain and Joseph Henry in the United States both found that moving a loop of wire through a magnetic field causes an electric current to flow in the wire. They also found that moving a magnet through a loop of wire produces a current. In both cases, the mechanical energy associated with the motion of the wire loop or the magnet is converted into electrical energy associated with the current in the wire. The magnet and wire loop must be moving relative to each other for an electric current to be produced. This causes the magnetic field inside the loop to change with time. In addition, if the current in a wire changes with time, the changing magnetic field around the wire can also induce a current in a nearby coil. The generation of a current by a changing magnetic field is **electromagnetic induction.**

Figure 16 The coil in a generator is rotated by an outside source of mechanical energy. Here the student supplies the mechanical energy that is converted into electrical energy by the generator.

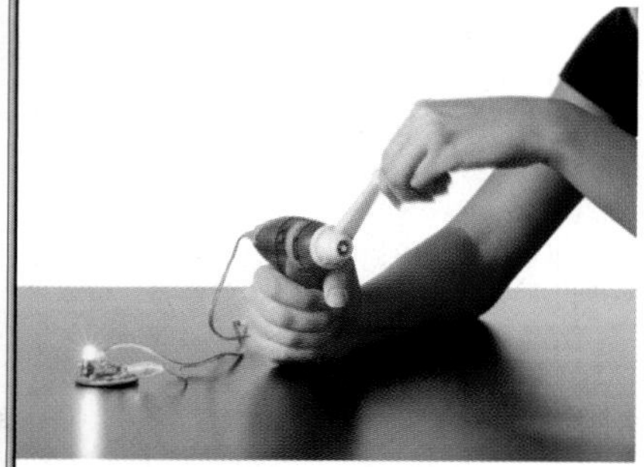

Generators Most of the electrical energy you use every day is provided by generators. A **generator** uses electromagnetic induction to transform mechanical energy into electrical energy. **Figure 16** shows one way a generator converts mechanical energy to electrical energy. The mechanical energy is provided by turning the handle on the generator.

An example of a simple generator is shown in **Figure 17.** In this type of generator, a current is produced in the coil as the coil rotates between the poles of a permanent magnet.

Section 3 Resource Manager

Chapter *FAST FILE* Resources
- Transparency Activity, pp. 46, 47–48
- Directed Reading for Content Mastery, pp. 21–22
- Enrichment, p. 32
- Reinforcement, p. 29
- Lab Worksheet, pp. 5–6, 7–8

Home and Community Involvement, p. 37
Cultural Diversity, p. 53
Performance Assessment in the Science Classroom, p. 53

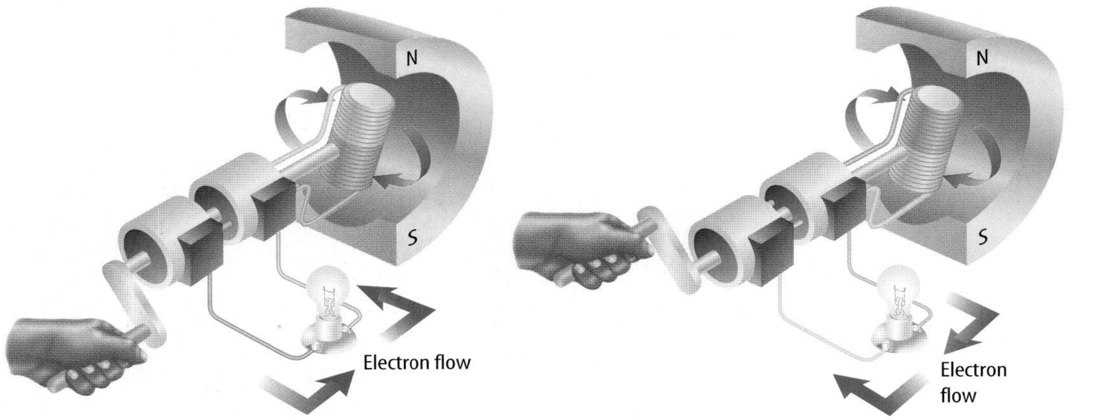

Switching Direction As the generator's wire coil rotates through the magnetic field of the permanent magnet, current flows through the coil. After the wire coil makes one-half of a revolution, the ends of the coil are moving past the opposite poles of the permanent magnet. This causes the current to change direction. In a generator, as the coil keeps rotating, the current that is produced periodically changes direction. The direction of the current in the coil changes twice with each revolution, as **Figure 17** shows. The frequency with which the current changes direction can be controlled by regulating the rotation rate of the generator. In the United States, current is produced by generators that rotate 60 times a second, or 3,600 revolutions per minute.

Reading Check *For each revolution of the coil, how many times does the current change direction?*

The Electromagnetic Force There is a relationship between electricity and magnetism. A changing magnetic field can cause electric charges to move in a wire. Also, a moving electric charge produces a magnetic field. The atoms of magnetic materials, such as iron, are magnets because of the motion of electric charges in the atoms. As a result, the magnetic field around a permanent magnet is due to electric charges that are in motion.

This connection occurs because the electric force and the magnetic force are two different aspects of the same force. This force is the electromagnetic force and is one of the fundamental forces in nature. An electromagnetic force exists between all objects that have electric charge. Just like the magnetic and the electric force, the electromagnetic force can be attracted or repulsive.

Figure 17 The current in the coil changes direction each time the ends of the coil move past the poles of the permanent magnet. **Explain** *how the frequency of the changing current can be controlled.*

2 Teach

Reading Check

Answer twice

IDENTIFYING Misconceptions

Magnetic Fields Some students may think that a magnetic field alone is enough to produce a current. Emphasize that the magnetic field must be changing to induce a current in the wire coil. A stationary magnet and loop will not generate a current.

Use Science Words

Word Meaning The expression *electromagnetic induction* is related to the word *induce*. Have students find the common meaning of induce and use it in a sentence. Induce means to move to a course of action, to cause; sample sentence: The king induced his knights to follow his lead. L2 LS **Linguistic**

Caption Answer

Figure 17 by regulating the rotation rate of the generator

Science Journal

History of Technology A turbine transforms straight-line motion into rotational motion. One of the oldest means of transforming motion this way is the waterwheel. Have students write paragraphs in their Science Journals comparing the design of a waterwheel with that of a hydroelectric turbine. L2 LS **Linguistic**

Discussion

Number of Power Plants Why is electricity usually generated at a few large plants, rather than many small ones? Possible answer: Generating plants are often located near rivers, dams, or other energy sources. Multiple small plants would require redundant resources and would be more expensive to build. L3 IS **Logical-Mathematical**

INTEGRATE Career

Power-Plant Operator These operators control and monitor the boilers, turbines, generators, and other equipment at power generating plants. Power-plant operators may use computers for many tasks including generating reports of daily operations or unusual incidents.

Research Have students research the future employment outlook for this career.

Quick Demo
Generating Current

Materials hand-operated generator, wire, bulb socket, lightbulb

Estimated Time ten minutes

Procedure Attach wire leads to the hand generator and to the bulb socket containing a lightbulb. Slowly turn the hand generator to light the bulb. Additional lightbulbs can be added in parallel or in series. Vary the speed that you turn the hand generator and show students the effect on the brightness of the lights.

Figure 18 Each of these generators at Hoover Dam can produce over 100,000 kW of electric power. In these generators, a rotating magnet induces an electric current in a stationary wire coil.

INTEGRATE Career

Power-Plant Operator
Many daily activities require electricity. Power-plant operators control the machinery that generates electricity. Operators must have a high school diploma. College-level courses may be helpful. Research to find employers in your area that hire power plant operators.

Generating Electricity for Your Home You probably do not have a generator in your home that supplies the electrical energy you use at home. This electrical energy comes from a power plant with huge generators like the one in **Figure 18.** The coils in these generators have many coils of wire wrapped around huge iron cores. The rotating magnets are connected to a **turbine,** which is a large wheel that rotates when pushed by water, wind, or steam.

Some power plants first produce thermal energy by burning fossil fuels or using the heat produced by nuclear reactions. This thermal energy is used to heat water and produce steam. Thermal energy is then converted to mechanical energy as the steam pushes the turbine blades. The generator then changes the mechanical energy of the rotating turbine into the electrical energy you use. In some areas, fields of windmills, such as those in **Figure 18,** can be used to capture the mechanical energy in wind to turn generators. Other power plants use the mechanical energy in falling water to rotate the turbines. Both generators and electric motors use magnets to produce energy conversions between electrical and mechanical energy. **Figure 20** summarizes the differences between electric motors and generators.

Figure 19 The propeller on each of these windmills is connected to an electric generator. The rotating propeller rotates a coil or a permanent magnet.

Curriculum Connection

Geography Solar power can be used to generate electricity. A very large array is needed to generate enough electricity for a city, and only very sunny sites will do. Ask students to research and report on areas in the United States that are suitable for such solar generators. Large solar arrays have been proposed for the Southwest's deserts, particularly those in California. L2 P IS **Linguistic**

Visual Learning

Figure 19 In the 1920s and 1930s, before rural areas had access to electricity from power plants, people sometimes used small windmills to run water pumps or household generators. The windmills shown are much larger, of course. Windmills on "wind farms," such as the one shown in the figure, can be as big as 50 m in diameter and stand several building stories high.

NATIONAL GEOGRAPHIC **VISUALIZING MOTORS AND GENERATORS**

Figure 20

Electric motors power many everyday machines, from CD players to vacuum cleaners. Generators produce the electricity these motors need to run. Both motors and generators use electromagnets, but in different ways. The table below compares motors and generators.

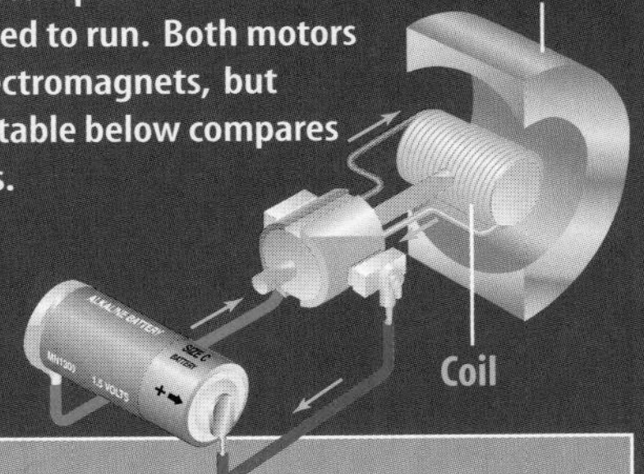

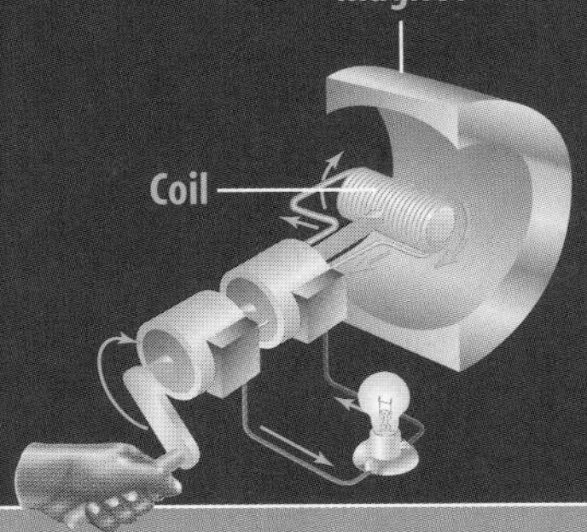

	Electric Motor	Generator
What does it do?	Changes electricity into movement 	Changes movement into electricity 
What makes its electromagnetic coil rotate?	Attractive and repulsive forces between the coil and the permanent magnet 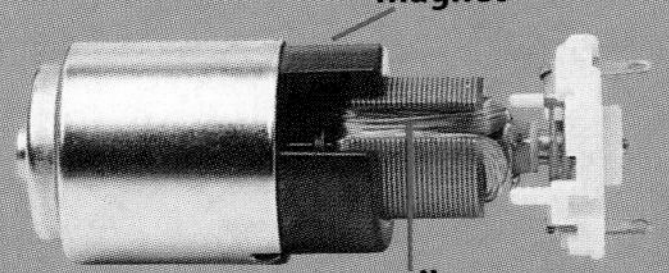	An outside source of mechanical energy 
What is the source of the current that flows in its coil?	An outside power source 	Electromagnetic induction from moving the coil through the field of the permanent magnet 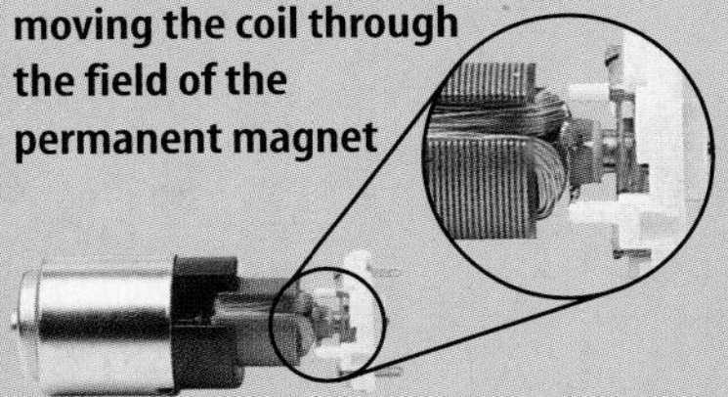
How often does the current in the coil change direction?	Twice during each rotation of the coil	Twice during each rotation of the coil

NATIONAL GEOGRAPHIC

Visualizing Motors and Generators

Have students examine the pictures and read the captions. Then ask the following questions.

In what way is an electric motor the opposite of a generator? In what way is it the same? Opposite: A motor changes electricity into movement, while a generator changes movement into electricity. Same: The current in the coil changes direction twice during each rotation of the coil.

What kind of movement produces the electricity in hydroelectric generators? moving water In windmills? moving air In a bicycle generator? moving bicycle wheel

Activity

Hand-Cranked Power Have small groups of students research power supplies used for camping or emergency situations that produce electricity from a hand-cranked generator. These devices include flashlights, lanterns, and radios. Have students make oral presentations about how these devices work and in what situations they would be most useful. L2 COOP LEARN

LS **Logical-Mathematical**

Differentiated Instruction

Challenge Students could research the differences between AC and DC generators and make labeled posters illustrating the differences between these two ways that electricity is transmitted. L3 LS **Visual-Spatial**

Teacher FYI

Current Disagreement Thomas Edison advocated the use of DC to transmit electric current. One of his workers, Nikola Tesla, argued that an AC current would be better. Edison and Tesla parted ways, and Tesla went to work for Edison's competitor, the Westinghouse Company. Today, electric current in the United States is distributed using AC.

Virtual Labs

Generators *How does a generator work?*

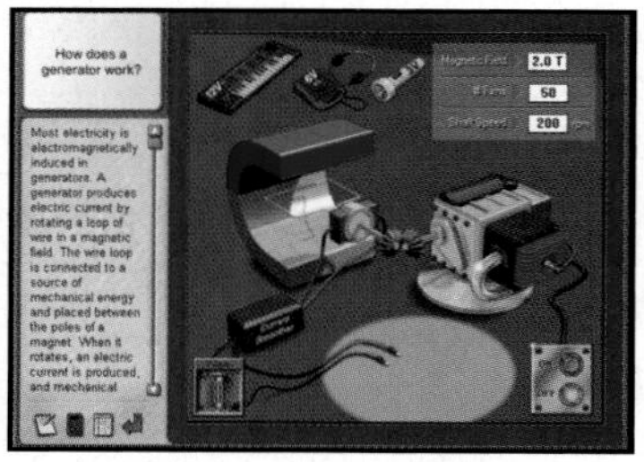

Reading Strategy

Cause and Effect Have students set up a chart with the headings *Cause* and *Effect*. Under *Effect*, have students list the following: a generator transforms mechanical energy into electrical energy, a radio plays music, and a transformer increases voltage. Have students use the text to find the cause for each effect.

Science Online

Topic: Transformers
Visit gpescience.com for links to information about how transformers transmit electric current.

Activity In England, voltage from an outlet is greater than required for U.S. appliances. Using information found at these links, diagram a transformer that would allow a U.S. appliance to operate in England.

Direct and Alternating Currents

Modern society relies heavily on electricity. Just how much you rely on electricity becomes obvious during a power outage. Out of habit, you might walk into a room and flip on the light switch. You might try to turn on a radio or television or check the clock to see what time it is. Because power outages sometimes occur, some electrical devices, such as the radio in **Figure 21,** use batteries as a backup source of electrical energy. However, the current produced by a battery is different from the current produced by an electric generator.

A battery produces a direct current. **Direct current** (DC) flows only in one direction through a wire. When you plug your CD player or any other appliance into a wall outlet, you are using alternating current. **Alternating current** (AC) reverses the direction of the current in a regular pattern. In North America, generators produce alternating current at a frequency of 60 cycles per second, or 60 Hz. The electric current produced by a generator changes direction twice during each cycle, or each rotation, of the coil. This means that a 60-Hz alternating current changes direction 120 times each second.

Electronic devices that use batteries as a backup energy source usually require direct current to operate. When the device is plugged into a wall outlet, electronic components inside the device convert the alternating current to direct current and also reduce the voltage of the alternating current.

Figure 21 Some devices, such as this radio, can use either direct or alternating current. Electronic components in these devices change alternating current from an electric outlet to direct current.

Transmitting Electrical Energy

The alternating current produced by an electric power plant carries electrical energy that is transmitted along electric transmission lines. However, when electrical energy is transmitted along power lines, some of the electrical energy is converted into heat because of the electrical resistance of the wires. The heat produced in the power lines warms the wires and the surrounding air and can't be used to power electrical devices. Also, the electrical resistance and heat production increase as the wires get longer. As a result, large amounts of heat can be produced when electrical energy is transmitted over long distances.

One way to reduce the heat produced in a power line is to transmit the electrical energy at high voltages, typically around 150,000 V. However, electrical energy at such high voltage cannot enter your home safely, nor can it be used in home appliances. Instead, a transformer is used to decrease the voltage.

Science Journal

Nikola Tesla Tell students that the inventor Nikola Tesla brought alternating current into wide usage. Have students find out where he was from, when he lived, and how he spread the use of alternating current, and write their findings in their Science Journals. Tesla lived from 1856 to 1943. He was Serbian, born in Croatia. He convinced businessman and inventor George Westinghouse that alternating current could be transported more efficiently than direct current. Westinghouse's company, General Electric, was able to develop commercial AC systems that soon were widely adopted. L2 IN **Linguistic**

442 CHAPTER 14 Magnetism

Transformers

A **transformer** is a device that increases or decreases the voltage of an alternating current. A transformer is made of a primary coil and a secondary coil. These wire coils are wrapped around the same iron core, as shown in **Figure 22.** As an alternating current passes through the primary coil, the coil's magnetic field magnetizes the iron core. The magnetic field in the primary coil changes direction as the current in the primary coil changes direction. This produces a magnetic field in the iron core that changes direction at the same frequency. The changing magnetic field in the iron core then induces an alternating current with the same frequency in the secondary coil.

The voltage in the primary coil is the input voltage, and the voltage in the secondary coil is the output voltage. The output voltage divided by the input voltage equals the number of turns in the secondary coil divided by the number of turns in the primary coil.

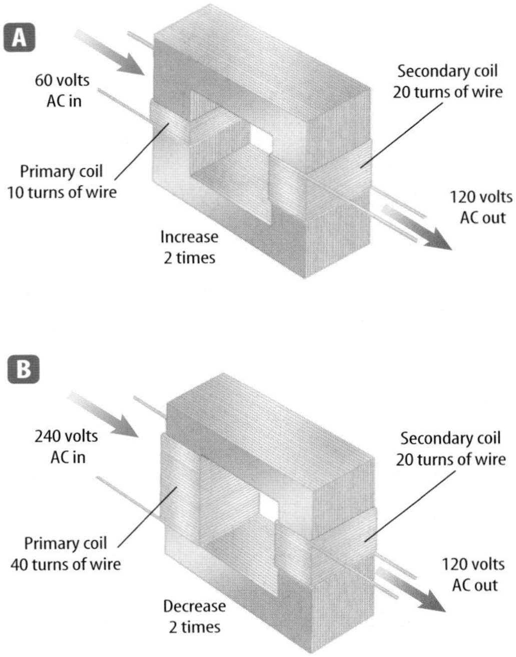

Figure 22 Transformers can increase or decrease voltage.
A A step-up transformer increases voltage. The secondary coil has more turns than the primary coil does. **B** A step-down transformer decreases voltage. The secondary coil has fewer turns than the primary coil does.
Infer *whether a transformer could change the voltage of a direct current.*

Reading Check *How does a transformer produce an alternating current in the secondary coil?*

Step-Up Transformer A transformer that increases the voltage so that the output voltage is greater than the input voltage is a step-up transformer. In a step-up transformer, the number of wire turns on the secondary coil is greater than the number of turns on the primary coil. For example, the secondary coil of the step-up transformer in **Figure 22A** has twice as many turns as the primary coil has. The ratio of the output voltage to the input voltage is 2:1, and the output voltage is twice as large as the input voltage. For this transformer, an input voltage of 60 V in the primary coil is increased to 120 V in the secondary coil.

Step-Down Transformer A transformer that decreases the voltage so that the output voltage is less than the input voltage is a step-down transformer. In a step-down transformer, the number of wire turns on the secondary coil is less than the number of turns on the primary coil. In **Figure 22B** the secondary coil has half as many turns as the primary coil has, so the ratio of the output voltage to the input voltage is 1:2. The input voltage of 240 V in the primary coil is reduced to a voltage of 120 V in the secondary coil.

Teacher FYI

Eddy Currents Eddy currents can be generated in transformers by the changing magnetic field around the core. Because the magnetic fields generated by the eddy current oppose the original field, power is lost. The cores of transformers are often made out of many thin, laminated strips of metal instead of one big iron loop. Insulating glue between the strips restricts the eddy currents to individual strips, where they cannot grow very large. This makes the transformer more efficient.

Activity

Finding Transformers Take students outside and find the transformers leading into the school. Ask students to find the transformers near their homes as well, and compare them. Caution students to not touch or get too close to the transformers. L1 ELL
Visual-Spatial

Reading Check

Answer The changing magnetic field in the iron core induces an alternating current with the same frequency in the secondary coil.

Caption Answer

Figure 22 No, a direct current does not produce a changing magnetic field in the primary or secondary coil. Electromagnetic induction does not occur.

Active Reading

Write-Draw-Discuss This strategy encourages students to actively participate in reading and lectures, assimilating content creatively. Have students write about electric motors, generators, and transformers, clarify their ideas, then make illustrations or drawings. Ask students to share responses with the class and display several examples. L2

Post Reading

Concept Map Starting with the central term *electric current,* have students draw five lines, similar to bicycle wheel spokes, each with one of the following: electromagnetic induction, generator, DC, AC, and transformers. Using more branching lines, have students explain these terms.

SECTION 3 Producing Electric Current 443

Caption Answer

Figure 23 the generator, step-up transformer, and step-down transformer

3 Assess

DAILY INTERVENTION

Check for Understanding

Visual-Spatial Have students draw a diagram of a generator and label the parts. Have students write a brief description about how the generator works. L2

Reteach

Visual-Spatial Use **Figure 20** to tie the electric generator to the electric motor. Have students explain what each is used for and how each uses the connection between electricity and magnetism. L2 LS

Assessment

Content Ask students to work in teams to design a human-powered device for generating electrical energy. As an example, describe how a stationary bicycle could be modified to rotate the electromagnet in a generator. Use **Performance Assessment in the Science Classroom,** p. 117. L2

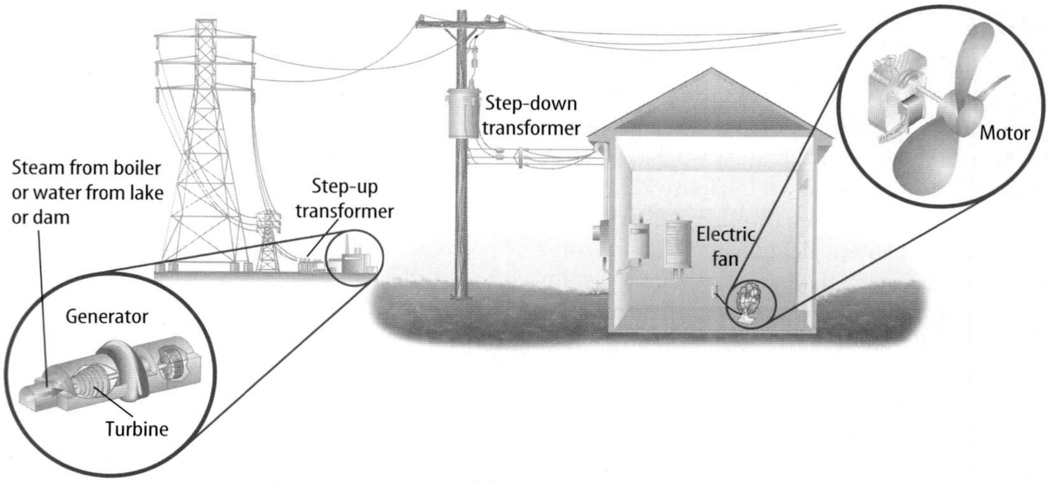

Figure 23 Many steps are involved in the creation, transportation, and use of the electric current in your home.
Identify *the steps that involve electromagnetic induction.*

Transmitting Alternating Current Power plants commonly produce alternating current because the voltage can be increased or decreased with transformers. Although step-up transformers and step-down transformers change the voltage at which electrical energy is transmitted, they do not change the amount of electrical energy transmitted. **Figure 23** shows how step-up and step-down transformers are used in transmitting electrical energy from power plants to your home.

section 3 review

Summary

From Mechanical to Electrical Energy

- An electric current is produced by moving a wire loop through a magnetic field or a magnet through a wire loop.
- A generator can produce an electric current by rotating a wire coil in a magnetic field.

Direct and Alternating Currents

- A direct current flows in one direction. An alternating current changes direction in a regular pattern.

Transformers

- A transformer changes the voltage of an alternating current. The voltage can be increased or decreased.
- The changing magnetic field in the primary coil of a transformer induces an alternating current in the secondary coil.

Self Check

1. **Describe** the energy conversions that occur when water falls on a paddle wheel connected to a generator that is connected to electric lights.
2. **Compare and contrast** a generator with an electric motor.
3. **Explain** why the output voltage from a transformer is zero if a direct current flows through the primary coil.
4. **Explain** why electric current produced by power plants is transmitted as alternating current.
5. **Think Critically** A magnet is pushed into the center of a wire loop and then stops. What is the current in the wire loop after the magnet stops moving? Explain.

Applying Math

6. **Use a Ratio** A transformer has 1,000 turns of wire in the primary coil and 50 turns in the secondary coil. If the input voltage is 2,400 V, what is the output voltage?

More Section Review gpescience.com

section 3 review

1. falling water strikes paddle wheel and wheel begins to turn—kinetic energy to mechanical energy; turning paddle wheel turns shaft of generator—mechanical energy to electrical energy; electrical energy flows to electric lights—electrical energy to heat and light
2. An electric motor converts electrical energy to mechanical energy and a generator coverts mechanical energy to electrical energy.
3. Only an alternating current induces the voltage in the transformer.
4. Alternating current is used because transformers can increase or decrease voltage. This enables power to be transmitted at high voltage to minimize the energy converted into heat. The voltage then is reduced to lower levels for safe use.
5. Zero; either the magnet or the wire loop must be moving to induce current.
6. $\frac{\text{Voltage}_{out}}{\text{Voltage}_{in}} = \frac{\text{turns}_{secondary}}{\text{turns}_{primary}}$

   $\frac{50}{1{,}000} = \frac{\text{Voltage}_{out}}{2{,}400\text{ V}}$

   $\text{Voltage}_{out} = 120\text{ V}$

LAB

El💡ctricity and Magnetism

Huge generators in power plants produce electricity by moving magnets past coils of wire. How does this produce an electric current?

Real-World Problem

How can a magnet and a wire coil be used to produce an electric current?

Goals

- **Observe** how a magnet and a wire coil can produce an electric current in a wire.
- **Compare** the currents created by moving the magnet and the wire coil in different ways.

Materials

cardboard tube
bar magnet
insulated wire
scissors
galvanometer or ammeter

Safety Precautions

WARNING: *Do not touch bare wires when current is running through them.*

Procedure

1. Wrap the wire around the cardboard tube to make a coil of about 20 turns. Remove the tube from the coil.
2. Use the scissors to cut and remove 2 cm of insulation from each end of the wire.
3. Connect the ends of the wire to a galvanometer or ammeter. Record the reading on your meter.
4. Insert one end of the magnet into the coil and then pull it out. Record the current. Move the magnet at different speeds inside the coil and record the current.
5. Watch the meter and move the bar magnet in different ways around the outside of the coil. Record your observations.
6. Repeat steps 4 and 5, keeping the magnet stationary and moving the wire coil.

Conclude and Apply

1. How was the largest current generated?
2. Does the current generated always flow in the same direction? How do you know?
3. **Predict** what would happen if you used a coil made with fewer turns of wire.
4. **Infer** whether a current would have been generated if the cardboard tube had been left in the coil. Why or why not? Try it.

Communicating Your Data

Compare the currents generated by different members of the class. What was the value of the largest current that was generated? How was this current generated?

BENCH TESTED

Video Lab available for this Lab.

Real-World Problem

Purpose Students observe electromagnetic induction of a current. L1 Kinesthetic

Process Skills observe and infer, interpret data, draw conclusions, recognize cause and effect, compare and contrast, make models

Time Required 45 minutes

Alternate Materials One end of a horseshoe magnet can replace the bar magnet.

Procedure

Teaching Strategy Be sure the galvanometer is on the most sensitive scale and that students form complete circuits.

Conclude and Apply

1. Faster motion produces more current, as does moving the magnet in the coil rather than outside it.
2. No; the needle was deflected in different directions depending on whether the magnet moved in or out of the coil.
3. A smaller current would be induced.
4. Yes; electric and magnetic fields are not affected by the cardboard.

Assessment

Performance Ask each student to make a poster that shows the design of the experiment they used and explains what each piece of equipment does. To one side, they should list how changes in the setup change the current induced. Use **PASC**, p. 145. L1

Communicating Your Data

Ask students to include suggestions for how they could make a stronger current. Possible answers: increase the number of coils; make the coils closer to the moving magnet; use a stronger magnet

BENCH TESTED

Real-World Problem

Purpose Students will assemble an electromagnet and then attempt to control its strength by changing its construction. L2

LS Kinesthetic

Process Skills form a hypothesis, identify and manipulate variables, make and use tables, observe

Time Required 60 minutes

Possible Materials Iron 16-penny nails are available through science supply companies. If nails are purchased locally, make sure they are made of iron.

Alternate Materials Students can use either an electric power supply or batteries for the electric current in their electromagnets. A knife switch can be included for easier current control.

Safety Precautions Closely monitor students who are using an electric power supply to ensure that they do not apply more than 6 volts.

Form a Hypothesis

Possible Hypothesis The more loops that are used in the construction of the electromagnet the stronger the magnetic field it will generate.

LAB Design Your Own

Controlling Electromagnets

Goals

- **Measure** relative strengths of electromagnets.
- **Determine** which factors affect the strength of an electromagnet.

Possible Materials

22-gauge insulated wire
16-penny iron nail
aluminum rod or nail
0-6 V DC power supply
three 1.5-V D cells
steel paper clips
magnetic compass
duct tape (to hold D cells together)

Safety Precautions

WARNING: *Do not leave the electromagnet connected for long periods of time because the battery will run down. Magnets will get hot with only a few turns of wire. Use caution in handling them when current is flowing through the coil. Do not apply voltages higher than 6 V to the electromagnets.*

Real-World Problem

You use electromagnets every day when you use stereo speakers, power door locks, and many other devices. To make these devices work properly, the strength of the magnetic field surrounding an electromagnet must be controlled. How can the magnetic field produced by an electromagnet be made stronger or weaker? Think about the components that form an electromagnet. Make a hypothesis about how changing these components would affect the strength of the electromagnet's magnetic field.

Form a Hypothesis

As a group, write down the components of an electromagnet that might affect the strength of its magnetic field.

Test Your Hypothesis

Make a Plan

1. Write your hypothesis about the best way to control the magnetic field strength of an electromagnet.
2. **Decide** how you will assemble and test the electromagnets. Which features will you change to determine the effect on the strength of the magnetic fields? How many changes will you need to try? How many electromagnets do you need to build?
3. **Decide** how you are going to test the strength of your electromagnets. Several ways are possible with the materials listed. Which way would be the most sensitive? Be prepared to change test methods if necessary.

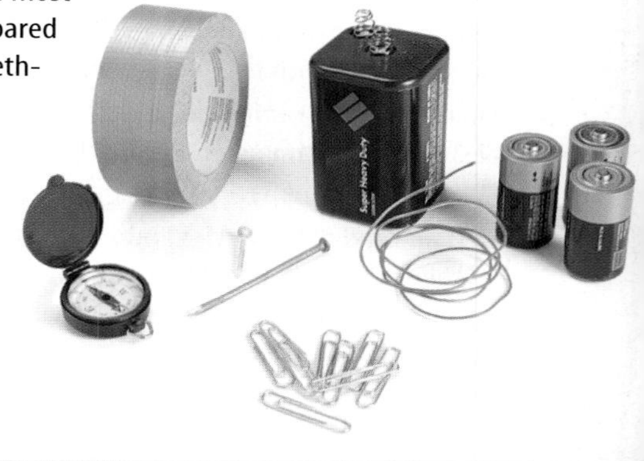

Alternative Inquiry Lab

Using Electromagnets Extend this Lab into an Inquiry Lab by building on the experience gained performing this lab. Encourage your students to use what they have learned to brainstorm uses for electromagnets. Have student groups each choose one question to explore. Ask them to list the materials they need to explore their questions. Unsafe or impractical questions should be eliminated. Students should have their plans for their additional experiments approved before continuing. Conduct the experiments after all necessary materials have been gathered. L3

446 CHAPTER 14 Magnetism

Using Scientific Methods

4. Write your plan of investigation. Make sure your plan tests only one variable at a time.

Follow Your Plan

1. Before you begin to build and test the electromagnets, make sure your teacher approves of your plan.
2. Carry out your planned investigation.
3. Record your results.

Analyze Your Data

1. **Make a table** showing how the strength of your electromagnet depends on changes you made in its construction or operation.
2. **Examine** the trends shown by your data. Are there any data points that seem out of line? How can you account for them?

Testing Electromagnets

Trial	Electromagnet Construction Features	Strength of Electromagnet
	Student answers will vary.	

Conclude and Apply

1. **Describe** how the electromagnet's magnetic-field strength depended on its construction or operation.
2. **Identify** the features of the electromagnet's construction that had the greatest effect on its magnetic-field strength. Which do you think would be easiest to control?
3. **Explain** how you could use your electromagnet to make a switch. Would it work with both AC and DC?
4. **Evaluate** whether or not your results support your hypothesis. Explain.

Communicating Your Data

Compare your group's result with those of other groups. Did any other group use a different method to test the strength of the magnet? Did you get the same results?

Assessment

Process Students should research how a doorbell works and make drawings illustrating what they find. Use **Performance Assessment in the Science Classroom,** p. 127. L2

Communicating Your Data

When comparing various methods used to test the strength of the magnet, students should consider the masses of the objects used and their composition. L2

Test Your Hypothesis

Possible Procedures Wrap wire around a nail about 15 times. Tape it in place, leaving about 20 cm loose on each end. Connect the wire ends to the terminals of a battery.

Determine how many paper clips the magnetized nail will pick up. Vary the number of wire loops and the number of batteries to observe the effect on the strength of the nail's magnetization.

Teaching Strategy Remind students that the polarity of the electromagnet can be reversed by changing the direction of the current flow.

Expected Outcome Increasing the number of loops in the electromagnet or the number of batteries increases the strength of the magnetic field.

Analyze Your Data

1. Check each group's table.
2. Answers will vary.

Error Analysis Have students compare their results and their hypotheses and explain why differences occurred.

Conclude and Apply

1. The strength of the magnetic field increased when the number of loops or number of batteries increased.
2. Adding additional batteries had the greatest effect and would be easiest to control.
3. Accept all reasonable responses. One way would be to use the electromagnet to pull a metal strip to close a circuit. Without current, a spring pulls the strip back and opens the circuit.
4. Answers will vary.

TIME

Content Background

Magnetic resonance imaging (MRI) is a noninvasive diagnostic technique that uses nuclear magnetic resonance (NMR) to image the structure of the body. Unhampered by bone and capable of producing images in a variety of planes, MRI is used in the diagnosis of brain tumors and disorders, spinal disorders, multiple sclerosis, and cardiovascular diseases. The procedure is considered to be without risk to the patient.

Types of magnetic resonance include electron paramagnetic resonance (EPR), also known as electron spin resonance (ESR), involving the magnetic effect of electrons, and nuclear magnetic resonance (NMR), involving the magnetic effects of protons and neutrons in the nuclei of atoms. The NMR resonant frequency provides information about the molecular material in which the nuclei reside.

Discussion

X Rays How are X rays used differently from MRI? Possible Answer: X rays are used for the diagnosis of problems in hard tissue areas of the body while MRI is used to diagnose soft tissue disorders. L2 **Logical-Mathematical**

Historical Significance

Make sure students understand that MRI has only been developed in the last twenty-five years, which is a very short period of time in the span of history. Start a discussion that will get students to think about the medical advances that have been made possible by MRI. For example, because of MRI doctors are now able to diagnose birth defects and operate on babies in the womb.

TIME SCIENCE AND HISTORY

SCIENCE CAN CHANGE THE COURSE OF HISTORY!

Body Art

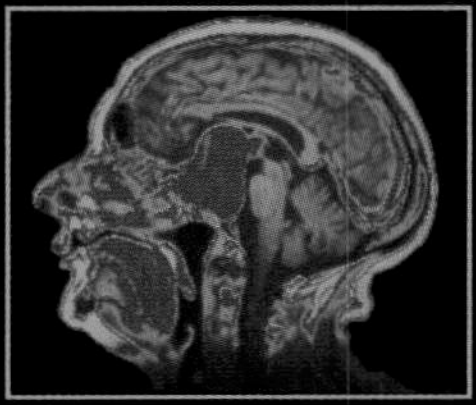

The surgeon turns the computer screen so the patient can see it. Pointing to a colorful image of the patient's brain, she reassures the worried patient. "This MRI shows exactly where your tumor is. We can remove it with little danger to you."

MRI for the Soft Stuff

MRI stands for "magnetic resonance imaging." It's a way to take 3-D pictures of the inside of your body. Before the 1980s, doctors could x-ray solid tissue such as bones, but had no way to see soft tissue such as the brain. Well, they had one way—surgery, which sometimes caused injury and infection, risking a patient's health.

MRI uses a strong magnet and radio waves. Tissues in your body contain water molecules that are made of oxygen and hydrogen atoms.

The nucleus of a hydrogen atom is a proton, which behaves like a tiny magnet. A strong magnetic field inside the MRI tube makes these proton magnets line up in the direction of the field. Radio waves are then applied to the body. The protons absorb some of the radio-wave energy, and flip their direction.

When the radio waves are turned off, the protons realign themselves with the magnetic field and emit the energy they absorbed. Different tissues in the body absorb and emit different amounts of energy. The emitted energy is detected, and a computer uses this information to form images of the body.

Your brain is getting bigger!

MRI has turned into an important research tool. For example, researchers using MRI have found that the brain grows rapidly through adolescence. Before this research, people thought that the brain stopped growing in childhood. MRI has proved that adolescents are getting bigger brains all the time.

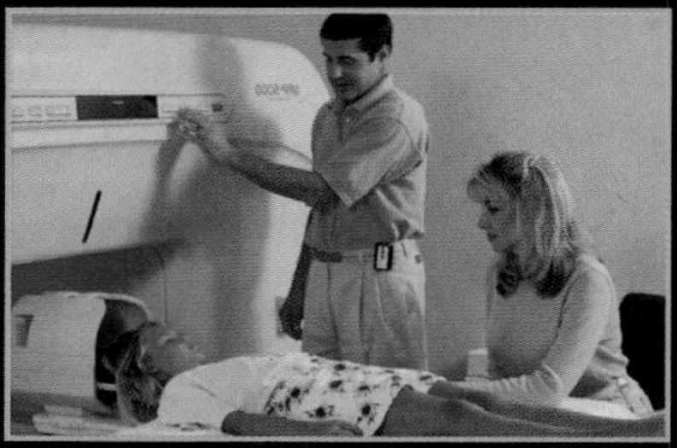

This patient is about to be placed in an MRI machine.

Interview As an oral history project, interview a retired physician or surgeon. Ask him or her to discuss with you how tools such as MRI changed during his or her career. Make a list of the tools and how they have helped improve medicine.

TIME For more information, visit gpescience.com

Interview If any of the students' parents work in the health field, ask them for suggestions of people students can interview. Conduct a brainstorming session to establish questions for the students to ask during their interviews to help them focus on relevant facts. Encourage them to write down their questions before the interview to ease this process. L2

Resources for Teachers and Students

Functional MRI (Medical Radiology) by C.T.W. Moonen (Editor) and P.A. Bandettini (Editor). Springer-Verlag, 2000

Imaging of Soft Tissue Tumors by A.M.A. De Schepper, and others, eds. Springer Verlag 2001

Reviewing Main Ideas

Section 1 Magnetism

1. A magnetic field surrounds a magnet and exerts a magnetic force.
2. All magnets have two poles: a south pole and a north pole.

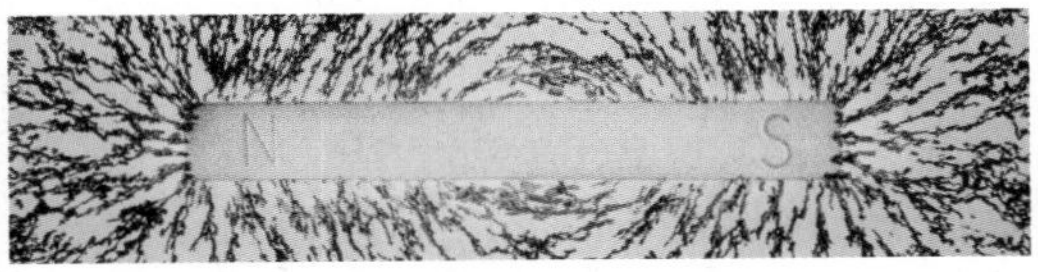

3. Opposite poles of magnets attract; like poles repel.
4. Groups of atoms with aligned magnetic poles are called magnetic domains.

Section 2 Electricity and Magnetism

1. An electric current flowing through a wire produces a magnetic field.
2. An electric current passing through a coil of wire can produce a magnetic field inside the coil. The coil becomes an electromagnet. One end of the coil is the north pole, and the other end is the south pole.

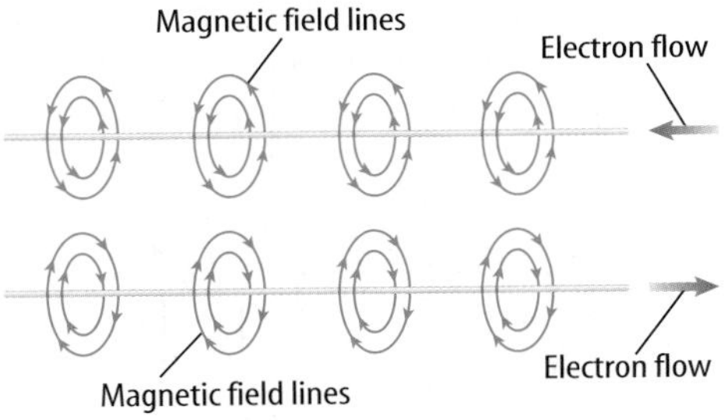

3. The magnetic field around an electromagnet depends on the current and the number of coils.
4. An electric motor contains a rotating electromagnet that converts electrical energy to mechanical energy.

Section 3 Producing Electric Current

1. By moving a magnet near a wire, you can create an electric current in the wire. This is called electromagnetic induction.

2. A generator produces electric current by rotating a coil of wire in a magnetic field. Generators at the base of this dam convert the kinetic energy in falling water into electrical energy.
3. Direct current flows in one direction through a wire; alternating current reverses the direction of current flow in a regular pattern.
4. The number of turns of wire in the primary and secondary coils of a transformer determines whether it increases or decreases voltage.

FOLDABLES Use the Foldable that you made at the beginning of this chapter to help you review magnets and magnetism.

Identifying Misconceptions

Assess

After students have done the lab on page 422F and completed the chapter, have them perform this lab.

Materials PVC pipe, aluminum or copper pipe, circular magnet

Procedure Drop a circular magnet down the length of each pipe and note how long it takes to get to the bottom.

Expected Outcome The magnet travels slower down the metal tube because the falling magnet creates an electric current in the pipe, which creates a magnetic field that slows it down. L2

chapter Study Guide 14

Reviewing Main Ideas

Summary statements can be used by students to review the major concepts of the chapter.

Science Online

Visit gpescience.com
More Section Review
Interactive Tutor
Vocabulary PuzzleMaker
More Chapter Review
Standardized Test Practice

Assessment Transparency

For additional assessment questions, use the *Assessment Transparency* located in the transparency book.

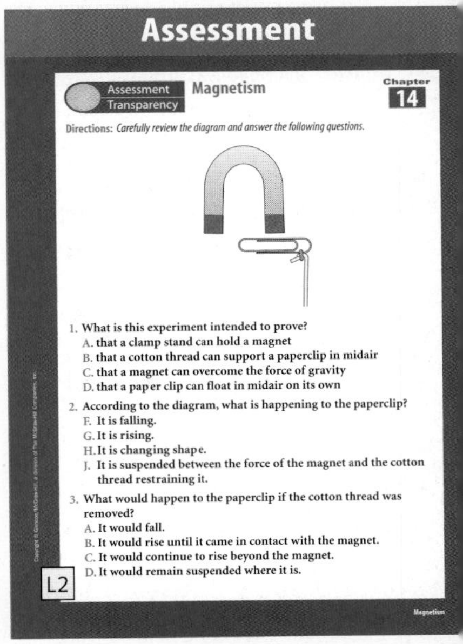

Assessment

Assessment Transparency **Magnetism** Chapter 14

Directions: *Carefully review the diagram and answer the following questions.*

1. What is this experiment intended to prove?
   A. that a clamp stand can hold a magnet
   B. that a cotton thread can support a paperclip in midair
   C. that a magnet can overcome the force of gravity
   D. that a paper clip can float in midair on its own
2. According to the diagram, what is happening to the paperclip?
   F. It is falling.
   G. It is rising.
   H. It is changing shape.
   J. It is suspended between the force of the magnet and the cotton thread restraining it.
3. What would happen to the paperclip if the cotton thread was removed?
   A. It would fall.
   B. It would rise until it came in contact with the magnet.
   C. It would continue to rise beyond the magnet.
   D. It would remain suspended where it is.

L2

Magnetism

FOLDABLES Have students use their Foldables to review the content of the chapter. On the back of the paper, have students write a paragraph describing how electric motors and electric generators work.

Using Vocabulary

1. transformer
2. magnetic pole
3. Direct current
4. magnetism
5. solenoid
6. magnetic domain
7. galvanometer

Checking Concepts

8. A
9. A
10. C
11. D
12. B
13. B
14. C

Interpreting Graphics

15. Both use a coil, an electromagnet, and a permanent magnet; in both cases the magnets move relative to one another. In an AC generator, a force turns one of the magnets, generating alternating electric current in the electromagnet. In a DC motor, electricity causes a magnet to turn, thereby turning whatever is attached to it.
16. permanent magnet—forces the electromagnet to spin; electromagnet—creates magnetic poles that try to align with the poles of the permanent magnet; the poles switch causing the electromagnet to spin which turns a shaft; current source—provides the electric current that creates the electromagnet
17. See **Figure 15.**
18. about 8 μT
19. The magnetic field strength decreases more rapidly closer to the wire. The magnetic field strength plunges until about 6 cm, then the strength begins to level off to about 2 μT.
20. 2 μT

chapter 14 Review

Using Vocabulary

alternating current (AC) p. 442	generator p. 438
direct current (DC) p. 442	magnetic domains p. 429
electric motor p. 435	magnetic field p. 425
electromagnet p. 432	magnetic pole p. 425
electromagnetic induction p. 438	magnetism p. 424
galvanometer p. 434	solenoid p. 432
	transformer p. 443
	turbine p. 440

Complete each statement with the correct vocabulary word or phrase.

1. A(n) _________ can be used to change the voltage of an alternating current.
2. A(n) _________ is the region where the magnetic field of a magnet is strongest.
3. _________ does not change direction.
4. The properties and interactions of magnets are called _________.
5. A(n) _________ can rotate in a magnetic field when a current passes through it.
6. The magnetic poles of atoms are aligned in a(n) _________.
7. A device that uses an electromagnet to measure electric current is a(n) _________.

Checking Concepts

Choose the word or phrase that best answers the question.

8. Where is the magnetic force exerted by a magnet strongest?
   A) both poles **C)** north pole
   B) south pole **D)** center
9. Which change occurs in an electric motor?
   A) electrical energy to mechanical energy
   B) thermal energy to wind energy
   C) mechanical energy to electrical energy
   D) wind energy to electrical energy
10. What happens to the magnetic force as the distance between two magnetic poles decreases?
   A) remains constant **C)** increases
   B) decreases **D)** becomes zero
11. Which of the following best describes what type of magnetic poles the domains at the north pole of a bar magnet have?
   A) north magnetic poles only
   B) south magnetic poles only
   C) no magnetic poles
   D) north and south magnetic poles
12. Which of the following would not change the strength of an electromagnet?
   A) increasing the amount of current
   B) changing the current's direction
   C) inserting an iron core inside the coil
   D) increasing the number of loops
13. Which of the following is NOT part of a generator?
   A) turbine **C)** electromagnet
   B) battery **D)** permanent magnet
14. Which of the following describes the direction of the electric current in AC?
   A) is constant **C)** changes regularly
   B) is direct **D)** changes irregularly

Interpreting Graphics

15. Copy and complete the Venn diagram below. Include the functions, part names, and power sources for these devices.

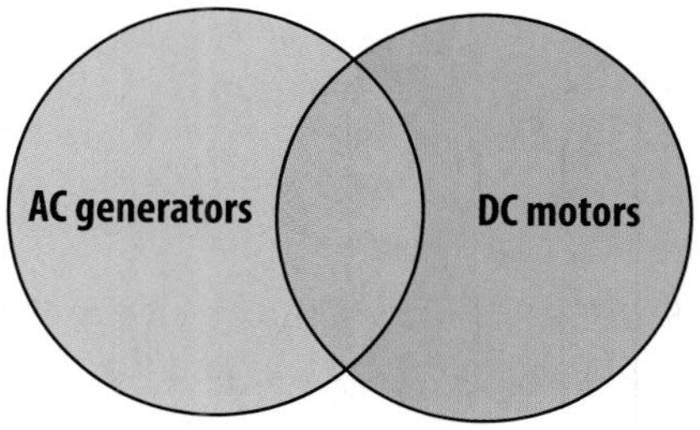

Vocabulary PuzzleMaker gpescience.com

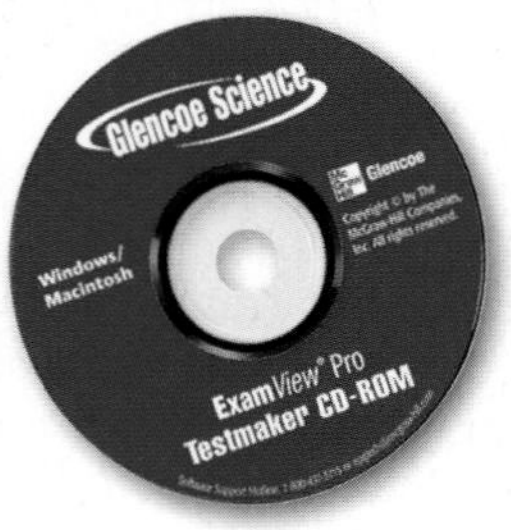

Use the Exam*View*® Pro Testmaker CD-ROM to:
- create multiple versions of tests
- create modified tests with one mouse click for inclusion students
- edit existing questions and add your own questions
- build tests aligned with state standards using built-in State Curriculum Tags
- change English tests to Spanish with one mouse click and vice versa

Use the diagram below to answer questions 16 and 17.

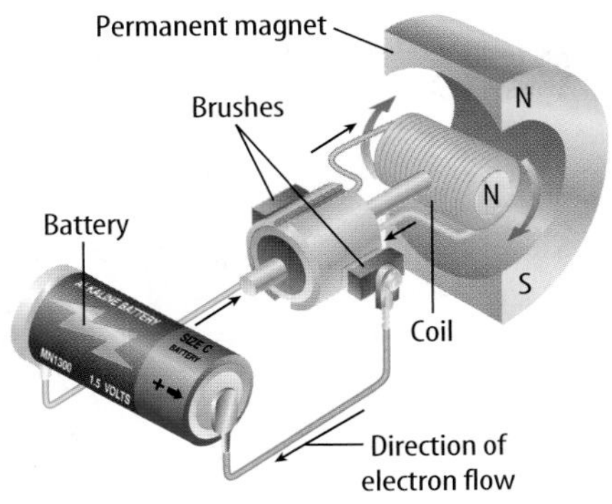

16. **Describe** Using the diagram, describe the function of the permanent magnet, the electromagnet, and the current source in a simple electric motor.

17. **Describe** the sequence of steps that occur in an electric motor that forces the coil to spin. Include the role of the commutator in your description.

Use the graph below to answer questions 18–20.

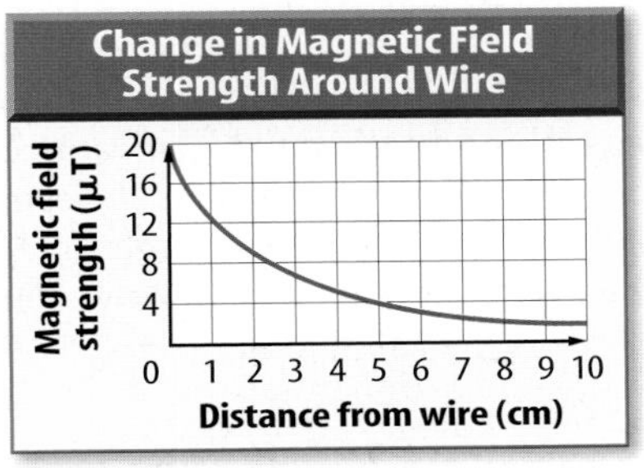

18. **Explain** How much larger is the magnetic field strength 1 cm from the wire compared to 5 cm from the wire?

19. **Explain** Does the magnetic field strength decrease more rapidly with distance closer to the wire or farther from the wire? Explain.

20. **Solve** Using the graph, estimate the magnetic field strength 11 cm from the wire.

Thinking Critically

21. **Infer** how you could you use a horseshoe magnet to find the north direction.

22. **Explain** In Europe, generators produce alternating current at a frequency of 50 Hz. Would the electric appliances you use in North America work if you plugged them into an outlet in Europe? Why or why not?

23. **Predict** Two generators are identical except for the loops of wire that rotate through their magnetic fields. One has twice as many turns of wire as the other one does. Which generator will produce the most electric current? Why?

24. **Explain** why a bar magnet will attract an iron nail to either its north pole or its south pole, but it will attract another magnet to only one of its poles.

25. **Compare and contrast** electromagnetic induction and the formation of electromagnets.

Applying Math

26. **Calculate** A step-down transformer reduces a 2,400-V current to 120 V. If the primary coil has 500 turns of wire, how many turns of wire are there on the secondary coil?

27. **Use a Ratio** To produce a spark, a spark plug requires a current of about 12,000 V. A car's engine uses a type of transformer called an induction coil to change the input voltage from 12 V to 12,000 V. In the induction coil, what is the ratio of the number of wire turns on the primary coil to the number of turns on the secondary coil?

More Chapter Review gpescience.com

Thinking Critically

21. Possible answer: suspend it by the middle so it can rotate; the south end should be attracted to magnetic north

22. No; North American appliances do not work in Europe unless they are made to operate at both frequencies. If the appliance is designed for dual operation, only an adapter is required. Most North American appliances require adapters, a converter, and a transformer to adjust the current and to accommodate the outlet designs in Europe.

23. The generator with twice as many loops will produce the most current because more wire loops pass through the magnetic field.

24. The magnetic domains in the nail become aligned so they are always attracted to the nearest pole of the bar magnet. The domains in a bar magnet are aligned in a fixed direction.

25. Both are related to current flowing in a wire. Electromagnetic induction is the generation of a current by a changing magnetic field. An electromagnet is formed when a wire is wrapped around an iron core and current flows through the wire.

Applying Math

Math Standards

National: 1, 2, 9

26. $\frac{\text{Voltage}_{out}}{\text{Voltage}_{in}} = \frac{\text{turns}_{seondary}}{\text{turns}_{primary}}$

$\frac{120\text{ V}}{2{,}400\text{ V}} = \frac{\text{turns}_{secondary}}{500\text{ turns}}$

$\text{turns}_{secondary} = 25\text{ turns}$

27. Use the reciprocal of the equation in problem 26.

$\frac{\text{turns}_{primary}}{\text{turns}_{secondary}} = \frac{\text{Voltage}_{in}}{\text{Voltage}_{out}};$

$\frac{\text{turns}_{primary}}{\text{turns}_{secondary}} =$

$\frac{12\text{ V}}{12{,}000\text{ V}} = \frac{1}{1000}$

the ratio is 1:1,000

✓ Assessment Resources

Reproducible Masters

Chapter *Fast File* Resources
- Chapter Review, pp. 37–38
- Chapter Tests, pp. 39–42
- Assessment Transparency Activity, p. 49

Glencoe Science Web site
- Chapter Review Test
- Standardized Test Practice

Glencoe Technology
- Assessment Transparency
- Exam*View*® Pro Testmaker
- MindJogger Videoquiz
- Interactive Chalkboard

Answer Sheet An answer sheet can be found at **gpescience.com**.

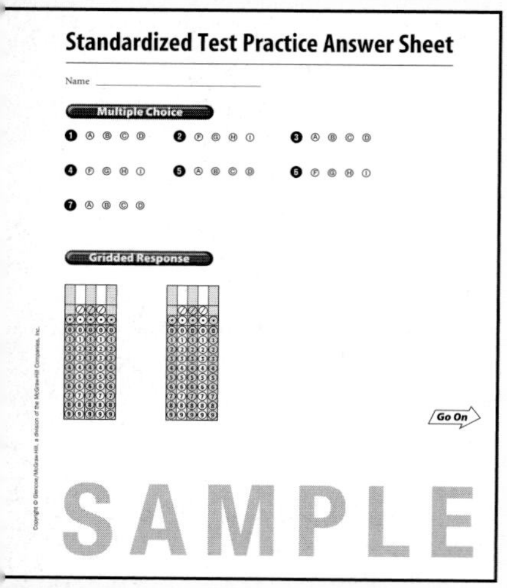

Multiple Choice

1. C
2. C
3. B
4. B

Record your answers on the answer sheet provided by your teacher or on a sheet of paper.

Multiple Choice

A transformer has 50 turns of wire on the primary coil and 10 turns of wire on the secondary coil. The effect of changing the input voltage is summarized in the table below.

Use the table below to answer questions 1 and 2.

Voltage and Current in a Transformer

Trial	Input Voltage (V)	Primary Coil Current (A)	Output Voltage (V)	Secondary Coil Current (A)
1	5	0.1	1	0.5
2	10	0.2	2	1.0
3	20	0.2	4	1.0
4	50	0.5	10	2.5

1. What is the ratio of the input voltage to the output voltage for this transformer?

A. 1:2.5

B. 4:1

C. 5:1

D. 1:5

2. What is the ratio of the secondary-coil current to the primary-coil current?

A. the ratio of the secondary-coil wire turns to the primary-coil wire turns

B. the ratio of the output voltage to the input voltage

C. the ratio of the primary-coil wire turns to the secondary-coil wire turns

D. It always equals one.

Use the figure below to answer question 3.

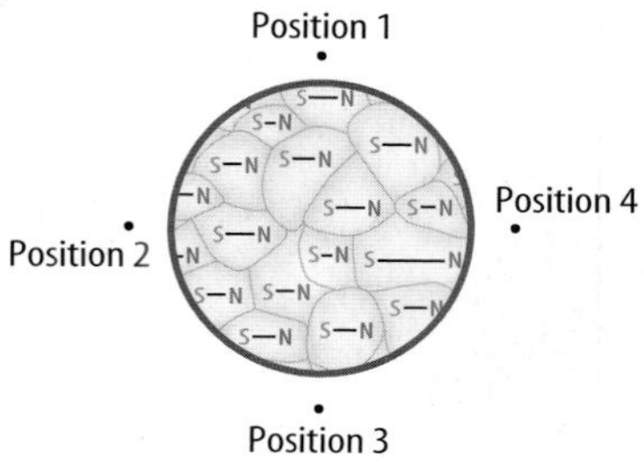

3. A steel paper clip is sitting on a desk. The figure above shows the magnetic domains in a section of the paper clip after the north pole of a magnet has been moved close to it. According to the diagram, the magnet's north pole is at which position?

A. position 1

B. position 2

C. position 3

D. position 4

4. A hydroelectric power plant uses water to spin a turbine attached to a generator. The generator produces 30,000 kW of electric power. If the turbine and generator are a combined 75 percent efficient, how much power does the falling water supply to the turbine?

A. 50,000 kW

B. 40,000 kW

C. 22,500 kW

D. 20,000 kW

Gridded Response

Use the figure below to answer questions 5 and 6.

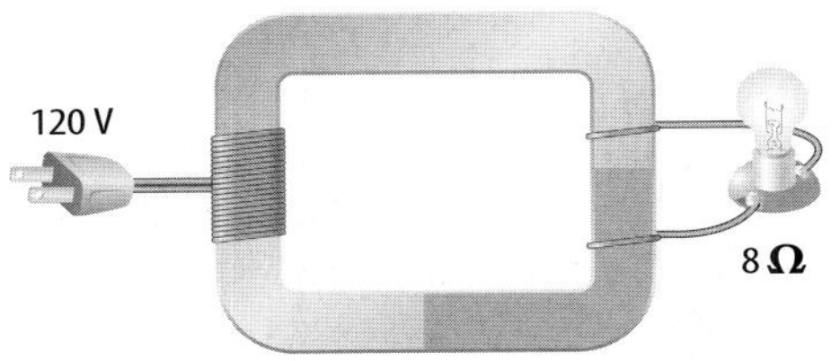

5. A step-down transformer is plugged into a 120-V electric outlet and a lightbulb is connected to the output coil. The transformer has 20 turns on the primary coil and 2 turns on the secondary coil. What is the voltage, in volts, at the output coil?

6. If the lightbulb has a resistance of 8 Ω, what is the current, in amperes, in the lightbulb?

Short Response

7. A bicycle has a small electric generator that is used to light a headlight. The generator is made to spin by rubbing against a wheel. Will the bicycle coast farther on a level surface if the light is turned on or turned off?

8. A student connects a battery to a step-up transformer to boost the voltage. Explain why a small electric motor does not spin when it is connected to the secondary coil of the transformer.

Extended Response

Use the figure below to answer question 9.

Effect of Rotation on Generator Voltage

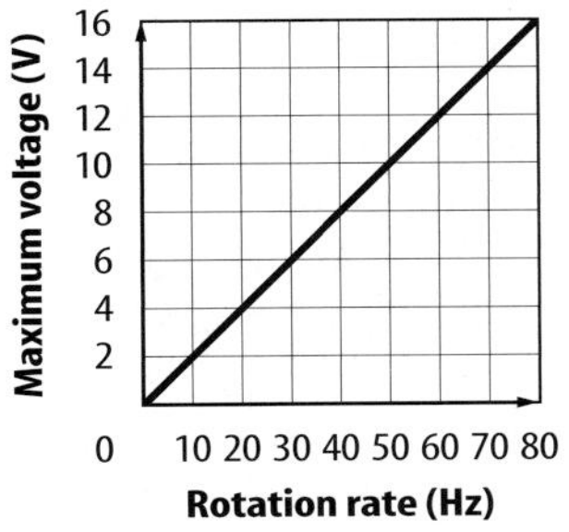

9. The graphic above shows how the voltage produced by a generator depends on the rotation rate of the coil. Explain whether this generator could produce household AC current that is 120 V at 60 Hz.

10. Compare and contrast the behavior and properties of positive and negative electric charges with north and south magnetic poles.

Test-Taking Tip

Read All the Information If a question includes a text passage and a graphic, carefully read the information in the text passage and the graphic before answering the question.

Question 1 Review the information in the text above the table and the information in the table.

Gridded Response

5. First find the output voltage:

$$\frac{\text{Voltage}_{out}}{\text{Voltage}_{in}} = \frac{\text{turns}_{secondary}}{\text{turns}_{primary}},$$

so: $\text{voltage}_{out} =$

$$(\text{voltage}_{in}) \times \frac{(\text{turns}_{secondary})}{(\text{turns}_{primary})}$$

$$= (120\text{ V}) \times \frac{(2\text{ turns})}{(20\text{ turns})}$$

$$= 12\text{ V}$$

6. Use Ohm's law to find the current.

$$I = \frac{V}{R} = \frac{(12\text{ V})}{(8\,\Omega)} = 1.5\text{ A}$$

Short Response

7. The kinetic energy of the coasting bicycle is converted into electrical energy if the generator is turned on. The bicycle will coast farther if the generator is turned off and the generator is not reducing the kinetic energy at a quicker rate.
8. Only an alternating current can induce a voltage in the secondary coil of a transformer. A battery supplies a direct current, so the output voltage is zero and no current flows.

Extended Response

9. When the generator is rotating at 60 Hz, it produces 12 V. Therefore this generator could not produce household AC current.
10. Similarities: Types of electric charge exist, positive and negative. Two types of magnetic poles exist, north and south. Electric charges exert forces on each other. Magnetic poles exert forces on each other. Like charges repel and unlike attract. Like poles repel, unlike attract. Differences: positive and negative charges exist separately, north and south poles don't exist separately.

Rubrics

For more help evaluating Short- and Extended-Response questions, see the rubrics on p. 9T.

chapter 15 Organizer

Section/Objectives	Standards		Labs/Features
	National	**State/Local**	
Chapter Opener	See pp. 16T–17T for a Key to Standards.		**Launch Lab:** Can electromagnetic waves change materials?, p. 455 **Foldables,** p. 455
Section 1 What are electromagnetic waves? 1 session .5 block 1. **Describe** how electric and magnetic fields form electromagnetic waves. 2. **Explain** how vibrating charges produce electromagnetic waves. 3. **Describe** properties of electromagnetic waves.	National Content Standards: UCP.1, UCP.2, UCP.3, UCP.5, A.1, A.2, B.2, B.4, B.6, G.3		**MiniLAB:** Investigating Electromagnetic Waves, p. 458 **Applying Math,** The Speed of Light in Water, p. 459
Section 2 The Electromagnetic Spectrum 2 sessions 1 block 4. **Describe** the waves in the different regions of the electromagnetic spectrum. 5. **Compare** the properties of different electromagnetic waves. 6. **Identify** uses for different types of electromagnetic waves.	National Content Standards: UCP.1, UCP.2, UCP.3, UCP.5, A.1, A.2, B.2, B.4, B.6, D.1		**MiniLAB:** Heating with Microwaves, p. 463 **Integrate Health,** p. 465 **Lab:** The Shape of Satellite Dishes, p. 468 Video Lab
Section 3 Radio Communication 3 sessions 1.5 blocks 7. **Explain** how modulating carrier waves enables information to be transmitted by radio waves. 8. **Distinguish** between amplitude modulation and frequency modulation. 9. **Identify** various ways of communicating using radio waves.	National Content Standards: UCP.1, UCP.2, UCP.3, UCP.5, A.1, A.2, B.2, B.4, B.6, G.3		**Visualizing Radio Broadcasts,** p. 471 **Integrate Career,** p. 472 **Science Online,** p. 473 **Science Online,** p. 474 **Lab:** Radio Frequencies, pp. 476-477 **Science and History:** Riding a Beam of Light, p. 478

StudentWorks Plus | Glencoe Exclusive! TeacherWorks™ All-In-One Planner and Resource Center

Lab Materials	Reproducible Resources	Section Assessment	Technology
LaunchLAB: red construction paper	**Chapter *Fast File* Resources** Foldables Worksheet, p. 17 Note-taking Worksheets, pp. 33–35 Directed Reading Overview, p. 19	Glencoe's Assessment Advantage	TeacherWorks includes: • Interactive Teacher Edition • Lesson Planner with calendar • Access to all program blacklines • Correlations to standards • Web links
MiniLAB: television with remote control, glass, book, paper, metal pan	**Chapter *Fast File* Resources** Transparency Activity, p. 44 MiniLAB, p. 3 Enrichment, p. 30 Reinforcement, p. 27 Directed Reading, p. 20 **Performance Assessment in the Science Classroom,** p. 35 **Science Inquiry Labs,** pp. 41–42	Portfolio Assessment, p. 461 Performance MiniLAB, p. 458 Applying Math, p. 459 Applying Math, p. 461 Content Section Assessment, p. 461	Section Focus Transparency Interactive Chalkboard CD-ROM StudentWorks Plus
MiniLAB: microwave, thermometer, small beakers or baby-food jars (2), 100 mL of dry sand, 20 mL of room-temperature water **Lab:** flashlight, several books, aluminum foil, small bowl	**Chapter *Fast File* Resources** Transparency Activity, p. 45 MiniLAB, p. 4 Enrichment, p. 31 Reinforcement, p. 28 Directed Reading, p. 21 Lab Worksheet, pp. 5–6 Lab Activity, pp. 9–12 Transparency Activity, pp. 47–48 **Reading and Writing Skill Activities,** p. 33	Performance MiniLAB, p. 463 Applying Math, p. 467 Content Section Assessment, p. 467	Section Focus Transparency Teaching Transparency Virtual Labs CD-ROM Interactive Chalkboard CD-ROM StudentWorks Plus Video Lab
Need materials? Contact Science Kit at 1-800-828-7777 or www.sciencekit.com.	**Chapter *Fast File* Resources** Transparency Activity, p. 46 Enrichment, p. 32 Reinforcement, p. 29 Directed Reading, pp. 21–22 Lab Worksheet, pp. 7–8 Lab Activity, pp. 13–16 **Lab Management and Safety,** p. 37 **Earth Science Critical Thinking/Problem Solving,** p. 5	Portfolio Science Journal, p. 473 Performance Applying Math, p. 475 Content Section Assessment, p. 475	Section Focus Transparency Interactive Chalkboard CD-ROM StudentWorks Plus

End of Chapter Assessment

Glencoe's Assessment Advantage

Blackline Masters	Technology	Professional Series
Chapter *Fast File* Resources Chapter Review, pp. 37–38 Chapter Tests, pp. 39–42 **Standardized Test Practice,** pp. 64–67	MindJogger Videoquiz Virtual Labs CD-ROM Exam*View*® Pro Testmaker TeacherWorks CD-ROM Interactive Chalkboard CD-ROM	**Performance Assessment in the Science Classroom (PASC)**

Transparencies

Section Focus

SECTION 1 Section Focus Transparency — Rainbows — Chapter 15

Have you ever met Roy G. Biv? Roy G. Biv isn't a person; it's a common device to help you remember the colors that comprise visible light. Each letter in Roy G. Biv stands for the first letter of a color—red, orange, yellow, green, blue, indigo, and violet.

1. Looking at the photo, which color of light bends the most as it passes through the prism? Which color bends the least?
2. Light is a type of wave. What other kinds of waves can you think of?
3. What do all these waves have in common? What are some possible differences?

L2

SECTION 2 Section Focus Transparency — Whoa, Not So Fast! — Chapter 15

Radio waves are part of the electromagnetic spectrum. These waves can do more than just carry a signal to your radio. Here, a radar gun is being used to measure speed. *Radar* stands for "radio detecting and ranging."

1. Which of the devices in the photo is using electromagnetic waves to measure speed?
2. Is wave speed or wavelength and frequency more useful for differentiating among different types of electromagnetic waves?
3. The prefix *infra-* means below, and the prefix *ultra-* means beyond. Knowing this, what do the terms *infrared* and *ultraviolet* mean?

L2

SECTION 3 Section Focus Transparency — Could it be a growth spurt? — Chapter 15

The Global Positioning System (GPS) uses electromagnetic waves and satellites to determine locations and measurements on Earth. For example, one group of scientists found that Mount Everest is actually 8,850 m (29,035 feet) tall, 2.1 m higher than the figure accepted since 1954. This man is demonstrating another use of the GPS. By connecting a receiver to a computer, he is able to map his location.

1. Name some ways people might use the GPS.
2. Could the GPS function using sound waves? Explain.

L2

This is a representation of key blackline masters available in the Teacher Classroom Resources. See Resource Manager boxes within the chapter for additional information.

Assessment

Assessment Transparency — Electromagnetic Waves — Chapter 15

Directions: *Carefully review the table and answer the following questions.*

Electromagnetic Waves	
Type of wave	**Wavelength range (m)**
Gamma rays	10^{-15}–10^{-11}
X rays	10^{-11}–10^{-8}
Ultraviolet	10^{-8}–10^{-7}
Infrared	10^{-6}–10^{-3}
Microwave	10^{-3}–10^{-1}
Radio wave	10^{-1}–10^{6}

1. Which of the following wavelengths could be broadcast by a rock-and-roll radio station?
   A 10^{-12} meters
   B 10^{-8} meters
   C 10^{5} meters
   D 10^{-3} meters
2. If a device emits an electromagnetic wave with a wavelength of 10^{-10} meters, then it is probably___.
   F an X-ray machine
   G an AM/FM car radio
   H a microwave
   J a light bulb
3. Food can be heated rapidly in your own home using an electromagnetic wave with a wavelength of ___.
   A 10^{-13}
   B 10^{-9}
   C 10^{-2}
   D 100

L2

Teaching

SECTION 2 Teaching Transparency — Electromagnetic Waves — Chapter 15

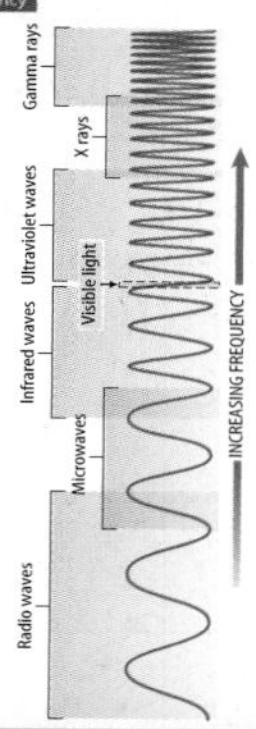

L2

Key to Teaching Strategies

The following designations will help you decide which activities are appropriate for your students.

- L1 Level 1 activities should be appropriate for students with learning difficulties.
- L2 Level 2 activities should be within the ability range of all students.
- L3 Level 3 activities are designed for above-average students.
- ELL ELL activities should be within the ability range of English Language Learners.
- COOP LEARN Cooperative Learning activities are designed for small group work.
- LS Multiple Learning Styles logos, as described on page 12T, are used throughout to indicate strategies that address different learning styles.
- P These strategies represent student products that can be placed into a best-work portfolio.
- PBL Problem-Based Learning activities apply real-world situations to learning.

Hands-on Activities

Student Text Lab Worksheet

Name Date Class

LAB The Shape of Satellite Dishes

Hands-On Activities

Lab Preview

Directions: *Answer these questions before you begin the Lab.*

1. What is the light source used in this lab?
2. Which side of the book should you hold toward the light source?

Communications satellites transmit signals with a narrow beam pointed toward a particular area of Earth. To detect this signal, receivers are typically large, parabolic dishes.

Real-World Problem

How does the shape of a satellite dish improve reception?

Materials

flashlight
several books
aluminum foil
small bowl
*large, metal spoon
*Alternate material

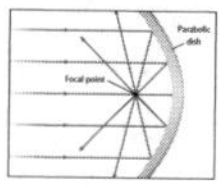

Goals

- **Make** a model of a satellite reflecting dish.
- **Observe** how the shape of the dish affects reception.

Safety Precautions

Procedure

1. Cover one side of a book with aluminum foil. Be careful not to wrinkle the foil.
2. Line the inside of the bowl with foil, also keeping it as smooth as possible.
3. Place some of the books on a table. Put the flashlight on top of the books so that its beam of light will shine several centimeters above and across the table.
4. Hold the foil-covered book on its side at a right angle to the top of the table. The foil-covered side should face the beam of light.
5. **Observe** the intensity of the light on the foil.
6. Repeat steps 4 and 5, replacing the foil-covered book with the bowl.

Electromagnetic Radiation L2

Laboratory Activities

Name Date Class

LAB 1 Laboratory Activity — Observing the Electromagnetic Spectrum

Hands-On Activities

Electromagnetic waves are produced by electric charges that move or vibrate back and forth. The frequency of the electromagnetic wave is the same as the frequency at which the charge vibrates. Except for their frequency and wavelength, all electromagnetic waves are the same and travel at the same speed, 300,000 km/s in a vacuum. The electromagnetic spectrum is used to classify electromagnetic waves according to their frequency and wavelength. Humans are only able to see visible light, which is one small portion of the spectrum. In this activity, you will create a model of the infrared, visible, and ultraviolet portions of the electromagnetic spectrum. The model you create will be made to scale based on wavelength.

Strategy

You will create a scale model of portions of the electromagnetic spectrum.
You will demonstrate that visible light makes up a very small portion of the electromagnetic spectrum.

Materials

calculator
meterstick or metric ruler (marked in millimeters)
scissors
one piece of paper in each of the following colors: red, orange, yellow, green, blue, violet, white, and black
black marker
cellophane tape
flashlight
prism

Procedure

1. The wavelengths for the visible, infrared, and ultraviolet portions of the spectrum are represented in meters in the data table. Complete a metric conversion calculation to find the length of the waves in nanometers. One nanometer is 1×10^{-9} of a meter.
   Use the following conversion factors to convert the wavelengths to nanometers:
   10^{-6}M = 1,000 nanometers;
   10^{-7}M = 100 nanometers; and
   10^{-8}M = 10 nanometers.
2. The scale that will be used to build the model of the spectrum is 1 nanometer equals 1 millimeter. Therefore, if a wavelength is *x* nanometers, the model for that wavelength should measure *x* millimeters. Record your calculations for scale wavelength in millimeters in the table in the Data and Observations section.
3. Work together as a class on the metric conversion calculation for red light. It is good to begin with red light rather than infrared, which is listed first in the data table, because the length of the scale model for infrared light is significantly longer than the scale models of any of the visible light colors.
4. Fill in the scale length in the millimeters column in your data table for red light. This column should always be the same as the final answer for wavelength in nanometers.
5. Use the colored paper to represent the different colors in the visible spectrum. Red paper will be used for the wavelength of red light, orange paper for orange light, and so on. White paper will represent infrared, and black paper will represent ultraviolet.

L2

Electromagnetic Waves 9

Meeting Different Ability Levels

Content Outline

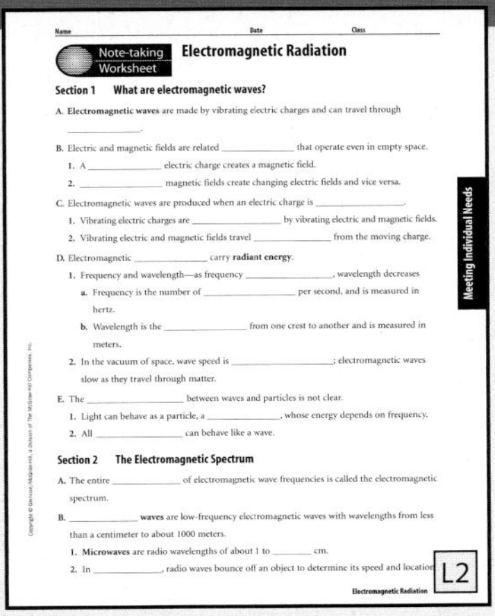
Note-taking Worksheet — Electromagnetic Radiation

Section 1 What are electromagnetic waves?

Section 2 The Electromagnetic Spectrum

L2

Reinforcement

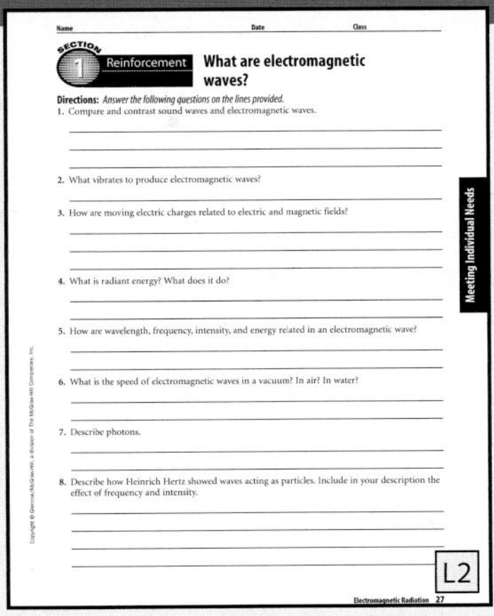
Section 1 Reinforcement — What are electromagnetic waves?

L2

Enrichment

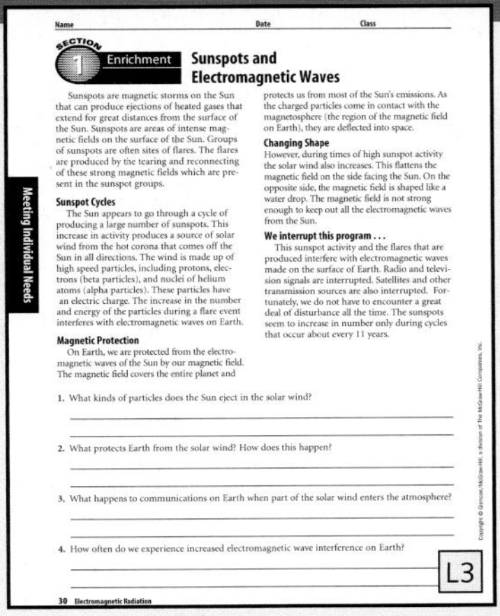
Section 1 Enrichment — Sunspots and Electromagnetic Waves

L3

Directed Reading (English/Spanish)

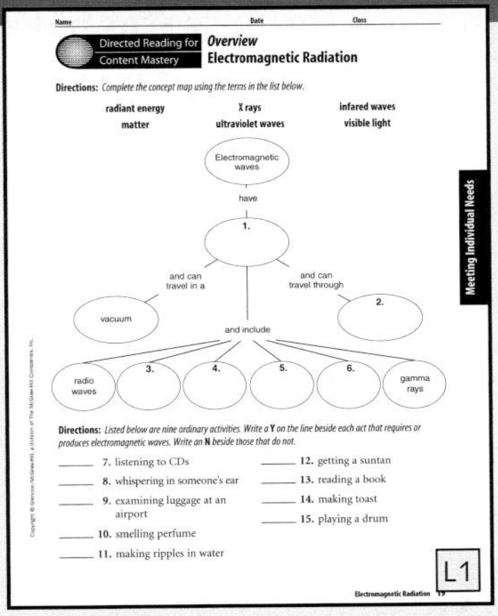
Directed Reading for Content Mastery — Overview: Electromagnetic Radiation

L1

Study Guide

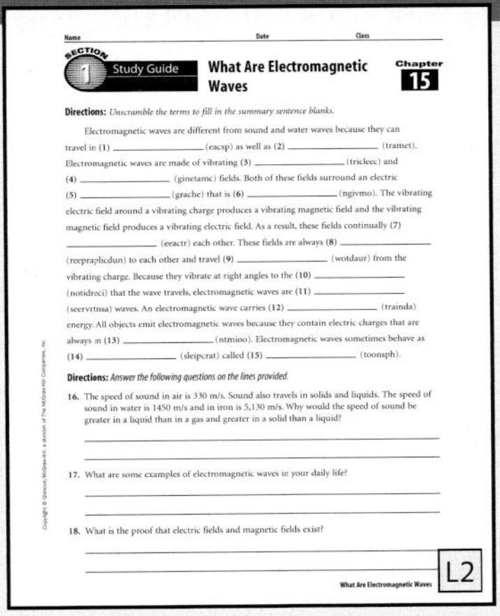
Section 1 Study Guide — What Are Electromagnetic Waves — Chapter 15

L2

Reading Essentials

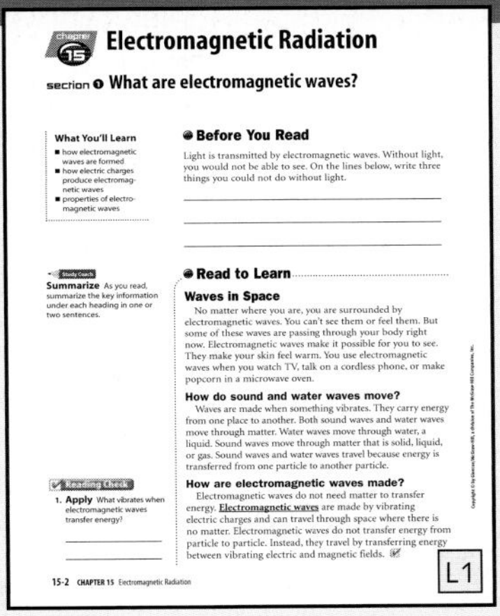
Chapter 15 Electromagnetic Radiation

section 1 What are electromagnetic waves?

L1

Assessment

Test Practice Workbook

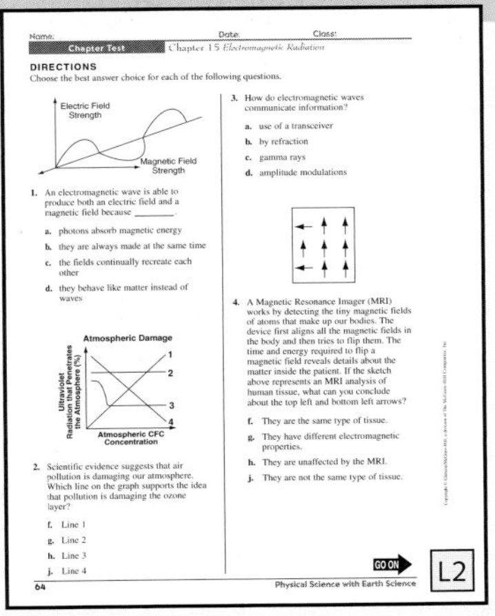
Chapter Test — Chapter 15 Electromagnetic Radiation

L2

Chapter Review

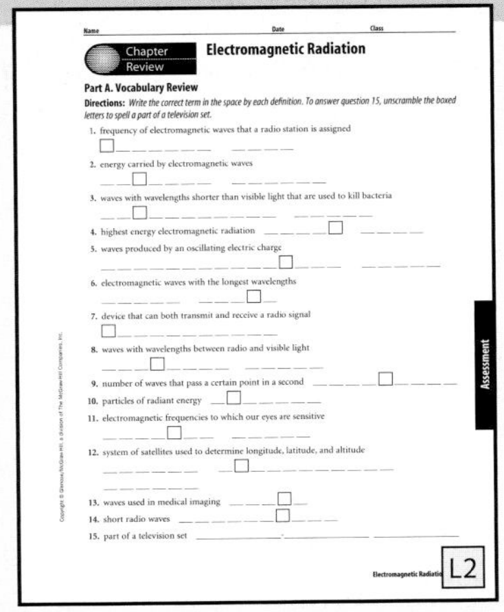
Chapter Review — Electromagnetic Radiation

L2

Chapter Tests

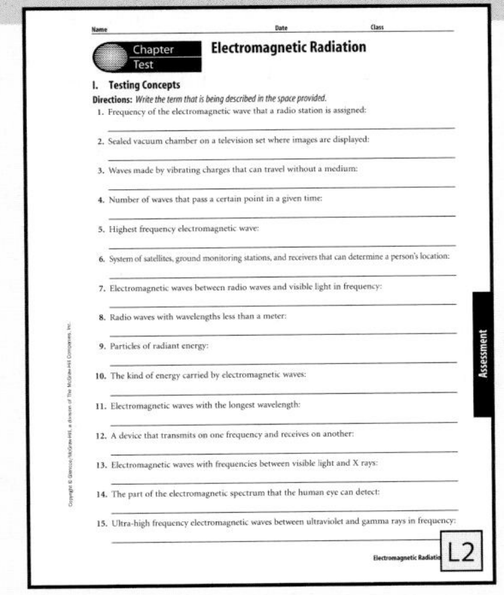
Chapter Test — Electromagnetic Radiation

L2

Science Content Background

section 1 What are electromagnetic waves?

Waves in Space

Throughout history, people have learned about the universe from the visible light that reached their eyes. For the past 100 years, people have been able to detect other types of electromagnetic radiation as well. Instruments such as radio telescopes and ultraviolet detectors have made this possible.

The Nature of Electromagnetic Waves

Electricity and magnetism are related. For example, a moving electric charge produces a magnetic field. James Clerk Maxwell in the 1860s realized that a changing electric field can produce a magnetic field. He also realized that because changing electric and magnetic fields can create each other, an electromagnetic wave that consisted only of oscillating electric and magnetic fields could exist.

An electromagnetic wave can be produced by an electric charge that is moving back and forth. The oscillating charge produces a changing electric field. The changing electric field produces a changing magnetic field, which produces a changing electric field and so on. In this way, the electric and magnetic fields oscillate in time and induce each other.

The two fields oscillate perpendicular to each other and perpendicular to the direction the wave is traveling. The frequency of the wave is the frequency at which the fields oscillate.

section 2 The Electromagnetic Spectrum

Infrared Waves

All objects emit electromagnetic waves. The warmer an object is, the more radiation it emits. Infrared waves are emitted by heat lamps at fast-food restaurants to keep food warm. Remote control devices use infrared waves to send signals that control TVs, VCRs and stereo equipment.

Snakes in the pit viper family, which includes rattlesnakes, have "pits" in their heads that allow them to detect infrared radiation. They use this ability when hunting small, warm-blooded mammals in dark tunnels.

Ultraviolet Waves

Skin cells contain melanocytes, which form the pigment melanin when exposed to UV rays. Melanin causes people to tan, and it blocks some UV radiation. Some insects, such as bees, can see UV radiation.

X Rays and Gamma Rays

Radiation detectors use the tendency of X rays and gamma rays to ionize atoms as a means for detection. Workers who may be exposed to these types of radiation often wear radiation badges. The badges are periodically developed to determine the total amount of radiation the worker has been exposed to.

chapter content resources

Internet Resources

For additional content background, visit gpescience.com to:

- access your book online
- find references to related articles in popular science magazines
- access Web links with related content background
- access current events with science journal topics

Print Resources

Waves: The Electromagnetic Universe, by Gloria Skurzynski, National Geographic Society, 1996

The Visual Dictionary of Physics, Eyewitness Visual Dictionaries, Dorling Kindersley, 1995

Understanding Science—Atoms and Molecules, by Phil Roxbee and Max Parsonage, Usborne Publishing, 1992

section 3 Radio Communication

Radio Transmission

Although Guglielmo Marconi was given credit for inventing radio, much of the credit should be given to Nikola Tesla. Tesla invented the means to turn electrical energy into radio waves.

Antennae are made of materials that are good conductors of electricity, so they allow easy movement of electrons. Electrons accelerating up and down a vertical antenna produce radio waves. If an antenna is aligned vertically, incoming radio waves cause the electrons to accelerate up and down the antenna. For a 1.5 million Hz AM radio wave, the electrons move up and down 1.5 million times per second.

AM radio has a relatively small frequency range of 1.165 MHz, and FM has a range of 20 MHz. The AM band is fine for voices, but the FM band is better for listening to music because it produces a richer sound.

On some nights you can pick up AM stations several hundred miles from where they are broadcast. This is because AM radio waves reflect off the ionosphere. FM radio waves are not reflected by the ionosphere and need to travel in a straight line to reach a receiver. This limits their range.

Teacher to Teacher
Dr. Judith Doyle, Retired Teacher
Newark High School
Newark, Ohio

"To demonstrate how microwaves impact water molecules, place a marshmallow on a paper plate into a microwave and cook for two minutes at 50%-60% power. The marshmallow will expand rapidly, deflate slightly during off cycles, and then inflate more each time power resumes. (Microwaves vary, so test different power levels beforehand to determine best visual effect.) Microwaves cause the water molecules in the marshmallow to flip billions of times per second which in turn causes them to bump into each other and warm up, so as the marshmallow warms up, it expands."

Dr. Judith Doyle

Image Credit

chapter 15

Chapter Vocabulary

electromagnetic wave, p. 456
radiant energy, p. 459
photon, p. 460
visible light, p. 462
radio wave, p. 463
microwave, p. 463
infrared wave, p. 464
ultraviolet wave, p. 465
X ray, p. 467
gamma ray, p. 467
carrier wave, p. 469
cathode-ray tube, p. 472
transceiver, p. 473
Global Positioning System (GPS), p. 475

Science Journal Student responses will vary, but may include: TV, tanning beds, stove, lightbulbs, toaster.

INTERACTIVE CHALKBOARD with Image Bank

PowerPoint® Presentations

This CD-ROM is an editable Microsoft® PowerPoint® presentation that includes:

- a pre-made presentation for every chapter
- interactive graphics
- animations
- audio clips
- image bank
- all new section and chapter questions
- Standardized Test Practice
- transparencies
- Foldables directions
- links to gpescience.com

chapter 15

Electromagnetic Radiation

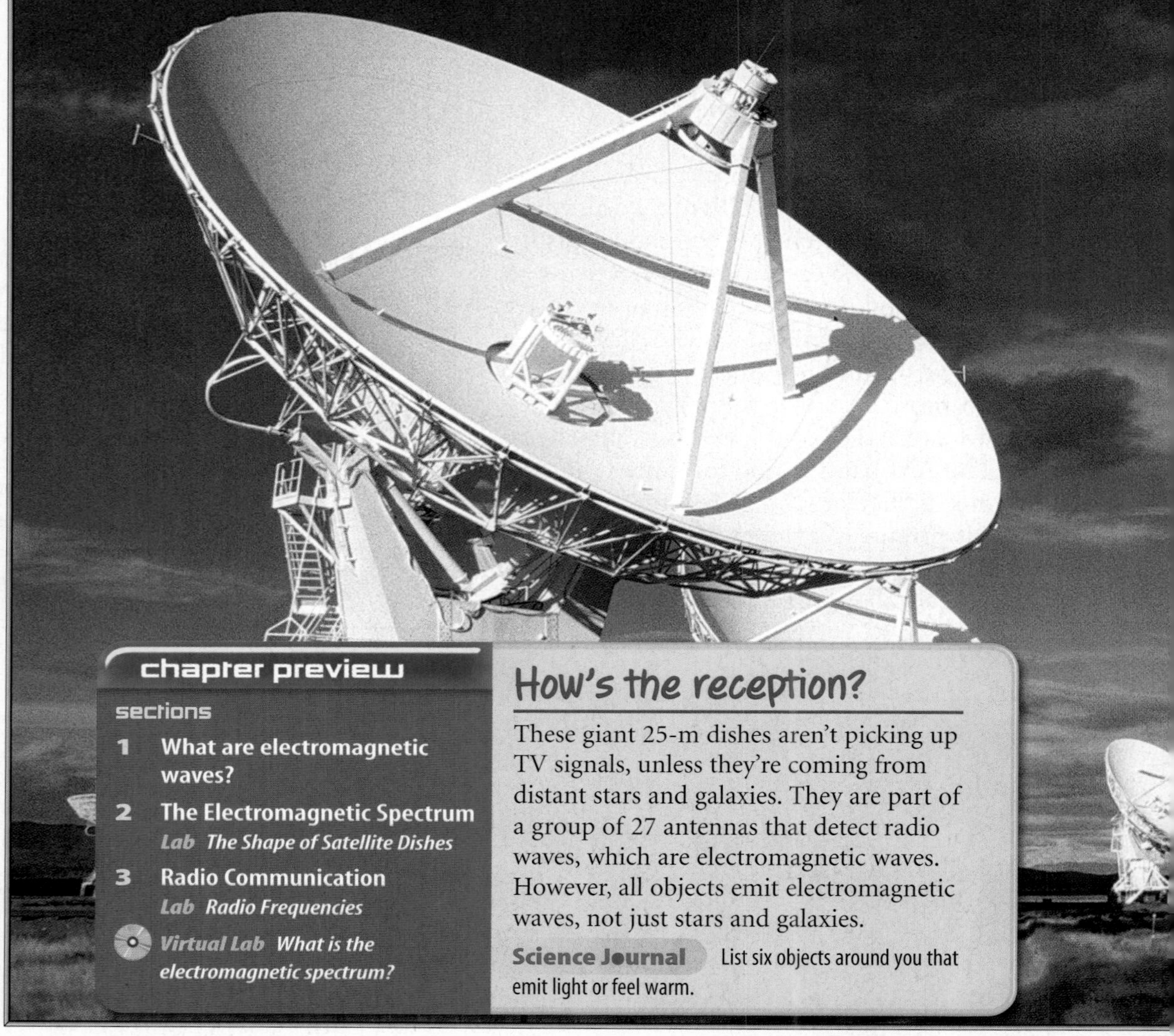

chapter preview

sections

1 What are electromagnetic waves?
2 The Electromagnetic Spectrum
Lab The Shape of Satellite Dishes
3 Radio Communication
Lab Radio Frequencies
Virtual Lab What is the electromagnetic spectrum?

How's the reception?

These giant 25-m dishes aren't picking up TV signals, unless they're coming from distant stars and galaxies. They are part of a group of 27 antennas that detect radio waves, which are electromagnetic waves. However, all objects emit electromagnetic waves, not just stars and galaxies.

Science Journal List six objects around you that emit light or feel warm.

Theme Connection

Energy Electromagnetic waves transfer energy. The electromagnetic spectrum ranges from low-energy radio waves to high-energy gamma rays. People often use low-energy radio waves for communication.

About the Photo

The VLA These receiver dishes are part of the Very Large Array (VLA) radio telescope, located near Socorro, New Mexico. The 27 separate receivers together gather radio waves emitted by stars, galaxies, and other deep-space objects. Images are formed from the data that show details of the radio wave emission from the objects being studied. To view images produced by the VLA go to gpescience.com and follow the links to your chapter.

Start-Up Activities

Launch LAB

Can electromagnetic waves change materials?

You often hear about the danger of the Sun's ultraviolet rays, which can damage the cells of your skin. When the exposure isn't too great, your cells can repair themselves, but too much at one time can cause a painful sunburn. Repeated overexposure to the Sun over many years can damage cells and cause skin cancer. In the lab below, observe how energy carried by ultraviolet waves can cause changes in other materials.

1. Cut a sheet of red construction paper in half.
2. Place one piece outside in direct sunlight. Place the other in a shaded location.
3. Keep the construction paper in full sunlight for at least 45 min. If possible, allow it to stay there for 3 h or more before taking it down. Be sure the other piece remains in the shade.
4. **Think Critically** In your Science Journal, describe any differences you notice in the two pieces of construction paper. Comment on your results.

FOLDABLES™ Study Organizer

Electromagnetic Waves Make the following Foldable to help you understand electromagnetic waves.

STEP 1 **Fold** a sheet of paper vertically in half from top to bottom.

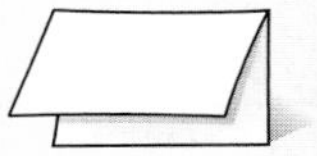

STEP 2 **Fold** in half from side to side with the fold at the top.

STEP 3 **Unfold** the paper once. **Cut** only the fold of the top flap to make two tabs.

STEP 3 **Write** on the front tabs as shown.

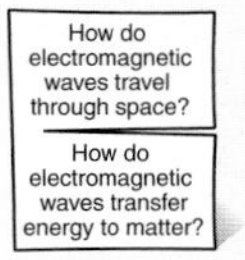

Identify Questions As you read the chapter, write answers to the questions on the back of the appropriate tabs.

Science Online | Preview this chapter's content and activities at gpescience.com

455

Launch LAB

Purpose Students observe how electromagnetic waves from the Sun affect the dye in colored paper. L1 ELL LS **Visual-Spatial**

Materials Although any color of construction paper will work for this activity, red will show the most dramatic results. Be sure to use construction paper that has not previously been exposed to sunlight.

Teaching Strategies

- Construction paper that is exposed to sunlight through a window will fade more slowly than construction paper in direct sunlight. The glass blocks much of the ultraviolet light.
- The construction paper should be exposed to sunlight for as long as possible. If time permits, allow students to observe the effects after different time intervals.

Think Critically

The color of the construction paper exposed to the Sun is faded compared to that of the paper left in the shade. Ultraviolet waves from the Sun have broken down some of the dye molecules.

Assessment

Process Ask students to compare how the ultraviolet waves affected the construction paper with what happens to their skin when they stay out too long in the Sun. Use **Performance Assessment in the Science Classroom,** p. 89.

FOLDABLES™ Study Organizer **Dinah Zike Study Fold**

Student preparation materials for this Foldable are available in the **Chapter *Fast File* Resources.**

1 Motivate

An editable Microsoft® PowerPoint® presentation is available on **Interactive Chalkboard** CD-ROM.

Bellringer

Section Focus Transparencies also are available on the Interactive Chalkboard CD-ROM. L2 ELL

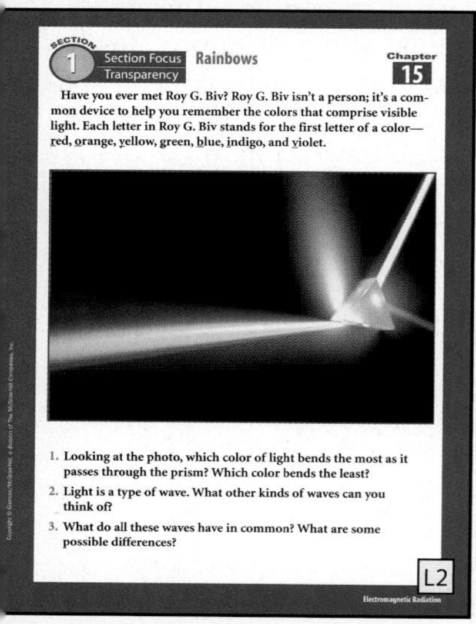
Section 1 Section Focus Transparency — Rainbows — Chapter 15

Have you ever met Roy G. Biv? Roy G. Biv isn't a person; it's a common device to help you remember the colors that comprise visible light. Each letter in Roy G. Biv stands for the first letter of a color—red, orange, yellow, green, blue, indigo, and violet.

1. Looking at the photo, which color of light bends the most as it passes through the prism? Which color bends the least?
2. Light is a type of wave. What other kinds of waves can you think of?
3. What do all these waves have in common? What are some possible differences?

L2

Electromagnetic Radiation

Reading Preview

Tie to Prior Knowledge

Magnets Show students how a magnet pulls on a nearby paper clip, even if they are not touching. Remind students that this is because a magnetic field surrounds the magnet. Tell students that in this section they will learn about magnetic fields and electric fields.

Word Analysis Write the term *electromagnetic wave* on the board. Ask students to study the word closely, and then infer which forces are involved in producing this type of wave. *electric and magnetic* Make sure students know the meanings of each of the word parts.

section 1

What are electromagnetic waves?

Reading Guide

What You'll Learn

- **Describe** how electric and magnetic fields form electromagnetic waves.
- **Explain** how vibrating charges produce electromagnetic waves.
- **Describe** properties of electromagnetic waves.

Why It's Important

You, and all the objects and materials around you, are radiating electromagnetic waves.

Review Vocabulary

hertz: the SI unit of frequency, abbreviated Hz; 1 Hz equals one vibration per second

New Vocabulary

- electromagnetic wave
- radiant energy
- photon

Waves in Space

Stay calm. Do not panic. As you are reading this sentence, no matter where you are, you are surrounded by electromagnetic waves. Even though you can't feel them, some of these waves are traveling right through your body. They enable you to see. They make your skin feel warm. You use electromagnetic waves when you watch television, talk on a cordless phone, or prepare popcorn in a microwave oven.

Figure 1 Water waves and sound waves require matter to move through. Energy is transferred from one particle to the next as the wave travels through the matter.

Sound and Water Waves Waves are produced by something that vibrates, and they transmit energy from one place to another. Look at the sound wave and the water wave in **Figure 1.** Both waves are moving through matter. The sound wave is moving through air and the water wave through water. These waves travel because energy is transferred from particle to particle. Without matter to transfer the energy, waves cannot move.

Electromagnetic Waves However, electromagnetic waves do not require matter to transfer energy. **Electromagnetic waves** are made by vibrating electric charges and can travel through space where matter is not present. Instead of transferring energy from particle to particle, electromagnetic waves travel by transferring energy between vibrating electric and magnetic fields.

Section 1 Resource Manager

Chapter *FAST FILE* Resources

Transparency Activity, p. 44
Directed Reading for Content Mastery, pp. 19, 20
Note-taking Worksheets, pp. 33–35
Enrichment, p. 30
MiniLAB, p. 3
Reinforcement, p. 27

Science Inquiry Labs, pp. 41–42
Performance Assessment in the Science Classroom, p. 35
Mathematics Skill Activities, p. 1

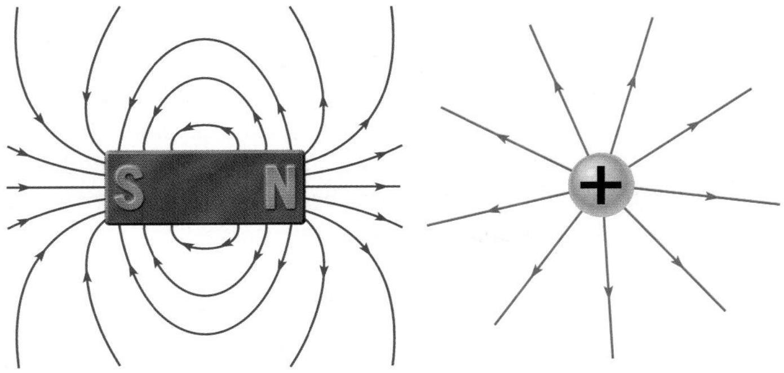

A magnetic field surrounds all magnets.

An electric field surrounds all charges.

Figure 2 Fields enable magnets and charges to exert forces at a distance. These fields extend throughout space.
Explain *how you could detect a magnetic field.*

Electric and Magnetic Fields

When you bring a magnet near a metal paper clip, the paper clip moves toward the magnet and sticks to it. The paper clip moves because the magnet exerts a force on it. The magnet exerts this force without having to touch the paper clip because all magnets are surrounded by a magnetic field, as shown in **Figure 2.** Magnetic fields exist around magnets even if the space around the magnets contains no matter.

Just as magnets are surrounded by magnetic fields, electric charges are surrounded by electric fields, also shown in **Figure 2.** An electric field enables charges to exert forces on each other even when they are far apart. Just as a magnetic field around a magnet can exist in empty space, an electric field exists around an electric charge even if the space around it contains no matter.

Magnetic Fields and Moving Charges Electric charges also can be surrounded by magnetic fields. It is the motion of electrons that generates the magnetic field. An electric current, the net flow of electrons in one direction, is always surrounded by a magnetic field. In fact, any moving electric charge is surrounded by a magnetic field, as well as an electric field. For example, an electric current flowing through a wire is surrounded by a magnetic field, as illustrated in **Figure 3.**

Figure 3 Electrons moving in a wire are surrounded by a magnetic field.
Describe *how you would confirm that a magnetic field exists around a current-carrying wire.*

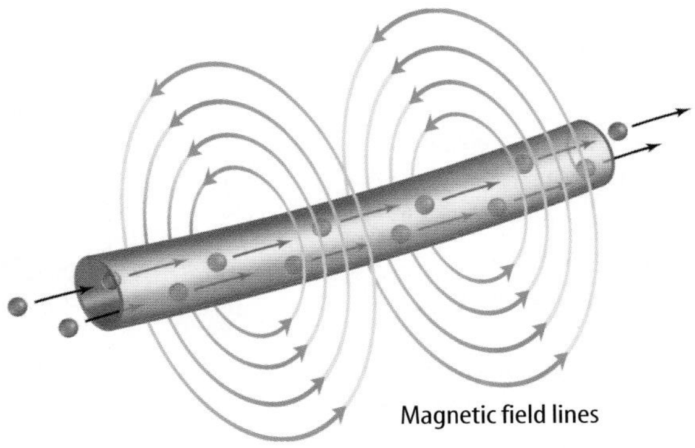

Differentiated Instruction

Challenge Have students research scientists who did early investigations on the relationship between electricity and magnetism, such as Oersted, Faraday, and Henry. Have students select an early experiment to demonstrate. L3

2 Teach

Caption Answers

Figure 2 Place a magnet where the field exists and see if there is a force exerted on the magnet.

Figure 3 Bring a compass near the wire.

Quick Demo

Seeing Magnetic Fields

Materials iron filings, iron bar magnet, plexiglass (optional: overhead projector, plastic wrap)

Estimated Time ten minutes

Procedure If using overhead, wrap writing surface with plastic wrap to protect. Place bar magnet on overhead or other flat surface. Lay plexiglass on top of magnet, and lightly sprinkle with iron filings above magnet. Point out how magnetic field drops off rapidly as distance from magnet increases. L2 LS **Visual-Spatial**

IDENTIFYING Misconceptions

No Magnetic Charge Students may believe that, since an electric field surrounds an electric charge, a magnetic field surrounds a magnetic charge. Explain that there is no magnetic charge. Magnetism is caused by moving electric charges. This is true even for magnetic materials. Electrons in all atoms move in a way that induces a small magnetic field. In most materials, these fields cancel, but in magnetic materials the atoms are arranged so that the fields combine to form a macroscopic field.

Mini LAB

Purpose Students investigate the behavior of electromagnetic waves. L2 ELL LS **Kinesthetic**

Materials television with remote control, glass, book, paper, metal pan

Teaching Strategy Suggest that students hold the objects both very close to the receiver and farther away from it. This will enable them to observe how the beam spreads out and can travel around objects.

Analysis

1. No (for most), because the infrared beam spreads out as it leaves its source.
2. The signal will travel through transparent or translucent materials.

Assessment

Process Some receivers are more sensitive and require the remote to be aimed directly at them. Ask students to suggest ways to control such a television without pointing the remote directly at the receiver. Possible answer: Aim the remote at an object in such a way that the reflected ray will hit the receiver. Use **Performance Assessment in the Science Classroom,** p. 93.

Try at Home

Reading Check

Answer an electric charge moving back and forth

Caption Answer

Figure 4 a transverse wave

Mini LAB

Investigating Electromagnetic Waves

Procedure

1. Point your **television remote control** in different directions and observe whether it will still control the **television.**
2. Place various materials in front of the infrared receiver on the television and observe whether the remote control still will operate the television. Some materials you might try are **glass, a book, your hand, paper,** and a **metal pan.**

Analysis

1. Was it necessary for the remote control to be pointing exactly toward the receiver to control the television? Explain.
2. Did the remote control continue to work when the various materials were placed between it and the receiver? Explain why or why not.

Try at Home

Changing Electric and Magnetic Fields A changing magnetic field creates a changing electric field. For example, in a transformer, changing electric current in the primary coil produces a changing magnetic field. This changing magnetic field then creates a changing electric field in the secondary coil that produces current in the coil. The reverse is also true: a changing electric field creates a changing magnetic field.

Making Electromagnetic Waves

Waves such as sound waves are produced when something vibrates. Electromagnetic waves also are produced when something vibrates—an electric charge that moves back and forth.

Reading Check *What produces an electromagnetic wave?*

When an electric charge vibrates, the electric field around it changes. Because the electric charge is in motion, it also has a magnetic field around it. This magnetic field also changes as the charge vibrates. As a result, the vibrating electric charge is surrounded by changing electric and magnetic fields.

How do the vibrating electric and magnetic fields around the charge become a wave that travels through space? The changing electric field around the charge creates a changing magnetic field. This changing magnetic field then creates a changing electric field. This process continues, with the magnetic and electric fields continually creating each other. These vibrating electric and magnetic fields are perpendicular to each other and travel outward from the moving charge, as shown in **Figure 4.** Because the electric and magnetic fields vibrate at right angles to the direction the wave travels, an electromagnetic wave is a transverse wave.

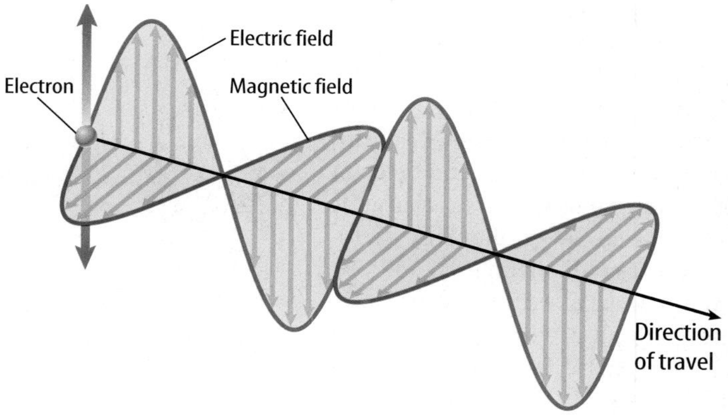

Figure 4 A vibrating electric charge creates an electromagnetic wave that travels outward in all directions from the charge. The wave in only one direction is shown here.
Determine *whether an electromagnetic wave is a transverse wave or a compressional wave.*

Visual Learning

Figure 4 The electromagnetic wave is shown in one direction to make it easier to visualize. In reality, a vibrating charge produces electromagnetic waves that travel in almost all directions. The wave shown here is vertically polarized: the electric field oscillates up and down, and the magnetic field oscillates right and left. In a horizontally polarized wave, the electric field oscillates right and left and the magnetic field oscillates up and down. Ask students to describe how the amplitude, frequency, and wavelength of the electric and magnetic fields are related. When the amplitude of the electric field is maximum, the amplitude of the magnetic field is maximum. The frequencies and wavelengths of the fields are the same.

Properties of Electromagnetic Waves

All matter contains charged particles that are always in motion. As a result, all objects emit electromagnetic waves. The wavelengths of the emitted waves become shorter as the temperature of the material increases. As an electromagnetic wave moves, its electric and magnetic fields encounter objects. These vibrating fields can exert forces on charged particles and magnetic materials, causing them to move. For example, electromagnetic waves from the Sun cause electrons in your skin to vibrate and gain energy, as shown in **Figure 5.** The energy transferred by an electromagnetic wave is **radiant energy.** Radiant energy makes a fire feel warm and enables you to see.

Figure 5 As an electromagnetic wave strikes your skin, electrons in your skin gain energy from the vibrating electric and magnetic fields.

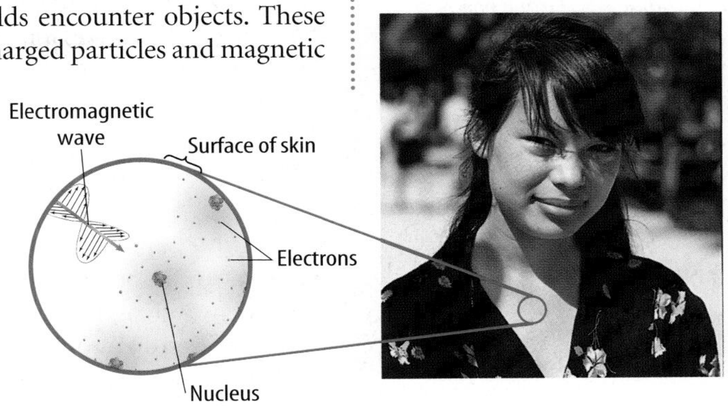

Applying Math — Using Scientific Notation

THE SPEED OF LIGHT IN WATER The speed of light in water is 226,000 km/s. Write this number in scientific notation.

IDENTIFY known values and the unknown value

Identify the known values:

The speed of light in water is 226,000 km/s.

Identify the unknown value:

the number 226,000 written in scientific notation

SOLVE the problem

A number written in scientific notation has the form $M \times 10^N$. N is the number of places the decimal point in the number has to be moved so that the number M that results has only one digit to the left of the decimal point.

Write the number in scientific notation:	$226{,}000. \times 10^N$
Move the decimal point so there is only one digit to its left:	2.26000×10^N
The decimal point was moved 5 places, so N equals 5:	2.26000×10^5
Delete remaining zeroes at the end of the number.	2.26×10^5

CHECK your answer

Add zeroes to the end of the number and move the decimal point in the opposite direction five places. The result should be the original number.

Practice Problems

Write the following numbers in scientific notation: 433; 812,000,000; 73,000,000,000; 84,500.

For more practice problems go to page 879, and visit Math Practice at gpescience.com.

Quick Demo

Waves

Materials coiled metal spring toy

Estimated Time 5–10 minutes

Procedure Have two volunteers hold each end of the spring on the floor. Demonstrate a transverse wave (a wave for which the medium moves at right angles to the direction the wave travels) by moving one end of the spring left and right. Demonstrate a longitudinal wave (a wave for which the medium moves along the same direction the wave travels) by holding both ends still, then gathering coils together and releasing them.

Applying Math

Math Standards

National: 1

Answer to Practice Problem

$433 = 4.33 \times 10^2$

$812{,}000{,}000 = 8.12 \times 10^8$

$73{,}000{,}000{,}000 = 7.3 \times 10^{10}$

$84{,}500 = 8.45 \times 10^4$

Discussion

Scientific Notation Why is scientific notation useful when studying electromagnetic radiation? Wavelength, frequency, and wave speed are often very large or very small numbers.

Fun Fact

By 1800, many scientists suspected a relationship between electricity and magnetism. Then, in 1820, Hans Christian Oersted accidentally brought a wire carrying direct current near a compass needle while teaching class. The compass needle moved, demonstrating that the current-carrying wire was surrounded by a magnetic field.

Science Journal

Radiant Energy Warm objects emit more radiant energy than cool objects do. Have students investigate this topic and each write a paragraph summarizing what he/she learns. All objects contain charged particles, such as electrons, that are always moving. These charged particles emit electromagnetic waves whose frequency depends on the frequency of vibration of the charges. As the temperature of the object increases, these charged particles move faster. Their frequency of vibration increases and the frequency of the electomagnetic radiation they emit increases. L3 **Logical-Mathematical**

Activity

Drawing Waves To help students understand how frequency and wavelength are related, have one student draw a series of waves across the board, end to end, each having a similar wavelength. Have another student draw a series of waves with a much longer wavelength below the first set. The drawings should demonstrate that over the same distance, there are more waves with shorter wavelengths and fewer waves with longer wavelengths. L2

LS **Visual-Spatial**

Teacher FYI

Light History There is a rich scientific history leading to the idea that light has both particle and wave nature. In the fifth century B.C., the Pythagoreans thought streams of light were emitted by the eye. Newton formed a particle theory of light in the early eighteenth century, around the same time Huygens concluded that light was a wave. In 1905, Einstein proposed that electromagnetic waves can also behave as particles.

Reading Check

Answer 300,000 km/s in a vacuum

Reading Strategy

Target Supporting Evidence As students read about wave speed, ask them to find evidence in the text that supports the following statement: The speed of electromagnetic waves depends on the material they travel through. Have them list the evidence and compare notes with a partner.

Table 1 Speed of Visible Light

Material	Speed (km/s)
Vacuum	300,000
Air	slightly less than 300,000
Water	226,000
Glass	200,000
Diamond	124,000

Wave Speed All electromagnetic waves travel at 300,000 km/s in the vacuum of space. Because light is an electromagnetic wave, the speed of electromagnetic waves in space is usually called the speed of light. The speed of light is nature's speed limit—nothing travels faster than the speed of light. In matter, the speed of electromagnetic waves depends on the material they travel through. Electromagnetic waves usually travel most slowly in solids and fastest in gases. **Table 1** lists the speed of visible light in various materials.

Reading Check *What is the speed of light?*

Wavelength and Frequency Like all waves, electromagnetic waves can be described by their wavelengths and frequencies. The wavelength of an electromagnetic wave is the distance from one crest to another, as shown in **Figure 6.**

The frequency of any wave is the number of wavelengths that pass a point in 1 s. The frequency of an electromagnetic wave also equals the frequency of the vibrating charge that produces the wave. This frequency is the number of vibrations, or back-and-forth movements, of the charge in one second. The frequency and wavelength of an electromagnetic wave are related. As the frequency increases, the wavelength becomes smaller.

Waves and Particles

The difference between a wave and a particle might seem obvious—a wave is a disturbance that carries energy, and a particle is a piece of matter. However, in reality, the difference is not so clear.

Waves as Particles In 1887, Heinrich Hertz found that by shining light on a metal, electrons were ejected from the metal. Hertz found that whether or not electrons were ejected depended on the frequency of the light and not on the amplitude. Because the energy carried by a wave depends on its amplitude and not its frequency, this result was mysterious. Years later, Albert Einstein provided an explanation: electromagnetic waves can behave as a particle, called a **photon,** whose energy depends on the frequency of the waves.

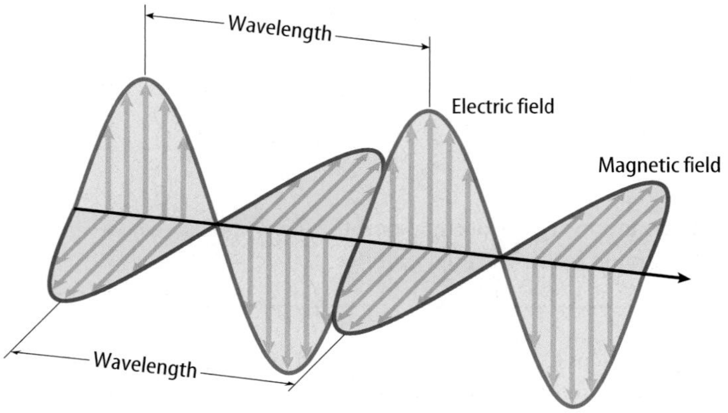

Figure 6 The wavelength of an electromagnetic wave is the distance between the crests of the vibrating electric field or magnetic field.

Differentiated Instruction

Challenge Ask students to research the early discoveries of Hertz, Planck, and Einstein on the quantum theory, black body radiation, and the photoelectric affect. Have students create a time line illustrating key concepts and experiments. L3

Behavioral Disorder Have students draw two waves on a piece of paper. Count the wavelengths in each wave. Discuss which wave has the highest frequency. For review, label resting point, amplitude, crest, trough, wavelength.

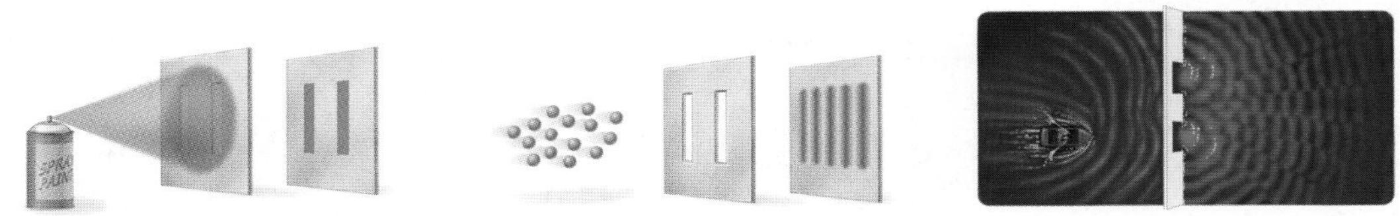

Particles of paint sprayed through two slits coat only the area behind the slits.

Electrons fired at two closely spaced openings form a wavelike interference pattern.

Water waves produce an interference pattern after passing through two openings.

Particles as Waves Because electromagnetic waves could behave as a particle, other scientists wondered whether matter could behave as a wave. If a beam of electrons were sprayed at two tiny slits, you might expect that the electrons would strike only the area behind the slits, like the spray paint in **Figure 7.** Instead, it was found that the electrons formed an interference pattern. This type of pattern is produced by waves when they pass through two slits and interfere with each other, as the water waves do in **Figure 7.** This experiment showed that electrons can behave like waves. It is now known that all particles, not only electrons, can behave like waves.

Figure 7 When electrons are sent through two narrow slits, they behave as a wave.

section 1 review

Summary

Making Electromagnetic Waves

- Moving electric charges are surrounded by an electric field and a magnetic field.
- A vibrating electric charge produces an electromagnetic wave.
- An electromagnetic wave consists of vibrating electric and magnetic fields that are perpendicular to each other and travel outward from the vibrating electric charge.

Properties of Electromagnetic Waves

- Electromagnetic waves carry radiant energy.
- In empty space, electromagnetic waves travel at 300,000 km/s, the speed of light.
- Electromagnetic waves travel more slowly in matter, with a speed that depends on the material.

Waves and Particles

- Electromagnetic waves can behave as particles that are called photons.
- In some circumstances, particles, such as electrons, can behave as waves.

Self Check

1. **Explain** why an electromagnetic wave is a transverse wave and not a compressional wave.
2. **Compare** the frequency of an electromagnetic wave with the frequency of the vibrating charge that produces the wave.
3. **Describe** how electromagnetic waves transfer radiant energy to matter.
4. **Explain** how an electromagnetic wave can travel through space that contains no matter.
5. **Think Critically** Suppose a moving electric charge were surrounded only by an electric field. Infer whether or not a vibrating electric charge would produce an electromagnetic wave.

Applying Math

6. **Calculate Time** How many minutes does it take an electromagnetic wave to travel 150,000,000 km?
7. **Use Scientific Notation** Calculate the distance an electromagnetic wave in space would travel in one day. Express your answer in scientific notation.

More Section Review gpescience.com

section 1 review

1. The vibrating electric and magnetic fields that create electromagnetic waves are perpendicular to the direction the wave travels. A compressional wave causes a disturbance that moves back and forth along the direction the wave travels.
2. They're equal.
3. by causing charged particles within objects to move
4. An electromagnetic wave is made of vibrating electric and magnetic fields that continually produce each other; matter is not needed for this to occur.
5. No, an electromagnetic wave would not be produced. Both a vibrating electric and magnetic field are needed to produce an electromagnetic wave that travels away from the vibrating charge.
6. 500 s = 8.33 min
7. 2.592×10^{10} km

Post Reading

Compare and Contrast Have students compare and contrast the behavior of waves and photons. Does the energy of a wave depend on its amplitude or frequency? What about a photon—on what does its energy depend? Have half the class share similarities and half the class note differences.

3 Assess

DAILY INTERVENTION

Check for Understanding

Logical-Mathematical Using two columns, chart the characteristics of sound waves and electromagnetic waves comparing and contrasting the properties of each.

Reteach

Seeing Waves Radio waves are long-wavelength, low-frequency electromagnetic waves, and gamma rays are short-wavelength, high-frequency waves. Have students model the relationship between wavelength and frequency of waves by vertically shaking a rope attached to a door handle. First, they can shake it with low frequency to see long wavelengths, then with higher frequency to see shorter wavelengths. L2 ELL IS **Kinesthetic**

Assessment

Portfolio Have students write several paragraphs that describe how electric and magnetic fields together form electromagnetic waves, and how these waves vary in frequency and wavelength. Use **Performance Assessment in the Science Classroom,** p. 159. P

1 Motivate

An editable Microsoft® PowerPoint® presentation is available on **Interactive Chalkboard** CD-ROM.

Bellringer

Section Focus Transparencies also are available on the Interactive Chalkboard CD-ROM. L2 ELL

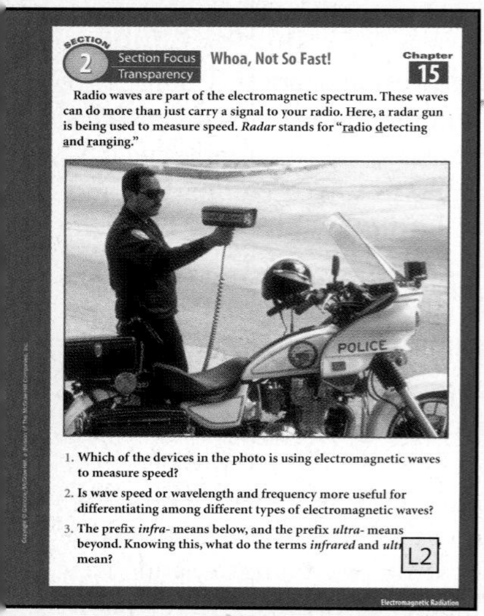
Section 2 Section Focus Transparency — Whoa, Not So Fast! — Chapter 15

Radio waves are part of the electromagnetic spectrum. These waves can do more than just carry a signal to your radio. Here, a radar gun is being used to measure speed. *Radar* stands for "radio detecting and ranging."

1. Which of the devices in the photo is using electromagnetic waves to measure speed?
2. Is wave speed or wavelength and frequency more useful for differentiating among different types of electromagnetic waves?
3. The prefix *infra-* means below, and the prefix *ultra-* means beyond. Knowing this, what do the terms *infrared* and *ult*[illegible] mean? L2

Electromagnetic Radiation

Reading Preview

Tie to Prior Knowledge

X Rays Ask students if they have ever had an X-ray image taken by an X-ray technician. X rays are one form of electromagnetic waves that they will be studying in this section.

Activate Background Knowledge Ask students to identify any familiar vocabulary words. Students will likely know *microwave* and *X ray*. Ask: What are these things and how do they work? Students may describe the words in terms of objects. Explain that a microwave oven uses microwaves and an X-ray machine uses X rays. Both are types of electromagnetic radiation.

section 2

The Electromagnetic Spectrum

Reading Guide

What You'll Learn

- **Describe** the waves in the different regions of the electromagnetic spectrum.
- **Compare** the properties of different electromagnetic waves.
- **Identify** uses for different types of electromagnetic waves.

Why It's Important

Waves in different regions of the electromagnetic spectrum are used every day in many ways.

Review Vocabulary

spectrum: a continuous sequence arranged by a particular property

New Vocabulary

- visible light
- radio wave
- microwave
- infrared wave
- ultraviolet wave
- X ray
- gamma ray

A Range of Frequencies

Electromagnetic waves can have a wide variety of frequencies. They might vibrate once each second or trillions of times each second. The entire range of electromagnetic wave frequencies is known as the electromagnetic spectrum, shown in **Figure 8.** Various portions of the electromagnetic spectrum interact with matter differently. As a result, they are given different names. The electromagnetic waves that humans can detect with their eyes, called **visible light,** are a small portion of the entire electromagnetic spectrum. However, various devices have been developed to detect the other frequencies. For example, the antenna of your radio detects radio waves.

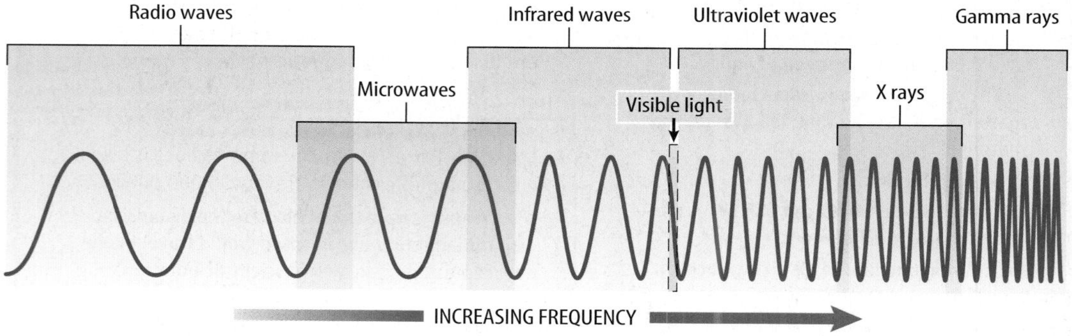

Figure 8 Electromagnetic waves are described by different names, depending on their frequencies and wavelengths.

Section 2 Resource Manager

Chapter *Fast File* Resources

Transparency Activity, p. 45, 47–48

Directed Reading for Content Mastery, p. 21

MiniLAB, p. 4

Enrichment, p. 31

Lab Activity, pp. 9–12

Reinforcement, p. 28

Lab Worksheets, pp. 5–6

Reading and Writing Skill Activities, p. 33

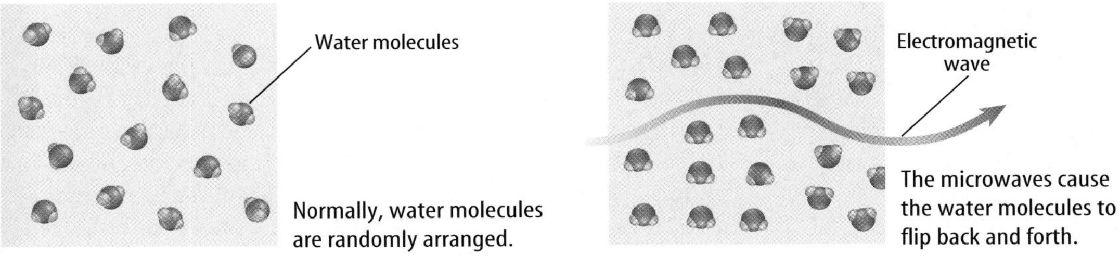

Figure 9 Microwave ovens use electromagnetic waves to heat food.

Radio Waves

Stop and look around you. Even though you can't see them, radio waves are moving everywhere you look. Some radio waves carry an audio signal from a radio station to a radio. However, even though these radio waves carry information that a radio uses to create sound, you can't hear radio waves. You hear a sound wave when the compressions and rarefactions the sound wave produces reach your ears. A radio wave does not produce compressions and rarefactions as it travels through air.

Microwaves **Radio waves** are low-frequency electromagnetic waves with wavelengths longer than about 1 mm. Radio waves with wavelengths of less than 30 cm are called **microwaves.** Microwaves with wavelengths of about 20 cm to 1 cm are widely used for communication, such as for cellular telephones and satellite signals. You are probably most familiar with microwaves because of their use in microwave ovens.

Reading Check *What is the difference between a microwave and a radio wave?*

Microwave ovens heat food when microwaves interact with water molecules in food, as shown in **Figure 9.** Each water molecule is positively charged on one side and negatively charged on the other side. The vibrating electric field inside a microwave oven causes water molecules in food to rotate back and forth billions of times each second. This rotation causes a type of friction between water molecules that generates thermal energy. It is the thermal energy produced by the interactions between the water molecules that causes your food to cook.

Radar Another use for radio waves is to find the position and movement of objects by a method called radar. Radar stands for **RA**dio **D**etecting **A**nd **R**anging. With radar, radio waves are transmitted toward an object. By measuring the time required for the waves to bounce off the object and return to a receiving antenna, the location of the object can be found. Law-enforcement officers use radar to measure how fast a vehicle is moving. Radar also is used for tracking the movement of aircraft, watercraft, and spacecraft.

Mini LAB

Heating with Microwaves

Procedure

1. Obtain two small **beakers or baby-food jars.** Place 50 mL of **dry sand** in each. To one of the jars, add 20 mL of **room-temperature water** and stir well.
2. Record the temperature of the sand in each jar.
3. Together, **microwave** both jars of sand for 10 s and immediately record the temperature again.

Analysis

1. Compare the initial and final temperatures of the wet and dry sand.
2. Infer why there was a difference.

2 Teach

Make a Model

Water Waves Use a pan of water to model how altering the frequency of a vibrating object creates waves with different frequencies. L1 ELL IS **Kinesthetic**

Mini LAB

Purpose Students observe how microwave ovens heat food. L2 ELL IS **Kinesthetic**

Materials microwave oven, two small beakers or baby food jars, dry sand, water, thermometer

Safety Precautions Do not overheat the sand.

Analysis

1. Wet sand becomes much hotter than dry sand.
2. The microwaves increase the kinetic energy of the water molecules, which then transfer some of this energy to the sand.

Assessment

Process Ask students to infer why the inside of a microwave oven doesn't get hot. It is made of materials that don't absorb the energy transferred by microwaves. Use **PASC,** p. 89.

Reading Check

Answer Microwaves are radio waves with wavelengths of less than a meter.

Differentiated Instruction

Learning Disabled Draw a diagram on the board or on a long piece of paper similar to **Figure 8.** As each type of wave is discussed, tape examples of things that use that type of wave under the correct heading.

Visual Learning

Figure 9 Point out to students that water molecules are polar. The side with the hydrogen atoms has a slightly positive charge and the side with the oxygen atom has a slightly negative charge. Because of this polarity, the molecules tend to align themselves with an electric field. The changing electric field in microwaves causes the water molecules to rotate. L2 IS **Visual-Spatial**

Fun Fact

While working with radar in the 1940s, Percy Spencer discovered that the candy in his pockets had melted. He also discovered that directing the radar toward popcorn caused the kernels to pop. From these observations, Spencer went on to develop the microwave oven.

Virtual Labs

Wavelength *What is the electromagnetic spectrum?*

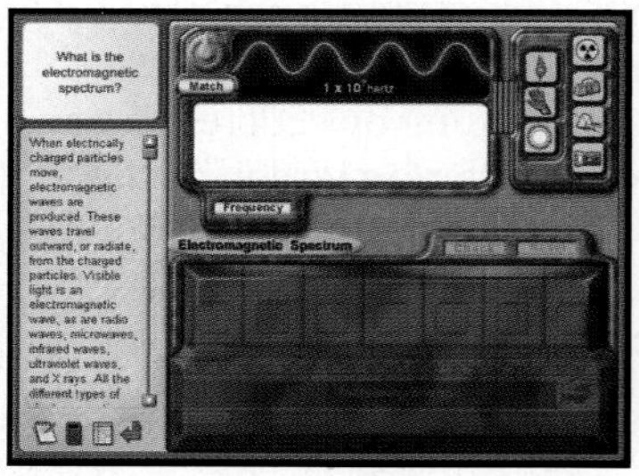

Inquiry Lab

Investigating Infrared Photographs

Purpose To investigate the uses of infrared photography and conduct a simple investigation using an infrared photograph.

Possible Materials internet access, infrared photographs

Estimated Time 3–4 class sessions

Teaching Strategies

- Have students research uses of infrared photography and select one use to investigate in more detail. Examples: geology, vegetation health, environmental pollution, land use.
- Have students obtain a photograph related to their area of research, form a question and hypothesis that could be answered with the photo, and then answer the question.
- Students can present their findings to the class.
- U.S. Department of the Interior/U.S. Geological Survey has a fact sheet and a list of contacts. For more information go to gpescience.com and follow the links to your chapter.

For additional inquiry activities, see Science Inquiry Lab Manual.

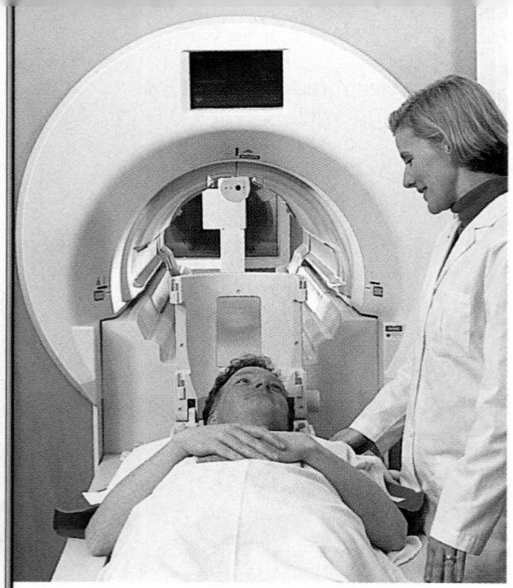

Figure 10 Magnetic resonance imaging technology uses radio waves as an alternative to X-ray imaging.

Magnetic Resonance Imaging (MRI) In the early 1980s, medical researchers developed a technique called magnetic resonance imaging, which uses radio waves to help diagnose illness. The patient lies inside a large cylinder, such as the one shown in **Figure 10.** Housed in the cylinder is a powerful magnet, a radio-wave emitter, and a radio-wave detector. Protons in hydrogen atoms in bones and soft tissue behave like magnets and align with the strong magnetic field. Energy from radio-waves causes some of the protons to flip their alignment. As the protons flip, they release radiant energy. A radio receiver detects this released energy. The amount of energy a proton releases depends on the type of tissue it is part of. The released energy detected by the radio receiver is used to create a map of the different tissues. A picture of the inside of the patient's body is produced painlessly.

Infrared Waves

Most of the warm air in a fireplace moves up the chimney, yet when you stand in front of a fireplace, you feel the warmth of the blazing fire. Why do you feel the heat? The warmth you feel is thermal energy transmitted to you by **infrared waves,** which are a type of electromagnetic wave with wavelengths between about one millimeter and 750 billionths of a meter.

You use infrared waves every day. A remote control emits infrared waves to control your television. A computer uses infrared waves to read CD-ROMs. In fact, every object emits infrared waves. Hotter objects emit more infrared waves than cooler objects emit. The wavelengths emitted also become shorter as the temperature increases. Infrared detectors can form images of objects from the infrared radiation they emit. Infrared sensors on satellites can produce infrared images that can help identify the vegetation over a region. **Figure 11** shows how cities appear different from surrounding vegetation in infrared satellite imagery.

Figure 11 Infrared images and visible light images can provide different types of information.

This visible light image of the region around San Francisco Bay in California was taken from an aircraft at an altitude of 20,000 m.

This infrared image of the same area was taken from a satellite. In this image, vegetation is red and buildings are gray.

Differentiated Instruction

Challenge Have students investigate other uses of infrared radiation, such as infrared spectroscopy and Forward-Looking Infrared Systems. Have them create informative posters conveying the various uses. L3

Science Journal

Imaging Safety Have students write short paragraphs in their Science Journals explaining why magnetic resonance imaging is safer than X rays. The radio waves used for magnetic resonance imaging have much lower energy than X rays, and they do not harm the body. L2 LS **Linguistic**

464 CHAPTER 15 Electromagnetic Radiation

Visible Light

Visible light is the range of electromagnetic waves that you can detect with your eyes. Light differs from radio waves and infrared waves only by its frequency and wavelength. Visible light has wavelengths around 750 billionths to 400 billionths of a meter. Your eyes contain substances that react differently to various wavelengths of visible light, so you see different colors. These colors range from long-wavelength red to short-wavelength blue. If all the colors are present, you see the light as white.

Ultraviolet Waves

Ultraviolet waves are electromagnetic waves with wavelengths from about 400 billionths to 10 billionths of a meter. Ultraviolet waves are energetic enough to enter skin cells. Overexposure to ultraviolet rays can cause skin damage and cancer. Most of the ultraviolet radiation that reaches Earth's surface is longer-wavelength UVA rays. The shorter-wavelength UVB rays cause sunburn, and both UVA and UVB rays can cause skin cancers and skin damage such as wrinkling. Although too much exposure to the Sun's ultraviolet waves is damaging, some exposure is necessary. Ultraviolet light striking the skin enables your body to make vitamin D, which is needed for healthy bones and teeth.

Useful UVs A useful property of ultraviolet waves is their ability to kill bacteria on objects such as food and medical supplies. When ultraviolet light enters a cell, it damages protein and DNA molecules. For some single-celled organisms, damage can mean death, which can be a benefit to human health. Ultraviolet waves are also useful because they make some materials fluoresce. Fluorescent materials absorb ultraviolet waves and reemit the energy as visible light. As shown in **Figure 12,** police detectives sometimes use fluorescent powder to show fingerprints when solving crimes.

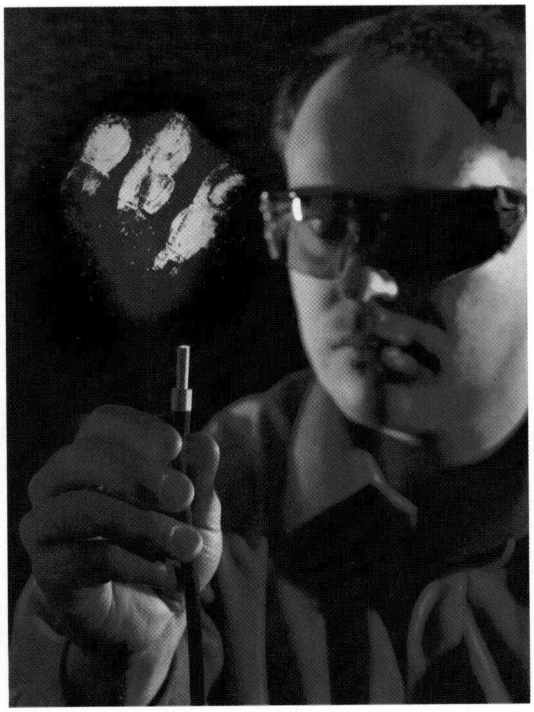

Figure 12 The police detective in this picture is shining ultraviolet light on a fingerprint dusted with fluorescent powder.

INTEGRATE Health

CT Scans In certain situations, doctors will perform a computerized tomography (CT) scan on a patient instead of taking a traditional X ray. Research to find out more about CT scans. Compare and contrast CT scans with X rays. What are the advantages and disadvantages of a CT scan? Write a paragraph about your findings in your Science Journal.

Use Science Words

Word Meanings Ask students to find the meaning of the prefix infra- and explain why it is appropriate for describing infrared waves. *Infra-* means "below." It is appropriate because infrared waves have frequencies just below that of red light. L2 LS **Linguistic**

INTEGRATE Health

CT Scans In both traditional X-ray imaging and CT (computerized tomography, also known as CAT, computerized axial tomography) scanning, X rays are passed through the body to provide an inside view. Traditional X-ray images are not appropriate for some purposes because they show only dense body parts. CT scans provide much clearer cross-sectional images made by rotating an X-ray beam around the patient. CT scans are more expensive.

Research Have students research specific uses for X rays and CT scans, and explain why each is best suited for that use.

Quick Demo
Visible Light Waves

Materials prism, light source, white screen

Estimated Time five minutes

Procedure Shine light onto a white screen. Refract light using a prism to show colors of light. Point out how each frequency refracted to a different degree with violet refracting the most and red the least.

LAB DEMONSTRATION

Purpose to demonstrate fluorescence L2 ELL LS **Kinesthetic**

Materials ultraviolet lamp; fluorescent rock kit or samples of calcite, fluorite, or opal; dry laundry detergent containing whiteners

Procedure In a darkened room, shine the UV lamp on the rocks and laundry detergent. Turn the lamp on and off comparing the affect of UV vs. visible light. Shine the light on clothing to check for fluorescent whiteners.

WARNING: *Be careful not to shine ultraviolet light in anyone's eyes.*

Expected Outcome Students will observe the materials fluoresce.

Assessment

Why do the materials fluoresce? When ultraviolet light strikes the materials, the electrons absorb the energy, then reemit it as light at a lower frequency.

Use Science Words

Word Origins Have students find out where the word *ozone* comes from. The word *ozone* comes from the Greek word *ozein* meaning "to smell." Point out that ozone can be formed when electricity or ultraviolet rays pass through oxygen. Its sharp smell can often be detected near electrical machinery or during a thunderstorm. L2 IN **Linguistic**

Reading Check

Answer It absorbs harmful UV waves.

INTEGRATE Environment Content Background

Ozone in the stratosphere is necessary to protect life on Earth, but ozone near the ground is harmful. Ground-level ozone is the result of reactions between chemical pollutants mainly from factories and car exhaust. The reaction requires thermal energy and sunlight, so ozone pollution is most prevalent during the summer and in warm, sunny climates. Breathing in ozone can induce coughing and chest pain; prolonged exposure can cause permanent lung damage. It also damages plant foliage and reduces agricultural productivity.

Discussion

Upper Limit Ask students whether or not they believe there is an upper limit to the energy of electromagnetic waves. Gamma rays with energies greater than a trillion electron volts (Tev) have been detected. By comparison, photons of visible light have energies of only a few electron volts. Astronomers believe that gamma rays with energies a thousand times greater should be emitted by certain galaxies, and have built instruments to detect these high-energy gamma rays. L3 IN **Logical-Mathematical**

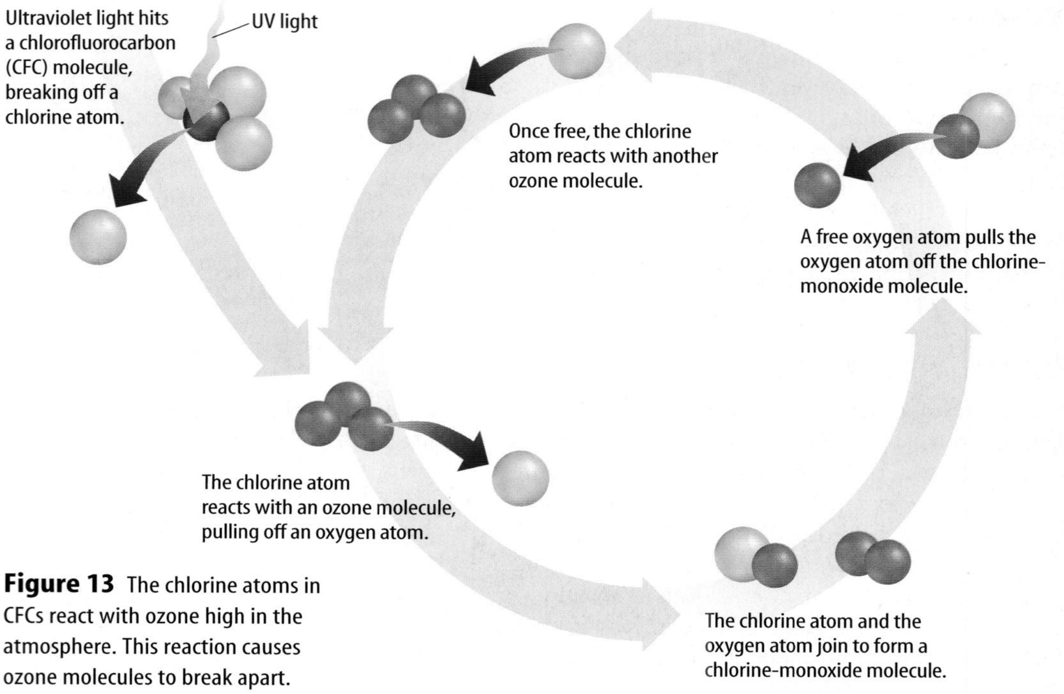

Figure 13 The chlorine atoms in CFCs react with ozone high in the atmosphere. This reaction causes ozone molecules to break apart.

The Ozone Layer About 20 to 50 km above Earth's surface in the stratosphere is a region called the ozone layer. Ozone is a molecule composed of three oxygen atoms. It is continually being formed and destroyed by ultraviolet waves high in the atmosphere. The ozone layer is vital to life on Earth because it absorbs most of the Sun's harmful ultraviolet waves. However, over the past few decades, the amount of ozone in the ozone layer has decreased. Averaged globally, the decrease is about three percent, but it is greater at higher latitudes.

Reading Check ***Why is the ozone layer vital to life on Earth?***

INTEGRATE Environment The decrease in ozone is caused by the presence of certain chemicals, such as CFCs, high in Earth's atmosphere. CFCs are chemicals called chlorofluorocarbons that have been widely used in air conditioners, refrigerators, and cleaning fluids. When CFC molecules reach the ozone layer, they react chemically with ozone molecules, as shown in **Figure 13.** One chlorine atom from a CFC molecule can break apart thousands of ozone molecules. As a result, many countries are reducing the use of CFCs and other ozone-depleting chemicals.

Reading Strategy

Sequence Have students sequence the steps in writing or with drawings that lead to ozone destruction in the atmosphere, beginning with the release of CFC molecules. Students can use **Figure 13** as a guide.

X Rays and Gamma Rays

The electromagnetic waves with the shortest wavelengths and highest frequencies are X rays and gamma rays. Both X rays and gamma rays are high-energy electromagnetic waves. **X rays** have wavelengths between about 10 billionths of a meter and 10 trillionths of a meter. Doctors and dentists use low doses of X rays to form images of internal organs, bones, and teeth, like the image shown in **Figure 14.** X rays also are used in airport screening devices to examine the contents of luggage.

Electromagnetic waves with wavelengths shorter than about 10 trillionths of a meter are **gamma rays.** These are the highest-energy electromagnetic waves and can penetrate through several centimeters of lead. Gamma rays are produced by processes that occur in atomic nuclei. Both X rays and gamma rays are used in a technique called radiation therapy to kill diseased cells in the human body. A beam of X rays or gamma rays can damage the biological molecules in living cells, causing both healthy and diseased cells to die. However, by carefully controlling the amount of X-ray or gamma-ray radiation received by the diseased area, the damage to healthy cells can be reduced.

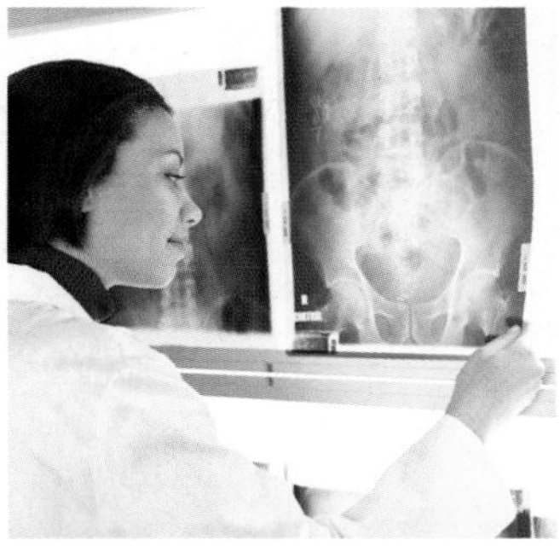

Figure 14 Bones are more dense than surrounding tissues and absorb more X rays. The image of a bone on an X ray is the shadow cast by the bone as X rays pass through the soft tissue.

section 2 review

Summary

Radio Waves and Infrared Waves

- Radio waves are electromagnetic waves with wavelengths longer than about 1 mm.
- Microwaves are radio waves with wavelengths between about 30 cm and 1 mm.
- Infrared waves have wavelengths between about 1 mm and 750 billionths of a meter.

Visible Light and Ultraviolet Waves

- Visible light waves have wavelengths between about 750 and 400 billionths of a meter.
- Ultraviolet waves have wavelengths between about 400 and 10 billionths of a meter.
- Most of the harmful ultraviolet waves emitted by the Sun are absorbed by the ozone layer.

X Rays and Gamma Rays

- X rays and gamma rays are the most energetic electromagnetic waves.
- Gamma rays have wavelengths less than 10 trillionths of a meter and are produced in the nuclei of atoms.

Self Check

1. **Explain** A mug of water is heated in a microwave oven. Explain why the water gets hotter than the mug.
2. **Describe** why you can see visible light waves but not other electromagnetic waves.
3. **List** the beneficial effects and the harmful effects of human exposure to ultraviolet rays.
4. **Identify** three objects in a home that produce electromagnetic waves and describe how the electromagnetic waves are used.
5. **Think Critically** What could an infrared image of their house reveal to homeowners?

Applying Math

6. **Use Scientific Notation** Express the range of wavelengths corresponding to visible light, ultraviolet waves, and X rays in scientific notation.
7. **Convert Units** A nanometer, abbreviated nm, equals one billionth of a meter, or 10^{-9} m. Express the range of wavelengths corresponding to visible light, ultraviolet waves, and X rays in nanometers.

section 2 review

1. The molecules of which the mug is made do not absorb the energy transferred by microwaves; water molecules do absorb microwave energy.
2. Human eyes contain chemical compounds that absorb the energy carried by visible light waves.
3. beneficial effects: production of Vitamin D in human body; harmful affects: damage protein and DNA molecules in cells, can damage skin and cause skin cancer
4. answers will vary
5. Possible answer: where thermal energy is escaping from the house, and where insulation would be needed to reduce energy loss
6. visible light = 7.5 to 4.0×10^{-7} m, ultraviolet = 40 to 1.0×10^{-8} m, X rays = 1.0×10^{-8} m to 1.0×10^{-11} m
7. visible light = 750 to 400 nm, ultraviolet = 400 to 10 nm, X rays = 10 to 0.01 nm

Post Reading

Panel Discussion Ask students to conduct further research on the ozone layer. Then have the class engage in a panel discussion about ozone depletion. What causes the problem? What steps are being taken to solve it? Should more action be taken?

3 Assess

DAILY INTERVENTION

Check for Understanding

Auditory-Musical Divide the class into six groups, assigning each one segment of the electromagnetic spectrum. Have groups write poems or rap songs highlighting key features of their segment.

Reteach

Wave Displays Divide the class into six groups. Ask each group to discuss and make a poster showing various properties and uses of one type of electromagnetic waves. Posters can be displayed in the classroom for reference. L2 COOP LEARN

LS **Visual-Spatial**

Assessment

Process Ask students to write paragraphs comparing and contrasting MRI and X-ray imaging. Both provide an inside view of a patient. MRI uses radio waves and is safer but more expensive. X-ray imaging uses potentially harmful X rays, but is less expensive. MRI provides clearer images. Use **Performance Assessment in the Science Classroom,** p. 157.

BENCH TESTED

Video Lab available for this Lab.

Real-World Problem

Purpose Students learn how the shape of a satellite dish affects reception. L2 ELL
LS **Kinesthetic**

Process Skills observe and infer, communicate, compare and contrast, recognize cause and effect, make models

Time Required 30 minutes

Alternate Materials Any small parabolic object can be used.

Procedure

Teaching Strategy For accurate comparison, be sure students have the flashlight at the same distance from the receptor for all measurements.

Conclude and Apply

1. The light on the flat surface is spread out, but the light on the curved surface is mostly an intense spot in the middle.
2. The light from the flashlight spreads out as it leaves the flashlight. When it hits a flat surface, this light remains spread out. When it hits a curved surface, the light is reflected to the center, forming the intense spot.
3. This activity uses visible light as a model for the microwaves used in satellite communication. A curved satellite dish focuses the signal so that reception is much better.

LAB

The Shape of Satellite Dishes

Communications satellites transmit signals with a narrow beam pointed toward a particular area of Earth. To detect this signal, receivers are typically large, parabolic dishes.

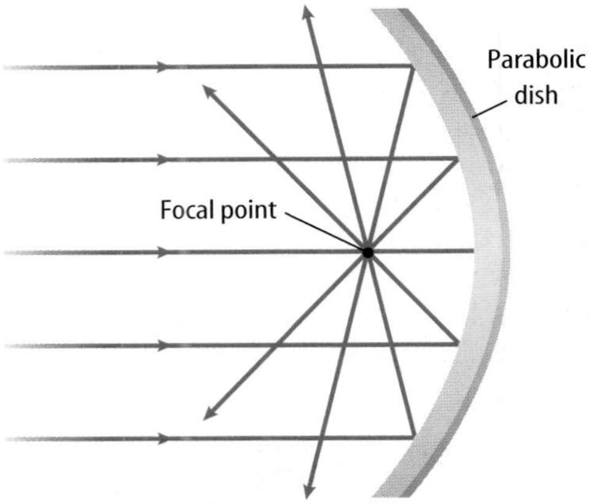

Real-World Problem

How does the shape of a satellite dish improve reception?

Goals

- **Make** a model of a satellite reflecting dish.
- **Observe** how the shape of the dish affects reception.

Materials

flashlight	small bowl
several books	**large, metal spoon*
aluminum foil	**Alternate materials*

Safety Precautions

Procedure

1. Cover one side of a book with aluminum foil. Be careful not to wrinkle the foil.
2. Line the inside of the bowl with foil, also keeping it as smooth as possible.
3. Place some of the books on a table. Put the flashlight on top of the books so that its beam of light will shine several centimeters above and across the table.
4. Hold the foil-covered book on its side at a right angle to the top of the table. The foil-covered side should face the beam of light.
5. **Observe** the intensity of the light on the foil.
6. Repeat steps 4 and 5, replacing the foil-covered book with the bowl.

Conclude and Apply

1. **Compare** the brightness of the light reflected from the two surfaces.
2. **Explain** why the light you see from the curved surface is brighter.
3. **Infer** why bowl-shaped dishes are used to receive signals from satellites.

Communicating Your Data

Compare your conclusions with those of other students in your class. **For more help, refer to the Science Skill Handbook.**

Communicating Your Data

Have students use a computer graphics program to prepare sketches of the models they created in this activity. The sketches should show how the light is reflected directly back from a flat surface, but is reflected toward the center of a curved surface. Have students compare their sketches.

Assessment

Oral After students have completed the activity, ask them to explain why focusing a satellite signal is important. Focusing increases the intensity of the satellite signal. Use **Performance Assessment in the Science Classroom,** p. 89.

section 3

Radio Communication

Reading Guide

What You'll Learn

- **Explain** how modulating carrier waves enables information to be transmitted by radio waves.
- **Distinguish** between amplitude modulation and frequency modulation.
- **Identify** various ways of communicating using radio waves.

Why It's Important

Every day, you use radio waves to communicate.

Review Vocabulary

modulate: to vary the amplitude or frequency of a wave to transmit information

New Vocabulary

- carrier wave
- cathode-ray tube
- transceiver
- Global Positioning System (GPS)

Radio Transmission

When you listen to the radio, you hear music and words that are produced at a distant location. The music and words are sent to your radio by radio waves. The metal antenna of your radio detects radio waves. As the electromagnetic waves pass by your radio's antenna, the electrons in the metal vibrate, as shown in **Figure 15.** These vibrating electrons produce a changing electric current that contains the information about the music and words. An amplifier boosts the current and sends it to speakers, causing them to vibrate. The vibrating speakers create sound waves that travel to your ears. Your brain interprets these sound waves as music and words

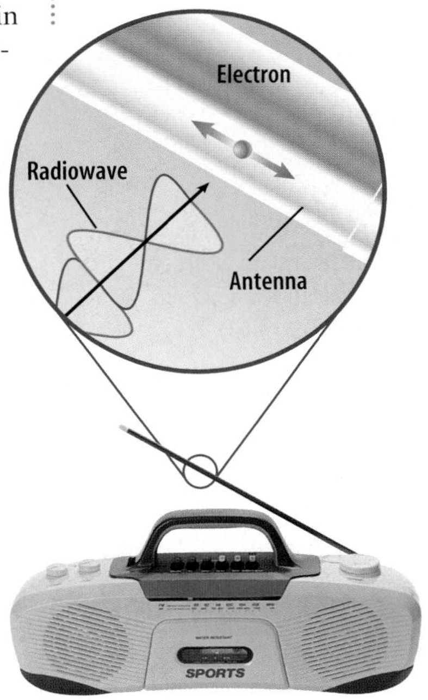

Figure 15 Radio waves exert a force on the electrons in an antenna, causing the electrons to vibrate.

Dividing the Radio Spectrum Each radio station is assigned to broadcast at one particular radio frequency. Turning the tuning knob on your radio allows you to select a particular frequency to listen to. The specific frequency of the electromagnetic wave that a radio station is assigned is called the **carrier wave.**

The radio station must do more than simply transmit a carrier wave. The station has to send information about the sounds that you are to receive. This information is sent by modifying the carrier wave. The carrier wave is modified to carry information in one of two ways, as shown in **Figure 16.**

Section 3 Resource Manager

Chapter *Fast File* Resources

Transparency Activity, p. 46

Enrichment, p. 32

Directed Reading for Content Mastery, pp. 21–22

Lab Activity, pp. 13–16

Reinforcement, p. 29

Lab Worksheet, pp. 7–8

Earth Science Critical Thinking/Problem Solving, p. 5

Lab Management and Safety, p. 37

1 Motivate

INTERACTIVE CHALKBOARD An editable Microsoft® PowerPoint® presentation is available on **Interactive Chalkboard** CD-ROM.

Bellringer

Section Focus Transparencies also are available on the Interactive Chalkboard CD-ROM.

L2 ELL

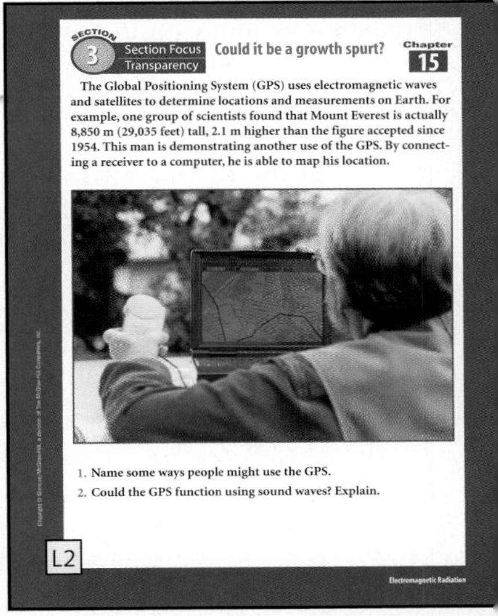
Section 3 Section Focus Transparency — Could it be a growth spurt? Chapter 15

The Global Positioning System (GPS) uses electromagnetic waves and satellites to determine locations and measurements on Earth. For example, one group of scientists found that Mount Everest is actually 8,850 m (29,035 feet) tall, 2.1 m higher than the figure accepted since 1954. This man is demonstrating another use of the GPS. By connecting a receiver to a computer, he is able to map his location.

1. Name some ways people might use the GPS.
2. Could the GPS function using sound waves? Explain.

L2

Electromagnetic Radiation

Reading Preview

Tie to Prior Knowledge

Communication Ask students to name different forms of electronic communication. They might mention radio, television, telephone, or the Internet. Tell them that much communication relies on the use of radio waves.

Make Connections Tell students to imagine they are lost in the woods. How could they find their way out? After allowing discussion, explain that technology exists that allows the user to pinpoint his or her exact location. The technology is called the Global Positioning System (GPS). Ask them to predict how they think it may work.

2 Teach

Use an Analogy

Boat's Sail Having a larger sail on a boat increases the amount of wind you catch, so the boat moves faster. Similarly, lengthening a radio's antenna frequently improves reception because a larger area of the electromagnetic field is intercepted.

Quick Demo

Favorite Frequencies

Materials AM/FM radio

Estimated Time ten minutes

Procedure Bring a radio to class and have students tune it to AM and FM stations. Stress that radios are tuned in by the frequency of the carrier wave. List students' favorite radio stations on the board in order of increasing frequency. L2

LS **Auditory-Musical**

IDENTIFYING Misconceptions

Wave Frequency Students might assume that AM stations broadcast with higher-frequency carrier waves than FM stations. For example, a station at 620 AM might seem to have a higher frequency than a station at 98 FM because 620 is greater than 98. Explain that the AM frequencies are in thousands of vibrations per second, while the FM frequencies are in millions of vibrations per second.

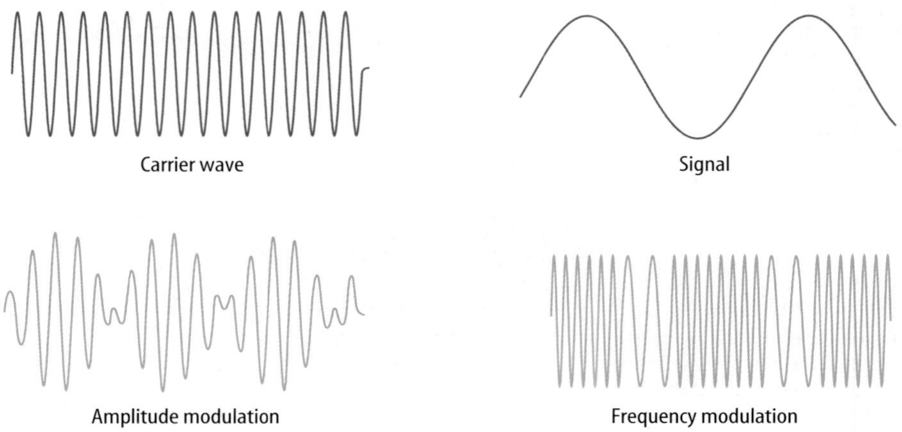

Figure 16 A carrier wave broadcast by a radio station can be altered in one of two ways to transmit a signal: amplitude modulation (AM) or frequency modulation (FM).

AM Radio An AM radio station broadcasts information by varying the amplitude of the carrier wave, as shown in **Figure 16.** Your radio detects the variations in amplitude of the carrier wave and produces a changing electric current from these variations. The changing electric current makes the speaker vibrate. AM carrier-wave frequencies range from 540,000 to 1,600,000 Hz.

FM Radio Electronic signals are transmitted by FM radio stations by varying the frequency of the carrier wave, as in **Figure 16.** Your radio detects the changes in frequency of the carrier wave. Because the strength of the FM waves is kept fixed, FM signals tend to be more clear than AM signals. FM carrier frequencies range from 88 million to 108 million Hz. This is much higher than AM frequencies, as shown in **Figure 17. Figure 18** shows how radio signals are broadcast.

Figure 17 Cell phones, TVs, and radios broadcast at frequencies that range from more than 500,000 Hz to almost 1 billion Hz.

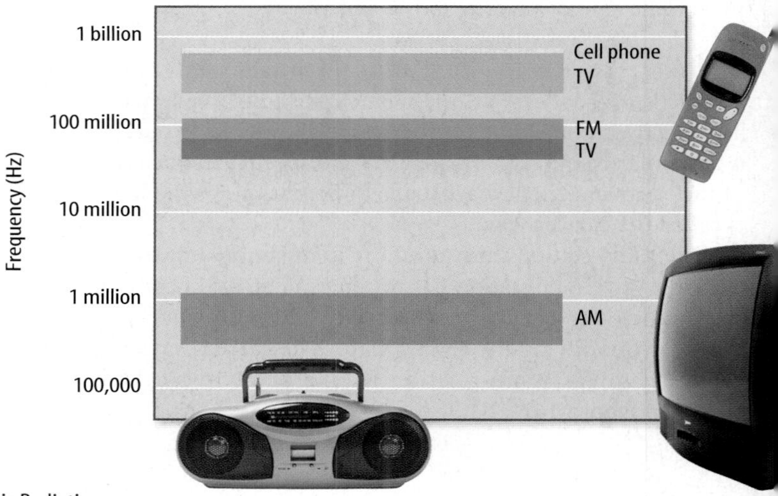

Differentiated Instruction

English-Language Learners To help students understand the meaning of *frequency* and *hertz*, have a student draw high-frequency waves on one end of the board and low-frequency waves on the other. When you list radio stations, write each radio station near the appropriate picture. Point to the pictures often as you use the terms *frequency*, *vibrations per second*, and *hertz*. L1 ELL

Curriculum Connection

Math The frequencies of AM radio stations are in kilohertz and those of FM stations are in megahertz. Have students use the equation wavelength = c/f to determine the wavelengths of the signals transmitted by local radio stations. (c = 300,000,000 m/s) Possible answer: For 98.6 FM, the wavelength is λ = 300,000,000 m/s/ 98,600,000 Hz = 3.04 m L3 LS **Logical-Mathematical**

NATIONAL GEOGRAPHIC

VISUALIZING RADIO BROADCASTS

Figure 18

You flick a switch, turn the dial, and music from your favorite radio station fills the room. Although it seems like magic, sounds are transmitted over great distances by converting sound waves to electromagnetic waves and back again, as shown here.

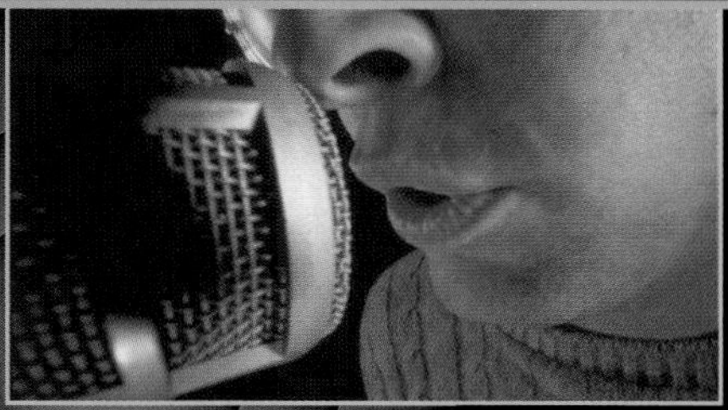

Ⓐ At the radio station, musical instruments and voices create sound waves by causing air molecules to vibrate. Microphones convert these sound waves to a varying electric current, or electronic signal.

Ⓑ This signal then is added to the station's carrier wave. If the station is an AM station, the electronic signal modifies the amplitude of the carrier wave. If the station is an FM station, the electronic signal modifies the frequency of the carrier wave.

AM Waves

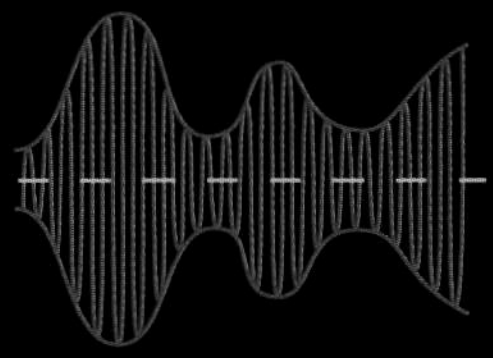

FM Waves

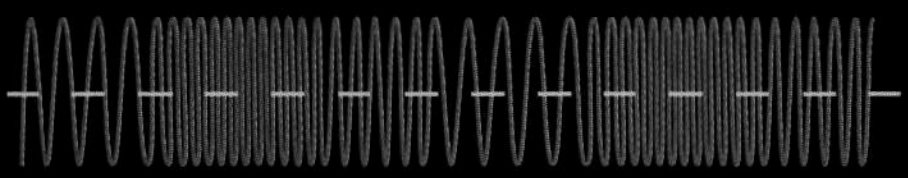

Ⓒ The modified carrier wave is used to vibrate electrons in the station's antenna. These vibrating electrons create a radio wave that travels out in all directions at the speed of light.

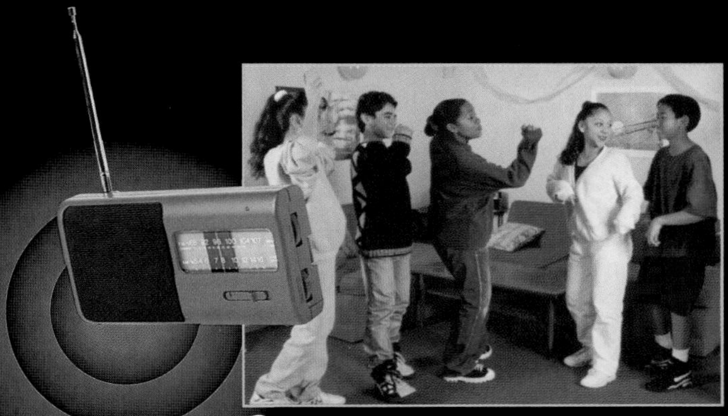

Ⓓ The radio wave from the station makes electrons in your radio's antenna vibrate. This creates an electric current. If your radio is tuned to the station's frequency, the carrier wave is removed from the original electronic signal. This signal then makes the radio's speaker vibrate, creating sound waves that you hear as music.

NATIONAL GEOGRAPHIC

Visualizing Radio Broadcasts

Have students examine the pictures and read the captions. Then ask the following questions.

Compare and contrast how electromagnetic waves are modified to create AM and FM radio signals. Both signals are made by modifying electromagnetic waves and adding them to a carrier wave. The amplitude of the AM carrier wave is modified. The frequency of the FM carrier wave is modified.

Explain the roles of antennas in radio transmission and reception. In transmission, electrons in an antenna are caused to vibrate, sending the electromagnetic wave out in all directions at the speed of light. In reception, the electromagnetic wave makes electrons in an antenna vibrate. The vibrating electrons in the antenna form an electric current that is detected by a receiver.

Activity

Wave Skit Have students write and perform a skit about the life of a radio wave from birth (original sound wave) to death (final conversion back to a sound wave and then dampened). L2

LS **Kinesthetic**

Fun Fact

Radio had only been in use for a few years when the *Titanic* sent its distress calls in 1912. Although radio is credited in aiding *Titanic's* survivors, it was the lack of radio communication with the ship *Californian* that sealed the fate of many who perished.

Reading Strategy

Ask Questions After students have read about radio broadcasts, ask them to think of questions they might have for a radio disc jockey. Tell them to write the questions in the form of an interview. If possible, invite a local disc jockey to the class for a group interview.

Differentiated Instruction

Challenge Ask students to find out how radio frequencies are assigned in the United States and how the Federal Communications Commission (FCC) regulates the industry. Have them present their findings to the class. L3

Use an Analogy

Jigsaw Puzzle The tiny rectangles or lines on a television or computer screen form a complete image the same way pieces of a jigsaw puzzle do. Individually the pieces seem meaningless, but when put together they form a picture.

INTEGRATE Career

Astronomers Learning about objects in distant space requires observing the universe with the entire range of electromagnetic waves. The *Compton Gamma Ray Observatory*, for example, detected gamma rays to look for pulsars at the centers of galaxies. The *Chandra X-ray Observatory* detects X rays to search for binary stars and black holes. The *Hubble Space Telescope* detects electromagnetic waves from ultraviolet to infrared to look at stars and galaxies.

Research Have students investigate what an astronomer does during a typical work day and the type of challenges they face. Present findings to the class.

Teacher FYI

Dispaly Options To avoid large cathode-ray tubes, flat-screen televisions and the displays on laptop computers use liquid crystal displays or gas-plasma displays.

Reading Check

Answer a sealed vacuum tube in which one or more beams of electrons are produced

INTEGRATE Career

Astronomers Do you ever look up at the stars at night and wonder how they were formed? With so many stars and so many galaxies, life might be possible on other planets. Research ways that astronomers use electromagnetic waves to investigate the universe. Choose one project astronomers currently are working on that interests you, and write about it in your Science Journal. Discuss the benefits of a career in astronomy.

Television

What would people hundreds of years ago have thought if they had seen a television? Televisions might seem like magic, but not if you know how they work. Television and radio transmissions are similar. At the television station, sounds and images are changed into electronic signals. These signals are broadcast by carrier waves. The audio part of television is sent by FM radio waves. Information about the color and brightness is sent at the same time by AM signals.

Cathode-Ray Tubes In many television sets, images are displayed on a cathode-ray tube (CRT), as shown in **Figure 19.** A **cathode-ray tube** is a sealed vacuum tube in which one or more beams of electrons are produced. The CRT in a color TV produces three electron beams that are focused by a magnetic field and strike a coated screen. The screen is speckled with more than 100,000 rectangular spots that are of three types. One type glows red, another glows green, and the third type glows blue when electrons strike it. The spots are grouped together, with a red, green, and blue spot in each group.

An image is created when the three electron beams of the CRT sweep back and forth across the screen. Each electron beam controls the brightness of each type of spot, according to the information in the video signal from the TV station. By varying the brightness of each spot in a group, the three spots together can form any color so that you see a full-color image.

Reading Check *What is a cathode-ray tube?*

Figure 19 Cathode-ray tubes produce the images you see on television. The inside surface of a television screen is covered by groups of spots that glow red, green, or blue when struck by an electron beam.

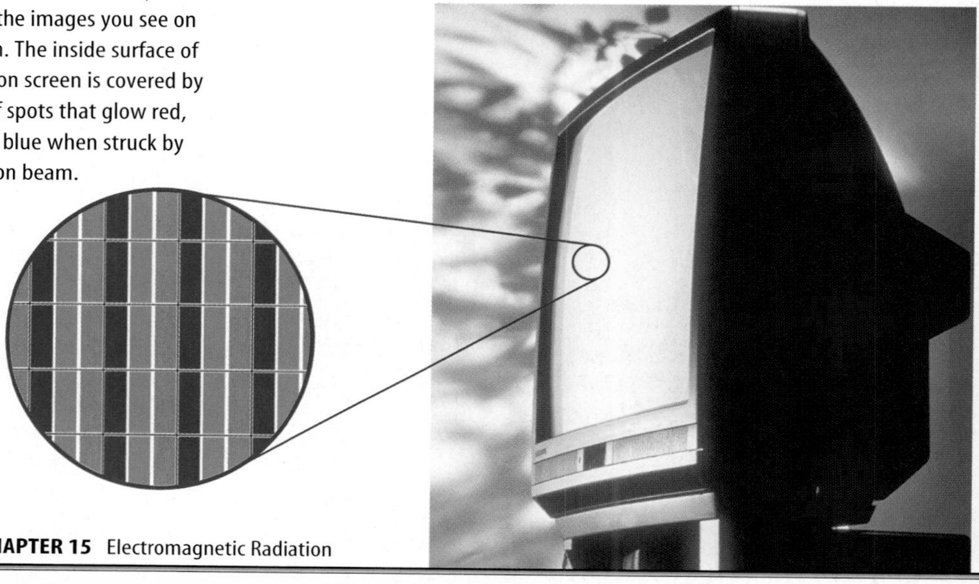

Cultural Diversity

Television As a young boy, Kenjito Takayanagi was a slow learner in school, but hard work enabled him to overcome his difficulties. In 1926, he transmitted the first television signal in Japan. Today he is honored as the founder of Japanese television. Have students make a class time line showing this and other contributions to the invention of television.

Visual Learning

Figure 19 The tiny rectangular spots on a television screen are colored red, green, and blue because these are the primary colors of light. Our eyes combine these into different colors, depending on the intensity of each rectangle. To demonstrate this idea, allow students to experiment with additive color filters or paddles. L2 LS **Visual-Spatial**

Telephones

Until about 1950, human operators were needed to connect telephone calls between people. Just 20 years ago, you never would have seen someone walking down the street talking on a telephone. Today, cell phones are seen everywhere. When you speak into a telephone, a microphone converts sound waves into an electrical signal. In cell phones, this current is used to create radio waves that are transmitted to and from a microwave tower, as shown in **Figure 20.** A cell phone uses one radio signal for sending information to a tower at a base station. It uses another signal for receiving information from the base station. The base stations are several kilometers apart. The area each one covers is called a cell. If you move from one cell to another while using a cell phone, an automated control station transfers your signal to the new cell.

Figure 20 The antenna at the top of a microwave tower receives signals from nearby cell phones. **Determine** *whether any microwave towers are located near your school or home. Describe their locations.*

Reading Check *What are the cells in a cell-phone system?*

Cordless Telephones Like a cellular telephone, a cordless telephone is a transceiver. A **transceiver** transmits one radio signal and receives another radio signal from a base unit. Having two signals at different frequencies allows you to talk and listen at the same time. Cordless telephones work much like cell phones. With a cordless telephone, however, you must be close to the base unit. Another drawback is that when someone nearby is using a cordless telephone, you could hear that conversation on your phone if the frequencies match. For this reason, many cordless phones have a channel button. This allows you to switch your call to another frequency.

Pagers Another method of transmitting signals is a pager, which allows messages to be sent to a small radio receiver. A caller leaves a message at a central terminal by entering a callback number through a telephone keypad or by entering a text message from a computer. At the terminal, the message is changed into an electronic signal and transmitted by radio waves. Each pager is given a unique number for identification. This identification number is sent along with the message. Your pager receives all messages that are transmitted in the area at its assigned frequency. However, your pager responds only to messages with its particular identification number. Newer pagers can send data as well as receive them.

Science Online

Topic: Radio Wave Technology

Visit gpescience.com for Web links to information about advances in radio-wave technology.

Activity List the advances you find, and write about the significance of each one in your Science Journal.

Discussion

Cell Limit Why is there a limit to the number of people who can talk on cell phones in a particular cell at the same time? Each phone uses a different frequency of electromagnetic waves. If all of the assigned frequencies are being used, no other phones can be used at that time. L2

LS Logical-Mathematical

Caption Answer

Figure 20 Students should be encouraged to look for microwave towers on both freestanding towers and on other tall objects, such as buildings or water towers.

Discussion

Building Block Why is it difficult to talk on a cell phone if you are inside a metal building? The metal reflects the incoming and outgoing microwaves. L2

LS Logical-Mathematical

Reading Check

Answer the area that can receive signals from a base station

Science Journal

Telephones of the Future Technology associated with telephones is changing rapidly, and the difference between computers and telecommunication devices is becoming less distinct. Have students write in their Science Journals descriptions of what they think telephones will be like in ten years. L2 LS P **Linguistic**

Use Science Words

Word Origin The word *satellite* has many meanings. Ask students to look up the origin of the word *satellite* and list various types of satellites. For each one, they should describe why the word satellite is an appropriate term. *Satellite* comes from the Latin word *satelles* meaning "attendant." Possible types: moons, satellite countries

Activity

GEO v. GPS Most communication satellites follow a geostationary equatorial orbit (GEO), also called a geosynchronous orbit. This is not the case with satellites for the Global Positioning System (GPS). Have students research the difference between a GEO and a GPS orbit. In a GEO, the satellite orbits Earth directly above the equator once every 24 hours, so that it is always above the same point on the equator. It maintains an altitude of about 35,800 km. In contrast, each of the 24 GPS satellites follows a different, circular orbit, circling Earth every 12 hours at an altitude of about 20,000 km. L2 IS **Linguistic**

Figure 21 Communications satellites, like the one shown here, use solar panels to provide the electrical energy they need to communicate with receivers on Earth. The solar panels are the structures on either side of the central body of the satellite.

Communications Satellites

Since satellites were first developed, thousands have been launched into Earth's orbit. Many of these, like the one in **Figure 21,** are used for communication. A station broadcasts a high-frequency microwave signal to the satellite. The satellite receives the signal, amplifies it, and transmits it to a particular region on Earth. To avoid interference, the frequency broadcast by the satellite is different from the frequency broadcast from Earth.

Satellite Telephone Systems If you have a mobile telephone, you can make a phone call when sailing across the ocean. To make a call on a mobile telephone, the telephone transmits radio waves directly to a satellite. The satellite relays the signal to a ground station, and the call is passed on to the telephone network. Satellite links work well for one-way transmissions, but two-way communications can have an annoying delay caused by the large distance the signals must travel to and from the satellite.

Television Satellites The satellite-reception dishes that you sometimes see in yards or attached to houses are receivers for television satellite signals. Satellite television is used as an alternative to ground-based transmission. Television satellites use microwaves rather than the longer-wavelength radio waves used for normal television broadcasts. Short-wavelength microwaves travel more easily through the atmo-sphere. The ground receiver dishes are rounded to help focus the microwaves onto an antenna.

Science Online

Topic: Satellite Communication
Visit gpescience.com for Web links to information about ways satellites are used for communication.

Activity Write a paragraph describing the advantages of placing a communications satellite in a geosynchronus orbit. Include a diagram.

Active Reading

Metacognition Journal In this strategy, each student analyzes his or her own thought processes. Have students divide the paper in half. On the left, have them record what they have learned about a topic. On the right, have them record the reason they learned it. Have students write a Metacognition Journal about electromagnetic waves and communication.

The Global Positioning System

Getting lost while hiking is not uncommon, but if you are carrying a Global Positioning System receiver, this is much less likely to happen. The **Global Positioning System (GPS)** is a system of satellites, ground monitoring stations, and receivers that determine a person's or object's exact location at or above Earth's surface. The 24 satellites necessary for 24-hour, around-the-world coverage became fully operational in 1995. GPS satellites are owned and operated by the United States Department of Defense, but the microwave signals they send out can be used by anyone. As shown in **Figure 22,** signals from four satellites are needed to determine the location of an object using a GPS receiver. Today, GPS receivers are used in airplanes, ships, cars, and even by hikers.

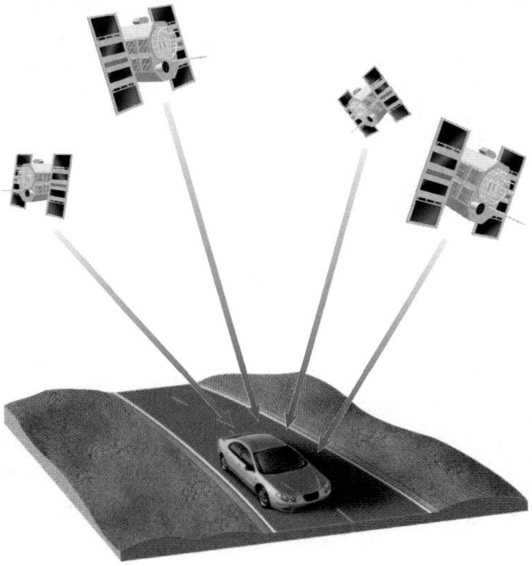

Figure 22 A GPS receiver uses signals from orbiting satellites to determine the receiver's location.

section 3 review

Summary

Radio Transmission

- Radio stations transmit electromagnetic waves that receivers convert to sound waves.
- Each AM radio station is assigned a carrier-wave frequency and varies the amplitude of the carrier waves to transmit a signal.
- Each FM radio station is assigned a carrier-wave frequency and varies the frequency of the carrier waves to transmit a signal.

Television

- TV sets use cathode-ray tubes to convert electronic signals from TV stations into both sounds and images.

Telephones

- Telephones contain transceivers that convert sound waves into electrical signals and also convert electrical signals into sound waves.
- Wires, microwave towers, and satellites are used to transmit and receive telephone signals.

Global Positioning System (GPS)

- The GPS uses a system of satellites to determine a person's or object's exact position.

Self Check

1. **Explain** the difference between AM and FM radio. Make a sketch of how a carrier wave is modulated in AM and FM radio.
2. **Define** a cathode-ray tube, and explain how it is used in a television.
3. **Describe** what happens if you are talking on a cell phone while riding in a car and you travel from one cell to another cell.
4. **Explain** some of the uses of the Global Positioning System. Why might emergency vehicles be equipped with GPS receivers?
5. **Think Critically** Why do cordless telephones stop working if you move too far from the base unit?

Applying Math

6. **Calculate a Ratio** A group of red, green, and blue spots on a TV screen is a pixel. A standard TV has 460 pixels horizontally and 360 pixels vertically. A high-definition TV has 1,920 horizontal and 1,080 vertical pixels. What is the ratio of the number of pixels in a high-definition TV to the number in a standard TV?

Post Reading

Supplemental Related Resources Obtain several manuals for televisions, portable phones, radios, or pagers. Have students scan through the booklets. Ask them to point out concepts in the manuals that they now understand, having read this section. Possible concepts might include AM and FM frequencies.

3 Assess

DAILY INTERVENTION

Check for Understanding

Visual-Spatial In pairs or small groups, have students create diagrams that illustrate the steps required for a radio, television, telephone, or satellite to transmit a message.

Reteach

How It Works Bring a radio or television into your classroom. Have students demonstrate the use of each device with proper physics explanations. They should include explanations about how the radio waves are picked up and what happens when you change the channel. L2 LS **Kinesthetic**

Assessment

Performance Have students work in pairs to make posters that show how one form of radio communication described in this section works. Posters can be displayed in the classroom to help students remember what they have studied. Use **Performance Assessment in the Science Classroom,** p. 145. L2 COOP LEARN LS **Visual-Spatial**

section 3 review

1. For AM, amplitude is modulated. For FM, frequency is modulated. Check students' sketches.
2. A sealed vacuum tube in which beams of electrons are produced. The electron beams hit dots on a coated screen, causing them to glow.
3. A central controller transfers your signal to the base station in the new cell.
4. GPS is used by hikers, airplanes, ships, cars, and others to identify their location on Earth. Emergency vehicles have GPS receivers to help them find places quickly.
5. The radio waves broadcast by the base unit become too weak for the handset to detect.
6. 12.5 to 1

BENCH TESTED

Real-World Problem

Purpose

Internet Students will use Internet sites that can be accessed through gpescience.com. They will investigate AM and FM radio station transmission frequencies and ranges.

Non-Internet Sources Contact the Federal Communications Commission (FCC) for information about station transmission frequencies and ranges.

Process Skills follow a procedure, compare and contrast, infer

Time Required two days

Make a Plan

Preparation Access gpescience.com to run through the steps that the students will follow.

Non-Internet Sources Organize FCC information about local radio stations by frequency and range.

Follow Your Plan

Teaching Strategy Remind students that AM stations broadcast at a lower frequency. These signals reflect off the ionosphere, providing a greater range. FM signals must travel by line of sight, so their range is less.

LAB Use the Internet

Radio Frequencies

Goals

- **Research** which frequencies are used by different radio stations.
- **Observe** the reception of your favorite radio station.
- **Make** a chart of your findings and communicate them to other students.

Data Source

Internet Lab

Visit gpescience.com for more information on radio frequencies, different frequencies of radio stations around the country, and the ranges of AM and FM broadcasts.

Real-World Problem

The signals from many radio stations broadcasting at different frequencies are hitting your radio's antenna at the same time. When you tune to your favorite station, the electronics inside your radio amplify the signal at the frequency broadcast by the station. The signal from your favorite station is broadcast from a transmission site that may be several miles away.

You may have noticed that if you're listening to a radio station while driving in a car, sometimes the station gets fuzzy and you hear another station at the same time. Sometimes you lose the station completely. How far can you drive before this happens? Does the distance vary depending on the station you listen to? What are the ranges of radio stations? Form a hypothesis about how far you think a radio station can transmit. Which type of signal, AM or FM, has a greater range? Form a hypothesis about the range of your favorite radio station.

Make a Plan

1. **Research** what frequencies are used by AM and FM radio stations in your area and other areas around the country.
2. **Determine** these stations' broadcast locations.
3. **Determine** the broadcast range of radio stations in your area.
4. **Observe** how frequencies differ. What is the maximum difference between frequencies for FM stations in your area? AM stations?

Alternative Inquiry Lab

Student Investigation To make this Lab an Inquiry Lab, have students design a way to compare the reception of local AM and FM stations under various conditions, such as day/night or clear/cloudy.

Using Scientific Methods

Follow Your Plan

1. **Make** sure your teacher approves your plan before you start.
2. Visit the Web site shown below for links to different radio stations.
3. **Compare** the different frequencies of the stations and the locations of the broadcasts.
4. **Determine** the range of radio stations in your area and the power of their broadcast signals in watts.
5. **Record** your data in your Science Journal.

Analyze Your Data

1. **Make** a map of the radio stations in your area. Do the ranges of AM stations differ from those of FM stations?
2. **Make** a map of different radio stations around the country. Do you see any patterns in the frequencies for stations that are located near each other?
3. **Write** a description that compares how close the frequencies of AM stations are and how close the frequencies of FM stations are. Also compare the power of their broadcast signals and their ranges.
4. **Share** your data by posting it at the Web site shown below.

Conclude and Apply

1. **Compare** your findings with those of your classmates and other data that are posted at the Web site shown below. Do all AM stations and FM stations have different ranges?
2. **Observe** your map of the country. How close can stations with similar frequencies be? Do AM and FM stations appear to be different in this respect?
3. **Infer** The power of a broadcast signal also determines its range. How does the power (wattage) of the signals affect your analysis of your data?

Communicating Your Data

Find this lab using the Web site below. Post your data in the table provided. **Compare** your data with those of other students. Then combine your data with theirs and make a map for your class that shows all of the data.

Internet Lab
gpescience.com

Analyze Your Data

1. AM stations have longer ranges than FM stations. AM signals are reflected by the ionosphere, which enables the signals to travel farther. The higher frequency FM signals are not reflected.
2. If two stations' transmitters are close to each other, their stations' frequencies will not be the same.
3. AM stations are spaced no closer than 10 kHz. FM stations are spaced no closer than 200 kHz.
4. Students can compare radio stations' ranges and frequencies in different locations around the country.

Conclude and Apply

1. AM stations and FM stations have different ranges. Broadcast range depends on a station's transmitter power.
2. Station transmitters with similar frequencies cannot be very close together because their signals would interfere with one another. AM stations differ from FM stations in how close their transmitters can be, because AM stations have a greater broadcast range than FM stations.
3. Students should use information about signal power and frequency to determine the ranges of radio stations.

Assessment

Performance Show radio station transmitter locations on a map of your area. Have students draw each station's range on the map to understand how reception and interference can affect the ability to receive a station's signal. Use **Performance Assessment in the Science Classroom,** p. 127.

Communicating Your Data

Use a spreadsheet program to collect information about radio stations. Include the station's call letters, locations of transmitters, frequency, and power.

TIME

Content Background

By the nineteenth century, it was widely believed that because light was a wave, it required a medium in which to travel, just as sound travels through air. The medium was called the ether, and was believed to be stationary. As a result, the ether provided an absolute reference system to which measurements in all other reference systems could be compared.

Several attempts were made to detect the ether, but failed. In 1887, Albert Michelson and Edward Morley attempted to measure the motion of Earth through the ether. To their surprise, they found no effects on the speed of light due to Earth's motion through the ether.

Einstein's paper on the special theory of relativity appeared in 1905. It postulated that physical laws have the same form and that the speed of light is a constant in any reference frame that is not accelerating. It was soon realized that the special theory could account for the results of the Michelson-Morley experiment, which was now seen as proving that the ether did not exist.

Discussion

Resisting Change Why are new theories often met with resistance? Possible answer: When theories are first proposed, they may not be supported by enough experimental evidence to convince people of their validity.

Historical Significance

Additional Ideas Einstein's theory of special relativity led to the idea that matter and energy are equivalent ($E=mc^2$). The theory also provides a more accurate description of phenomena involving objects moving near the speed of light than was provided by Newton's laws of motion.

TIME SCIENCE AND HISTORY

SCIENCE CAN CHANGE THE COURSE OF HISTORY!

Riding a Beam of Light

Einstein and the Special Theory of Relativity

Catch a Wave

At age 16, Albert Einstein wondered, "What would it be like to ride a beam of light?" He imagined what might happen if he turned on a flashlight while riding a light beam. Because the flashlight already would be traveling at the speed of light, would light from the flashlight travel at twice the speed of light?

What's so special?

Einstein thought about this problem, and in 1905, he published the special theory of relativity. This theory states that the speed of light will be the same when measured by any observer that moves with a constant speed. The measured speed of light will not depend on the speed of the observer or on how fast the source of light is moving. Einstein answered the question he had asked himself when he was 16. He found the universal speed limit that can't be broken.

It Doesn't Add Up

According to Einstein, electromagnetic waves such as light waves behave very differently from other waves. For example, sound waves from the siren of an ambulance moving toward you move faster than they would if the ambulance were not moving. The speed of the ambulance adds to the speed of the sound waves. However, for light waves, the speed of a light source doesn't add to the speed of light.

Very Strange, but True

Einstein's special theory of relativity makes other strange predictions. According to this theory, no object can travel faster than the speed of light. Another prediction is that the measured length of a moving object is shorter than when the object is at rest. Also, moving clocks should run more slowly than when they are at rest. These predictions have been confirmed by experiments. Measurements have shown, for example, that a moving clock does run more slowly.

Communicate **Research the life of Albert Einstein and make a time line showing important events in his life. Also include on your time line major historical events that occurred during Einstein's lifetime.**

TIME For more information, visit gpescience.com

Communicate Encourage students to include international events; examine how these events impacted Einstein's research. Also, there are many visual metaphors and cartoons available to explain Einstein's theories in simple terms. Go to gpescience.com for more information.

Resources for Teachers and Students

Albert Einstein: Physicist and Genius by Joyce Goldenstern, Enslow Publishers, Inc., 1994

Einstein's Universe by Nigel Calder, Random House Value Publishing, Inc., 1990

Reviewing Main Ideas

Section 1 What are electromagnetic waves?

1. Electromagnetic waves consist of vibrating electric and magnetic fields, and are produced by vibrating electric charges.

2. Electromagnetic waves carry radiant energy and can travel through a vacuum or through matter.
3. Electromagnetic waves sometimes behave like particles called photons.

Section 2 The Electromagnetic Spectrum

1. Electromagnetic waves with the longest wavelengths are called radio waves. Radio waves have wavelengths greater than about 1 mm. Microwaves are radio waves with wavelengths between about 30 cm and 1 mm.
2. Infrared waves have wavelengths between about 1 mm and 750 billionths of a meter. Warmer objects emit more infrared waves than cooler objects do.
3. Visible light rays have wavelengths between about 750 and 400 billionths of a meter. Substances in your eyes react with visible light to enable you to see.
4. Ultraviolet waves have frequencies between about 400 and 10 billionths of a meter. Excessive exposure to ultraviolet waves can damage human skin.
5. X rays and gamma rays are high-energy electromagnetic waves with wavelengths less than 10 billionths of a meter. X rays are used in medical imaging.

Section 3 Radio Communication

1. Modulated radio waves are used often for communication. AM and FM are two forms of carrier-wave modulation.
2. Television signals are transmitted as a combination of AM and FM waves.
3. Cellular telephones, cordless telephones, and pagers use radio waves to transmit signals. Communications satellites are used to relay telephone and television signals over long distances.
4. The Global Positioning System (GPS) enables the exact position of a person or object on Earth to be determined.

FOLDABLES™ Use the Foldable that you made at the beginning of this chapter to help you review electromagnetic radiation.

chapter 15 Study Guide

Reviewing Main Ideas

Summary statements can be used by students to review the major concepts of the chapter.

Science Online

Visit gpescience.com
More Section Review
Interactive Tutor
Vocabulary PuzzleMaker
More Chapter Review
Standardized Test Practice

Assessment Transparency

For additional assessment questions, use the *Assessment Transparency* located in the transparency book.

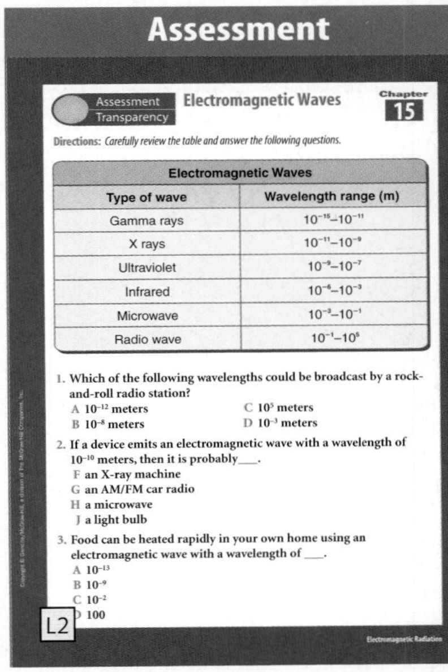

Assessment

Assessment Transparency **Electromagnetic Waves** Chapter 15

Directions: *Carefully review the table and answer the following questions.*

Electromagnetic Waves	
Type of wave	**Wavelength range (m)**
Gamma rays	10^{-15}–10^{-11}
X rays	10^{-11}–10^{-9}
Ultraviolet	10^{-9}–10^{-7}
Infrared	10^{-6}–10^{-3}
Microwave	10^{-3}–10^{-1}
Radio wave	10^{-1}–10^{5}

1. Which of the following wavelengths could be broadcast by a rock-and-roll radio station?
   A 10^{-12} meters
   B 10^{-8} meters
   C 10^{5} meters
   D 10^{-3} meters
2. If a device emits an electromagnetic wave with a wavelength of 10^{-10} meters, then it is probably ___.
   F an X-ray machine
   G an AM/FM car radio
   H a microwave
   J a light bulb
3. Food can be heated rapidly in your own home using an electromagnetic wave with a wavelength of ___.
   A 10^{-13}
   B 10^{-9}
   C 10^{-2}
   D 100

L2

Electromagnetic Radiation

FOLDABLES™ Have students use their Foldables to review the content of the chapter. On the back of the paper, have students explain how they would likely make use of each type of electromagnetic wave in the course of their day.

Using Vocabulary

1. Radio waves
2. infrared waves
3. radiant energy
4. ultraviolet waves
5. carrier waves
6. cathode ray tube
7. electromagnetic waves

Checking Concepts

8. A
9. D
10. B
11. A
12. C
13. B
14. A

Interpreting Graphics

15. See student page.
16. See student page.

Thinking Critically

17. They have enough energy to pass through the body's soft tissue but still be blocked by hard tissue. This causes a shadow image of the hard tissue to be formed on photographic film.
18. No, because the electric field must be changing to produce the magnetic field and the magnetic field must be changing to produce the electric field.
19. Visible light has a very high frequency, on the order of 10^{15} Hz. The magnetic field in visible light changes direction much too rapidly for the compass needle to respond.
20. Answers will vary.
21. Possible answer: Ultraviolet waves would be absorbed by Earth's ozone layer.

chapter 15 Review

Using Vocabulary

carrier wave p. 469	microwave p. 463
cathode-ray tube p. 472	photon p. 460
electromagnetic wave p. 456	radiant energy p. 459
gamma ray p. 467	radio wave p. 463
Global Positioning System (GPS) p. 475	transceiver p. 473
infrared wave p. 464	ultraviolet wave p. 465
	visible light p.462
	X ray p. 467

Complete each statement using the correct word or phrase from the vocabulary list above.

1. _________ are the type of electromagnetic waves often used for communication.
2. A remote control uses _________ to communicate with a television set.
3. Electromagnetic waves transmit _________.
4. If you stay outdoors too long, your skin might be burned by exposure to _________ from the Sun.
5. A radio station broadcasts radio waves called _________, which have the specific frequency assigned to the station.
6. The image on a television screen is produced by a _________.
7. Transverse waves that are produced by vibrating electric charges and consist of vibrating electric and magnetic fields are _________.

Checking Concepts

Choose the word or phrase that best answers each question.

8. Which type of electromagnetic wave is the most energetic?
   - **A)** gamma rays
   - **B)** ultraviolet waves
   - **C)** infrared waves
   - **D)** microwaves

Use the figure below to answer question 9.

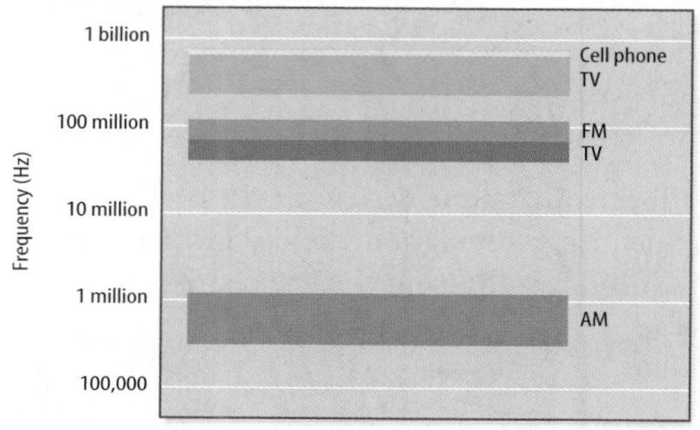

9. What signal has the longest wavelength?
   - **A)** cell phone
   - **B)** TV
   - **C)** FM
   - **D)** AM
10. Which type of electromagnetic wave enables skin cells to produce vitamin D?
    - **A)** visible light
    - **B)** ultraviolet waves
    - **C)** infrared waves
    - **D)** X rays
11. Which of the following describes X rays?
    - **A)** short wavelength, high frequency
    - **B)** short wavelength, low frequency
    - **C)** long wavelength, high frequency
    - **D)** long wavelength, low frequency
12. Which of the following is changing in an AM radio wave?
    - **A)** speed
    - **B)** frequency
    - **C)** amplitude
    - **D)** wavelength
13. Which type of electromagnetic wave has wavelengths greater than about 1 mm?
    - **A)** X rays
    - **B)** radio waves
    - **C)** gamma rays
    - **D)** ultraviolet waves
14. Which of these colors of visible light has the shortest wavelength?
    - **A)** blue
    - **B)** green
    - **C)** red
    - **D)** white

Vocabulary PuzzleMaker gpescience.com

Use the ExamView® Pro Testmaker CD-ROM to:

- create multiple versions of tests
- create modified tests with one mouse click for inclusion students
- edit existing questions and add your own questions
- build tests aligned with state standards using built-in State Curriculum Tags
- change English tests to Spanish with one mouse click and vice versa

Interpreting Graphics

15. Copy and complete the following table about the electromagnetic spectrum.

Uses of Electromagnetic Waves

Type of Electromagnetic Waves	Examples of How Electromagnetic Waves Are Used
radio waves	radio, TV transmission
Infrared waves	remote control transmitters
Visible light	vision
ultraviolet light	fluorescent materials
X rays	medical imaging
gamma rays	destroying harmful cells

16. Copy and complete the following events chain about the destruction of ozone molecules in the ozone layer by CFC molecules.

CFCs are released into the air.
↓
CFCs drift into the ozone layer.
↓
CFCs release chlorine atoms.
↓
Chlorine atoms react with ozone molecules.
↓
Ozone is changed to oxygen atoms and molecules.

Thinking Critically

17. **Explain** why X rays are used in medical imaging.

18. **Predict** whether an electromagnetic wave would travel through space if its electric and magnetic fields were not changing with time. Explain your reasoning.

19. **Infer** Electromagnetic waves consist of vibrating electric and magnetic fields. A magnetic field can move a compass needle. Why doesn't a compass needle move when visible light strikes the compass?

20. **Classify** Look around your home, school, and community. Make a list of the different devices that use electromagnetic waves. Beside each device, write the type of electromagnetic wave the device uses.

21. **Form a hypothesis** to explain why communications satellites don't use ultraviolet waves to receive information and transmit signals to Earth's surface.

22. **Compare** the energy of photons corresponding to infrared waves with the energy of photons corresponding to ultraviolet waves.

23. **Determine** whether or not all electromagnetic waves always travel at the speed of light. Explain.

Applying Math

24. **Use Fractions** When visible light waves travel in ethyl alcohol, their speed is three-fourths of the speed of light in air. What is the speed of light in ethyl alcohol?

25. **Use Scientific Notation** The speed of light in a vacuum has been determined to be 299,792,458 m/s. Express this number to four significant digits using scientific notation.

26. **Calculate Wavelength** A radio wave has a frequency of 540,000 Hz and travels at a speed of 300,000 km/s. Use the wave speed equation to calculate the wavelength of the radio wave. Express your answer in meters.

22. Photons corresponding to electromagnetic waves with higher frequencies have greater energy; photons corresponding to ultraviolet waves will have greater energy than infrared photons.

23. No. They travel at their maximum speed in a vacuum. When moving through matter their speed is slower.

Applying Math

Math Standards

National: 1, 2, 9

24. 225,000 km/s

25. 2.998×10^8 m/s

26. $v = f\lambda$, so $\lambda = v/f = \dfrac{(300{,}000 \text{ km/s})}{(540{,}000 \text{ Hz})} =$ 0.55 km = 550 m

Assessment Resources

Reproducible Masters

Chapter *Fast File* Resources
- Chapter Review, pp. 37–38
- Chapter Tests, pp. 39–42
- Assessment Transparency Activity, p. 49

Glencoe Science Web site
- Chapter Review Test
- Standardized Test Practice

Glencoe Technology
- Assessment Transparency
- Exam*View*® Pro Testmaker
- MindJogger Videoquiz
- Interactive Chalkboard

Answer Sheet An answer sheet can be found at **gpescience.com**.

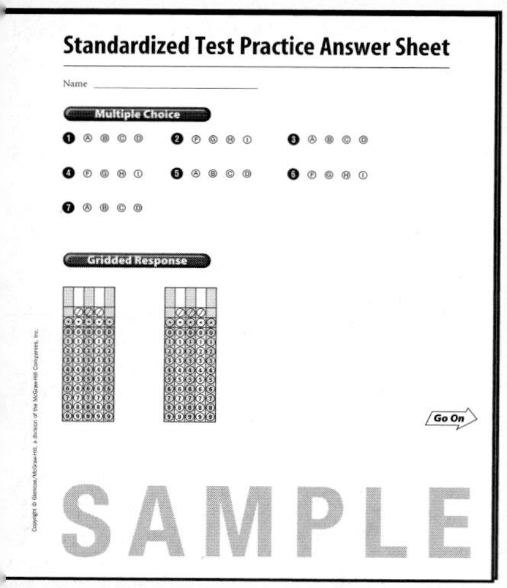

Multiple Choice

1. A
2. D
3. B
4. C
5. C
6. B
7. D

chapter 15 Standardized Test Practice

Record your answers on the answer sheet provided by your teacher or on a sheet of paper.

Multiple Choice

1. Which of the following produces electromagnetic waves?

   A. vibrating charge

   B. constant electric field

   C. static charge

   D. constant magnetic field

Use the photograph below to answer questions 2 and 3.

2. A television image is produced by three electron beams. What device inside a television set produces the electron beams?

   A. transceiver

   B. transmitter

   C. antenna

   D. cathode-ray tube

Test-Taking Tip

Marking on Tests Be sure to ask if it is okay to write on the test booklet when taking the test, but make sure you mark all answers on your answer sheet.

3. What colors are the three types of glowing spots that form the different colors on the television screen?

   A. red, yellow, blue

   B. red, green, blue

   C. cyan, magenta, yellow

   D. cyan, magenta, blue

4. Which of the following explains how interference is avoided between the signals communications satellites receive and the signals they broadcast?

   A. The signals travel at different speeds.

   B. The signals have different amplitudes.

   C. The signals have different frequencies.

   D. The signals are only magnetic.

Use the table below to answer questions 5 and 6.

Regions of the Electromagnetic Spectrum		
Infrared waves	Radio waves	Gamma rays
X rays	Visible light	Ultraviolet waves

5. If you arranged the list of electromagnetic waves shown above in order from shortest to longest wavelength, which would be first on the list?

   A. radio waves

   B. X rays

   C. gamma rays

   D. visible light

6. Which region of the electromagnetic spectrum listed in the table above includes microwaves?
   A. gamma rays
   B. radio waves
   C. ultraviolet waves
   D. infrared waves

7. The warmth you feel when you stand in front of a fire is thermal energy transmitted to you by what type of electromagnetic waves?
   A. X rays
   B. microwaves
   C. ultraviolet waves
   D. infrared waves

Gridded Response

8. Electromagnetic radiation travels through space at 3.00×10^5 km/s. The moon is, on average, 382,000 km from Earth. How many seconds would it take radio waves broadcast from Earth to reach the moon?

Short Response

Use the illustrations below to answer question 9.

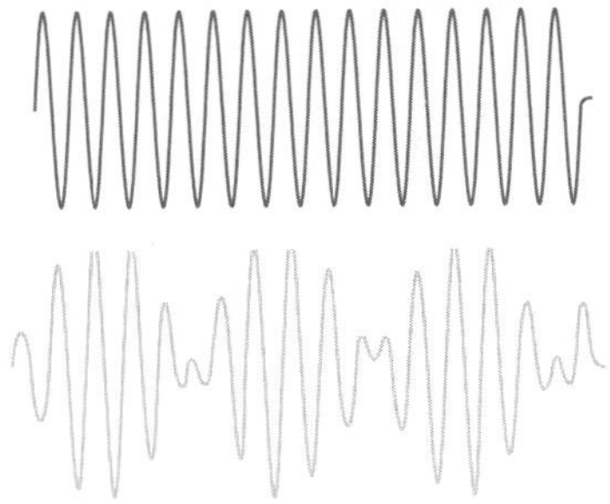

9. The illustrations above show two radio waves broadcast by a radio station. The upper, unmodulated wave is the carrier wave. The lower figure shows the same wave that has been modulated to carry sound information. What type of modulation does it show?

10. Even on a cloudy day, you can get sunburned outside. However, inside a glass greenhouse, you won't get sunburned. Based on this fact, which type of electromagnetic waves will pass through clouds but not glass?

Extended Response

11. Explain how an electromagnetic wave that strikes a material transfers radiant energy to the atoms in the material.

Use the illustration below to answer question 12.

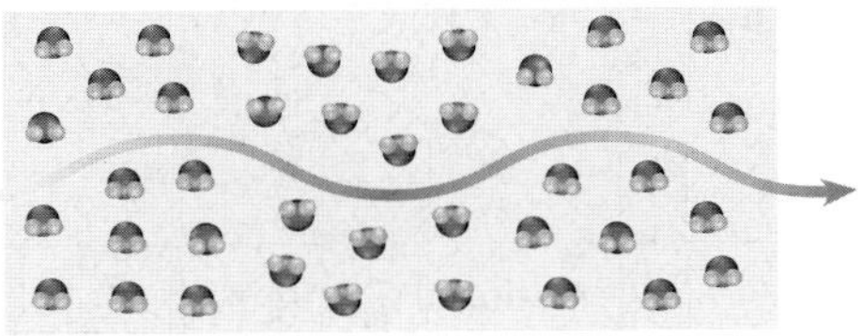

12. The illustration above shows a microwave interacting with water molecules in food.
   Part A How does the electric field in microwaves affect water molecules?
   Part B Describe how thermal energy is produced by microwaves interacting with water molecules inside food.

Gridded Response

8. 1.27

Short Response

9. AM, amplitude modulation
10. ultraviolet waves

Extended Response

11. by causing charged particles within articles to vibrate
12. Sample Answers
Part A: causes water molecules to rotate back and forth
Part B: The friction that occurs as rotating water molecules interact with each other is converted into thermal energy.

Rubrics

For more help evaluating Short- and Extended-Response questions, see the rubrics on p. 9T.

chapter 16 Organizer

Section/Objectives	Standards		Labs/Features
	National	State/Local	
Chapter Opener	See pp. 16T–17T for a Key to Standards.		**Launch Lab:** Heating with Solar Energy, p. 485 **Foldables,** p. 485
Section 1 Fossil Fuels 2 sessions 1 block 1. **Discuss** properties and uses of fossil fuels. 2. **Explain** how fossil fuels are formed. 3. **Describe** how the chemical energy in fossil fuels is converted into electrical energy.	National Content Standards: UCP.1–3, UCP.5, A.1, A.2, B.2, B.6 D.1–3		**Visualizing the Formation of Fossil Fuels,** p. 488 **MiniLAB:** Designing an Efficient Water Heater, p. 489
Section 2 Nuclear Energy 1 session 0.5 block 4. **Explain** how a nuclear reactor converts nuclear energy to thermal energy. 5. **Describe** advantages and disadvantages of using nuclear energy to produce electricity. 6. **Discuss** nuclear fusion as a possible energy source.	National Content Standards: UCP.1–3, UCP.5, A.1, A.2, B.1, B.2, F.2, F.4		**Integrate Earth Science,** p. 496 **Integrate Social Studies,** p. 497 **Science Online,** p. 498 **Applying Science:** Can a contaminated radioactive site be reclaimed?, p. 499
Section 3 Renewable Energy Sources 3 sessions 1.5 block 7. **Analyze** the need for alternate energy sources. 8. **Describe** alternate methods for generating electricity. 9. **Compare** the advantages and disadvantages of various alternate energy sources.	National Content Standards: UCP.1–3, UCP.5, A.1, A.2, D.1–3, F.2, F.4		**MiniLAB:** Using Solar Power at Home, p. 502 **Science Online,** p. 505 **Lab:** Solar Heating, p. 507 Video Lab **Lab:** How much does energy really cost?, pp. 508–509 **Science and Society:** Reacting to Nuclear Energy, p. 510

StudentWorks Plus

Glencoe Exclusive! TeacherWorks™ All-In-One Planner and Resource Center

Lab Materials	Reproducible Resources	Section Assessment	Technology
Launch Lab: scissors, coffee cans with lids (2), thermometers (2), white paint, black paint, water	**Chapter *Fast File* Resources** Foldables Worksheet, p. 17 Directed Reading Overview, p. 19 Note-taking Worksheets, pp. 33–35	Glencoe's Assessment Advantage	TeacherWorks includes: • Interactive Teacher Edition • Lesson Planner with calendar • Access to all program blacklines • Correlations to standards • Web links
MiniLAB: candle, water, beaker, aluminum foil	**Chapter *Fast File* Resources** Transparency Activity, p. 44 MiniLAB, p. 3 Enrichment, p. 30 Reinforcement, p. 27 Directed Reading, p. 20 **Science Inquiry Labs,** pp. 31–32	**Portfolio** Curriculum Connection, p. 487 Activity, p. 492 **Performance** MiniLAB, p. 489 Applying Math, p. 493 **Content** Section Review, p. 493	Section Focus Transparency Virtual Labs CD-ROM Interactive Chalkboard CD-ROM StudentWorks Plus
Need materials? Contact Science Kit at 1-800-828-7777 or www.sciencekit.com.	**Chapter *Fast File* Resources** Transparency Activity, p. 45 Enrichment, p. 31 Reinforcement, p. 28 Directed Reading, p. 20 Transparency Activity, pp. 47–48 **Mathematics Skill Activities,** p. 47	**Portfolio** Reteach, p. 500 **Performance** Applying Science, p. 499 Applying Math, p. 500 **Content** Section Review, p. 500	Section Focus Transparency Teaching Transparency Interactive Chalkboard CD-ROM StudentWorks Plus
MiniLAB: pieces of cloth (2) **Lab:** small cardboard boxes; black, white, and colored paper; tape or glue; thermometer; watch with a second hand **Lab:** Internet or other resources on energy costs	**Chapter *Fast File* Resources** Transparency Activity, p. 46 MiniLAB, p. 4 Enrichment, p. 32 Reinforcement, p. 29 Directed Reading, pp. 21, 22 Lab Worksheets, pp. 5–6, 7–8 Lab Activities, pp. 9–12, 13–16 **Reading and Writing Skill Activities,** p. 19 **Home and Community Involvement,** p. 42	**Portfolio** Differentiated Instruction, p. 504 **Performance** MiniLAB, p. 502 Applying Math, p. 506 **Content** Section Review, p. 506	Section Focus Transparency Interactive Chalkboard CD-ROM StudentWorks Plus Video Lab

End of Chapter Assessment

Glencoe's Assessment Advantage

Blackline Masters	Technology	Professional Series
Chapter *Fast File* Resources Chapter Review, pp. 37–38 Chapter Tests, pp. 39–42 **Standardized Test Practice,** pp. 68–71	MindJogger Videoquiz Virtual Labs CD-ROM Exam*View*® Pro Testmaker TeacherWorks CD-ROM Interactive Chalkboard CD-ROM	**Performance Assessment in the Science Classroom (PASC)**

chapter 16 Energy Sources

Transparencies

Section Focus

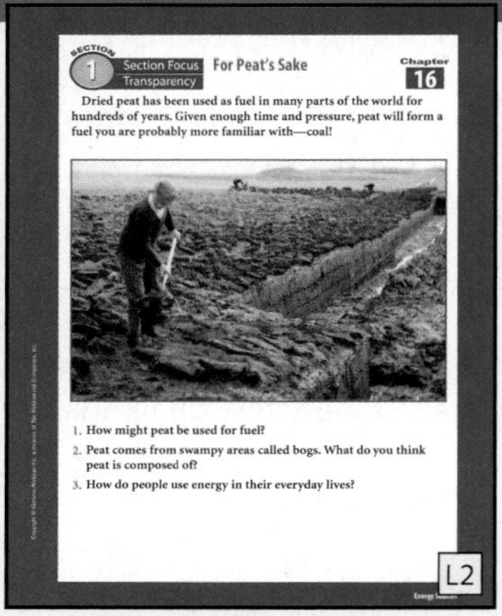
SECTION 1 Section Focus Transparency — For Peat's Sake — Chapter 16

Dried peat has been used as fuel in many parts of the world for hundreds of years. Given enough time and pressure, peat will form a fuel you are probably more familiar with—coal!

1. How might peat be used for fuel?
2. Peat comes from swampy areas called bogs. What do you think peat is composed of?
3. How do people use energy in their everyday lives?

L2

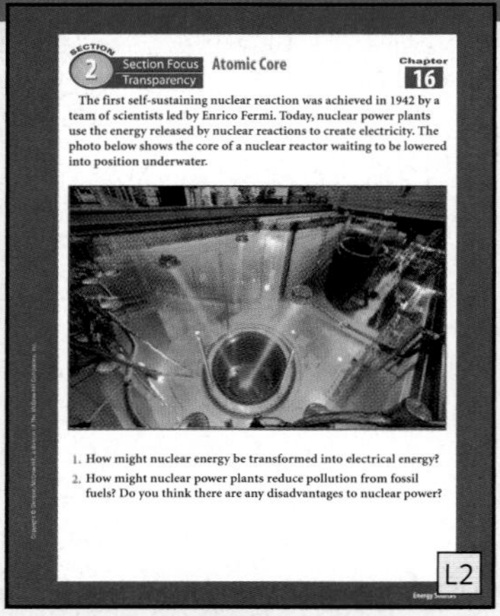
SECTION 2 Section Focus Transparency — Atomic Core — Chapter 16

The first self-sustaining nuclear reaction was achieved in 1942 by a team of scientists led by Enrico Fermi. Today, nuclear power plants use the energy released by nuclear reactions to create electricity. The photo below shows the core of a nuclear reactor waiting to be lowered into position underwater.

1. How might nuclear energy be transformed into electrical energy?
2. How might nuclear power plants reduce pollution from fossil fuels? Do you think there are any disadvantages to nuclear power?

L2

SECTION 3 Section Focus Transparency — Sun Power! — Chapter 16

NASA is developing solar-powered aircraft that have the ability to stay in the air for months at a time! They can be used for studying the atmosphere, storms, crop damage, or fires.

1. What might be a big difficulty for solar-powered aircraft? What are the advantages?
2. Name some organisms that collect the Sun's energy.
3. What other uses of solar power can you name?

L2

This is a representation of key blackline masters available in the Teacher Classroom Resources. See Resource Manager boxes within the chapter for additional information.

Assessment

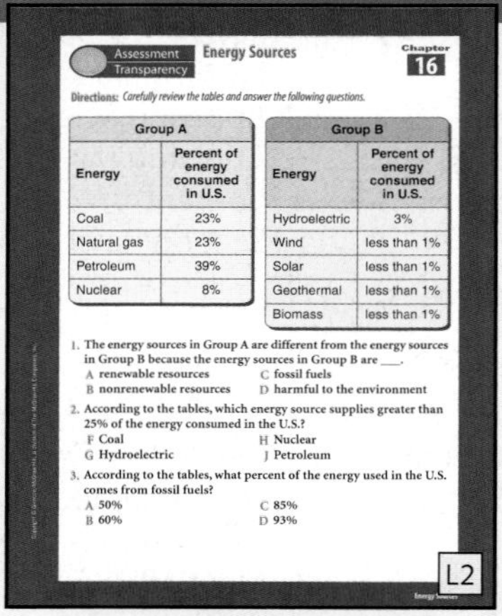
Assessment Transparency — Energy Sources — Chapter 16

Directions: Carefully review the tables and answer the following questions.

Group A	
Energy	Percent of energy consumed in U.S.
Coal	23%
Natural gas	23%
Petroleum	39%
Nuclear	8%

Group B	
Energy	Percent of energy consumed in U.S.
Hydroelectric	3%
Wind	less than 1%
Solar	less than 1%
Geothermal	less than 1%
Biomass	less than 1%

1. The energy sources in Group A are different from the energy sources in Group B because the energy sources in Group B are ____.
A renewable resources C fossil fuels
B nonrenewable resources D harmful to the environment
2. According to the tables, which energy source supplies greater than 25% of the energy consumed in the U.S.?
F Coal H Nuclear
G Hydroelectric J Petroleum
3. According to the tables, what percent of the energy used in the U.S. comes from fossil fuels?
A 30% C 85%
B 60% D 93%

L2

Teaching

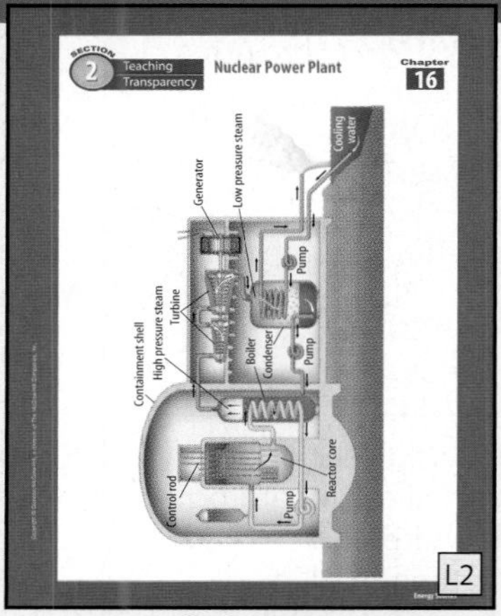
SECTION 2 Teaching Transparency — Nuclear Power Plant — Chapter 16

L2

Key to Teaching Strategies

The following designations will help you decide which activities are appropriate for your students.

- L1 Level 1 activities should be appropriate for students with learning difficulties.
- L2 Level 2 activities should be within the ability range of all students.
- L3 Level 3 activities are designed for above-average students.
- ELL ELL activities should be within the ability range of English Language Learners.
- COOP LEARN Cooperative Learning activities are designed for small group work.
- LS Multiple Learning Styles logos, as described on page 12T, are used throughout to indicate strategies that address different learning styles.
- P These strategies represent student products that can be placed into a best-work portfolio.
- PBL Problem-Based Learning activities apply real-world situations to learning.

Hands-on Activities

Student Text Lab Worksheet

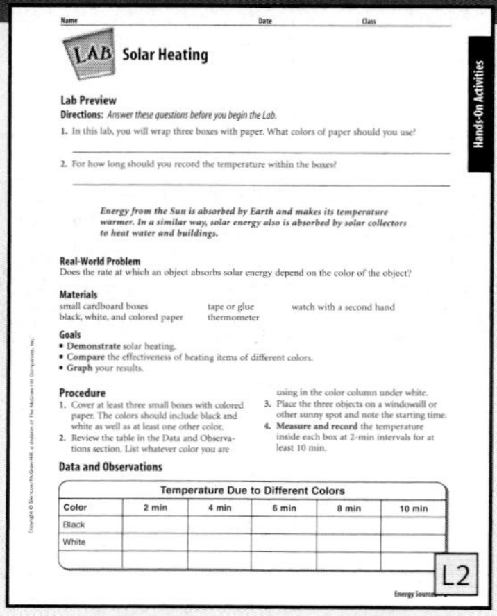
LAB Solar Heating

Lab Preview

Directions: Answer these questions before you begin the Lab.

1. In this lab, you will wrap three boxes with paper. What colors of paper should you use?
2. For how long should you record the temperature within the boxes?

Energy from the Sun is absorbed by Earth and makes its temperature warmer. In a similar way, solar energy also is absorbed by solar collectors to heat water and buildings.

Real-World Problem

Does the rate at which an object absorbs solar energy depend on the color of the object?

Materials

Goals
- Demonstrate solar heating.
- Compare the effectiveness of heating items of different colors.
- Graph your results.

Procedure

Data and Observations

Temperature Due to Different Colors					
Color	2 min	4 min	6 min	8 min	10 min
Black					
White					

L2

Laboratory Activities

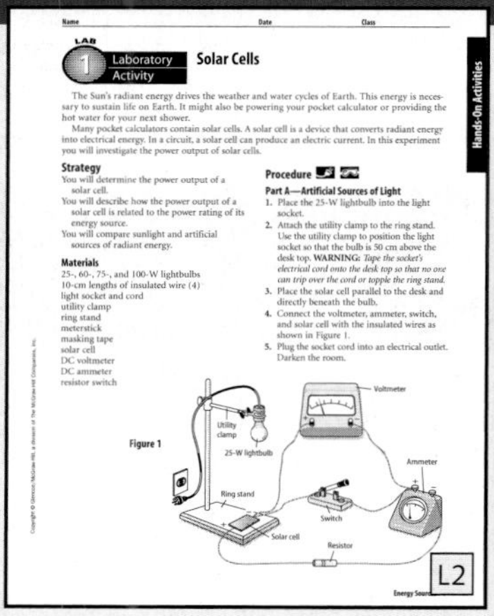
LAB 1 Laboratory Activity — Solar Cells

The Sun's radiant energy drives the weather and water cycles of Earth. This energy is necessary to sustain life on Earth. It might also be powering your pocket calculator or providing the hot water for your next shower.

Strategy

Materials

Procedure

Part A—Artificial Sources of Light

Figure 1

L2

Meeting Different Ability Levels

Content Outline

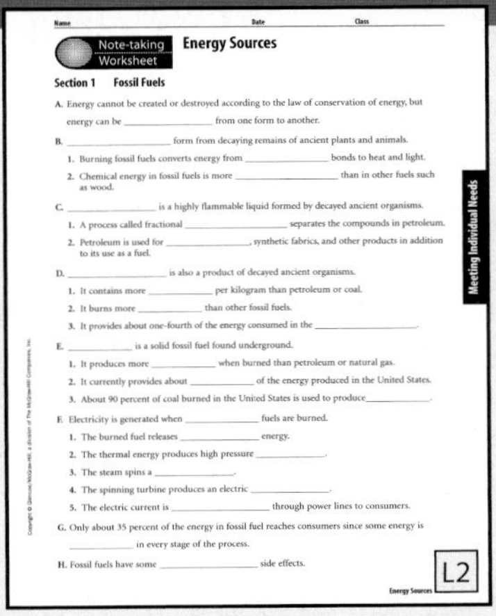

Reinforcement

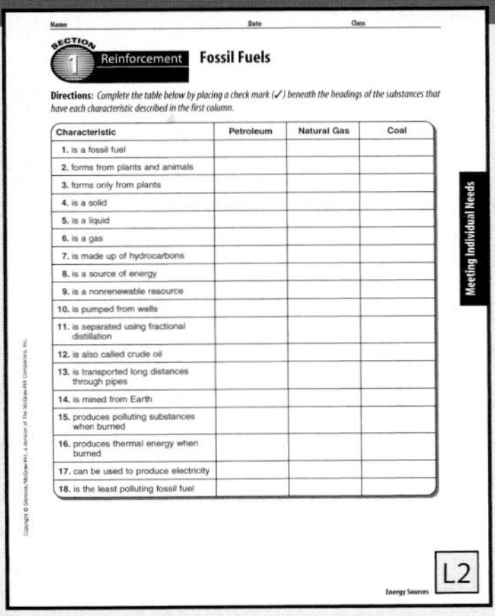

Enrichment

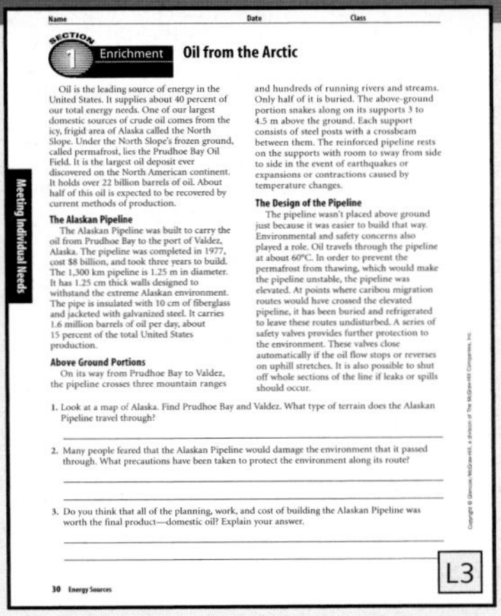

Directed Reading (English/Spanish)

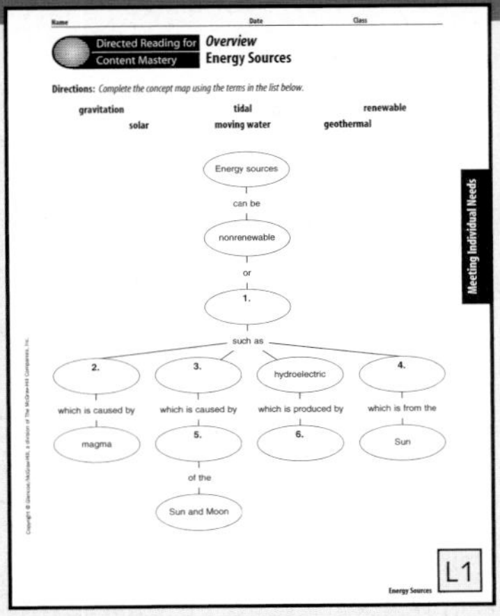

Study Guide

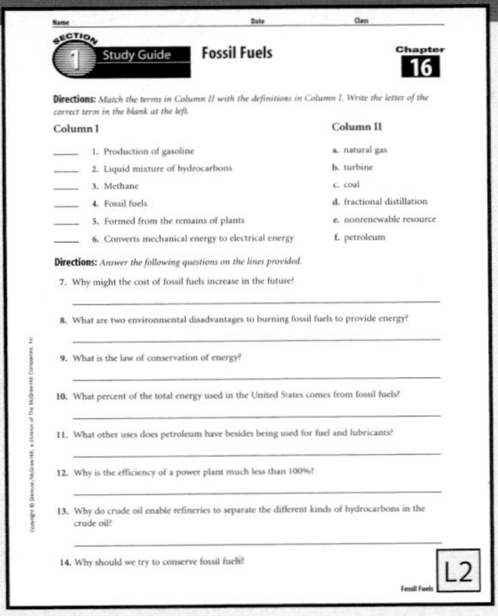

Reading Essentials

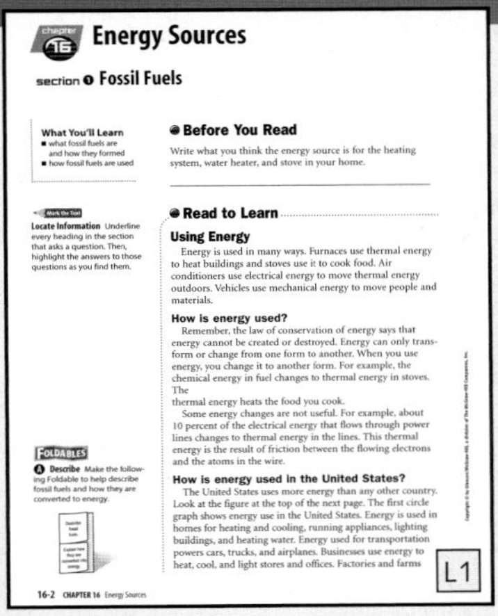

Assessment

Test Practice Workbook

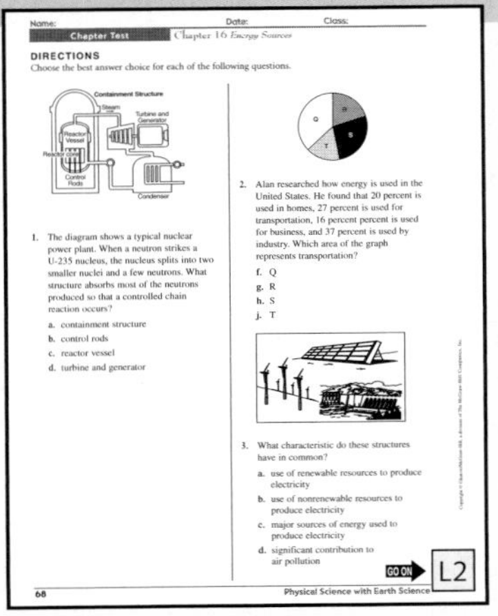

Chapter Review

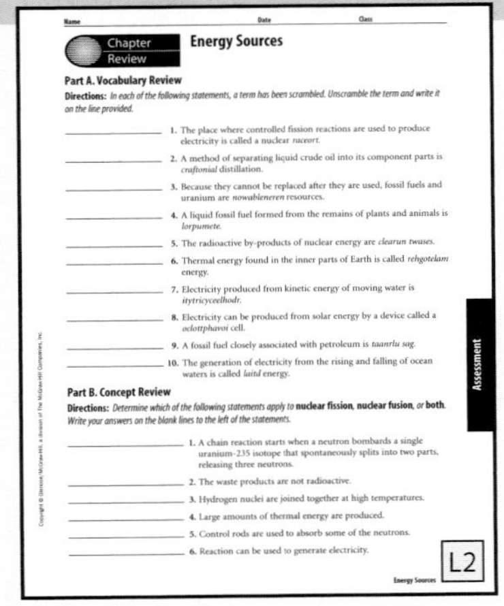

Chapter Tests

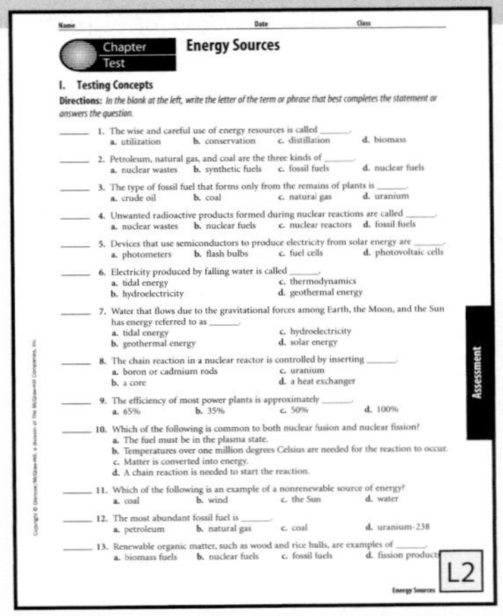

Science Content Background

section 1 Fossil Fuels

Making Fossil Fuels

Fossil fuels were once living organisms that obtained energy directly or indirectly from the Sun and can therefore be considered a type of solar energy. Unlike the direct use of solar energy, burning fossil fuels produces carbon dioxide gas and other pollutants.

Kerosene was once the most important product from petroleum because of its use in kerosene lanterns. Kerosene is now used mainly as a fuel for jet engines.

Generating Electricity

Whether using fossil fuels, geothermal energy, or nuclear power, the generation of electricity involves heating water to produce steam to turn turbines. Hydropower, wind, and tidal energy turn turbines, but water is not heated to produce steam.

Teacher to Teacher
Erin Peters,
Lead Science Teacher
Williamsburg Middle School
Arlington, VA

"I ask the students to think of an activity such as doing your homework. Trace the energy sources back to the Sun. For example, pushing your pencil is mechanical energy, which comes from the chemical energy of eating lunch, which comes from food, which gets its energy from the Sun."

Erin Peters

section 2 Nuclear Energy

Using Nuclear Energy

When nuclear fission and nuclear fusion occur, a small amount of mass is converted into energy. The connection between mass and energy is given by Einstein's famous equation $E=mc^2$. This equation showed that a small amount of mass is converted into an enormous amount of energy.

Gamma ray exposure is sometimes compared to the equivalent exposure in X rays. For example, a nuclear weapons worker may have had a yearly dose that is equivalent to one chest X ray. Compared to X rays or other types of nuclear radiation, gamma rays are the most energetic. As a result, they penetrate the farthest into living tissue and can cause the most biological damage.

France is the world leader in electrical power generation from nuclear fission. Approximately three-quarters of France's electrical energy is generated by this process.

The only approved permanent storage site in the United States for radioactive wastes is Yucca Mountain in Nevada. Some scientists believe this is a good site because it is far from major populations, it has low levels of rainfall, and the water table is very deep.

section 3 Renewable Energy Sources

Energy from the Sun

The materials required to generate electricity from solar energy are expensive. The materials to use the Sun's energy for heating are, however, relatively inexpensive. Piping and a box with a glass roof are the fundamental parts of many solar water heaters. Currently about one million homes in the United States use solar water heating. Some states, such as North Carolina and Arizona, give tax incentives for the installation of solar water heaters. Passive solar heating of spaces in houses is another low-cost way to use the Sun's energy. New houses are increasingly being designed with windows facing the south to absorb the Sun's energy in wintertime. Overhangs on the houses prevent the Sun's entry in the summertime.

Energy from Inside Earth

You don't need to live near a volcano to use geothermal energy. Heat pumps, in use in 400,000 United States homes, take advantage of fairly constant below-ground temperatures. The temperature range in the first ten feet of soil is 10° to 15.5°C (50° to 60°F). This usually means the soil is warmer than the winter air and cooler than the summer air. In a heat pump, air either gains or loses heat to the ground before entering a heating or cooling unit.

Alternative Fuels

When animal manure is decomposed by anaerobic fermentation, methane gas is produced. This can be collected and used as a source of fuel for, among other things, generating electricity. Farms with 700 head of cattle can produce enough methane to power approximately 50 homes. Methane is a greenhouse gas, and this process helps prevent additional methane from entering the atmosphere.

chapter content resources

Internet Resources

For additional content background, visit **gpescience.com** to:

- access your book online
- find references to related articles in popular science magazines
- access Web links with related content background
- access current events with science journal topics

Print Resources

Achieving Energy Independence—One Step at a Time, by Jeffrey R. Yago, Dunimis Technology, 1999

Power with Nature: Solar and Wind Energy Demystified, by Rex A. Ewing, PixyJack Press, 2003

Alternative Energy: Facts, Statistics, and Issues, by Paula Berinstein, Oryx Press, 2001

Tomorrow's Energy: Hydrogen, Fuel Cells, and the Prospects for a Cleaner Planet, by Peter Hoffmann, MIT Press, 2002

Bill Banaszewski/Visuals Unlimited

chapter 16

Chapter Vocabulary

fossil fuel, p. 487
petroleum, p. 489
nonrenewable resource, p. 493
nuclear reactor, p. 494
nuclear waste, p. 498
renewable resource, p. 501
photovoltaic cell, p. 501
hydroelectricity, p. 503
geothermal energy, p. 505
biomass, p. 506

Science Journal Student responses will vary. The majority of the United States uses fossil fuels to generate electrical power, but there are areas of the country that have other energy sources.

INTERACTIVE CHALKBOARD with Image Bank

PowerPoint® Presentations

This CD-ROM is an editable Microsoft® PowerPoint® presentation that includes:

- a pre-made presentation for every chapter
- interactive graphics
- animations
- audio clips
- image bank
- all new section and chapter questions
- Standardized Test Practice
- transparencies
- Foldables directions
- links to gpescience.com

chapter 16

Energy Sources

chapter preview

sections

1 Fossil Fuels
2 Nuclear Energy
3 Renewable Energy Sources
Lab *Solar Heating*
Lab *How much does energy really cost?*
Virtual Lab *How much electricity is used in a house?*

That's a lot of kilowatts!

Look closely at this photo. Can you identify at least three items that require energy to operate? The welding torches require energy to join the pieces of the car together. The robots require energy to assemble the pieces. When the car is finished, energy will be required to operate the car.

Science Journal Describe how your day would be different if the electric power were off all day.

484

Theme Connection

Energy People use energy from many different sources. Fossil fuels are the primary source of energy, but nuclear reactions, solar power, hydroelectric power, and geothermal power also are used.

About the Photo

Robot Workers The 1970s energy crisis began a major push to automate manufacturing processes in the United States. Recent developments in robots used in automobile manufacturing can significantly reduce energy needs of a factory and thereby reduce environmental pollutants, such as carbon dioxide, by as much as 50 percent.

Start-Up Activities

Launch LAB

Heating with Solar Energy

The Sun constantly bathes our planet with enormous amounts of energy. This energy can be captured and used to make electricity, heat homes, and provide hot water. How can the Sun's energy be used to heat water?

1. Use scissors to poke a small hole in the center of two coffee can lids.
2. Fill a coffee can that has been painted black with water at room temperature. Snap on the lid and push a thermometer through the hole in the lid. Record the temperature.
3. Repeat step 2 using the coffee can that has been painted white.
4. Place both cans in direct sunlight. After 15 min, record the temperature of the water in both cans again.
5. **Think Critically** Write a paragraph explaining why the temperature change differed between the two cans.

Science Online | Preview this chapter's content and activities at gpescience.com

FOLDABLES™ Study Organizer

Energy Sources There are many sources of energy. Make the following Foldable to help you organize information about various types of energy sources.

STEP 1 **Fold** a sheet of paper in half lengthwise. Make the back edge about 5 cm longer than the front edge.

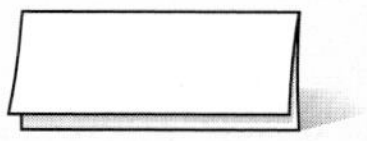

STEP 2 **Turn** the paper so the fold is on the bottom. Then **fold** it into thirds.

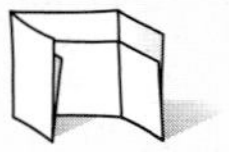

STEP 3 **Unfold and cut** only the top layer along both folds to make three tabs.

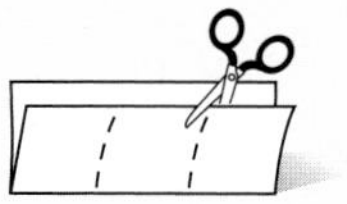

STEP 4 **Label** the Foldable as shown.

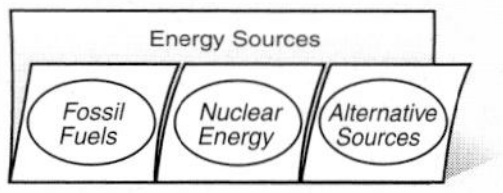

Summarize As you read this chapter, summarize important information about each type of energy source under the appropriate tab.

Launch LAB

Purpose Use the Launch Lab to show students how one form of energy can be transformed into another form that we can use. L2 ELL LS **Kinesthetic**

Preparation To save time, you may want to paint coffee cans and cut holes in the lids ahead of time.

Materials scissors, coffee cans with lids, white paint, black paint, water, thermometer

Teaching Strategy Identify a place that gets direct sunlight where students can leave the cans for 15 minutes.

Think Critically

The temperature change is greater in the black can because the color black absorbs more energy than the color white.

Assessment

Process Ask students to make data tables and to record in the tables the temperature readings for each can every two minutes. Use **Performance Assessment in the Science Classroom,** p. 109.

FOLDABLES™ Study Organizer — Dinah Zike Study Fold

Student preparation materials for this Foldable are available in the **Chapter *Fast File* Resources.**

section 1 Fossil Fuels

1 Motivate

INTERACTIVE CHALKBOARD An editable Microsoft® PowerPoint® presentation is available on **Interactive Chalkboard** CD-ROM.

Bellringer

Section Focus Transparencies also are available on the Interactive Chalkboard CD-ROM. L2 ELL

Section Focus Transparency 1 — For Peat's Sake — Chapter 16

Dried peat has been used as fuel in many parts of the world for hundreds of years. Given enough time and pressure, peat will form a fuel you are probably more familiar with—coal!

1. How might peat be used for fuel?
2. Peat comes from swampy areas called bogs. What do you think peat is composed of?
3. How do people use energy in their everyday lives?

L2

Energy Sources

Reading Preview

Tie to Prior Knowledge

Energy Source Ask students to name the last time they rode in a bus or car. Tell them that the energy that made the vehicle move came from fossil fuels. In this section, they will learn about various types of fossil fuels that are useful sources of energy.

Activate Vocabulary Knowledge Ask students to identify the ways in which the new vocabulary words are connected. Allow students to use the text as a resource. Have them identify other familiar terms that could be connected to the vocabulary words.

Reading Guide

What You'll Learn
- **Discuss** properties and uses of fossil fuels.
- **Explain** how fossil fuels are formed.
- **Describe** how the chemical energy in fossil fuels is converted into electrical energy.

Why It's Important

Fossil fuels are used to generate most of the energy you use every day.

Review Vocabulary

chemical potential energy: the energy stored in the chemical bonds between atoms in molecules

New Vocabulary
- fossil fuel
- petroleum
- nonrenewable resource

Using Energy

How many different ways have you used energy today? Today you might have ridden in a car or bus, or used a hair dryer or a toaster. If you did, you used energy. Furnaces and stoves use thermal energy to heat buildings and cook food. Air conditioners use electrical energy to move thermal energy outdoors. Cars and other vehicles use mechanical energy to carry people and materials from one part of the country to another.

Transforming Energy According to the law of conservation of energy, energy cannot be created or destroyed. Energy can only be transformed, or converted, from one form to another. To use energy means to transform one form of energy to another form of energy that can perform a useful function. For example, energy is used when the chemical energy in fuels is transformed into thermal energy that heats your home.

Sometimes energy is transformed into a form that isn't useful. For example, power lines, like those shown in **Figure 1,** carry electrical energy. When electric current flows in power lines, about 10 percent of the electrical energy is transformed into thermal energy. This thermal energy flows into the air surrounding the power lines, and can no longer be used.

Figure 1 Power lines like these carry the electrical energy you use every day.

Section 1 Resource Manager

Chapter *FAST FILE* Resources
- Transparency Activity, p. 44
- Note-taking Worksheets, pp. 33–35
- Directed Reading for Content Mastery, pp. 19–20
- MiniLAB, p. 3
- Enrichment, p. 30
- Reinforcement, p. 27

Cultural Diversity, p. 45, 49

Performance Assessment in the Science Classroom, p. 48

Science Inquiry Labs, pp. 31–32

Physical Science Critical Thinking/Problem Solving, p. 14

Energy Use in the United States More energy is used in the United States than in any other country in the world. **Figure 2** shows energy usage in the United States. About 20 percent of the energy is used in homes for heating and cooling, to run appliances, and to provide lighting and hot water. About 27 percent is used for transportation powering vehicles such as cars, trucks, and aircraft. Another 16 percent is used by businesses to heat, cool, and light stores, shops, and office buildings. Finally, about 37 percent of this energy is used by industry and agriculture to manufacture products and produce food. **Figure 2** also shows the main sources of the energy used in the United States. Almost 85 percent of the energy used in the United States comes from burning petroleum, natural gas, and coal. Nuclear power plants provide about eight percent of the energy used in the United States.

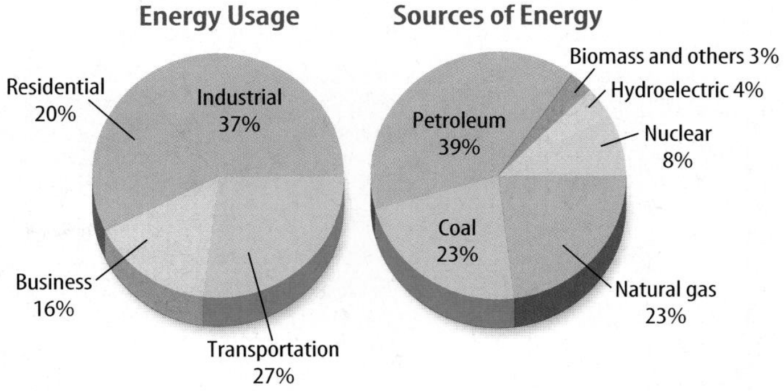

Figure 2 These circle graphs show where energy is used in the United States and sources of this energy.

Making Fossil Fuels

In one hour of freeway driving a car might use several gallons of gasoline. It may be hard to believe that it took millions of years to make the fuels that are used to produce electricity, provide heat, and transport people and materials. **Figure 4** on the next page shows how coal, petroleum, and natural gas are formed by the decay of ancient plants and animals. Fuels such as petroleum, or oil, natural gas, and coal are called **fossil fuels** because they are formed from the decaying remains of ancient plants and animals.

Concentrated Energy Sources When fossil fuels are burned, carbon and hydrogen atoms combine with oxygen molecules in the air to form carbon dioxide and water molecules. This process converts the chemical potential energy that is stored in the chemical bonds between atoms to heat and light. Compared to other fuels such as wood, the chemical energy that is stored in fossil fuels is more concentrated. For example, burning 1 kg of coal releases two to three times as much energy as burning 1 kg of wood. **Figure 3** compares the amount of energy that is produced by burning different fossil fuels.

Figure 3 The bar graph shows the amount of energy released by burning one gram of four different fuels. **Determine** *the ratio of the energy content of natural gas to the energy content of wood.*

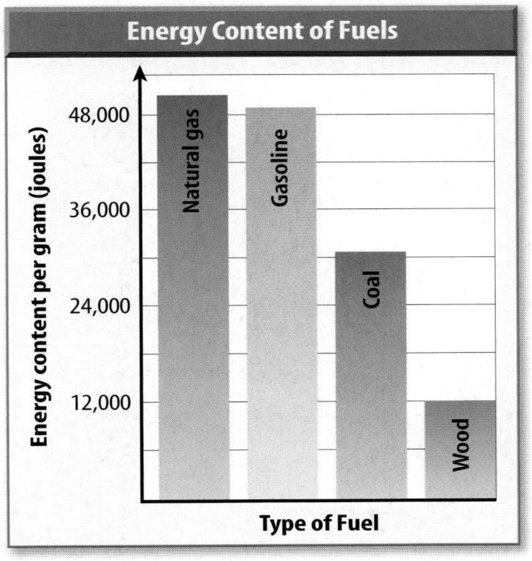

2 Teach

Fun Fact

Fossil fuels currently supply nearly 90 percent of all the energy consumed by the industrially developed nations of the world

Caption Answer

Figure 3 about 4:1

Discussion

Fossil Fuels Are fossil fuels still being made today? The physical and chemical processes that made fossil fuels are still acting on decaying organic matter on Earth's crust. However, the rate at which new fuel is being made is tiny compared with the rate at which it is being used. L3

LS **Logical-Mathematical**

Reading Strategy

K-W-L Chart Have students set up a three-column chart. In the first column, students will indicate what they know about Petroleum, Natural Gas, Coal, and Electricity Generation. In the second column, they will state what they want to know about each. Finally, after reading, students will state what they've learned about the topics.

Differentiated Instruction

Challenge Ask students to find out how much energy is used per person in other developed nations, compared with the amount used in the United States. Have students make a graph showing their results. In most other developed nations, about half as much energy is used per person as is used in the United States. L3 LS **Logical-Mathematical**

Curriculum Connection

Language Arts Power outages sometimes occur because of severe snowstorms, flooding, or other natural disasters. Have each student write a story about how he or she would survive an imaginary week-long loss of electricity, natural gas, and gasoline. Students should describe their daily routines and include ideas for alternate sources of energy. L2 LS **Linguistic** P

Visualizing the Formation of Fossil Fuels

Have students examine the pictures and read the captions. Then ask the following question.

Why do oil and gas sometimes bubble to the surface, while coal never does? Oil (a liquid) and natural gas (a gas) are less dense than the surrounding rock. Coal is a solid and its density is not low enough for it to rise to the surface.

Activity

Fossil Fuel Concentrations Divide the class into three groups. Assign each group a different fossil fuel: coal, oil, and natural gas. Have students in each group research the locations of deposits of the fuel and plot the distribution on an outline map of the world. Display the three maps and discuss which parts of the world have the largest concentrations of each fossil fuel. L2 LS **Visual-Spatial**

Teacher FYI

OPEC The Organization of Petroleum Exporting Countries (OPEC) is a group of eleven countries that own most of the world's crude oil reserves. They work together to coordinate petroleum policy. Member nations are Algeria, Indonesia, Iran, Iraq, Kuwait, Libya, Nigeria, Qatar, Saudi Arabia, the United Arab Emirates, and Venezuela.

NATIONAL GEOGRAPHIC VISUALIZING THE FORMATION OF FOSSIL FUELS

Figure 4

Oil and natural gas form when organic matter on the ocean floor, gradually buried under additional layers of sediment, is chemically changed by heat and crushing pressure. The oil and gas may bubble to the surface or become trapped beneath a dense rock layer. Coal forms when peat—partially decomposed vegetation—is compressed by overlying sediments and transformed first into lignite (soft brown coal) and then into harder, bituminous coal. These two processes are shown below.

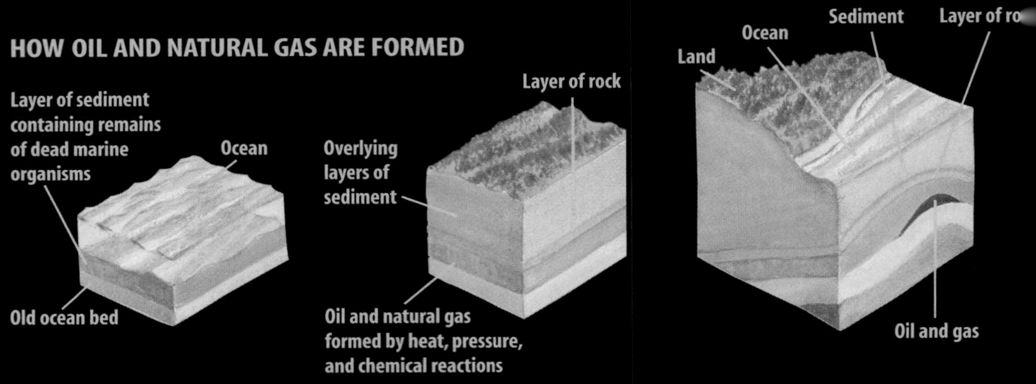

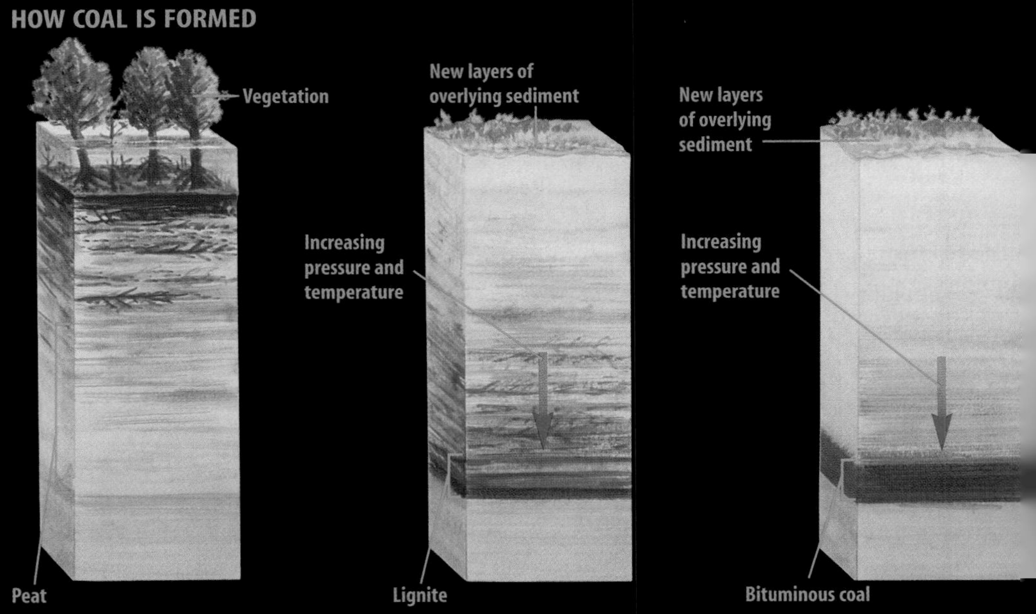

Differentiated Instruction

Challenge Have students research the discoveries of bog mummies that have been made by peat cutters in northern Europe where peat is still sometimes used as a fuel. Have students write reports on the conditions that caused the peat bogs to form and that also mummified the bodies. L3 LS **Linguistic**

Petroleum

Millions of gallons of petroleum, or crude oil, are pumped every day from wells deep in Earth's crust. **Petroleum** is a highly flammable liquid formed by decayed ancient organisms, such as microscopic plankton and algae. Petroleum is a mixture of thousands of chemical compounds. Most of these compounds are hydrocarbons, which means their molecules contain only carbon atoms and hydrogen atoms.

Separating Hydrocarbons The different hydrocarbon molecules found in petroleum have different numbers and arrangements of carbon and hydrogen atoms. The composition and structure of hydrocarbons determines their properties.

The many different compounds that are found in petroleum are separated in a process called fractional distillation. This separation occurs in the tall towers of oil-refinery plants. First, crude oil is pumped into the bottom of the tower and heated. The chemical compounds in the crude oil boil and vaporize according to their individual boiling points. Materials with the lowest boiling points rise to the top of the tower as vapor and are collected. Hydrocarbons with high boiling points, such as asphalt and some types of waxes, remain liquid and are drained off through the bottom of the tower.

Reading Check *What is fractional distillation used for?*

Other Uses for Petroleum Not all of the products obtained from petroleum are burned to produce energy. About 15 percent of the petroleum-based substances that are used in the United States go toward nonfuel uses. Look around at the materials in your home or classroom. Do you see any plastics? In addition to fuels, plastics and synthetic fabrics are made from the hydrocarbons found in crude petroleum. Also, lubricants such as grease and motor oil, as well as the asphalt used in surfacing roads, are obtained from petroleum. Some synthetic materials produced from petroleum are shown in **Figure 5.**

Figure 5 The objects shown here are made from chemical compounds found in petroleum.
Identify *four objects in your classroom that are made from petroleum.*

Mini LAB

Designing an Efficient Water Heater

Procedure

1. Measure and record the mass of a **candle.**
2. Measure 50 mL of **water** into a **beaker.** Record the temperature of the water.
3. Use the lighted candle to increase the temperature of the water by 10°C. Put out the candle and measure its mass.
4. Repeat steps 1 to 3 with an **aluminum foil** chimney surrounding the candle.

Analysis

1. Compare the mass change in the two trials. Which heater was more efficient?
2. Explain why adding the chimney changed the efficiency of the water heater.

Mini LAB

Purpose Students determine how heating efficiency can be improved. L2 ELL IS **Kinesthetic**

Materials candle, water, foil, 100-mL beaker, thermometer, ring stand and ring, balance, wire gauze, graduated cylinder

Teaching Strategies

- Demonstrate how to set up the equipment. Place wire gauze between the ring stand and the beaker for more even heating.
- Encourage students to experiment with the chimney size, shape, and location. Soot on the beaker improves the efficiency of heating.

Analysis

1. The mass changes less when the chimney is used. The chimney heater was more efficient because less of the candle was needed to raise the temperature of the water.
2. The chimney directed the thermal energy from the candle to the beaker.

Assessment

Oral How would the results differ if the temperature of the water were increased by 30°C in each case? There would be a greater change in the candle's mass, especially if the chimney were not used.

Reading Check

Answer to separate the many different compounds found in petroleum

Caption Answer

Figure 5 Student answers will vary but may include tennis shoes, plastic chairs, plastic trash bags, and synthetic fabrics such as fleece, polyester, nylon, and rayon.

Cultural Diversity

Oil-Rich Countries More than 65 percent of the world's oil reserves are in the Middle East. Have students research some of the changes that have occurred in these countries since oil was discovered in them. Possible answer: The economies of these countries are now based on income from the sale of oil. They have better health care, roads, schools, and other public facilities than they had before. L3 IS **Linguistic**

Curriculum Connection

History In 1973, the Arab oil embargo caused an energy crisis in the United States that forced people to carefully examine their dependence on oil. Have groups of students research this topic and create computer presentations about related major events since that time. Topics might include the economic recession caused by the oil crisis or causes of the Persian Gulf War. L3 IS **Interpersonal**

Discussion

Odorless Gas Natural gas has almost no odor. Why might natural gas distributors add an odorant to the gas? so you can tell if there is a gas leak L2 LS **Logical-Mathematical**

Inquiry Lab

Conserving Resources

Purpose to survey fellow students' efforts to conserve energy, to compile results, and to offer energy conservation tips and techniques

Possible Materials copies of student-generated survey to pass out to fellow students

Estimated Time 2 class periods or 2 hours outside of class

Teaching Strategies

- Students should be divided into small groups. Have students write a student survey that will ask questions about energy conservation, such as "Do you turn the lights off when you leave the room?"
- Students should compile the results of the survey. Students can use their math skills to determine the percentages of the types of responses.
- Have students prepare a brochure to be distributed to students in their school presenting their compilation and tips and techniques for conserving energy.

For additional inquiry activities, see *Science Inquiry Lab*.

Figure 6 Coal mines usually are located deep underground.

Natural Gas

The chemical processes that produce petroleum as ancient organisms decay also produce gaseous compounds called natural gas. These compounds rise to the top of the petroleum deposit and are trapped there. Natural gas is composed mostly of methane, CH_4, but it also contains other hydrocarbon gases such as propane, C_3H_8, and butane, C_4H_{10}. Natural gas is burned to provide energy for cooking, heating, and manufacturing. About one fourth of the energy consumed in the United States comes from burning natural gas. There's a good chance that your home has a stove, furnace, hot-water heater, or clothes drier that uses natural gas.

Natural gas contains more energy per kilogram than petroleum or coal does. It also burns more cleanly than other fossil fuels, produces fewer pollutants, and leaves no residue such as ash.

Coal

Coal is a solid fossil fuel that is found in mines underground, such as the one shown in **Figure 6.** In the first half of the twentieth century, most houses in the United States were heated by burning coal. In fact, during this time, coal provided more than half of the energy that was used in the United States. Now, almost two-thirds of the energy used comes from petroleum and natural gas, and only about one-fourth comes from coal. About 90 percent of all the coal that is used in the United States is burned by power plants to generate electricity.

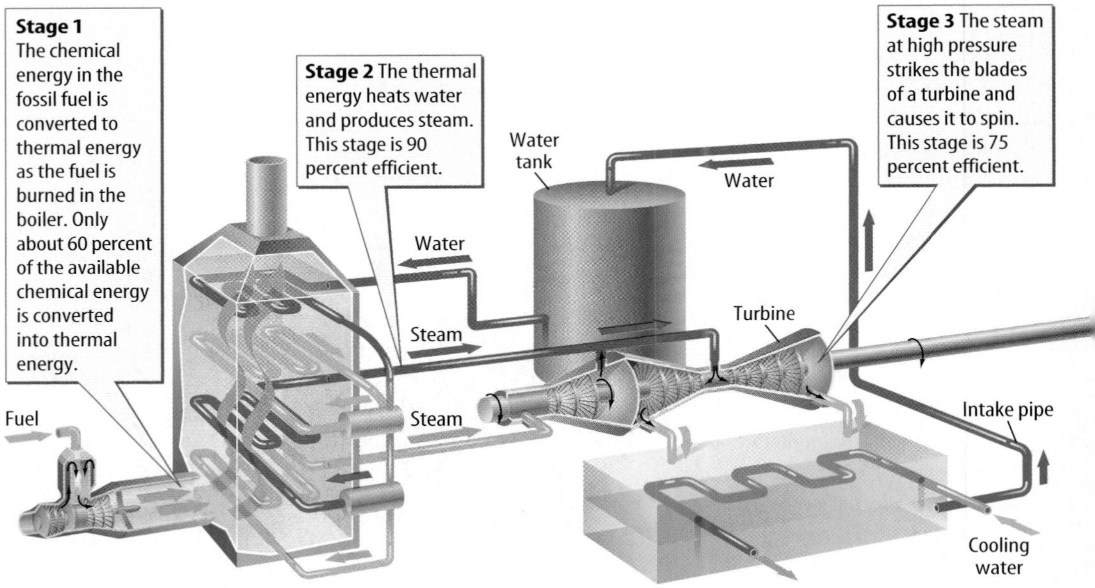

Differentiated Instruction

Challenge Fluidized-bed combustion of coal burns coal more efficiently and produces fewer pollutants than conventional coal boilers. Have students find out more about this technology. Have students draw a diagram detailing how this process works. L3 LS **Logical-Mathematical**

Teacher FYI

U.S. Coal Reserves The four largest coal reserves in the United States are the Four Corners Region near northern New Mexico, the Powder River Basin in Montana and Wyoming, the Eastern Interior Region around Illinois, and the Appalachian Region from Pennsylvania to Alabama.

Origin of Coal Coal mines were once the sites of ancient swamps. Coal formed from the organic material that was deposited as the plants that lived in these swamps died. Worldwide, the amount of coal that is potentially available is estimated to be 20 to 40 times greater than the supply of petroleum.

Coal also is a complex mixture of hydrocarbons and other chemical compounds. Compared to petroleum and natural gas, coal contains more impurities, such as sulfur and nitrogen compounds. As a result, more pollutants, such as sulfur dioxide and nitrogen oxides, are produced when coal is burned.

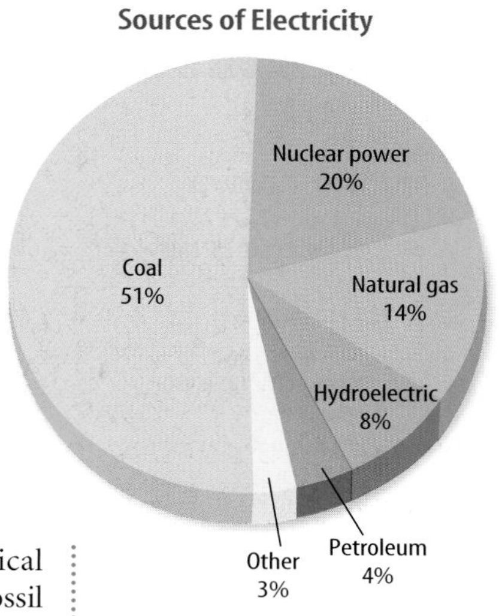

Figure 7 This circle graph shows the percentage of electricity generated in the United States that comes from various energy sources.

Generating Electricity

Figure 7 shows that almost 70 percent of the electrical energy used in the United States is produced by burning fossil fuels. How is the chemical energy contained in fossil fuels converted to electrical energy in an electric power station?

The process is shown in **Figure 8.** In the first stage, fuel is burned in a boiler or combustion chamber, and it releases thermal energy. In the second stage, this thermal energy heats water and produces steam under high pressure. In the third stage, the steam strikes the blades of a turbine, causing it to spin. The shaft of the turbine is connected to an electric generator. In the fourth stage, electric current is produced when the spinning turbine shaft rotates magnets inside the generator. In the final stage, the electric current is transmitted to homes, schools, and businesses through power lines.

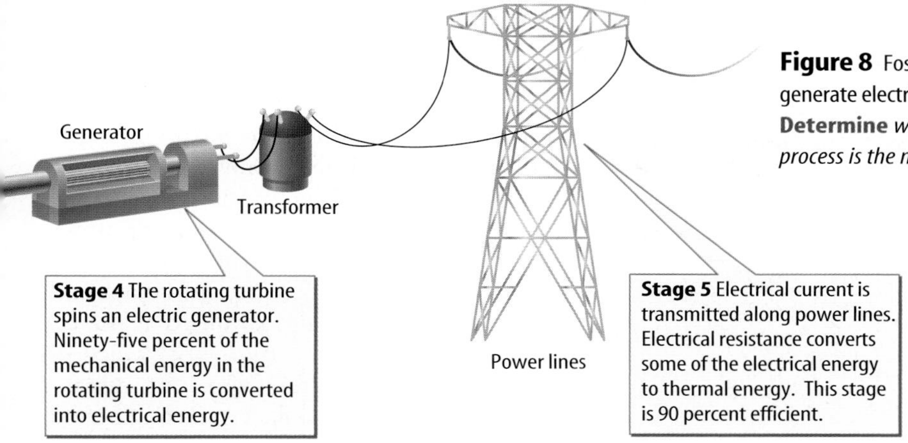

Figure 8 Fossil fuels are burned to generate electricity in a power plant. **Determine** *which stage in this process is the most inefficient.*

Quick Demo
Coal Formation

Materials peat; four different types of coal such as lignite, subbituminous, bituminous, and anthracite

Estimated Time 10 minutes

Procedure Have students examine the peat and the different types of coal. Have students infer how the coal was formed. What are the differences in the conditions that formed the coal? The four types of coal are distinguished by the pressure that produced them. Lignite is produced when rock and soil pressed down on buried peat, causing it to dry out and harden. Further pressure produces subbituminous coal, then bituminous coal, and finally anthracite. L2 LS **Visual-Spatial**

Discussion

Power Sources Electricity became the major source of power in the United States during the twentieth century. What were the sources of power before that? Possible answers include running water and steam. L2 LS **Logical-Mathematical**

Caption Answer

Figure 8 stage 1

Virtual Labs

Household Electricity *How much electricity is used in a house?*

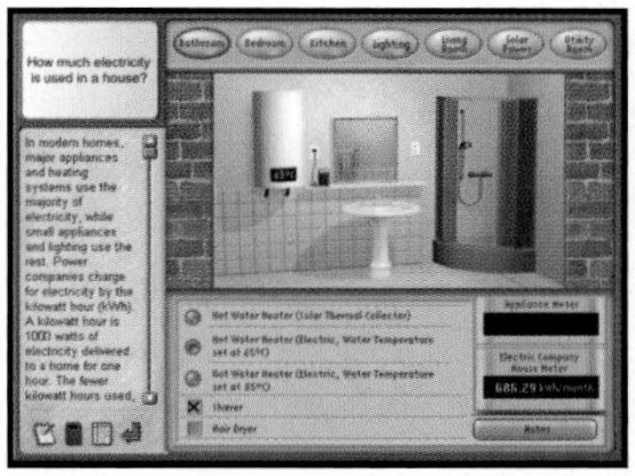

Visual Learning

Figure 7 Review with students the information shown in **Figure 7.** What are the percentages of the three energy sources that are fossil fuels? What do they add up to? Coal 51%, natural gas 14%, and petroleum 4%. These add up to 69%. L2 LS **Visual-Spatial**

Curriculum Connection

History Electricity has been a major source of power in the United States for less than 100 years. Have students research the early history of the use of electricity in the United States. In 1882, Edison opened an electric power plant that lit light bulbs. The first electric power was direct current. Power plants now produce alternating current. L3 LS **Linguistic**

SECTION 1 Fossil Fuels **491**

Table 1 Efficiency of Fossil Fuel Conversion	
Process	**Efficiency (%)**
Chemical to thermal energy	60
Conversion of water to steam	90
Steam-turning turbine	75
Turbine spins electric generator	95
Transmission through power lines	90
Overall efficiency	35

Efficiency of Power Plants

When fossil fuels are burned in power plants, not all of the chemical energy stored in the fuels is converted into electrical energy. In each energy transformation, some energy is converted into thermal energy that cannot be used. As a result, no stage of the process is 100 percent efficient.

The efficiency of each stage of the process in a fossil-fuel burning power plant is given in **Table 1.** The overall efficiency is found by multiplying the efficiencies together, and is only about 35 percent. This means that only about 35 percent of the chemical energy contained in fossil fuels is converted into electrical energy by power plants. The other 65 percent is converted into thermal energy that is transferred to the environment.

The Costs of Using Fossil Fuels

Although fossil fuels are a useful source of energy for generating electricity and providing the power for transportation, their use has some undesirable side effects. When petroleum products and coal are burned, smoke is given off that contains small particles called particulates. These particulates cause breathing problems for some people. Burning fossil fuels also releases carbon dioxide. **Figure 9** shows how the carbon dioxide concentration in the atmosphere has increased from 1960 to 2000. One consequence of increasing the atmospheric carbon dioxide concentration could be to cause Earth's surface temperature to increase.

Figure 9 The carbon dioxide concentration in Earth's atmosphere has been measured at Mauna Loa in Hawaii. From 1960 to 2000, the carbon dioxide concentration has increased by about 16 percent.

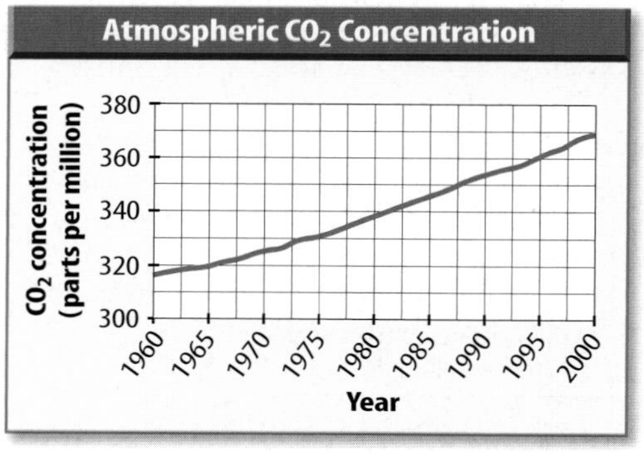

Using Coal The most abundant fossil fuel is coal, but coal contains even more impurities than oil or natural gas. Many electric power plants that burn coal remove some of these pollutants before they are released into the atmosphere. Removing sulfur dioxide, for example, helps to prevent the formation of compounds that might cause acid rain. Mining coal also can be dangerous. Miners risk being killed or injured, and some suffer from lung diseases caused by breathing coal dust over long periods of time.

Discussion

Energy Loss What is the primary way in which energy is lost in power plants? Energy is lost as heat.

Activity

Pollution Diagrams Have students draw diagrams showing how burning fossil fuels causes pollution. Diagrams might illustrate smog formed when fossil fuels are burned, and the effects of ozone near Earth's surface. Students might also draw plants using devices that remove the pollutants before they can reach the air. L3 LS **Visual-Spatial** P

Discussion

Alternatives What might happen when readily available fossil fuels are used up? Possible answers: Alternative energy sources will be developed; companies will exploit more expensive sources of fossil fuels; people's way of life will change because energy will become more expensive to use. L2 LS **Logical-Mathematical**

Differentiated Instruction

Learning Disabled To help students understand the math involved in finding the total efficiency of a power plant, discuss a two-step process in which the efficiency of the first step is 50 percent and the efficiency of the second step is 50 percent. Fill a beaker with water. Pour off half (100% × 50% = 50%). Then pour off half again (50% × 50% = 25%).

492 **CHAPTER 16** Energy Sources

Nonrenewable Resources

All fossil fuels are **nonrenewable resources,** which means they are resources that cannot be replaced by natural processes as quickly as they are used. Therefore, fossil fuel reserves are decreasing at the same time that population and industrial demands are increasing. **Figure 10** shows how the production of oil might decline over the next 50 years as oil reserves are used up. As the production of energy from fossil fuels continues, the remaining reserves of fossil fuels will decrease. Fossil fuels will become more difficult to obtain, causing them to become more costly in the future.

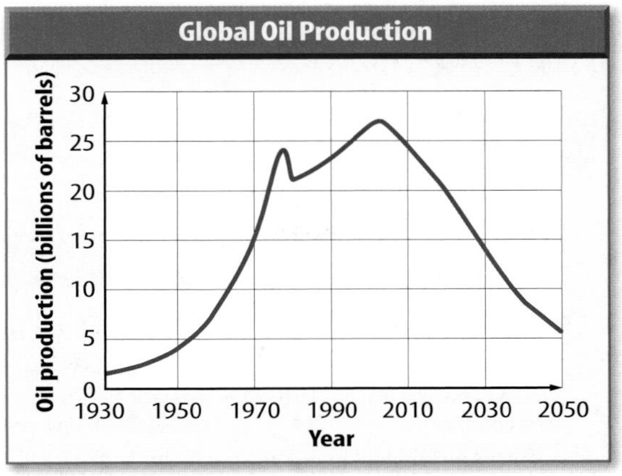

Figure 10 Some predictions show that worldwide oil production will peak by 2005 and then decline rapidly over the following 50 years.

Conserving Fossil Fuels

Even as reserves of fossil fuels decrease and they become more costly, the demand for energy continues to increase as the world's population increases. One way to meet these energy demands would be to reduce the use of fossil fuels and obtain energy from other sources.

section 1 review

Summary

Using Energy

- Energy cannot be created or destroyed, but can only be transformed from one form to another.

Fossil Fuels

- Petroleum, natural gas, and coal are fossil fuels formed by the decay of ancient plants and animals.
- Petroleum is a mixture of thousands of chemical compounds, most of which are hydrocarbons.
- About 90 percent of all coal used in the United States is burned by power plants to produce electricity.

Generating Electricity

- Power plants burn fossil fuels to produce steam that spins turbines attached to electric generators.

Self Check

1. **Describe** the advantages and disadvantages of using fossil fuels to generate electricity.
2. **Explain** how the different chemical compounds in crude oil are separated.
3. **Describe** how fossil fuels are formed.
4. **Name** three materials that are derived from the chemical compounds in petroleum.
5. **Think Critically** If fossil fuels are still forming, why are they considered to be a nonrenewable resource?

Applying Math

6. **Interpret a Graph** According to the graph in **Figure 9,** by how many parts per million did the concentration of atmospheric carbon dioxide increase from 1960 to 2000?
7. **Use a Table** In **Table 1,** if the efficiency of converting chemical to thermal energy was 90 percent, what would the overall efficiency be?

More Section Review gpescience.com

section 1 review

1. Advantages: Fossil fuels are an inexpensive source of energy. They are plentiful for the near-term; Disadvantages: Fossil fuels may cause environmental damage when removed from Earth, when transported, and when burned.
2. They are separated by fractional distillation, in which each compound vaporizes at its own boiling point, rises, and is collected.
3. Fossil fuels are formed when organic matter is chemically changed by heat and pressure.
4. Possible answers: plastics, grease, gasoline, asphalt
5. We are using fossil fuels faster than they are being replaced.
6. about 50 parts per million
7. 52 percent

Post Reading

Extended Research
Scientists predict that the demand for fossils fuels will increase while supplies continue to decrease. It will soon become necessary to consider alternative energy sources. Have students research alternatives to fossils fuels. They may report findings as a written paper or in a poster format.

3 Assess

DAILY INTERVENTION

Check for Understanding

Interpersonal Divide the class into small groups. Assign each group a topic from the section. Each group should present the main ideas from that section to the rest of the class.

Reteach

Evaluating Fossil Fuels Organize the class into teams of three. Have each team consider the advantages and disadvantages of using petroleum, natural gas, and coal. Have the teams combine their lists and report their conclusions. L2 COOP LEARN

LS **Interpersonal**

Assessment

Process Have students make a bulletin board comparing and contrasting the ways people obtain petroleum and coal. Petroleum is a liquid, so it is pumped from wells drilled deep into Earth's crust. Coal also comes from underground, but it is a solid, so it must be mined. Use **Performance Assessment in the Science Classroom,** p. 131.

1 Motivate

INTERACTIVE CHALKBOARD PowerPoint® Presentations An editable Microsoft® PowerPoint® presentation is available on **Interactive Chalkboard** CD-ROM.

Bellringer

Section Focus Transparencies also are available on the Interactive Chalkboard CD-ROM. L2 ELL

Section 2 Section Focus Transparency — Atomic Core — Chapter 16

The first self-sustaining nuclear reaction was achieved in 1942 by a team of scientists led by Enrico Fermi. Today, nuclear power plants use the energy released by nuclear reactions to create electricity. The photo below shows the core of a nuclear reactor waiting to be lowered into position underwater.

1. How might nuclear energy be transformed into electrical energy?
2. How might nuclear power plants reduce pollution from fossil fuels? Do you think there are any disadvantages to nuclear power?

L2

Energy Sources

Reading Preview

Tie to Prior Knowledge
Nuclear Energy Uses Ask students to name ways that nuclear energy is used. Possible answers: diagnose and treat illnesses, nuclear weapons, generate power.

Predict and Anticipate Have students scan the section to find the new vocabulary words. Suggest that they read figures and captions to obtain clues to meaning. Ask students to anticipate how the words may be used in future chapters.

section 2

Nuclear Energy

Reading Guide

***What* You'll Learn**
- **Explain** how a nuclear reactor converts nuclear energy to thermal energy.
- **Describe** advantages and disadvantages of using nuclear energy to produce electricity.
- **Discuss** nuclear fusion as a possible energy source.

***Why* It's Important**
Using nuclear energy to produce electricity can help reduce the use of fossil fuels. However, like all energy sources, the use of nuclear energy has advantages and disadvantages.

Review Vocabulary
nuclear fission: the process of splitting an atomic nucleus into two or more nuclei with smaller masses

New Vocabulary
- nuclear reactor
- nuclear waste

Using Nuclear Energy

Over the past several decades, electric power plants have been developed that generate electricity without burning fossil fuels. Some of these power plants, such as the one shown in **Figure 11,** convert nuclear energy to electrical energy. Energy is released when the nucleus of an atom breaks apart. In this process, called nuclear fission, an extremely small amount of mass is converted into an enormous amount of energy. Today almost 20 percent of all the electricity produced in the United States comes from nuclear power plants. Overall, nuclear power plants produce about eight percent of all the energy consumed in the United States. In 2003, there were 104 nuclear reactors producing electricity at 65 nuclear power plants in the United States.

Figure 11 A nuclear power plant generates electricity using the energy released in nuclear fission. Each of the domes contain a nuclear reactor. A cooling tower is on the left.

Nuclear Reactors

A **nuclear reactor** uses the energy from controlled nuclear reactions to generate electricity. Although nuclear reactors vary in design, all have some parts in common, as shown in **Figure 12.** They contain a fuel that can be made to undergo nuclear fission; they contain control rods that are used to control the nuclear reactions; and they have a cooling system that keeps the reactor from being damaged by the heat produced. The actual fission of the radioactive fuel occurs in a relatively small part of the reactor known as the core.

Section 2 Resource Manager

Chapter *Fast File* Resources
Transparency Activity, pp. 45, 47–48
Directed Reading for Content Mastery, p. 20
Transparency Activity, pp. 47–48
Enrichment, p. 31
Reinforcement, p. 28

Earth Science Critical Thinking/Problem Solving, p. 2
Cultural Diversity, p. 59
Mathematics Skill Activities, p. 47

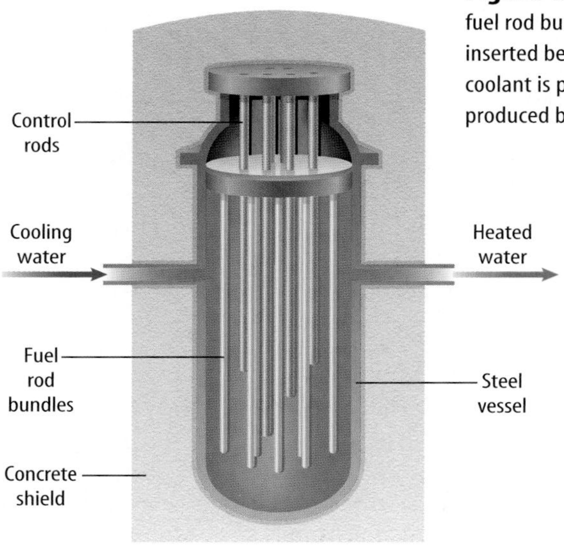

Figure 12 The core of a nuclear reactor contains the fuel rod bundles. Control rods that absorb neutrons are inserted between the fuel rod bundles. Water or another coolant is pumped through the core to remove the heat produced by the fission reaction.

Nuclear Fuel Only certain elements have nuclei that can undergo fission. Naturally occurring uranium contains an isotope, U-235, whose nucleus can split apart. As a result, the fuel that is used in a nuclear reactor is usually uranium dioxide. Naturally occurring uranium contains only about 0.7 percent of the U-235 isotope. In a reactor, the uranium usually is enriched so that it contains three percent to five percent U-235.

Figure 13 Nuclear fuel pellets are stacked together to form fuel rods. The fuel rods are bundled together, and the bundle is covered with a metal alloy.

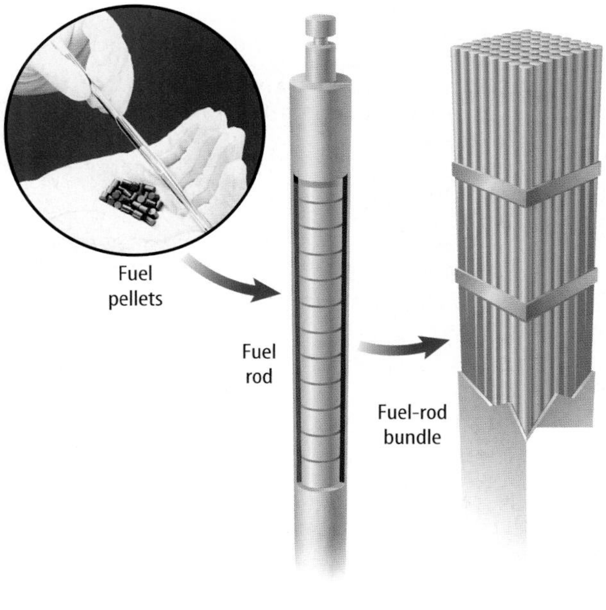

The Reactor Core The reactor core contains uranium dioxide fuel in the form of tiny pellets like the ones in **Figure 13.** The pellets are about the size of a pencil eraser and are placed end to end in a tube. The tubes are then bundled and covered with a metal alloy, as shown in **Figure 13.** The core of a typical reactor contains about a hundred thousand kilograms of uranium in hundreds of fuel rods. For every kilogram of uranium that undergoes fission in the core, 1 g of matter is converted into energy. The energy released by this gram of matter is equivalent to the energy released by burning more than 3 million kg of coal.

2 Teach

Reading Strategy

Visualize the Text Read the sections titled Nuclear Fuel, The Reactor Core, and Nuclear Fission aloud to students. As you read, ask students to close their eyes and imagine what is being described in the text. After listening to the reading, have students draw their visualizations.

Visual Learning

Figure 12 The distance the control rods extend into the reactor core controls the reaction. If the control rods are inserted completely, they absorb too many neutrons and the reaction halts. If they are removed completely, the reaction is uncontained. How do you think control rods are programmed to respond in an emergency? They insert completely to stop the reaction. L2 IS **Logical-Mathematical**

Discussion

Rod-Shaped Why do you think the fuel and control used in the reactor are rod-shaped? to allow the water to flow freely around them and provide cooling L2 IS **Visual-Spatial**

Quick Demo

Nuclear Fuel Pellets

Materials mini-marshmallows, test tubes (larger diameter than marshmallows), rubber band

Estimated Time five minutes

Procedure Use mini-marshmallows to represent the uranium dioxide fuel. Use test tubes to represent the reactor rods. Put the mini-marshmallows into the test tubes. Bundle several test tubes together with the rubber band to represent the bundled fuel rods.

Differentiated Instruction

Visually Impaired Use refillable erasers for mechanical pencils to symbolize the fuel pellets, allow students to feel what the fuel pellets are shaped like. A large soda straw can be used to symbolize the fuel rods. Students can put the erasers in the straw to symbolize packing the fuel rod.

Curriculum Connection

Social Studies The use of nuclear reactions in commercial power plants to produce electricity has been the subject of intense controversy. Organize the class into two teams and have them debate the issue. Arguments for nuclear power include its efficiency and nonreliance on fossil fuels. Arguments against nuclear power include safety hazards and disposal of nuclear waste. L3 IS **Logical-Mathematical**

Use an Analogy

Foxes and Rabbits If rabbits live and breed in an environment rich in rabbit food but in which there are no rabbit predators, the rabbit population will boom very quickly. This is analogous to the uncontrolled chain reaction that can occur in a nuclear reactor. The introduction of foxes into the rabbit environment controls the size of the rabbit population just as the introduction of control rods controls the number of neutrons available to participate in the nuclear reaction.

Caption Answer

Figure 14 The neutrons strike other U-235 nuclei, breaking them apart into fission products and neutrons, or they are absorbed by control rods.

Reading Check

Answer a nuclear reaction in which the products of one reaction start another reaction

Make a Model

Reactor Core Have students work in pairs to make models of the core of a nuclear reactor. Models should include some fuel rods, some control rods, and a coolant. One possible model could use test tubes filled with different substances to represent the fuel rods and the control rods, a test tube rack to represent the core, and water as the coolant. L2 LS **Kinesthetic**

INTEGRATE Earth Science

Uranium-Lead Dating The ratio of amounts of thorium-230 to uranium-234 has been used to date calcium carbonate. Rocks are also dated from the fossils they contain.

Figure 14 When a neutron strikes the nucleus of a U-235 atom, the nucleus splits apart into two smaller nuclei. In the process two or three neutrons also are emitted. The smaller nuclei are called fission products.
Explain *what happens to the neutrons that are released in this reaction.*

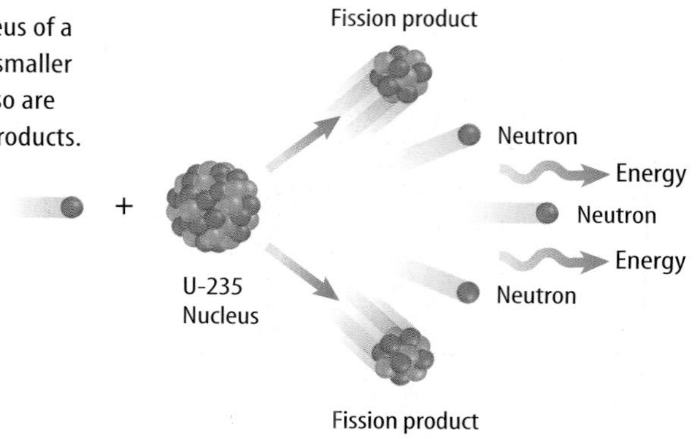

Nuclear Fission How does the nuclear reaction proceed in the reactor core? Neutrons that are produced by the decay of U-235 nuclei are absorbed by other U-235 nuclei. When a U-235 nucleus absorbs a neutron, it splits into two smaller nuclei and two or three additional neutrons, as shown in **Figure 14.** These neutrons strike other U-235 nuclei, causing them to release two or three more neutrons each when they split apart.

Because every uranium atom that splits apart releases neutrons that cause other uranium atoms to split apart, this process is called a nuclear chain reaction. In the chain reaction involving the fission of uranium nuclei, the number of nuclei that are split can more than double at each stage of the process. As a result, an enormous number of nuclei can be split after only a small number of stages. For example, if the number of nuclei involved doubles at each stage, after only 50 stages more than a quadrillion nuclei might be split.

Nuclear chain reactions take place in a matter of milliseconds. If the process isn't controlled, the chain reaction will release energy explosively rather than releasing energy at a constant rate.

Reading Check *What is a nuclear chain reaction?*

Controlling the Chain Reaction To control the chain reaction, some of the neutrons that are released when U-235 splits apart must be prevented from striking other U-235 nuclei. These neutrons are absorbed by rods containing boron or cadmium that are inserted into the reactor core. Moving these control rods deeper into the reactor causes them to absorb more neutrons and slow down the chain reaction. Eventually, only one of the neutrons released in the fission of each of the U-235 nuclei strikes another U-235 nucleus, and energy is released at a constant rate.

INTEGRATE Earth Science

Uranium-Lead Dating
Uranium is used to determine the age of rocks. As uranium decays into lead at a constant rate, the age of a rock can be found by comparing the amount of uranium to the amount of lead produced. Uranium-lead dating is used by scientists to date rocks as old as 4.6 billion years. Research other methods used to determine the age of rocks.

Visual Learning

Figure 14 The tremendous energy from the fission process shown here is mostly transferred to the smaller nuclei and the neutrons, but part of the energy is released as gamma radiation. What are two ways a chain reaction can be avoided? by introducing materials that absorb neutrons and by decreasing the amount of U-235 so there aren't enough atoms to continue the process L2 LS **Logical-Mathematical**

Active Reading

Think-Pair-Share This strategy encourages students to think first before discussing their ideas or thoughts about a topic. Students are asked to respond to a question by writing a response. After thinking for a few minutes, partners share responses to the question. Finally, ask students to share responses with the class.

Nuclear Power Plants

Nuclear fission reactors produce electricity in much the same way that conventional power plants do. **Figure 15** shows how a nuclear reactor produces electricity. The thermal energy released in nuclear fission is used to heat water and produce steam. This steam then is used to drive a turbine that rotates an electric generator. To transfer thermal energy from the reactor core to heat water and produce steam, the core is immersed in a fluid coolant. The coolant absorbs heat from the core and is pumped through a heat exchanger. There thermal energy is transferred from the coolant and boils water to produce steam. The overall efficiency of nuclear power plants is about 35 percent, similar to that of fossil fuel power plants.

The Risks of Nuclear Power

Producing energy from nuclear fission has advantages. Nuclear power plants do not produce the air pollutants that are released by fossil-fuel burning power plants. Also, nuclear power plants don't produce carbon dioxide.

The nuclear generation of electricity also has disadvantages. The mining of the uranium can cause environmental damage. Water that is used as a coolant in the reactor core must cool before it is released into streams and rivers. Otherwise, the excess heat could harm fish and other animals and plants in the water.

INTEGRATE Social Studies

Ukraine The worst nuclear accident in history occurred at the Chernobyl nuclear power plant in the Ukraine in 1986. Many people in the area suffered from radiation sickness. Use a map or atlas to find the location of the Ukraine. Write a description of the location in your Science Journal.

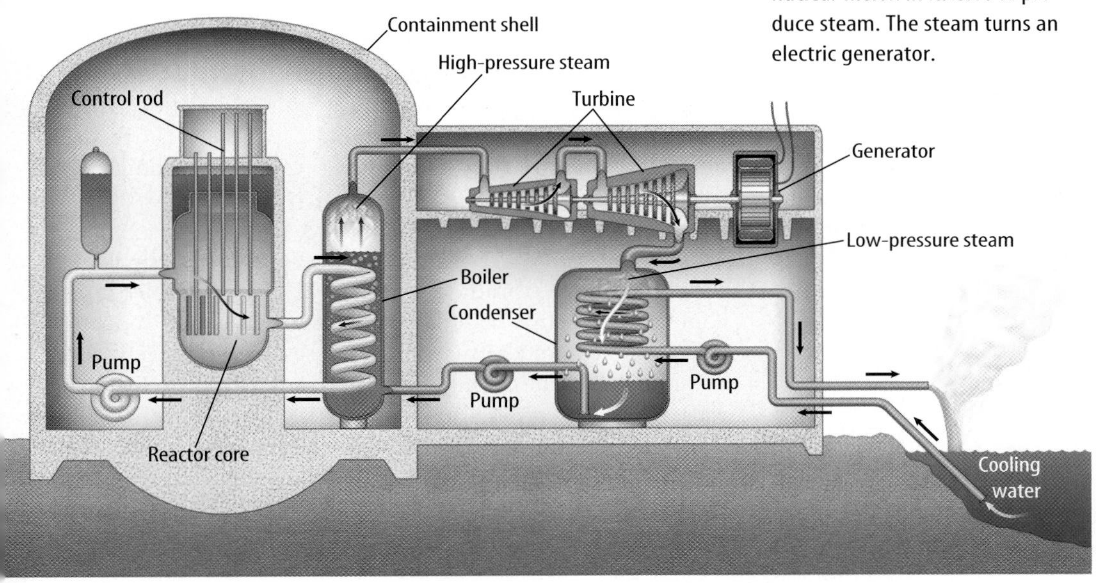

Figure 15 A nuclear power plant uses the heat produced by nuclear fission in its core to produce steam. The steam turns an electric generator.

INTEGRATE Social Studies

Ukraine The Ukraine borders eastern Europe and is located east of Poland and north of Romania.

Research Have students research the Chernobyl accident. Have them find out what caused the accident and the damages that resulted from it.

IDENTIFYING Misconceptions

Contaminated Water The water that is used as a coolant in reactor cores becomes contaminated with radioactive material. This water is not the same water that is cooled and released into streams and rivers. The water that is released into the environment does not come into direct contact either with the reactor core or with the water that cools the reactor core. It exchanges heat with the contaminated water through a heat exchanger.

Teacher FYI

Energy Supplies In an average American's lifetime, more than 1 million kg of coal would be needed to supply the person's energy needs. In contrast, if nuclear reactors were used instead of coal, about 1,100 uranium fuel pellets would be needed to supply the same amount of energy.

Science Journal

Nuclear Power Plants Ask students to identify the nuclear power plant located closest to their community and write their findings in their Science Journals. Have them include the plant's name and location, when it began operation, how much electricity it generates, and its operating history. Answers will depend on the location of their community. L3

LS **Linguistic**

Teacher FYI

Chernobyl After the Chernobyl accident in 1986, people all over the world became concerned about the safety of nuclear reactors. Although all reactors have some risks, reactors in the United States are far safer than the one in Chernobyl. Most importantly, the Chernobyl reactor did not have a containment shell that could prevent the escape of radioactive materials.

Activity

Nuclear Waste Disposal Ask students to generate ideas for nuclear waste disposal. Remind them to consider short-term and long-term effects as well as the various types of waste. Have students share their ideas in small groups and arrive at a class consensus about the best methods of disposal. L2 LS **Interpersonal**

Figure 16 An explosion occurred at the Chernobyl reactor in the Ukraine after graphite control rods caught fire. The explosion shattered the reactor's roof.

The Release of Radioactivity One of the most serious risks of nuclear power is the escape of harmful radiation from power plants. The fuel rods contain radioactive elements with various half-lives. Some of these elements could cause damage to living organisms if they were released from the reactor core. Nuclear reactors have elaborate systems of safeguards, strict safety precautions, and highly trained workers in order to prevent accidents. In spite of this, accidents have occurred.

For example, in 1986 in Chernobyl, Ukraine, an accident occurred when a reactor core overheated during a safety test. Materials in the core caught fire and caused a chemical explosion that blew a hole in the reactor, as shown in **Figure 16.** This resulted in the release of radioactive materials that were carried by winds and deposited over a large area. As a result of the accident, 28 people died of acute radiation sickness. In the United States, power plants are designed to prevent accidents such as the one that occurred at Chernobyl.

The Disposal of Nuclear Waste

After about three years, not enough fissionable U-235 is left in the fuel pellets in the reactor core to sustain the chain reaction. The spent fuel contains radioactive fission products in addition to the remaining uranium. These fuel pellets are a form of nuclear waste. **Nuclear waste** is any radioactive by-product that results when radioactive materials are used. Nuclear wastes are classified as low-level waste and high-level waste.

Low-Level Waste Low-level nuclear wastes usually contain a small amount of radioactive material. They usually do not contain radioactive materials with long half-lives. Products of some medical and industrial processes are low-level wastes, including items of clothing used in handling radioactive materials. Low-level wastes also include used air filters from nuclear power plants and discarded smoke detectors. Low-level wastes usually are sealed in containers and buried in trenches 30 m deep at special locations. When dilute enough, low-level waste sometimes is released into the air or water.

Science Online

Topic: Storing Nuclear Wastes

Visit gpescience.com for Web links to information about storing nuclear wastes.

Activity Obtain a map or sketch an outline of the United States. Mark the locations of the nuclear waste sites that you found. What do these locations have in common? Why do you think these locations were chosen over other sites that were closer to the nuclear waste generating sites?

Differentiated Instruction

Challenge On March 28, 1979, an accident occurred at the Three-Mile Island Nuclear Plant near Harrisburg, Pennsylvania. Have students find out more about this incident and report their findings to the class. The accident caused a small amount of hydrogen gas to escape the containment shell. Emergency cooling systems eventually contained the problem, but some radiation was released. This accident focused the nation's attention on the potential dangers of nuclear reactors. L3 LS **Linguistic**

High-Level Waste High-level nuclear waste is generated in nuclear power plants and by nuclear weapons programs. After spent fuel is removed from a reactor, it is stored in a deep pool of water, as shown in **Figure 17.** Many of the radioactive materials in high-level nuclear waste have short half-lives. However, the spent fuel also contains materials that will remain radioactive for tens of thousands of years. For this reason, the waste must be disposed of in extremely durable and stable containers.

One method proposed for the disposal of high-level waste is to seal the waste in ceramic glass, which is placed in protective metal-alloy containers. The containers then are buried hundreds of meters below ground in stable rock formations or salt deposits. It is hoped that this will keep the material from contaminating the environment for thousands of years.

Figure 17 Spent nuclear fuel rods are placed underwater after they are removed from the reactor core. The water absorbs the nuclear radiation and prevents it from escaping into the environment.

Reading Check *What is the difference between low-level and high-level nuclear wastes?*

Applying Science

Can a contaminated radioactive site be reclaimed?

In the early 1900s, with the discovery of radium, extensive mining for the element began in the Denver, Colorado, area. Radium is a radioactive element that was used to make watch dials and instrument panels that glowed in the dark. After World War I, the radium industry collapsed. The area was left contaminated with 97,000 tons of radioactive soil and debris containing heavy metals and radium, which is now known to cause cancer. The soil was used as fill, foundation material, left in place, or mishandled.

Radium
88
Ra
(226)

Identifying the Problem

In the 1980s, one area became known as the Denver Radium Superfund Site and was cleaned up by the Environmental Protection Agency. The land then was reclaimed by a local commercial establishment.

Solving the Problem

1. The contaminated soil was placed in one area and a protective cap was placed over it. This area also was restricted from being used for residential homes. Explain why it is important for the protective cap to be maintained and why homes could not be built in this area.
2. The advantages of cleaning up this site are economical, environmental, and social. Give an example of each.

Discussion

Nuclear Waste Sites What are some problems that must be addressed when deciding on a site for nuclear waste? Safe transportation from other sites, possible terrorist plans for theft, political changes on policies and funding, proper storage capability to prevent the risk of radioactive materials from entering the environment L2

LS **Logical-Mathematical**

Reading Check

Answer Low-level nuclear wastes usually contain only a small amount of radioactive material with short half-lives. High-level nuclear wastes are usually highly radioactive and contain material with long half-lives.

Applying Science

Answers

1. The cap has to be maintained to prevent contaminated soil from reaching people. Homes can't be built in this area because all of the contaminated soil may not have been removed and some contamination may have reached the groundwater.
2. Advantages: Economic—jobs, revenue for the community, tax for the state, increase in property values; environmental—elimination of long-term risks for contaminated material, prevention of the migration of metals through the soil, protection of the public from contaminated land and water; social—improvement of the aesthetic quality of the land, commercial buildings can be built.

LAB DEMONSTRATION

Purpose to demonstrate how shielding decreases radiation levels

Materials alpha, beta, and gamma sources; Geiger counter; 3 lead sheets

Procedure Place the alpha source near the Geiger counter. Note the intensity measured by the counter. Place a lead sheet between the source and the counter, and note the change in intensity. Repeat for the beta source using one lead sheet and for the gamma source using first one, then two, then three lead sheets.

Expected Outcome One lead sheet blocks the alpha and beta radiation. The intensity of the gamma radiation decreases with additional shielding.

Assessment

How were measurements affected by the amount of shielding? Increased shielding meant less radiation was measured.

SECTION 2 Nuclear Energy 499

Caption Answer

Figure 18 A small amount of mass is converted into energy.

Post Reading

Debates and Discussions Ask students to research the pros and cons of using nuclear energy. Then, engage the class in a discussion of the topic, encouraging students to take a position on the use of nuclear energy in the United States.

3 Assess

DAILY INTERVENTION

Check for Understanding

Visual-Spatial Have students draw a diagram of atoms undergoing nuclear fission and nuclear fusion. Students should label the reactants and products of each reaction, as well as the type of atom that is undergoing the process.

Reteach

Nuclear Reactors Have each student make a simple sketch of a nuclear reactor, showing the major parts of the reactor and describing the function of each of them. L2 LS **Visual-Spatial** P

Assessment

Content Have students draw diagrams showing a nuclear fission chain reaction and how it is controlled in nuclear power plants. Use **PASC,** p. 163.

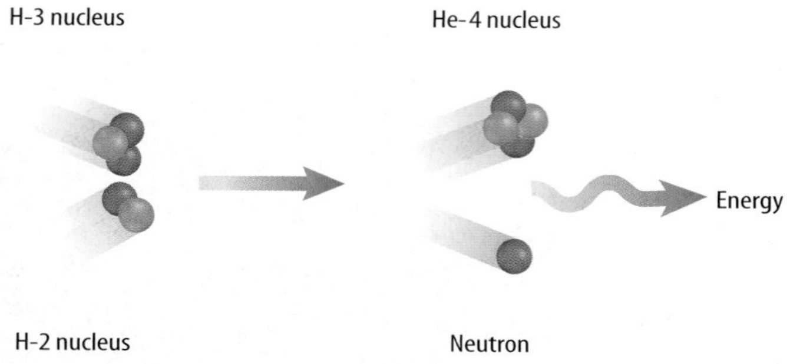

Figure 18 In nuclear fusion, two smaller nuclei join together to form a larger nucleus. Energy is released in the process. In the reaction shown here, two isotopes of hydrogen come together to form a helium nucleus.
Identify *the source of the energy released in a fusion reaction.*

Nuclear Fusion

The Sun gives off a tremendous amount of energy through a process called thermonuclear fusion. Thermonuclear fusion is the joining together of small nuclei at high temperatures, as shown in **Figure 18.** In this process, a small amount of mass is converted into energy. Fusion is the most concentrated energy source known.

An advantage of producing energy using nuclear fusion is that the process uses hydrogen as fuel. Hydrogen is abundant on Earth. Another advantage is that the product of the reaction is helium. Helium is not radioactive and is chemically nonreactive.

One disadvantage of fusion is that it occurs only at temperatures of millions of degrees Celsius. Research reactors often consume more energy to reach and maintain these temperatures than they produce. Another problem is how to contain a reaction that occurs at such extreme conditions. Until solutions to these and other problems are found, the use of nuclear fusion as an energy source is not practical.

section 2 review

Summary

Using Nuclear Energy

- Nuclear power plants produce about eight percent of the energy used each year in the United States.

Nuclear Power Plants

- Nuclear reactors use the energy released in the fission of U-235 to produce electricity.
- The energy released in the fission reaction is used to make steam. The steam drives a turbine that rotates an electric generator.

The Risks of Nuclear Energy

- Organisms could be damaged if radiation is released from the reactor.
- Nuclear waste is the radioactive by-product produced by using radioactive materials.
- Nuclear power generation produces high-level nuclear wastes.

Self Check

1. **Explain** why a chain reaction occurs when uranium-235 undergoes fission.
2. **Describe** how the chain reaction in a nuclear reactor is controlled.
3. **Compare** the advantages and disadvantages of nuclear power plants and those that burn fossil fuels.
4. **Describe** the advantages and disadvantages of using nuclear fusion reactions as a source of energy.
5. **Think Critically** A research project produced 10 g of nuclear waste with a short half-life. How would you classify this waste, and how would it be disposed of?

Applying Math

6. **Use Percentages** Naturally occurring uranium contains 0.72 percent of the isotope uranium-235. What is the mass of uranium-235 in 2,000 kg of naturally-occurring uranium?

More Section Review gpescience.com

section 2 review

1. Neutrons are produced when U-235 undergoes decay. These neutrons are absorbed by other U-235 neutrons which release more neutrons when they decay.
2. Control rods are used to absorb excess neutrons.
3. Advantages: Nuclear power plants do not release air pollutants or carbon dioxide; Disadvantages: The mining of uranium can cause environmental damage. The possible escape of harmful radiation and the disposal of nuclear wastes are additional disadvantages of nuclear power generation.
4. Advantages: A small amount of mass is converted into a large amount of energy. Hydrogen is an abundant fuel source; Disadvantages: The reaction occurs at difficult-to-maintain temperatures. The extreme temperatures involved make the reaction hard to contain.
5. It is a low-level waste that should be sealed in an insulated container and buried in a repository.
6. 14.4 kg

section 3

Renewable Energy Sources

Reading Guide

What You'll Learn

- **Analyze** the need for alternate energy sources.
- **Describe** alternate methods for generating electricity.
- **Compare** the advantages and disadvantages of various alternate energy sources.

Why It's Important

Alternative energy sources need to be explored because the primary sources of energy used in the United States are nonrenewable.

Review Vocabulary

radiant energy: the energy carried by an electromagnetic wave

New Vocabulary

- renewable resource
- photovoltaic cell
- hydroelectricity
- geothermal energy
- biomass

Energy Options

The demand for energy continues to increase, but supplies of fossil fuels are decreasing. Using more nuclear reactors to produce electricity will produce more high-level nuclear waste that has to be disposed of safely. As a result, other sources of energy that can meet Earth's increasing energy demands are being developed. Some alternative energy sources are considered to be renewable resources. A **renewable resource** is an energy source that is replaced nearly as quickly as it is used.

Energy from the Sun

The average amount of solar energy that falls on the United States in one day is more than the total amount of energy used in the United States in one year. Because only about one billionth of the Sun's energy falls on Earth, and because the Sun is expected to continue producing energy for several billion years, solar energy cannot be used up. Solar energy is a renewable resource.

Many devices use solar energy for power including solar-powered calculators similar to the one in **Figure 19.** These devices use a **photovoltaic cell** that converts radiant energy from the Sun directly into electrical energy. Photovoltaic cells also are called solar cells.

Figure 19 This calculator uses a solar cell to produce the electricity it needs to operate.

Section 3 Resource Manager

Chapter *FAST FILE* Resources

Transparency Activity, p. 46

MiniLAB, p. 4

Enrichment, p. 32

Directed Reading for Content Mastery, pp. 21–22

Reinforcement, p. 29

Lab Worksheet, pp. 5–6, 7–8

Lab Activities, pp. 9–12, 13–16

Home and Community Involvement, p. 42

Mathematics Skill Activities, p. 31

1 Motivate

INTERACTIVE CHALKBOARD An editable Microsoft® PowerPoint® presentation is available on **Interactive Chalkboard** CD-ROM.

Bellringer

Section Focus Transparencies also are available on the Interactive Chalkboard CD-ROM.

L2 ELL

Section 3 Section Focus Transparency **Sun Power!** Chapter 16

NASA is developing solar-powered aircraft that have the ability to stay in the air for months at a time! They can be used for studying the atmosphere, storms, crop damage, or fires.

1. **What might be a big difficulty for solar-powered aircraft? What are the advantages?**
2. **Name some organisms that collect the Sun's energy.**
3. **What other uses of solar power can you name?**

L2

Energy Sources

Reading Preview

Tie to Prior Knowledge

Alternative Energy Sources Every day we turn on lights and ride in cars. Ask students what it would be like if suddenly our sources of fossil fuels ran out. Explain that this section describes alternative sources of energy.

Structural Word Analysis Have students break the new vocabulary words into parts (prefixes, suffixes, and base words) to identify meaning. For example, *geothermal* can be broken down into the parts *geo* meaning "earth" and *thermal*, relating to heat. Students should then predict word meaning.

2 Teach

Use Science Words

Word Meaning Why are solar cells also known as photovoltaic cells? *Photo* - means "light," and *voltaic* refers to electricity. L2 LS **Linguistic**

Caption Answer

Figure 20 Possible answers are a calculator and a highway sign that displays messages using lights.

Mini LAB

Purpose Students analyze the use of solar energy. L2 ELL LS **Kinesthetic**

Materials piece of cloth, watch or clock, water, scissors

Analysis

1. the cloth in direct sunlight
2. The energy absorbed from the Sun warms the cloth and makes the water evaporate quicker.

Assessment

Oral Ask students to identify the dependent and independent variables and the constants in this experiment. The dependent variable is drying time and the independent variable is location of the cloth. Constants include size, type, and initial dampness of the cloth.

Try at Home

Figure 20 Solar cells convert radiant energy from the Sun to electricity. **Identify** *two devices that use solar cells for power.*

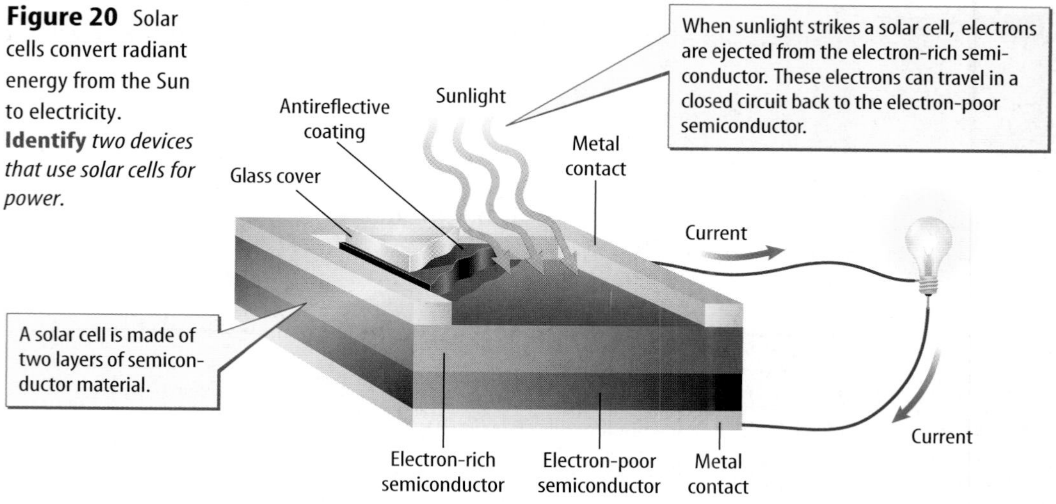

Mini LAB

Using Solar Power at Home

Procedure

1. Cut a **piece of cloth** into two pieces about 10 cm on each side.
2. Wet both pieces and wring them out so they are equally damp.
3. Spread the pieces out to dry outside. One piece should be in sunlight and the other should be in shade.
4. Record the time it takes for each piece to dry.

Analysis

1. Which piece of cloth received more solar energy?
2. Explain why the drying time for a piece of cloth depends on the amount of solar energy it receives.

Try at Home

How Solar Cells Work Solar cells are made of two layers of semiconductor materials sandwiched between two layers of conducting metal, as shown in **Figure 20.** One layer of semiconductor is rich in electrons, while the other layer is electron poor. When sunlight strikes the surface of the solar cell, electrons flow through an electrical circuit from the electron-rich semiconductor to the electron-poor material. This process of converting radiant energy from the Sun directly to electrical energy is only about 7 percent to 11 percent efficient.

Using Solar Energy Producing large amounts of electrical energy using solar cells is more expensive than producing electrical energy using fossil fuels. However, in remote areas where electric distribution lines are not available, the use of solar cells is a practical way of providing electrical power.

Currently, the most promising solar technologies are those that concentrate the solar power into a receiver. One such system is called the parabolic trough. The trough focuses the sunlight on a tube that contains a heat-absorbing fluid such as synthetic oil or liquid salt. The heated fluid is circulated through a boiler where it generates steam to turn a turbine, generating electricity.

The world's largest concentrating solar power plant is located in the Mojave Desert in California. This facility consists of nine units that generate over 350 megawatts of power. These nine units can generate enough electrical power to meet the needs of approximately 500,000 people. These units use natural gas as a backup power source for generating electricity at night and on cloudy days when solar energy is unavailable.

Visual Learning

Figure 20 The semiconductor layers of this solar cell form a diode, a device that allows current to flow in only one direction. Thin metal strips on top of the cell serve as contacts for collecting the current. One advantage of solar cells is that they have no moving parts. Why does this make them attractive for use on satellites in space? Solar cells require no maintenance and no fuel.

Differentiated Instruction

Learning Disabled Have students bring in devices that use solar cells, such as toys and calculators. Show how the devices stop working if the solar cell's light source is blocked. L1 ELL LS **Visual-Spatial**

Energy from Water

Just as the expansion of steam can turn an electric generator, rapidly moving water can as well. The gravitational potential energy of the water can be increased if the water is retained by a high dam. This potential energy is released when the water flows through tunnels near the base of the dam. **Figure 21** shows how the rushing water spins a turbine, which rotates the shaft of an electric generator to produce electricity. Dams built for this purpose are called hydroelectric dams.

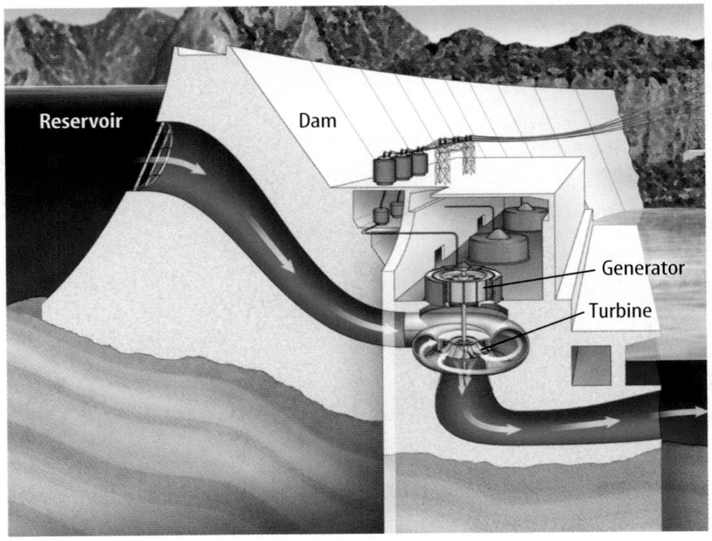

Figure 21 The potential energy in water stored behind the dam is converted to electrical energy in a hydroelectric power plant.
Diagram *the energy conversions that occur as a hydroelectric dam produces electrical energy.*

Using Hydroelectricity Electricity produced from the energy of moving water is called **hydroelectricity.** Currently about 8 percent of the electrical energy used in the United States is produced by hydroelectric power plants. Hydroelectric power plants are an efficient way to produce electricity with almost no pollution. Because no exchange of heat is involved in producing steam to spin a turbine, hydroelectric power plants are almost twice as efficient as fossil fuel or nuclear power plants.

Reading Check *Why are hydroelectric power plants more efficient than fossil fuel power plants?*

Another advantage is that the bodies of water held back by dams can form lakes that can provide water for drinking and crop irrigation. These lakes also can be used for boating and swimming. Also, after the initial cost of building a dam and a power plant, the electricity is relatively cheap.

However, artificial dams can disturb the balance of natural ecosystems. Some species of fish that live in the ocean migrate back to the rivers in which they were hatched to breed. This migration can be blocked by dams, which causes a decline in the fish population. Fish ladders, such as those shown in **Figure 22,** have been designed to enable fish to migrate upstream past some dams. Also, some water sources suitable for a hydroelectric power plant are located far from the regions needing power.

Figure 22 Fish ladders enable fish to migrate upstream past dams.

Discussion

Water Use Water is a free and renewable resource. Why, then, doesn't it supply more of our energy needs? Most sites suitable for developing hydroelectric power are already in use. Hydroelectric plants cannot be built in other locations because they disrupt the natural ecosystems or the geography of the location does not make it practical. L2 LS **Logical-Mathematical**

Caption Answer

Figure 21 The kinetic energy of falling water produces mechanical energy when it strikes and rotates the turbine. The turbine rotates a shaft of an electric generator that transforms mechanical energy to electrical energy.

IDENTIFYING Misconceptions

Alternative Energy Sources Students may think that because an alternative energy source isn't economical on a large scale that it isn't useful. Explain that many alternative energy sources, such as hydroelectricity, solar power, and wind power, are ideal for use on a small scale in rural areas or in developing societies.

Reading Check

Answer Hydroelectric power plants do not have a loss of energy converting thermal energy to mechanical energy. The falling water provides the mechanical energy required to turn the turbine to generate electricity.

Reading Strategy

Metacognitive Strategy Have students read the sections titled Energy from Water, Energy from the Tides, and Harnessing the Wind. As students read, ask them to notice where they struggle with comprehension. Engage the class in a discussion of how, where, and when comprehension breaks down.

Cultural Diversity

The Amish and Electricity The Amish in the United States avoid modern technology and focus on a simple life based on family, church, and community. Have students find out more about how the Amish use technology. Some Amish will use such things as telephones and cars without owning them. Some have their own electrical generators, but do not tap into public power supplies. L3 LS **Linguistic**

SECTION 3 Renewable Energy Sources **503**

Teacher FYI

Tidal Energy The Annapolis Royal tidal energy plant is located on the Bay of Fundy between New Brunswick and Nova Scotia in Canada, which has tides up to 17 meters high. These are the highest tides in the world. L3

LS **Linguistic**

Discussion

Tide Height Why do some coastal areas have higher tides than others? The height of the tide is increased by geographical features, such as the shapes of bays and inlets and the slope of the ocean floor.

Fun Fact

Tidal energy is possible only if the difference between high and low tides is more than 5 m. A higher tide difference means the plant can produce more electricity at a lower cost. A dam is needed to hold back the water at high tide. The dam's high construction cost makes it cheaper to build tidal plants on narrow inlets.

Quick Demo

Windmills

Materials toy pinwheel

Estimated Time five minutes

Procedure Use a toy pinwheel to demonstrate how a windmill works. Blow gently into the pinwheel forcing it to spin.

Figure 23 This tidal energy plant at Annapolis Royal, Nova Scotia, generates 20 megawatts of electric power.

Energy from the Tides

The gravity of the Moon and Sun causes bulges in Earth's oceans. As Earth rotates, the two bulges of ocean water move westward. Each day, the level of the ocean on a coast rises and falls continually. Hydroelectric power can be generated by these ocean tides. As the tide comes in, the moving water spins a turbine that generates electricity. The water is then trapped behind a dam. At low tide the water behind the dam flows back out to the ocean, spinning the turbines and generating electric power.

Tidal energy is nearly pollution free. The efficiency of a tidal power plant is similar to that of a conventional hydroelectric power plant. However, only a few places on Earth have large enough differences between high and low tides for tidal energy to be a useful energy source. The only tidal power station in use in North America is at Annapolis Royal, Nova Scotia, shown in **Figure 23.** Tidal energy probably will be a limited source of energy in the future.

Harnessing the Wind

You might have seen a windmill on a farm or pictures of windmills in a book. These windmills use the energy of the wind to pump water. Windmills also can use the energy of the wind to generate electricity. Wind spins a propeller that is connected to an electric generator. Windmill farms, like the one shown in **Figure 24,** may contain several hundred windmills.

Figure 24 Wind energy is converted to electricity as the spinning propeller turns a generator.

However, only a few places on Earth consistently have enough wind to rely on wind power to meet energy needs. Also, windmills are only about 20 percent efficient on average. Research is underway to improve the design of wind generators and increase their efficiency. Other disadvantages of wind energy are that windmills can be noisy and change the appearance of a landscape. Also, they can disrupt the migration patterns of some birds. However, wind generators do not consume any nonrenewable natural resources, and they do not pollute the atmosphere or water.

Teacher FYI

Tidal Power Plants The world's first and largest tidal power plant began operating in 1967 at the Rance River in France, with a capacity of 240 MW. The Annapolis Royal plant in Canada has a 20-MW capacity, and the tidal plant near Murmansk in Russia has a capacity of 0.4 MW.

Differentiated Instruction

English-Language Learners Have students create a poster showing different types of renewable energy sources. Have students find a real location or an example that uses each type of renewable energy to generate power. Include these examples on the poster. P

Energy from Inside Earth

INTEGRATE Earth Science Earth is not completely solid. Heat is generated within Earth by the decay of radioactive elements. This heat is called geothermal heat. Geothermal heat causes the rock beneath Earth's crust to soften and melt. This hot molten rock is called magma. The thermal energy that is contained in hot magma is called **geothermal energy.**

In some places, Earth's crust has cracks or thin spots that allow magma to rise near the surface. Active volcanoes, for example, permit hot gases and magma from deep within Earth to escape. Perhaps you have seen a geyser, like Old Faithful in Yellowstone National Park, shooting steam and hot water. The water that shoots from the geyser is heated by magma close to Earth's surface. In some areas, this hot water can be pumped into houses to provide heat.

Reading Check *What two natural phenomena are caused by geothermal heat?*

Science Online

Topic: Geothermal Energy
Visit gpescience.com for Web links to information about geothermal energy.

Activity Using the information that you find, write a paragraph describing why geothermal power plants are located where they are.

Geothermal Power Plants

Geothermal energy also can be used to generate electricity, as shown in **Figure 25.** Where magma is close to the surface, the surrounding rocks are also hot. A well is drilled and water is pumped into the ground, where it makes contact with the hot rock and changes into steam. The steam then returns to the surface, where it is used to rotate turbines that spin electric generators.

The efficiency of geothermal power plants is about 16 percent. Although geothermal power plants can release some gases containing sulfur compounds, pumping the water created by the condensed steam back into Earth can help reduce this pollution. However, the use of geothermal energy is limited to areas where magma is relatively close to the surface.

Figure 25 A geothermal power plant converts geothermal energy to electrical energy.

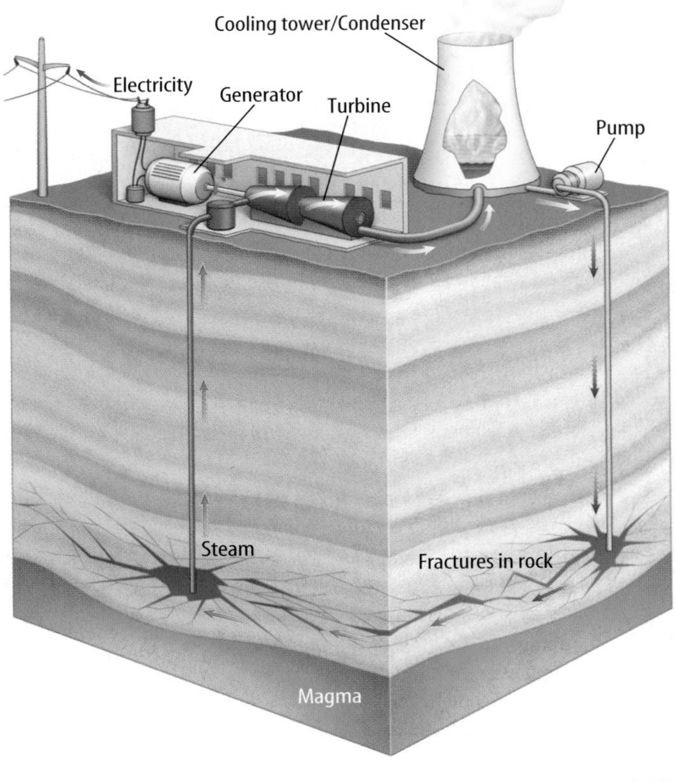

INTEGRATE Earth Science Content Background
Most sources of geothermal energy are in areas with high volcanic activity. Geothermal energy is used on a large scale in Japan, Iceland, Italy, New Zealand, and California.

Discussion

Geothermal Energy Is geothermal energy renewable? Heat from a particular reservoir can be used up faster than it can be replaced, so it is not renewable. However, radioactive decay will provide a constant heat source for millions of years. L3 LS **Logical-Mathematical**

Use Science Words

Word Meaning Why is heat from Earth called "geothermal"? *Geo* means "Earth," and *thermal* means "heat." L2 LS **Linguistic**

Reading Check

Answer volcanoes and geysers

Visual Learning

Figure 25 In a geothermal plant such as the one shown here, after the steam has turned the turbine, the steam is condensed and returned to the rock through the injection well. Why is the water returned to the rock formation? to maintain the supply of water needed to produce steam L2 LS **Logical-Mathematical**

Post Reading

Semantic Feature Analysis Have students list renewable energy sources across the top of a grid. Along the sides, they should list features the energy sources might possess. For example, they might list "can be burned to provide heat." To analyze the energy sources, students will write "+" if the feature is present, and "−" if it is not.

Differentiated Instruction

Challenge Have students research and write descriptions of the various forces that affect wind. They might write about the effects of temperature and pressure, surface obstacles, Earth's rotation, sea breezes, and mountain breezes. L3 LS **Logical-Mathematical**

Discussion

Alternative Fuels Using biomass and other alternative fuels reduces dependence on foreign oil. Why is this desirable? Political disagreements could reduce access to foreign oil because of strained relations with some countries. L3 LS **Logical-Mathematical**

3 Assess

DAILY INTERVENTION

Check for Understanding

Interpersonal Have the students work in small groups. Each group should choose one of the energy sources discussed in the chapter. Have the students devise a plan describing how their chosen energy source could be used in their community.

Reteach

Renewable Energy Sources Ask students to list the six energy sources discussed in this section. Once the students have a complete list, ask them to write a sentence about each source, describing how it can be used to provide energy. L2 LS **Linguistic**

Assessment

Performance Have students work in small groups to design and create a system for heating water using solar power. Use **PASC,** p. 117.

Figure 26 Hydrogen may one day replace gasoline as a fuel for automobiles. Burning hydrogen produces water vapor, instead of carbon dioxide.

Alternative Fuels

The use of fossil fuels would be greatly reduced if cars could run on other fuels or sources of energy. For example, cars have been developed that use electrical energy supplied by batteries as a power source. Hybrid cars use both electric motors and gasoline engines. Hydrogen gas is another possible alternative fuel. It produces only water vapor when it burns and creates no pollution. **Figure 26** shows a car that is equipped to use hydrogen as fuel.

Biomass Fuels Could any other materials be used to heat water and produce electricity like fossil fuels and nuclear fission? Biomass can be burned in the presence of oxygen to convert the stored chemical energy to thermal energy. **Biomass** is renewable organic matter, such as wood, sugarcane fibers, rice hulls, and animal manure. Converting biomass is probably the oldest use of natural resources for meeting human energy needs.

section 3 review

Summary

Energy Options

- The development of alternative energy sources can help reduce the use of fossil fuels.

Solar Energy

- Photovoltaic cells, or solar cells, convert radiant energy from the Sun into electrical energy.
- Producing large amounts of energy from solar cells is more expensive than using fossil fuels.

Other Renewable Energy Sources

- Hydroelectric power plants convert the potential energy in water to electrical energy.
- Tidal energy, wind energy, and geothermal energy can be converted into electrical energy, but are useable only in certain locations.
- Alternative fuels such as hydrogen could be used to power cars, and biomass can be burned to provide heat.

Self Check

1. **Explain** the need to develop and use alternative energy sources.
2. **Describe** three ways that solar energy can be used.
3. **Explain** how the generation of electricity by hydroelectric, tidal, and wind sources are similar to each other.
4. **Explain** why geothermal energy is unlikely to become a major energy source.
5. **Think Critically** What single energy source do most energy alternatives depend on, either directly or indirectly?

Applying Math

6. **Use Percentages** A house uses solar cells that generate 6.0 kW of electrical power to supply some of its energy needs. If the solar panels supply the house with 40 percent of the power it needs, how much power does the house use?

More Section Review gpescience.com

section 3 review

1. The use of alternative energy sources can cause the use of fossil fuels to be reduced. This would make the supply of fossil fuels last longer, and reduce the emission of pollutants and carbon dioxide into the atmosphere.
2. Possible answers: Let the sun warm and light rooms. Use solar panels for heating water or air. Use photovoltaic cells to produce electricity.
3. They are all renewable sources. Each of these spins a turbine to rotate the shaft of an electric generator.
4. It is limited to areas where magma is relatively close to the surface.
5. the Sun
6. 15 kW

LAB

Solar Heating

Energy from the Sun is absorbed by Earth and makes its temperature warmer. In a similar way, solar energy also is absorbed by solar collectors to heat water and buildings.

Real-World Problem

Does the rate at which an object absorbs solar energy depend on the color of the object?

Goals

- **Demonstrate** solar heating.
- **Compare** the effectiveness of heating items of different colors.
- **Graph** your results.

Materials

small cardboard boxes
black, white, and colored paper
tape or glue
thermometer
watch with a second hand

Procedure

1. Cover at least three small boxes with colored paper. The colors should include black and white as well as at least one other color.
2. Copy the data table into your Science Journal. Replace *Other color* with whatever color you are using.
3. Place the three objects on a windowsill or other sunny spot and note the starting time.
4. **Measure and record** the temperature inside each box at 2-min intervals for at least 10 min.

Temperature Due to Different Colors

Color	2 min	4 min	6 min	8 min	10 min
Black	Student answers will vary.				
White					
Other color					

Conclude and Apply

1. **Graph** your data using a line graph.
2. **Describe** the shapes of the lines on your graph. What color heated up the fastest? Which heated up the slowest?
3. **Explain** why the colored boxes heated at different rates.
4. **Infer** Suppose you wanted to heat a tub of water using solar energy. Based on the results of this activity, what color would you want the tub to be? Explain.
5. **Explain** why you might want to wear a white or light-colored shirt on a hot, sunny, summer day.

Communicating Your Data

Compare your results with those of other students in your class. Discuss any differences found in your graphs, particularly if different colors were used by different groups.

BENCH TESTED

Video Lab available for this Lab.

Real-World Problem

Purpose Students demonstrate how various colors absorb solar energy differently and graph the results. L2 LS **Kinesthetic**

Process Skills observe, infer, compare and contrast, recognize cause and effect, communicate, make and use tables, make and use graphs, interpret data

Time Required 45 minutes

Procedure

Teaching Strategy Suggest students work in pairs to make measurements. One student can read the thermometer as the other student fills in the data table. Have students work individually to prepare their graphs.

Troubleshooting Students should cover each box in a way that does not allow heat to escape.

Conclude and Apply

1. Suggest students use a different color line for each color of paper.
2. The lines all sloped upward. Black heated the fastest. White heated the slowest.
3. Black absorbs more light energy, which makes it heat faster, and white absorbs less light energy, which makes it heat more slowly.
4. Because black heats up faster, you would want the tub to be black.
5. You would want to wear a white or light-colored shirt because it absorbs less light energy and wouldn't heat up as quickly.

Assessment

Content Have students make cartoons illustrating situations in which the color of something is important to its temperature. For example, dark-colored car seats are hotter in summer than those with a light color. Use **Performance Assessment in the Science Classroom,** p. 133.

Communicating Your Data

Have students use a computer graphing program to prepare their graphs. Encourage them to make their graphs as clear as possible so that others can understand the results easily. Remind students that a clear presentation of data is important to help others benefit from their work.

BENCH TESTED

Real-World Problem

Purpose

Internet Students will use Internet sites that can be accessed by visiting gpescience.com. They will investigate the costs and environmental impacts of different energy sources.

Non-Internet Sources Product information publications often have comparison data for energy sources such as batteries, as well as energy efficiency ratings for appliances.

Process Skills gather and organize information, evaluate sources of information, make and use tables, compare and contrast, evaluate, infer

Time Required about three days

Make a Plan

Preparation

Internet Visit gpescience.com to run through the steps students will follow.

Non-Internet Sources Collect magazines and periodicals that list efficiencies of energy sources and appliances.

Follow Your Plan

Teaching Strategy Remind students that they should consider how different energy sources, such as rechargeable batteries and disposable batteries, affect the environment.

LAB Use the Internet

How much does energy really co$t?

Goals

- **Identify** three energy sources that people use.
- **Determine** the cost of the energy produced by each source.
- **Describe** the environmental impact of each source.

Data Source

Internet Lab

Visit gpescience.com for more information about energy sources and for data collected by other students.

Real-World Problem

You know that it costs money to produce energy. Using energy also can have an impact on the environment. For example, coal costs less than some other fuels. However, combustion is a chemical reaction that can produce pollutants, and burning coal produces more pollution than burning other fossil fuels, such as natural gas. Even energy sources, such as hydroelectric power, that don't produce pollution can have an impact on the environment. What are some of the environmental impacts of the evergy sources used in the United States? How can these environmental impacts be compared to the cost of the energy produced?

Make a Plan

1. **Research** the various sources of energy used in different areas of the United States and choose three energy sources to investigate.
2. **Research** the cost of the consumer of 1 kWh of electrical energy generated by energy sources you have choosen.
3. **Determine** the effects each of the three energy sources has on the environment.
4. **Use** your data to create a table showing the energy sources, and the energy cost and environmental impact of each energy source.
5. **Decide** how you will evaluate the environmental impact of each of your energy sources.
6. **Write** a summary describing which of your three energy sources is the most cost-effective for producing energy. Consider the cost of the energy and your evaluation of the environmental impact in making your decision. Use information from your research to support your conclusions.

Alternative Inquiry Lab

Real-World Connection To make this Lab an Inquiry Lab, give the students a more personal investment into the problem by connecting it to the real world. Divide the students into small groups. Each group will start a small imaginary manufacturing facility. The facility must be powered primarily by some type of renewable energy. At least 60 percent of the power for the facility must come from an on-site renewable energy source. Have students investigate the types of energy sources available for their area. Students should develop a site plan for their facility that includes a site for their renewable energy source. This Lab will help students develop problem-solving skills, critical-thinking skills, and team-building skills.

Using Scientific Methods

Follow Your Plan

1. Make sure your teacher approves your plan before you start.
2. **Record** your data in your Science Journal.

Analyze Your Data

1. Of the energy sources you investigated, which is the most expensive to use? The least expensive?
2. Which energy source do you think has the most impact on the environment? The least impact?

Energy Sources

Energy Source	Cost per kWh	Environmental Impacts
Energy source 1	Student answers will vary.	
Energy source 2		
Energy source 3		

Conclude and Apply

1. **Explain** Of the energy sources you investigated, which is the least expensive energy source? Which is the best choice to use? Why?
2. **Explain** Of the energy sources you investigated, how did the environmental impact of using that energy source influence your choice of the best energy solution?
3. **Evaluate** Which data support your decision?

Communicating Your Data

Find this lab using the link below. Post your data in the table provided. **Compare** your data to those of other students.

Internet Lab
gpescience.com

Analyze Your Data

1. Answers may vary. Remind students to consider the costs of producing energy sources as they evaluate the cost of using each source.
2. Answers may vary. Students should evaluate different environmental impacts of energy sources, such as water pollution and pollutants released into the ground.

Conclude and Apply

1. To support their answers, ask students to provide specific facts to explain why an energy source is the least expensive or the most expensive and the best choice.
2. Student responses should describe how the chosen energy source affects the environment.
3. Information from scientific and energy industry sources may provide data to support students' hypotheses.

Assessment

Process Have students make displays describing their findings. Displays should include the items that were investigated, students' hypotheses, different energy sources that could be used to operate the items, and the cost and environmental impact of each energy source. Use **Performance Assessment in the Science Classroom,** p. 135.

Communicating Your Data

Have students design a rating system to evaluate the environmental impact of various energy sources. After analyzing each energy source for each criterion, students can make bar graphs representing their results.

TIME

Content Background

Nuclear energy is a complicated subject. Images of the devastation from atomic explosions and sensational accounts of the dangers of radiation have created fear regarding anything labeled *nuclear*. The abstract nature of the subject offers little comfort to the layman.

Radiation occurs when an unstable atom ejects particles or energy from its nucleus in the process of becoming stable. Fission, the splitting of an atom into two smaller atoms, releases neutrons. These neutrons collide with other nuclei, causing them to split and emit neutrons. This process can cause a chain reaction. Nuclear fission reactions can release high-energy electromagnetic radiation called gamma rays, which can only be blocked by lead or thick concrete.

Discussion

Drawbacks Are there any drawbacks to wind, hydroelectric, or tidal power technologies? Possible answers: Wind and tide generation are variable and restricted to a localized area. Hydroelectric power requires building dams, which then have an impact on wildlife habitats. Wind and hydro power use much more land area per kilowatt than the other sources of power.

Investigate the Issue

Have students research the feasibility of power sources not discussed in the article such as fusion and fuel cells. Discuss whether any of these might replace currently available sources.

TIME SCIENCE AND Society SCIENCE ISSUES THAT AFFECT YOU!

Reacting to Nuclear Energy

Most people agree that thanks to energy sources, we have many things that make our quality of life better. Energy runs our cars, lights our homes, and powers our appliances. What many people don't agree on is where that energy should come from.

Almost all of the world's electric energy is produced by thermal power plants. Most of these plants burn fossil fuels—such as coal, oil, and natural gas—to produce energy. Nuclear energy is produced by fission, which is the splitting of an atom's nucleus. People in favor of nuclear energy argue that, unlike fossil fuels, nuclear energy is nonpolluting.

Opponents counter, though, that the poisonous radioactive waste created in nuclear reactors qualifies as pollution—and will be lingering in the ground and water for hundreds of thousands of years.

Supporters of nuclear energy also cite the spectacular efficiency of nuclear energy—one metric ton of nuclear fuel produces the same amount of energy as up to 3 million tons of coal. Opponents point out that uranium is in very short supply and, like fossil fuels, is likely to run out in the next 100 years.

Opponents worry that as utilities come under less government regulation, safety standards will be ignored in the interest of profit. This could result in more accidents like the one that occurred at Chernobyl in the Ukraine. There, an explosion in the reactor core released radiation over a wide area.

Supporters counter that it will never be in the best interests of those running nuclear plants to relax safety standards since those safety standards are the best safeguard of workers' health. They cite the overall good safety record of nuclear power plants.

This site at Yucca Mountain, Nevada, is the location of a proposed high-level nuclear waste storage facility. Here, radioactive materials would be buried for tens of thousands of years.

Debate Form three teams and have each team defend one of the views presented here. If you need more information, go to the link at the right. "Debrief" after the debate. Did the arguments change your understanding of the issues?

TIME For more information, visit gpescience.com

Debate Have the teams use the knowledge they gained from the activity and investigation above to help them investigate the cost per kilowatt of one of the technologies discussed. Remind students to keep in mind the amount and type of pollution caused by each technology and by processing its fuel. Ask teams for recommendations about future energy production.

Resources for Teachers and Students

American Nuclear Society, 555 North Kensington Avenue, LaGrange Park, Illinois 60526 USA

Quarks and Sparks: The Story of Nuclear Power (Science and Society Series), by J. S. Kidd and Renee A. Kidd, New York: Facts on File (1999)

American Wind Energy Association, 122 C Street, NW, Suite 380, Washington, DC 20001

Reviewing Main Ideas

Section 1 Fossil Fuels

1. Fossil fuels include oil, natural gas,and coal. They formed from the buried remains of plants and animals.
2. Fossil fuels can be burned to supply energy for generating electricity. Petroleum also is used to make plastics and synthetic fabrics.

3. Fossil fuels are nonrenewable energy resources. They can be replaced, but it takes millions of years.

Section 2 Nuclear Energy

1. A nuclear reactor transforms the nuclear energy from a controlled nuclear chain reaction into electrical energy.
2. Nuclear wastes must be contained and disposed of carefully so radiation from nuclear decay will not leak into the environment. These low-level nuclear wastes are buried to protect living organisms.

3. Nuclear fusion releases energy when two nuclei combine. Fusion only occurs at high temperatures that are difficult to produce in a laboratory.

Section 3 Renewable Energy Sources

1. Alternative energy resources can be used to supplement or replace nonrenewable energy resources.
2. Other sources of energy for generating electricity include hydroelectricity and solar, wind, tidal, and geothermal energy. Each source has its advantages and disadvantages. Also, some of these sources can damage the environment.
3. Although some alternative energy sources produce less pollution than fossil fuels do and are renewable, their use often is limited to the regions where the energy source is available. For example, tides can be used to generate electricity in coastal regions only.

4. It may be possible to use hydrogen as a fuel for automobiles and other vehicles. Biomass, such as wood and other renewable organic matter, has been used as fuel for thousands of years.

FOLDABLES Use the Foldable that you made at the beginning of the chapter to help you review energy sources.

Reviewing Main Ideas

Summary statements can be used by students to review the major concepts of the chapter.

Science Online

Visit gpescience.com
More Section Review
Interactive Tutor
Vocabulary PuzzleMaker
More Chapter Review
Standardized Test Practice

Assessment Transparency

For additional assessment questions, use the *Assessment Transparency* located in the transparency book.

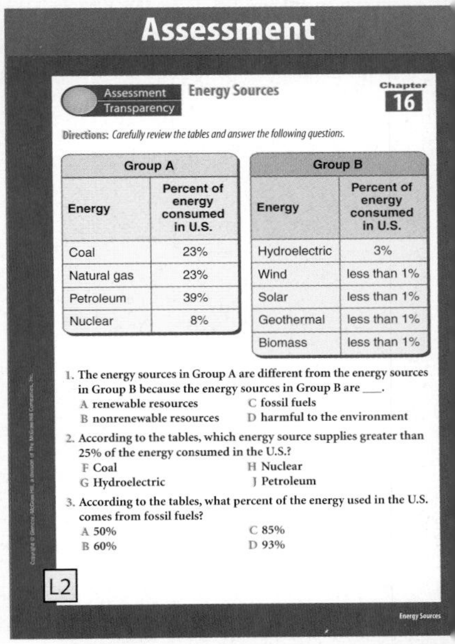

Assessment

Assessment Transparency **Energy Sources** Chapter 16

Directions: *Carefully review the tables and answer the following questions.*

Group A	
Energy	Percent of energy consumed in U.S.
Coal	23%
Natural gas	23%
Petroleum	39%
Nuclear	8%

Group B	
Energy	Percent of energy consumed in U.S.
Hydroelectric	3%
Wind	less than 1%
Solar	less than 1%
Geothermal	less than 1%
Biomass	less than 1%

1. The energy sources in Group A are different from the energy sources in Group B because the energy sources in Group B are ____.
   A renewable resources C fossil fuels
   B nonrenewable resources D harmful to the environment
2. According to the tables, which energy source supplies greater than 25% of the energy consumed in the U.S.?
   F Coal H Nuclear
   G Hydroelectric J Petroleum
3. According to the tables, what percent of the energy used in the U.S. comes from fossil fuels?
   A 50% C 85%
   B 60% D 93%

L2

Energy Sources

FOLDABLES Have students use their Foldables to review the content of the chapter. On the back of the paper, have the students write the advantages and disadvantages of each type of energy source that is listed on the Foldable.

Using Vocabulary

1. photovoltaic cell
2. Geothermal energy
3. renewable resource
4. Fossil fuel
5. nonrenewable
6. nuclear waste

Checking Concepts

7. C
8. A
9. C
10. B
11. A
12. C
13. D
14. B

chapter 16 Review

Using Vocabulary

biomass p. 506	nuclear reactor p. 494
fossil fuel p. 487	nuclear waste p. 498
geothermal energy p. 505	petroleum p. 489
hydroelectricity p. 503	photovoltaic cell p. 501
nonrenewable resource p. 493	renewable resource p. 501

Complete each statement using a term from the vocabulary list above.

1. A(n) _________ uses the Sun to generate electricity.
2. _________ makes use of thermal energy inside the Earth.
3. Energy produced by the rise and fall of ocean levels is a(n) _________.
4. _________ includes the following: oil, natural gas, and coal.
5. Fossil fuels are a(n) _________ because they are being used up faster than they are being made.
6. A special caution should be taken in disposing of _________.

Checking Concepts

Choose the word or phrase that best answers the question.

7. Why are fossil fuels considered to be nonrenewable resources?
   A) They are no longer being produced.
   B) They are in short supply.
   C) They are not being produced as fast as they're being used.
   D) They contain hydrocarbons.
8. To generate electricity, nuclear power plants produce which of the following?
   A) steam **C)** plutonium
   B) carbon dioxide **D)** water
9. What is a major disadvantage of using nuclear fusion reactors?
   A) use of hydrogen as fuel
   B) less radioactivity produced
   C) extremely high temperatures required
   D) use of only small nuclei
10. How are spent nuclear fuel rods usually disposed of?
    A) burying them in a community landfill
    B) storing them in a deep pool of water
    C) burying them at the reactor site
    D) releasing them into the air

Use the graph below to answer question 11.

Sources of Energy

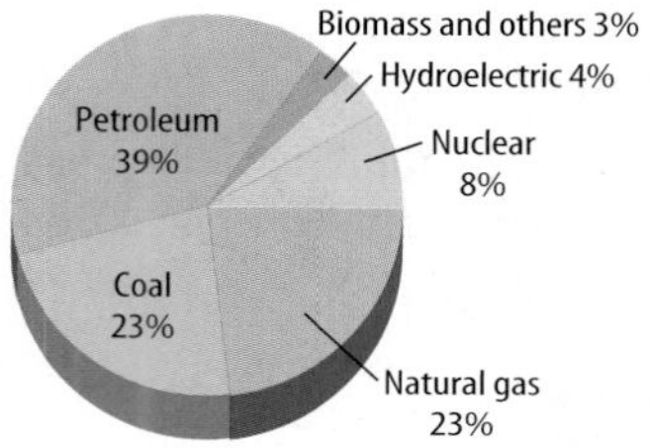

11. How much energy in the United States comes from burning fossil fuels?
    A) 85% **C)** 65%
    B) 35% **D)** 25%
12. What do hydrocarbons react with when fossil fuels are burned?
    A) carbon dioxide **C)** oxygen
    B) carbon monoxide **D)** water
13. Which of the following is NOT a source of nuclear waste?
    A) products of fission reactors
    B) materials with short half-lives
    C) some medical and industrial products
    D) products of coal-burning power plants
14. Which of the following is the source of almost all of Earth's energy resources?
    A) plants **C)** magma
    B) the Sun **D)** fossil fuels

Vocabulary PuzzleMaker gpescience.com

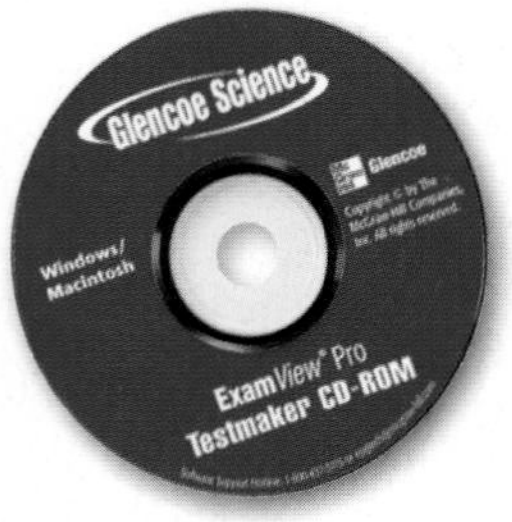

Use the Exam*View*® Pro Testmaker CD-ROM to:

- create multiple versions of tests
- create modified tests with one mouse click for inclusion students
- edit existing questions and add your own questions
- build tests aligned with state standards using built-in State Curriculum Tags
- change English tests to Spanish with one mouse click and vice versa

Interpreting Graphics

15. Copy and complete the table below describing possible effects of changes in the normal operation of a nuclear reactor.

Reactor Problems

Cause	Effect
The cooling water is released hot.	Pollution of the environment results.
The control rods are removed.	More heat is produced in the core.
The cooling system fails.	The reactor core overheats and meltdown occurs.

16. Copy and complete this concept map.

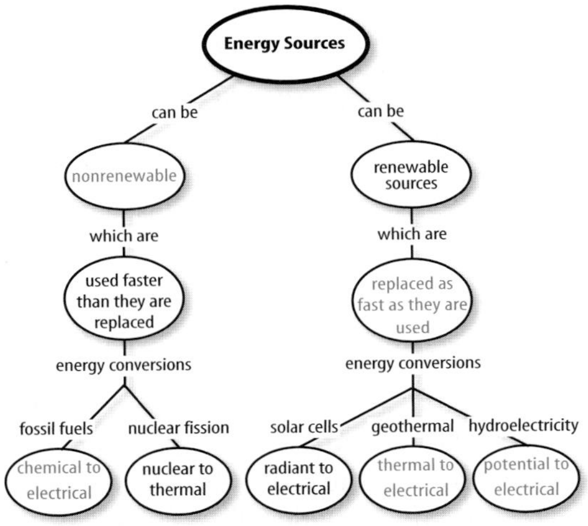

Thinking Critically

17. **Infer** why alternative energy resources aren't more widely used.

18. **Infer** whether fossil fuels should be conserved if renewable energy sources are being developed.

19. **Infer** Suppose new reserves of fossil fuels were found and a way to burn these fuels was developed that did not release pollutants and carbon dioxide into the atmosphere. Should fossil fuels still be conserved? Explain

20. **Explain** why coal is considered a nonrenewable energy source, but biomass, such as wood, is considered a renewable energy source.

21. **Make a table** listing two advantages and two disadvantages for each of the following energy sources: fossil fuels, hydroelectricity, wind turbines, nuclear fission, solar cells, and geothermal energy.

Applying Math

22. **Convert Units** Crude oil is sold on the world market in units called barrels. A barrel of crude oil contains 42 gallons. If 1 gallon is 3.8 liters, how many liters are there in a barrel of crude oil?

Use the table below to answer question 25.

High-Production Coal Mines

Coal Mine	Metric tons/year
North Antelope Rochelle	6.78×10^7
Black Thunder	6.13×10^7

23. **Use Percentages** Nine of the top coal producing mines are located in Wyoming. Production information on two of the mines is in the table above. A total of about 1.02×10^9 metric tons is produced per year in the United States. What percentage do these two coal mines contribute to the total yearly coal production in the U.S.?

Assessment Resources

Reproducible Masters

Chapter *Fast File* Resources
Chapter Review, pp. 37–38
Chapter Tests, pp. 39–42
Assessment Transparency Activity, p. 49

Glencoe Science Web site
Chapter Review Test
Standardized Test Practice

Glencoe Technology
Assessment Transparency
Exam*View*® Pro Testmaker
MindJogger Videoquiz
Interactive Chalkboard

Interpreting Graphics

15. See student page.
16. See student page.

Thinking Critically

17. Alternative energy resources are not widely used because the necessary technology does not yet exist, is too expensive, or has limited applicability.
18. Fossil fuels should be conserved because they are used to produce useful materials, such as plastic.
19. These new sources would still be nonrenewable energy sources. Conserving fossil fuel would make them last longer.
20. Biomass can be replaced in several years by replanting. Coal takes millions of years to form.
21. Fossil fuels: inexpensive and plentiful, but are nonrenewable and produce pollutants. Hydroelectricity: renewable and inexpensive, but can affect local ecosystems and has limited availability. Wind turbines: nonpolluting and use a renewable energy source, but are noisy and have limited availability. Nuclear power: nonpolluting and inexpensive, but problems exist with nuclear waste disposal, and risks of nuclear accidents. Solar cells : use a renewable resource that is available everywhere, but inefficient and expensive. Geothermal energy: uses Earth's heat as a renewable resource and does not produce carbon dioxide, but is inefficient and has limited availability.

Applying Math

Math Standards

National: 1, 5, 9

22. $\frac{42 \text{ gallons}}{1 \text{ barrel}} \times \frac{3.8 \text{ liters}}{1 \text{ gallon}} =$

$159.6 \frac{\text{liters}}{\text{barrel}} = 160 \frac{\text{liters}}{\text{barrel}}$

23. $\frac{1.291 \times 10^8 \text{ metric tons/year}}{1.02 \times 10^9 \text{ metric tons/year}} =$

$0.127 = 12.7\%$

Answer Sheet An answer sheet can be found at **gpescience.com**.

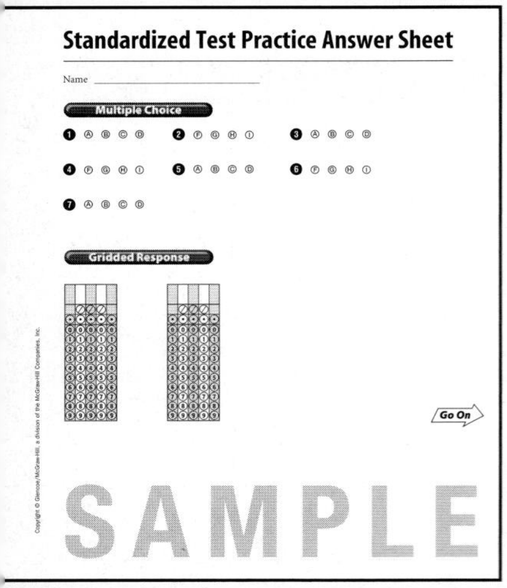

Multiple Choice

1. D
2. B
3. A
4. A
5. B

chapter 16 Standardized Test Practice

Record your answers on the answer sheet provided by your teacher or on a sheet of paper.

Multiple Choice

Use the graph below to answer questions 1 and 2.

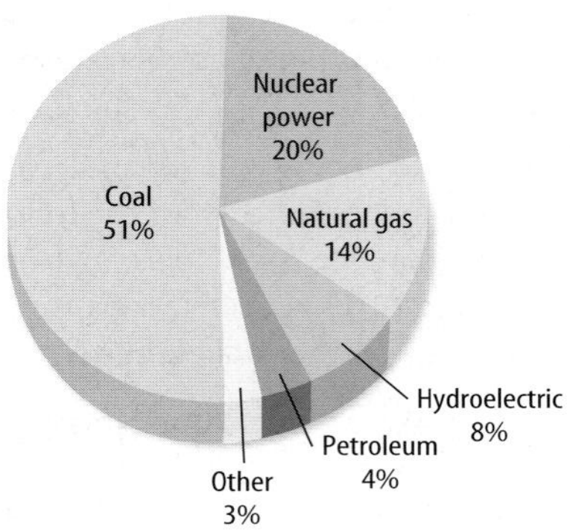

1. The graph above shows the percentage of electricity generated in the United States that comes from various energy sources. According to the graph, about what percentage comes from fossil fuels?

A. 51%

B. 55%

C. 65%

D. 69%

2. The graph shows that approximately what percentage of electricity comes from nonrenewable energy sources?

A. 97%

B. 89%

C. 69%

D. 55%

3. Which of the following is a typical efficiency for a solar cell?

A. 10%

B. 50%

C. 75%

D. 95%

4. Which of the following forms only from ancient plant material, not from ancient animal remains?

A. coal

B. crude oil

C. natural gas

D. petroleum

Use the table below to answer questions 5 and 6.

Efficiency of Fossil-fuel Conversion	
Process	**Efficiency (%)**
Chemical to thermal energy	60
Conversion of water to steam	90
Steam spins turbine	75
Turbine spins electric generator	95
Transmission through power lines	90

5. The table above shows the efficiency of different steps in the conversion of fossil fuels to electricity at a power plant. According to the table, what is the efficiency for converting chemical energy in the fossil fuels to thermal energy, and then converting water to steam?

A. 40%

B. 54%

C. 25%

D. 90%

Gridded Response

6. What is the overall efficiency shown in the table for converting chemical energy in fossil fuels to electricity?

Short Response

Use the illustration below to answer question 7.

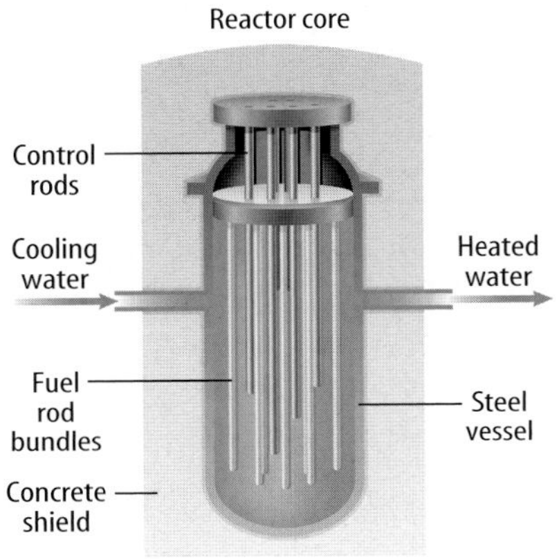

7. Describe the purpose of the control rods and explain how their placement in the reactor affects the nuclear chain reaction.

8. Fusion is the most concentrated energy source known. Why, then, is it not used at nuclear plants to make electricity?

Extended Response

Use the illustration below to answer question 9.

9. The illustration above shows a nuclear power plant that generates electricity using the energy released in nuclear fission of uranium-235. Draw a sketch showing this fission process. Describe your sketch and explain how the process results in a chain reaction.

10. Describe two advantages and two disadvantages of using fossil fuels as a source of energy.

Test-Taking Tip

Determine the Information Needed Concentrate on what the question is asking about a table, instead of all the information in the table.

Question 5 Read the question carefully to determine which rows in the table contain the information needed to answer the question.

Gridded Response

6. 35

Short Response

7. to stop or slow the nuclear chain reaction by absorbing neutrons released during the reaction; Moving these control rods deeper into the reactor allows them to absorb more neutrons and slow down the reaction.
8. Fusion reactions occur only at temperatures of millions of degrees Celsius. Creating and maintaining these high temperatures requires enormous amounts of energy.

Extended Response

9. Use **Figure 14** to check students' sketches.
10. Advantages: relatively inexpensive and easy to transport from place to place.
    Disadvantages: causes pollution and nonrenewable.

Rubrics

For more help evaluating Short- and Extended-Response questions, see the rubric on p. 9T.

chapter 17 Organizer

Section/Objectives	Standards		Lab/Features
	National	State/Local	
Chapter Opener	See pp. 16T–17T for a Key to Standards.		**Launch Lab:** Atmospheric Pressure, p. 517 **Foldables,** p. 517
Section 1 Earth's Atmosphere 2 sessions 1 block 1. **Describe** the composition of the atmosphere. 2. **Explain** how the atmosphere is heated and include the role of land surface and water. 3. **Describe** Earth's system of water cycling.	National Content Standards: UCP.1–3, UCP.5, A.1, A.2, C.6, D.1, D.2		**MiniLAB:** Visualizing Convection, p. 519 Video Lab **Integrate Life Science,** p. 522 **Lab,** Visualizing a Temperature Inversion, p. 523
Section 2 Weather 1 session 1.5 blocks 4. **Explain** what causes Earth's major wind and pressure systems. 5. **Describe** typical daily weather patterns around lows and fronts. 6. **Describe** the most important storm systems and forms of severe weather.	National Content Standards: UCP.1–3, UCP.5, A.1, A.2, D.1, D.2, B.4, B.6, D.1, D.2		**MiniLAB:** Modeling the Coriolis Effect, p. 525 **Science Online,** p. 528
Section 3 Climate 1 session 1.5 blocks 7. **Describe** what determines climate. 8. **Explain** how latitude, oceans, and other factors affect the climate of a region. 9. **Classify** climate systems. 10. **Describe** climate distribution over the United States.	National Content Standards: UCP.1–3, UCP.5, A.1, A.2, B.4, B.6, C.5, D.1		**Science Online,** p. 530 **Visualizing Earth's Biogeophysical System,** p. 531
Section 4 Earth's Changing Climates 3 sessions 1.5 blocks 11. **Explain** how climate changes seasonally. 12. **Explain** causes of climate change. 13. **Describe** how we influence climate. 14. **Describe** El Niño's effect on weather.	National Content Standards: UCP.1–5, A.1, A.2, D.1, D.3, F.4, F.5		**Integrate History,** p. 536 **Applying Math:** Carbon Dioxide (CO_2) Concentration, p. 537 **Lab:** Investigating Microclimate, pp. 540–541 **Science and Language Arts:** The Grapes of Wrath, p. 542

StudentWorks Plus

Glencoe Exclusive! TeacherWorks™ All-In-One Planner and Resource Center

Lab Materials	Reproducible Resources	Section Assessment	Technology
Launch Lab: glass, thick paper or cardboard, water	**Chapter *Fast File* Resources** Foldables Worksheet, p. 17, Directed Reading Overview, p. 19 Note-taking Worksheets, pp. 35–37	Glencoe's Assessment Advantage	TeacherWorks includes: • Interactive Teacher Edition • Lesson Planner with calendar • Access to all program blacklines • Correlations to standards • Web links
MiniLAB: ice cube, water, beaker, food coloring **Lab:** 10-mL beaker, 500-mL beaker, 1,000-mL beaker, food coloring, ladle, long-stem dropper, freezer, hot plate, thermal mitt, water	**Chapter *Fast File* Resources** Transparency Activity, p. 46, 51–52 MiniLAB, p. 3 Enrichment, p. 31 Reinforcement, p. 27 Directed Reading, p. 20 Lab Worksheets, pp. 5–6 Lab Activity, pp. 13–16	**Performance** Applying Math, p. 522 **Content** Section Review, p. 522	Section Focus Transparency Teaching Transparency Interactive Chalkboard CD-ROM StudentWorks Plus Video Lab
MiniLAB: cardboard, turntable, ruler, pen or pencil	**Chapter *Fast File* Resources** Transparency Activity, p. 47 MiniLAB, p. 4 Enrichment, p. 32 Reinforcement, p. 28 Directed Reading, p. 20 **Cultural Diversity,** pp. 47–48 **Lab Management and Safety,** p. 61 **Mathematics Skill Activities,** pp. 41–42	**Portfolio** Assessment p. 528 **Performance** Applying Math, p. 528 **Content** Section Review, p. 528	Section Focus Transparency Interactive Chalkboard CD-ROM StudentWorks Plus
Need materials? Contact Science Kit at 1-800-828-7777 or www.sciencekit.com.	**Chapter *Fast File* Resources** Transparency Activity, p. 48 Lab Activity, pp. 9–12 Enrichment, p. 33 Reinforcement, p. 29 Directed Reading, p. 21 **Reading and Writing Skills Activities,** pp. 3–4	**Performance** Applying Math, p. 534 **Content** Section Review, p. 534	Section Focus Transparency Interactive Chalkboard CD-ROM StudentWorks Plus
Lab: directional compass, thermometer, rain gauge, meterstick, small plastic cups	**Chapter *Fast File* Resources** Transparency Activity, p. 49 Enrichment, p. 34 Reinforcement, p. 30 Directed Reading, pp. 21–22 Lab Worksheets, pp. 7–8	**Performance** Applying Math, p. 537 Applying Math, p. 539 **Content** Section Review, p. 539	Section Focus Transparency Interactive Chalkboard CD-ROM StudentWorks Plus

End of Chapter Assessment

Glencoe's Assessment Advantage

Blackline Masters	Technology	Professional Series
Chapter *Fast File* Resources Chapter Review, pp. 39–40 Chapter Test, pp. 41–44 **Standardized Test Practice,** pp. 72–75	MindJogger Videoquiz Exam*View*® Pro Testmaker TeacherWorks CD-ROM Interactive Chalkboard CD-ROM	**Performance Assessment in the Science Classroom (PASC)**

Transparencies

Section Focus

Section 1 Section Focus Transparency — Satellite View of Earth — Chapter 17

1. At what latitude and longitude is the satellite located?
2. If you were to draw a circle around the diagram to show the troposphere and stratosphere, where would the circles be?
3. Where is the sun located in this picture?

Weather and Climate

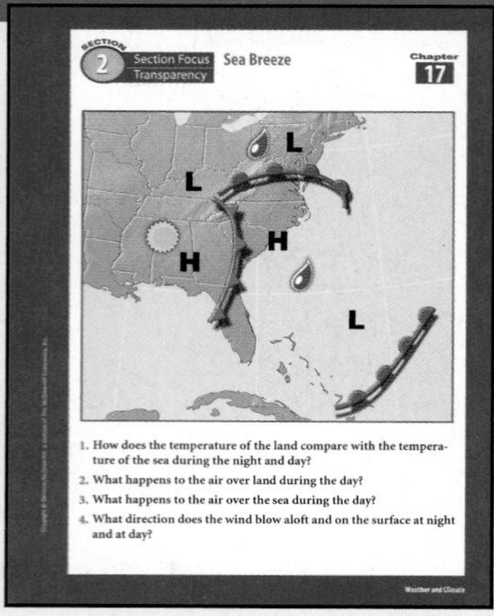

Section 2 Section Focus Transparency — Sea Breeze — Chapter 17

1. How does the temperature of the land compare with the temperature of the sea during the night and day?
2. What happens to the air over land during the day?
3. What happens to the air over the sea during the day?
4. What direction does the wind blow aloft and on the surface at night and at day?

Weather and Climate

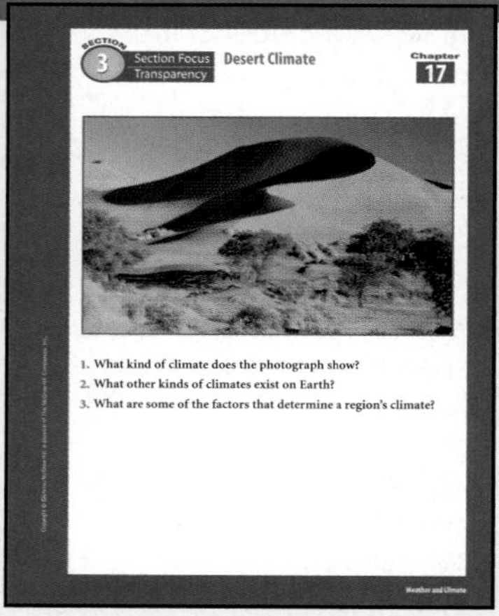
Section 3 Section Focus Transparency — Desert Climate — Chapter 17

1. What kind of climate does the photograph show?
2. What other kinds of climates exist on Earth?
3. What are some of the factors that determine a region's climate?

Weather and Climate

Section 4 Section Focus Transparency — Holgate Glacier — Chapter 17

1. What will happen to the sea level if glaciers melt?
2. What would cause the volume of solid ice on Earth to increase?
3. What is a reason that glaciers, snow, and icecaps can be said to decrease average temperatures of Earth?

Weather and Climate

This is a representation of key blackline masters available in the Teacher Classroom Resources. See Resource Manager boxes within the chapter for additional information.

Assessment

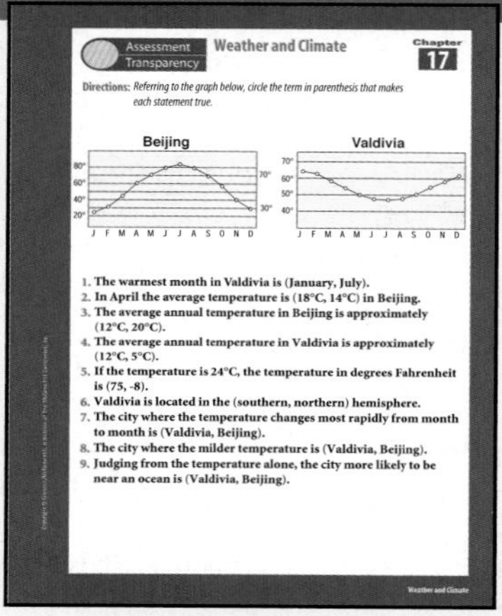
Assessment Transparency — Weather and Climate — Chapter 17

Directions: Referring to the graph below, circle the term in parentheses that makes each statement true.

1. The warmest month in Valdivia is (January, July).
2. In April the average temperature is (18°C, 14°C) in Beijing.
3. The average annual temperature in Beijing is approximately (12°C, 20°C).
4. The average annual temperature in Valdivia is approximately (12°C, 5°C).
5. If the temperature is 24°C, the temperature in degrees Fahrenheit is (75, -8).
6. Valdivia is located in the (southern, northern) hemisphere.
7. The city where the temperature changes most rapidly from month to month is (Valdivia, Beijing).
8. The city where the milder temperature is (Valdivia, Beijing).
9. Judging from the temperature alone, the city more likely to be near an ocean is (Valdivia, Beijing).

Weather and Climate

Teaching

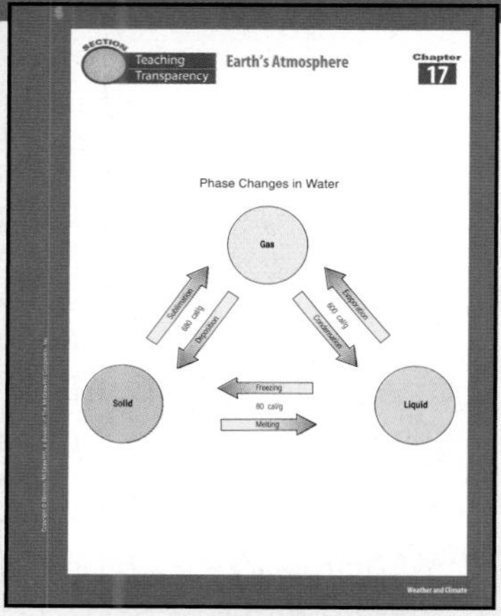
Teaching Transparency — Earth's Atmosphere — Chapter 17

Weather and Climate

Key to Teaching Strategies

The following designations will help you decide which activities are appropriate for your students.

- L1 Level 1 activities should be appropriate for students with learning difficulties.
- L2 Level 2 activities should be within the ability range of all students.
- L3 Level 3 activities are designed for above-average students.
- ELL ELL activities should be within the ability range of English Language Learners.
- COOP LEARN Cooperative Learning activities are designed for small group work.
- LS Multiple Learning Styles logos, as described on page 12T, are used throughout to indicate strategies that address different learning styles.
- P These strategies represent student products that can be placed into a best-work portfolio.
- PBL Problem-Based Learning activities apply real-world situations to learning.

Hands-on Activities

Student Text Lab Worksheet

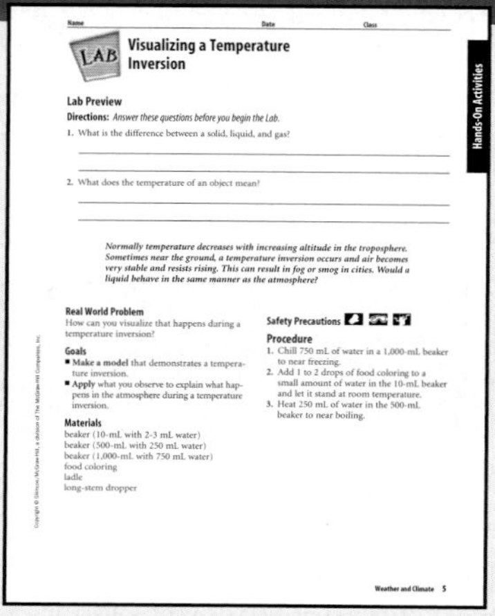
LAB — Visualizing a Temperature Inversion

Hands-On Activities

Lab Preview

Directions: Answer these questions before you begin the Lab.

1. What is the difference between a solid, liquid, and gas?
2. What does the temperature of an object mean?

Normally temperature decreases with increasing altitude in the troposphere. Sometimes near the ground, a temperature inversion occurs and air becomes very stable and resists rising. This can result in fog or smog in cities. Would a liquid behave in the same manner as the atmosphere?

Real World Problem

How can you visualize that happens during a temperature inversion?

Goals

- Make a model that demonstrates a temperature inversion.
- Apply what you observe to explain what happens in the atmosphere during a temperature inversion.

Materials

beaker (10-mL with 2-3 mL water)
beaker (500-mL with 250 mL water)
beaker (1,000-mL with 750 mL water)
food coloring
ladle
long-stem dropper

Safety Precautions

Procedure

1. Chill 750 mL of water in a 1,000-mL beaker to near freezing.
2. Add 1 to 2 drops of food coloring to a small amount of water in the 10-mL beaker and let it stand at room temperature.
3. Heat 250 mL of water in the 500-mL beaker to near boiling.

Weather and Climate 5

Laboratory Activities

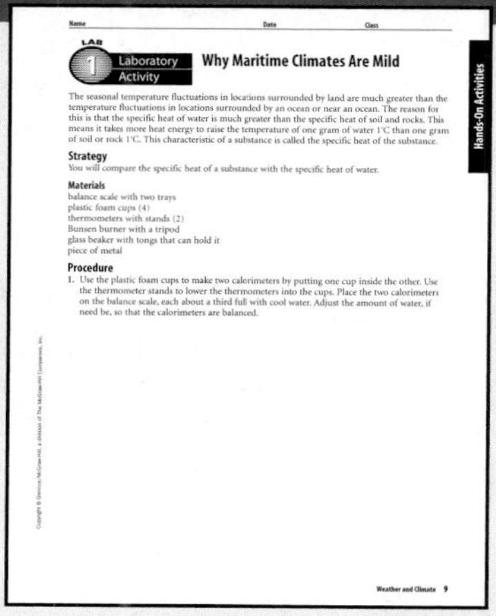
LAB 1 Laboratory Activity — Why Maritime Climates Are Mild

Hands-On Activities

The seasonal temperature fluctuations in locations surrounded by land are much greater than the temperature fluctuations in locations surrounded by an ocean or near an ocean. The reason for this is that the specific heat of water is much greater than the specific heat of soil and rocks. This means it takes more heat energy to raise the temperature of one gram of water 1°C than one gram of soil or rock 1°C. This characteristic of a substance is called the specific heat of the substance.

Strategy

You will compare the specific heat of a substance with the specific heat of water.

Materials

balance scale with two trays
plastic foam cups (4)
thermometers with stands (2)
Bunsen burner with a tripod
glass beaker with tongs that can hold it
piece of metal

Procedure

1. Use the plastic foam cups to make two calorimeters by putting one cup inside the other. Use the thermometer stands to lower the thermometers into the cups. Place the two calorimeters on the balance scale, each about a third full with cool water. Adjust the amount of water, if need be, so that the calorimeters are balanced.

Weather and Climate 9

Meeting Different Ability Levels

Content Outline

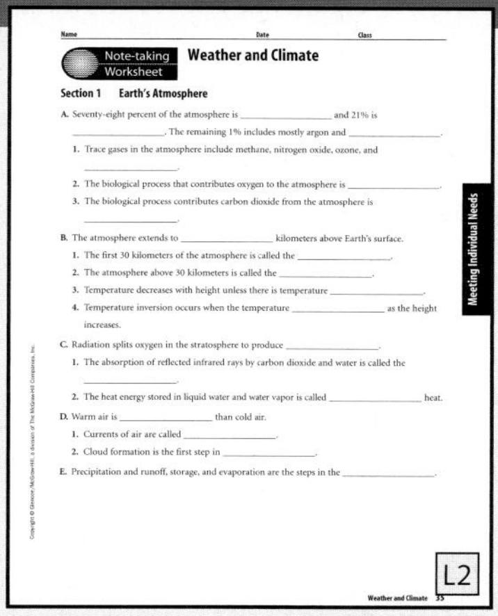
Name Date Class

Note-taking Worksheet **Weather and Climate**

Section 1 Earth's Atmosphere

A. Seventy-eight percent of the atmosphere is ____________ and 21% is ____________. The remaining 1% includes mostly argon and ____________.
1. Trace gases in the atmosphere include methane, nitrogen oxide, ozone, and ____________.
2. The biological process that contributes oxygen to the atmosphere is ____________.
3. The biological process contributes carbon dioxide from the atmosphere is ____________.

B. The atmosphere extends to ____________ kilometers above Earth's surface.
1. The first 30 kilometers of the atmosphere is called the ____________.
2. The atmosphere above 30 kilometers is called the ____________.
3. Temperature decreases with height unless there is temperature ____________.
4. Temperature inversion occurs when the temperature ____________ as the height increases.

C. Radiation splits oxygen in the stratosphere to produce ____________.
1. The absorption of reflected infrared rays by carbon dioxide and water is called the ____________.
2. The heat energy stored in liquid water and water vapor is called ____________ heat.

D. Warm air is ____________ than cold air.
1. Currents of air are called ____________.
2. Cloud formation is the first step in ____________.

E. Precipitation and runoff, storage, and evaporation are the steps in the ____________.

Meeting Individual Needs

L2

Weather and Climate 35

Reinforcement

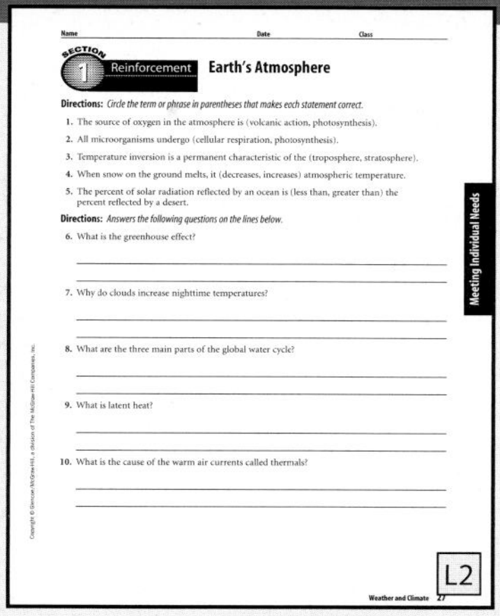
Name Date Class

Section 1 Reinforcement **Earth's Atmosphere**

Directions: *Circle the term or phrase in parentheses that makes each statement correct.*
1. The source of oxygen in the atmosphere is (volcanic action, photosynthesis).
2. All microorganisms undergo (cellular respiration, photosynthesis).
3. Temperature inversion is a permanent characteristic of the (troposphere, stratosphere).
4. When snow on the ground melts, it (decreases, increases) atmospheric temperature.
5. The percent of solar radiation reflected by an ocean is (less than, greater than) the percent reflected by a desert.

Directions: *Answer the following questions on the lines below.*
6. What is the greenhouse effect?
7. Why do clouds increase nighttime temperatures?
8. What are the three main parts of the global water cycle?
9. What is latent heat?
10. What is the cause of the warm air currents called thermals?

Meeting Individual Needs

L2

Weather and Climate 27

Enrichment

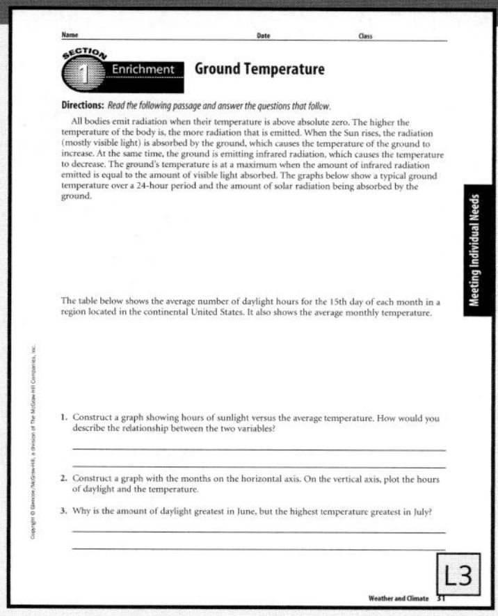
Name Date Class

Section 1 Enrichment **Ground Temperature**

Directions: *Read the following passage and answer the questions that follow.*

All bodies emit radiation when their temperature is above absolute zero. The higher the temperature of the body is, the more radiation that is emitted. When the Sun rises, the radiation (mostly visible light) is absorbed by the ground. When the Sun rises, the radiation ... increase. At the same time, the ground is emitting infrared radiation, which causes the temperature to decrease. The ground's temperature is at a maximum when the amount of infrared radiation emitted is equal to the amount of visible light absorbed. The graphs below show a typical ground temperature over a 24-hour period and the amount of solar radiation being absorbed by the ground.

The table below shows the average number of daylight hours for the 15th day of each month in a region located in the continental United States. It also shows the average monthly temperature.

1. Construct a graph showing hours of sunlight versus the average temperature. How would you describe the relationship between the two variables?
2. Construct a graph with the months on the horizontal axis. On the vertical axis, plot the hours of daylight and the temperature.
3. Why is the amount of daylight greatest in June, but the highest temperature greatest in July?

Meeting Individual Needs

L3

Weather and Climate 31

Directed Reading (English/Spanish)

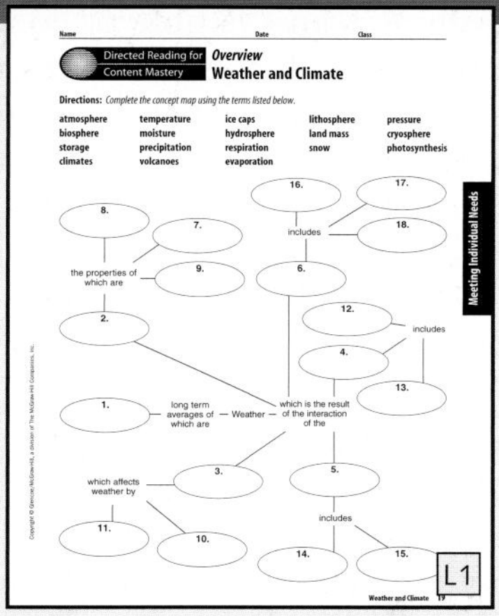
Name Date Class

Directed Reading for Content Mastery *Overview* **Weather and Climate**

Directions: *Complete the concept map using the terms listed below.*

atmosphere	temperature	ice caps	lithosphere	pressure
biosphere	moisture	hydrosphere	land mass	cryosphere
storage	precipitation	respiration	snow	photosynthesis
climates	volcanoes	evaporation		

Meeting Individual Needs

L1

Weather and Climate 19

Study Guide

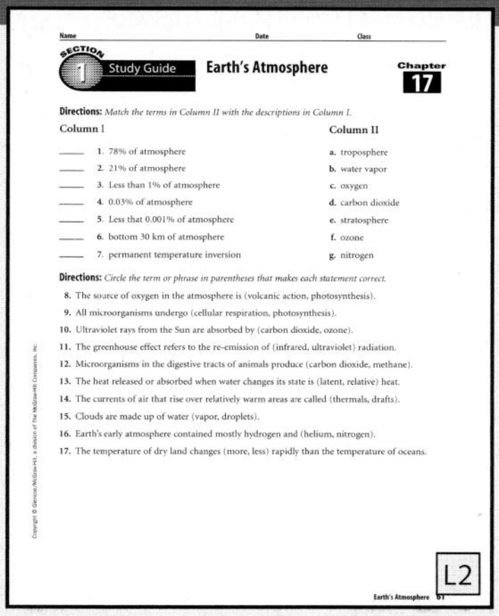
Name Date Class

Section 1 Study Guide **Earth's Atmosphere** Chapter 17

Directions: *Match the terms in Column II with the descriptions in Column I.*

Column I	Column II
____ 1. 78% of atmosphere	a. troposphere
____ 2. 21% of atmosphere	b. water vapor
____ 3. Less than 1% of atmosphere	c. oxygen
____ 4. 0.03% of atmosphere	d. carbon dioxide
____ 5. Less that 0.001% of atmosphere	e. stratosphere
____ 6. bottom 30 km of atmosphere	f. ozone
____ 7. permanent temperature inversion	g. nitrogen

Directions: *Circle the term or phrase in parentheses that makes each statement correct.*
8. The source of oxygen in the atmosphere is (volcanic action, photosynthesis).
9. All microorganisms undergo (cellular respiration, photosynthesis).
10. Ultraviolet rays from the Sun are absorbed by (carbon dioxide, ozone).
11. The greenhouse effect refers to the re-emission of (infrared, ultraviolet) radiation.
12. Microorganisms in the digestive tracts of animals produce (carbon dioxide, methane).
13. The heat released or absorbed when water changes its state is (latent, relative) heat.
14. The currents of air that rise over relatively warm areas are called (thermals, drafts).
15. Clouds are made up of water (vapor, droplets).
16. Earth's early atmosphere contained mostly hydrogen and (helium, nitrogen).
17. The temperature of dry land changes (more, less) rapidly than the temperature of oceans.

L2

Earth's Atmosphere 61

Reading Essentials

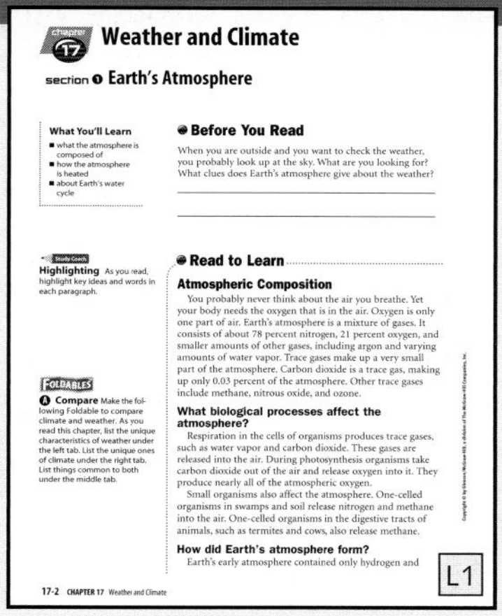
chapter 17 **Weather and Climate**

section 1 **Earth's Atmosphere**

What You'll Learn
- what the atmosphere is composed of
- how the atmosphere is heated
- about Earth's water cycle

Before You Read

When you are outside and you want to check the weather, you probably look up at the sky. What are you looking for? What clues does Earth's atmosphere give about the weather?

Study Coach **Highlighting** As you read, highlight key ideas and words in each paragraph.

Read to Learn

Atmospheric Composition

You probably never think about the air you breathe. Yet your body needs the oxygen that is in the air. Oxygen is only one part of air. Earth's atmosphere is a mixture of gases. It consists of about 78 percent nitrogen, 21 percent oxygen, and smaller amounts of other gases, including argon and varying amounts of water vapor. Trace gases make up a very small part of the atmosphere. Carbon dioxide is a trace gas, making up only 0.03 percent of the atmosphere. Other trace gases include methane, nitrous oxide, and ozone.

FOLDABLES **A Compare** Make the following Foldable to compare climate and weather. As you read this chapter, list the unique characteristics of weather under the left tab. List the unique ones of climate under the right tab. List things common to both under the middle tab.

What biological processes affect the atmosphere?

Respiration in the cells of organisms produces trace gases, such as water vapor and carbon dioxide. These gases are released into the air. During photosynthesis organisms take carbon dioxide out of the air and release oxygen into it. They produce nearly all of the atmospheric oxygen.

Small organisms also affect the atmosphere. One-celled organisms in swamps and soil release nitrogen and methane into the air. One-celled organisms in the digestive tracts of animals, such as termites and cows, also release methane.

How did Earth's atmosphere form?

Earth's early atmosphere contained only hydrogen and

17-2 CHAPTER 17 Weather and Climate

L1

Assessment

Test Practice Workbook

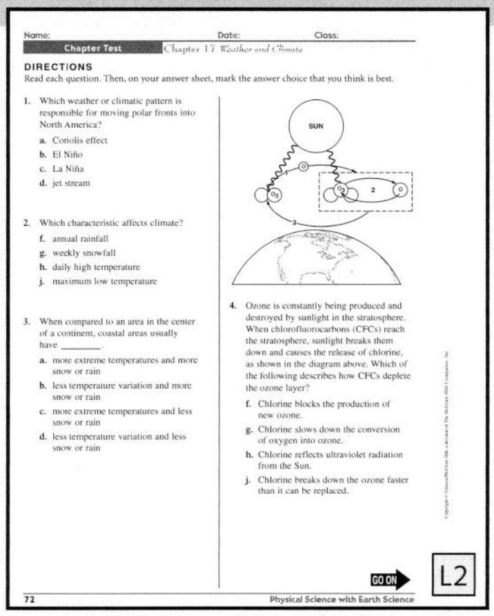
Name: Date: Class:

Chapter Test *Chapter 17 Weather and Climate*

DIRECTIONS

Read each question. Then, on your answer sheet, mark the answer choice that you think is best.

1. Which weather or climatic pattern is responsible for moving polar fronts into North America?
   a. Coriolis effect
   b. El Niño
   c. La Niña
   d. jet stream
2. Which characteristic affects climate?
   f. annual rainfall
   g. weekly snowfall
   h. daily high temperature
   j. maximum low temperature
3. When compared to an area in the center of a continent, coastal areas usually have ____.
   a. more extreme temperatures and more snow or rain
   b. less temperature variation and more snow or rain
   c. more extreme temperatures and less snow or rain
   d. less temperature variation and less snow or rain
4. Ozone is constantly being produced and destroyed by sunlight in the stratosphere. When chlorofluorocarbons (CFCs) reach the stratosphere, sunlight breaks them down and causes the release of chlorine, as shown in the diagram above. Which of the following describes how CFCs deplete the ozone layer?
   f. Chlorine blocks the production of new ozone.
   g. Chlorine slows down the conversion of oxygen into ozone.
   h. Chlorine reflects ultraviolet radiation from the Sun.
   j. Chlorine breaks down the ozone faster than it can be replaced.

GO ON

L2

72 Physical Science with Earth Science

Chapter Review

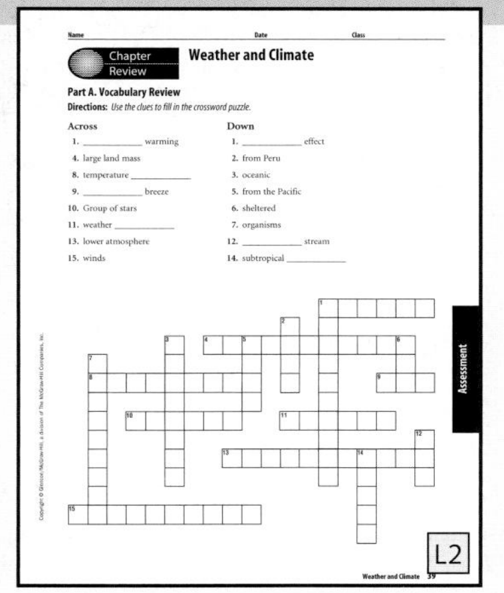
Name Date Class

Chapter Review **Weather and Climate**

Part A. Vocabulary Review

Directions: *Use the clues to fill in the crossword puzzle.*

Across	Down
1. ____________ warming	1. ____________ effect
4. large land mass	2. from Peru
8. temperature ____________	3. oceanic
9. ____________ breeze	5. from the Pacific
10. Group of stars	6. sheltered
11. weather ____________	7. organisms
13. lower atmosphere	12. ____________ stream
15. winds	14. subtropical ____________

Assessment

L2

Weather and Climate 39

Chapter Tests

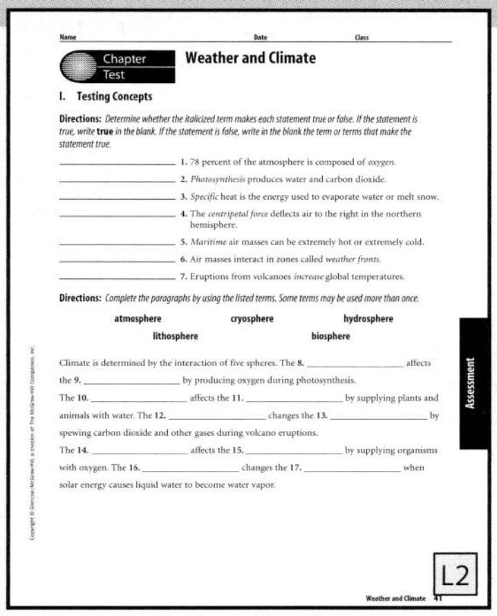
Name Date Class

Chapter Test **Weather and Climate**

I. Testing Concepts

Directions: *Determine whether the italicized term makes each statement true or false. If the statement is true, write* **true** *in the blank. If the statement is false, write in the blank the term or terms that make the statement true.*

____________ 1. 78 percent of the atmosphere is composed of *oxygen*.
____________ 2. *Photosynthesis* produces water and carbon dioxide.
____________ 3. *Specific* heat is the energy used to evaporate water or melt snow.
____________ 4. The *centripetal force* deflects air to the right in the northern hemisphere.
____________ 5. *Maritime* air masses can be extremely hot or extremely cold.
____________ 6. Air masses interact in zones called *weather fronts*.
____________ 7. Eruptions from volcanoes *increase* global temperatures.

Directions: *Complete the paragraphs by using the listed terms. Some terms may be used more than once.*

atmosphere cryosphere hydrosphere lithosphere biosphere

Climate is determined by the interaction of five spheres. The 8. ____________ affects the 9. ____________ by producing oxygen during photosynthesis. The 10. ____________ affects the 11. ____________ by supplying plants and animals with water. The 12. ____________ changes the 13. ____________ by spewing carbon dioxide and other gases during volcano eruptions. The 14. ____________ affects the 15. ____________ by supplying organisms with oxygen. The 16. ____________ changes the 17. ____________ when solar energy causes liquid water to become water vapor.

Assessment

L2

Weather and Climate 41

Science Content Background

section 1 Earth's Atmosphere

Atmospheric Layers

Earth's atmosphere can be divided into distinct layers based on differences in temperature. The troposphere extends from the surface to an altitude of about 10 km. Temperatures in the troposphere generally decrease with height. The stratosphere extends from roughly 10 km above the surface to 50 km. Temperatures here increase with height. The mesosphere is located between 50 km and 90 km above Earth's surface. Here, temperatures again decrease with altitude. Above the mesosphere lies the thermosphere, which extends into space. Temperatures in the thermosphere are high. However, because there are so few air molecules present at this altitude, the air would not feel warm.

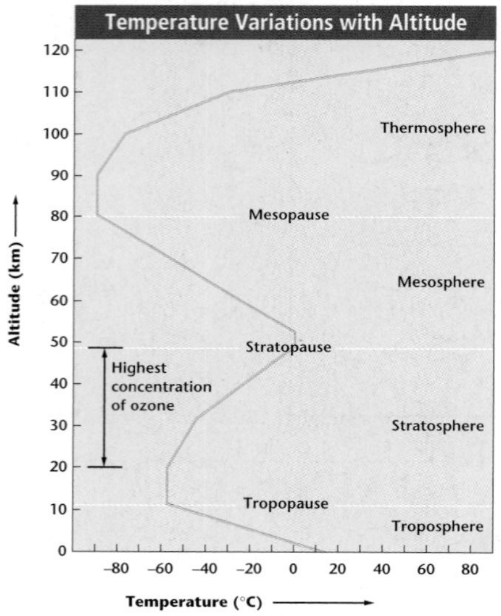

section 2 Weather

Heat Transfer

Energy from the Sun powers global winds and creates the unequal heating of Earth's surface that results in weather. Solar energy is transferred throughout the atmosphere in four different ways. Radiation involves the transfer of energy by electromagnetic radiation, which includes visible light. Sunshine is an example of energy transfer by radiation. Conduction involves the transfer of energy that occurs when molecules collide. In this process, the Sun warms the ground. Heat from the ground is transferred by conduction to the layer of air nearest the surface. Convection involves the transfer of energy by the flow of a heated substance. In the atmosphere, convection plays a role in creating global wind patterns, local winds, and certain types of severe weather. The Sun's energy is also transferred to the atmosphere by latent heat. Solar radiation heats liquid water and converts it into vapor. This stored energy is released when water vapor condenses as precipitation. Water heats and cools slowly. For this reason large bodies of water have a moderating effect on climate.

chapter content resources

Internet Resources

For additional content background, visit **gpescience.com** to:

- access your book online
- find references to related articles in popular science magazines
- access Web links with related content background
- access current events with science journal topics

Print Resources

Meteorology Today, Fifth Edition, by C. Donald Ahrens, West Publishing Company, 1994

section 3 Climate

Climatic Data

Climate normals represent standard climatic data for a given location. These data might include high and low temperatures, rainfall amounts, wind speed and direction, and air pressure. Often, the normals include daily, monthly, and yearly mean values. The mean daily temperature, for example, is the average of the highest and lowest temperature within a 24-hour period. The mean monthly temperature is the average of mean daily temperatures over a 30-day period. Likewise, the mean yearly temperature is the average of mean monthly temperatures over 12 months. An area's annual temperature range is simply the difference between the mean temperatures of the warmest and coldest months.

section 4 Earth's Changing Climates

Global Warming

Scientists estimate that Earth's climate may have been as much as 15°C warmer during much of the planet's history. These warm periods of geologic time were interspersed with periods of glaciation, known as ice ages.

Ice ages occur in cycles lasting millions of years. At the peaks, the poles are covered with thick ice, glaciers advance into the mid latitudes, and sea levels fall. Between glaciations, Earth warms, the glaciers retreat, and sea levels rise. The last ice age peaked about 18,000 years ago when falling sea levels exposed land- bridges between England and Europe and between Asia and North America that may have allowed humans and animals to migrate.

Teacher to Teacher

Tracey L. Smeltzer
Library Specialist
Derry Area High School
Derry, PA

"After discussing atmospheric pressure, have students speculate about the effects that altitude has on an open carbonated beverage. For example, will an opened container remain carbonated longer in Denver, Colorado or Acapulco, Mexico? Ask students to support their ideas."

Tracey L. Smeltzer

Currently, Earth is warming again as would be expected based on glaciation cycles. However, the rate of warming has accelerated over the last century, raising concern that human activities, such as burning of fossil fuels, may be interfering with natural cycles. The term *global warming* refers these concerns.

To what degree human activities have interfered with natural cycles is unclear. Most scientists agree that increased greenhouse gases contribute greatly to global warming. However, they cannot identify this as the sole cause. The complexity of the interactions among Earth's systems makes it difficult to predict the effect of changing any one variable. A model must consider the effects of warming on ocean currents and levels, cloud formation, and rainfall distribution, and at the same time consider contributions from other sources, such as glaciation and volcanoes. Meanwhile, scientists continue to collect information and discuss the problem.

chapter 17

Chapter Vocabulary

troposphere, p. 519
temperature inversion, p. 519
greenhouse effect, p. 520
latent heat, p. 520
westerlies, p. 524
jet stream, p. 525
subtropical high, p. 525
weather front, p. 526
biosphere, p. 529
continental climate, p. 532
maritime climate, p. 532
lee rain shadow, p. 533
sea breeze, p. 533
global warming, p. 538
El Niño, p. 539
La Niña, p. 539

Science Journal Student observations will vary. They will likely find that short-term weather forecasts are more accurate than long-term forecasts.

INTERACTIVE CHALKBOARD with Image Bank

PowerPoint® Presentations

This CD-ROM is an editable Microsoft® PowerPoint® presentation that includes:

- a pre-made presentation for every chapter
- interactive graphics
- animations
- audio clips
- image bank
- all new section and chapter questions
- Standardized Test Practice
- transparencies
- Foldables directions
- links to gpescience.com

chapter 17

Weather and Climate

chapter preview

sections

Flash Flood!

When cool, dry air meets warm, moist air dramatic things can happen. Many desert environments are familiar with flash floods that can result from such an event. Dry river beds can suddenly become raging torrents of water, rocks, and mud.

Science Journal In your Science Journal, describe some of your observations of severe weather. Hypothesize what might cause these weather events.

516

Theme Connection

Change and Constancy The state of the atmosphere is in constant flux, as weather factors such as temperature and pressure vary day by day or hour by hour. Climates may also change; however, these changes usually occur in long-term cycles.

About the Photo

Storm in the Desert This photo shows a lightning storm over an Arizona desert. When relative humidity is very low, rain can fall from clouds and evaporate before it hits the ground. However, during a heavy rain, dry gulches or arroyos can fill rapidly with raging torrents of water and sediment.

Start-Up Activities

Launch LAB

Atmospheric Pressure

Changes in atmospheric pressure are involved in producing winds and weather. You may not be aware of how much pressure the atmosphere exerts, but you can see it in this Lab.

1. Fill a glass to the brim with water.
2. Place a piece of thick paper or cardboard on top.
3. Hold the paper or cardboard securely to the brim of the glass. Turn the glass upside down.
4. Release your hand from the paper
5. **Think Critically** What keeps the paper or cardboard against the brim of the glass and the water from flowing out?

FOLDABLES™ Study Organizer

Weather and Climate Make the following Foldable to compare and contrast the characteristics of weather and climate.

STEP 1 **Fold** one sheet of paper lengthwise.

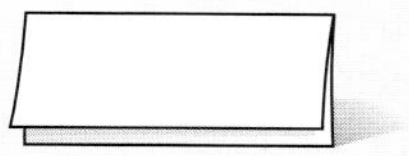

STEP 2 **Fold** into thirds.

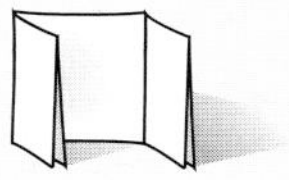

STEP 3 **Unfold and draw** overlapping ovals. **Cut** the top sheet along the folds.

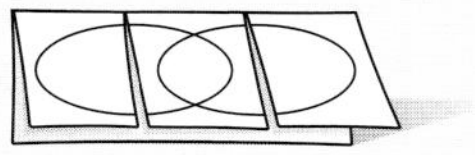

STEP 4 **Label** the ovals as shown.

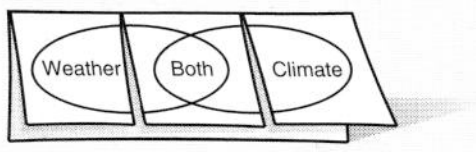

Constructing a Venn Diagram As you read the chapter, list the characteristics unique to weather under the left tab, those unique to climate under the right tab, and those elements common to both under the middle tab.

Science Online Preview this chapter's content and activities at gpescience.com

Launch LAB

Purpose Use this Launch Lab to introduce students to atmospheric pressure. L2

Materials water, glass, piece of thick paper or cardboard

Teaching Strategy Remind students that air exerts pressure in all directions. Have students take turns performing the Lab at the sink.

Think Critically

the pressure of the atmosphere against the paper or cardboard

Assessment

Performance Have students use a balloon and a balance to determine if air has mass. Students can find the mass of a deflated balloon. Then they can blow up the balloon and find its mass. Students should note that the increase in mass of the inflated balloon corresponds to the mass of the air.

FOLDABLES™ Study Organizer **Dinah Zike Study Fold**

Student preparation materials for this Foldable are available in the **Chapter *Fast File* Resources.**

section 1

Earth's Atmosphere

Reading Guide

What You'll Learn

- **Describe** the composition of the atmosphere.
- **Explain** how the atmosphere is heated and include the role of land surface and water.
- **Describe** Earth's system of water cycling.

Why It's Important

Heat and water are essential for life on Earth.

Review Vocabulary

nucleus: a central point about which concentration or accretion takes place

New Vocabulary

- troposphere
- temperature inversion
- greenhouse effect
- latent heat

Atmospheric Composition

You probably never think about the air you breathe. Your body uses only oxygen, but air is a mixture of gases. Nitrogen is the largest component with 78 percent and oxygen is next with 21 percent by volume. Most of the remaining one percent is the inactive gas argon and water vapor in varying amounts. The small remaining portion is a mixture of trace gases, so called because they are present in such small, barely detectable amounts. For example, carbon dioxide makes up only about 0.03 percent, and the other trace gases—methane, nitrous oxide, and ozone—together make up less than 0.001 percent of the atmosphere. Still, these trace gases are critical for life on Earth.

Reading Check *What are the trace gases?*

Biological Processes Living organisms produce trace gases, except ozone. Cellular respiration by organisms produces water vapor and carbon dioxide (CO_2). Photosynthetic organisms use carbon dioxide and produce almost all the oxygen in the atmosphere. Organisms alter atmospheric CO_2 concentration at various latitudes throughout the year, as shown in **Figure 1.** Microorganisms in swamps, rice paddies, and soil produce nitrogen and methane. The microorganisms in the digestive tracts of animals such as termites, cows, and sheep produce methane.

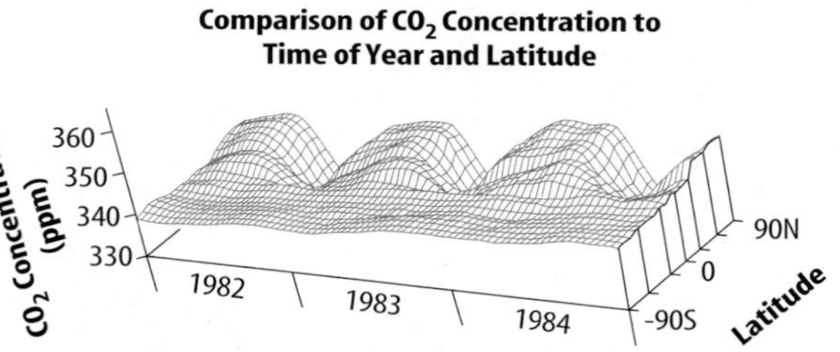

Figure 1 In northern latitudes, carbon dioxide concentration increases during summer and decreases during winter.

1 Motivate

An editable Microsoft® PowerPoint® presentation is available on **Interactive Chalkboard** CD-ROM.

Bellringer

Section Focus Transparencies also are available on the Interactive Chalkboard CD-ROM. L2 ELL

Reading Preview

Tie to Prior Knowledge

Clouds Have students describe different cloud shapes they have seen in the sky. Tell students that in this section, they will learn how clouds form and take the shapes they do. L2

Word Map Have students divide a sheet of paper into quadrants and then write a new vocabulary word in the center. In the upper left have students write a definition in their own words; in the upper right have them write an example of the term; in the lower left have them write a sentence using the word; in the lower right have them draw a picture depicting the word.

Section 1 Resource Manager

Chapter *Fast File* Resources

Directed Reading for Content Mastery, pp. 19–20

Note-taking Worksheets, pp. 35–37

Transparency Activity, p. 46, 51–52

MiniLAB, p. 3

Enrichment, p. 31

Reinforcement, p. 27

Lab Worksheets, pp. 5–6

Lab Activity, pp. 13–16

Earth Science Critical Thinking/Problem Solving, p. 13

Life Science Critical Thinking/Problem Solving, p. 8

Formation of the Atmosphere Earth's early atmosphere contained mostly hydrogen and helium. These gases were lost and were replaced by gases from volcanic eruptions, including water vapor and CO_2. Oxygen from photosynthetic marine organisms accumulated in the atmosphere and intense solar radiation converted some of it into ozone. The ozone layer shielded Earth from harmful ultraviolet rays. This allowed photosynthetic organisms to emerge on land, where they produced more oxygen.

Some scientists think it took millions of years for our atmosphere to reach its current state—a delicate equilibrium between processes producing and destroying atmospheric gases. Unfortunately, human activities might be threatening this equilibrium.

Atmospheric Structure

Earth's atmosphere extends more than 1,000 km above Earth's surface. Most of our weather takes place within the **troposphere,** a layer extending 30 km above Earth's surface. In this layer, as shown in **Figure 2,** temperature normally decreases with height. Sometimes, however, temperature increases with height. This is called a **temperature inversion.** When this happens, the air is very stable—it resists the rising motion needed to form clouds or to disperse air pollution.

The Stratosphere Above the troposphere is the stratosphere, which is extremely dry and rich in ozone. Here, temperature always increases with height, creating a permanent temperature inversion. The place where this temperature inversion begins is called the tropopause. It acts like a lid that keeps air in the troposphere from rising into the stratosphere. The uppermost layers, the mesophere and thermosphere, are very low in density and do not affect weather.

Mini LAB

Visualizing Convection

Procedure

1. Place an **ice cube** in the center of a **beaker.**
2. Add room-temperature **water** until the beaker is three-fourths full.
3. Place one drop of **food coloring** on the surface of the water.
4. Observe what happens.

Analysis

1. Describe what happened to the color.
2. Explain why this occurred.

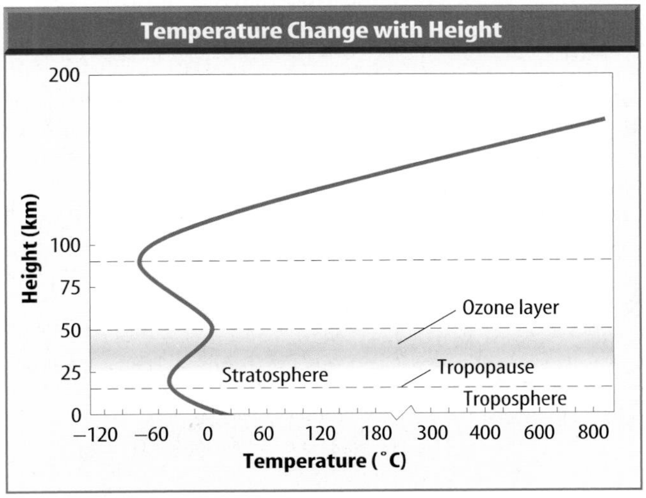

Figure 2 Temperature decreases with height in the troposphere up to the tropopause. Above the tropopause, temperature increases with height in the stratosphere.
Identify *The ozone layer is found in which atmospheric layer?*

Teacher FYI

Air Pollution Temperature inversions are particularly harmful in urban areas, which are plagued by air pollution. A temperature inversion can trap the pollution over a city for days. In December 1952, for example, a temperature inversion in London lasted one week. Pollutants from coal-burning factories and homes were trapped over the city. The air pollution trapped by the inversion caused the deaths of 4,000 people.

2 Teach

Reading Check

Answer gases that are found in very small amounts in the atmosphere, including carbon dioxide, methane, nitrous oxide, and ozone

Mini LAB

Video Lab available.

Purpose Students will model convection.

Materials water, dropper, food coloring, beaker, ice cube

Preparation If only gel colors are available, add a few drops of water and mix well before giving to students.

Teaching Strategy Remind students that molecules move faster at higher temperatures. Hold a lighted candle near one of the student's beakers and ask them to observe the effect.

Analysis

1. The color should drop to the bottom, spread out, and then move up the sides of the beaker.
2. Movement of the coloring was caused by convection. The coloring near the ice cooled, became denser, and sank. Away from the ice, the coloring warmed, became less dense, and rose.

Assessment

Oral In their own words, have students summarize how air temperature changes with height in the troposphere and explain where convection has the greatest effect. In the troposphere, air temperature decreases with height. Convection is most effective in the lower troposphere closer to the surface. L2

Caption Answer

Figure 2 stratosphere

SECTION 1 Earth's Atmosphere **519**

Discussion

The Greenhouse Effect Have students discuss how the greenhouse effect received its name. Point out that the greenhouse effect works much like a greenhouse. Have students explain the connection. The greenhouse effect traps heat on Earth just as a greenhouse traps heat within its walls. L2

Use Science Words

Word Meaning Have students use dictionaries to look up the meaning of the word *latent.* present or potential, but not active Have them relate the definition to the concept of latent heat. Latent heat is stored energy that is present, but not yet active, in the atmosphere. L1 ELL

Quick Demo

Rates of Absorption

Materials two cake pans, soil, water, two thermometers, lamp

Estimated Time 25 minutes

Procedure Fill a cake pan with water at room temperature. Fill the second pan with soil. Have students observe while you record the temperature of the water and soil. Place the lamp over the pans. Turn on the lamp and let it shine on the pans for 20 min. Take the temperature of the water and soil. Students should see that the water heated more slowly than the soil.

Motivated students might expand this activity by measuring the temperature increases of the two materials at intervals and graphing the results. L2 ELL IS

Caption Answer

Figure 3 A blanket traps a person's body heat, keeping the person warm.

Heating the Atmosphere

The energy that heats the atmosphere ultimately comes from the Sun. In the stratosphere, solar rays split oxygen molecules into single atoms. The oxygen atoms then react with other oxygen molecules, forming ozone. Ozone absorbs nearly all of the Sun's ultraviolet radiation. This absorption by ozone is why temperature increases with height in the stratosphere.

The remaining solar rays pass to Earth's surface where they are either absorbed or reflected back to the atmosphere. As Earth's surface is heated, it emits long-wave, infrared radiation. Trace gases, such as carbon dioxide and water vapor, absorb long wavelengths and re-emit some of them back to Earth's surface. The term **greenhouse effect** refers to this re-emission of infrared radiation back to Earth's surface, as shown in **Figure 3.**

Oxygen and nitrogen absorb little radiation and contribute little to atmospheric heating. Although water vapor and trace gases make up less than 0.03 percent of the atmosphere, they are strong absorbers and heat the atmosphere the most.

Conduction, convection, and latent heat also contribute to heating Earth's atmosphere. **Latent heat** is heat energy released or absorbed during the phase changes of water, such as evaporating water or melting snow. It is released to the atmosphere when water vapor condenses as clouds.

Figure 3 Trace gases absorb infrared radiation and are heated. These gases then re-emit infrared in all directions, sending part of it back to Earth's surface.
Infer *How does this compare to being covered by a blanket at night?*

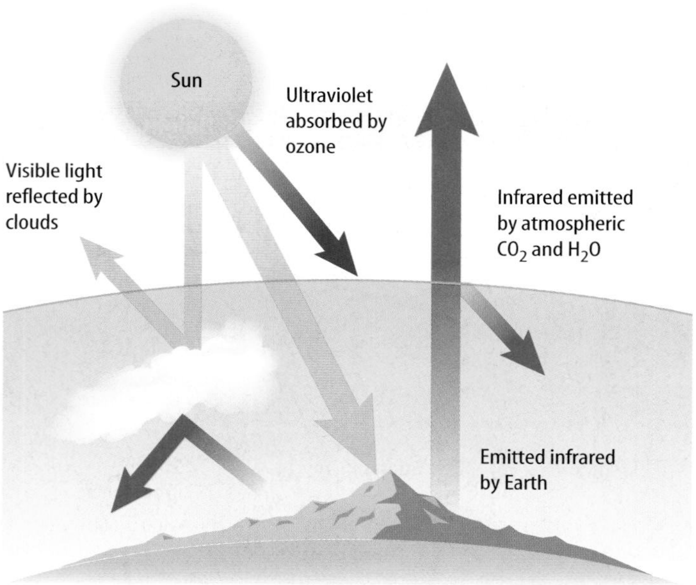

A Varied Surface

Earth's surface is not uniform and therefore, heats the atmosphere unevenly. Snow, ice, water, vegetation, and bare soil reflect different amounts of solar radiation back to space and heat at different rates when they absorb radiation. For example, dry land heats rapidly and emits much radiation to the atmosphere. In contrast, water temperature changes slowly and stores heat, releasing it at a later time. This uneven pattern of surface heating gives rise to pressure differences and wind.

Visual Learning

Figure 3 Ask students to compare the diagram to what they know about greenhouses used for growing plants. Ask them about similarities and differences. L2 ELL

Fun Fact

Weather data are gathered by two different types of satellites. A geostationary satellite orbits at the same speed as Earth spins, so it remains above a fixed point. This allows the satellite to continually study one area. A polar-orbiting satellite orbits the poles. With each orbit of the satellite, Earth has rotated slightly, allowing the satellite to monitor different areas.

Water in the Atmosphere

Uneven heating has another effect. It produces currents of air that carry water vapor aloft and form clouds. Air generally rises over warm surfaces and sinks over cold surfaces. Many birds and hang gliders soar on these warm currents, called thermals.

As air rises, it expands and cools. To form clouds, moist air must rise high enough to cool to its dew point. At this temperature, air is saturated and water vapor condenses to form cloud droplets. Small particles in the air, called condensation nuclei, trigger this process. When present in high quantities, such as in dust or polluted city air, these nuclei can trigger condensation in unsaturated air. This is how smog forms.

Reading Check *Explain how smog forms.*

Precipitation Cloud formation is the first step in the precipitation process. Two basic cloud types are the puffy cumulus type and the flat, elongated, stratus type. Cumulus clouds form from rising air parcels. If they produce rain, it is usually only brief showers. Stratus-type clouds form mainly when layers of air rise gently. They usually produce drizzle or long-lasting rain. Many in-between forms of clouds exist, depending on how stable the air is and how high in the atmosphere the clouds form. You can see some of these types in **Figure 4.** One type you might recognize is the cumulonimbus, or thunderhead. This cloud forms from unstable air and usually brings intense rain.

Cloud droplets are so small that they might be kept aloft by turbulence or evaporate before reaching Earth. For precipitation to occur, droplets must grow large. Growth can occur when droplets collide and combine. This is called warm rain. Droplets grow faster when they combine with ice crystals high in the atmosphere. This is called cold rain.

Figure 4 Clouds affect atmospheric heating by absorbing or blocking solar radiation and trapping Earth's radiation. Cloud cover also helps to reduce daytime temperature and increase nighttime temperature.

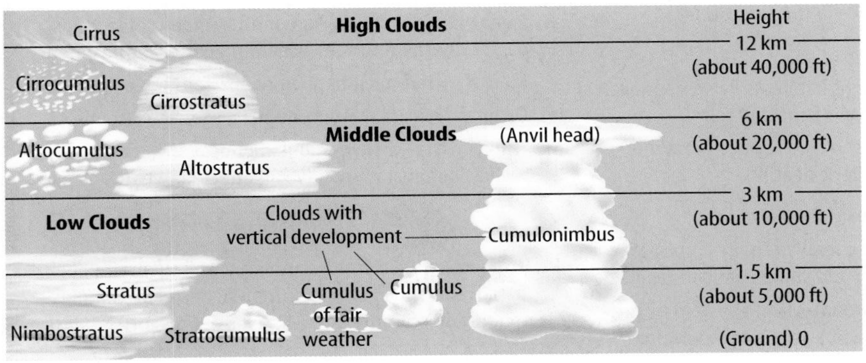

Reading Check

Answer Smog forms when pollutants trigger condensation in air that is not fully saturated with water vapor.

Inquiry Lab

Modeling Atmospheric Composition

Question How can you use liquids to model the composition of atmospheric gases?

Possible Materials 100-mL graduated cylinder, beaker, water, vegetable oil, rubbing alcohol, food dye

Estimated Time 20 minutes

Teaching Strategies

- Students should wear safety goggles and clothes aprons.
- Have students use a graduated cylinder to measure 78 mL of water into a beaker. This will represent the percentage of nitrogen in the atmosphere. They can measure 21 mL of vegetable oil to represent oxygen and pour the oil into the flask. 1 mL of an alcohol can be poured into the flask to represent trace gases.
- Food dye can be used to color the water and alcohol.

For additional inquiry activities, see *Science Inquiry Lab Manual*.

Activity

Modeling Raindrops Give each pair of students a dropper, water, and a long, rectangular, plastic container with a lid. Have students prop the lid in the container so that it forms a steep slope. Tell them to dribble drops of water down the lid making sure that the entire lid is used. Students should observe that the water droplets collide and combine into bigger drops. Explain that this same process occurs in the clouds during the formation of precipitation. L2 ELL LS **Visual-Spatial**

Reading Strategy

Synthesize and Summarize Have students write summary paragraphs for each of the following topics: Atmospheric Structure, Atmospheric Heating, and Water in the Atmosphere. Remind students to look for main ideas and supporting points as they read. They then should synthesize the information into their own words.

Differentiated Instruction

Hearing Impaired To help students with hearing impairments, be sure to write important points on the board when lecturing. Also, use hand gestures to explain key concepts. For example, outline the process of cloud formation on the board. As you discuss rising air, use your hands to show how the air expands. L2 ELL

SECTION 1 Earth's Atmosphere **521**

INTEGRATE Life Science

Plants Transpiration is affected mostly by the relative humidity of the atmosphere. The greater the relative humidity of the air is, the lesser the rate of transpiration in plants.

Post Reading

Graphic Organizer Provide slips of paper with the terms *atmosphere, troposphere, temperature inversion, stratosphere, greenhouse effect.* Students should write the relationships between words as they create a graphic organizer. For example, between *atmosphere* and *troposphere* students might write *layer.*

3 Assess

DAILY INTERVENTION

Check for Understanding

Visual-Spatial Have students sketch the water cycle. Sketches should show evaporation, condensation, and precipitation. L2 ELL

Reteach

Earth's Atmosphere On the board, outline the steps in the formation of Earth's atmosphere, including original atmosphere; hydrogen and helium; gases from volcanic eruptions; photosynthesis and accumulation of oxygen; and formation of ozone layer. L1 ELL

Figure 5 Earth's continual cycling of water strongly affects weather and climate.

INTEGRATE Life Science

Plants Transpiration is the loss of water through pores in the leaves of plants. More than 90 percent of the water that enters a plant returns to the atmosphere through the process of transpiration. Research how humidity and air temperature affect transpiration rates in plants. Share your findings with your class.

Global Water Cycle

Precipitation, runoff, storage, and evaporation make up the global water cycle, shown in **Figure 5.** Plants are an important part of the water cycle. They affect absorption and runoff and return water to the air by evaporation from their surfaces.

People affect the water cycle in many ways. They use groundwater for irrigation or pump it from wells. They replace forests with agricultural fields and pave land to build cities. Many of these changes have reduced water quality and resources. Conserving water resources requires careful planning.

section 1 review

Summary

Atmospheric Structure

- The stratosphere and the troposphere are two lower layers of Earth's atmosphere. Most weather takes place in the troposphere.

Atmospheric Heating

- Most solar radiation first heats Earth's surface, which then heats the atmosphere.
- Characteristics of the land surface greatly influence atmospheric heating.

Water in the Atmosphere

- Cloud formation generally requires moist air, rising and cooling, and condensation nuclei.
- Water is cycled through Earth's system by precipitation, runoff, storage, and evaporation.

Self Check

1. **Describe** how temperature of the atmosphere changes with height and explain why.
2. **Explain** the greenhouse effect.
3. **Explain** why small changes in the amount of trace gasses are so important in heating Earth's atmosphere.
4. **Identify** what must happen before rain can occur.
5. **Compare and contrast** cumulus and stratus clouds.
6. **Think Critically** How might changes on Earth's surface, such as deforestation, have an effect on weather?

Applying Math

7. **Use Percentages** If the southern hemisphere contains 10 percent land and the northern hemisphere contains roughly 40 percent land, what percent of Earth is land?

More Section Review gpescience.com

section 1 review

1. In the stratosphere, temperature increases with height; in the troposphere it decreases with height.
2. Water vapor, carbon dioxide, and trace gases transmit solar radiation to the surface, but absorb the Earth's infrared radiation, preventing it from escaping into space.
3. Trace gases are stronger absorbers than nitrogen and oxygen and heat the atmosphere more.
4. First, the air must be completely saturated. Then the water vapor must condense into droplets, usually around condensation nuclei.
5. Both types of clouds form as water vapor condenses. Stratus clouds are layered, form slowly, and produce drizzle or slow rain. Cumulus clouds are large and puffy, form rapidly, and usually produce showers.
6. Changes on Earth's surface, such as deforestation, alter the absorption of solar radiation. This leads to uneven heating of Earth's atmosphere that causes differences in air pressure, wind, and other weather conditions. Also, deforestation alters concentrations of atmospheric CO_2 and water vapor, which are trace gases.
7. 25 percent

LAB

Visualizing a Temperature Inversion

Normally temperature decreases with increasing altitude in the troposphere. Sometimes near the ground, a temperature inversion occurs and air becomes very stable and resists rising. This can result in fog or smog in cities. Will a liquid behave in the same manner as the atmosphere?

Real-World Problem

How can you visualize what happens during a temperature inversion?

Goals

- **Make a model** that demonstrates a temperature inversion.
- **Apply** what you observe to explain what happens in the atmosphere during a temperature inversion.

Materials

10-mL beaker containing 2–3 mL water
500-mL beaker containing 250 mL water
1,000-mL beaker containing 750 mL water

food coloring	ladle
long-stem dropper	thermal mitt
freezer	hot plate

Safety Precautions

Procedure

1. Chill 750 mL of water in a 1,000-mL beaker to near freezing.
2. Add one to two drops of food coloring to the water in the 10-mL beaker and let it stand at room temperature.
3. Heat 250 mL of water in the 500-mL beaker to near boiling.
4. Hold the ladle at the surface of the chilled water. Very slowly pour all the heated water into the ladle and allow it to slowly flow out of the ladle onto the surface of the chilled water. You should have a bottom layer of cold water and a top layer of hot water.
5. Use the long-stem dropper to inject a few drops of the colored water from step 2 into the cold water in the 10-mL beaker.

Conclude and Apply

1. **Describe** what happened to the colored water.
2. **Explain** why this happened in terms of the temperatures of the water layers.
3. **Infer** how this is related to temperature inversions in the atmosphere.

Communicating Your Data

Write a brief paragraph describing your experiment and your observations. Include a labeled diagram showing the temperature layers and explain what happened to the colored water.

BENCH TESTED

Real-World Problem

Purpose Students use a liquid to model a temperature inversion in the atmosphere.

Process Skills make models, observe, predict

Time required about 30 minutes or one class period

Procedure

Safety Precautions Caution students to handle the hot water carefully and not to touch the hot plate.

Teaching Strategies

- Chill water before class and divide it among student groups.
- Demonstrate the proper way to pour the hot water and suggest that one student hold the ladle while another pours.

Conclude and Apply

1. The colored water remained trapped between the layers.
2. The room-temperature colored water floated on the cold water because it was less dense and sank beneath the hot water because it was denser.
3. The cold water at the bottom is similar to the cooler air near the ground during a temperature inversion. The colored water models a stagnant air mass that might hold pollutants.

Assessment

Process Ask students to predict the effects of rapidly pouring more cold water into the container. How might this relate to atmospheric conditions? L2

Communicating Your Data

Ask students to use their paragraphs and diagrams to explain temperature inversions to friends and family members.

1 Motivate

An editable Microsoft® PowerPoint® presentation is available on **Interactive Chalkboard** CD-ROM.

Bellringer

Section Focus Transparencies also are available on the Interactive Chalkboard CD-ROM. L2 ELL

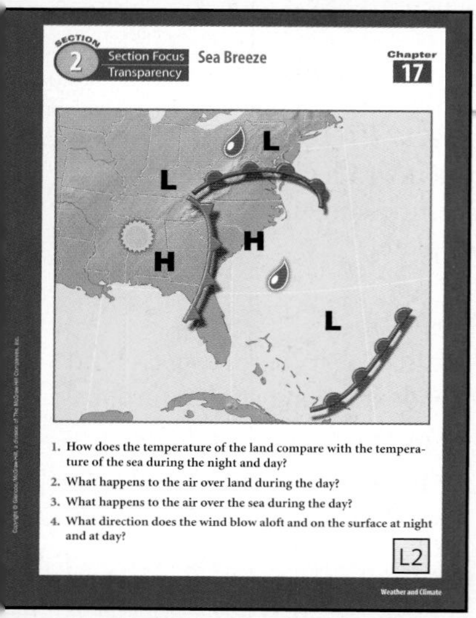

Reading Preview

Tie to Prior Knowledge

Weather Ask students if they watch the weather forecasts on television. Ask them how accurate they think these forecasts are and why they are sometimes incorrect. Ask them how weather forecasts affect their lives. L2

Structural Word Analysis Have students break new vocabulary words into word parts. Ask them to predict meaning by examining the word parts. For example, *jet* refers to a high-speed fluid stream. *Stream* implies a steady current. From this, students could determine that *jet stream* is a high-speed wind current.

section 2

Weather

Reading Guide

What You'll Learn

- **Explain** what causes Earth's major wind and pressure systems.
- **Describe** typical daily weather patterns around lows and fronts.
- **Describe** the most important storm systems and forms of severe weather.

Why It's Important

Weather affects the health, life, and livelihood of everyone on Earth.

Review Vocabulary

gradient: the rate of change of a quantity with distance

New Vocabulary

- westerlies
- jet stream
- subtropical high
- weather front

Atmospheric Pressure

Although you usually are unaware of it, the atmosphere presses down on you with a pressure equivalent to one kilogram per square centimeter. This pressure is caused by gas molecules moving and colliding with each other and any surfaces they touch. Because the number of air molecules decreases as altitude increases, pressure always decreases with altitude. This is why air is said to be thinner in the upper atmosphere. The number of air molecules, including oxygen, decreases in proportion to pressure. This is why jet aircraft cabins are pressurized and why climbers can get mountain sickness at altitudes over 3,000 m.

Figure 6 In the northern hemisphere, four major pressure belts produce three major wind belts.
Infer *How does pressure affect wind direction?*

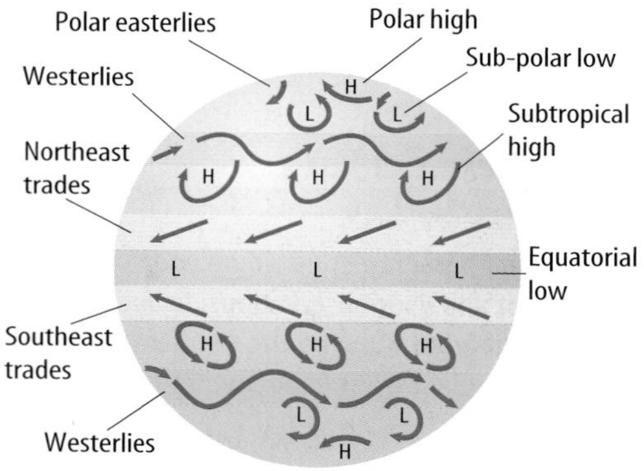

Global Winds and Pressure Systems Weather patterns result from complex global patterns of wind and pressure. **Figure 6** shows a simplified picture of the Earth's major pressure belts that give rise to major wind belts. The most important of these are the **westerlies**—winds that blow from the west in the middle latitudes—and the trade winds, which blow from the east, in the tropics.

Two factors produce these global patterns—unequal heating between the equator and poles and the rotation of Earth. Warm air rising near the equator and sinking over the poles creates general north-south wind circulation. Earth's rotation produces an east-west deflection of this general circulation pattern.

Section 2 Resource Manager

Chapter *Fast File* Resources

Transparency Activity, p. 47
MiniLAB, p. 4
Enrichment, p. 32
Reinforcement, p. 28
Directed Reading for Content Mastery, p. 20

Home and Community Involvement, p. 41
Cultural Diversity, pp. 47–48
Lab Management and Safety, p.61
Mathmatics Skill Activities, pp. 41–42
Reading and Writing Skills Activities, pp. 45–46

524 CHAPTER 17 Weather and Climate

Jet Streams Imbedded in these wind systems are fast and powerful **jet streams** that control many weather processes, such as storm development. Most important for the United States is the polar front jet stream, a wind maximum in the westerlies located about 12 km above the surface. Its speeds can exceed 500 km/h. Major storm tracks follow it as it moves north and south with the seasons.

High and Low Pressure Systems

The large-scale weather systems that have the most effect on the United States are the subpolar lows, westerlies, and the subtropical highs. **Subtropical highs** are relatively stable belts of high pressure near latitudes of 30°. In contrast, sub-polar lows and the westerlies tend to meander as smaller cells of high and low pressure develop. The lows generally develop from a disturbance in the polar front jet and move eastward with the jet stream.

Specific patterns of weather are associated with high and low pressure cells because of the way air flows around them. In the northern hemisphere, winds blow counterclockwise around lows and clockwise around highs, as shown in **Figure 7.** In the southern hemisphere, the directions reverse. Lows are associated with rainfall and storms, and highs with calm winds and clear skies.

INTEGRATE Physics

Coriolis Effect Airflow around low or high pressure areas results from the net forces acting on the air. First, the pressure gradient pulls the air toward low pressure. Then an apparent force, called the Coriolis effect, deflects the air to the right in the northern hemisphere. When these forces are balanced, air flows perpendicular to lines of equal pressure. Near the surface, friction slows air and modifies its direction, turning it slightly toward low-pressure centers and slightly away from high-pressure centers. This causes air to rise in the center of lows and to sink in the center of highs.

Mini LAB

Modeling the Coriolis Effect

Procedure

1. Put a **large, round piece of cardboard** or paper on a **turnable surface** such as a turntable.
2. Hold a **ruler** just above the diameter of the cardboard.
3. Ask someone to turn the surface while you draw a line across the turning cardboard with your **pen or pencil** against the ruler.
4. Repeat step 3 but turn the surface in the opposite direction.

Analysis

1. Compare the outlines drawn on the cardboard.
2. Explain how these outlines represent the Coriolis effect.

Try at Home

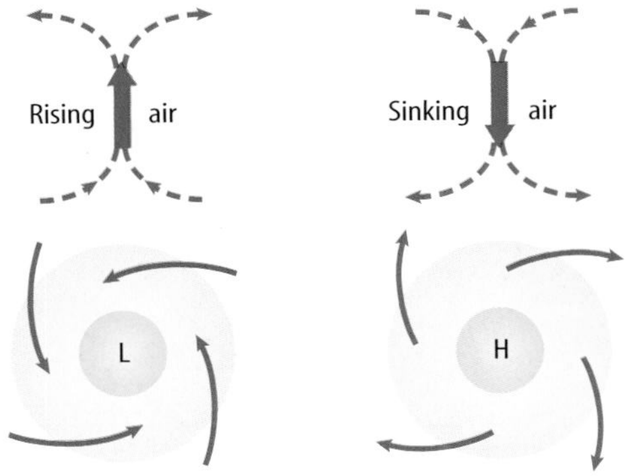

Figure 7 At Earth's surface in the northern hemisphere, air moves counterclockwise toward low pressure and clockwise from high pressure.
Infer *How does air move when it is high above Earth's surface, above each pressure system?*

2 Teach

Caption Answer

Figure 6 Wind blows from high pressure to low pressure.

Mini LAB

Purpose Students will model the Coriolis force.

Materials cardboard, turntable, ruler, marker

Teaching Strategy Advise students to first rotate the turntable in a counterclockwise direction. In doing so, they will model the direction of Earth's rotation from the point of view of an observer over the north pole.

Analysis

1. When the turntable turns counterclockwise, the line curves to the right; when the turntable is turned clockwise, the line curves to the left.
2. The first line represents the Coriolis force in the northern hemisphere; the second represents the Coriolis force in the southern hemisphere.

Assessment

Content Explain that the Coriolis force is an effect caused by Earth's rotation. Ask students the following question: How would air move across Earth's surface if Earth did not rotate? in a straight line

Try at Home

Visual Learning

Figure 6 Make sure students understand that winds are named for the direction from which they blow. Thus, westerlies blow from the west toward the east; easterlies blow from the east toward the west. Also, point out that the model of global winds is greatly simplified. It does not take into account many factors that affect wind flow, such as land masses. L2 ELL

Caption Answer

Figure 7 Above a surface high pressure system is an atmospheric low. In the northern hemisphere, the air moves counterclockwise toward the atmospheric low. It moves clockwise away from an atmospheric high.

INTEGRATE Physics

Content Background

The amount of deflection associated with the Coriolis force is affected by latitude and wind speed. The Coriolis effect is nearly nonexistent at the equator. It is strongest near the poles. The effect also increases with wind speed. Thus, a strong wind blowing at a high latitude will exhibit a much greater deflection than a weak wind blowing at a low latitude.

Air Masses and Weather Fronts

Weather around low-pressure cells is produced by interaction of air masses—large units of air with relatively uniform moisture and temperature. These form when air remains stationary for a time, such as in regions of high pressure. The air then takes on the characteristics of the surface. Air masses can be polar or tropical and continental or maritime. Continental air originates over land. It is relatively dry and can be extremely cold or extremely warm. Maritime air masses are moist because they originate over the oceans. The maritime air masses affecting the United States come from the Atlantic Ocean, the Pacific Ocean, or the Gulf of Mexico.

Air masses interact in zones called **weather fronts,** as shown in **Figure 8,** which are associated with low pressure systems. Warm and cold fronts create different types of precipitation. In a warm front, warm air rises gently above the cold air, usually forming layered, stratus-type clouds or fog—a cloud with its base on the ground. Most layered clouds produce only drizzle or steady rain. In a cold front, cold air pushes the warm air aloft in a random and chaotic fashion forming cumulus clouds. These often produce showers and thunderstorms.

Reading Check *What are weather fronts?*

Figure 8 The symbols shown below each of these weather fronts are used by meteorologists to represent the respective fronts on weather maps.

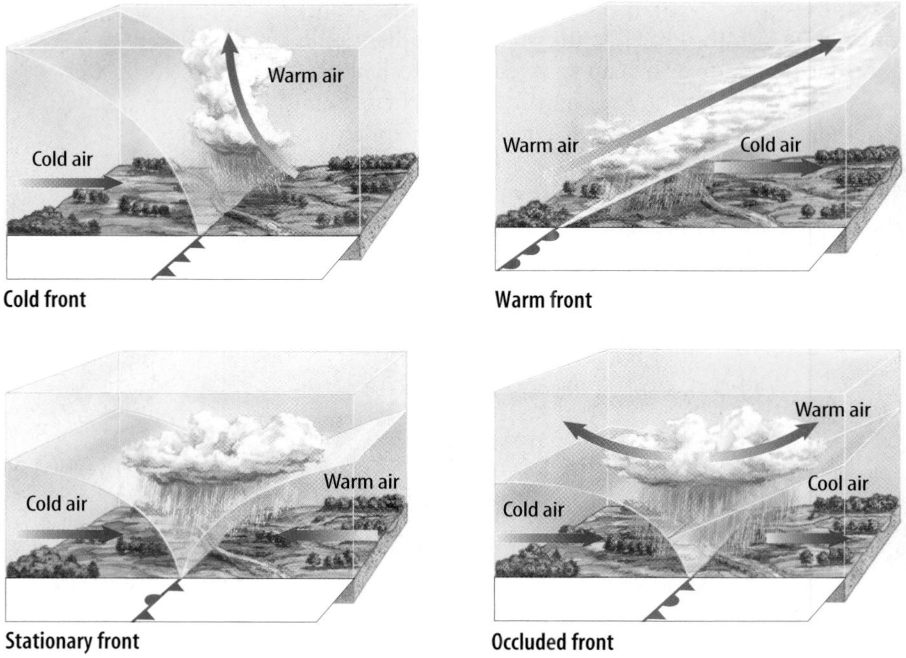

Discussion

Air Masses To assess students' understanding of air masses, ask them to describe the temperature and moisture characteristics of an air mass that originated over northern Canada. The air mass would be cold and dry.

Teacher FYI

Weather Fronts A fast-moving cold front can sometimes overtake a warm front. The new frontal boundary forms an occluded front. Depending upon the type of occlusion, precipitation may be heavy or light. Two air masses can also meet and simply stall. The resulting boundary is called a stationary front. Stationary fronts are often associated with light winds and some precipitation.

Reading Check

Answer zones of interaction between air masses

Activity

Weather Maps Use colored chalk to draw the symbols for warm fronts and cold fronts on the board. Warm fronts are represented by red semicircles on a line. Cold fronts are represented by blue triangles on a line. Have students study weather maps to locate fronts and areas of high pressure and low pressure. Have them use the maps to develop weather forecasts for their area. L2 ELL IN **Visual-Spatial**

Fun Fact

Although fast-moving cirrus clouds had long hinted their existence, jet streams were discovered only in the 1940s by pilots flying high altitude aircraft in World War II.

Science Journal

Weather Log Have students keep a log of local weather conditions for one week. Encourage them to incorporate sketches of clouds, types of precipitation, and other weather factors in their logs. You may want to set up a weather station so that students can record daily temperature, air pressure, and precipitation amounts. At the end of the week, have students write short paragraphs relating their observations to possible pressure systems and frontal boundaries. L3

Severe Weather

The continental United States is prone to severe weather because of the extreme temperatures of warm and cold air masses and the availability of moisture from tropical oceans. Such conditions lead to severe thunderstorms, hurricanes, tornadoes, and violent wind storms called downbursts.

Thunderstorms Recall that cumulonimbus clouds formed from unstable air produce thunderstorms. A typical cumulonimbus cloud has ice crystals near its top, as shown in **Figure 9.** Sometimes these ice crystals act as nuclei to trigger further growth of cloud droplets, and turbulence adds layers of ice during many cycles of sinking and rising. This forms hail. Hailstones can grow to the size of softballs and can cause extensive damage to crops and structures.

Downdrafts and Squalls The force of the falling precipitation in a thunderstorm may pull with it cold air bursts from higher in the cloud. This is why the air often feels cool after a thunderstorm. This sinking current of cold air is called a downdraft. When a downdraft hits the surface with particularly strong force, it spreads out in a series of windy gusts called squalls. In arid regions, squalls produce dust storms.

Downbursts Cold air downdrafts can produce even more severe forms of weather. One example of an extreme form of wind shear is a downburst. Here, cold air descends from a thunderstorm and hits the ground. When it hits the ground, it bursts outward like the spokes on a wheel. The rapid change in wind speed and/or direction that a downburst causes can be dangerous for aircraft during both take-off and landing. The winds that result from downbursts can be as high as 260 km/h. Fortunately, automated warning systems now alert pilots to look for signs of downbursts when approaching an airport.

Figure 9 When hailstones fall, they are repeatedly caught in updrafts, coated with moisture, and frozen. This gives them a layered, onionlike appearance.
Infer *Why does this cumulonimbus cloud have an anvil-shaped top?*

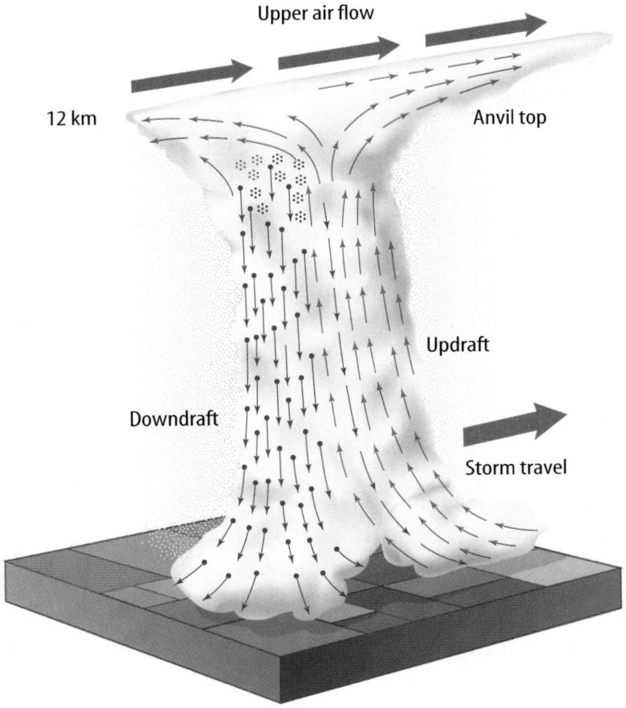

Quick Demo
Downdrafts

Materials plastic container about 10 cm deep, large plastic sheet, sand, fan

Estimated Time 10 minutes

Procedure Place the plastic sheet in a clear area on the floor. Center the container on the sheet. Pour sand into the container to a depth of 3 cm. Hold the fan horizontally over the container so that the blades of the fan are about 15 cm above the sand. Turn the fan on high. Have students observe how the "downdraft" scatters the sand.
L2 ELL **Visual-Spatial**

IDENTIFYING Misconceptions

Thunder Many students mistakenly believe that thunder occurs when two clouds collide. Explain that thunder occurs when lightning heats the air, causing it to rapidly expand. This expansion, in turn, causes a sound wave known as thunder. To be sure students understand the concept, ask: Can thunder ever occur without lightning? No, thunder is the sound wave produced when lightning heats air, causing it to expand rapidly.

Caption Answer

Figure 9 Updrafts are stopped by the low temperature at high altitudes. Cloud tops are spread out by the upper air flow.

Reading Strategy

Predict Have students scan the sections High and Low Pressure Systems, Fronts and Air Masses, and Severe Weather. Ask students to note figures, bold print, and headings. For each section, students should make predictions regarding the content. As students read, they may confirm or alter their predictions.

Differentiated Instruction

English-Language Learners Students whose first language is not English may have trouble visualizing the processes that form hurricanes. Show students satellite images that illustrate the stages of development of a hurricane. Point out the distinctive cyclonic nature of these storms. Have students locate the eye in the center of the storm.

Post Reading

Illustrations Have students make illustrations of the following: global wind patterns, fronts, and wind patterns in a severe storm, such as a thunderstorm or a hurricane. Students should refer to the text and can do research using library resources. Remind students to label all illustrations.

3 Assess

DAILY INTERVENTION

Check for Understanding

Kinesthetic Have students use their hands to model the movement of air around low-pressure systems and high-pressure systems. In the northern hemisphere, air blows counterclockwise around a low-pressure system and clockwise around a high-pressure system. L1 ELL

Reteach

Fronts Make a table on the board comparing and contrasting the characteristics of warm fronts and cold fronts. L1 ELL

Assessment

Portfolio Have students research safety tips for thunderstorms, tornadoes, or hurricanes. Students can use their research to make brochures informing the public of safety measures to take during severe weather events. L2

Science Online

Topic: Hurricane Tracking
Visit gpescience.com for Web links to information about hurricanes and hurricane tracking.

Activity Research six hurricanes. Make a table that lists how each was tracked as a tropical depression and then as a hurricane.

Tornadoes and Hurricanes Two types of violent wind storms that differ greatly in their origins and effects are tornadoes and hurricanes. Tornadoes are intense, short-lived, localized storms in the mid-latitudes. They originate in cumulonimbus clouds under special conditions. Typically, tornadoes that occur in the United States form when dry air from the deserts of Mexico and the southwest overrides warm, moist air from the Gulf of Mexico. This happens frequently in the Great Plains, the lower midwest, and parts of the south, as shown in **Figure 10.** In the south, they often accompany hurricanes.

A twisting, funnel-shaped tornado cloud can move across land at a speed of around 50 km/h creating a path 150 m wide and 10 km long. Intense, circular winds in the funnel can reach speeds up to 400 km/h. The extreme low pressure at the center can result in more damage than that from the wind.

Figure 10 Texas, Oklahoma, and Kansas frequently experience tornadoes.

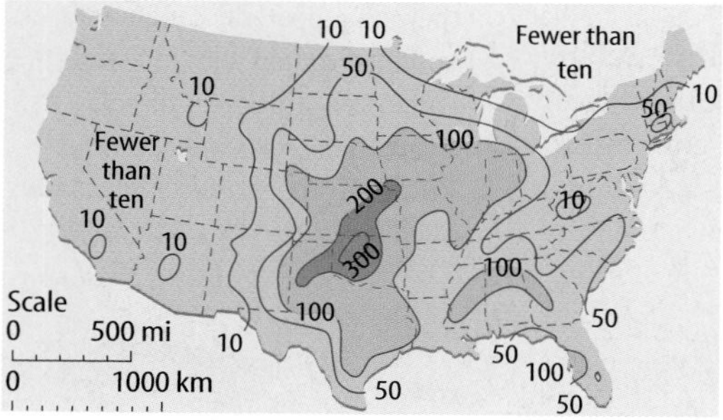

Hurricanes are tropical storms that cover vast areas and last for days. Those affecting the United States often form as tropical depressions over the warm waters of the southern Atlantic off the coast of Africa. When winds exceed 118 km/h, the storms are called hurricanes. A typical hurricane consists of vast cloud bands that spiral inward toward the clear center, called the eye. Scientists often fly into the eye to study the storm. Western Pacific hurricanes are called typhoons.

section 2 review

Summary

Global Wind and Pressure Systems

- Four major pressure systems produce three major wind systems in each hemisphere.

High and Low Pressure Systems

- Air flows counterclockwise around lows and clockwise around highs in the northern hemisphere.
- Air rises in the center of lows and sinks in the center of highs.

Weather Fronts and Severe Weather

- Air masses interact at weather fronts.
- Warm fronts are associated with stratus-type clouds and cold fronts with cumulus-type clouds.
- Severe weather includes hurricanes, tornadoes, and downbursts.

Self Check

1. **Explain** how Earth's rotation affects winds.
2. **Compare and contrast** tornadoes and hurricanes.
3. **Infer** the wind directions around a high in the southern hemisphere.
4. **Describe** common differences between continental air masses and maritime air masses.
5. **Compare and contrast** warm fronts and cold fronts.
6. **Think Critically** If the polar front jet stream were to move southward over the U.S., what other weather systems are likely to be affected?

Applying Math

7. **Use Percentage** A tornado watch was issued on 25 days during one year in a midwest city. What percent of the year does this represent?

More Section Review gpescience.com

section 2 review

1. In the northern hemisphere, winds are deflected counterclockwise toward low pressure and clockwise away from high pressure.
2. Tornadoes and hurricanes are storms with violent winds. Tornadoes are brief, cover small areas, and occur in the mid-latitudes. Hurricanes are of longer duration, cover large areas, and begin in the tropics.
3. counterclockwise
4. Continental air masses originate over land, are relatively dry, and commonly exhibit extreme temperature variations. Maritime air masses originate over oceans, are relatively moist, and usually exhibit less extreme temperature variations.
5. Both are zones where air masses interact. In warm fronts, cold air gently pushes warm air above it, bringing layered clouds and light or steady rain. In cold fronts, cold air chaotically pushes warm air upward, forming cumulus and cumulonimbus clouds, which can produce brief showers.
6. Because the major storm track follows the polar front jet, it would move southward too.
7. 25/365 = 6.8 percent

section 3

Climate

Reading Guide

What You'll Learn

- **Describe** what determines climate.
- **Explain** how latitude, oceans, and other factors affect the climate of a region.
- **Classify** climate systems.
- **Describe** climate distribution over the United States.

Why It's Important

Climate affects the way you live.

Review Vocabulary

boreal: relating to northern regions

New Vocabulary

- biosphere
- continental climate
- maritime climate
- lee rain shadow
- sea breeze

Climate and Weather

What is the climate where you live? Traditionally, climate means the long-term average of weather conditions—wind, temperature, precipitation, moisture, and other aspects of weather. Climate also describes the annual variations of these conditions and their extremes.

Averages of data collected monthly over 30 years or longer are used to define climatic normals. These normals do not describe usual weather conditions of an area, but are only averages of conditions measured at one local site. For example, the conditions in a city might vary from what is measured at an airport weather station outside the city.

Climate System Climate is best considered as part of the whole Earth system. This biogeophysical system can be visualized as five spheres that interact to create the environments in which we live, as shown in **Figure 11.** The atmosphere includes the air around us. The **biosphere** is everything organic, including plants, animals, and humans. The hydrosphere is liquid water in oceans, lakes, rivers, soil, and underground. The cryosphere is frozen water in snow, ice, and glaciers. Finally, the lithosphere is the solid Earth, including its soil, rocks, and mantle.

Figure 11 All of the five spheres shown below interact. Each sphere causes changes in, and is changed by, the others.
Research *What does the prefix* cryo- *mean?*

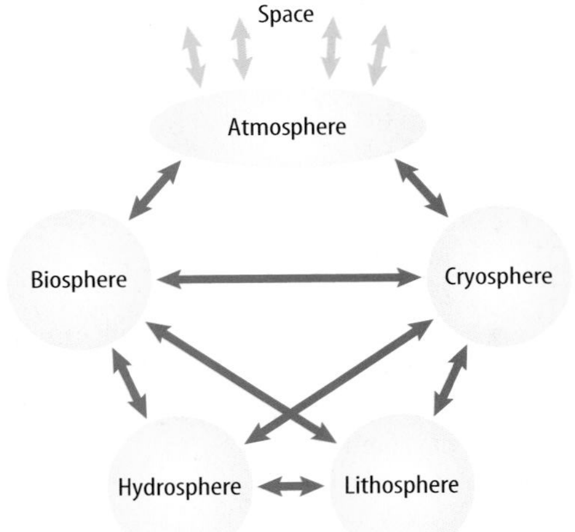

1 Motivate

An editable Microsoft® PowerPoint® presentation is available on **Interactive Chalkboard** CD-ROM.

Bellringer

Section Focus Transparencies also are available on the Interactive Chalkboard CD-ROM. L2 ELL

Reading Preview

Tie to Prior Knowledge

Climate Characteristics Ask students to name types of climates. Students might mention terms such as mild, rainy, cold, or warm. Ask them what aspects of weather these terms include. L2

Activate Background Knowledge Have students preview new vocabulary terms. As a class, ask them to brainstorm ideas related to each term. Guide students toward a deeper understanding of the terms by asking clarifying questions.

Section 3 Resource Manager

Chapter *Fast File* Resources

Transparency Activity, p. 48
Lab Activity, pp. 9–12
Enrichment, p. 33
Reinforcement, p. 29
Directed Reading for Content Mastery, p. 21
Reading and Writing Skills Activities, pp. 3–4

2 Teach

Caption Answer

Figure 11 cold, freezing

Use an Analogy

Weather v. Climate To help students distinguish between weather and climate, tell them that weather is like a single test score. That score represents what a student knows at one point in time. Climate is like a final grade. It is the average of many different factors over a longer period of time.

Make a Model

Earth's Spheres Form small groups of students and have them make models showing Earth's five spheres. Students can use plants, water, crushed ice, and sand to represent the biosphere, hydrosphere, cryosphere, and lithosphere, respectively. Have students set up their models in large plastic containers. Then place an electric fan near one of the models. Turn it on and have students observe interactions among the spheres. Ask: What does the fan or drier represent? atmosphere What interactions did you observe among Earth's spheres? Students might note that the "wind" caused the sand to erode. They might see the melting ice cause the water level to rise or that wind caused the plants to wilt. The breeze of the fan might cause waves that erode the sand. Ask students about the consequences of removing one of the spheres. Removing the hydrosphere might affect the biosphere. Removing the cryosphere might affect the hydrosphere. You might extend the activity by having students observe the model over a period of time and note changes among the spheres. L2 ELL IN **Visual-Spatial**

Caption Answer

Figure 12 The northern hemisphere is tilted toward the Sun.

Science Online

Topic: World Climates

Visit gpescience.com for Web links to data on mean annual temperature and rainfall of world cities.

Activity Use a world atlas, globe, or large classroom map to find a city corresponding to each of the eight climate divisions shown in **Figure 17.**

Sphere Interactions Gases, water, soluble materials, energy, and particulates are exchanged among these spheres. Each sphere affects all the other spheres. For example, volcanic eruptions transfer gases and particles from the lithosphere to the atmosphere. The atmosphere provides and regulates the amount of water in the hydrosphere and cryosphere, and provides water, carbon, and oxygen for the biosphere. Through winds, atmosphere causes erosion, creates soil, and absorbs and emits energy from the Sun. When you consider all these complex interactions, you can see why it's better to define climate as the average weather conditions, their variability and causes, and inter-relationships of many individual systems within the global Earth system. One example how such systems are inter-related is illustrated in **Figure 12.**

What causes climate?

Latitude is the primary factor that determines climate at a given location. The amount of radiation received from the Sun and the prevailing circulation features depend on latitude. Other factors are location near high mountains or on the east or west sides of a continent and distance from major bodies of water.

Causes of Mean Temperature The amount of solar radiation received and surface temperatures vary greatly from the equator to the poles. In the winter, the amount of solar radiation varies, because of the low angle at which it strikes Earth. As a result, temperatures decrease rapidly with increasing latitude. The high reflectance, or albedo, of snow and ice in high latitudes adds to this decrease. In summer, temperature decrease is less pronounced as sunlight strikes at a higher angle and periods of daylight are longer. The temperature patterns over the United States illustrate this, as shown in **Figure 12.** The strong temperature gradients in winter and spring help to create storms and severe weather.

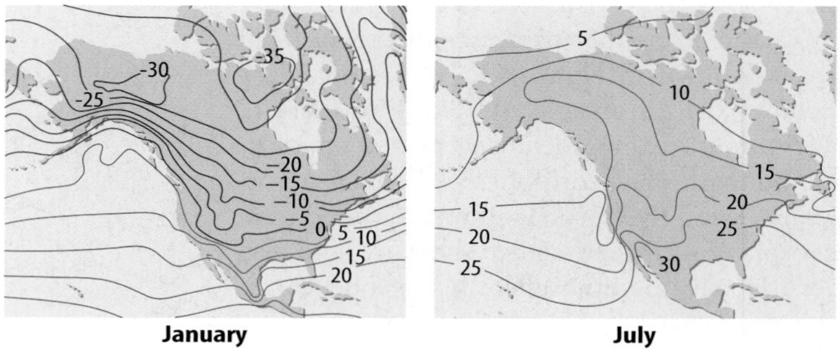

Figure 12 Lines drawn on a weather map that connect points of equal temperature are called isotherms.
Infer *Why are warmer temperatures shifted northward in July?*

Curriculum Connection

Geography Remind students that latitude is the distance in degrees north or south of the equator. Longitude is the distance in degrees east or west of the prime meridian. Have students use a world map or globe to locate the equator, the prime meridian, and the latitude and longitude of where they live. L1 ELL

Teacher FYI

Red Tides Scientists have found a connection between giant dust clouds from Africa that deposit dust containing high levels of iron in waters near Florida and toxic algae. Increased iron levels encourage growth of algae in the water that kills large numbers of sea animals—the red tide. This shows the interactions of four of the five spheres.

NATIONAL GEOGRAPHIC VISUALIZING EARTH'S BIOGEOPHYSICAL SYSTEM

Figure 13

The Namib desert illustrates the interconnectedness of climate, geology, plants, and animals. It is created by high pressure, wind, and cold ocean currents along the west coast of southern Africa.

Transverse dunes form perpendicular to the wind.

The desert is constantly reshaped by the wind. Transverse dunes show that the wind blows in one preferred direction. Dunes also begin when isolated plants trap sand. However, most deserts are not covered with sand dunes—they are made of stony pavement left behind when wind strips the desert surface. Winds and water remove the finer surface materials, leaving stones behind. This process is called deflation.

Star-shaped dunes form when winds are variable.

Dense coastal fog forms when the air above cold ocean currents interacts with moist desert air. Although deserts may appear to be dry, the air above ground contains lots of moisture. Condensation from fog produces fog-water, which drips into desert pavement and dissolves rocks, forming new sediment. It also forms small pools below the stony surface, which support plant growth. Desert plants have special adaptations such as a dense, compact form and thick, waxy coats. This helps protect them from both heat and animals.

Stone pavement is more common in a desert than dunes.

The Welwitschia plant grows in this barren land by absorbing fog-water through its elongated leaves. It is a relic of millions of years ago and is found only in the Namib.

Beetles capture fog-water by basking upside down or forming trenches at the bottom of dunes. They also survive beneath the leaves of Welwitschia plants where temperatures may be 30°C cooler than the surround bare ground.

NATIONAL GEOGRAPHIC

Visualizing Earth's Biogeophysical Systems

Have students examine the pictures and read the captions. Then ask the following questions: Explain why some areas of the Namib appear so different from others. Wind shapes dunes. Some winds blow exclusively from one direction and produce dunes with crests perpendicular to the wind. Variable winds produce star-shaped dunes. Explain why so many deserts might consist of stony pavement rather than sand. Dunes usually start when sand is trapped by isolated vegetation. With no vegetation, sand does not collect, but may be blown thousands of miles. Also, the type of rock present may not be easily eroded by wind. If coastal fog contains so much moisture, why don't more plants exist along the coast? Fog condenses only when the temperature drops below its dew point. This happens only in the cool night or morning and in shaded crevices, so only plants that can absorb moisture rapidly and retain it can survive.

Activity

Ask students to research mechanisms that help plants and animals survive under harsh environmental conditions. Ask each student to find one example and present it to the class along with a photo or drawing. The pictures can then be grouped on posters, according to the conditions—for example, aridity, heat, or cold. L2 LS **Visual-Spatial**

Differentiated Instruction

Challenge Have students research a desert in the southwestern United States and make a presentation to the class. The presentation should include how the desert formed, conditions, and the survival mechanisms of plants and animals. During the presentation they might ask students to compare and contrast aspects of this desert with the Namib. L2 LS **Linguistics**

Discussion

Factors that Influence Climate After students have read about types of climates, have them summarize the factors that affect the climate of San Francisco. San Francisco is located near the coast so it is influenced by ocean currents. The city also lies in the path of the prevailing westerlies. This strengthens the influence of the ocean currents, giving San Francisco a strongly developed maritime climate. L2

Teacher FYI

ITCZ Near the equator, the trade winds converge along a shifting boundary known as the Intertropical Convergence Zone (ITCZ). In July, the Sun is more directly over the northern hemisphere. This area receives the maximum amount of radiant energy. In response, the ITCZ moves north. The opposite occurs during January. The sun is more directly over the southern hemisphere, and the ITCZ moves south. This seasonal movement of the ITCZ strongly affects the amount of precipitation received throughout the year by areas located north or south of 30° latitude.

Caption Answer

Figure 14 equal

Ocean and Land Influence Oceans and ocean currents modify the basic climate. Areas with little direct ocean influence are called **continental climates** and have steep temperature gradients. A climate with strong ocean influence is called a **maritime climate.** Maritime climates are milder—summers are cooler, winters are warmer, and daily temperatures vary less. The continental climate of Peoria, Illinois, and the maritime climate of San Francisco, California, illustrate the contrast. Although both are near 40° N latitude, the temperature difference between the warmest and coldest months is about 8° C in San Francisco and 30° C in Peoria. Maritime effects are strong enough to keep winters at arctic Spitsbergen, Norway at 78° N latitude, warmer than in International Falls, Minnesota at 48° N latitude.

Precipitation Wind and pressure patterns determine precipitation. Humid climates are associated with low-pressure areas in the tropics and the middle latitudes. Rainfall is greater near the equator because the trade winds of both hemispheres converge there, increasing the rising motion. Arid climates are common where high pressure prevails, and aridity is particularly intense in the subtropics on the eastern sides of the subtropical highs.

Superimposed upon this general pattern are differences related to location on a continent, as shown for North America in **Figure 14.** The west coast lies east of the subtropical high, which brings cold water currents and stable air. This creates the dry climates of California and the southwest. The east coast lies west of the subtropical high, where southerly winds bring warm, unstable air from the Gulf of Mexico that increases precipitation. Air masses can also influence the amount of precipitation an area receives. When continental polar air masses, which originate in the cold, dry artic regions, move across the Midwestern states in the winter, cold, dry weather results.

Another factor affecting precipitation is the prevailing winds. Because westerlies prevail in the middle latitudes, the maritime influence is stronger on the west coast. This explains why San Francisco has a strongly developed maritime climate, but Boston has a continental climate.

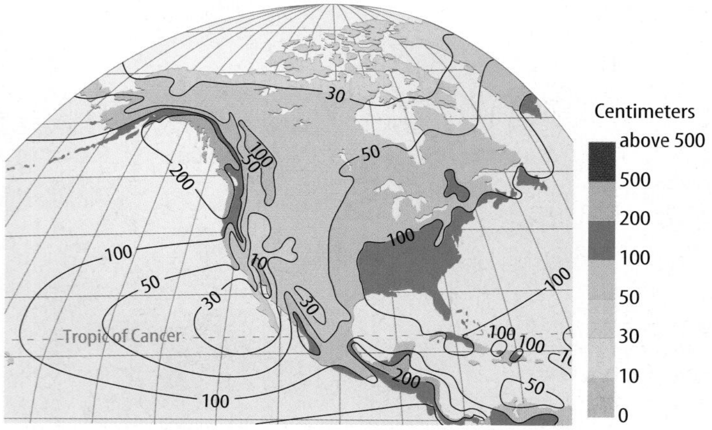

Figure 14 Lines drawn on a map that connect points of equal precipitation are called isohyets or isohyetal lines.
Research *What does the prefix iso- mean?*

Fun Fact

The world record for the hottest temperature belongs to El Azizia, Libya. In 1922, a temperature of 58°C (136°F) was recorded. The world record for the coldest temperature is held by Vostok, Antarctica. In 1983, a temperature of -89°C (-129°F) was recorded.

Reading Strategy

K-W-L Have students make a four-column tabl In the first column, students should list *mean ten perature, ocean/land influence, precipitation, an mountain and water influence.* In the secon column, they should write what they know abo each. In the third column, they should list wh they want to know. After they read, have studen record what they learned in the last column.

532 CHAPTER 17 Weather and Climate

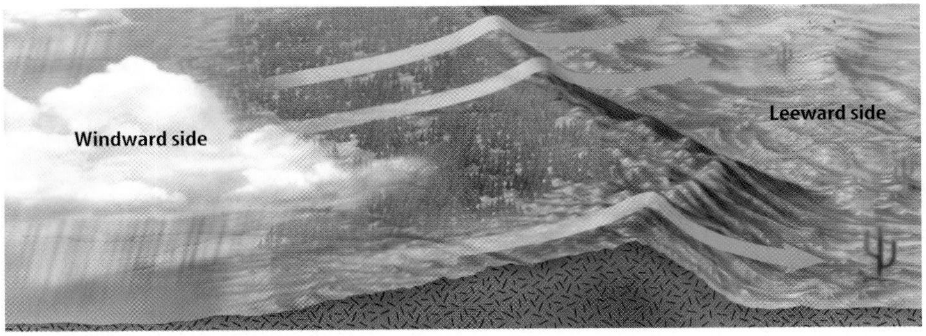

Influence of Mountains The Rocky Mountains and the Sierra Nevada also influence the climate of the west. They act as barriers in the wind, blocking weather systems and altering patterns of precipitation. When the wind blows perpendicular to one side of a mountain range, a **lee rain shadow** forms on the opposite side, as shown in **Figure 15.** The Great Plains lie in the lee shadow of the Rocky Mountains and are relatively dry.

Figure 15 The lee rain shadow of the Sierra Nevada and Rocky Mountains accounts for much of the decreased precipitation shown in Figure 14.

Influence of Water Coasts and lakeshores can affect regional climates in several ways. In winter, lake-effect snow often results in regions around the Great Lakes, like those shown in **Figure 16.** As cold, continental air from the north passes over warmer lake water, the air mass gains heat and moisture. When the air mass reaches the colder land to the south or east of a lake, heavy precipitation, in the form of snow, occurs.

Another example of how coasts affect regional climate is a sea breeze. A **sea breeze** (or lake breeze) blows from the water toward the land in the afternoon, when the land is warmer than the water. Warm air rises over the land creating low pressure that allows cool, dense air to blow from the sea toward land. The reverse happens at night when the land is cooler than the water. A land breeze occurs when cool, dense air over land creates high pressure causing the air to blow from the land toward the sea.

Climate Scale Many small-scale variations are superimposed upon the large-scale climate patterns. Some are regional or local and others, termed microclimates, are variations within small distances. For example, cities create a condition called the heat island effect. Building and pavement materials heat more rapidly than bare land. Vehicles and industry produce pollution that retains heat. Air rises over a heat island, pulling in air from the surrounding countryside. On some clear, calm nights, downtown San Francisco can be as much as 8°C warmer than the surrounding rural areas.

Figure 16 People often experience similar weather events near large bodies of water. Cities east of the Great Lakes experience lake-effect snow.

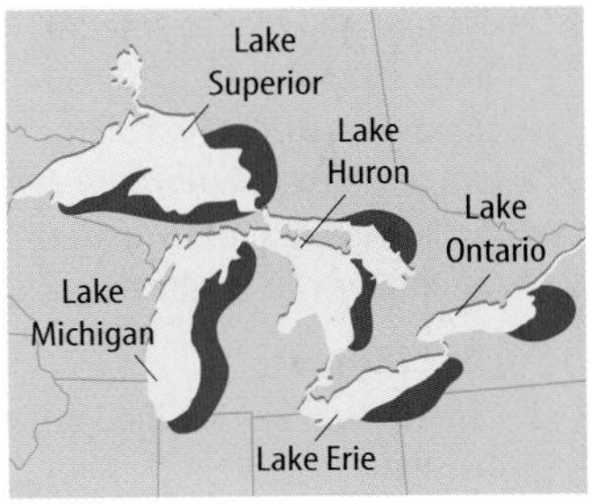

Quick Demo
Lee Rain Shadow

Materials sponge, water, plastic folder, large plastic container

Estimated Time 15 minutes

Procedure Open the plastic folder and turn it upside down within the plastic container, so that the folder forms a model mountain. Dampen the sponge and squeeze it as you move the sponge up the windward side of the "mountain." Continue to move the sponge, now dry, down the leeward side of the mountain. Ask students what type of climate would be found on the leeward side of the mountain. dry climate L3

Activity

Microclimates Have students take temperature readings in a sunny field on the school grounds and in the shadow of the school building. Have them explain the differences in temperature moisture, and plant growth. The area in the shadow of the school building is a microclimate. Its temperatures are generally cooler than those in the open field. The area might be drier if an overhang shields it from rain and might be wetter if near a downspout. Plant growth might vary, depending on available light and moisture. L2 ELL

LS **Visual-Spatial**

Differentiated Instruction

Learning Disabled Help clarify the connection between vegetation, temperature, and precipitation for students with learning disabilities. Point out that some plants, such as fir trees, can withstand cold temperatures. Other plants, such as cacti, thrive in warm climates. Plants also have different moisture requirements. When scientists study an area's climate, they also study the area's vegetation, among other factors. Vegetation is a visible clue, indicating the temperature and precipitation amounts for an area. L1 ELL

Caption Answer

Figure 17 temperature and moisture

Visual Learning

Figure 17 Have students use the map to describe the characteristics of their area's climate. Answers will vary depending upon students' location. L2

Post Reading

Reflection Ask students to respond to the following prompt in their Science Journals: Describe the climate in the reigon in which you live or in a place you've visited. Using the knowledge gained from reading the text, try to determine influences affecting climate in your area of choice.

3 Assess

DAILY INTERVENTION

Check for Understanding

Visual-Spatial Display a globe. Ask students which area receives the most direct sunlight. equator Ask students to describe how temperature changes with latitude. Temperature decreases with distance from the equator. L1

Reteach

Climate Factors Have students work in pairs to quiz one another on the factors that influence climate. L2 ELL

Assessment

Performance Have students work in small groups to design a plan to help reduce the heat-island effect in an urban area. Encourage students to research real solutions used by several different cities. Potential solutions include planting more trees along streets, enlarging parks, and painting rooftops white—most rooftops are dark-colored and absorb heat. L2 ELL PBL **Linguistic**

Cold Arid	*tundra*
Cold Dry winter	*boreal evergreen forest*
Warm Arid	*desert*
Warm Semi-arid	*grassland*
Wet winter Dry summer	*Mediterranean forest*
Wet summer Dry winter	*temperate woodland*
Warm Wet	*subtropical deciduous forest*
Warm Wet	*tropical deciduous forest*

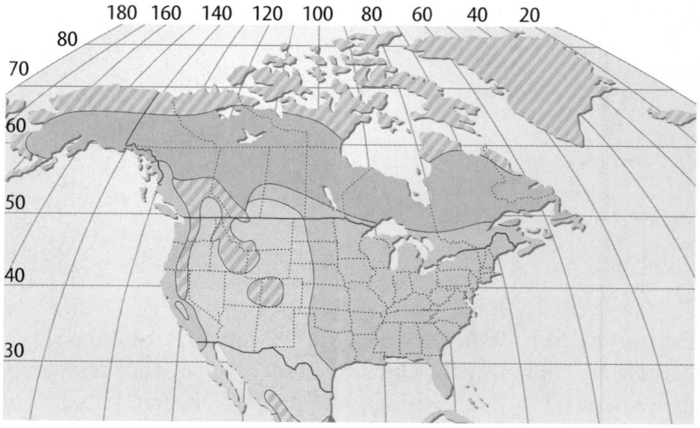

Figure 17 Climate zone influences the types of vegetation that will grow there.
Infer *What are two major factors that characterize climate types?*

Types of Climates

Geographer Glenn Trewartha and meteorologist Lyle Horn designed a system to classify climates, shown in **Figure 17.** It has three major divisions—cold or boreal, arid and semi-arid, and climates with adequate heat and precipitation. The last includes temperate, subtropical, and tropical climates. These divisions are closely correlated with vegetation.

section 3 review

Summary

Climate and Weather

- Climate is the net result of interactions involving all aspects of the biogeophysical system called Earth.

What causes climate?

- The main causes of climate are the distribution of solar radiation and the location of pressure and wind systems.
- Oceans, land masses, mountains, and large lakes also affect climate.
- Climates are classified on the basis of temperature and moisture availability.
- Prevailing high pressure or the rain shadow of mountains can produce dry climates.

Types of climate

- Climates can be classified into three major divisions.

Self Check

1. **Explain** why a climatic normal does not tell you exactly what to expect where you live.
2. **Identify** the five elements of the biogeophysical system called Earth.
3. **Explain** the association between climate and latitude.
4. **Compare and contrast** continental and maritime climates.
5. **Think Critically** Would you expect the daily temperature range to be greater in a maritime climate or a continental climate? Explain.

Applying Math

6. **Calculate Range** The coolest average summer temperature in the United States is 2°C at Barrow, Alaska, and the warmest is 37°C at Death Valley, California. Calculate the range of average summer temperatures in the United States.

More Section Review gpescience.com

section 3 review

1. A climatic normal is an average of conditions over a 30-year period. It does not predict what to expect on any specific day.
2. atmosphere, hydrosphere, lithosphere, cryosphere, and biosphere
3. Latitude is a major factor that determines climate because it governs the amount of solar radiation received.
4. Both are types of climate that depend on location. Maritime climates have a strong ocean influence and usually have a narrow range of temperatures. Continental climates have little or no ocean influence and experience extreme temperature differences between winter and summer.
5. The daily temperature range would be greater in a continental climate because the maritime effect would lessen daily differences.
6. 35°C

section 4

Earth's Changing Climates

Reading Guide

What You'll Learn
- **Explain** how climate changes seasonally.
- **Explain** causes of climate change.
- **Describe** how we influence climate.
- **Explain** El Niño's effect on weather.

Why It's Important
Changing climates affect all life on Earth.

Review Vocabulary
trace: a minute, barely detectable amount present

New Vocabulary
- global warming
- El Niño
- La Niña

Seasonal Changes

Seasonal changes occur as Earth completes a revolution around the Sun. The hemisphere tilted toward the Sun experiences summer while the hemisphere tilted away from the Sun experiences winter. During the summer, a hemisphere receives more intense solar radiation and temperatures rise. During winter, the intensity and amount of solar radiation decreases and temperatures drop. Seasonal changes are magnified in the mid-latitudes by the temperature contrast between land and oceans. The oceans are generally colder than land in the summer, but warmer than land in the winter.

Long-term Changes

Cycles of glaciations, called ice ages, represent long-term climatic change. The peak of the last ice age was 18,000–22,000 years ago when global was about 6°C cooler than present. Glaciers covered much of the middle and high latitudes, as shown in **Figure 18A.** Deserts expanded in the tropics and rainforests all but disappeared.

However, by 5,000 years ago, most of the glacial ice had melted, rainforests returned, and grasslands spread into low latitude deserts. World climate reached its current pattern only about 3,000 years ago, but even since then, large variations have occurred. In the Medieval period, parts of the northern hemisphere were warm and much of the North Atlantic was free of ice, enabling the Vikings to sail to Greenland and establish colonies. A few centuries later, a cooler period called the Little Ice Age occurred, as shown in **Figure 18B.**

Figure 18 The last glacial maximum was 18,000 years ago when Earth's temperature was 6°C cooler than present.

A

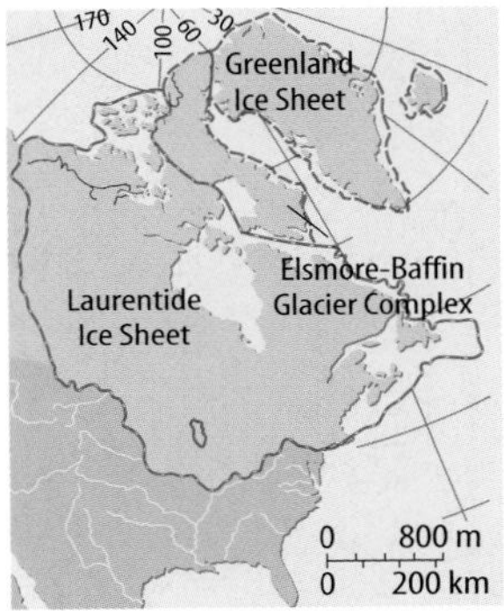

B

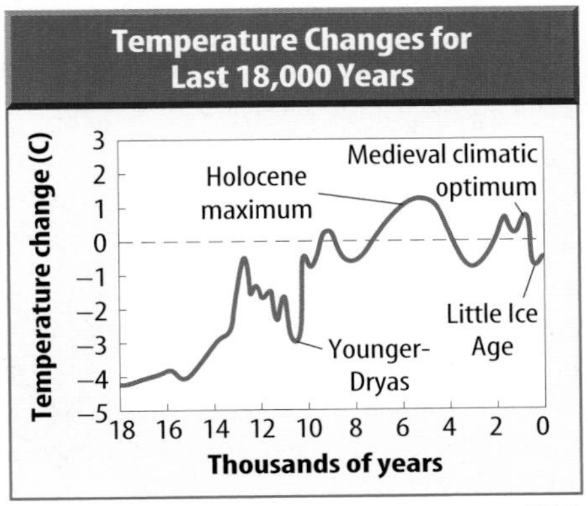

Section 4 Resource Manager

Chapter *FAST FILE* Resources
- Transparency Activity, p. 49
- Enrichment, p. 34
- Reinforcement, p. 30
- Directed Reading for Content Mastery, pp. 21–22
- Lab Worksheets, pp. 7–8

Physical Science Critical Thinking/Problem Solving, p. 18

Performance Assessment in the Science Classroom, pp. 48–49

Reading and Writing Skills Activities, pp. 19–20

1 Motivate

INTERACTIVE CHALKBOARD An editable Microsoft® PowerPoint® presentation is available on **Interactive Chalkboard** CD-ROM.

Bellringer

Section Focus Transparencies also are available on the Interactive Chalkboard CD-ROM. L2 ELL

Reading Preview

Tie to Prior Knowledge

Climate Change Ask students what climate change they experience yearly. If they mention seasonal changes tell them that seasons are short-term climate changes, but climate changes can take place over a few years to a few million years. L2

Set the Purpose Refer to the new vocabulary terms and ask students to set a purpose for reading the text by forming a question related to the word. For the term *global warming,* students might set this purpose: What influences global warming? What influences global warming? As they read, students should record the answers to their questions.

2 Teach

Quick Demo
Seasons

Materials unshaded lamp, globe

Procedure Place a lamp on a desk in front of the classroom and turn it on. Tilt a globe toward a wall, then circle the lamp, spinning the globe but keeping it tilted toward the wall. Students should observe that different areas of the globe directly face the Sun during Earth's revolution. Ask: What season is it in the northern hemisphere when that hemisphere is tilted toward the Sun? summer L2 ELL LS **Visual-Spatial**

Discussion

Ask students to explain why it is difficult for scientists to determine which factor is causing a specific climate change. Climate is the net result of different factors acting on different times scales. L3

INTEGRATE History

Dinosaur Extinction In 1980, Luis Alvarez published his discovery of the rare earth element iridium, found in a thin layer of clay in Italy. Iridium is common in meteoroids, comets, and asteroids. Further studies showed that iridium had been deposited about the time that dinosaurs became extinct.

Caption Answer

Figure 19 Trees absorb CO_2 and release O_2 into the atmosphere.

Visual Learning

Figure 19 Have students trace the path of a carbon atom through the carbon cycle. Have them begin with photosynthesis in a producer. L2 ELL **Visual-Spatial**

INTEGRATE History

Dinosaur Extinction
The impact of a large asteroid 65 million years ago on Mexico's Yucatán peninsula may have caused the extinction of dinosaurs and other species. The dust from such an impact would have caused months of darkness and drastically lowered temperatures. Animals like dinosaurs that needed large supplies of food would have suffered most. Research what evidence scientists have for such an impact and report your findings to your class.

Causes of Climate Change Numerous factors influence climate and act on diverse time scales. Over millions of years, factors such as mountain building and continental movement are important. Over years and decades, ocean currents, temperatures, and snow and ice cover play a big role. Climate is the net result of all factors on all timescales.

Variations in the receipt of solar radiation are important on a scale of hundreds to thousands of years. Changes related to Earth's orbit are the most important factors, producing changes that determine the rhythmic cycles of glaciation. These include changes in the tilt of Earth's axis of rotation, the shape of its orbit, and the timing of the seasons with respect to distance from the Sun. The tilt, for example, is now 23.5°, but has varied between 21.5° and 24.5°. These changes alter the amount and distribution of solar radiation that reaches Earth.

Sunspots similarly affect the amount of radiation received by Earth. During one period from 1645 to 1715 sunspot activity was very low. This period is correlated with long winters and extreme cold temperatures in Western Europe, known as the Little Ice Age. Sunspots are important on historical time scales. Volcanoes also play a role on this scale. They spew out vast amounts of dust that can block sunlight for years. For example, the eruption of Mt. Tambora in Indonesia in 1815 created the cold weather conditions that gave 1816 the name "The Year Without a Summer."

The Human Factor

Human activities, such as the burning of fossil fuels, manufacturing processes, deforestation, draining of wetlands, and intensive agriculture, have influenced Earth's atmosphere significantly. These activities modify the surface heating and the water and carbon cycles. They also increase the atmospheric concentrations of trace gases, dust and air pollution.

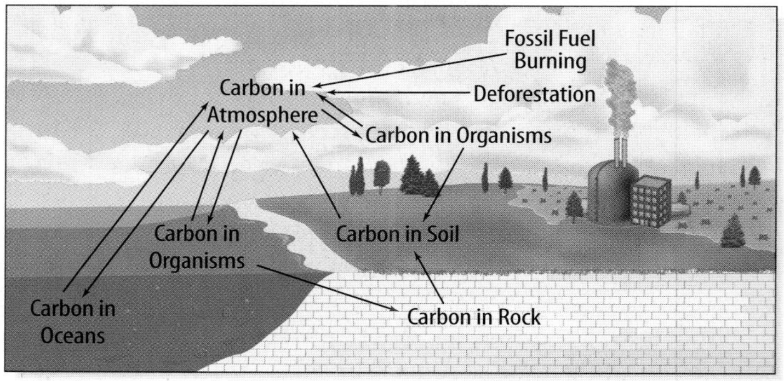

Figure 19 When organisms die and decay, some carbon is stored as humus in the soil and some is released back to the atmosphere as carbon dioxide.
Describe *how trees affect levels of carbon dioxide and oxygen in the atmosphere.*

Differentiated Instruction

Behaviorally Disordered Help keep students with behavioral disorders engage in classroom activities by assigning them small tasks. For example, students can take turns reading the text aloud and summarize the causes of climate change. They can also outline important points on the board as you lecture, or help distribute hand-outs. L2

Active Reading

Cause-and-Effect Chart This strategy is used to focus on cause-effect relationships. Have students write *Global Warming* in the center. To the left, write the apparent causes of the topic. On the right, have students record the effects.

The Carbon Cycle The carbon cycle, as shown in **Figure 19,** follows the exchange of carbon among the ocean, land, and atmosphere. Carbon is the basis of all organic matter. The changes in the carbon cycle are particularly important both meteorologically and ecologically. The carbon cycle is affected in two ways by deforestation and loss of vegetation—less carbon dioxide is absorbed from the atmosphere during photosynthesis, and decaying and burning wood adds carbon dioxide to the atmosphere.

Applying Math — Calculate

CARBON DIOXIDE (CO_2) CONCENTRATION Concentration of CO_2 in the atmosphere has increased at a constant rate of about 4.2 percent per decade over at least the last 30 years. Assuming this rate remains constant, you can predict its concentration in the future by using the following formula:

CO_2 (year + 10) = CO_2 (year) + CO_2 (year) × rate of CO_2 increase

IDENTIFY known values and unknown values

Identify the known values:

The concentration of CO_2 in 2000 was 369 ppm

Rate of CO_2 increase between 1990 and 2000 was 4.2 percent

Identify the unknown value:

What will be the concentration of carbon dioxide in 2010?

Concentration of CO_2 = ? ppm

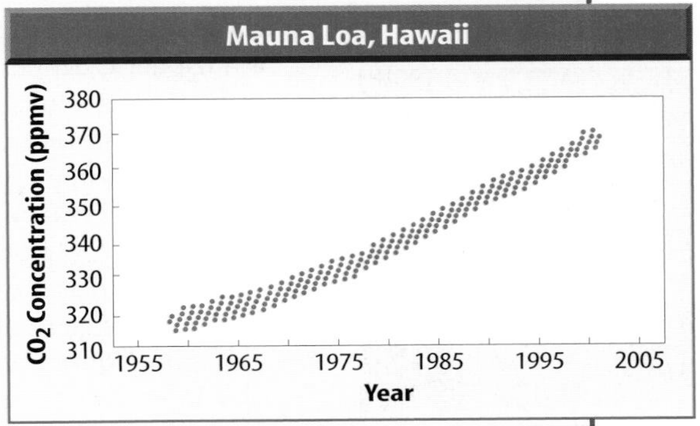

SOLVE the problem

Substitute the known values into the equation:

Concentration in 2010 = 369 ppm + 369 × 0.042

Concentration in 2010 = 384.5

CHECK your answer

Multiply 369 × .042 and subtract from 384.5 to get the value in 2000.

Practice Problems

1. Use the same method to find carbon dioxide concentration in 2020.
2. Assuming that conservation efforts reduce the rate of carbon dioxide increase to 2.6 percent per decade, predict the concentration in 2010?

For more practice problems, go to page 879 and visit Math Practice at gpescience.com.

Reading Strategy

Dialogue Have students create a written dialogue between themselves and a family member. In the conversation, the student should explain how carbon cycles between the living and nonliving world and the effect of human activities on this cycle.

Teacher FYI

Effects of Burning Fossil Fuels The burning of fossil fuels adds carbon dioxide to the air and removes oxygen. This activity has caused a slight decrease in atmospheric oxygen over the last century. However, oxygen is much more abundant than carbon dioxide in the atmosphere. Currently, scientists are monitoring the oxygen cycle, but they do not foresee any serious consequences to global climate.

Applying Math

Math Standards

National: 1, 2, 9

Answers to Practice Problems

1. 400.7 ppm
2. 378.6 ppm

LAB DEMONSTRATION

Purpose to demonstrate that burning fossil fuels releases carbon dioxide into the air

Materials balloons, tire pump, car, twist ties, straws, funnel, test tubes, water, bromthymol blue, dropper

Preparation Using a funnel, fill one balloon with car exhaust. Fill the second using a tire pump. Seal both with twist ties.

Procedure Add 10 drops of bromthymol blue, which turns yellow in the presence of carbon dioxide, to each test tube. Drop a straw into each test tube. Test the contents of each balloon by placing its open end over one of the straws and carefully releasing the twist tie.

Expected Outcome The exhaust fumes cause the solution to turn yellow.

Assessment

How might levels of carbon dioxide in the atmosphere be reduced? By reducing emissions from vehicles

Teacher FYI

Environmental Solutions The city in Mexico having the most air pollution is the capital, Mexico City. Many of the city's four million vehicles do not contain modern emission controls. In response, the government has provided incentives to industry and private citizens, promoting the manufacture and use of cleaner vehicles. For example, since 1991, new cars are now equipped with emission controls. Residents in urban areas either must equip their vehicles with catalytic converters or be banned from driving one day each week.

Visual Learning

Figure 20 Have students identify trends they observe in the images of the ozone layer. The concentration of ozone has decreased dramatically since 1979. L2

Caption Answer

Figure 20 Ozone shields Earth from ultraviolet radiation.

Activity

Deforestation Have students design and carry out experiments to determine how deforestation affects soil erosion. They can compare rates of erosion in two different containers. One container could hold both plants and soil. The second container could hold soil only. L3

Fun Fact

Scientists have determined the historical concentrations of atmospheric carbon dioxide by analyzing samples of air that can be accurately dated. These include air bubbles in ice layers and air trapped in hollow buttons on military uniforms and in sealed bottles of vintage wines.

Trace Gases Today's atmosphere contains on average about 380 ppm of carbon dioxide. This is an increase of 66 ppm, or 21 percent, since measurements began in 1957. This level is far greater still than at the beginning of the nineteenth century, when levels were stable at 280 ppm. Human activities have also increased the concentration of other trace gases—methane by more than 100 percent, nitrous oxide by about 10 percent. All of these gases are important in heating the atmosphere.

Global Warming **Global warming** is an increase in the average global temperature of Earth. Global temperatures have increased over the last century by about 1°C. This may seem small, but the entire global temperature increase since the last ice age is only 6°C. Our understanding of global warming is incomplete, but evidence strongly suggests that the increase in trace gases is an important component.

Figure 20 The concentration of ozone over Antarctic has dramatically decreased between 1979 and 2003. Concentrations in the hole are about eighty percent lower than what would be there naturally. **Explain** *why scientists are concerned about decreasing concentration of ozone in the stratosphere.*

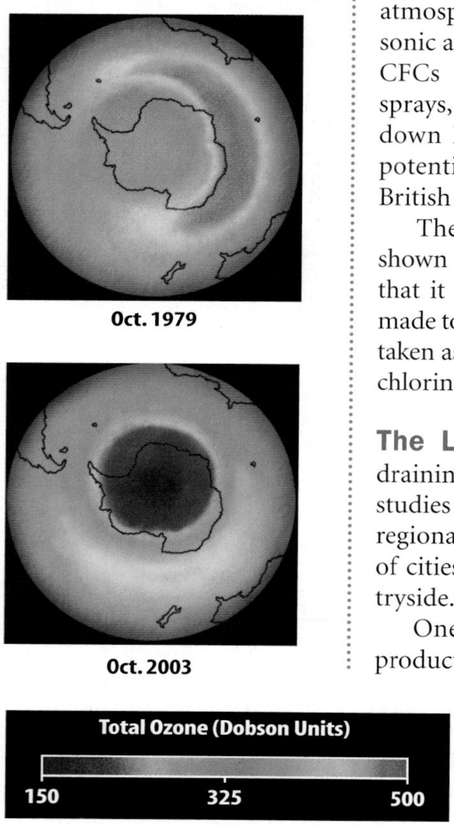

The Ozone Hole As early as the 1970s, scientists were concerned that synthetic chemical compounds could destroy atmospheric ozone. They worried about exhaust from supersonic aircraft and chlorine and fluorine compounds, such as the CFCs (chlorofluorocarbons) used in refrigeration, aerosol sprays, and other processes. Since ultraviolet radiation breaks down DNA, less protection from solar ultraviolet radiation potentially could affect the quality of life on Earth. In 1985, British scientists found a hole in the ozone layer over Antarctica.

The change in the ozone layer between 1979 and 2003 is shown in **Figure 20.** When study of the air in this hole showed that it was largely man-made, an international agreement was made to limit the use of CFCs. Recent studies indicate that actions taken as a result of the agreement are having an effect on levels of chlorine in the atmosphere, which are decreasing each year.

The Land Surface Humans change the land surface by draining swamps, plowing fields, and building cities. Extensive studies have suggested that these processes might affect local or regional climate, but the issue is still controversial. The climate of cities is different than the climate of the surrounding countryside. Effects on larger scales are not as clear.

One concern is desertification. Desertification is the end product of many types of changes that make once-productive land unusable. Human activities such as overgrazing of livestock, deforestation, and irrigation of crops may contribute to the process of desertification in some areas of the world.

Cultural Diversity

Adapting to Extremes You have seen how plants and animals can adapt to extreme climatic conditions. Humans use ingenuity and available materials to build shelters. Many Inuits build long- and short-term shelters from blocks of snow. Snow is a good insulation against frigid arctic temperatures. Around the Persian Gulf where summer temperatures are a threat, people once cooled their homes naturally using wind towers. These tall structures had openings in all directions and internal, diagonal walls. Breezes were captured, forced downward and channeled through certain rooms that were used in summer.

El Niño and La Niña

El Niño is a climatic event that involves the atmosphere and oceans. Normally, the trade winds blow warm surface water westward toward a low pressure area in the western Pacific. The warm surface water is replaced by cold, nutrient-rich water that is upwelled from below the surface. When the tradewinds weaken, surface pressure patterns break down and the flow of warm water is reversed. Nutrient-rich cold water is no longer upwelled and warm, nutrient-poor water remains at the surface.

Fewer fish and other marine life can be supported by the nutrient-poor water. Rainfall in the western Pacific decreases, where as heavy rain and flooding can occur on the normally dry coast of Peru. El Niño can dramatically alter global weather patterns. For example, a strong El Niño can lead to flooding and mudslides in California, as shown in **Figure 21,** and droughts in India, Australia, and parts of Africa.

The opposite of El Niño is **La Niña,** which occurs when tradewinds in the Pacific are unusually strong and equatorial oceanic surface temperatures are colder than normal. La Niña can cause drought in the southern United States and excess rainfall in the northwest.

Figure 21 Parts of the Pacific Coast Highway in California have been disrupted by erosion and mudslides caused by El Niño.

section 4 review

Summary

Seasonal Changes

- The tilt of Earth's axis changes the amount of solar radiation received by the northern and southern hemispheres throughout the year, causing the seasons.

Long-term Climate Changes

- Cycles of glaciation occur on the scale of tens of thousands of years.
- Sunspots and volcanoes influence climate on shorter timescales.

The Human Factor

- Human activities have increased the concentration of trace gases and decreased stratospheric ozone.

El Niño and La Niña

- El Niño is a warming of the Pacific Ocean with worldwide effects. La Niña is the opposite of El Niño.

Self Check

1. **Identify** ways that humans may be affecting climate.
2. **Explain** why the contrast between land and water changes with the seasons.
3. **Explain** why it is difficult to identify any single cause of an observed climate change.
4. **Think Critically** What can be done to stop global warming? What can you do to help?

Applying Math

5. **Use Percentages** The eruption of Mount Pinatubo in 1991 put large amounts of dust into the atmosphere. Scientists say this decreased the average global temperature about 0.8 percent during the next year. How would this affect an area with an average temperature of 25°C before the eruption?
6. **Calculate** Areas of the southeastern United States may receive 15 percent of their rain during hurricanes. If average rainfall for this area ranges from 100–200 cm, how much of this might be from hurricanes?

More Section Review gpescience.com

Post Reading

Debate and Discuss Have students research the following topics in preparation for a class discussion/debate: causes of global warming, human influence on climate, and causes of the ozone hole. Encourage them to make a case that argues for specific causes and effects.

3 Assess

DAILY INTERVENTION

Check for Understanding

Linguistic Ask students to describe the connection between the greenhouse effect and global warming. The greenhouse effect is a natural process wherein certain gases trap heat from the Sun. Global warming is a rise in Earth's overall surface temperature possibly caused by an increase in greenhouse gases. L2

Reteach

Climate Change Draw an oval on the board. Inside the oval write *Climate Change.* Under this oval, draw two more ovals. In the first oval, write *Caused by Natural Processes.* In the second oval, write *Caused by Human Activities.* Use lines to connect the second row of ovals to the center oval. Draw a third row of ovals, connected to the second row. With student input, fill in the ovals with examples of different types of climate change. L1 ELL **Visual-Spatial**

Assessment

Oral Tell students that scientists disagree on the causes and effects of global warming. Have students conduct further research on the topic and then debate what the U.S. government should be doing about global warming. L3 IS **Visual-Spatial**

section 4 review

1. Answers include burning fossil fuels, deforestation, paving land, draining swamps, and releasing chemicals that damage the ozone layer.
2. Water absorbs heat slowly but retains heat longer than land. Oceans are generally warmer than land in winter, but cooler in summer.
3. Because climate depends on many factors that operate on different time scales, it is hard to determine which is most important.
4. Answers might include reduce emissions of trace gases, conserve electricity, enact stronger antipollution laws, plant more forests, and develop alternate energy sources.
5. lower average temperature by 0.2°C
6. 15–30 cm

BENCH TESTED

Real-World Problem

Purpose Students will identify a microclimate and investigate how conditions there differ from the surroundings and determine how this affects life forms or other factors.

Process Skills observe, measure, form and test hypotheses, make a graph, evaluate, infer, predict

Time Required 10-15 minutes a day for one or two weeks

Materials thermometer, rain gauge, meter stick or metric ruler, magnifying glass, camera

Alternate Materials small plastic cups, graduated cylinder

Form a Hypothesis

Possible Hypotheses

Encourage students to look for small areas that appear different either in plant growth or presence of snow, ice, or water.

After students have identified a possible microclimate, have them select one variable to study. Moisture enhances plant growth, so areas with more precipitation might have more vegetation. Sunlight also encourages plant growth, but some plants require less light than others, so vegetation may vary in size and variety.

Temperature may be a factor also. Sheltered areas protect against freezing temperatures and winds. Shade from buildings affects temperature, and this can cause snow to last longer or have positive and negative effects on life forms. Air temperature at ground level differs from that at higher elevations.

LAB Design Your Own

Investigating Microclimate

Goals

- **Investigate** how environmental variables respond to various microclimates.

Possible Materials

directional compass
thermometer
rain gauge
meter stick
small plastic cups
**graduated cylinder*
**Alternate materials*

Safety Precautions

Real World Problem

While we can talk about global climate or regional climate, we also can discuss climate on the scale of a few meters. We call climate at this scale a microclimate. For example, because cold, heavy air drains downhill, valley fog sometimes forms in moist, low-lying areas. Along the California coast, coastal fog collects on the needles of redwood trees, drips to the ground, and is absorbed by the tree's shallow root system. This microclimate helps the coastal redwoods survive, nestled in the fog belt along the California coast. In this lab, you will investigate local differences in microclimate.

Form a Hypothesis

Choose an aspect of climate, such as precipitation, light, or temperature. Form a hypothesis to explain how this aspect influences local environments. Predict how these factors will vary in response to differences in your microclimate variable.

Test Your Hypothesis

Possible Procedure Encourage students to take measurements at various distances to define the boundaries of their microclimate. Measure conditions over several days at about five sites.

Teaching Strategy

- Help students choose variables appropriate for the season.
- Make sure that the variable is measurable with the tools available.
- Help students choose appropriate sites and decide when and where to make measurements.

540 CHAPTER 17 Weather and Climate

Using Scientific Methods

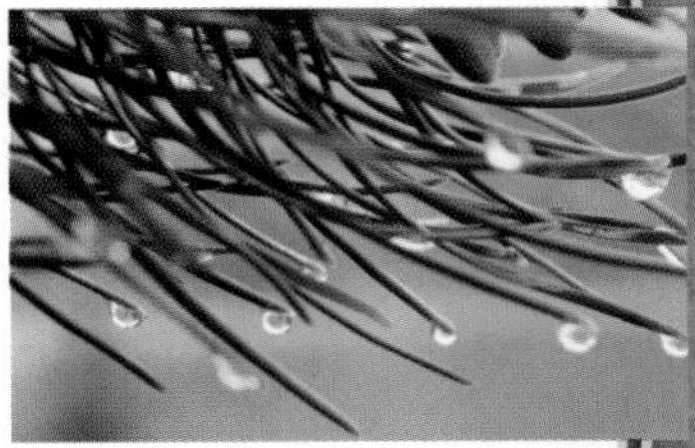

Test Your Hypothesis

Make a Plan

1. Decide what microclimate factor you will investigate, and what environmental factor you will monitor for effects.
2. How will you measure the selected microclimate variable? What equipment will you need? How often will you make measurements?
3. Choose sites for making measurements. Will these sites vary in microclimate? Is the environmental variable you chose present in these places?
4. Decide how you will measure your environmental variable. What equipment will you need? How often will you make measurements? Should the microclimate measurement happen at the same time?
5. Prepare a data table to record your measurements. Will you record the time of the measurements? Should you record the weather at the time of measurements?
6. Before you begin, list the steps of your procedure. Include all materials needed for each step. Does your procedure give you the data necessary to test your hypothesis?

Follow Your Plan

1. Be sure that your teacher approves your plan before you start.
2. Carry out your experiment as planned. Be sure to record all data in the appropriate places. Follow all appropriate safety precautions.
3. Record all observations and data in your Science Journal.

Analyze Your Data

1. **Make a graph** of your data. Put the microclimate variable on the *y*-axis, and the environmental variable on the *x*-axis.
2. **Discuss** any trends you see in the data based on your graph.
3. **Infer** any effects that the weather had on microclimate variables. How did this affect your environmental variable?

Conclude and Apply

1. **Discuss** your predicted environmental response to microclimate. Did your results support your hypothesis?
2. **Predict** how changes in global climate would affect the microclimate and response variables that you studied.

Communicating Your Data

Compare your results with the data of other students who measured the same microclimate variable. Present the combined data to the class. **For more help, refer to the** Science Skills Handbook.

Troubleshooting If no changes are observed in the first few days, encourage students to modify their plans and choose a different area or different variables.

Expected Outcome Varying amounts of shade, warmth, and precipitation will have measurable impacts on snow cover, plant growth, and evaporation rates at different sites.

Analyze Your Data

Answers to questions will vary. Accept all reasonable answers.

Conclude and Apply

Conclusions will vary. Be sure that the results are clearly expressed using diagrams and graphs where possible.

Assessment

Content Have students find other sites similar to those they investigated. Ask them to predict the microclimate in these sites based on their original observations. Use **Performance Assessment in the Science Classroom,** p. 89. L2

Alternative Inquiry Lab

A Controlled Microclimate To extend this lab, have students confirm their observations and conclusions in a controlled system. For example, they might compare growth of two or three plants. Be sure that they modify only one selected variable, such as moisture, light, or temperature while keeping other variables constant. L3

Communicating Your Data

Help students to present their results clearly, using drawings and graphs where possible, so that they can explain them to students who studied different microclimates.

Understanding Literature

The dust bowl was a tragic period for southern plains states in the 1930s. Ask students what other events took place during the 1930s. Possible answers: the Great Depression, Roosevelt's New Deal, and the rise of Nazi Germany

Respond to the Reading

1. It buries them in dust, damages leaves, stalks, and roots, and blocks essential sunlight.
2. Dust storms have a number of causes, including over-farming and grazing, erosion, removing trees, and drought.
3. **Linking Science and Reading** The effects of different types of severe weather can be similar. Crops are damaged, trees and homes are damaged or destroyed, and lives are disrupted.

INTEGRATE Earth Science **Dust Storms** With no moisture to bring rain, the wind picks up fine soil particles that often remain suspended in air. This irritates eyes and makes breathing difficult. The suspended dust also produces sunset colors. The particle content of the air is high enough to filter out all the blue light. What remains are the longer wavelengths of yellow, orange, and red.

Science and Language Arts

The Grapes of Wrath

by John Steinbeck

In *The Grapes of Wrath,* Steinbeck tells the story of the fictional Joad family, who lived in Oklahoma in the 1930s. Like thousands of families living in the drought-stricken dust bowl of the central United States, the Joads were tenant farmers who lost their farm. Such families piled their belongings into rickety trucks and migrated to California seeking work as fruit pickers.

Although the drought alone caused much hardship, it was gigantic dust storms that finally destroyed their crops. Steinbeck describes such a storm in the following words:

"The wind grew stronger, whisked under stones, carried up straws and old leaves, and even little clods, marking its course as it sailed across the fields. The air and the sky darkened and through them the sun shone redly, and there was a raw sting in the air. During a night the wind raced faster over the land, dug cunningly among the rootlets of the corn, and the corn fought the wind with its weakened leaves until the roots were freed by the prying wind and then each stalk settled wearily sideways toward the earth and pointed the direction of the wind."

When the storm finally ended, the buildings, fences, and trees were blanketed with thick layers of dust—a grim reminder of how the Joads' lives had been changed forever.

Understanding Literature

Historical Novels Authors often use historical events as inspiration. When a piece of fiction combines historical events or characters with fictional plot and dialogue, it becomes a historical novel. Well-written historical fiction can aid the reader in understanding how people actually experienced an important time in history.

Respond to the Reading

1. How does the dust storm affect the crops?
2. What might cause such a dust storm?
3. **Linking Science and Reading** Write a paragraph describing the effects of a hurricane or tornado.

INTEGRATE Earth Science The dust bowl resulted from interactions between natural elements, such as climate, plants, and soil, and human elements, such as farming practices and economics. When the dust bowl occurred, vegetation was already sparse. This reduced friction and allowed the wind to gain speed. With no moisture to bind soil particles together, the soil eroded. Dust from these storms was carried up to 3,000 km away from its original source. The dust storms were a type of squall that sometimes bring rain to these semi-arid plains.

542 **CHAPTER 17** Weather and Climate

Resources for Teachers and Students

Out of the Dust, by Karen Hesse, Scholastic Press, 1999.

Survival in the Storm, The Dust Bowl Diary of Grace Edwards, by Katelan Janke, Scholastic Press, 2002.

Reviewing Main Ideas

Section 1 Earth's Atmosphere

1. Earth's atmosphere is 78 percent nitrogen, 21 percent oxygen, one percent argon, and includes small amounts of trace gases.
2. The stratosphere is the upper layer of the atmosphere where temperature always increases with height. The troposphere is the lower layer where most weather occurs.
3. The troposphere is heated primarily by Earth's surface after it absorbs radiation from the Sun.
4. Land absorbs and emits heat efficiently, but water resists temperature change.
5. Clouds form when warm air carrying water vapor rises until it is cool enough to condense.

Section 2 Weather

1. Major pressure belts and wind belts are caused by unequal heating between the equator and the poles and modifications resulting from Earth's rotation.

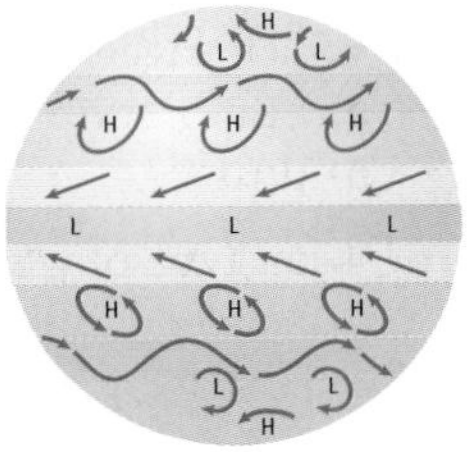

2. Specific weather patterns are associated with high and low pressure cells.
3. Air masses are large blocks of air with similar properties of moisture and temperature throughout. They interact in zones called weather fronts.
4. Severe weather includes thunderstorms, downbursts, tornadoes, and hurricanes.

Section 3 Climate

1. Climate refers to the mean weather conditions and their annual variations in an area.
2. Climate is part of an Earth system that includes the atmosphere, biosphere, hydrosphere, cryosphere, and lithosphere.
3. Latitude is the most important factor in determining climate.
4. Continents, mountains, and oceans influence climate on a large scale, and small-scale variations are termed microclimates.

Section 4 Earth's Changing Climates

1. Long-term changes include cycles of glaciation. Causes of climate change include changes in Earth's orbit, solar activity, volcanism, and human intervention.
2. Global warming has been documented. The reasons for it are complex and not fully understood.
3. Increased concentrations of trace gases and damage to the ozone layer are probably caused by human activities.

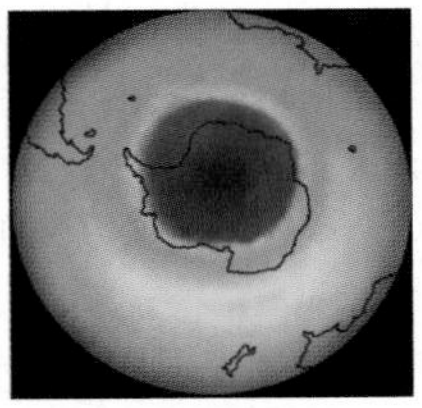

4. El Niño and La Niña affect ocean currents and coastal winds, causing serious droughts and flooding in some areas.

FOLDABLES™ Use the Foldable that you made at the beginning of this chapter to review what you have learned about weather and climate.

chapter Study Guide 17

Reviewing Main Ideas

Summary statements can be used by students to review the major concepts of the chapter.

Science Online

Visit gpescience.com
More Section Review
Interactive Tutor
Vocabulary PuzzleMaker
More Chapter Review
Standardized Test Practice

Assessment Transparency

For additional assessment questions, use the *Assessment Transparency* located in the transparency book.

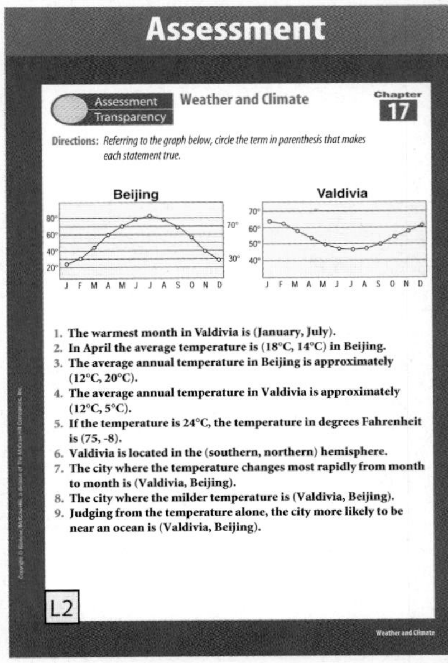

Assessment

Assessment Transparency — Weather and Climate — Chapter 17

Directions: *Referring to the graph below, circle the term in parenthesis that makes each statement true.*

1. The warmest month in Valdivia is (January, July).
2. In April the average temperature is (18°C, 14°C) in Beijing.
3. The average annual temperature in Beijing is approximately (12°C, 20°C).
4. The average annual temperature in Valdivia is approximately (12°C, 5°C).
5. If the temperature is 24°C, the temperature in degrees Fahrenheit is (75, -8).
6. Valdivia is located in the (southern, northern) hemisphere.
7. The city where the temperature changes most rapidly from month to month is (Valdivia, Beijing).
8. The city where the milder temperature is (Valdivia, Beijing).
9. Judging from the temperature alone, the city more likely to be near an ocean is (Valdivia, Beijing).

L2

Weather and Climate

FOLDABLES™ Have students use their Foldables to review weather and climate.

Using Vocabulary

1. weather fronts
2. maritime climate
3. latent heat
4. troposphere
5. El Nino/La Nina
6. westerlies
7. jet streams
8. lee rain shadow
9. temperature inversion
10. greenhouse effect

Checking Concepts

11. A	15. B
12. A	16. A
13. C	17. D
14. C	18. C

Interpreting Graphics

19. Accept reasonable diagrams showing subpolar lows and subtropical highs with westerlies in between the lows and highs. Trade winds blow from northeast in the northern hemisphere and southeast in the southern hemisphere.
20. Continental climates have little or no ocean influence and experience extreme temperature differences between winter and summer. Maritime climates have a strong ocean influence and usually have a narrow range of temperatures.
21. Cities at latitudes 41 and 45 have maritime climates; that at 72 and 40 have continental climates.

Thinking Critically

22. The continental U.S. has extreme temperatures of cold and warm air masses and the availability of moisture from tropical oceans.
23. Because ozone filters out harmful ultraviolet radiation, loss of ozone exposes us to this danger.

chapter 17 Review

Using Vocabulary

biosphere p. 529	maritime climate p. 532
continental climate p. 532	sea breeze p. 533
El Niño p. 539	subtropical high p. 525
global warming p. 538	temperature inversion p. 519
greenhouse effect p. 520	troposphere p. 519
jet stream p. 525	weather front p. 526
La Niña p. 539	westerlies p. 524
latent heat p. 520	
lee rain shadow p. 533	

Match the correct vocabulary word(s) with each definition given below.

1. area of interaction between air masses
2. climate with a strong ocean influence
3. energy used to evaporate water
4. layer of the atmosphere where most weather occurs
5. global weather event(s) that involve oceans and the atmosphere
6. most important of three major wind belts
7. fast, powerful air current that affects many weather processes
8. area of reduced precipitation on one side of a mountain range
9. a region of very stable air that resists rising needed to form clouds and dispel pollution
10. warming of the atmosphere involving heat absorption by trace gases

Checking Concepts

Choose the word or phrase that best answers the question.

11. Which has great ranges in temperature and little ocean influence?
    A) continental climate
    B) El Niño
    C) La Niña
    D) maritime climate

12. Which is the percent of solar radiation reflected from the surface?
    A) albedo
    B) Coriolis effect
    C) greenhouse effect
    D) urban heat island

13. Which is the most important factor in determining climate at a given location?
    A) altitude **C)** latitude
    B) continents **D)** mountains

Use the illustration below to answer question 14.

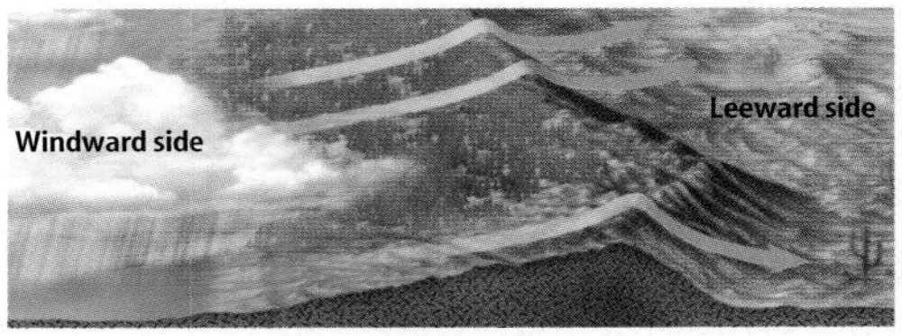

14. Which influence on regional climate is shown above?
    A) continental location
    B) lake effect
    C) lee rain shadow
    D) maritime location

15. Which triggers droplet formation in clouds?
    A) evaporation **C)** ozone
    B) dust **D)** thermals

16. What type of weather is most closely associated with a warm front?
    A) drizzle or steady rain
    B) downbursts or windshear
    C) hurricanes or tornadoes
    D) thunderstorms

17. Which is a trace gas?
    A) argon **C)** oxygen
    B) nitrogen **D)** ozone

18. Which surface reflects solar radiation the most?
    A) bare soil **C)** snow fields
    B) forest **D)** ocean

Vocabulary PuzzleMaker gpescience.com

Use the ExamView® Pro Test Bank CD-ROM to:

- create multiple versions of tests
- create modified tests with one mouse click for inclusion students
- edit existing questions and add your own questions
- build tests aligned with state standards using built-in State Curriculum Tags
- change English tests to Spanish with one mouse click and vice versa

Interpreting Graphics

19. **Illustrate** Earth's major pressure belts and wind belts, with labels showing the westerlies and the trade winds.

20. **Make a table** comparing characteristics of continental and maritime climates.

Use the data in the following table to answer question 21.

City Temperatures

Cities at Degrees N Latitude	Average July Temperature (°C)	Average January Temperature (°C)
72	20	−45
41	21	9
45	29	−2
40	31	−10

21. **Identify** Based on the data in the table above, identify the latitudes of the cities that have maritime and continental climates.

Thinking Critically

22. **Explain** why the continental United States is prone to severe weather, such as tornadoes and hurricanes.

23. **Infer** why scientists are so concerned about finding a hole in the ozone layer over Antarctica.

24. **Form a hypothesis** about how we might determine whether human activities have played a role in global warming.

25. **Identify** some ways that plants and animals might adapt to changing climate patterns. *Hint: Think of how organisms adapt to extreme conditions.*

Use the illustration below to answer question 26.

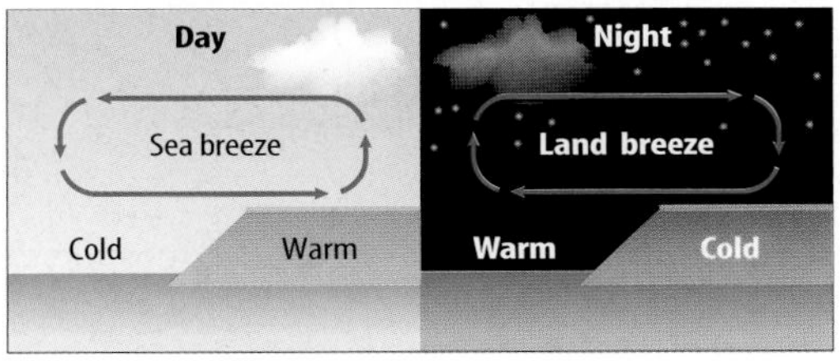

26. **Explain** why a sea breeze blows toward the land in the afternoon, and a land breeze blows toward the water in the evening.

27. **Infer** how global warming might increase the frequency of severe weather, such as hurricanes.

28. **Describe** the carbon cycle and explain how human activities might interfere with it.

29. **Explain** how water droplets form in clouds and the conditions needed to make them fall as some form of precipitation.

30. **Identify** some of the ways that human activities have interfered with the water cycle and describe some results of these activities.

31. **Explain** how El Niño affects global weather patterns.

Applying Math

32. **Convert Units** The high temperature of a summer day in the United States might be 81°F. What would this temperature be in France where they use Celsius temperatures? *Hint: Use the formula* $°C = (°F - 32) \times 5/9$.

33. **Compare Ratios** City A had 175 cloudy days in 2004. In 2004, 56 percent of city B's days were cloudy. Which city had more cloudy days? Show the calculations you did to find your answer.

More Chapter Review gpescience.com

Assessment Resources

Reproducible Masters

Chapter *Fast File* Resources
- Chapter Review, pp. 39–40
- Chapter Tests, pp. 41–44
- Assessment Transparency Activity, p. 53

Glencoe Science Web site
- Chapter Review Test
- Standardized Test Practice

Glencoe Technology
- Assessment Transparency
- Exam*View*® Pro Testmaker
- MindJogger Videoquiz
- Interactive Chalkboard

Thinking Critically

24. Hypotheses may involve correlating human activities as global temperature increases, for example, increases in irrigation, industrialization, and grazing animals or decreases in forest cover caused by deforestation

25. Students may mention that plants adapt to dry conditions by having small leaves or waxy coatings on their leaves. Also, plants and animals may become dormant during dry periods and begin growth only when moisture is available.

26. Cooler, denser air over water blows toward land during the day pushing up warmer, less dense air. A land breeze occurs during the evening when cooler, denser air over land flows toward warmer, less dense air over water.

27. Because hurricanes arise over warm tropical waters, global warming would make hurricanes more likely over wider areas.

28. Carbon is exchanged among three major areas, the ocean, land, and atmosphere. The major ways humans interfere with it are by deforestation and burning fossil fuels.

29. Water droplets form when cloud temperature drops to the dew point. Moisture condenses around fine particles called condensation nuclei.

30. Answers should include draining swamps, paving land, irrigation using well water, replacing forests with agricultural fields.

31. Heavy rain and flooding can occur on the normally dry coast of Peru. Rainfall in the western Pacific decreases. A strong El Niño can lead to flooding and mudslides in California and droughts in India, Australia, and parts of Africa.

Applying Math

Math Standards

National: 1,4,9

32. 27.2°C

33. City B; 0.56 × 365 days = 204 days

Answer Sheet An answer sheet can be found at **gpescience.com**.

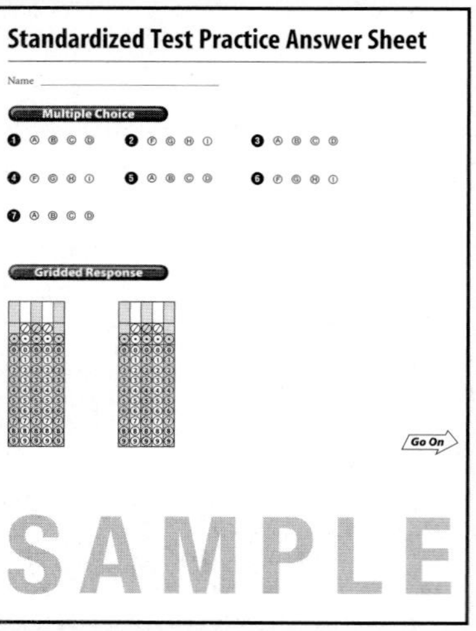

Multiple Choice

1. C	**5.** B
2. B	**6.** B
3. D	**7.** D
4. D	**8.** A

chapter 17 Standardized Test Practice

Record your answers on the answer sheet provided by your teacher or on a sheet of paper.

Multiple Choice

1. Which makes up most of Earth's atmosphere?

A. carbon dioxide

B. carbon monoxide

C. nitrogen

D. oxygen

Use the figure below to answer question 2.

Comparison of CO_2 Concentration to Time of Year and Latitude

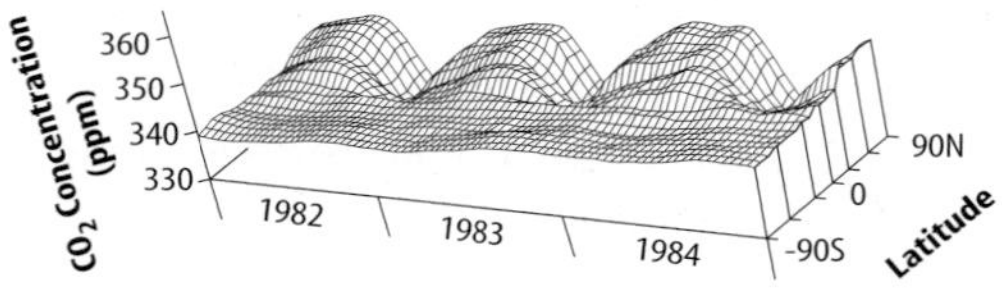

2. Which is used by photosynthetic organisms to produce almost all of Earth's atmospheric oxygen?

A. carbon monoxide

B. carbon dioxide

C. methane

D. nitrogen

3. Which accumulated in the stratosphere over millions of years and shielded Earth from ultraviolet rays from the Sun?

A. argon

B. nitrogen

C. oxygen

D. ozone

4. Which type of air mass would most likely be moist and warm?

A. continental polar

B. continental tropical

C. maritime polar

D. maritime tropical

5. Which is a series of windy gusts formed when a downdraft hits Earth's surface with particularly strong force?

A. hail

B. squall

C. thunderstorm

D. tornado

Use the diagram below to answer question 6.

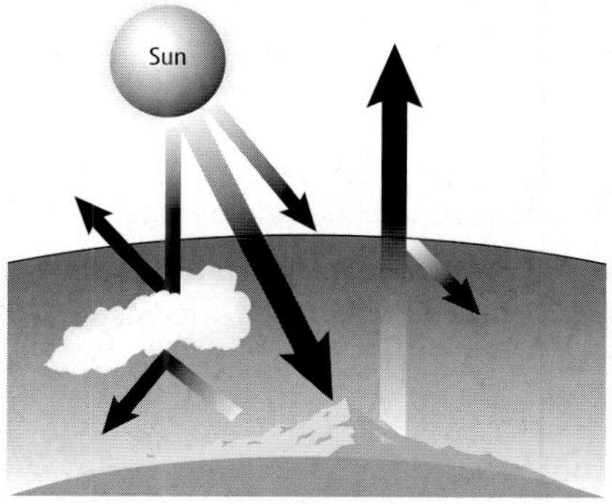

6. Which is caused by absorption of long wavelength radiation by trace gases?

A. condensation

B. greenhouse effect

C. latent heat

D. precipitation

546 STANDARDIZED TEST PRACTICE

Use the table below to answer question 7.

Land Surface	Albedo
Bare soil	25
Snow	90
Desert	50
Dense forest	10

7. Over which surface is the least amount of solar radiation absorbed?

A. bare soil

B. dense forest

C. desert

D. snow

8. Which are fast, powerful flows of wind imbedded in global wind systems?

A. jet streams

B. sea breezes

C. subtropical highs

D. westerlies

Gridded Response

9. If the average concentration of carbon dioxide in Earth's atmosphere at the beginning of the nineteenth century was 280 ppm and it presently is 380 ppm, what percentage of today's concentration existed at the beginning of the nineteenth century?

Test-Taking Tip

Review Never leave any answer blank.

Short Response

10. Describe the major differences between the conditions that existed 18,000 years ago from the conditions of the present. Include descriptions of the climatic, geological, and biological conditions.

11. Explain how the stratospheric ozone layer is formed. Also explain its importance in regard to the quality of life on Earth.

12. What causes uneven patterns of heating on Earth's surface?

13. Which factors cause climate?

Extended Response

Use diagram below to answer question 14.

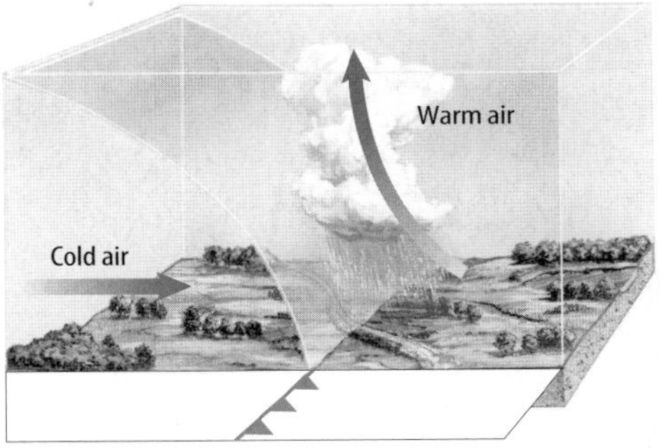

14. PART A What are weather fronts?

PART B How do air masses interact at a cold front?

chapter 17 Standardized Test Practice

Gridded Response

9. 73.7 %

Short Response

10. Climate was colder 18,000 years ago. Glaciers covered much of the middle and high latitudes and deserts expanded into the tropics. Rainforests were much smaller.

11. Oxygen from photosynthetic organisms accumulates in the atmosphere. Intense solar radiation converts some of it to ozone. Since ultraviolet radiation breaks down DNA, intense ultraviolet radiation from the Sun could be harmful to life on Earth. Stratospheric ozone shields Earth from ultraviolet radiation.

12. Dry land heats more rapidly than water. This, along with the different amounts of radiation that are reflected from different surfaces causes an uneven pattern of surface heating.

13. Latitude on Earth determines the amount of radiation Earth gets from the Sun and sets up prevailing air and water circulation. Other factors include distance from major bodies of water and the location of mountain ranges on a continent.

Extended Response

14. Part A: Weather fronts are zones in which air masses interact.

Part B: In a cold front, a cold air mass pushes the warm air mass upward in a random and chaotic fashion forming cumulus clouds. This often produces showers and thunderstorms.

Rubrics

For more help evaluating Short- and Extended-Response questions, see the rubrics on p. 9T.

unit 5

Unit Contents

WebQuest *Art of Neon* is a motivating and challenging investigation of the chemistry of noble gases and how they are used in colorful neon signs and glowing sculptures. Students will research how the noble gases are inserted into bent tubing and made to glow. As a culminating activity, students will design a "blueprint" of their own neon sign, its components, colors, shape, size, and use.

unit 5

Matter and Earth Materials

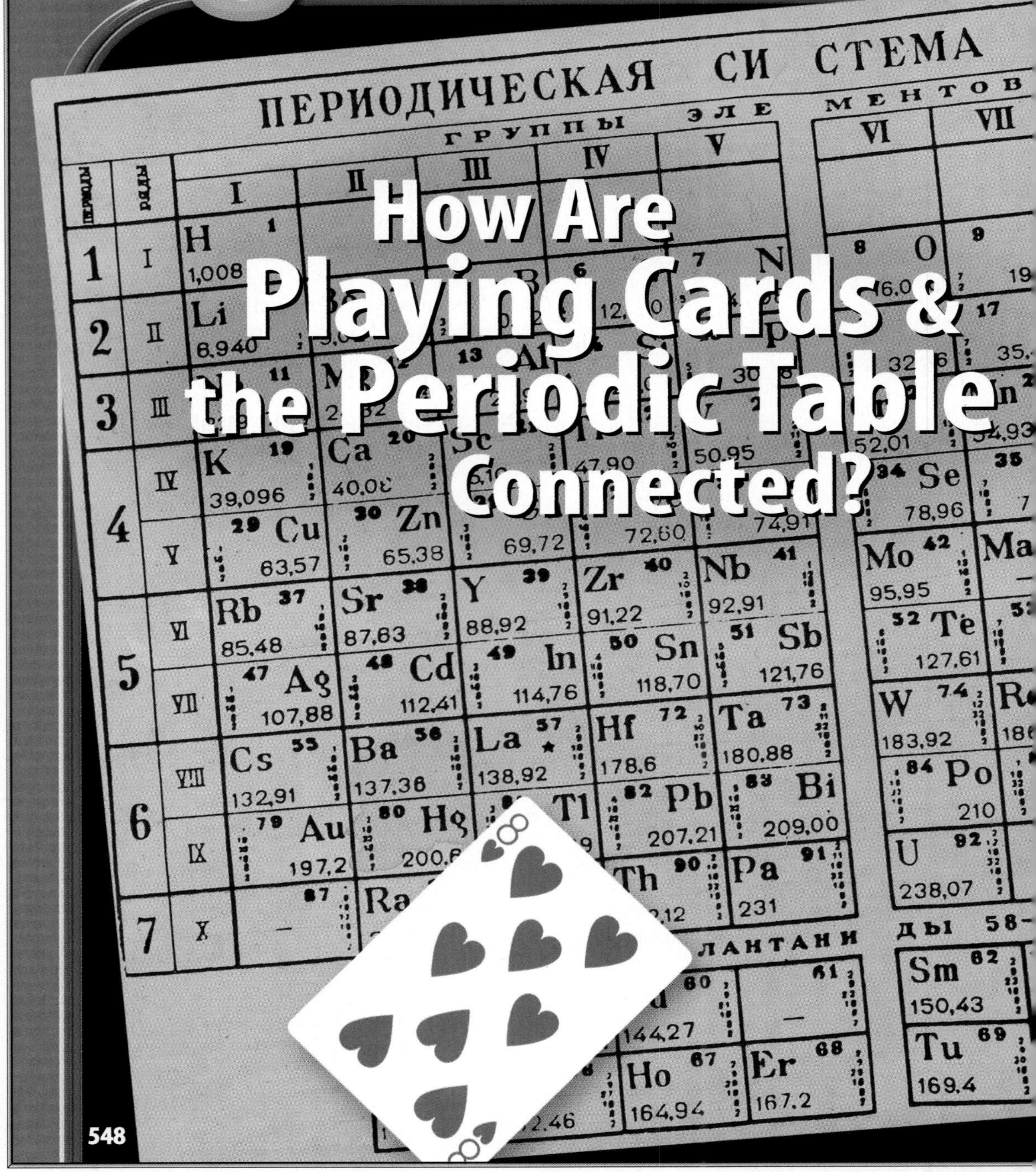

How Are Playing Cards & the Periodic Table Connected?

548

PROJECT CRISS

Study Skills

Discussion Several students are assigned to research each group on the periodic table or each collection of elements that belong together. After reading silently about the elements, the students take turns asking questions or making comments about the material until they have answers to the following questions: How reactive are the elements in each group? What evidence do the students use to discuss this? What properties do the elements share? Whole-class discussion follows.

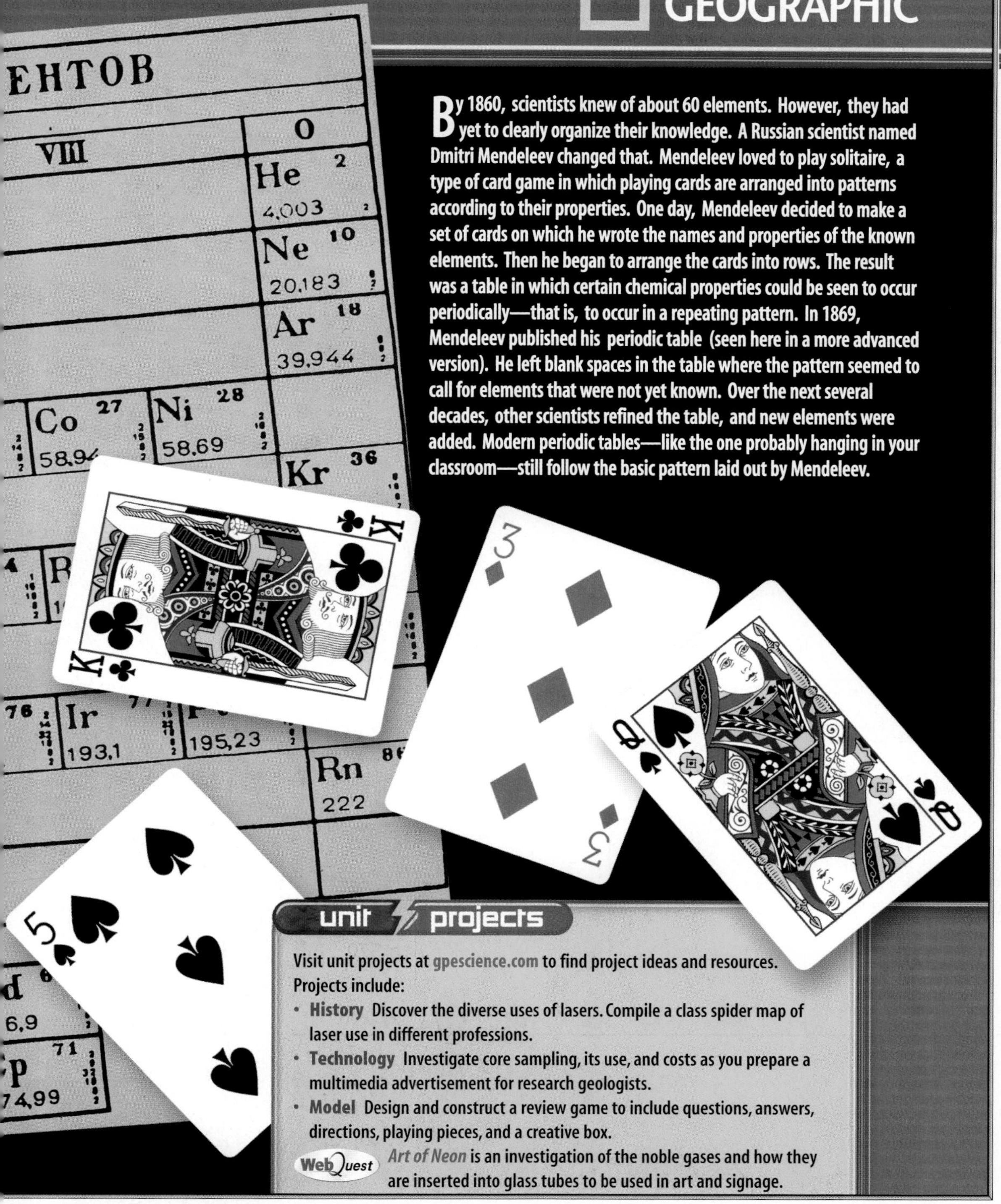

By 1860, scientists knew of about 60 elements. However, they had yet to clearly organize their knowledge. A Russian scientist named Dmitri Mendeleev changed that. Mendeleev loved to play solitaire, a type of card game in which playing cards are arranged into patterns according to their properties. One day, Mendeleev decided to make a set of cards on which he wrote the names and properties of the known elements. Then he began to arrange the cards into rows. The result was a table in which certain chemical properties could be seen to occur periodically—that is, to occur in a repeating pattern. In 1869, Mendeleev published his periodic table (seen here in a more advanced version). He left blank spaces in the table where the pattern seemed to call for elements that were not yet known. Over the next several decades, other scientists refined the table, and new elements were added. Modern periodic tables—like the one probably hanging in your classroom—still follow the basic pattern laid out by Mendeleev.

unit projects

Visit unit projects at gpescience.com to find project ideas and resources. Projects include:

- **History** Discover the diverse uses of lasers. Compile a class spider map of laser use in different professions.
- **Technology** Investigate core sampling, its use, and costs as you prepare a multimedia advertisement for research geologists.
- **Model** Design and construct a review game to include questions, answers, directions, playing pieces, and a creative box.

WebQuest *Art of Neon* is an investigation of the noble gases and how they are inserted into glass tubes to be used in art and signage.

unit projects

Career Working in small groups, have students explore the diverse use of lasers in a variety of careers—medical, military, police, educational, or artistic light and sound shows. Students should investigate how electrical engineers are designing new equipment for each field to help technicians be more precise and efficient. As a class, design a spider map for lasers and compile each group's information into one large informative display.

Technology Have students research the technology and use of core sampling by geologists. Information should include the mechanics of the actual drilling equipment, range of possible drilling depth, reasons a core sample might be useful in a variety of geological areas, and cost of equipment and drilling process. Students may then design a multimedia advertisement, as if selling drilling equipment to research geologists.

Model Ask students to design an entertaining and engaging game that will review concepts presented in this unit, giving them an opportunity to apply their new knowledge. Ideas might include card games, board games, trivia cards, dice, spinners, and game pieces, as well as complete directions, questions and answers, and a colorful intriguing container.

Additional Resources Visit unit projects at gpescience.com for more information, resources, and assessment rubrics.

NATIONAL GEOGRAPHIC **How Are Playing Cards & the Periodic Table Connected?**

- Tape a deck of cards sequentially on poster board. Ask students how all the cards in a row (period) are alike, and how all the cards in a column (family or group) are alike. They are all of one suit; the same card value is shown.
- Remind students that Mendeleev left blank spaces in his periodic table where elements seemed to be missing. Randomly remove several cards and ask students to identify the properties of the cards that belong in the empty spaces. Have them justify their answers and relate them to the empty spaces on Mendeleev's periodic table.

Section/Objectives	Standards		Lab/Features
	National	State/Local	
Chapter Opener	See pp. 16T–17T for a Key to Standards.		**Launch Lab:** Demonstrate the Distillation of Water, p. 551 Video Lab **Foldables,** p. 551
Section 1 Composition of Matter 3 sessions 1.5 blocks 1. **Define** substances and mixtures. 2. **Identify** elements and compounds. 3. **Compare and contrast** solutions, colloids, and suspensions.	National Content Standards: UCP.1–3, UCP.5, A.1, A.2, B.2		**Visualizing Elements,** p. 553 **MiniLAB:** Classifying Materials, p. 555 **Science Online,** p. 557 **Lab:** Comparing Pure Substances and Mixtures, p. 559
Section 2 Properties of Matter 4 sessions 2 blocks 4. **Identify** substances using physical properties. 5. **Compare and contrast** physical and chemical changes. 6. **Identify** chemical changes. 7. **Determine** how the law of conservation of mass applies to chemical changes.	National Content Standards: UCP.1, UCP.2, UCP.3, B.2, B.3, B.6		**Integrate Environment,** p. 561 **MiniLAB:** Separating Ink, p. 562 **Integrate History,** p. 564 **Integrate Earth Science,** p. 565 **Applying Math:** The Law of Conservation of Mass, p. 565 **Science Online,** p. 566 **Lab:** Measuring the Conservation of Mass, pp. 568–569 **Science Stats:** Intriguing Elements, p. 570

StudentWorks Plus | Glencoe Exclusive! TeacherWorks™ All-In-One Planner and Resource Center

Lab Materials	Reproducible Resources	Section Assessment	Technology
Launch Lab: hot plate, ice, 200-mL beaker, water, blue food dye, evaporating dish, heat-resistant gloves, graduated cylinder, white paper	**Chapter *Fast File* Resources** Foldables Worksheet, p. 17 Directed Reading Overview, p. 19 Note-taking Worksheets, pp. 31–32	Glencoe's Assessment Advantage	TeacherWorks includes: • Interactive Teacher Edition • Lesson Planner with calendar • Access to all program blacklines • Correlations to standards • Web links Video Lab
MiniLAB: Science Journal **Lab:** salt, iron fillings, pepper water,sugar water, graduated cylinder, 250-mL beakers, magnet, balance, funnel, filter paper, magnifying lens	**Chapter *Fast File* Resources** Transparency Activity, p. 42 MiniLAB, p. 3 Enrichment, p. 29 Reinforcement, p. 27 Lab Worksheet, pp. 5–6 Transparency Activity, pp. 45–46 Directed Reading, p. 20 Lab Activity, pp. 9-12 **Cultural Diversity,** p. 67 **Physical Science Critical Thinking/Problem Solving,** p. 9	Portfolio Science Journal, p. 554 Performance MiniLAB, p. 555 Applying Math, p. 558 Content Section Review, p. 558	Section Focus Transparency Teaching Transparency Virtual Labs CD-ROM Interactive Chalkboard CD-ROM StudentWorks Plus
Lab: antacid tablet, empty plastic bottle, balloon, beacker, spatula, water, balance, mortar, pestle, funnel *Need materials?* Contact Science Kit at 1-800-828-7777 or www.sciencekit.com.	**Chapter *Fast File* Resources** Transparency Activity, p. 43 MiniLAB, p. 4 Enrichment, p. 30 Reinforcement, p. 28 Lab Worksheet, pp. 7–8 Directed Reading, pp. 21, 22 Lab Activity, pp. 13–16 **Home and Community Involvement,** p. 43 **Mathematics Skill Activities,** p. 9	Portfolio Science Journal, p. 564 Performance MiniLAB, p. 562 Applying Math, p. 566 Applying Math, p. 567 Content Section Review, p. 567	Section Focus Transparency Interactive Chalkboard CD-ROM StudentWorks Plus

End of Chapter Assessment

Glencoe's Assessment Advantage

Blackline Masters	Technology	Professional Series
Chapter *Fast File* Resources Chapter Review, pp. 34–35 Chapter Tests, pp. 36–38 **Standardized Test Practice,** pp. 76–79	MindJogger Videoquiz Virtual Labs CD-ROM Exam*View*® Pro Testmaker TeacherWorks CD-ROM Interactive Chalkboard CD-ROM	**Performance Assessment in the Science Classroom (PASC)**

Transparencies

Section Focus

This is a representation of key blackline masters available in the Teacher Classroom Resources. See Resource Manager boxes within the chapter for additional information.

Assessment

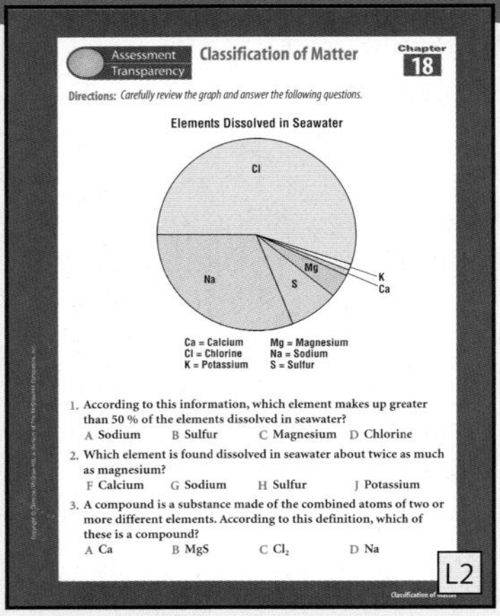

Teaching

Key to Teaching Strategies

The following designations will help you decide which activities are appropriate for your students.

- L1 Level 1 activities should be appropriate for students with learning difficulties.
- L2 Level 2 activities should be within the ability range of all students.
- L3 Level 3 activities are designed for above-average students.
- ELL ELL activities should be within the ability range of English Language Learners.
- COOP LEARN Cooperative Learning activities are designed for small group work.
- LS Multiple Learning Styles logos, as described on page 12T, are used throughout to indicate strategies that address different learning styles.
- P These strategies represent student products that can be placed into a best-work portfolio.
- PBL Problem-Based Learning activities apply real-world situations to learning.

Hands-on Activities

Student Text Lab Worksheet

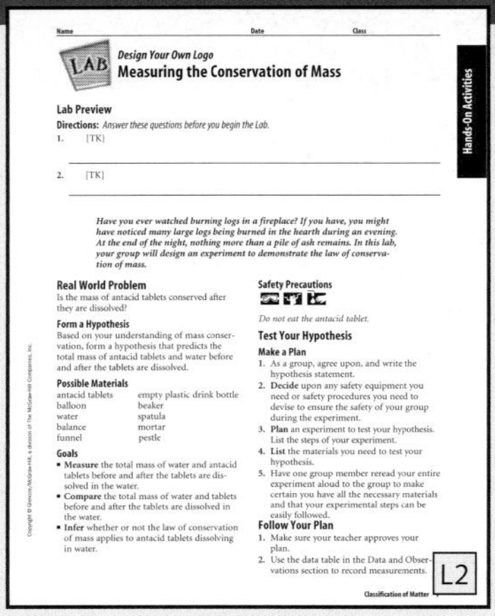

Laboratory Activities

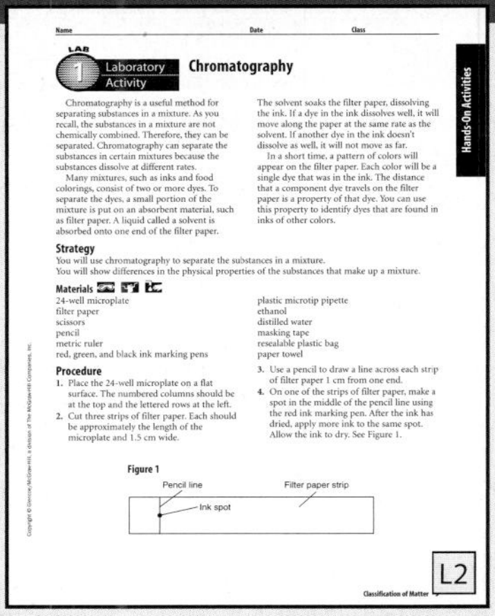

Meeting Different Ability Levels

Content Outline

Note-taking Worksheet — Classification of Matter

L2

Reinforcement

Section 1 Reinforcement — Composition of Matter

L2

Enrichment

Section 1 Enrichment — Classification of Matter

L3

Directed Reading (English/Spanish)

Directed Reading for Content Mastery — Overview — Classification of Matter

L1

Study Guide

Section 1 Study Guide — Composition of Matter — Chapter 18

L2

Reading Essentials

Chapter 18 Classification of Matter — section 1 Composition of Matter

L1

Assessment

Test Practice Workbook

Chapter Test — Chapter 18 Classification of Matter

L2

Chapter Review

Chapter Review — Classification of Matter

L2

Chapter Tests

Chapter Test — Classification of Matter

L2

Science Content Background

section 1 Composition of Matter

Pure Substances

Matter can be divided into mixtures and pure substances. Pure substances can be described as either elements or chemical compounds. Mixtures can be either heterogeneous or homogeneous. Homogeneous mixtures are usually called solutions and have a constant composition. Heterogeneous mixtures have regions with visibly different compositions. Homogeneous liquid mixtures tend to be transparent, whereas heterogeneous liquid mixtures are often cloudy and separate on standing.

Elements

At this time there are at least 111 known elements. All the compounds found on Earth are formed when atoms of two or more different elements combine, creating new materials with new properties.

section 2 Properties of Matter

Physical Properties

The characteristics, or properties, that are used to describe matter can be classified in several ways. Physical properties are those that can be determined without changing the chemical composition of the sample, whereas chemical properties are those that do involve a chemical change in the sample. Intensive properties are those that have values that do not depend on the size of the sample. Extensive properties do depend on the size of the sample. Density, the intensive property that relates mass to volume, is an important and useful physical property. Knowing the density of a substance can be very useful, because it is often easier to measure the volume of a liquid than its mass.

Conservation of Mass

The law of conservation of matter states that matter is not created or destroyed but only converted from one form into another. Thus in a chemical reaction, the amount of matter before the reaction is the same as after the reaction. This is equally true for phase changes. Although a material may turn from a solid to a liquid to a gas, the amount of matter is conserved.

chapter content resources

Internet Resources

For additional content background, visit **gpescience.com** to:

- access your book online
- find references to related articles in popular science magazines
- access Web links with related content background
- access current events with science journal topics

Print Resources

Chemistry, The Molecular Nature of Matter and Change, Martin S. Silberberg, McGraw-Hill, 2003

Chemistry, Steve S. Zumdahl, Susan A. Zumdahl, Houghton Mifflin Company, 2003

IDENTIFYING Misconceptions

Find Out What Students Think

Students may think that . . .

Matter is not conserved in physical or chemical changes.

Perceptions are often more dominant than logic, and for students it may look as though matter simply vanishes when it turns into an invisible gas. When wood burns in a fire, it is obvious that only ashes remain, but it is not obvious what has happened to the bulk of the wood. For these reasons, students may not recognize the conservation of matter in physical or chemical changes.

Demonstration

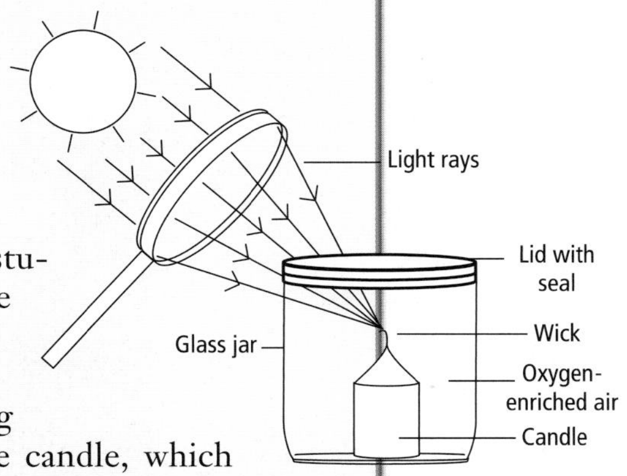

Present Figure 1 to students. Tell them that the mass of the jar with everything in it is 500 g. Suppose the magnifying glass is used to light the candle, which then burns in the oxygen-enriched air for about one minute before going out. Ask students to describe any changes that have occurred in the jar. Is the mass of the jar and everything in it now less than, the same as, or greater than 500 g? The mass is still 500 g. L2 LS **Kinesthetic**

Promote Understanding

Activity

Prior to class fill small plastic soda bottles two-thirds full of water, cap the bottles, and freeze.

On the day of the activity, provide each group of students with one frozen bottle and a paper towel. Then ask students in each group to

- dry the outside of the bottle and find its mass.
- predict what the mass of the bottle will be when the water melts.
- leave the bottles overnight so that the water inside them melts.

On the next day, have students dry the outside of the bottles and find their masses.

Make a table on the board with columns labeled *Mass of Bottle with Frozen Water* and *Mass of Bottle with Liquid Water* and a row for each group. Ask a member of each group to fill in the data for that group. With the class, analyze the data in the table. Discuss why the masses stayed the same. Help students realize that the bottles were closed so no mass was added to or subtracted from them. L2 LS **Visual-Spatial, Kinesthetic, Interpersonal**

Assess

After completing the chapter, see *Identifying Misconceptions* in the Study Guide at the end of the chapter.

chapter 18

Chapter Vocabulary

substance, p. 552
element, p. 552
compound, p. 554
heterogeneous mixture, p. 555
homogeneous mixture, p. 556
solution, p. 556
colloid, p. 556
Tyndall effect, p. 557
suspension, p. 558
physical property, p. 560
physical change, p. 562
distillation, p. 563
chemical property, p. 563
chemical change, p. 564
law of conservation of mass, p. 567

Science Journal The physical changes are the wet paint becoming a solid when dried and the evaporation of the solvent.

INTERACTIVE CHALKBOARD with Image Bank

PowerPoint® Presentations

This CD-ROM is an editable Microsoft® PowerPoint® presentation that includes:

- a pre-made presentation for every chapter
- interactive graphics
- animations
- audio clips
- image bank
- all new section and chapter questions
- Standardized Test Practice
- transparencies
- Foldables directions
- links to gpescience.com

chapter 18

Classification of Matter

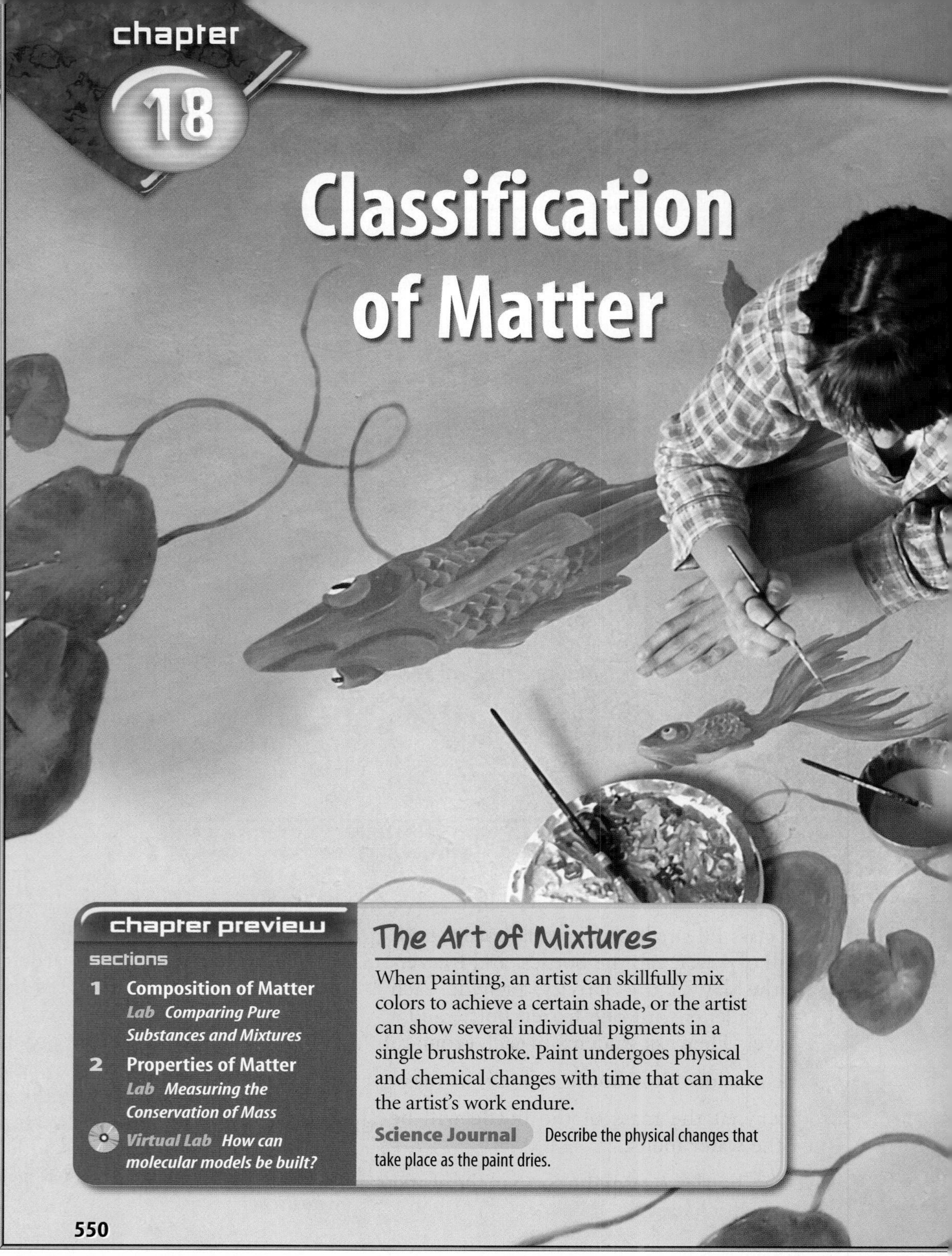

chapter preview

sections

1 **Composition of Matter**
Lab Comparing Pure Substances and Mixtures

2 **Properties of Matter**
Lab Measuring the Conservation of Mass

Virtual Lab How can molecular models be built?

The Art of Mixtures

When painting, an artist can skillfully mix colors to achieve a certain shade, or the artist can show several individual pigments in a single brushstroke. Paint undergoes physical and chemical changes with time that can make the artist's work endure.

Science Journal Describe the physical changes that take place as the paint dries.

Theme Connection

Stability and Change Matter can undergo physical and chemical changes. The stability of a substance affects how and when it will change.

About the Photo

Paints Although the solid colors look homogeneous, pigments are in a solvent or water-based solution to form a mixture called a suspension. Larger particles will settle out, while smaller particles remain in suspension and form a colloid. As paint dries, physical changes and chemical reactions occur, making the final properties of paint different from its original state.

Start-Up Activities

Launch Lab

Demonstrate the Distillation of Water

Matter is classified according to the different properties that it exhibits. These differences in properties allow drinking water to be obtained from seawater. These properties could be very important to you if you were stranded on a desert island and needed drinking water. Purified water can be obtained through a process called distillation.

1. Place 75 mL of water in a 200-mL beaker and add 20 drops of blue food coloring.
2. Place the beaker on a hot plate.
3. Add ice to an evaporating dish until the dish is half full. Place the evaporating dish on the beaker as shown in the photo.
4. Turn on the hot plate and slowly bring the water and food-coloring solution to a boil.
5. After boiling the solution for five minutes, carefully remove the evaporating dish using heat-resistant gloves. Touch the drops of liquid on the bottom of the dish to a piece of white paper.
6. Observe the liquid on the paper.
7. **Think Critically** In your Science Journal, write a paragraph explaining where the liquid came from. What was in the beaker that is not in the liquid on the paper?

FOLDABLES™ Study Organizer

Classification of Matter Make the following Foldable to ensure that you understand the content by defining the vocabulary terms from this chapter.

STEP 1 **Fold** a sheet of paper vertically from side to side. Make the front edge about 1.25 cm shorter than the back edge.

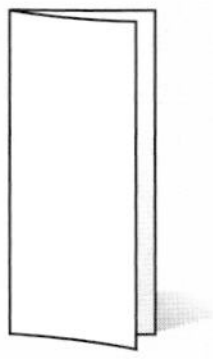

STEP 2 **Turn** lengthwise, with the fold on top, and **fold** into thirds.

STEP 3 **Unfold and cut** only the top layer along both folds to make three tabs.

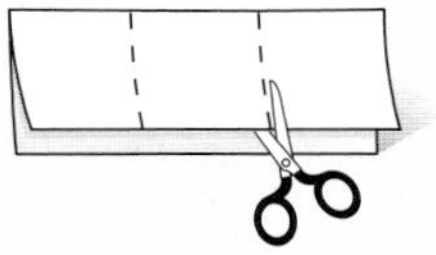

STEP 4 **Label** the tabs *Elements, Compounds,* and *Mixtures* as shown.

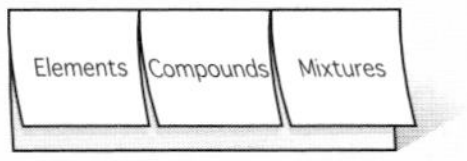

Define As you read the chapter, define each term and list examples of each under the appropriate tab.

Science Online — Preview this chapter's content and activities at gpescience.com

Launch Lab

Video Lab available for this Lab.

Purpose Use this Launch Lab to demonstrate for students how water can be distilled and purified.

Preparation Set up a hotplate and acquire ice for each group.

Materials 200-mL beaker, water, food dye, 100-mL graduated cylinder, evaporating dish, ice, tongs, white paper, and a hot-plate for each group

Teaching Strategy To extend this activity, stage a contest to determine who can design an experiment that produces the maximum distillation rate.

Think Critically

Water droplets from the steam rising from the boiling water will condense on the evaporating dish. The water will be colorless. The distillation process will separate the water from the food dye.

Assessment

Content Have each group imagine they are marooned on a tropical island without supplies. Ask them what island materials or materials they are wearing they could use to construct an apparatus for distilling water. The lens of a pair of glasses could magnify sunlight on dried grass to produce a fire. Empty coconut shells could replace beakers and large tropical leaves could replace the evaporating dish.

FOLDABLES™ Study Organizer **Dinah Zike Study Fold**

Student preparation materials for this Foldable are available in the **Chapter *Fast File* Resources.**

section 1 Composition of Matter

1 Motivate

INTERACTIVE CHALKBOARD PowerPoint® Presentations An editable Microsoft® PowerPoint® presentation is available on **Interactive Chalkboard** CD-ROM.

Bellringer

Section Focus Transparencies also are available on the Interactive Chalkboard CD-ROM. L2 ELL

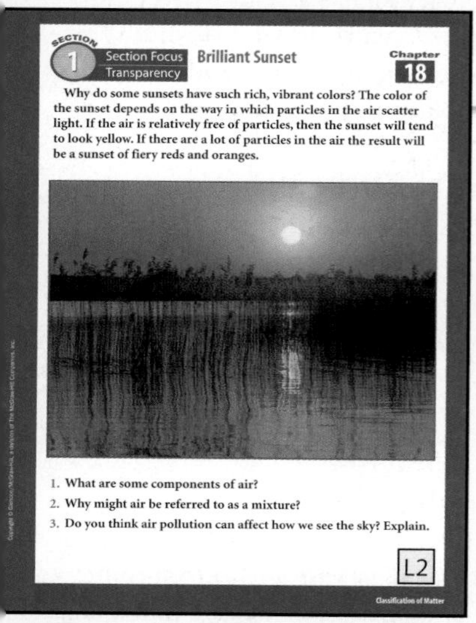
Section 1 Section Focus Transparency — Brilliant Sunset — Chapter 18

Why do some sunsets have such rich, vibrant colors? The color of the sunset depends on the way in which particles in the air scatter light. If the air is relatively free of particles, then the sunset will tend to look yellow. If there are a lot of particles in the air the result will be a sunset of fiery reds and oranges.

1. What are some components of air?
2. Why might air be referred to as a mixture?
3. Do you think air pollution can affect how we see the sky? Explain.

L2

Classification of Matter

Reading Guide

What You'll Learn

- **Define** substances and mixtures.
- **Identify** elements and compounds.
- **Compare and contrast** solutions, colloids, and suspensions.

Why It's Important

You will have a better knowledge of your world when you understand the concepts of elements and compounds.

Review Vocabulary

property: characteristic or essential quality

New Vocabulary

- substance
- element
- compound
- heterogeneous mixture
- homogeneous mixture
- solution
- colloid
- Tyndall effect
- suspension

Figure 1 All the atoms of an element are alike.

Pure Substances

Have you ever seen a photo hanging on a wall that looked just like a real painting? Did you have to touch it to find out? If so, the rough or smooth surface told you whether it was a painting or a photo. Every material has its own properties. The properties of materials can be used to classify them into general categories.

Every material is made of a pure substance or a mixture of substances. A pure **substance** is a type of matter with a fixed composition. A substance can be either an element or a compound. Some substances you might recognize are helium, aluminum, water, and salt.

Elements All substances are built from atoms. If all the atoms in a substance have the same identity, that substance is an **element.** The graphite in your pencil point and the copper coating of most pennies are examples of elements. In graphite, all atoms are carbon atoms, and in a copper sample, all the atoms are copper atoms. The metal substance beneath the copper in a penny is another element—zinc. About 90 elements are found on Earth. More than 20 others have been made in laboratories, but most of these are unstable and exist only for short periods of time. Some elements you might recognize are shown in **Figure 1.** Some less-common elements and their properties are shown in **Figure 2.**

Reading Preview

Tie to Prior Knowledge

Ice Cream Sodas Ask students to describe the types of substances in an ice cream soda. Tell students that whipped cream is a colloid—a heterogeneous mixture in which the particles are very small. L2

Activate Vocabulary Knowledge Have students compare the vocabulary list to the words in **Figure 6.** Explain that each oval in **Figure 6** represents a type of matter. Subgroups of matter are in the connected ovals. What can they infer about the vocabulary words by reading the graphic organizer?

Section 1 Resource Manager

Chapter *FAST FILE* Resources

Transparency Activity, pp. 42, 45–46

Directed Reading for Content Mastery, pp. 19, 20

Note-taking Worksheets, pp. 31–32

MiniLAB, p. 3

Lab Activity, pp. 9–12

Lab Worksheet, pp. 5–6

Physical Science Critical Thinking/Problem Solving, p. 9

Cultural Diversity, p. 67

NATIONAL GEOGRAPHIC **VISUALIZING ELEMENTS**

Figure 2

Most of us think of gold as a shiny yellow metal used to make jewelry. However, it is also an element that is used in more unexpected ways, such as in spacecraft parts. On the other hand, some less-common elements, such as americium (am uh REE see um), are used in everyday objects. Some elements and their uses are shown here.

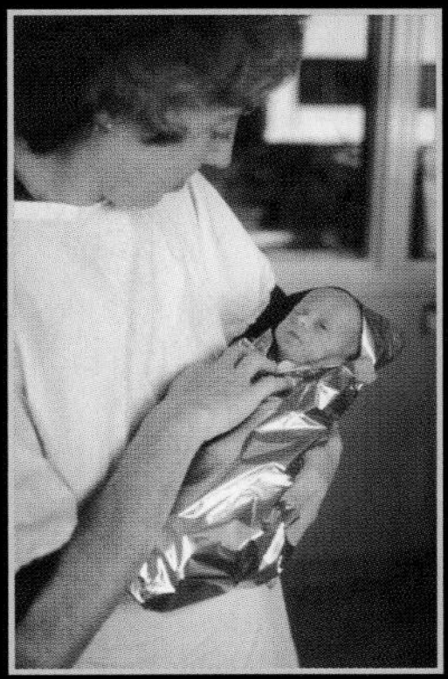

▲ ALUMINUM Aluminum is an excellent reflector of heat. Here, an aluminum plastic laminate is used to retain the body heat of a newborn baby.

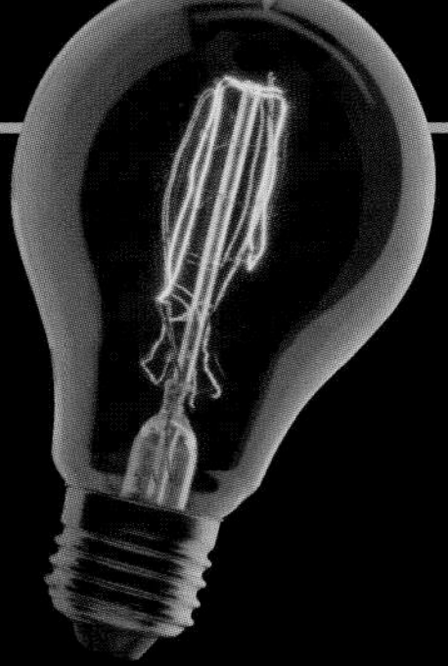

▲ TUNGSTEN Although tungsten can be combined with steel to form a very durable metal, in its pure form it is soft enough to be stretched to form the filament of a lightbulb. Tungsten has the highest melting point of any metal.

▲ TITANIUM (tie TAY nee um) Parts of the exterior of the Guggenheim Museum in Bilbao, Spain, are made of titanium panels. Strong and lightweight, titanium is also used for body implants.

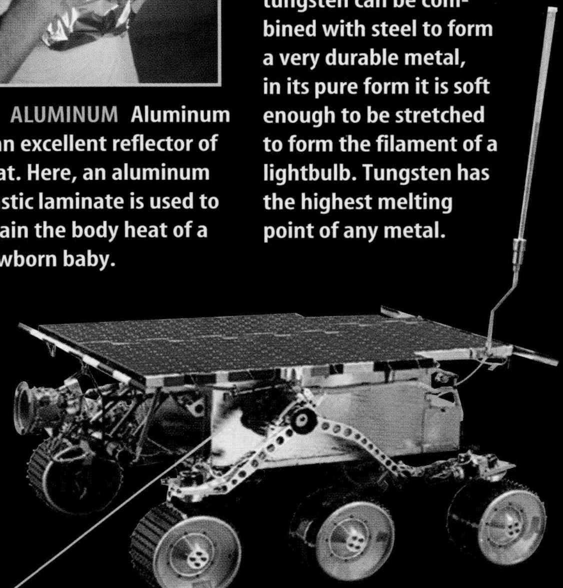

▲ GOLD Gold's resistance to corrosion and its ability to reflect infrared radiation make it an excellent coating for space vehicles. The electronic box on the six-wheel *Sojourner Rover,* above, part of NASA's Pathfinder 1997 mission to Mars, is coated with gold.

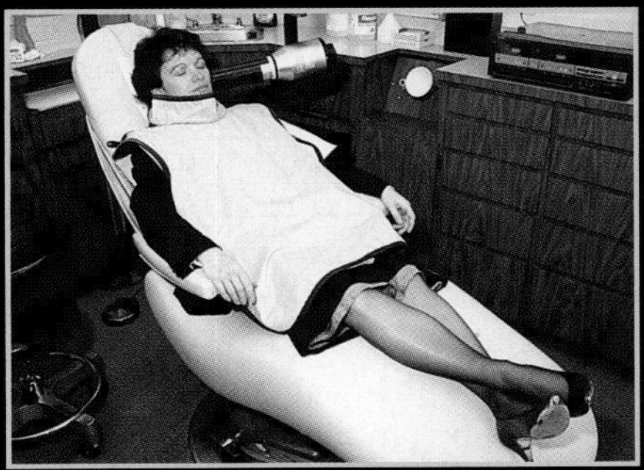

▲ LEAD Because lead has a high density, it is a good barrier to radiation. Dentists drape lead aprons on patients before taking X rays of the patient's teeth to reduce radiation exposure.

◀ AMERICIUM Named after America, where it was first produced, americium is a component of this smoke detector. It is a radioactive metal that must be handled with care to avoid contact.

NATIONAL GEOGRAPHIC

Visualizing Elements

Have students examine the pictures and read the captions. Then ask the following questions.

Why is pure tungsten used for the filaments of light bulbs? Because it is durable and stretchable, and has the highest melting point of any metal.

Why is it important to drape the trunk of your body during X rays? To avoid unnecessary radiation exposure to your vital organs.

Can you think of other ways that the reflective properties of aluminum are used? Answers will vary but may include some of the following: cooking, emergency blankets, and signaling mirrors.

Why would the Sojourner Rover need to reflect infrared radiation? To protect the equipment inside the box from excessive infrared radiation. L2 LS **Visual-Spatial**

Activity

Smoke Detectors Have students research and find out why americium is used in smoke detectors. Have the students report their findings to the class. L2

LS **Linguistic, Intrapersonal**

Differentiated Instruction

Challenge Have students find out why titanium is used for body implants and why it is used in aircraft landing gear. The students should report their findings to their class. L3

SECTION 1 Composition of Matter 553

2 Teach

Discussion

Two Liquids Describe for students two liquids. Tell them that both liquids contain only hydrogen and oxygen, and both liquids are transparent and colorless. How can the two liquids have different identities? They have different combinations of atoms. One liquid is water, H_2O; the other is hydrogen peroxide, H_2O_2. L2

LS **Logical-Mathematical**

IDENTIFYING Misconceptions

Definition of Compounds Students may think that elements made from more than one atom, such as Cl_2, H_2, S_8, or P_4, are compounds. However, compounds must be made from combinations of different elements.

Use an Analogy

Pedal Power In pedal-powered vehicles, the ratio of one frame to one wheel makes a unicycle. One frame to two wheels forms a bicycle. One frame to three wheels produces a tricycle. Similarly, one carbon to one atom of oxygen makes carbon monoxide. One carbon to two oxygen atoms is carbon dioxide. These compounds do not have the same properties.

Reading Check

Answer Compounds contain two or more different elements.

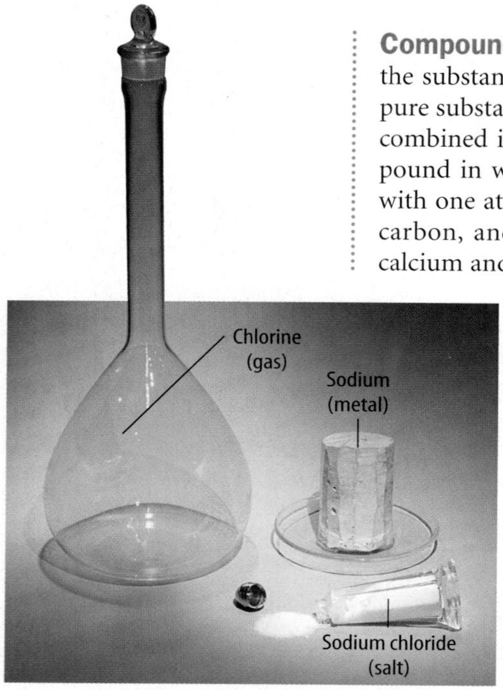

Figure 3 Chlorine gas and sodium metal combine dramatically in the ratio of one to one to form sodium chloride.

Compounds When two or more different elements combine, the substance formed is called a compound. A **compound** is a pure substance in which the atoms of two or more elements are combined in a fixed proportion. For example, water is a compound in which two atoms of the element hydrogen combine with one atom of the element oxygen. Chalk contains calcium, carbon, and oxygen in the proportion of one atom each of calcium and carbon to three atoms of oxygen.

Reading Check *How are elements and compounds related?*

Can you imagine yourself putting something made from a silvery metal and a greenish-yellow, poisonous gas on your food? You might have shaken some on your food today—table salt is a chemical compound that fits this description. Even though it looks like white crystals and adds flavor to food, its components—sodium and chlorine—are neither white nor salty, as shown in **Figure 3.** Like salt, other compounds usually look different from the elements in them.

Molecules A particle consisting of two or more atoms that are bonded together is called a molecule. Oxygen in the air, as an example, is a diatomic (two-atom) molecule. A molecule is a basic unit of a molecular compound. The simple sugars you eat; the proteins in your body; and the wool and cotton fibers in your clothes all consist of molecules formed from bonded atoms.

Figure 4 The number of mixtures that can be created by combining substances is unlimited.

Mixtures

Are pizza and a soft drink one of your favorite lunches? If so, you enjoy two foods that are classified as mixtures, but two different kinds of mixtures. A mixture, such as the pizza or soft drink shown in **Figure 4,** is a material made up of two or more substances that can be easily separated by physical means.

Science Journal

Elements and Compounds Ask students to list in their Science Journals all the elements and chemical compounds they can think of without looking them up. Have them look up the chemical symbols for the elements and the chemical formulas for the compounds. Have them write the formulas next to the names of the substances. L2 ELL P LS **Linguistic**

Differentiated Instruction

English-Language Learners Provide physical examples of various elements, compounds, and mixtures, and have them labeled to aid the students in developing their vocabulary.

Heterogeneous Mixtures Unlike compounds, mixtures do not always contain the same proportions of the substances that make them up. For example, a pizza chef doesn't measure precisely how much of each topping is sprinkled on a pizza. You easily can see most of the toppings on a pizza. A mixture in which different materials can be distinguished easily is called a **heterogeneous** (he tuh ruh JEE nee us) **mixture.** Granite, concrete, and dry soup mixes are other heterogeneous mixtures you can recognize.

You might be wearing another heterogeneous mixture—clothing made of a permanent-press fabric like the one shown in **Figure 5A.** Such a fabric contains fibers of two materials—polyester and cotton. The amounts of polyester and cotton can vary from one article of clothing to another, as shown by the label. Though you might not be able to distinguish the two fibers just by looking at them, you probably could if you used a microscope, as shown in **Figure 5B.**

Most of the substances you come in contact with every day are heterogeneous mixtures. Some components are easy to see, such as the ingredients in pizza, but others are not. In fact, a component you see can be a mixture itself. For example, the cheese in pizza is also a mixture, but you cannot see the individual components. Cheese contains many compounds, such as milk proteins, butterfat, colorings, and other food additives.

Mini LAB

Classifying Materials

Procedure

1. In your **Science Journal,** create a data table with four columns and 11 rows. Label the columns *Elements, Compounds, Mixtures,* and *Explanation.*
2. Choose ten items in your home and classify each as an element, a compound, or a mixture. List them in your table in the appropriate columns.
3. In the *Explanation* column, explain why you classified the items as you did.

Analysis

1. How many elements did you find?
2. Which column has the greatest number of items? Is this the same for all students?

Try at Home

Figure 5 Heterogeneous mixtures can be hard to detect.

A You can't tell at a glance that this fabric is a mixture of cotton and polyester.

Cotton fiber

Polyester fiber

B With a microscope, however, the difference between the two fibers is clear; the polyester fiber is perfectly smooth, and the cotton is rough.

Magnification: 600×

Mini LAB

Purpose Students learn to distinguish between elements, mixtures, and compounds.

Materials Science Journal, pen or pencil

Teaching Strategies

Have a class discussion on the items that students classified.

Have students classify the mixtures as either heterogeneous or homogeneous.

Analysis

1. Student responses will vary.
2. Student responses will vary.

Assessment

Content Have students work in groups of two or three to develop a picture book that explains the difference between elements, compounds, and mixtures. Use **Performance Assessment in the Science Classroom,** p. 169

Try at Home

Virtual Labs

Modeling *How can molecular models be built?*

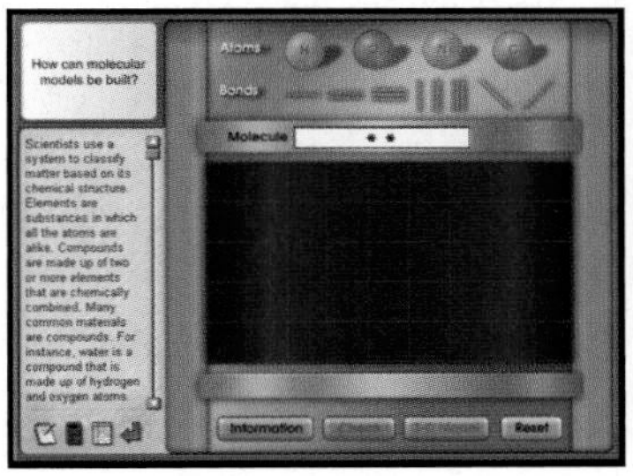

Reading Strategy

Graphic Organizer Tell students to copy **Figure 6** in their notes, leaving some space to add more information and examples of each type of matter. They will use the graphic organizer as a way of making notes as they read the section. Have them look for the missing vocabulary words *colloid* and *suspension* and add them in the correct locations.

Teacher FYI

Phases Heterogeneous mixtures contain more than one phase. A phase is a region with uniform properties that has a boundary between itself and other areas of uniform properties. For example, the structure, heat capacity, and density of floating ice vary from the liquid water in which it is floating.

Discussion

Homogeneous Mixtures Remind students that the components of a homogeneous mixture are blended evenly throughout the mixture. Tell students that an alloy can be a solid homogeneous mixture of metals. How can two solid metals mix homogeneously? The metals are melted, mixed as liquids, and then allowed to become solid again. L2 LS **Logical-Mathematical, Visual-Spatial**

Activity

Bag Project Bring four bags to class. Using large lettering, label the bags *Element*, *Compound*, *Homogeneous*, **and** *Heterogeneous*. Have students bring objects from home and place each one in the proper bag. After a week, empty the bags and discuss their contents and their classifications with the class. L2 ELL LS **Kinesthetic**

Visual Learning

Figure 7 Bring to class some aluminum foil, cereal with raisins, and liquid made from powdered, flavored drink mix dissolved in water. Have students classify these materials using the chart shown in **Figure 7.** Aluminum foil is an element; raisin cereal is a heterogeneous mixture; powdered, flavored drink mix dissolved in water is a homogeneous mixture. L2 LS **Visual-Spatial, Kinesthetic**

Reading Check

Answer a homogeneous mixture

Homogeneous Mixtures Remember that soft drink you like with your pizza? Some soft drinks contain water, sugar, flavoring, coloring, and carbon-dioxide gas.

Soft drinks in sealed bottles are examples of homogeneous mixtures. A **homogeneous** (hoh muh JEE nee us) **mixture** contains two or more gaseous, liquid, or solid substances blended evenly throughout. However, a soft drink in which you can see bubbles of carbon-dioxide gas and ice cubes is a heterogeneous mixture.

Vinegar is another homogeneous mixture. It appears to be clear, even though it is made up of particles of acetic acid mixed with water. Another name for a homogeneous mixture such as vinegar and a bottled soft drink is a solution. A **solution** is a homogeneous mixture of particles so small that they cannot be seen with a microscope and will never settle to the bottom of their container. Solutions remain constantly and uniformly mixed. The differences between substances and mixtures are summarized in **Figure 6.**

Reading Check *What kind of mixture is a solution?*

Colloids Milk is an example of a specific kind of mixture called a colloid. Like a heterogeneous mixture, milk contains water, fats, and proteins in varying proportions. Like a solution, its components won't settle when it is left standing. A **colloid** (KAH loyd) is a type of mixture with particles that are larger than those in solutions but not heavy enough to settle out. The word *colloid* comes from a Greek word for *glue*. The first colloids studied were in gelatin, a source of some types of glue.

Paint is an example of a liquid with suspended colloid particles. Gases and solids can contain colloidal particles, too. For example, fog consists of particles of liquid water suspended in air, and smoke contains solids suspended in air.

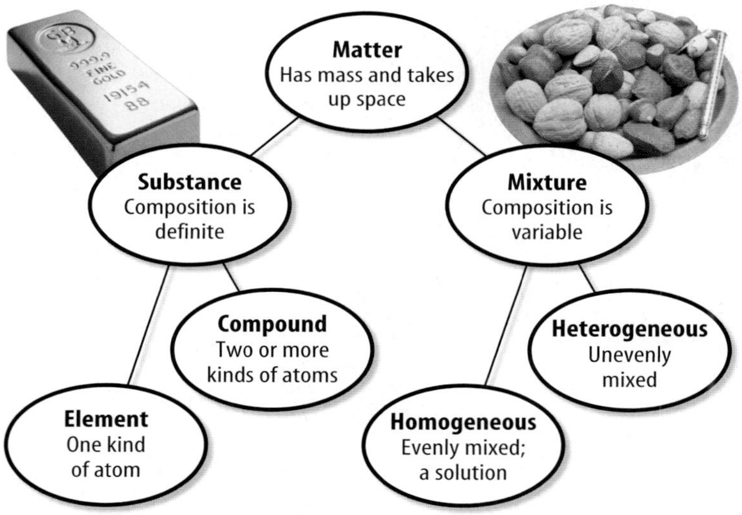

Figure 6 All matter can be divided into substances and mixtures.

Curriculum Connection

Math Have students express the particle diameter given for solutions (0.000,000,001 m) in exponential notation. 1×10^{-9} m Then, ask them to calculate how many particles it would take to go across one cm. 1×10^{-9} m $\times$ (100 cm/1 m) $= 1 \times 10^{-7}$ cm/particle, then 1 cm $\times$ (1 particle/1×10^{-7} cm) $= 1 \times 10^{7}$ or 10,000,000 particles L3 LS **Logical-Mathematical**

Figure 7 Fog is a colloid composed of water droplets suspended in air.

The light from the headlights is scattered by the fog.

The same colloid allows you to see the sunlight as it streams through the trees.

Detecting Colloids One way to distinguish a colloid from a solution is by its appearance. Fog appears white because its particles are large enough to scatter light as shown in **Figure 7.** Sometimes it is not so obvious that a liquid is a colloid. For example, some shampoos and gelatins are colloids called gels that appear almost clear. You can tell for certain if a liquid is a colloid by passing a beam of light through it, as shown in **Figure 8.** A light beam cannot be seen as it passes through a solution, but can be seen readily as it passes through a colloid. This occurs because the particles in the colloid are large enough to scatter light, but those in the solution are not. This scattering of light by colloidal particles is called the **Tyndall effect.**

Reading Check *How can you distinguish a colloid from a solution?*

Science Online

Topic: John Tyndall

Visit gpescience.com for Web links to information about the discoverer of the Tyndall effect.

Activity Prepare a book cover describing the various activities of John Tyndall.

Figure 8 Because of the Tyndall effect, a light beam is scattered by the colloid suspension on the right, but it passes invisibly through the solution on the left.

Use Science Words

Word Meaning Have students find out the names of colloids in which liquids contain liquids, liquids contain solids, and gases contain liquids or solids. Colloids of liquids in liquids are emulsions, colloids of solids in liquids are sols (once cooled, they are called gels), colloids of liquids or solids in gases are called aerosols. L3 LS **Linguistic**

Fun Fact

The Tyndall effect is named after Irish scientist John Tyndall, who first described the effect in the mid-1800s.

Quick Demo

Tyndall Effect

Materials flashlight, clear drinking glass, water, milk

Estimated Time five minutes

Procedure Bring a small bright flashlight close to a clear drinking glass containing water. Have students observe the light on the wall as it passes through the water. Then add a couple drops of milk to the water and shine the light again. Ask students to name the light-scattering effect that they see. the Tyndall effect L2

Reading Check

Answer Pass a beam of light through it and check for the Tyndall effect.

Post Reading

Paired Learning In their own words have students explain to each other how the Tynnall Effect can be used to determine if something is a *colloid* or *solution.* Have them summerize the similarities and differences between these two types of matter that cause the effect. Encourage students to look back into the text if they cannot remember the details.

Active Reading

Learning Journal This strategy encourages students to interact with the reading, allowing personal responses. The left column entries can be research notes, lectures notes, or vocabulary terms. The right column entries are the student's response to, interpretation of, questions about, or analysis of the left column entries. L2 LS **Linguistic, Visual-Spatial**

Differentiated Instruction

Challenge Ask students to determine the connection between beautiful red sunsets and suspensions. The atmosphere around Earth has many suspended particles that scatter light. The more of these particles the light passes through, the redder the light appears. During a sunset, the Sun is low in the sky, so we see its light through a large number of scattering particles. Sunsets are particularly beautiful in years in which volcanic eruptions take place. L3 LS **Logical Mathematical**

INTEGRATE Earth Science **Content Background**

Another type suspension is found in the melt-water of glaciers. This water has an opaque appearance caused by suspended soil and rock particles that eventually settle out. Ask students what size the particles in meltwater must be. greater than 100 nm

Caption Answer

Figure 9 10 km

3 Assess

DAILY INTERVENTION

Check for Understanding

Kinesthetic Place red food coloring, sand, milk, water, vinegar, and a clear drinking glass on a table. Allow students to mix these various substances in the order they choose. Have students write down observations and explain what qualities the mixtures exhibit after each addition of a new substance. L2

LS **Linguistic, Visual-Spatial**

Reteach

Compounds Place some NaCl and sand in a clear container and stir them together. Next, place some NaCl and water in a clear beaker and stir them together. Ask the class whether a new compound was formed in either process. no L2

LS **Visual-Spatial**

Assessment

Oral Burn a small sample of paper, and ask students to identify any elements, compounds, or mixtures. element: oxygen; compounds: carbon dioxide, the cellulose in the paper; mixtures: air, smoke particles in the air Use **PASC,** p. 89. L2 **Visually Impaired** LS **Visual-Spatial, Kinesthetic**

Figure 9 The mud deposited by the Mississippi River is thought to be more than 10,000 m thick. **Calculate** *in kilometers how thick the mud in the Mississippi River is.*

Table 1 Comparing Solutions, Colloids, and Suspensions

Description	Solutions	Colloids	Suspensions
Settle upon standing?	no	no	yes
Separate using filter paper?	no	no	yes
Particle size	0.1–1 nm	1–1,000 nm	>1,000 nm
Scatter light?	no	yes	yes

Suspensions Some mixtures are neither solutions nor colloids. One example is muddy pond water. If pond water stands long enough, some mud particles will fall to the bottom, and the water clears. Pond water is a **suspension,** which is a heterogeneous mixture containing a liquid in which visible particles settle. **Table 1** summarizes the properties of different types of mixtures.

INTEGRATE Earth Science River deltas are large scale examples of how a suspension settles. Rivers flow swiftly through narrow channels, picking up soil and debris along the way. As a river widens, it flows more slowly. Suspended particles settle and form a delta at the mouth, as shown in **Figure 9.**

section 1 review

Summary

Pure Substances

- An element is a substance in which all atoms have the same identity.
- A compound is a substance that has two or more elements combined in a fixed proportion.

Mixtures

- A heterogeneous mixture is a mixture in which different materials can be distinguished easily.
- A homogeneous mixture contains two or more gaseous, liquid, or solid substances that are blended evenly throughout.
- Mixtures can be heterogeneous, homogeneous, colloids, or suspensions.

Self Check

1. **Describe** How is a compound similar to a homogeneous mixture? How is it different?
2. **Distinguish** between a substance and a mixture. Give two examples of each.
3. **Describe** the differences between colloids and suspensions.
4. **Think Critically** Why do the words "Shake well before using" indicate that a fruit juice is a suspension?

Applying Math

5. **Use Numbers** A polyester fabric is a mixture of 90 percent cotton and 10 percent polyester. If the fabric has a mass of 500 g, what is the mass of cotton in the fabric?

More Section Review gpescience.com

section 1 review

1. Both compounds and homogeneous mixtures are made of more than one element and are homogeneous. However, compounds must be made from elements in an exact ratio and involve chemical bonds between the elements in them.
2. A substance must be either an element or a compound. Mixtures can be made from combinations of compounds or elements.
3. Colloids do not settle out; suspensions eventually do settle out. Particles in colloids are smaller than particles in suspensions.
4. Materials in suspensions settle out.
5. 450 g

LAB

Comparing Pure Substances and Mixtures

Everything you see that is made of matter is either a pure substance or a mixture. Some things, such as iron nails and aluminum foil, are elements; others, such as water and salt, are compounds. Steel, lemonade, concrete, and a bowl of fruit are all examples of mixtures.

Real-World Problem

How do the properties of different pure substances and mixtures compare?

Goals

- **Classify** matter.
- **Calculate** density.
- **Compare** the properties of elements, compounds, and mixtures.

Materials

salt
iron filings
pepper water
sugar water
graduated cylinder
250-mL beakers (5)
magnet
balance
funnel
filter paper
magnifying lens

Safety Precautions

Procedure

1. Copy the data table into your Science Journal.
2. **Determine** the color of each sample. Record all data in your table.
3. **Classify** the materials as an element, compound, or mixture.

Properties Table

Substance	Matter Classification	Color	Magnetic Attraction	Density

4. **Determine** if each sample has a magnetic attraction.
5. **Determine** the mass of a 10 mL sample of each material. Calculate the density of each sample.
6. Try to separate the particles of the pepper/water mixture and the sugar water.
7. **Infer** if the different particles of each sample can be separated by using physical properties.

Conclude and Apply

1. **Describe** the separation methods of the mixture samples.
2. **Infer** how you can identify a substance as an element.
3. **Calculate** the density of each material.

Communicating Your Data

Identify experimental errors that might have occurred during the collection of your data.

BENCH TESTED

Real-World Problem

Purpose Students will identify samples of elements, compounds, and mixtures.

Process Skills observe, measure, use data tables, compare and contrast, infer

Time Required 45 minutes

Procedure

Alternate Materials copper wire, aluminum foil, sugar, pepper, lemonade, soil/water mixture

Safety Precautions Have students wear safety goggles. Warn students that hot and cold glasses appear the same.

Teaching Strategies Prepare the five samples of matter in small beakers before the activity.

Troubleshooting Be certain all the sugar dissolves in the water samples by using hot tap water and only 1–2 g of sugar.

Conclude and Apply

1. The salt and iron filings are easily separated by using a magnet to attract the filings, and the pepper is easily filtered out of the water. Students will not be able to separate the sugar from the solution.
2. All elements are listed on the periodic table of the elements.
3. iron filings—1.94 g/mL
   table salt—1.32 g/mL
   sugar water—1.0 g/mL
   pepper in water—1.0 g/mL

Assessment

Content Have students test other matter samples such as concrete, copper wire, sugar, dry soup mix, and lemonade mix. Use **PASC,** p. 97

Communicating Your Data

As a class, discuss reasons for any differences in students' results. L2 LS **Logical-Mathematical**

section 2

Properties of Matter

1 Motivate

INTERACTIVE CHALKBOARD PowerPoint® Presentations An editable Microsoft® PowerPoint® presentation is available on **Interactive Chalkboard** CD-ROM.

Bellringer

Section Focus Transparencies also are available on the Interactive Chalkboard CD-ROM. L2 ELL

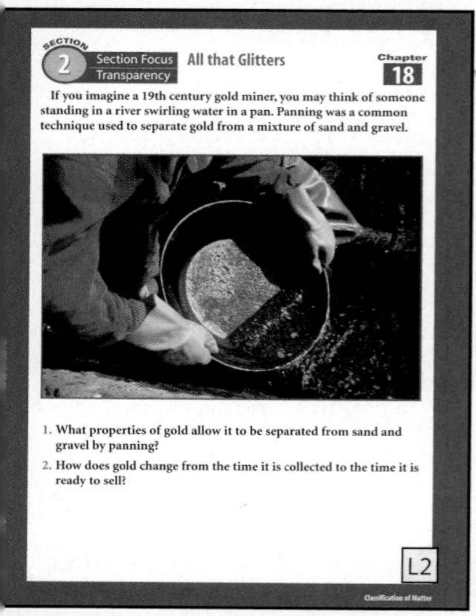
SECTION 2 Section Focus Transparency — All that Glitters — Chapter 18

If you imagine a 19th century gold miner, you may think of someone standing in a river swirling water in a pan. Panning was a common technique used to separate gold from a mixture of sand and gravel.

1. What properties of gold allow it to be separated from sand and gravel by panning?
2. How does gold change from the time it is collected to the time it is ready to sell?

L2

Classification of Matter

Reading Preview

Tie to Prior Knowledge

Visiting Places Ask students to describe, without naming it, a place that they have visited. As others try to determine the site, remind students that any description, whether of matter or of a place, requires careful attention to important properties. L1 **Visual-Spatial**

Content-Specific Words Have students use the text to find the meaning of the new vocabulary terms. Ask them to create cartoons that describe each of the words. For *physical change* they may draw a girl with straight hair; for *chemical change* they may draw brown hair to blond hair.

Reading Guide

What You'll Learn

- **Identify** substances using physical properties.
- **Compare and contrast** physical and chemical changes.
- **Identify** chemical changes.
- **Determine** how the law of conservation of mass applies to chemical changes.

Why It's Important

Understanding chemical and physical properties can help you use materials properly.

Review Vocabulary

state of matter: one of three physical forms of matter: solid, liquid, or gas

New Vocabulary

- physical property
- physical change
- distillation
- chemical property
- chemical change
- law of conservation of mass

Physical Properties

You can stretch a rubber band, but you can't stretch a piece of string very much, if at all. You can bend a piece of wire, but you can't easily bend a matchstick. In each case, the materials change shape, but the identity of the substances—rubber, string, wire, and wood—does not change. The abilities to stretch and bend are physical properties. Any characteristic of a material that you can observe without changing the identity of the substances that make up the material is a **physical property.** Examples of other physical properties are color, shape, size, density, melting point, and boiling point. What physical properties can you use to describe the items in **Figure 10?**

Figure 10 Appearance is the most obvious physical property. **Describe** *the appearance of these items.*

Appearance How would you describe a tennis ball? You could begin by describing its shape, color, and state of matter. You might describe the tennis ball as a brightly colored, hollow sphere. You can measure some physical properties, too. For instance, you could measure the diameter of the ball. What physical property of the ball is measured with a balance?

To describe a soft drink in a cup, you could start by calling it a liquid with a brown color. You could measure its volume and temperature. Each of these characteristics is a physical property of that soft drink.

Section 2 Resource Manager

Chapter *FAST FILE* Resources

Transparency Activity, p. 43

Directed Reading for Content Mastery, pp. 21, 22

Lab Activity, pp. 13–16

MiniLAB, p. 4

Lab Worksheet, pp. 7–8

Home and Community Involvement, p. 43

Mathematics Skill Activities, p. 9

Physical Science Critical Thinking/Problem Solving, p. 10

Figure 11 The best way to separate substances depends on their physical properties. Size is the property used to separate poppy seeds from sunflower seeds in this example.

Behavior Some physical properties describe the behavior of a material or a substance. As you might recall, objects that contain iron, such as a safety pin, are attracted by a magnet. Attraction to a magnet (magnetism) is a physical property of the substance iron. Every substance has a specific combination of physical properties that make it useful for certain tasks. Some metals, such as copper, can be drawn out into wires. Others, such as gold, can be pounded into sheets as thin as 0.1 micrometers (µm), about 4-millionths of an inch. This property of gold makes it useful for decorating picture frames and other objects. Gold that has been beaten or flattened in this way is called gold leaf.

Think again about your soft drink. If you spill it, the drink will spread out over the table or floor. If you knock over a jar of molasses, however, it does not flow as easily. The ability to flow is a physical property of liquids.

Using Physical Properties to Separate Removing the seeds from a watermelon can be easily done based on the physical properties of the seeds compared to the rest of the fruit. **Figure 11** shows a mixture of poppy seeds and sunflower seeds. You can identify the two kinds of seeds by differences in color, shape, and size. By sifting the mixture, you could separate the poppy seeds from the sunflower seeds quickly because their sizes differ.

Now look at the mixture of iron filings and sand shown in **Figure 11.** You probably wouldn't be able to sift out the iron filings because they are similar in size to the sand particles. What you could do is pass a magnet through the mixture. The magnet will attract only the iron filings and pull them from the sand. This is an example of how a physical property, such as magnetic attraction, can be used to separate substances in a mixture. Something like this is done to separate iron for recycling.

Reading Check *What physical properties could be used to separate two different substances?*

Magnetism easily separates iron from sand.

INTEGRATE Environment

Recycling and Physical Properties Recycling conserves natural resources. In some large recycling projects, aluminum metal must be separated from scrap iron. What physical properties of the two metals could be used to separate them?

2 Teach

Text Question Answer

size, shape, color, surface, density, mass

Text Question Answer

Mass could be measured with a balance.

Caption Answer

Figure 10 The ball is spherical, fuzzy, all one color, and has a curved line on it. The rock is rough, has many colors, has several dark straight lines, and has an irregular shape.

INTEGRATE Environment

Recycling and Physical Properties Since metallic iron is magnetic and metallic aluminum is not, strong magnets could attract iron from a mixture of iron and aluminum.

Quick Demo
Chemical Change

Materials beaker, candle, matches

Estimated Time 4 minutes

Procedure Hold the bottom of a glass beaker directly over a burning candle for a few minutes. What clues indicate that a chemical change has taken place? Carbon deposits begin to form on the outside of the beaker caused by the breakdown of the hydrocarbon candle wax. Carbon is released from its bonds with other carbon and hydrogen atoms. L2 LS **Visual-Spatial, Kinesthetic**

Reading Check

Answer color, shape, size, magnetism

Differentiated Instruction

Challenge Tell students that viscosity is a measure of a fluid's resistance to flow. Have students contact a service station or an auto parts store and ask about viscosity ratings of motor oils. Higher viscosity oils have more resistance to flow and are used in warm weather, while lower viscosity motor oils flow more easily and are used in cold temperatures. L3

LS **Logical-Mathematical**

Learning Disabled Bring a magnet and some iron filings to class. Prepare a mixture of the iron filings and sugar. Ask students how they know the mixture is not the result of a chemical change, and how the mixture can be separated. The mixture looks like the components from which it was made; add water to dissolve the sugar but not the iron, or use a magnet to separate the iron from the sugar particles. L1

LS **Kinesthetic, Visual-Spatial**

Reading Check

Answer No, the identity of the element or compound remains the same.

Mini LAB

Purpose Students will use physical change to separate the colors in black ink. L2 ELL COOP LEARN

Materials black marker (not permanent), coffee filter or filter paper, water, plate, eyedropper, Science Journal, pen or pencil

Teaching Strategies

Have students use different brands of black markers and black felt-tip pens.

Remind students to handle the coffee filter as little as possible. The oil from their fingers will distort the results.

Analysis

physical change

Assessment

Oral Ask students what colors were mixed together to make the black ink. Answers will vary based on the ink used. Use **Performance Assessment in the Science Classroom,** p. 89 L2

Caption Answer

Figure 12 state of matter

Mini LAB

Separating Ink

Procedure

1. Cut a circle out of a **clean, white coffee filter** with a 9-cm diameter. Draw a spot using a **nonpermanent black marker** in the center of the filter.
2. Place the filter on a **plate.** Using a **dropper,** place ten drops of water on the spot.

Analysis

Make a labeled drawing of your results in your **Science Journal.** What type of change did you observe? Explain.

Physical Changes

If you break a piece of chewing gum, you change some of its physical properties—its size and shape. However, you do not change the identity of the materials that make up the gum.

The Identity Remains the Same When a substance freezes, boils, evaporates, or condenses, it undergoes physical changes. A change in size, shape, or state of matter is called a **physical change.** Such a change might involve energy changes, but the kind of substance—the identity of the element or compound—does not change. Because all substances have distinct properties, such as densities, specific heats, and boiling and melting points, which are constant, these properties can be used to help identify them when a particular mixture contains substances that are not yet identified.

Reading Check *Does a change in state mean that a new substance has formed? Explain.*

Iron is a substance that can change states if it absorbs or releases enough energy; at high temperatures, it melts. However, in both the solid and liquid state, iron has physical properties that identify it as iron. Color changes can accompany a physical change, too. For example, when iron is heated, it first glows red. Then, if it is heated to a higher temperature, it turns white, as shown in **Figure 12.**

Using Physical Change to Separate A cool drink of water is something most people take for granted, but in some parts of the world, drinkable water is scarce. Not enough drinkable water can be obtained from wells. Many such areas that lie close to the ocean obtain drinking water by using the physical properties of water to separate it from the salt. One separation method, which uses the property of boiling point, is distillation.

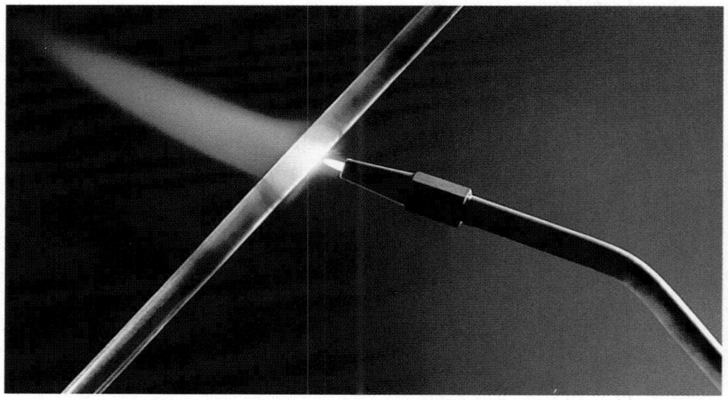

Figure 12 Heating iron raises its energy level and changes its color. These energy changes are physical changes because the substance is still iron.
Define *When liquid water becomes a solid, what type of physical change occurs?*

LAB DEMONSTRATION

Purpose to determine whether an observed change is chemical or physical

Materials water, potassium permanganate, sodium hydrogen sulfite, 250-mL beaker, stirring rod

Procedure Add water to the beaker until it is half full. Add a crystal of potassium permanganate to the water. Add 1 g of sodium hydrogen sulfite to the solution and stir until the solution becomes colorless.

Expected Outcome The addition of sodium hydrogen sulfite to potassium permanganate in water will cause a change in color.

Assessment

Is dissolving a chemical or physical change? physical change What evidence of a chemical change did you see? The change in color from purple to colorless indicated that new substances were being formed.

Distillation The process used for separating substances in a mixture by evaporating a liquid and recondensing its vapor is **distillation.** It usually is done in the laboratory using an apparatus similar to that shown in **Figure 13.** The liquid vaporizes and condenses, leaving the solid material behind.

Two liquids having different boiling points can be separated in a similar way. The mixture is heated slowly until it begins to boil. Vapors of the liquid with the lowest boiling point form first and are condensed and collected. Then, the temperature is increased until the second liquid boils, condenses, and is collected. Distillation is used often in industry. Natural oils such as mint are distilled.

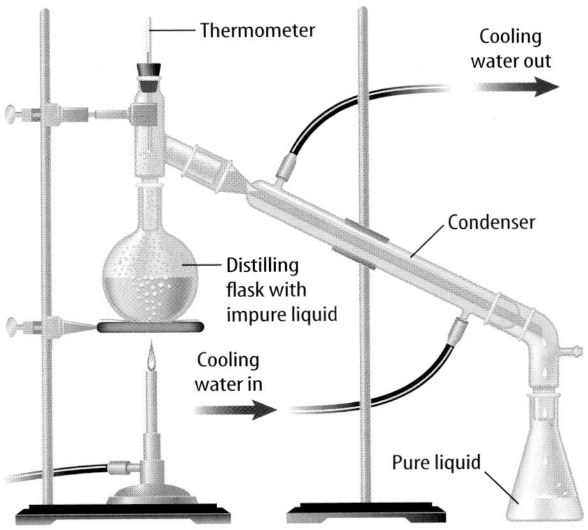

Figure 13 Distillation can easily separate liquids from solids dissolved in them. The liquid is heated until it vaporizes and moves up the column. Then, as it touches the water-cooled surface of the condenser, it becomes liquid again.

Chemical Properties and Changes

You probably have seen warnings on cans of paint thinners and lighter fluids for charcoal grills that say these liquids are flammable (FLA muh buhl). The tendency of a substance to burn, or its flammability, is an example of a chemical property. Burning produces a new substance during a chemical change. A **chemical property** is a characteristic of a substance that indicates whether it can undergo a certain chemical change. Many substances used around the home, such as lighter fluids, are flammable. Knowing which ones are flammable helps you to use them safely.

A less-dramatic chemical change can affect some medicines. Look at **Figure 14.** You probably have seen bottles like this in a pharmacy. Many medicines are stored in dark bottles because they contain compounds that can change chemically if they are exposed to light.

Figure 14 The brown color of these bottles tells you that these vitamins may react to light. Reaction to light is a chemical property.

Make a Model

Magnetism and Iron Turn a shoebox lid upside down and place iron filings and sand in the lid. Place a bar magnet underneath the lid and move it around while holding it against the bottom of the lid. Observe how the iron filings are both attracted and repulsed by the magnet depending upon the position of magnet. **Visual-Spatial**

Activity

Element Properties Ask students to pick a chemical element and use an encyclopedia or Internet source to make a list of its properties. Have them then divide the list into chemical and physical properties. L2 ELL
LS **Linguistic**

Discussion

Flammability What is involved in determining the flammability of a substance? Some of the factors used to determine flammability are temperature, vapor concentration, and ability to sustain combustion. Air is usually considered the oxidant in these measurements.

Fun Fact

Air, or oxygen, is not the only oxidant required for a substance to burn, there are also substances that will burn in fluorine gas.

Reading Strategy

Fix-Up Strategy Read aloud to students the text on distillation while interjecting questions about how you make sense of text as you read. Show students how to use the related illustration, **Figure 13,** to help unlock the text. Then, have students find their own difficult passages and practice close reading with a partner.

Visual Learning

Figure 14 Review with students the distillation process, and ask a volunteer to trace the path of water through the apparatus shown in the figure. Explain that the distillate moves through the inner portion of the condenser, while cold water, which helps cool the distillate, runs through the outer portion. L2 LS **Visual-Spatial**

Curriculum Connection

History Compounds called nitrates played a major role in the history of Chile. Have students find out what chemical property makes nitrates important and what role they played in Chile. Nitrates are one component of explosives. Nitrates were Chile's largest export in the late 1800s, giving the country money for economic development. The nitrate market collapsed during World War I, when chemists discovered a way to synthesize nitrates. L3 LS **Linguistic**

SECTION 2 Properties of Matter 563

INTEGRATE History

Alchemy Even though most people connect alchemy with the middle ages, alchemy started many years before that. References to alchemy can be found in Chinese, Egyptian, and Arabian histories.

Research Have students select and research a culture that has played a role in alchemy. Have students present their findings.

Reading Check

Answer a change of one substance to another

Caption Answer

Figure 15 formation of bubbles or solids, heat, cooling

Inquiry Lab

Oxidation and Food

Purpose to demonstrate chemical reactions in common foods

Possible Materials potato, lemon juice, peach, pear, apple, bowls (2)

Teaching Strategies

- Cut the potato, peach, pear, and apple in half. Dip the exposed inner surface of one of the food items in the lemon juice, then place in bowl.
- Place the other half in another bowl and allow both items to sit for 30 minutes. Encourage students to explain the reactions that occurred and allow them to explore other questions that arise. L2 IN **Kinesthetic, Visual-Spatial**

For additional inquiry activities, see *Science Inquiry Lab Manual*.

INTEGRATE History

Alchemy In the Middle Ages, alchemy was an early form of chemistry devoted to the study of changing baser metals into gold and also to finding the elixir of perpetual youth. Based on what we know now about the properties of metals and biology, it is easy to understand why this field of study is no longer practiced.

Detecting Chemical Changes

If you leave a pan of chili cooking unattended on the stove for too long, your nose soon tells you that something is wrong. Instead of a spicy aroma, you detect an unpleasant smell that alerts you that something is burning. This burnt odor is a clue that a new substance has formed.

The Identity Changes The smell of rotten eggs and the formation of rust on bikes or car fenders are signs that chemical changes have taken place. A change of one substance to another is a **chemical change.** The foaming of an antacid tablet in a glass of water and the smell in the air after a thunderstorm are other signs of new substances being produced. In some chemical changes, a rapid release of energy—detected as change of heat, light, and/or sound production—is a clue that changes are occurring.

Reading Check *What is a chemical change?*

A clue such as heat, cooling, or the formation of bubbles or solids in a liquid is a helpful indicator that a chemical reaction is taking place. However, the only sure proof is that a new substance is produced. Consider the following example. The heat, light, and sound produced when hydrogen gas combines with oxygen in a rocket engine are clear evidence that a chemical reaction has taken place. But no clues announce the reaction that takes place when iron combines with oxygen to form rust because the reaction takes place so slowly. The only clue that iron has changed into a new substance is the presence of rust. Burning and rusting are chemical changes because new substances form. You sometimes can follow the progress of a chemical reaction visually. For example, you can see lead nitrate forming in **Figure 15.**

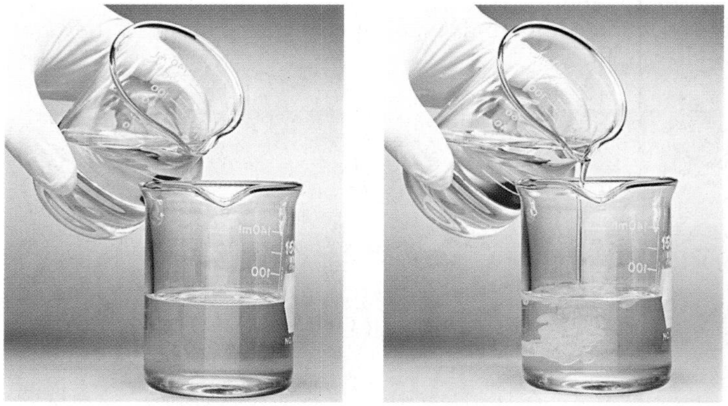

Figure 15 The solid forming from two liquids is another sign that a chemical reaction has taken place.
Identify *clues that show a reaction has taken place.*

Science Journal

Chemical Changes in Daily Life Have students keep a log of chemical changes they encounter in a 24-hour period. The logs should describe each change and list clues that helped students conclude that the change was chemical. Answers could include: respiration—oxygen used, carbon dioxide released; combusting gasoline—carbon dioxide produced, heat released; cooking—an egg becomes white and solid. L2 P IN **Linguistic, Visual-Spatial**

Using Chemical Change to Separate You might separate substances using a chemical change when cleaning tarnished silver. Tarnish is a chemical reaction between silver metal and sulfur compounds in the air that results in silver sulfide. It can be changed back into silver with a chemical reaction. This chemical reversal back to silver takes place when the tarnished item is placed in a warm water bath with baking soda and aluminum foil. You don't usually separate substances using chemical changes in the home. In industry and chemical laboratories, however, this kind of separation is common. For example, many metals are separated from their ores and then purified using chemical changes.

Weathering—Chemical or Physical Change?

The forces of nature continuously shape Earth's surface. Rocks split, deep canyons are carved out, sand dunes shift, and curious limestone formations decorate caves. Do you think these changes, often referred to as weathering, are physical or chemical? The answer is both. Geologists, who use the same criteria that you have learned in this chapter, say that some weathering changes are physical and some are chemical.

Physical Large rocks can split when water seeps into small cracks, freezes, and expands. However, the smaller pieces of newly exposed rock still have the same properties as the original sample. This is a physical change. Streams can cut through softer rock, forming canyons, and can smooth and sculpt harder rock, as shown on the left in **Figure 16.** In each case, the stream carries rock particles far downstream before depositing them. Because the particles are unchanged, the change is a physical one.

INTEGRATE Earth Science

Chemical Reactions and Lightning In a thunderstorm, light and sound tell you that changes have occurred. The pungent smells of ozone indicates that a chemical reaction also took place. Lightning converts oxygen gas, O_2, into ozone, O_3. Ozone is unstable and soon breaks up, forming oxygen again.

Flowing water shaped and smoothed these rocks in a physical process.

Both chemical and physical changes shaped the famous White Cliffs of Dover lining the English Channel.

Figure 16 Weathering can involve physical or chemical change.

Cultural Diversity

Chinese Chemistry The Chinese used chemical reactions to separate silver from lead and other impurities. In a process known as cupellation, they used high temperatures and blasts of air to oxidize the lead and other impurities, leaving pure silver behind.

INTEGRATE Earth Science

Chemical Reactions and Lightning Ask students why the sound of thunder indicates a physical change rather than a chemical change. To produce thunder, air molecules are driven closer together, then spread apart, setting up a sound wave. the air molecules are not chemically changed in this process. L3 LS **Logical-Mathematical**

Career Meteorologists are scientists who study the earth's climate. They do more than just forecast the weather. Meteorologists are responsible for researching and analyzing weather patterns, air pollution, and global warming trends. They can work for the governmant, universities, or for private industries.

Quick Demo

Physical and Chemical Changes

Materials chalk, file, dilute hydrochloric acid

Estimated Time five minutes

Safety Precautions

WARNING: *Wear goggles, gloves, and an apron. Avoid direct contact with the acid.*

Procedure A piece of chalk can be used to show the physical and chemical changes discussed in the text. Have students observe the chalk and note its size, appearance, and color. Next, file the chalk to show bits of it breaking away and reducing its size and form. This illustrates physical changes such as those produced by wind, geological movements, or cracking. Now take the same chalk, and place it in dilute hydrochloric acid. A noticeable gas-producing reaction ensues. This is a chemical change that produces new products, including carbon dioxide gas. L2 ELL LS **Visual-Spatial, Kinesthetic**

IDENTIFYING Misconceptions

Matter Conservation Students may think that matter is not conserved in physical or chemical changes. Refer to page F at the beginning of this chapter for teaching strategies that address this misconception.

Reading Check

Answer The mass of all substances present before a chemical change equals the mass of all the substances remaining after the change.

Applying Math

Math Standards

National: 1, 2, 9

Teaching Strategy

Have students count the atoms of each type of element. The number is the same on both sides of the equation. The total number of atoms of reactants will equal the total number of atoms of products. In the example, there are a total of four atoms: two hydrogens on each side. L2

LS **Logical-Mathematical**

Answers to Practice Problems

1. $(24\ g\ CH_4 + 96\ g O_2) = (66\ g\ CO_2 + x\ g\ H_2O)$
   $120\ g = 66\ g + x\ g\ H_2O$
   $120\ g - 66\ g = 54\ g\ H_2O$
2. $(54\ g\ Al + 409.2\ g\ ZnCl_2) = (196.2\ g\ Zn + x\ g\ AlCl_3)$
   $463.2\ g = 196.2\ g + x\ g\ AlCl_3$
   $463.2\ g = 196.2\ g + 267\ g\ AlCl_3$

Science Online

Topic: Caves

Visit gpescience.com for Web links to information about cave formations.

Activity Describe the formation of stalactites and stalagmites. Explain the differences between the two and whether they are the result of a physical and/or chemical process.

Chemical In other cases, the change is chemical. For example, solid calcium carbonate, a compound that mostly makes up limestone, does not dissolve easily in water. However, when the water is even slightly acidic, as it is when it contains some dissolved carbon dioxide, calcium carbonate reacts. It changes into a new substance, calcium hydrogen carbonate, which does dissolve in water. This change in limestone is a chemical change because the identity of the calcium carbonate changes. The White Cliffs of Dover, shown on the right in **Figure 16,** are made of limestone and undergo such chemical changes, as well as physical changes. A similar chemical change produces caves and the icicle-shaped rock formations that often are found in them.

Applying Math — Calculate

THE LAW OF CONSERVATION OF MASS When a chemical reaction takes place, the total mass of reactants equals the total mass of products. If 18 g of hydrogen reacts completely with 633 g of chlorine, how many grams of HCl are formed? $H_2 + Cl_2 \rightarrow 2HCl$

IDENTIFY known values and the unknown value

Identify the known values:

mass of H_2 = 18 g

mass of Cl_2 = 633 g

mass of reactants = mass of products

Identify the unknown value:

mass of HCl means ? g

SOLVE the problem

Solve for the mass of HCl. $g\ H_2 + g\ Cl_2 = g\ HCl$

Substitute the known values. $18\ g + 633\ g = 651\ g\ HCl$

CHECK the answer

Does your answer seem reasonable? Check your answer by subtracting the mass of H_2 from the mass of HCl. Do you obtain the mass of the Cl_2? If so, the answer is correct.

Practice Problems

1. In the following reaction, 24 g of CH_4 (methane) reacts completely with 96 g of O_2 to form 66 g of CO_2. How many grams of H_2O are formed? $CH_4 + 2O_2 \rightarrow CO_2 + 2H_2O$
2. In the following equation, 54.0 g of Al reacts completely with 409.2 g of $ZnCl_2$ to form 196.2 g of Zn metal. How many grams of $AlCl_3$ are formed? $2Al + 3ZnCl_2 \rightarrow 3Zn + 2AlCl_3$

For more practice problems go to page 879, and visit Math Practice at gpescience.com.

Teacher FYI

Changing Limestone The weathering of Dover's white cliffs involves the breakdown of limestone into soluble compounds. The formation of stalactites in caves involves the precipitation of limestone from water solutions. Thus, the formation of stalactites is the reverse of the weathering of the cliffs of Dover.

Post Reading

Cooperative Learning Working in small groups, have students create a chart with the headings *Grand Canyon*, *Sinkholes*, *Sand Beaches*, and *Rock Formations.* Have them list physical and chemical changes that contributed to the formation of each. Encourage students to find pictures or interesting facts to add to their charts.

The Conservation of Mass

Wood is combustible, or burnable. As you just learned, this is a chemical property. Suppose you burn a large log in a fireplace, as shown in **Figure 17,** until nothing is left but a small pile of ashes. Smoke, heat, gas, and light are given off, and the changes in the appearance of the log confirm that a chemical change took place. You might think that matter was lost during this change because the pile of ashes looks much smaller than the log did. In fact, the mass of the ashes is less than that of the log. Suppose that you could collect all the oxygen in the air that was combined with the log during the burning and all the smoke, heat, light, and gases that escaped from the burning log and measure their masses, too. Then you would find that no mass was lost after all.

Not only is no mass lost during burning, mass is not gained or lost during any chemical change. In other words, matter is neither created nor destroyed during a chemical change. According to the **law of conservation of mass,** the mass of all substances that are present before a chemical change equals the mass of all the substances that remain after the change.

Figure 17 This reaction appears to be destroying these logs. When it is over, only ashes will remain. Yet you know that no mass is lost in a chemical reaction. **Explain** *why this is so.*

Reading Check *Explain what is meant by the law of conservation of mass.*

section 2 review

Summary

Physical Properties

- You can observe physical properties without changing the identity of a substance.

Physical Changes

- Change in the size, shape, or state of matter is a physical change.

Chemical Properties and Changes

- A chemical property is a characteristic of a substance that indicates whether it can undergo a certain chemical change.
- A change of one substance to another is a chemical change.
- Many metals are separated from their ores and purified using chemical changes.

Self Check

1. **Explain** why evaporation of water is a physical change and not a chemical change.
2. **List** four physical properties you could use to describe a liquid.
3. **Describe** why flammability is a chemical property rather than a physical property.
4. **Explain** how the law of conservation of mass applies to chemical changes.
5. **Think Critically** How might you demonstrate the law of conservation of mass for melting ice and distilling water?

Applying Math

6. **Calculate** In the following equation, 417.96 g of Bi (bismuth) reacts completely with 200 g of F (fluorine). How many grams of BiF_3 (bismuth fluoride) are formed? $2\ Bi + 3\ F_2 \longrightarrow 2\ BiF_3$

Caption Answer

Figure 17 Some of the log's components combine with oxygen to form gases.

3 Assess

DAILY INTERVENTION

Check for Understanding

Kinesthetic Have a student light a match and allow it to burn. Also, place an ice cube in a glass container and allow it to melt. Have students explain what type of changes took place with each item and describe the final properties of each. L2 LS **Visual-Spatial**

Reteach

Mass Place a small, open vial of dilute silver nitrate solution carefully inside a large flask containing a dilute solution of sodium chloride. Determine the mass of the entire assembly. Then tip the flask to intentionally spill the contents of the small vial. A white precipitate will quickly form. Re-mass the assembly. Ask students what law is demonstrated when the two masses are in agreement. law of conservation of mass L2 ELL

LS **Visual-Spatial, Kinesthetic**

Assessment

Oral Display several similar but slightly different candles. Have a student describe each candle using a minimum number of physical properties. Other students must identify the candle from its physical properties. Use **Performance Assessment in the Science Classroom,** p. 89. L1

section 2 review

1. The makeup of the water units is unchanged.
2. color, odor, volume, temperature
3. Because the original materials are changed into new substances.
4. The mass of all substances present before a chemical change equals the mass of all the substances remaining after the change.
5. Let the ice melt on a balance, and show that the balance doesn't move. Find the mass of the liquid water, boil it and collect the condensed vapor and any solids. Find the mass of the condensed vapor and solids.
6. 617.96 g

BENCH TESTED

Real-World Problem

Purpose Students will design an experiment to observe the law of conservation of mass.

Process Skills observe, measure, use and make data tables, collect and organize data, communicate, form hypotheses, infer

Time Required 45 minutes

Procedure

Possible Materials Different brands of antacid tablets and different sized plastic drink bottles can be used.

Safety Precautions Caution students never to eat or drink anything during science class.

Form a Hypothesis

Possible Hypothesis Students should hypothesize that the mass of the reactants should be approximately equal to the mass of the products.

Test Your Hypothesis

Possible Procedures Students can use a mortar and pestle to grind the antacid tablets. The powdered tablet is placed into a dry balloon. Sudents should measure the mass of the balloon bottle with water before and after the reaction. The balloon should be fitted over the mouth of the bottle. The powder will be poured into the bottle, then gently swirled.

LAB Design Your Own

Measuring the Conservation of Mass

Goals

- **Measure** the total mass of water and antacid tablets before and after the tablets are dissolved in the water.
- **Compare** the total mass of water and tablets before and after the tablets are dissolved in the water.
- **Infer** whether or not the law of conservation of mass applies to antacid tablets dissolving in water

Possible Materials

antacid tablets
empty plastic drink bottle
balloon
beaker
water
spatula
balance
mortar
pestle
funnel

Safety Precautions

Do not eat the antacid tablet.

Real-World Problem

Have you ever watched burning logs in a fireplace? If you have, you might have noticed many large logs being burned in the hearth during an evening. At the end of the night, nothing more than a pile of ash remains. In this lab, your group will design an experiment to demonstrate the law of conservation of mass. Is the mass of antacid tablets conserved after they are dissolved?

Form a Hypothesis

Based on your understanding of mass conservation, form a hypothesis that predicts the total mass of antacid tablets and water before and after the tablets are dissolved.

Test Your Hypothesis

Make a Plan

1. As a group, agree upon and write the hypothesis statement.
2. Decide upon any safety equipment you need or safety procedures you need to devise to ensure the safety of your group during the experiment.

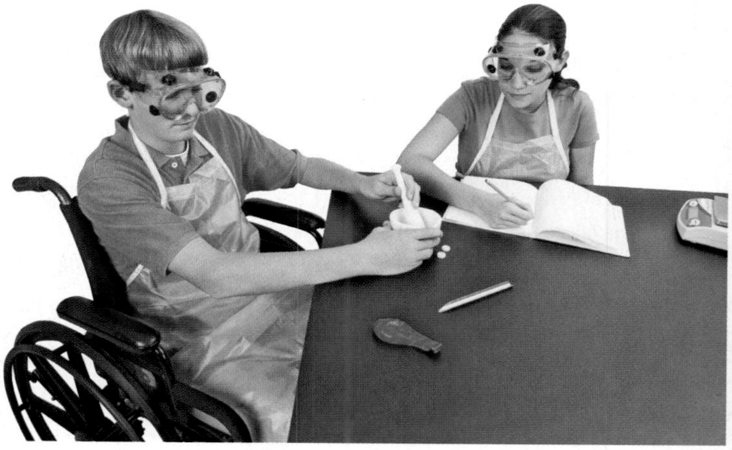

Alternative Inquiry Lab

Open and Closed Systems To make this Lab into an Inquiry Lab, have students compare the initial and final masses of an open system and closed system. They can create a closed system by following the procedure they devised during their lab, and they can create an open system by placing the powder directly into the bottle and leaving the container open.

Students can also research the chemical reactions involved when antacids are used to neutralize excess stomach acid. Citric acid (C6H8O7) and sodium bicarbonate (NaHCO3) are the main ingredients in antacid tablets. When the tablets are dropped into water with dissolved H+ ions, a chemical reaction occurs to produce water and carbon dioxide.

Using Scientific Methods

3. **Plan** an experiment to test your hypothesis. List the steps of your experiment.
4. **List** the materials you need to test your hypothesis.
5. Have one group member reread your entire experiment aloud to the group to make certain you have all the necessary materials and that your experimental steps can be easily followed.

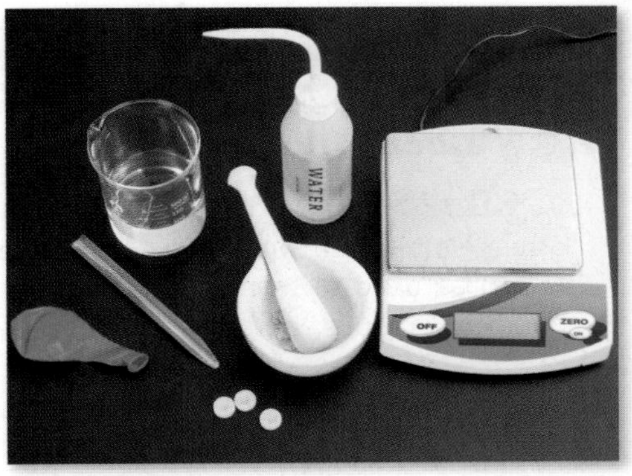

Follow Your Plan

1. Make sure your teacher approves your plan.
2. Copy the data table into your Science Journal to record measurements.
3. While doing the experiment, write your observations, and complete the data table in your Science Journal.

Data Table

Trial Number	Mass Before Reaction	Mass After Reaction

Analyze Your Data

1. **Describe** the effects of the chemical reaction between the antacid powder and the water.
2. **Compare** the total mass of the substances before the reaction to their mass after the reaction.
3. **Graph** the mass of the substances before and after the reaction using a bar graph.
4. **Explain** if your data supported your hypothesis.

Conclude and Apply

1. **Identify** possible experimental errors in your experiment design.
2. **Infer** how mass might have been lost or added between the initial and final weighing of the substances.
3. **Infer** what the expected mass of the substances should be after the chemical reaction occurred.

Communicating Your Data

Compare the data your group collected with the data collected by the other groups and discuss possible reasons for differences in the data

Teaching Strategies

- Explain that the mass of the system before the reaction will probably not be exactly the same as the mass after the reaction due to some form of experimental error. There is always some margin of error during an experiment.

Troubleshooting One student needs to stretch the balloon's opening while a second student scoops the powdered tablet into the balloon. Make certain the plastic bottle and attached balloon will fit on your classroom balances.

Expected Outcome Although the initial mass and final mass of the substances may not be identical, the mass of the reactants should be nearly equal to the mass of the products. A small amount of mass will probably be lost due to experimental error.

Analyze Your Data

1. The water will fizz vigorously, and the balloon will partially inflate with released carbon dioxide.
2. Results will vary depending upon the measurements collected by each group.
3. Graphs will vary.
4. Answers will vary.

Error Analysis Discuss with students possible errors in their data. Students might make inaccurate measurements, or gases produced during the reaction might escape.

Conclude and Apply

1. Answers may vary.
2. Answers may vary.
3. Answers may vary.

Assessment

Content Have students write and act out a skit demonstrating the law of conservation of mass at work during a chemical reaction such as paper burning or the joining of two elements to form a compound. Use **PASC,** p. 147.

Communicating Your Data

Encourage students to create data tables and bar graphs electronically.

LAB 569

Content Background

Scientists constantly attempt to create or discover new elements. Recently discovered elements do not exist in nature but have been synthesized by bombarding existing elements with high-speed particles. The element seaborgium was synthesized by bombarding the element californium by highly accelerated oxygen nuclei.

Discussion

Oxygen The element oxygen makes up 46 percent of Earth's crust, yet it makes up only 21 percent of Earth's atmosphere. Most oxygen is contained in compounds. For example, sand is silicon dioxide, SiO_2.

Activity

Changing Elements Unless an element is radioactive and its nucleus changes, each atom remains the same element. However, elements change form and location. Provide students with the following statements. Have them draw an illustration that uses arrows and the statements to show how the element nitrogen is cycled on Earth. Statements:

- Plants obtain nitrogen from the soil.
- Bacteria on certain plants change atmospheric nitrogen to a useful form.
- Animals eat plants.
- Animals and plants die and decompose.

L2 IS **Visual-Spatial, Logical-Mathematical**

SCIENCE Stats

Intriguing Elements

Did you know...

... Silver-white cobalt, which usually is combined with other elements in nature, is used to create rich paint pigments. It can be used to form powerful magnets, treat cancer patients, build jet engines, and prevent disease in sheep.

... Gold is the most ductile (stretchable) of all the elements. Just 29 g of gold—about ten wedding bands—can be pulled into a wire 100 km long. That's long enough to stretch from Toledo, Ohio, to Detroit, Michigan, and beyond.

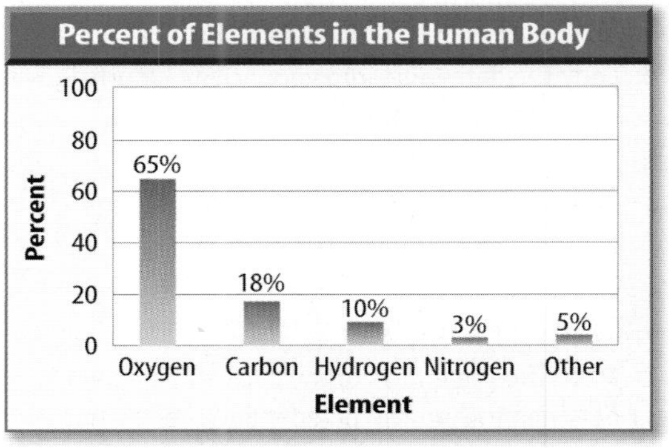

... Zinc makes chewing gum taste better. Up to 0.3 mg of zinc acetate can be added per 1000 mg of chewing gum to provide a tart, zingy flavor.

Applying Math

1. Zinc acetate is approximately 35 percent zinc. How many grams of chewing gum would be needed to provide a total of 10.0 mg of zinc?
2. If you wanted to produce a gold wire with the same diameter as mentioned in the example above, how many grams would be needed to make a wire one meter in length?
3. Table sugar has the chemical formula $C_{12}H_{22}O_{11}$. If you were going to build a scale model of sucrose (table sugar) and you had 36 model carbon atoms, how many of each of the others (hydrogen and oxygen) would you need to build an accurate, complete sucrose model?

Applying Math

Teaching Strategies

- Review with students how to set up a proportion. Remind students that 1,000 mg equals 1 g.
- Discuss with students that they need to convert meters to kilomters or kilomters to meters in order to set up a proportion to solve.
- Review ratios with students to determine the scale factor, 3.

Answers

1. about 33 g
2. 0.00029 g
3. H—66 atoms; O—33 atoms

Reviewing Main Ideas

Section 1 Composition of Matter

1. Elements and compounds are substances. A mixture is composed of two or more substances.
2. You can distinguish between the different materials in a heterogeneous mixture using either your unaided eye or a microscope.
3. Colloids and suspensions are two types of heterogeneous mixtures. The particles in a suspension will settle eventually. Particles of a colloid will not. Milk is an example of a colloid.

4. In a homogeneous mixture, the particles are distributed evenly and are not visible, even when using a microscope. Homogeneous mixtures can be composed of solids, liquids, or gases.
5. A solution is another name for a homogeneous mixture that remains constantly and uniformly mixed.

This is a clear indication that this mixture is a suspension.

Section 2 Properties of Matter

1. Physical properties are characteristics of materials that you can observe without changing the identities of the substances.
2. Chemical properties indicate what chemical changes substances can undergo. Many medicines are stored in dark bottles because they react with light.

3. In physical changes, the identities of substances remain unchanged.
4. In chemical changes, the identities of substances change: new substances are formed. A visible chemical change takes place when rust is cleaned with bleach.

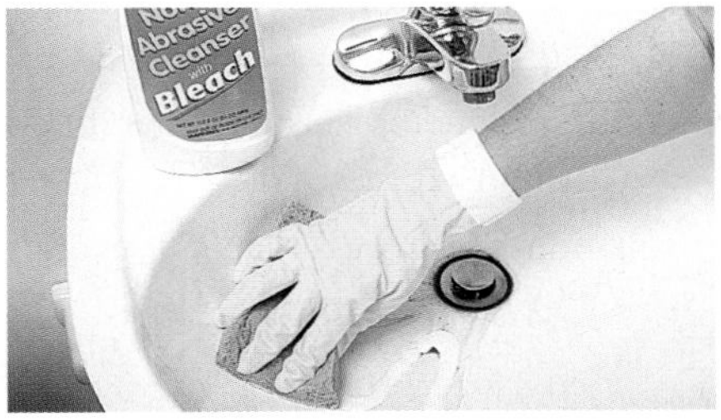

5. The law of conservation of mass states that during any chemical change, matter is neither created nor destroyed.

FOLDABLES Use the Foldable that you made at the beginning of the chapter to help you review the classification of matter.

Identifying Misconceptions

Assess

Materials photograph of a sealed terrarium that contains a plant, an animal, and food for the animal

Procedure Show students the photograph. Explain that the terrarium is completely sealed. Suppose we measure the mass of this terrarium today, leave it for three months in a place where the plant gets enough light, and then measure the mass again. What is the terrarium's mass? L2 LS **Visual-Spatial**

Expected Outcome Students should realize that the mass of the terrarium would stay the same because it is a closed system.

Reviewing Main Ideas

Summary statements can be used by students to review the major concepts of the chapter.

Science Online

Visit gpescience.com
More Section Review
Interactive Tutor
Vocabulary PuzzleMaker
More Chapter Review
Standardized Test Practice

Assessment Transparency

For additional assessment questions, use the *Assessment Transparency* located in the transparency book.

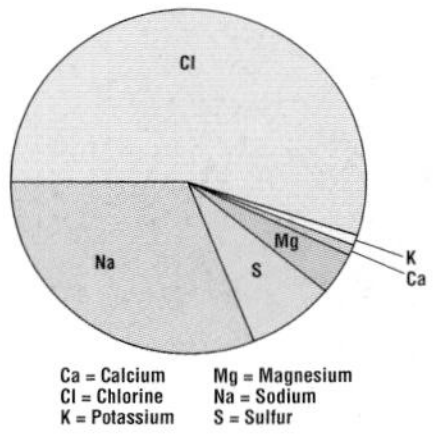

Assessment

Assessment Transparency — Classification of Matter — Chapter 18

Directions: *Carefully review the graph and answer the following questions.*

1. According to this information, which element makes up greater than 50 % of the elements dissolved in seawater?
   A Sodium B Sulfur C Magnesium D Chlorine
2. Which element is found dissolved in seawater about twice as much as magnesium?
   F Calcium G Sodium H Sulfur J Potassium
3. A compound is a substance made of the combined atoms of two or more different elements. According to this definition, which of these is a compound?
   A Ca B MgS C Cl_2 D Na

L2

Classification of Matter

FOLDABLES Have students use their Foldables to review the content of the chapter.

Using Vocabulary

1. compounds
2. suspension
3. physical change
4. law of conservation of mass
5. heterogeneous mixture
6. elements
7. physical change

Checking Concepts

8. D
9. D
10. B
11. A
12. D
13. D
14. C
15. B
16. A
17. D

Interpreting Graphics

18. See student page.
19. See student page.

chapter 18 Review

Using Vocabulary

chemical change p. 564
chemical property p. 563
colloid p. 556
compound p. 554
distillation p. 563
element p. 552
heterogeneous mixture p. 555
homogeneous mixture p. 556
law of conservation of mass p. 567
physical change p. 562
physical property p. 560
solution p. 556
substance p. 552
suspension p. 558
Tyndall effect p. 557

Complete each sentence with the correct vocabulary word or words.

1. Substances formed from atoms of two or more elements are called _________.
2. A(n) _________ is a heterogeneous mixture in which visible particles settle.
3. Freezing, boiling, and evaporation are all examples of _________.
4. According to the _________, matter is neither created nor destroyed during a chemical change.
5. A mixture in which different materials are easily identified is _________.
6. Compounds are made from different atoms of two or more _________.
7. Distillation is a process that can separate two liquids using _________.

Checking Concepts

Choose the word or phrase that best answers the question.

8. Bending a copper wire is an example of what property?
   A) chemical **C)** element
   B) conservation **D)** physical
9. Which is **NOT** an element?
   A) carbon **C)** oxygen
   B) hydrogen **D)** water
10. Which is an example of a chemical change?
   A) boiling **C)** evaporation
   B) burning **D)** melting
11. What is gelatin?
   A) colloid **C)** substance
   B) compound **D)** suspension
12. Which is an example of a visible sunbeam?
   A) an element **C)** a compound
   B) a solution **D)** the Tyndall effect
13. How would you classify the color of a rose?
   A) chemical change
   B) chemical property
   C) physical change
   D) physical property
14. How would you describe the process of evaporating water from seawater?
   A) chemical change
   B) chemical property
   C) physical change
   D) physical property
15. Which is a substance?
   A) colloid **C)** mixture
   B) element **D)** solution
16. Which property can be used to help identify an unknown substance?
   A) specific heat **C)** temperature
   B) combustion **D)** Tyndall effect
17. Which statement about the law of conservation of mass is **TRUE**?
   A) Mass is created only.
   B) Mass is created and destroyed.
   C) Mass is destroyed only.
   D) Mass is neither created nor destroyed.

 Vocabulary PuzzleMaker gpescience.com

Use the Exam*View*® Pro Testmaker CD-ROM to:
- create multiple versions of tests
- create modified tests with one mouse click for inclusion students
- edit existing questions and add your own questions
- build tests aligned with state standards using built-in State Curriculum Tags
- change English tests to Spanish with one mouse click and vice versa

Interpreting Graphics

18. Copy and complete the concept map below about matter.

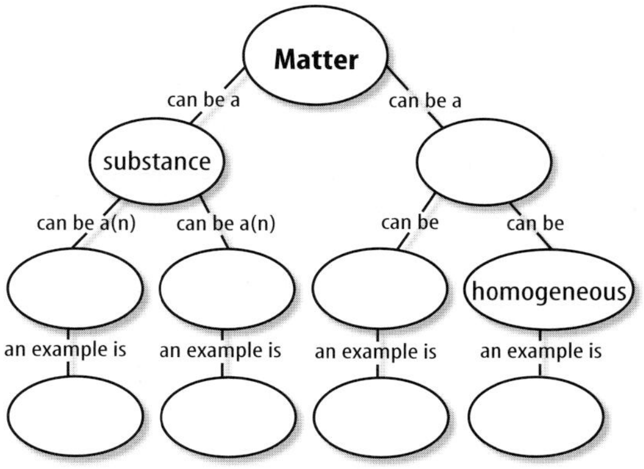

Use the table below to answer question 19.

Common Colloids

Colloid	Example
Solid in a liquid	Gelatin
Solid in a gas	
Gas in a solid	
Solid in a liquid	
Liquid in a gas	

19. Identify how different colloids can involve different states. For example, gelatin is formed from solid particles in a liquid. Complete the table using these colloids: *smoke, marshmallow, fog,* and *paint.*

Thinking Critically

20. Compare and contrast elements and compounds. Give two examples of each.

21. Explain Carbon and the gases hydrogen and oxygen combine to form sugar. How do you know sugar is a compound?

22. Use a nail rusting in air to explain the law of conservation of mass.

23. Use Variables, Constants, and Controls Marcos took a 100-cm^3 sample of a suspension, shook it well, and poured equal amounts into four different test tubes. He placed one test tube in a rack, one in hot water, one in warm water, and the fourth in ice water. He then observed the time it took for each suspension to settle. What was the variable in the experiment? What was one constant?

24. Concept Map Make a network tree to show types of liquid mixtures. Include these terms: *homogeneous mixtures, heterogeneous mixtures, solutions, colloids,* and *suspensions.*

Applying Math

Use the graph below to answer question 25.

Percent of Elements in the Human Body

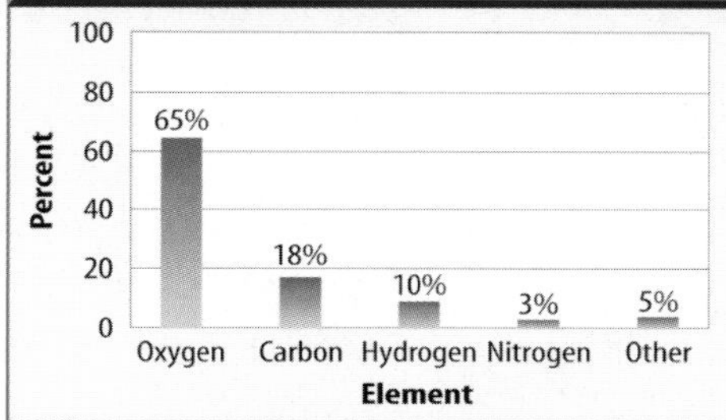

25. Use Proportions If you had 50 atoms of hydrogen, how many atoms each of oxygen, carbon, and nitrogen would you need to have the elements in the same proportion as they are in your body?

26. Use Numbers In the following equation, 243.5 g of Sb (antimony) reacts completely with 1000 g of I_2 (iodine) to form 1004.9 g of SbI_3 (antimony triiodide). How many grams of I_2 were consumed in the reaction? $2\ Sb + 3\ I_2 \rightarrow 2\ SbI_3$

Assessment Resources

Reproducible Masters

Chapter *Fast File* Resources
- Chapter Review, pp. 35–36
- Chapter Tests, pp. 37–40
- Assessment Transparency Activity, p. 47

Glencoe Science Web site
- Chapter Review Test
- Standardized Test Practice

Glencoe Technology
- Assessment Transparency
- Exam*View*® Pro Testmaker
- MindJogger Videoquiz
- Interactive Chalkboard

Thinking Critically

20. Elements and compounds are made from atoms. An element has all the same atoms whereas a compound is made of atoms of two or more elements. Accept all reasonable examples of elements and compounds.

21. It can't be separated by physical means; it looks different from the elements that make it up.

22. The combined mass of the oxygen and the iron before the reaction is equal to the mass of the rust after the reaction.

23. The variable was temperature. One constant was the amount of suspension put into each tube.

24. Mixtures include homogeneous mixtures, which are solutions, and heterogeneous mixtures, which include colloids or suspensions.

Applying Math

Math Standards

National: 2, 6, 9

Answers to Practice Problems

25. approximately 325 atoms of oxygen, 90 atoms of carbon, and 15 atoms of nitrogen

26. 238.6 g.

Answer Sheet An answer sheet can be found at **gpescience.com**.

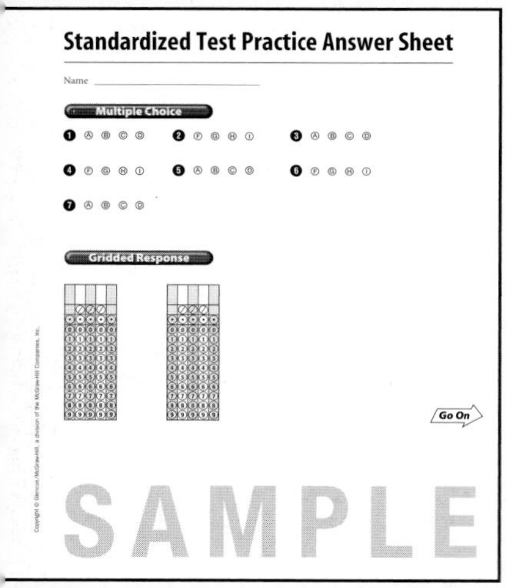
Standardized Test Practice Answer Sheet

Name

Multiple Choice

Gridded Response

Go On

SAMPLE

Multiple Choice

1. B
2. C
3. A
4. B
5. A
6. D

Gridded Response

7. 54
8. 33.38

chapter 18 Standardized Test Practice

Record your answers on the answer sheet provided by your teacher or on a sheet of paper.

Multiple Choice

1. $CaCO_3$ is an example of which type of material?

A. colloid

B. compound

C. element

D. mixture

Use the graph to answer question 2.

Elements in the Universe

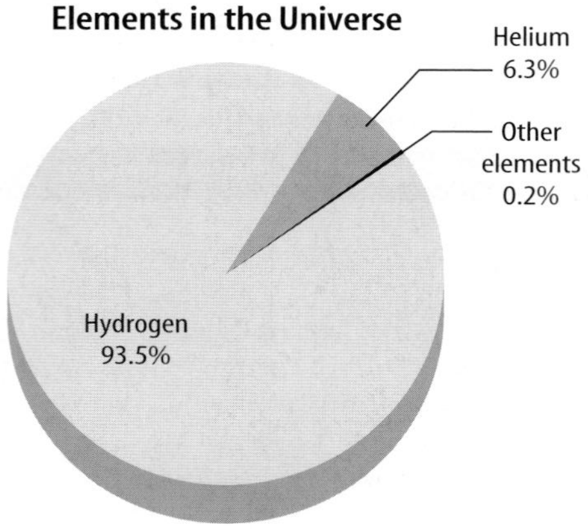

2. What percentage do the elements hydrogen and helium account for in the universe?

A. 100 percent

B. 99.9 percent

C. 99.8 percent

D. 98 percent

Use the graph below to answer question 3.

Elements in Earth's Crust

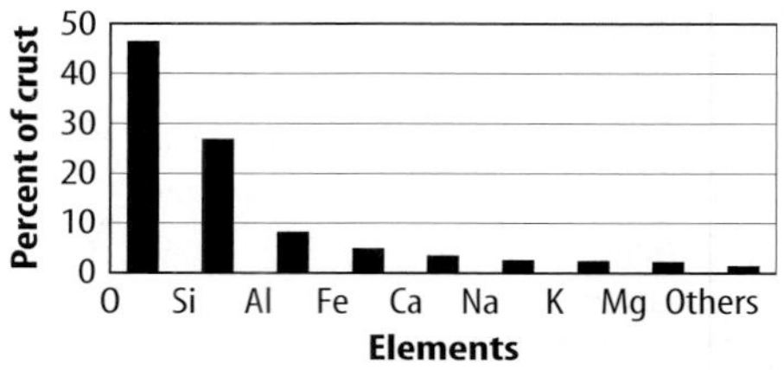

3. Which element makes up 8 percent of Earth's crust?

A. aluminum

B. iron

C. oxygen

D. silicon

4. Which element has the physical property of magnetism?

A. calcium

B. iron

C. oxygen

D. sodium

5. Which statement best decribes the law of conservation of mass?

A. The mass of the products is always greater than the mass of the materials that react in a chemical change.

B. The mass of the products is always less than the mass of the materials that react in a chemical change.

C. A certain mass of material must be present for a reaction to occur.

D. Matter is neither lost nor gained during a chemical change.

6. The most plentiful element in the universe readily burns in air. What is this chemical property called?
   - **A.** flammability
   - **B.** ductility
   - **C.** density
   - **D.** boiling point

Gridded Response

7. In the following reaction, 24 g of CH_4 (methane) react completely with 96 g of O_2 to form 66 g of CO_2. How many grams of H_2O are formed?

8. A reaction of 22.85 g of sodium hydroxide (NaOH) with 20.82 g of hydrogen chloride (HCl) gives off 10.29 g of water (H_2O). What mass of sodium chloride (NaCl) is formed in this reaction?

Short Response

Use the illustration below to answer questions 9.

9. What physical properties could be used to identify these minerals?

10. You are given a mixture of iron filings, sand, and salt. Describe how to separate this mixture.

Extended Response

11. Describe how a compound is a combination of elements in a fixed proportion. Give two examples.

Use the illustration below to answer question 12.

12. Design an experiment that shows that this type of chemical change is governed by the law of conservation of mass.

Test-Taking Tip

Directions and Instructions Listen carefully to the instructions from your teacher. Read the directions and each question carefully.

Short Response

9. Physical properties of these minerals include color, shape, magnetism, density, melting point, and boiling point.
10. Add water to the mixture. Stir until all the salt is dissolved, then pour the water/salt solution off of the sand/iron mixture. Use a magnet to separate the iron and sand.

Extended Response

11. By definition, a compound is a substance made from two or more elements. All compounds are fixed in the proportions of that compound. If the ratio of the elements changes, then a new compound is formed. Examples are: water, carbon dioxide, salt, and sugar. Accept answers that students may provide as long as they are compounds.
12. The experiment should include these components: Design an enclosure to trap all solid and gas products of the reaction. With the enclosure covering the reactants, measure the total mass (enclosure plus all reactants to be burned.) With enclosure in place, start the reaction. Once burning is complete, measure the total mass again. The initial and final masses will be equal.

Rubrics

For more help evaluating Short- and Extended-Response questions, see the rubrics on p. 10T.

chapter 19 Organizer

Section/Objectives	Standards		Labs/Features
	National	State/Local	
Chapter Opener	See pp. 16T–17T for a Key to Standards.		**Launch Lab:** Inferring What You Can't Observe, p. 577 Video Lab **Foldables,** p. 577
Section 1 Structure of the Atom 2 sessions 1 block 1. **Identify** the names and symbols of common elements. 2. **Identify** quarks as subatomic particles of matter. 3. **Describe** the electron cloud model of the atom. 4. **Explain** how electrons are arranged in an atom.	National Content Standards: UCP.1–3, UCP.5, A.1, A.2, B.2, B.5, B.6, G.3		**Science Online,** p. 579 **MiniLAB:** Modeling an Aluminum Atom, p. 581 **Visualizing the Atomic Model,** p. 582
Section 2 Masses of Atoms 3 sessions 1.5 blocks 5. **Compute** the atomic mass and mass number of an atom. 6. **Identify** the components of isotopes. 7. **Interpret** the average atomic mass of an element.	National Content Standards: UCP.1–3, UCP.5, A.1, A.2, B.2, B.5, B.6, G.3		**Integrate Life Science,** p. 586 **Applying Science,** p. 586
Section 3 The Periodic Table 3 sessions 1.5 blocks 8. **Explain** the composition of the periodic table. 9. **Use** the periodic table to obtain information. 10. **Explain** what the terms *metal, nonmetal,* and *metalloid* mean.	National Content Standards: UCP.1–3, UCP.5, A.1, A.2, B.2, B.5, B.6 G.3		**MiniLAB:** Organizing a Personal Periodic Table, p. 589 **Integrate Career,** p. 592 **Science Online,** p. 593 **Science Online,** p. 595 **Lab:** A Periodic Table of Foods, p. 597 **Lab:** What's in a name?, pp. 598–599 **Science and History:** A Chilling Story, p. 600

StudentWorks Plus

Glencoe Exclusive!
TeacherWorks™
All-In-One Planner and Resource Center

Lab Materials	Reproducible Resources	Section Assessment	Technology
Launch Lab: chalk, eraser, thimble, bottle, washer, envelope	**Chapter *Fast File* Resources** Foldables Worksheet, p. 17 Directed Reading Overview, p. 19 Note-taking Worksheets, pp. 33–35	Glencoe's Assessment Advantage	TeacherWorks includes: • Interactive Teacher Edition • Lesson Planner with calendar • Access to all program blacklines • Correlations to standards • Web links • Video Lab
MiniLAB: 13 3-cm circles cut from orange paper, 14 3-cm circles cut from blue paper, red paper, hole punch	**Chapter *Fast File* Resources** Transparency Activity, p. 44 MiniLAB, p. 3 Enrichment, p. 30 Reinforcement, p. 27 Directed Reading, p. 20 Transparency Activity, pp. 47–48 **Reading and Writing Skill Activities,** p. 43	Portfolio Check for Understanding, p. 583 Performance MiniLab, p. 581 Applying Math, p. 583 Content Section Review, p. 583	Section Focus Transparency Teaching Transparency Interactive Chalkboard CD-ROM StudentWorks Plus
Need materials? Contact Science Kit at 1-800-828-7777 or www.sciencekit.com.	**Chapter *Fast File* Resources** Transparency Activity, p. 45 Enrichment, p. 31 Reinforcement, p. 28 Directed Reading, p. 20 Lab Activity, pp. 9–12 **Mathematics Skill Activities,** p. 7 **Science Inquiry Labs,** pp. 49–50	Portfolio Check for Understanding, p. 587 Performance Applying Science, p. 586 Content Section Review, p. 587	Section Focus Transparency Interactive Chalkboard CD-ROM StudentWorks Plus
MiniLAB: feather, penny, container of water, pencil, dime, strand of hair, container of milk, container of orange juice, container of soda, square of cotton cloth, nickel, crayon, quarter, golf ball, sheet of paper, baseball, marble, leaf, and paper clip **Lab:** 11 × 17 paper, 12- or 18-inch ruler, colored pencils or markers	**Chapter *Fast File* Resources** Transparency Activity, p. 46 MiniLAB, p. 4 Enrichment, p. 32 Reinforcement, p. 29 Directed Reading, pp. 21–22 Lab Worksheet, pp. 5–6, 7–8 Lab Activity, pp. 13–15 **Reading and Writing Skill Activities,** p. 47 **Home and Community Involvement,** p. 25	Portfolio Differentiated Instruction, p. 592 Assessment, p. 599 Performance MiniLab, p. 589 Applying Math, p. 596 Content Section Review, p. 596	Section Focus Transparency Virtual Labs CD-ROM Interactive Chalkboard CD-ROM StudentWorks Plus

End of Chapter Assessment

Glencoe's Assessment Advantage

Blackline Masters	Technology	Professional Series
Chapter *Fast File* Resources Chapter Review, pp. 37–38 Chapter Tests, pp. 39–42 **Standardized Test Practice,** pp. 80–83	MindJogger Videoquiz Virtual Labs CD-ROM Exam*View*® Pro Testmaker TeacherWorks CD-ROM Interactive Chalkboard CD-ROM	**Performance Assessment in the Science Classroom (PASC)**

Transparencies

Section Focus

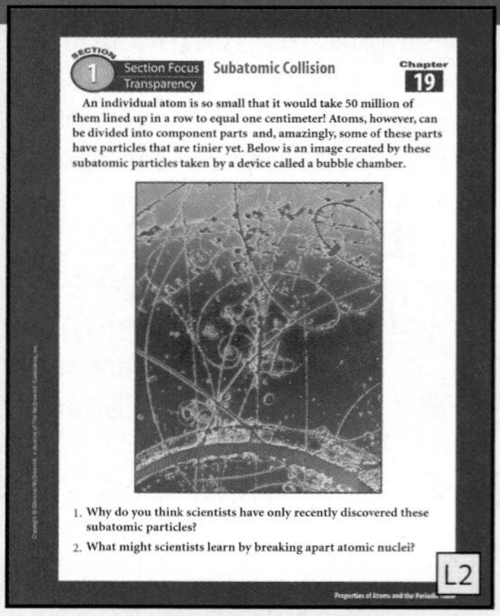
SECTION 1 Section Focus Transparency — Subatomic Collision — Chapter 19

An individual atom is so small that it would take 50 million of them lined up in a row to equal one centimeter! Atoms, however, can be divided into component parts and, amazingly, some of these parts have particles that are tinier yet. Below is an image created by these subatomic particles taken by a device called a bubble chamber.

1. Why do you think scientists have only recently discovered these subatomic particles?
2. What might scientists learn by breaking apart atomic nuclei?

L2

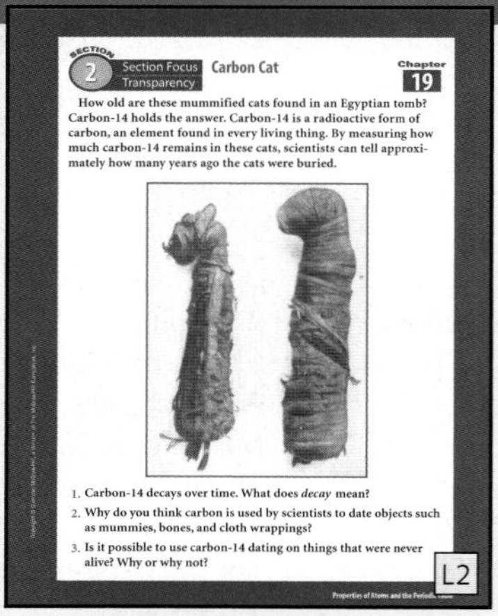
SECTION 2 Section Focus Transparency — Carbon Cat — Chapter 19

How old are these mummified cats found in an Egyptian tomb? Carbon-14 holds the answer. Carbon-14 is a radioactive form of carbon, an element found in every living thing. By measuring how much carbon-14 remains in these cats, scientists can tell approximately how many years ago the cats were buried.

1. Carbon-14 decays over time. What does *decay* mean?
2. Why do you think carbon is used by scientists to date objects such as mummies, bones, and cloth wrappings?
3. Is it possible to use carbon-14 dating on things that were never alive? Why or why not?

L2

SECTION 3 Section Focus Transparency — What makes the glass glow? — Chapter 19

When you hear the word uranium, you might think of nuclear power. Uranium, though, was used in the 19th century by European glassmakers to create what was called uranium glass. This interesting glass had a yellowish-green color and glows under certain lighting conditions.

1. Of what materials is glass usually made?
2. Why do you think the uranium glass glows?
3. Why might prolonged work with such glass be dangerous?

L2

This is a representation of key blackline masters available in the Teacher Classroom Resources. See Resource Manager boxes within the chapter for additional information.

Assessment

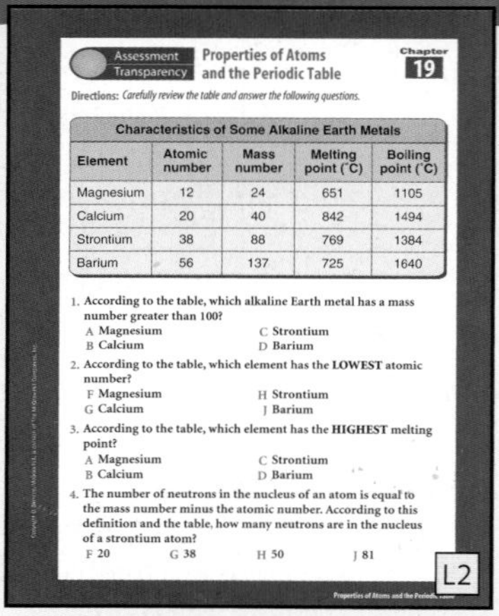
Assessment Transparency — Properties of Atoms and the Periodic Table — Chapter 19

Directions: Carefully review the table and answer the following questions.

Characteristics of Some Alkaline Earth Metals

Element	Atomic number	Mass number	Melting point (°C)	Boiling point (°C)
Magnesium	12	24	651	1105
Calcium	20	40	842	1494
Strontium	38	88	769	1384
Barium	56	137	725	1640

1. According to the table, which alkaline Earth metal has a mass number greater than 100?
   A Magnesium C Strontium
   B Calcium D Barium
2. According to the table, which element has the **LOWEST** atomic number?
   F Magnesium H Strontium
   G Calcium J Barium
3. According to the table, which element has the **HIGHEST** melting point?
   A Magnesium C Strontium
   B Calcium D Barium
4. The number of neutrons in the nucleus of an atom is equal to the mass number minus the atomic number. According to this definition and the table, how many neutrons are in the nucleus of a strontium atom?
   F 20 G 38 H 50 J 81

L2

Teaching

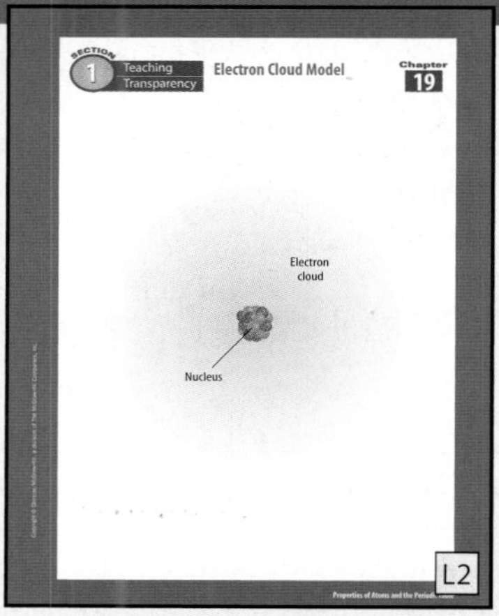
SECTION 1 Teaching Transparency — Electron Cloud Model — Chapter 19

L2

Key to Teaching Strategies

The following designations will help you decide which activities are appropriate for your students.

- L1 Level 1 activities should be appropriate for students with learning difficulties.
- L2 Level 2 activities should be within the ability range of all students.
- L3 Level 3 activities are designed for above-average students.
- ELL ELL activities should be within the ability range of English Language Learners.
- COOP LEARN Cooperative Learning activities are designed for small group work.
- LS Multiple Learning Styles logos, as described on page 12T, are used throughout to indicate strategies that address different learning styles.
- P These strategies represent student products that can be placed into a best-work portfolio.
- PBL Problem-Based Learning activities apply real-world situations to learning.

Hands-on Activities

Student Text Lab Worksheet

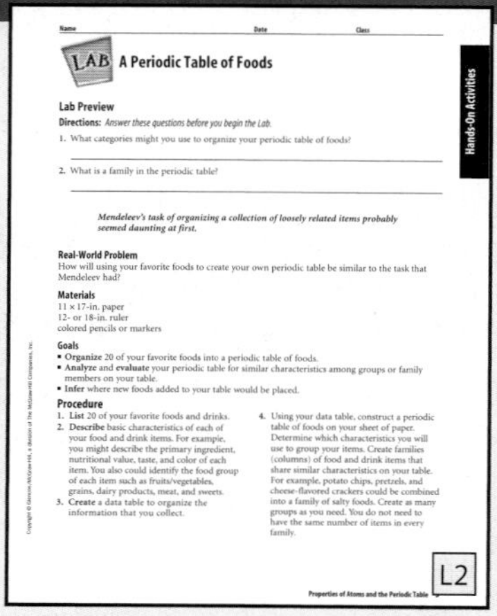
LAB A Periodic Table of Foods

Lab Preview

Directions: Answer these questions before you begin the Lab.

1. What categories might you use to organize your periodic table of foods?
2. What is a family in the periodic table?

Mendeleev's task of organizing a collection of loosely related items probably seemed daunting at first.

Real-World Problem

How will using your favorite foods to create your own periodic table be similar to the task that Mendeleev had?

Materials

11 × 17-in. paper
12- or 18-in. ruler
colored pencils or markers

Goals

- **Organize** 20 of your favorite foods into a periodic table of foods.
- **Analyze** and **evaluate** your periodic table for similar characteristics among groups or family members on your table.
- **Infer** where new foods added to your table would be placed.

Procedure

1. **List** 20 of your favorite foods and drinks.
2. **Describe** basic characteristics of each of your food and drink items.
3. **Create** a data table to organize the information that you collect.
4. Using your data table, construct a periodic table of foods on your sheet of paper.

Hands-On Activities

L2

Laboratory Activities

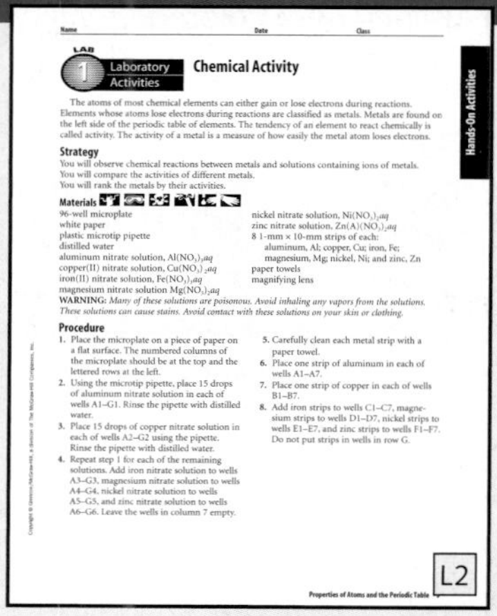
LAB 1 Laboratory Activities — Chemical Activity

Strategy

Materials

Procedure

Hands-On Activities

L2

Meeting Different Ability Levels

Content Outline

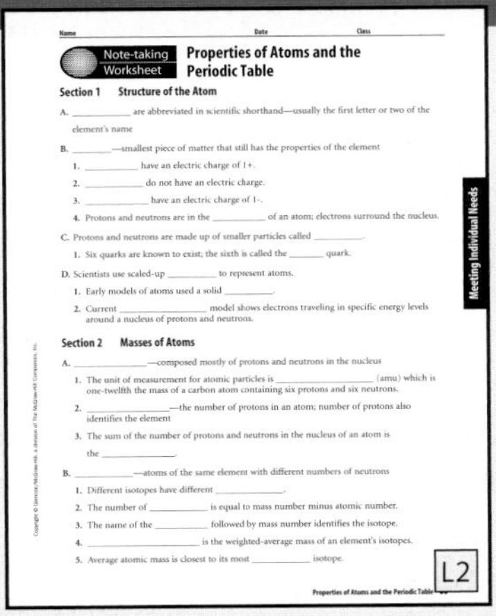

Reinforcement

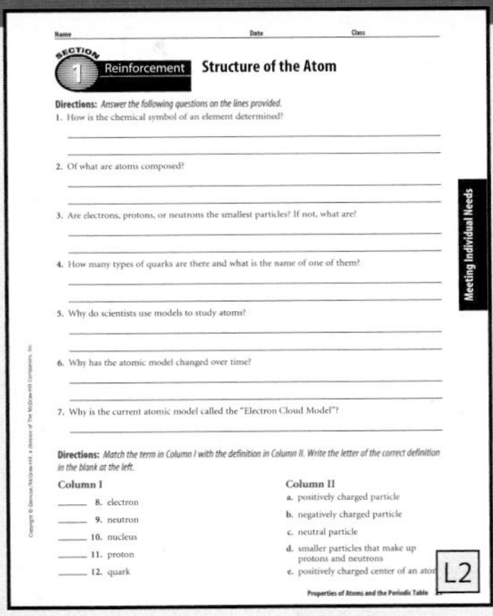

Enrichment

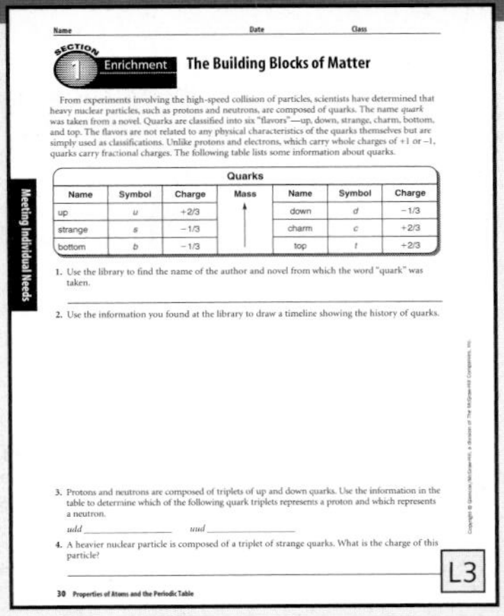

Directed Reading (English/Spanish)

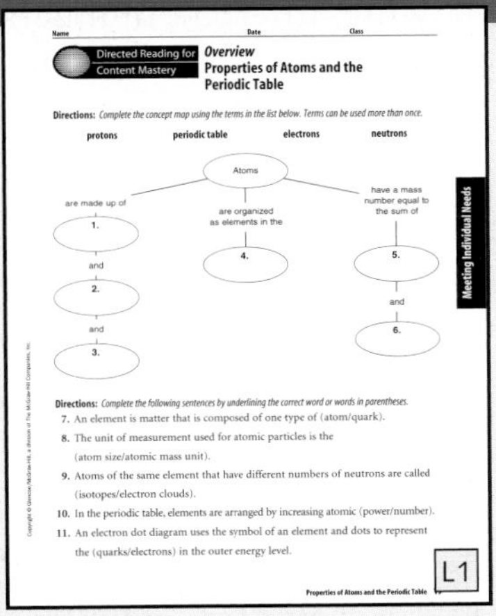

Study Guide

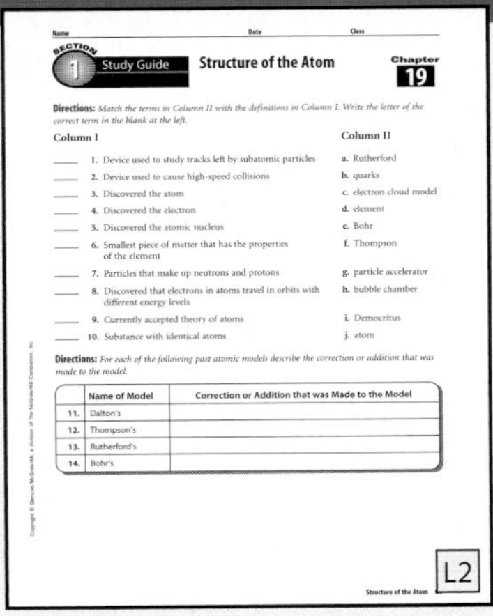

Reading Essentials

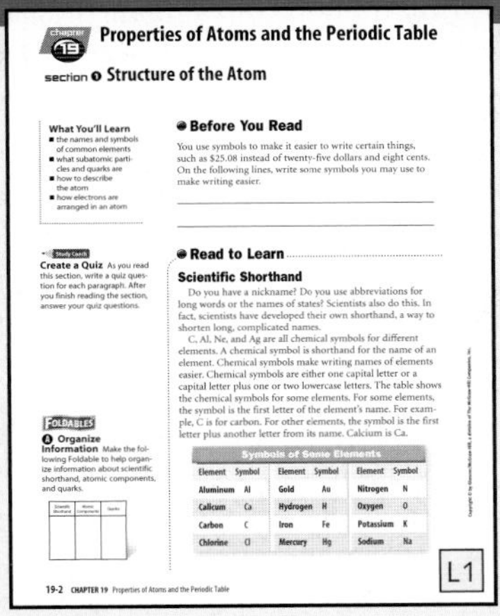

Assessment

Test Practice Workbook

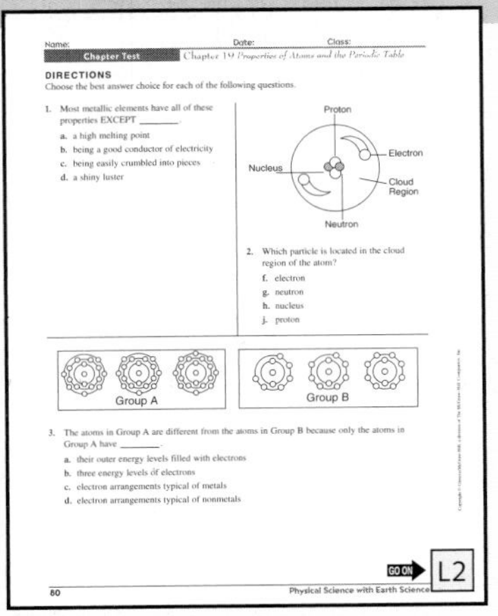

Chapter Review

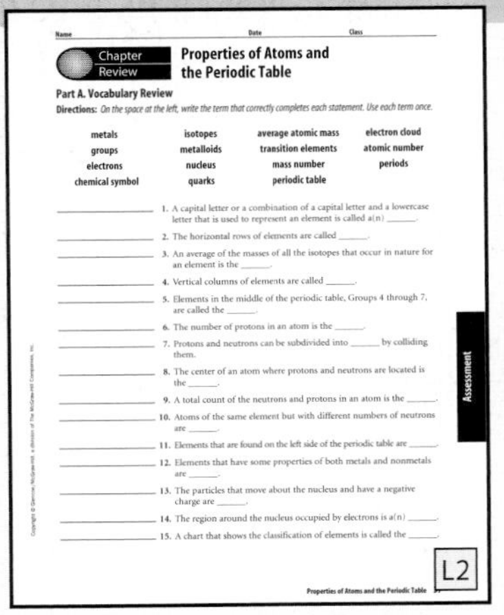

Chapter Tests

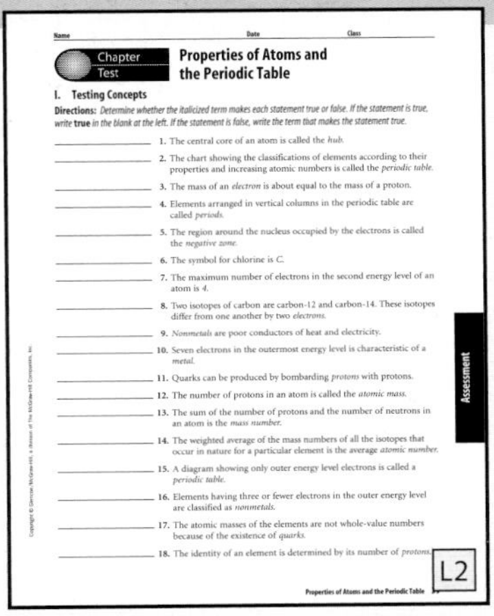

Science Content Background

section 1 Structure of the Atom

Models—Tools for Scientists

In 1926, Austrian physicist Erwin Schrodinger (1887–1961) proposed the quantum mechanical model of the atom. The model was based on the wavelike properties of the electron. Electrons were no longer seen as small particles moving around the nucleus in a defined path. In fact, it was shown in 1927 by Werner Heisenberg (1901–1976), described in the Heisenberg Uncertainty Principle, that it is impossible to know precisely both an electron's position and momentum at a given time. Since that time, the location of electrons in an atom has been described as an electron cloud. An electron cloud is a volume of space where an electron with a certain amount of energy is most likely to be found.

Teacher to Teacher

Petrolia Moss, Teacher
North Heights Junior High
Texarkana, AR

"Multicolored modeling clay is an inexpensive and reusable material for middle school students to use to visualize science concepts. Students use their creativity to make 'atoms' that have touchable protons, neutrons, and electrons."

Petrolia Moss

section 2 Masses of Atoms

Isotopes

Isotopes are atoms of the same element with different numbers of neutrons. Many isotopes, such as carbon-14, occur naturally, and scientists have succeeded in producing many artificial isotopes. Isotopes that are radioactive are called radioisotopes. Among other applications, radioisotopes are used as tracers in medicine, geology, and biology research and are used to measure the thickness of materials in industry.

1 H 1.01																	2 He 4.00
3 Li 6.94	4 Be 9.01											5 B 10.8	6 C 12.0	7 N 14.0	8 O 16.0	9 F 19.0	10 Ne 20.2
11 Na 23.0	12 Mg 24.3											13 Al 27.0	14 Si 28.1	15 P 31.0	16 S 32.1	17 Cl 35.5	18 Ar 40.0
19 K 39.1	20 Ca 40.1	21 Sc 45.0	22 Ti 47.9	23 V 50.9	24 Cr 52.0	25 Mn 54.9	26 Fe 55.8	27 Co 58.9	28 Ni 58.7	29 Cu 63.5	30 Zn 65.4	31 Ga 69.7	32 Ge 72.6	33 As 74.9	34 Se 79.0	35 Br 79.9	36 Kr 83.8
37 Rb 85.5	38 Sr 87.6	39 Y 88.9	40 Zr 91.2	41 Nb 92.9	42 Mo 95.9	43 Tc 98	44 Ru 101	45 Rh 103	46 Pd 106	47 Ag 108	48 Cd 112	49 In 115	50 Sn 119	51 Sb 122	52 Te 128	53 I 127	54 Xe 131
55 Cs 133	56 Ba 137	57 La 139	72 Hf 178	73 Ta 181	74 W 184	75 Re 186	76 Os 190	77 Ir 192	78 Pt 195	79 Au 197	80 Hg 201	81 Tl 204	82 Pb 207	83 Bi 209	84 Po 210	85 At 210	86 Rn 222
87 Fr 223	88 Ra 226	89 Ac 227	104 Rf 227	105 Db 262	106 Sg 263	107 Bh 264	108 Hs 265	109 Mt 268	110 Ds 281	111 Rg 269	112 Uub 277	113	114 Uuq 289	115	116	117	118

58 Ce 140	59 Pr 141	60 Nd 144	61 Pm 147	62 Sm 150	63 Eu 152	64 Gd 157	65 Tb 159	66 Dy 163	67 Ho 165	68 Er 167	69 Tm 169	70 Yb 173	71 Lu 175
90 Th 232	91 Pa 231	92 U 238	93 Np 237	94 Pu 244	95 Am 243	96 Cm 247	97 Bk 247	98 Cf 251	99 Es 254	100 Fm 257	101 Md 258	102 No 255	103 Lr 256

color code = light metals -brittle metals -ductile metals -low melting metals -non-metals -noble gases -lanthanides -actinides

section 3 The Periodic Table

Organizing the Elements

In 1817, the German chemist Johann Dobereiner found that he could arrange many elements into groups that he called triads. He noticed for example that lithium, sodium, and potassium react vigorously with water. Similar regularities were uncovered for calcium, strontium, and barium, and for fluorine, chlorine, and bromine.

Dobereiner's early work laid the groundwork for other chemists as they searched for an organizing principle by which to classify elements. In 1863, English chemist John Newlands proposed that when the known elements were arranged according to atomic mass, similarities in chemical properties occurred with every eighth element. He called this regularity the law of octaves. This regularity was also noticed by Dmitri Mendeleev. Mendeleev arranged the elements into a periodic table, which he published in 1869.

The modern periodic table didn't come into being until a Dutch physicist, Anton van den Broek, proposed that the elements should be arranged according to nuclear charge rather than atomic mass. Henry Mosely confirmed this hypothesis through studies of the X-ray spectra of a series of elements that had consecutive positions on the table. The change to ordering by atomic number resulted in the reversal of the positions of a few elements.

The Atom and the Periodic Table

The period in which an element appears in the periodic table indicates how many main electron energy levels that are in that atom. For example, oxygen is in the second period, so the oxygen atom has two main energy levels. The group number (for main group elements) indicates how many electrons are in the outermost energy level. Oxygen has six outer or valence electrons, so oxygen is in Group 6A. It is these outermost electrons that determine how an atom reacts.

For every principle quantum number (period or horizontal row), there are sublevels designated by letters, such as *s*, *p*, *d*, and *f*. In the sublevels, electron pairs are found in orbitals. There is a maximum of one *s* orbital, three *p* orbitals, five *d* orbitals, and seven *f* orbitals in an energy level. As you move across any period of the table, Groups 1 and 2 are filling *s* orbitals with two electrons. Groups 13–18 are filling *p* orbitals with six electrons. In periods 4 through 7, the transition elements, Groups 2–12, are filling five *d* orbitals with ten electrons. The inner transition elements, located below the periodic table, are filling the 4*f* and 5*f* orbitals with 14 electrons.

chapter content resources

Internet Resources

For additional content background, visit gpescience.com to:
- access your book online
- find references to related articles in popular science magazines
- access Web links with related content background
- access current events with science journal topics

Print Resources

Essential Elements: Atoms, Quarks, and the Periodic Table, by Matt Tweed, Walker and Company, 2003

Conceptual Chemistry: Understanding Our World of Atoms and Molecules, Second Edition, by John Suchocki, Pearson Benjamin Cummins, 2003

Fizz, Bubble, and Flash: Element Explorations and Atom Adventures (Williamson Kids Can! Series), by Anita Brandolini, Ph.D., Williamson Publishing, 2003

chapter 19

Chapter Vocabulary

atom, p. 579
nucleus, p. 579
proton, p. 579
neutron, p. 579
electron, p. 579
quark, p. 579
electron cloud, p. 583
atomic number, p. 585
mass number, p. 585
isotope, p. 586
average atomic mass, p. 587
periodic table, p. 588
group, p. 592
electron dot diagram, p. 594
period, p. 595

Science Journal Student responses will vary, but may include information about the components that make up atoms or the methods of studying atoms.

INTERACTIVE CHALKBOARD with Image Bank

PowerPoint® Presentations

This CD-ROM is an editable Microsoft® PowerPoint® presentation that includes:

- a pre-made presentation for every chapter
- interactive graphics
- animations
- audio clips
- image bank
- all new section and chapter questions
- Standardized Test Practice
- transparencies
- Foldables directions
- links to gpescience.com

chapter 19

Properties of Atoms and the Periodic Table

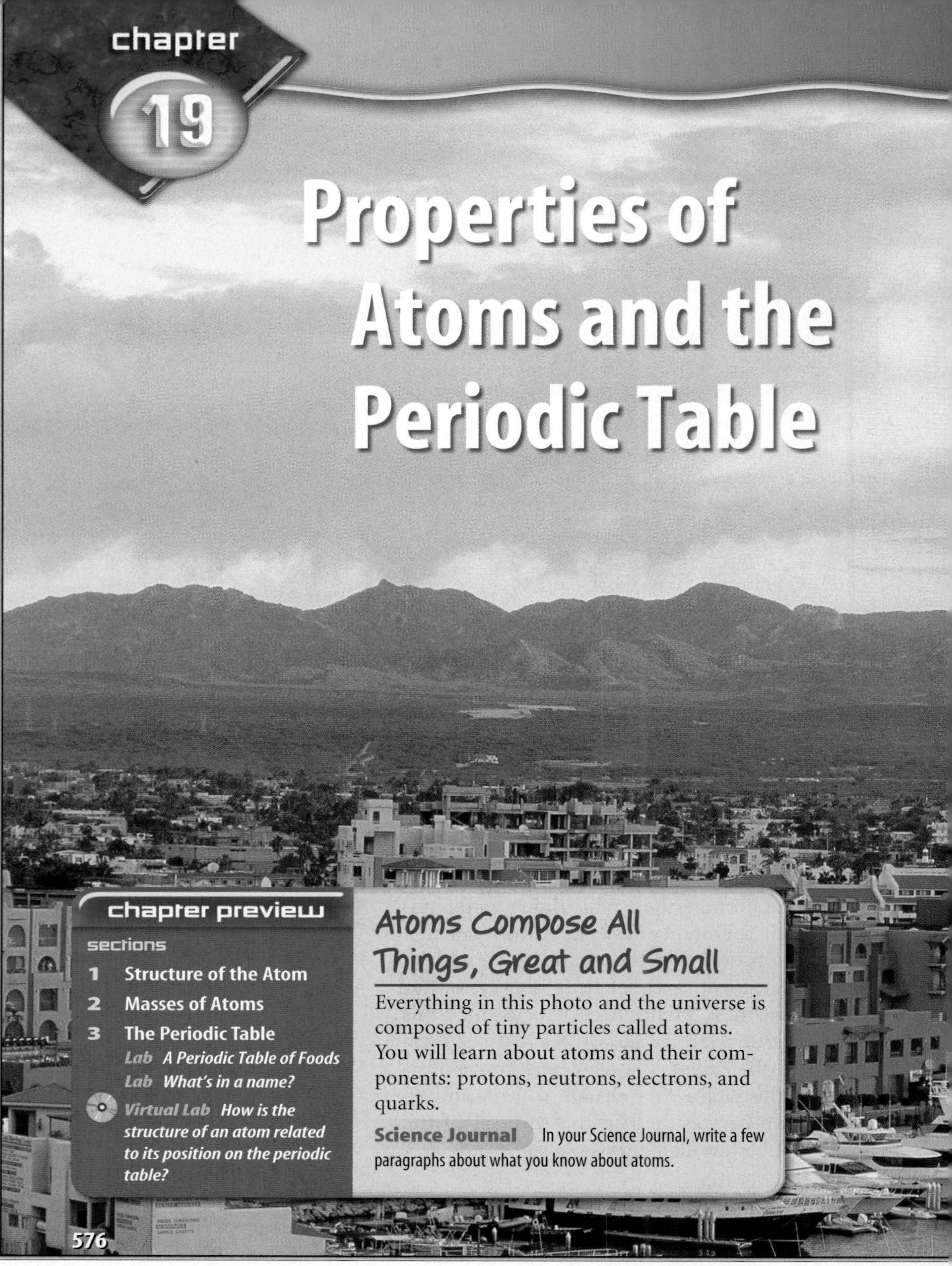

chapter preview

sections

1 Structure of the Atom
2 Masses of Atoms
3 The Periodic Table
Lab A Periodic Table of Foods
Lab What's in a name?
Virtual Lab How is the structure of an atom related to its position on the periodic table?

Atoms Compose All Things, Great and Small

Everything in this photo and the universe is composed of tiny particles called atoms. You will learn about atoms and their components: protons, neutrons, electrons, and quarks.

Science Journal In your Science Journal, write a few paragraphs about what you know about atoms.

576

Theme Connection

Scale and Structure The underlying small-scale structure of atoms determines the properties of elements and their positions on the periodic table of elements.

About the Photo

Atoms It is important for students to understand that all things are composed of atoms. Some students may not realize that even substances found in space are composed of atoms. In fact, stars like the Sun produce energy through the fusion of hydrogen to helium. Heavier elements are formed through fusion processes too.

Start-Up Activities

Launch LAB

Inferring What You Can't Observe

How do detectives solve a crime when no witnesses saw it happen? How do scientists study atoms when they cannot see them? In situations such as these, techniques must be developed to find clues to answer questions. Do the lab below to see how clues might be gathered.

1. Take an envelope and several items from your teacher.
2. Place an assortment of items in the envelope and seal it.
3. Trade envelopes with another group.
4. Without opening the envelope, try to figure out the types and number of items that are in the envelope. Record a hypothesis about the contents of the envelope in your Science Journal.
5. After you record your hypothesis, open the envelope and see what is inside.
6. **Think Critically** Describe the contents of your envelope. Was your hypothesis correct?

Science Online | Preview this chapter's content and activities at gpescience.com

FOLDABLES™ Study Organizer

Atoms You have probably studied atoms before. Make the following Foldable to help identify what you already know, what you want to know, and what you learn about atoms.

STEP 1 **Fold** a sheet of paper vertically from side to side. Make the front edge about 1.25 cm shorter than the back edge.

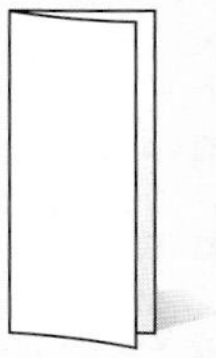

STEP 2 **Turn** lengthwise and **fold** into thirds.

STEP 3 **Unfold and cut** only the top layer along both folds to make three tabs.

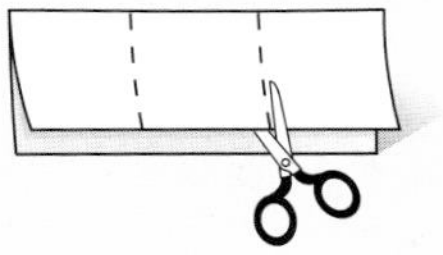

STEP 4 **Label** each tab as shown.

Identify Questions Before you read the chapter, write what you already know about atoms under the left tab of your Foldable, and write questions about what you'd like to know under the center tab. After you read the chapter, list what you learned under the right tab.

Launch LAB

Video Lab available for this Lab.

Purpose Use the Launch Lab to show students how to use inference to describe something they cannot see. L2 LS **Kinesthetic**

Preparation Obtain several items, such as chalk, eraser, thimble, bottle cap, or washer.

Materials envelopes, chalk, eraser, thimble, bottle cap, washer.

Teaching Strategy Suggest that students:

- lay a piece of thin paper over the sealed envelope and rub the side of a pencil over the items.
- hold the envelope up to a bright light to see an outline of the items.
- shake the envelope from side to side to see whether the items are flat or round.

Think Critically

Answers will vary depending on the assortment of items. The clues students find should be used in their conclusions.

Assessment

Oral Ask students whether they have ever attempted to guess the contents of a wrapped gift. Have them explain how they used inference to get clues. Finally, ask them to explain how their gift-guessing might be similar to the reasoning used by atomic scientists to determine atomic structure. Use **Performance Assessment in the Science Classroom,** p. 89.

FOLDABLES™ Study Organizer **Dinah Zike Study Fold**

Student preparation materials for this Foldable are available in the **Chapter *Fast File* Resources.**

1 Motivate

INTERACTIVE CHALKBOARD An editable Microsoft® PowerPoint® presentation is available on **Interactive Chalkboard** CD-ROM.

Bellringer

Section Focus Transparencies also are available on the Interactive Chalkboard CD-ROM. L2 ELL

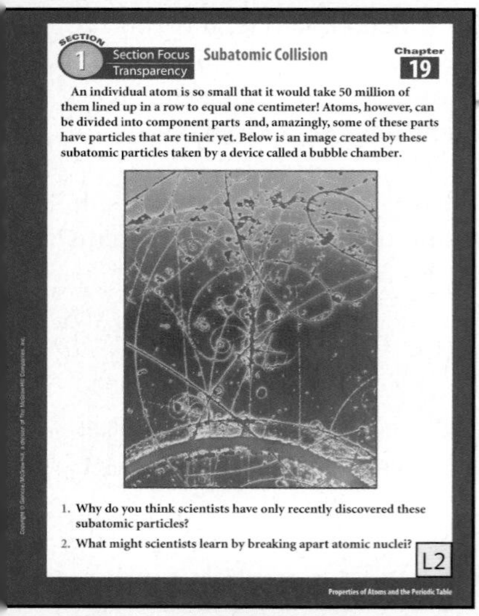
Section 1 Section Focus Transparency — Subatomic Collision — Chapter 19

An individual atom is so small that it would take 50 million of them lined up in a row to equal one centimeter! Atoms, however, can be divided into component parts and, amazingly, some of these parts have particles that are tinier yet. Below is an image created by these subatomic particles taken by a device called a bubble chamber.

1. Why do you think scientists have only recently discovered these subatomic particles?
2. What might scientists learn by breaking apart atomic nuclei? L2

Properties of Atoms and the Periodic Table

Reading Preview

Tie to Prior Knowledge

Brainstorm Names Have students brainstorm a list of the names of elements that they know without referring to a periodic table. Record the list on the board or on chart paper. Make sure that things like brass or steel, which are mixtures of elements, are not accepted. L2

Activate Vocabulary Knowledge Ask students to discuss with a partner the following question: What is the smallest piece of matter that makes up an element? Atom Point out **Figure 6**, the most current atomic model. Have them locate the vocabulary words in **Figure 6** and predict where the other words may fit.

section 1

Structure of the Atom

Reading Guide

What You'll Learn

- **Identify** the names and symbols of common elements.
- **Identify** quarks as subatomic particles of matter.
- **Describe** the electron cloud model of the atom.
- **Explain** how electrons are arranged in an atom.

Why It's Important

Everything that you see, touch, and breathe is composed of tiny atoms.

Review Vocabulary

element: substance with atoms that are all alike

New Vocabulary

- atom
- nucleus
- proton
- neutron
- electron
- quark
- electron cloud

Scientific Shorthand

Do you have a nickname? Do you use abbreviations for long words or the names of states? Scientists also do this. In fact, scientists have developed their own shorthand for dealing with long, complicated names.

Do the letters C, Al, Ne, and Ag mean anything to you? Each letter or pair of letters is a chemical symbol, which is a short or abbreviated way to write the name of an element. Chemical symbols, such as those in **Table 1,** consist of one capital letter or a capital letter plus one or two lowercase letters. For some elements, the symbol is the first letter of the element's name. For other elements, the symbol is the first letter of the name plus another letter from its name. Some symbols are derived from Latin. For instance, *argentum* is Latin for "silver." Elements have been named in a variety of ways. Some elements are named to honor scientists, for places, or for their properties. Other elements are named using rules established by an international committee. Regardless of the origin of the names, scientists derived this international system for convenience. It is much easier to write H for hydrogen, O for oxygen, and H_2O for dihydrogen oxide (water) than to write out the names. Because scientists worldwide use this system, everyone understands what the symbols mean.

Table 1 Symbols of Some Elements

Element	Symbol	Element	Symbol
Aluminum	Al	Iron	Fe
Calcium	Ca	Mercury	Hg
Carbon	C	Nitrogen	N
Chlorine	Cl	Oxygen	O
Gold	Au	Potassium	K
Hydrogen	H	Sodium	Na

Section 1 Resource Manager

Chapter *FAST FILE* Resources

Transparency Activity, pp. 44, 47–48

Directed Reading for Content Mastery, pp. 19–20

Note-taking Worksheets, pp. 33–35

Enrichment, p. 30

MiniLAB, p. 3

Reinforcement, p. 27

Reading and Writing Skill Activities, p. 43

Physical Science Critical Thinking/Problem Solving, p. 13

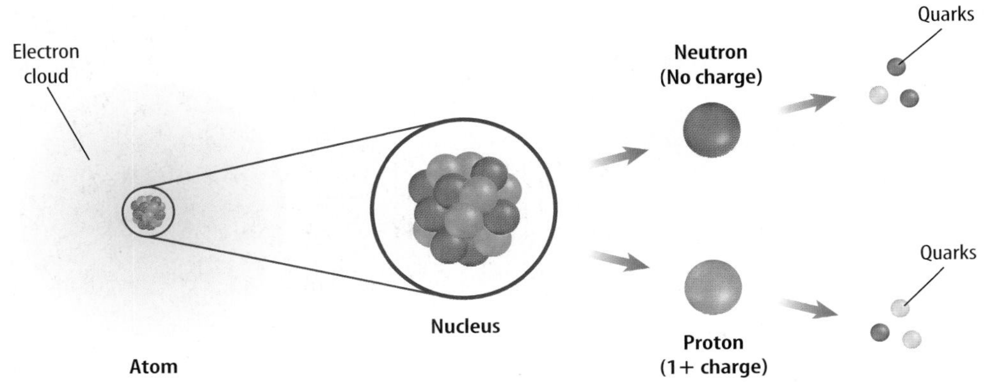

Figure 1 The nucleus of the atom contains protons and neutrons that are composed of quarks. The proton has a positive charge and the neutron has no charge. A cloud of negatively charged electrons surrounds the nucleus of the atom.
Explain *how atoms of different elements differ.*

Atomic Components

An element is matter that is composed of one type of **atom,** which is the smallest piece of matter that still retains the property of the element. For example, the element silver is composed of only silver atoms, and the element hydrogen is composed of only hydrogen atoms. Atoms are composed of particles called protons, neutrons, and electrons, as shown in **Figure 1.** Protons and neutrons are found in a small, positively-charged center of the atom called the **nucleus,** which is surrounded by a cloud containing electrons. **Protons** are particles with an electrical charge of 1+. **Neutrons** are neutral particles that do not have an electrical charge. **Electrons** are particles with an electrical charge of 1−. Atoms of different elements differ in the number of protons they contain.

Reading Check *What are the particles that make up the atom and where are they located?*

Quarks: Even Smaller Particles

Are the protons, electrons, and neutrons that make up atoms the smallest particles that exist? Scientists hypothesize that electrons are not composed of smaller particles and are one of the most basic types of particles. Protons and neutrons, however, are made up of smaller particles called **quarks.** So far, scientists have confirmed the existence of six uniquely different quarks. Scientists theorize that an arrangement of three quarks held together with the strong nuclear force produces a proton. Another arrangement of three quarks produces a neutron. The search for the composition of protons and neutrons is an ongoing effort.

Science Online
Topic: Particle Research
Visit gpescience.com for Web links to information about particle research at Fermi National Accelerator Laboratory.

Activity Write a paragraph describing the information that you found at the site.

2 Teach

Caption Answer

Figure 1 by the number of protons they contain

Use Science Words

Word Usage Have students compare and contrast the use of the word *nucleus* in biology and in physical science. In biology, *nucleus* refers to the cellular organelle where control of cell functions originates. It is in the interior of the cell, but not necessarily at the center. In physical science, the nucleus is also a sort of control area because the number of protons found in the nucleus determines the identity of the atom. The nucleus of an atom, however, is located at the center of the atom. L2 LS **Linguistic**

Reading Check

Answer Particles that make up atoms include protons and neutrons, which are located in the nucleus, and electrons, which are located in a cloud surrounding the nucleus.

Make a Model

Nesting Dolls Obtain a set of nesting dolls and place them in the front of the room. Ask students what they think is inside. After they respond, open the largest figure and reveal the smaller one. Continue this until you reach the last doll. How are the dolls similar to the search for smaller nuclear particles? Scientists thought several times that they had found the smallest particles, but each time they found even smaller particles. Now scientists would say that the last doll is like a quark. L2 LS **Visual-Spatial**

Discussion

Quarks Why are scientists having trouble determining the composition of protons and neutrons? Until recently, technology was not available to determine the existence of quarks. Subatomic particles are difficult to study because of their size.

Reading Strategy

Illustrations As they read, have students write their own definitions of the vocabulary words based on the information found in the text. Ask them to begin a drawing of an atom using **Figure 6** as a starting point. Tell them to add more detail as they read. Ask them to label all the parts using the vocabulary words.

Differentiated Instruction

English-Language Learners Have students use colored pencils to draw a diagram of an atom of the element lithium. Students should draw the correct numbers of protons, neutrons, and electrons. Students should color code the components and provide a key to their diagram. Have students use 3 protons, 4 neutrons, and 3 electrons in their diagram. L2 ELL

Use an Analogy

Snow Tracks People walking in snow or skiing down a mountain leave their tracks behind. If there were no snow, tracks of activity would be much more difficult to see. When detecting quarks or other atomic particles, scientists create an environment that helps them see the tracks the moving particles leave behind. In a cloud chamber, a dense cloud condenses to an even denser track when a particle passes through. Just as skiers leave a different track than do snowboarders, an electron moving through the dense cloud leaves a different track than does a proton. L2

Caption Answer

Figure 2 to accelerate the particles so they will have enough energy to break each other apart when they collide

Quick Demo

Gathering Evidence

Materials one large sheet of poster board, various types of markers and pens, tape, magnifying lens

Estimated Time 10 minutes

Procedure Display a large poster in front of the class on which you have made several curved lines using different markers and pens. Tape the markers and pens to the poster board and provide a magnifying lens. Ask students to match the pen with the appropriate line by examining the pen tip with the lens. Next, ask what other method they could use to identify the lines. Make comparison marks with each pen or marker. Tell students that nuclear scientists use both predictions and matching techniques.

Figure 2 The Tevatron is a huge machine. The aerial photograph of Fermi National Accelerator Laboratory shows the circular outline of the Tevatron particle accelerator. The close-up photograph of the Tevatron gives you a better view of the tunnel.

Infer *Why is such a long tunnel needed?*

Finding Quarks To study quarks, scientists accelerate charged particles to tremendous speeds and then force them to collide with—or smash into—protons. This collision causes the proton to break apart. The Fermi National Accelerator Laboratory, a research laboratory in Batavia, Illinois, houses a machine that can generate the forces that are required to make protons collide. This machine, the Tevatron, shown in **Figure 2,** is approximately 6.4 km in circumference. Electric and magnetic fields are used to accelerate, focus, and make the fast-moving particles collide.

The particles that result from the collision can be detected by various collection devises. Often, scientists use multiple collection devices to collect the greatest possible amount of information about the particles created in a collision. Just as police investigators can reconstruct traffic accidents from tire marks and other clues at the scene, scientists are able to examine and gather information about the particles, as shown in **Figure 3.** Scientists use inferences to identify the subatomic particles and to discover information about each particle's inner structure.

Figure 3 Bubble chambers can be used by scientists to study the tracks left by subatomic particles.

The Sixth Quark Finding evidence for the existence of quarks was not an easy task. Scientists found five quarks and hypothesized that a sixth quark existed. However, it took a team of nearly 450 scientists from around the world several years to find the sixth quark. The tracks of the sixth quark were hard to detect because only about one-billionth of a percent of the proton collisions performed showed the presence of a sixth quark, typically referred to as the *top* quark.

Teacher FYI

Cloud Chambers The first cloud chambers were developed near the beginning of the 1900s by C.T.R. Wilson, a Scottish physicist. He was trying to reproduce weather conditions in a closed chamber. Supersaturated vapor formed in the chamber and formed visible vapor trails when X rays passed through. This led to more sophisticated bubble chambers for detailed study of the vapor trails formed as beta and alpha particles passed through the supersaturated vapor.

580 CHAPTER 19 Properties of Atoms and the Periodic Table

Models—Tools for Scientists

Scientists and engineers use models to represent things that are difficult to visualize or picture in the mind. You might have seen models of buildings, the solar system, or airplanes. These are scaled-down models. Scaled-down models allow you to see either something too large to see all at once or something that has not been built yet. Scaled-up models are often used to visualize things that are too small to see. To give you an idea of how small the atom is, it would take about 24,400 atoms stacked one on top of the other to equal the thickness of a sheet of aluminum foil. To study the atom, scientists have developed scaled-up models that they can use to visualize how the atom is constructed. For the model to be useful, it must support all of the information that is known about matter and the behavior of atoms. As more information about the atom is collected, scientists change their models to include the new information.

Reading Check *Explain how models can simplify science.*

The Changing Atomic Model You know now that all matter is composed of atoms, but this was not always known. Around 400 B.C., Democritus proposed the idea that atoms make up all substances. However, another famous Greek philosopher, Aristotle, disputed Democritus's theory and proposed that matter is uniform throughout and is not composed of smaller particles. Aristotle's incorrect theory was accepted for about 2000 years. In the 1800s, John Dalton, an English scientist, was able to offer proof that atoms exist.

Dalton's model of the atom, a solid sphere shown in **Figure 4,** was an early model of the atom. As you can see in **Figure 5,** the model has changed somewhat over time. Dalton's modernization of Aristotle's idea of the atom provided a physical explanation for chemical reactions. Scientists could then express these reactions in quantitative terms using chemical symbols and equations.

Mini LAB

Modeling an Aluminum Atom

Procedure

1. Arrange thirteen 3-cm circles cut from **orange paper** and fourteen 3-cm circles cut from **blue paper** on a **flat surface** to represent the nucleus of an atom. Each orange circle represents one proton, and each blue circle represents one neutron.
2. Position two holes punched from **red paper** about 20 cm from your nucleus.
3. Position eight punched holes about 40 cm from your nucleus.
4. Position three punched holes about 60 cm from your nucleus.

Analysis

1. How many protons, neutrons, and electrons does an aluminum atom have?
2. Explain how your circles model an aluminum atom.
3. Explain why your model does not accurately represent the true size and distances in an aluminum atom.

Figure 4 John Dalton's atomic model was a simple sphere.

Mini LAB

Purpose to make a model showing the particles in an atom L2

Materials blue, orange, and red paper, metric ruler, hole punch

Teaching Strategy To save time, prepare the circles and the punched holes ahead of time.

Analysis

1. 13 protons, 14 neutrons, and 13 electrons
2. Like an aluminum atom, the model has 13 protons and 14 neutrons. It also has three energy levels with 2 electrons in the first level, 8 in the second, and 3 in the third.
3. In reality, protons and neutrons are more than 1,800 times larger than electrons. This activity does not attempt to model subatomic particle radii nor their exact locations in the cloud. It is merely modeling the grouping that occurs within the cloud.

Assessment

Process Have students use their materials to make models of atoms of as many different elements as they can. Ask them to make lists of the atoms they made, and draw a quick sketch of each one. Use **Performance Assessment in the Science Classroom,** p. 97.

Reading Check

Answer Models are less expensive to build than the actual item and they allow the study of things that are difficult to visualize or duplicate.

Differentiated Instruction

Challenge Have students research models that are used in other fields such as architecture, aerospace, or the automotive industry. Have students bring in a model of their choice and make a presentation to the class on how the models are used by scientists and engineers in their selected field. L3

Visual Learning

Figure 4 Tell students that the wooden sphere atom models that Dalton constructed are on display in the Science Museum in London. Many of his contemporaries ridiculed his idea of atoms simply on the basis that atoms could not be seen and, therefore, did not exist. What are some other things that exist but can't be seen? Possible answers: electromagnetic waves, air L2 IN **Visual-Spatial**

SECTION 1 Structure of the Atom 581

NATIONAL GEOGRAPHIC

Visualizing The Atomic Model

Have students examine the pictures and read the captions. Then ask the following questions.

What significant changes occurred in the atomic model between **Figure 5A** and **Figure 5B?** Scientists found that the atom was not "uncuttable" but was composed of positive and negative particles.

What significant changes occurred in the atomic model between **Figure 5B** and **Figure 5C?** Scientists found that the mass of the atom was concentrated in the center instead of throughout the atom and that electrons orbit the nucleus.

What significant changes occurred in the atomic model between **Figure 5C** and **Figure 5D?** Scientists found that the orbits of the electrons are not random but are at fixed distances from the nucleus. Scientists also found that the nucleus is composed of protons and neutrons.

Activity

Rutherford Report Have students research and find out how Rutherford discovered that the mass of the atom is concentrated primarily in the center of the atom. Ask students to write brief reports in their Science Journals describing Rutherford's experiment. L2 IN **Linguistic**

NATIONAL GEOGRAPHIC **VISUALIZING THE ATOMIC MODEL**

Figure 5

The ancient Greek philosopher Democritus proposed that elements consist of tiny, solid particles that cannot be subdivided (A). He called these particles *atomos,* meaning "uncuttable." This concept of the atom's structure remained largely unchallenged until the 1900s, when researchers began to discover through experiments that atoms are composed of still smaller particles. In the early 1900s, a number of models for atomic structure were proposed (B-D). The currently accepted model (E) evolved from these ideas and the work of many other scientists.

A DEMOCRITUS'S UNCUTTABLE ATOM

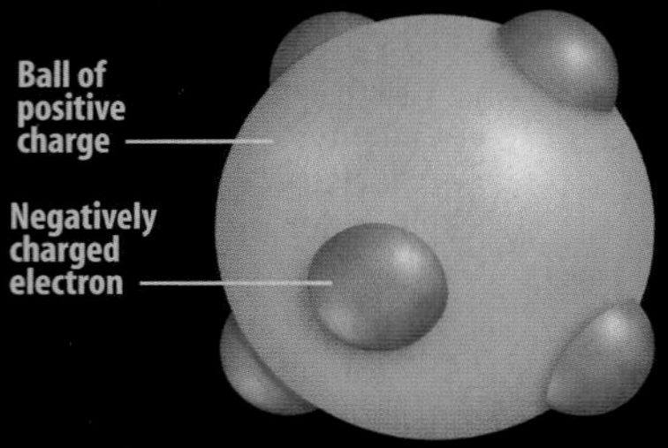

B THOMSON MODEL, 1904 **English physicist Joseph John Thomson inferred from his experiments that atoms contain small, negatively charged particles. He thought these "electrons" (in red) were evenly embedded throughout a positively charged sphere, much like chocolate chips in a ball of cookie dough.**

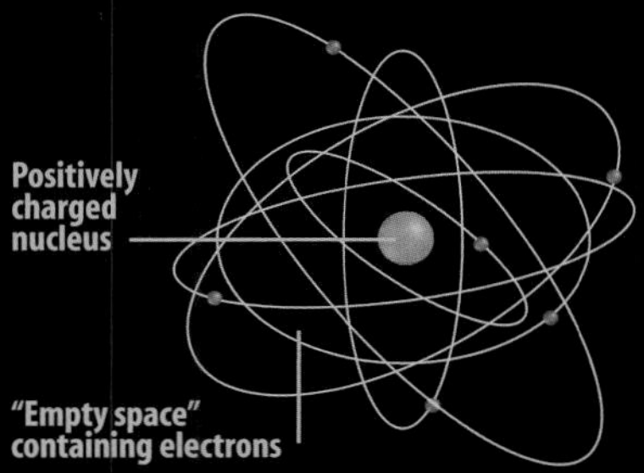

C RUTHERFORD MODEL, 1911 **Another British physicist, Ernest Rutherford, proposed that almost all the mass of an atom—and all its positive charges—is concentrated in a central atomic nucleus surrounded by electrons.**

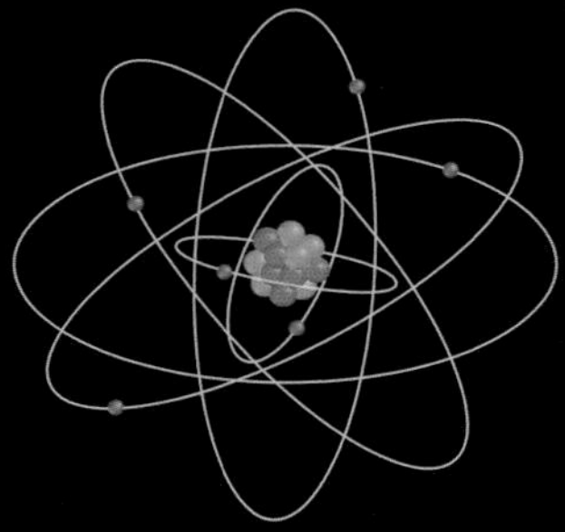

D BOHR MODEL, 1913 **Danish physicist Niels Bohr hypothesized that electrons travel in fixed orbits around the atom's nucleus. James Chadwick, a student of Rutherford, concluded that the nucleus contains positive protons and neutral neutrons.**

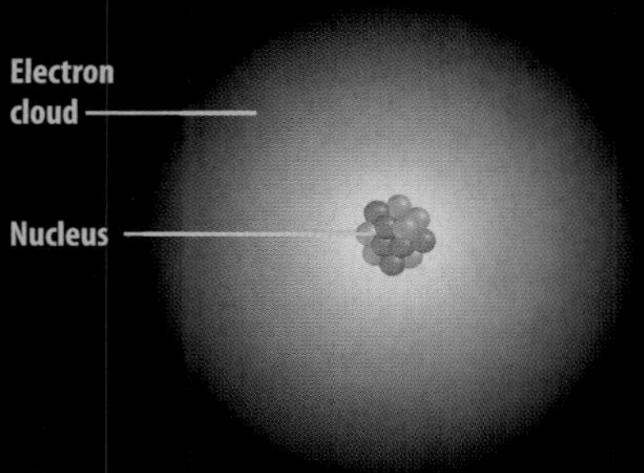

E ELECTRON CLOUD MODEL, CURRENT **According to the currently accepted model of atomic structure, electrons do not follow fixed orbits but tend to occur more frequently in certain areas around the nucleus at any given time.**

The Electron Cloud Model By 1926, scientists had developed the electron cloud model of the atom that is in use today. An **electron cloud** is the area around the nucleus of an atom where its electrons are most likely found. The electron cloud is 100,000 times larger than the diameter of the nucleus. In contrast, each electron in the cloud is much smaller than a single proton.

Because an electron's mass is small and the electron is moving so quickly around the nucleus, it is impossible to describe its exact location in an atom. Picture the spokes on a moving bicycle wheel. They are moving so quickly that you can't pinpoint any single spoke. All you see is a blur that contains all of the spokes somewhere within it. In the same way, an electron cloud is a blur containing all of the electrons of the atom somewhere within it. **Figure 6** illustrates what the electron cloud might look like.

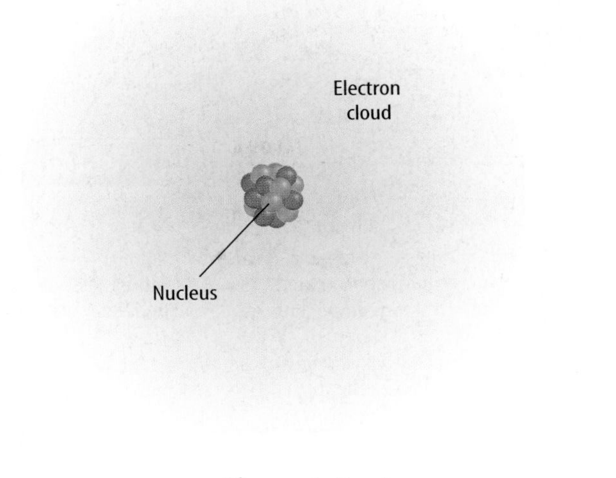

Figure 6 The electrons are located in an electron cloud surrounding the nucleus of the atom.

section 1 review

Summary

Scientific Shorthand
- Scientists use chemical symbols as shorthand when writing the names of elements.

Atomic Components
- Atoms are composed of small particles that have known charges.
- Atoms of different elements differ in the number of protons they contain.

Quarks: Even Smaller Particles
- So far, scientists have confirmed the existence of six different quarks.

Models: Tools for Scientists
- Models are used by scientists to simplify the study of concepts and things.
- The current atomic model is an accumulation of over 200 years of knowledge.
- The electron cloud model is the current atomic model.

Self Check

1. **List** the chemical symbols for the elements carbon, aluminum, hydrogen, oxygen, and sodium.
2. **Identify** the names, charges, and locations of three kinds of particles that make up an atom.
3. **Identify** the smallest particle of matter. How were these particles discovered?
4. **Describe** the electron cloud model of the atom.
5. **Think Critically** Explain how a rotating electric fan might be used to model the atom. Explain how the rotating fan is unlike an atom.

Applying Math

6. **Use Numbers** The mass of a proton is estimated to be 1.6726×10^{-24} g, and the mass of an electron is estimated to be 9.1093×10^{-28} g. How many times larger is the mass of a proton than the mass of an electron?
7. **Calculate** What is the difference between the mass of a proton and the mass of an electron?

Post Reading

Metacognition Working in groups, have students devise a metacognitive method to help them remember and more fully understand the charges and locations of the subatomic particles neutron, proton, and electron. Have groups report any analogies, word associations, or study strategies they created to remember the terms and the structure of an atom.

3 Assess

DAILY INTERVENTION

Check for Understanding

Linguistic Have students write a narrative describing the changes in the atomic model through time. L2 P

Reteach

Demonstrating Atoms Place some sesame seeds inside a balloon and carefully (do not breathe in any seeds) inflate and tie off the balloon. As you shake the balloon, ask students how this model could represent electrons in an atom. The seeds are small compared to the balloon, they are constantly moving, their locations are difficult to predict. Ask students how this model does not parallel the electrons in an atom. The balloon has a specific boundary beyond which the seeds cannot move. Electrons can move away from atoms. L2 IN **Visual-Spatial**

section 1 review

1. C; Al; H; O; Na
2. proton, +1, nucleus; neutron, 0, nucleus; electron, −1, electron cloud
3. quark; by accelerating protons and making them collide with so much force that they broke apart
4. This model says electrons are most likely to be found in a cloud surrounding the nucleus; it is 100,000 times larger than the diameter of the nucleus.
5. The blades on a rotating fan appear as a smooth metal surface around the center hub. The probability area for electrons in an atom also presents a solid appearance. The fan blades are different from electrons because they are much larger and, when the fan stops, can easily be seen.
6. 1,836 times larger
7. 1.6717×10^{-24}

Assessment

Oral Tell students that a fundamental particle is one that cannot be divided into other particles. Ask whether protons, neutrons, or electrons are fundamental particles. Electrons are fundamental particles. Protons and neutrons are not. Use **Performance Assessment in the Science Classroom**, p. 89. L2

section 2

Masses of Atoms

Reading Guide

***What* You'll Learn**

- **Compute** the atomic mass and mass number of an atom.
- **Identify** the components of isotopes.
- **Interpret** the average atomic mass of an element.

***Why* It's Important**

Some elements naturally exist in more than one form—radioactive and nonradioactive.

Review Vocabulary

mass: amount of matter in an object

New Vocabulary

- atomic number
- mass number
- isotope
- average atomic mass

Atomic Mass

The nucleus contains most of the mass of an atom because protons and neutrons are far more massive than electrons. The mass of a proton is about the same as that of a neutron—approximately 1.6726×10^{-24} g, as shown in **Table 2.** The mass of each is approximately 1,836 times greater than the mass of an electron. An electron's mass is so small that it is considered negligible when finding the mass of an atom.

Table 2 Subatomic Particle Masses

Particle	Mass (g)
Proton	1.6726×10^{-24}
Neutron	1.6749×10^{-24}
Electron	9.1093×10^{-28}

If you were asked to estimate the height of your school building, you probably wouldn't give an answer in kilometers. The number would be too cumbersome to use. Considering the scale of the building, you would more likely give the height in a smaller unit, meters. When thinking about the small masses of atoms, scientists found that even grams were not small enough to use for measurement. Scientists need a unit that results in more manageable numbers. The unit of measurement used for atomic particles is the atomic mass unit (amu). The mass of a proton or a neutron is almost equal to 1 amu. This is not coincidence: the unit was defined that way. The atomic mass unit is defined as one-twelfth the mass of a carbon atom containing six protons and six neutrons. Remember that the mass of the carbon atom is contained almost entirely in the mass of the protons and neutrons that are located in the nucleus. Therefore, each of the 12 particles in the nucleus must have a mass nearly equal to 1 amu.

Reading Check *Where is the majority of the mass of an atom located?*

1 Motivate

INTERACTIVE CHALKBOARD An editable Microsoft® PowerPoint® presentation is available on **Interactive Chalkboard** CD-ROM.

Bellringer

Section Focus Transparencies also are available on the Interactive Chalkboard CD-ROM. L2 ELL

Section 2 Section Focus Transparency **Carbon Cat** Chapter 19

How old are these mummified cats found in an Egyptian tomb? Carbon-14 holds the answer. Carbon-14 is a radioactive form of carbon, an element found in every living thing. By measuring how much carbon-14 remains in these cats, scientists can tell approximately how many years ago the cats were buried.

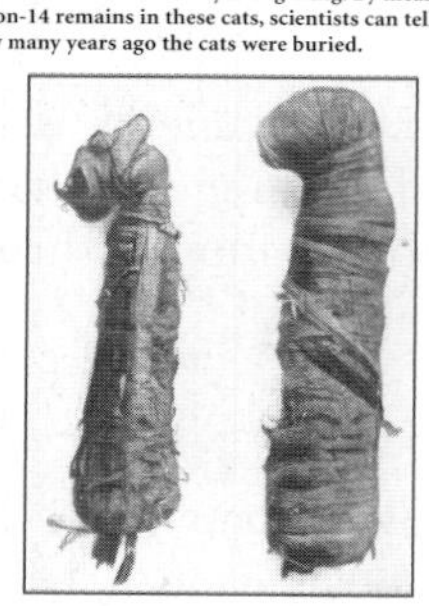

1. Carbon-14 decays over time. What does *decay* mean?
2. Why do you think carbon is used by scientists to date objects such as mummies, bones, and cloth wrappings?
3. Is it possible to use carbon-14 dating on things that were never alive? Why or why not?

L2

Properties of Atoms and the Periodic Table

Reading Preview

Tie to Prior Knowledge

Mass, Volume, and Weight Ask students to explain the differences among mass, weight, and volume. Mass is the amount of matter in an object, weight is a measure of the force of gravity on an object, and volume is the amount of space the object occupies. L2

SQ3R This five step preview strategy helps promote active reading. Have students first **S**urvey the section, focusing on headings. Students should develop **Q**uestions about key concepts. Next, have students **R**ead the section, keeping their questions in mind. Last, have students **R**ecite the vocabulary words and **R**eview their definitions.

Section 2 Resource Manager

Chapter *FAST FILE* Resources

Transparency Activity, p. 45

Directed Reading for Content Mastery, p. 20

Lab Activity, pp. 9–12

Reinforcement, p. 28

Enrichment, p. 31

Mathematics Skill Activities, p. 7

Science Inquiry Labs, pp. 49–50

Table 3 Mass Numbers of Some Atoms

Element	Symbol	Atomic Number	Protons	Neutrons	Mass Number	Average Atomic Mass*
Boron	B	5	5	6	11	10.81 amu
Carbon	C	6	6	6	12	12.01 amu
Oxygen	O	8	8	8	16	16.00 amu
Sodium	Na	11	11	12	23	22.99 amu
Copper	Cu	29	29	34	63	63.55 amu

*The atomic mass units are rounded to two decimal places.

Protons Identify an Element You learned earlier that atoms of different elements are different because they have different numbers of protons. In fact, the number of protons tells you what type of atom you have and vice versa. For example, every carbon atom has six protons. Also, all atoms with six protons are carbon atoms. Atoms with eight protons are oxygen atoms. The number of protons in an atom is equal to a number called the **atomic number.** The atomic number of carbon is 6. Therefore, if you are given any one of the following—the name of the element, the number of protons in the element, or the atomic number of the element—you can determine the other two.

Reading Check *Which element is an atom with six protons in the nucleus?*

Mass Number The **mass number** of an atom is the sum of the number of protons and the number of neutrons in the nucleus of the atom. Look at **Table 3** to see that this is true.

If you know the mass number and the atomic number of an atom, you can calculate the number of neutrons. The number of neutrons is equal to the atomic number subtracted from the mass number.

number of neutrons = mass number − atomic number

Atoms of the same element with different numbers of neutrons can have different properties. For example, carbon with a mass number equal to 12, or carbon-12, is the most common form of carbon. Carbon-14 is present on Earth in much smaller quantities. Carbon-14 is radioactive, while carbon-12 is not.

2 Teach

Reading Check

Answer in the nucleus

Answer carbon

Discussion

Atom Charge How many electrons are found in a neutral atom of carbon? six What would the charge be on the carbon atom if it lost four electrons? Explain. + 4; The atom now has 4 more protons than electrons. How does neutron count affect atomic charge? It has no effect. L2

Quick Demo

Modeling Atoms

Materials modeling clay (three different colors)

Estimated Time 20 minutes

Procedure Create models of the atoms in **Table 3** using three different colors of modeling clay. Use small balls from two of the colors to create the protons and neutrons in the nucleus. Use the third color to represent the electrons.

Discussion

Atom Numbers Have students determine the number of neutrons, protons, and electrons in neon −20, potassium −39, and gold −197. Ne: 10 protons, 10 neutrons, 10 electrons; K: 19 protons, 20 neutrons, 19 electrons; Au: 79 protons, 118 neutrons, 79 electrons L3

LS **Logical-Mathematical**

Activity

Element Game Have students play the element game in pairs. One student should write down the name of an element on a piece of paper. This student gives the other student a hint about the name of the element. The student keeps giving hints until the other student guesses the element. L2

Teacher FYI

Isotopes Nearly all elements have isotopes, some of which are radioactive. The mass of an element listed on the periodic table is the weighted average of the masses of the isotopes of that element.

Differentiated Instruction

Visually Impaired If **Table 3** is difficult for some to read, use one type of object, such as small corks, to represent protons and another type, such as rubber stoppers, to represent neutrons. Have students assemble the right numbers of protons and neutrons for the atoms listed in **Table 3**. L2

IDENTIFYING Misconceptions

Protons v. Neutrons Students may think that since many of the lighter elements have the same number of protons as neutrons, all elements have this property. Remind them that this is not true. Large atoms have more neutrons than protons because neutrons play a role in stabilizing the repulsive forces between the protons in the nucleus.

INTEGRATE Life Science

Carbon Dating Archaeologists are most interested in carbon-13 and carbon-14 because these isotopes are radioactive. The longer a once-living organism has been dead, the less radioactive it will be per gram of carbon. This gives archaeologists a way to determine the approximate age of once-living organisms.

Reading Check

Answer 146 neutrons

Applying Science

Answers

1. 48,800 million years; 97,600 million years
2. 8,920 million years; lead-206

Reading Strategy

Clarify Text Have students read the text about Atomic Mass. Ask: Are any of the concepts unclear? Write student concerns or misconceptions on the board. Model ways of clarifying the text, such as referring to **Table 3** and using supporting facts. Encourage students who understand the concepts to explain them in their own words.

INTEGRATE Life Science

Carbon Dating Living organisms on Earth contain carbon. Carbon-12 makes up 99 percent of this carbon. Carbon-13 and carbon-14 make up the other one percent. Which isotopes are archaeologists most interested in when they determine the age of carbon-containing remains? Explain your answer in your Science Journal.

Isotopes

Not all the atoms of an element have the same number of neutrons. Atoms of the same element that have different numbers of neutrons are called **isotopes.** Suppose you have a sample of the element boron. Naturally occurring atoms of boron have mass numbers of 10 or 11. How many neutrons are in a boron atom? It depends upon the isotope of boron to which you are referring. Obtain the number of protons in boron from the periodic table. Then use the formula on the previous page to calculate the number of neutrons in each boron isotope. You can determine that boron can have five or six neutrons.

Reading Check ***Uranium-238 has 92 protons. How many neutrons does it have?***

Applying Science

How can radioactive isotopes help tell time?

Atoms can be used to measure the age of bones or rock formations that are millions of years old. The time it takes for half of the radioactive atoms in a piece of rock or bone to change into another element is called its half-life. Scientists use the half-lives of radioactive isotopes to measure geologic time.

Half-Lives of Radioactive Isotopes

Radioactive Element	Changes to This Element	Half-Life
Uranium-238	lead-206	4,460 million years
Potassium-40	argon-40, calcium-40	1,260 million years
Rubidium-87	strontium-87	48,800 million years
Carbon-14	nitrogen-14	5,715 years

Identifying the Problem

The table above lists the half-lives of some radioactive isotopes and into which elements they change. For example, it would take 5,715 years for half of the carbon-14 atoms in a rock to change into atoms of nitrogen-14. After another 5,715 years, half of the remaining carbon-14 atoms will change, and so on. You can use these radioactive clocks to measure different periods of time.

Solving the Problem

1. How many years would it take half of the rubidium-87 atoms in a piece of rock to change into strontium-87? How many years would it take for 75 percent of the atoms to change?
2. After a long period, only 25 percent of the atoms in a rock remained uranium-238. How many years old would you predict the rock to be? The other 75 percent of the atoms are now which radioactive element?

Visual Learning

Figure 7 Have students draw diagrams in their Science Journals of the nuclei of carbon-12, carbon-13, and carbon-14. Carbon-12 has 6 protons and 6 neutrons, carbon-13 has 6 protons and 7 neutrons, and carbon-14 has 6 protons and 8 neutrons. L2 IS **Visual-Spatial**

Differentiated Instruction

Challenge Have students research radioactive isotopes that are used in medicine. Have students give a presentation to the class about the types of isotopes used and what they are used for. L3

Identifying Isotopes Models of two isotopes of boron are shown in **Figure 7.** Because the numbers of neutrons in the isotopes are different, the mass numbers are also different. You use the name of the element followed by the mass number of the isotope to identify each isotope: boron-10 and boron-11. Because most elements have more than one isotope, each element has an average atomic mass. The **average atomic mass** of an element is the weighted-average mass of the mixture of its isotopes. For example, four out of five atoms of boron are boron-11, and one out of five is boron-10. To find the weighted-average, or the average atomic mass of boron, you would use the following equation:

$$\frac{4}{5}(11 \text{ amu}) + \frac{1}{5}(10 \text{ amu}) = 10.8 \text{ amu}$$

The average atomic mass of the element boron is 10.8 amu. Note that the average atomic mass of boron is close to the mass of its most abundant isotope, boron-11.

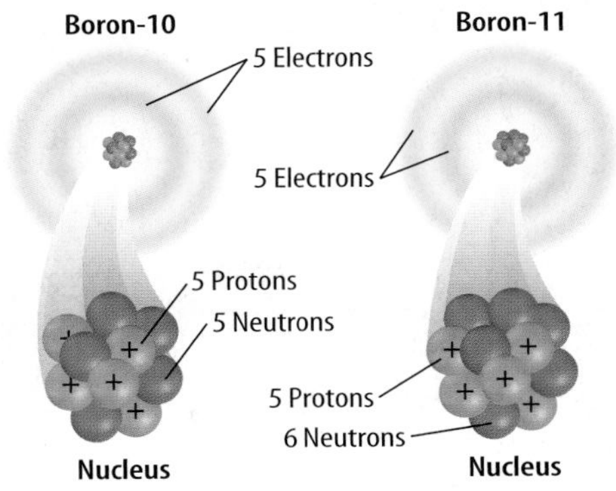

Figure 7 Boron-10 and boron-11 are two isotopes of boron. These two isotopes differ by one neutron.
Explain *why these atoms are isotopes.*

section 2 review

Summary

Atomic Mass

- The nucleus contains most of the mass of an atom.
- The masses of a proton and neutron are approximately equal.
- The mass of an electron is considered negligible when finding the mass of an atom.
- The unit of measurement for atomic particles is the atomic mass unit (amu).
- The carbon-12 isotope was used to define the atomic mass unit.
- The number of protons identifies an element.

Isotopes

- Atoms of the same element with different numbers of neutrons are called isotopes.
- The average atomic mass of an element is the weighted-average mass of the mixture of isotopes.

Self Check

1. **Identify** the mass number and atomic number of a chlorine atom that has 17 protons and 18 neutrons.
2. **Explain** how the isotopes of an element are alike and how are they different.
3. **Explain** why the atomic mass of an element is an average mass.
4. **Explain** how you would calculate the number of neutrons in potassium-40.
5. **Think Critically** Chlorine has an average atomic mass of 35.45 amu. The two naturally occurring isotopes of chlorine are chlorine-35 and chlorine-37. Why does this indicate that most chlorine atoms contain 18 neutrons?

Applying Math

6. **Use Numbers** If a hydrogen atom has two neutrons and one proton, what is its mass number?
7. **Use Tables** Use the information in **Table 2** to find the mass in kilograms of each subatomic particle.

section 2 review

1. Mass number = 35; atomic number = 17
2. Isotopes have the same number of protons but different numbers of neutrons.
3. Elements have several isotopes with different numbers of neutrons, and thus different masses. The average atomic mass is the weighted average of the masses of the element's isotopes.
4. Mass number − atomic number = number of neutrons = 40 − 19 = 21
5. The average of 35.45 lies closer to the 35 mass number than to the 37 mass number.
6. 3
7. proton = 1.6726×10^{-27} kg
neutron = 1.6749×10^{-27} kg
electron = 9.1093×10^{-31} kg

Post Reading

Ask Questions Have students review the list of questions generated during the **SQ3R** activity. Now that students have read about atomic mass and isotopes, have volunteers provide answers to the questions. Ask if students have new questions.

Caption Answer

Figure 7 These atoms are isotopes because they have the same number of protons, but differ in the number of neutrons.

3 Assess

DAILY INTERVENTION

Check for Understanding

Visual-Spatial Have students use colored pencils to draw the electron cloud model for lithium. Students should include the correct number of protons and electrons. Tell students to include four neutrons in their drawing. L2 P

Reteach

Weighted Averages Have students calculate the weighted average of student quiz scores if the following results were obtained: 5 students scored 80%; 19 students scored 90%.

$$\left(\frac{5}{24} \times 80\right) + \left(\frac{19}{24} \times 90\right) = 88$$

L2 LS **Logical-Mathematical**

Assessment

Oral Place a small plastic container on a table. Have students count as you place colored marbles, representing protons, into the bowl. When you stop, ask them to identify the element. Then ask them to predict the number of neutrons needed for a particular isotope of that element. Use **PASC,** p. 89. L2

section 3

The Periodic Table

Reading Guide

What You'll Learn

- **Explain** the composition of the periodic table.
- **Use** the periodic table to obtain information.
- **Explain** what the terms *metal, nonmetal,* and *metalloid* mean.

Why It's Important

The periodic table is an organized list of the elements that compose all living and nonliving things known to exist in the universe.

Review Vocabulary

chemical property: any characteristic of a substance that indicates whether it can undergo a certain chemical change

New Vocabulary

- periodic table
- group
- electron dot diagram
- period

Organizing the Elements

On a clear evening, you can see one of the various phases of the Moon. Each month, the Moon seems to grow larger, then smaller, in a repeating pattern. This type of change is periodic. *Periodic* means "repeated in a pattern." The days of the week are periodic because they repeat themselves every seven days. The calendar is a periodic table of days and months.

In the late 1800s, Dmitri Mendeleev, a Russian chemist, searched for a way to organize the elements. When he arranged all the elements known at that time in order of increasing atomic masses, he discovered a pattern. **Figure 8** shows Mendeleev's early periodic chart. Chemical properties found in lighter elements could be shown to repeat in heavier elements. Because the pattern repeated, it was considered to be periodic. Today, this arrangement is called the periodic table of elements. In the **periodic table,** the elements are arranged by increasing atomic number and by changes in physical and chemical properties.

Figure 8 Mendeleev discovered that the elements have a periodic pattern in their chemical properties.

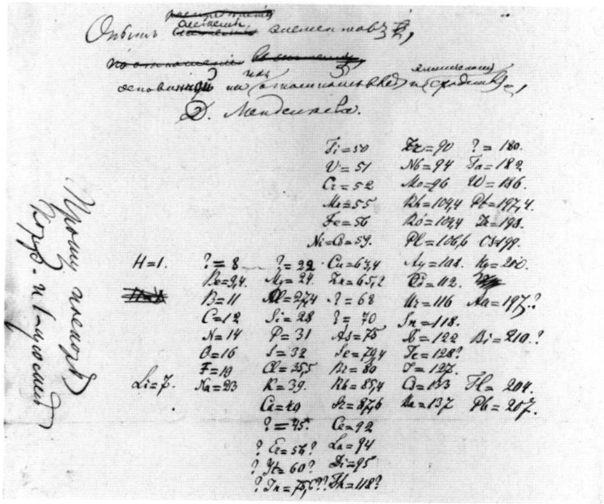

1 Motivate

INTERACTIVE CHALKBOARD PowerPoint® Presentations An editable Microsoft® PowerPoint® presentation is available on **Interactive Chalkboard** CD-ROM.

Bellringer

Section Focus Transparencies also are available on the Interactive Chalkboard CD-ROM. L2 ELL

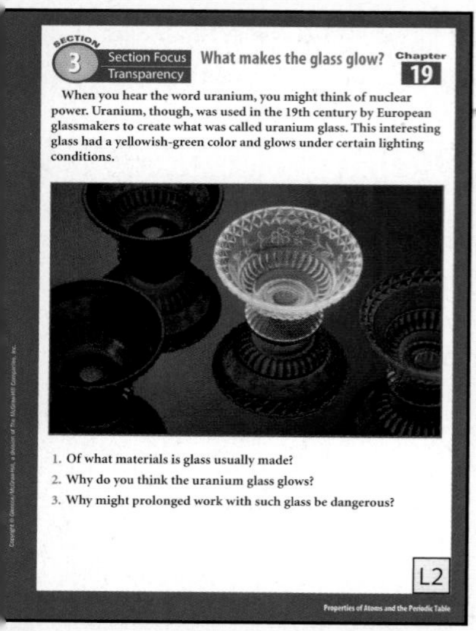

Section 3 Section Focus Transparency What makes the glass glow? Chapter 19

When you hear the word uranium, you might think of nuclear power. Uranium, though, was used in the 19th century by European glassmakers to create what was called uranium glass. This interesting glass had a yellowish-green color and glows under certain lighting conditions.

1. Of what materials is glass usually made?
2. Why do you think the uranium glass glows?
3. Why might prolonged work with such glass be dangerous?

L2

Properties of Atoms and the Periodic Table

Reading Preview

Tie to Prior Knowledge

Repeating Patterns Students are already familiar with the repeating pattern of the days of the week. Point out that just as a calendar illustrates the periodic pattern of the days of the week, the periodic table illustrates the periodic patterns of the chemical properties of chemical elements. L2

Facets of Meaning Ask students why their class sessions are called periods. Tell them *Periodical* is a name for a magazine that is published weekly or at regular intervals. Then tell them they will learn about a similar pattern that led to the table of elements being named the periodic table.

Section 3 Resource Manager

Chapter *FAST FILE* Resources

Transparency Activity, p. 46
MiniLAB, p. 4
Lab Activity, pp. 13–15
Directed Reading for Content Mastery, pp. 21–22
Enrichment, p. 32
Reinforcement, p. 29
Lab Worksheet, pp. 5–6, 7–8

Reading and Writing Skill Activities, p. 47
Home and Community Involvement, p. 25
Cultural Diversity, p. 59

Table 4 Mendeleev's Predictions

Predicted Properties of Ekasilicon (Es)	Actual Properties of Germanium (Ge)
Existence Predicted: 1871	*Actual Discovery: 1886*
Atomic mass = 72	Atomic mass = 72.61
High melting point	Melting point = 938°C
Density = 5.5 g/cm^3	Density = 5.323 g/cm^3
Dark gray metal	Gray metal
Density of EsO_2 = 4.7 g/cm^3	Density of GeO_2 = 4.23 g/cm^3

Mendeleev's Predictions Mendeleev had to leave blank spaces in his periodic table to keep the elements properly lined up according to their chemical properties. He looked at the properties and atomic masses of the elements surrounding these blank spaces. From this information, he was able to predict the properties and the mass numbers of new elements that had not yet been discovered. **Table 4** shows Mendeleev's predicted properties for germanium, which he called ekasilicon. His predictions proved to be accurate. Scientists later discovered these missing elements and found that their properties were extremely close to what Mendeleev had predicted.

Reading Check *How did Mendeleev organize his periodic table?*

Improving the Periodic Table Although Mendeleev's arrangement of elements was successful, it did need some changes. On Mendeleev's table, the atomic mass gradually increased from left to right. If you look at the modern periodic table, shown in **Table 5,** you will see several examples, such as cobalt and nickel, in which the mass decreases from left to right. You also might notice that the atomic number always increases from left to right. In 1913, the work of Henry G. J. Moseley, a young English scientist, led to the arrangement of elements based on their increasing atomic numbers instead of an arrangement based on atomic masses. This new arrangement seemed to correct the problems that had occurred in the old table. The current periodic table uses Moseley's arrangement of the elements.

Reading Check *How is the modern periodic table arranged?*

Mini LAB

Organizing a Personal Periodic Table

Procedure

1. Collect as many of the following items as you can find: **feather, penny, container of water, pencil, dime, strand of hair, container of milk, container of orange juice, square of cotton cloth, nickel, crayon, quarter, container of soda, golf ball, sheet of paper, baseball, marble, leaf, paper clip.**
2. Organize these items into several columns based on their similarities to create your own periodic table.

Analysis

1. Explain the system you used to group your items.
2. Were there any items on the list that did not fit into any of your columns?
3. Infer how your activity modeled Mendeleev's work in developing the periodic table of the elements.

Try at Home

2 Teach

Mini LAB

Purpose Students classify objects that are very different. L2

LS **Logical-Mathematical**

Materials a variety of objects that can be sorted into several categories

Teaching Strategy A wide variety of objects will force the students to work harder to find common traits.

Analysis

1. Answers will vary but possible groups include metal objects, coins, organic items, spheres, liquids, and writing implements.
2. Answers will vary.
3. Just as Mendeleev searched for similarities and repeating patterns among the elements, students searched for commonalities among the objects to place them in groups.

Assessment

Performance Provide students with an assortment of bolts, screws, and nails. Have them build another periodic table using these items. Use **Performance Assessment in the Science Classroom,** p. 121.

Try at Home

Reading Check

Answer He arranged the elements by increasing atomic mass and aligned them in columns based on chemical and physical properties.

Answer by atomic number

Teacher FYI

Mendeleev's Predictions Mendeleev predicted several elements in addition to ekasilicon. These included successful predictions of ekaaluminum and ekaboron, which were later found to be gallium and scandium, and unsuccessful predictions of ekaniobium and ekacesium, which do not exist. The prefix *eka* is Sanskrit for the numeral one.

Quick Demo

Singing the Elements

Materials compact disc, record, or tape of *An Evening Wasted with Tom Lehrer,* compact disc player, record player, or tape player

Estimated Time 10 minutes

Procedure Play the fourth song, *The Elements.* The song's lyrics, which are set to a Gilbert and Sullivan tune, contain the names of the chemical elements. Make a list of puns related to the names or symbols of the elements. Ask students to come up with the correct elements. Some examples include policeman, copper; smelliest element, Pu; foolish prisoner, silicon.

Teacher FYI

Nonmetallic The elements have an increasing nonmetallic characteristic as you read from left to right across the table. Along the stair-step line are metalloids, which have properties of both metals and nonmetals.

Activity

Atomic Mass Chart Have students list the elements in the first six periods that would be out of sequence if the chart were arranged by atomic mass. Ar and K, Co and Ni, Te and I L2 **Logical-Mathematical**

Visual Learning

Periodic Table Which element has an average mass greater than 75 but less than 79? selenium Is is possible to have more than one element that could fit that restriction? No; based on average masses, there are no missing atomic numbers from 33 to 34 to 35.

Table 5 Periodic Table of the Elements

Columns of elements are called groups. Elements in the same group have similar chemical properties.

Element — Hydrogen
Atomic number — 1
Symbol — H
Atomic mass — 1.008
State of matter

Gas
Liquid
Solid
Synthetic

The first three symbols tell you the state of matter of the element at room temperature. The fourth symbol identifies elements that are not present in significant amounts on Earth. Useful amounts are made synthetically.

Period	1	2	3	4	5	6	7	8	9
1	Hydrogen 1 H 1.008								
2	Lithium 3 Li 6.941	Beryllium 4 Be 9.012							
3	Sodium 11 Na 22.990	Magnesium 12 Mg 24.305							
4	Potassium 19 K 39.098	Calcium 20 Ca 40.078	Scandium 21 Sc 44.956	Titanium 22 Ti 47.867	Vanadium 23 V 50.942	Chromium 24 Cr 51.996	Manganese 25 Mn 54.938	Iron 26 Fe 55.845	Cobalt 27 Co 58.933
5	Rubidium 37 Rb 85.468	Strontium 38 Sr 87.62	Yttrium 39 Y 88.906	Zirconium 40 Zr 91.224	Niobium 41 Nb 92.906	Molybdenum 42 Mo 95.94	Technetium 43 Tc (98)	Ruthenium 44 Ru 101.07	Rhodium 45 Rh 102.906
6	Cesium 55 Cs 132.905	Barium 56 Ba 137.327	Lanthanum 57 La 138.906	Hafnium 72 Hf 178.49	Tantalum 73 Ta 180.948	Tungsten 74 W 183.84	Rhenium 75 Re 186.207	Osmium 76 Os 190.23	Iridium 77 Ir 192.217
7	Francium 87 Fr (223)	Radium 88 Ra (226)	Actinium 89 Ac (227)	Rutherfordium 104 Rf (261)	Dubnium 105 Db (262)	Seaborgium 106 Sg (266)	Bohrium 107 Bh (264)	Hassium 108 Hs (277)	Meitnerium 109 Mt (268)

The number in parentheses is the mass number of the longest-lived isotope for that element.

Rows of elements are called periods. Atomic number increases across a period.

The arrow shows where these elements would fit into the periodic table. They are moved to the bottom of the table to save space.

Lanthanide series	Cerium 58 Ce 140.116	Praseodymium 59 Pr 140.908	Neodymium 60 Nd 144.24	Promethium 61 Pm (145)	Samarium 62 Sm 150.36
Actinide series	Thorium 90 Th 232.038	Protactinium 91 Pa 231.036	Uranium 92 U 238.029	Neptunium 93 Np (237)	Plutonium 94 Pu (244)

Differentiated Instruction

Challenge The chemical symbols for the following elements are not abbreviations of their English names. Have students use reference books to determine the symbols for the following elements and the names upon which the symbols are based: copper (Cu, cuprum); gold (Au, aurum); iron (Fe, ferrum); lead (Pb, plumbum); tin (Sn, stannum); mercury (Hg, hydrargyrum); silver (Ag, argentum); sodium (Na, natrium); potassium (K, kalium); antimony (Sb, stibium); tungsten (W, wolfram). Have students present their research results to their class. L3 **Linguistic**

590 CHAPTER 19 Properties of Atoms and the Periodic Table

Metal

Metalloid

Nonmetal

The color of an element's block tells you if the element is a metal, nonmetal, or metalloid.

Science Online

Topic: Periodic Table Updates

Visit gpescience.com for updates to the periodic table.

10	11	12	13	14	15	16	17	18
								Helium 2 **He** 4.003
			Boron 5 **B** 10.811	Carbon 6 **C** 12.011	Nitrogen 7 **N** 14.007	Oxygen 8 **O** 15.999	Fluorine 9 **F** 18.998	Neon 10 **Ne** 20.180
			Aluminum 13 **Al** 26.982	Silicon 14 **Si** 28.086	Phosphorus 15 **P** 30.974	Sulfur 16 **S** 32.065	Chlorine 17 **Cl** 35.453	Argon 18 **Ar** 39.948
Nickel 28 **Ni** 58.693	Copper 29 **Cu** 63.546	Zinc 30 **Zn** 65.409	Gallium 31 **Ga** 69.723	Germanium 32 **Ge** 72.64	Arsenic 33 **As** 74.922	Selenium 34 **Se** 78.96	Bromine 35 **Br** 79.904	Krypton 36 **Kr** 83.798
Palladium 46 **Pd** 106.42	Silver 47 **Ag** 107.868	Cadmium 48 **Cd** 112.411	Indium 49 **In** 114.818	Tin 50 **Sn** 118.710	Antimony 51 **Sb** 121.760	Tellurium 52 **Te** 127.60	Iodine 53 **I** 126.904	Xenon 54 **Xe** 131.293
Platinum 78 **Pt** 195.078	Gold 79 **Au** 196.967	Mercury 80 **Hg** 200.59	Thallium 81 **Tl** 204.383	Lead 82 **Pb** 207.2	Bismuth 83 **Bi** 208.980	Polonium 84 **Po** (209)	Astatine 85 **At** (210)	Radon 86 **Rn** (222)
Darmstadtium 110 **Ds** (281)	Roentgenium * 111 **Rg** (272)	Ununbium * 112 **Uub** (285)		Ununquadium * 114 **Uuq** (289)				

* The names and symbols for elements 112 and 114 are temporary. Final names will be selected when the elements' discoveries are verified.

Europium 63 **Eu** 151.964	Gadolinium 64 **Gd** 157.25	Terbium 65 **Tb** 158.925	Dysprosium 66 **Dy** 162.500	Holmium 67 **Ho** 164.930	Erbium 68 **Er** 167.259	Thulium 69 **Tm** 168.934	Ytterbium 70 **Yb** 173.04	Lutetium 71 **Lu** 174.967
Americium 95 **Am** (243)	Curium 96 **Cm** (247)	Berkelium 97 **Bk** (247)	Californium 98 **Cf** (251)	Einsteinium 99 **Es** (252)	Fermium 100 **Fm** (257)	Mendelevium 101 **Md** (258)	Nobelium 102 **No** (259)	Lawrencium 103 **Lr** (262)

IDENTIFYING Misconceptions

A Disadvantage Mendeleev did not have the advantage of knowing atomic structure when he made his periodic chart. Electrons were not discovered until the late 1890s. His chart was based on mass and properties of the elements.

Use an Analogy

Orderly Classification Remind students that orderly classification allows them to enter a music store and quickly find a desired selection without examining every CD in the store. The periodic table gives chemists the same advantage when they are looking for elements with particular properties.

Fun Fact

Hydrogen, by its electron arrangement, is part of Group 1. However, because it has only one electron in an energy level that can hold two electrons, it has its own unique set of properties.

LAB DEMONSTRATION

Purpose to choose a criterion for arranging items

Materials 5 clear plastic cups, water, blue food coloring

Preparation Add an equal amount of water to each cup. Add 1 drop of food coloring to cup 1, 2 drops to cup 2, and so on. Make one with $3\frac{1}{2}$ drops and put it aside.

Procedure Mix the order of the cups and display them. Have students place the cups in a sequence. Display the solution made with $3\frac{1}{2}$ drops of food coloring and ask them to place it in its proper location.

Expected Outcome The sequence may be from diluted to concentrated or the opposite.

Assessment

How does this activity demonstrate the thinking Mendeleev used for his chart? He made a sequence of chemical elements based on their properties and could tell where new discoveries fit in. L2

INTEGRATE Career

Research Physicist The amount of energy an electron contains determines its behavior. Physicists can apply this knowledge to the fields of nuclear energy, electronics, optics, and communications.

Research Have students research who employs research physicists and what the future job outlook statistics are for this career.

Visual Learning

Figure 9 Point out to students that this diagram is not intended to represent relative sizes of the electrons, atom, or nucleus.

Reading Strategy

Think-Aloud Choose a challenging piece of text, such as Electron Dot Diagrams, and read it aloud while interjecting questions and strategies to aid comprehension. Show students how to use related figures to help with comprehension. Then have students find their own difficult passages and practice close reading with a partner.

Caption Answer

Figure 9 *number of electrons in the outer energy level*

INTEGRATE Career

Research Physicist The study of nuclear interactions is shared by chemists and physicists. Research physicists use their knowledge of the physical laws of nature to explain the behavior of the atom and its composition. Explain in your Science Journal why physicists would study the amount of energy that electrons contain.

The Atom and the Periodic Table

Objects often are sorted or classified according to the properties they have in common. This also is done in the periodic table. The vertical columns in the periodic table are called **groups,** or families, and are numbered 1 through 18. Elements in each group have similar properties. For example, in Group 11, copper, silver, and gold have similar properties. Each is a shiny metal and a good conductor of electricity and heat. What is responsible for the similar properties? To answer this question, look at the structure of the atom.

Electron Cloud Structure You have learned about the number and location of protons and neutrons in an atom. But where are the electrons located? How many are there? In a neutral atom, the number of electrons is equal to the number of protons. Therefore, a carbon atom, with an atomic number of 6, has six protons and six electrons. These electrons are located in the electron cloud surrounding the nucleus.

Scientists have found that electrons within the electron cloud have different amounts of energy. Scientists model the energy differences of the electrons by placing the electrons in energy levels, as in **Figure 9.** Energy levels nearer the nucleus have lower energy than those levels that are farther away. Electrons fill these energy levels from the inner levels (closer to the nucleus) to the outer levels (farther from the nucleus).

Elements that are in the same group have the same number of electrons in their outer energy levels. It is the number of electrons in the outer energy level that determines the chemical properties of an element. It is important to understand the link between the location on the periodic table, chemical properties, and the structure of the atom.

Figure 9 Energy levels in atoms can be represented by a flight of stairs. Each stair step away from the nucleus represents an increase in the amount of energy within the electrons.
Explain *what determines the chemical properties of an element.*

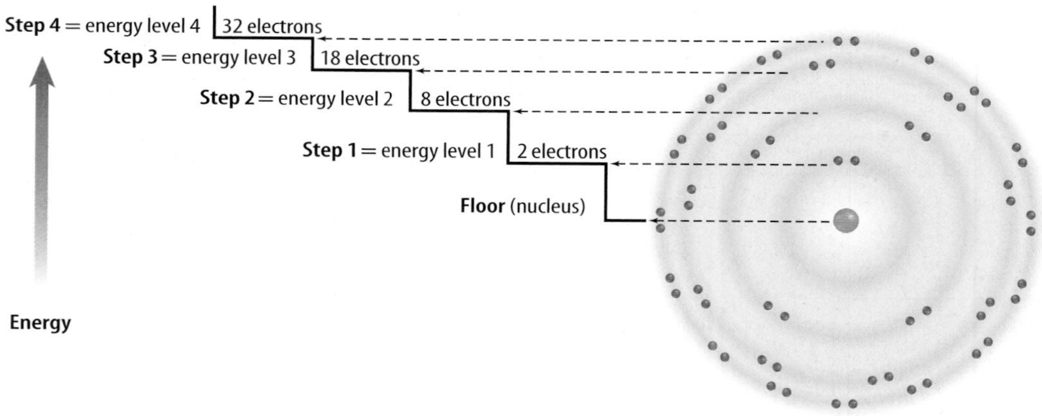

Differentiated Instruction

Challenge Each energy level contains sublevels, which in turn contain atomic orbitals. Have students find out more about the distribution of electrons in sublevels and atomic orbitals. Have students make a chart showing the information found about sublevels. The first energy level has only one sublevel, while the second level has two sublevels, and the third has three. The first sublevel in any level contains one *s* orbital, which can contain up to two electrons. The second sublevel in any level contains three *p* orbitals. Each *p* orbital can contain up to two electrons, so this sublevel can contain a maximum of six electrons. The third sublevel contains five *d* orbitals, each of which can contain up to two electrons, so this sublevel can contain up to ten electrons. The fourth sublevel contains seven *f* orbitals, each of which can contain up to two electrons, so this sublevel can contain up to fourteen electrons. L3 LS **Linguistic** P

Energy Levels Energy levels are named using the numbers one to seven. The maximum number of electrons that can be contained in each of the first four levels is shown in **Figure 9.** For example, energy level one can contain a maximum of two electrons. Energy level two can contain a maximum of eight electrons. Notice that energy levels three and four contain several electrons. A complete and stable outer energy level will contain eight electrons. In elements in periods three and higher, additional electrons can be added to inner energy levels, although the outer energy level contains only eight electrons.

Rows on the Table Remember that an atomic number found on the periodic table is equal to the number of electrons in an atom. Look at **Figure 10.** The first row has hydrogen with one electron and helium with two electrons both in energy level one. Because energy level one is the outermost level containing an electron, hydrogen has one outer electron. Helium has two outer electrons. Recall from **Figure 9** that energy level one can hold only two electrons. Therefore, helium has a full or complete outer energy level.

The second row begins with lithium, which has three electrons, two in energy level one and one in energy level two. Lithium has one outer electron. Lithium is followed by beryllium, with two outer electrons, boron with three, and so on until you reach neon, with eight outer electrons. Again, looking at **Figure 9,** energy level two can hold only eight electrons. Therefore, neon has a complete outer energy level. Do you notice how the row in the periodic table ends when an outer energy level is filled? In the third row of elements, the electrons begin filling energy level three. The row ends with argon, which has a full outer energy level of eight electrons.

Reading Check *How many electrons are needed to fill the outer energy level of sulfur?*

Science Online

Topic: Atomic Energy Level Structure

Visit gpescience.com for Web links to information about the structure of atomic energy levels.

Activity Draw a diagram that details how the energy levels are structured.

Hydrogen 1 **H**							Helium 2 **He**
Lithium 3 **Li**	Beryllium 4 **Be**	Boron 5 **B**	Carbon 6 **C**	Nitrogen 7 **N**	Oxygen 8 **O**	Fluorine 9 **F**	Neon 10 **Ne**
Sodium 11 **Na**	Magnesium 12 **Mg**	Aluminum 13 **Al**	Silicon 14 **Si**	Phosphorus 15 **P**	Sulfur 16 **S**	Chlorine 17 **Cl**	Argon 18 **Ar**

Figure 10 One proton and one electron are added to each element as you go across a period in the periodic table.
Explain *what the elements in the last column share in relation to their outer energy levels.*

Fun Fact

The maximum number of electrons in a level is $2n^2$, where n is the level number. For example, when $n = 3$ there can be a maximum of $2(3^2) = 18$ electrons.

Discussion

Row Questions In which row do you find the metalloid germanium? fourth row Which row contains the fewest elements? first row Which row probably contains the largest atoms on the periodic table? seventh row L2 LS **Visual-Spatial**

IDENTIFYING Misconceptions

Lanthenides and Actinides Students may be confused by the depiction of the last two rows of the periodic table below the rest of the table. These two rows, called the lanthanides and actinides, respectively, are shown below to allow the table to be displayed in a manner that is easy to read.

Caption Answer

Figure 10 Each element in the last column has a full outer-energy level.

Reading Check

Answer two additional electrons

Curriculum Connection

Music In music, the syllables *do, re, mi, fa, sol, la, ti, do* give the pitches of the diatonic scale. Have students find out how this scale is similar to the periodic table. The scale *do, re, mi, fa, sol, la, ti, do* can be related to Li, Be, B, C, N, O, F, and Na in the periodic table. Na repeats the properties of Li just as the second *do* is one octave higher than the first *do.* L2 LS **Auditory-Musical**

Differentiated Instruction

Learning Disabled Obtain samples of several elements, such as tin, copper, sulfur, silver, and aluminum. Have students examine and record the characteristics of each element. They should look for such properties as color, hardness, texture, and brittleness. They can play a game in which one student lists the characteristics and another identifies the element. L1

Activity

Energy Levels With a periodic table prominently displayed, or while students look at the one in the text, select various elements by name and atomic number. Have students determine the correct number of outer level electrons and write the dot diagram on the board. Do not use the elements from Groups 3–12 for this activity. These groups, called the transition elements, have their new electrons added to a lower energy level. L2

LS **Visual-Spatial**

Use an Analogy

Wearing a Hat Remind students that when atoms gain or lose electrons, they become charged, negatively if they gain electrons and positively if they lose electrons, but the atoms retain their identity because the number of protons in the nucleus remains the same. This is analogous to the way a person can wear a hat and easily take it off without losing his or her identity. L2

Fun Fact

The elements in Group 18, known as the noble gases, had no recognized compounds until 1962 when xenon and fluorine were combined. Since then, other noble gas compounds have been formed. As recently as 2000, argon was found to combine. These are rare cases. In nature, noble gases are found uncombined.

Reading Check

Answer All members of a group have the same number of electrons in their outer energy level.

Caption Answer

Figure 11 *determines the chemical properties of an element*

Figure 11 The elements in Group 1 have one electron in their outer energy level. This electron dot diagram represents that one electron.
Explain *why the outer electrons of an element are important.*

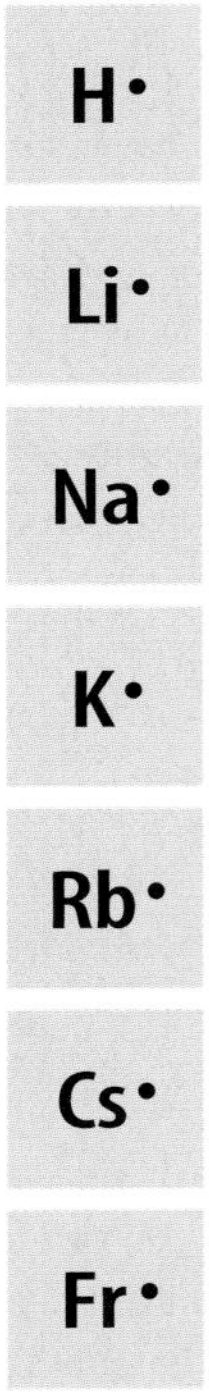

Electron Dot Diagrams Did you notice that hydrogen, lithium, and sodium each have one electron in their outer energy levels? Elements that are in the same group have the same number of electrons in their outer energy levels. These outer electrons are so important in determining the chemical properties of an element that a special way to represent them has been developed. American chemist G. N. Lewis created this method while teaching a college chemistry class. An **electron dot diagram** uses the symbol of the element and dots to represent the electrons in the outer energy level. **Figure 11** shows the electron dot diagram for Group 1 elements. The electron configuration of an atom determines how that atom reacts with other atoms. Electron dot diagrams also are used to show how the electrons in the outer energy levels are bonded when elements combine to form compounds.

Same Group, Similar Properties The elements in Group 17, the halogens, have electron dot diagrams similar to chlorine, shown in **Figure 12.** All halogens have seven electrons in their outer energy levels. Because all of the members of a group on the periodic table have the same number of electrons in their outer energy levels, group members will undergo chemical reactions in similar ways.

A common property of the halogens is the ability to form compounds readily with elements in Group 1. Group 1 elements each have only one electron in their outer energy levels. **Figure 12** shows an example of a compound formed by one such reaction. The Group 1 element, sodium, reacts easily with the Group 17 element, chlorine. The result is the compound sodium chloride, or NaCl, ordinary table salt.

Not all elements will combine readily with other elements. The elements in Group 18 have complete outer energy levels. This special configuration makes Group 18 elements relatively unreactive. You will learn more about why and how bonds form between elements in later chapters.

Reading Check ***Why do elements in a group undergo similar chemical reactions?***

Figure 12 Electron dot diagrams show the electrons in an element's outer energy level.

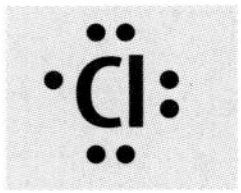

The electron dot diagram for Group 17 consists of three sets of paired dots and one single dot.

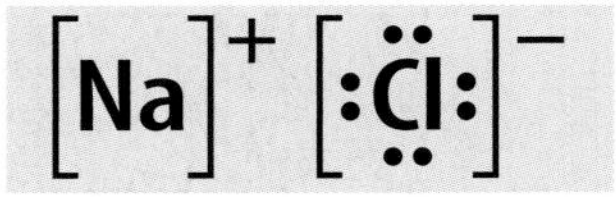

Sodium combines with chlorine to give each element a complete outer energy level in the resulting compound.

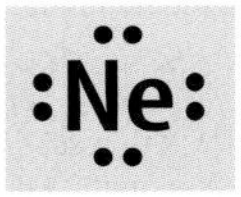

Neon, a member of Group 18, has a full outer energy level. Neon has eight electrons in its outer energy level, making it unreactive.

Active Reading

Jigsaw In this collaborative learning technique, individuals become experts on a portion of a text and share their expertise with a small group, called their home group. Everyone shares responsibility for learning the assigned reading. Assign each person in each home group an expert number. Have students gather into the expert groups that correspond to the numbers they were assigned. Have them read, discuss, and master chapter concepts and determine how best to teach them to their home groups. Have students return to their home groups and share the content they learned in their expert groups. Have students use this strategy to help them learn about the characteristics of elements and how they are grouped on the periodic table. L2

Regions on the Periodic Table

The periodic table has several regions with specific names. The horizontal rows of elements on the periodic table are called **periods.** The elements increase by one proton and one electron as you go from left to right in a period.

All of the elements in the blue squares in **Figure 13** are metals. Iron, zinc, and copper are examples of metals. Most metals exist as solids at room temperature. They are shiny, can be drawn into wires, can be pounded into sheets, and are good conductors of heat and electricity.

Those elements on the right side of the periodic table, in yellow, are classified as nonmetals. Oxygen, bromine, and carbon are examples of nonmetals. Most nonmetals are gases, are brittle, and are poor conductors of heat and electricity at room temperature. The elements in green are metalloids or semimetals. They have some properties of both metals and nonmetals. Boron and silicon are examples of metalloids.

Reading Check *What are the properties of the elements located on the left side of the periodic table?*

A Growing Family Scientists around the world are continuing their research into the synthesis of elements. In 1994, scientists at the Heavy-Ion Research Laboratory in Darmstadt, Germany, discovered element 111. As of 1998, only one isotope of element 111 had been found. This isotope had a life span of 0.002 s. In 1996, element 112 was discovered at the same laboratory. As of 1998, only one isotope of element 112 had been found. The life span of this isotope was 0.00048 s. Both of these elements are produced in the laboratory by joining smaller atoms into a single atom. The search for elements with higher atomic numbers continues. Scientists think they have synthesized elements 114 and 116. However, the discovery of these elements has not yet been confirmed.

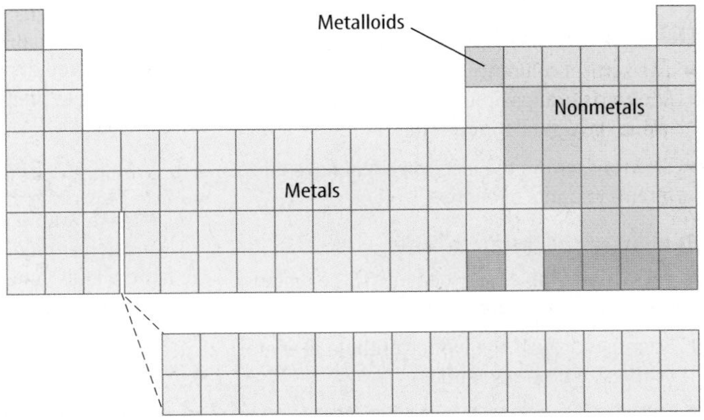

Figure 13 Metalloids are located along the green stair-step line. Metals are located to the left of the metalloids. Nonmetals are located to the right of the metalloids.

Science Online

Topic: New Elements
Visit gpescience.com for Web links to information about newly synthesized elements.

Activity Write an article explaining how several new elements were synthesized and who synthesized them.

Reading Check

Answer The elements on the left side of the table are metals, which are solids at room temperature, shiny, and good conductors of heat and electricity. Hydrogen is an exception to these properties.

Virtual Labs

Periodic Table *How is the structure of an atom related to its position on the periodic table?*

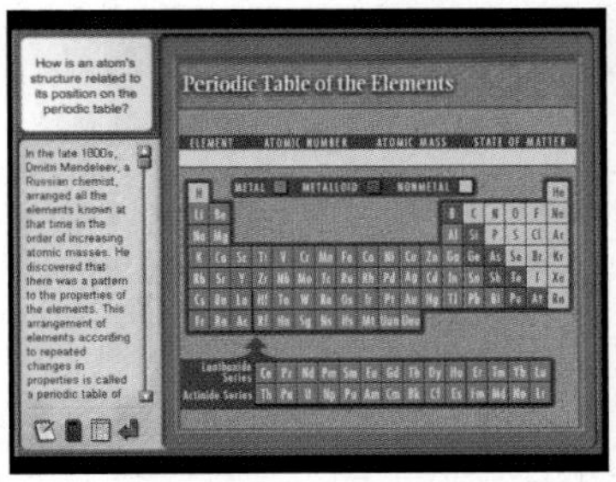

Inquiry Lab

Purpose to explore compounds that may form between elements

Possible Materials index cards or paper and markers

Estimated Time one class session

Teaching Strategies

- Students make cards with electron dot diagrams for elements in Groups 1–2 and 13–17.
- Students will need more than one card for some elements.
- Students can predict compounds that will form between the elements using electron dot diagrams.
- Have students make a list of the compounds that may form.

For additional inquiry activities, see *Science Inquiry Labs*.

Post Reading

Science Journal Have students work in pairs as they review the history of the periodic table. In their own words, have them respond to this prompt: What characteristics of the elements led to the periodic table being named *periodic*? Have students discuss their responses with different partner.

Science Journal

New Elements Have students research and identify the newest synthesized element. Have them write in their Science Journals the element's name, atomic number, isotope, half-life, and where the element was discovered. L2 LS **Linguistic**

INTEGRATE Astronomy **Content Background**

A star in Earth's galaxy explodes as a supernova about once a century. The most famous supernova of this galaxy occurred in 1084. The explosion was so powerful that it could be seen during the day and its brightness lasted for weeks.

3 Assess

DAILY INTERVENTION

Check for Understanding

Visual-Spatial Have students draw a generic dot diagram for elements in Groups 1, 2, and 13-18. L2

Reteach

Classifying Elements Using a poster-sized periodic table, point to various elements and ask students to identify the group number and period number of each element and classify it as a metal, nonmetal, or metalloid. L2 LS **Visual-Spatial**

Assessment

Performance Gather pens and pencils from the class and have students suggest ways to group them that place similar ones together. Then have students arrange the pens and pencils by approximate mass in a pencil-pen periodic table. Give students a new pen or pencil and ask them to decide where to place it in the table. How is this similar to Mendeleev's activities? He arranged chemical elements by mass and by properties and could predict and classify new elements. Use **PASC**, p. 121. L2

Figure 14 Scientists think that some elements are found in nature only within stars.

Elements in the Universe

INTEGRATE Astronomy Using the technology that is available today, scientists are finding the same elements throughout the universe. They have been able to study only a small portion of the universe because it is so vast. Many scientists believe that hydrogen and helium are the building blocks of other elements. Atoms join together within stars to produce elements with atomic numbers greater than 1 or 2, the atomic numbers of hydrogen and helium. Exploding stars, or supernovas, shown in **Figure 14,** give scientists evidence to support this theory. When stars reach the supernova stage, which is characterized by a massive explosion, a mixture of elements, including the heavy elements such as iron, are flung into the galaxy. Many scientists believe that supernovas have spread the elements that are found throughout the universe. Some of these elements are found only in trace amounts in Earth's crust as a result of uranium decay. Others have been found only in stars.

section 3 review

Summary

Organizing the Elements

- Mendeleev organized the elements using increasing atomic mass and chemical and physical properties.
- Mendeleev left blank spaces in his table to allow for elements that were yet undiscovered.
- Moseley corrected the problems in the periodic table by arranging the elements in order of increasing atomic number.

The Atom and the Periodic Table

- The vertical columns in the periodic table are known as groups or families. Elements in a group have similar properties.
- Electrons within the electron cloud have different amounts of energy.

Regions of the Periodic Table

- The periodic table is divided into these regions: periods, metals, nonmetals, and metalloids.
- Scientists around the world continue to try to synthesize new elements.

Self Check

1. **Identify** Use the periodic table to find the name, atomic number, and average atomic mass of the following elements: N, Ca, Kr, and W.
2. **List** the period and group in which each of these elements is found: nitrogen, sodium, iodine, and mercury.
3. **Classify** each of these elements as a metal, a nonmetal, or a metalloid and give the full name of each: K, Si, Ba, and S.
4. **Think Critically** The Mendeleev and Mosely periodic tables have gaps for the as-then-undiscovered elements. Why do you think the table used by Mosely was more accurate at predicting where new elements would be placed?

Applying Math

5. **Make a Graph** Construct a circle graph showing the percentage of elements classified as metals, metalloids, and nonmetals. Use markers or colored pencils to distinguish clearly between each section on the graph. Record your calculations in your Science Journal.

More Section Review gpescience.com

section 3 review

1. N, nitrogen, 7,14.007; Ca ,calcium; 20, 40.078; Kr, krypton, 36, 83.798; W, tungsten, 74, 183.84
2. nitrogen, period 2, Group 15; sodium, period 3, Group 1; iodine, period 5, Group 17; mercury, period 6, Group 12
3. K, potassium, metal; Si, silicon, metalloid; Ba, barium, metal; S, sulfur, nonmetal
4. One could not be certain that the gaps in Mendeleev's table would be filled by only one element. However, Moseley's table was arranged by number of protons. Therefore, if the gap were between two elements differing by two protons, only one element could fit.
5. The graph should indicate that about 79% of the elements are metals; about 7% are metalloids, and about 14% are nonmetals.

LAB

BENCH TESTED

A Periodic Table of Foods

Real-World Problem

Mendeleev's task of organizing a collection of loosely related items probably seemed daunting at first. How will using your favorite foods to create your own periodic table be similar to the task that Mendeleev had?

Goals

- **Organize** 20 of your favorite foods into a periodic table of foods.
- **Analyze** and **evaluate** your periodic table for similar characteristics among groups or family members on your table.
- **Infer** where new foods added to your table would be placed.

Materials

11 × 17-in paper
12- or 18-in ruler
colored pencils or markers

Procedure

1. **List** 20 of your favorite foods and drinks.
2. **Describe** basic characteristics of each of your food and drink items. For example, you might describe the primary ingredient, nutritional value, taste, and color of each item. You also could identify the food group of each item such as fruits/vegetables, grains, dairy products, meat, and sweets.
3. **Create** a data table to organize the information that you collect.
4. Using your data table, construct a periodic table of foods on your sheet of paper. Determine which characteristics you will use to group your items. Create families (columns) of food and drink items that share similar characteristics on your table.

For example, potato chips, pretzels, and cheese-flavored crackers could be combined into a family of salty tasting foods. Create as many groups as you need. You do not need to have the same number of items in every family.

Conclude and Apply

1. **Evaluate** the characteristics you used to make the groups on your periodic table. Do the characteristics of each group adequately describe all the family members? Do the characteristics of each group distinguish its family members from the family members of the other groups?
2. **Analyze** the reasons why some items did not fit easily into a group.
3. **Infer** why chemists have not created a periodic table of compounds.

Communicating Your Data

Construct a bulletin board of the periodic tables of foods created by the class. Compare and contrast the tables.

Real-World Problem

Purpose Students create a periodic table to organize foods. L2
LS **Logical-Mathematical**

Process Skills classify, compare and contrast, sequence, make and use tables

Procedure

Time Required 30 minutes

Teaching Strategies Have references available from which students can find the nutritional content of foods, such as fruits, that have no labels.

Conclude and Apply

1. Answers will vary, but food items containing several major ingredients such as pizza or ice cream cones often present classification problems.
2. Individual foods such as mangos or tuna are easily grouped into the major food groups, but when food ingredients are combined into items such as cakes or soups, classification becomes difficult.
3. There are about 114 elements, many with common characteristics. There are millions of compounds, which makes a table of compounds impractical to construct and apply.

✓ Assessment

Process Have students repeat the activity using only unprocessed foods. Does this make it easier or more difficult to divide foods into families? Use **Performance Assessment in the Science Classroom,** p. 121.

Communicating Your Data

Students may want to use a spreadsheet program to determine the layout of the class periodic table of foods for the bulletin board.

BENCH TESTED

Real-World Problem

Internet Students use Internet sites that can be accessed at gpescience.com. Students can post their findings on the site and get information from other schools around the country.

Non-Internet Sources In its entry for an element, an encyclopedia often will give the history of the discovery and naming of that element. Find books about the history of science, including biographies of famous scientists and descriptions of important discoveries and inventions.

Time Required about two days

Make a Plan

Preparation

Internet To run through the steps that the students will follow, visit gpescience.com.

Non-Internet Sources Bring to class books on the history of chemistry and the history of science that describe how elements were discovered and named.

LAB **Use the Internet**

What's in a name?

Goals

- **Research** the names and symbols of various elements.
- **Study** the methods that are used to name elements and how they have changed through time.
- **Organize** your data by making your own periodic table.
- **Study** the history of certain elements and their discoveries.
- **Create** a table of your findings and communicate them to other students.

Data Source

Internet Lab

Visit gpescience.com for more information about naming elements, elements' symbols, and the discovery of new elements, and for data collected by other students.

Real-World Problem

The symbols used for different elements sometimes are easy to figure out. After all, it makes sense for the symbol for carbon to be C and the symbol for nitrogen to be N. However, some symbols aren't as easy to figure out. For example, the element silver has the symbol Ag. This symbol comes from the Latin word for *silver, argentum.* How are symbols and names chosen for elements?

Make a Plan

1. Make a list of particular elements you wish to study.
2. **Identify** the symbols for these elements.
3. **Research** the discovery of these elements. Do their names match their symbols? Were they named after a property of the element, a person, their place of discovery, or a system of nomenclature? What was that system?

Alternative Inquiry Lab

Real-World Connection To make this Lab an Inquiry Lab, give the students more personal investment into the problem by connecting it to the real world. Tell the students that they must devise a system for naming new elements that are discovered. Have them devise a naming system that can be used by scientists world wide. After students have devised their system, have them compare and contrast their system to the system devised by the International Union of Pure and Applied Chemistry. L2

Using Scientific Methods

Follow Your Plan

1. Make sure your teacher approves your plan before you start.
2. Visit the Web site provided for links to different sites about elements, their history, and how they were named.
3. **Research** these elements.
4. Carefully record your data in your Science Journal.

Analyze Your Data

1. **Record** in your Science Journal how the symbols for your elements were chosen. What were your elements named after?
2. **Construct** an element key that includes the research information that you found for your elements.
3. Make a chart of your class's findings. Sort the chart by year of discovery for each element.
4. How are the names and symbols for newly discovered elements chosen? Make a chart that shows how the newly discovered elements will be named.

Conclude and Apply

1. **Compare** your findings to those of your classmates. Did anyone's data differ for the same element? Were all the elements in the periodic table covered?
2. **Explain** the system that is used to name the newly discovered elements today.
3. **Explain** Some elements were assigned symbols based on their name in another language. Do these examples occur for elements discovered today or long ago?

Communicating Your Data

Find this lab using the link below. Post your data in the table provided. **Compare** your data to those of other students.

Internet Lab
gpescience.com

Follow Your Plan

Teaching Strategies

- Suggest that students include in their lists of elements to study some elements discovered long ago and some elements discovered more recently.
- Suggest that each student study at least ten elements.
- Have books on Greek and Roman mythology available so students can learn more about the characters from these myths for whom some of the elements are named.

Analyze Your Data

1. Students should report how the names and symbols of the elements were determined.
2. The student's element key should resemble the element key on the periodic table.
3. Answers will vary.
4. Different scientific organizations have created naming recommendations for newly discovered elements.

Conclude and Apply

1. Student data for the same element should not differ. Have students write their names next to the elements they researched to see if all the elements were investigated.
2. The International Union of Pure and Applied Chemistry has specific recommendations for giving names and symbols to newly-discovered elements.
3. elements discovered long ago

Communicating Your Data

Students can build an interactive periodic table of the elements. Have them use the computer and a Web page development program to display the periodic table. Suggest they design the table so that when an element is clicked, the computer will display information about the origin of the name and symbol for that element.

Assessment

Portfolio Ask students to prepare written reports of their findings about the way elements were named hundreds of years ago and the way they are named today. Have them include in their reports their original hypotheses and discussions of how the information they found proved or disproved their hypotheses. Use **Performance Assessment in the Science Classroom**, p. 157.

TIME

Content Background

Air trapped in ice cores contains traces of whatever the lower atmosphere contained at the time the ice formed. Large increases in the concentration of sulfates indicate volcanic activity. Changes in types of pollen provide clues to general trends in temperature.

Discussion

Finding Clues Why do we know more about what caused the Greenland colony to vanish today than the people who discovered the colonists missing? Possible answer: The scientific knowledge and technology to extract and analyze ice cores did not exist until recently. L2

Historical Significance

Climate change is not a relic of the past, but a continuing cyclical process. Obtain for the class a cross sectional slab of tree trunk or a large photo of one. The tree should be approximately three feet in diameter. Make sure you know where the tree grew and when. Have students determine how long the tree lived by counting the rings and then determine where and when it lived. With this knowledge, students can research local temperatures over the lifespan of the tree and plot them using small flags on pins placed at the appropriate rings. Discuss with students the relation between ring size and temperature. Discuss any anomalous variations in ring size and other possible environmental conditions that may have been responsible for them.

TIME **SCIENCE AND HISTORY** SCIENCE CAN CHANGE THE COURSE OF HISTORY!

A CHILLING STORY

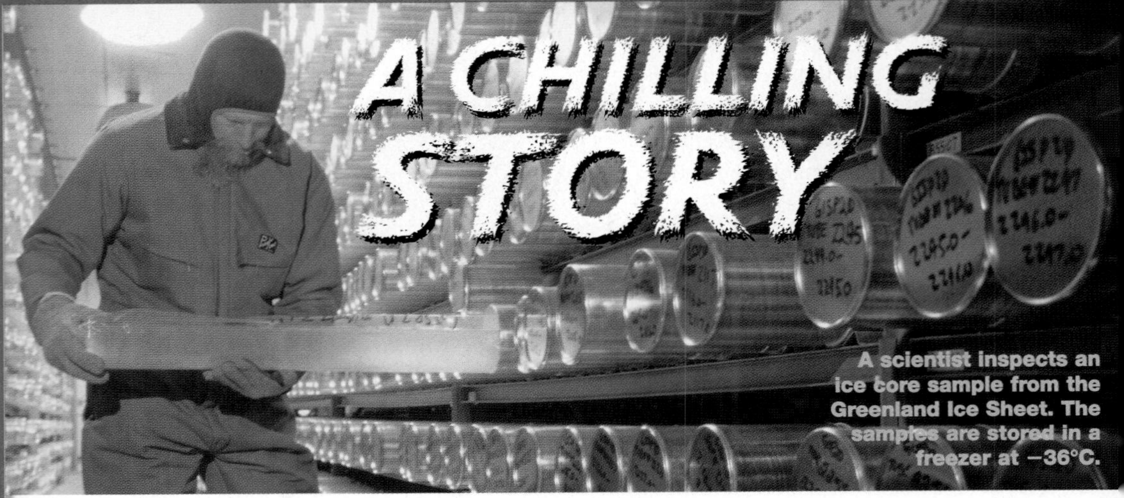

A scientist inspects an ice core sample from the Greenland Ice Sheet. The samples are stored in a freezer at −36°C.

Picture this: It's 1361. A ship from Norway arrives at a Norwegian settlement in Greenland. The ship's crew members hope to trade its cargo with the people living there. The crew members get off the ship. They look around. The settlement is deserted. More than 1,000 people had vanished!

New evidence has shed some light on the mysterious disappearance of the Norse settlers. The evidence came from a place on the Greenland Ice Sheet over 600 km away from the settlement. This part of Greenland is so cold that snow never melts. As new snow falls, the existing snow is buried and turns to ice. By drilling deep into this ice, scientists can recover an ice core. The core is made up of ice formed from snowfalls way, way back in time.

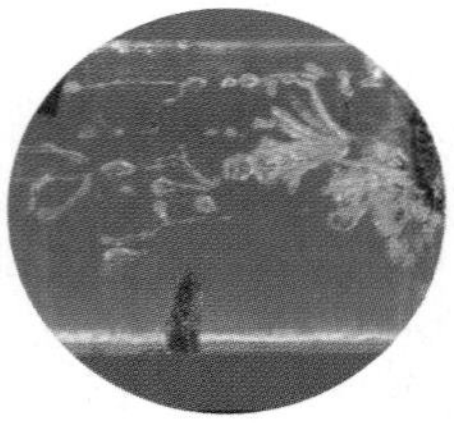

Air bubbles and dirt trapped in ice provide clues to Earth's past climate.

By measuring the ratio of oxygen isotopes in the ice core, scientists can estimate Greenland's past air temperatures. The cores provide a detailed climate history going back over 80,000 years. Individual ice layers can be dated much like tree rings to determine their ages. The air bubbles trapped within each layer are used to learn about climate variations. Dust and pollen trapped in the ice also yield clues to ancient climates.

A Little Ice Age

Based on their analysis, scientists think the Norse settlers moved to Greenland during an unusually warm period. Then, in the 1300s, the climate started to cool and a period known as the Little Ice Age began. The ways the Norse people hunted and farmed were inadequate for survival in this long chill. Because they couldn't adapt to their colder surroundings, the settlers died out.

Research Report Evidence seems to show that Earth is warming. Rising temperatures could affect our lives. Research global warming to find out how Earth may change. Share your report with the class.

TIME For more information, visit gpescience.com

Research Report Research periods of glaciation over the history of Earth and discuss the cycles in light of present climate conditions. You might want to construct a timeline for students showing Earth's average temperatures at different points in time and the percentage of Earth's surface covered with ice at those times. L2

Resources for Teachers and Students

U.S. National Ice Core Laboratory, United States Geological Survey, MS-975, Box 25046, DFC, Denver, CO 80225

"Core Values. (Samplings)." *Natural History*, March, 2003

chapter 19 Study Guide

Reviewing Main Ideas

Section 1 Structure of the Atom

1. A chemical symbol is a shorthand way of writing the name of an element.
2. An atom consists of a nucleus made up of protons and neutrons surrounded by an electron cloud, as shown in the figure to the right.

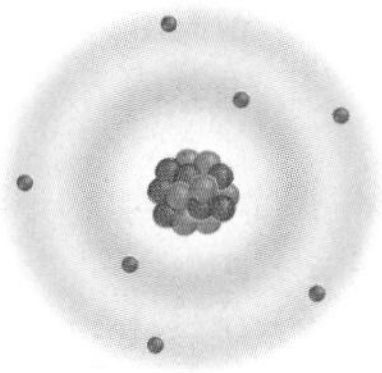

3. Quarks are particles of matter that make up protons and neutrons.
4. The model of the atom changes over time. As new information is discovered, scientists incorporate it into the model.

Section 2 Masses of Atoms

1. The number of neutrons in an atom can be computed by subtracting the atomic number from the mass number.
2. The isotopes of an element are atoms of the same element that have different numbers of neutrons. The figure below shows the isotopes of hydrogen.

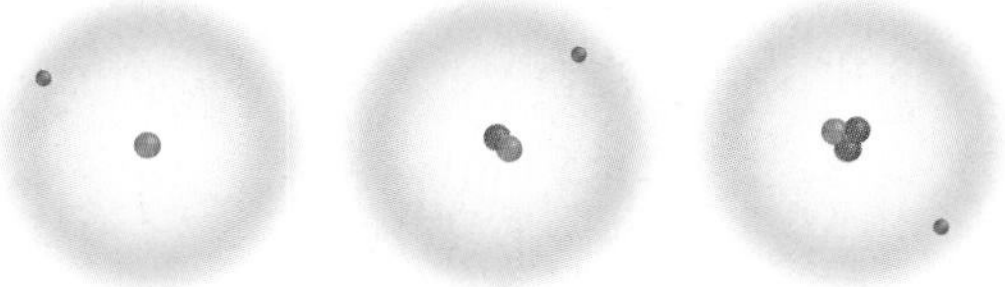

3. The average atomic mass of an element is the weighted-average mass of the mixture of its isotopes. Isotopes are named by using the element name, followed by a dash, and its mass number.

Section 3 The Periodic Table

1. In the periodic table, the elements are arranged by increasing atomic number, resulting in periodic changes in properties. Knowing that the number of protons, electrons, and atomic number are equal gives you a partial composition of an atom.
2. In the periodic table, the elements are arranged in 18 vertical columns, or groups, and seven horizontal rows, or periods.
3. Metals are found at the left of the periodic table, nonmetals at the right, and metalloids along the line that separates the metals from the nonmetals, as shown below.

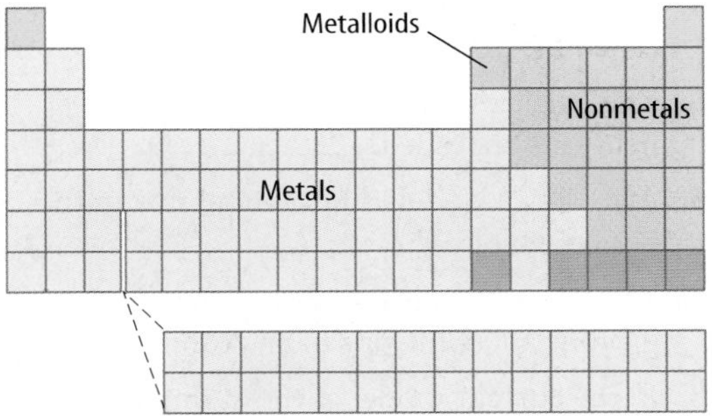

4. Elements are placed on the periodic table in order of increasing atomic number. A new row on the periodic table begins when the outer energy level of an element is filled.

FOLDABLES Use the Foldable that you made at the beginning of the chapter to help you review properties of atoms and the periodic table.

Reviewing Main Ideas

Summary statements can be used by students to review the major concepts of the chapter.

Science Online

Visit gpescience.com
More Section Review
Interactive Tutor
Vocabulary PuzzleMaker
More Chapter Review
Standardized Practice Test

Assessment Transparency

For additional assessment questions, use the *Assessment Transparency* located in the transparency book.

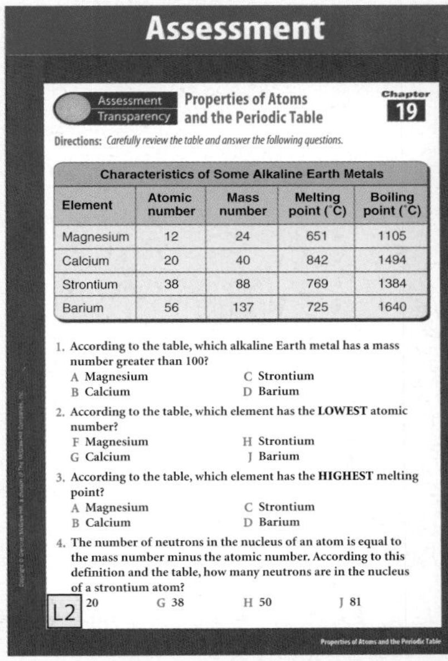

Assessment

Assessment Transparency — Properties of Atoms and the Periodic Table — Chapter 19

Directions: *Carefully review the table and answer the following questions.*

Characteristics of Some Alkaline Earth Metals

Element	Atomic number	Mass number	Melting point (°C)	Boiling point (°C)
Magnesium	12	24	651	1105
Calcium	20	40	842	1494
Strontium	38	88	769	1384
Barium	56	137	725	1640

1. According to the table, which alkaline Earth metal has a mass number greater than 100?
   A Magnesium C Strontium
   B Calcium D Barium
2. According to the table, which element has the **LOWEST** atomic number?
   F Magnesium H Strontium
   G Calcium J Barium
3. According to the table, which element has the **HIGHEST** melting point?
   A Magnesium C Strontium
   B Calcium D Barium
4. The number of neutrons in the nucleus of an atom is equal to the mass number minus the atomic number. According to this definition and the table, how many neutrons are in the nucleus of a strontium atom?
   20 G 38 H 50 J 81

L2

Properties of Atoms and the Periodic Table

FOLDABLES Have students use their Foldables to review the content of the chapter. On the back of the paper, have students write a paragraph about how the atomic model looks today.

chapter 19 Review

Using Vocabulary

1. periodic table
2. isotopes
3. Average atomic mass
4. nucleus
5. quarks
6. period
7. mass number
8. electron cloud

Checking Concepts

9. D
10. C
11. B
12. B
13. A
14. A
15. B
16. B

chapter 19 Review

Using Vocabulary

atom p. 579	mass number p. 585
atomic number p. 585	neutron p. 579
average atomic mass p. 587	nucleus p. 579
electron p. 579	period p. 595
electron cloud p. 583	periodic table p. 588
electron dot diagram p. 594	proton p. 579
group p. 592	quark p. 579
isotope p. 586	

Complete the statement with the correct vocabulary word or phrase.

1. Mendeleev created an organized table of elements called the ________.
2. Two elements with the same number of protons but a different number of neutrons are called ________.
3. ________ is the weighted-average mass of all the known isotopes for an element.
4. The positively charged center of an atom is called the ________.
5. The particles that make up protons and neutrons are called ________.
6. A(n) ________ is a horizontal row in the periodic table.
7. The ________ is the sum of the number of protons and neutrons in an atom.
8. In the current model of the atom, the electrons are located in the ________.

Checking Concepts

Choose the word or phrase that best answers the question.

9. In which state of matter are most of the elements to the left of the stair-step line in the periodic table?
   A) gas **C)** plasma
   B) liquid **D)** solid

10. Which term describes a pattern that repeats?
   A) isotopic **C)** periodic
   B) metallic **D)** transition

11. Which element has similar properties to those of neon?
   A) aluminum **C)** arsenic
   B) argon **D)** silver

12. Which term describes boron?
   A) metal **C)** noble gas
   B) metalloid **D)** nonmetal

13. How many outer-level electrons do lithium and potassium have?
   A) one **C)** three
   B) two **D)** four

14. Which is **NOT** found in the nucleus of an atom?
   A) electron **C)** proton
   B) neutron **D)** quark

15. The atomic number of rhenium is 75. The atomic mass of one of its isotopes is 186. How many neutrons are in an atom of this isotope?
   A) 75 **C)** 186
   B) 111 **D)** 261

Use the photo below to answer question 16.

16. Which scientist developed this atomic model?
   A) Bohr **C)** Rutherford
   B) Dalton **D)** Thomson

Vocabulary PuzzleMaker gpescience.com

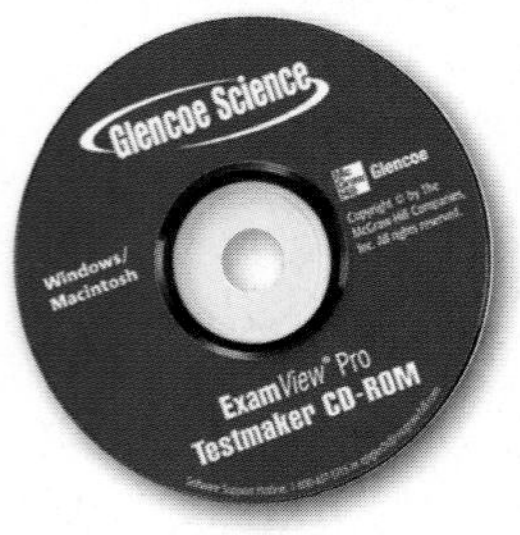

Use the Exam*View*® Pro Testmaker CD-ROM to:
- create multiple versions of tests
- create modified tests with one mouse click for inclusion students
- edit existing questions and add your own questions
- build tests aligned with state standards using built-in State Curriculum Tags
- change English tests to Spanish with one mouse click and vice versa

Interpreting Graphics

17. Construct As a star dies, it becomes more dense. Its temperature rises to a point at which He nuclei are combined with other nuclei. When this happens, the atomic numbers of the other nuclei are increased by 2 because each gains the two protons contained in the He nucleus. For example, Cr fuses with He to become Fe. Copy and complete the concept map showing the first four steps in He fusion.

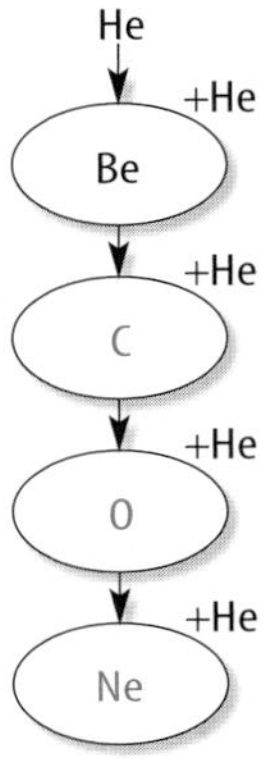

18. Copy and complete the concept map below.

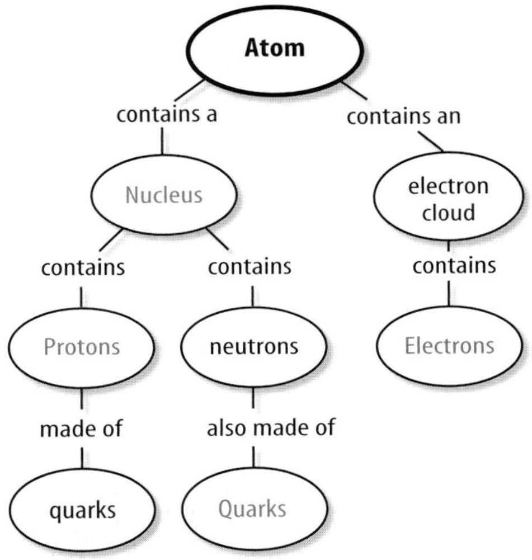

Thinking Critically

19. Infer Lead and mercury are two pollutants in the environment. From information about them in the periodic table, determine why they are called heavy metals.

20. Explain why it is necessary to change models as new information becomes available.

21. Infer Why did scientists choose carbon as a base for the atomic mass unit? Which isotope of carbon did they use?

22. Infer Ge and Si are used in making semiconductors. Are these two elements in the same group or the same period?

23. Explain Using the periodic table, predict how many outer level electrons will be in elements 114, 116, and 118. Explain your answer.

24. Infer Ca is used by the body to make bones and teeth. Sr-90 is radioactive. Ca is safe for people, and Sr-90 is hazardous. Why is Sr-90 hazardous to people?

Applying Math

25. Solve One-Step Equations The atomic number of yttrium is 39. The atomic mass of one of its isotopes is 89. How many neutrons are in an atom of this isotope?

Use the table below to answer question 26.

Electrons per Energy Level

Energy Level	Maximum Number of Electrons
1	2
2	8
3	8
4	0

26. Use Tables Use the information in **Figure 9** to determine how many electrons should be in the second, third, and fourth energy levels for argon, atomic number 18. Copy and complete the table above with the number of electrons for each energy level.

More Chapter Review gpescience.com

Interpreting Graphics

17. See student page.
18. See student page.

Thinking Critically

19. Compared to many metals, both lead and mercury have large average atomic masses.
20. Models must be updated to reflect the new information that is found. If the models are not updated, they are obsolete when the new information is found. The model would be useless.
21. Student answers may vary. It is possible that carbon was chosen because living organisms contain a significant amount of carbon. carbon-12
22. same group
23. 114-4; 116-6; 118-8; because these elements are in groups 14, 16, and 18 respectively
24. The radioactive nature of Sr can damage human cells.

Applying Math

Math Standards

National: 1, 5, 9

25. 50
26. See student page.

Assessment Resources

Reproducible Masters

Chapter *Fast File* Resources
Chapter Review, pp. 37–38
Chapter Tests, pp. 39–42
Assessment Transparency Activity, p. 49

Glencoe Science Web site
Chapter Review Test
Standardized Test Practice

Glencoe Technology

Assessment Transparency
Exam*View*® Pro Testmaker
MindJogger Videoquiz
Interactive Chalkboard

Answer Sheet An answer sheet can be found at **gpescience.com**.

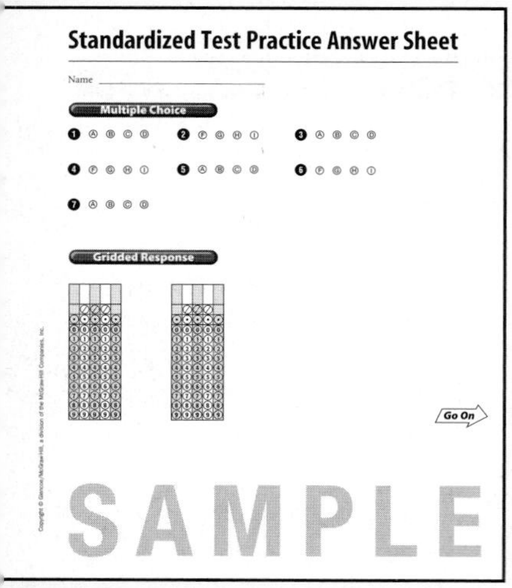

Multiple Choice

1. D
2. D
3. C
4. C
5. C
6. D

Gridded Response

7. 125
8. 35.5 amu

chapter 19 Standardized Test Practice

Record your answers on the answer sheet provided by your teacher or on a sheet of paper.

Multiple Choice

1. Which group of elements on the periodic table do not combine readily with other elements?

A. Group 1

B. Group 2

C. Group 17

D. Group 18

Use the illustration below to answer question 2.

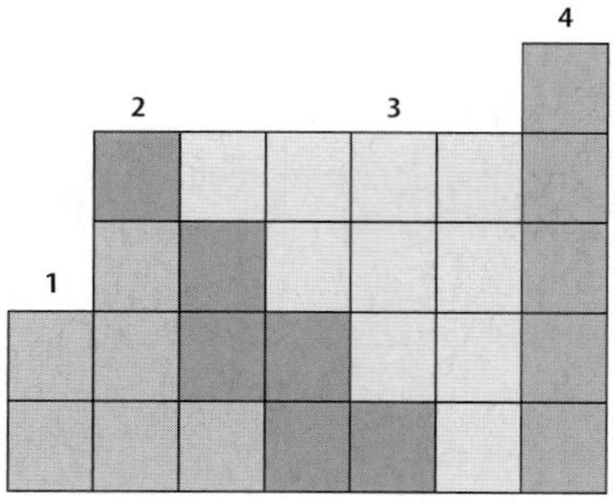

2. Which of the regions shown on the periodic table contains mostly elements that are gases at room temperature?

A. region 1

B. region 2

C. region 3

D. region 4

Test-Taking Tip

Have Breakfast The morning of the test, eat a healthy breakfast with a balanced amount of protein and carbohydrates.

3. Which scientist proposed the idea that atoms make up all substances?

A. Aristotle

B. Dalton

C. Democritus

D. Galileo

Use the table below to answer question 4.

Element	Electrons in a Neutral Atom	Electrons in Outer Energy Level
Carbon	6	4
Oxygen	8	6
Neon	10	8
Sodium	11	1
Chlorine	17	7

4. Which element would you expect to be located in Group 1 of the periodic table?

A. oxygen

B. neon

C. sodium

D. chlorine

5. The element nickel has five naturally occurring isotopes. Which of the following describes the relationship of these isotopes?

A. same mass, same atomic number

B. same mass, different atomic number

C. different mass, same atomic number

D. different mass, different atomic number

6. Atoms of different elements are different because they have different numbers of what type of particle?
   - **A.** electrons
   - **B.** photons
   - **C.** protons
   - **D.** neutrons

Gridded Response

7. According to the periodic table, an atom of lead has an atomic number of 82. How many neutrons does lead-207 have?

8. About three out of four chlorine atoms are chlorine-35, and about one out of four is chlorine-37. What is the average atomic mass of chlorine?

Short Response

Use the illustration below to answer question 9.

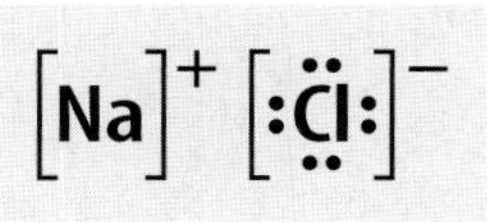

9. The electron dot diagram above shows how a sodium atom, Na, combines with a chlorine atom, Cl, to form sodium chloride. What do the + and the − symbols indicate in the diagram?

10. Why isn't the mass of the electron included in the mass of an atom on the periodic table?

Extended Response

Use the illustration below to answer questions 11 and 12.

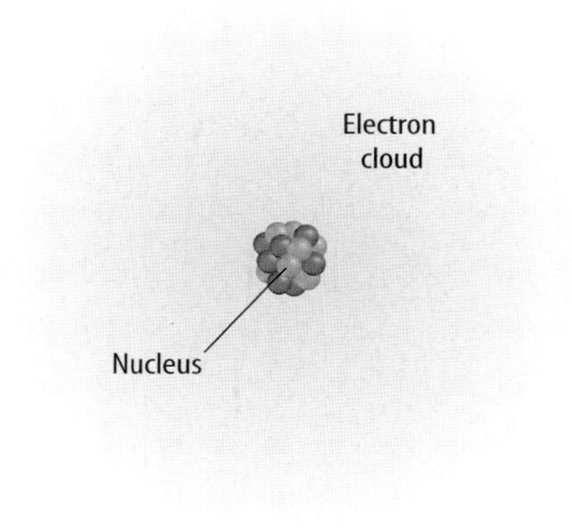

11. The illustration above shows the currently accepted model of atomic structure. Describe this model.

12. Compare and contrast the model shown above with Bohr's model of an atom.

13. How can you use the periodic table to determine the average number of neutrons an element has, even though the number of neutrons is not listed?

14. Describe how Dalton's modernization of the ancient Greeks' ideas of elements, atoms, and compounds provided a basis for understanding chemical reactions. Give an example.

Rubrics

For more help evaluating Short- and Extended-Response questions, see the rubrics on p. 9T.

Short Response

9. The + indicates that the sodium atom loses an electron, and the indicates the chlorine atom gains an electron when the ionic bond forms.

10. You can determine the average number of neutrons by subtracting the atomic number from the average atomic mass.

Extended Response

11. A cloud of negatively-charged electrons moves in an area around the nucleus of the atom.

12. Bohr hypothesized that electrons travel in fixed orbits around the atom's nucleus. In the electron cloud model of an atom, the electrons do not follow fixed orbits. Both models agree that the nucleus contains positively-charged protons and neutrons with no charge.

13. You can determine the average number of neutrons by subtracting the atomic number from the average atomic mass.

chapter 20 Organizer

Section/Objectives	Standards: National	Standards: State/Local	Labs/Features
Chapter Opener	See pp. 16T–17T for a Key to Standards.		**Launch Lab:** Earth Materials at Home and School, p. 607 **Foldables,** p. 607
Section 1 Minerals 2 sessions 1 block 1. **Describe** characteristics of all minerals. 2. **Indentify** common minerals using physical properties. 3. **Compare and contrast** some conditions of mineral formation.	National Content Standards: UCP.1–3, UCP.5, A.1, A.2, B.2, D.1, D.2, G.2, G.3, F.3		**MiniLAB:** Identifying Salt's Crystal System, p. 612 **Integrate Chemistry,** p. 613 **Science Online,** p. 614 **Integrate Language Arts,** p. 615 **Lab:** Be a Mineral Detective, p. 616 Video Lab
Section 2 Igneous Rocks 1 session .5 block 4. **Describe** the types of materials present in most rocks. 5. **Explain** how and where igneous rocks form. 6. **Classify** igneous rocks.	National Content Standards: UCP.1–3, UCP.5, A.1, A.2, D.1, D.2,		**Applying Math:** Extrusive Igneous Rock Classification, p. 621 **Science Online,** p. 622
Section 3 Sedimentary Rocks 2 sessions 1 block 7. **Explain** how and where sedimentary rocks form. 8. **Discuss** how sedimentary rocks are used to interpret Earth's history. 9. **Describe** how sedimentary rocks are classified.	National Content Standards: UCP.1–3, UCP.5, A.1, A.2, D.1, D.2,		**Integrate Chemistry,** p. 627 **MiniLAB:** Modeling Evaporites p. 628
Section 4 Metamorphic Rocks 2 sessions 1 block 10. **Identify** physical conditions that cause metamorphism. 11. **Explain** where metamorphism occurs. 12. **Classify** metamorphic rocks.	National Content Standards: UCP.1–3, UCP.5, A.1, A.2, D.1, D.2,		**Science Online,** p. 632 **Visualizing Shock Metamorphic Rock,** p. 633 **Lab:** Identifying Rocks, pp. 636–637 **Science and Society:** Earth Materials at Work, p. 638

StudentWorks Plus

Glencoe Exclusive! TeacherWorks™ All-In-One Planner and Resource Center

Lab Materials	Reproducible Resources	Section Assessment	Technology
Launch Lab: various movable items in the classroom, sheets of paper, ruler	**Chapter *Fast File* Resources** Foldables Worksheet, p. 19 Directed Reading Overview, p. 21 Note-taking Worksheets, pp. 37–39	Glencoe's Assessment Advantage	**TeacherWorks** includes: • Interactive Teacher Edition • Lesson Planner with calendar • Access to all program blacklines • Correlations to standards • Web links
MiniLAB: salt, dark surface, magnifying lens **Lab:** mineral supplies, penny, unglazed porcelian tile, Mohs hardness scale, nail, glass plate, Reference Handbook "Minerals"	**Chapter *Fast File* Resources** Transparency Activity, pp. 48, 53–54 MiniLAB, p. 3 Enrichment, p. 34 Reinforcement, p. 29 Directed Reading, p. 22 Lab Worksheets, pp. 5–6	**Portfolio** Assessment, p. 615 **Performance** MiniLab, p. 612 Applying Math, p. 615 **Content** Section Review, p. 615	Section Focus Transparency Teaching Transparency Interactive Chalkboard CD-ROM StudentWorks Plus Video Lab
Need materials? Contact Science Kit at 1-800-828-7777 or www.sciencekit.com.	**Chapter *Fast File* Resources** Transparency Activity, p. 49 Enrichment, p. 34 Reinforcement, p. 30 Directed Reading, p. 22	**Performance** Applying Math, p. 621 Applying Math, p. 623 **Content** Section Review, p. 623	Section Focus Transparency Interactive Chalkboard CD-ROM StudentWorks Plus
MiniLAB: sauce pan with lid, tap water, salt, spoon, hotplate, thermal mitts, saucers (2)	**Chapter *Fast File* Resources** Transparency Activity, p. 50 MiniLAB, p. 4 Lab Activity, pp. 15–17 Enrichment, p. 35 Reinforcement, p. 31 Directed Reading, p. 23	**Performance** MiniLab, p. 628 Applying Math, p. 629 **Content** Section Review, p. 629	Section Focus Transparency Interactive Chalkboard CD-ROM StudentWorks Plus
Lab: rock samples, nail, pre-1986 penny, magnifying lens, particle size chart, dilute HCl, paper, towels, glass plate, unglazed porcelain tile, Reference Handbook "Rocks"	**Chapter *Fast File* Resources** Transparency Activity, p. 51 Lab Activity, pp. 11–13 Enrichment, p. 36 Reinforcement, p. 32 Directed Reading, p. 23–24 Assessment Transparency Activity, p. 55 Lab Worksheets, pp. 7–8	**Performance** Applying Math, p. 635 **Content** Section Review, p. 635	Section Focus Transparency Interactive Chalkboard CD-ROM StudentWorks Plus

End of Chapter Assessment

Glencoe's Assessment Advantage

Blackline Masters	Technology	Professional Series
Chapter *Fast File* Resources Chapter Review, pp. 41–42 Chapter Tests, pp. 43–46 **Standardized Test Practice,** pp. 84–87	MindJogger Videoquiz Exam*View*® Pro Testmaker TeacherWorks CD-ROM Interactive Chalkboard CD-ROM	**Performance Assessment in the Science Classroom (PASC)**

Transparencies

Section Focus

Section 1 Section Focus Transparency — A Sea of Diamonds (Chapter 20)

Over the past 100 million years, up to 1,400 meters have eroded from the land's surface, sending billions of carats of diamonds on a trip to the sea. An estimate of diamonds eroded from just one mine, South Africa's Kimberley mine—the "Big Hole"— is 500,000 carats! Rivers carried most of the eroded diamonds to the Atlantic Ocean, although about ten percent were stored in the alluvial deposits of the drainage systems. Because powerful ocean waves break poorer quality diamonds, 90-95 percent of marine diamonds are of gem quality. That makes the Atlantic coast the focus of intense mining activity.

1. How are diamonds formed?
2. Why are diamonds so valuable?
3. How do diamonds fit the definition of a mineral?

L2

Section 2 Section Focus Transparency — Earth Power! (Chapter 20)

Geothermal power plants are electricity-generating stations. They get their energy from hot water circulating deep underground in rocks heated by contact with magma. Geothermal plants are often located in geologically active locations, such as the Philippines and Indonesia. Geothermal power has great potential as an alternative source of energy to lessen the world's dependence on increasingly diminishing oil supplies.

1. How might a geothermal power plant gain access to the hot water underground?
2. How could magma heat water that comes in contact with it?
3. Do you think geothermal power could be the answer to the world's energy needs? Why or why not?

L2

Section 3 Section Focus Transparency — Fossil Fascination (Chapter 20)

Most fossils are actually casts of animals or plants. When an animal dies and sinks to the sea floor, the body begins to decay and is buried under layers of sediment, such as mud or sand. These layers become rock, and the hard parts of the animal are replaced with minerals, such as iron pyrites or silicia. These minerals then form the fossil. Usually, fossils show the hard parts of the animal or plant such as shell or bones. Most fossils are found in sedimentary rocks — rocks that are created when shells or small loose bits of rock are laid down in layers. Examples of sedimentary rocks are limestone, sandstone, clay, and chalk.

1. Why do fossils usually show only the hard parts of animals or plants?
2. How can fossils help us learn about the past?
3. Where might you go in your area to hunt for fossils?

L2

Section 4 Section Focus Transparency — Marvelous Marble (Chapter 20)

Marble is a metamorphic rock that is frequently used in sculpture and architecture because of its beauty. It is finely grained and dense, with a nondirectional structure. It is capable of taking a high polish and is often irregularly veined and colored by impurities. White marble has been quarried in Greece, Italy, Turkey, India, China, and the United States. Among the most renowned sources have been the quarries of Carrara in the Apuan Alps of Italy. Confusingly, the name "marble" is sometimes used to refer to any stone that takes a polish, although such stones may also include alabasters, granites, and serpentines. Many of the world's great structures, such as the Lincoln Memorial, are made of marble.

1. Why might marble be veined or colored with impurities?
2. Name a marble building or structure in or near where you live.
3. What is a common sedimentary rock that is also popular as a building material?

L2

This is a representation of key blackline masters available in the Teacher Classroom Resources. See Resource Manager boxes within the chapter for additional information.

Key to Teaching Strategies

The following designations will help you decide which activities are appropriate for your students.

- **L1** Level 1 activities should be appropriate for students with learning difficulties.
- **L2** Level 2 activities should be within the ability range of all students.
- **L3** Level 3 activities are designed for above-average students.
- **ELL** ELL activities should be within the ability range of English Language Learners.
- **COOP LEARN** Cooperative Learning activities are designed for small group work.
- **LS** Multiple Learning Styles logos, as described on page 12T, are used throughout to indicate strategies that address different learning styles.
- **P** These strategies represent student products that can be placed into a best-work portfolio.
- **PBL** Problem-Based Learning activities apply real-world situations to learning.

Assessment

Assessment Transparency — Earth Materials (Chapter 20)

Directions: *Carefully review the diagrams of various crystal systems. Use the diagrams to answer the following questions.*

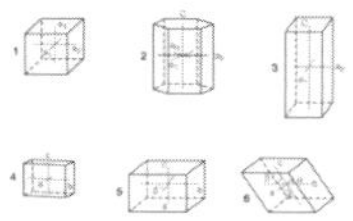

1. Which diagram represents a cubic system?
   - A Diagram 1
   - B Diagram 3
   - C Diagram 4
   - D Diagram 6
2. Which crystal system does Diagram 6 identify?
   - F Hexagonal
   - G Orthorhombic
   - H Triclinic
   - J Tetragonal
3. A monoclinic system is represented by
   - A Diagram 1
   - B Diagram 2
   - C Diagram 3
   - D Diagram 5

L2

Teaching

Teaching Transparency — Using the Mohs Scale (Chapter 20)

Directions: *Study the incomplete Mohs scale carefully. Then write the correct hardness number in the blank next to each mineral.*

Mohs Scale	Hardness	Hardness of Common Objects
	1	(softest)
	2	fingernail (2.5)
	3	piece of copper (2.5 to 3.0)
	4	iron nail (4.5)
	5	glass (5.5)
	6	Steel file (6.5)
	7	streak plate (7.0)
	8	
	9	
	10	(hardest)

L2

Hands-on Activities

Student Text Lab Worksheet

Name Date Class

LAB Be a Mineral Detective

Hands-On Activities

Lab Preview

Directions: *Answer these questions before you begin the Lab.*

1. Why is it important for you to be descriptive and broad in your observations of the unknown mineral specimens?
2. How will the penny, nail, and glass objects help you identify the mineral specimens?

Detectives must gather facts and physical evidence to deduce the events that took place during a crime. Much like detectives, geologists gather physical evidence to better understand Earth processes. First, minerals are identified, and then their histories sometimes can be interpreted.

Real-World Problem

How is it possible to distinguish similar-looking materials from each other?

Safety Precautions

Goals

- **Observe and record** physical properties of minerals.
- **Determine** mineral names using your observations and identification keys.

Materials

mineral samples
nail
penny
glass plate
unglazed porcelain tile
Mohs hardness scale
Reference Handbook "Minerals"

Procedure

1. Use the table provided to record your data. Note the columns labeled: *Mineral Number, Color, Hardness, Streak, Cleavage, Fracture, Other Observations* (like smell, feel, or heft), and *Mineral Name.*
2. Obtain numbered mineral specimens from your teacher. Observe each mineral and accurately record the data based on your tests for physical properties. Be descriptive and broad in your observations.

Hints: When determining hardness, test several different spots on the sample. Remember the hardness of your fingernail is a little more than 2; penny, a bit more than 3; steel nail, 5-6; glass, about 5-5.5. Minerals can have both cleavage and fracture at the same time. Cleavage is expressed as how many unique planar directions are present, and the angles formed when more than one direction occurs.

Earth Materials L2

Laboratory Activities

Name Date Class

LAB 1 Laboratory Activity — The Colored Ribbons of Gneiss

Hands-On Activities

Gneiss is a high-grade metamorphic rock that originates from either sedimentary rock (usually shale) or from the igneous rock granite. It is often used as building or paving stone. Gneiss is labeled high-grade because it was subjected to more heat and compression than schist, the first stage of the metamorphism of shale. As a result, it is coarser and has distinct color layers, or banding.

You may remember that color variation within sedimentary rock is due to the difference in particle size of the various sediments. However, particle size is no longer a factor in metamorphic rock because intense heat and pressure have made particle size more uniform. The color banding in the metamorphic rock gneiss, therefore, comes solely from the difference in mineral colors. Gneiss is usually composed of mica, feldspar, and quartz, although it can also contain hornblende, kyanite, garnet, tourmaline, magnetite, and other minerals.

Glassy in appearance, quartz can appear white, gray, yellow, or even red in sedimentary rock, but it is gray in igneous rock. Glassy-faced potassic feldspars—microline and orthoclase—are pink or tan in appearance, although occasionally they look white. Another type of feldspar, plagioclase feldspar, ranges from white to dark grey (sometimes black) and may show small flashes of green or blue. The plagioclase feldspars are albite and labradorite.

The micas (muscovite and biotite) are thin flakes or flake layers, that peel easily off a rock sample. Muscovite ranges from silver to brown, while biotite is black. Other "flaky" minerals are the chlorite group, although their flakes aren't as thin as the mica group's. Chlorite always has a green cast and varies from medium to dark green, although it can also be black with a green tinge.

Although gneiss is usually light-colored, it can also appear dark. A rock hunter who observes fairly broad color stripes in a coarse-textured, hard rock can be fairly certain that the rock is gneiss. However, if this gneiss sample is compared with another, the difference in coloration can be dramatic.

In this experiment, you will create "gneiss," observe banding, identify the "minerals" that create the banded colors, and observe the different combinations that can make gneiss rocks differ greatly from one another. Predict how your model will compare with those of your classmates. Record your prediction and observations in the Data and Observations below.

Strategy

You will create a model of the metamorphic rock gneiss.
You will observe mineral banding in the model.
You will hypothesize about specific minerals that contribute to banding.
You will compare and contrast your model with those of other students.

Materials

sheet of newspaper
wide-mouthed canning jar, 1-quart or 1-L (must be clear and colorless)
granulated sugar (not extra-fine)
colored sugar (yellow, red, green, blue, pink, black)
clean, dry beach sand
small scoop

*colored sand (such as that used in candle-making)
*small serving spoon
*Alternate materials

Earth Materials L2

Meeting Different Ability Levels

Content Outline

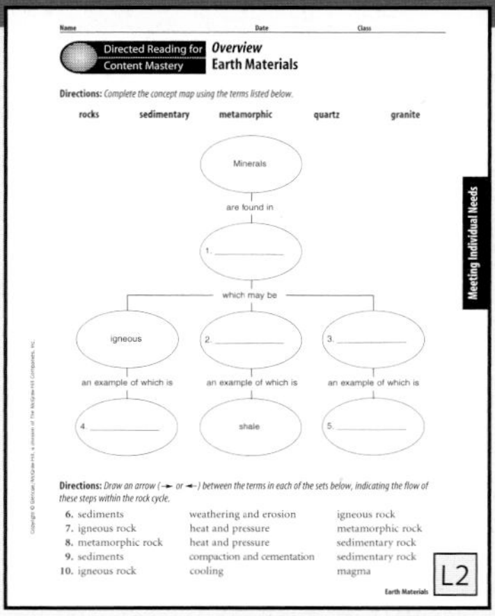

Reinforcement

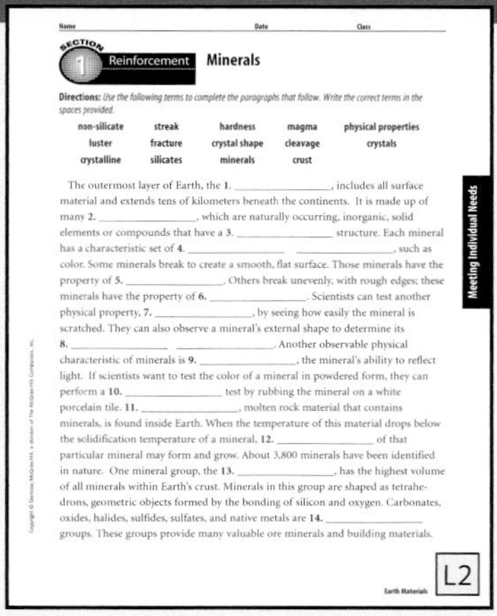

Enrichment

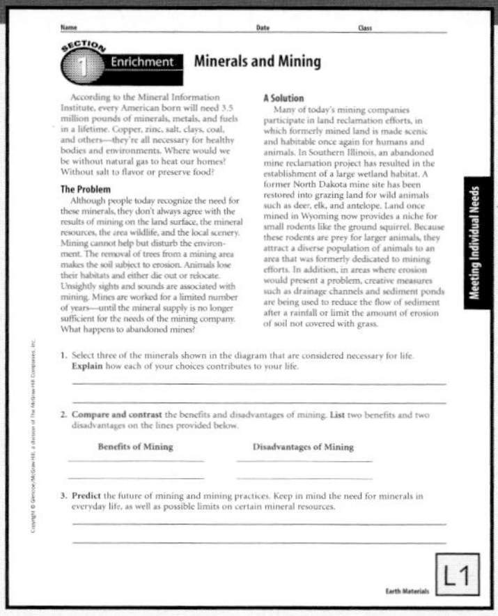

Directed Reading (English/Spanish)

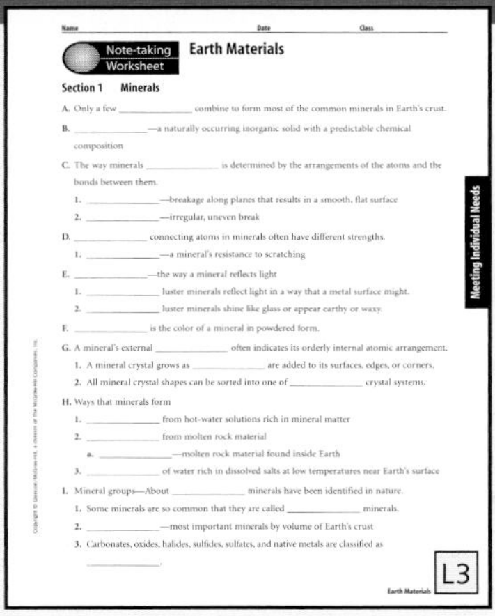

Spanish Directed Reading

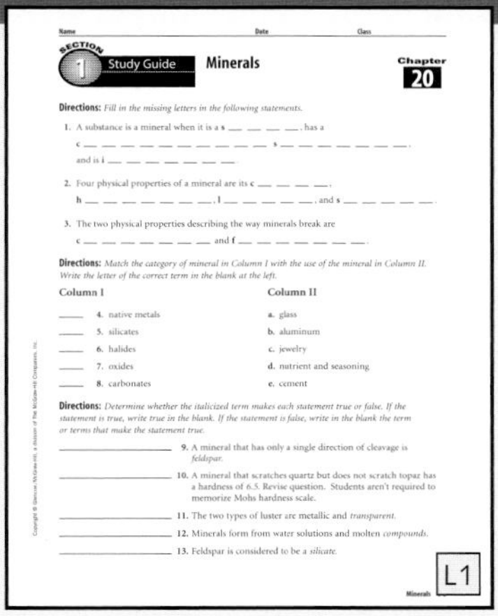

Reading Essentials

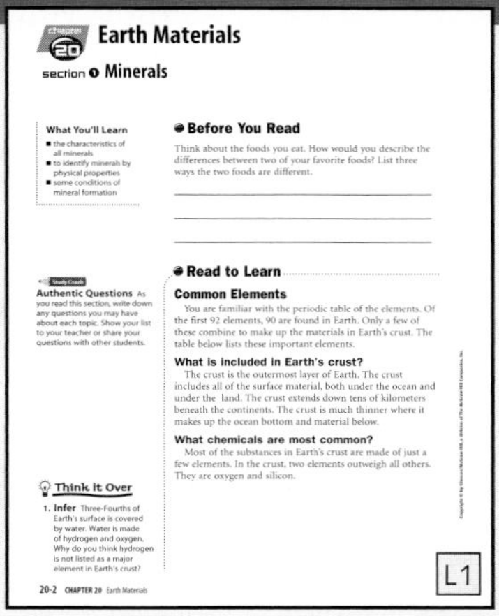

Assessment

Test Practice Workbook

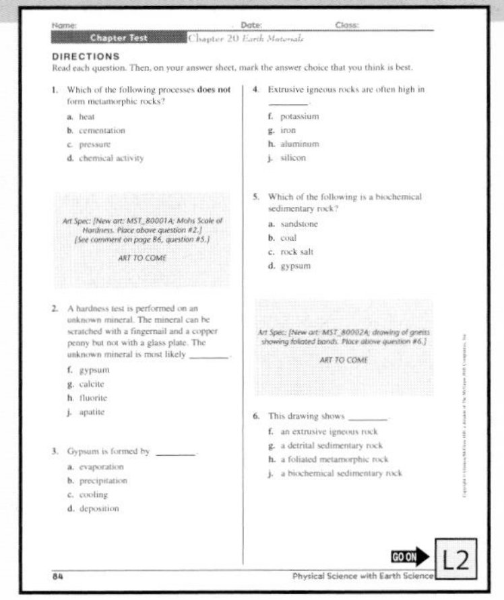

Chapter Review

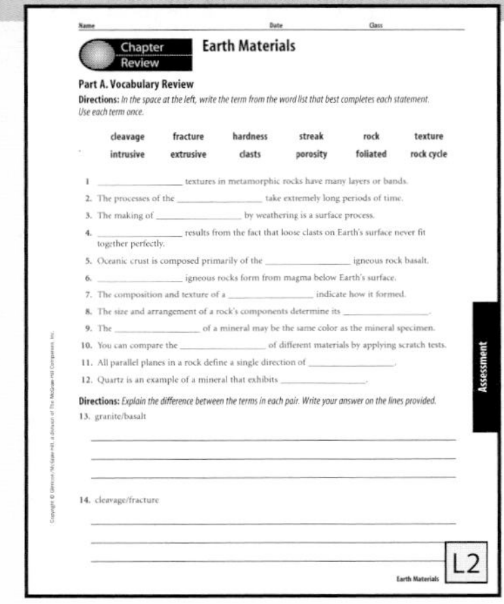

Chapter Tests

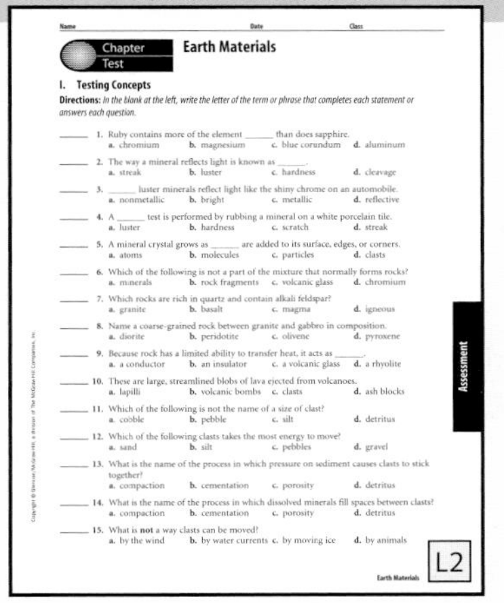

Science Content Background

section 1 Minerals

Common Elements

An important idea is that all matter, not just minerals, is made up of very few of the known elements. Most minerals are composed of only eight elements; expand the list of elements to 15 and you'll cover Earth's atmosphere, oceans, and living things. These 15 elements are common, simple, and have an atomic mass of less than 30.

Most rock forming minerals are more complex variations of a simple form. For example, the many types of silicates are composed of the simple silicon-oxygen tetrahedron. The addition of small amounts of an impurity changes these structures and creates a new set of physical properties.

section 2 Igneous Rocks

Crystalization Temperature

Magma can be thought of as a solution controlled by temperature. At a given temperature a mineral might exist as a solid or liquid. Magmas can be thought of as an element or an ionic soup. As the soup cools, ions will slow down and begin to form mineral crystals. Bowen's Reaction Series explains which minerals form first. The soup now has chunks of minerals. These chunks have a melting temperature that is higher than the temperature of the magma and will not melt as the magma continues to cool. Should temperatures rise, the minerals will melt in the reverse order from which they crystallized.

Magma rich in low-mass elements will produce minerals such as quartz or potassium feldspar, and will be low in density. Such low-density magmas produce continental crustal rocks such as granite. This density difference accounts for Earth's less-dense crust and denser mantle. The mantle is composed of minerals with higher densities such as olivine and pyroxene.

If magma cools rapidly, elements have less time to form large crystals. Crystal size, or texture, provides information on the rate of formation. The first rocks to be formed from a magma can be determined by their composition. These two factors—texture and composition—are key to classifying and interpreting igneous rocks.

chapter content resources

Internet Resources

For additional content background, visit **gpescience.com** to:

- access your book online
- find references to related articles in popular science magazines
- access Web links with related content background
- access current events with science journal topics

Print Resources

Physical Geology, Fifth Edition, by Charles C. Plummer and David McGeary, Wm. C. Brown Publishers, 1991

Petrology, by Loren A. Raymond, Wm. C. Brown Publishers, 1995

Manual of Mineralogy, Twenty-First Edition, by Cornelis Klein and Cornelius S. Hurlbut, Jr., John Wiley & Sons, Inc., 1993

section 3 Sedimentary Rocks

Texture and Composition Clues

The classification of sedimentary rock is based mainly on texture, followed by composition. Textural factors in detrital sedimentary rocks are particle size, shape, and sorting (range of size variation). These factors provide clues to the energy level and possible changes of the transporting medium.

Generally, large-sized clasts equate to high energy—mountain streams or beaches with heavy surf. Smaller sizes equate to low energy—swamps, lake bottoms, or deltas.

Shape factors give clues to the distance of transport. Angular clasts indicate near source locations. Well-rounded clasts indicate long distances of transport or longer periods of residence in an abrasive environment.

Size variation or sorting indicates variability of energy. Well-sorted clasts, all roughly the same size, indicate a consistent energy level. Beach sand tends to be well-sorted because wave action winnows away fine clasts and abrades and reduces larger clasts.

Composition depends on the nature of the parent rock. Rocks from the eastern United States yield a light-colored, quartz-rich sand like that of the Florida beaches. The basalt of Hawaii produces black sand. Poor sorting usually indicates a constant supply of new clasts or an extreme variability in energy levels. Chemical and organic sedimentary rocks tend to be composed of one mineral.

section 4 Metamorphic Rocks and the Rock Cycle

Degree of Metamorphism

Texture and composition are used equally when classifying metamorphic rock. Metamorphic rocks are first sorted by degree of foliation. Generally, as the degree of metamorphism increases, the rock will display a more-pronounced foliation pattern and will contain more mica minerals. Non-foliated metamorphic rocks tend to exhibit increased growth in grain size. The grains are often similar in size and composition. To avoid confusion in identifying igneous and metamorphic rocks, recall that igneous rocks have a broader range of grain sizes and mineral composition.

Teacher to Teacher

Nancy Bridge
Olympia High School
Orlando, Florida

For a hands-on experience with the rock cycle, I give each lab group four different colored crayons and a pencil sharpener. Students sharpen the crayons and collect the shavings on a piece of tag-board paper. This is the sediment step. Have students fold the tag board over, place it on the floor, and step on it. This is the sedimentary step. You still can see the individual colors and shapes but they cling together. Students bring the tag-board pockets to the teacher. The teacher places a warm iron (heat and pressure) on top of the tag-board pocket, which slightly melts the crayons together and makes a harder rock sample—the metamorphic step. We place a sample form the metamorphic step on a piece of foil, put it on a hot plate, and completely melt it. You no longer can distinguish any colors but it has changed into a new color—the igneous step.

Nancy Bridge

chapter 20

Chapter Vocabulary

mineral, p. 609
cleavage, p. 610
fracture, p. 610
hardness, p. 611
streak, p. 611
magma, p. 613
rock, p. 617
texture, p.617
intrusive igneous rock, p. 617
extrusive igneous rock, p. 620
clast, p. 624
porosity, p. 625
cementation, p. 625
foliated, p. 631
rock cycle, p. 634

Science Journal Student answers will vary. If students continue to trace the origins of materials, they will discover that all of the materials we use eventually come from Earth.

INTERACTIVE CHALKBOARD with Image Bank

PowerPoint® Presentations

This CD-ROM is an editable Microsoft® PowerPoint® presentation that includes:

- a pre-made presentation for every chapter
- interactive graphics
- animations
- audio clips
- image bank
- all new section and chapter questions
- Standardized Test Practice
- transparencies
- Foldables directions
- links to gpescience.com

chapter 20

Earth Materials

chapter preview

sections

1 Minerals
Lab Be a Mineral Detective
2 Igneous Rocks
3 Sedimentary Rocks
4 Metamorphic Rocks and the Rock Cycle
Lab Identifying Rocks

Mountain of Oxygen

We often think of oxygen as being in the air we breathe, but we also walk on it everyday. By weight, almost half of Earth's crust is oxygen. Imagine half the weight of this mountain being made of oxygen!

Science Journal In your Science Journal, list ten of the most important materials you can think of and where you think they come from.

606

Theme Connection

Law of Conservation of Mass This law states that mass can be neither created nor destroyed during chemical changes. In the rock cycle, minerals are being transformed by physical and chemical processes into different rock types, without the loss of the starting mass.

About the Photo

Gem of the Rockies Glacier-studded mountains tower above Maligne Lake, in Jasper National Park, Canada. These mountains are made of sedimentary rocks and a metamorphic rock called quartzite. Common minerals include silica, feldspar, mica, and olivine. Glaciers scour valley floors and grind rocks into rock flour. In the lake, this suspended material distorts light into emeralds and blues.

Start-Up Activities

Launch LAB

Earth Materials at Home and School

You come in contact with Earth materials every day. Many of the objects around you are Earth materials, or items processed using minerals or rocks as raw materials. 

1. Obtain several items from your teacher.
2. Make a three-column table on a separate sheet of paper.
3. In the first column, list each item.
4. In the second column, decide whether each item listed is a natural Earth material or a product made from Earth materials.
5. In the third column, indicate whether the item is found at home, school, or both places.
6. **Think Critically** Select three of the items in your first column and imagine that they no longer exist. Explain how you could cope without these materials. What other materials could be used instead?

Science Online | Preview this chapter's content and activities at gpescience.com

FOLDABLES™ Study Organizer

Textures Make the following Foldable to help you organize the types of textures in igneous, sedimentary, and metamorphic rocks.

STEP 1 **Fold** a sheet of paper in half lengthwise. Make the back edge about 2 inches longer than the front edge.

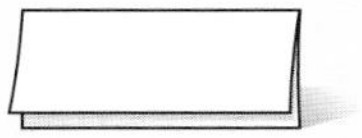

STEP 2 **Turn** the paper so the fold is on the bottom. Then **fold** it into thirds.

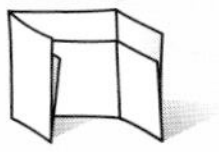

STEP 3 **Unfold and cut** only the top layer along both folds to make three tabs.

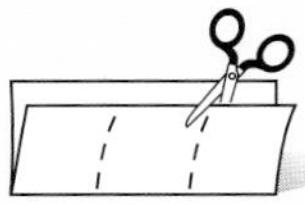

STEP 4 **Label** the Foldable as shown

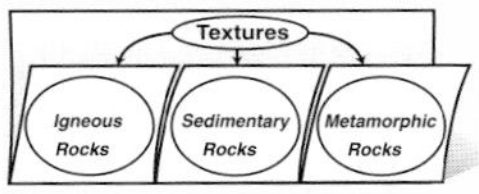

Making a Concept Map As you read the chapter, write about and illustrate the texture types shown by each group of rocks represented in your concept map.

Launch LAB

Purpose Use the Launch Lab to introduce students to the idea that most of the manufactured objects we use today require raw materials from Earth. L2 **Kinesthetic**

Preparation Prepare a collection of different objects to show the class or compile a list of common items for the class to consider.

Materials Suggested objects: paper clip, beverage can, plastic pen cap, piece of ceramic tile, piece of glass, cotton cloth, straw basket, leather item, wood item

Teaching Strategies

- Show the class an item and allow students to record their responses.
- Give students an object and have them explain their decisions to the class.

Think Critically

Possible answer: Students should speak of using alternative materials, such as using plastics instead of metals.

Assessment

Oral Have students formulate a list of Earth materials that we use today, but may run out of in the future. Have them include steps that could be taken to avoid this problem.

FOLDABLES™ Study Organizer **Dinah Zike Study Fold**

Student preparation materials for this Foldable are available in the Chapter *FAST FILE* Resources.

1 Motivate

INTERACTIVE CHALKBOARD An editable Microsoft® PowerPoint® presentation is available on **Interactive Chalkboard** CD-ROM.

Bellringer

Section Focus Transparencies also are available on the Interactive Chalkboard CD-ROM. L2 ELL

Section 1 Section Focus Transparency — A Sea of Diamonds — Chapter 20

Over the past 100 million years, up to 1,400 meters have eroded from the land's surface, sending billions of carats of diamonds on a trip to the sea. An estimate of diamonds eroded from just one mine, South Africa's Kimberley mine—the "Big Hole"— is 500,000 carats! Rivers carried most of the eroded diamonds to the Atlantic Ocean, although about ten percent were stored in the alluvial deposits of the drainage systems. Because powerful ocean waves break poorer quality diamonds, 90-95 percent of marine diamonds are of gem quality. That makes the Atlantic coast the focus of intense mining activity.

1. How are diamonds formed?
2. Why are diamonds so valuable?
3. How do diamonds fit the definition of a mineral?

L2

Earth Materials

Reading Preview

Tie to Prior Knowledge

Compounds Have students recall that compounds are composed of two or more different elements. Minerals are compounds found naturally on Earth. L2

Vocabulary Chart Have students develop a chart containing the new vocabulary words. Most of the terms are properties of minerals. Have students fill out the chart as they read, explaining the characteristics represented by each term.

section 1

Minerals

Reading Guide

What You'll Learn

- **Describe** characteristics of all minerals.
- **Identify** common minerals using physical properties.
- **Compare and contrast** some conditions of mineral formation.

Why It's Important

Minerals are a source of raw materials used to support civilization.

Review Vocabulary

ionic bond: attraction formed between oppositely charged ions in an ionic compound

New Vocabulary

- mineral
- cleavage
- fracture
- hardness
- streak
- magma

Common Elements

You're familiar with the periodic table of elements. Of the first 92 elements, 90 are found in Earth, and of these, only a small number combine to make up most of the common minerals in Earth's crust. **Table 1** lists these important elements. Most of the chemical formulas of common minerals contain some of these elements.

Composition of Earth's Crust The crust is the outermost layer of Earth. It includes all continental material and the material that forms the ocean bottom. The crust extends down tens of kilometers beneath the continents, but it is much thinner where it makes up the ocean bottom and material below, as shown in **Figure 1.**

Table 1 Major Elements in Earth's Crust

Element	Percent (by mass)	Element	Percent (by mass)
Oxygen	46.6%	Sodium	2.8%
Silicon	27.7%	Potassium	2.6%
Aluminum	8.1%	Magnesium	2.1%
Iron	5.0%	All others	1.5%
Calcium	3.6%		

Section 1 Resource Manager

Chapter *FAST FILE* Resources

- Transparency Activity, pp. 48, 53–54
- Note-taking Worksheets, pp. 37–39
- MiniLAB, p. 3
- Enrichment, p. 33
- Reinforcement, p. 29
- Directed Reading for Content Mastery, p. 22
- Lab Worksheets, pp. 5–6

Home and Community Involvement, p. 39

Life Science Critical Thinking/Problem Solving, p. 16

Cultural Diversity, pp. 37–38

Lab Management and Safety, p. 56

608 CHAPTER 20 Earth Materials

Chemical Element Building Blocks Imagine Earth's chemical parts being like a set of interlocking blocks. In the set you are given lots of common types of blocks from which you can make thousands of forms. But, you are given only a few of the special blocks. The bulk of the forms you build consist of the common blocks. Elements and minerals in Earth's crust are a lot like the block set. For example, most minerals of the crust, whether beneath the land surface or ocean water, contain abundant oxygen and silicon.

What's a mineral?

Remember that atoms of different elements can bond chemically to form compounds. A **mineral** is a naturally occurring element or compound that is inorganic, solid, and has a crystalline structure. In addition, minerals have predictable chemical compositions that are indicated as single elements or chemical formulas. For example, the native element gold is a mineral with chemical formula Au. Similarly, the compound fluorite is a mineral that contains Ca and F in a 1:2 ratio, resulting in chemical formula CaF_2.

Physical Properties

A mineral has a characteristic set of physical properties, but some of these properties can differ from sample to sample. For example, some minerals come in several different colors. This color variation may be due to chemical impurities in the mineral. This is true for the gem varieties of the mineral corundum, Al_2O_3. Ruby is red corundum, and sapphire is blue corundum. Ruby contains more of the element chromium, which substitutes for Al in the crystalline structure. You should take care when observing mineral properties, particularly when studying their colors.

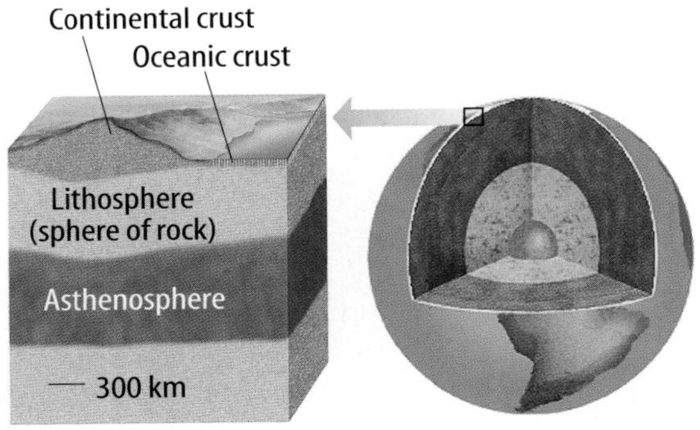

Figure 1 The crust and a thin layer of the upper mantle make up the lithosphere, which means rock sphere. The lithosphere floats on a dense, plasticlike layer called the asthenosphere.

2 Teach

Teacher FYI

Gemstone Market Diamonds are often viewed as the king of gemstones. There is a diamond cartel, which means that a few producers in the world strictly control the price of diamonds. The mining, grading, cutting, and marketing of diamonds do not allow for price to reflect demand. Colored stones, such as emeralds, rubies and sapphires, are not subject to this control and therefore change in value according to the effects of supply and demand.

Differentiated Instruction

English-Language Learners Have students create a dual-language glossary for common rock and mineral names. Having hand specimens available to illustrate the glossary could be helpful. L2 **Visual-Spatial**

Curriculum Connection

Geography Have students prepare a world map showing the distribution of metal (iron, copper, aluminum, gold, silver) or valuable mineral (emerald, ruby, diamond) production. Discuss whether the countries where these are found are enjoying economic growth because of this.

Make A Model

Construct a model of the atomic arrangement of a common mineral, such as sodium chloride (NaCl) or calcium carbonate ($CaCO_3$). L2 ELL LS **Visual-Spatial, Kinesthetic**

Activity

Special Properties of Minerals Discuss with students that some minerals have distinct properties that help in their identification. Provide small groups with samples of halite, calcite, magnetite, specular hematite, and sphalerite. In addition, provide them with dilute HCl, a small magnet and a streak plate. If possible, demonstrate the effect that fluorescent light has on calcite. Encourage students to discover the special properties that each of these minerals has. Halite tastes salty, calcite fizzes with HCl, magnetite is magnetic, specular hematite is silver but shows a reddish-brown streak, and sphalerite is brown but steaks pale yellow and the streak smells like sulphur. Calcite appears orange under fluorescent light.

Reading Check

Answer Quartz fractures, but does not cleave.

IDENTIFYING Misconceptions

Cleavage v. Crystals Students may confuse a crystal face for a cleavage plane. Explain, using a quartz crystal as a guide, that crystal faces are not cleavage features.

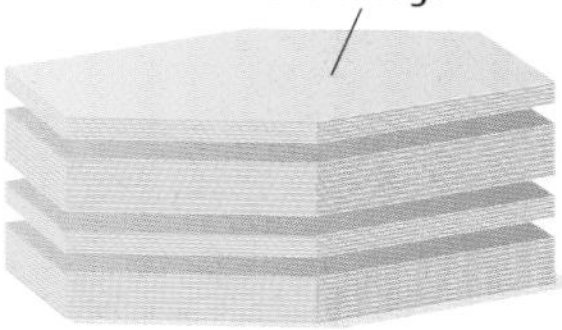

Figure 2 Because mica has one direction of cleavage, it can be separated in layers.

Atom Arrangement Some physical properties are controlled by the orderly arrangement of atoms in a mineral's structure. This orderly pattern is what makes a mineral crystalline. The arrangement of atoms and the bonds between them can reflect the way a mineral breaks, how hard it is, and what type of crystal shape it has.

How Minerals Break When minerals break along planes that cut across relatively weak chemical bonds, a smooth, flat surface is created. The ability of a mineral to do this is the physical property called **cleavage.** All parallel cleavage planes define a single direction of cleavage. The mica family of minerals exhibits only one direction of cleavage, as shown in **Figure 2.** Other minerals may show two or more different directions of cleavage, as in **Figure 3.** If this happens, those different planar directions have to meet each other at an angle.

Some minerals do not split along well-defined flat surfaces. In such cases, a mineral will break unevenly. This type of irregular break is called **fracture.** Quartz is an example of a common mineral that does not cleave, but exhibits fracture. This physical property is a key aspect in distinguishing quartz from other minerals.

Reading Check *What distinguishes quartz from other minerals?*

Figure 3 Feldspar is an example of a mineral with two planes of cleavage.

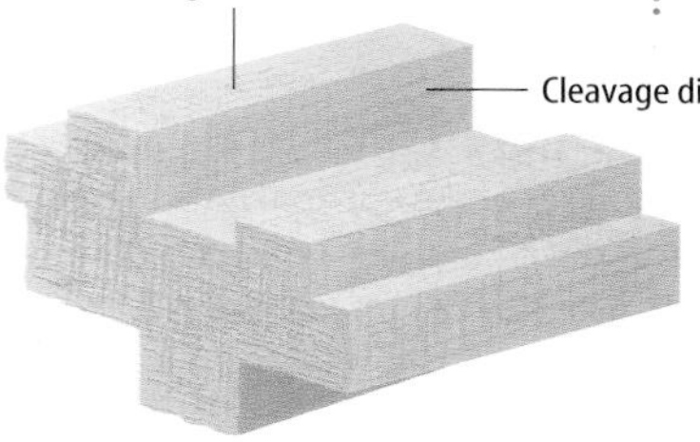

610 CHAPTER 20 Earth Materials

Visual Learning

Figure 2 Observe the mica in the photo. What can you say about the chemical bonds that form this mineral? Because the mineral splits into sheets, you can say that the bonds are weak. L2 LS **Visual-Spatial**

Teacher FYI

Cleavage Cleavage doesn't have to display entire planar surfaces. Imagine the corner of a box projecting above a surface. You can see three cleavage faces; top, end, and side. It is not necessary to see the opposite planar surface of these to infer their presence.

Hardness Bonds connecting atoms in materials often have different strengths. When you scratch a mineral with another material you will be breaking bonds and leaving a scratch. The physical property that measures resistance to scratching is called **hardness.** You can compare the hardness of different materials by applying scratch tests and using Mohs Scale, as shown in **Table 2.** When a hardness test is performed by rubbing two objects together, the softer of the two will wear away.

Table 2 Mohs Scale of Hardness

1. Talc	6. Feldspar
2. Gypsum (fingernail 2.2)	7. Quartz (streak plate 7.0)
3. Calcite (copper penny 3.2)	8. Topaz
4. Fluorite	9. Corundum
5. Apatite (glass plate 5.5)	10. Diamond

Today, you might be using a pencil that takes advantage of the softness of a mineral. The graphite in the core of some pencils has one plane of cleavage and very weak bonds. The weak bonds make the lead soft. As you write with the pencil, thin plates of graphite are left on your paper and the pencil becomes dull.

Luster and Streak The way a mineral reflects light is the physical property known as luster. Two main types of luster, metallic and nonmetallic, help subdivide minerals and often give a clue about their compositions. Just as you might guess, metallic luster minerals reflect light in a way that a metal surface might, such as the shiny chrome on a car or bicycle. Nonmetallic luster, shown in **Figure 4,** includes descriptions of all other types, such as those minerals that shine like glass or appear earthy or waxy.

The color of a mineral in powdered form is called **streak.** The streak of a mineral may be the same color as the mineral specimen, but when a mineral shows different colors or types of luster, the streak powder color generally stays the same, which helps identify the mineral. A streak test is performed by rubbing a mineral on a white porcelain tile.

Figure 4 The mineral on the left produces a glassy luster; the mineral on the right produces a metallic luster.

Quick Demo
Testing for Hardness

Materials penny, steel nail, wire nail, glass plate.

Estimated Time 20 minutes

Procedure Demonstrate the technique for determining hardness.

- The test is for resistance to scratching.
- The pressure used is similar to that for writing.
- Show testing in several directions on the same surface of the specimen. Often, specimens contain more than one mineral. Be sure to test different surfaces of the same mineral.
- Caution students to always hold either the sample or the testing materials on the table. They should always place the glass plate on the table, never in their hands. L2 ELL **Visual-Spatial**

Discussion

What makes diamonds, sapphires, and rubies so valuable? There are two possible answers. Rarity for those minerals that have extreme value; supply and demand for all the others. Quartz sand has little value because it is so abundant; extremely pure quartz, which is rare, has a higher value because of its use in making computer chips.

Activity

Before having a formal lab experience with minerals, have students sort the minerals they will use in the lab into groups of their choice. Have them explain their sorting criteria. Students will most likely use color. Use several colors of quartz as an example to explain the problem of using color alone. L2 ELL LS **Visual-Spatial**

Visual Learning

Figure 4 What color streak would the two minerals shown here produce? Streak testing is generally useful only for metallic minerals. Can you explain why this is so? The streak produced by non-metallic minerals is usually white, while metallic minerals produce streaks that range from black to grey to even reddish-brown. A colored streak provides more information about a particular mineral than a white streak does.

SECTION 1 Minerals **611**

Mini LAB

Purpose Students will learn and identify the shape of salt (NaCl) crystals. L2 ELL LS **Visual-Spatial**

Materials table salt, magnifying glass

Analysis

1. sketches of cubes
2. Cubes may stick together to form rectangles.
3. cubic; The length of all of the sides of the smallest particle are equal.

Assessment

Content Have students imagine the placement of the sodium and chlorine atoms to form a cube and to form a repeated structure of cubes.

Reading Strategy

Summarize Have students compose a summary paragraph in which they describe how scientists identify minerals by their properties. Remind students to explain each mineral property by using the mineral charts they created earlier.

Teacher FYI

Common Minerals and Crystal Systems The six crystal systems can be difficult to visualize. Sometimes the crystal takes the form of the system. For example, halite and calcite belong to the cubic and triclinic systems, respectively. A well-formed quartz crystal has six sides and belongs to the hexagonal system. Biotite, which occurs in sheets, belongs to the monoclinic system. Remember that identification of minerals seldom is based on identifying its crystal system.

Mini LAB

Identifying Salt's Crystal System

Procedure

1. Sprinkle a small quantity of **salt** onto a **dark surface.**
2. Using a **magnifying lens,** observe the individual grains of salt.

Analysis

1. Make a sketch showing the shapes of several salt grains.
2. Why are some of the grains more elongated than others?
3. To which crystal system does salt belong? Support your answer with details from the text.

Try at Home

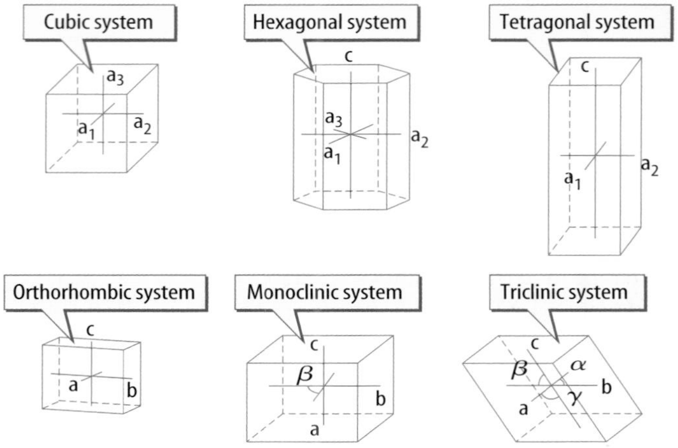

Figure 5 Minerals can be classified using six basic crystal forms.

Crystal Shape The orderly internal arrangement of atoms in a mineral often is indicated by its external crystal shape. In fact, some minerals take on a geometric shape that is a larger version of their internal atomic arrangement. Even though many unique shapes are exhibited by mineral crystals in nature, each can be sorted into one of the six crystal systems, as shown in **Figure 5.** The types of symmetry shown by the crystal are key elements in determining the crystal system to which a mineral belongs.

Mineral Formation

A mineral crystal grows as atoms are added to its surfaces, edges, or corners. The types of atoms that are added depend on what atoms are available in the growing crystal's surroundings. Growth also is controlled by how fast atoms can migrate to the crystal and by the temperature and pressure conditions of the surroundings. Some ways that minerals form include precipitation from hot, water-rich fluids, solidification from molten rock material, and evaporation of water rich in dissolved salts at low temperatures near Earth's surface.

Minerals from Hot Water Some minerals are produced from hot-water solutions rich in dissolved mineral matter. You know that sugar dissolves fastest in hot water. As hot water cools, its atoms slow down and atoms of dissolved material are able to form chemical bonds. Minerals often form around the edges of hot springs, as shown in **Figure 6.** When hot water passes through cracks in cooler rock, minerals may form within the cracks. The cracks become lined and filled with mineral matter. Sometimes, veins or halos of concentrated minerals like gold, silver, or copper are produced in fractures.

Figure 6 Hydrothermal minerals form on the rims of hot springs.

Differentiated Instruction

Learning Disabled Some students may have a difficult time envisioning dissolved minerals in solution. Demonstrate the concept of evaporation and precipitation with a simple activity using salt and warm water. Have students dissolve 2–3 teaspoons of salt in 200 mL of warm water and stir until dissolved. Explain that the mineral halite (salt) is now in solution. Pour the water into a shallow Petri dish and allow it to evaporate overnight. Explain that the water evaporated into the air (became water vapor) and the substance that remains on the dish is halite. It precipitated from the solution as the water evaporated.

Minerals from Magma Molten rock material found inside Earth is called **magma.** As magma cools, atoms slow down and begin to arrange into an orderly structure. When the temperature of magma drops well below the solidification temperature of a mineral, crystals of that particular mineral may form and grow.

Reading Check *How do minerals form in magma?*

Minerals from Evaporation Minerals also form from water at Earth's surface. When water slowly evaporates, concentrated dissolved mineral material may be left behind to form crystals. You might have seen films of material left behind in a pan that once was filled with water. Crusty material is left on the surface of the pan after the water evaporates.

Mineral Groups

About 3,800 minerals have been identified in nature. Some minerals are so common that they are called rock-forming minerals. Recall that few elements are needed to make up almost the entire crust of Earth. Similarly, a few important mineral groups make up most of Earth's crust.

Silicates The atomic arrangement and composition of minerals allow them to be sorted into groups. Among these, the most important by volume of Earth's crust are the silicate groups.

Most minerals contain silica. Silica is a common term for a compound that contains silicon plus oxygen or silicon dioxide (SiO_2). The mineral quartz is pure silica that has crystallized. In silicate minerals, the elements silicon and oxygen bond together to form a geometric structure called a tetrahedron, as shown in **Table 3.** Other metal atoms can attach to the oxygen atoms. Most silicate minerals contain silicon, oxygen, and one or more other elements.

Table 3 Silicate Minerals

Mineral		Photos	Silicate Structure
Olivine			 Single tetrahedron
Pyroxene group (Augite)			 Single chains
Amphibole group (Hornblende)			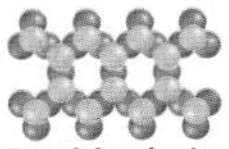 Double chains
Micas	Biotite		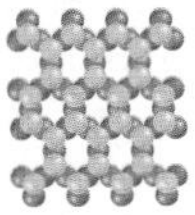 Sheets
	Muscovite		
Feldspars	Potassium feldspar		 Three-dimensional networks
	Plagioclase		
Quartz			

INTEGRATE Chemistry

Si-O Bond The silicon-oxygen tetrahedron is the base unit for the silicates in the nonliving world. Carbon chains are fundamental units for living things. Research carbon chains and compare and contrast them with the Si-O tetrahedrons.

Reading Check

Answer When magma is cooled well below the solidification temperature of the minerals, atoms arrange themselves into orderly groups and solids form.

INTEGRATE Chemistry

Si-O Bond Compare and contrast carbon chains with Si-O tetrahedrons. Both carbon and silicon are in Group 14 of the periodic table. Both elements form chains. However, carbon forms covalent bonds with many elements and often produces flexible molecular structures. In the Si-O tetrahedron, the bond between silicon and oxygen is an ionic bond, which often produces a rigid structure.

IDENTIFYING Misconceptions

Mineral Precipitation Students may think that mineral matter gets sprayed or spread on the surface as hot water sprays or flows from a spring. The process is more complex. Minerals such as calcium and bicarbonate are dissolved in the hot water. Below the surface, the water is under pressure, which keeps the minerals in solution. At the surface, pressure is less. Carbon dioxide, which under pressure is dissolved in the water, escapes as a gas. This leaves the carbonate to combine with calcium, forming calcium carbonate as a precipitate. The chemical equation is as follows:
$Ca^{2+} + 2HCO_{3-} > CO_2$ (gas) $+ CaCO_{3-} + H_2O$

Fun Fact

Silica, which is pure quartz, has a wide variety of uses. It is used to make glass, added to tires to extend their life, added to highway asphalt to harden it, used in crystal as the time keeping element in watches, and is the foundation material in making computer chips.

Using Science Words

Word Meaning Introduce the word *phyllo* to the students. It means "leaf" in Greek. Phyllo dough is thin, sheet-like dough used to make a variety of pastries and foods. Challenge the students to determine which type of silicate the mineral mica is and explain why it is classified as such. Mica is a phyllosicate. These are made of sheets of silica tetrahedra that are weakly joined together. Mica occurs as sheets that are easily peeled apart. Thus, it is just like phyllo dough.

Reading Check

Answer oxides

Inquiry Lab

Mineral Search

Question How many things in your home are made from important silicate and non-silicate minerals?

Possible Materials items found at home, textbook

Estimated Time 30 minutes

Teaching Strategies

- Have students use their textbook and other sources to research and prepare a list of silicate minerals and non-silicate minerals that are commonly used for household items.
- Explain that quartz, a silicate, is used in glass, watches, clocks, computers, televisions, and electronic games. Talc, a silicate, is used in talcum powder, paint, ceramics, paper, and rubber.
- Important non-silicates include fluorite (toothpaste), calcite (cement and antacids), graphite (pencil lead), gypsum (drywall), and halite (table salt). Other non-silicates include some gemstones and metals such as iron (used in steel), copper, zinc, aluminum, tin, gold, and silver.

For additional inquiry activities, see *Science Inquiry Lab Manual*.

Science Online

Topic: Economic Minerals
Visit gpescience.com for Web links to information about uses for minerals.

Activity Make a table for at least ten minerals. Your table headings should include *Common Minerals, Occurrences,* and *Uses or Products.*

Silicate Structures You probably have watched buildings go up in your neighborhood. All the buildings are put together using similar construction materials. What really makes them different is how these materials are put together. Silicate mineral groups are similar. Silicates all contain silicon-oxygen tetrahedrons that are linked together in different ways.

The simplest silicate structures have silicon-oxygen tetrahedrons that are not linked together. By joining silicon-oxygen tetrahedrons together, chains, sheets, and three-dimensional framework structures can form, as shown in **Table 3.** Keep in mind that each group of silicates has a different structure, but most contain the silicon-oxygen tetrahedron as a basic structural unit.

Minerals of the Crust Several important silicate groups form most of Earth's crust. Quartz and some feldspar group minerals, shown in **Table 3,** are relatively low in density and form at relatively low temperatures compared to other silicate minerals. Together, quartz and feldspar group silicates make up most of Earth's continental crust.

In contrast, Earth's oceanic crust is denser and contains a larger percentage of silicates whose tetrahedrons are not linked together as much. For example, chain silicates such as the pyroxene group, and single tetrahedron silicates of the olivine group, along with plagioclase feldspars, make up the majority of crust beneath the oceans.

Figure 7 Calcite, shown above, is a common mineral found in limestone. Hematite, below, is an ore used to produce iron and steel.

Important Non-silicates Many important mineral groups are not silicates. These include the carbonates, oxides, halides, sulfides, sulfates, and native metals. The non-silicate groups are a source of many valuable ore minerals and building materials. To be an ore, a mineral must occur in large enough quantities to be economically recoverable. One example of an important ore of iron is the mineral hematite, an iron oxide. Aluminum comes in part from bauxite, a mixture of aluminum oxides. People eat salt processed from the halide mineral halite, and use calcite (a carbonate) to make cement. Common non-silicate minerals are shown in **Figure 7.**

Reading Check *To which mineral group does hematite belong?*

Fun Fact

Fun Fact Enrique Camarena Salazar was an American drug enforcement agent who was murdered and found buried on a ranch in Mexico. Forensic evidence and careful examination of the dirt found on his body determined that he had been killed somewhere else and had been moved to the ranch later.

Post Reading

Extended Research Have students research a mineral using library resources. Ask them to develop a report in which they discuss mineral extraction, uses, and properties. For example, a student may choose to study quartz, which is used in glass manufacturing and as a part of computers.

Mineral Uses

For centuries, humans have relied on minerals for their everyday needs, for example, humans have always needed salt. Civilizations have advanced themselves through the use of their mineral wealth. Think of the exploration and conflicts that took place over gold. Europeans spent vast sums of money and risked many lives to search for gold.

People use minerals either directly as objects of wealth, or as raw materials to make things. Those regions fortunate enough to have large quantities of hematite, iron ore, advanced rapidly. Think of all of the things made from iron and steel. Without iron there would be no machinery as we know it today for manufacturing goods.

Not all minerals need to provide metals to be valuable. Nonmetallic minerals are valuable as well. For example, quartz is used to make glass and glass fibers. Glass fiber is used to make fiber optical cables. Most sands and gravels are largely quartz. When mixed with cement (calcite), quartz is used to make concrete. Think of all the things that are made of concrete.

INTEGRATE Language Arts

Salt Mining Because of its use as a preservative for food in ancient times, salt was a valuable resource. Salt has been collected by evaporating seawater and by mining deposits from below Earth's surface. Research the word *salary* in terms of its connection with salt.

section 1 review

Summary

Common Elements

- Few elements form the bulk of materials in Earth's crust.

Mineral Properties

- A mineral is an inorganic solid with a predictable chemical composition.
- All minerals occur in nature and have orderly internal atomic arrangements.
- Physical properties of minerals may reflect their chemical composition and orderly atomic arrangement.

Mineral Formation and Mineral Groups

- Minerals crystallize mainly from fluids and molten rock material, as atoms come together to form crystalline structures.
- Minerals can be sorted into two broad categories: silicates and non-silicates.

Mineral Uses

- Civilization depends on minerals for a wide range of uses, from direct wealth to making products.

Self Check

1. **Determine** whether diamonds produced in laboratories are considered to be minerals.
2. **Describe** two ways that minerals form.
3. **Compare and contrast** mineral cleavage and mineral fracture.
4. **Explain** why it is useful to test more than one physical property when attempting to identify a mineral.
5. **Think Critically** What does the fact that mower blades become dull tell you about the hardness of the blades?

Applying Math

6. **Calculate Area** Imagine you have a halite cube that measures 3 cm on each edge. What is the total surface area of the cube?
7. **Calculate Area** Imagine cleaving the halite cube in question 6 exactly in half, perpendicular to one of its faces. What is the total surface area now?
8. **Analyzing Variables** What is the relationship between particle size and surface area for a given volume of material?

INTEGRATE Language Arts

Salt Mining Because of its use as a food preservative, in ancient times salt was more valuable than gold. Through the ages salt has been collected by evaporating seawater or briny river water or through mining.

Research Have students research the origin of the word *salary*. *Salary* comes from Latin *salarium*, meaning "pension of salt," which comes from sal which means "salt." ELL

3 Assess

DAILY INTERVENTION

Check for Understanding

Linguistic Have students write a short, detailed description of the process used to identify a mineral. L2

Reteach

Identification Display a variety of mineral samples. Call on students to choose one and, using correct terms and materials, identify the sample. L1 ELL

Visual-Spatial

Assessment

Portfolio A murder has occurred and the body is found in the woods. Have students create a poster describing the kinds of mineral evidence a crime sceneinvestigator might collect and how that evidence might be used. Use **PASC,** p. 145. L2 P

section 1 review

1. Synthetic diamonds are not minerals because they do not occur naturally.
2. cooling of magma; precipitation from a solution; material left after evaporation
3. fracture leaves uneven surfaces; cleavage leaves smooth, parallel planar surfaces
4. For any given property there will be many minerals (there are many white minerals); however, for a set of properties the choices become fewer.
5. Grass contains silica, which has a hardness of 5.5. But the hardness of iron is 4.5, thus allowing the blades to wear down.
6. 54 cm^3
7. 72 cm^3
8. Surface area increases as the particle sizes decrease.

BENCH TESTED

Video Lab available for this lab.

Real-World Problem

Purpose Students will gain experience in observation, classification, and use of a classification key. L2

Process Skills observe, evaluate, interpret data, record, collect data

Time Required Two 40-minute sessions

Safety Precautions

Pennies and steel nails are sufficient to establish hardness; glass plates can be omitted.

Place glass plates flat on surface and hold mineral sample in your hand.

Dispose of broken glass plates in proper containers.

Procedure

Teaching Strategies Remind students to be open-minded in observations.

Troubleshooting If specimens are in short supply, give each group only two specimens at a time and rotate the specimens from group to group.

Conclude and Apply

1. Some minerals have no outstanding properties.
2. Some minerals have outstanding and unique properties, such as mica with one plane of cleavage, galena with a high specific gravity, or halite with cubic cleavage.
3. Answers will vary. Students may list hardness, cleavage, fracture, and luster.
4. Answers will vary but may include color and luster.

LAB

Be a Mineral Detective

Detectives must gather facts and physical evidence to deduce the events that took place during a crime. Much like detectives, geologists gather physical evidence to better understand Earth processes. First, minerals are identified, and then their histories sometimes can be interpreted.

Real-World Problem

How is it possible to distinguish similar-looking materials from each other?

Goals

- **Observe and record** physical properties of minerals.
- **Determine** mineral names using your observations and identification keys.

Materials

mineral samples
unglazed porcelain tile
Mohs hardness scale
Reference Handbook, "Minerals"
penny
nail
glass plate

Procedure

1. Set up a data table on your paper. Label the columns using, at least: *Mineral Number, Color, Hardness, Streak, Cleavage, Fracture, Other Observations* (like smell, feel, or heft), and *Mineral Name.*
2. Obtain numbered mineral specimens from your teacher. Observe each mineral and accurately record the data based on your tests for physical properties. Be descriptive and broad in your observations.

   Hints: When determining hardness, test several different spots on the sample. Remember the hardness of your fingernail is a little more than 2; penny, a bit more than 3; steel nail, 5–6; glass, about 5–5.5. Minerals can have both cleavage and fracture at the same time. Cleavage is expressed as how many unique planar directions are present, and the angles formed when more than one direction occurs.
3. Using the Reference Handbook, "Minerals" at the back of your book, attempt to identify each unknown mineral. Your teacher may tell you when you are incorrect and allow you try again.

Conclude and Apply

1. **Explain** why certain minerals seemed to be difficult to identify.
2. **Explain** why certain minerals seemed to be easy to identify.
3. **Determine** which physical properties were most reliable for identification overall.
4. **Determine** which physical properties seemed to be least reliable.

Communicating Your Data

Compare your results with your classmates. Discuss what kind of mineral evidence a detective might obtain from a crime scene and how it might be used.

Communicating Your Data

Detectives may compare mineral or soil particles found on the clothing, shoes, or other objects belonging to the accused with corresponding particles from the crime scene.

Assessment

Oral Ask students to select a single identifying characteristic for each mineral they worked with. This will not be possible for some minerals. Reinforce the idea that identification relies on a set of characteristics. L2

section 2

Igneous Rocks

Reading Guide

What You'll Learn
- **Describe** the types of materials present in most rocks.
- **Explain** how and where igneous rocks form.
- **Classify** igneous rocks.

Why It's Important
Igneous rocks make up the majority of Earth's crust and mantle and contain clues about processes that form them.

Review Vocabulary
mixture: combination of two or more substances that can be physically separated

New Vocabulary
- rock
- texture
- intrusive igneous rock
- extrusive igneous rock

What's a rock?

A **rock** is a naturally formed consolidated mixture containing minerals, rock fragments, or volcanic glass. Most rocks contain crystals of minerals that may or may not be well-formed. Rocks are identified by their composition and texture. **Texture** is a description that includes the size and arrangement of the rock's components. The rock-making process is a continuous cycle. Part of this cycle involves rock formed from magma inside Earth.

Reading Check *What types of materials compose rocks?*

Figure 8 These light-colored veins of intrusive igneous rock formed when molten rock material cut through surrounding rock layers.

Intrusive Igneous Rocks

Igneous rocks are those that form from molten rock material called magma. Geologists have termed igneous rocks from inside Earth plutonic, after Pluto, the Greek god of the underworld. Such rocks also are called **intrusive igneous rocks** because they form within, or push into, regions of Earth's crust, as shown in **Figure 8.**

Section 2 Resource Manager

Chapter FAST FILE Resources
- Transparency Activity, p. 49
- Enrichment, p. 34
- Reinforcement, p. 30
- Directed Reading, p. 22
- **Physical Science Critical Thinking/Problem Solving,** p. 9

1 Motivate

INTERACTIVE CHALKBOARD An editable Microsoft® PowerPoint® presentation is available on **Interactive Chalkboard** CD-ROM.

Bellringer

Section Focus Transparencies also are available on the Interactive Chalkboard CD-ROM. L2 ELL

Section 2 Section Focus Transparency Earth Power! Chapter 20

Geothermal power plants are electricity-generating stations. They get their energy from hot water circulating deep underground in rocks heated by contact with magma. Geothermal plants are often located in geologically active locations, such as the Philippines and Indonesia. Geothermal power has great potential as an alternative source of energy to lessen the world's dependence on increasingly diminishing oil supplies.

1. How might a geothermal power plant gain access to the hot water underground?
2. How could magma heat water that comes in contact with it?
3. Do you think geothermal power could be the answer to the world's energy needs? Why or why not?

L2

Earth Materials

Reading Preview

Tie to Prior Knowledge
Rocks and Minerals Generally, minerals are naturally occurring mixtures of elements; rocks are mixtures of minerals.

Visualize Have students scan the text to find the new vocabulary words and predict the meanings. Ask them to develop a mental picture of each term. For *intrusive igneous rock,* students might picture Earth with an interior made of magma and solid rock.

Reading Check

Answer a mixture of minerals, rock fragments, and/or volcanic glass

2 Teach

IDENTIFYING Misconceptions

Magma A common misconception is that magma comes from the outer core. Some magma is formed in the asthenosphere. The asthenosphere is a semisolid layer below the crust, within the upper part of the upper mantle. This magma is composed of the heavier, denser minerals such as olivine and pyroxene. Magma is also formed within the crust, particularly at convergent plate tectonic boundaries. This magma is less dense than that formed from the asthenosphere.

Use Science Words

Students often confuse the word freezing with being exclusive to the freezing of water at 0°C or 32° F. Ask what the freezing temperature of a magma is.
Stress that freezing is the action of going from a liquid to a solid; Hawaiian basalt flows freeze at temperatures in excess of 1,000°C. Also stress that freezing and melting temperatures are the same at a given pressure. L1 ELL
LS **Linguistic**

Caption Answer

Figure 9 Responses will vary, but mineral pairs should always be at approximately the same temperature level.

Nature of Magma As it passes through rock, magma might cause partial melting of the rock it intrudes. Geologists have learned that minerals melt at different temperatures, so some will melt when exposed to the thermal energy of the magma. This interaction between magma and surrounding rock can cause changes in the rock, contamination of the magma, or both.

You're familiar with the freezing of liquid water to form ice at 0°C on Earth's surface. Minerals freeze at very high temperatures, ranging from several hundred to more than 1,000°C. However, magmas generally must be cooled below the solidification temperature of a mineral in order for it to begin crystallizing.

Intrusive Igneous Rock Composition As crystals solidify in cooling magma, they use up certain atoms. High-temperature magmas tend to crystallize olivine and pyroxene group minerals and plagioclase feldspars first. These minerals are dense and tend to settle toward the bottom of the magma chamber. Late-forming, less dense minerals tend to solidify at lower temperatures and float to the top of the magma chamber. These relationships are shown in **Figure 9.**

Figure 9 The Bowen's reaction series, shown below, illustrates the sequence in which minerals crystallize from magma at different temperatures.
Identify *two pairs of minerals that are likely to be found in the same rock.*

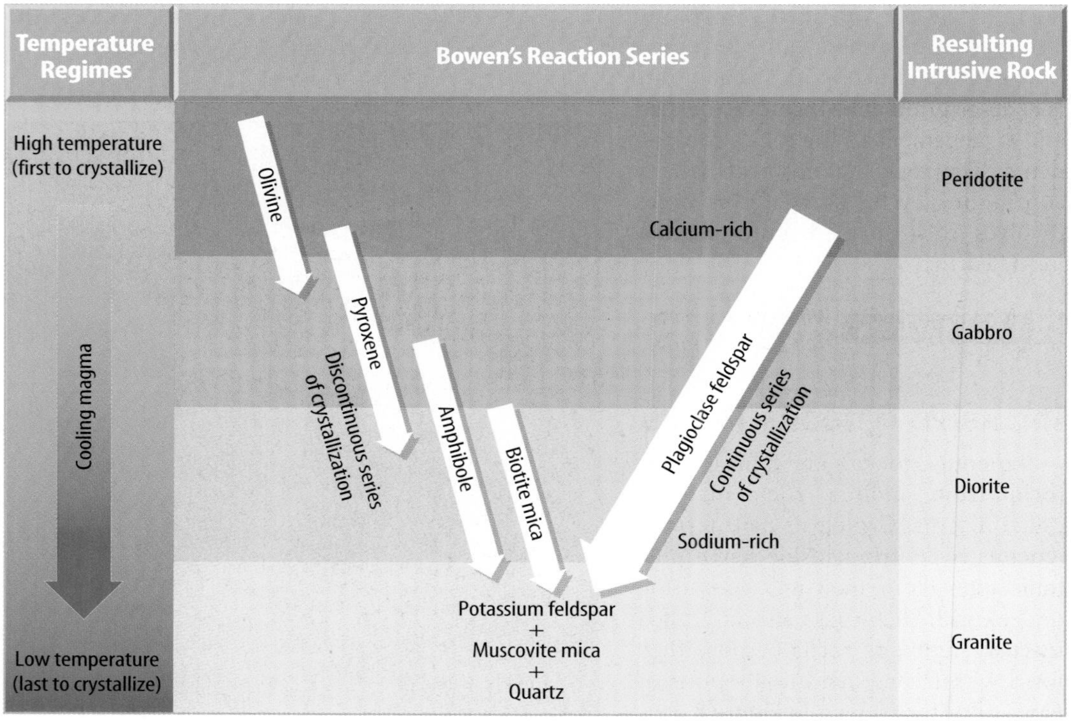

Reading Strategy

Double-Entry Notes Have students divide a sheet of paper into two columns. In the left column, students will take notes from the text. The right column is reserved for reflections regarding the notes, such as connections to previous content, opinions, or questions.

Visual Learning

Figure 9 Observe that on the continuous series side of the diagram, the feldspar composition changes from sodium-rich at the low-temperature end to calcium-rich at the high-temperature end. Based on the minerals present at either end, what can you say about the color of sodium-rich and calcium-rich feldspar? Sodium-rich feldspar is lighter in color than calcium-rich feldspar. L2 LS **Visual-Spatial**

Figure 10 Intrusive igneous rocks often can be distinguished from extrusive igneous rocks because of their large grain size.

The composition of intrusive igneous rocks gives you clues as to where in Earth they formed. Igneous rocks with abundant quartz generally are associated with continental crust, while those with little or no quartz generally are associated with deep locations in continental crust or with oceanic crust. The minerals found in the rock depend on what atoms were available in the magma. If a particular element is not present in the magma, then minerals requiring that element can't be formed.

Reading Check *Where might you find igneous rocks with little or no quartz?*

Intrusive Igneous Rock Texture Recall that texture describes the size and arrangement of rock components. In intrusive igneous rocks, grain size, which means the size of individual mineral crystals, gives you clues as to how fast magma cooled to form it. Magma that cools slowly, over many thousands or millions of years, allows atoms time to migrate about and form large crystals. Large grains are those big enough to see with the unaided eye. Such materials are termed coarse-grained, like the rock shown in **Figure 10.**

Classification of Intrusive Igneous Rocks It is worthwhile to consider a few igneous rock compositions that represent end-members of a large range in possible rock compositions. Rocks that are quartz-rich and contain potassium feldspar and plagioclase feldspar are called granite. Rocks with no quartz and abundant plagioclase feldspar and pyroxene are called gabbro. The low density of granite allows it to be a dominant rock in continental crust. Coarse-grained diorite is an igneous rock between granite and gabbro in composition. Peridotite is denser than gabbro, is composed mainly of olivine and pyroxene, and is thought to compose the bulk of Earth's uppermost mantle.

Reading Check

Answer deep in continental crust or within oceanic crust

Use an Analogy

Crystals Forming in Magma At high temperatures, the ions in magma are far apart and movement from one area to another is easy. As magma cools, ions move closer to each other and eventually bond, forming crystals. These ions and crystals block the flow of any remaining ions. If a group of students represents ions, a single class in a gymnasium is free to move about. A student representing a silicon atom could easily migrate to find a student representing an oxygen atom. Imagine several classes in the gym with most of the students holding hands to represent chemical bonds in crystals. Any remaining silicon students will have difficulty migrating to find an oxygen ion student. L2 ELL

Quick Demo

Igneous Characteristics

Materials large hand samples of common igneous rocks; granite, basalt, rhyolite, andesite, obsidian, and pumice

Estimated Time 20 minutes

Procedure Use the samples to reinforce the distinction between large and small crystal size, dark and light color, and vesicular and glassy textures. L2 ELL

LS **Visual-Spatial**

Differentiated Instruction

English-Language Learners Have the students describe what they see in the Quick Demo and/or Activity in their native language and immediately translate it to English.

Activity

Natural v. Synthetic Have students compare and contrast the crystallization of synthetic materials like metals and glass to the crystallization of igneous rocks. Students should come to the conclusion that synthetic materials resemble natural glass and very fine-grained extrusive igneous rocks. This is due to the rapid cooling rates of the manufacturing processes. L2

Discussion

Decorative Use of Granite Discuss with your students the common use of igneous rocks as countertops and flooring in homes and businesses. If possible, bring in samples of the types of rocks used. Ask students to explain why it is incorrect to call all of these samples granite. Students should now know that there are many types of igneous rocks. Even though a rock is crystalline, it does not mean that it is granite. Dark-colored counters are actually forms of diorite or gabbro.

Extrusive Igneous Rocks

When magma reaches Earth's surface, it is called lava. **Extrusive igneous rocks** are those that cool from lava that has erupted at Earth's surface, as shown in **Figure 11.** These rocks may have the same compositions as intrusive igneous rocks, but they always will have different textures. Rapid cooling causes small, microscopic grains to be present, or no grains at all. Volcanic glass represents an extreme in that it cools almost instantaneously, or is quenched, in air or water.

Magma often becomes contaminated with material that is melted from surrounding rocks as it passes through them on its way to Earth's surface. The greater the distance the magma travels, the more likely it will be contaminated. For example, magma traveling several kilometers to the surface is more likely to change in composition. Magma traveling a much shorter distance might remain unchanged. Another factor is the amount of time the magma was in contact with the surrounding rock material. If the magma is rapidly erupted at Earth's surface, it is less likely to have had enough time to melt the surrounding rock material. Composition of the surrounding rock material will also affect the extrusive magma. If the surrounding rock material is similar to the magma, contamination is less likely.

Figure 11 This type of lava, called pahoehoe, has a smooth, ropy surface.

620 CHAPTER 20 Earth Materials

Extrusive Igneous Rock Composition The compositions of extrusive igneous rocks is much like the compositions of their intrusive cousins. A magma rich in silica (SiO_2) forms granite if it cools slowly, and rhyolite if it cools rapidly. Similarly, gabbro's fine-grained volcanic counterpart is basalt, which is a common rock in Earth's oceanic crust. An extrusive rock intermediate in the amount of SiO_2 is andesite, the volcanic equivalent of intrusive diorite. Many intrusive igneous rock compositions have extrusive igneous rock equivalents.

Applying Math — Use Percentages

EXTRUSIVE IGNEOUS ROCK CLASSIFICATION The amount of silica (SiO_2) in an extrusive rock formed when magma cools is used as a classification system. Balsatic rock contains 45 percent to 55 percent SiO_2, andesitic rock contains 55 percent to 65 percent SiO_2, and rhyolitic rock contains 65 percent to 75 percent SiO_2. A 151-g rock is found to contain 89 g of SiO_2. Based on the percentage of SiO_2 in this rock, how would you classify it?

IDENTIFY known values and the unknown value

Identify the known values:

151-g rock — means — $m_{rock} = 151$ g

89 g of SiO_2 — means — $m_{silica} = 89$ g

Identify the unknown value:

percentage of SiO_2 — means — percent SiO_2 = ? %

SOLVE the problem

Divide the mass of SiO_2 by the total mass of the rock and multiply by 100%:

$$\text{percent } SiO_2 = \frac{m_{silica}}{m_{rock}} \times 100\% = \frac{89\text{ g}}{151\text{g}} \times 100\% = 59\%$$

The rock should be classified as andesitic.

CHECK your answer

Does your answer seem reasonable? Check your answer by multiplying the percentage you calculated (expressed as a decimal) by the mass of the rock. The answer should be the mass of silica given in the problem.

Practice Problems

1. What is the greatest mass of SiO_2 that could be found in a 212-g rhyolitic rock?
2. A 120-kg balsatic boulder found in Hawaii contains 47 percent SiO_2. How many kilograms of SiO_2 are in the boulder?

For more practice problems, go to page 879 and visit Math Practice at gpescience.com.

Quick Demo
Indentifying Igneous Rocks

Materials igneous rock samples, igneous rock identification chart showing both diagrammatic and percentage of mineral composition

Estimated Time 15 minutes

Procedure Beginning with granite, describe the overall color and texture of the sample and then show how it fits into the identification chart. Granite is light in color and it has large crystals so it is positioned at the left end of the chart. Work your way through rhyolite, andesite, diorite, gabbro, basalt, scoria, and obsidian, each time illustrating how the overall color, mineral composition, and grain size allow for its identification.

Applying Math
Math Standards

National: 1, 4, 9

Teaching Strategy

Have students practice their estimating skills as a method of checking their answers. In the sample problem, 89 g of a 151-g rock is silica. 89 g/151 g is approximately 90 g/150 g. 90/150 = 9/15 = 3/5 = 60%. Since 60% is very close to 59%, it appears that the problem was calculated properly.

Answers to Practice Problems

1. 75% x 212 g = 159 g
2. 47% x 120 kg = 56.4 kg

SECTION 2 Igneous Rocks 621

Fun Fact

Some names of rocks and minerals have something to do with how they look or how they formed. Obsidian refers to neither. Its name comes from the Latin word obsidianus, which is actually a misprint of the Latin word obsianus (lapis). It literally means "stone of Obsius". Obsius, as described by Pliny, was a Roman man who allegedly found this rock in Ethiopia.

Reading Check

Answer Cooling starts off slowly, but finishes at a faster rate.

Caption Answer

Figure 12 Intrusive igneous rocks have larger crystals and, because individual mineral crystals can be seen, may exhibit a variety of colors. Extrusive igneous rocks have small crystals and are generally uniform in color.

Activity

Pumice Provide students with containers of a carbonated beverage and another solution that will not fizz. Have students pour each solution into a new container and observe. They should see gases released from the carbonated beverage and no gas release from the other solution. The frothy head is equivalent to pumice, while the liquid below it is a glass. They have the same composition but different textures.

Science Online

Topic: Igneous Rock Textures

Visit gpescience.com for Web links to information about igneous rock textures.

Activity Select gabbro and granite from plutonic microtextures. Make a detailed, colored sketch of each of the photomicrographs of these rocks. Label your drawings. Repeat the activity by selecting nepheline basalt and rhyolite from the volcanic microtextures file.

Extrusive Igneous Rock Textures Rock has a limited ability to transfer thermal energy and so acts like an insulator, allowing magma to cool slowly. Should magma erupt into air or water, thermal energy loss is much faster. When magma nears the surface it meets up with much cooler surroundings. Depending on composition, magmas have temperatures ranging from about 650°C to 1,200°C. The surface of Earth might be 35°C on a hot day.

Recall that rapid cooling results in small crystals or no crystals at all and slow cooling results in large crystals, as shown in **Figure 12.** If cooling starts off slowly below the surface with large crystals, but then finishes at a faster rate to form small or no crystals, the extrusive rock is called a porphyry. If you observed a volcanic porphyry, you would see larger crystals embedded in a mass of small crystals or glass. The term *porphyritic* is used as an adjective to describe this texture. You might then have a porphyritic rhyolite or porphyritic basalt.

Reading Check *What conditions cause a porphyritic texture to form?*

Figure 12 Igneous rocks often are described as being basaltic or granitic. Basaltic rocks are dense and rich in magnesium and iron, but low in silica. Granitic rocks usually are less dense and are silica-rich, containing higher quantities of quartz.
Compare and contrast *the textures and colors of extrusive igneous rocks and their intrusive counterparts.*

	Granitic	Basaltic
Intrusive	 Granite	 Gabbro
Extrusive	 Rhyolite	 Basalt

Science Journal

Crystal Size and Igneous Intrusions A well-known igneous intrusion occurs in the Bighorn Mountains of Wyoming. It is called the Leopard Lode. It's central part consists of large, well-formed feldspar crystals that appear to be floating in a fine-grained, greenish-black background (ground-mass). The margins or sides of the intrusion consist of a fine-grained reddish/black rock. Have students write a history of the Leopard Lode to explain the difference in grain sizes and why they occur where they do. Accept all reasonable explanations. The central portion is a porphyry—the groundmass is basalt. The sides are called a chill margin. As the intruding magma came in contact with the cold surrounding rock, it cooled quickly forming a fine-grained rock.

Volcanic eruptions can result in many different extrusive rock textures and forms as shown in **Figure 13.** Lava can be ejected into the air as large, streamlined blobs that solidify in flight called volcanic bombs, or smaller droplets known as lapilli. Solids of varying size from large blocks to ash can be expelled from a volcano.

Effect of Gases Should magma contain dissolved gases, the gases expand in response to decreasing pressure at the surface, escape, and break apart or disrupt the lava into ash flows. In addition, lava that flows across the surface also can have many tiny holes, somewhat like Swiss cheese. Such a texture is called vesicular, and it mainly forms near the top surface of a flow where gases escape. The extrusive rock pumice results when the holes are left behind. Some pumice has so many gas-bubble holes that its density is reduced and it can float in water.

Figure 13 Some volcanic bombs develop a streamlined shape when they are hurled rapidly through the air during a volcanic explosion.

section 2 review

Summary

What's a rock?
- Rocks are mixtures of a wide variety of natural materials.
- The composition and texture of a rock indicate how it formed.

Intrusive Igneous Rocks
- Intrusive igneous rocks form from magma below Earth's surface, cool slowly, and are coarse-grained.
- The composition of granite is similar to the composition of continental crust as a whole.

Extrusive Igneous Rocks
- Some extrusive igneous rocks form from lava at Earth's surface, cool rapidly, and are fine-grained or glassy.
- Other extrusive rocks are consolidated solid materials expelled from volcanoes.
- Oceanic crust is composed primarily of the extrusive igneous rock basalt.

Self Check

1. **List** the materials that can form a rock.
2. **Describe** how the texture of a porphyritic andesite indicates its cooling history.
3. **Discuss** what happens to the dissolved gases in magma as the magma ascends toward the surface of Earth.
4. **Explain** why you would not expect to observe an igneous rock with quartz and olivine in it.
5. **Think Critically** Lava flows that are relatively low in SiO_2 tend to have low viscosities, or flow easily. Name an igneous rock that you would expect to form from a low-viscosity lava flow. Explain your answer.

Applying Math

6. **Calculate Granite Volume** Granite occurs in very large masses called batholiths. The Sierra Nevada in California is a batholith made up of many separate intrusions. Suppose the mountain range averaged 8.33 km in thickness, extended 700 km north to south, and averaged 91.66 km wide. Approximately how many cubic kilometers of granite are in that mountain range?

More Section Review gpescience.com

Teacher FYI

Not all rocks that appear welded and vesicular are pumice. If they formed from ash and other ejected materials that became welded together, they are called tuff.

Post Reading

Chart Have students set up a chart with the headings *Intrusive Rocks* and *Extrusive Rocks.* In each column, students should list each rock type's characteristics and properties and include examples. For instance, granite is an intrusive rock and basalt is an extrusive rock.

3 Assess

DAILY INTERVENTION

Check for Understanding

Intrapersonal Display several igneous rocks. To confirm an understanding of igneous rock classification, have students state at least two criteria that they can use to correctly identify each sample. L1

Reteach

Speed of Crystallization Show photos and samples of igneous rocks with differing crystal sizes. Have students tell the relative rate of crystal formation—slow, fast, or very fast—and whether the sample formed near, beneath or above the surface. L2 IN **Visual-Spatial**

section 2 review

1. minerals and rock fragments
2. Large crystals indicate that cooling began slowly; the finer-grained background indicates that cooling sped up.
3. Gases expand as they rise, creating bubbles that burst at the surface, leaving a vesicular texture.
4. Because olivine crystallizes at high temperatures and quartz crystallizes at lower temperatures, by the time quartz crystals form, the olivine is already incorporated into solid rock. It is unlikely that both minerals will occur in the same rock.
5. Gabbro and basalt both contain low amounts of silica. Because basalt is a volcanic rock, you would find basaltic lava flows.
6. 5.3×10^5 km^3

Assessment

Oral Have each student prepare a quiz-show style answer for the category *Igneous Rocks.* Critique each answer and save the best ones for a game at the end of the chapter. L2

1 Motivate

INTERACTIVE CHALKBOARD PowerPoint® Presentations An editable Microsoft® PowerPoint® presentation is available on **Interactive Chalkboard** CD-ROM.

Bellringer

Section Focus Transparencies also are available on the Interactive Chalkboard CD-ROM. L2 ELL

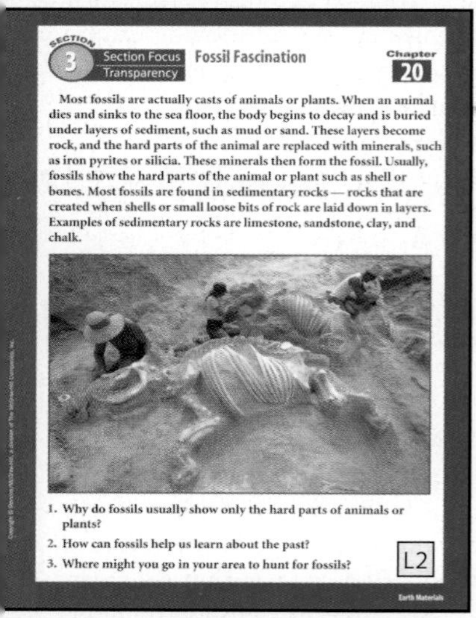

Section 3 Section Focus Transparency **Fossil Fascination** Chapter 20

Most fossils are actually casts of animals or plants. When an animal dies and sinks to the sea floor, the body begins to decay and is buried under layers of sediment, such as mud or sand. These layers become rock, and the hard parts of the animal are replaced with minerals, such as iron pyrites or silicia. These minerals then form the fossil. Usually, fossils show the hard parts of the animal or plant such as shell or bones. Most fossils are found in sedimentary rocks — rocks that are created when shells or small loose bits of rock are laid down in layers. Examples of sedimentary rocks are limestone, sandstone, clay, and chalk.

1. Why do fossils usually show only the hard parts of animals or plants?
2. How can fossils help us learn about the past?
3. Where might you go in your area to hunt for fossils? L2

Earth Materials

Reading Preview

Tie to Prior Knowledge

Surface Igneous Rocks Have students recall that some igneous rocks, such as those from lava flows, form at the surface where they are exposed to wind, rain, and ice. L2

Frayer Model Have students divide a sheet of paper into quadrants. Instruct students to write a new vocabulary word in the center of the page. In the upper left, they should write the word's definition. In the upper right, they should list characteristics associated with the word. Have them record examples in the lower left and non-examples in the lower right.

section 3

Sedimentary Rocks

Reading Guide

What You'll Learn

- **Explain** how and where sedimentary rocks form.
- **Discuss** how sedimentary rocks are used to interpret Earth's history.
- **Describe** how sedimentary rocks are classified.

Why It's Important

Knowledge of sedimentary rocks helps you understand where resources such as fossil fuels and groundwater come from.

Review Vocabulary

precipitate: an insoluble compound that comes out of solution during a chemical reaction

New Vocabulary

- clast
- porosity
- cementation

Rocks from Surface Materials

Recall that rock is a consolidated mixture of minerals. Some of these minerals could be in bits and pieces of other rocks. Such small bits and pieces are called **clasts.** The word *clast* is from the Greek *klastos* which means "broken."

Figure 14 Rocks that are tumbled more than 3,000 km along the bottom of the Colorado River, shown below, can be broken into fine particles before they reach the Gulf of California.

Surface Attack What could reduce rocks of the crust to smaller sizes? Rocks inside Earth are protected from surface conditions. They are squeezed and heated and are reasonably stable under those physical conditions. In contrast, rock exposed at the surface is attacked by the weather. This action over a long time breaks rocks down into smaller-sized pieces and loosens them from their original positions. Loose chunks of rock, in turn, are attacked more easily by water and air, and are able to smash into each other. It is this slow, but constant smashing, grinding, and dissolving of clasts that can take place in rivers and streams, as shown in **Figure 14,** and in other environments.

Section 3 Resource Manager

Chapter *FAST FILE* Resources

Transparency Activity, p. 50
MiniLAB, p. 4
Lab Activity, pp. 15–17
Enrichment, p. 35
Reinforcement, p. 31
Directed Reading, p. 23

Performance Assessment in the Science Classroom, pp. 50–51

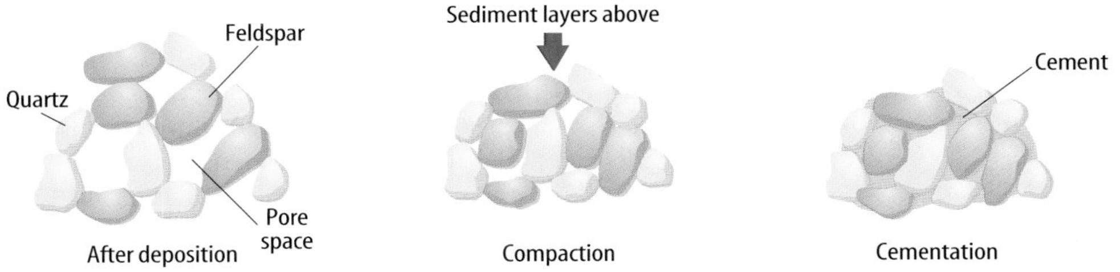

Figure 15 Sandstone can form when sand grains are deposited, compacted, and cemented together.

Transportation and Deposition Mechanical weathering processes break rocks into smaller clasts, making it possible for the clasts to be eroded or removed from their original locations. When clasts are transported to new locations, they often become rounded before being deposited.

When clasts are loose on Earth's surface, they don't fit together perfectly. For example, a pile of baseballs will have plenty of space between the balls. This empty space is called **porosity.** Now imagine a pile of clasts, some rounded as they were transported by a river. Although smaller than the baseballs, the pile of clasts also will have some porosity. Sedimentary rock starts off with some porosity. When the clasts are clay minerals, which are sheet silicates that fit together tightly when compressed, porosity is minimal. It is in the porosity that water, oil, and natural gas are stored within Earth.

Buried Clasts Eventually, clasts can become consolidated into sedimentary rock. The making of clasts by weathering is a surface process, while the making of sedimentary rock occurs below the surface. What processes below the surface could hold clasts together tightly enough to make a rock?

When buried by more sediment deposited above them, clasts can be smashed together with such great force that they become compressed and stick together. The force is pressure created by gravity pulling down on all the material that overlies the clasts. Pressure increases the deeper in Earth that the clasts are, increasing the chance that the clasts will stick together. This process is called compaction.

Reading Check *What force causes compaction?*

Water moving between clasts carries dissolved minerals that can act as cement. Common minerals that are cement materials include quartz, calcite, hematite, and clay minerals. Under the right conditions these minerals slowly precipitate out of water and begin to fill spaces between clasts. This process is called **cementation.** Most of the time both compaction and cementation work together to make sedimentary rock. **Figure 15** shows how sedimentary rock becomes consolidated.

Reading Check

Answer gravity or compression

Quick Demo

Modeling Concentration

Materials clean sand and/or gravel, clear-plastic cups, petroleum jelly, water-based glue.

Procedure Make a thin solution of glue and water. Coat the inside of the cup with a thin layer of petroleum jelly as a release agent.

Loosely fill the cup with the sand and/or gravel mix. Slowly pour the glue solution over the sediment mix. Set it aside to harden. Break away the cup and examine your synthetic rock. L2 ELL **Visual-Spatial**

Teacher FYI

Cement is dehydrated limestone. Mortar is a mixture of varying amounts of sand and cement with water. When water is added, the cement rehydrates and an exothermic reaction starts. The end product of this reaction is a gluelike substance that binds the sand together. Concrete is similar to mortar, but gravel is added to further increase the strength of the hardened product. It is sometimes mistaken for the sedimentary rock conglomerate because of its appearance. Concrete must cure for a long time to gain its full strength. Keeping mortar or concrete moist slows the hardening process and adds strength to the material.

Quick Demo
Sediment Settling

Materials Large, clear-plastic jar and lid, water, mixture of sand, gravel and clay (such as the clay on a baseball diamond.

Estimated Time 10 minutes or more

Procedure Fill the jar until it is half full of sediment mix and top it off with water. Cap the jar and shake vigorously. Set it down and allow the sediment to settle. The gravel will quickly settle out, but the water will remain murky for a long time, possibly days. In advance, ask what will happen; afterward, ask why the water remained cloudy. Ask for suggestions on how to measure the clarity of the water. Very fine sediments take a long time to settle and the water must be completely still; possible suggestions may include shining a flashlight through the jar or trying to read or see an image through the jar.

L2 ELL IN **Visual-Spatial**

Discussion

After the Quick Demo, engage students in a brainstorm setting to formulate a rule about settling rates for sediments and a rule for the vertical grain size distribution in a layer deposited by a flood. L2

Activity

Natural or Synthetic Have students compare and contrast a piece of broken concrete to a specimen of conglomerate. Conglomerate is likely to have a wider variety of clast sizes and the cementing agent will be less well-distributed. L2 ELL IN **Visual-Spatial**

Detrital Sedimentary Rocks

Detritus, from the Latin *deterere,* which means "to lessen or wear away," is another name given to clasts. Sedimentary rocks that are made mostly of clasts are called detrital sedimentary rocks. Clasts can come in many sizes. In order of decreasing size, clasts are known as gravel, sand, silt, or clay. Most people use size names loosely, but to geologists, each size name has a specific meaning, as shown in **Figure 16.** These size names only tell the dimension of a particle, not its composition.

Detrital Sedimentary Rock Textures If someone asked you to define sand, what would you say? Some people might think sand is made only of quartz, or the common silica sand available in hardware stores. In fact, a sand-sized particle could be made of any kind of material. Some kinds of materials, such as quartz and feldspar, hold up better against the effects of weather than others, such as olivine and pyroxene, and are more common in sedimentary rocks.

Why would anyone care about the exact size of a clast? Geologists have found that size works well as a clue to the kind of environment in which a rock formed. One clast of gravel is large and heavy compared to one clast of sand. It takes more force, or energy, to lift or move gravel than it does to lift or move sand. The larger particles in a mix of clasts often can't be lifted by air or water, and instead bounce or scoot along Earth's surface. If you sampled a muddy river you might be surprised to find gravel or sand on the bottom of the river, but a jar of river water might contain millions of tiny silt and clay particles. When water is calm, most clast sizes settle out. As water speeds up, the smallest clasts are lifted first, then larger clasts. During a flood, when the water is moving swiftly, all but the very largest particles are moved. The reverse happens as the water slows. Largest particles settle out first, followed by smaller particles.

Detrital Sedimentary Rocks

Texture (grain size)		Sediment Name	Rock Name
Coarse (over 2mm)		Gravel (Rounded fragments) Gravel (Angular fragments)	Conglomerate Breccia
Medium (1/16 to 2 mm)	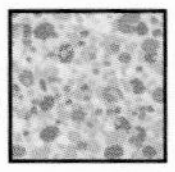	Sand	Sandstone
Fine (1/16 to 1/256 mm)	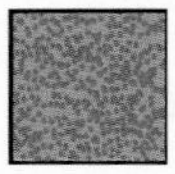	Mud	Siltstone
Very fine (less than 1/256 mm)		Mud	Shale

Figure 16 Sand is defined by size, not by composition. Sand doesn't even have to be made from rock material; it can be made from shells.

Differentiated Instruction

Visually Impaired Sedimentary rocks lend themselves to identification by touch because the rock name is determined by clast size. Provide visually impaired students with samples of siltstone, sandstone, and conglomerate to handle and compare.

L2 ELL IN **Kinesthetic**

Detrital Sedimentary Rock Compositions Detrital sedimentary rock composition depends on sources of rock material that were eroded, transported, and eventually deposited. Original rock material can be dislodged and carried by streams or water currents, blown by the wind, or rafted along by moving ice. The clasts can come from all the regions that these carriers moved over or through. The number of possible combinations of different kinds of clasts is large. However, the size of clasts is controlled by the ability of the carrier to move them.

Some minerals tend to be more common in detrital sediments because they are harder or more resistant to being dissolved. Quartz is such a mineral, which is why you might have thought clasts are always made of quartz. Geologists examine sedimentary rock compositions and try to reconstruct what happened to form them. You can try to reconstruct a sedimentary rock's history by imagining all the places that clasts could have come from and how they got there.

Reading Check *What factors control the composition of a detrital sedimentary rock?*

Detrital Rock Classification Just as igneous rocks are classified according to composition and texture, similar observations are used to classify detrital sedimentary rocks. Mineral composition is extremely variable, so adjectives are used to modify the general name of the rock. The general rock name is determined by clast size. The names of detrital sedimentary rocks are given in **Table 4.**

Clast size also provides clues to help determine the deposition environment of the sediment that formed the detrital rock. Suppose you have a sample of siltstone that contains shells of marine animals. You might conclude that the sediments were deposited in a shallow, calm area along the coast. The calm water allows small particles like silt to settle out. The shells give you a clue that the environment was near the ocean. Perhaps the sample also has fossils in the form of marine worm tubes. The fossils are traces of organisms that might have lived in soft mud.

Table 4 Common Clast Sizes Used to Name Sedimentary Rocks

Common Clast Size	Rock Name
Gravel or larger	Conglomerate
Sand	Sandstone
Silt	Siltstone
Clay	Shale

INTEGRATE Chemistry

Cementation Though sedimentary rocks may form in arid, desert conditions or from compaction by glaciers, most sedimentary rocks are created from being deposited in water. Dissolved minerals in the water may precipitate onto the surfaces of the clastic particles and become the cement to hold grains of sand, silt and clay together. The minerals may also precipitate to form layered rock crystals as well. Make a supersaturated solution and allow the liquid to evaporate. Do the crystals form in layers?

Reading Check

Answer Composition is dependent on what is available in the region and capable of being picked up by the transporting agent.

Fun Fact

Fun Fact Students might think that gold is the most valuable earth material. But the total value of all building aggregates (such as sand, gravel, cement and building stone) has a greater value than the amount of gold mined in a year.

INTEGRATE Chemistry

Cementation In a homogenous solution, crystals can grow as material is added to the surface of existing crystals. However, imperfections on the crystal's surface can cause reorientation of crystal development. Also, changes in the composition or temperature of the solution can produce a layering effect. If enough material is available in solution, crystal growth can fill the space between grains of sediment and cement the grains together.

LAB DEMONSTRATION

Formation of Ripple Marks

Purpose Demonstrate how ripple marks indicate direction of water flow.

Materials pan, sand, electrical fan, spatula

Preparation Into the pan, pour sand to a depth of about 2.5 cm. Cover the sand with about 2.5 cm of water.

Procedure Use the fan to blow the water in one direction until ripple marks form. Have students describe the ripples. Smooth out the sand. Simulate wave action by moving the spatula back and forth in the water until ripple marks form. Have students describe the ripples.

Expected Outcome First set of ripples is asymmetrical; second set is symmetrical.

Assessment

What environmental conditions form each type of ripple? asymmetrical–water or wind move in one direction; symmetrical–back-and-forth waves

Mini LAB

Purpose Simulate the formation of evaporite rocks

Materials sauce pan, measuring spoons, two saucers, thermal mitts, stove, water, salt

Analysis

1. There will be a white crust in the saucer that contained water from the pan; the saucer that contained water from the lid will contain nothing.
2. The salt in the saucer is a crust of cubic crystals.

Assessment

Oral What position on the saucer had the greatest amount of crystal growth? Outer edges should have the thickest growth.

Reading Check

Answer calcium carbonate; the hard parts of marine organisms

Reading Strategy

Find Supporting Details Have students start with the main idea: *There are three types of sedimentary rocks. Each type originates in a particular way.* Using this idea, students should find supporting examples and facts. Ask them to compose a paragraph incorporating the main idea and the supporting details.

Mini LAB

Modeling Evaporites

Procedure

1. Add to a **sauce pan** 1 L of **tap water** and 34 g (about 6 level teaspoons) of **salt** and stir with a **spoon.**
2. Place a **lid** on the pan and heat it on a **hotplate** to boiling. Droplets of a solution should be forming underneath the lid. This solution will be hot. Use **thermal mitts** to carefully remove the lid and drain off the liquid from the lid into a **saucer.** Replace the lid.
3. Repeat step 2 several times until you have several teaspoons worth of liquid from the lid.
4. Carefully pour enough of the pan's contents to half-fill a **second saucer.** Label each saucer to identify which water came from the lid and which came from the pan.
5. Allow both saucers to sit undisturbed until all of the water evaporates from each.

Analysis

1. What do you observe in the saucers after all of the water has evaporated?
2. Compare and contrast any substance you observe with some salt grains directly from the salt container. Use a magnifying lens to observe the substance in each saucer.

Chemical Sedimentary Rocks

Some sedimentary rocks form through the activity of chemicals dissolved in water. If the water contains more dissolved material than it can hold, then some of that dissolved material begins to form crystals that settle out of the water. These crystals build up to form new rock. There are two ways that this process gets started.

Precipitation If water receives more dissolved materials than it can hold in solution, then the excess must precipitate out as microscopic crystals. This crystallization of excess dissolved material is called precipitation. In a small percentage of limestones called oolites, calcium carbonate precipitates directly from sea water around preexisting particles, such as grains of silt or sand.

Evaporation The other option is for some water to evaporate. This leaves an oversupply of dissolved matter and again crystals are forced to form. Rock salt and rock gypsum are common chemical rocks formed in this way. They are often are called evaporites because evaporation of water initiates their formation.

Biochemical Sedimentary Rocks

If sedimentary rocks contain the remains of living organisms they are called biochemical sedimentary rocks. Most of Earth's limestone is composed, at least partially, of the remains of marine organisms that had hard parts made of calcium carbonate. The shells of the organisms were cemented together by calcite mud. If you found a rock composed almost entirely of shells and shell fragments, you would have found limestone. Coquina is a variety of limestone that is formed mostly from broken shell fragments. The shells accumulated on the seafloor and were later cemented together with calcium carbonate. Most organisms whose shells contributed to the limestone-making process lived in warm, shallow seas. Animals without shells rarely contributed enough debris to make rock. More often, their soft remains deteriorated or were scavenged before they became part of a sedimentary rock.

Reading Check ***What chemical compound is limestone made of and where does it come from?***

Another common rock that originates from the remains of organisms is coal. The starting material for coal is mostly plant matter. Coal is sedimentary rock composed almost entirely of the carbon that remains after plant material is compressed underground.

628 CHAPTER 20 Earth Materials

Figure 17 As sediment accumulates above a layer of peat, shown at the upper triangle, the peat becomes more compressed. Continual compression drives out water and other compounds, leaving behind a form of carbon called coal, shown at the lower triangle.

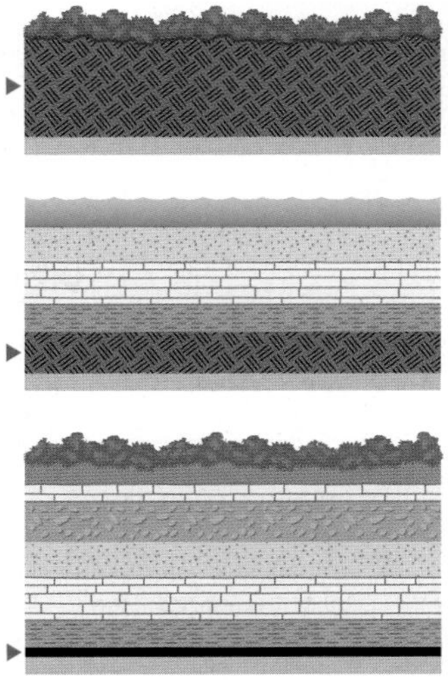

Coal usually develops from peat, a brown, lightweight deposit of moss and other plant matter. Shallow swamps or bogs in a temperate or tropical climate are likely environments of deposition. Partial decay of the plant matter uses up oxygen in the swamp water. This stops further decay and the remaining organic matter is preserved. Peat is transformed into coal largely by compaction after it has been buried by sediment.

Look at **Figure 17.** Coal goes through a series of changes as it forms from peat. Each stage of compaction drives out more impurities and leaves behind a more concentrated form of carbon. Coal often lies within repeated sequences of sandstone, shale, and limestone, which indicate alternating continental and marine conditions. This implies a low-lying environment near the sea, such as lagoons, large deltas, and swampy coastal plains. By studying coal fields, changes in Earth's climate, geological activity, and life forms may be traced and compared.

section 3 review

Summary

Rocks from Surface Materials

- Sedimentary rocks have three main types that reflect their origins: Detrital, chemical, and biochemical.

Detrital Sedimentary Rocks

- Detrital sedimentary rocks can be composed of a wide variety of clasts.
- Clasts vary widely in size.
- Many possible combinations of clast composition and clast size produce a large number of detrital sedimentary rocks.

Chemical Sedimentary Rocks

- Chemical sedimentary rocks form as minerals precipitate from water rich in dissolved mineral matter.

Biochemical Sedimentary Rocks

- Biochemical sedimentary rocks form from the remains of organisms.

Self Check

1. **Describe** the requirements for a material to be classified as a sedimentary rock.
2. **Compare and contrast** the formation of an evaporite rock to one of detrital origin.
3. **Explain** how clast size affects transportation of different-sized clasts. Also, explain the order in which different-sized clasts are deposited.
4. **Think Critically** Suppose a stream floods over its banks. If you dug a hole through the layers of sediment deposited near the edge of the channel after the water receded, what would you likely see?

Applying Math

5. **Calculating Sedimentation Rate** Imagine that thin layers of sediment are being added to a lake that is 10 m deep. Suppose the average yearly influx of sediment is 2.5 mm. About how long would it take to fill in the lake with sediment?

Post Reading

Cooperative Project Have groups of three students choose a particular sedimentary rock, such as conglomerate, to study. Ask them to develop a poster that describes these aspects of their rock: formation, composition, and common locations. Students also should include a picture of their rock type.

3 Assess

DAILY INTERVENTION

Check for Understanding

Sedimentary Rock Identification

Display several sedimentary rocks. To confirm an understanding of igneous rock classification, have students identify at least two criteria they can use to correctly identify each sample. L1 ELL

IS **Visual-Spatial**

Reteach

Remind students that sedimentary rocks are formed from sediments that have been cemented together. Show them a variety of sediments (gravel, sand, silt or clay, mud) and have students predict what type of rock would form if the sediments were cemented together. L1 ELL

Assessment

Content Have each student prepare a quiz-show style answer for the category *Sedimentary Rocks*. Critique each answer and save the best answers for a game at the end of the chapter. L2

section 3 review

1. compacted and/or cemented mixture of minerals and/or rock fragments (or plant matter in coal)
2. Both rocks are sedimentary and form in water environments. Detrital—composed of sediment cemented together, variety of minerals, individual grains can be seen; evaporite—forms when water evaporates leaving minerals behind, crystalline texture, one mineral, generally one color.
3. Large clasts require faster-moving water or wind to be lifted and transported; they are the first to be dropped as the water or wind slows down.
4. You would find layers of sediment with the largest clast sizes in the bottom layers and progressively smaller clast sizes upward.
5. assuming no sinking or settling occurs on the lake bottom—4,000 years

1 Motivate

An editable Microsoft® PowerPoint® presentation is available on **Interactive Chalkboard** CD-ROM.

Bellringer

Section Focus Transparencies also are available on the Interactive Chalkboard CD-ROM. L2 ELL

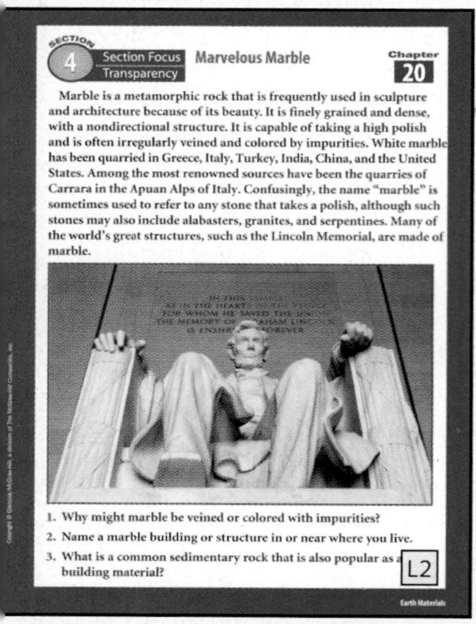
Section 4 Section Focus Transparency — Marvelous Marble — Chapter 20

Marble is a metamorphic rock that is frequently used in sculpture and architecture because of its beauty. It is finely grained and dense, with a nondirectional structure. It is capable of taking a high polish and is often irregularly veined and colored by impurities. White marble has been quarried in Greece, Italy, Turkey, India, China, and the United States. Among the most renowned sources have been the quarries of Carrara in the Apuan Alps of Italy. Confusingly, the name "marble" is sometimes used to refer to any stone that takes a polish, although such stones may also include alabasters, granites, and serpentines. Many of the world's great structures, such as the Lincoln Memorial, are made of marble.

1. Why might marble be veined or colored with impurities?
2. Name a marble building or structure in or near where you live.
3. What is a common sedimentary rock that is also popular as a building material? L2

Earth Materials

Reading Preview

Tie to Prior Knowledge

Metamorphic Rock Rocks that form near the surface may become buried. Burial increases heat and pressure, which metamorphoses the rock. L2

Preview Each new vocabulary word has a corresponding figure in the text. Have students study the figure to predict the word's meaning. They also might sketch their version of the figure. As students read the text, have them confirm or modify their ideas.

section 4

Metamorphic Rocks and the Rock Cycle

Reading Guide

What You'll Learn
- **Identify** physical conditions that cause metamorphism.
- **Explain** where metamorphism occurs.
- **Classify** metamorphic rocks.

Why It's Important

An awareness of change leads to an improved ability to adapt to change.

Review Vocabulary

chemical reaction: process in which one or more substances are changed into new substances

New Vocabulary
- foliated
- rock cycle

Metamorphic Rocks

In the last section you learned that sedimentary rocks show great variety with many different combinations of composition and texture. The same is true for metamorphic rocks. Metamorphic rocks, like the one shown in **Figure 18,** are rocks that have been changed by some combination of thermal energy, pressure, and chemical activity. As these agents begin to act on a preexisting rock, its atoms rearrange and sometimes form new minerals. The word metamorphic comes from two stems, "meta" (to change) and "morph" (form). Any igneous, sedimentary, or metamorphic rock is subject to change through metamorphism.

Figure 18 Sharp folds sometimes display intense transformations in metamorphic rocks.

Conditions that form metamorphic rocks are somewhere between the sedimentary and igneous environments. In other words, consolidation of sediment to form sedimentary rock occurs at lower pressures and temperatures than typical metamorphic conditions. On the other hand, igneous rock formation requires rock to melt and solidify. Igneous processes operate at higher temperatures than metamorphism which occurs while rock remains solid.

Section 4 Resource Manager

Chapter *FAST FILE* Resources

Transparency Activity, p. 51
Lab Activity, pp. 11–13
Enrichment, p. 36
Reinforcement, p. 32
Directed Reading, p. 23–24
Lab Worksheets, pp. 7–8
Earth Science Critical Thinking/Problem Solving, p. 4
Reading and Writing Skills Activities, pp. 21–22

630 CHAPTER 20 Earth Materials

Metamorphic Rock Composition

INTEGRATE Chemistry The agents of metamorphism are thermal energy, pressure, and chemical activity. Water and carbon dioxide are common active chemicals that exist as a fluid and chemically react with rock. This fluid can come from molecular water or carbonate locked in the rock itself, or can be introduced from a nearby intrusion of magma.

Reading Check *What are three causal agents of metamorphism?*

Changing Minerals Clay minerals, micas, and amphiboles are examples of minerals that contain water in their crystal structures. Clay minerals tend to form micas with increasing metamorphic conditions. If metamorphic conditions of pressure and temperature continue to increase, the water can be driven away completely. Minerals, such as garnet, that contain some of the same elements found in clays (aluminum and silicon) can result. In this way, some new minerals form by dehydration at higher temperature and pressure.

Environments of Metamorphism So, what's causing these changes? Deep burial or regional movements of large parts of Earth's crust and uppermost mantle are possible causes. These large-scale changes, called regional metamorphism, produce huge areas of changed rock. Another smaller-scale cause is local contact of any preexisting rock with magma. This is called contact metamorphism. You produce contact metamorphism when you place food in a hot pan coated with oil and it quickly begins to burn. One important difference is that in cooking, chemical reactions take place rapidly, while metamorphic changes occur over thousands or millions of years.

Figure 19 *Folio* means "leaf." Foliated texture has the appearance of layered leaves or pages of a book. The texture of the first metamorphic rock shown below is foliated; the second is nonfoliated.

Metamorphic Rock Textures

Metamorphic processes create many rock textures, but a few general types can help you understand the processes that formed them. **Foliated** textures in metamorphic rocks have lots of layers or bands. Nonfoliated metamorphic textures include rocks whose grains are in more random orientations. Some nonfoliated textures resemble igneous rock textures, in which grains are locked tightly together. **Figure 19** shows examples of these textures.

2 Teach

Reading Check

Answer thermal energy, pressure, chemical activity

INTEGRATE Chemistry **Content Background**

Water is the most important fluid involved in metamorphism. Water is thought to affect metamorphic chemical reactions by dissolving mineral ions and carrying them to other locations where they react with other mineral ions. Ask students where they think the water might come from in metamorphic rock. Some water is subducted along with sediment at convergent plate boundaries. Water also might come from the molecular structure of some minerals or magma.

Discussion

Metamorphism Place time frames on the process of metamorphism. Ask students how long they think these changes take. What are the variables? Responses will vary, but all the time frames should range from millions to billions of years. Variables include depth of burial, heat sources, additional heat from Earth's interior or tectonism, presence or absence of fluids. L2 ELL IS **Visual-Spatial**

Quick Demo

Metamorphic Textures

Materials large hand specimens of slate, phyllite, schist, gneiss, marble, and quartzite

Estimated Time 15 minutes

Procedure Use the hand samples to reinforce the distinction between foliated and non-foliated textures and to show the progressive degree of metamorphism from slate to gneiss. L2 ELL IS **Visual-Spatial**

Visual Learning

Figure 18 What can you observe about the rock in this figure that indicates it is not sedimentary? Sedimentary rocks display layering, but these layers are distorted just as they are in metamorphic rocks. Some layers also show signs of stress by thinning and thickening in the folds. L2 ELL IS

Differentiated Instruction

Learning Disabled Identification of metamorphic rocks relies on visual characteristics. Provide several sets of metamorphic rocks that show the gradation from slate to gneiss. Help the students recognize the physical changes as they examine the samples from lowest degree of metamorphism to highest degree. L1 ELL

Reading Check

Answer Grains align perpendicular to the direction of compression.

Discussion

Index Minerals Using the information in the content background below, introduce students to the concept of index minerals. Obtain a map showing their distribution to help illustrate the concept. In order of decreasing temperature, the minerals are: sillimanite, and alusite and staurolite/kyanite, garnet, biotite and chlorite. Ask students to compare and contrast the use of index minerals to the use of index fossils. Both occur in specific areas; minerals in an area that experienced a specific temperature, fossils in rocks that represent a specific period of time. Their occurrence in rocks can be used to fine-tune an interpretation of the rock body they occur in.

Teacher FYI

Mapping and Metamorphic Minerals Contact metamorphism can result in the formation of a new assemblage of minerals. Research has determined the temperature ranges under which certain minerals form. These minerals are called index minerals. They form over a narrow range of temperature and can be used to characterize a particular degree of metamorphism. When an igneous intrusion occurs, the temperature is hottest closest to the intrusion and decreases farther away. The minerals that form as a result of this contact metamorphism record the change in temperature away from the intrusion. The location of the intrusive igneous body can be located by mapping the occurrence of index minerals and following the apparent increase in temperature.

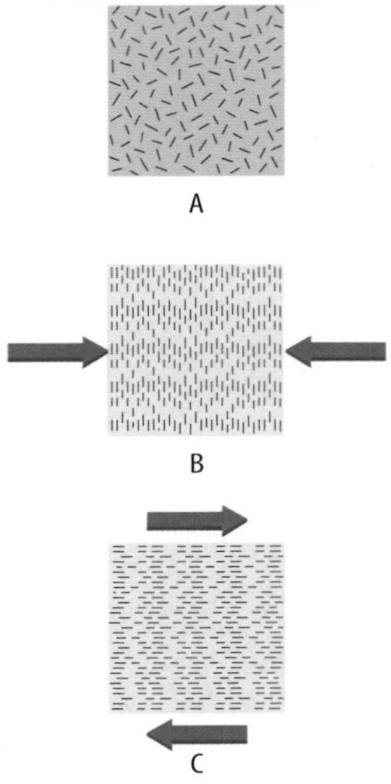

Figure 20 Direction of applied force affects orientation of mineral grains.

- **A** Mineral grains are randomly oriented when no directed force is involved.
- **B** Orientation of mineral grains is perpendicular to the direction of pressure caused by compression.
- **C** Mineral grains are parallel to the direction of shearing force.

Science Online

Topic: Metamorphic Rock Textures

Visit gpescience.com for Web links to information about metamorphic rock textures.

Activity: Select from metamorphic microtextures: Gneiss, marble and foliation. Make a detailed colored sketch of each of the photomicrographs showing these textures. Label your drawings.

Foliated Rocks The most common sedimentary rocks in Earth's crust are mudrocks such as shale and siltstone. These rocks contain abundant clay minerals, and when metamorphosed, the clays change to minerals in the mica group, such as muscovite. The mica group minerals also change in grain size with increasing degrees of metamorphism.

When squeezed and heated, layers of mica line up in a direction that is perpendicular to the direction of compression or parallel to the direction of shearing, as shown in **Figure 20.** For example, slate is a fine-grained, foliated metamorphic rock that splits easily along flat, parallel planes. It typically formed when shale was compressed, causing mica grains to orient perpendicular to the compression.

Reading Check *How does compression affect the orientation of mica grains in metamorphic rocks?*

Sometimes it's easiest to consider foliated rocks as a progression of increasing metamorphic conditions. The smallest-grain sizes in foliated textures occur in slate, which forms thin layers and exhibits rock cleavage. The rock cleavage comes from the parallel alignment of mineral grains within the rock. If the metamorphic conditions increase, some of the mineral grains in the slate grow and produce phyllite. With continued grain growth, a shiny mass of mica sheets called schist (SHIHST) forms. Finally, at the highest level of change a rock called gneiss (NISE) is produced. Gneiss rock textures often are banded, and gneisses generally represent the limit between metamorphic and igneous conditions.

Nonfoliated Rocks Similar in texture to intrusive igneous rocks, nonfoliated metamorphic rocks tend to have random crystal orientation and uniform grain size. In general, mineral grains tend to grow as the grade of metamorphism increases. Imagine a limestone with microscopic grains. Under the influence of thermal energy, pressure, and fluids, such a limestone recrystallizes in large beautiful grains of calcite that are readily visible in a hand specimen. This resulting rock is marble, and it is essentially chemically equivalent to the limestone.

Metamorphic Rock Classification

Much like other rock types, metamorphic rocks can be classified based on texture and composition. Beginning with texture, you can determine whether a metamorphic rock is foliated or nonfoliated. Remember that in any classification, there are exceptions, as illustrated in **Figure 21.**

Cultural Diversity

Have the students research the use of Earth materials in the construction of housing in different regions on Earth.

Active Reading

Learning Journal Have students divide a sheet of paper in half and record research notes, lecture notes, or vocabulary terms in the left column. In the right column, they respond to, interpret, question, or analyze the left column entries. Students can write a Learning Journal while reading about metamorphic rock.

NATIONAL GEOGRAPHIC VISUALIZING SHOCK METAMORPHIC ROCK

Figure 21

Earth materials undergo change, even when buried far below the surface. Deep in the crust, high temperature and pressure conditions alter the chemical composition and structure of rocks in predictable ways over time, producing metamorphic rocks. Metamorphism, however, also can occur rapidly, violently, and without warning.

Scientists estimate that the force created by a meteorite impact could be nine million times greater than atmospheric pressure. This type of collision would send enormous shock waves throughout surrounding rock strata, rearranging atoms into new crystal structures stable at higher temperature, and pressure conditions.

Large meteorite impacts leave scars that can remain visible for millions of years. Taken from the space shuttle, this image shows the *International Space Station* above the Manicouagan impact crater in Quebec, Canada. The meteorite that created this crater struck Earth 214 million years ago, hurling debris high into the atmosphere and leaving evidence in the rock record worldwide.

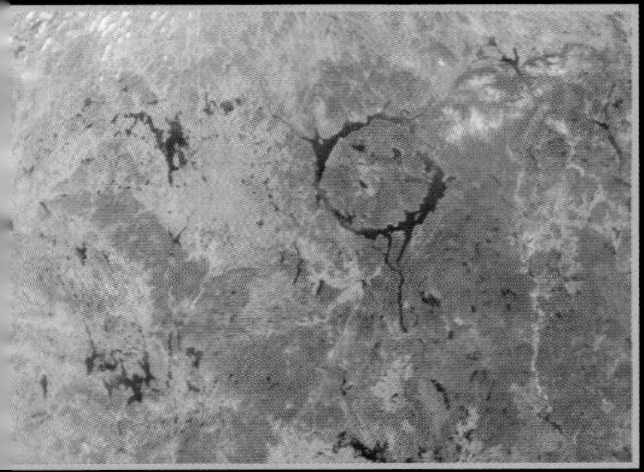

With a diameter of 100 km, the Manicouagan crater is one of the largest impact structures preserved on Earth. The force of the collision caused rock melting and rock metamorphism to a depth of about 9 km. Mineral grains in metamorphic rocks at the site are deformed extensively, evidence that an intense compression wave shocked the strata.

NATIONAL GEOGRAPHIC

Visualizing Shock Metamorphic Rocks

Have students examine the pictures. Then provide them with the following information and ask them to provide their own explanations.

Most of the rock found at the center of the Manicouagan impact crater is either igneous or metamorphic rock. Explain the presence of igneous rock at this location. Possible answer: The force of the meteorite impact resulted in the release of a tremendous amount of heat energy. High temperatures in the rock strata caused some material to melt. As the molten material cooled and hardened, igneous rock was formed.

In 2002, geologists published the discovery of a 2-cm layer of impact material in the rock strata in western England. Based on the decay of radioactive potassium, the debris layer was dated at 214 million years old and tied to the formation of the Manicouagan impact crater. Explain how material from Canada made its way into rock strata in England. Possible answer: The meteorite struck with such force that debris was ejected far into the atmosphere, then carried away from the impact site by various atmospheric processes. Eventually, heavy materials settled back to Earth, creating a layer in the rock strata in certain locations.

Activity

Manicouagan Imagine that you viewed the Manicouagan meteorite impact from a safe distance 214 million years ago. Write a description of what you saw and heard before, during, and after the collision. Share your observations with other classmates.

Teacher FYI

Rock Cycle Activity In the rock cycle, volcanic activity occurs fastest, while cooling of igneous intrusions and the heat and pressure of metamorphism occurs slowest. The processes of erosion, transport, and deposition all can be interrupted by new episodes of uplift and erosion. This recycling is possible until sediments reach the deep ocean floor. Metamorphic rocks also can be recycled through mountain-building processes.

Discussion

Have students speculate about what rocks would look like if there were three lava flows of a gas-rich lava, one atop another. It would look like a layer cake; a glassy layer (cake) with a frothy layer atop it (icing), then glass, froth, glass, and froth on top. L2 ELL IN **Visual-Spatial**

What would happen if all weathering processes stopped? Without weathering, the cycle would not continue. L2

Reading Strategy

Brainstorm Post four large sheets of paper. Each should have one of the following headings: *Weathering Rock Composition*, *Texture*, *Classification*, or *The Rock Cycle.* Form four student groups—one for each topic. Students will have three minutes to brainstorm and record ideas that fit their category. Groups rotate to other topics until all have visited each one.

Mineral Composition Next, consider the mineral composition. Mineral composition provides clues about the original rock type before metamorphism, and also indicates to what degree a rock has been metamorphosed. The original rock material, often called the parent rock, and the conditions of metamorphism together control the resulting metamorphic rock. So, in studying rocks from the field, geologists must work backwards. Field samples are the results of many geologic conditions, most of which cannot be accurately reproduced in the laboratory. Some conditions have been reproduced, however, and scientists can use mineral composition to estimate the pressure, temperature, and chemical activity that resulted in the formation of a metamorphic rock.

The Rock Cycle

Illustrations often simplify complex ideas. A diagram of the rock cycle, shown in **Figure 22,** summarizes processes that you have learned about in this chapter. Processes of the **rock cycle** include any chemical and physical conditions that continuously form and change rocks. Notice that some processes happen at Earth's surface, while others happen deep below the surface.

Figure 22 The rock cycle is a continual process in which rocks change from one form to another.

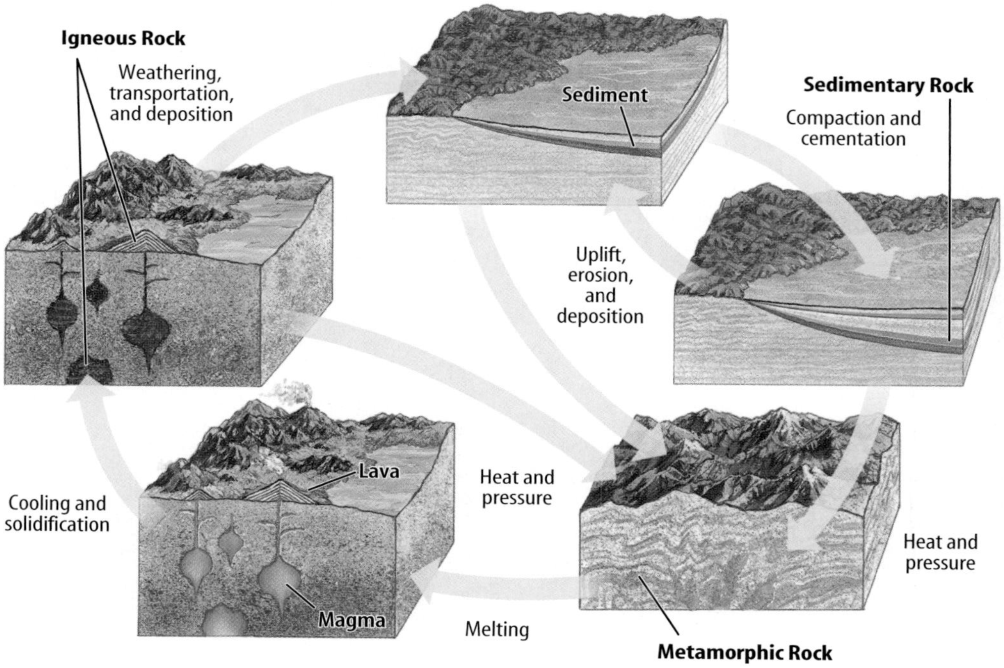

LAB DEMONSTRATION

Purpose Review the rock cycle.

Materials: rock specimens of the rock cycle; 3 ring stands with rings; 3-in × 5-in cards (7); jumbo paper clips, hole punch; large rubber bands; hole reinforcers

Preparation Label the cards *crystallization, erosion, transportation, deposition, burial, increase in heat and temperature,and recrystallization.* Punch a hole at each end of a card and reinforce. Connect two jumbo clips to a rubber band. Attach a clip to each end of a card.

Procedure Place a rock on a ring. Use an action card to connect the ring to another ring. Continue the process until a rock cycle is constructed.

Expected Outcome Students should be able to model the rock cycle.

Assessment

What would happen if all weathering processes stopped? Without weathering, the cycle would not continue. L2

As rock material moves through stages of the cycle, all matter is conserved. Minerals from granite are found in the sediments that were eroded from those igneous rocks. Those same minerals could be present in sedimentary rocks formed later. Atoms that have been mobilized during weathering or metamorphic chemical reactions are not destroyed, but can end up as dissolved materials in solutions. Mineral crystals later can precipitate from those solutions. The atoms are never destroyed, only rearranged into new forms that are stable under the present conditions.

Also note that many different paths, indicated by arrows in **Figure 22,** can be taken by rock material as it changes within the cycle. Understand that these processes may take long periods of time, occurring over millions of years. Other processes happen suddenly, such as an erupting volcano, but this does not change the fact that there is no beginning and no end to the rock cycle.

Reading Check *Describe several examples of how matter is conserved in the rock cycle.*

section 4 review

Summary

Metamorphic Rocks

- Metamorphic rocks can form from any preexisting rocks.

Metamorphic Rock Composition

- Agents of metamorphism can cause new textures and new minerals to form.

Metamorphic Rock Textures

- Metamorphic rocks are foliated or non-foliated.
- As metamorphic conditions increase in magnitude, mineral grains may grow larger.

Metamorphic Rock Classification

- Metamorphic rocks are classified based on mineral composition and texture.
- As with all rock classifications, some metamorphic rocks are exceptional and not easily categorized.

The Rock Cycle

- Although rocks are subject to many changes, matter is conserved through processes of the rock cycle.

Self Check

1. **Explain** the requirements for a material to be called a metamorphic rock.
2. **Compare and contrast** foliated and non-foliated textures.
3. **List** the following sedimentary rocks: limestone and shale. Provide the respective common names of the metamorphic rocks that each one becomes.
4. **Identify** which rock in question 3 is foliated.
5. **Critical Thinking** A marble contains occasional layers of the mineral muscovite. What possible parent rock composition could have been metamorphosed to produce this rock?

Applying Math

6. **Calculate Mass** Suppose a sculptor wants to use marble with an average density of about 2.7 g/cm^3. The block of marble is one meter on every side. What is the mass of the block? If the sculptor knows from experience that the finished product will only use 45% of the block, and the rest is waste, then what will the mass of the statue be?

Reading Check

Answer Minerals can be eroded from granite and incorporated into sedimentary rock and minerals from sedimentary rock can be dissolved and precipitate as different minerals.

Post Reading

Article Ask students to imagine that they are writing an article for a geology journal about their discovery of metamorphic rocks in an old mine. Ask them to include information about the type of metamorphic rock and its mineral composition, texture, and method of formation. Make a booklet of all the articles.

3 Assess

DAILY INTERVENTION

Check for Understanding

Metamorphic Textures

Display several metamorphic rocks. Have students state at least two criteria they can use to correctly identify each sample. L2

Reteach

Demonstrate how foliation develops perpendicular to the direction of pressure. Knead a ball of clay until it is soft. Add some uncooked, long-grained rice and knead the clay until the grains are randomly scattered. Place the clay ball on the table. Slowly and firmly, apply pressure to the top of it. When the ball is about half its original height, cut it in half. Students will observe that the rice grains are now aligned, as in foliation. L1 ELL **Visual-Spatial**

section 4 review

1. The rock must show evidence of the effects of heat, pressure, and/or chemical activity such as foliation, increased crystal size, or new minerals.
2. Both form from an increase in heat and pressure. They also show a change in mineral composition and grain size. Foliated—ranges from faint compact layering and uniform color to distinct light and dark bands with visible crystals of uneven sizes; non-foliated—mostly monomineralic, one color, crystals uniform in size, blocky in shape
3. limestone to marble; shale to slate
4. slate
5. alternating layers of shale (muscovite) and limestone (marble)
6. Density of marble = 2.7 g/cm^3; 1 m^3 block = 1 million cm^3; 1 million cm^3 $\times$ 2.7 g/cm^3 = 2.7 $\times$ 10^{6}g; the statue weighs 1.215 $\times$ 10^{6}g

Assessment

Content Have each student prepare a quiz-show style answer for the category *Metamorphic Rocks*. Critique each answer and save the best answers for a game at the end of the chapter. L2

BENCH TESTED

Real-World Problem

Purpose Students will gain experience in observation, classification, and use of a classification key.

Process Skills observe, evaluate, interpret data, record, collect data

Time Required Three 40-minute sessions

Safety Precautions

- Damage to clothing from sharp objects and chemicals is possible.
- Dilute/hydrochloric acid—5%

Procedure

Teaching Strategy

- Identify rocks from one major rock group during each session.
- Give each lab group pairs of rocks and limit their time (5 min) to observe and record data. When time is up, rotate the rocks to the next group.
- If time allows, during the third session, provide samples from the first two sessions for comparison.

Troubleshooting

Have one or two acid test stations, which you monitor closely. Do not give every group acid. Stress that only ONE drop of acid is necessary and the sample must be blotted dry with paper towel after the test.

LAB

Identifying Rocks

Goals

- **Observe** physical properties of minerals in rocks to determine their compositions.
- **Classify** each rock according to general type: Igneous, sedimentary, or metamorphic.
- **Identify** each rock based on its composition and texture.

Materials

rock samples
nail
penny (pre-1986)
magnifying lens or particle size chart
dilute HCl
paper towels
glass plate
* binocular microscope
unglazed porcelain tile
Resource Handbook, "Rocks"

**Alternate material*

Safety Precautions

Real-World Problem

You've learned to identify most everything around you. This is an automatic process most of the time. You learned by repetition and by asking what things are called. By the time you were five years old you could name many different kinds of objects. You could identify the people in your life. You might not have had the same experience in identifying rocks—at least not yet. In this lab, you will identify rocks using a more formal approach. How can you determine the composition and texture of common rocks? What can a rock's composition and texture indicate to you about how it was formed?

Procedure

1. Construct a horizontal data table with ten columns and four rows.
2. Label the tops of columns 1 through 10, in the top row, as follows:
   1) Sample number
   2) General rock type (igneous, sedimentary, metamorphic)
   3) Crystals (yes/no)
   4) Grain size (large/small/none)
   5) Gas-bubble holes (yes/no)
   6) Fossils (yes/no)
   7) Particle size (gravel/sand/silt/clay)
   8) Foliations (yes/no)
   9) Additional observations
   10) Rock name

Alternative Inquiry Lab

Rocks from Home Many students collect rocks. They can be encouraged to bring some rocks from home to be evaluated during this lab. Many of these rocks have novel characteristics, such as an attractive color, unusual shape or texture, fossils, petrifaction, etc. Be aware that sometimes these items are not rocks. Byproducts from industrial processes, such as slag, often are mistaken for rocks. Knowing where a rock was found can be important when learning about rocks.

636 CHAPTER 20 Earth Materials

Using Scientific Methods

3. Obtain three rocks provided by your teacher.
4. **Observe** each rock. First, try to determine if it is igneous, sedimentary, or metamorphic. Then record everything else you observe. Your data table columns will serve as a checklist to help organize your observations.

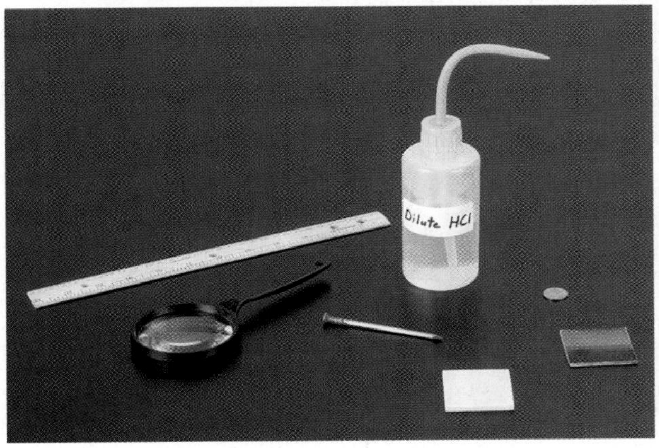

WARNING: *If you choose to use the acid test for calcite identification, use only one drop of HCl. A positive reaction to acid is the presence of tiny bubbles rising through the drop. Blot the liquid off the sample with a paper towel before leaving it. Be careful to keep acid away from skin and clothing.*

5. **Identify** the rock with the help of Resource Handbook, "Rocks," at the back of your textbook.
6. **Repeat** steps 4 and 5 to check that your results are replicated. Keep an open mind.

Analyze Your Data

1. **Identify** the texture observations that helped you distinguish igneous rocks from sedimentary rocks.
2. **Determine** which rock samples required the fewest tests to identify them and explain why.

Conclude and Apply

1. **Evaluate** rocks according to difficulty for identifying and classifying.
2. **Explain** which observations were useful for the largest number of rock samples.
3. **Evaluate** your data table in terms of including important observations. Explain whether there were any observations you left out of your data table that are critical for distinguishing rocks.

Communicating Your Data

Present your findings to the class. Discuss any observations that were different from those of your classmates. Discuss the column headings you included in your data table and defend your choices.

Analyze Your Data

1. igneous rocks—interlocking crystals, polymineralic (many minerals); sedimentary rocks—individual grains cemented together, some are layered, some contain fossils, generally uniform in color
2. Answers will vary. Rocks that have distinguishing characteristics will be easy to identify; granite—large crystals and generally light colored, some limestones have fossils and all react to acid

Expected Outcome At the very least, students should be able to accurately group specimens into the three main rock categories and name at least two rocks in each category.

Error Analysis Have students compare results with others to discover common errors.

Conclude and Apply

1. Answers will vary. Students may mention grain size, mineral composition and special features such as foliation.
2. Texture patterns should rank high as most useful, such as grain size, clast size, foliation, or banding. General color may be also ranked as useful.
3. Answers will vary. Students may point out the specialized characteristics that only a few rocks may exhibit; such as acid reaction or feel (rough or slick).

Communicating Your Data

Have students compare experiences in identifying the specimens and develop a flowchart of strategies or procedures for speeding up the identification process.

Assessment

Oral Ask students to differentiate between those rock characteristics that allowed them to sort the specimens into the three main rock categories and those characteristics that allowed for identifying the rock. L2

TIME

Content Background

Kaolinite, $Al_2Si_2O_5(OH)_4$, is one of the most important minerals found in clay. Because kaolinite crystals occur in interlocking layers, little water can penetrate the mineral. This prevents materials made from kaolinite from swelling in the presence of liquids or expanding when heated. The absence of water also makes ceramic materials very heat-resistant.

Kaolinite is one of the most common minerals on Earth. It is a weathering product of the mineral feldspar. It is stable only under conditions of low temperature and pressure such as those present at Earth's surface. Deposits of kaolinite often are formed through the weathering of granite and other rocks that are rich in feldspar. In the United States, major deposits are mined in Georgia, North Carolina, and Pennsylvania.

Discussion

What's your opinion? Imagine that a large company is planning to mine kaolinite in your area. How would local residents feel about a kaolinite mining operation being established near the schools, homes, and farms? Possible answer: Kaolinite is not a radioactive or otherwise dangerous mineral. Positive effects for the local economy are likely. However, any type of mining operation raises environmental and safety concerns, including surface water contamination, landscape and habitat destruction, dust generation, and noise pollution, among others. L2

Investigate the Issue

Kaolinite Mines in the United States
Have student groups research the location of kaolinite mining operations in the United States, and then plot locations on a U.S. map. L2 ELL

TIME SCIENCE AND Society

SCIENCE ISSUES THAT AFFECT YOU!

Earth Materials at Work

Kaolinite, a type of clay, is a common mineral on Earth.

What is clay, and where does it come from?

What do a commode, a brick, and a coffee mug have in common? While these items have widely different uses, they share an important component—a material called clay. Clay is found in many locations worldwide. Because of its unique properties and availability, clay has been used by civilizations throughout history to make items including building materials, pottery, and tablets for recording information.

Clay forms through weathering, crystallization, and deposition of Earth materials. The word *clay* really represents an entire group of many different minerals. These minerals have particles with a diameter of 0.004 mm or less. When wet, most clay minerals can be molded into a variety of shapes. When water is driven off under high temperature conditions, the material may become as hard as stone.

Clay minerals are used to make many items of pottery and dinnerware.

Clay deposits typically are found in sedimentary rock layers close to Earth's surface. As a result, clay mines are generally shallow, with depths of less than 150 m. Companies in the United States often reclaim the landscape that they mine. First, the topsoil and uppermost clay layer are removed and stored at another location. After clay is mined from an area, leftover Earth materials are returned to the pit. This layer is covered with topsoil, into which vegetation is planted.

Ceramic materials have diverse applications in manufacturing, building, art, and everyday life. Products made from clay minerals include floor tiles, fine china, and dental porcelain. The import, export, and use of clay materials contribute significantly to the world economy.

Brainstorm **Ceramic products can be found at school, at home, and in stores. Make a list of ceramic products that you encounter or use on a regular basis.**

TIME
For more information, visit gpescience.com

Brainstorm Students should be able to identify many items made from ceramic materials such as pottery, bricks, cement, floor and wall tiles, sinks, bathtubs, planters, fine porcelain, table ware, sewer pipes, and many others. Remind students that the unique properties of the clay which forms these materials enables them to withstand high temperatures and resist liquid infiltration. L3

Resources for Teachers and Students

Mineral Information Institute, 501 Violet Street, Golden, Colorado, 80401

A Field Guide to Rocks and Minerals (Peterson Field Guides), Frederick H. Pough and Roger Tory Peterson, Houghton Mifflin Company, 1998

Reviewing Main Ideas

Section 1 Minerals

1. Only eight elements compose more than 98 percent, by mass, of Earth's crust.
2. Minerals are naturally occurring, inorganic solids that have a crystalline structure and predictable chemical composition.

3. Major mineral groups that form the bulk of Earth's crust are known as the rock-forming minerals.
4. Every mineral has characteristic physical properties that help in its identification.

Section 2 Igneous Rocks

1. Igneous rocks must form from solidification of magma or lava.
2. Igneous rocks can be separated into two categories: Intrusive—those that form in Earth—and extrusive—those that form at Earth's surface.

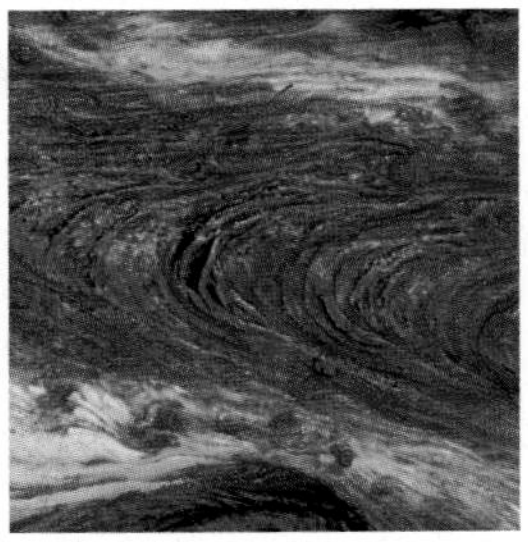

3. Igneous rocks are classified based on their texture and composition.
4. Igneous rocks with granite-like compositions are associated with continental crust, while igneous rocks with basalt-like compositions are associated with oceanic crust.

Section 3 Sedimentary Rocks

1. Sedimentary rocks are consolidated mixtures of minerals, rock fragments, organic debris, or other natural materials.
2. Sedimentary rocks can contain or be made entirely of the remains of organisms.

3. Detrital sedimentary rocks form through the processes of cementation and compaction.
4. Sedimentary rocks are classified based on clast size and composition.

Section 4 Metamorphic Rocks and the Rock Cycle

1. Metamorphic rocks are made through the effects of heat, pressure, and chemical activity on preexisting rocks.
2. Metamorphic rocks can be divided into two categories: Foliated—having layers or bands—and nonfoliated—with grains in random orientations.
3. Parent rock material and conditions of metamorphism control the composition of a metamorphic rock.
4. The rock cycle describes all processes in Earth that continuously change Earth materials.

FOLDABLES™ Use the Foldable that you made at the beginning of this chapter to help you review Earth materials.

Reviewing Main Ideas

Summary statements can be used by students to review the major concepts of the chapter.

Science Online

Visit gpescience.com
More Section Review
Interactive Tutor
Vocabulary PuzzleMaker
More Chapter Review
Standardized Test Practice

Assessment Transparency

For additional assessment questions, use the *Assessment Transparency* located in the transparency book.

Assessment

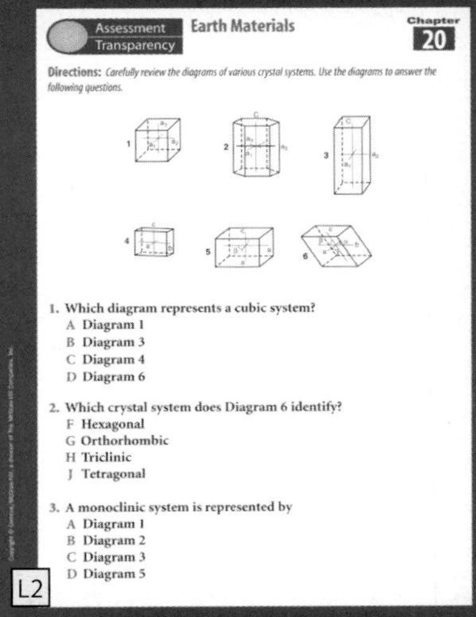

Assessment Transparency — Earth Materials — Chapter 20

Directions: *Carefully review the diagrams of various crystal systems. Use the diagrams to answer the following questions.*

1. Which diagram represents a cubic system?
   A Diagram 1
   B Diagram 3
   C Diagram 4
   D Diagram 6
2. Which crystal system does Diagram 6 identify?
   F Hexagonal
   G Orthorhombic
   H Triclinic
   J Tetragonal
3. A monoclinic system is represented by
   A Diagram 1
   B Diagram 2
   C Diagram 3
   D Diagram 5

L2

Earth Materials

FOLDABLES™ Have students use their Foldable to review the content of the chapter. On the back of the paper, describe textures of igneous, sedimenentary, and metamorphic rocks.

Using Vocabulary

1. magma
2. texture
3. intrusive igneous rock
4. hardness
5. fracture
6. rock
7. clast
8. foliation
9. porosity
10. cementation
11. cleavage
12. mineral

Checking Concepts

13. B
14. C
15. C
16. D
17. A
18. D

chapter 20 Review

Using Vocabulary

cementation p. 625
clast p. 624
cleavage p. 610
extrusive igneous rock p. 620
foliated p. 631
fracture p. 610
hardness p. 611
intrusive igneous rock p. 617
magma p. 613
mineral p. 609
porosity p. 625
rock p. 617
rock cycle p. 634
streak p. 611
texture p. 617

Match the correct vocabulary terms with each description below.

1. molten rock
2. grain size and arrangement
3. coarse grained
4. scratch resistance
5. uneven break
6. consolidated minerals
7. particle of rock
8. layers or bands
9. empty space
10. fills porosity
11. planar break
12. natural, inorganic, crystalline solid

Checking Concepts

Choose the word or phase that best answers the question.

13. What is the most common group of minerals?
    A) carbonates
    B) silicates
    C) sulfates
    D) oxides

14. What is a factor that controls grain size in igneous rocks?
    A) porosity
    B) cleavage
    C) cooling rate
    D) temperature

15. What do all the silicate minerals have?
    A) the same hardness
    B) the same crystal structure
    C) silicon and oxygen
    D) silicon and carbon as common elements

16. Through what process does chemical sedimentary rock usually form?
    A) cementation of sand
    B) compaction of clasts
    C) evaporation of melt
    D) precipitation of crystals

17. Which of the following features are extrusive igneous rocks least likely to have?
    A) fossils
    B) small grains
    C) vesicular texture
    D) porphyrtic texture

Use the photo below to answer question 18.

18. Which of the following descriptions best describes the large-grained igneous rock shown above?
    A) extrusive and basaltic
    B) extrusive and granitic
    C) intrusive and basaltic
    D) intrusive and granitic

Vocabulary PuzzleMaker gpescience.com

Use the Exam*View*® Pro Test Bank CD-ROM to:

- create multiple versions of tests
- create modified tests with one mouse click for inclusion students
- edit existing questions and add your own questions
- build tests aligned with state standards using built-in State Curriculum Tags
- change English tests to Spanish with one mouse click and vice versa

Interpreting Graphics

19. Copy and complete the concept map on igneous rocks.

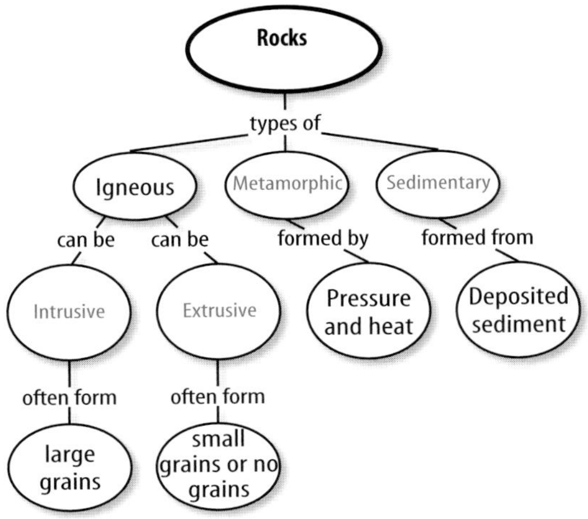

20. Copy the following table on a separate sheet of paper. Use Bowen's reaction series to fill in the blanks.

Crystalization Temperature Ranges for Mineral 1 and Mineral 2

Temperature Range	Mineral 1	Mineral 2	Rock Name
Low	mica	quartz or K-feldspar	granite or rhyolite
Intermediate/ High	pyroxene	calcium plagioclase	gabbro or basalt

Thinking Critically

21. **Explain** how cooling rate affects the texture of an igneous rock.

22. **List** the characteristics that help you identify sedimentary rocks.

23. **Determine** the identity of each rock from the following descriptions.
    - **a.** quartz-rich, coarse interlocking grains, with noticeable amounts of potassium feldspar
    - **b.** foliated mass of mica group minerals with some garnet
    - **c.** nearly pure mass of fossil shells cemented by calcite
    - **d.** dense black, fine-grained, with some gas bubble holes
    - **e.** light colored, very low density, frothy (vesicular), glassy

Use the photo below to answer question 24.

24. Describe the kind of force and the direction it was most likely applied to produce this foliated metamorphic rock.

Applying Math

25. If a miner were extracting rock that contained 0.015% gold by mass, how many kilograms of rock must be processed to obtain one kilogram of gold?

26. The body of ore described in question 25 is estimated to have an average density of 6.0 g/cm^3 and contain 1.5×105 m^3 of ore. How many kilograms of gold potentially could come from this body of ore?

Interpreting Graphics

19. See student page.
20. See student page.

Thinking Critically

21. the faster the rate of cooling, the smaller the crystals
22. presence of clasts and/or fossil, evidence of cementation and/or porosity
23. **a.** granite
    b. schist
    c. limestone
    d. vesicular basalt
    e. pumice
24. Compression was perpendicular to the foliation

Applying Math

Math Standards

National: 1, 4, 9

25. 1.5×10^5 m^3 = 1.5×10^{11} cm^3 of ore; 1.5×10^{11} cm^3 $\times$ 6.0 g/cm^3 and = 9×10^{11} g of ore; 9×10^{11} g x 0.00015 = 1,350,000 g of gold or 1,350 Kg of gold

26. 1,350 kg $\times$ 32.15 troy ounces/kg = 43,402.5 troy ounces $\times$ \$450/troy ounce = \$19,531,125.

Assessment Resources

Reproducible Masters

Chapter *Fast File* Resources
- Chapter Review, pp. 41–42
- Chapter Tests, pp. 43–46
- Assessment Transparency Activity, p. 55

Glencoe Science Web site
- Chapter Review Test
- Standardized Test Practice

Glencoe Technology
- Assessment Transparency
- Exam*View*® Pro Testmaker
- MindJogger Videoquiz
- Interactive Chalkboard

chapter 20 Standardized Test Practice

Answer Sheet An answer sheet can be found at **gpescience.com**.

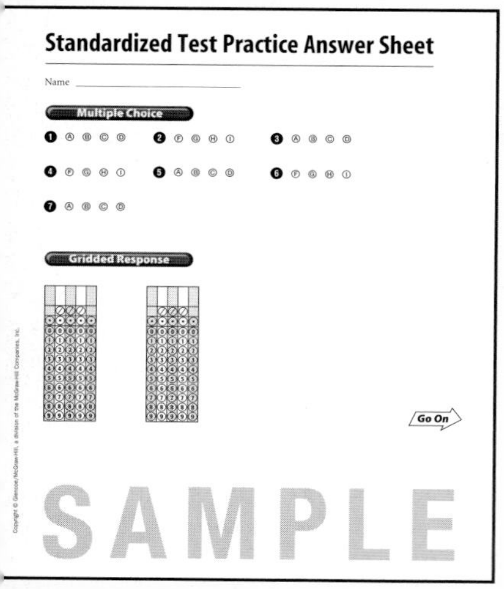
Standardized Test Practice Answer Sheet

Name

Multiple Choice

Gridded Response

Go On

SAMPLE

Multiple Choice

1. B
2. A
3. B
4. B
5. C
6. C
7. A

Gridded Response

8. 5.5 times more
9. C is calcium (14.0% of 25.7 is 3.6% of 100); E is potassium (10.1% of 25.7 is 2.6% of 100)

chapter 20 Standardized Test Practice

Record your answers on the answer sheet provided by your teacher or on a sheet of paper.

Multiple Choice

1. Which is the most common element in Earth's crust?

A. aluminum

B. oxygen

C. potassium

D. silicon

Use the image below to answer question 2.

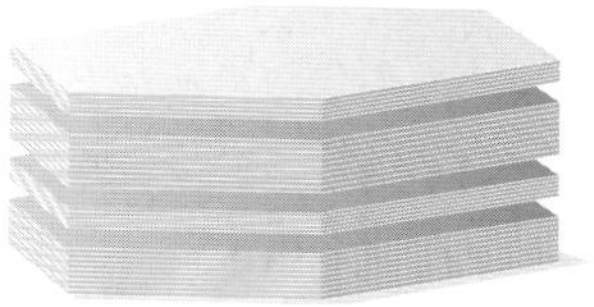

2. Which property of a mineral, used in its identification, is shown?

A. cleavage

B. fracture

C. hardness

D. luster

3. Which is a measure of a mineral's resistance to scratching?

A. cleavage

B. hardness

C. luster

D. streak

4. Why is graphite used in the core of some pencils?

A. Its hardness is high enough to leave a scratch on paper.

B. Its hardness is low enough to leave a streak on paper.

C. Its metallic luster gives it a dark color.

D. Its metallic luster makes it shine on paper.

5. Which mineral is very important to the production of machinery for manufacturing goods?

A. feldspar

B. halite

C. hematite

D. quartz

Use the photo below to answer question 6.

6. The formation of which type of rock produced the rock feature shown above?

A. foliated metamorphic rock

B. extrusive igneous rock

C. intrusive igneous rock

D. nonfoliated metamorphic rock

7. Which is a dark-colored igneous rock with small grains?

   A. basalt

   B. gabbro

   C. granite

   D. rhyolite

Gridded Response

8. If the percent by mass of silicon in Earth's crust is 27.7 percent and the percent by mass of iron is 5.0 percent, how much more silicon is present in Earth's crust than iron?

Use the circle graph below to answer question 9.

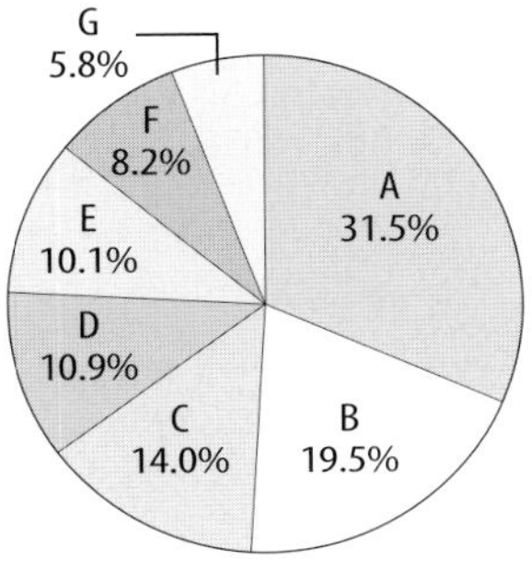

9. The percent by mass of elements in Earth's crust are: 46.6% oxygen; 27.7% silicon; 8.1% aluminum; 5.0% iron; 3.6% calcium; 2.8% sodium; 2.6% potassium; 2.1% magnesium; and 1.5% all others. When oxygen and silicon are not considered, the relative abundance of the remaining elements in Earth's crust are shown in the circle graph above. Which material represents the abundance of calcium?

Short Response

10. How does coal form? Describe the initial material, deposition environment, and geological conditions that lead to its formation.

11. Describe the rock cycle. Discuss what can happen to rock material within the cycle and the amount of time it might take for rocks to be transformed.

12. How does a mineral crystal grow during mineral formation?

13. What are some of the factors that affect the way a crystal grows?

Extended Response

Use photos below to answer question 14.

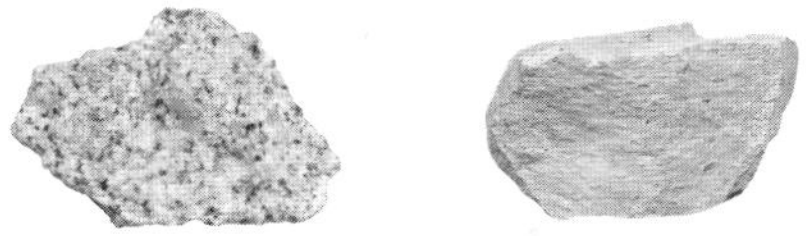

14. **PART A** Identify each of the igneous rocks shown.

    PART B Describe how each rock most likely formed.

Test-Taking Tip

Review Double check your answers before turning in the test.

chapter 20 Standardized Test Practice

Short Response

10. Coal usually develops from peat, a deposit of plant matter that has been buried in shallow swamps in temperate or tropical climates. Low levels of oxygen in swamp water slow the decay of the plant matter before it is buried and compacted by sediment. Several stages of compaction drive out impurities, leaving behind a concentrated form of carbon. Coal often lies within repeated sequences of sandstone, shale, and limestone, which indicate alternating continental and marine conditions or low-lying environments near the sea, such as large deltas and swampy coastal plains.

11. Processes of the rock cycle include any chemical and physical conditions that continuously form and change rocks. Some processes happen at Earth's surface, while others happen deep below the surface. Rock material can be changed into igneous, sedimentary, or metamorphic rock. However, many different paths can be taken by rock material as it changes within the cycle. These processes can take extremely long periods of time, occurring over millions of years, or happen suddenly, such as an erupting volcano. As rock material moves through stages of the cycle, all matter is conserved.

12. As the mineral forms, atoms are added to the surfaces, edges, and corners of the mineral crystal.

13. which atoms are available and their concentration, how fast atoms can migrate, and by the temperature and pressure conditions present

Extended Response

14. **Part A:** The dark, fine-grained rock is basalt. The light-colored, coarse-grained rock is granite.

    Part B: Basalt forms from iron-rich magma that cools quickly at Earth's surface. Granite forms from silica-rich magma that cools slowly deep inside Earth.

Rubrics

For more help evaluating Short- and Extended-Response questions, see the rubrics on p. 9T.

chapter 21 Organizer

Section/Objectives	Standards: National	Standards: State/Local	Lab/Features
Chapter Opener	See pp. 16T–17T for a Key to Standards.		**Launch Lab:** Have you got the time?, p. 645 **Foldables,** p. 645
Section 1 Weathering and Soil 2 sessions 1 block 1. **Explain** the role of weathering in recycling Earth materials. 2. **Discuss** the processes of mechanical and chemical weathering. 3. **Describe** the process of and controls on soil formation. 4. **Discuss** some methods for controlling soil loss.	National Content Standards: UCP. 1–5, A.1, A.2, B.3		**MiniLAB:** Observing a Disappearing Seasoning, p. 647 **Integrate Chemistry,** p. 648 **Lab:** Graphing Soil Textures, p. 653
Section 2 Shaping the Landscape 2 sessions 1 block 5. **Explain** how agents of erosion operate. 6. **Describe** kinds of landforms created by erosion. 7. **Identify** landforms created by deposition of eroded material.	National Content Standards: UCP.1–3, UCP. 5, A.1, A.2, D.1, D.2		**MiniLAB:** Modeling Runoff, p. 656 Video Lab **Science Online,** p. 657 **Science Online,** p. 658
Section 3 Groundwater 1 session 1.5 blocks 8. **Explain** the importance of groundwater. 9. **Describe** how groundwater is stored and obtained. 10. **List** some concerns about future groundwater use.	National Content Standards: UCP. 1–3, UCP. 5, A.1, A.2, D.2, F.4, F.5		**Applying Math:** Porosity Volume, p. 665 **Visualizing The Role of Groundwater in Shaping Earth's Surface,** p. 666 **Integrate Environment,** p. 667 **Science Online,** p. 667
Section 4 Geologic Time 3 sessions 1.5 blocks 11. **Distinguish** among geologic eras, periods, and epochs. 12. **Explain** how scientists decide when a geologic time period ends and another begins. 13. **Explain** the methods and logic used in relative dating. 14. **Interpret** a geologic cross section. 15. **Describe** the methods and logic used in absolute dating.	National Content Standards: UCP. 1–5, A. 1, A.2, B.1, B.2, D.3, E.1, G.2		**Integrate History,** p. 670 **Lab:** It's about time—relative, that is., pp. 676–677 **Science and Society:** Tapping into the Underground, p. 678

Glencoe Exclusive!

StudentWorks Plus | TeacherWorks™ All-In-One Planner and Resource Center

Lab Materials	Reproducible Resources	Section Assessment	Technology
Launch Lab: adding machine tape, meterstick	**Chapter *Fast File* Resources** Foldables Worksheet, p. 15 Directed Reading Overview, p. 17 Note-taking Worksheets, pp. 33–35	Glencoe's Assessment Advantage	TeacherWorks includes: • Interactive Teacher Edition • Lesson Planner with calendar • Access to all program blacklines • Correlations to standards • Web links
MiniLAB: sugar, paper plate, salt, drinking glasses, water, watch, spoon **Lab:** soil texture triangular diagram	**Chapter *Fast File* Resources** Transparency Activity, p. 44 MiniLAB, p. 3 Lab Activity, pp. 9–11 Enrichment, p. 29 Reinforcement, p. 25 Directed Reading, p. 18 Lab Worksheet, pp. 5–6	**Performance** MiniLab, p. 647 Applying Math, p. 652 **Content** Section Review, p. 652	Section Focus Transparency Teaching Transparency Interactive Chalkboard CD-ROM StudentWorks Plus
MiniLAB: baking sheet, water	**Chapter *Fast File* Resources** Transparency Activity, p. 45 MiniLAB, p. 4 Enrichment, p. 30 Reinforcement, p. 26 Directed Reading, p. 18	**Portfolio** Assessment, p. 662 **Performance** MiniLab, p. 656 Applying Math, p. 662 **Content** Section Review, p. 662	Section Focus Transparency Interactive Chalkboard CD-ROM StudentWorks Plus Video Lab
Need materials? Contact Science Kit at 1-800-828-7777 or www.sciencekit.com.	**Chapter *Fast File* Resources** Transparency Activity, p. 46 Lab Activity, pp. 13–14 Enrichment, p. 31 Reinforcement, p. 27 Directed Reading, pp. 19	**Portfolio** Differentiated Instruction, p. 667 **Performance** Applying Math, p. 665 Applying Math, p. 668 **Content** Section Review, p. 668	Section Focus Transparency Interactive Chalkboard CD-ROM StudentWorks Plus
Lab: geologic cross sections	**Chapter *Fast File* Resources** Transparency Activity, p. 47, 49–50 Enrichment, p. 32 Reinforcement, p. 28 Directed Reading, p. 19–20 Lab Worksheets, pp. 7–8	**Performance** Applying Math, p. 675 **Content** Section Review, p. 675	Section Focus Transparency Interactive Chalkboard CD-ROM StudentWorks Plus

End of Chapter Assessment

Glencoe's Assessment Advantage

Blackline Masters	Technology	Professional Series
Chapter *Fast File* Resources Chapter Review, pp. 37–38 Chapter Tests, pp. 39–42 **Standardized Test Practice,** pp. 88–91	MindJogger Videoquiz Exam*View*® Pro Testmaker TeacherWorks CD-ROM Interactive Chalkboard CD-ROM	**Performance Assessment in the Science Classroom (PASC)**

Earth's Changing Surface

Transparencies

Section Focus

Section Focus Transparency 1 — Significance of Soil — Chapter 21

The United States Department of Agriculture puts a lot of time and money into studying various soils within the United States and around the world. It has officially classified twelve different types of soils called *soil orders* with 64 recognized suborders. Soil data are made available to the general public for use in various agricultural and industrial purposes.

1. Why is so much effort put into studying soil?
2. What are some non-agricultural uses of soil surveys?
3. How can conservationists use this soil data in their work?

L2

Section Focus Transparency 2 — Landscape with Nature — Chapter 21

How would you like to never have to mow your lawn again? If that idea appeals to you, landscaping with native plants may be the answer. Native plants flourish since they are well acclimated to the local environment and have little need for pesticides, fertilizers, or any water other than the natural rainfall. Such a natural landscape can make us feel more connected to nature and enhance the beauty of our home environments.

1. How could natural landscaping be good for the soil?
2. How might periodic burning be beneficial for a natural landscape?
3. What is biodiversity?

L2

Section Focus Transparency 3 — All's Well that Ends Well — Chapter 21

For many people around the world, wells are the only source of fresh water. People have been digging wells for thousands of years, yet wells can pose problems. A poorly built well or one that has been tainted by poisonous substances is useless. Fortunately, there are ways to test well water for contaminants, and many people who depend on wells for water perform such tests on a regular basis.

1. How could toxic material spilled on Earth's surface affect groundwater?
2. Why should a person with a well limit the use of pesticides and fertilizers?
3. Why would water conservation be important for people who get their water from wells?

L2

This is a representation of key blackline masters available in the Teacher Classroom Resources. See Resource Manager boxes within the chapter for additional information.

Assessment

Assessment Transparency — Earth's Changing Surface — Chapter 21

1. Wind transports the _____ materials of soil such as organic matter, clays, and silts.
   A heaviest B lightest
   C most colorful D most dense
2. Wind erosion lowers the agricultural _____ of the soil.
   F productivity G infertility
   H input J shortage
3. There is also a(n) _____ impact associated with wind erosion as city funds are spent clearing and cleaning affected areas.
   A social C economical
   B emotional D philosophical

L2

Teaching

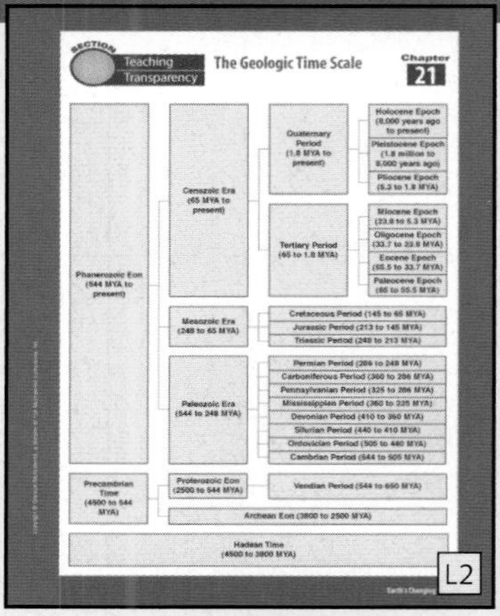
Teaching Transparency — The Geologic Time Scale — Chapter 21

L2

Key to Teaching Strategies

The following designations will help you decide which activities are appropriate for your students.

- L1 Level 1 activities should be appropriate for students with learning difficulties.
- L2 Level 2 activities should be within the ability range of all students.
- L3 Level 3 activities are designed for above-average students.
- ELL ELL activities should be within the ability range of English Language Learners.
- COOP LEARN Cooperative Learning activities are designed for small group work.
- LS Multiple Learning Styles logos, as described on page 12T, are used throughout to indicate strategies that address different learning styles.
- P These strategies represent student products that can be placed into a best-work portfolio.
- PBL Problem-Based Learning activities apply real-world situations to learning.

Hands-on Activities

Student Text Lab Worksheet

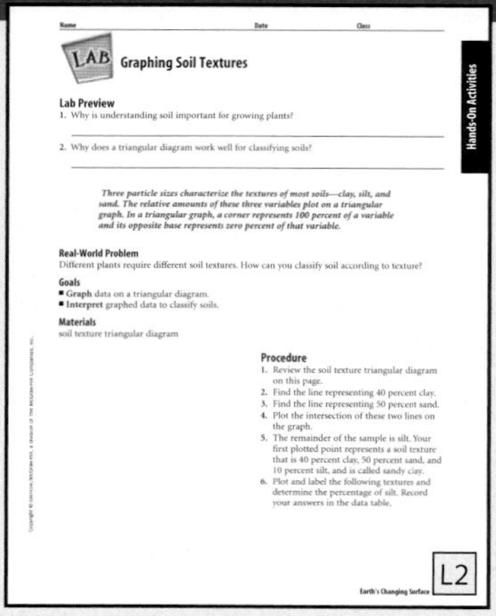
LAB — Graphing Soil Textures

Lab Preview
1. Why is understanding soil important for growing plants?
2. Why does a triangular diagram work well for classifying soils?

Real-World Problem
Different plants require different soil textures. How can you classify soil according to texture?

Goals
- Graph data on a triangular diagram.
- Interpret graphed data to classify soils.

Materials
soil texture triangular diagram

Procedure
1. Review the soil texture triangular diagram on this page.
2. Find the line representing 40 percent clay.
3. Find the line representing 50 percent sand.
4. Plot the intersection of these two lines on the graph.
5. The remainder of the sample is silt. Your first plotted point represents a soil texture that is 40 percent clay, 50 percent sand, and 10 percent silt, and is called sandy clay.
6. Plot and label the following textures and determine the percentage of silt. Record your answers in the data table.

L2

Laboratory Activities

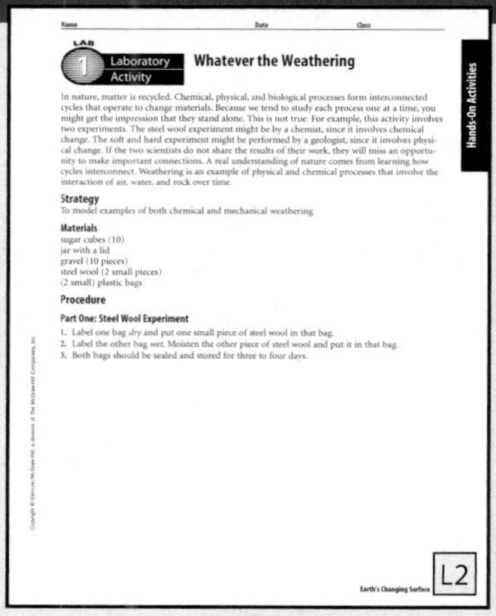
Laboratory Activity 1 — Whatever the Weathering

Strategy
To model examples of both chemical and mechanical weathering

Materials
sugar cubes (10)
jar with a lid
gravel (10 pieces)
steel wool (2 small pieces)
(2 small) plastic bags

Procedure
Part One: Steel Wool Experiment
1. Label one bag *dry* and put one small piece of steel wool in that bag.
2. Label the other bag *wet*. Moisten the other piece of steel wool and put it in that bag.
3. Both bags should be sealed and stored for three to four days.

L2

Resource Manager

Meeting Different Ability Levels

Content Outline

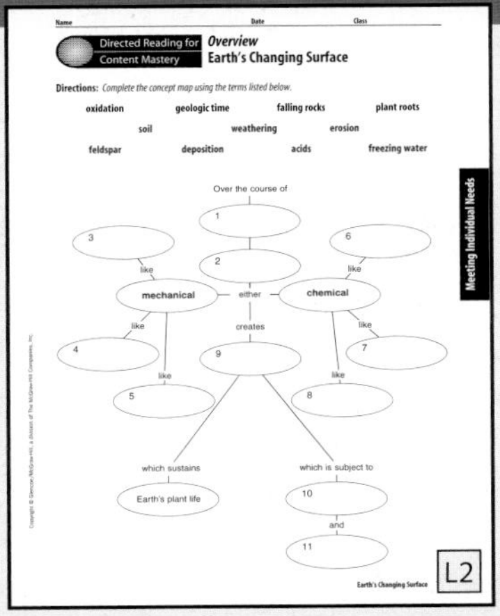
Directed Reading for Content Mastery — Overview — Earth's Changing Surface

Directions: Complete the concept map using the terms listed below.

oxidation, geologic time, falling rocks, plant roots, soil, weathering, erosion, feldspar, deposition, acids, freezing water

L2

Reinforcement

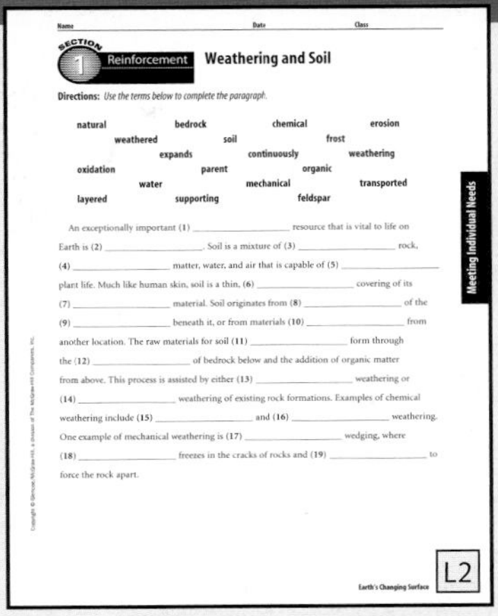
Section 1 Reinforcement — Weathering and Soil

Directions: Use the terms below to complete the paragraph.

L2

Enrichment

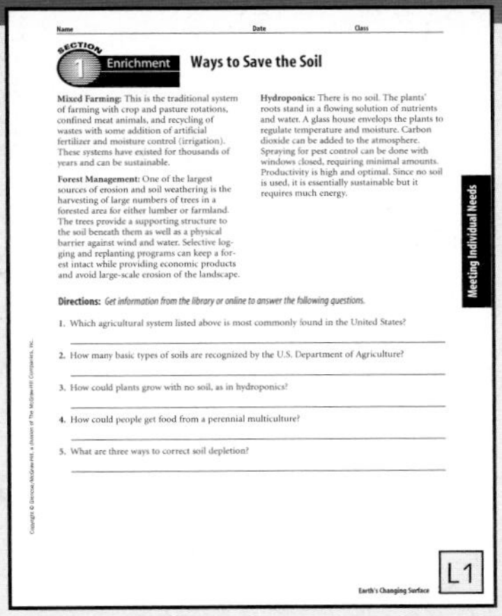
Section 1 Enrichment — Ways to Save the Soil

L1

Directed Reading (English/Spanish)

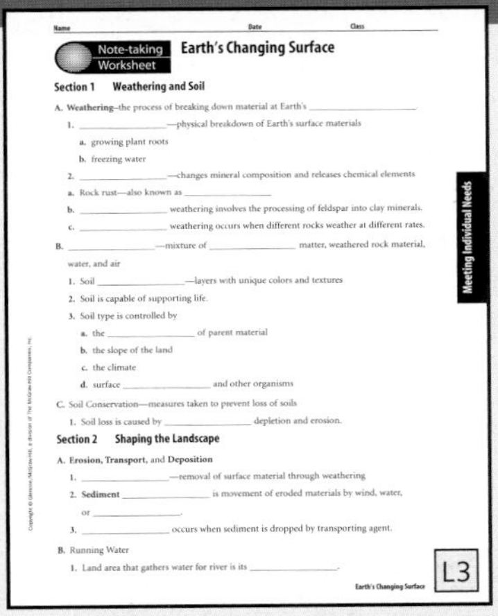
Note-taking Worksheet — Earth's Changing Surface

Section 1 Weathering and Soil

L3

Study Guide

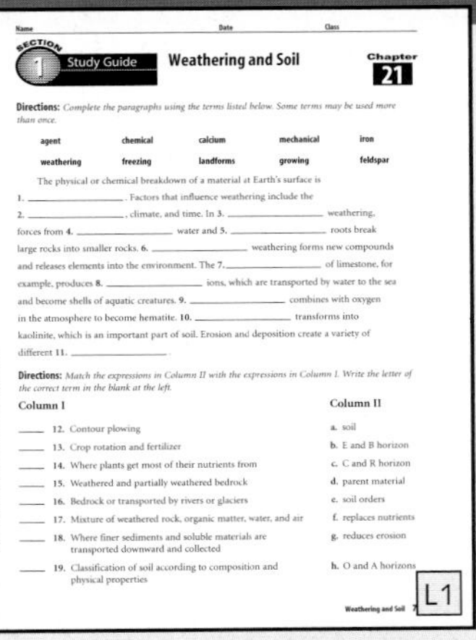
Section 1 Study Guide — Weathering and Soil — Chapter 21

L1

Reading Essentials

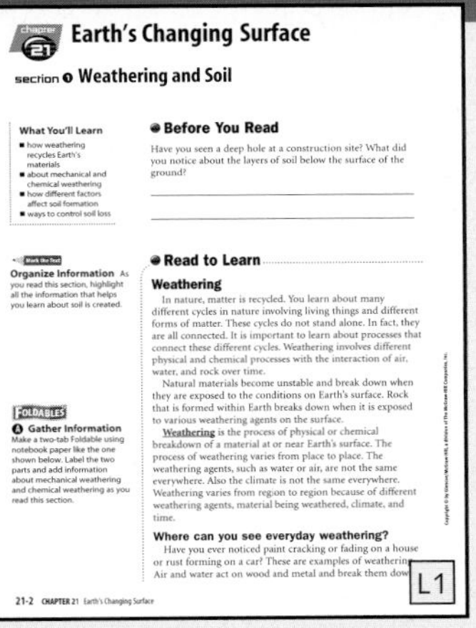
Chapter 21 Earth's Changing Surface

section 1 Weathering and Soil

Before You Read

Read to Learn

Weathering

L1

Assessment

Test Practice Workbook

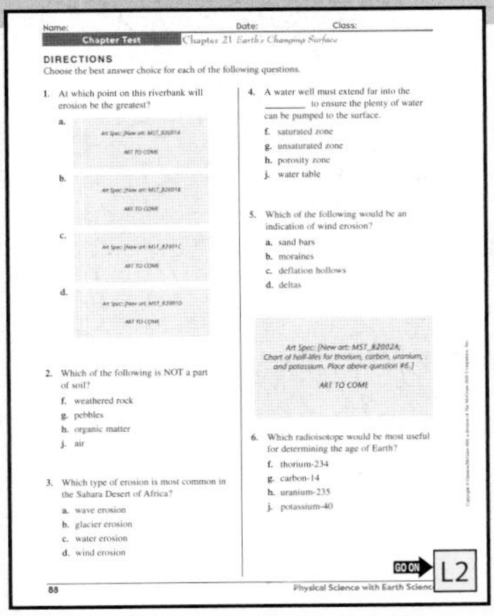
Chapter Test — Chapter 21 Earth's Changing Surface

DIRECTIONS

Choose the best answer choice for each of the following questions.

L2

Chapter Review

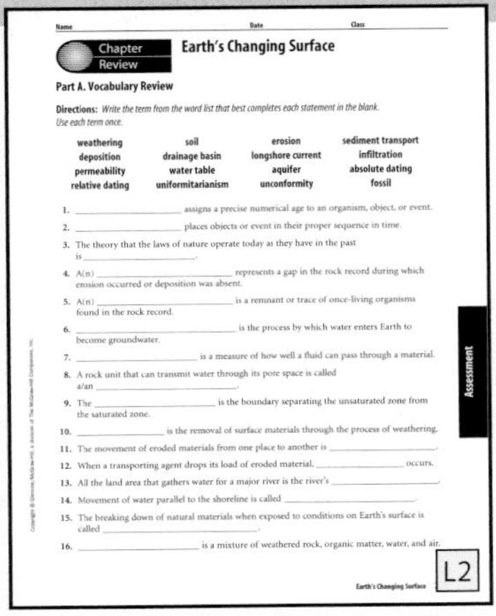
Chapter Review — Earth's Changing Surface

Part A. Vocabulary Review

L2

Chapter Tests

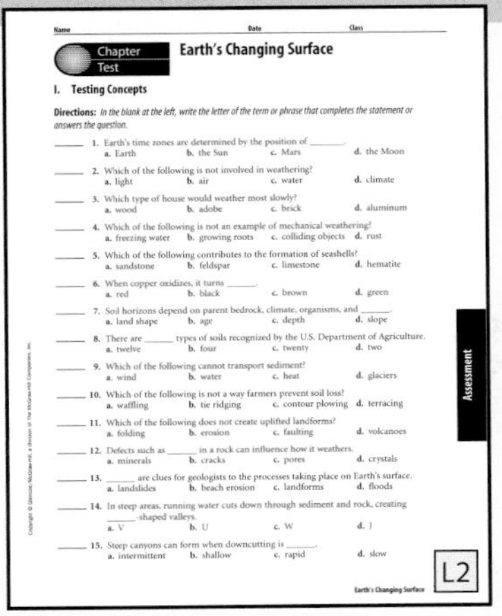
Chapter Test — Earth's Changing Surface

I. Testing Concepts

L2

Science Content Background

section 1 Weathering and Soil

Response to Changing Conditions

Weathering is a natural response to changing conditions in the environment. If a material was created in a specific environment, remains in that environment, and the environment never changes, then weathering should not take place. Exposure to change is an important factor in weathering. The deep-sea environment, for example, is exceedingly constant. Pressure, temperature, salinity, and light levels do not change and weathering is non-existent.

Archeologists find artifacts in the forms of pottery and glass, which have survived thousands of years. These materials are stable on Earth's surface and weather very slowly, if at all. On the other hand, ancient paper or cloth are not as commonly found; they are not stable and are subject to weathering.

Environmental Concerns

A modern environmental concern is that we are creating new synthetic materials that do not weather; i.e. disposable diapers and plastics. In landfills, these materials do not decay, rot, decompose, or weather. These products are also difficult to recycle. Recycling amounts to synthetic weathering and reformation into a new object.

Most fertile soils on Earth have been cultivated for hundreds of years, often with the same crop. This practice results in soil depletion on a colossal scale. A consequence of this is that much of the food grown on or in this soil lacks the nutrient value it once possessed. We are eating food, but it is not as nourishing at it once was. One solution is vitamin supplements for those that can afford them. Unfortunately, many can't afford them. Therefore, soil management and fertility is a concern for everyone.

section 2 Shaping the Landscape

Causes and Effects of Erosion

The agents of erosion are persistent. These actions are often so gradual that in a person's lifetime, little change to the Earth's surface is noticed. But occasionally catastrophes happen which draw peoples' attention to erosion. It is this harmful set of changes that strips Earth of soil and leads to disasters, such as landslides and flooding.

Running water as an erosional agent is by far the most important. Most of Earth's land surface is affected by this agent. Even in deserts, running water is responsible for most of the surface erosion. Glacial activity is equally destructive, but is confined to mountain peaks and polar regions. Wind erosion is limited to areas with little surface cover and persistent winds.

Human activity, such as road building, farming, and the building of housing, can all promote erosion. Erosion can't be stopped, but it can be controlled and limited. Breakwaters, different farming techniques, and paving less land can all help to reduce it.

section 3 Groundwater

A Precious Resource

The majority of municipal water supplies come from groundwater sources and are built atop those same aquifers. Municipal waste is stored in landfills, which act like giant tea bags, leaching their contents into the groundwater below. Some populations also carelessly dump household waste on the surface and overuse pesticides and fertilizers, which leach into the groundwater supplies.

Conventional wisdom says, "out of sight, out of mind." It also says that Earth's soils and rocks will filter out the contaminants and no harm will be done. Earth's soil and rock cover does filter out contaminants. But like all filters, there is a limit to the rate of filtration and the total amount of contaminants that can be absorbed.

In some regions of our country there are proposals for treating surface water and then injecting it into the groundwater supply, thus bypassing the infiltration process. Many regions use treated surface water. We frequently hear of cities in a water crisis blamed on drought; however, many of these crises are due to natural infiltration being unable to keep up with demand. While infiltration takes years, pumped withdrawal takes minutes.

section 4 Geologic Time

Uniformitarianism

Geologic time is one of the most difficult concepts to understand. Support for the belief in the vastness of geologic time was slow in coming. The principles of relative dating based on the global study of fossils laid the foundation for the concept that Earth was old. If it were not for breakthroughs in chemistry, specifically radioisotope studies, we would still only be using relative dating methods.

Attached to the understanding of relative dating is the concept of uniformitarianism. Set forth by James Hutton in the late 1700s, this concept unto itself is at the heart of all science. In a nutshell, uniformitarianism says that the laws of nature are fixed and immutable. Chemical reactions occur today as they did yesterday or even a million years ago. The same applies to the laws of physics. And so it goes for all the other laws of nature.

Hutton shocked the geologic community with some simple reasoning. He observed that each year the streams of Scotland flooded and left a new, thin layer of mud on the seafloor. If he dug a hole into that seafloor at low tide, he found a "layer cake" of past mud accumulations. He assumed that each thin layer amounted to a year's time. Inland there are hillsides exposed by erosion that showed enough of these thin layers to account for hundreds of thousands of years. Hutton properly reasoned that it would take time for the layers to accumulate, be compressed to rock and then uplifted and eroded—the beginnings of the notion of a rock cycle.

chapter content resources

Earth Revealed video series Episodes 15, 19, 20, 22, 23, 24, 21, 10
www.learner.org/resources/series78.html

Internet Resources
For additional content background, visit gpescience.com to:
- access your book online
- find references to related articles in popular science magazines
- access Web links with related content background
- access current events with science journal topics

Print Resources
Physical Geology, Fifth Edition, by Charles C. Plummer and David McGeary, Wm. C. Brown Publishers, 1991

chapter 21

Chapter Vocabulary

weathering, p. 646
soil, p. 650
erosion, p. 654
sediment transport, p. 654
deposition, p. 654
drainage basin, p. 655
longshore current, p. 660
infiltration, p. 663
water table, p. 664
permeability, p. 664
aquifer, p. 664
absolute dating, p. 669
relative dating, p. 669
uniformitarianism, p. 670
principle of superposition, p. 670
unconformity, p. 671
fossil, p. 671

Science Journal Answers will vary. Answers might include U-shaped valley, hanging valley, moraines and eskers, poorly-sorted glacial till, or glacial grooves and striations.

INTERACTIVE CHALKBOARD with Image Bank

PowerPoint® Presentations

This CD-ROM is an editable Microsoft® PowerPoint® presentation that includes:

- a pre-made presentation for every chapter
- interactive graphics
- animations
- audio clips
- image bank
- all new section and chapter questions
- Standardized Test Practice
- transparencies
- Foldables directions
- links to gpescience.com

chapter 21

Earth's Changing Surface

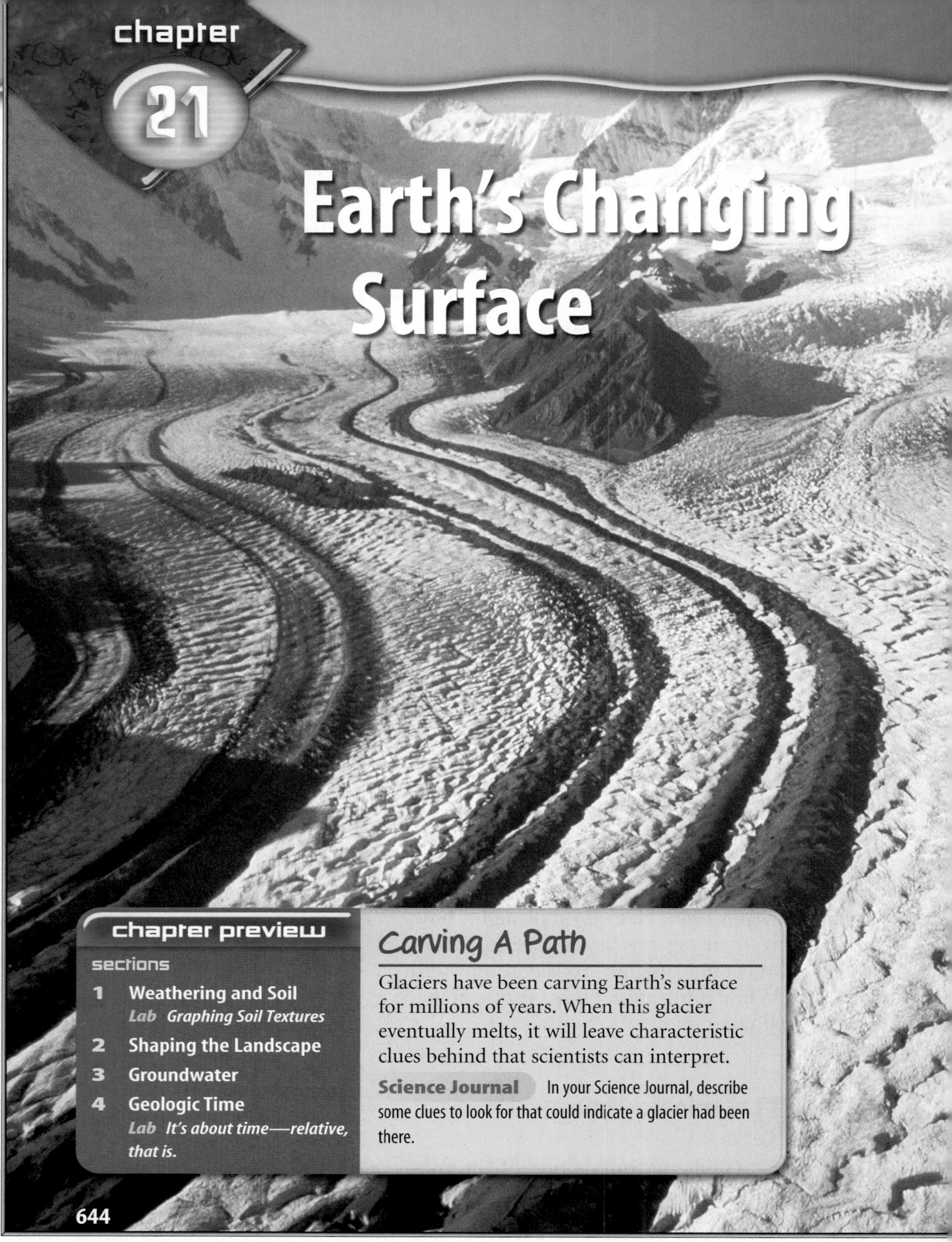

chapter preview

sections

1. Weathering and Soil
   Lab *Graphing Soil Textures*
2. Shaping the Landscape
3. Groundwater
4. Geologic Time
   Lab *It's about time—relative, that is.*

Carving A Path

Glaciers have been carving Earth's surface for millions of years. When this glacier eventually melts, it will leave characteristic clues behind that scientists can interpret.

Science Journal In your Science Journal, describe some clues to look for that could indicate a glacier had been there.

Theme Connection

Processes The surface of Earth is constantly changing as it adjusts to new conditions. Weathering, erosion, soil formation, and land-form development are the result of a variety of processes as they operate over the immensity of geologic time.

About the Photo

Kennicott Glacier Medial moraines run through the Kennicott Glacier at Wrangell-St. Elias National Park in Alaska. Medial moraines form when lateral moraines converge.

Start-Up Activities

Launch LAB

Have you got the time?

We usually think of time in terms of hours, days, and years. Earth processes operate in much longer time units. Imagine that Earth's age—about 4.5 billion years—were equal to an average human lifespan of 75 years. Then one million years of Earth's existence would represent about six days of a human life.

1. Obtain a 5-m length of adding machine tape and a meterstick.
2. Draw a horizontal line across one end of the tape and label it *Present*.
3. Using a scale of 1 mm = 1 million years, draw and label lines across the tape behind *Present* to mark the beginning of each of the following divisions of time:
   Cenozoic Era: 66 million years ago (mya)
   Mesozoic Era: 248 mya
   Paleozoic Era and beginning of Phanerozoic Eon: 540 mya
   Proterozoic Eon: 2,500 mya
   Archean Eon: 3,800 mya
4. **Think Critically** Eons are the longest subdivisions of geologic time. An eon is subdivided into eras. Infer why eons and eras are different lengths of time. What kind of events might end one time interval and begin a new one?

FOLDABLES™ Study Organizer

Surface Features Make the following Foldable to help you organize features that result from erosion and deposition on Earth's surface.

STEP 1 **Fold** one piece of paper lengthwise into thirds.

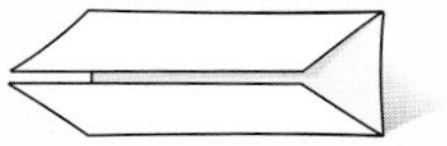

STEP 2 **Fold** the paper widthwise into fourths.

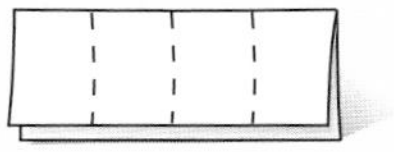

STEP 3 **Unfold**, lay the paper lengthwise, and draw lines along the folds.

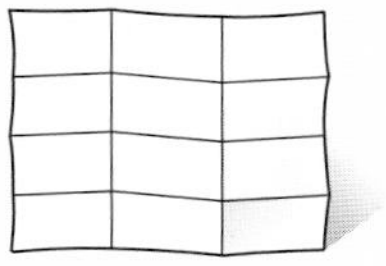

STEP 4 **Label** your table as shown.

Surface-Changing Agent	Erosion	Deposition
Wind		
Water		
Glaciers		

Making a Table As you read the chapter, complete the table describing erosional and despositional features.

Science Online | Preview this chapter's content and activities at gpescience.com

Launch LAB

Purpose to introduce students to the concept and scope of geologic time L2

Preparation Pre-cut the adding-machine tape into 5-m-long strips.

Materials adding-machine tape, meterstick, colored pencils

Teaching Strategy Remind students of proper measurement techniques.

Troubleshooting Some students still have difficulty finding millimeter markings on the meterstick. Help students to read the markings correctly.

Think Critically

Students are likely to say that the extinction of a dominant life-form ends intervals. This is true, but point out that most intervals are also accompanied by a global geologic event.

Assessment

Oral Have students speculate about future events that might result in the end of the current epoch (Holocene), period (Neogene), or era (Cenozoic).

FOLDABLES™ Study Organizer **Dinah Zike Study Fold**

Student preparation materials for this Foldable are available in the **Chapter *Fast File* Resources.** L2

Weathering and Soil

1 Motivate

An editable Microsoft® PowerPoint® presentation is available on **Interactive Chalkboard** CD-ROM.

Bellringer

Section Focus Transparencies also are available on the Interactive Chalkboard CD-ROM. L2 ELL

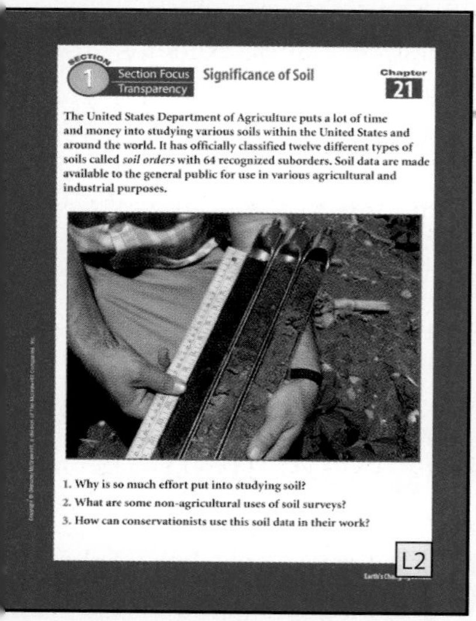
Section 1 Section Focus Transparency — Significance of Soil — Chapter 21

The United States Department of Agriculture puts a lot of time and money into studying various soils within the United States and around the world. It has officially classified twelve different types of soils called *soil orders* with 64 recognized suborders. Soil data are made available to the general public for use in various agricultural and industrial purposes.

1. Why is so much effort put into studying soil?
2. What are some non-agricultural uses of soil surveys?
3. How can conservationists use this soil data in their work?

L2

Reading Preview

Tie to Prior Knowledge

New Materials Chemical change results in new substances being formed. Chemical weathering forms new Earth materials. L2

Brainstorm Have students write a new vocabulary word in the center of a sheet of paper. Ask them to brainstorm the meaning of the word and write ideas radiating from the central word like spokes of a bicycle wheel. Students can verify or modify their definitions as they read the text.

Reading Check

Answer action of water, wind, ice, and air

Reading Guide

What You'll Learn

- **Explain** the role of weathering in recycling Earth materials.
- **Discuss** the processes of mechanical and chemical weathering.
- **Describe** the process of and controls on soil formation.
- **Discuss** some methods for controlling soil loss.

Why It's Important

The processes of weathering and soil formation are critical in forming a base to support plant growth and ecosystems.

Review Vocabulary

sediment: particles of rock deposited on Earth's surface that may become sedimentary rocks

New Vocabulary

- weathering
- soil

Weathering

In nature, matter is recycled. Chemical, physical, and biological processes form interconnected cycles that operate to change materials. Because we tend to study each process one at a time, you might get the impression that they stand alone. This is not true. A real understanding of nature comes from learning how the cycles interconnect. Weathering is an example of physical and chemical processes that involve the interaction of air, water, and rock over time.

Natural materials become unstable and break down when exposed to conditions on Earth's surface. **Figure 1** illustrates the results of rock weathering. The minerals in this rock formed under higher temperatures and pressures compared to those on the surface. When these minerals were subjected to the conditions at the surface, they broke down. **Weathering** is the process of physical or chemical breakdown of a material at or near Earth's surface. Factors that influence weathering include the agent, such as water or air, the nature of the material being weathered, climate, and time. Weathering varies from region to region because different weathering conditions are present.

Figure 1 The corners and edges of rocks are more rapidly weathered than smooth rock faces. This often produces rounded forms.

Reading Check *What causes weathering?*

Section 1 Resource Manager

Chapter *FAST FILE* Resources
- Transparency Activity, p. 44
- Note-taking Worksheets, pp. 33–35
- MiniLAB, p. 3
- Lab Activity, pp. 9–11
- Enrichment, p. 29
- Reinforcement, p. 25
- Directed Reading for Content Mastery, pp. 17–18
- Lab Worksheets, pp. 5–6

Earth Science Critical Thinking/Problem Solving, p. 6

Performance Assessment in the Science Classroom, pp. 44–45

Everyday Weathering You can notice weathering going on all around you. Paint on a house eventually will crack or fade in color. Roadways eventually develop cracks and potholes. Some metal items on cars might start to rust. All of these take place at different rates depending on where you live and whether or not you have taken measures to prevent weathering.

Mechanical Weathering

You can think of mechanical weathering as turning big pieces into little pieces. For this to take place, a force must be applied to the material. Forces that can cause mechanical weathering include impact, expansion or contraction of materials, and biological effects. Variables that control mechanical weathering include the nature of the material being weathered, climate, and time. Of these variables, time is the least noticeable. Extremely slow changes often go unnoticed until their long-term accumulated effects get our attention.

Prying Rock Apart If a rock contains natural fractures, water can enter them. When water freezes, it expands. This forces the cracks apart and ultimately forces the rock apart. This type of weathering is called frost wedging. Any place that has sufficient surface water and temperatures that change from freezing to above freezing can experience this type of mechanical weathering.

Growing plant roots are an example of a biological force that can cause mechanical weathering. As roots grow, they increase in diameter and exert forces that widen cracks.

Rocks can also act as impact agents. Large rocks falling from a cliff or tumbling down a slope can break other rocks into smaller pieces. **Figure 2** illustrates what happens when a large object breaks apart. As a large particle breaks into smaller particles, the amount of surface area increases. More surface area compared to volume increases the likelihood that a material will be attacked by chemical agents.

Mini LAB

Observing a Disappearing Seasoning

Procedure

1. Sprinkle a teaspoon of **sugar** on a **paper plate.** Using the back of a **metal spoon,** crush the sugar into the finest powder you can. Do the same for a teaspoon of **salt.**
2. Half-fill **four clear drinking glasses** with **tap water.** Allow them to stand for several minutes.
3. Have a **watch with a second hand** ready. Drop a teaspoon of uncrushed sugar into a glass of water and stir. Record how long it takes the sugar to completely dissolve.
4. Repeat step 3 using the powdered sugar, the powdered salt, and a teaspoon of uncrushed salt.

Analysis

1. Which substance dissolved fastest? Why?
2. How does particle size affect dissolving rate?
3. List some variables other than particle size that could affect dissolving rate.

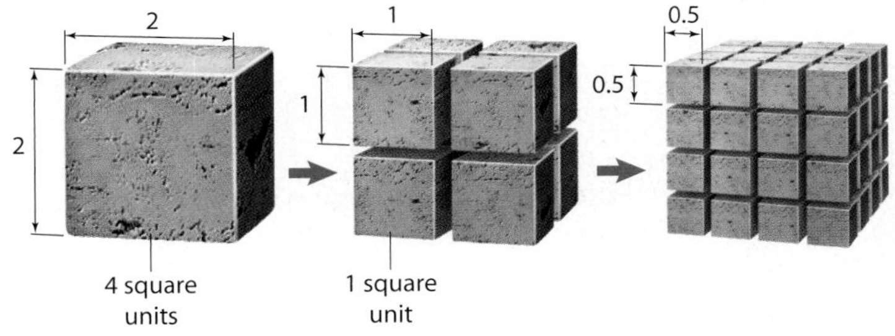

Figure 2 The cube on the right has exposed, inner surfaces that the cube on the left does not have.

2 Teach

Mini LAB

Purpose Students will observe the effect of grain size on solution rate.

Materials four clear drinking glasses, salt, sugar, tap water, metal spoons, plastic stirring spoon, clock or watch that shows seconds

Teaching Strategy Have the students attempt to crush the sugar and salt to approximately the same sized particles. Use the back of a spoon against a plate to crush the materials. Running the material through a sieve will ensure uniform grain size.

Analysis

1. powdered salt; because salt is more soluble than sugar
2. smaller-sized particles increase the dissolving rate
3. temperature or quantity of water

Assessment

Oral Have students relate the difficulties they had in doing this procedure. Probable responses might include: determining when the last of the product dissolved—salt is difficult to determine because it clouds the water; making sure the crush size was consistent. Use **PASC**, p. 89. L2

Reading Strategy

Causal Relationships Have students make a chart with the headings *Cause* and *Effect.* Under *Effect,* have students write *prying rock apart, moving matter, rock rust, feldspar weathering,* and *differential weathering.* Have students read the text to determine the cause of each effect.

SECTION 1 Weathering and Soil 647

INTEGRATE Chemistry

Illegible Rocks These two obelisks stand 21 m tall. They are made of red granite. Thothmes III erected them in Heliopolis, Egypt around 1500 B.C. In 1200 B.C., Ramses II added inscriptions commemorating his military victories. The obelisks were moved to Alexandria by the Romans in 12 B.C. and sometime later feil over into the mud. It was this unplanned burial that helped prevent chemical weathering of the granite. Unfortunately, the humid climates of New York City and London accelerated the weathering process by reacting with salts contained in the mud.

Reading Check

Answer water, oxygen, and naturally occurring acids

INTEGRATE Chemistry

Illegible Rocks The Egyptians carved tall, slender granite obelisks. One is displayed in New York City and another in London. Over time, these two obelisks have become almost smooth and the hieroglyphs barely can be seen. Form a hypothesis stating why the obelisks changed.

Chemical Weathering

The process of chemical weathering forms new compounds and releases elements into the environment. Water and oxygen are the key agents of chemical weathering, along with naturally occurring acids. Elements released by chemical weathering enrich soil and nourish plants. Without weathering of rocks there would be no soil to support land plants, terrestrial ecosystems, and humans.

Reading Check *List three key agents of chemical weathering.*

Matter on the Move Cycles of chemical weathering affect all surface environments from land to sea. If streams carry elements released on land into the ocean, then those elements become raw materials that support marine ecosystems. For example, marine organisms that build shells require dissolved products such as calcium ions (Ca^{2+}) and bicarbonate ions (HCO_3^-) to make their shells. These ions come from the weathering of limestone on land and from the dissolving of other seashells.

Rock Rust Oxidation is a common chemical weathering process. Iron that is present in minerals is released through weathering and combines with oxygen to form iron oxides. You might know that when something made of iron or steel is exposed to air and water, it quickly begins to rust. The mineral hematite is natural "rust" produced through oxidation reactions. Hematite is mined to obtain iron for steel production.

Recall that natural materials tend to convert to a more stable form at Earth's surface. Unstable iron released by weathering forms stable hematite. Hematite is easily spotted in rocks because it stains them a brownish-red color, as shown in **Figure 3.** Other metals also form oxide minerals. Examples include copper, which oxidizes to a greenish-colored patina or silver, which oxidizes to a black coating.

Figure 3 When iron-bearing rocks are weathered and eroded, they often produce reddish sediment. Iron oxidation also can give some soils a reddish color.

Active Reading

Reflection In this strategy, students record responses to an activity. Have students divide sheets of paper into columns. Have them record their thoughts under headings What I Did, What I Learned, Questions I Have, Suprises I Experienced, and Overall Response. Have students write a Science Journal entry for the MiniLAB in this section.

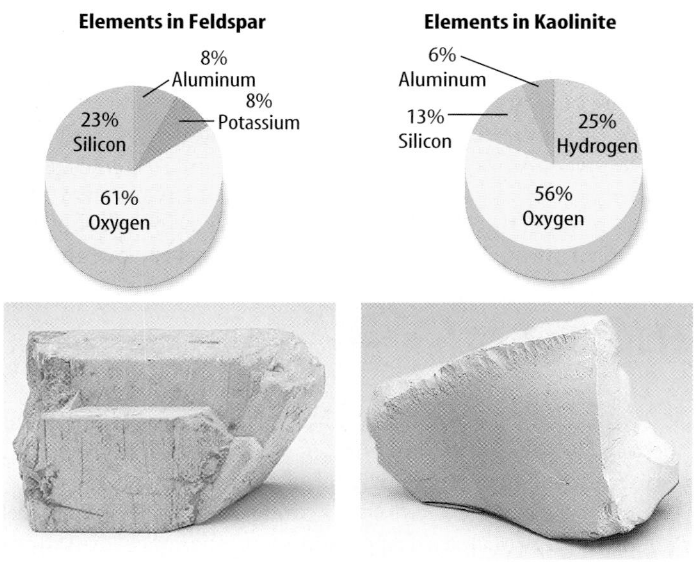

Feldspar reacts with carbonic acid. The mineral kaolinite is formed.

Figure 4 Chemical weathering changes the chemical composition of minerals and rocks.
Describe *how kaolinite is different from feldspar.*

Feldspar Weathering An important chemical weathering process for continental rocks is the weathering of feldspar minerals into clay minerals.

This reaction starts with a common rock-forming mineral shown in **Figure 4,** and ends with minerals that are common in continental sediment and soil. The silica end product often forms quartz cement in sedimentary rocks. The kaolinite is a clay mineral that helps soil hold water and nutrients. Chemical elements freed by weathering now are available for use by plants. Similar chemical weathering reactions of other minerals provide particles necessary for roots to anchor themselves and nutrient elements to support plant growth.

Differential Weathering Different rock formations tend to weather at different rates. The types of minerals, cementing agent, and the presence of defects, such as fractures, influence how a rock formation weathers. As a result, rocks that are the most resistant to weathering remain in the landscape. They are products of differential weathering and erosion.

Together, erosion and deposition of sediment create a variety of landforms. They also represent important processes of the rock cycle. Landforms, such as those in **Figure 5,** are geologists' clues to the processes taking place on Earth's surface. Some of these processes include floods, landslides, and beach erosion.

Figure 5 As water seeks a path of least resistance, it acts as a differential weathering agent. This type of weathering creates many interesting landforms.

Teacher FYI

Feldspar Weathering Carbonic acid causes the mineral feldspar to weather to the clay mineral kaolinite. The chemical reaction can be written as follows:

$$2KAlSi_3O_8 + 2(H^+ + HCO_3) + H_2O \rightarrow$$
K feldspar carbonic acid water

$$Al_2Si_2O_5(OH)_4 + 2K^+ + 2HCO_3^- + 4SiO_2$$
kaolinite (potassium) (bicarbonate) (silica) (in solution)

Caption Answer

Figure 4 It contains hydrogen and no potassium.

Identifying Misconceptions

Cave Formation Many students think caves are formed by the work of underground rivers. The process is actually quite different. Students should understand that solid rock once was present where a cave now exists. When rock develops fractures, perhaps from the action of yearly freeze and thaw, water is able to seep into the cracks. Water that is slightly acidic begins to chemically dissolve the rock. As the cracks become larger, more dissolution occurs, eventually forming a cave.

Discussion

Surface Area Water also flows along bedding planes or joints in the rock. Explain to the students that cracks begin to branch out as they increase in size. Ask them to compare these cracks to river drainage patterns. Which one do they resemble? Cracks resemble dendritic or rectangular patterns. How does this help in the formation of a cave? As the cracks grow larger, more branches form, increasing the amount of surface area that is exposed to chemical weathering. L2

Visual Learning

Figure 5 Have students examine the rocks in the photo. Tell them to recall Moh's hardness scale and the three major types of rocks. Why is resistance to weathering based on a combination of factors? If based on rock type alone, rocks made of soft minerals would be easily weathered. But, limestone bluffs and cliffs such as the Redwall Limestone in Grand Canyon National Park indicate otherwise. Limestone is resistant to weathering in the arid southwest but not in the humid northeast. Here, climate must be considered as well. L2 LS **Visual-Spatial**

Reading Check

Answer weathered rock material, organic matter, water, and air

Quick Demo
Soil Components

Materials soil, cookie sheet, colander, plastic jar with lid, tablespoon, powdered dish detergent, water

Estimated Time 15 minutes

Procedure Collect at least four cups of soil and allow it to air dry on a cookie sheet. Sift the sample through a kitchen colander to get rid of stones, twigs, or leaves, and break up any lumps. Place a cupful of the dry soil into a clear, plastic, straight-sided jar. Add a tablespoon of powdered dish detergent and fill with water. Cap and shake for several minutes and set aside. Observe the settling process and record what you see. Sand settles out first, then silt, and lastly clay. It will likely take several days for the final settling. Measure the thickness of each layer and calculate the ratios. This is a rough way to determine the ratio of sand to silt to clay. Ask the students why the dishwashing powder was added to the soil mixture. The detergent is a surfactant, which helps to separate the particles.

Caption Answer
Figure 6 Organic materials, fine sediments, and soluble materials are leached from this horizon and transported downward, leaving light materials such as quartz behind.

Soil

One natural resource that is vital to life on Earth is soil. **Soil** is a mixture of weathered rock, organic matter, water, and air that is capable of supporting plant life. Much like human skin, soil is a thin, layered covering of its parent material. Soil originates from weathering of the bedrock beneath it or from materials transported from another location. The raw materials for soil continuously form through the weathering of bedrock below and the addition of organic matter from above.

Reading Check *Soil is made up of what?*

Soil Horizons Digging a deep hole allows you to see the soil horizons, or layers. Each horizon has its own unique texture and color. **Figure 6** illustrates a sequence of soil horizons, called a profile. Soil profiles don't always contain every horizon. The horizons present depend on the composition of the parent bedrock, climate, and the kind and amount of organisms on the surface. In addition, the shape of the land on which the soil forms is important. As slope angles increase, thin, poor-quality soil is more likely to develop.

Figure 6 This illustration provides a generalized view of a soil profile. Soil horizons vary in color and thickness. Some horizons don't appear in certain soils. Notice that the E horizon is lighter in color than the B horizon.
Explain *why the E horizon is light in color.*

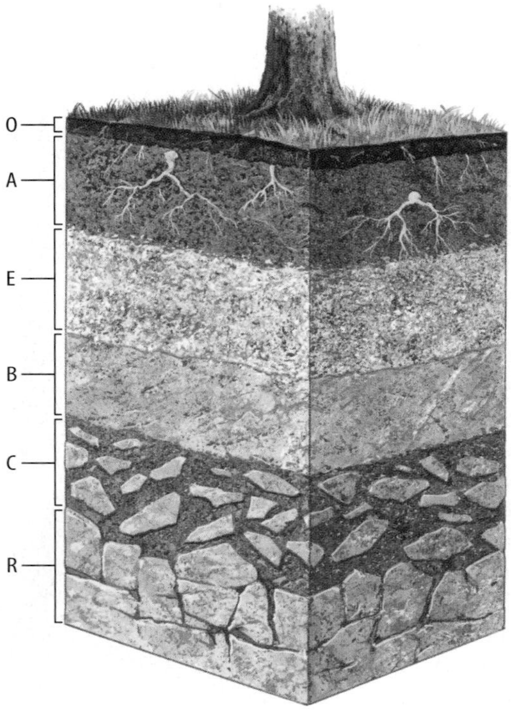

Figure 6 shows a complete set of horizons, designated as O, A, E, B, C, and R from the surface to bedrock. The O horizon, for organic, and the A horizon often are referred to as topsoil. Plants get most of their nutrients from the topsoil.

The E horizon, for eluviation, is a zone in which finer sediments and soluble materials are transported downward. The process of dissolving soluble elements and transporting them deeper into the soil is called leaching. This is much like a coffee maker that leaches flavors from ground coffee. The B horizon collects the materials from above and is usually darker than the E horizon. Sometimes so much material accumulates that water can't easily penetrate this zone. This formation is referred to as hardpan. The E horizon and the B horizon often are referred to as subsoil. Roots from large trees sometimes penetrate these horizons to get water and are able to anchor themselves in the subsoil.

Collectively, horizons O, A, E, and B make up the true soil. The C horizon is partially crumbled and weathered bedrock. The R horizon is unweathered bedrock.

Teacher FYI

Given the same parent material, different climates will produce different soils. Pioneer plants contribute organics to the soil and change its chemistry. Through time, a climax community of plants is established. Agriculture is largely adaptive in nature. For example, if the native soil supports a climax community of grasses, then agriculture is focused on cultivated grasses—wheat, oats, corn, and barley.

650 CHAPTER 21 Earth's Changing Surface

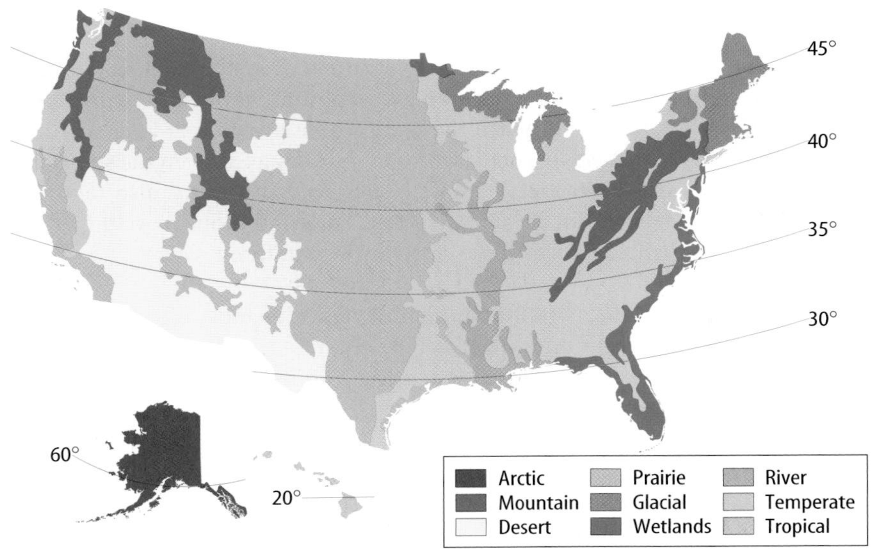

Figure 7 Glacial soil in the northeastern U.S. often is composed of poorly-sorted glacial till. The eastern U.S. receives large amounts of precipitation which contribute to wetland soil.

Soil Types There are many different types of soil. Climate often is used as a basis to characterize many different types of soil, as illustrated in **Figure 7.** They are separated according to composition and physical properties. The amount of precipitation and the temperature range of a region, together with the type of parent material, affect the soil that forms. Vegetation, if present, also is important for providing a supply of organic matter. For example, topsoils that develop beneath the forests of the eastern U.S. are acidic, sandy in texture and light in color. This contrasts with soils that develop beneath the grasses of the western U.S. These often are enriched in calcite and are whitish in color. In tropical environments, the soils are strongly leached. They are rich in insoluble aluminum, iron oxides, and clay minerals. Finally, in the arctic or desert regions, where little or no vegetation grows, there is no soil. Without organic material, a true soil cannot develop.

Parent Material Some soils form in the same place as the parent bedrock. Other soils form from materials transported from distant sources. Rivers and glaciers are important transporting agents for soils. Some of the most fertile soils form when rivers flood and deposit new sediment on floodplains or when glaciers transport and deposit sediment. The ancient Egyptians relied for thousands of years on the annual flooding of the Nile River to deposit nutrient-rich sediment. During the most recent ice advance, glaciers in North America transported materials that later would become some of the world's most fertile soils.

Activity

Soil Texture Using a soils classification triangle, create several soils of your own design. Use a variety of materials from a garden center. Use the triangle to determine the types of soils you have. See how many different soils you can identify. Students will identify a variety of soils. What is present in each will depend on the type of materials acquired from the garden center. Ordinarily the organic content can be determined by how black the soil is. Judging percentages of sand, silt, and clay is very difficult to do visually. The way the soil feels is often a better technique to use in texture classification.

Discussion

Soil Type Have the students discuss the role that soil type would have on agriculture in different regions. Why are certain crops grown where they are? Plants have requirements for growth. Not all soils can support all plants. Is climate the only control? Climate is only part of the control; nature of the parent material also determines soil type. Does climate control the nature of the soil? Yes, heavy rain, for example, can cause erosion or leaching of nutrients; plant growth provides organic material. L2 ELL

Post Reading

Extended Research Ask students to research mechanical and chemical weathering. Have them write a paper that describes a specific example of each weathering type. For example, a student might write about weathering of granitic rock in Yosemite National Park.

3 Assess

DAILY INTERVENTION

Check for Understanding

Visual-Spatial Display unlabeled photos of soil profiles and ask students to identify the soil horizons. Photos can be obtained from your county/state agriculture department. L2 ELL

Reteach

Analyze soil samples (as in the Activity) that students have brought in or use homemade soils of your creation. Following each analysis, the students should use the soil classification triangle and determine the amount and kind of changes needed to give the soil a sandy loam texture. If a soil test kit is available, perform tests for nitrogen, potash, and phosphorous. County horticultural agents probably can provide pamphlets for the class on soil amending (fertilizing). L2

Assessment

Performance Have students create a community service presentation that focuses on the techniques and values of soil conservation in their region. Use **PASC,** p. 143

Figure 8 The tie-ridging method makes fields look like waffles.

Soil Conservation

Plants and animals continuously remove elements from soil. Soil depletion is a serious agricultural problem in many regions. For example, when the same crop is grown year after year in the same field, particular elements are depleted from the soil. Soils in areas with heavy rainfall, such as rain forests, also tend to be deficient in certain elements. The continuous recycling of plant matter returns these elements to rain forest soils.

Adding Nutrients Soil depletion is most often corrected by the addition of fertilizers containing nitrogen, phosphorous, or potassium. Farmers often use crop rotation to help preserve the quality of soils. This is because what one crop removes from the soil, another crop may return. For example, some crops, such as legumes, return nutrients to the soil. Crop rotation also helps prevent erosion and reduces the risk of diseases and attack by pests. Another alternative is to allow the soil to rest, called going fallow, by not planting crops. This gives the soil time to replenish some of its lost nutrients.

Preventing Soil Loss Most soil lost to erosion occurs because the vegetative cover has been removed or because the land is overly steep. Modern farmers use contour plowing, which runs the furrows around a hill instead of up and down a slope, to reduce erosion. In the tie-ridging method, shown in **Figure 8,** crops are planted on ridges and rainfall collects in basins. Slowing the downhill flow of water helps prevent erosion.

section 1 review

Summary

Mechanical and Chemical Weathering

- Weathering is the breakdown of materials that are not stable under the physical conditions at Earth's surface.
- Physical breakdown of surface materials is accomplished by mechanical weathering.
- Chemical reactions at Earth's surface change mineral composition and release elements.

Soil and Soil Conservation

- Soil is a mixture of organic matter, weathered rock material, water, and air.
- Measures are taken to prevent soil depletion and soil erosion.

Self Check

1. **Explain** how mechanical and chemical weathering processes are related.
2. **Describe** how the controls on soil formation affect soil.
3. **Distinguish** between soil depletion and soil erosion.
4. **Think Critically** Outline the soil conservation measures you expect from any contractor building new roads in your region.

Applying Math

5. **Calculate** Suppose that soil erosion in your area averages 2.65 cm per year. The average soil profile is 3 m thick, and 45 percent of that is topsoil. Estimate how long it will take for the topsoil to erode.

More Section Review gpescience.com

section 1 review

1. Both result from outside forces or processes, which alter Earth materials. An increase in physical weathering leads to an increase in chemical weathering.
2. Possible answers: the amount of moisture will guide the amount of chemical weathering of rock and plant material; moisture also determines plant growth which in turn contributes to the organic component.
3. Soil depletion is a change in the soils chemistry that effects its fertility; soil erosion is the physical removal and loss of soil.
4. Where excavation or steepening of slopes will take place, the contractor must take measures to keep soil from eroding—retaining walls, temporary barriers to control runoff; steps should be taken to limit loss of soil by wind erosion; once construction is finished grass or other plant material must be replaced to anchor the soil.
5. 135 cm/2.65 cm/year = 50.9 years

LAB

Graphing Soil Textures

Three particle sizes characterize the textures of most soils—clay, silt, and sand. The relative amounts of these three variables plot on a triangular graph. In a triangular graph, a corner represents 100 percent of a variable and its opposite base represents 0 percent of that variable.

Real-World Problem

Different plants require different soil textures. How can you classify soil according to texture?

Goals

- **Graph** data on a triangular diagram.
- **Interpret** graphed data to classify soils.

Materials

soil texture triangular diagram

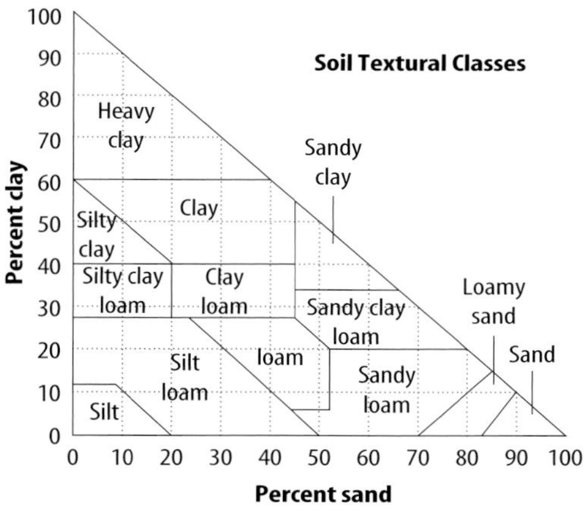

Procedure

1. Obtain a copy of a soil texture triangular diagram from your teacher.
2. Find the line representing 40 percent clay.
3. Find the line representing 50 percent sand.
4. Plot the intersection of these two lines on your copy of the graph.
5. The remainder of the sample is silt. Your first plotted point represents a soil texture that is 40 percent clay, 50 percent sand, and 10 percent silt, and is called sandy clay.
6. Plot and label the following textures and determine the percentage of silt. Record your answers in a data table.

Soil Texture Data

Sample #	% Clay	% Sand	% Silt
1	20	40	40
2	10	70	20
3	15	15	70
4	60	20	20
5	25	65	10

Conclude and Apply

1. **Describe** the composition of any soil that plots along the base of the triangle.
2. **List** the texture names for each sample.
3. **Evaluate** each sample for its ability to retain or drain water.
4. **Predict** which soil samples would be best for root crops such as potatoes or carrots.

Communicating Your Data

Prepare a brief oral presentation outlining how to use the soil texture triangle.

BENCH TESTED

Real-World Problem

Plants require different soil textures. How can we classify soil textures?

Purpose Demonstrate the use of a triangular diagram to classify soil texture.

Process Skills graph, interpret, infer

Time Required 60 minutes

Procedure

Teaching Strategy Use a transparency of the diagram and a sample problem to illustrate the mechanics of the graph's use.

Troubleshooting Point out to students that if they find the intersection of two of the values, the third value acts as a check. Stress that the base of the diagram is 0 percent and the peak is 100 percent.

Conclude and Apply

1. It contains 0 percent of that component.
2. 1. loam
   2. sandy loam
   3. silt loam
   4. clay/heavy clay
   5. sandy clay loam
3. 1. good
   2. excellent
   3. good
   4. very poor
   5. good
4. 2 best; 1, 3, 5 good; 4 poor

Communicating Your Data

Have students discuss the variations on opinion that will arise in answering questions 3 and 4.

section 2

Shaping the Landscape

Reading Guide

What You'll Learn
- **Explain** how agents of erosion operate.
- **Describe** kinds of landforms created by erosion.
- **Identify** landforms created by deposition of eroded material.

Why It's Important

Some erosion events, such as floods and landslides, have catastrophic effects on lives and property.

Review Vocabulary

physical change: any change in size, shape, or state in which the identity of a substance remains the same

New Vocabulary
- erosion
- sediment transport
- deposition
- drainage basin
- longshore current

Erosion, Transport, and Deposition

You've learned about forces capable of building mountains. Forces with origins within Earth can create uplifted landforms through folding, faulting, or volcanic activity. Although they might seem like permanent features, mountains and other landforms are subject to continuous change. Gravity is a factor in all change. Some of these changes also involve the action of agents at the surface of Earth, such as air, water, or ice. The shape of the land you see is what is left over after material has been removed or added by these agents.

Erosion is the removal of surface material through the processes of weathering. **Sediment transport** is the movement of eroded materials from one place to another by water, wind, and/or glaciers. When a transporting agent drops its load of eroded material, **deposition** occurs. The characteristics of landforms created on the surface, such as the eskers and moraines shown in **Figure 9,** can help identify the type of agent that formed it. Analyzing the sediment in a surface deposit can reveal clues about its point of origin. For this reason surface sediment often is used to piece together the plate tectonic history of a region.

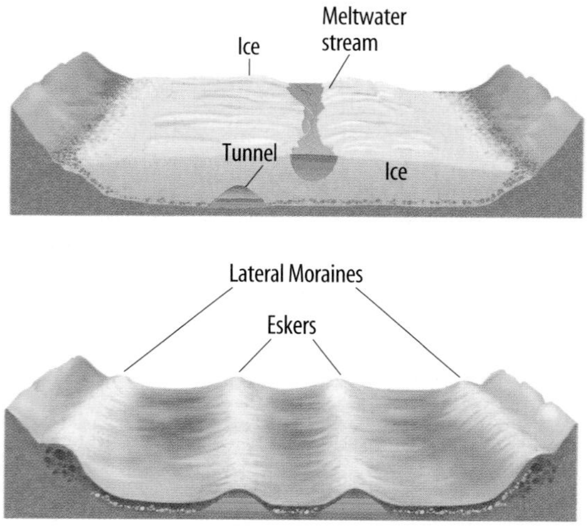

Figure 9 When valley glaciers melt they deposit sediment in characteristic landforms. Moraines consist of poorly sorted glacial till and eskers consist of layers of sediment.

1 Motivate

INTERACTIVE CHALKBOARD An editable Microsoft® PowerPoint® presentation is available on **Interactive Chalkboard** CD-ROM.

Bellringer

Section Focus Transparencies also are available on the Interactive Chalkboard CD-ROM. L2 ELL

Section 2 Section Focus Transparency — Landscape with Nature — Chapter 21

How would you like to never have to mow your lawn again? If that idea appeals to you, landscaping with native plants may be the answer. Native plants flourish since they are well acclimated to the local environment and have little need for pesticides, fertilizers, or any water other than the natural rainfall. Such a natural landscape can make us feel more connected to nature and enhance the beauty of our home environments.

1. How could natural landscaping be good for the soil?
2. How might periodic burning be beneficial for a natural landscape?
3. What is biodiversity?

L2

Earth's Changing Surface

Reading Preview

Tie to Prior Knowledge

Causes of Erosion When force is applied to a mass, it may cause motion. The forces of running water, glaciers, breaking waves, gravity, and wind all combine to erode and transport loose Earth materials.

Word Chart Post the new vocabulary words in a prominent place in the classroom. Give students a sheet of paper with definitions and ask them to predict which vocabulary word corresponds to each definition. Students can check their ideas by reading the text and noting the meanings of the words.

Section 2 Resource Manager

Chapter *Fast File* Resources
- Transparency Activity, p. 45
- MiniLAB, p. 4
- Enrichment, p. 30
- Reinforcement, p. 26
- Directed Reading for Content Mastery, p. 18
- **Cultural Diversity**, pp. 33–34

654 CHAPTER 21 Earth's Changing Surface

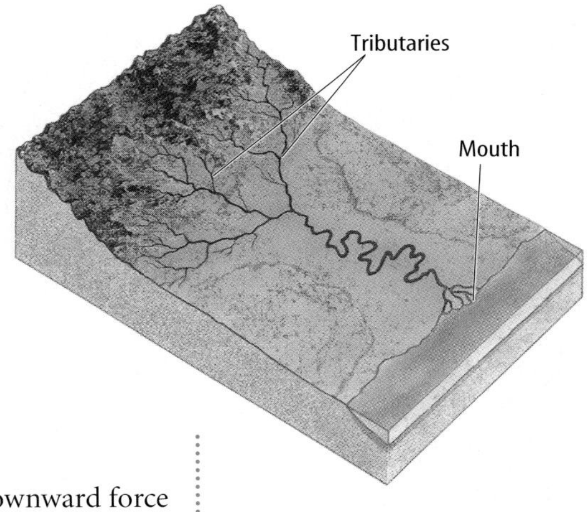

Figure 10 Gradient, or slope, affects the shape of a stream and its containing valley. **Compare and contrast** *how a steep gradient and a gentle gradient affect the shape of a stream.*

Running Water

An important agent of erosion that exerts a downward force on slopes is running water. In steep areas, running water cuts down through sediment and rock, creating V-shaped valleys. As the steepness of a slope decreases, more force is exerted sideways. Lateral cutting broadens river valleys and allows for floodplains to develop. The mouth of a river is where it meets the body of water or land surface into which it ultimately flows. Near the mouth, a river might wind back and forth, or meander, across its valley. **Figure 10** shows how characteristics of a river can change as it flows from its source to its mouth.

Drainage Basins In most river systems, small streams called tributaries flow into larger streams, which in turn flow into even larger streams. This process of branching is much like a tree with small branches that can be traced to larger branches, and then to a trunk. Most major river systems are well-known, such as the Mississippi River. All of the land area that gathers water for a major river is the river's **drainage basin.** Drainage basins are larger in area for major rivers and include all of the drainage basins of its tributaries. The Mississippi River drainage basin extends from the Appalachian Mountains westward to the Rocky Mountains. Both of these mountain ranges represent drainage divides. A drainage divide is a boundary line separating distinct drainage basins. **Figure 11** illustrates the Mississippi River drainage basin.

Figure 11 The Mississippi River drainage basin is the largest drainage basin in the United States.

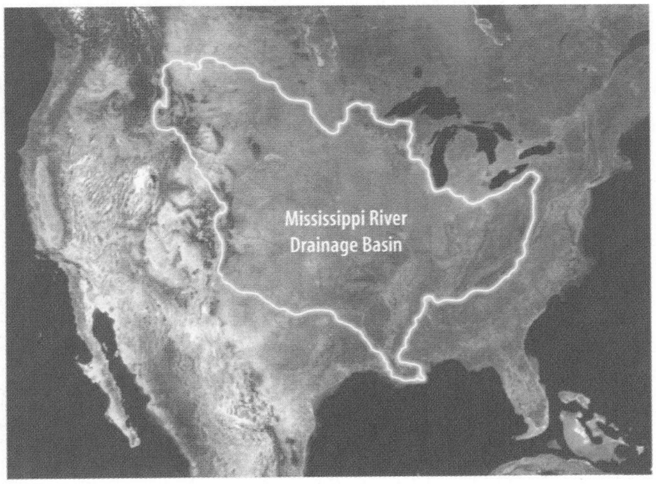

2 Teach

Caption Answer

Figure 10 Rivers with steep gradients develop V-shaped valleys and have narrow floodplains. Rivers with gentle gradients develop broad valleys, several oxbows, and have wide floodplains.

Visual Learning

Figure 10 Erosion is occurring at several places in this diagram. Where is deposition occurring? Deposition is occurring in the river channels, on along the river banks, on the river floodplain, and in the delta at the mouth of the river.

Activity

Land Analysis Obtain topographic maps (now available on CD-ROMs) and current local land-use maps for your area. Have students examine these maps to identify remnant landforms and areas of potential erosion and/or flooding.

Curriculum Connection

Social Studies As areas were settled, towns sprang up at various locations. Most often these towns were found along the banks of rivers, particularly where obstacles in the river were large enough to require portage around the obstacle. Lakes afforded easy transport, so lake ports were also important. Many of towns have "Falls," "Rapids," "Lake," or the suffix "-ford" in their names. Have students use a map of your region and highlight those towns or cities which fit the descriptions above. Have them give a reason they think that city was key in the development of the area. Your state museum can probably provide copies of early maps of the state, which show the earliest settlements. Many towns have internet sites which include a brief town history. L2 LS **Visual-Spatial**

Mini LAB

Video Lab available.

Purpose Students will model runoff.

Materials cookie sheet, faucet that will produce a thin, laminar stream of water

Teaching Strategy It is important to stress that the cookie sheet is clean and grease-free and that the stream of water is as fine and laminar as possible.

Troubleshooting Students may need to unscrew the aerator from the faucet to get the fine stream of water.

Analysis

It begins to meander over the sheet more.

The two forces acting in the system are friction and gravity. Assuming that friction is uniform over the surface, we can assume that the water is responding only to gravity. When the sheet is at a steep angle (high gradient) the gravity component is directed straight off the sheet by the shortest path. As the angle of the sheet (river bed) lessens (low gradient) the influence of gravity also decreases. The water flows along the strongest pull of gravity. This translates into meandering.

Assessment

Oral Have the students predict the shape of stream valleys with different gradients. Mountain streams (high gradient) tend to be straighter; streams that are less confined and have a low gradient will develop numerous meanders and broad flood plains. L2

Try at Home

Reading Check

Answer Young streams cut V-shaped valleys. L2

Figure 12 This portion of the Colorado River is cutting a deep, V-shaped valley as the Colorado Plateau is being uplifted.

Mini LAB

Modeling Runoff

Procedure

1. Obtain a clean, flat, smooth **baking sheet.**
2. Turn on a faucet and adjust the flow of **water** to a slow, smooth stream about the diameter of a pencil lead.
3. Place the baking sheet at a steep angle under the stream of water. Hold the sheet so that the water runs off along the length of the sheet. Record your observations.
4. Make several more observations reducing the steepness each time until your last observation is with the stream perpendicular to the sheet. Record all observations.

Analysis

What happened to the stream flow pattern as you decreased the angle of the sheet? Explain.

Try at Home

Channel Development As surface water flows downhill under the influence of gravity, water erodes the surface, creating its own path or following existing paths called channels. V-shaped valleys are formed from rivers cutting down through sediment and rock, eroding material from a slope. Steep canyons can form when downcutting is rapid. This is often a result of a recent uplift of land, as shown in **Figure 12.**

Reading Check *What is the shape of a valley that is cut by a young stream?*

Stream Deposits Maybe you've seen accumulations or bars of sediment in stream channels. When running water slows down, it drops part of the sediment load it is carrying, largest particles first. Generally, bars form on the inside of bends in a river channel, where water speeds are slowest. But in regions where sediment is plentiful, bars might interrupt the flow of water right in the middle of the channel, as shown in **Figure 13.**

Figure 13 Streams with many bars within their channels are called braided streams.

Use an Analogy

Oxbow Lakes Meandering streams often develop distinct features called oxbows. An oxbow is a U-shaped frame around an ox's neck used to support a yoke. As water flows along a meander, it slows down on the inside of the bend and deposits the heavier sediment. The water speeds up and flows faster around the outside of the bend. This causes erosion at this point. Over time, the erosion results in the narrowing of the land between two meanders. This can be seen in several figures in this section. Continued erosion will cause the river to break through the narrow strip of land. This will cause the river to straighten out at that point and will leave behind an isolated lake that is shaped like an oxbow.

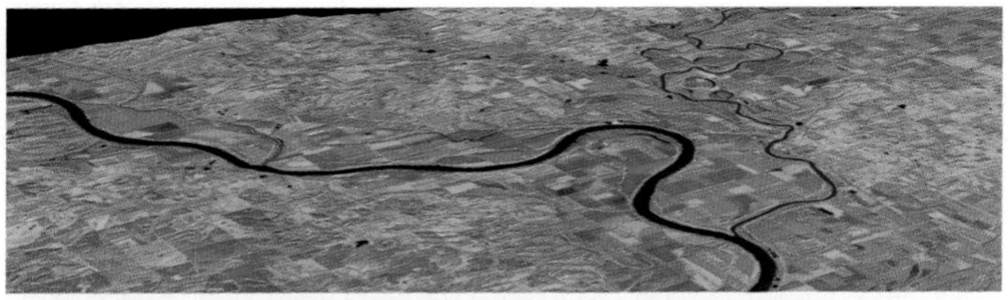

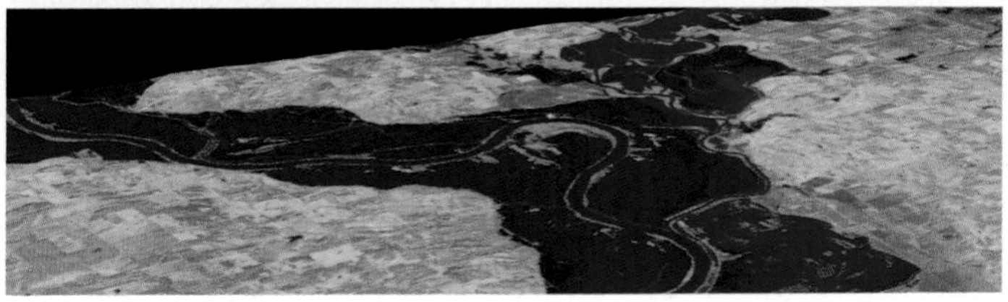

Figure 14 The Missouri River, shown above, sometimes overflows its banks and spills onto its floodplain, shown below.

Science Online

Topic: Bayou

Visit gpescience.com for Web links to information about the Louisiana Bayous.

Activity A bayou can be a creek, secondary watercourse, or any of various, usually marshy or sluggish bodies of water. Research the origin of the word *bayou.* Locate the Louisiana Bayous on a United States map.

Floodplains After a river floods, and as floodwaters subside, slow, and drop their sediment, floodplains form along the valley sides. These floodplains are part of a river, but they are only submerged during floods. **Figure 14** shows a satellite image of a portion of the Missouri river before and during the 1993 flood. While they can be catastrophic to property, a beneficial effect of such a flood event is to rejuvenate soil quality.

Deltas At the mouth of a stream that empties into a body of water, a fan-shaped sediment deposit called a delta will form. Deltas often have branching channels, like roots of a tree, called distributaries. Distributaries distribute water and mud into the water body they enter, as shown in **Figure 15.** Similar depositional features, called alluvial fans, form where the mouth of a stream enters dry land.

Figure 15 Both tributaries and distributaries are sometimes compared to branches or roots of a tree. Some distributaries of the Mississippi River are shown here.
Compare and contrast *tributaries and distributaries.*

Quick Demo
Meandering Streams

Materials sand, baking tray, water

Estimated Time 10 minutes

Procedure A stream table filled with about 3 cm of clean sandbox sand can be used to perform the MiniLAB from this section. You can substitute a large baking tray for the stream table works. Follow the MiniLAB directions. The tray of sand should have a drain that flows into another pan (trap). The trap, in turn, overflows into a sink. The trap is critical so that eroded sand doesn't clog the sink drain. Smooth the sand and change the gradient between trial runs. This apparatus can be left up for student inquiry after the demo.

Teacher FYI

Stream Styles Natural meanders usually start as a stream redirects itself around obstacles in the streambed. These patterns can be quite complex if there are multiple obstacles. At very low gradients or when the streambed is composed of soft mud, streams develop multiple intertwined streamlets. Then it is called a braided stream.

Caption Answer

Figure 15 Tributaries carry water into the main channel, distributaries carry water away from the main channel.

Cultural Diversity

Explorers from many different countries led the way into our country. Some places, therefore, have distinct ethnic characteristics. Place names of rivers, towns, and mountains often are Native American in origin. Have your students use state maps to identify features that have non-English names and research the origins of the place names they identify. L2 ELL LS **Visual-Spatial**

Fun Fact

Earth's longest river is the Nile River in Africa, at 6,484 km.
The river with the highest discharge is the Amazon at 180,000 m^3/s.
The Amazon also has the largest drainage basin at 5,879,273 sq. Km.

Discussion

Erosion at Home Ask students to identify the kinds of erosion that are taking place in your region today. Extend the discussion to include the forms of erosion that have affected the region in the past and the resulting landforms that exist today. Have them speculate as to how those landforms shaped the land use of the region. Answers will vary by region—consult your state/local museums and universities for specifics to your region. For example: thick deposits of glacial outwash and loess in central Illinois formed the basis for the fertile soils and subsequent farming that developed. L2

Reading Check

Answer Winter snow fall must exceed summer melt.

Fun Fact

Some well-known features in the United States are actually glacial in origin. Bunker Hill is a drumlin. Walden Pond (Thoreau, 1840s) is a kettle lake.

Caption Answer

Figure 16 A trunk valley is formed when valley glaciers move through regions once occupied by streams. A hanging valley is formed by a tributary glacial valley whose mouth is above the main valley.

Science Online

Topic: Isostatic Rebound
Visit gpescience.com for Web links to information about the effect of the weight of glacial ice on Earth's crust.

Activity In your Science Journal, describe evidence that supports the fact that Earth's crust rebounded upward at a location where the weight of glacial ice was removed.

Glaciers

A region where winter snowfall exceeds summer melt has the potential to form a glacier. This excess snowfall must take place year after year for hundreds to thousands of years. Compaction within a thick mass of snow eventually can change it to glacial ice. Valley glaciers form at the top, or head, of river valleys in mountainous regions. They move down slope, usually following the path of the preexisting valleys as shown in **Figure 16.** Continental glaciers, which occupy huge land areas, cover all but the highest peaks. Ice moves away in all directions from where it accumulates.

Reading Check *What is a requirement for a glacier to form?*

Imagine what happens when you pour pancake batter onto a cooking surface. It spreads out under its own weight. The more you pour the more it spreads. As ice accumulates, the pressure at its base increases and causes it to flow outward. The polar ice sheets of Greenland and Antarctica move in this manner.

Glaciers become effective agents of erosion as they move either down slope as in valley glaciers or under their own weight as in continental glaciers. As the ice moves, it acts like a giant bulldozer scraping, gouging, and plucking soil and surface rocks.

Figure 16 Valley glaciers create a variety of alpine, or mountainous, features. Along their paths, they accumulate soil and surface rocks that become abrasive material used to transform the landscape. **Compare and contrast** *trunk valleys and hanging valleys.*

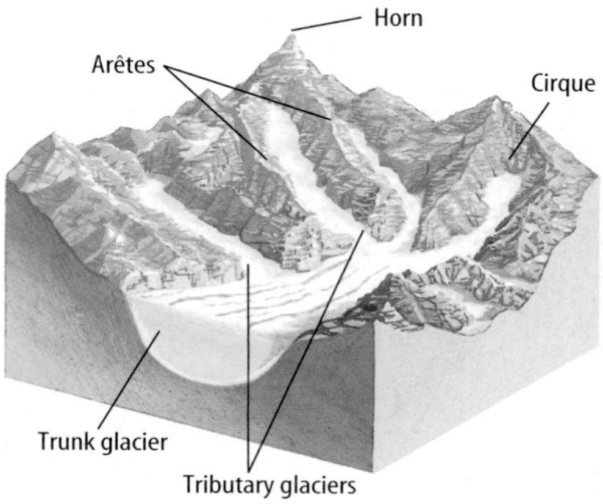

Bowl-shaped basins called cirques form by erosion at the start of a valley glacier. Arêtes form where two adjacent valley glaciers meet and erode a long, sharp ridge. Horns are sharpened peaks formed by glacial action at three or more cirques.

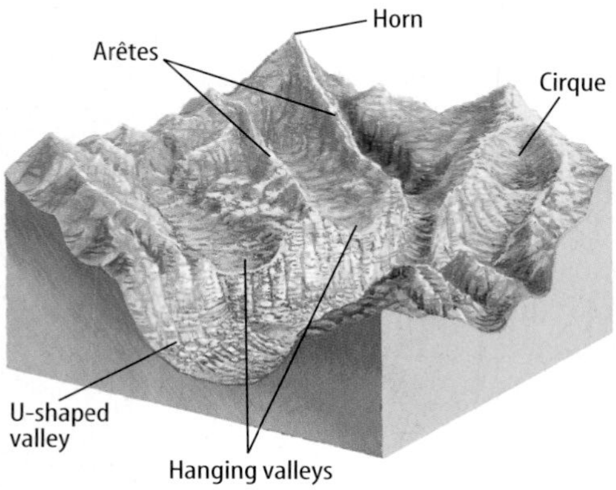

U-shaped valleys result when valley glaciers move through regions once occupied by streams. A tributary glacial valley whose mouth is high above the floor of the main, trunk valley is called a hanging valley. The discordance between the different valley floors is due to the greater erosive power of the trunk glacier.

Curriculum Connection

Social Studies Students have learned that Earth's asthenosphere is partially molten and flows under pressure. The extreme thickness and weight of glacial ice causes deformation of the asthenosphere and a decrease in the crust's elevation. When the weight of the ice is removed, the crust rises back up in a process called isostatic rebound. Evidence of this rebound can be observed in areas where large continental ice sheets once covered the land. Have students discuss the evidence for isostatic rebound provided by Viking ship moorings along the coasts of Canada and Scandinavia. Alternatively, they can discuss the changes observed at Sloop Cove NHS near Churchill, Manitoba. Guide them to note that sea level has not changed appreciably since the time of the Vikings. L2

Erosional Features Valley and continental glaciers leave behind deep grooves or striations, which give clues about the direction the ice was moving. Continental glaciers gouged out the Great Lakes and the finger lakes of New York. Valley glaciers convert V-shaped stream valleys into distinctive U-shaped valleys. The downcutting force of valley glaciers differs from those of streams. Rather than simply cutting downward, glacial ice exerts pressure to the sides as well. This creates the distinct and easily recognized U-shaped valley.

Reading Check ***What is the shape of a valley that is cut by glaciers?***

This downward cutting force of ice is a function of mass. Tributary glaciers with less mass cut less deeply. Larger trunk glaciers have more mass and erode more deeply. This produces tributary valleys that enter the main valley at different elevations, creating hanging valleys. Stream divides are eroded into sharp ridges called arêtes. Where ice first accumulates, a bowl-shaped depression called a cirque is formed. The formation of several cirques around a mountain results in the formation of a horn. **Figure 16** illustrates some glacial landforms that form in mountainous areas.

Glacier Deposits Ice cannot sort material like moving water does. So, when continental and valley glaciers melt, they dump all the rock material they are carrying. This material, known as till, is composed of random sediment sizes ranging from tiny clay particles to house-sized boulders. The large ridges of till that accumulate at the edge of a glacier are called moraines. An end moraine forms at the front of the ice, and lateral moraines form at the side of the ice. If two valley glaciers join together down slope, their lateral moraines get sandwiched together to form medial moraines. A ground moraine forms underneath melting continental ice sheets.

Some of the smaller-sized particles ranging from clay to gravel are carried away by meltwater and form layered deposits on outwash plains. Deposits of outwash material are layered and sorted by size because of the action of water in transporting and depositing them. Glacial deposits in flat outwash plains often become fertile soils that support plant growth. **Figure 17** shows examples of landforms deposited by melting ice.

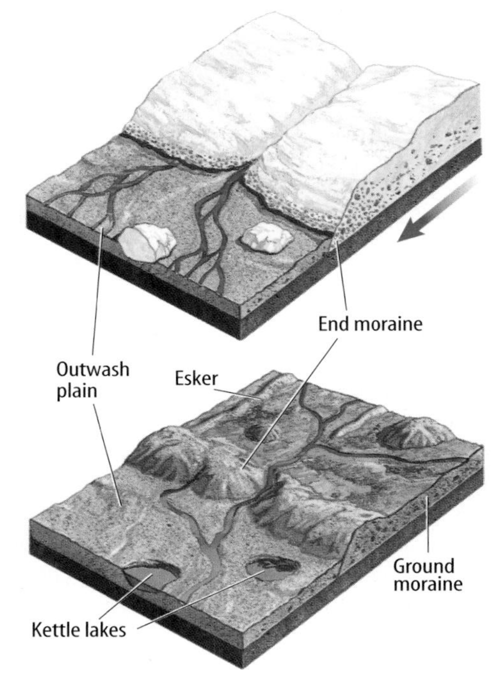

Figure 17 End moraines are composed of poorly sorted soil and rocks that were scraped up by the glacier, moved ahead of it, and then deposited where it melted. Eskers are composed of finer soil and rock material that was deposited within the glacier.

Reading Check

Answer U-shaped

Inquiry Lab

Melting Ice

Purpose to help students visualize till deposition more clearly

Materials two large glass jars with lids, water, assortment of sediment sizes, ice, hammer, large resealable bags

Preparation Fill one jar one-third full with sediment. Add water to fill the jar and put on the lid. Crush the ice inside the plastic bag using the flat side of the hammer. Add sediment to the ice and quickly mix. Pour into the second jar and seal. Immediately put the jar into a freezer.

Teaching Strategies

- Remove the jar from the freezer at the beginning of class. Shake the first jar to free the sediment and set it on the table. Place the second jar next to it. Do not move either jar during the class period.
- Students will observe that the sediment in the first jar will settle out by size, just as it does in a river or stream. The sediment in the second jar will settle out as the ice melts but it will not be sorted. This is what happens as a glacier melts and till is deposited.

For additional inquiry activities, see *Science Inquiry Lab Manual.* L2 ELL

LAB DEMONSTRATION

Purpose demonstrate glacial erosion

Materials sand, large cookie sheet, ice cubes, paper towels

Alternate Materials box lid or shallow box

Preparation Spread a 2- to 3-inch layer of sand on the cookie sheet. Make ice cubes.

Procedure Have a student push an ice cube over the sand and note where the sand erodes and where it accumulates. Have another student push a second cube beside the first. Repeat, but this time have the ice cubes start apart and come closer together.

Expected Outcome Erosion occurs along the bottom and sides of the ice cubes while sand accumulates along the sides.

Assessment

Oral What types of moraines formed? Lateral, end, and medial moraines formed.

Caption Answer

Figure 18 Particles are blown by the wind until they are dropped. The leeward side of a dune is protected from the wind. The wind looses energy and the particles are dropped.

Discussion

What are dunes? Obtain photos or transparencies of the five major dune types: transverse, barchan, longitudinal, star, and parabolic. Explain that dune shape is dependent upon sand supply, wind velocity, variation in wind direction, and surface characteristics. Have small groups choose one dune type and speculate on the nature of the four characteristics listed above that result in the formation of their dune. Transverse—large sand supply, constant wind direction perpendicular to dune zpoints face downwind; Longitudinal—limited sand supply, strong winds from two slightly different directions, parallel to combined wind direction; Star—ample sand supply, three or four wind directions; Parabolic—limited sand supply, constant wind direction, points face upwind L2

ELL IN **Visual-Spatial**

Science Journal

Dust Bowl Experiences Have students write an eye witness account of a "black blizzard" during the dust bowl of the 1930s. Encourage them to discuss why the dust storms were called black blizzards and how these blizzards differ from snow blizzards. Snow melts, and the dust remains where it settles. Information is available from historical societies of any of the dust bowl states, such as Kansas and North Dakota. L2

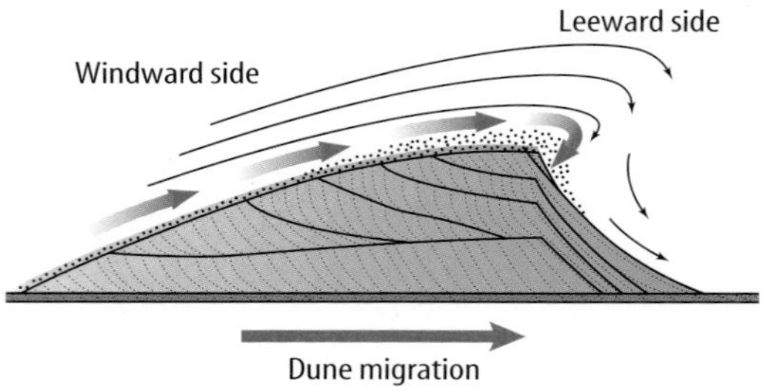

Figure 18 Erosion on the windward side and deposition on the leeward side can cause sand dunes to appear to move.
Infer *Why does deposition occur on the leeward side of a dune?*

Wind

You might think that wind is the most important agent of erosion in deserts, but this is not so. Running water erodes more, especially during infrequent flash floods. Compared to water and ice, wind lacks the ability to pick up and carry large particles. However, wind can act as a sand blaster, blowing sediment around and polishing and smoothing landforms. In places where sand and smaller particles are abundant and not held in place by vegetation, wind can be a very effective agent of erosion.

Erosion by Wind The removal of small particles by wind, leaving heavier particles behind, is called deflation. Deserts often are pictured as endless sand dunes, but this is misleading. Many deserts have a rocky, rough texture caused by deflation. The remaining surface is known as desert pavement. Blowouts, or deflation hollows, are common landforms where wind is the dominant agent of erosion. These landforms are shallow depressions where wind has scooped out surface material, leaving high places behind.

Wind Deposits As wind velocity decreases, the load of sediment is dropped. The shapes and sizes of landforms that form depend on how constant the wind velocity is and on the supply of sediment. Fine silt from glacial outwash plains or deserts is picked up and deposited as thick, unlayered deposits called loess (LUS). Dunes form as the wind moves sand-sized particles into distinct forms, as shown in **Figure 18.**

Wave Action

The zone where land meets open water is an area where extreme forces operate. One cubic meter of water has a large mass. The force generated by breaking waves is large and provides the energy to change surface features.

Currents from Wave Action When waves approach a shoreline at an angle, they change directions, or are refracted. They wash up at a slight angle to the beach. The backwash returns to the sea perpendicular to the shoreline. Waves churn up beach sediment, which is carried back toward the sea with the backwash, then moved toward shore at an angle again. This process results in net sediment transport parallel to the shoreline, as illustrated in **Figure 19.** The resulting movement of water parallel to the shoreline is called a **longshore current.**

Differentiated Instruction

English-Language Learners Have students cut photos out of magazines, such as National Geographic or a travel magazine, to create a collage or poster of landforms created by erosion. Students should label or provide a key for their work in both English and their native language. The label should include the erosive agent that created the landform.

Reading Strategy

Panel Discussion Choose five students to be experts for a discussion about erosion. Each expert will study the part of the text that corresponds with one of the following: running water, glaciers, wind, wave action, and mass wasting. Other students in the class will ask questions of the student experts.

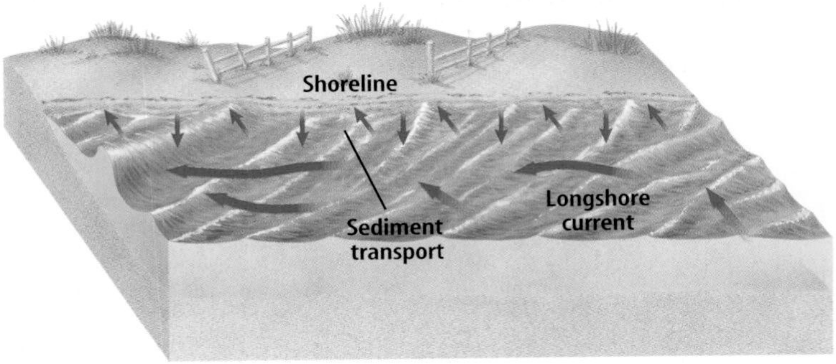

Erosion from Wave Action The action of waves loaded with sediment works like sandpaper and causes abrasion. This results in rounded pebbles and cobbles on the beach. Coastal cliffs often are eroded at their bases by wave action. This results in periodic collapse of cliff material into the sea. This material then is battered by waves and eventually reduced to smaller sizes that can be transported by the longshore current. Shorelines that are rock-bound with steep cliffs tend to experience differential weathering. A wide variety of landforms, such as sea stacks, sea arches, and headlands, are characteristic of rocky shorelines.

Reading Check *How does beach sand become rounded?*

Deposition by Wave Action Shorelines commonly lack erosional landforms when they have a thick sediment cover. Instead, the sediment on these beaches is constantly reworked producing a variety of depositional landforms. Longshore currents move sediment along the shore. Where this current slows, sediments are deposited as offshore sand ridges or bars. Sandbars run parallel to the shore. A sandbar that seals off a bay from the open ocean is called a baymouth bar. Spits are sand bars that project into the water from land and curve back toward land in a hook shape. Cape Cod is a well-known spit off the coast of Massachusetts. During severe storms, water levels can rise and create sand deposits known as barrier islands that can serve as protection for the mainland. The shallow lagoons between the islands and the mainland are nurseries for many forms of marine life.

Mass Wasting

When erosion occurs primarily as a result of gravity, whether triggered by an influx of water, by earthquakes, or by human activity, mass wasting occurs. Mass wasting takes place where slopes are overly steep or lacking vegetation. Events usually begin when support at the base of a slope is removed and the material above moves downhill.

Figure 19 Longshore currents run parallel to the shoreline. They can completely remove some beaches by erosion and later deposit the sediment, forming new beaches farther down-current.

Visual Learning

Figure 19 Have students examine the figure and ask the following: The beach is often called a "river of sand." How can this figure be used to explain this name? The longshore current transports sand parallel to the shoreline. This process never stops, so sand is moving constantly. The movement of the sand can be seen as a river of sand. L2

Reading Check

Answer Wave action transports sediment and rolls it around—sediment acts like sandpaper and erodes adjacent particles.

Post Reading

Reflection Ask students to think about a place they've seen that has experienced erosion. Have them write a description of the area and an explanation of the erosion process. Write the terms *wave action* and *running water* on the board to prompt thinking.

SECTION 2 Shaping the Landscape **661**

3 Assess

DAILY INTERVENTION

Check for Understanding

Visual-Spatial Use the posters created for the Differentiated Instruction or Performance activities as an opportunity for class review and critique. L2 ELL

Reteach

Wind Erosion Use eye protection. Use three trays filled with different-sized particles: sand, gravel, or silt. Have students gently blow across the surface of each tray, as if they were blowing out birthday candles. They should repeat this several times, blowing stronger each time. Have them observe the amount of effort it takes to get each particle to begin to move. Silt will take little effort, sand more, but gravel may be immovable. L1 ELL

Assessment

Performance Have students create a poster of photos that illustrate landforms created by an erosional agent. Use **PASC,** p. 145 P

Figure 20 In 1985 in Colombia, the Nevado del Ruiz volcano erupted. Meltwater from its glacier-covered peak created a mudflow that took 23,000 lives. In 1991 in the Philippines, Mount Pinatubo erupted and covered its slopes with ash and pyroclastic flows. Heavy rains mixed with the volcanic debris, creating a lahar, or mudflow, that covered much of Bacolor Village, shown above.

Erosion by Mass Wasting Erosion caused by mass wasting is dependent upon the type of event and the type of materials involved. For example, slumps, which are common in soil along hillsides, produce concave, upward scars from which material has detached and moved downward. Landslides or rockslides also can produce distinct scars on slopes. Mudflows move rapidly and are as dense and damaging as fluid cement. These most often occur following heavy rainfall or snowmelt. **Figure 20** illustrates an example of a mass wasting event.

Deposition by Mass Wasting Mass wasting events tend to dump their material in disorganized masses. This material replaces the undermined material at the base of the landform. When sufficient material builds up, the slope becomes stabilized and mass wasting stops. Geologists often can identify ancient landslides by their disorganized structure.

section 2 review

Summary

Erosion, Transport, and Deposition

- Features resulting from erosion, transport, and deposition of sediment give clues about the natural processes that formed them.

Running Water and Glaciers

- Regions along streams have specific characteristics depending on whether they are near the head or near the mouth of the stream.
- Glaciers create characteristic landforms.

Wind, Wave Action, and Mass Wasting

- Wind erosion creates landforms such as blowouts and dunes.
- Wave action creates longshore currents.
- Mass wasting occurs when material moves downslope mainly due to gravity.

Self Check

1. **Define** the general process of erosion.
2. **Describe** the process of sediment transport by running water, glaciers, wind, wave action, and mass wasting.
3. **List** at least two landforms associated with each of processes listed in question 2.
4. **Think Critically** How can you explain a sediment deposit that contains unlayered and randomly sorted material at the bottom and layered, well-sorted material at the top?

Applying Math

5. **Calculate** If a glacier moves 0.5 m per day, how far does it move in 100 years?

More Section Review gpescience.com

section 2 review

1. loosening and removal of weathered material from Earth's surface by an agent of erosion
2. running water: load is transported until velocity decreases—the largest particles settle out first; glaciers: moving ice rafts or pushes sediment along until the ice melts—all the particles are deposited; wind: wind-blown load is limited to sand and smaller particles, which are transported until wind velocity decreases—the largest particles are deposited first; wave action: particles are suspended and deposited with each wave and are transported along the shore by the longshore current; mass wasting: downhill transport due to gravity, sometimes with the aid of water
3. running water—bars, floodplain, delta, alluvial fan; glaciers—striations, U-shaped valley, moraines; wind—deflation hollows, dunes; wave action—sea stacks, sea arches, sand bars, barrier islands; mass wasting—slumps, rockslides, landslides, mudflows.
4. The bottom layer was deposited by a glacier; the top layer was deposited by running water.
5. 18.3 km

section 3

Groundwater

Reading Guide

What You'll Learn
- **Explain** the importance of groundwater.
- **Describe** how groundwater is stored and obtained.
- **List** some concerns about future groundwater use.

Why It's Important
Groundwater is a main source of drinking water for society.

Review Vocabulary
porosity: the percentage of open space in a material

New Vocabulary
- infiltration
- water table
- permeability
- aquifer

The Water Cycle

The oceans contain 97.2 percent of Earth's water. That leaves only 2.8 percent as freshwater, three-quarters of which is tied up in glacial ice. This means less than 1.0 percent of Earth's water is available for use.

Water Cycle Freshwater supplies are constantly being replenished through the water cycle. For example, large amounts of freshwater enter the water cycle by evaporation of seawater. A lesser amount enters the cycle through transpiration—the plant process in which water enters roots and is released through leaves as water vapor. The energy to power both evaporation and transpiration comes from the Sun. Water vapor in the air forms clouds, which in turn provide precipitation. Precipitation is freshwater, but it often is contaminated with pollutants washed from the air. Most precipitation goes back into the ocean. The water that falls back on land can evaporate, runoff as stream flow, or infiltrate Earth. **Infiltration** is the process by which water enters Earth to become groundwater below the surface. **Figure 21** illustrates how these processes are interconnected through the water cycle.

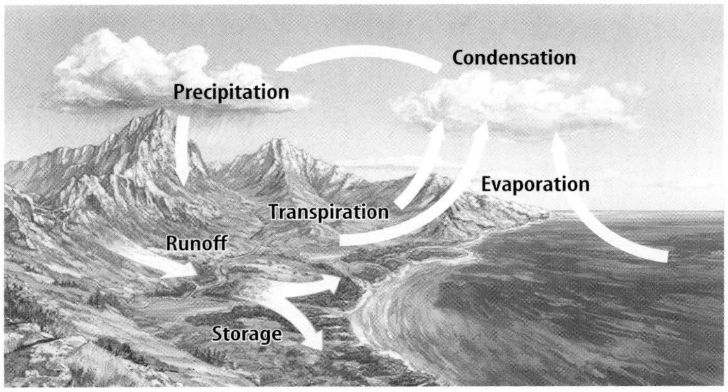

Figure 21 The water cycle continually redistributes Earth's water.

1 Motivate

INTERACTIVE CHALKBOARD PowerPoint® Presentations An editable Microsoft® PowerPoint® presentation is available on **Interactive Chalkboard** CD-ROM.

Bellringer

Section Focus Transparencies also are available on the Interactive Chalkboard CD-ROM. L2 ELL

SECTION 3 Section Focus Transparency **All's Well that Ends Well** Chapter 21

For many people around the world, wells are the only source of fresh water. People have been digging wells for thousands of years, yet wells can pose problems. A poorly built well or one that has been tainted by poisonous substances is useless. Fortunately, there are ways to test well water for contaminants, and many people who depend on wells for water perform such tests on a regular basis.

1. How could toxic material spilled on Earth's surface affect groundwater?
2. Why should a person with a well limit the use of pesticides and fertilizers?
3. Why would water conservation be important for people who get their water from wells?

L2

Earth's Changing Surface

Reading Preview

Tie to Prior Knowledge

Porosity Fluids can be stored in the empty or pore spaces of materials. Some rocks are able to store water and other fluids. These rocks have porosity.

Predict Meaning Ask students to scan the text to find new vocabulary words. Suggest that they note bold print, headings, and figures for clues to meaning. Have students predict the meaning of each word. Students can then read the text to verify or modify meanings.

Section 3 Resource Manager

Chapter *FAST FILE* Resources
- Transparency Activity, p. 46
- Lab Activity, pp. 13–14
- Enrichment, p. 31
- Reinforcement, p. 27
- Directed Reading for Content Mastery, p. 19

Life Science Critical Thinking/Problem Solving, p. 23

Lab Management and Safety, p. 71

2 Teach

Quick Demo
Porosity

Materials glass beakers, non-absorbent materials, water, graduated cylinder

Estimated Time 20 minutes

Procedure Four 500-mL or larger glass beakers can be used to illustrate different porosities. Select three different particle sizes of a non-absorbent material, such as gravel, sand, marbles, ball bearings, or pellets. Fill three of the beakers with a single particle size. Fill the fourth with a mix of the three sizes chosen. Have the students predict the percent porosity for each beaker.

Then pour measured amounts of water into each beaker, recording the amount necessary to cover the particles and fill the beaker.

The amount of water to cover (mL) divided by the amount of particles (mL) times 100 equals porosity. Typical answers should be less than 30 percent.

Teacher FYI

Porosities Single-sized particles (well-sorted) tend to have higher porosities than mixtures of different particle sizes (poorly sorted). Typical rock porosities range from 0–20 percent to as high as 30 percent. Most people tend to overestimate porosity.

Reading Check

Answer the process of surface water seeping into the ground

Groundwater

All the water that is naturally stored underground is called groundwater, as illustrated in **Figure 22.** When water moves underground through infiltration into the pore spaces of sediment and rock, groundwater is replenished. The region near the surface where water can infiltrate freely is the unsaturated zone. The region below that, where water completely fills the pore space, is the saturated zone. The **water table** is the boundary separating these two zones. Factors affecting how easily water can infiltrate and recharge groundwater supplies include the slope of the land, the nature of the surface material, and the type and amount of vegetation.

Reading Check *What is infiltration?*

Groundwater Storage A material must be capable of absorbing water in order for it to allow infiltration. If a material is not already saturated and enough time is available for water to pass through it, infiltration will occur. Unsaturated, porous sand or gravel will generally allow rapid infiltration. Surfaces made of clay or other impermeable material will generally allow little water to infiltrate. Most rainfall or snow melt runs off steep surfaces or evaporates. Plants take in significant amounts of infiltrated water before the water can move deep enough to be stored. In some regions, the supply of groundwater has been stored for millions of years, but humans are withdrawing it faster than it can naturally be replaced. This is particularly bad in arid climates where rainfall is low.

A rock unit that can transmit water through its pore space is called an **aquifer.** Sandstone and limestone often make good aquifers. A rock that slows or stops infiltration is an aquitard. A shale or clay layer makes a good aquitard. Small, local water tables can happen where an aquitard prevents downward infiltration. In this case water is said to be perched, or positioned above an aquitard.

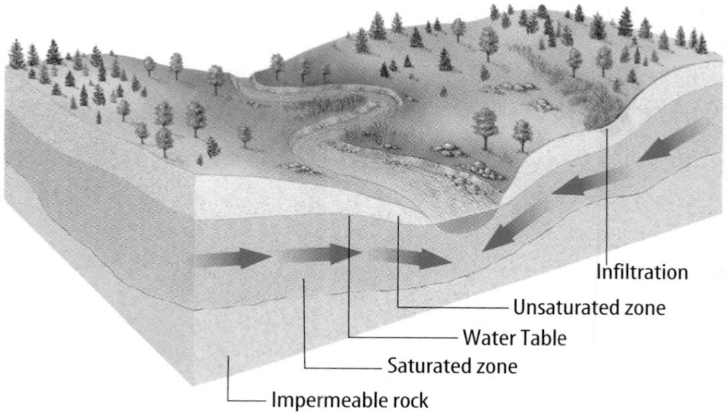

Figure 22 Groundwater is stored in porous rock called aquifers. It is often recharged, or replenished, by infiltration in wetlands.

Visual Learning

Figure 22 Note the positions of the saturated and unsaturated zones and the water table. What will happen to the position of the water table after a heavy rain? It will move up as more ground becomes saturated with water. L2 ELL

Porosity and Permeability Water infiltrates through pore spaces, which are open spaces in sediments or rock. The combined volume of these spaces defines the material's porosity. If porosity is low or if the pores don't interconnect, then water will not flow easily, if at all. Such a condition is called low permeability. **Permeability,** illustrated in **Figure 23,** is a measure of how well a fluid can pass through a material. Water can continue to move through sediment and rock as long as there are interconnected pores available. This can cause the water table to rise and the zone of saturation to grow. When the water table rises to the surface, water can no longer infiltrate and run-off or flooding from more rainfall is likely.

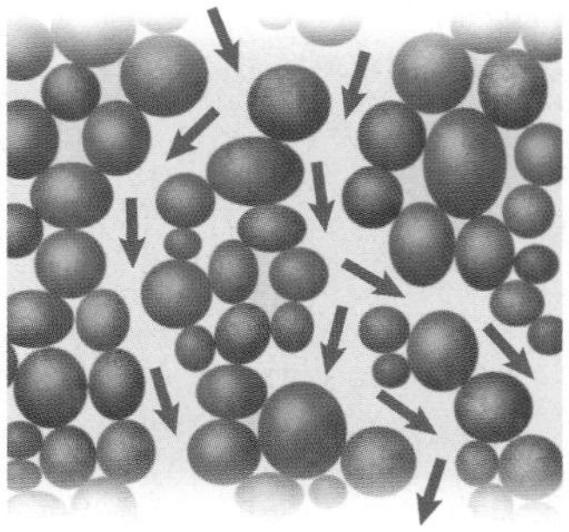

Figure 23 Fluids pass through interconnected pores but cannot pass through isolated pores.

Applying Math — Use Geometry

POROSITY VOLUME Suppose that an aquifer with dimensions of about 450 km in length and 200 km in width is 75 m thick. It has an average porosity of 7 percent. About how much water can the aquifer potentially hold?

IDENTIFY known values and the unknown value

Identify the known values:

Length of aquifer (L) = 450 km or 450,000 m

Width of aquifer (W) = 200 km, or 200,000 m

Thickness of aquifer (T) = 75 m

Porosity = 7% = 0.07

Identify the unknown value: the porosity volume

SOLVE the problem

Volume of aquifer = $L \times W \times T$ = 450,000 m × 200,000 m × 75 m

$(4.5 \times 10^5 \text{m}) \times (2.0 \times 10^5 \text{ m}) \times (75 \text{ m}) = 6.8 \times 10^{12} \text{ m}^3$

Total volume of porosity = volume × porosity (%)

$6.8 \times 10^{12} \text{ m}^3 \times .07 = 4.7 \times 10^{11} \text{ m}^3$

CHECK the answer

Does your answer seem reasonable? Check your answer by dividing it by the porosity, thickness, and width values. The result should be the length of the aquifer in meters.

Practice Problems

The Dakota Sandstone is 925 km long, 560 km wide, averages 4,200 m in thickness, and has an average porosity of 9.3 percent. What is its water storage volume?

For more practice problems, go to page 879 and visit Math Practice at gpescience.com.

Applying Math

Math Standards

National: 1, 4, 9

Teaching Strategy

It is helpful to liken this to determining how much water a sponge can hold when you can't wring out the sponge. Stress that it is a two-part problem: determine total volume of the aquifer and then reduce that value to the amount equal to empty space.

Answer to Practice Problem

$2.02 \times 10^{14} \text{ m}^3$

Activity

Absorption and Infiltration Rate Have students time the rate at which different materials such as paper towels, cloth, and sponges absorb a given amount of water. Use similar materials to time how long it takes water to soak through (infiltrate) a stack of the same material. L2

Reading Strategy

Question a Partner After reading a section, students should write questions to ask a partner. Students will alternate asking and answering questions. The following topics can be used for questions: the water cycle, groundwater, and water resources. Encourage students to write higher-order comprehension questions.

LAB DEMONSTRATION

Purpose demonstrate permeability

Materials juice cans, plastic screens, rubber bands, clock, sand, gravel, tray, paper towels

Preparation Cut one end out of a juice can. Make a large hole (5 cm) in the other end. Construct several more set-ups.

Procedure Place a paper towel over the end of a can with a 5-cm hole, followed by layers of plastic screening. Secure with rubber bands. Fill the can with gravel. Hold the can above the tray and pour water into the can. Time how long it takes for the water to wet the paper. Repeat the procedure with different sizes and mixes of sediment.

Expected Outcome Gravel has the fastest time, then sand, and finally the mixes.

Assessment

Ask students to explain the different flow rates. As pore sizes decrease, friction increases, lowering the permeability. L2

NATIONAL GEOGRAPHIC

Visualizing the Role of Groundwater in Shaping Earth's Surface

Have students examine the pictures and read the captions. Then ask the following questions: Why are karst features most frequently found in areas with limestone bedrock? Limestone is more soluble in water than most other kinds of rock. Why can't groundwater be considered a large underground lake? Because the water is spread out in cracks and openings in the soil and rock. When groundwater evaporates in a glass, it leaves a solid film, but rainwater does not. What is the film? Dissolved calcium carbonate from the bedrock.

Activity

Caves Have students play a block game in which blocks of various sizes and shapes are stacked to form a structure. Carefully remove blocks from the bottom or middle of the stack to form openings and tunnels. Is it possible to create a cave that extends through the structure without causing a collapse? Repeat several times to determine an approximate percentage of blocks that can be removed while keeping the structure intact. L2

NATIONAL GEOGRAPHIC **VISUALIZING THE ROLE OF GROUNDWATER IN SHAPING EARTH'S SURFACE**

Figure 24

Some of the rainwater that falls on the ground flows into rivers and lakes. However, much of the water flows between soil particles and travels underground. Below ground, acidic water gradually dissolves limestone. Landforms that result from acidic water dissolving underground limestone are known as karst topography. Indications of karst areas include springs, caves, and sinkholes.

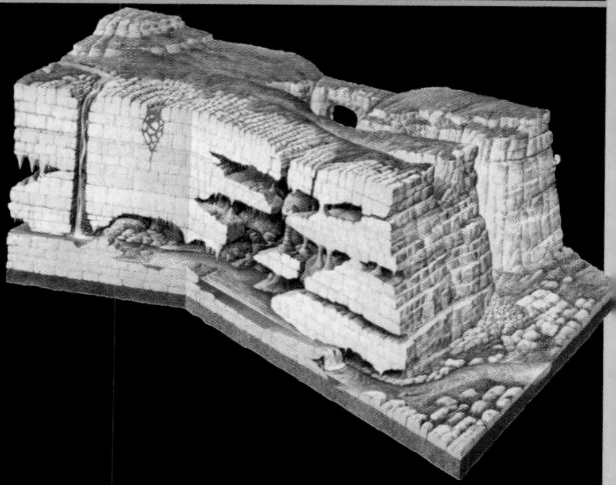

Spring waters flow from the ground where the zone of saturation meets Earth's surface. Depending on the level of the water table, springs can be either permanent or intermittent features of the landscape.

Caves form as acidic groundwater flows through bedrock and dissolves limestone. When the water table drops, open channels remain as caves. Limestone caves can extend many kilometers underground and include chambers that are tens of meters high.

Sinkholes can form when the roof of a cave collapses. Sinkholes can range from small, sloping depressions where water can slowly work its way underground, to large chasms where the flow of a stream or river can be transferred to an underground cave.

666 **CHAPTER 21** Earth's Changing Surface

Differentiated Instruction

Challenge Have students find the average annual rainfall for your location. If all the rain could be collected, how large an area (in square meters) would be required to supply the water used by a typical household, about 250,000 liters/year? Use the following factors: 1,000 L = 1 m^3; one inch = 0.0025 m. L3

Water Resources

Life is dependent on the availability of freshwater. Because of this, supplies are monitored and attempts are made to preserve water resources. Humans have a responsibility to protect freshwater no matter what its source is.

Obtaining Groundwater Some groundwater comes naturally from springs, which are where the water table intersects the ground surface. Alternatively, wells are holes dug or drilled into Earth. When a drill hole encounters the water table, water can be pumped to the surface. As water is removed from the zone of saturation, the water table is lowered. You might expect the water table's surface to remain horizontal as water is taken away. This does not happen near the well because the groundwater flow path changes.

Much like surface water, groundwater flows downhill. The natural flow path of groundwater has both horizontal and vertical components, as illustrated in **Figure 24.** Also, groundwater flow rates usually are slow. As water is withdrawn, the direction of water flow shifts downward toward the well, depressing the water table around it into what is called a cone of depression. Depending on the rate of pumping, the cone of depression can affect water availability from other local wells, or force wells to be drilled deeper into an aquifer to obtain water. **Figure 25** illustrates this situation.

Water Under Pressure Wells drilled into aquifers that are under sufficient natural pressure to force water up into a well are called artesian wells. They form when an aquifer is sandwiched between two aquitards. One example might be sandstone positioned between two shale layers. The aquitards keep the water confined to the aquifer. When the aquifer is sloped, gravity on the water provides pressure on the low side of the slope. These wells usually are free flowing at the surface.

Figure 25 As areas become more populated, more water wells often are drilled. This lowers the water table, causing some existing water wells to go dry.
Infer *Why is a cone of depression created in the water table at the base of a water well?*

INTEGRATE Environment

Not In My Back Yard (NIMBY) In the past, abandoned mines and parts of uninhabited valleys were used as landfill sites. Trash was thrown into these landfills. When it was discovered that many hazardous materials in trash were leaching into nearby water supplies, something had to be done. Research problems associated with locating sites for landfills and current improvements in landfill technology. Hold a class debate about the pros and cons of landfills.

Science Online

Topic: Hard v. Soft Water
Visit gpescience.com for Web links to information about the difference between hard and soft water and where they occur.

Activity Create a map showing locations of hard and soft water across the United States. Explain what makes water hard or soft and how the effects can be reduced.

INTEGRATE Environment

Not In My Back Yard (NIMBY) In the past, abandoned mines and parts of uninhabited valleys were used as landfills to hold trash. When it was discovered that many hazardous materials in trash were leaching into nearby water supplies, something had to be done. Research problems associated with locating sites for landfills and current improvements in landfill technology. Hold a class debate about the pros and cons of landfills. New technology and engineering techniques are continuing to improve the quality of landfill construction. However, as population increases and availability of land decreases, finding locations for landfills becomes increasingly more difficult.

Discussion

Water Issues Have students compile a class list of actions they could take to conserve water. Introduce local water issues here.

Science Journal

Fluoride—Good or Bad? Provide students with information on the addition of fluoride to municipal drinking water. The U.S. Environmental Protection Agency is a good place to start. Have students write an essay declaring whether this practice is good or not by comparing the pros and cons of fluoride in drinking water. Students should be able to defend their decision. L2

Caption Answer

Figure 25 As water is drawn up into the well, groundwater moves slowly through the pore spaces.

Curriculum Connection

Chemistry Introduce the idea of water as the universal solvent and conduct a discussion of how this property creates hard and soft water. To help with this discussion, your local water provider can give you information on the physical properties of the water in your area. If your municipality does not use groundwater, ask your water company to help you locate a nearby town or city that does. L2

Differentiated Instruction

English-Language Learners Have students prepare a campaign poster for "Save Our Water" groundwater conservation. Suggest using print-media clippings or drawings and data from your region to keep the campaign local. Another topic could be "Help Control Water Pollution—Do Your Part". L2 P

Reading Check

Answer from natural pollutants, such as arsenic, or infiltration from runoff

Caption Answer

Figure 26 Polluted groundwater is sometimes impossible to clean.

Post Reading

Illustrations Have students create illustrations of groundwater moving through rock. Ask them to label impermeable rock, saturated and unsaturated zones, and the water table. Also, have them draw and label a sketch of the water cycle.

3 Assess

DAILY INTERVENTION

Check for Understanding

Auditory-Musical Have students write a jingle or song with lyrics describing the water cycle. L2

Reteach

Obtain information from your local or state water conservation organization that addresses local water concerns. Have the students read through the information and list the problems their area is dealing with and any solutions that have been employed. L2

Assessment

Content Have students outline factors in their region that have an effect on the amount and quality of the region's groundwater. Ask what can be done or is being done in their region to protect their water supply. For regions that use surface water as the source, apply the same ideas and ask why groundwater is not used. L2

Figure 26 Pollution can enter groundwater through infiltration. Cleaning polluted groundwater can be difficult and costly.
Infer *Why is it important to prevent groundwater resources from being polluted?*

Pollution and Groundwater Resources Pollutants that are spilled or dumped on the ground and even air pollutants, washed from the air by precipitation, enter groundwater through infiltration, as shown in **Figure 26.** Particles of soil can filter larger contaminants and prevent them from moving deeper. But, natural pollutants such as arsenic can contaminate infiltrated water. Such groundwater is not useful as a freshwater source.

Reading Check *How can groundwater become polluted?*

section 3 review

Summary

Water Cycle
- Only about three percent of Earth's water sources are freshwater. Freshwater is renewed through water cycle processes.
- Supplies of groundwater are replenished when surface water infiltrates into Earth.

Groundwater
- The slope of the land, nature of the surface material, and the kind and amount of vegetation control infiltration.
- Porosity, permeability, and gravity control how water will move through materials.

Water Resources
- Both surface and groundwater resources are susceptible to human and natural contamination.

Self Check

1. **Explain** the importance of groundwater.
2. **Discuss** the role of porosity and permeability in the transmission of water through rock.
3. **Distinguish** among the unsaturated zone, the saturated zone, and the water table.
4. **Think Critically** In a rapidly growing neighborhood, streets, shopping centers, and homes are being built. Discuss the possible long-term effects of such growth on groundwater infiltration and supplies.

Applying Math

5. **Calculate** Suppose a community of 1,500 uses water at a rate of 1,000 L per person per day. This community relies on an aquifer that contains 1.5 billion L of water. How many years will this water supply last?

More Section Review gpescience.com

section 3 review

1. Groundwater is the source from which most communities draw their water supply.
2. Porosity determines the quantity of water that can be stored; permeability determines the ease of transmission of water between the pores
3. The unsaturated zone has pores that are not filled with water, the saturated zone has pores that are filled with water, and the water table is the boundary separating the two.
4. These factors limit infiltration and increase runoff and flood potential; if unchecked, less water will enter the ground and groundwater supplies can be used up.
5. 1,000 days or 2.7 years

section 4

Geologic Time

Reading Guide

What You'll Learn

- **Distinguish** among geologic eras, periods, and epochs.
- **Explain** how scientists decide when a geologic time period ends and another begins.
- **Explain** the methods and logic used in relative dating.
- **Interpret** a geologic cross section.
- **Describe** the methods and logic used in absolute dating.

Why It's Important

An understanding of geologic time allows you to put current geologic events into a realistic perspective.

Review Vocabulary

radioactivity: the process that occurs when a nucleus decays and emits alpha, beta, and gamma radiation

New Vocabulary

- absolute dating
- relative dating
- uniformitarianism
- principle of superposition
- unconformity
- fossil

Time

In your daily life you have become accustomed to the length of a year, a day, or an hour. These units of time are ancient and were established by observing astronomical events. **Figure 27** shows a globe illustrating Earth's time zones. They are determined by the position of Earth with respect to the Sun during one cycle of Earth's rotation.

Figure 27 Earth is divided into 24 time zones.

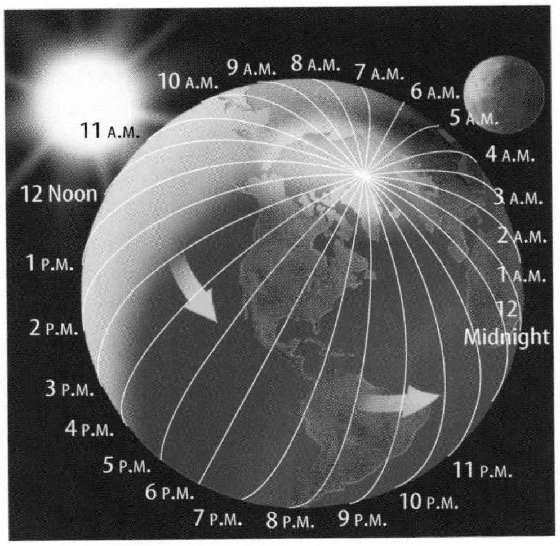

Absolute and Relative Dating You can give your age in years, months, days, and even hours. To do this you must have a starting reference—your birth date. Birth records often give the exact hour and minute of birth. This is an example of absolute dating. **Absolute dating** is the process of assigning a precise numerical age to an organism, object, or event. Technology allows scientists to add precision to their findings involving geologic time. **Relative dating** is the process of placing objects or events in their proper sequence in time. When you date events relatively, you know which came first, second, and so on. For example, students could be asked to line up in order of birth date, with oldest first. The key to relative dating is that the order is controlled by logical relationships, which might or might not involve the use of numbers.

Section 4 Resource Manager

Chapter FAST FILE Resources

Transparency Activity, pp. 47, 49–50

Enrichment, p. 32

Reinforcement, p. 28

Directed Reading for Content Mastery, pp. 19–20

Lab Worksheets, pp. 7–8

Home and Community Involvement, p. 43

Physical Science Critical Thinking/Problem Solving, p. 11

Reading and Writing Skills Activities, pp. 15–16

Mathematics Skills Activities, pp. 19–20

1 Motivate

INTERACTIVE CHALKBOARD PowerPoint® Presentations An editable Microsoft® PowerPoint® presentation is available on **Interactive Chalkboard** CD-ROM.

Bellringer

Section Focus Transparencies also are available on the Interactive Chalkboard CD-ROM. L2 ELL

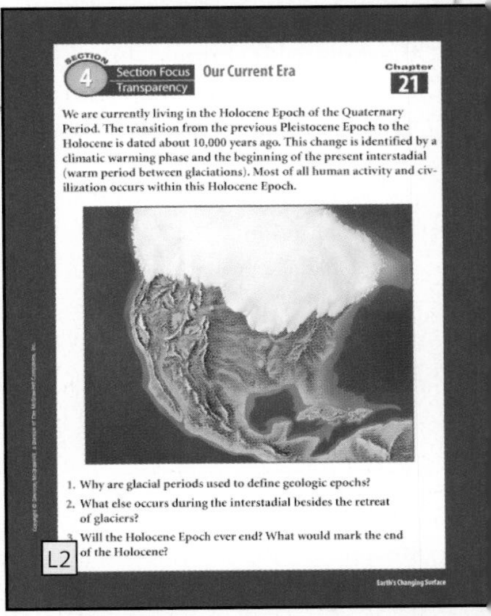
SECTION 4 Section Focus Transparency Our Current Era Chapter 21

We are currently living in the Holocene Epoch of the Quaternary Period. The transition from the previous Pleistocene Epoch to the Holocene is dated about 10,000 years ago. This change is identified by a climatic warming phase and the beginning of the present interstadial (warm period between glaciations). Most of all human activity and civilization occurs within this Holocene Epoch.

1. Why are glacial periods used to define geologic epochs?
2. What else occurs during the interstadial besides the retreat of glaciers?
3. Will the Holocene Epoch ever end? What would mark the end of the Holocene?

L2

Earth's Changing Surface

Reading Preview

Tie to Prior Knowledge

Fossil Clues Sedimentary rocks may contain fossils. Students will learn how these can be used to help interpret the age of the rocks or the history of their deposition.

Vocabulary Chart Have students make a three-column chart. Have students write the new vocabulary words in the first column and the meanings in the second column. In the last column, they should create a memory cue by drawing a sketch to represent the word or writing a sentence.

2 Teach

Discussion

Time Have students define *time* in their own words and then describe the methods used to establish common units of time—day, month, and year. day = repetition of the Sun on your meridian; month = repetition of a full moon on you meridian; year = repetition of the Sun at its highest or lowest point in the sky. L2

INTEGRATE History

It's how old? James Hutton is considered the father of modern geology. Research Hutton's life to discover how he became such an important scientific figure. James Hutton profoundly changed people's thinking. He was controversial in his day, just as Charles Darwin was some years later for his view on the origin of species. Hutton's observations led to the modern notions of a very old Earth.

Reading Check

Answer statement that says that oldest rock layers occur at the bottom of a formation, and become younger upward

Quick Demo
Fossil or Just Bone

Materials bones, fossil bones

Estimated Time 10 minutes

Procedure Obtain some clean bones from a butcher. Contact a college or state museum to borrow some fossil bones. Have the students handle both and briefly discuss how they are different. Ask the question: How does a forensics expert know if the bones found in a woods are recent or fossils? Fossils will have been replaced by mineral matter and should be heavier and denser than recent bones. Replacement can change the color of the bone as well; brown or black usually indicates replacement by the mineral phosphate. Variegated colors often indicate silica replacement. L2

INTEGRATE History

It's how old? James Hutton was instrumental in changing the way scientists think about Earth history. Research Hutton's life to discover how a gentleman farmer became such an important scientific figure.

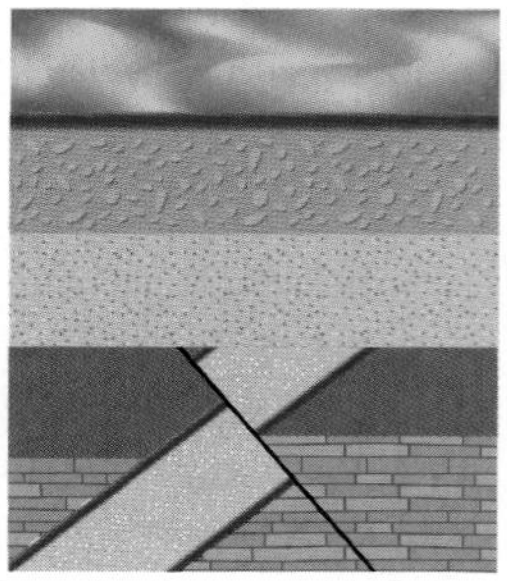

Figure 28 The principle of cross cutting relationships often can be used to determine the chronological order of some of Earth's geologic events. This illustration shows an intrusion of igneous rock that was separated later by a fault.

Uniformitarianism Geologic time is so vast that when James Hutton introduced his ideas for relative dating of rocks in his native Scotland and proposed that they might be millions of years old, he was seriously doubted. Hutton proposed the idea of **uniformitarianism,** which states that the laws of nature operate today as they have in the past. The only changes might be in their rate or scale. By studying how geologic events take place today, scientists can infer how events took place in the past. Uniformitarianism often is stated "the present is the key to the past." The idea of uniformitarianism is supported by many observations.

Principles of Relative Dating

To accurately date an event requires a set of logical rules that help determine the order of events. In the mid-1600s, Nicolaus Steno, a Danish physician, stated four principles that became the basis for understanding geologic events and the order in which they occurred. Suppose you were throwing papers into a wastebasket all day long, and at the end of the day you discovered you needed to find a paper from early that morning. You would know to look at the bottom of the basket, because the first things tossed away, or oldest papers, are at the bottom. In much the same way, the **principle of superposition** states that the oldest rocks in an undisturbed sequence of rock layers will be at the bottom of the sequence.

Reading Check *What is the principle of superposition?*

Original Horizontality In formulating the principle of original horizontality, Steno recognized that sedimentary layers always start off as horizontal layers. If you saw sedimentary layers that were not horizontal, you should know that they had been disturbed. You could infer that they began as horizontal layers of sediment, were formed into rock, and then were moved out of the horizontal position by some force.

Overlapping Features Another point of logic that helps establish a relative age is the principle of cross cutting relationships. This principle states that any rock formation or fault is younger than the rock or feature that it cuts through. How could an igneous rock intrusion squeeze through something that is not there? It seems apparent that the rocks affected by the intrusion in **Figure 28** had to be there first in order to be affected. Likewise, if a piece of rock were to become embedded in part of another rock, the piece had to exist before the rock into which it was incorporated. These rock pieces are called inclusions.

Science Journal

Travel Log Have students pretend that they are time travelers on a journey through one of the geologic eras. Have the students write a science log for their journey from the beginning to the end of the era. The log should include descriptions of the animals and plants they saw along the way. A complete journal would include some geologic events as well.

Reading Strategy

Determine Main Ideas Have students determine main ideas for the following sections: Time, Principles of Relative Dating, Fossils, Absolute Dating, and Geologic Maps. Remind them that main ideas can be implied. Encourage students to put themselves in the author's place and examine phrases for clues to what is important.

Unconformities Rock sequences are like Earth's diary. If you keep a diary there might be days when you make no new entries. Also, there might be days when you make entries, but tear them out later and destroy them. Deposition is similar. Rocks that occur in their proper time sequence might have gaps within the sequence. There are times when no sediments are being deposited that can be observed later. Also, there are times when erosion destroys existing rock layers. **Unconformities** represent gaps in the rock record during which erosion occurred or deposition was absent. **Figure 29** shows a sequence of rocks that contains several unconformities.

Reading Check *What is an unconformity?*

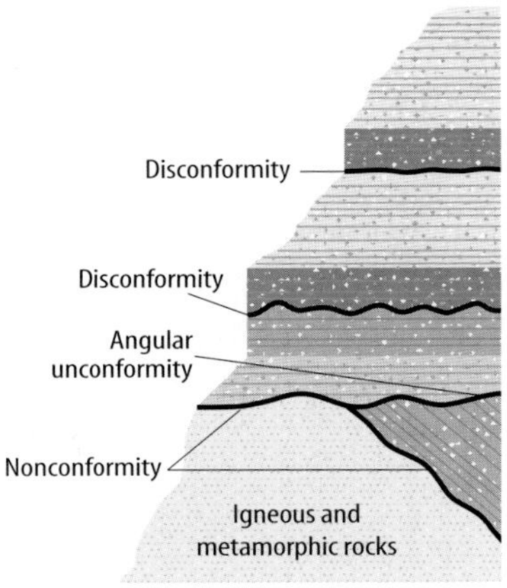

Figure 29 Three types of unconformities are shown above: disconformity, angular unconformity, and nonconformity. A disconformity is an erosional surface between horizontal rock layers. An angular unconformity is an erosional surface between rock layer segments that intercept at an angle. A nonconformity is an erosional surface between sedimentary rock and igneous or metamorphic rock.

Fossils

The remains or traces of organisms found in the geologic rock record are called **fossils.** Fossils can be direct remains, such as an actual bone or shell. Sometimes fossil remains, such as the inside of a shell, act as molds that form casts when filled with sediment that later hardens to rock. In a process called replacement, water containing dissolved mineral material might replace original shell or bone material with different minerals such as pyrite or quartz. In other cases, only a trace impression such as a footprint or burrow is left for paleontologists to observe.

Correlation While working as a canal engineer in England at the end of the eighteenth century, William Smith proposed the principle of faunal succession. Smith noticed that fossils appeared in the same order in the rock layers dug out to build the canals, no matter where he found them. For example, if fossil Q were found in a sedimentary rock layer above fossil F, then Q also appeared above F in a different geographic region. If you apply the law of superposition to this observation, you can conclude that fossil Q is younger than fossil F.

The process of matching distinctive rock units from different regions is called correlation. **Figure 30** illustrates how this is done. Paleontologists have been successful in correlating fossil-bearing rock units on a global scale. Fossils that are most useful as global time markers often are from organisms that were widespread geographically, but lived in only a narrow, well-defined period of time. Such fossils are called index fossils.

Not all fossil organisms existed over a wide area, however. Some fossils are not useful as time markers because they appear the same over millions of years. In addition, recall that geologic processes such as mountain building and erosion can destroy fossils, making correlation difficult.

Figure 30 Sometimes the relative age of rock units can be found by matching distinctive fossil-bearing rock units from different locations.

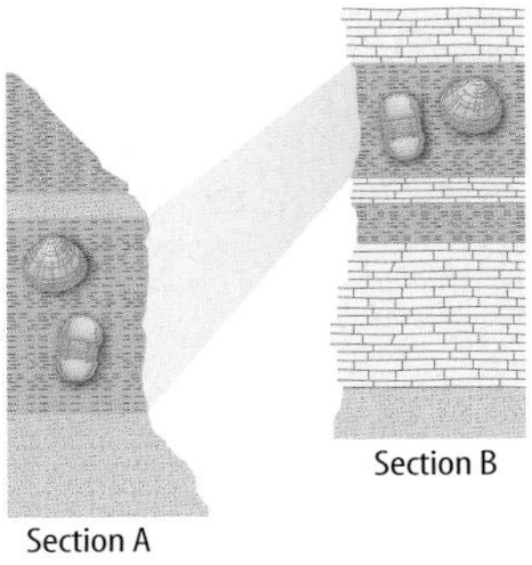

Reading Check

Answer a gap in the rock record caused by periods of erosion or non-deposition

Quick Demo
Molds and Casts

Materials paper cups, plaster of paris, water, petroleum jelly, cotton swabs.

Estimated Time 15 minutes per day (2)

Procedure Mix the plaster of paris to the consistency of peanut butter. Half-fill a paper cup with plaster of paris. Coat an object with a very thin film of petroleum jelly and press it into the plaster surface to make an impression. Do not push it in all the way. Set it aside to harden. The next day, remove the object and coat the entire top surface of the plaster in the cup with a very thin film of petroleum jelly. Cotton swabs help with this. Fill the cup with a second batch of plaster. Set it aside to harden. The next day, peel the paper cup away and separate the two halves. If done properly, a large amount of detail will be preserved. The bottom half is a mold; the top half is a cast.

Teacher FYI

Fossils Very few fossils are actual remains. The most common forms of fossils are molds and casts and replacement fossils. In replacement fossils, minerals in groundwater replace the original bone, shell, or wood of the organism. Details and internal structures are well preserved. For example, thin slices of petrified wood show cell walls of the original wood. The fossils are denser and heavier than the original material.

Visual Learning

Figure 29 An unconformity is a surface that represents a break in the geologic record. Usually a disconformity can be detected only by studying fossils in a sequence of sedimentary rock layers. A disconformity can occur when a surface is eroded and sediment is deposited on it at a later time. A disconformity also can occur when significant geologic time passes between depositions. L2 ELL

Differentiated Instruction

Learning Disabled Have students mix the plaster for the mold and cast activity. The plaster mix should not be too watery. A watery, soupy mix dries too slowly and the objects sink into the plaster. L1

SECTION 4 Geologic Time 671

Teacher FYI

As time passes, there is an increased possibility that evidence needed for dating will be destroyed. With this scant evidence, precision is lessened; therefore, the limits of each time segment are set by very noticeable or revolutionary changes in the rock and fossil record.

In more recent rocks there is an abundance of evidence and therefore finer definitions of time are possible.

Use Science Words

Prefixes Have students research the meaning of some of the prefixes used in the geologic time scale.

Paleo = *old/ancient*
Meso = *middle*
Ceno = *new*
Oligo = *little/few*
Neo = *new*
Eo = *dawn*
Mio = *less*
Holo = *entirely*

IDENTIFYING Misconceptions

Time Relationships Films often portray dinosaurs and humans in the same scenes. The last dinosaur died millions of years before the first humans appeared. It is worthwhile to consult a geologic time scale and review the first occurrence of major animal and plant groups.

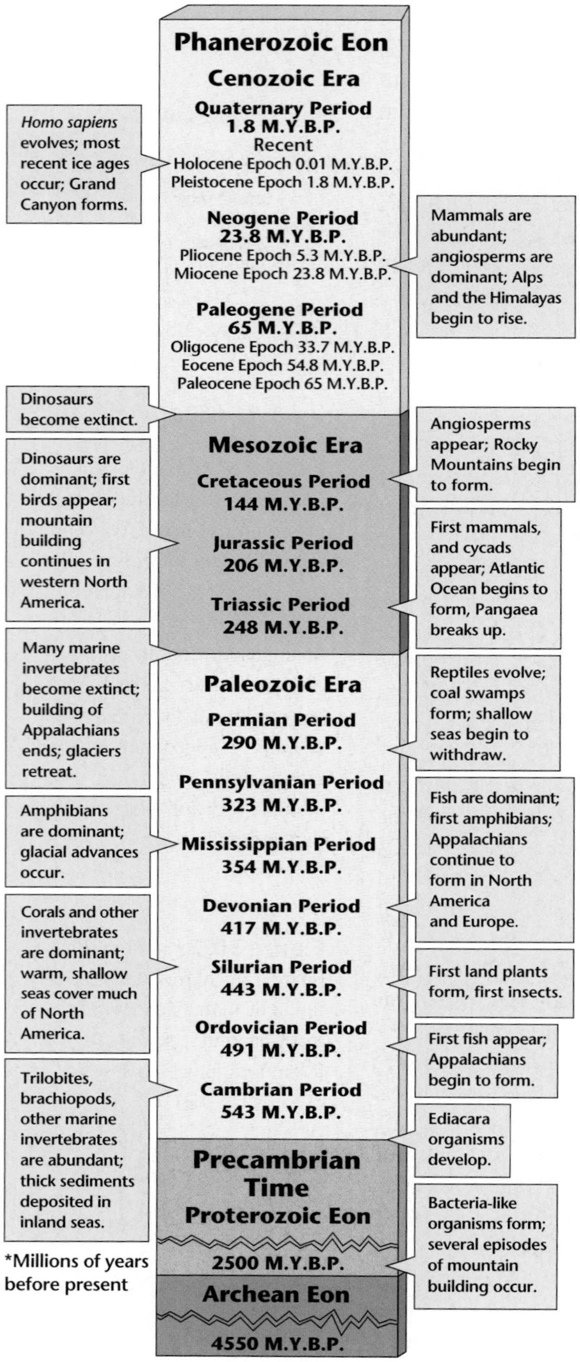

Geologic Time Scale Historians speak of the Industrial Revolution, and musicians refer to the Classical Period. These time periods began and ended with some event that marked a noticeable change in society and music. Similarly, paleontologists observe changes in the fossil record and associate them with boundaries of time units, shown in **Figure 31.** At these boundaries, fossils of certain life forms are no longer present and new life forms begin to appear. Boundaries also might be established by evidence of a catastrophic geologic event. Such events might have caused environmental changes that led to extinctions or changes in life forms.

Absolute Dating

Some atoms in minerals of a newly-formed igneous rock are like a clock that has been reset. A quantity of unstable radioactive element—the parent isotope—starts its decay at the time of mineral formation and gradually decays to a stable daughter isotope. Because radioactive isotopes decay in predictable ways, scientists can analyze the ratio of parent to daughter isotopes in a mineral to calculate the time that has elapsed since that mineral formed.

Radioactive Decay Some types of atoms are unstable and decay by casting off, or emitting, parts of their nuclei. Decay mechanisms produce new isotopes—some produce daughters with different atomic numbers, some involve a change in atomic mass, and some involve a change in both.

Figure 31 *Phanerozoic* means "visible life."
Calculate *What fraction of Earth's history does the Phanerozoic eon represent?*

Visual Learning

Figure 31 Have students examine the geologic time scale and note how each era is subdivided. Ask students to suggest reasons why the Cenozoic is subdivided into more units than the other eras. The Cenozoic contains the youngest rocks on Earth and the youngest fossils. There has been less time to destroy fossil material. Because the abundance of fossils is higher in these younger rocks, the formations can be subdivided with greater detail. L2

Fun Fact

Most dinosaur skeletons found in nature aren't complete. The bones become scattered and many are not preserved. Skeletons displayed in museums display those available bones. The curators create copies of the missing parts. For example, if the right foreleg is found, but there is no left foreleg, the right is used as a model for the missing left.

Table 1 Commonly Used Isotopes for Dating Earth Materials		
Radioactive Parent	**Stable Daughter**	**Half-Life**
Carbon-14	Nitrogen-14	5,730 years
Uranium-235	Lead-207	713 million years
Potassium-40	Argon-40	1.3 billion years
Uranium-238	Lead-206	4.5 billion years
Thorium-232	Lead-208	14.1 billion years
Rubidium-87	Strontium-87	49.0 billion years

INTEGRATE Physics

Half-Life Every radioactive isotope has a half-life. The half-life is the time it takes for one-half of a radioactive parent sample to decay to its stable daughter. After one half-life, the ratio of parent atoms to daughter atoms is 50:50, or 1:1. For example, if the half-life of a parent isotope is 500,000 years and a rock is analyzed and the observed daughter/parent ratio is 1:1, one half-life has elapsed and the age of that rock is 500,000 years. During the next half-life, there is decay of one-half of the remaining parent isotope, resulting in one-fourth parent to three-fourths daughter, or 25:75.

Reading Check *What is half-life?*

Useful Isotopes All of the isotopes in **Table 1** except carbon-14 are common in many types of rocks. Carbon-14 is useful for dating organic Earth materials such as wood and peat.

Generally, absolute ages are determined from unaltered minerals in igneous rocks. This is because sedimentary and metamorphic processes involve water or other fluids. When they interact with the rock it can cause the amount of parent isotopes, daughter isotopes, or both to change. When this happens, the age that is determined will be too young or old.

To see how geologists combine relative dating techniques with absolute dating techniques, look at **Figure 32.** You could conclude from the rock layers at Location A that Fossil C is between 2.1 and 2.4 million years old, Fossil A is older than 2.4 million years, and Fossil E is younger than 2.1 million years. These conclusions use radiometric dating for the age values and superposition for the order of events. What age relations can you determine for Fossils C, B, E and F at Location B?

Figure 32 Relative dating and absolute dating techniques can be combined to help determine the ages of some fossils.
Infer *Why is Fossil C considered to be between 2.1 and 2.4 million years old?*

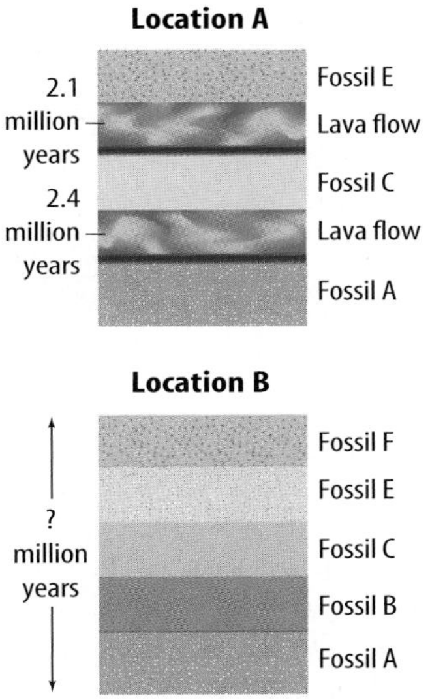

INTEGRATE Physics **Content Background**

Radioactive decay occurs when unstable atoms spontaneously break apart releasing alpha particles making them a more stable element. The rate at which the atoms decay depends on the element. Radiocarbon dating was recently used to determine the fate of a set of human skeletal remains found near Kennewick, Washington. If they could be determined to be Native American, they would be protected by the Native American Graves Protection and Repatriation Act of 1990 (NAGPRA). In 1999, four small bone samples were tested at three independent laboratories. Results indicated that the chronological age of the bones is between 9510 to 9320 years ago. This age predates the arrival of any European explorers. So, the remains are considered to be Native American.

Reading Check

Answer applies to radioactive isotopes; is the length of time required for half the set amount of an isotope to decay to its stable daughter product

Caption Answer

Figure 32 The rock layer below Fossil C has been radiometricly dated to be 2.4 million years old, the rock layer above Fossil C has been radiometricly dated to be 2.1 million years old.

SECTION 4 Geologic Time 673

Reading Check

Answer a two-dimensional representation of the rocks at Earth's surface

Make A Model

Geologic Structures Students enjoy making models of geologic cross-sections or geologic structures. Anticlines, synclines, basins, domes, or more elaborate cross-sections can be made of any material. A novel twist is to create them from edible materials.

A variation is to create a cross-section cake, where the icing hides the structure. Straws pushed through the cake act like drill cores. Students can infer the structure and test their hypothesis by cutting (and eating) the cake. L2 ELL LS **Visual-Spatial**

Caption Answer

Figure 33 uplift from below the rock layers, or lateral forces converging toward a central area

Geologic Maps

Geologic cross-sections, like the simplified sketch in **Figure 32,** represent a vertical slice taken through Earth. Geologic maps, on the other hand, show the horizontal surface distribution of various rock formations. Most geologic maps also include a legend that indicates the ages of the rock formations at the surface. Geologic maps are two-dimensional models of Earth's crust for a given region. Geologists plot the location, orientation, and boundaries of rocks found at the surface. These data are obtained by direct field observation, through drill cores, aerial photography, and satellite observations.

Reading Check *What is a geologic map?*

Basins and Domes Recall that rock layers can be deformed by tectonic processes that result in the formation of faults and folds. One example of a deformed structure is a basin. Recall that the principle of original horizontality states that sediments are laid down in horizontal layers as shown in **Figure 33A.** Compressional forces due to plate tectonic activity cause the layers to fold and to dip downward. **Figure 33B** shows the surface map expression of a basin. In basins, the youngest rocks are exposed in the center and tilt or dip inward.

Domes are essentially the opposite of basins. In this case, the rock layers are uplifted at the center of the structure. The surface appearance of a dome, shown in map view in **Figure 33C,** is similar to a basin. In this case, the oldest rocks are at the center and dip outward. Visualize this by warping up a stack of papers into a hill. Next, imagine sawing off the top of the paper hill. The sawing would expose the bottom layers of paper in the middle. In the case of rock formations, the sawing represents erosion, and the lower paper layers represent the oldest rock layers.

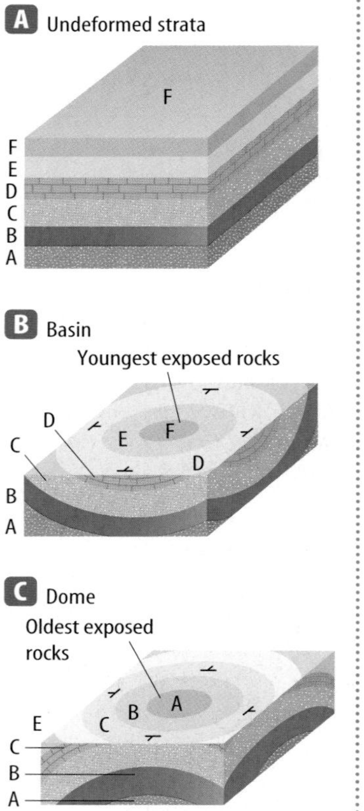

Figure 33 Tectonic processes can cause Earth's plates to shift, collide, and separate. Sometimes this leads to the deformation of horizontal rock layers.
Infer *What direction(s) of force might be needed to create a dome?*

Folds Folding of the crust can also be recognized on geologic maps. Recall that compressional stresses tend to squeeze and shorten materials. If the forces on part of Earth's crust are mainly compression forces, then rocks subjected to the compression might wrinkle up or fold. Hold a sheet of paper flat with both hands and push the sides together. The paper wrinkles either up or down. Folds of rock appear much the same way. An upward wrinkle of rock formations is an anticline and a downward wrinkle is a syncline, shown in **Figure 34A.** Try the paper trick again, but hold one hand still and push with the other. You get a fold that flops over horizontally. This is called a recumbent fold.

Visual Learning

Figure 33 Examination of the diagram indicates that up-folded layers should form a mountain and down-folded layers should form a valley. However, a well-known rock exposure in the Appalachian Mountains of Maryland exhibits the opposite. The road cut through the mountain shows down-folded layers. Ask students how this might be possible. Accept reasonable answers. The Appalachian Mountains are so old that erosion has worn down the original high mountains. In many places, what once were valleys are now the high points, thus down-folded layers make up what are now the mountains that we see. L2 ELL

674 CHAPTER 21 Earth's Changing Surface

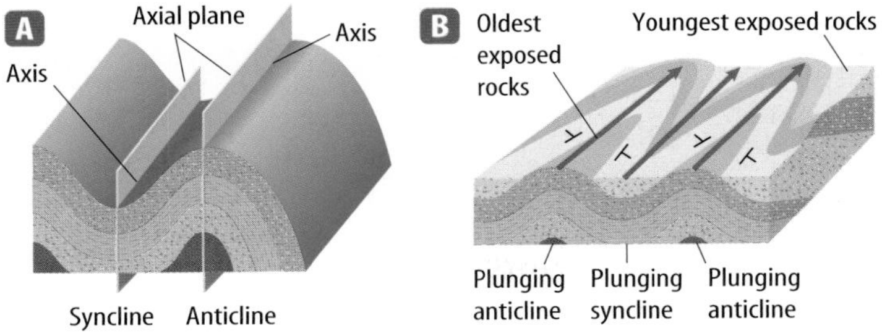

Figure 34 Two basic types of folds are found in rock layers.
A Synclines form a trough and anticlines form an arch.
B If these folds are tilted, they form plunging folds. On a geologic map, plunging folds appear as V-shaped or horseshoe patterns.

Plunging Folds The axis of a fold is an imaginary line where Earth's surface meets the axial plane. The axial plane divides the fold in half, and is usually perpendicular to the compression force. If the forces are applied unevenly the axis of the fold might plunge back into the Earth, producing a surface pattern of rock like the one shown in **Figure 34B.**

These structural features can give you an idea of how geologists illustrate what the surface of the crust looks like in given locations. Practice viewing the structures in cross section and map view, and apply relative dating logic to the structures. You will soon be able to reconstruct the events that formed the features, and tell a story about their history.

section 4 review

Summary

Time

- Uniformitarianism states the processes occurring today are the same as they have been in the past. Rate and extent may have changed.

Principles of Relative Dating

- Steno's principles helped to develop an understanding of geologic events.

Fossils

- Fossils are the remains or traces of once-living organisms. Correlation is the matching of rock outcrops from one region to another.

Absolute Dating

- Analyzing the radioactive decay of radioactive isotopes helps to establish numerican dates for objects and events.

Geologic Maps

- Geologic maps are two-dimensional models of a region of Earth's crust.

Self Check

1. **Discuss** how events in Earth history determine boundaries for geologic time units.
2. **Compare and contrast** absolute and relative dating.
3. **Describe** three lines of logic used in relative dating. Draw and label respective diagrams.
4. **Think Critically** You're hiking down a canyon that has been deeply eroded, exposing numerous folds. One fold is recumbent, with layers turned completely over. Describe the problems this structure could cause for relative dating, if only a small portion of its rock layers were exposed.

Applying Skills

5. **Calculate an Age** Suppose the ratio of radioactive parent to stable daughter isotope in a mineral within an igneous rock is 12.5:87.5. The half-life of the parent isotope is 7.13×10^8 years. How old is the rock sample?

More Section Review gpescience.com

section 4 review

1. Mass extinction of key animal forms or global geologic events establish boundaries.
2. Both are used to establish time relationships; absolute dating establishes numerical dates while relative dating establishes the order of events.
3. superposition—oldest material is at the bottom of an undisturbed sequence of rock; cross-cutting—features which cut across other features are younger than the feature they transect; original horizontality—sedimentary rocks start off as horizontal layers
4. The dates would be in reverse order, but fossil inclusions may alert you to the reversed order.
5. 3 half-lives $\times$ 713,000,000 years = 2.1 billion years

Post Reading

Fix-Up Strategy Model this strategy by reading a challenging passage aloud. As you read, ask clarifying questions, change reading pace, review figures, and reread when necessary. Have students practice the strategy with a partner, using a passage they find particularly difficult.

3 Assess

DAILY INTERVENTION

Check for Understanding

Visual-Spatial Have the class construct a living geologic time scale on the school's football field. Assuming Earth is 4.5 billion years old, 1 inch equals 1,250,000 years. Have students make large pennants on stakes to mark geologic and biologic events on the time line. L2 ELL

Reteach

Use the Launch Lab time line that was created and have the students add detail to it by including periods, eras, and epochs. Have them illustrate the timeline by correctly sketching in the animals and plants common to specific periods. L1 ELL

Assessment

Create Have each student prepare a game-show-style answer that asks a question for the category *Geologic Time*. Critique each answer and use the best answers for an end-of-chapter review. Use **PASC**, p. 91. L2

BENCH TESTED

Real-World Problem

Purpose Demonstrate the methods used in relative dating of geologic cross sections.

Process Skills observe, interpret, infer

Time Required 90 minutes

Procedure

Teaching Strategy Have students carefully examine the example(s) given and stress that the list of events will include more than just the layers of rock shown in the cross section.

Analyze Your Data

Expected Outcome Students will be able to apply the laws of relative dating.

Answers to Chronologies

Tiltin Hilton

1. B conglomerate
2. C sandstone
3. D limestone
4. F sandstone
5. G shale w/inclusions of F
6. tectonic movement
7. angular unconformity
8. L conglomerate
9. M limestone
10. N shale

Criss Cross

1. F sandstone
2. angular unconformity
3. M limestone
4. O shale
5. S limestone
6. T conglomerate w/inclusions of S
7. disconformity
8. W shale
9. G intrusive igneous rock any time after S
10. H intrusive igneous rock anytime after G and S

No Fault of Mine

1. A limestone
2. C shale
3. D sandstone
4. F limestone
5. G conglomerate
6. disconformity
7. I shale
8. J sandstone
9. Fault X

Intruder

1. Q limestone
2. R sandstone
3. S extrusive igneous rock
4. K sandstone
5. T extrusive igneous rock
6. C shale
7. folding
8. angular unconformity
9. B sandstone
10. disconformity
11. M shale
12. N intrusive igneous rock anytime after B sandstone

LAB

It's about time—relative, that is.

Goals

- **Observe** geologic cross sections.
- **Interpret** events that caused the observed features.
- **Infer** a probable chronology for the events.

Materials

copies of geologic cross sections

Real-World Problem

When interpreting the geologic history of a region, geologists follow the principles of relative dating. As with all scientific disciplines, they might get help by exchanging information with other scientists. Some rocks in an area of interest might have been dated using radioactive isotopes or index fossils. How can geologists determine a chronological order of events that took place in a section of Earth's crust over many millions of years?

Procedure

1. Familiarize yourself with the symbols in the legend that signify different rock types and other cross section features.
2. Examine the cross sections. On your own paper, list the order of events that took place for each cross section, listing the oldest first. Note that the number of steps is not simply the number of rock layers in the cross section.

Legend

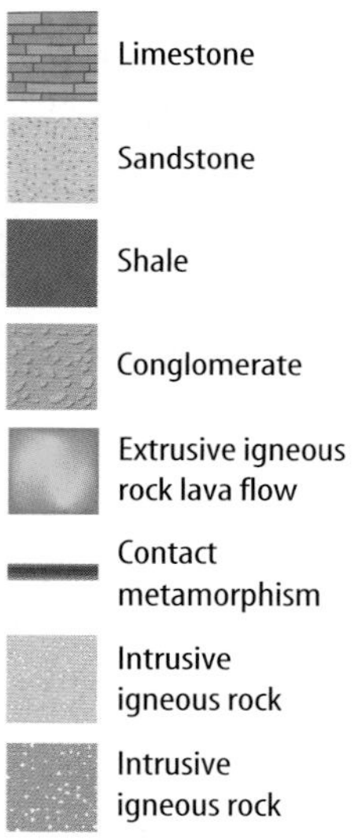

Tiltin Hilton

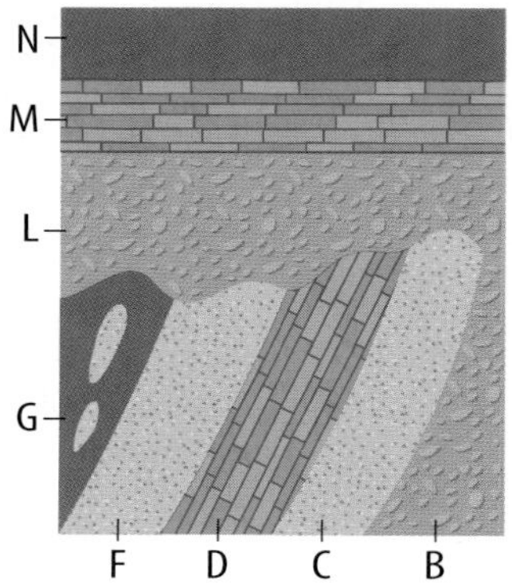

Criss cross

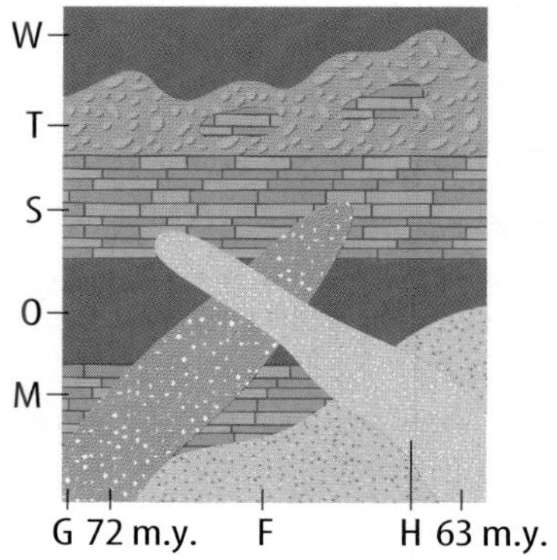

676 CHAPTER 21 Earth's Changing Surface

Using Scientific Methods

3. Be sure to include all of the events or actions that changed or helped form the Earth materials shown in each of the four cross sections. For example, unconformities, faulting, folding, or other changes also need to be placed in proper order.

No fault of mine

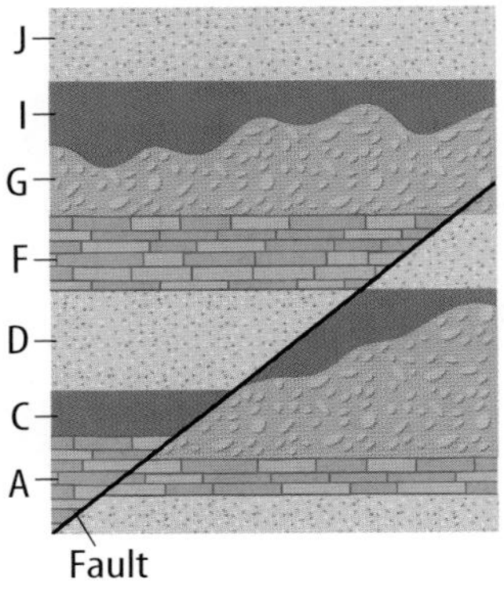

Analyze Your Data

1. **Analyze** each cross section and determine whether there is more than one possible chronological interpretation.
2. **Identify** features that are most useful in supporting relative age relationships.

Conclude and Apply

1. **Evaluate** cross sections that apparently have more than one possible explanation for a geologic history.
2. **Explain** whether or not the absolute ages for the intrusions in cross section *Crisscross* agree with the relative ages of the intrusions.
3. How would your answer have changed for cross section *Crisscross* if you did not have absolute age data?
4. **Summarize** your reasoning for establishing a relative age for fault X in the cross section *No Fault of Mine*.

Intruder

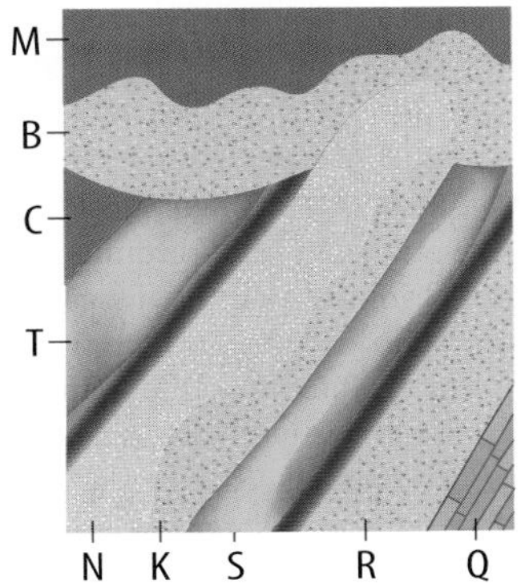

Communicating Your Data

Prepare an oral defense for your interpretation of one of the cross sections. Answer questions from classmates who might have made different conclusions about the same cross section.

Answers to Questions

1. Student answers will vary.
2. Cross cutting features and intrusions are most helpful.

Error Analysis Have students compare their chronologies and resolve any differences. More than one solution is possible for those cross sections with the answer statement "anytime after."

Conclude and Apply

1. Student answers will vary. The key to apply is "anytime after."
2. Absolute ages agree; relative age would not change; absolute ages are used for confirmation.
3. Relative age would not change; absolute ages are to establish ages of rocks before or after intrusions.
4. Fault X has to come after the youngest layer that it effects aligning the sequences on both sides of the fault reveals the same sequence G, I, J.

Assessment

Performance Ask students to draw a simple, labeled, geologic cross section that illustrates each of the relative dating principles: superposition, cross cutting, and original horizontality. Then have them create labeled drawings to illustrate a cross section of a geologic structure: basin, dome, anticline/syncline. L2

Alternative Inquiry Lab

What was the sequence? Students can model geologic events by using different colors of clay to represent horizontal, angular, and folded rock layers. Using plastic knives and spoons to create erosion surfaces and faults. Exchange cross sections with other students and have them infer the sequence in which the original models were made.

Communicating Your Data

Have students relate their interpretation of a cross section as part of the Error Analysis process.

LAB 677

TIME

Content Background

Groundwater flow is a very complex, poorly understood subject. Channels underground can carry water in directions unrelated to the surface topography. Because the patterns of water distribution are not generally mapped and groundwater often travels tens or hundreds of miles from the recharge zone, disturbance of groundwater can have unexpected effects. In addition to problems of water shortage, this makes pollution of groundwater particularly problematic. Groundwater mining frequently causes the surface to subside as water is removed from the aquifer, creating structural problems to buildings as the grounds settles inches or feet per year. Also, once the water is removed, many subsurface soils become compacted by the weight of soil above. These soils cannot be recharged with fresh water, permanently destroying that part of the aquifer.

Discussion

Water Sources What other sources of water could be used in order to avoid mining groundwater? Possible answers: streams, water collected from surface runoff in mountains; desalination of seawater; catching water that falls on roofs for use in building; recycling wastewater

Activity

Have students measure the capacity of a large plastic or metal bowl by filling it with water from a graduated cylinder or measuring cup. Empty the bowl and fill it completely with coarse gravel. Have students add a measured amount of water to the rim of the bowl. Determine what percent of the bowl of gravel is actually open space between rocks. Several groups of students can use different sizes of gravel and compare the results.

TIME **SCIENCE AND Society** SCIENCE ISSUES THAT AFFECT YOU!

Tapping into the Underground

Freshwater is one of our most important natural resources. Although it may seem that there is an unlimited supply of water—just turn on the faucet and there it is—water supplies can run out. Much of Earth's freshwater is stored in aquifers, inside the cracks and pores of rock and soil. Some of this water flows to the surface and is continually replaced by rainfall that filters through the ground. Other aquifers lie far below the surface, holding water that fell as rain thousands of years ago.

Humans pump water from underground for many uses including drinking, bathing, irrigating crops, and for manufacturing. Because the time needed for water to move into an aquifer can be years or even centuries, these uses consume water faster than it can be replaced by natural processes. When that happens, water is no longer a renewable resource and groundwater shortages become likely.

If water is pumped from a well faster than it can be replaced, the area around it becomes depeleted. This results in wells must be drilled deeper and deeper. Eventually the water flow becomes too slow to be useful. Groundwater shortages don't just affect the amount of water, but they can also affect its quality. Under normal conditions, the direction of underground water flow tends to be the same as the slope of the surface. As the supply is depleted, water flows from all directions toward the well. In places near the ocean, salt water flowing into the aquifer can make the water useless.

Water conservation—using less water—slows the depletion of the aquifer. This helps the supply refill naturally. Many communities are taking steps to avoid groundwater shortages. In some places, wastewater is cleaned and recycled for other uses to reduce the amount of underground water needed. Another way to use recycled wastewater is ro refill the groundwater supply. Treated wastewater is either pumped back into the ground or allowed to filter back into the aquifer from constructed wetlands.

Interview **Contact a local hydrologist for an interview. Before the interview, do research to determine the sources of water for your community and what happens to treated wastewater. Make a list of interview questions. Conduct the interview and write a summary.**

TIME
For more information, visit gpescience.com

Research Provide time for students to discuss whether there are possible alternative sources for water supply and disposal and advantages and disadvantages of each. Ask for suggestions for reducing water usage.

Resources for Teachers and Students

The Hidden Sea: Ground Water, Springs, and Wells by Francis H. Chapelle, Geoscience Press, Tucson, AZ, 1997

Understanding Groundwater by W. Jesse Schwalbaum, Nova Science Publishers, Commack, NY 1997

USEPA, Water Resource Center (RC-4100)
1200 Pennsylvania Avenue NW,
Washington DC 20460

Reviewing Main Ideas

Section 1 Weathering and Soil

1. Mechanical weathering reduces the size of materials. Chemical weathering creates new materials or dissolves material through chemical reactions.
2. Differential weathering causes rock that is resistant to particular climate conditions to stand out in the landscape.
3. Soil is composed of weathered rock, decaying organic matter, water, and air. Soil type depends on the nature of the material from which it forms, climate type, and location.

4. Erosion and chemical depletion of soil are global problems.

Section 2 Shaping the Landscape

1. Erosion is a set of processes that physically remove material at Earth's surface.
2. All the land area that collects water for a major river is a drainage basin.
3. In order to develop, glaciers require long periods of time in which winter snowfall exceeds summer melt. Glaciers create erosional and depositional features.
4. Erosion by wind generally is limited to particle sizes that are sand-sized or smaller.
5. Erosion by wave action on rocky coastlines leaves resistant landforms behind, such as sea stacks and arches. Beach erosion and deposition is caused partly by movement of sediment by longshore currents.
6. Mass wasting is any form of erosion driven by gravity, such as landslides and mudflows.

Section 3 Groundwater

1. Groundwater accumulates by the infiltration of surface water. Infiltration is controlled by slope of land, type of surface material and type and amount of vegetation.
2. Groundwater is stored in aquifers. The movement of groundwater in an aquifer is influenced by gravity, the structure of the aquifer, and by the porosity and permeability of the aquifer.

3. Groundwater might return to the surface naturally by springs or be brought to the surface by human-made wells.

Section 4 Geologic Time

1. Relative dating principles are used to determine the order of geologic events. Radiometric dating uses the decay of radioactive isotopes to establish a numerical age for materials.
2. Geologic maps illustrate the horizontal distribution of rock formations.

FOLDABLES™ Use the Foldable that you made at the beginning of this chapter to help you review Earth's erosional and depositional features.

chapter Study Guide 21

Reviewing Main Ideas

Summary statements can be used by students to review the major concepts of the chapter.

Science Online

Visit gpescience.com
More Section Review
Interactive Tutor
Vocabulary PuzzleMaker
More Chapter Review
Standardized Test Practice

Assessment Transparency

For additional assessment questions, use the *Assessment Transparency* located in the transparency book.

Assessment

Assessment Transparency — Earth's Changing Surface — Chapter 21

1. Wind transports the ____ materials of soil such as organic matter, clays, and silts.
   A heaviest B lightest
   C most colorful D most dense
2. Wind erosion lowers the agricultural ____ of the soil.
   F productivity G infertility
   H input J shortage
3. There is also a(n) ____ impact associated with wind erosion as city funds are spent clearing and cleaning affected areas.
   A social C economical
   B emotional D philosophical

L2

Earth's Changing Surface

FOLDABLES™ Have students use their Foldables to review erosional and depositional features.

Using Vocabulary

1. aquifer
2. relative dating
3. drainage basin
4. uniformitarianism
5. permeability
6. weathering
7. soil
8. water table
9. unconformity

Checking Concepts

10. B
11. D
12. C
13. A
14. B
15. B
16. D
17. B

Interpreting Graphics

18.

H.L.	% P	% D
1	50	50
2	25	75
3	12.5	87.5
4	6.25	93.75

Using Vocabulary

absolute dating p. 669
aquifer p. 664
deposition p. 654
drainage basin p. 655
erosion p. 654
fossil p. 671
infiltration p. 663
longshore current p. 660
permeability p. 664
principle of superposition p. 670
relative dating p. 669
sediment transport p. 654
soil p. 650
unconformity p. 671
uniformitarianism p. 670
water table p. 664
weathering p. 646

Match the correct vocabulary word(s) with each definition given below.

1. a rock layer that stores and transmits water
2. a means of establishing the order of events
3. region that collects water for a stream system
4. concept that the laws of nature act today as they have in the past
5. a measure of the ability of a fluid to pass through a material
6. processes of chemical or physical breakdown of a substance
7. Earth's surface covering consisting of weathered rock, decaying organic matter, water, and air
8. boundary separating the saturated zone and the unsaturated zone
9. a surface representing a period of erosion or non-deposition

Checking Concepts

10. What is a process that leaves resistant rock remaining in the landscape?
A) deposition
B) differential weathering
C) sediment transport
D) infiltration

Use the illustration below to answer questions 11–12.

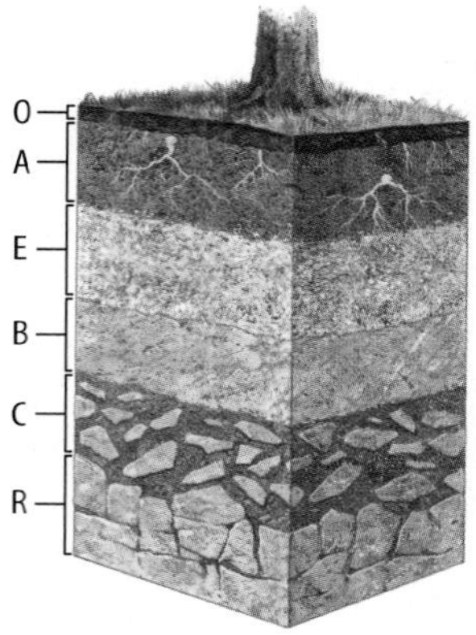

11. Which soil horizon contains the greatest amount of organic matter?
A) A horizon
B) B horizon
C) C horizon
D) O horizon

12. Which soil horizon represents weathered bedrock?
A) A horizon
B) B horizon
C) C horizon
D) O horizon

13. Which of the following is NOT a typical soil texture component?
A) gravel
B) sand
C) silt
D) clay

14. Which of the following is formed by glaciers?
A) V-shaped valleys
B) moraines
C) flood plain
D) deltas

Vocabulary PuzzleMaker gpescience.com

Use the Exam*View*® Pro Test Bank CD-ROM to:

- create multiple versions of tests
- create modified tests with one mouse click for inclusion students
- edit existing questions and add your own questions
- build tests aligned with state standards using built-in State Curriculum Tags
- change English tests to Spanish with one mouse click and vice versa

15. Select the material that slows or stops movement of ground water.
 A) aquifer
 B) aquitard
 C) water table
 D) saturated zone

16. Select the relative principle that states: *The oldest rock layer is on the bottom.*
 A) original horizontality
 B) cross cutting relationships
 C) faunal succession
 D) superposition

17. Which time unit of the geological time scale is the shortest?
 A) eon
 B) epoch
 C) period
 D) era

Interpreting Graphic

18. Copy and complete the table below.

Radioactive Decay

Half-lives	% Parent	% Daughter
1	25 50	75 50
2	12.5	87.5
3	6.25	93.75
4		

Thinking Critically

19. **Explain** why a soluble rock such as limestone can stand out as cliffs in the western United States.

20. **Infer** how water from a natural spring could become contaminated.

21. **Explain** the difference between a confined aquifer and an unconfined aquifer.

22. **Infer** why cities that draw their water from a drainage basin need to understand how surrounding land is used.

23. **Infer** why rocks or fossils that are found lying on the ground are not useful for relative dating.

Use the illustration below to answer question 24.

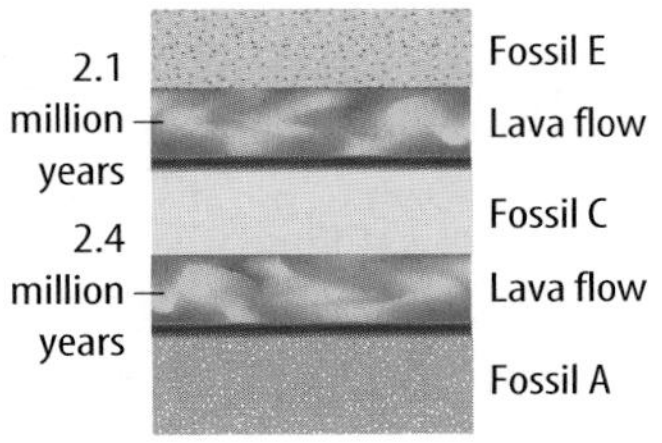

24. **Describe** how absolute dates from ancient lava flows could be used to determine the absolute ages of fossils.

25. **Apply** The half-life of carbon-14 is 5730 years. Explain why carbon-14 is useful for dating objects that are 75,000 years old and younger.

26. **Apply** Explain why glacial deposits made of till are often poorly drained and swampy.

Applying Math

27. Suppose an aquifer is known to be 200 km long and 75 km wide. If its average saturated thickness is 40 m and it has an average porosity of 3 percent, estimate how many cubic kilometers of water could potentially be stored in the aquifer.

28. An igneous rock sample was dated using radioactive potassium. Measurement indicates that 1/32 of the original parent potassium is left in the sample. The half-life of potassium is 1.3 billion years. How old is this igneous rock?

More Chapter Review gpescience.com

chapter 21 Review

Thinking Critically

19. The climate is arid. With little rainfall, dissolution of carbonate rocks such as limestone is minimal.

20. The infiltration area that supplies the spring is contaminated.

21. A confined aquifer has an aquitard above and below it.

22. If contaminants are dumped or vegetation is cut away in these areas, the resulting water will enter the drainage basin in a degraded condition.

23. Loose fossils could have come from anywhere and have no direct connection to any rock.

24. Fossils found in layers between the absolutely dated lava flows must be of an age between those absolute ages.

25. If an object is 75,000 years old, 13 half-lives have elapsed. Because so little of the parent material remains, it is difficult to obtain a reliable date for objects that are older.

26. Till is poorly sorted, which means that pore spaces are few and small. Porosity is low and water does not drain well through till.

Applying Math

Math Standards

National: 1, 4, 9

27. 18 km^3

28. If 1/32 of the parent isotope remains, five half-lives have elapsed. 1.3 billion years $\times$ 5 = 6.5 billion years.

Assessment Resources

Reproducible Masters

Chapter *Fast File* Resources
 Chapter Review, pp. 37–38
 Chapter Tests, pp. 39–42
 Assessment Transparency Activity, p. 51

Glencoe Science Web site
 Chapter Review Test
 Standardized Test Practice

Glencoe Technology
 Assessment Transparency
 Exam*View*® Pro Testmaker
 MindJogger Videoquiz
 Interactive Chalkboard

Answer Sheet An answer sheet can be found at **gpescience.com**.

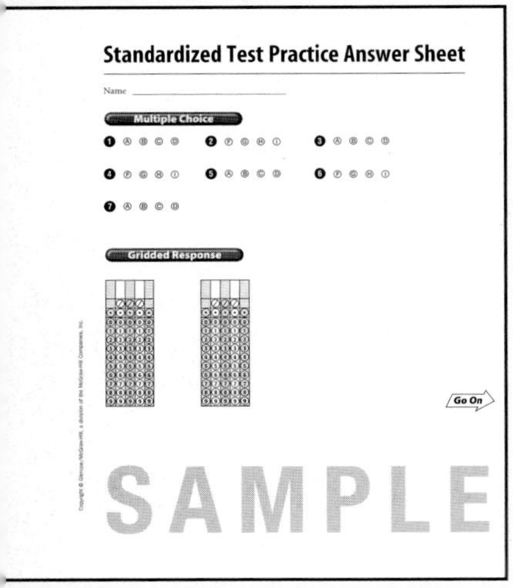
Standardized Test Practice Answer Sheet

Name

Multiple Choice

Gridded Response

Go On

SAMPLE

Multiple Choice

1. B
2. D
3. A
4. A
5. C
6. B
7. A
8. C

Gridded Response

9. 40
10. 14,000 years
11. 20 years

chapter 21 Standardized Test Practice

Record your answers on the answer sheet provided by your teacher or on a sheet of paper.

Multiple Choice

Use the illustration below to answer question 1.

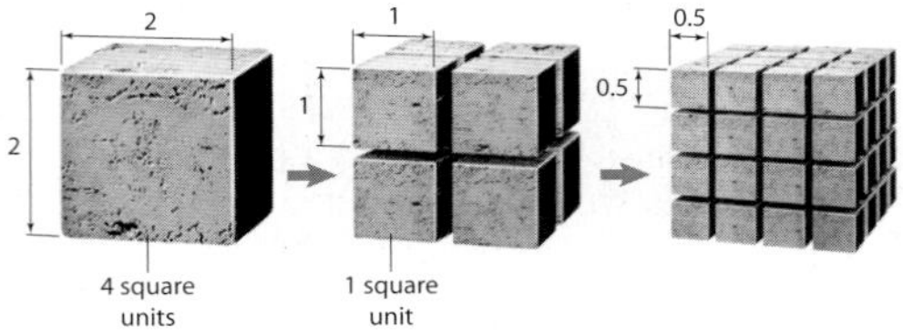

1. How does mechanical weathering affect rock material?

A. alters chemical composition

B. increases rock surface area

C. increases rock volume

D. slows chemical weathering

2. Which is a mixture of weathered rock, organic matter, water, and air?

A. feldspar

B. parent material

C. rock rust

D. soil

3. Which is the dropping of sediment load?

A. deposition

B. erosion

C. transporting

D. weathering

Test-Taking Tip

Remember Never leave any answer blank.

4. Which develops as force within a stream is exerted sideways?

A. floodplain

B. mouth

C. source

D. tributary

Use the illustration below to answer question 5.

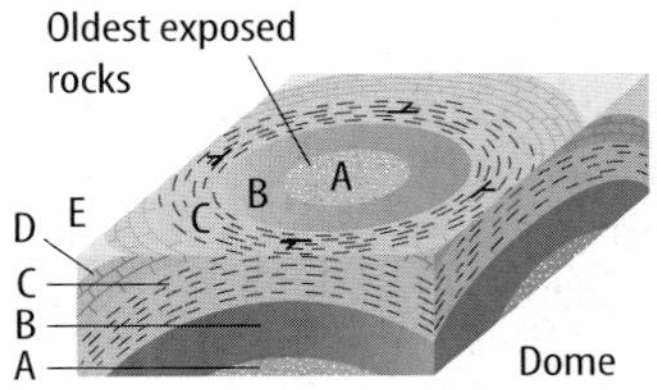

5. Which structural form is illustrated above?

A. anticline

B. basin

C. dome

D. syncline

6. Which is where a stream's water flows into another body of water?

A. floodplain

B. mouth

C. source

D. tributary

7. Which forms at the front of a glacier?

A. end moraine

B. ground moraine

C. lateral moraine

D. medial moraine

682 STANDARDIZED TEST PRACTICE

8. Which forms when sand is moved by wind?
   - **A.** currents
   - **B.** delta
   - **C.** dunes
   - **D.** loess

Gridded Response

Use the illustration below to answer question 9.

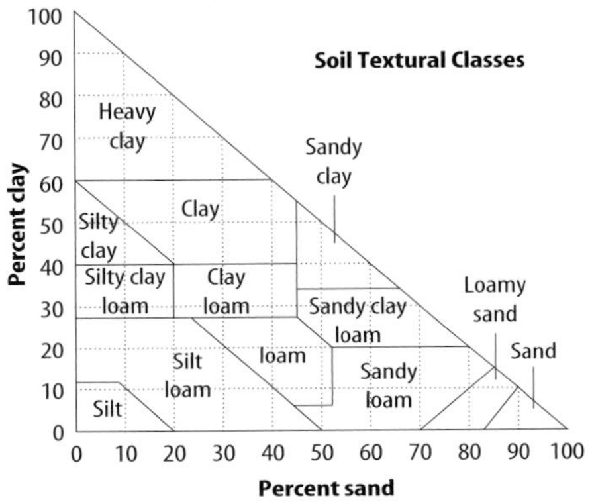

9. Which soil texture consists of 50 percent sand and 40 percent clay?

10. If the half-life of an isotope is 7,000 years and the amount of that isotope present in an igneous rock is only one-fourth of the original amount, how old is the rock?

11. Soil erosion in an area is 3.0 cm per year. The soil profile is 2.4 m thick and 25 percent of that is topsoil. How long will it take for the topsoil to erode away?

Short Response

12. How does water work to cause mechanical weathering called frost wedging?

13. How does slope affect the soil horizon?

14. Why is vegetation important to the type of soil that forms?

15. What is the drainage basin of a river?

16. How does a delta form?

17. How does a bar form on the inside of a bend in a stream?

18. How does a glacier erode the land's surface?

Extended Response

Use the art below to answer question 19.

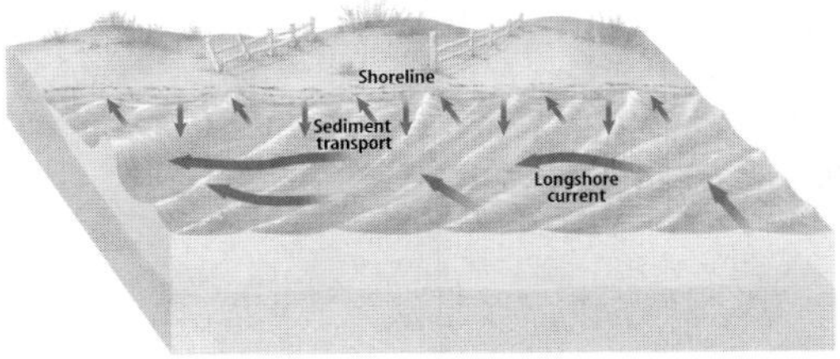

19. **PART A** How does a longshore current form?

    PART B Explain how a longshore current affects erosion and deposition.

chapter 21 Standardized Test Practice

Short Response

12. Water enters cracks in the rocks where it then freezes. As the water freezes, it expands, forcing the cracks apart.
13. Steep slopes cause thin, poor-quality soils. As slope decreases, thicker soil horizons will develop.
14. Vegetation provides a supply of organic material for the soil.
15. All of the land area that gathers water for the river.
16. At the mouth of a stream where it empties into another body of water, sediment is deposited in a fan-shaped deposit.
17. Water flow is the slowest at the inside of a bend in a stream. When the water flow slows, sediment is deposited forming a bar.
18. A glacier acts like a bulldozer, scrapping, gouging, and plucking soil and surface rocks.

Extended Response

19. **Part A:** Movement of water parallel to the shoreline is caused by the refraction of waves that approach the shoreline at an angle.

    Part B: As water recedes from the beach, it erodes material and carries it out to sea. As the water approaches the beach at an angle, it transports and deposits that material farther downcurrent.

Rubrics

For more help evaluating Short- and Extended-Response questions, see the rubrics on p. 9T.

unit 6

Unit Contents

WebQuest ***Chemistry of Fireworks*** is designed to engage students in researching the chemical components of fireworks, how chemicals are used to produce different colors, the history of fireworks, and how firework displays are created. Students will answer a set of questions following their Web research to demonstrate the knowledge they have gained.

unit 6 Interactions of Matter

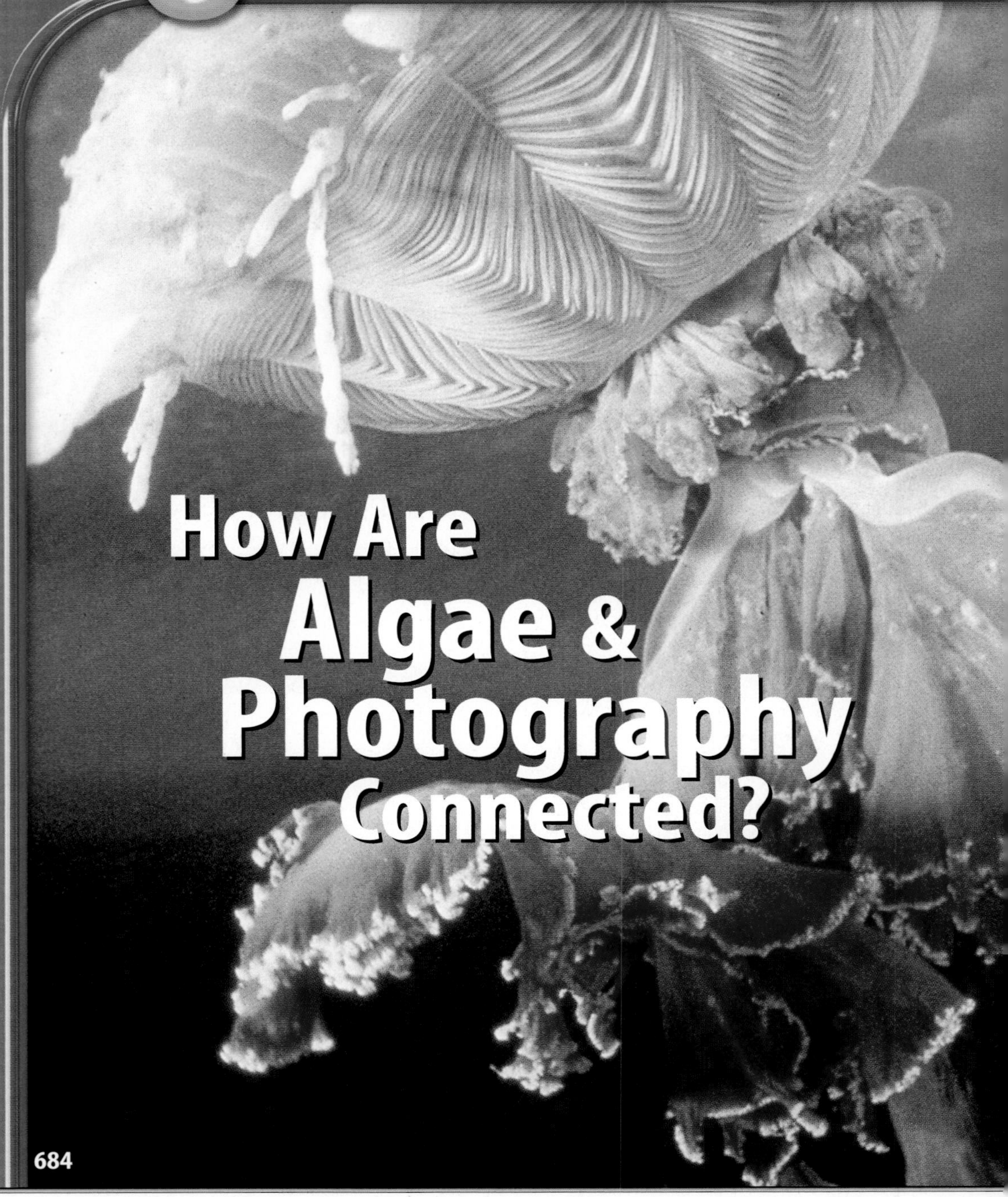

684

PROJECT CRISS[SM]

Study Skills

Organize Information Main idea-detail notes help students organize content from reading assignments. After studying solutions and chemical reactions, students use the two-column strategy. In the left column, students list a variety of acids and bases. In the right-hand column, students write pertinent details about each, such as the properties, pH, and uses.

Main Idea	Detail
Acid	Properties: • ____________ • ____________ pH: __________ Uses: __________
Base	

NATIONAL GEOGRAPHIC

In the mid-1800s, scientists experimented with light-sensitive chemicals. They found that when paper was treated with such chemicals and then exposed to light, the resulting reaction changed the paper's color. If an object blocked some of the light, a silhouette of the object was created. One set of chemicals produced prints—called cyanotypes—of white images on a blue background. A botanist named Anna Atkins saw the potential of this process. Until that time, the only way to create pictures of plants had been to draw them. Atkins used cyanotypes to create impressions of the plants. In 1843, she published a book of cyanotype images of algae, including the two seen at lower right. It was the first book ever to be illustrated by photography. Since Atkins' time, photography has gone through many changes. But it is still a powerful tool for making images of the natural world—which includes this giant jellyfish, whose image is being captured by an underwater photographer.

unit projects

Visit unit projects at gpescience.com to find project ideas and resources.
Projects include:

- **Career** Explore careers in space travel. Design a creative want-ad and work as a class to compile a mock newspaper classified section.
- **Technology** Discover what elements are used to make salts, how they are made, where they can be found, and where they are used. Create a formula for personal bath salts or salt scrubs.
- **Model** Research the Mars rovers. Design blueprints, and construct a model with moveable parts.

WebQuest *Chemistry of Fireworks* explores the chemical compounds of fireworks, what chemicals are used, and how firework displays are created.

NATIONAL GEOGRAPHIC How Are Algae & Photography Connected?

- Students are probably familiar with a specific application of the cyanotype process—blueprints. If any of their families have blueprints of their homes, have students share them with the class.
- Ask students to hypothesize how cyanotypes can be used to photocopy something. The item to be photocopied can be placed over treated paper and then exposed to light. Tell students that this type of copying was first done in the mid-1800s.
- Tell students that they will study many such interactions of matter and energy. All chemical reactions involve energy transfer.

unit projects

Career Have students explore the field of astro-geology, cosmology, aerospace engineering, or other space travel careers. Using the information they have gathered, students may design a creative want-ad advertising an employment opportunity. A class mock newspaper classified section may be compiled to share student work.

Technology Assign a specific salt to a pair of students. Using a variety of resources, have students research what elements are used to make their salt, how it is made, where it can be found, and where it is used. Some students may be interested in researching bath salts and their popularity in today's society. Salt research suggestions might include:
sodium chloride ($NaCl$),
potassium chloride (KCl),
ammonium chloride (NH_4Cl),
magnesium sulfate ($MgSO_4$),
sodium sulfate (Na_2SO_4),
potassium acetate (CH_3CO_2K),
sodium nitrate ($NaNO_3$),
barium sulfate ($BaSO_4$),
copper(II) acetate ($Cu(CH_3CO_2)$),
or ammonium sulfate
($(NH_4)_2SO_4$).

Model In small groups, have students research the Mars rovers. Students may design blueprints of an electronic robot including remote controls and the capability to move, scoop, and retrieve. Actual working models may be possible using donated and recycled materials.

Additional Resources Visit unit projects at gpescience.com for more information, resources, and assessment rubrics.

chapter 22 Organizer

Section/Objectives	Standards: National	Standards: State/Local	Labs/Features
Chapter Opener	See pp. 16T–17T for a Key to Standards		**Launch Lab:** Chemical Bonds and Mixing, p. 687 **Foldables,** p. 687
Section 1 Stability in Bonding 2 sessions 1 block 1. **Describe** how a compound differs from its component elements. 2. **Explain** what a chemical formula represents. 3. **Explain** that the electric forces between electrons and protrons, which are oppositely charged, are essential to forming compounds. 4. **State** a reason why chemical bonding occurs.	National Content Standards: UCP.1–3, UCP.5, A.1, A.2, B.2, B.4, B.6		**Science Online,** p. 691 **Lab:** Atomic Trading Cards, p. 693
Section 2 Types of Bonds 3 sessions 1.5 blocks 5. **Describe** ionic bonds and covalent bonds. 6. **Identify** the particles produced by ionic bonding and by covalent bonding. 7. **Distinguish** between a nonpolar covalent bond and a polar covalent bond.	National Content Standards: UCP.1–3, UCP.5, A.1, A.2, B.2, B.4, B.6, F.1		**Integrate Life Science,** p. 695 **MiniLAB:** Observing a Bond Type, p. 698 **Visualizing Polar Molecules,** p. 699
Section 3 Writing Formulas and Naming Compounds 3 sessions 1.5 blocks 8. **Explain** how to determine oxidation numbers. 9. **Write** formulas and names for ionic compounds. 10. **Write** formulas and names for covalent compounds.	National Content Standards: UCP.1–3, UCP.5, A.1, A.2, B.4, B.6, G.3		**Integrate History,** p. 705 **Applying Math:** Determing a Formula, p. 705 **Applying Science:** Can you name binary ionic compounds?, p. 706 **MiniLAB:** Making a Hydrate, p. 708 Video Lab **Lab:** Modeling Chemical Bonding, pp. 710–711 **Oops! Accidents in Science:** A Sticky Subject, p. 712

StudentWorks Plus

Glencoe Exclusive! TeacherWorks™ All-In-One Planner and Resource Center

Lab Materials	Reproducible Resources	Section Assessment	Technology
Launch Lab: water, vegetable oil, rubbing alcohol, food dye, 100-mL graduated cylinder, dropper	**Chapter *Fast File* Resources** Foldables Worksheet, p. 17 Directed Reading Overview, p. 19 Note-taking Worksheets, pp. 33–35	Glencoe's Assessment Advantage	TeacherWorks includes: • Interactive Teacher Edition • Lesson Planner with calendar • Access to all program blacklines • Correlations to standards • Web links
Lab: 4-in × 6-in cards, periodic table *Need materials?* Contact Science Kit at 1-800-828-7777 or www.sciencekit.com.	**Chapter *Fast File* Resources** Transparency Activity, p. 44 Enrichment, p. 30 Reinforcement, p. 27 Directed Reading, p. 20 Lab Worksheets, pp. 5–6 Lab Activity, pp. 9–12 **Cultural Diversity,** p. 69	**Portfolio** Assessment, p. 687 Differentiated Instruction, p. 690 **Performance** Applying Math, p. 692 **Content** Section Review, p. 692	Section Focus Transparency Interactive Chalkboard CD-ROM StudentWorks Plus
MiniLAB: inflated balloon, wool or fur, running water	**Chapter *Fast File* Resources** Transparency Activity, p. 45 MiniLAB, p. 3 Enrichment, p. 31 Reinforcement, p. 28 Directed Reading, p. 20 Lab Activity, pp. 13–16 **Science Inquiry Labs,** pp. 43–44	**Portfolio** Differentiated Instruction, p. 699 **Performance** MiniLAB, p. 708 Applying Math, p. 702 **Content** Section Review, p. 702	Section Focus Transparency Virtual Labs CD-ROM Interactive Chalkboard CD-ROM StudentWorks Plus
MiniLAB: plaster of paris, water, small bowl, rubber hammer, hair dryer **Lab:** small samples of crushed ice, table salt, and sugar; wire test-tube holder; test tubes; laboratory burner; stopwatch	**Chapter *Fast File* Resources** Transparency Activity, p. 46 MiniLAB, p. 4 Enrichment, p. 32 Reinforcement, p. 29 Directed Reading, pp. 21, 22 Transparency Activity, pp. 47–48 Lab Worksheets, pp. 7–8	**Portfolio** Cultural Diversity, p. 707 **Performance** Applying Math, p. 705 Applying Science, p. 706 MiniLAB, p. 708 Applying Math, p. 709 **Content** Section Review, p. 709	Section Focus Transparency Teaching Transparency Interactive Chalkboard CD-ROM StudentWorks Plus Video Lab

End of Chapter Assessment

Blackline Masters	Technology	Professional Series
Chapter *Fast File* Resources Chapter Review, pp. 37–38 Chapter Tests, pp. 39–42 **Standardized Test Practice,** pp. 92–95	MindJogger Videoquiz Virtual Labs CD-ROM Exam*View*® Pro Testmaker TeacherWorks CD-ROM Interactive Chalkboard CD-ROM	**Performance Assessment in the Science Classroom (PASC)**

Transparencies

Section Focus

Section 1 Section Focus Transparency — Picking Up the Pieces — Chapter 22

Jigsaw puzzles can have hundreds—even thousands—of pieces. To complete the puzzle, you need to infer how each piece fits together. Size, shape, and markings all give clues as to how the pieces should be placed to make a picture.

1. Where do the remaining pieces belong? How do you know?
2. How might a compound and its individual elements compare to a puzzle and its pieces?

L2

Section 2 Section Focus Transparency — A Crystal Nature — Chapter 22

This picture shows salt crystals on the Dead Sea shore. When a salt crystal is pure, it is in the shape of a colorless cube. Impurities can make salt appear to be different colors, like white or gray. Table salt is a compound of sodium and chlorine.

1. Describe the appearance of the salt in the picture.
2. What happens to salt in water? How might you recover salt from ocean water?
3. How do people use salt?

L2

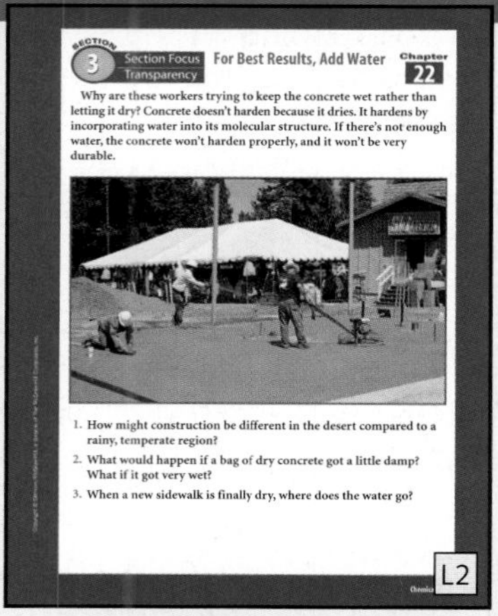
Section 3 Section Focus Transparency — For Best Results, Add Water — Chapter 22

Why are these workers trying to keep the concrete wet rather than letting it dry? Concrete doesn't harden because it dries. It hardens by incorporating water into its molecular structure. If there's not enough water, the concrete won't harden properly, and it won't be very durable.

1. How might construction be different in the desert compared to a rainy, temperate region?
2. What would happen if a bag of dry concrete got a little damp? What if it got very wet?
3. When a new sidewalk is finally dry, where does the water go?

L2

This is a representation of key blackline masters available in the Teacher Classroom Resources. See Resource Manager boxes within the chapter for additional information.

Assessment

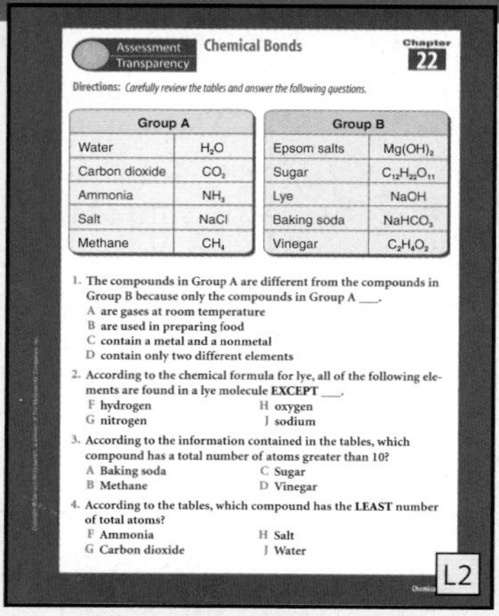
Assessment Transparency — Chemical Bonds — Chapter 22

Directions: Carefully review the tables and answer the following questions.

Group A	
Water	H_2O
Carbon dioxide	CO_2
Ammonia	NH_3
Salt	NaCl
Methane	CH_4

Group B	
Epsom salts	$Mg(OH)_2$
Sugar	$C_{12}H_{22}O_{11}$
Lye	NaOH
Baking soda	$NaHCO_3$
Vinegar	$C_2H_4O_2$

1. The compounds in Group A are different from the compounds in Group B because only the compounds in Group A ___.
A are gases at room temperature
B are used in preparing food
C contain a metal and a nonmetal
D contain only two different elements
2. According to the chemical formula for lye, all of the following elements are found in a lye molecule EXCEPT ___.
F hydrogen H oxygen
G nitrogen J sodium
3. According to the information contained in the tables, which compound has a total number of atoms greater than 10?
A Baking soda C Sugar
B Methane D Vinegar
4. According to the tables, which compound has the LEAST number of total atoms?
F Ammonia H Salt
G Carbon dioxide J Water

L2

Teaching

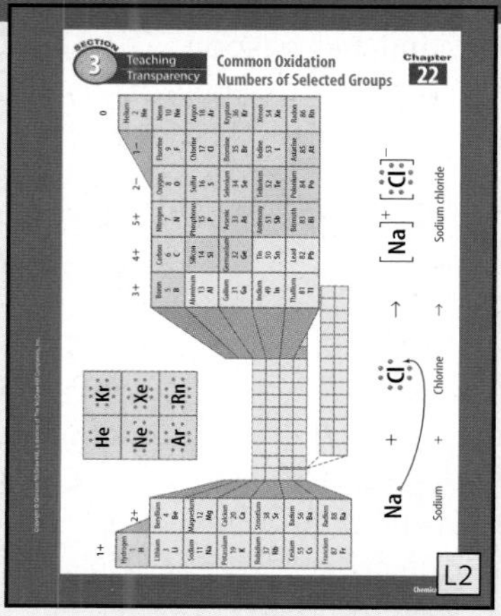
Section 3 Teaching Transparency — Common Oxidation Numbers of Selected Groups — Chapter 22

L2

Key to Teaching Strategies

The following designations will help you decide which activities are appropriate for your students.

- L1 Level 1 activities should be appropriate for students with learning difficulties.
- L2 Level 2 activities should be within the ability range of all students.
- L3 Level 3 activities are designed for above-average students.
- ELL ELL activities should be within the ability range of English Language Learners.
- COOP LEARN Cooperative Learning activities are designed for small group work.
- LS Multiple Learning Styles logos, as described on page 12T, are used throughout to indicate strategies that address different learning styles.
- P These strategies represent student products that can be placed into a best-work portfolio.
- PBL Problem-Based Learning activities apply real-world situations to learning.

Hands-on Activities

Student Text Lab Worksheet

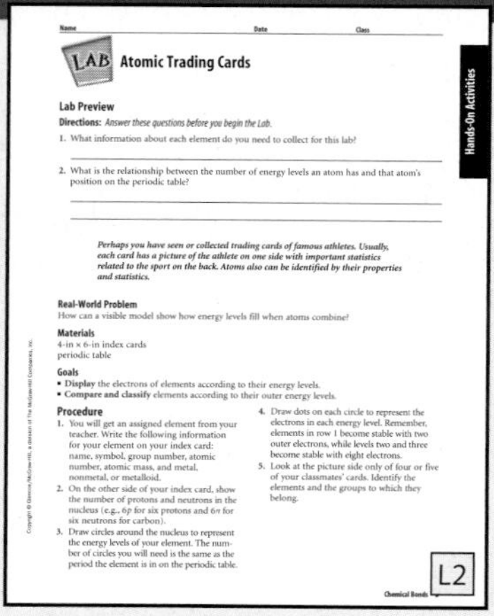
LAB Atomic Trading Cards

Lab Preview

L2

Laboratory Activities

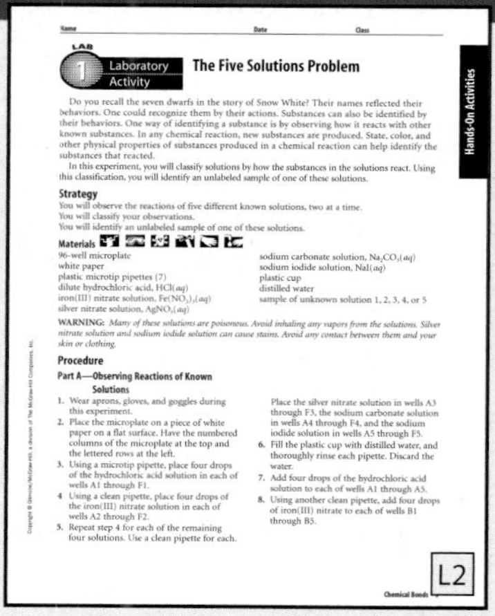
Laboratory Activity 1 — The Five Solutions Problem

L2

Meeting Different Ability Levels

Content Outline

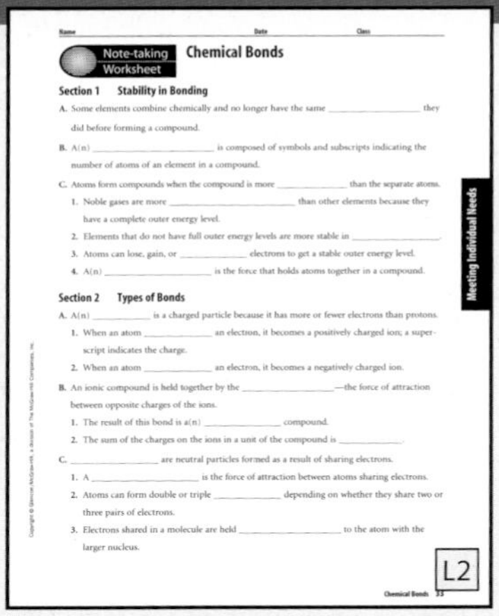
Note-taking Worksheet
Chemical Bonds
Section 1 Stability in Bonding
Section 2 Types of Bonds
L2

Reinforcement

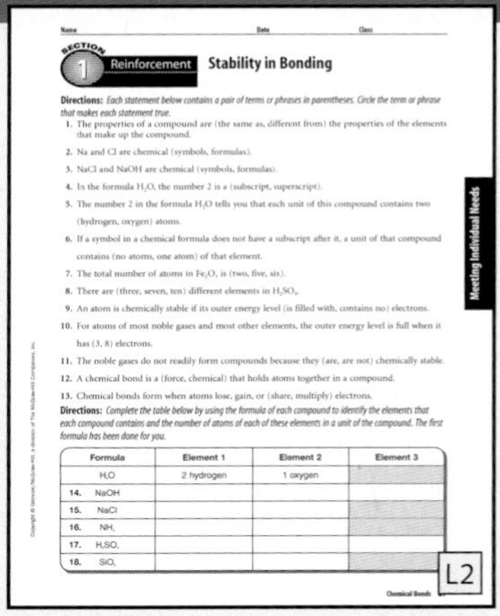
Section 1 Reinforcement
Stability in Bonding
L2

Enrichment

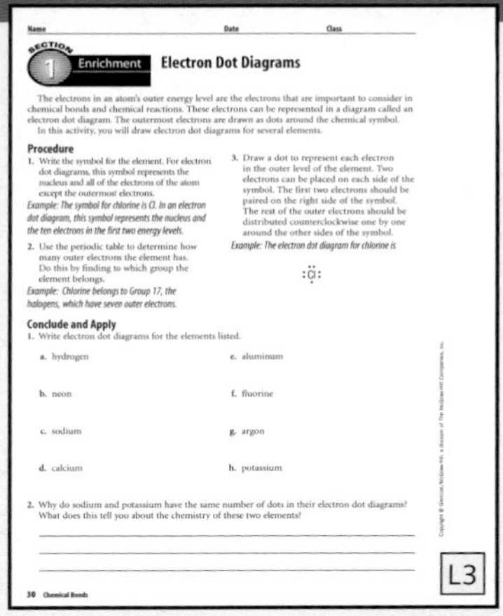
Section 1 Enrichment
Electron Dot Diagrams
Procedure
Conclude and Apply
L3

Directed Reading (English/Spanish)

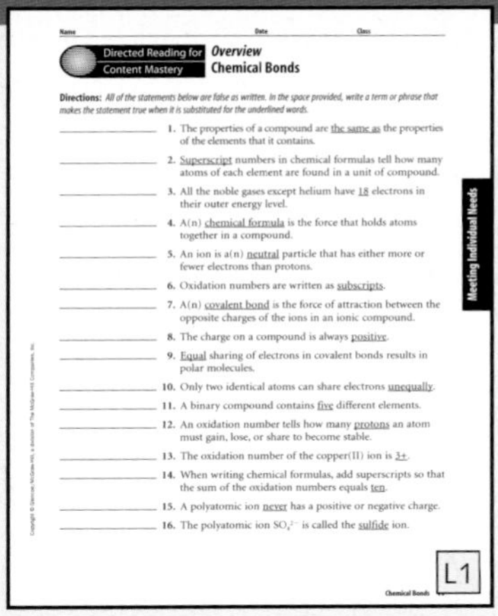
Directed Reading for Content Mastery
Overview
Chemical Bonds
L1

Study Guide

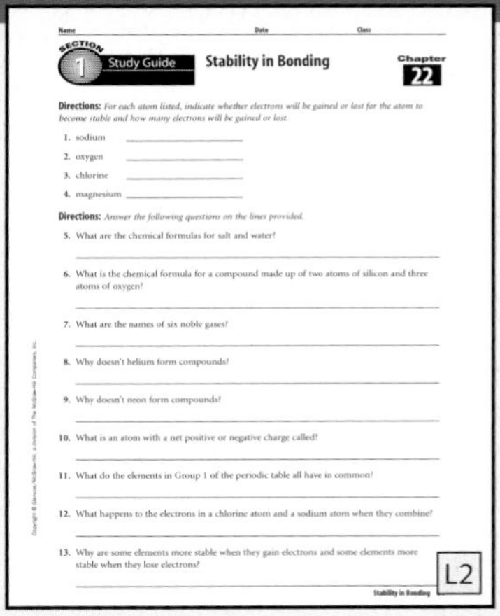
Section 1 Study Guide
Stability in Bonding
Chapter 22
L2

Reading Essentials

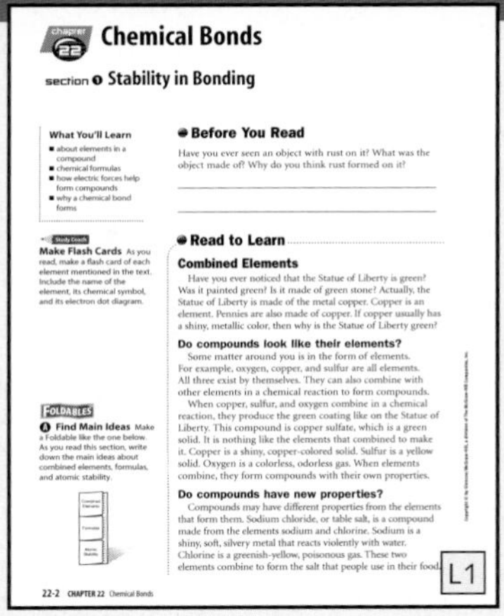
Chapter 22 Chemical Bonds
section 1 Stability in Bonding
Before You Read
Read to Learn
Combined Elements
Do compounds look like their elements?
Do compounds have new properties?
L1

Assessment

Test Practice Workbook

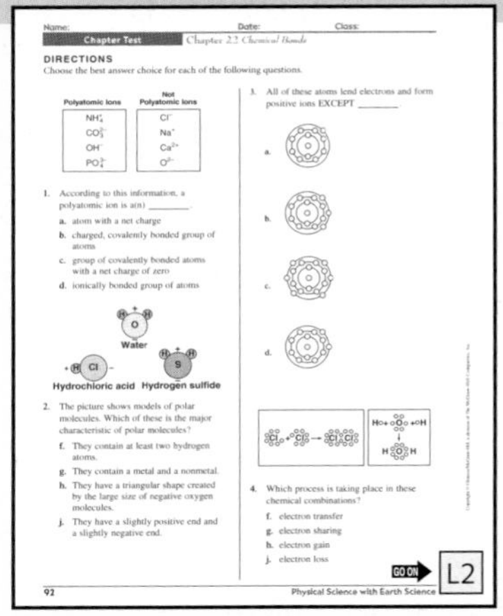
Chapter Test
Chapter 22 Chemical Bonds
DIRECTIONS
L2

Chapter Review

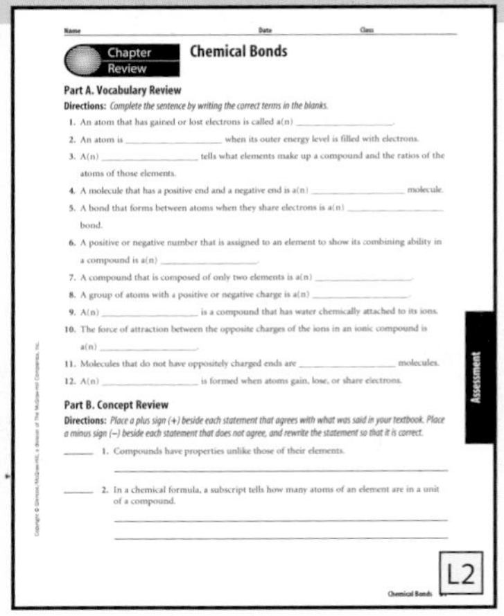
Chapter Review
Chemical Bonds
Part A. Vocabulary Review
Part B. Concept Review
L2

Chapter Tests

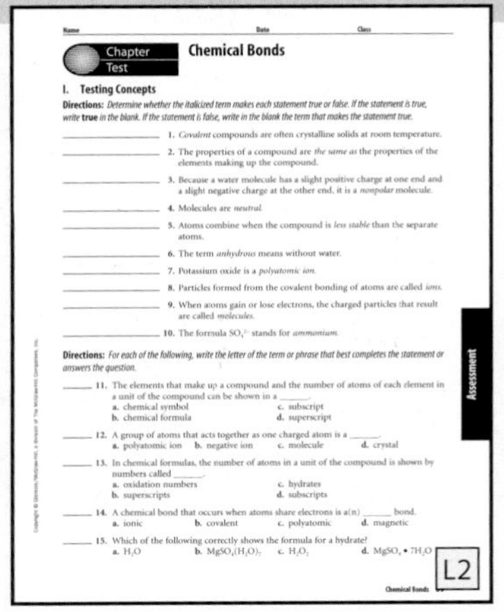
Chapter Test
Chemical Bonds
I. Testing Concepts
L2

Science Content Background

section 1 Stability in Bonding

Atomic Stability

Atoms undergo rearrangements of electrons to become more stable. This concept forms the basis for understanding chemical bonding. The most stable configuration of electrons is found in the noble gases. Atoms gain, lose, or share electrons, some more easily than others, so that they have the same electron configurations as the noble gases. For example, a chlorine atom gains an electron (Cl^-) and attains an electron structure like the chemically stable noble gas argon. Sodium loses one of its 11 electrons (Na^+) to attain an electron structure like neon. In general, metals tend to form positively charged ions (lose electrons) and nonmetals form negatively charged ions (gain electrons).

section 2 Types of Bonds

Electron Dot Structures

One of the most convenient ways to picture the sharing of electrons between atoms in covalent or polar covalent bonds is to use electron dot structures. Electron dot structures are often called Lewis structures, after American chemist G. N. Lewis (1875–1946), who invented this symbolism. Electron dot structures represent an atom's outer-level, or valence, electrons by dots. Atoms form covalent bonds by sharing electron pairs, with the resulting molecules drawn by assigning the correct number of valence electrons to each atom. Group 13 atoms have three valence electrons, Group 14 atoms have four valence electrons, and so on across the periodic table.

Group 18 elements, such as neon and argon, rarely form covalent bonds because they have a stable configuration of eight electrons in their outer energy levels. This is called the octet rule—representative elements react so that they attain eight electrons in their outer energy level.

Lewis dot structures can be used to model covalent bonding and predict the number of bonds between atoms in a compound. For example, in N_2, the atoms share three pairs of electrons. Each pair represents a bond, so N_2 has a triple bond. Multiple bonds are shorter and stronger than single bonds because there are more electrons holding the nuclei together.

Although Lewis dot structures are accurate models of bonding for most compounds, laboratory data from some compounds do not always agree with conclusions drawn from these models. This is the case with O_2. The Lewis dot structure predicts that O_2 will contain a double bond and four electron pairs. Bond length studies have shown that the O_2 bond length is consistent with that of a double bond. However, O_2 is known to be paramagnetic (it has unpaired electrons). This apparent discrepancy has been resolved by applying quantum-based molecular orbital (MO) theory.

Barry L. Runk/Grant Heilman Photography, Inc.

Electronegativity

When two different kinds of atoms share a pair of electrons, a bond forms in which electrons are shared unequally. The attractive force that an atom of an element has for shared electrons in a molecule is known as its electronegativity. Nobel laureate Linus Pauling (1901–1994) developed a scale of relative electronegativities, in which the most electronegative element, fluorine, is assigned a value of 4.0. The higher the electronegativity, the stronger an atom attracts electrons within a bond. Electronegativity generally increases from left to right across a period and decreases down a group for typical elements.

Teacher to Teacher
Mark Resch,
Ripon High School
Ripon, Wisconsin

"I balance an 8-inch piece of 2 × 4 lumber on a watch glass. Then, I induce a charge in an inflated balloon by rubbing it in my hair. I hold the charged balloon to the side near one end of the 2 × 4. The balloon will be attracted to the wood. I move the balloon to the other side to reverse direction. Unless the air is very humid, this will work."

Mark Resch

Polar or Nonpolar?

A general knowledge of electronegativities can be used to make predictions about bond polarity. A general guideline is that bonds between atoms with the same or similar values are nonpolar covalent, bonds between atoms whose values differ by more than 1.7 are substantially ionic, and bonds between atoms whose values differ by less than 1.7 are polar covalent. At the extreme, one or more electrons are actually transferred and an ionic bond results. It is important to realize that bonding is a continuum—the difference between ionic and covalent is a gradual change.

chapter content resources

Internet Resources
For additional content background, visit gpescience.com to:
- access your book online
- find references to related articles in popular science magazines
- access Web links with related content background
- access current events with science journal topics

Print Resources
Chemistry; The Molecular Nature of Matter and Change, by Martin S. Silberberg, McGraw-Hill, 2003
Structure and Bonding, by Jack Barrett and Eddie Abel, Wiley, John & Sons, Incorporated, 2002

section 3 Writing Formulas and Naming Compounds

Hydrates

The best-known hydrates are crystalline solids that lose their structure upon removal of their bound water. Although the number of molecules of water in a given hydrate is fixed, some substances can form several different hydrates. For example, there are four different hydrates of iron (II) sulfate, each with separate and unique physical properties.

chapter 22

Chapter Vocabulary

chemical formula, p. 689
ion, p. 692
chemical bond, p. 694
ionic bond, p. 696
covalent bond, p. 697
molecule, p. 697
polar molecule, p. 700
nonpolar molecule, p. 700
binary compound, p. 703
oxidation number, p. 703
polyatomic ion, p. 707
hydrate, p. 708

Science Journal Sample answer: Glue joins separate pieces together to form a stable object. Atoms bond with other atoms to form molecules and compounds. The glue that holds atoms together is the chemical bond.

INTERACTIVE CHALKBOARD with Image Bank

PowerPoint® Presentations

This CD-ROM is an editable Microsoft® PowerPoint® presentation that includes:

- a pre-made presentation for every chapter
- interactive graphics
- animations
- audio clips
- image bank
- all new section and chapter questions
- Standardized Test Practice
- transparencies
- Foldables directions
- links to gpescience.com

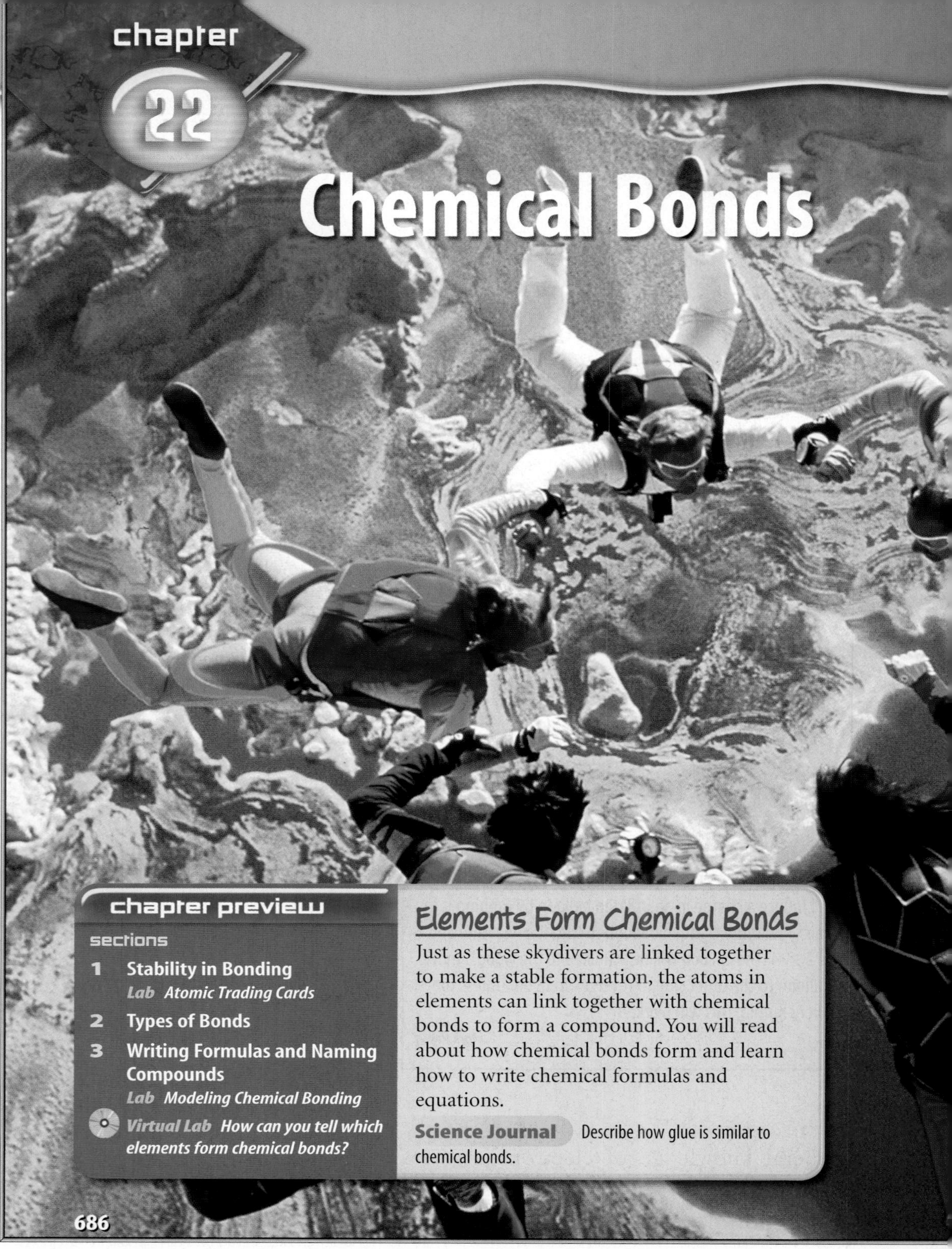

chapter 22

Chemical Bonds

chapter preview

sections

Elements Form Chemical Bonds

Just as these skydivers are linked together to make a stable formation, the atoms in elements can link together with chemical bonds to form a compound. You will read about how chemical bonds form and learn how to write chemical formulas and equations.

Science Journal Describe how glue is similar to chemical bonds.

686

Theme Connection

Stability and Change The relationship between an atom's electronic structure and its stability is described in this chapter. Chemical bonding enables atoms to become stable. Chemical changes take place when existing bonds are broken and new bonds form.

About the Photo

Bond Strength Use the analogy of these skydivers gripping hands to associate bond strength with the formation of stable and unstable formations.

Start-Up Activities

Launch Lab

Chemical Bonds and Mixing

You probably have noticed that some liquids such as oil-and-vinegar salad dressings will not stay mixed after the bottle is shaken. However, rubbing alcohol and water will mix. The compounds that make up the two liquids are different. This lab will demonstrate the influence the types of chemical bonds have on how the compounds mix.

1. Pour 20 mL of water into a 100-mL graduated cylinder.
2. Pour 20 mL of vegetable oil into the same cylinder. Vigorously swirl the two liquids together, and observe for several minutes.
3. Add two drops of food dye and observe.
4. After several minutes, slowly pour 30 mL of rubbing alcohol into the cylinder.
5. Add two more drops of food dye and observe.
6. **Think Critically** In your Science Journal, write a paragraph describing how the different liquids mixed. Would your final results be different if you added the liquids in a different order? Explain.

FOLDABLES™ Study Organizer

Chemical Formulas Every compound has a chemical formula that tells exactly which elements are present in that compound and exactly how many atoms of each element are present in that compound. Make the following Foldable to help identify the chemical formulas in this chapter.

STEP 1 **Fold** a sheet of notebook paper vertically from side to side.

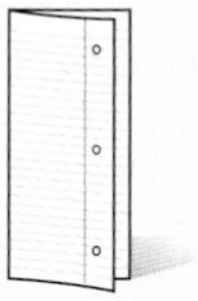

STEP 2 **Cut** along every third line of only the top layer to form tabs.

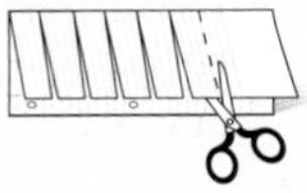

Read and Write Go through the chapter, find ten chemical formulas, and write them on the front of the tabs. As you read the chapter, write what compound each formula represents under the appropriate tab.

Science Online — Preview this chapter's content and activities at gpescience.com

Launch Lab

Purpose Use the Launch Lab to introduce students to the interaction between liquids with polar bonds and liquids with nonpolar bonds. L2 LS **Visual-Spatial**

Preparation Prepare small beakers of each liquid for each group.

Materials two 100-mL graduated cylinders, water, vegetable oil, rubbing alcohol, food dye, dropper

Teaching Strategy Explain that the molecules in water, food dye, and rubbing alcohol have polar chemical bonds, but the molecules in vegetable oil have nonpolar chemical bonds.

Think Critically

When the oil was added to the water and the cylinder was shaken, the oil formed bubbles that quickly separated from the water when the cylinder was allowed to sit. The oil then formed a layer on top of the water. The drops of food dye moved through the nonpolar oil as droplets. Once the drops of food dye passed through the oil/water boundary, they mixed with the water molecules, exploding with color. The alcohol, which is polar, remained on top of the oil, and the food dye dissolved in it immediately.

Assessment

Portfolio Ask students to draw a labeled diagram of their graduated cylinder filled with liquids. Use **Performance Assessment in the Science Classroom**, p. 127.

FOLDABLES™ Study Organizer **Dinah Zike Study Fold**

Student preparation materials for this Foldable are available in the **Chapter *Fast File* Resources.**

1 Motivate

An editable Microsoft® PowerPoint® presentation is available on **Interactive Chalkboard** CD-ROM.

Bellringer

Section Focus Transparencies also are available on the Interactive Chalkboard CD-ROM.

L2 ELL

SECTION 1 Section Focus Transparency — Picking Up the Pieces — Chapter 22

Jigsaw puzzles can have hundreds—even thousands—of pieces. To complete the puzzle, you need to infer how each piece fits together. Size, shape, and markings all give clues as to how the pieces should be placed to make a picture.

1. **Where do the remaining pieces belong? How do you know?**
2. **How might a compound and its individual elements compare to a puzzle and its pieces?**

L2

Chemical Bonds

Reading Preview

Tie to Prior Knowledge

Jigsaw Puzzle Have students consider how pieces of a jigsaw puzzle fit together in an orderly, exact way. Explain that it is possible to predict how atoms of different elements fit together in an exact way. As an example, discuss how water forms when two parts hydrogen combine with one part oxygen. The "parts" in this case are atoms that form chemical bonds with one another.

Content-Specific Words Ask students to create cartoons that describe each of the vocabulary words. For *ion*, students might draw an atom character giving away the letter "e," which represents an electron.

section 1

Stability in Bonding

Reading Guide

What You'll Learn

- **Describe** how a compound differs from its component elements.
- **Explain** what a chemical formula represents.
- **Explain** that the electric forces between electrons and protons, which are oppositely charged, are essential to forming compounds.
- **State** a reason why chemical bonding occurs.

Why It's Important

The millions of different kinds of matter around us are a result of chemical bonds.

Review Vocabulary

compound: substance formed from two or more elements in which the exact combination and proportion of elements is always the same

New Vocabulary

- chemical formula
- ion

Figure 1 The difference between the elemental copper metal and the copper compound formed on the Statue of Liberty is striking.

Combined Elements

Have you noticed the color of the Statue of Liberty? It is green. The Statue of Liberty is made of copper, which is an element. Uncombined, elemental copper is a bright, shiny copper color. When copper is exposed to the weather over a long period of time, the metal combines with substances in the atmosphere and changes color.

Compounds Some of the matter around you is in the form of uncombined elements such as copper, sulfur, and oxygen. However, like many other sets of elements, these three elements can unite chemically to form a compound when the conditions are right. The green coating on the Statue of Liberty and some old pennies is a result of this chemical change. One compound in this coating, seen in contrast with the elemental copper in **Figure 1,** is a compound called copper sulfate. Copper sulfate isn't shiny and copper colored like elemental copper. Nor is it a pale-yellow solid like sulfur or a colorless, odorless gas like oxygen. It has its own unique properties.

Section 1 Resource Manager

Chapter *FAST FILE* Resources

- Transparency Activity, p. 44
- Directed Reading for Content Mastery, pp. 19–20
- Note-taking Worksheets, pp. 33–35
- Lab Activity, pp. 9–12
- Enrichment, p. 30
- Reinforcement, p. 27
- Lab Worksheet, pp. 5–6

Cultural Diversity, p. 69

Physical Science Critical Thinking/Problem Solving, p. 1

New Properties An observation you will make is that the compound formed when elements combine often has chemical and physical properties that aren't anything like those of the individual elements. Sodium chloride, for example, shown in **Figure 2,** is a compound made from the elements sodium and chlorine. Sodium is a shiny, soft, silvery metal that reacts violently with water. Chlorine is a poisonous greenish yellow gas. Would you have guessed that these elements combine to make ordinary table salt?

Figure 2 Sodium is a soft, silvery metal that combines with chlorine, a greenish yellow gas, to form sodium chloride, which is a white crystalline solid. **Describe** *how the properties of table salt are different from those of sodium and chlorine.*

Formulas

The chemical symbols Na and Cl represent the elements sodium and chlorine. When written as NaCl, the symbols make up a formula, or chemical shorthand, for the compound sodium chloride. A **chemical formula** tells what elements a compound contains and the exact number of the atoms of each element in a unit of that compound. The compound that you are probably most familiar with is H_2O, commonly known as water. This formula contains the symbols H for the element hydrogen and O for the element oxygen. Notice the number 2 written as a subscript after the H for hydrogen. *Subscript* means "written below." A subscript written after a symbol tells how many atoms of that element are in a unit of the compound. If a symbol has no subscript, the unit contains only one atom of that element. A unit of H_2O contains two hydrogen atoms and one oxygen atom.

Look at the formulas for each compound listed in **Table 1.** What elements combine to form each compound? How many atoms of each element are required to form each of the compounds?

Table 1 Some Familiar Compounds

Familiar Name	Chemical Name	Formula
Sand	Silicon dioxide	SiO_2
Milk of magnesia	Magnesium hydroxide	$Mg(OH)_2$
Cane sugar	Sucrose	$C_{12}H_{22}O_{11}$
Lime	Calcium oxide	CaO
Vinegar	Acetic acid	CH_3COOH
Laughing gas	Dinitrogen oxide	N_2O
Grain alcohol	Ethanol	C_2H_5OH
Battery acid	Sulfuric acid	H_2SO_4
Stomach acid	Hydrochloric acid	HCl

Reading Check *Describe what a chemical formula tells you.*

2 Teach

Caption Answer

Figure 2 Table salt is a stable, white solid. Sodium is very reactive with water, silver in color, soft, and a metal. Chlorine is a poisonous, greenish-yellow gas.

Discussion

Similar Formulas Point out that H_2O and H_2O_2 have similar chemical formulas. Does this mean they are similar compounds? Explain. They are not similar compounds. The addition of one oxygen atom changes H_2O (water), a substance that is critical for life, into H_2O_2 (hydrogen peroxide), a substance that is used as a disinfectant and quickly reacts with many other compounds. L1 LS **Logical-Mathematical**

Text Question Answer

sand: 1 atom of silicon (Si), 2 of oxygen (O); milk of magnesia: 1 atom of magnesium (Mg), 2 of oxygen (O), 2 of hydrogen (H); cane sugar: 12 atoms of carbon (C), 22 of hydrogen (H), 11 of oxygen (O); lime: 1 atom (ion) of calcium (Ca), 1 of oxygen (O); vinegar: 2 atoms of carbon (C), 2 of oxygen (O), and 4 of hydrogen (H); laughing gas: 2 atoms of nitrogen (N), 1 of oxygen (O); grain alcohol: 2 atoms of carbon (C), 6 of hydrogen (H), 1 of oxygen (O); battery acid: 2 atoms of hydrogen (H), 1 of sulfur (S), 4 of oxygen (O); stomach acid: 1 atom of hydrogen (H), 1 of chlorine (Cl) L2 LS **Logical-Mathematical**

Reading Check

Answer tells what elements are present in a compound and the exact number of the atoms of each element in a unit of that compound

Reading Strategy

Preview Prior to reading, ask students to scan the text. remind them to notice figures and bold print. Provide discussion prompts such as the following, to heighten interest: What does H_2O represent, and why do we use symbols?

Visual Learning

Figure 3 Have students predict whether each atom shown would more likely gain or lose electrons to form an octet. An atom with fewer than four electrons in the outer energy level tends to give up electrons, while those with more than four tend to gain electrons to form an octet. L1 **Visual-Spatial**

Use an Analogy

Gloves In a cold climate, each person would seek to have two gloves to keep his or her hands warm. Someone with fewer than two would try to get warm by gaining a glove or two. A person with more than two gloves might give up those not needed for warmth. Individuals with exactly two gloves would not be involved in any rearrangements. Similarly, some atoms give up electrons to have eight in their outer energy levels, while others must obtain electrons to have eight. An atom with exactly eight electrons in its outer level does not need to gain or lose electrons, so it does not participate in rearrangements of electrons between atoms. The atoms of all the nonreactive noble gases except helium have eight electrons in their outer energy levels. Helium's outer level is complete with two electrons.

Activity

Binary Compounds Have the students create binary compounds using the periodic chart. Then have the student research that compound and describe it to the other students.

Caption Answer

Figure 5 Group 18

Reading Check

Answer Helium has a full outer energy level and is chemcally stable.

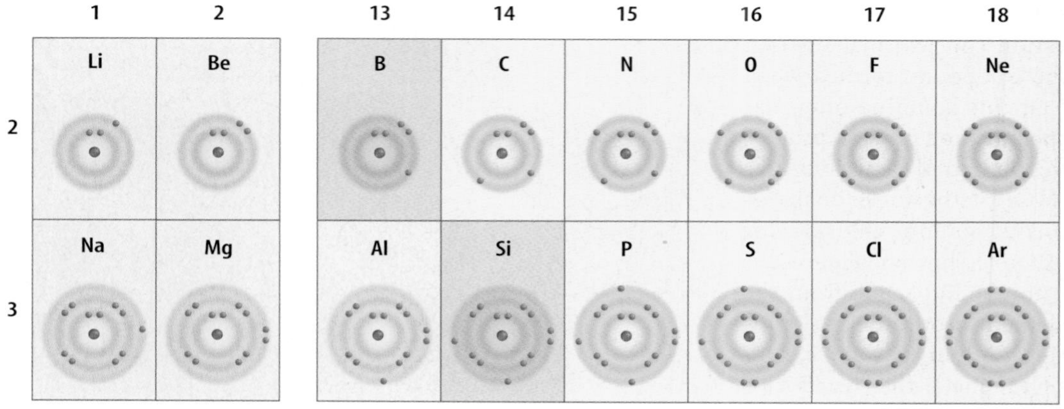

Figure 3 The number of electrons in each group's outer level increases across the table until the noble gases in Group 18, where each has a complete outer energy level.

Atomic Stability

Why do atoms form compounds? The electric forces between electrons and protons, which are oppositely charged, hold atoms and molecules together, and thus they are the forces that cause compounds to form. The periodic table on the inside back cover of your book lists the known elements. However, the six noble gases in Group 18 do not form compounds, or do so with difficulty. Atoms of noble gases are unusually stable. Compounds of these atoms rarely form because they are almost always less stable than the original atoms.

The Unique Noble Gases To understand the stability of the noble gases, it is helpful to look at electron dot diagrams across a period. Electron dot diagrams show only the electrons in the outer energy level of an atom. They contain the chemical symbol for the element surrounded by dots representing its outer electrons. How do you know how many dots to make? For Groups 1 and 2 and 13 through 18, you can use the periodic table or the portion of it shown in **Figure 3.** Elements in Group 1 each have one outer electron. Those in Group 2 each have two. Those in Group 13 each have three, those in Group 14, four, and so on to Group 18, the noble gases, which each have eight.

Chemical Stability An atom is chemically stable when its outermost energy level has the maximum number of electrons. The outer energy levels of helium and hydrogen are stable with two electrons. The outer energy levels of all the other elements are stable when they contain eight electrons. **Figure 4** shows electron dot diagrams of some of the noble gases. Notice that eight dots surround Kr, Ne, Xe, Ar, and Rn, and two dots surround He.

Figure 4 Electron dot diagrams of noble gases show that they each have a stable outer energy level.

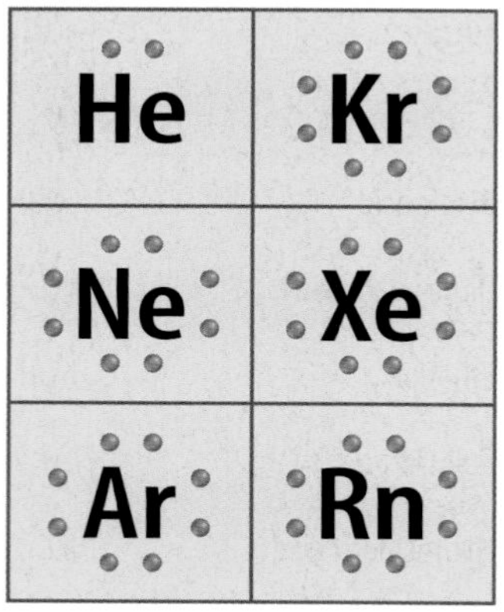

Teacher FYI

New Elements The number of known elements may change during your use of this text. Research teams in Dubna, Russia; Darmstadt, Germany; and Berkeley, California are working to synthesize new elements.

Differentiated Instruction

Challenge Some students will wonder why the text skips elements in Group 3 to Group 12 when talking about outer-level electrons. Encourage these students to research and write brief reports about why these transition metals are skipped. The outer energy levels of these elements are similar to those of elements in Groups 1 or 2. As electrons are added, they fill in incomplete lower electron energy levels. L3 IN **Linguistic** P

Energy Levels and Other Elements How do the dot diagrams represent other elements, and how does this relate to their ability to make compounds? Hydrogen and helium, the elements in period 1 of the periodic table, can hold a maximum of two electrons in their outer energy levels. Hydrogen contains one electron in its lone energy level. A dot diagram for hydrogen has a single dot next to its symbol. This means that hydrogen's outer energy level is not full. It is more stable when it is part of a compound.

In contrast, helium's outer energy level contains two electrons. Its dot diagram has two dots—a pair of electrons—next to its symbol. Helium has a full outer energy level and is chemically stable. Helium rarely forms compounds and the element is a commonly used gas.

When you look at the elements in Groups 13 through 17, you see that none of the elements has a stable energy level. Each group contains too few electrons for a stable level of eight electrons.

Reading Check *Why is it rare for helium to form a compound?*

Outer Levels—Getting Their Fill As you just learned, hydrogen is an element that does not have a full outer energy level. How does hydrogen, or any other element, become stable? Atoms with partially stable outer energy levels can lose, gain, or share electrons to obtain stable outer energy levels. They do this by combining with other atoms that also have partially complete outer energy levels. As a result, each becomes stable. **Figure 5** shows electron dot diagrams for sodium and chlorine. When they combine, sodium loses one electron and chlorine gains one electron. You can see from the electron dot diagram that chlorine now has a stable outer energy level, similar to a noble gas. But what about sodium?

Science Online

Topic: Dot Diagrams

Visit gpescience.com for Web links to information about using dot diagrams to represent outer energy level electrons.

Activity Draw a dot diagram of methane, CH_4.

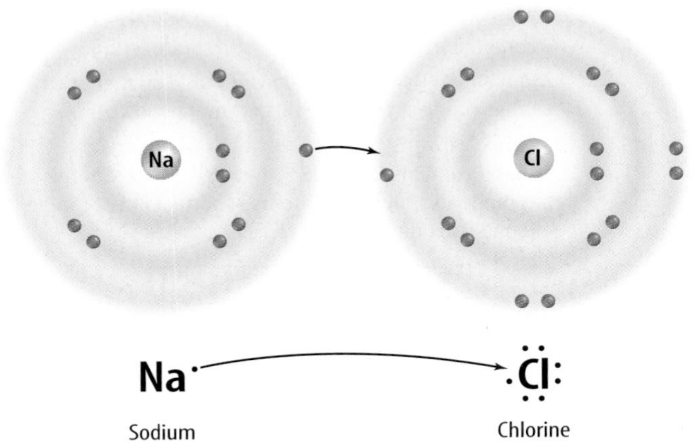

Figure 5 Sodium, as a Group 1 element, will lose one electron. It will have the same number of electrons as neon. Chlorine, which belongs to Group 17, will gain one electron. It will have the same number of electrons as argon.
Identify *the group number where neon and argon can be found.*

Quick Demo
Chemical Reactions

Materials calcium metal, 1 M HCl, beaker

Estimated Time 10 minutes

Safety Precautions

Procedure Place a pea-sized piece of calcium metal in a small amount of 1 M HCl. Have students note the production of bubbles as H_2 is given off. Carefully evaporate the liquid, leaving $CaCl_2$. On the board, write the dot diagram for the ions contained in this ionic compound. Both Ca^{2+} and Cl^- contain eight outer electrons. (If zinc metal is used instead of Ca, $ZnCl_2$ will form.) L2 ELL IN **Visual-Spatial**

Make a Model

Elements Have students use various colors of modeling clay to make spheres that represent metals and nonmetals. Tell them to use smaller spheres of a specific color to show electrons. Attach the correct number of electrons to each model sphere to represent the outer energy level of the selected atoms. Challenge students to use a periodic table to identify possible elements that each model represents. Then have them explain how the element in each model can obtain eight outer electrons through various combinations with other elements. L2 ELL IN **Kinesthetic**

Text Question Answer

Its outer level is filled, too.

Differentiated Instruction

Learning Disabled Prepare physical models of various atoms and have the students assemble them. Then they can see how the electrons are essential to forming stable chemical bonds between atoms.

Challenge Use dot diagrams with one carbon atom and two oxygen atoms to make an arrangement that gives the carbon and oxygen atoms an octet. Place carbon in the center and make double bonds between the carbon and oxygen atoms. In this arrangement, the carbon atom shares two electrons with one oxygen atom and two with the other. Each oxygen atom shares two electrons with the carbon atom. L3 IN **Visual-Spatial**

Fun Fact

The minimum amount of energy needed to remove the outermost (highest energy) electron from a neutral atom in the gaseous state is referred to as the first ionization potential.

Post Reading

Fix-Up Strategy Choose a challenging piece of text and read it aloud while interjecting questions and strategies to aid comprehension. Show students how to use reflated figures to help unlock the text. Then, have students find their own difficult passage and practice close reading with a partner.

3 Assess

DAILY INTERVENTION

Check for Understanding

Logical-Mathematical Have students review the periodic table and identify which groups would most likely form binary compounds with each other. Then have them give examples of some of the possible binary compounds and draw the dot diagrams of each one.

Reteach

Electron Distribution Remind students that giving up electrons can sometimes provide a new outer level of eight electrons. Make a poster with sodium's electron distribution written out—two in the first level, eight in the second. Loosely tape a page with the single electron in the third energy level written on it over the poster. Demonstrate that when the outer page is removed (losing the electron), the new outer level is shown to contain eight electrons. L1 ELL IS **Visual-Spatial**

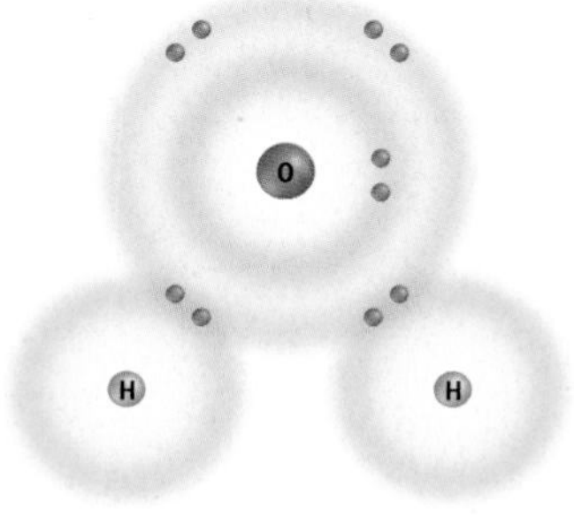

Figure 6 In water, hydrogen and oxygen each contribute one electron to each hydrogen-oxygen bond. The atoms share those electrons instead of giving them up.

Stability Is Reached Sodium had only one electron in its outer energy level, which it lost when it combined with chlorine to form sodium chloride. However, look back to the next, outermost energy level of sodium. This is now the new outer energy level, and it is stable with eight electrons. When the outer electron of sodium is removed, a complete inner energy level becomes the new outer energy level. Sodium and chlorine are stable now because of the exchange of an electron.

In the compound water, each hydrogen atom needs one electron to have a stable outer energy level. The oxygen atom needs two electrons for its outer level to be stable with eight electrons. Hydrogen and oxygen become stable and form bonds in a different way from sodium and chlorine. Instead of gaining or losing electrons, they share them. **Figure 6** shows how hydrogen and oxygen share electrons to achieve a more stable arrangement of electrons.

Atoms, too, lose or gain to meet a goal—a stable energy level. They do not lose or gain an advantage. Instead, they lose or gain electrons. An atom that has lost or gained electrons is called an ion. An **ion** is a charged particle because it now has either more or fewer electrons than protons. The positive and negative charges are not balanced. It is the electric forces between oppositely charged particles, such as ions, that hold compounds together.

section 1 review

Summary

Combined Elements

- When elements combine, the new compound has unique properties that are different from the original properties of the elements.

Formulas

- Chemical symbols and numbers are shorthand for the elements and their amounts in chemical formulas.

Atomic Stability

- The elements of Group 18, the noble gases, rarely combine with other elements.
- Electron dot diagrams show the electrons in the outer energy level of an atom.
- Most atoms need eight electrons to complete their outer energy levels.

Self Check

1. **Compare and contrast** the properties of the individual elements that combine to make salt with the compound salt.
2. **Identify** what the formula BaF_2 tells you about this compound.
3. **Explain** why some elements are stable on their own while others are more stable in compounds.
4. **Think Critically** The label on a box of cleanser states that it contains CH_3COOH. What elements are in this compound? How many atoms of each element can be found in a unit of CH_3COOH?

Applying Math

5. **Use Percentages** Given that the molecular weight of $Mg(OH)_2$, magnesium hydroxide, is 58.32 g, what percentage of this compound is oxygen?

More Section Review gpescience.com

Assessment

Performance Have students write out the dot diagrams for two atoms of aluminum and for three atoms of oxygen. Then have them show how this combination gives all atoms eight outer, shared electrons. Use **PASC,** p. 127.

section 1 review

1. Sodium, as an element, is a solid metal. Chlorine is a gas. When the two combine to form sodium chloride, they form a solid compound.
2. The compound ratio is made up of one barium ion and two floride ions. Also, since the compound is made up of a metal and a nonmetal, it is likely ionic.
3. If an element has eight electrons in its outer energy level, it has a tendency not to react because the element is stable. Other elements form compounds as a way to complete their outer energy levels in order to become stable.
4. Hydrogen, carbon, and oxygen are in the compound. Each unit contains four hydrogen, two carbon, and two oxygen atoms.
5. 54.86%

LAB

Atomic Trading Cards

Perhaps you have seen or collected trading cards of famous athletes. Usually, each card has a picture of the athlete on one side with important statistics related to the sport on the back. Atoms also can be identified by their properties and statistics.

Real-World Problem

How can a visible model show how energy levels fill when atoms combine?

Goals

- **Display** the electrons of elements according to their energy levels.
- **Compare and classify** elements according to their outer energy levels.

Materials

4-in × 6-in index cards
periodic table

Procedure

1. You will get an assigned element from your teacher. Write the following information for your element on your index card: name, symbol, group number, atomic number, atomic mass, and metal, nonmetal, or metalloid.
2. On the other side of your index card, show the number of protons and neutrons in the nucleus (e.g., 6*p* for six protons and 6*n* for six neutrons for carbon).
3. Draw circles around the nucleus to represent the energy levels of your element. The number of circles you will need is the same as the period the element is in on the periodic table.
4. Draw dots on each circle to represent the electrons in each energy level. Remember, elements in row 1 become stable with two outer electrons, while levels two and three become stable with eight electrons.
5. Look at the picture side only of four or five of your classmates' cards. Identify the element and the group to which it belongs.

Conclude and Apply

1. As you classify the elements according to their group number, what pattern do you see in the number of electrons in the outer energy levels?
2. Atoms that give up electrons combine with atoms that gain electrons to form compounds. In your Science Journal, predict some pairs of elements that combine in this way.

Communicating Your Data

Make a graph that relates the groups to the number of electrons in their outer energy levels. **For more help, refer to the** Science Skill Handbook.

BENCH TESTED

Real-World Problem

Purpose Students make models showing the number of electrons in the outer energy levels of atoms of various elements and compare and classify those elements. L2 LS **Visual-Spatial**

Process Skills formulate models, classify, use numbers, compare and contrast, make and use graphs

Time Required 40 minutes

Procedure

Teaching Strategy To avoid confusion, assign elements from Groups 1, 2, and 13–18 only.

Troubleshooting Emphasize to students that the circles around the nucleus are only representations of the energy levels of electrons. Electrons do not actually move in circles.

Conclude and Apply

1. They are the same in each group.
2. Sodium and potassium give up the only electron in their respective outer energy levels to chlorine and iodine, forming the chemically stable compounds sodium chloride and potassium iodide.

Assessment

Oral Ask students to which group carbon and silicon belong and whether these two elements are more likely to gain electrons, lose electrons, or share electrons when they form compounds. Group 14; because they have four electrons in their outer energy levels they most likely share electrons. Use **Performance Assessment in the Science Classroom,** p. 89.

Communicating Your Data

Have students enter the number of electrons in the outer energy levels of atoms and the numbers of the groups to which the atoms belong in a computer spreadsheet. Then have them use the spreadsheet's graphing function to make the graph.

section 2 Types of Bonds

1 Motivate

INTERACTIVE CHALKBOARD An editable Microsoft® PowerPoint® presentation is available on **Interactive Chalkboard** CD-ROM.

Bellringer

Section Focus Transparencies also are available on the Interactive Chalkboard CD-ROM. L2 ELL

Section 2 Section Focus Transparency — A Crystal Nature — Chapter 22

This picture shows salt crystals on the Dead Sea shore. When a salt crystal is pure, it is in the shape of a colorless cube. Impurities can make salt appear to be different colors, like white or gray. Table salt is a compound of sodium and chlorine.

1. Describe the appearance of the salt in the picture.
2. What happens to salt in water? How might you recover salt from ocean water?
3. How do people use salt?

L2

Chemical Bonds

Reading Preview

Tie to Prior Knowledge

Electrolytes Ask students if they have ever consumed sports drinks. Explain that the electrolytes that are advertised to be in sports drinks are ions that are found naturally in human blood.

Word Associations Ask students to associate new vocabulary terms with related words. For example, *chemical bond* might be associated with *link*. Have students brainstorm associations and write them on the board.

Reading Guide

What You'll Learn

- **Describe** ionic bonds and covalent bonds.
- **Identify** the particles produced by ionic bonding and by covalent bonding.
- **Distinguish** between a nonpolar covalent bond and a polar covalent bond.

Why It's Important

Bond type determines how compounds mix and interact with other compounds.

Review Vocabulary

atom: the smallest particle of an element that still retains the properties of the element

New Vocabulary

- chemical bond
- ionic bond
- covalent bond
- molecule
- polar molecule
- nonpolar molecule

Gain or Loss of Electrons

You and a friend decide to go to the movies. When you arrive at the theater, you discover that you do not have enough money to buy a ticket. Your friend has enough money for both tickets and loans you the money. Now you both have enough money to go to the movies.

Recall that atoms also can loan electrons to other atoms so that both can reach a stable energy level. When atoms gain, lose, or share electrons, an attraction forms that pulls the atoms together to form a compound. This attraction is called a chemical bond. A **chemical bond** is the force that holds atoms together in a compound. A compound has different physical and chemical properties from those of the atoms that make up the compound.

Some of the most common compounds are made by the loss and gain of just one electron. These compounds contain an element from Group 1 on the periodic table and an element from Group 17. Some examples are sodium chloride, commonly known as table salt, and potassium iodide, an ingredient in iodized salt.

Figure 7 A goiter, an enlargement of the thyroid gland in the neck, can be caused by iodine deficiency.

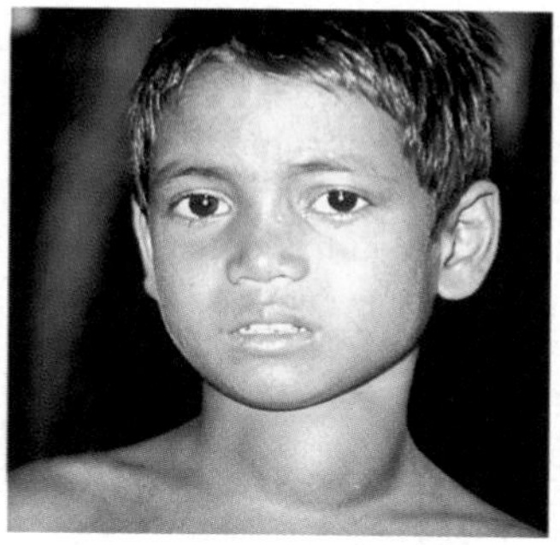

INTEGRATE Health Why do people need iodized salt? A lack of iodine causes a wide range of problems in the human body. The most obvious is an enlarged thyroid gland, as shown in **Figure 7,** but the problems can include mental retardation, neurological disorders, and physical problems.

694 CHAPTER 22 Chemical Bonds

Section 2 Resource Manager

Chapter *FAST FILE* Resources

- Transparency Activity, p. 45
- Directed Reading for Content Mastery, p. 20
- Enrichment, p. 31
- MiniLAB, p. 3
- Lab Activity, pp. 13–16
- Reinforcement, p. 28

Science Inquiry Labs, pp. 43–44

Physical Science Critical Thinking/Problem Solving, p. 13

A Bond Forms What happens when potassium and iodine atoms collide? A neutral atom of potassium has one electron in its outer level. This is not a stable outer energy level. When potassium forms a compound with iodine, potassium loses one electron from its fourth level, and the third level becomes the complete outer level. However, the atom is no longer neutral. The potassium atom has become an ion. When a potassium atom loses an electron, the atom becomes positively charged because there is one electron less in the atom than there are protons in the nucleus. The 1+ charge is shown as a superscript written after the element's symbol, K^+, to indicate its charge. *Superscript* means "written above."

The iodine atom in this reaction undergoes change as well. An iodine atom has seven electrons in its outer energy level. Recall that a stable outer energy level contains eight electrons. During the reaction with potassium, the iodide atom gains an electron, leaving its outer energy level with eight electrons. This atom is no longer neutral because it gained an extra negative particle. It now has a charge of 1− and is called an iodide ion, written as I^-. The compound formed between potassium and iodine is called potassium iodide. The dot diagrams for the process are shown in **Figure 8.**

Reading Check *What part of an ion's symbol indicates its charge?*

Another way to look at the electron in the outer shell of a potassium atom is as an advertisement to other atoms saying, "Available: One electron to lend." The iodine atom would have the message, "Wanted: One electron to borrow." When the two atoms get together, each becomes a stable ion. Notice that the resulting compound has a neutral charge because the positive and negative charges of the ions cancel each other.

INTEGRATE Life Science

Ions and Nerve Cells Ions are important in many processes in your body. The movement of muscles is just one of these processes. Muscle movement would be impossible without the movement of ions in and out of nerve cells. Research the type of ions used by the nerve cells.

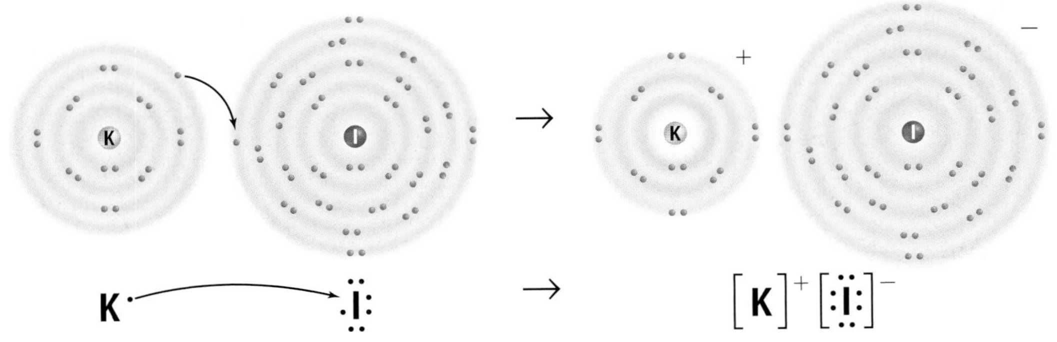

Figure 8 Potassium and iodine must perform a transfer of one electron. Potassium and iodine end up with stable outer energy levels. **Infer** *why the size of the ion changes with the change in electron distribution.*

2 Teach

Reading Check

Answer the superscript written after the element's symbol

INTEGRATE Life Science

Ions and Nerve Cells The primary ions needed for nerve impulses are Na^+ and K^+. Remind students that the properties of an ion of an element are different from those of the neutral atom. For example, both sodium and potassium metals react violently with water, while their ions do not.

Discussion

Atom Identity How many protons and electrons are in an atom of chlorine? 17 protons and 17 electrons How many protons and electrons are in a common ion of Cl? 17 protons and 18 electrons Remind students that while atoms gain or lose electrons fairly easily, changing the number of protons changes the identity of the atom. L2 LS **Logical-Mathematical**

Caption Answer

Figure 8 An ion has fewer electrons. The attraction between the positive nucleus and the electrons become greater.

INTEGRATE Health **Content Background**

Iodine, as well as other elements such as copper and iron, is necessary to have a healthy body. These elements, which are called trace minerals, regulate many chemical reactions in the body.

Visual Learning

Figure 8 Have students find potassium and iodine on the periodic table. How many electrons does potassium have? 19 How many does iodine have? 53 Have students count the electrons in each atom and ion in **Figure 8.** Explain that the first energy level in any atom can contain up to 2 electrons, the second level can contain up to 8 electrons, the third level can contain up to 18 electrons, and the fourth level can contain up to 32 electrons. L3 LS **Visual-Spatial**

Differentiated Instruction

Learning Disabled Provide students with two bar magnets. Have them use the magnets to determine that opposite ends (charges) of the magnets attract and like ends (charges) repel. Relate this concept to the attractions that bring opposite ions together. L1 LS **Kinesthetic**

Figure 9 This sparkler contains iron, which burns in air to produce an ionic compound that contains iron and oxygen.

The Ionic Bond

When ions attract in this way, a bond is formed. An **ionic bond** is the force of attraction between the opposite charges of the ions in an ionic compound. In an ionic bond, a transfer of one or more electrons takes place. With this transfer of electrons to form an ionic compound, a large amount of energy is released, as shown in **Figure 9**.

Now that you have seen how an ionic bond forms when one electron is involved, see how it works when more than one electron is involved. The formation of magnesium chloride, $MgCl_2$, is another example of ionic bonding. When magnesium reacts with chlorine, a magnesium atom loses two electrons and becomes a positively charged ion, Mg^{2+}. At the same time, two chlorine atoms gain one electron each and become negatively charged chloride ions, Cl^-. In this case, a magnesium atom has two electrons to lend, but a single chlorine atom needs to borrow only one electron. Therefore, it takes two chlorine atoms, as shown in **Figure 10,** to take the two electrons from the magnesium ion to form the compound magnesium chloride.

Zero Net Charge The result of this bond is a neutral compound. The compound as a whole is neutral because the sum of the charges on the ions is zero. The positive charge of the magnesium ion is equal to the negative charge of the two chloride ions. In other words, when different atoms form an ionic compound, electrons move from one atom to a different atom, but the overall number of protons and electrons of the combined atoms remains equal and unchanged. Therefore, the compound is neutral.

Metals and nonmetals usually combine by forming ionic bonds. Looking at the periodic table, you will see that the elements that bond ionically are often across the table from each other. Ionic compounds are often crystalline solids with high melting points.

Figure 10 A magnesium atom gives an electron to each of two chlorine atoms to form $MgCl_2$.

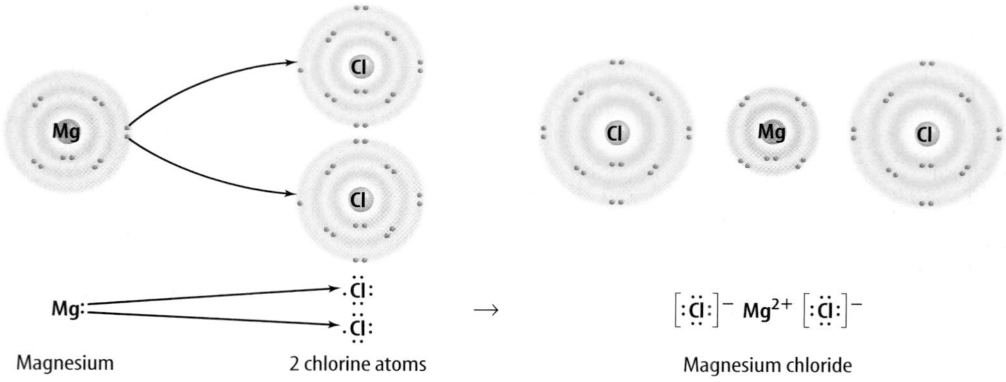

Discussion

Electron Moves Explain to students that a metal may give up an electron when forming an ionic bond. What type of charge does the metal have after it loses an electron? positive L1
LS **Logical-Mathematical**

Activity

Ionic Bonds Using a classroom periodic table, or the one in the textbook, point out potassium (K) on the left of the table. Ask a volunteer to name a nonmetal that would likely form an ionic bond with that element. Possible answers: O or F (K_2O; KF) Repeat with barium (Ba). Possible answers: Cl or S ($BaCl_2$; BaS) Use this exercise to point out that the metals and nonmetals that form ionic bonds often are located far apart on the periodic table. L2 LS **Logical-Mathematical**

Fun Fact

Most ionic compounds are soluble in water, but are not soluble in nonpolar solvents.

Quick Demo

Conductivity in Salt

Materials 9-volt battery, two insulated copper wires, flashlight bulb, salt, distilled water, one beaker

Estimated Time 15 minutes

Procedure Pour distilled water into beaker. Connect one wire to positive pole of battery and put other end in one side of beaker into water. Run another wire from negative pole of battery to flashlight bulb and another wire from bulb to water at other end of beaker. After students see that bulb does not light up, add salt to beaker and stir water to dissolve salt, bulb should then light up if enough salt is added.

Teacher FYI

Ion Attraction A positive ion is always smaller than its original neutral atom, and a negative ion is always larger than its original neutral atom. The charge on an ion acts as though it were located exactly in the center of the ion. Therefore, large ions have less attraction toward other ions; the center of charge is farther away. The more highly charged an ion is, the stronger the force around it. The strongest attractions take place between small, highly charged ions such as Al^{3+} and highly negative ions such as O^{2-}. Large, singly charged ions such as K^+ and I^- have less attractive force between them.

Sharing Electrons

Some atoms of nonmetals are unlikely to lose or gain electrons. For example, the elements in Group 14 of the periodic table have four electrons in their outer levels. They would have to either gain or lose four electrons to have a stable outer level. Losing four electrons takes a great deal of energy. Each time an electron is removed, the nucleus holds the remaining electrons even more tightly. These atoms become more chemically stable by sharing electrons, rather than by losing or gaining electrons.

The attraction that forms between atoms when they share electrons is known as a **covalent bond.** A neutral particle that forms as a result of electron sharing is called a **molecule,** as shown in **Figure 11.**

Figure 11 Each of the pairs of electrons between the two hydrogens and the oxygen is shared as each atom contributes one electron to the pair to make the bond.

Single Covalent Bonds A single covalent bond is made up of two shared electrons. Usually, one of the shared electrons comes from one atom in the bond and the other comes from the other atom in the bond. A water molecule contains two single bonds. In each bond, a hydrogen atom contributes one electron to the bond, and the oxygen atom contributes the other. The two electrons are shared, forming a single bond. The result of this type of bonding is a stable outer energy level for each atom in the molecule.

Multiple Bonds A covalent bond also can contain more than one pair of shared electrons. An example of this is the bond in nitrogen (N_2), shown in **Figure 12.** A nitrogen atom has five electrons in its outer energy level and needs three more electrons to become stable. It does this by sharing three of its electrons with another nitrogen atom. The other nitrogen atom also shares three of its electrons. When each atom contributes three electrons, they share six electrons, or three pairs of electrons. Each pair of electrons represents a bond. Therefore, three pairs of electrons represent three bonds, or a triple bond. Each nitrogen atom is stable with eight electrons in its outer energy level. In a similar way, a bond that contains two shared pairs of electrons is a double bond. Carbon dioxide is an example of a molecule with double bonds.

Covalent bonds form between nonmetallic elements. These elements are close together in the upper right-hand corner of the periodic table. Many covalent compounds are liquids or gases at room temperature.

Figure 12 The dot diagram shows that the two nitrogen atoms in nitrogen gas share six electrons. **Explain** *which of these gases would require the most energy to react with another element to form a compound, H_2 or N_2.*

Activity

Bond Types Point out that in general the closer together reacting elements are on the periodic table, the more likely it is that they will share electrons with one another rather than form ionic bonds. Have students use this information to predict the type of bond that will form between carbon and oxygen. covalent Have them predict the type of bond formed between each of the following: sodium and oxygen, ionic; phosphorus and oxygen, covalent; magnesium and oxygen, ionic; aluminum and oxygen, ionic; chlorine and oxygen, covalent; sulfur and oxygen, covalent. L2 LS **Logical-Mathematical**

Inquiry Lab

Energy Levels

Purpose to familiarize students with the energy levels of elements

Possible Materials periodic table of elements

Estimated Time 30 minutes

Teaching Strategy Assign students to groups and give each group a different element from the periodic table. Then, have students sketch their element and its various energy levels to represent electrons making up those levels. Have students brainstorm questions about elements. Allow them to explore these questions as time allows.

For additional inquiry activities, see Science Inquiry Lab Manual.

Caption Answer

Figure 12 N_2

Differentiated Instruction

English-Language Learners Use the dot diagrams to explain how atoms form covalent bonds in order to complete their outer electron energy level. Explain that the more covalent bonds that a compound has, the more energy that is required to separate the atoms with these bonds. **Visual-Spatial**

Science Journal

Dot Diagrams Have students research the work of American chemist Gilbert N. Lewis and write short paragraphs in their Science Journals about his contribution to dot diagrams. The diagrams are called Lewis diagrams because he developed the idea as a way of explaining attractions besides ionic bonding between atoms. The dots allowed him to better explain bonding to his students. L2 LS **Linguistic**

MiniLAB

Purpose Students observe that water molecules are polar. L2

LS **Kinesthetic**

Materials water faucet, balloon, wool

Teaching Strategy Practice to determine the amount of static charge that can be built up on the balloon. High humidity reduces the buildup, causing a smaller deflection of the water stream.

Analysis

1. The balloon acquires a charge when rubbed against the wool. When brought near a thin stream of water, the charge attracts water, causing the stream to bend.
2. In both cases, opposites attract. A water molecule contains a negative region and a positive region that are similar to the opposite poles of a magnet.

Assessment

Oral Explain to students that pentane (C_5H_{12}) is a nonpolar molecule. Ask students to predict whether a stream of pentane would bend if they used the same procedure followed in the MiniLAB. No; pentane is nonpolar and therefore will not be attracted to the static charge on the balloon. Use **Performance Assessment in the Science Classroom,** p. 89. L2 LS **Logical-Mathmatical**

Try at Home

Caption Answer

Figure 13 Chlorine atoms have a stronger attraction for electrons than hydrogen atoms.

MiniLAB

Observing a Bond Type

Procedure

1. Turn on the faucet to produce a thin **stream of water.**
2. Rub an inflated **balloon** with **wool or fur.**
3. Bring the balloon near the stream of water, and describe what you see.

Analysis

1. Explain your observations.
2. Relate the attraction between the balloon and the water to the attraction between the north and south poles of two magnets. Why might water act like a magnet?

Try at Home

Unequal Sharing Electrons are not always shared equally between atoms in a covalent bond. The strength of the attraction of each atom to its electrons is related to the size of the atom, the charge of the nucleus, and the total number of electrons the atom contains. Part of the strength of attraction has to do with how far the electron being shared is from the nucleus. For example, a magnet has a stronger pull when it is right next to a piece of metal rather than several centimeters away. The other part of the strength of attraction has to do with the size of the positive charge in the nucleus. Using a magnet as an example again, a strong magnet will hold the metal more firmly than a weak magnet will.

One example of this unequal sharing is found in a molecule of hydrogen chloride, HCl, which is shown in **Figure 13.** In water, HCl is hydrochloric acid, which is used in laboratories and in industry to clean metal, and is found in your stomach, where it helps to digest food. Chlorine atoms have a stronger attraction for the shared electrons than hydrogen atoms do. As a result, the shared electrons in hydrogen chloride will spend more time near the chlorine atom than near the hydrogen atom. The chlorine atom has a partial negative charge, represented by a lowercase Greek symbol *delta* followed by a negative superscript, δ^-. The hydrogen atom has a partial positive charge, represented by a δ^+.

Reading Check ***What determines the strength of attraction of an atom?***

Tug-of-War You might think of a covalent bond as the rope in a tug-of-war, and the shared electrons as the knot in the center of the rope. **Figure 14** illustrates this concept. Each atom in the molecule attracts the electrons that they share. However, sometimes the atoms aren't the same size.

The same thing happens in tug-of-war. Sometimes one team has more people or stronger participants than the other. When this is true, the knot in the middle of the rope ends up closer to the stronger team. Similarly, the electrons being shared in a molecule are held more closely to the atoms with the stronger pull or larger nucleus.

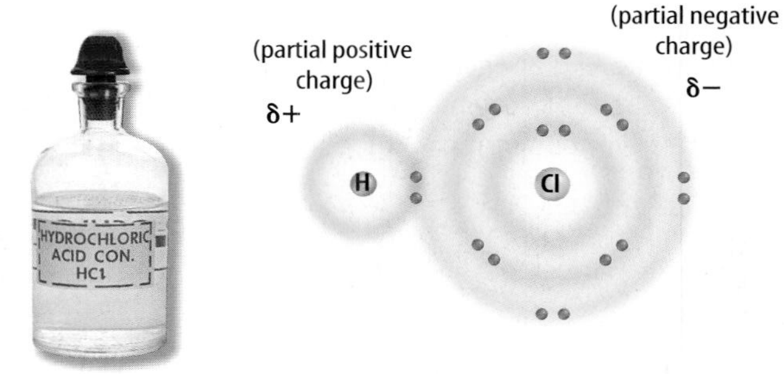

Figure 13 The chlorine atom exerts the greater pull on the electrons in hydrogen chloride, which forms hydrochloric acid in water.
Explain *why the chlorine atom has a greater pull than the hydrogen atom.*

Differentiated Instruction

Challenge Have students research the electronegativity scale developed by Linus Pauling and relate the information they find to the formation of covalent, polar covalent, and ionic bonds. Pauling's electronegativity scale is a way of ranking the ability of an atom to attract electrons within a bond. Two atoms that have a small or no electronegativity difference form a covalent bond. Those with a great electronegativity difference form an ionic bond. If the difference is moderate, a polar covalent bond forms. Each element is given a numerical ranking, so simple subtraction gives the electronegativity difference. L3 LS **Linguistic**

698 CHAPTER 22 Chemical Bonds

NATIONAL GEOGRAPHIC

VISUALIZING POLAR MOLECULES

Figure 14

When playing tug-of-war, if there are more—or stronger—team members on one end of the rope than the other, there is an unequal balance of power. The stronger team can pull harder on the rope and has the advantage. A similar situation exists in polar molecules, in which electrons are attracted more strongly by one type of atom in the molecule than another. Because of this unequal sharing of electrons, polar molecules have a slightly negative end and a slightly positive end, as shown below.

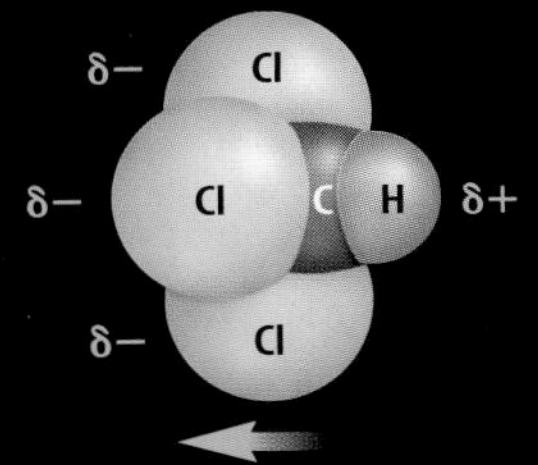

CHLOROFORM **In a molecule of chloroform ($CHCl_3$), or trichloromethane (tri klor oh ME thayn), the three chlorine atoms attract electrons more strongly than the hydrogen atom does, creating a partial negative charge on the chlorine end of the molecule and a partial positive charge on the hydrogen end. This polar molecule is a clear, sweet-smelling liquid once widely used as an anesthetic in human and veterinary surgery.**

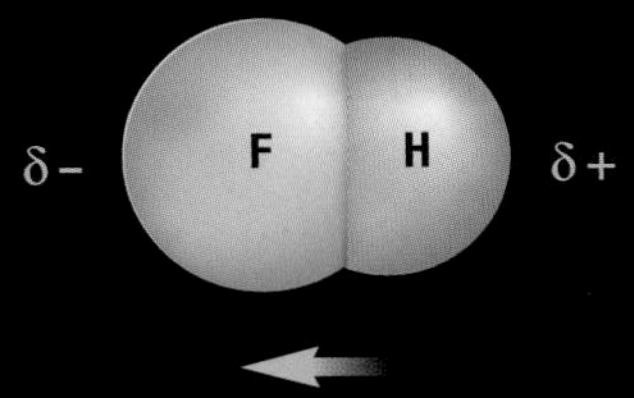

HYDROGEN FLUORIDE **Hydrogen and fluorine react to form hydrogen fluoride (HF). In an HF molecule, the two atoms are bound together by a pair of electrons, one contributed by each atom. However, the electrons are not shared equally because the fluorine atom attracts them more strongly than the hydrogen atom does. The result is a polar molecule with a slightly positive charge near the hydrogen end and a slightly negative charge near the fluorine end.**

NATIONAL GEOGRAPHIC

Visualizing Polar Molecules

Have students examine the pictures and read the captions. Then ask the following questions.

In your own words, describe why charge is distributed unevenly in chloroform molecules. Possible answer: The chlorine molecules have a stronger attraction for electrons than the hydrogen molecule.

Why are the hydrogen sides of both chloroform molecules and hydrogen fluoride molecules partially positive? The electrons have been pulled away, leaving an exposed proton in each hydrogen nucleus.

Activity

Electron Dot Diagrams Work together as a class to draw on the board the electron dot diagrams for both molecules. Students should easily see that the electrons are concentrated on one side of each molecule, which leads to a partial negative charge on that side. Have students draw these diagrams in their Science Journals. LS **Visual-Spatial**

Differentiated Instruction

Challenge Ask students to find out what an induced dipole is. Direct students to make posters showing examples of induced dipoles and explain their posters to the class. L3 LS **Visual-Spatial** P

Reading Check

Answer a molecule that has a slightly negative end and a slightly positive end

Using an Analogy

Similarities Draw an analogy between the positive and negative poles of a polar molecule and the magnetic north and south poles of Earth. Point out that one meaning of the word *polar* is "directly opposite."

Use Science Words

Word Origin Have students use reference books to learn about the origins of various element names. Ask students to write each element symbol, name, and the source of its name. Many elements were named after countries or people. For example, polonium was named for Poland, the native land of its discoverer, Marie Curie.

Discussion

Compounds Ask students to describe various materials in the classroom and to suggest which elements make up each material. Typical responses are water—hydrogen and oxygen; metal objects—iron, aluminum, mixtures of iron with other elements, such as carbon.

Caption Answer

Figure 15 unequal sharing of electrons

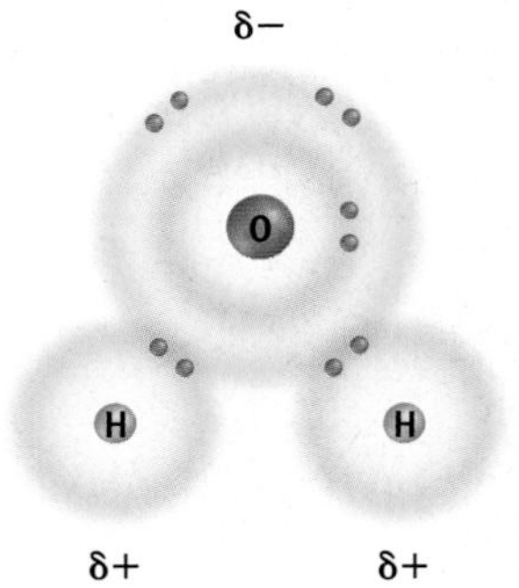

Figure 15 The polarity of water is responsible for many of its unique properties.
Explain *the cause of polarity.*

Polar or Nonpolar? For the molecule involved in this electron tug-of-war, there is another consequence. Again, look at the molecule of hydrogen chloride. The unequal sharing of electrons gives each chlorine atom a slight negative charge and each hydrogen atom a slight positive charge. The atom holding the electron more closely always will have a slightly negative charge. The charge is balanced but not equally distributed. This type of molecule is called polar. The term *polar* means "having opposite ends." A **polar molecule** is one that has a slightly positive end and a slightly negative end, although the overall molecule is neutral. Water is an example of a polar molecule, as shown in **Figure 15.**

Reading Check *What is a polar molecule?*

Two atoms that are exactly alike can share their electrons equally, forming a nonpolar molecule. A **nonpolar molecule** is one in which electrons are shared equally in bonds. Such a molecule does not have oppositely charged ends. This is true of molecules made from two identical atoms or molecules that are symmetric, such as CCl_4.

Properties of Compounds

Recall that atoms can form two types of bonds: covalent and ionic. A compound whose atoms are held together by covalent bonds is a covalent compound.

Sugar is a covalent compound. A compound that is composed of ions is an ionic compound. Table salt, NaCl, is an ionic compound. Looking at both substances, you would think they would have similar physical and chemical properties.

Both sugar and salt, as shown in **Figure 16,** are used to change the taste of foods. You add sugar to lemonade or iced tea to make the drink sweet. Table salt is used to enhance the flavors of foods, such as meats and vegetables. Sugar and salt have different physical and chemical properties.

Figure 16 Table sugar is an example of a covalent compound that is a crystalline solid soluble in water. Ionic compounds, such as table salt, are also soluble in water.

Reading Strategy

Classify Text Provide students with three key questions related to the text. Have students categorize information from the text under the key questions. A key question might be: How do different types of bonds form? Students should take notes and categorize information on ionic bonds and covalent bonds under the key question.

700 CHAPTER 22 Chemical Bonds

Figure 17 Candle wax and propane are covalent compounds that are insoluble in water.

Covalent and Ionic Properties The chemical and physical properties of covalent compounds and ionic compounds are different. This difference in properties, as shown in **Table 2,** is due to differences in attractive forces of the bonds.

Covalent Compounds The covalent bonds between atoms in molecules are strong. However, the attraction between individual molecules is weak. It is the weak forces between individual molecules that are responsible for the properties of covalent compounds.

Melting and boiling points of covalent compounds are relatively lower when compared to ionic compounds. Sugar will melt at approximately 185°C, whereas table salt will melt at 801°C. Covalent compounds, which will form soft solids, have poor electrical and thermal conductivity. Candles and propane gas shown in **Figure 17** are covalent compounds.

Table 2 Comparison of Covalent and Ionic Compounds

	Covalent Compounds	Ionic Compounds
Bond Type	Electron Sharing	Electron Transfer
Melting and Boiling Points	Lower	Higher
Electrical Conductivity	Poor	Good
State at Room Temperature	Solid, liquid, or gas	Solid
Forces Between Particles	Strong bonds between atoms; weak attraction between molecules	Strong attraction between positive and negative ions

IDENTIFYING Misconceptions

Water Students probably believe that water is an electrolyte that conducts electricity. Point out that what we call "water" is usually a solution containing small amounts of dissolved molecules and ions. The ions act as electrolytes, which allow the solution to conduct electricity.

Virtual Labs

Bonding *How can you tell which elements form chemical bonds?*

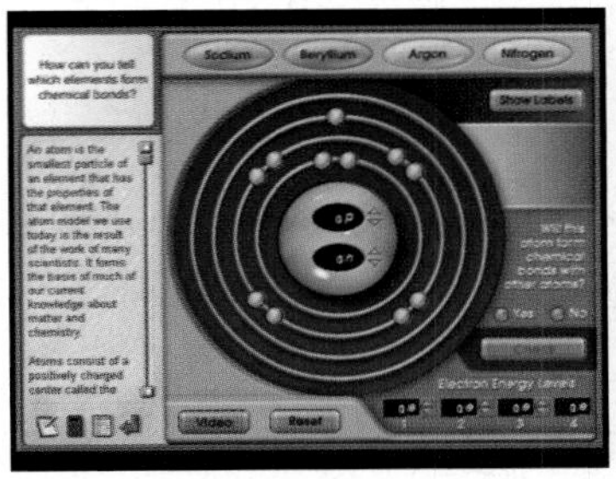

Post Reading

Illustrations Have students develop pictures to show ionic and covalent bonding. Allow them to creatively personify characters representing bonding atoms. Ask them to choose a particular compound, such as salt, to represent in the illustrations. Allow students to work in pairs or groups to encourage deeper understanding.

Cultural Diversity

Salt of the Earth Salt has been recognized as an important and essential substance in all cultures for thousands of years. One of the major uses of salt in all parts of the worlds is as a preservative. Salt is used to symbolize fidelity and permanence of relationships in many societies. The Hebrew expression "to eat the salt of the palace" means to think highly of someone, just as the English phrase describing a person as "salt of the earth."

SECTION 2 Types of Bonds 701

Reading Check

Answer Ionic bonding causes brittleness.

3 Assess

DAILY INTERVENTION

Check for Understanding

Interpersonal Assign students to groups and have them develop a brief presentation for the class explaining the differences between polar and nonpolar molecules.

Reteach

Identify Compounds List the formulas for HCl, H_2O, NaCl, and $MgCl_2$ on the board. Have students identify each compound as ionic or covalent. HCl, covalent; H_2O, covalent; NaCl, ionic; $MgCl_2$, ionic.

L2 LS **Logical-Mathematical**

Assessment

Performance Have each student write the symbol of one of the first 30 elements on a sheet of paper. Now have the student use the periodic table to try to find an element that would form a covalent bond with the first element. Have students repeat the exercise for an ionic compound and explain their choices. Emphasize that both electron configuration and attraction for electrons determine whether two atoms will bond with each other. Use **PASC,** p. 93.

Figure 18 Some common ionic compounds used in everyday life are potassium chloride as a salt substitute; potassium iodide added to table salt; and sodium fluoride added to toothpaste.

Ionic Compounds The ionic bonds between ions are relatively strong. This accounts for the high melting and boiling points of ionic compounds such as table salt. Examples of common ionic compounds are shown in **Figure 18.** Ionic compounds are hard and brittle. When in a liquid or aqueous state, ionic compounds can conduct electric current.

Strong attractive forces hold the ions in place. Ionic compounds are stable due to the attraction between unlike charges. The ions are drawn together and energy is released. Formation of ionic compounds is always exothermic.

Reading Check *Why are ionic compounds brittle?*

section 2 review

Summary

Gain or Loss of Electrons

- An ion is a charged particle that has either fewer or more electrons than protons, resulting in a negative or positive charge.

Ionic Bond

- An ionic bond is the force or attraction between opposite charges of ions in an ionic bond.
- An ionic compound is neutral because the sum of the ion charges is zero.

Sharing Electrons

- Some atoms, such as those in Group 4, share electrons instead of losing or gaining them.
- Covalent bonds can form single, double, or triple bonds.
- In a polar molecule, the electrons are shared unequally in the bond. This results in slightly charged ends.
- Electrons are shared equally in a nonpolar molecule.

Self Check

1. **Explain** why an atom makes an ionic bond only with certain other atoms.
2. **Compare and contrast** the possession of electrons in ionic and covalent bonds.
3. **Name** the types of particles formed by covalent bonds.
4. **Concept Map** Using the following terms, make a network-tree concept map of chemical bonding: *ionic, covalent, ions, positive ions, negative ions, molecules, polar,* and *nonpolar.* Define the terms *atom* and *molecule*.
5. **Think Critically** Choose two elements that are likely to form an ionic bond: O, Ne, S, Ca, K. Next, select two elements that would likely form a covalent bond. Explain.

Applying Math

6. **Solve One-Step Equations** Aluminum oxide, Al_2O_3, can be produced during space shuttle launches. Show that the sum of the positive and negative charges in a unit of Al_2O_3 equals zero.

More Section Review gpescience.com

section 2 review

1. In ionic bonds, one atom accepts electrons from another. This happens only among elements having large differences in their attractions for electrons.
2. In ionic bonds, one atom accepts an electron from another atom. In covalent bonds, electrons are shared, sometimes unequally.
3. Covalent bonding produces molecules.
4. Check students' work.
5. Ionic: Ca–O and K–O, because K and Ca are metals far from O on the periodic table; covalent: S–O because S and O are nonmetals close to each other on the periodic table
6. The charge on Al is +3 and the charge on O is $[2(+3)] + [3(-2)] = 0$.

section 3

Writing Formulas and Naming Compounds

Reading Guide

What You'll Learn

- **Explain** how to determine oxidation numbers.
- **Write** formulas and names for ionic compounds.
- **Write** formulas and names for covalent compounds.

Why It's Important

The name and the formula convey information about the compound.

Review Vocabulary

anion: a negatively charged ion

New Vocabulary

- binary compound
- oxidation number
- polyatomic ion
- hydrate

Binary Ionic Compounds

Does the table in **Figure 19** look like it has anything to do with chemistry? It is an early table of the elements made by alchemists, scientists who tried to make gold from other elements. The alchemists used symbols to write the formulas of substances. The first formulas of compounds that you will write are for binary ionic compounds. A **binary compound** is one that is composed of two elements. Potassium iodide, the salt additive mentioned in Section 2, is a binary ionic compound. Before you can write a formula, you must have all the needed information at your fingertips. What will you need to know?

Oxidation Numbers You need to know which elements are involved and what number of electrons they lose, gain, or share to become stable. Section 1 discussed the relationship between an element's position on the periodic table and the number of electrons it gains or loses. Because all elements in a given group have the same number of electrons in their outer energy levels, they must gain or lose the same number of electrons. Metals always lose electrons and nonmetals always gain electrons when they form ions. The charge on the ion is known as the **oxidation number** of the atom.

For ionic compounds, the oxidation number is the same as the charge on the ion. For example, a sodium ion has a charge of 1+ and an oxidation number of 1+. A chloride ion has a charge of 1− and an oxidation number of 1−.

Figure 19 This old chart of the elements used pictorial symbols to represent elements.

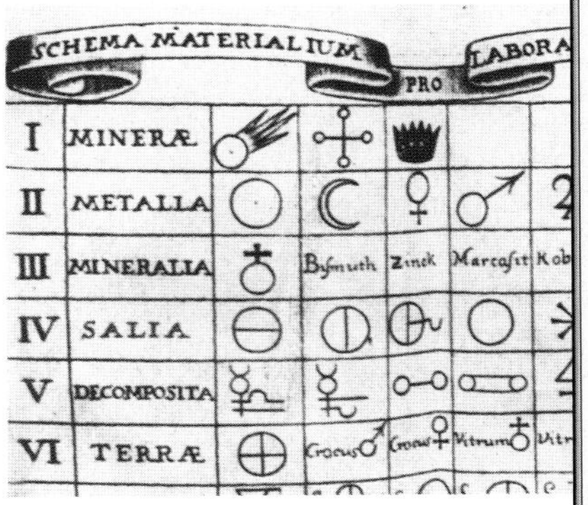

1 Motivate

An editable Microsoft® PowerPoint® presentation is available on **Interactive Chalkboard** CD-ROM.

Bellringer

Section Focus Transparencies also are available on the Interactive Chalkboard CD-ROM.
L2 ELL

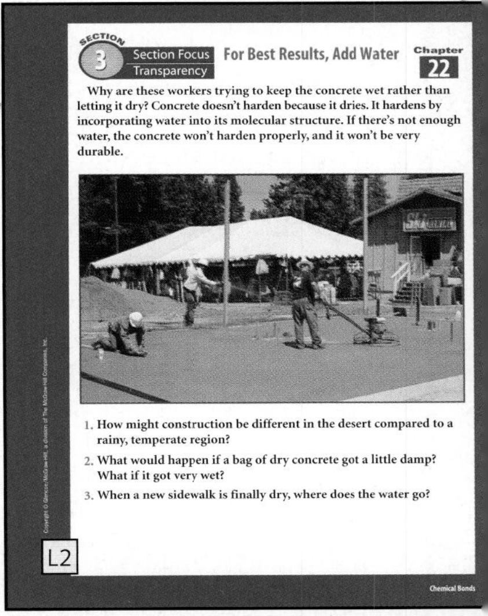
Section 3 Section Focus Transparency — For Best Results, Add Water — Chapter 22

Why are these workers trying to keep the concrete wet rather than letting it dry? Concrete doesn't harden because it dries. It hardens by incorporating water into its molecular structure. If there's not enough water, the concrete won't harden properly, and it won't be very durable.

1. How might construction be different in the desert compared to a rainy, temperate region?
2. What would happen if a bag of dry concrete got a little damp? What if it got very wet?
3. When a new sidewalk is finally dry, where does the water go?

L2

Chemical Bonds

Reading Preview

Tie to Prior Knowledge

Common Formulas Bring in labels from common substances, such as antacids, that contain chemical formulas. Identify the substances shown by each formula. Then explain that students will discover how to read and interpret such formulas and how to name the compounds they represent.

Word Parts Ask students to identify word parts that offer clues to meaning. For instance, *binary compound* could be broken apart. *Bi* indicates "two" com means "joining". A *binary compound* is made up of two elements, as suggested by the word parts.

Section 3 Resource Manager

Chapter FAST FILE Resources

Transparency Activity, pp. 46, 47–48
Directed Reading for Content Mastery, pp. 21–22
Reinforcement, p. 29
Enrichment, p. 32
MiniLAB, p. 4
Lab Worksheet, pp. 7–8

Home and Community Involvement, p. 46
Mathematics Skill Activities, p. 29
Reading and Writing Skill Activities, p. 41
Lab Management and Safety, p. 49

2 Teach

Quick Demo

Ion Charge

Materials cellophane tape

Estimated Time 5 minutes

Procedure Binary ionic compounds form when oppositely charged ions attract each other. Demonstrate the basic forces involved by placing two 25-cm pieces of cellophane tape side by side on a plastic surface. Pull both up at the same time. As they are brought close together they will repel. Explain that this happens because both pieces of tape have acquired the same charge. Place one piece of tape on the surface and a second piece directly on top of the first. Pull them off the table and separate them. They now attract each other. Why? They have acquired opposite charges, which causes them to attract each other. L1 **Visual-Spatial**

IDENTIFYING Misconceptions

Roman Numerals The use of Roman numerals can be confusing. Copper(II) oxide is CuO, with one copper atom for each oxygen atom. The compound copper(I) oxide is written as Cu_2O, with two copper atoms for each oxygen atom. Remind students that the Roman numeral represents the charge on an atom, while Arabic subscript numbers, such as 2 and 3, show the number of atoms of each element.

Caption Answer

Figure 20 charge on the ion

Reading Check

Answer 2^+

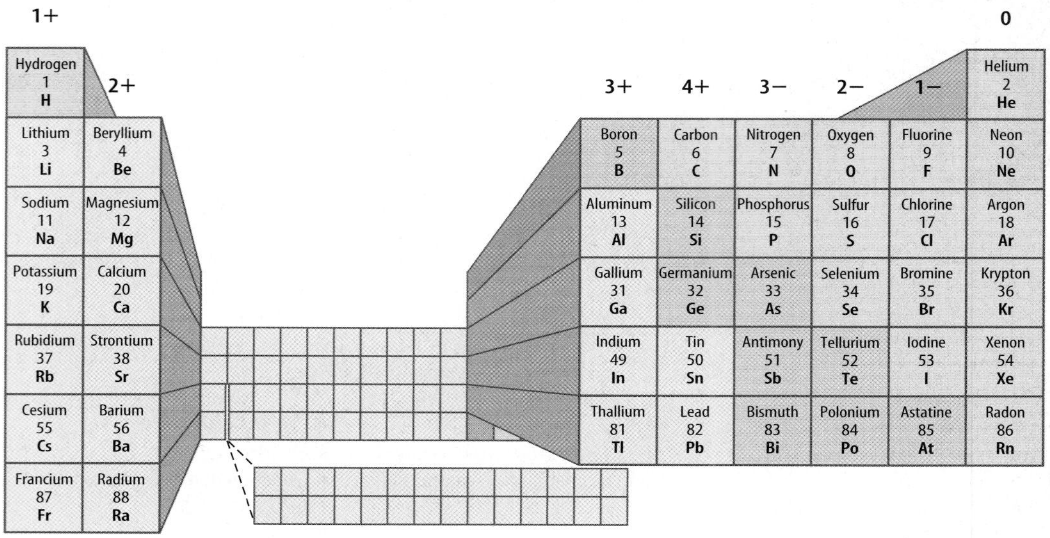

Figure 20 The number at the top of each column is the most common oxidation number of elements in that group.
Define *oxidation number.*

Oxidation Numbers and the Periodic Table The numbers with positive or negative signs in **Figure 20** are the oxidation numbers for the elements in the columns below them. Notice how they fit with the periodic-table groupings.

The elements in **Table 3** can have more than one oxidation number. When naming these compounds, the oxidation number is expressed in the name with a roman numeral. For example, the oxidation number of iron in iron(III) oxide is 3+.

Reading Check *What is the oxidation number for barium, Ba?*

Table 3 Special Ions

Name	Oxidation Number
Copper(I)	1+
Copper(II)	2+
Iron(II)	2+
Iron(III)	3+
Chromium(II)	2+
Chromium(III)	3+
Lead(II)	2+
Lead(IV)	4+

Ionic Compounds Are Neutral When writing formulas, it is important to remember that although the individual ions in a compound carry charges, the compound itself is neutral. A formula must have the same number of positive ions and negative ions so the charges balance. For example, sodium chloride is made up of a sodium ion with a 1+ charge and a chloride ion with a 1− charge.

However, what if you have a compound such as calcium fluoride? A calcium ion has a charge of 2+ and a fluoride ion has a charge of 1−. In this case, you need to have two fluoride ions for every calcium ion for the charges to cancel and the compound to be neutral with the formula CaF_2.

Some compounds require more thought. Aluminum oxide contains an ion with a 3+ charge and an ion with a 2− charge. You must find the least common multiple of 3 and 2 to determine how many of each ion you need. You need two aluminum ions and three oxygen ions to have a 6+ charge and, a 6− charge and, therefore, the neutral compound Al_2O_3.

Science Journal

Oxidation Number Have students use a periodic table to identify the oxidation numbers of the elements in Groups 1, 2, and 13–18. Ask students to make tables containing this information in their Science Journals. L1 IN **Visual-Spatial**

Active Reading

Reflective Journal Have students identify what they learned from activities. Then divide sheets of paper into several columns and record their thoughts under headings such as *What I did, What I learned, Questions I have, Surprises I experienced,* and *Overall response.* Have students write a Reflective Journal for writing formulas.

Writing Formulas After you've learned how to find the oxidation numbers and their least common multiple, you can write formulas for ionic compounds. Write the formula for an ionic compound containing sodium and oxygen by using the following rules in this order.

1. Write the symbol of the element that has the positive oxidation number or charge. Sodium, a Group 1 element, has an oxidation number of 1+.
2. Write the symbol of the element with the negative number. Nonmetals other than hydrogen have negative oxidation numbers. Oxygen has an oxidation number of 2−.
3. To have a neutral compound, the positive charges have to balance the negative charges. It takes two sodium ions to balance the one oxygen ion. Thus, the formula becomes Na_2O.

INTEGRATE History

Jöns Jakob Berzelius As a Swedish chemist, Berzelius is credited with developing the concepts of ions and ionic compounds. Because of his many interests and discoveries in chemistry, Berzelius, like Antoine Lavoisier, is known as one of the founders of modern chemistry.

Applying Math — Writing Chemical Formulas

DETERMINING A FORMULA What is the formula for lithium nitride?

IDENTIFY known values

Identify the known values:

Symbol and oxidation number of the positive element:

Lithium —means→ Li^{1+}

Symbol and oxidation number of the negative element:

Nitrogen —means→ N^{3-}

SOLVE the problem

To have a neutral compound, it takes three Li^{1+} ions to balance the one N^{3-} ion.

$3Li^{1+} = 1N^{3-}$ —means→ Li_3N_1 or Li_3N

Reduce the subscripts to the smallest whole numbers that retain the ratios of ions.

CHECK the answer

Does your answer seem reasonable? Check your answer by determining whether your compound is neutral.

Practice Problems

1. What is the formula for lead (IV) phosphide?
2. What is the formula for iron (III) oxide?

For more practice problems go to page 879, and visit Math Practice at gpescience.com.

INTEGRATE History

Jöns Jakob Berzelius Berzelius, who was trained as a medical doctor, was a professor at Stockholm School of Surgery. He started in the chemical field by writing a chemistry book for his medical students. While doing research for his book, he discovered the law of constant proportion.

Research Have students research which elements that Berzelius discovered. silicon, selenium, thorium, cerium

Applying Math

Math Standards

National: 2, 6, 9

This is what you know: Write the symbol and oxidation number of the positive element: Lead (Pb) = 4+

Write the symbol and oxidation number of the negative element:

Phosphorus (P) = 3−

Least common multiple = 12

This is what you need to do:

Add subscripts so that the sum of the oxidation numbers is zero.

3Pb = (3) (4+) = 12 +;

4P = (4) (3−) = 12−

Complete the formula.

Answers to Practice Problems

1. Pb_3P_4
2. Fe_2O_3

Activity

Ion Names Give students a list of compound names that consist of the various ions presented in this chapter. Have them write and balance the formula so that the net charge is zero.

Differentiated Instruction

Challenge Have the students inspect the ingredient list on the side of various containers and find five chemical formulas. Have them determine the oxidation numbers of the various elements in each of the five compounds and make a table to exhibit their findings. L3

Curriculum Connection

Language Arts The binary ionic compound Fe_3O_4 is the naturally magnetic mineral magnetite. Magnetite was used in the ancient world as a compass; it was called a *lodestone*. Ask students to find out where the name magnetite comes from. Magnetite was named by the ancient Greeks after the place it was originally found, Magnesia in what is now Turkey. L2

LS **Linguistic**

SECTION 3 Writing Formulas and Naming Compounds 705

Activity

Compound Teams Organize the class into two teams. Have team one make a list of the names of compounds and write the names on the board. Team two must then write the correct formula next to each compound. Award one point for each correct answer. Then have team two make a list of compound formulas and write them on the board for team one to name. Alternate between the teams until one reaches a score of 10. L2 ELL COOP LEARN LS **Intrapersonal**

Visual Learning

Table 3 In a binary compound involving oxygen, what name is given to the second part of the compound? oxide L1 LS **Visual-Spatial**

Applying Science

Answers

1. copper(II) oxide
2. aluminum chloride

Reading Strategy

Metacongnitive Strategies Metacongnitive involves self-regulation of thinking and the use of strategies to support comprehension. Model this strategy by reading aloud. Articulate thoughts regarding word meaning, content, and integration of ideas. Show students how to use prior knowlege to aid comprehension.

Table 4 Elements in Binary Compounds

Element	*-ide* Name
Oxygen	oxide
Phosphorus	phosphide
Nitrogen	nitride
Sulfur	sulfide

Writing Names You can name a binary ionic compound from its formula by using these rules.

1. Write the name of the positive ion.
2. Using **Table 3,** check to see if the positive ion is capable of forming more than one oxidation number. If the ion has only one possible oxidation number, proceed to step 3. If it has more than one, determine the oxidation number of the ion from the formula of the compound. To do this, keep in mind that the overall charge of the compound is zero and the negative ion has only one possible charge. Write the charge of the positive ion using roman numerals in parentheses after the ion's name.
3. Write the root name of the negative ion. The root is the first part of the element's name. For chlorine, the root is *chlor-*.
4. Add the ending *-ide* to the root. **Table 4** lists several elements and their *-ide* counterparts. For example, sulfur in a binary compound becomes sulfide.

Subscripts do not become part of the name for ionic compounds. However, subscripts can be used to help determine the charges of these metals that have more than one positive charge.

Applying Science

Can you name binary ionic compounds?

What would a chemist name the compound CuCl?

Identifying the Problem

There are four simple steps in naming binary ionic compounds.

1. Write the name of the positive ion in the compound. In CuCl, the name of the positive ion is copper.
2. Check **Table 3** to determine whether copper is one of the elements that can have more than one oxidation number. Looking at **Table 3,** you can see that copper can have a 1+ or a 2+ oxidation number. You need to determine which to use. Looking at the compound, you see that there is one copper atom and one chlorine atom. You know that the overall charge of the compound is zero and that chlorine only forms a 1− ion. For the charge of the compound to be zero, the charge of the copper ion must be 1+. Write this charge using roman numerals in parentheses after the element's name, copper(I).
3. Write the root name of the negative ion. The negative ion is chlorine and its root is *chlor-*.
4. Add the ending *-ide* to the root, *chloride.*
5. The full name of the compound CuCl is copper(I) chloride.

Solving the Problem

1. What is the name of CuO?
2. What is the name of $AlCl_3$?

706 **CHAPTER 22** Chemical Bonds

Teacher FYI

Hydrogen's Assignment Hydrogen is nearly always found with a +1 charge. However, when hydrogen combines with active metals such as those found in Groups 1 and 2, it is assigned a −1 charge. This assignment is made because of the ease with which those metals lose electrons to become + 1 ions. Examples include NaH and MgH_2. These compounds are called sodium hydride and magnesium hydride.

Compounds with Polyatomic Ions

Not all ionic compounds are binary. Baking soda—used in cooking, as a medicine, and for brushing your teeth—has the formula $NaHCO_3$. This is an example of an ionic compound that is not binary. Some ionic compounds are composed of more than two elements. They contain polyatomic ions. The prefix *poly-* means "many," so the term *polyatomic* means "having many atoms." A **polyatomic ion** is a positively or negatively charged, covalently bonded group of atoms. Thus, the polyatomic ions as a whole contain two or more elements. The polyatomic ion in baking soda is the bicarbonate or hydrogen carbonate ion, HCO_3^-.

Table 5 Polyatomic Ions

Charge	Name	Formula
1+	ammonium	NH_4^+
1−	acetate	$C_2H_3O_2^-$
	chlorate	ClO_3^-
	hydroxide	OH^-
	nitrate	NO_3^-
2−	carbonate	CO_3^{2-}
	sulfate	SO_4^{2-}
3−	phosphate	PO_4^{3-}

Writing Names Several polyatomic ions are listed in **Table 5.** To name a compound that contains one of these ions, first write the name of the positive ion. Use **Table 5** to find the name of a polyatomic ion. Then write the name of the negative ion. For example, K_2SO_4 is potassium sulfate. What is the name of $Sr(OH)_2$? Begin by writing the name of the positive ion, strontium. Then find the name of the polyatomic ion, OH^-, which is hydroxide. Thus, the name is strontium hydroxide.

Writing Formulas To write formulas for these compounds, follow the rules for binary compounds, with one addition. When more than one polyatomic ion is needed, write parentheses around the polyatomic ion before adding the subscript. How would you write the formula of barium chlorate?

First, identify the symbol of the positive ion. Barium has the symbol Ba and forms a 2+ ion, Ba^{2+}. Next, identify the negative chlorate ion. **Table 5** shows that it is ClO_3^-. Finally, you need to balance the charges of the ions to make the compound neutral. It will take two chlorate ions with a 1− charge to balance the 2+ charge of the barium ion. Because the chlorate ion is polyatomic, you use parentheses before adding the subscript. The formula is $Ba(ClO_3)_2$. Another example of naming complex compounds is shown in **Figure 21.**

Figure 21 Naming Complex Compounds

How would a scientist write the chemical formula for ammonium phospate?
To write the formula, answer the following questions:

1. What is the positive ion and its charge?
   The positive ion is NH_4^{1+} and its charge is 1+.
2. What is the negative ion and its charge?
   The negative ion is PO_4^{3-} and its charge is 3−.
3. Balance the charges to make the compound neutral.
   a) three NH_4^{1+} ions (+3) balance one PO_4^{3-} (3−)
   b) The charge of one ion (without the sign) becomes the subscript of the other. Add parentheses for subscripts greater than 1.
   NH_4^{1+} PO_4^{3-} gives $(NH_4)_3PO_4$

The chemical formula for ammonium phosphate is $(NH_4)_3PO_4$.

Discussion

Polyatomic Ions Provide practice using polyatomic ions by having students name each of the following compounds and determine the number of atoms of the underlined element in each: $Na_3P\underline{O}_4$, 4 oxygen atoms, sodium phosphate; $Al_2(\underline{C}O_3)_3$, 3 carbon atoms, aluminum carbonate; $Ca(C_2\underline{H}_3O_2)_2$, 6 atoms of hydrogen, calcium acetate L2 LS **Logical-Mathematical**

Fun Fact

Anhydrous compounds such as $CaCl_2$ are sometimes sold as products to reduce humidity. Anhydrous calcium chloride absorbs moisture to become a hydrate in a moist basement.

Cultural Diversity

Silicon Dioxide The binary covalent compound silicon dioxide, SiO_2, also known as quartz or rock crystal, has been revered in many cultures since ancient times. Have students report on some of the legends associated with SiO_2. Japanese, ancient Greek, Cherokee Indian, Burmese, Irish, and Scottish are some of the cultures that have legends surrounding SiO_2. P

Differentiated Instruction

Challenge Have students find the formulas, names, or charges of the following polyatomic ions: nitrite, NO_2^-; sulfite, SO_3^{2-}; MnO_4^-, permanganate; ClO_2^-, chlorite. L3 LS **Logical-Mathematical**

SECTION 3 Writing Formulas and Naming Compounds 707

Use Science Words

Word Usage Have students use the word *hydrate* in a sentence in a way that describes its meaning. Possible answer: A hydrate forms when water molecules become attached to the ions of a compound. L1 LS **Linguistic**

Mini LAB

Video Lab available.

Purpose Students will create their own hydrates.

Materials plaster of paris, water, small bowl, rubber hammer, hair dryer for each student

Teaching Strategy Ask students to show their final products to the class.

Analysis

1. The plaster should not crack when tapped before it is heated, but it becomes brittle and cracks easily after being heated.
2. Steam will rise from the plaster, and it will easily crumble and become powder. The heat removes water molecules from the hydrated gypsum causing the plaster to lose its strength.

Assessment

Performance Ask students to experiment with different proportions of water and plaster of paris to create hydrates with different heat and stress-resistant properties. Use **Performance Assessment in the Science Classroom,** p. 89.

Caption Answer

Figure 22 $CaSO_4$

Mini LAB

Making a Hydrate

Procedure

1. Mix 150 g of **plaster of paris** with 75 mL of **water** in a small **bowl.**
2. Let the plaster dry overnight and then take the hardened plaster out of the bowl.
3. Lightly tap the plaster with a **rubber hammer.**
4. Heat the plaster with a **hair dryer** on the hottest setting and observe.
5. Place a towel over the sample, then lightly tap the plaster with the hammer after heating it.

Analysis

1. What happened to the plaster when you tapped it before and after heating it?
2. What did you observe happening to the plaster as you heated it? Explain.

Compounds with Added Water

Some ionic compounds have water molecules as part of their structure. These compounds are called hydrates. A **hydrate** is a compound that has water chemically attached to its ions and written into its chemical formula.

Common Hydrates The term *hydrate* comes from a word that means "water." When a solution of cobalt chloride evaporates, pink crystals that contain six water molecules for each unit of cobalt chloride are formed. The formula for this compound is $CoCl_2 \cdot 6H_2O$ and is called cobalt chloride hexahydrate.

You can remove water from these crystals by heating them. The resulting blue compound is called anhydrous, which means "without water." When anhydrous (blue) $CoCl_2$ is exposed to water, even from the air, it will revert back to its hydrated state.

The plaster of paris shown in **Figure 22** also forms a hydrate when water is added. It becomes calcium sulfate dihydrate, which is also known as gypsum. The water that was added to the powder became a part of the compound.

To write the formula for a hydrate, write the formula for the compound and then place a dot followed by the number of water molecules. The dot in the formula represents a ratio of a compound to water molecules. For example, calcium sulfate dihydrate, $CaSO_4 \cdot 2H_2O$, is the formula for the hydrate of calcium sulfate that contains two molecules of water.

Naming Binary Covalent Compounds

Covalent compounds are those formed between elements that are nonmetals. Some pairs of nonmetals can form more than one compound with each other. For example, nitrogen and oxygen can form N_2O, NO, NO_2 and N_2O_5. In the system you have learned so far, each of these compounds would be called nitrogen oxide. You would not know from that name what the composition of the compound is.

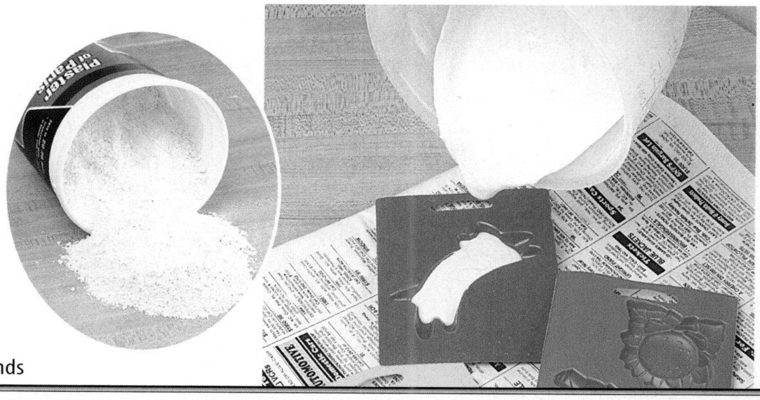

Figure 22 The presence of water changes this powder into a material that can be used to create art.
Identify *the formula for this powder prior to the addition of water.*

LAB DEMONSTRATION

Purpose to observe the difference between a hydrated and a dehydrated compound

Materials copper(II) sulfate pentahydrate, test tube, Bunsen burner, water, dropper

Procedure Place a small amount of copper(II) sulfate pentahydrate in the tube and heat it in a flame. Have students observe the change. Let tube cool, then add a few drops of water.

Expected Outcome When heated, the deep blue copper(II) sulfate pentahydrate gradually changes into the white powder of the anhydrous compound. When water is added, the blue hydrate is restored.

Assessment

Write the formula for copper(II) sulfate pentahydrate. $CuSO_4 \cdot 5H_2O$ Was this a chemical change or a physical change? A chemical change; it changed the identity of the material.

Using Prefixes Scientists use the Greek prefixes in **Table 6** to indicate how many atoms of each element are in a binary covalent compound. The nitrogen and oxygen compounds N_2O, NO, NO_2, and N_2O_5 would be named dinitrogen oxide, nitrogen oxide, nitrogen dioxide, and dinitrogen pentoxide. Notice that the last vowel of the prefix is dropped when the second element begins with a vowel, as in pentoxide. Often, the prefix *mono-* is omitted, although it is used for emphasis in some cases. Carbon monoxide is one example.

Reading Check ***What prefix would be used for seven atoms of one element in a covalent compound?***

These same prefixes are used when naming the hydrates previously discussed. The main ionic compound is named the regular way, but the number of water molecules in the hydrate is indicated by the Greek prefix.

You have learned how to write formulas of binary ionic compounds and of compounds containing polyatomic ions. Using oxidation numbers to write formulas, you can predict the ratio in which atoms of elements might combine to form compounds. You also have seen how hydrates have water molecules as part of their structures and formulas. Finally, you have learned how to use prefixes in naming binary covalent compounds. As you continue to study, you will see many uses of formulas.

Table 6 Prefixes for Covalent Compounds

Number of Atoms	Prefix
1	*mono-*
2	*di-*
3	*tri-*
4	*tetra-*
5	*penta-*
6	*hexa-*
7	*hepta-*
8	*octa-*

Reading Check

Answer *hepta-*

Post Reading

Science Journal Have students respond to the following prompt: Explain how binary compounds and compounds with complex ions are named. Include information reguarding the formation of these compounds and the chemical formulas used to represent them. Have students read and discuss their responses with a partner.

section 3 review

Summary

Binary Ionic Compounds

- A binary compound is one composed of two elements.
- The oxidation number tells how many electrons an atom has gained, lost, or shared to become stable.
- The net charge of a compound is zero.

Compounds with Complex Ions

- A polyatomic ion is a positively or negatively charged, covalently bonded group of atoms.
- A hydrate is a compound that has water chemically attached to its ions.
- Greek prefixes are used to indicate how many atoms of each element are in a binary covalent compound.

Self Check

1. **Use Formulas** Write formulas for the following compounds: potassium iodide, magnesium hydroxide, aluminum sulfate, and chlorine heptoxide.
2. **Use Formulas** Write the names of these compounds: KCl, Cr_2O_3, $Ba(ClO_3)_2$, NH_4Cl, and PCl_3.
3. **Name** $Mg_3(PO_4)_2 \cdot 4H_2O$ and write the formula for calcium nitrate trihydrate.
4. **Think Critically** Explain why sodium and potassium will or will not react to form a bond with each other.

Applying Math

5. **Solve One-Step Equations** The overall charge on the polyatomic sulfate ion, found in some acids, is 2^-. Its formula is SO_4^{2-}. If the oxygen ion has a 2^- oxidation number, determine the oxidation number of sulfur in this polyatomic ion.

More Section Review gpescience.com

3 Assess

DAILY INTERVENTION

Check for Understanding

Logical-Mathematical Have students read the labels of various products and find five compounds that have names with the numeric prefixes. Have them write out the formula for each of these compounds.

Reteach

Prefix Ask students why calcium chloride ($CaCl_2$) is named without using the prefix system shown in **Table 5,** while carbon tetrachloride (CCl_4) does use a prefix to designate the number of chlorine atoms. The prefix system is used for covalent compounds between nonmetals. $CaCl_2$ is ionic. L2 LS **Logical-Mathematical**

Assessment

Performance The common name for $Na_2B_4O_5(OH)_4 \cdot 8H_2O$ is borax. It is used as an important source of boron and can also be used as a washing powder. Ask students to determine the number of oxygen atoms in the molecule. Use **PASC,** p.101.

section 3 review

1. KI; $Mg(OH)_2$; $Al_2(SO_4)_3$; Cl_2O_7
2. potassium chloride; chromium(III) oxide; barium chlorate; ammonium chloride; phosphorus trichloride
3. magnesium phosphate tetrahydrate; $Ca(NO_3)_2 \cdot 3H_2O$
4. Sodium and potassium will bond with atoms that are able to easily accept electrons. They would have a difficult time bonding with each other because both tend to lose electrons.
5. Oxygen contributes $4 \times -2 = -8$. The total charge is -2, so sulfur must contribute $+6$.

BENCH TESTED

Real-World Problem

Purpose Students will compare and contrast chemical formulas by making models of chemical bonding using outer energy levels. L3 LS **Kinesthetic**

Process Skills classify, communicate, compare and contrast, draw, label, infer, interpret scientific illustrations, organize data, think critically

Time Required class period

Safety Precautions Do not use candy in place of beans. You should not encourage eating in the lab.

Form a Hypothesis

Possible Hypothesis Students may hypothesize that ionic bonding occurs with the transfer of electrons to form ions and that covalent bonding occurs when electrons are shared between atoms.

Test Your Hypothesis

Possible Procedures Give students three to nine beans. This will allow them to model lithium to flourine. Encourage students to work with other students to model ionic bonding (transfer of electrons) and covalent bonding (sharing of electrons).

Teaching Strategies

- Using the egg carton, block off two of the egg spaces and review with students the capacity of first and second energy levels.

LAB **Model and Invent**

Modeling Chemical Bonding

Goals

- **Infer** chemical formulas by making models of outer electron levels.
- **Compare and contrast** models of ionic and covalent bonding.
- **Draw and label** diagrams to illustrate chemical bonding.

Possible Materials

modified egg carton
beans
**pennies*
**buttons*
**Alternate materials*

Safety Precautions

Complete a safety worksheet before you begin.

Real-World Problem

Chemical bonding is one of the most important concepts in chemistry. Bonding is what makes different compounds. Even though atoms have a nucleus containing protons and neutrons, the part of the atom that is most important to chemists is outside the nucleus. How are electrons involved in chemical bonding?

Make a Model

1. Obtain a modified egg carton and beans from your teacher. The egg carton represents the first and second energy levels of an atom. The beans represent electrons.
2. **Decide** which elements you can model by the number of beans you have. Consider how the periodic table can be used to determine the number of outer electrons in an element.
3. **Model** all the elements that you can create using the modified egg carton and beans.
4. **Draw** the models of elements that you created in your Science Journal.
5. **Determine** if the elements form ionic or covalent bonding. Record your conclusions in your Science Journal.

710 **CHAPTER 22** Chemical Bonds

Using Scientific Methods

Test Your Model

1. Look for element combinations that could represent chemical formulas for compounds and molecules. Some formulas may require more than one atom to form some types of elements and compounds.
2. Work with other students to make models of compounds and molecules produced by chemical bonding.
3. **Draw** the models of the compounds and molecules you made in your Science Journal. Record the type of bonding used to make the compounds and molecules.

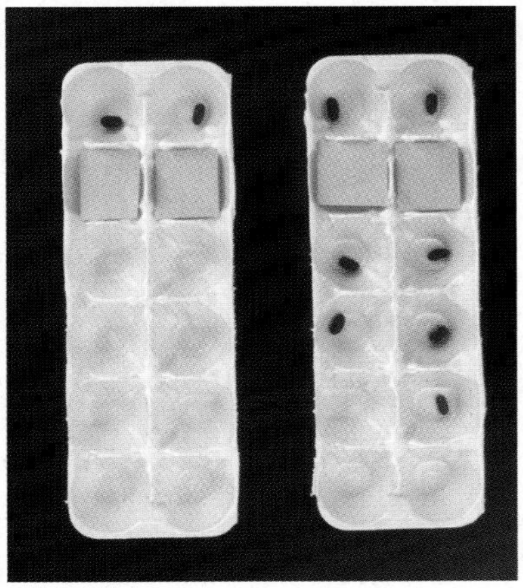

Analyze Your Data

1. **Explain** how you can use the periodic table to identify the element that represents your model.
2. **Explain** whether elements in the metal groups on the periodic table have more or fewer electrons in their outer energy levels than the nonmetals.
3. The combinations of elements could represent chemical formulas. Explain why some formulas require more than one atom of an element.

Conclude and Apply

1. **Describe** why your model could be used to show examples of both ionic and covalent bonding.
2. **Predict** what element your model would be if you received ten beans. Explain your reasoning.

Communicating Your Data

Compare your conclusions with other students' conclusions. What elements did their models represent? Explain how their elements differed in ability to form ionic and covalent bonds.

Expected Outcome Monitor students so they discover simple matchups such as LiF and progress to compounds such as BeF_2, Li_2O, BeO, and Be_3N_2. Remind students that elements can achieve stability by losing, gaining, or sharing electrons.

Analyze Your Data

1. Using the periodic table, three beans would represent lithium, four beans beryllium, and so forth up to nine beans representing flourine.
2. In general, metals have fewer electrons than nonmetals.
3. Formulas such as BeF_2 show more flourine is needed to balance the charge in this compound.

Conclude and Apply

1. Elements have the ability to lose, gain, or share electrons.
2. This would represent neon, a noble gas that has a stable arrangement of eight outer level electrons.

✔ Assessment

Oral Have students explain compounds or molecules using their model that were not done during the experiment. Use **Performance Assessment in the Science Classroom,** p. 143.

Communicating Your Data

Share drawings of models with other students.

Content Background

Glue has been around for a long time. Egyptian carvings dating back 3,300 years show figures gluing thin pieces of veneer to sycamore planks. Throughout history, most glues came from a variety of natural sources, including beeswax, flour paste, egg whites, cheese, and extracts from animal horns and fish. Only in the recent century did synthetic glues become more prominent. Glues work because they are able to seep into the crevices of a surface and form chemical welds to the molecules on that surface. Strong polymer chains give glues their strength and flexibility.

Activity

Glue Experiment Let small groups of students experiment with their own glue. Give each group 15 mL of unflavored gelatin in a small beaker. Pour 25 mL of boiling water into the gelatin **WARNING:** *Be careful with the hot water.* Have students stir the mixture until the gelatin dissolves. Let them use paintbrushes to apply the glue to various types of materials such as paper, wood, and plastic to see which kinds of materials the glue will bond together.

Analyze the Event

Explain to students that Louis Pasteur was a French scientist who discovered, among other things, the rabies vaccine and the pasteurization process for milk. Write the following quote of Pasteur's on the board: "In the field of observation, chance favors the prepared mind." Ask students to brainstorm what they think the quote means and how it applies to this feature. Possible answers: The first group of researchers didn't realize the possibilities of the discovery, but the later group did, so the later group had "prepared minds."

Oops! Accidents in SCIENCE

SOMETIMES GREAT DISCOVERIES HAPPEN BY ACCIDENT!

A Sticky Subject

In 1942, a research team was working on creating a new kind of glass. The group was working with some cyanoacrylate monomers (si uh noh A kruh layt • MAH nuh muhrz) that showed promise, but a problem kept coming up. Everything the monomers touched stuck to everything else!

Cyanoacrylate is the chemical name for instant, supertype glues. The researchers were so focused on finding a different type of glass that at the time, none of them recognized that they were working with an important new adhesive.

In 1952, a member of the research team, working on new materials for jet plane canopies, made a similar complaint. The ethyl cyanoacrylate the team was working with again made everything stick together. This time, the insight stuck to the scientists like, well, like GLUE! "I began gluing everything I could lay my hands on—glass plates, rubber stoppers, metal spatulas, wood, paper, plastic. Everything stuck to everything, almost instantly, and with bonds I could not break apart," recalls the head of the research group.

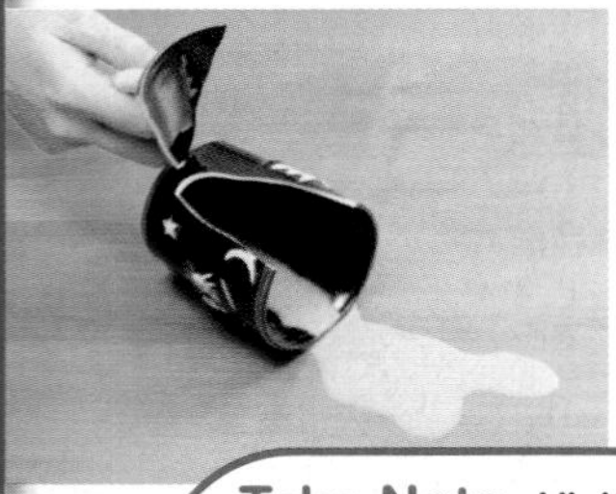

Stick to It

Most adhesives, commonly called glues, are long chains of bonded molecules called polymers. Cyanoacrylate, however, exists as monomers—single molecules with double bonds. And it stays that way until it hits anything with moisture in it, such as air. Yes, even the small amount of moisture in air and on the surfaces of most materials is enough to dissolve the double bonds in the monomers of cyanoacrylate, making them join together in long chains. The chains bond to surfaces as they polymerize.

The discovery of cyanoacrylates had an immediate impact on the automobile and airplane industries. And it soon "held" a spot in almost every household toolbox. Since the 1990s, cyanoacrylate glues have also found a place in doctors' offices. A doctor can apply a thin layer of instant glue instead of putting stitches in a cut. This specially made medical glue was approved by the U.S. Food and Drug Administration in 1998.

Take Note **Visit a store and make a table of different kinds of glues. List their common names, their chemical names, what they are made of, how long it takes them to set, and the types of surfaces for which they are recommended. Note any safety precautions.**

Oops! For more information, visit gpescience.com

Take Note Tell students to pay careful attention to the recommended uses for each type of glue. Ask students why one glue cannot meet all people's needs. (Possible answers: Some glues can be toxic and so wouldn't be useful for gluing drinking cups, as shown in the feature. Some glues might react chemically with paper or wood. Some glues aren't waterproof.)

Resources for Teachers and Students

"Adhesion," Encyclopedia Brittanica

The Encyclopedia of Modelmaking Techniques, by Christopher Payne and P. Quatro, 1996

The Crafter's Guide to Glues, by Tammy Young, Chilton Book Company, 1995

Sticky, Rigby Interactive Library, 1996

Reviewing Main Ideas

Section 1 Stability in Bonding

1. The properties of compounds are generally different from the properties of the elements they contain.
2. A chemical formula for a compound indicates the composition of a unit of the compound. This model of a water molecule shows the shape of the molecule and the relative sizes of the atoms.

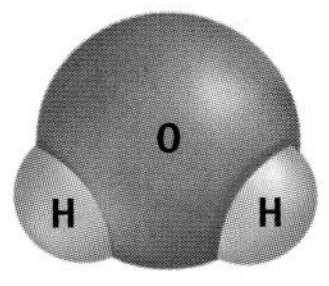

3. Chemical bonding occurs because atoms of most elements become more stable by gaining, losing, or sharing electrons to obtain stable outer energy levels.

Section 2 Types of Bonds

1. Covalent bonds are formed by the sharing of electrons. Ionic bonds between atoms are formed by the attraction between ions. Below is an example of an ionically bonded compound.

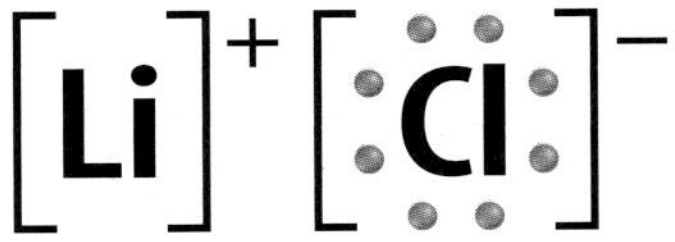

2. Ionic bonding occurs between charged particles called ions and produces ionic compounds. Covalent bonding produces units called molecules and occurs between nonmetallic elements.
3. The unequal sharing of electrons produces compounds that contain polar bonds, and the equal sharing of electrons produces nonpolar compounds.

Section 3 Writing Formulas and Naming Compounds

1. An oxidation number indicates how many electrons an atom has gained, lost, or shared when bonding with other atoms.
2. In the formula of an ionic compound, the element or ion with the positive oxidation number is written first, followed by the one with the negative oxidation number.
3. The name of a binary compound is derived from the names of the two elements that compose the compound. Salt is an example of a binary compound, sodium chloride.

4. A hydrate is a compound that has water chemically attached to its ions and written into its formula.
5. Greek prefixes are used in the names of covalent compounds. These indicate the number of each atom present.

FOLDABLES™ Use the Foldable that you made at the beginning of this chapter to help you review chemical bonds.

Reviewing Main Ideas

Summary statements can be used by students to review the major concepts of the chapter.

Science Online

Visit gpescience.com
More Section Review
Interactive Tutor
Vocabulary PuzzleMaker
More Chapter Review
Standardized Test Practice

Assessment Transparency

For additional assessment questions, use the *Assessment Transparency* located in the transparency book.

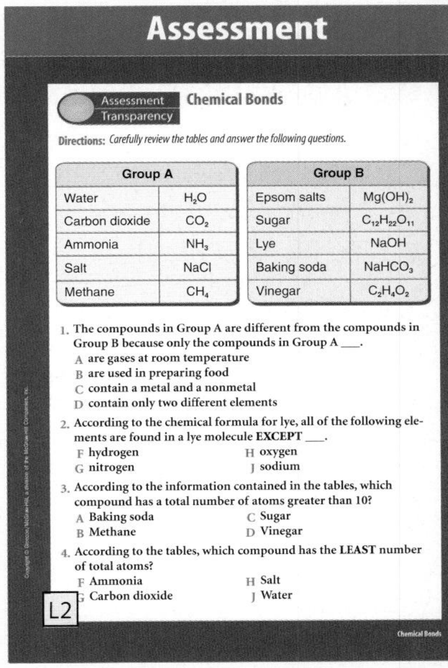

Assessment

Assessment Transparency **Chemical Bonds**

Directions: *Carefully review the tables and answer the following questions.*

Group A	
Water	H_2O
Carbon dioxide	CO_2
Ammonia	NH_3
Salt	NaCl
Methane	CH_4

Group B	
Epsom salts	$Mg(OH)_2$
Sugar	$C_{12}H_{22}O_{11}$
Lye	NaOH
Baking soda	$NaHCO_3$
Vinegar	$C_2H_4O_2$

1. The compounds in Group A are different from the compounds in Group B because only the compounds in Group A ___.
   A are gases at room temperature
   B are used in preparing food
   C contain a metal and a nonmetal
   D contain only two different elements
2. According to the chemical formula for lye, all of the following elements are found in a lye molecule **EXCEPT** ___.
   F hydrogen H oxygen
   G nitrogen J sodium
3. According to the information contained in the tables, which compound has a total number of atoms greater than 10?
   A Baking soda C Sugar
   B Methane D Vinegar
4. According to the tables, which compound has the **LEAST** number of total atoms?
   F Ammonia H Salt
   G Carbon dioxide J Water

L2

Chemical Bonds

FOLDABLES™ Use the Foldables that you made at the beginnning of the chapter to help you review chemical bonds.

chapter 22 Review

Using Vocabulary

1. polyatomic ion
2. binary compound
3. polar molecule
4. ion
5. ionic bond
6. covalent bond
7. hydrate
8. molecule
9. oxidation number
10. chemical formula

Checking Concepts

11. B
12. C
13. A
14. C
15. B
16. B
17. A
18. D

Interpreting Graphics

19. More stable; Different from; Ionic; Gained and lost; Covalent; Shared
20. hydrogen sulfide; H_2S
21. TeF_6, Na_2SO_4, CS_2, $BaCO_3$

chapter 22 Review

Using Vocabulary

binary compound p. 703	ionic bond p. 696
chemical bond p. 694	molecule p. 697
chemical formula p. 689	nonpolar molecule p. 700
covalent bond p. 697	oxidation number p. 703
hydrate p. 708	polar molecule p. 700
ion p. 692	polyatomic ion p. 707

Match each phrase with the correct vocabulary word or phrase.

1. a charged group of atoms
2. a compound composed of two elements
3. a molecule with partially charged areas
4. a positively or negatively charged particle
5. a chemical bond between oppositely charged ions
6. a bond formed from shared electrons
7. a crystalline substance that contains water
8. a particle made of covalently bonded atoms
9. shows an element's combining ability
10. tells which elements are in a compound and their ratios.

Checking Concepts

Choose the word or phrase that best answers the question.

11. Which elements are least likely to react with other elements?
    A) metals **C)** nonmetals
    B) noble gases **D)** transition elements

12. What is the name of CuO?
    A) copper oxide
    B) copper(I) oxide
    C) copper(II) oxide
    D) copper(III) oxide

13. Which formula represents a nonpolar molecule?
    A) N_2 **C)** NaCl
    B) H_2O **D)** HCl

14. How many electrons are in the outer energy levels of Group 17 elements?
    A) 1 **C)** 7
    B) 2 **D)** 17

15. Which is a binary ionic compound?
    A) O_2 **C)** H_2SO_4
    B) NaF **D)** $Cu(NO_3)_2$

16. Which is an anhydrous compound?
    A) H_2O **C)** $CuSO_4 \cdot 5H_2O$
    B) $CaSO_4$ **D)** $CaSO_4 \cdot 2H_2O$

17. Which atom has gained an electron?
    A) negative ion
    B) positive ion
    C) polar molecule
    D) nonpolar molecule

18. Which is a covalent compound?
    A) sodium chloride
    B) calcium fluoride
    C) calcium chloride
    D) sulfur dioxide

Interpreting Graphics

19. Copy and complete the concept map.

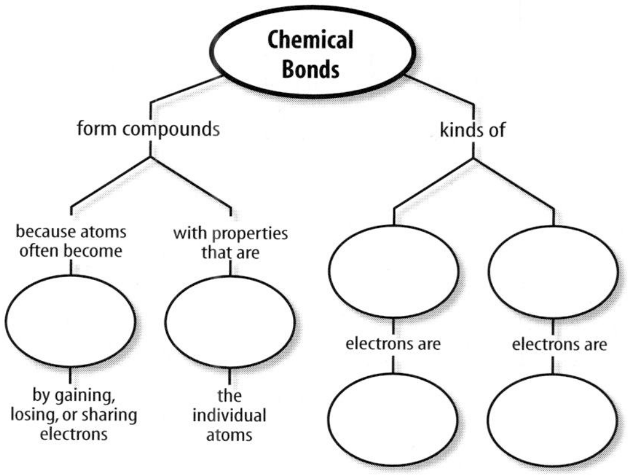

Use the ExamView® Pro Testmaker CD-ROM to:
- create multiple versions of tests
- create modified tests with one mouse click for inclusion students
- edit existing questions and add your own questions
- build tests aligned with state standards using built-in State Curriculum Tags
- change English tests to Spanish with one mouse click and vice versa

20. **Identify** and write the name and formula for the compound illustrated to the right.

Use the table below to answer question 21.

Which compounds exist?

Formula	Possible Compounds
SF_6	AlF_6 or TeF_6
K_2SO_4	Na_2SO_4 or Ba_2SO_4
CO_2	CCl_2 or CS_2
$CaCO_3$	OCO_3 or $BaCO_3$

21. **Predict** Elements from one family (vertical column) of the periodic table generally combine with elements from another family and polyatomic ions in the same ratio. For example, one calcium atom combines with two chlorine atoms to give $CaCl_2$ (calcium chloride), as it does with two fluorine atoms to give CaF_2 (calcium fluoride). Using the periodic table as a guide, predict which of the two compounds on the right side of the table above is more likely to exist based upon the formula on the left side.

Thinking Critically

22. **Draw** Anhydrous magnesium chloride is used to make wood fireproof. Draw a dot diagram of magnesium chloride.

23. **Use Formulas** Artificial diamonds are made using thallium carbonate. If thallium has an oxidation number of 1+, what is the formula for the compound?

24. **Compare and contrast** polar and nonpolar molecules.

25. **Write** Baking soda, which is sodium hydrogen carbonate, and vinegar, which contains hydrogen acetate, can be used as household cleaners. Write the chemical formulas for these two compounds.

26. **Draw Conclusions** Ammonia gas and water react to form household ammonia, which contains NH_4^+ and OH^- ions. The formula for water is H_2O. What is the formula for ammonia gas?

27. **Draw Conclusions** The name of a compound called copper(II) sulfate is written on a bottle. What is the charge of the copper ion? What is the charge of the sulfate ion?

28. **Explain** what electric forces between oppositely charged electrons and protons have to do with chemical reactions.

29. **Name Compounds** Write the chemical name for the following compounds.
A) Fe_2S_3 **C)** $Ca(PO_4)_2$
B) $Cu(ClO_3)_2$ **D)** $(NH_4)_2SO_4$

30. **Model** One common form of phosphorus, white phosphorus, has the formula P_4 and is formed by four covalently bonded phosphorus atoms. Make a model of this molecule, showing that all four atoms are now chemically stable.

31. **Determine** the chemical formulas for the following compounds.
A) potassium chloride
B) calcium carbonate
C) copper sulfate
D) sodium oxide

Applying Math

32. **Use Numbers** What is the oxidation number of Fe in the compound Fe_2S_3?
A) 1^+ **C)** 3^+
B) 2^+ **D)** 4^+

chapter 22 Review

Thinking Critically

22. $[:\ddot{\underset{..}{Cl}}:]^-Mg^{2+}[:\ddot{\underset{..}{Cl}}:]^-$
23. Tl_2CO_3
24. A polar molecule has opposite charges (positive and negative) on each end because of an unequal sharing of electrons. A nonpolar molecule does not have oppositely charged ends because the electrons involved are shared equally.
25. $NaHCO_3$; $HC_2H_3O_2$
26. NH_3
27. Cu^{+2} SO_4^{-2}
28. In order to form an ionic charge, the quantity of electrons and protons are unequal. If one element loses electrons, another must gain in order to keep the neutral charge of the compound
29. **a.** iron sulfide
b. copper (II) chlorate
c. calcium phosphate
d. ammonium sulfate
30. :P::P:
:P::P:
Use **PASC,** p. 123
31. **a.** KCl
b. $CaCO_3$
c. $CuSO_4$
d. Na_2O

Applying Math

Math Standards

National: 2, 6, 9

32. +3

Assessment Resources

Reproducible Masters

Chapter *Fast File* Resources
Chapter Review, pp. 37–38
Chapter Tests, pp. 39–42
Assessment Transparency Activity, p. 49

Glencoe Science Web site
Chapter Review Test
Standardized Test Practice

Glencoe Technology
Assessment Transparency
Exam*View*® Pro Testmaker
MindJogger Videoquiz
Interactive Chalkboard

Answer Sheet An answer sheet can be found at **gpescience.com**.

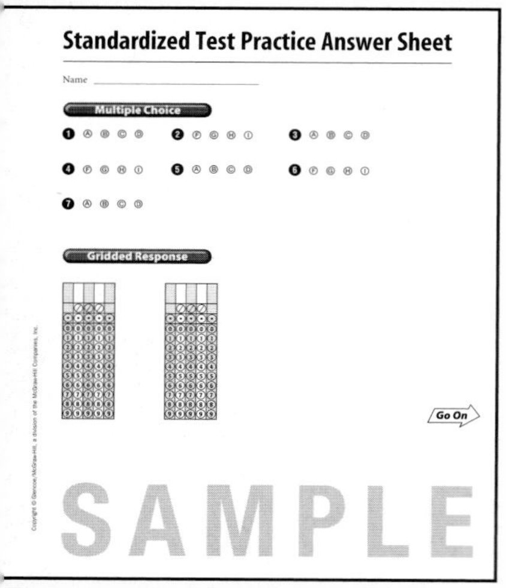

Multiple Choice

1. D
2. A
3. A
4. B
5. A
6. C
7. B

Gridded Response

8. 18
9. 18

Short Response

10. Nitrogen and fluorine have oxidation numbers of 23 and 21, respectively. Nitrogen must gain three electrons to fill its outer energy level, while fluorine must gain one.
11. NaCl is an ionic bond. In an ionic bond, a transfer of electrons takes place. Because you have a1 and a2 you get a zero net charge. Na1 1 Cl2, which gives you a zero net charge.

chapter 22 Standardized Test Practice

Record your answers on the answer sheet provided by your teacher or on a sheet of paper.

Multiple Choice

1. Which statement about this molecule is TRUE?

A. This is a nonpolar molecule.

B. The electrons are shared equally in the bonds of this molecule.

C. This molecule does not have oppositely charged ends.

D. This is a polar molecule.

Use the figure below to answer question 2.

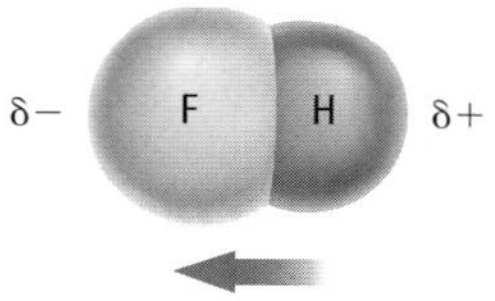

2. What type of bond holds the atoms of this molecule together?

A. covalent

B. ionic

C. triple

D. double

3. What do the Group 7A elements become when they react with Group 1A elements?

A. negative ions

B. neutral

C. positive ions

D. polyatomic ions

4. What is the name of $KC_2H_3O_2$?

A. potassium carbide

B. potassium acetate

C. potassium hydroxide

D. potassium oxide

5. What is the chemical formula for lead(II) oxide?

A. PbO

B. Pb_2O

C. PbO_2

D. Pb_2O_2

Use the illustration below to answer question 6.

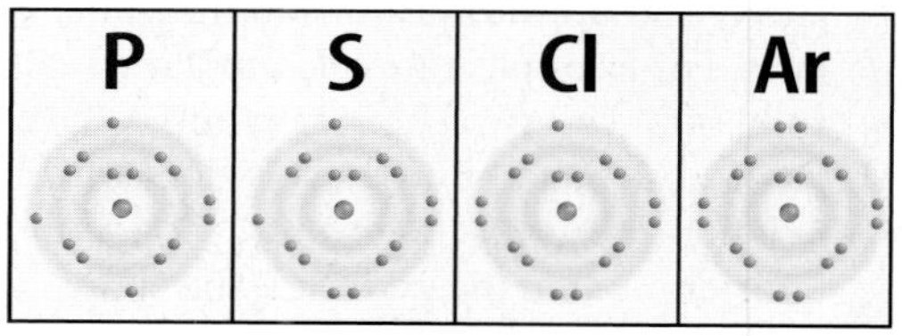

6. How many electrons are required to complete the outer energy level of a phosphorous atom?

A. one

B. two

C. three

D. four

Test-Taking Tip

Comprehension Be sure you understand the question before you read the answer choices. Make special note of words like NOT or EXCEPT. Read and consider all the answer choices before you mark your answer sheet.

Extended Response

12. HCL is an example of covalent bonding of unequal sharing. Chlorine atoms have a stronger attraction for electrons than hydrogen does. Therefore, the electrons shared in hydrogen chloride will spend more time near the chlorine atom than the hydrogen atom. The example of a tug-of-war with the knot being the electron shows how the bonding happens. Therefore the electron goes more with the chlorine which is bigger.
Ionic bonding is an equal sharing of electrons so that they equal 0. Potassium is a 11 and chlorine is a 21 which when you put 11 1 21 5 0.
13. This is a covalent bond, formed from sharing of electrons. It is a triple bond, as three pairs of electrons are shared.
14. H:H :O::O: :F:F: :Cl:Cl: :Br:Br: :I:I:

7. Which element is **NOT** part of the compound NH_4NO_3?

A. nitrogen

B. nickel

C. oxygen

D. hydrogen

Gridded Response

8. When an atom is chemically stable, how many electrons are in its outer energy level?

9. How many electrons are there in an argon atom?

Short Response

Use the illustration below to answer question 10.

Oxidation Numbers of Some Period 2 Elements

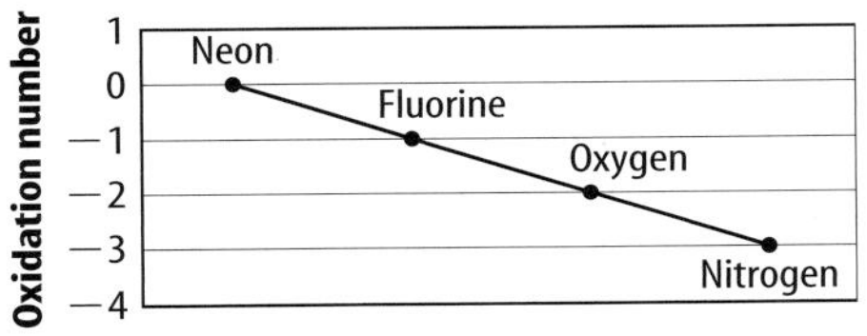

10. Compare the oxidation numbers of nitrogen and fluorine. Why do they differ?

11. The bonding of atoms and molecules is the result of oppositely charged electrons and protons being held together by electric forces within the atoms. Using this information, explain the bonding of NaCl.

Extended Response

12. KCl is an example of ionic bonding. HCl is an example of covalent bonding. Describe the difference in the bonds in terms of electrons and outer energy levels.

Use the illustration below to answer question 13.

13. Describe the bond holding the nitrogen atoms together in this molecule.

14. Nitrogen occurs naturally as a diatomic molecule because N_2 molecules are more stable than nitrogen atoms. H_2, O_2, F_2, Cl_2, Br_2, and I_2 are other diatomic molecules. Draw dot diagrams for three of these molecules.

15. Explain why elements in Groups 4A, which have four electrons in their outer energy levels, are unlikely to lose all of the electrons in their outer energy levels.

16. What factors affect how strongly an atom is attracted to its electrons?

17. Create a chart that compares the properties of polar and nonpolar molecules. Your chart should include several examples of each type of molecule.

18. What is the difference between nitrogen oxide and dinitrogen pentoxide? Why are prefixes used to name these compounds?

18. Nitrgen oxide is NO, while dinitrogen pentoxide is N2O5. Prefixes are used to identify the composition of compounds which are made of elements that can form more than one compound with each other.

Rubrics

For more help evaluating Short- and Extended-Response questions, see the rubrics on p. 10T.

15. These elements have four outer shell electrons. It would take a lot of energy to lose four electrons, because each time an electron was lost, the other electrons would be held even more tightly by the nucleus.

16. The size of the atom, the size of the positive charge in the nucleus, and the total number of electrons an atom has all affect the strength of the attraction between an atom and its electrons.

17.

Polar Molecules	Nonpolar Molecules
Have covalent bonds	Have covalent bonds
Electrons are held more closely by one atom of the molecule	Electrons are shared equally
Have slightly positive and slightly negative ends	Do not have oppositely charged ends
Examples: NH_3, H_2O	Examples: CCl_4, CH_4

chapter 23 Organizer

Section/Objectives	Standards: National	Standards: State/Local	Labs/Features
Chapter Opener	See pp. 16T–17T for a Key to Standards.		**Launch LAB:** Rusting—A Chemical Reaction, p. 719 **Foldables,** p. 719
Section 1 Chemical Changes 1 session; 1 block 1. **Identify** the reactants and products in a chemical reaction. 2. **Determine** how a chemical reaction satisfies the law of conservation of mass. 3. **Determine** how chemists express chemical changes using equations.	National Content Standards: UCP.1–UCP.5, A.1, A.2, B.2, B.3, G.3		**Science Online,** p. 722 **MiniLAB:** Designing a Team Equation, p. 724 Video Lab
Section 2 Chemical Equations 2 sessions; 1 block 4. **Identify** what is meant by a balanced chemical equation. 5. **Determine** how to write balanced chemical equations.	National Content Standards: UCP.1–UCP.5, A.1, A.2, B.2, B.3		**Science Online,** p. 727 **Applying Math:** Barium Sulfate Reaction, p. 728
Section 3 Classifying Chemical Reactions 2 sessions; 1 block 6. **Identify** the five general types of chemical reactions. 7. **Identify** redox reactions. 8. **Predict** which metals will replace other metals in compounds.	National Content Standards: UCP.1–UCP.5, A.1, A.2, B.2, B.3, B.6		
Section 4 Reaction Rates and Energy 3 sessions; 1 block 9. **Identify** the source of energy changes in chemical reactions. 10. **Compare and contrast** exergonic and endergonic reactions. 11. **Examine** the effects of catalysts and inhibitors on the speed of chemical reactions.	National Content Standards: UCP.1–UCP.5, A.1, A.2, B.2, B.3, B.6, G.1, G.2, G.3		**Integrate Life Science,** p. 735 **Visualizing Chemical Energy,** p. 737 **MiniLAB:** Creating a Colorful Chemical Reaction, p. 738 **Integrate History,** p. 740 **Lab:** Catalyzed Reaction, p. 741 **Lab:** Investigating Reaction Conditions, pp. 742–743 **Oops! Accidents in Science:** A Clumsy Move Pays Off, p. 744

StudentWorks Plus | Glencoe Exclusive! TeacherWorks™ All-In-One Planner and Resource Center

Lab Materials	Reproducible Resources	Section Assessment	Technology
Launch Lab: teaspoon, agar, beaker, hot plate, graduated cylinder, 1% phenolphthalein solution, petri dishes, uncoated steel nails, aluminum pie tins or nails	**Chapter *Fast File* Resources** Foldables Worksheet, p. 17 Note-taking Worksheets, pp. 35–37 Directed Reading Overview, p. 19	Glencoe's Assessment Advantage	TeacherWorks includes: • Interactive Teacher Edition • Lesson Planner with calendar • Access to all program blacklines • Correlations to standards • Web links
MiniLAB: 15 index cards, markers	**Chapter *Fast File* Resources** Transparency Activity, p. 46 MiniLAB, p. 3 Enrichment, p. 31 Reinforcement, p. 27 Directed Reading, p. 20 Transparency Activity, pp. 51–52 Lab Activity, pp. 9–11	**Portfolio** Curriculum Connection, p. 722 **Performance** MiniLAB, p. 724 Applying Math, p. 725 **Content** Section Review, p. 725	Section Focus Transparency Teaching Transparency Interactive Chalkboard CD-ROM StudentWorks Plus Video Lab
	Chapter *Fast File* Resources Transparency Activity, p. 47 Enrichment, p. 32 Reinforcement, p. 28 Directed Reading, p. 20 Lab Activity, pp. 13–16	**Portfolio** Assessment, p. 729 **Performance** Applying Math, p. 728 Applying Math, p. 729 **Content** Section Review, p. 729	Section Focus Transparency Virtual Labs CD-ROM Interactive Chalkboard CD-ROM StudentWorks Plus
Need materials? Contact Science Kit at 1-800-828-7777 or www.sciencekit.com.	**Chapter *Fast File* Resources** Transparency Activity, p. 48 Enrichment, p. 33 Reinforcement, p. 29 Directed Reading, p. 21	**Performance** Applying Math, p. 733 **Content** Section Review, p. 733	Section Focus Transparency Interactive Chalkboard CD-ROM StudentWorks Plus
MiniLAB: water, test tube, copper(II) bromide **Lab:** test tubes, rack, H_2O_2, graduated cylinder, teaspoon, sand, hot plate, wooden splint, water, MnO_2 **Lab:** water, vinegar, baking soda, plastic bottle, test tube, beakers, graduated cylinder, marker, tape measure, stopwatch	**Chapter *Fast File* Resources** Transparency Activity, p. 49 MiniLAB, p. 4 Enrichment, p. 34 Reinforcement, p. 30 Directed Reading, pp. 21, 22 Lab Worksheet, pp. 5–6, 7–8	**Portfolio** Activity, p. 737 **Performance** MiniLAB, p. 738 Applying Math, p. 740 **Content** Section Review, p. 740	Section Focus Transparency Interactive Chalkboard CD-ROM StudentWorks Plus

End of Chapter Assessment

Glencoe's Assessment Advantage

Blackline Masters	Technology	Professional Series
Chapter *Fast File* Resources Chapter Review, pp. 39–40 Chapter Tests, pp. 41–44 **Standardized Test Practice,** pp. 96–99	MindJogger Videoquiz Virtual Labs CD-ROM Exam*View*® Pro Testmaker TeacherWorks CD-ROM Interactive Chalkboard CD-ROM	**Performance Assessment in the Science Classroom (PASC)**

Transparencies

Section Focus

SECTION 1 Section Focus Transparency — A Changing World — Chapter 23

This family is not only having fun, they're doing chemistry! Toasting marshmallows, burning wood, and getting energy from food all involve changes in substances.

1. Describe what you see in this campfire scene.
2. How do some of the things you named look different than they did before the fire was lit?
3. How will the marshmallows continue to change if kept in the fire?

L2

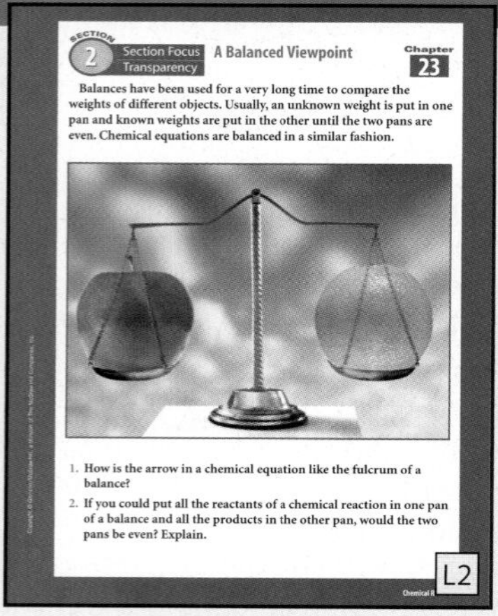
SECTION 2 Section Focus Transparency — A Balanced Viewpoint — Chapter 23

Balances have been used for a very long time to compare the weights of different objects. Usually, an unknown weight is put in one pan and known weights are put in the other until the two pans are even. Chemical equations are balanced in a similar fashion.

1. How is the arrow in a chemical equation like the fulcrum of a balance?
2. If you could put all the reactants of a chemical reaction in one pan of a balance and all the products in the other pan, would the two pans be even? Explain.

L2

SECTION 3 Section Focus Transparency — Free the Nitrogen! — Chapter 23

Nitrogen is the most abundant gas in the atmosphere. However, in the atmosphere, nitrogen is held in molecules by very strong triple bonds. In order to be used by living things, these triple bonds need to be broken. Lightning can supply energy that frees nitrogen atoms to form new compounds.

1. Do the nitrogen atoms freed by lightning undergo a chemical or physical change?
2. Describe what happens to the atoms in the reaction $N_2 + O_2 \rightarrow 2NO$.

L2

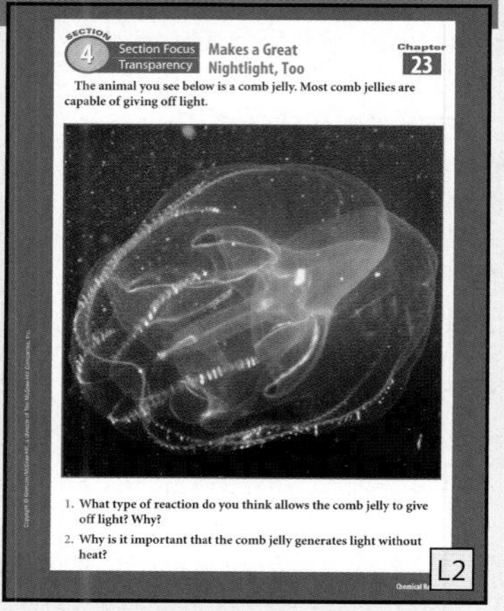
SECTION 4 Section Focus Transparency — Makes a Great Nightlight, Too — Chapter 23

The animal you see below is a comb jelly. Most comb jellies are capable of giving off light.

1. What type of reaction do you think allows the comb jelly to give off light? Why?
2. Why is it important that the comb jelly generates light without heat?

L2

This is a representation of key blackline masters available in the Teacher Classroom Resources. See Resource Manager boxes within the chapter for additional information.

Assessment

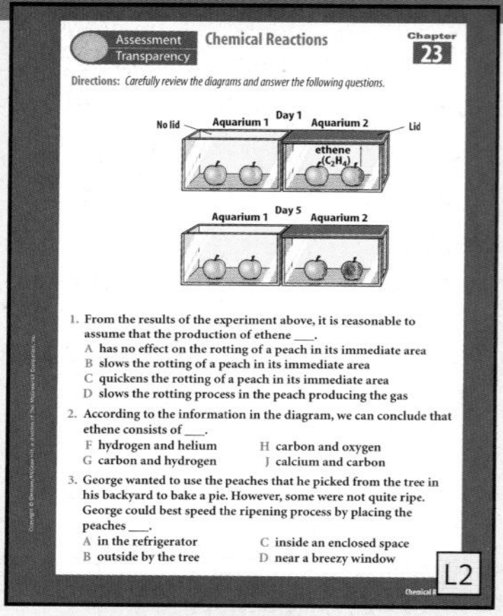
Assessment Transparency — Chemical Reactions — Chapter 23

Directions: *Carefully review the diagrams and answer the following questions.*

1. From the results of the experiment above, it is reasonable to assume that the production of ethene ___.
   A has no effect on the rotting of a peach in its immediate area
   B slows the rotting of a peach in its immediate area
   C quickens the rotting of a peach in its immediate area
   D slows the rotting process in the peach producing the gas
2. According to the information in the diagram, we can conclude that ethene consists of ___.
   F hydrogen and helium
   G carbon and hydrogen
   H carbon and oxygen
   J calcium and carbon
3. George wanted to use the peaches that he picked from the tree in his backyard to bake a pie. However, some were not quite ripe. George could best speed the ripening process by placing the peaches ___.
   A in the refrigerator
   B outside by the tree
   C inside an enclosed space
   D near a breezy window

L2

Teaching

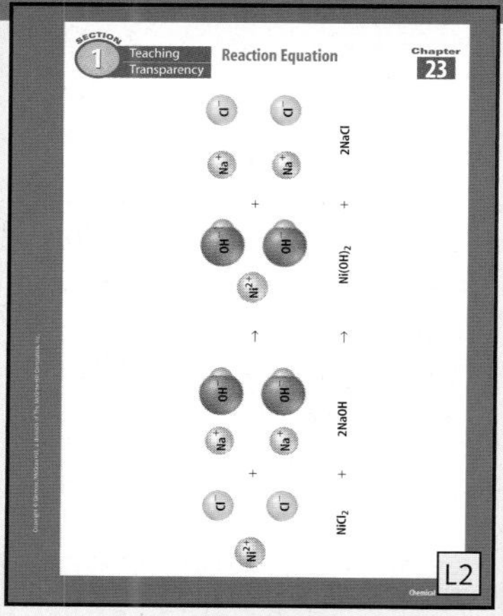
Teaching Transparency 1 — Reaction Equation — Chapter 23

L2

Key to Teaching Strategies

The following designations will help you decide which activities are appropriate for your students.

- L1 Level 1 activities should be appropriate for students with learning difficulties.
- L2 Level 2 activities should be within the ability range of all students.
- L3 Level 3 activities are designed for above-average students.
- ELL ELL activities should be within the ability range of English Language Learners.
- COOP LEARN Cooperative Learning activities are designed for small group work.
- LS Multiple Learning Styles logos, as described on page 12T, are used throughout to indicate strategies that address different learning styles.
- P These strategies represent student products that can be placed into a best-work portfolio.
- PBL Problem-Based Learning activities apply real-world situations to learning.

Hands-on Activities

Student Text Lab Worksheets

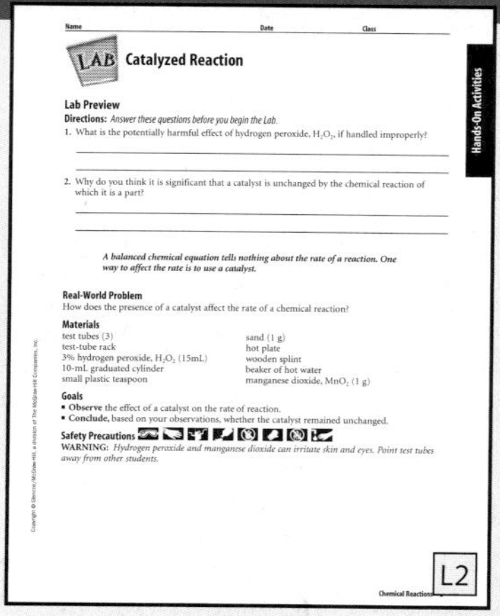
Name Date Class

LAB Catalyzed Reaction

Lab Preview

Directions: *Answer these questions before you begin the Lab.*

1. What is the potentially harmful effect of hydrogen peroxide, H_2O_2, if handled improperly?
2. Why do you think it is significant that a catalyst is unchanged by the chemical reaction of which it is a part?

A balanced chemical equation tells nothing about the rate of a reaction. One way to affect the rate is to use a catalyst.

Real-World Problem

How does the presence of a catalyst affect the rate of a chemical reaction?

Materials

test tubes (3)
test-tube rack
3% hydrogen peroxide, H_2O_2 (15mL)
10-mL graduated cylinder
small plastic teaspoon
sand (1 g)
hot plate
wooden splint
beaker of hot water
manganese dioxide, MnO_2 (1 g)

Goals

- **Observe** the effect of a catalyst on the rate of reaction.
- **Conclude,** based on your observations, whether the catalyst remained unchanged.

Safety Precautions

WARNING: *Hydrogen peroxide and manganese dioxide can irritate skin and eyes. Point test tubes away from other students.*

Hands-On Activities

L2

Laboratory Activities

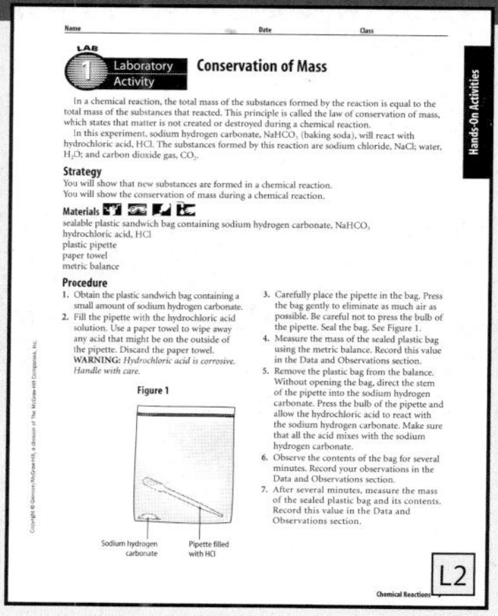
Name Date Class

LAB 1 Laboratory Activity — Conservation of Mass

In a chemical reaction, the total mass of the substances formed by the reaction is equal to the total mass of the substances that reacted. This principle is called the law of conservation of mass, which states that matter is not created or destroyed during a chemical reaction.

In this experiment, sodium hydrogen carbonate, $NaHCO_3$ (baking soda), will react with hydrochloric acid, HCl. The substances formed by this reaction are sodium chloride, NaCl; water, H_2O; and carbon dioxide gas, CO_2.

Strategy

You will show that new substances are formed in a chemical reaction.
You will show the conservation of mass during a chemical reaction.

Materials

sealable plastic sandwich bag containing sodium hydrogen carbonate, $NaHCO_3$
hydrochloric acid, HCl
plastic pipette
paper towel
metric balance

Procedure

1. Obtain the plastic sandwich bag containing a small amount of sodium hydrogen carbonate.
2. Fill the pipette with the hydrochloric acid solution. Use a paper towel to wipe away any acid that might be on the outside of the pipette. Discard the paper towel. **WARNING:** *Hydrochloric acid is corrosive. Handle with care.*
3. Carefully place the pipette in the bag. Press the bag gently to eliminate as much air as possible. Be careful not to press the bulb of the pipette. Seal the bag. See Figure 1.
4. Measure the mass of the sealed plastic bag using the metric balance. Record this value in the Data and Observations section.
5. Remove the plastic bag from the balance. Without opening the bag, direct the stem of the pipette into the sodium hydrogen carbonate. Press the bulb of the pipette and allow the hydrochloric acid to react with the sodium hydrogen carbonate. Make sure that all the acid mixes with the sodium hydrogen carbonate.
6. Observe the contents of the bag for several minutes. Record your observations in the Data and Observations section.
7. After several minutes, measure the mass of the sealed plastic bag and its contents. Record this value in the Data and Observations section.

Figure 1

Hands-On Activities

L2

Meeting Different Ability Levels

Content Outline

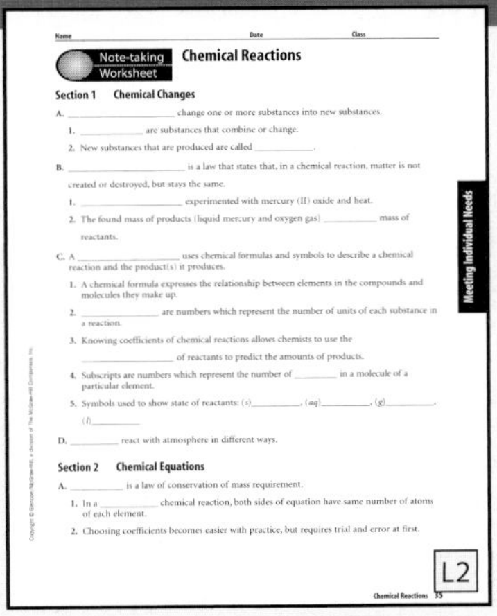

Reinforcement

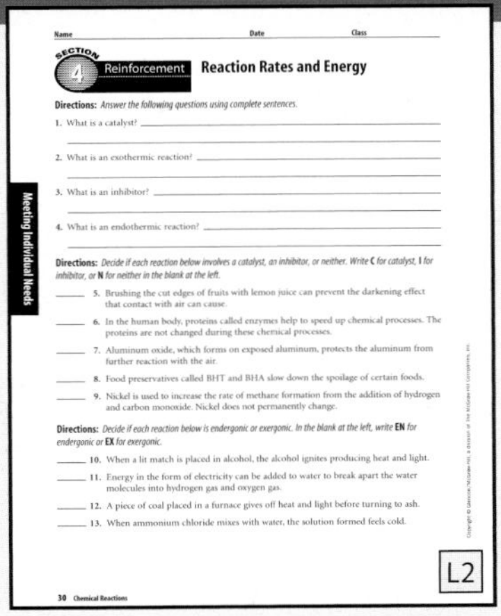

Enrichment

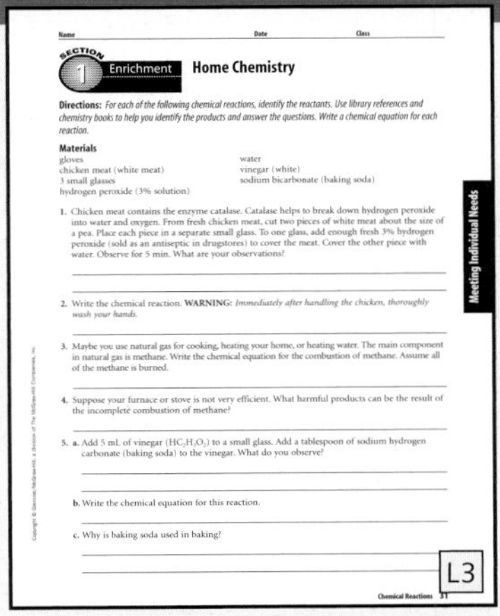

Directed Reading (English/Spanish)

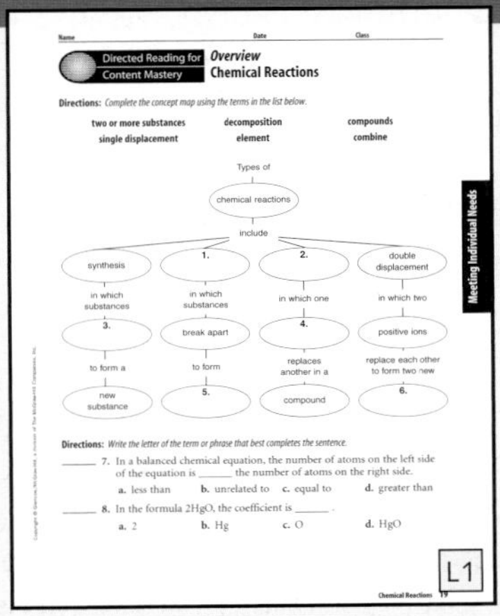

Study Guide

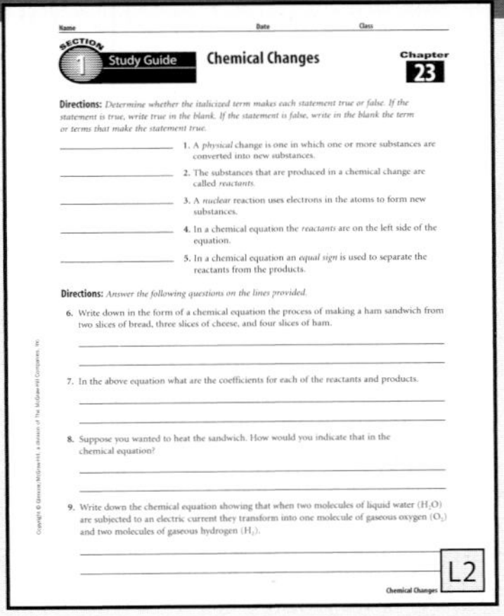

Reading Essentials

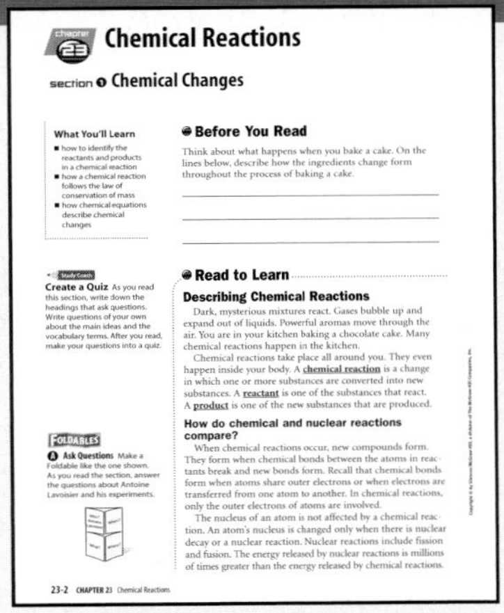

Assessment

Test Practice Workbook

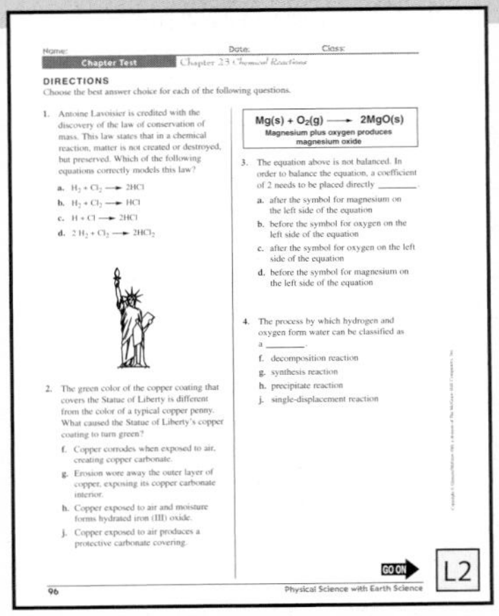

Chapter Review

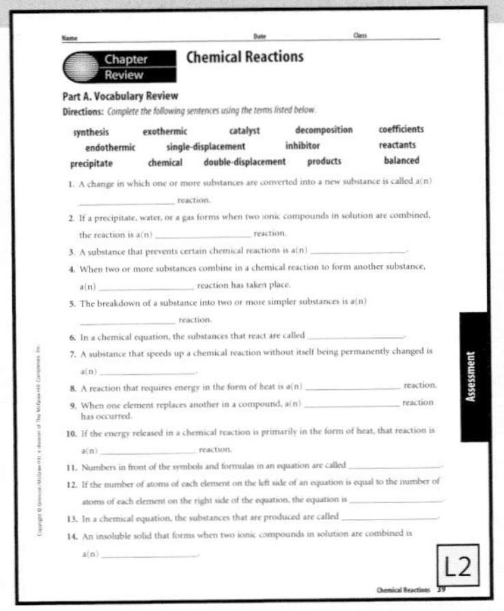

Chapter Tests

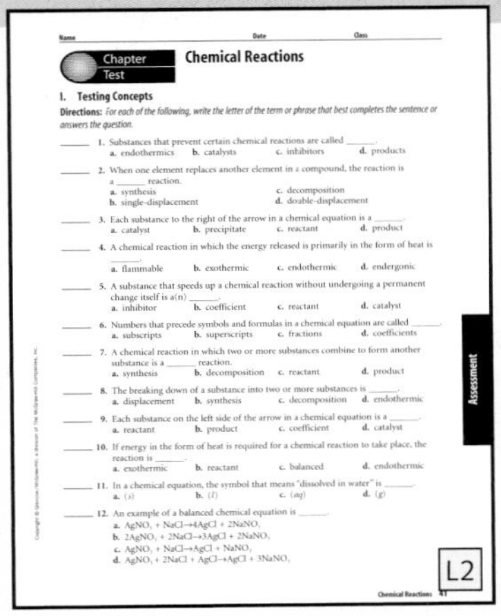

Science Content Background

section 1 Chemical Changes

Conservation of Mass

For his work on conservation of mass, many consider eighteenth-century French scientist Antoine-Laurent Lavoisier to be the founder of modern chemistry. Lavoisier's work, done during the late 1700s, included some of the first quantitative chemical experiments ever performed. He showed that the quantity of matter is the same at the end of a chemical reaction as it is at the beginning of the reaction.

Teacher to Teacher

Jaime A. Sullivan,
South Caldwell High School
Hudson, NC

"One way to get a reaction out of the kids is to demonstrate with fire. In this case, I use a mixture of baking soda and vinegar to produce carbon dioxide, then I douse a lit candle in the CO_2. Now that they're wondering how the flame was put out, I explain that a chemical reaction took place and I show them the chemical formulas for vinegar (aqueous acetic acid, $C_2H_4O_2(aq)$) and baking soda (sodium hydrogen carbonate, $NaHCO_3$). I let them determine on their own (and they eventually will) that what is actually produced is $CO_2(g)$."

Jaime A. Sullivan

While most of Lavoisier's experiments centered on combustion, he also investigated the composition of water. In fact, he named the two components of water—hydrogen and oxygen. With the help of other scientists, he devised a chemical naming system that served as the basis of the modern system.

Lavoisier held many public offices in France, working in areas such as finance, agriculture, education, hygiene, and social welfare. In these capacities, he attempted to introduce various reforms, among them changes in the French monetary and tax systems, and also in farming methods. During the French Revolution, he and other influential French leaders fell out of favor. Lavoisier was arrested in 1793. On May 8, 1794, after a trial that lasted less than a day, Lavoisier and 27 others were beheaded.

section 2 Chemical Equations

Balanced Equations

A chemical equation must show the identities and relative amounts of the reactants and products. However, it can also indicate the physical states of the reactants and products, whether energy is released or absorbed, and whether a catalyst is used. A chemical equation is not accurate unless the formulas are correct and the equation is balanced.

section 3 Classifying Chemical Reactions

Types of Reactions

Most chemical reactions can be classified as one of five types of reactions: synthesis, decomposition, single-displacement, double-displacement, and combustion. In a double-displacement reaction, two elements replace one another in two different compounds. Double-displacement reactions occur only in solution and only if a precipitate, a gas, or water is formed.

Charles D. Winters/Photo Researchers

Section 4 Reaction Rates and Energy

Chemical Reactions and Energy

Every reaction has a rate, or speed at which it proceeds. The study of reaction rates and reaction mechanisms is known as chemical kinetics. Temperature, concentration, particle size, catalysts, and the nature of the reactants determine the reaction rate. The rate of a reaction is not constant throughout the course of the reaction because the rate is proportional to reactant concentration. The concentration of reactants decreases as reactants are converted to products. In other words, as the reactants are used up to form products, the reactants cannot find one another as often as they could in the beginning of the reaction. This decreases the rate of reaction. To counteract this slowdown, an excess of one reactant is often used to keep the reaction from becoming impractically slow.

In 1888, the French chemist Henri Le Chatelier (1850–1936) set forth a simple important generalization on the behavior of equilibrium systems. This generalization, known as Le Chatelier's principle, states that if a stress is applied to a system at equilibrium, the system will shift to relieve that stress and restore equilibrium under a new set of conditions. The application of Le Chatelier's principle helps in predicting the effect of concentration, temperature, and volume on the rate of chemical reactions.

Endergonic Reactions

Catalysts are extremely important to industrial chemistry. Many industrial processes use catalysts to lower reaction temperatures, thus reducing energy costs. Once suitable catalysts are found, chemical reactions that are otherwise too slow to be of practical value may become cost-effective.

Enzymes are large proteins that act as catalysts for biological reactions. The enzyme amylase found in human digestive systems is able to catalyze the breakdown of starch to yield glucose but has no effect on cellulose, even though the two compounds are similar. This is why humans can digest a hamburger bun, but not the grass that fed the cow.

---

chapter content resources

Internet Resources

For additional content background, visit **gpescience.com** to:

- access your book online
- find references to related articles in popular science magazines
- access Web links with related content background
- access current events with science journal topics

Print Resources

Chemicals and Reactions, Jon Richards, Copper Beach Books, Brookfield, CT, 2000

Energy and Chemical Change, Brian J. Knapp, Grolier Educational, Danbury, CT, 1998

Oxidation and Reduction, Brian J. Knapp, Grolier Educational, Danbury, CT, 1998

Inquiry-Based Experiments in Chemistry, Valerie Lechtanski, Oxford University Press, 2000

John Paul Endress/The Stock Market

chapter 23

Chapter Vocabulary
chemical reaction, p. 720
reactant, p. 720
product, p. 720
chemical equation, p. 723
balanced chemical equation, p. 726
combustion reaction, p. 730
synthesis reaction, p. 731
decomposition reaction, p. 731
single-displacement reaction, p. 731
double-displacement reaction, p.732
activation energy, p.735
endothermic reaction, p. 735
rate of reaction, p. 738
exothermic reaction, p. 738
catalyst, p. 740
inhibitor, p. 740

Science Journal Most responses will be chemical reactions.

INTERACTIVE CHALKBOARD with Image Bank

PowerPoint® Presentations

This CD-ROM is an editable Microsoft® PowerPoint® presentation that includes:
- a pre-made presentation for every chapter
- interactive graphics
- animations
- audio clips
- image bank
- all new section and chapter questions
- Standardized Test Practice
- transparencies
- Foldables directions
- links to gpescience.com

chapter 23

Chemical Reactions

chapter preview

sections

All-American Chemistry

Few things are as American as fireworks on the Fourth of July. The explosions of color and deafening booms get huge reactions from crowds across the country. These sights and sounds are the results of chemical reactions involving various substances with oxygen.

Science Journal Describe several cause-and-effect types of events that might happen in your refrigerator. Later, decide which of the events are chemical reactions.

718

Theme Connection

Systems and Interactions Chemical reactions depend on interactions among chemical compounds. A chemical reaction can be considered to be a system into and out of which energy flows.

About the Photo

Fireworks All of the fireworks effects we enjoy, including the vibrant colors and the boom of the explosions, are the result of chemical reactions. The colors come from small amounts of metal ions-blue from copper, red from lithium, gold from sodium, and green from barium. The booms and bangs are the result of chemical reactions with oxygen.

Start-Up Activities

Launch LAB

Rusting—A Chemical Reaction

Like exploding fireworks, rusting is a chemical reaction in which iron metal combines with oxygen. Other metals combine with oxygen, too—some more readily than others. In this lab, you will compare how iron and aluminum react with oxygen.

1. Place a clean iron or steel nail in a dish prepared by your teacher.
2. Place a clean aluminum nail in a second dish. These dishes contain agar gel and an indicator that detects a reaction with oxygen.
3. Observe both nails after one hour. Record any changes around the nails in your Science Journal.
4. Carefully examine both of the dishes the next day.
5. **Think Critically** Record any differences you noticed between the two dishes. Predict if a reaction occurred. How can you tell? What might have caused the differences you observed between the two nails. Explain.

FOLDABLES™ Study Organizer

Chemical Reactions Make the following Foldable to help you classify chemical reactions.

STEP 1 **Fold** a sheet of paper in half lengthwise.

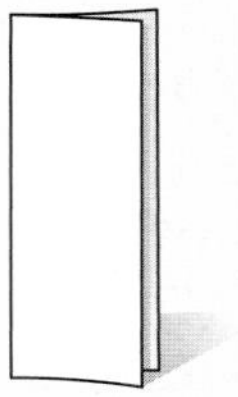

STEP 2 **Mark** four lines evenly spaced at even intervals down the page.

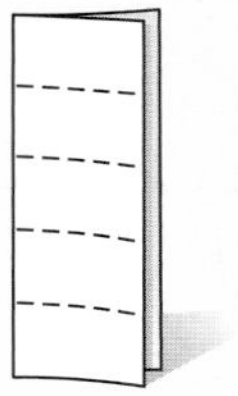

STEP 3 **Cut** only the top layer along the four marks to make five tabs. Label the tabs as shown.

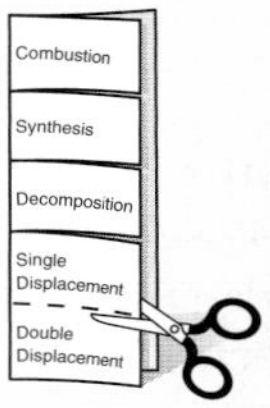

Classify As you read, record examples of each type of reaction from the book, then review the chapter and list other examples mentioned in the text or from classroom discussions.

Science Online — Preview this chapter's content and activities at gpescience.com

Launch LAB

Purpose Use this Launch Lab to introduce students to chemical reactions and to the evidence that a chemical change has occurred. L2 ELL LS **Visual-Spatial**

Preparation Prepare agar by dissolving about ½ teaspoon of agar in about 240 mL of water. Heat just until boiling. Cool slightly and stir in 2 mL of 1% phenolphthalein (in alcohol) solution. Pour enough solution into the petri dishes to partly submerge the nails. Strips of aluminum cut from aluminum pie tins may be used in place of aluminum nails. **WARNING:** aluminum strips may have sharp edges. For this lab, use only uncoated nails.

Materials agar mixture, petri dishes, aluminum nails, iron nails

Teaching Strategy Ask students how we know when a chemical change has taken place. evidence such as color changes

Think Critically

Rusting involves many chemical reactions. Among them is the formation of iron hydroxides, which cause the phenolphthalein to turn pink. The red-brown color that appears later indicates the formation of iron(III) oxide. Aluminum reacts slowly with oxygen, but this will not be visible here.

Assessment

Process Have students use colored markers to draw the two colors observed with the iron nail. Point out that these represent two different reactions. L2

FOLDABLES™ Study Organizer **Dinah Zike Study Fold**

Student preparation materials for this Foldable are available in the **Chapter *Fast File* Resources.**

1 Motivate

INTERACTIVE CHALKBOARD An editable Microsoft® PowerPoint® presentation is available on **Interactive Chalkboard** CD-ROM.

Bellringer

Section Focus Transparencies also are available on the Interactive Chalkboard CD-ROM. L2 ELL

Reading Preview

Tie to Prior Knowledge

Observing Reactions Ask students to describe evidence they have observed of chemical reactions. Examples will vary but could include evolution of a gas (baking soda and vinegar); production of heat and light (burning a fuel); color change (cooking a hot dog over a fire); formation of a precipitate (spoiling of milk.) L2

Activate Background Knowledge Place students in groups and have them brainstorm meanings of new vocabulary words. Assign a recorder in each group to take notes and share the class. After students read the text, have them return to their groups to elaborate on their definitions.

section 1 Chemical Changes

Reading Guide

What You'll Learn

- **Identify** the reactants and products in a chemical reaction.
- **Determine** how a chemical reaction satisfies the law of conservation of mass.
- **Determine** how chemists express chemical changes using equations.

Why It's Important

Chemical reactions cook our food, warm our homes, and provide energy for our bodies.

Review Vocabulary

chemical change: change of one substance into a new substance

New Vocabulary

- chemical reaction
- reactant
- product
- chemical equation

Describing Chemical Reactions

Dark mysterious mixtures react, gas bubbles up and expands, and powerful aromas waft through the air. Where are you? You are in the kitchen baking a chocolate cake. Nowhere in the house do so many chemical reactions take place as in the kitchen.

Chemical reactions are taking place all around you and even within you. A **chemical reaction** is a change in which one or more substances are converted into new substances. The substances that react are called **reactants.** The new substances produced are called **products.**

Chemical and Nuclear Reactions When chemical reactions occur, new compounds form when bonds between atoms in the reactants break and new bonds form. Recall that chemical bonds form when outer electrons, called valence electrons, are shared between atoms or are transferred from one atom to another. As a result, only the outer electrons of atoms are involved in chemical reactions. The nucleus of an atom is not affected by a chemical reaction. An atomic nucleus changes only when nuclear decay or a nuclear reaction, such as nuclear fission or fusion, occurs. The energy released by a nuclear reaction is millions of times greater than the energy released by a chemical reaction. **Figure 1** summarizes the difference between nuclear and chemical reactions.

Figure 1 Different parts of the atom are used in chemical and nuclear reactions.
Identify *how chemical bonds are formed.*

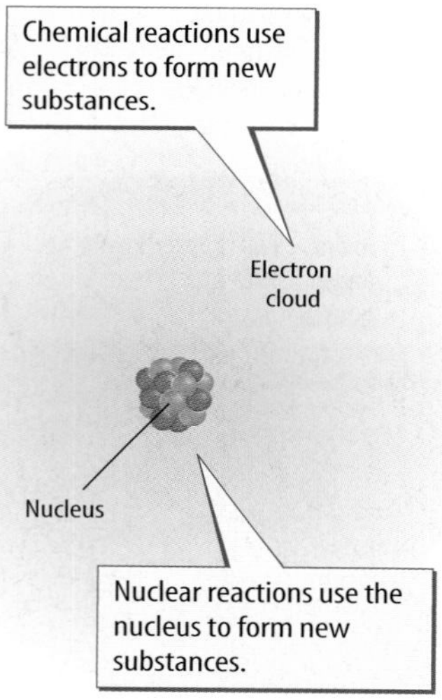

Section 1 Resource Manager

Chapter *FAST FILE* Resources

Transparency Activity, pp. 46, 51–52
Directed Reading for Content Mastery, pp. 19–20
Enrichment, p. 31
MiniLAB, p. 3
Reinforcement, p. 27

Conservation of Mass

By the 1770s, chemistry was changing from the art of alchemy to a true science. Instead of being satisfied with a superficial explanation of unknown events, scientists began to study chemical reactions more thoroughly. Through such study, the French chemist Antoine Lavoisier established that the total mass of the products always equals the total mass of the reactants. This principle is illustrated in **Figure 2.**

The Father of Modern Chemistry When Lavoisier demonstrated the law of conservation of mass, he set the field of chemistry on its modern path. In fact, Lavoisier is known today as the father of modern chemistry for his more accurate explanation of the conservation of mass and for describing a common type of chemical reaction called combustion, which you will learn about later in this chapter. Lavoisier also pioneered early experimentation on the biological phenomena of respiration and metabolism that contributed early milestones in the study of biochemistry, medicine, and even sports medicine.

Reading Check *How did Lavoisier's contributions earn him the title of Father of Modern Chemistry?*

Nomenclature Antoine Lavoisier's work led him to the conclusion that language terminology would be critical to communicate novel scientific ideas. Lavoisier began to develop the system of naming substances based on their composition that we still use today. In 1787, Lavoisier and several colleagues published *Méthode de Nomenclature Chimique* as one of the first sets of nomenclature guidelines.

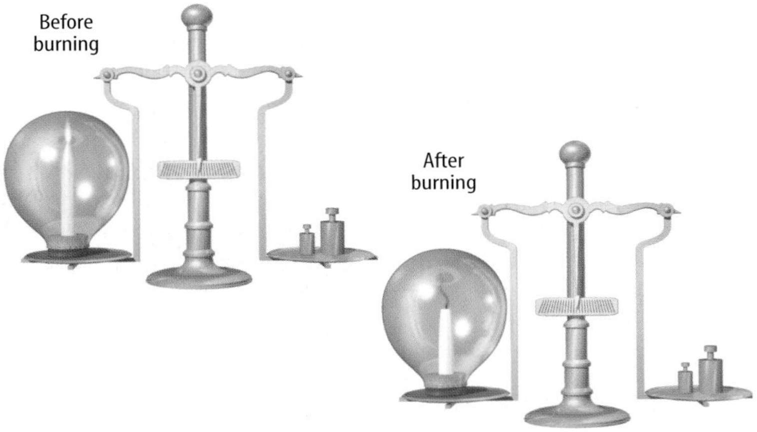

Figure 2 The mass of the candles and oxygen before burning is exactly equal to the mass of the remaining candle and gaseous products.
Describe *the principle that is represented in this figure.*

2 Teach

Caption Answer

Figure 1 Outer electrons are shared or transferred between atoms.

Activity

Table of Elements Lavoisier was an early contributor to what became the periodic table of elements. Have students use the library to find names of other scientists who helped shape and fill the table. L2

IDENTIFYING Misconceptions

Nomenclature Students may think that there is only one form of nomenclature that serves all branches of science. Explain that different disciplines have different forms of specific nomenclature, but at the same time emphasize that nomenclature is consistent within each area. Also emphasize that guidelines are established to maintain consistency and uniformity and that the guidelines for nomenclature are often similar across disciplines. This makes it possible for scientists whose work crosses scientific boundaries to communicate effectively.

Reading Check

Answer He explained the theory of conservation of mass and was key in developing modern chemical nomenclature.

Caption Answer

Figure 2 law of conservation of mass

Reading Strategy

Clarify Text Model this strategy by reading a challenging piece of text aloud. Demonstrate that when students encounter new vocabulary or difficult concepts, they can employ clarification strategies. As you read, articulate your thoughts, reread when necessary, and show students how to use the context of the passage to help them clarify.

Differentiated Instruction

Challenge Photographs are made using a chemical reaction driven by exposure to light. Ask students to find out what metal is typically involved in the process. Silver ions in silver bromide (AgBr) can be changed to silver metal when exposed to light. L3 **Linguistic**

Use an Analogy

Balancing a Ledger Lavoisier's background included tax collecting and auditing. Balancing a ledger is somewhat like balancing a chemical equation. One must carefully consider what goes in and what comes out without losing anything. L2

Quick Demo

Conservation of Mass

Materials balance, Erlenmeyer flask, sodium carbonate, water, calcium chloride, stopper, test tube

Estimated Time 15 minutes

Procedure Add 0.50 g of sodium carbonate and 25 mL of water in the flask. Add 10 mL of water and 0.10 g of calcium chloride to a small test tube. Put the test tube in the flask. Weigh the flask and contents. Shake the stoppered flask so that the tube contents mix with the flask content. Reweigh the stoppered flask. The mass of the flask and contents remain the same. L2

ELL IS **Visual-Spatial**

Reading Check

Answer In a chemical reaction, matter is not created or destroyed.

Figure 3 Antoine Lavoisier's wife, Marie-Anne, drew this view of Lavoisier in his laboratory performing studies on oxygen. She depicted herself at the right taking notes.

Science Online

Topic: Antoine Lavoisier

Visit gpescience.com for Web links to information about Antoine Lavoisier and his contributions to chemistry.

Activity In your Science Journal, write a brief biography of Antoine Lavoisier that includes some of his non-scientific activities and political interests, as well as his scientific contributions.

Lavoisier's Contribution One of the questions that motivated Lavoisier was the mystery of exactly what happened when substances changed form. He began to answer this question by experimenting with mercury. In one experiment, Lavoisier placed a carefully measured mass of solid mercury(II) oxide, which he knew as mercury calx, into a sealed container. When he heated this container, he noted a dramatic change. The red powder had been transformed into a silvery liquid that he recognized as mercury metal, and a gas was produced. When he determined the mass of the liquid mercury and gas, their combined masses were exactly the same as the mass of the red powder he had started with.

mercury(II) oxide		oxygen	plus	mercury
10.0 g	=	0.7 g	+	9.3 g

Lavoisier also established that the gas produced by heating mercury(II) oxide, which we call oxygen, was a component of air. He did this by heating mercury metal with air and saw that a portion of the air combined to give red mercury(II) oxide. He studied the effect of this gas on living animals, including himself. Hundreds of experiments carried out in his laboratory, as shown in **Figure 3,** confirmed that in a chemical reaction, matter is not created or destroyed, but is conserved. This principle became known as the law of conservation of mass. This means that the total starting mass of all reactants equals the total final mass of all products.

Reading Check *What does the law of conservation of mass state?*

Curriculum Connection

History Have students research and write a short report about the time period in France in which Lavoisier lived (mid- to late-eighteenth century). For comparison and perspective, have them relate the same period to the happenings in America. L2 P IS **Linguistic**

Differentiated Instruction

English-Language Learners Express to the class that scientists from many countries have made significant contributions to general science. Recount the scientific contributions of the Frenchman Lavoisier and have non-English language speakers read a chemical reaction so they can recognize that the formulas and notation are the same, regardless of the language of the scientist. L2

Writing Equations

If you wanted to describe the chemical reaction shown in **Figure 4,** you might write something like this:

> Nickel(II) chloride, dissolved in water, plus sodium hydroxide, dissolved in water, produces solid nickel(II) hydroxide plus sodium chloride, dissolved in water.

This series of words is rather cumbersome, but all of the information is important. The same is true of descriptions of most chemical reactions. Many words are needed to state all the important information. As a result, scientists have developed a shorthand method to describe chemical reactions. A **chemical equation** is a way to describe a chemical reaction using chemical formulas and other symbols. Some of the symbols used in chemical equations are listed in **Table 1.**

The chemical equation for the reaction described above in words and shown in **Figure 4** looks like this:

$$NiCl_2(aq) + 2NaOH(aq) \longrightarrow Ni(OH)_2(s) + 2NaCl(aq)$$

On the left side of the equation are the reactants, nickel(II) chloride and sodium hydroxide. On the right side of the equation are the products, nickel(II) hydroxide and sodium chloride.

It is much easier to tell what is happening by writing the information in this form. Later, you will learn how chemical equations make it easier to calculate the quantities of reactants that are needed and the quantities of products that are formed.

Table 1 Symbols Used in Chemical Equations

Symbol	Meaning
$\rightarrow$	produces or yields
+	plus
(s)	solid
(l)	liquid
(g)	gas
(aq)	aqueous, a substance is dissolved in water
heat $\rightarrow$	the reactants are heated
light $\rightarrow$	the reactants are exposed to light
elec. $\rightarrow$	an electric current is applied to the reactants

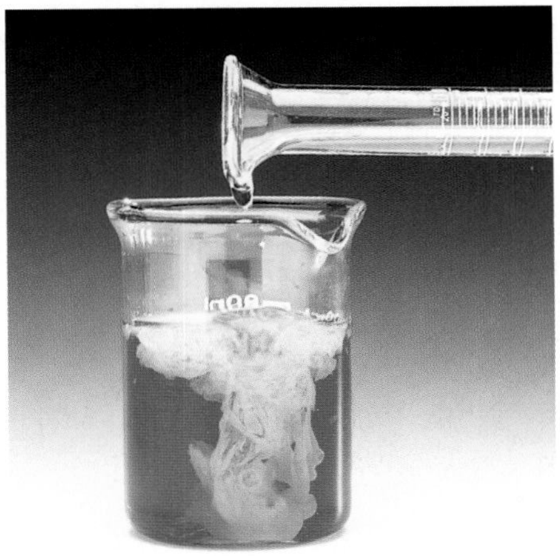

Figure 4 A white precipitate of nickel(II) hydroxide forms when sodium hydroxide is added to a green solution of nickel(II) chloride. Sodium chloride, the other product formed, is in solution.

Use an Analogy

Baseball Scores Have a baseball coach or interested student bring in a scorer's record book from a baseball game. The records are kept for each inning with accepted symbols for events such as strikeout (K), home run (HR), infield out made by throw from third to first base (5-3), etc. The symbols in baseball allow a great deal of information to be recorded accurately in a small space. Chemical equations do this as well. L2 LS **Logical-Mathematical**

Discussion

Burning Copper Burning a piece of copper in a flame will produce a product that has a greater mass than the original copper. Why doesn't this violate the law of conservation of mass? The mass of oxygen participating in the burning process must be included as part of the mass of the reactants. L2 LS **Logical-Mathematical**

Fun Fact

Lavoisier was an early advocate of the use of chemical equations. He used symbols to show both the identity and quantity of materials in reactions and thought that algebra was the best language for expressing scientific information. He wrote, "In order to show at a glance the results of what happens . . . I have constituted formulae of a kind that could at first be taken for algebraic formulae . . ."

Science Journal

Soda Coefficients Have students calculate the total amount of soft drink in two 2-L bottles, three six-packs of 355-mL cans, and one case of 355-mL cans. Total = 4,000 + 6,390 + 8,520 = 18,910 mL. The coefficients in *2 bottles, 3 six-packs,* and *1 case* indicate the number of packaged units. Coefficients in a chemical equation indicate the number of units of atoms. L2

Teacher FYI

Chemist Symbols Some chemists use the symbol (cr) to represent solids that are crystals and (amor) to represent amorphous solids, which have no definite structure.

SECTION 1 Chemical Changes 723

Mini LAB

Video Lab available.

Purpose Students see that coefficients are not conserved in a chemical equation but that mass is. L2 **Logical-Mathematical**

Materials 15 index cards per student, markers

Safety Precautions Request assistance from a parent or guardian.

Teaching Strategy Suggest students redo the activity, varying the composition of a team.

Analysis

1. G_2F_2C; 2 guards + 2 forwards + 1 center → 1 team
2. The equation uses coefficients like a chemical equation, and it shows conservation of mass. Only a specific number of each type of player can be used per team. Those left over sit on the bench (cannot be used).
3. The total number of cards at the beginning equals the number of leftover cards plus the cards being used for the team.

Assessment

Oral Ask students how many guards would be needed to make four teams. $4 \times 2 = 8$ How many complete teams could be made around 5 centers? $5 \times 1 = 5$ teams How many players would be left over when the following players assembled to make teams: 10 guards, 9 forwards, and 5 centers? $\frac{9}{2} = 4$ teams with 1 extra forward, 1 extra center, 2 extra guards Use **PASC**, p. 101.

Reading Check

Answer They act as unit managers, representing the number of units of each substance taking part in a reaction.

Mini LAB

Designing a Team Equation

Procedure

1. Obtain **15 index cards** and mark each as follows: five with *Guard,* five with *Forward,* and five with *Center.*
2. Group the cards to form as many complete basketball teams as possible. Each team needs two guards, two forwards, and one center.

Analysis

1. Write the formula for a team. Write the formation of a team as an equation. Use coefficients in front of each type of player needed for a team.
2. How is this equation like a chemical equation? Why can't you use the remaining cards?
3. How do the remaining cards illustrate the law of conservation of matter in this example?

Try at Home

Unit Managers

What do the numbers to the left of the formulas for reactants and products mean? Remember that according to the law of conservation of mass, matter is neither made nor lost during chemical reactions. Atoms are rearranged but never lost or destroyed. These numbers, called coefficients, represent the number of units of each substance taking part in a reaction. Coefficients can be thought of as unit managers.

Reading Check *What is the function of coefficients in a chemical equation?*

Imagine that you are responsible for making sandwiches for a picnic. You have been told to make a certain number of three kinds of sandwiches, and that no substitutions can be made. You would have to figure out exactly how much food to buy so that you had enough without any food left over. You might need two loaves of bread, four packages of turkey, four packages of cheese, two heads of lettuce, and ten tomatoes. With these supplies you could make exactly the right number of each kind of sandwich.

In a way, your sandwich-making effort is like a chemical reaction. The reactants are your bread, turkey, cheese, lettuce, and tomatoes. The number of units of each ingredient are similar to the coefficients of the reactants in an equation. The sandwiches are similar to the products, and the numbers of each kind of sandwich are similar to the coefficients.

Knowing the number of units of reactants enables chemists to add the correct amounts of reactants to a reaction. Also, these units, or coefficients, tell them exactly how much product will form. An example of this is the reaction of one unit of $NiCl_2$ with two units of NaOH to produce one unit of $Ni(OH)_2$ and two units of NaCl. You can see these units in **Figure 5.**

Figure 5 Each coefficient in the equation represents the number of units of each type in this reaction.

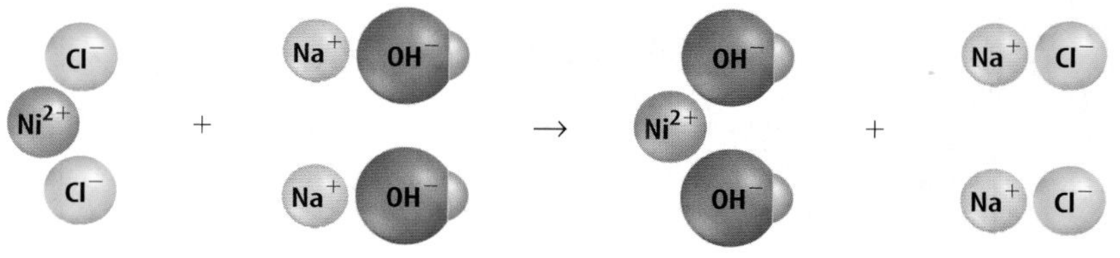

$NiCl_2 + 2NaOH \rightarrow Ni(OH)_2 + 2NaCl$

Visual Learning

Figure 5 Have students count the atoms in the illustration and match them with the formulas in the equation. Point out which atoms combine to form each product. L2 **Visual-Spatial**

Post Reading

Science Journal Have students respond to the following prompt in their Science Journals: What did you learn by reading about chemical reactions, chemical equations, and the law of conservation of mass? Encourage students to include their own opinions and thoughts regarding what they read.

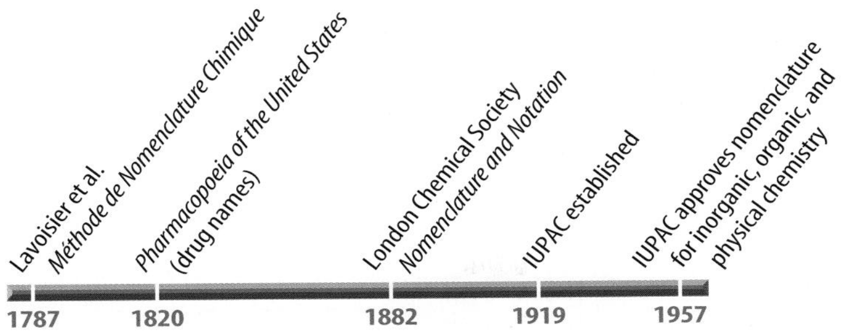

Figure 6 This time line of nomenclature development and publications does not end in 1957. In fact, today there are nomenclature organizations for almost every branch of scientific study, and the rules and guidelines for naming substances continue to evolve.

INTEGRATE History

IUPAC Antoine Lavoisier and his colleagues understood the importance of using a nomenclature system that helps scientists communicate their data. Since that time, the guidelines have continued to evolve with scientific discovery. In 1919, the International Union of Applied Chemistry (IUPAC) was formed. The primary mission of the IUPAC is to coordinate guidelines for naming chemical compounds systematically. **Figure 6** illustrates some of the early events in nomenclature development.

In addition to chemical nomenclature, IUPAC also is responsible for standardizing chemistry methods, evaluating atomic weights and environmental programs, along with many other areas relating to chemistry.

section 1 review

Summary

Describing Chemical Reactions

- A chemical reaction is a process that involves one or more reactants changing into one or more products.
- In chemical reactions and nuclear reactions, different parts of the atom form new substances.

Conservation of Mass

- A basic principle of chemistry is that matter, during a chemical change, can neither be created nor destroyed.

Writing Equations

- Chemical equations describe the change of reactants to products and obey the law of conservation of mass.

Unit Managers

- Coefficients represent how many units of each substance are involved in a chemical reaction.

Self Check

1. **Identify** the reactants and the products in the following chemical equation.
   $Cd(NO_3)_2(aq) + H_2S(g) \longrightarrow CdS(s) + 2HNO_3(aq)$
2. **Identify** the state of matter of each substance in the following reaction.
   $Zn(s) + 2HCl(aq) \longrightarrow H_2(g) + ZnCl_2(aq)$
3. **Compare and contrast** a chemical reaction and a nuclear reaction.
4. **Explain** the importance of the law of conservation of mass.
5. **Think Critically** How would global communication between scientists have been changed if IUPAC had not been established?

Applying Math

6. **Solve One-Step Equations** When making soap, if 890 g of a specific fat react completely with 120 g of sodium hydroxide, the products formed are soap and 92 g of glycerin. Calculate the mass of soap formed to satisfy the law of conservation of mass.

More Section Review gpescience.com

INTEGRATE History

Content Background

IUPAC is an international organization with one mission of promoting free exchange of scientific information. There are 65 countries whose scientists are affiliated with IUPAC. Countries such as Croatia and the Netherlands are members of IUPAC.

3 Assess

DAILY INTERVENTION

Check for Understanding

Chemistry Flashcards Create a set of chemistry flashcards by writing the chemical formulas for a variety of substances on standard index cards. Also write several forward-pointing arrows on some cards. Have students create basic chemical reactions demonstrating the concept of "reactants produce products". Remember when creating the flashcards to include appropriate product substances to pair with the reactants. L2

Reteach

Understanding Coefficients Show that the balanced equation for the decomposition of water is $2H_2O \rightarrow 2H_2 + O_2$. Ask students to use the coefficients to determine the number of hydrogen and oxygen atoms on each side of the equation. 4 hydrogens and 2 oxygens on the left side and 4 hydrogens and 2 oxygens on the right side L1 LS **Logical-Mathematical**

Assessment

Performance Have students examine this unbalanced equation for the rusting of iron ($Fe + O_2 + H_2O \rightarrow Fe_2O_3 \cdot 3H_2O$) to determine the products and reactants and use coefficients to balance the equation. $4Fe + 3O_2 + 6H_2O \rightarrow 2Fe_2O_3 \cdot 3H_2O$ Use **PASC,** p. 101. L2

section 1 review

1. reactants: $Cd(NO_3)_2$ and H_2S; products: CdS and HNO_3
2. Zn is a solid, HCl is dissolved in water, H_2 is a gas, and $ZnCl_2$ is dissolved in water.
3. Both reactions produce a change, resulting in a new product. In a chemical reaction, the electrons are rearranged to create new bonds. In a nuclear reaction, the nucleus of the atom is changed.
4. The law of conservation of mass explains why matter in the universe does not go away permanently.
5. Scientists from different countries would have a difficult time discussing discoveries due to a lack of a common language.
6. 890 + 120 = 1,010 g of reactant, which must equal 1,010 g of product; 1,010 − 92 = 918 g of soap.

section 2

Chemical Equations

Reading Guide

What You'll Learn

- **Identify** what is meant by a balanced chemical equation.
- **Determine** how to write balanced chemical equations.

Why It's Important

Chemical equations are the language used to describe chemical change, which allow scientists to develop products for our world.

Review Vocabulary

subscript: in a chemical formula, a number below and to the right of a symbol indicating number of atoms

New Vocabulary

- balanced chemical equation

Balanced Equations

Lavoisier's mercury(II) oxide reaction, shown in **Figure 7,** can be written as:

$$HgO(s) \xrightarrow{\text{heat}} Hg(l) + O_2(g)$$

Notice that the number of mercury atoms is the same on both sides of the equation but that the number of oxygen atoms is not the same. One oxygen atom appears on the reactant side of the equation and two appear on the product side.

Atoms	HgO	→	Hg	+	O_2
Hg	1		1		
O	1				2

But according to the law of conservation of mass, one oxygen atom cannot just become two. Nor can you simply add the subscript 2 and write HgO_2 instead of HgO. The formulas HgO_2 and HgO do not represent the same compound. In fact, HgO_2 does not exist. The formulas in a chemical equation must accurately represent the compounds that react.

Fixing this equation requires a process called balancing. Balancing an equation doesn't change what happens in a reaction—it simply changes the way the reaction is represented. The balancing process involves changing coefficients in a reaction to achieve a **balanced chemical equation,** which has the same number of atoms of each element on both sides of the equation.

Figure 7 Mercury metal forms when mercury oxide is heated. Because mercury is poisonous, this reaction is never performed in a classroom laboratory.

1 Motivate

INTERACTIVE CHALKBOARD PowerPoint® Presentations An editable Microsoft® PowerPoint® presentation is available on **Interactive Chalkboard** CD-ROM.

Bellringer

Section Focus Transparencies also are available on the Interactive Chalkboard CD-ROM. L2 ELL

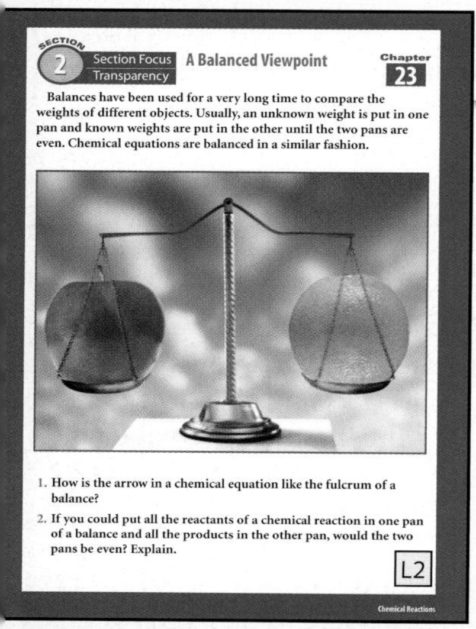

Reading Preview

Tie to Prior Knowledge

Building Blocks Ask students if they remember attachable plastic building blocks. Remind students that the structures could be disassembled to make different objects from the same blocks. In a similar way, a balanced chemical equation represents the rearrangement of a set of atoms into new compounds.

Word Analysis The new vocabulary term *balanced chemical equation* is composed of three words. Have students determine the meaning of each word. Then ask them to predict the meaning of the whole term. As they read, students may verify or modify their understanding of the term.

Section 2 Resource Manager

Chapter *Fast File* Resources

- Transparency Activity, p. 47
- Directed Reading for Content Mastery, p. 20
- Lab Activity, pp. 13–16
- Reinforcement, p. 28
- Enrichment, p. 32

Home and Community Involvement, p. 46

Choosing Coefficients Finding out which coefficients to use to balance an equation is often a trial-and-error process. In the equation for Lavoisier's experiment, the number of mercury atoms is balanced, but one oxygen atom is on the left and two are on the right. If you put a coefficient of 2 before the HgO on the left, the oxygen atoms will be balanced, but the mercury atoms become unbalanced. To balance the equation, also put a 2 in front of mercury on the right. The equation is now balanced.

Atoms	$2HgO$	$\rightarrow$	$2Hg$	$+$	O_2
Hg	2		2		
O	2				2

Balancing Equations Magnesium burns with such a brilliant white light that it is often used in emergency flares as shown in **Figure 8.** Burning leaves a white powder called magnesium oxide. To write a balanced chemical equation for this and most other reactions, follow these four steps.

Step 1 Write a chemical equation for the reaction using formulas and symbols. Recall that oxygen is a diatomic molecule.

$$Mg(s) + O_2(g) \longrightarrow MgO(s)$$

Step 2 Count the atoms in reactants and products.

Atoms	Mg	$+$	O_2	$\rightarrow$	MgO
Mg	1				1
O			2		1

The magnesium atoms are balanced, but the oxygen atoms are not. Therefore, this equation isn't balanced.

Step 3 Choose coefficients that balance the equation. Remember, never change subscripts of a correct formula to balance an equation. Try putting a coefficient of 2 before MgO.

$$Mg(s) + O_2(g) \longrightarrow 2MgO(s)$$

Step 4 Recheck the numbers of each atom on each side of the equation and adjust coefficients again if necessary. Now two Mg atoms are on the right side and only one is on the left side. So a coefficient of 2 is needed for Mg to balance the equation.

$$2Mg(s) + O_2(g) \longrightarrow 2MgO(s)$$

Reading Check *How can you balance a chemical equation using coefficients?*

Science Online

Topic: Balancing Chemical Equations

Visit gpescience.com for Web links to information about balancing chemical equations.

Activity Using the Web links, locate a website that offers practice problems for balancing chemical equations. Copy several of the unbalanced equations in your Science Journal and try to balance them. Check your work against the answers on the web site when you are done.

Figure 8 Magnesium combines with oxygen, giving an intense white light.

Differentiated Instruction

Learning Disabled The concept of coefficients may be difficult for students to understand. Take time to relate the use of coefficients in chemical equations to the students' mathematics experience. In this instruction use simple, non-chemical examples to illustrate the concept of coefficients.

Challenge Safety air bags in automobiles depend on a chemical reaction to inflate. Have students supply the coefficients needed to balance the equation: $NaN_3(s) \rightarrow Na(g) + N_2(g)$

$2NaN_3(s) \rightarrow 2Na(s) + 3N_2(g)$ L3

2 Teach

Teacher FYI

Calculating Fractions Fractions can be used to balance chemical equations. $Na + Cl_2 \rightarrow NaCl$ can be balanced as $2Na + Cl_2 \rightarrow 2NaCl$ or as $Na + \frac{1}{2}Cl_2 \rightarrow NaCl$. Fractions are used mainly when the calculations involve the formation of only one unit of a product.

Fun Fact

Air bags should really be called nitrogen bags. They are not filled with air, but with nitrogen.

Reading Check

Answer by a trial-and-error process, then by counting the number of atoms of reactant and product molecules

Reading Strategy

Synthesize and Summarize Have students summarize the steps required to balance a chemical equation. Remind them that they should put ideas together in a condensed form using their own words. This requires synthesizing. Ask students to include an example in their summaries to help clarify.

Discussion

Balancing Strategies Discuss with the class various techniques or strategies that might be helpful for students to visualize the number of atoms on each side of the equation and work through the process of assigning coefficients. Encourage students to share their individual processes.

SECTION 2 Chemical Equations 727

Applying Math

Math Standards

National: 1, 2, 9, 10

Answers to Practice Problems

1. $2HCl + Na_2CO_3 \rightarrow 2NaCl + H_2O + CO_2$
2. $2NaOH + CaBr_2 \rightarrow Ca(OH)_2 + 2NaBr$

IDENTIFYING Misconceptions

Students may think that when the body of a car rusts away, leaving holes in the metal, that the law of conservation of matter is not obeyed. Explain that the corrosion of iron in the presence of water and oxygen in fact does obey the law, and reinforce this fact by introducing the chemical equation for the oxidation of iron: $4Fe(s) + 3O_2(g) \rightarrow 2Fe_2O_3(s)$.

Virtual Labs

In Balance *What is a balanced chemical equation?*

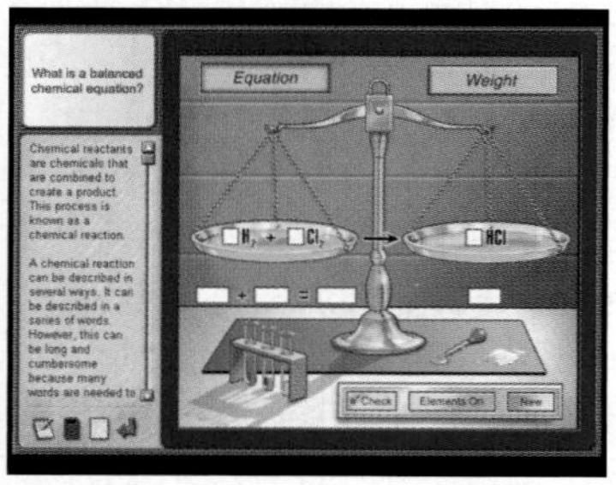

Applying Math — Use Coefficients

BARIUM SULFATE REACTION A sample of barium sulfate is placed on a piece of paper, which is then ignited. Barium sulfate reacts with the carbon from the burned paper producing barium sulfide and carbon monoxide. Write a balanced chemical equation for this reaction.

IDENTIFY known values

We know the substances that are involved in the reaction. From this, we can write a chemical equation showing reactants and products.

$$BaSO_4(s) + C(s) \rightarrow BaS(s) + CO(g)$$

SOLVE the problem

The chemical equation above is not balanced. There are more oxygen atoms on the left side of the equation than there are on the right side. This must be corrected while keeping all other atom counts in balance. Begin to balance the equation by first counting and listing the atoms before and after the reaction.

Kind of Atom	Number of Atoms Before Reaction	Number of Atoms After Reaction
Ba	1	1
S	1	1
O	4	1
C	1	1

Next, adjust the coefficients until all atoms are balanced on the left and right sides of the arrow. Try putting a 4 in front of CO. Now you have 4 oxygen atoms on the right, which balances on both sides, but the carbon atoms become unbalanced. To fix this, add a 4 in front of the C in the reactants. The balanced equation looks like this:

$$BaSO_4(s) + 4C(s) \rightarrow BaS(s) + 4CO(g)$$

CHECK your answer

Count the number of atoms on each side of the equation and verify that they are equal.

Practice Problems

1. Balance this equation: $NaOH(aq) + CaBr_2(aq) \rightarrow Ca(OH)_2(s) + NaBr(aq)$.
2. HCl is slowly added to aqueous Na_2CO_3 forming NaCl, H_2O, and CO_2. Follow the steps above to write a balanced equation for this reaction.

For more practice problems, go to page 879, and visit Math Practice at gpescience.com.

Post Reading

Fix-Up Strategy Model this strategy by going back to a challenging section of text. Articulate your thoughts. Make a connection between real-world concepts and the material in the text. Predict, stop to think, visualize, retell what you've read, and reread. Allow students to practice this strategy with a partner.

728 CHAPTER 23 Chemical Reactions

Polish Your Skill When lithium metal is treated with water, hydrogen gas and lithium hydroxide are produced, as shown in **Figure 9.**

Step 1 Write the chemical equation.

$$Li(s) + H_2O \longrightarrow LiOH(aq) + H_2(g)$$

Step 2 Check for balance by counting the atoms.

Atoms	Li	+	H_2O	$\rightarrow$	LiOH	+	H_2
Li	1				1		
H			2		1		2
O			1		1		

This equation is not balanced. There are three hydrogen atoms on the right and only two on the left. Complete steps 3 and 4 to balance the equation. After each step, count the atoms of each element. When equal numbers of atoms of each element are on both sides, the equation is balanced. The balanced chemical equation looks like this:

$$2Li + 2H_2O \longrightarrow 2LiOH + H_2$$

The coefficients and subscripts are multiplied together, not added, to determine the correct number of atoms for each element.

Figure 9 When lithium metal is added to water, it reacts, producing a solution of lithium hydroxide and bubbles of hydrogen gas.

section 2 review

Summary

Balanced Equations

- A chemical equation is a way to indicate reactants and products and relative amounts of each.
- A balanced chemical equation tells the exact number of atoms involved in the reaction.
- Balanced chemical equations must satisfy the law of conservation of matter; no atoms of reactant or product can be lost from one side to the other.
- Coefficients are used to achieve balance in a chemical equation.
- Chemical equations cannot be balanced by adjusting the subscript numerals in compound names because doing so would change the compounds.

Self Check

1. **Describe** two reasons for balancing chemical equations.
2. **Balance** this chemical equation: $Fe(s) + O_2(g) \longrightarrow FeO(s)$.
3. **Explain** why oxygen gas must always be written as O_2 in a chemical equation.
4. **Infer** What coefficient is assumed if no coefficient is written before a formula in a chemical equation?
5. **Think Critically** Explain why the sum of the coefficients on the reactant side of a balanced equation does not have to equal the sum of the coefficients on the product side of the equation.

Applying Math

6. **Use Numbers** Balance the equation for the reaction $Fe(s) + Cl_2(g) \longrightarrow FeCl_3(s)$.

More Section Review gpescience.com

3 Assess

DAILY INTERVENTION

Check for Understanding

Logical-Mathematical Bring a disposable butane lighter to class. Write the formula for butane, C_4H_{10}, on the chalkboard, and as you light the lighter, ask students to identify the chemical reaction taking place. Oxygen is combining with the carbon and hydrogen to produce water and carbon dioxide. Have them write and balance the equation for the reaction. $2C_4H_{10} + 13O_2 \rightarrow 8CO_2 + 10H_2O$ L3 LS

Reteach

Molecular View Using the style of **Figure 5,** draw on the chalkboard the structures of $Ca(OH)_2$, H_3PO_4, $Ca_3(PO_4)_2$, and H_2O. Tell students that calcium hydroxide reacts with hydrogen phosphate to produce calcium phosphate and water. Ask students to write the balanced chemical equation for this reaction. $3Ca(OH)_2 + 2H_3PO_4 \rightarrow Ca_3(PO_4)_2 + 6H_2O$ L2 LS **Visual-Spatial**

Assessment

Performance Have students draw Venn diagrams to contrast the changes in chemical reactions with those in nuclear reactions. In a chemical change, the atoms do not change their basic identity. In nuclear changes, the identity of an atom is often changed. Use **PASC,** p. 167. P L3

section 2 review

1. Conservation of mass requires that the number of atoms of an element on the left side equals the number of atoms on the right side. Balanced equations accurately depict chemical changes.
2. $2Fe + O_2 \rightarrow 2FeO$
3. Oxygen gas exists as a diatomic molecule.
4. 1
5. The coefficients represent the number of units of a compound, not the number of atoms.
6. $2Fe(s) + 3Cl_2(g) \rightarrow 2FeCl_3(s)$

SECTION 2 Chemical Equations 729

section 3

Classifying Chemical Reactions

Reading Guide

What You'll Learn

- **Identify** the five general types of chemical reactions.
- **Identify** redox reactions.
- **Predict** which metals will replace other metals in compounds.

Why It's Important

Classifying chemical reactions helps to understand what is happening and predict the outcome of reactions.

Review Vocabulary

states of matter: the physical forms in which all matter naturally exists, most commonly solid, liquid, and gas

New Vocabulary

- combustion reaction
- synthesis reaction
- decomposition reaction
- single-displacement reaction
- double-displacement reaction

Types of Reactions

You might have noticed that there are all sorts of chemical reactions. In fact, there are literally millions of chemical reactions that occur every day, and scientists have described many of them and continue to describe more. With all these reactions, it would be impossible to use the information without first having some type of organization. With this in mind, chemists have defined five main categories of chemical reactions: combustion, synthesis, decomposition, single displacement, and double displacement.

Combustion Reactions If you have ever observed something burning, you have observed a combustion reaction. As mentioned previously, Lavoisier was one of the first scientists to accurately describe combustion. He deduced that the process of burning (combustion) involves the combination of a substance with oxygen. A **combustion reaction** occurs when a substance reacts with oxygen to produce energy in the form of heat and light. Combustion reactions also produce one or more products that contain the elements in the reactants. For example, the reaction between carbon and oxygen produces carbon dioxide. Many combustion reactions also will fit into other categories of reactions. For example, the reaction between carbon and oxygen also is a synthesis reaction.

Figure 10 Rust has accumulated on the *Titanic* since it sank in 1912. **Identify** *the general formula for a synthesis reaction.*

1 Motivate

An editable Microsoft® PowerPoint® presentation is available on **Interactive Chalkboard** CD-ROM.

Bellringer

Section Focus Transparencies also are available on the Interactive Chalkboard CD-ROM. L2 ELL

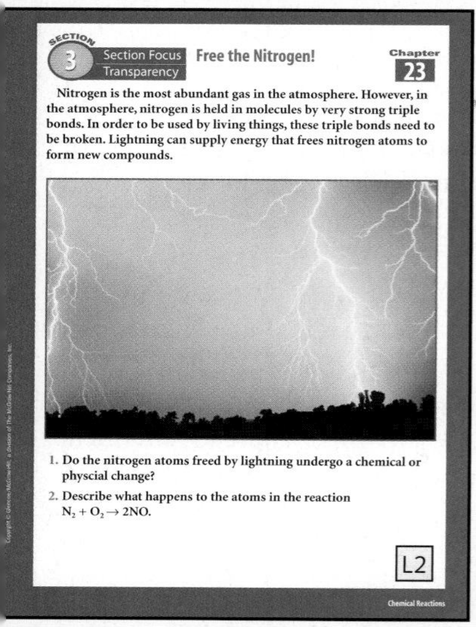

Section 3 Section Focus Transparency — **Free the Nitrogen!** — Chapter 23

Nitrogen is the most abundant gas in the atmosphere. However, in the atmosphere, nitrogen is held in molecules by very strong triple bonds. In order to be used by living things, these triple bonds need to be broken. Lightning can supply energy that frees nitrogen atoms to form new compounds.

1. Do the nitrogen atoms freed by lightning undergo a chemical or physcial change?
2. Describe what happens to the atoms in the reaction $N_2 + O_2 \rightarrow 2NO$.

L2

Chemical Reactions

Reading Preview

Tie to Prior Knowledge

Chemical Reactions The new vocabulary describes the five general types of chemical reactions. Ask students to think of situations in which these terms are used. Combustion—burning; Synthesis—joining carbon dioxide and water; decomposition—one substance converting to others as it falls apart, single and double displacement—similar to collectors trading one or two souvenirs. L2

Morphological Word Analysis Ask students to look at word parts they know within the term *decomposition reaction*. Discuss the meaning of the prefix *de-* and *re-*, and the words *compose*, *composition*, *act*, and *action*. Show students how meanings are hidden within words.

Section 3 Resource Manager

Chapter *Fast File* Resources

- Transparency Activity, p. 48
- Directed Reading for Content Mastery, p. 21
- Enrichment, p. 33
- **Home and Community Involvement,** p. 33

730 CHAPTER 23 Chemical Reactions

Synthesis Reactions One of the easiest reaction types to recognize is a synthesis reaction. In a **synthesis reaction,** two or more substances combine to form another substance. The generalized formula for this reaction type is as follows: $A + B \longrightarrow AB$.

The reaction in which hydrogen burns in oxygen to form water is an example of a synthesis reaction.

$$2H_2(g) + O_2(g) \longrightarrow 2H_2O(g)$$

This reaction is used to power some types of rockets. Another synthesis reaction is the combination of oxygen with iron in the presence of water to form hydrated iron(II) oxide or rust. This reaction is shown in **Figure 10.**

Decomposition Reactions A decomposition reaction is just the reverse of a synthesis. Instead of two substances coming together to form a third, a **decomposition reaction** occurs when one substance breaks down, or decomposes, into two or more substances. The general formula for this type of reaction can be expressed as follows: $AB \longrightarrow A + B$.

Most decomposition reactions require the use of heat, light, or electricity. An electric current passed through water produces hydrogen and oxygen as shown in **Figure 11.**

$$2H_2O(l) \xrightarrow{\text{elec.}} 2H_2(g) + O_2(g)$$

Single Displacement When one element replaces another element in a compound, it is called a **single-displacement reaction.** Single-displacement reactions are described by the general equation $A + BC \longrightarrow AC + B$. Here you can see that atom A displaces atom B to produce a new molecule AC. A single displacment reaction is illustrated in **Figure 12,** where a copper wire is put into a solution of silver nitrate. Because copper is a more active metal than silver, it replaces the silver, forming a blue copper(II) nitrate solution. The silver, which is not soluble, forms on the wire.

$$Cu(s) + 2AgNO_3(aq) \longrightarrow Cu(NO_3)_2\,(aq) + 2Ag(s)$$

Reading Check *Describe a single-displacement reaction.*

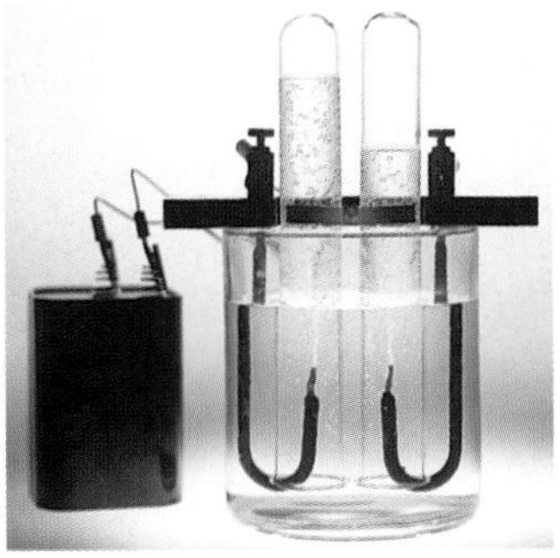

Figure 11 Water decomposes into hydrogen and oxygen when an electric current is passed through it. A small amount of sulfuric acid is added to increase conductivity. Notice the proportions of the gases collected. **Describe** *how this is related to the coefficients of the products in the equation.*

Figure 12 Copper in a wire replaces silver in silver nitrate, forming a blue-tinted solution of copper(II) nitrate.

2 Teach

Caption Answer

Figure 10 $A+B \longrightarrow AB$

Figure 11 There are twice as many molecules of hydrogen being produced than molecules of oxygen. The coefficient of hydrogen is 2 and the coefficient of oxygen is 1.

Reading Check

Answer One element replaces another in a compound.

Activity

Building Reactions Bring in a set of connecting, colored blocks and ask students to demonstrate the five types of chemical reactions using the blocks as the reactants and products. For example, they might combine a blue block with a red block to demonstrate a synthesis reaction or start with two blocks combined and separate them to demonstrate a decomposition reaction. Encourage capable students to use more than three or four blocks to demonstrate more complex reactions. L2

Quick Demo
Synthesis Reaction

Materials magnesium ribbon, Bunsen burner and lighter, tongs, crucible or glass catch plate

Estimated Time 15 minutes

Procedure Demonstrate the synthesis of magnesium oxide by burning magnesium ribbon in oxygen. Using tongs, position a small piece of magnesium ribbon in the flame of the Bunsen burner. *Hold the magnesium away from you and do NOT look directly into the flame.* Place the magnesium over a crucible or glass plate as it is burning to catch the ash (MgO). Reinforce the demonstration with the balanced chemical equation for the reaction: $2Mg_{(s)} + O2_{(g)} \longrightarrow 2MgO_{(s)}$.

Visual Learning

Figure 12 Ask students if the copper replacement of silver could have any practical use. It is a good way to retrieve silver for recycling. L2 LS **Logical-Mathematical**

Reading Strategy

Shared Reading Read the section Synthesis Reactions aloud to the class. Draw attention to headings, figures, and equations. Ask questions, clarify, and summarize as you read. Allow student volunteers to read other sections to small groups of four to five students as they practice effective reading strategies.

Discussion

Double-Displacement Reaction Refer to the Teacher to Teacher idea at the beginning of this chapter in which a chemical reaction created a gas that extinguished a candle. Discuss how this is a double-displacement reaction.

Make a Model

Electron Transfer Have students use themselves as model components to illustrate electron transfer in a redox reaction. Arrange several "electron" students around two nuclei, then have one or two of the "electrons" move over to the other atom. Describe how this model proves that a loss of electrons equals a gain of electrons somewhere else and that matters is neither created nor destroyed when electrons move. L2

Reading Check

Answer Double-displacement reactions frequently produce a precipitate.

Use an Analogy

Basketball Before a basketball game, the coach assembles the players and selects five to form the starting team. Which one of the four reactions does this resemble? synthesis One of the starting players on the basketball team fouls out of the game. The coach then substitutes a player from the bench into the game. Which one of the four reaction types does this resemble? single displacement L2 IN **Logical-Mathematical**

Figure 13 This figure shows the activity series of metals. A metal will replace any other metal that is less active.

The Activity Series Sometimes single-displacement reactions can cause problems. For example, if iron-containing vegetables such as spinach are cooked in aluminum pans, aluminum can displace iron from the vegetable. This causes a black deposit of iron to form on the sides of the pan. For this reason, it is better to use stainless steel or enamel cookware when cooking spinach.

We can predict which metal will replace another using the diagram shown in **Figure 13,** which lists metals according to how reactive they are. A metal can replace any metal below it on the list but not above it. Notice that copper, silver, and gold are the least active metals on the list. That is why these elements often occur as deposits of the relatively pure element. For example, gold is sometimes found as veins in quartz rock. Copper is found in pure lumps known as native copper. Other metals can occur as compounds.

Double Displacement In a **double-displacement reaction,** the positive ion of one compound replaces the positive ion of the other to form two new compounds. A double-displacement reaction takes place if a precipitate, water, or a gas forms when two ionic compounds in solution are combined. A precipitate is an insoluble compound that comes out of solution during this type of reaction. The generalized formula for this type of reaction is as follows: $AB + CD \longrightarrow AD + CB$.

Reading Check *What type of reaction produces a precipitate?*

The reaction of barium nitrate with potassium sulfate is an example of this type of reaction. A precipitate—barium sulfate—forms, as shown in **Figure 14.** The chemical equation is as follows:

$$Ba(NO_3)_2(aq) + K_2SO_4(aq) \longrightarrow BaSO_4(s) + 2KNO_3(aq)$$

These are a few examples of chemical reactions classified into types. Many more reactions of each type occur around you.

Figure 14 Solid barium sulfate settles to the bottom of a test tube containing potassium nitrate.
Observe *Has a chemical change occurred in this photo? How can you tell?*

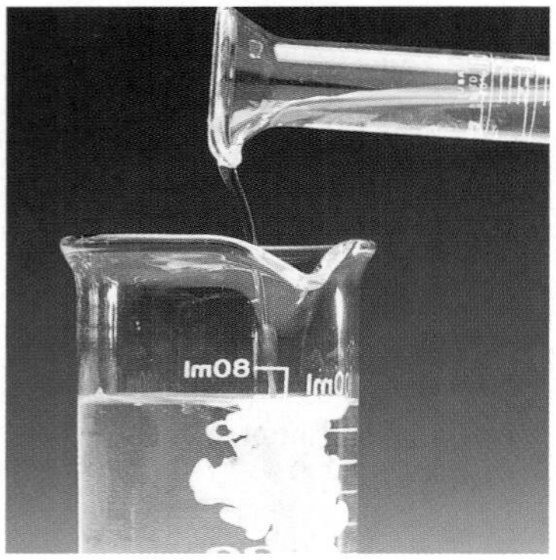

Differentiated Instruction

Learning Disabled Use visual learning techniques to describe the five main types of chemical reactions. Brightly colored blocks can be used to represent reactants products, and the reactions can be demonstrated physically in addition to the explanations in the text and teacher lectures. L1

Challenge Many single-displacement reactions involve oxidation and reduction. Challenge students to determine the importance of the two terms in determining the activity of a metal. Oxidation refers to losing electrons; reduction refers to gaining electrons. Chemical activity for metals usually involves the exchange of electrons. Active metals give up their electrons, or oxidize, easily. L3 IN **Linguistic**

Oxidation-Reduction Reactions One characteristic that is common to many chemical reactions is the tendency of the substances to lose or gain electrons. Chemists use the term oxidation to describe the loss of electrons and the term reduction to describe the gain of electrons. Chemical reactions involving electron transfer of this sort often involve oxygen, which is very reactive, pulling electrons from metallic elements. Corrosion of metal is a visible result, as shown in **Figure 15.**

The cause and effect of oxidation and reduction can be taken one step further by describing the substances after the electron transfer. The substance that gains an electron or electrons obviously becomes more negative, so we say it is reduced. On the other hand, the substance that loses an electron or electrons then becomes more positive, and we say it is oxidized. The electrons that were pulled from one atom were gained by another atom in a chemical reaction called reduction. Reduction is the partner to oxidation; the two always work as a pair, which is commonly referred to as redox.

Figure 15 One of the results of all of these electrons moving from one place to another might show up on the metal body of a tanker.

section 3 review

Summary

Types of Reactions

- Lavoisier was one of the first scientists to accurately describe a combustion reaction.
- For single-displacement reactions, we can predict which metal will replace another by comparing the activity characteristic of each.
- Some reactions produce a solid called a precipitate when two ionic substances are combined.
- Chemical reactions are organized into five basic classes: combustion, synthesis, decomposition, single displacement, and double displacement.

Oxidation-Reduction Reactions

- Oxidation is the loss of electrons and reduction is the corresponding gain of electrons.
- Redox reactions often result in corrosion and rust.
- A substance that gains elections is reduced, and a substance that loses elections is oxidized.

Self Check

1. **Classify** each of the following reactions:
   a. $CaO(s) + H_2O \longrightarrow Ca(OH)_2\,(aq)$
   b. $Fe(s) + CuSO_4(aq) \longrightarrow FeSO_4(aq) + Cu(s)$
   c. $NH_4NO_3(s) \longrightarrow N_2O(g) + 2H_2O(g)$
2. **Describe** what happens in a combustion reaction.
3. **Explain** the difference between synthesis and decomposition reactions.
4. **Determine,** using **Figure 13,** if zinc will displace gold in a chemical reaction and explain why or why not.
5. **Think Critically** In the reaction $2\,Na + Cl_2 \longrightarrow 2NaCl$, which atom is reduced and which atom is oxidized?

Applying Math

6. **Use Proportions** The following chemical equation is balanced, but the coefficients used are larger than necessary. Rewrite this balanced equation using the smallest coefficients.
   $9Fe(s) + 12H_2O(g) \longrightarrow 3Fe_3O_4(s) + 12H_2(g)$
7. **Use Coefficients** Sulfur trioxide, (SO_3), a pollutant released by coal-burning plants, can react with water in the atmosphere to produce sulfuric acid, H_2SO_4. Write a balanced equation for this reaction.

Caption Answer

Figure 14 Yes; a precipitate (barium sulfate) forms as a result of the reaction.

Post Reading

Essay Writing Ask students to choose a class of chemical reactions. Students will research the reaction type and compose an essay that includes a description of the reaction, including examples.

3 Assess

DAILY INTERVENTION

Check for Understanding

Auditory-Musical With the class, come up with some mnemonic devices to remember the five types of chemical reactions. You may devise a poem or jingle. Have the students write the results in their Science Journals to reinforce the topic and for future study reference. L2

Reteach

Play Cards Ask students to review the following four kinds of chemical reactions by using colored note cards. Synthesis: Tape two different colored cards together. Decomposition: Two cards that are taped could be pulled apart. Single-displacement: Two different cards are taped together and a third colored card replaces one of them. Double-displacement: Two cards, from each of two sets of two different colored, taped cards are traded. L3 ELL IN **Kinesthetic**

section 3 review

1. (a) synthesis (b) single displacement (c) decomposition
2. A substance combines with oxygen to produce energy.
3. Synthesis involves bringing elements or compounds together. Decomposition involves breaking compounds down.
4. Zinc will displace gold because zinc is more reactive than gold.
5. reduced – Cl; oxidized – Na
6. $3Fe(s) + 4H_2O(l) \longrightarrow Fe_3O_4(s) + 4H_2(g)$.
7. $SO_3 + H_2O \longrightarrow H_2SO_4$

Assessment

Performance Have students complete and balance the following single-displacement reaction:

$K + AlCl_3 \rightarrow$ _____ + _____

$3K + AlCl_3 \longrightarrow 3KCl + Al$

Use **PASC,** p. 101.

1 Motivate

An editable Microsoft® PowerPoint® presentation is available on **Interactive Chalkboard** CD-ROM.

Bellringer

Section Focus Transparencies also are available on the Interactive Chalkboard CD-ROM. L2 ELL

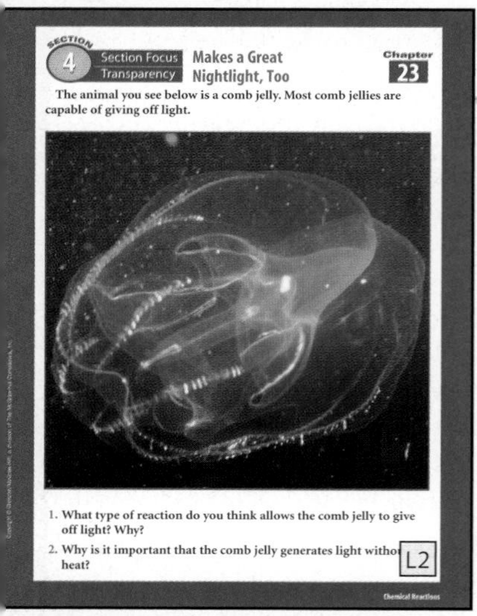

Reading Preview

Tie to Prior Knowledge

Eating Food Ask how energy is obtained from food. Chemical bonds in proteins, carbohydrates, and fats store energy. During digestion, those bonds are broken and new ones form. The energy required to break bonds is less than the energy released when new bonds form, so the net result is the release of energy. L2

Word Chart Post each new vocabulary word on a separate poster board. Give students simple definitions of all words. Ask them to probe "deeper meanings" of the words based on their background knowledge or a preview of the chapter. Have them record examples, word associations, or explanations after they have read the section.

section 4

Reaction Rates and Energy

Reading Guide

What You'll Learn

- **Identify** the source of energy changes in chemical reactions.
- **Compare and contrast** exergonic and endergonic reactions.
- **Examine** the effects of catalysts and inhibitors on the speed of chemical reactions.

Why It's Important

Chemical reactions provide energy to cook your food, keep you warm, and transform the food you eat into substances you need to live and grow.

Review Vocabulary

chemical bond: the force that holds two atoms together

New Vocabulary

- activation energy
- endothermic reaction
- exothermic reaction
- rate of reaction
- catalyst
- inhibitor

Chemical Reactions and Energy

Often a crowd gathers to watch a building being demolished using dynamite. In a few breathtaking seconds, tremendous structures of steel and cement that took a year or more to build are reduced to rubble and a large cloud of dust. A dynamite explosion, as shown in **Figure 16,** is an example of a rapid chemical reaction.

All chemical reactions release or absorb energy. This energy can take many forms, such as heat, light, sound, or electricity. The heat produced by a wood fire and the light emitted by a glow stick are two examples of reactions that release energy.

Figure 16 When its usefulness is over, a building is sometimes demolished using dynamite. Dynamite charges must be placed carefully so that the building collapses inward, where it cannot harm people or property.

Conservation of Energy in Chemical Reactions

According to the law of conservation of energy, energy cannot be created or destroyed, but can only change form. In compounds, chemical potential energy is stored in chemical bonds between atoms. In some chemical reactions, chemical potential energy is changed to other forms of energy, such as heat or light, and is released. In other chemical reactions, forms of energy such as heat or light are converted to chemical potential energy and stored in bonds that form, and energy is absorbed. In all chemical reactions, energy is never created or destroyed, but only changes form. All reactions follow the laws of conservation of mass and energy.

Section 4 Resource Manager

Chapter FAST FILE Resources

Transparency Activity, p. 49

Directed Reading for Content Mastery, pp. 21–22

Enrichment, p. 34

MiniLAB, p. 4

Lab Worksheet, pp. 5–6, 7–8

Reinforcement, p. 30

Physical Science Critical Thinking/Problem Solving, p. 14

Activation Energy

As you learned earlier, atoms and molecules have to bump into each other before a product can be formed. In order to form new bonds, atoms have to be close together. In addition to being close, the reactants require a certain amount of energy in order to allow the reaction to start. This minimum amount of energy needed to start a reaction is called **activation energy.** If there is not enough energy, the reaction will not start. Spilled gasoline does not ignite unless there is an energy source. Once ignited, the gasoline releases enough energy to keep going. Activation energy, which differs from reaction to reaction, is required for both exothermic and endothermic reactions.

INTEGRATE Life Science

Controlling Body Heat
Some animals, such as birds, are classified as endotherms because their body temperature remains constant. An animal whose body temperature varies with its environment, such as a reptile, is classified as an ectotherm. What other animals that can be classified as ectotherms?

Endergonic Reactions

Sometimes a chemical reaction requires more energy to break bonds than is released when new ones are formed. These reactions are called endergonic reactions. The energy absorbed can be in the form of light, heat, or electricity.

Electricity is often used to supply energy to endergonic reactions. For example, electroplating deposits a coating of metal onto a surface.

Heat Absorption When the energy needed is in the form of heat, the reaction is called an **endothermic reaction.** The term *endothermic* is not just related to chemical reactions. It also can describe physical changes. The process of dissolving a salt in water is a physical change. If you ever had to soak a swollen ankle in an Epsom salt solution, you probably noticed that when you mixed the Epsom salt in water, the solution became cold. The dissolving of Epsom salt absorbs heat. Thus, it is a physical change that is endothermic.

Some reactions are so endothermic that they can cause water to freeze. One such endothermic reaction is that of barium hydroxide ($Ba(OH)_2$) and ammonium chloride (NH_4Cl) in water, shown in **Figure 17.**

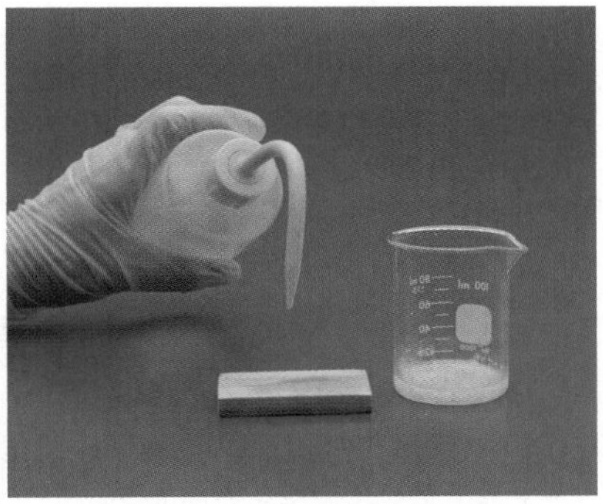

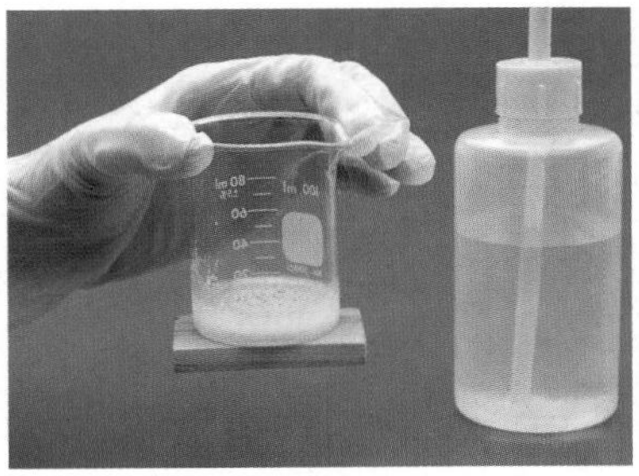

Figure 17 As an endothermic reaction happens, such as the reaction of barium hydroxide and ammonium chloride, energy from the surrounding environment is absorbed, causing a cooling effect. Here, the reaction absorbs so much heat that a drop of water freezes and the beaker holding the reaction sticks to the wood.

2 Teach

Activity

Hand Warmers Obtain several packaged hand warmers used for outdoor activities from a sports supply store. Have students carefully follow the directions and observe the results. Place the hand warmers around a small beaker of water and measure the temperature change in the water. What causes heat to be released? Many such packaged devices have a sealed sample of iron that slowly combines with oxygen (rusts) after the seal is broken and releases more heat than is required to get the reaction started. L2 ELL LS Kinesthetic

Use Science Words

Word Meanings Ask students to break the words *endergonic* and *exergonic* down into parts, and find out what each part means. Have them then explain why the words are appropriate for describing chemical processes that release or require energy. Ex-ergon-ic: *ex-* out of, *ergon-* work, *-ic* - having the character of. End-ergon-ic: *end-* into, *ergon-* work, *-ic-* having the character of. An exergonic reaction produces energy that can do work. An endergonic reaction requires energy, or work, in order to occur. L2 LS Linguistic

INTEGRATE Life Science

Controlling Body Heat Both birds and mammals are endotherms. Endotherms have internal processes that maintain a constant body temperature. The internal processes cool endotherms if they are too warm, and warm them if they are too cool. Amphibians are ectotherms, such as frogs, toads, and salamanders.

Active Reading

Bubble Map Using a bubble map helps students start ideas flowing about a given topic. Words are clustered to describe a topic or idea that is studied. Students can use a bubble map for a prewriting, to generate ideas before writing in their Science Journals, or to review for a test. Have students design a bubble map for energy exchanges in chemical reactions. L2

Teacher FYI

Tracking Energy A cold pack absorbs heat as ammonium nitrate dissolves. The dissolving process usually is considered a physical change, not a chemical reaction. In most changes, the energy can be tracked as it moves from the surroundings to the system and vice versa. In the cold pack, the system is the chemical dissolving in water. The surroundings are the plastic bag, the air, any injured body area, etc.

Visual Learning

Figure 19 Bring in several glow sticks and demonstrate the reaction. Be sure to quiet the class so they can hear the containers breaking inside the sticks. When the reaction is taking place, monitor how long it takes for the glow to be visible and how long it lasts.

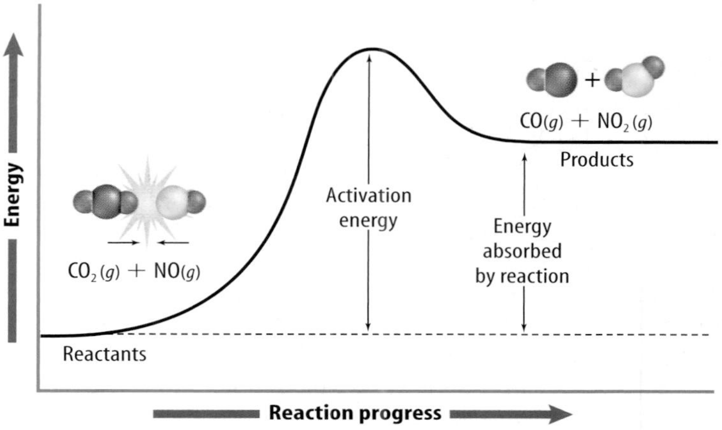

Figure 18 With an endothermic reaction, the reactants have a lower energy level than the products. The reactants must overcome the activation energy barrier in order to form new products.

Endothermic Reactions With an endothermic reaction, the chemical reaction will not take place unless energy is added. A constant source of energy must be added to keep the reaction going. The products have more stored energy than the reactants.

Figure 18 shows an energy diagram for the reaction of carbon dioxide (CO_2) and nitrogen monoxide (NO). With an endothermic reaction, the reactants have a lower energy level than the products. In order for the products to form, an input of energy is needed for the reactants to overcome the activation energy barrier.

Exergonic Reactions

You have seen many reactions that release energy. Chemical reactions that release energy are called exergonic (ek sur GAH nihk) reactions. In these reactions, less energy is required to break the original bonds than is released when new bonds are formed. As a result, some form of energy, such as light or heat, is given off by the reaction. The familiar glow from the reaction inside a glow stick, shown in **Figure 19,** is an example of an exergonic reaction, which produces visible light. In other reactions, however, energy is released as heat. This is the case with some heat packs that are used to treat muscle aches and other medical conditions. Another release of energy is used to power rockets, as shown in **Figure 20.**

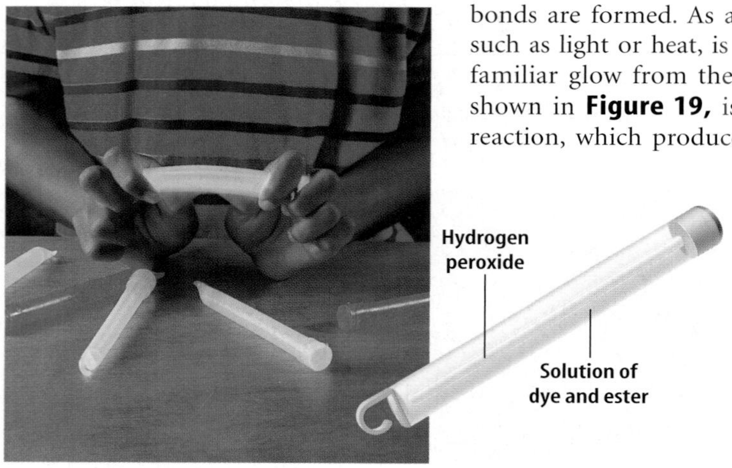

Figure 19 Glow sticks contain three different chemicals—an ester and a dye in the outer section and hydrogen peroxide in a center glass tube. Bending the stick breaks the tube and mixes the three components. The energy released is in the form of visible light.

LAB DEMONSTRATION

Purpose to demonstrate an exothermic process

Materials supersaturated solution of sodium acetate, sodium acetate crystal

Preparation Make a saturated solution of sodium acetate. Leave excess crystals in the bottom of the flask. Heat and stir until the crystals dissolve. Cool undisturbed to room temperature.

Procedure Drop an additional crystal of sodium acetate into the solution. Have students watch the solution and carefully feel the outside of the flask.

Expected Outcome The solution will crystallize, and the flask will become hot.

Assessment

Why did the solution release heat? The amount of energy required to break the bonds in the solution is less than the energy released when new crystals formed. The excess energy is released as heat. L2

736 CHAPTER 23 Chemical Reactions

NATIONAL GEOGRAPHIC

VISUALIZING CHEMICAL ENERGY

Figure 20

Rockets burn fuel to provide the thrust necessary to propel them upward. In 1926, engineer Robert Goddard used gasoline and liquid oxygen to propel the first ever liquid-fueled rocket. Although many people at the time ridiculed Goddard's space travel theories, his rockets eventually served as models for those that have gone to the Moon and beyond. A selection of rockets—including Goddard's—is shown here. The number below each craft indicates the amount of thrust—expressed in newtons (N)—produced during launch.

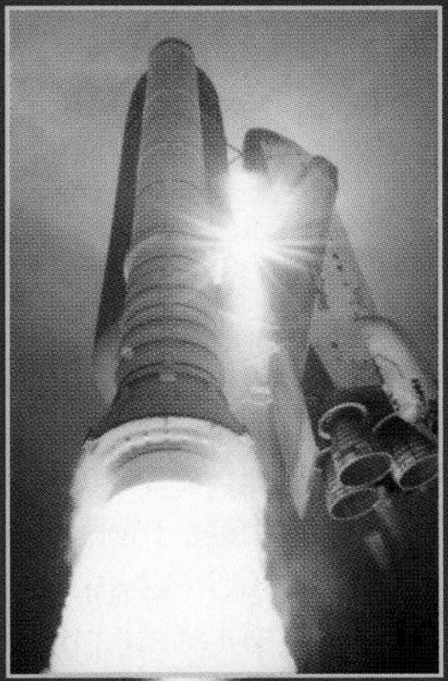

◀ SPACE SHUTTLE The main engines produce enormous amounts of energy by combining liquid hydrogen and oxygen. Coupled with solid rocket boosters, they produce over 32.5 million newtons (N) of thrust to lift the system's 2 million kg off the ground.

▶ JUPITER C This rocket launched the first United States satellite in 1958. It used a fuel called hydyne plus liquid oxygen.

▼ GODDARD'S MODEL ROCKET Although his first rocket rose only 12.6 m, Goddard successfully launched 35 rockets in his lifetime. The highest reached an altitude of 2.7 km.

▼ LUNAR MODULE Smaller rocket engines, like those used by the Lunar Module to leave the Moon, use hydrazine-peroxide fuels. The number shown below indicates the fixed thrust from one of the module's two engines; the other engine's thrust was adjustable.

400 N

369,350 N

32,500,000 N

15,920 N

Differentiated Instruction

Visually Impaired If students cannot see the model rocket you demonstrated in the Quick Demo activity, organize the class into small groups and have each group make its own model rocket. Visually impaired students can work with others to accomplish the rocket design and they can provide the thrust for the craft.

Challenge Ask students to research new developments in rocket technology and the projected dates that the new technology will be used. Ask students to give short oral reports to the class describing what they learn. L3

NATIONAL GEOGRAPHIC

Visualizing Chemical Energy

Have students examine the pictures and read the captions. Then ask the following questions.

How much more thrust did the Jupiter C rocket produce than Goddard's rocket? 369,350 N/400 N = 923.38 times more thrust

Why does the space shuttle require so much thrust to launch it into orbit? because it has so much mass

Activity

Rocket Technology Have students research the development of rocket technology throughout history and prepare time line posters showing the major milestones in this technology. L2 LS **Visual-Spatial** P

Quick Demo

Model Rocket

Materials various tube materials such as straws, towel tubes, plastic tubing

Estimated Time 30 minutes

Procedure Make several small "rockets" and demonstrate the amount of force it takes to launch them. Rockets can be simple straws (small inside a large straw) propelled by your lungs or tube constructions launched by a hand pump. Relate to the class that to use a greater force to launch the rocket requires a heavier, sturdier rocket to withstand the force. Demonstrate different designs to aid the flight of the rocket. Explain that the design to fly is an important consideration inside Earth's atmosphere, but is inconsequential in space. L2

Mini LAB

Purpose to observe evidence of a chemical reaction L2 ELL
LS **Visual Spatial**

Materials water, test tube, copper(II) bromide

Safety Precautions Use the safety symbols list to explain the safety hazards, examples, and precautions as they apply to this lab. Approve safety forms before work begins.

Teaching Strategies The chemical reaction that occurs is

1. $CuBr_2 + 4H_2O \rightarrow Cu(H_2O)_4^{2+} + 2Br^-$
2. $Cu(H_2O)_4^{2+} + H_2O \rightarrow Cu(H_2O)_3OH^+ + H_3O^+$

Analysis

1. brown
2. blue
3. A chemical reaction occurred.

Assessment

Performance Have students repeat the activity and look for signs of energy absorbed or released by the reaction. Use **Performance Assessment in the Science Classroom**, p. 97.

Reading Check

Answer The energy given off by the reaction is primarily in the form of heat.

Mini LAB

Creating a Colorful Chemical Reaction

Procedure

1. Sprinkle a few crystals of **copper(II) bromide** into the **test tube.** Record the color of the crystals in your Science Journal.
2. Pour 5 mL of **water** into the test tube. Observe the color change of the crystals.
3. Slowly add more water and observe what happens.

Analysis

1. What color were the copper(II) bromide crystals after you added them to the test tube of water?
2. What color were they when you added more water?
3. What caused this color change?

Exothermic Reactions When the energy given off in a reaction is primarily in the form of heat, the reaction is called an **exothermic reaction.** The burning of wood and the explosion of dynamite are exothermic reactions. Iron rusting is also exothermic, but, under typical conditions, the reaction proceeds so slowly that it's difficult to detect any temperature change.

Reading Check *Why is a log fire considered to be an exothermic reaction?*

Exothermic reactions provide most of the power used in homes and industries. Fossil fuels that contain carbon, such as coal, petroleum, and natural gas, combine with oxygen to yield carbon dioxide gas and energy. Unfortunately impurities in these fuels, such as sulfur, burn as well, producing pollutants such as sulfur dioxide. Sulfur dioxide combines with water in the atmosphere, producing acid rain.

Energy Release The energy diagram for an exothermic reaction is the reverse of an endothermic reaction. With an exothermic reaction, the products have less stored energy than the reactants. As shown in **Figure 21,** the reactants, carbon monoxide (CO) and nitrogen dioxide (NO_2) have a higher energy level than the products. The molecules have enough energy to overcome the activation energy barrier.

Chemical Reaction Rates

According to the kinetic theory of matter, atoms and molecules are always moving. In order for a chemical reaction to occur, the atoms and molecules that are the reactants have to bump into each other or collide. The **rate of reaction** is the speed at which reactants are consumed and products are produced in a given reaction.

Reaction rate is important in the manufacturing industry because the faster the product can be made, the less it usually costs. Sometimes a fast reaction rate is undesirable, such as the rate of reaction that causes food spoilage. In this case, the slower the reaction rate, the longer the food will stay edible. What conditions control the reaction rate, and how can the rate be changed?

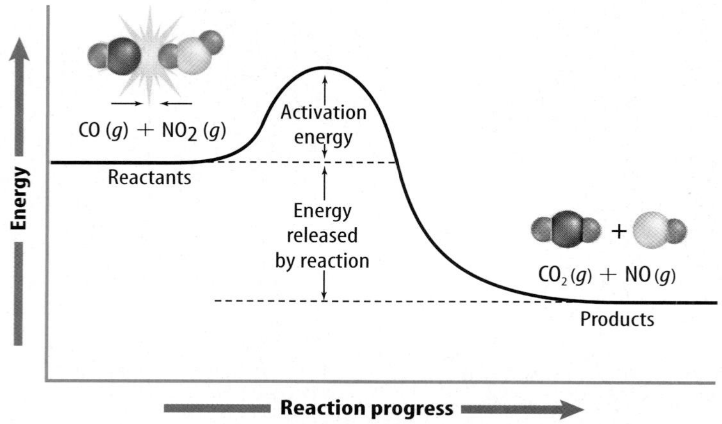

Figure 21 In an exothermic reaction, molecules have enough energy to overcome the activation energy barrier. Energy is released with the formation of new products.

Cultural Diversity

Japanese Chemistry In 1908, the Japanese chemist Kikunae Ikeda (1864–1936) used chemical reactions to make monosodium glutamate from hydrolyzed kelp protein. This synthesis became the foundation of Japan's chemical industry.

Reading Strategy

Discussion Groups Organize the class into groups of four students. Ask each group to discuss the following prompts: What role does energy play in chemical reactions? How are chemical reaction rates affected by different factors? Have students share a summary of their ideas with the class.

738 CHAPTER 23 Chemical Reactions

Temperature Energy is needed by atoms and molecules to break old bonds and to form new ones. One way to increase the activation energy is to add heat or increase the temperature. With an increase in temperature, atoms and molecules move faster and kinetic energy increases. With faster moving atoms and molecules, more molecules have kinetic energy greater than activation energy. The atoms and molecules now will have enough energy to break old bonds at higher temperature, which will increase the reaction rate. A chemical reaction will go faster at higher temperature and slower at lower temperature as shown in **Figure 22.**

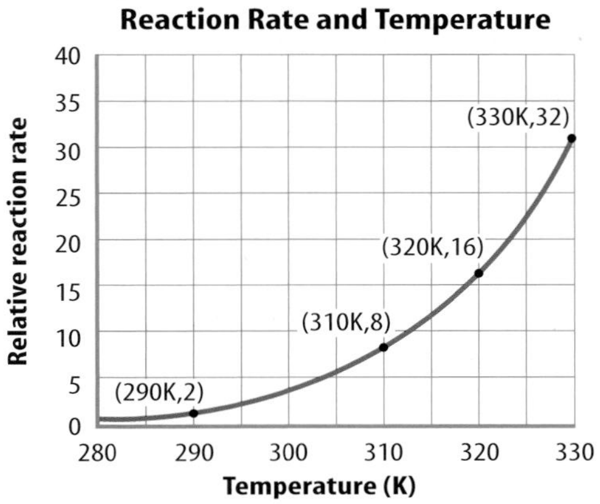

Figure 22 Increasing the temperature of a reaction increases the frequency of collisions, which will increase the rate of reaction.

Concentration When you walk through the hallways at school, you are more likely to bump into another student if the hallways are crowded. A similar situation is shown in **Figure 23.** The closer atoms and molecules are to each other, the greater the chance of collision. The amount of substance present in a certain volume is called its concentration. Increasing the concentration of a substance increases the reaction rate.

Surface Area Only atoms or molecules in the outer layer of a substance can collide with other reactants. When a substance is finely divided, it has a larger surface area than when it was whole. Increasing the surface area increases the chance for collisions, which will increase the reaction rate. A powdered reactant will produce a faster reaction rate than a lump of the same reactant. For instance, grain elevator operators have to be careful of explosions and fire. The dust from the grains in the bin has a larger surface area than the whole grains. With an ignition spark, the dust will catch fire rapidly and cause an explosion.

Agitation If you are making lemonade, the water, sugar, and lemon juice are mixed in order to get the product. Agitation or stirring is a physical process that allows reactants to mix. A low stirring rate will slow the reaction due to fewer collisions. Chemical reactions can be controlled by agitation.

Pressure Another way to influence the reaction rate is with pressure. By increasing the pressure of gases, molecules have less room to move about and the concentration of the reactants increases. This will boost the chance of collisions, which means the reaction rate increases. Decreasing the pressure means fewer collisions, and lower reaction rate.

Collisions are more frequent in a concentrated solution.

Collisions are less frequent in a dilute solution.

Figure 23 People are more likely to collide in crowds. Molecules behave similarly.

Inquiry Lab

Real-World Rust

Purpose To recognize that some chemical reactions have financial impacts, explain to students that when metal rusts, money must be spent to correct the problem and prevent further corrosion.

Possible Materials pencil and paper

Estimated Time 20 minutes

Teaching Strategies

- Start the brainstorming by giving an example of corrosion on a bridge support. Visit each group to be sure they are thinking of appropriate examples.
- Do not limit the brainstorming to the problem and solutions of rust. Accept and discuss other types of chemical reactions that may have financial impacts.
- Accept and discuss chemical reactions that can have real-world impacts on health or safety and encourage creative solutions to these types of situations.

For additional inquiry activities, see *Science Inquiry Lab Manual.* L2

Discussion

Reaction Factors Explain to students that in order to react, molecules must collide, must have sufficient energy, and must collide with the correct orientation. Any factor, such as concentration, temperature, and catalysts that influence those requirements will have an effect on the reaction rate.

Post Reading

Extended Research Ask students to research the purpose of catalysts and inhibitors. Have them develop a short paper that describes the function of each, along with specific examples. Have students present their findings to the class.

Teacher FYI

Determining Reaction Many reactions do not happen in a simple one-step process or mechanism. Two, three, or four more steps may be involved in the process that eventually converts the reactants to products. Each step may occur at a different rate.

INTEGRATE History

Catalysts The metals in exhaust catalysis help break down the unused hydrocarbon fuel molecules into less harmful compounds.

Research Have students research current trends in catalyst systems for automobiles and other vehicles that use fossil fuels. Findings can be noted in students' Science Journals.

Reading Check

Answer lowers the activation energy

3 Assess

DAILY INTERVENTION

Check for Understanding

Sounds of Chemistry Reiterate that the boom sounds from fireworks are also the results of chemical reactions. Have students name other sounds of chemical reactions. the backfire sound from a car or the pop sound from a toy cap gun L2

Reteach

Chemical Energy Write the following two equations on the board:

$A + B \rightarrow C + \text{heat}$

$X + Y + \text{heat} \rightarrow Z$

Which equation depicts an endothermic reaction? second one Which depicts an exothermic reaction? first one L2 IS **Logical-Mathematical**

Assessment

Oral Ask students to suppose that they are each holding a test tube that has a chemical change taking place inside. The tube is beginning to feel colder. Is the process in the tube endothermic or exothermic? Endothermic; the system is gaining energy from the surroundings—your hand. Use **PASC**, p. 89. L2

INTEGRATE History

Catalysts Metals, such as platinum and palladium, are used as catalysts in the exhaust systems of automobiles. What reactions do you think they catalyze?

Catalysts and Inhibitors Some reactions proceed too slowly to be useful. To speed them up, a catalyst reaction can be added. A **catalyst** is substance that speeds up a chemical reaction without being permanently changed itself. When you add a catalyst to a reaction, the mass of the product that is formed remains the same, but it will form more rapidly. A catalyst lowers the activation energy of the reaction. With the lowering of the activation energy, collisions among molecules now will become more effective, thus increasing the rate of reaction.

Reading Check *Explain how a catalyst speeds up a reaction.*

At times, it is worthwhile to prevent certain reaction from occurring. Substances that are used to slow down a chemical reaction are called **inhibitors.** The food preservations BHT and BHA are inhibitors that prevent spoilage of certain foods, such as cereals and crackers.

One thing to remember when thinking about catalysts and inhibitors is that they do not change the amount of product produced. They only change the rate of production. Catalysts increase the rate and inhibitors decease the rate. Other factors, including concentration, pressure, and temperature, also affect the rate of reaction and must be considered when catalyzing or inhibiting a reaction.

section 4 review

Summary

Conservation of Energy

- In a chemical reaction, the total amount of energy is the same. Energy is neither created nor destroyed.

Chemical Reactions and Energy

- Chemical reactions release or absorb energy, as chemical bonds are broken and formed.
- An endothermic reaction absorbs heat.
- An exothermic reaction releases heat.

Chemical Reaction Rates

- Temperature, concentration, and pressure can affect reaction rates.
- In an exothermic reaction, reactants have more energy than the products.
- In an endothermic reaction, the reactants have less energy than the products.

Self Check

1. **Explain** whether the term *endothermic* can be used to describe physical changes.
2. **Describe** how temperature can affect reaction rate.
3. **Illustrate** As an exothermic reaction, methane and oxygen will react to form carbon dioxide and water. Draw the activation energy chart showing where the reactants and products belong.
4. **Explain** why crackers containing BHT stay fresh longer than those without it.
5. **Think Critically** To develop a product that warms people's hands, would you choose an exothermic or endothermic reaction to use? Why?

Applying Math

6. **Calculate** If an endothermic reaction begins at 26°C and loses 2°C per minute, how long will it take to reach 0°C?
7. **Use Graphs** Create a graph of the data in question 6. After 5 min, what is the temperature of the reaction?

section 4 review

1. Endothermic can be used to describe physical changes.
2. A chemical reaction will go faster at a higher temperature and slower at a lower temperature.
3. The student's graph should be similar to **Figure 21**.
4. BHT slows the spoilage of the cracker.
5. Exothermic; it would release energy to warm people's hands.
6. 13 min
7. Check students' graphs. After 5 min, reaction is approximately 18°C.

LAB

CATALYZED Reaction

A balanced chemical equation tells nothing about the rate of a reaction. One way to affect the rate is to use a catalyst.

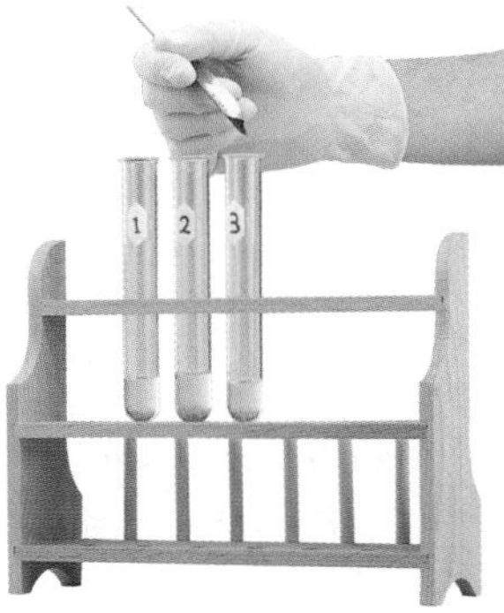

Real-World Problem

How does the presence of a catalyst affect the rate of a chemical reaction?

Goals

- **Observe** the effect of a catalyst on the rate of reaction.
- **Conclude,** based on your observations, whether the catalyst remained unchanged.

Possible Materials

test tubes (3)
test-tube rack
3% hydrogen peroxide, H_2O_2 (15 mL)
10-mL graduated cylinder
small plastic teaspoon
sand (1 g)
hot plate
wooden splint
beaker of hot water
manganese dioxide, MnO_2 (1 g)

Safety Precautions

WARNING: *Hydrogen peroxide and manganese dioxide can irritate skin and eyes. Point test tubes away from other students.*

Procedure

1. Label three test tubes and set them in a test-tube stand. Pour 5 mL of hydrogen peroxide into each tube.
2. Place about 1 g of sand in tube 2 and the same amount of MnO_2 in tube 3.
3. In the presence of a catalyst, H_2O_2 decomposes rapidly producing oxygen gas, O_2. Hypothesize what will happen when the smoldering wood is introduced to each test tube. Test each tube by lighting a wooden splint, blowing out the flame, and inserting the glowing splint into the tube. The splint will relight if oxygen is present.
4. Place all three tubes in a beaker of hot water. Heat on a hot plate until all of the remaining H_2O_2 is driven away and no liquid remains.

Conclude and Apply

1. **Observe** the changes that happened when the solids were added to the tubes.
2. **Infer** which substance, sand or MnO_2, was the catalyst.
3. **Identify** what remained in each tube after the H_2O_2 was driven away.

Communicating Your Data

Compare your results with those of your classmates and discuss any differences observed. **For more help refer to the** Science Skill Handbook.

BENCH TESTED

Real-World Problem

Purpose Students operationally define a catalyst and observe its action. L2 **Kinesthetic**

Process Skills observe, infer, form operational definitions, classify, recognize cause and effect

Time Required 30 minutes

Procedure

Safety Precautions Have students tie back long hair and keep clothing away from open flame. Use the safety symbols list to explain the safety hazards, examples, and precautions as they apply to this lab. Approve safety forms before work begins.

Teaching Strategy Demonstrate the glowing splint test for students.

Troubleshooting To ensure that the splint will relight, be sure the splints still have some glowing ember when introduced into the test tube. A completely cold splint will not relight.

Conclude and Apply

1. There was no observable change from the addition of sand, but the MnO_2 increased the rate of oxygen production.
2. manganese dioxide
3. the sand in one tube, the MnO_2 in the other tube

Assessment

Performance Have students repeat the test with a small piece of liver instead of MnO_2. Ask what was in the liver to cause increased O_2 production. an enzyme Use **Performance Assessment in the Science Classroom,** p. 97.

Communicating Your Data

Have students draw illustrations showing each test tube at each step of the procedure.

Real-World Problem

Purpose Explain and infer the factors of concentration, temperature, pressure, and catalyst that affect the rate of a chemical reaction.

Time Required 1 class period

Process Skills Analyze results, collect data, explain, infer, interpret data, observe, organize data, summarize, use scientific explanations

Procedure

Alternate Materials You can use small Erlenmeyer flasks instead of plastic water bottles. You can collect gases by water displacement to get more quantitative data.

Safety Precautions Use the safety symbols list to explain the safety hazards, examples, and precautions as they apply to this lab. Approve safety forms before work begins.

Follow Your Plan

Teaching Strategy You may want to demo the technique of setting up the balloons so students can see how it works.

LAB

Investigating Reaction Conditions

Goals
- **Evaluate** the effect of concentration on the rate of a chemical reaction.
- **Examine** the effect of temperature on the rate of a chemical reaction.

Materials
water
vinegar solution
baking soda
balloons (3)
plastic 0.5-liter soft-drink bottles (3)
test tube
150-mL beakers (3)
100-mL graduated cylinder
marker
tape measure
stop watch
**clock with second hand*

**Alternate material*

Safety Precautions

Real-World Problem

Many people believe that you cannot perform chemical reactions without expensive equipment or costly chemicals. But this isn't true; chemical reactions happen everywhere. All you need is a food store to find many substances that can produce exciting chemical reactions. What factors determine how much product is produced in a chemical reaction or how fast a reaction occurs?

Procedure

1. Copy the data tables into your Science Journal.
2. Prepare the following solutions: a 50% vinegar solution by mixing 50 mL of vinegar with 50 mL of water; a 30% vinegar solution by mixing 30 mL vinegar with 70 mL of water and a 10% vinegar solution by mixing 10 mL of vinegar with 90 mL of water. Pour these solutions into labeled 0.5-L plastic bottles.
3. Mark a small test tube about 1–2 cm from its bottom. Fill the test tube to the line with baking soda. Put the baking soda into one balloon. Repeat, adding baking soda to the other two balloons.

742 CHAPTER 23

Alternative Inquiry Lab

Real-World Connection To extend this lab, have students design an experiment that can collect quantitative results that can be graphed. Other reactions that can be carried out are the reaction of zinc with hydrochloric acid.

4. Place the mouth of one balloon over the mouth of one 0.5-L bottle. Do not let any of the baking soda fall into the solution.
5. Lift each balloon to allow the baking soda to fall into each vinegar solution. Observe time of reaction and measure how much each balloon inflates. Record your observations in your data table.
6. Rinse the plastic bottles with water. Prepare three 30% vinegar solutions. Bottle A will have cold water added. Bottle B will have room temperature water added. Bottle C will have hot water added.
7. Prepare the baking soda in the balloons as in step 3. Add the baking soda to the solution. Time how long it takes for the reaction to finish. Measure how much each balloon inflates. Record your observations in the data table.

Concentration Table

Concentration	50%	30%	10%
Observations			

Temperature Table

Temperature	Cold Temp	Room Temp	Hot Temp
Observations			

Analyze Your Data

1. **Describe** how increasing the concentration of a solution affects the rate of a chemical reaction.
2. **Summarize** how temperature affects the rate of a chemical reaction.
3. **Explain** why the balloons became inflated.

Conclude and Apply

1. **Infer** how a change in pressure can affect the rate of chemical reaction of this system.
2. **Explain** how temperature and balloon inflation are related.

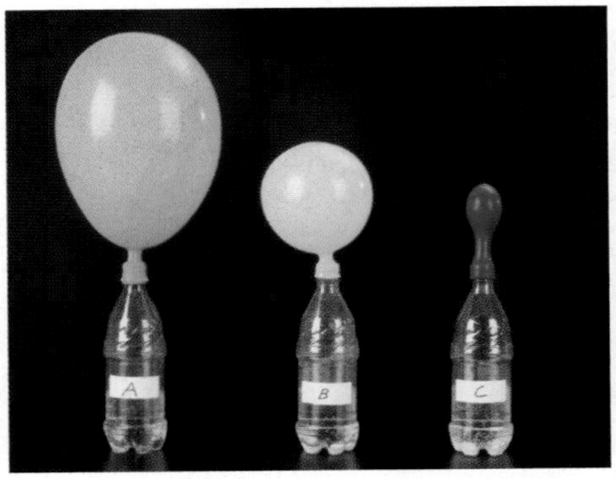

Communicating Your Data

Compare your results with other students in your class.

Analyze Your Data

1. The higher the concentration, the faster the rate of reaction.
2. The higher the temperature, the faster the rate of reaction.
3. The balloon became inflated because of the gas generated.

Conclude and Apply

1. Increasing the pressure has the same effect as increasing the concentration, so the rate of reaction will increase.
2. The higher the temperature, the more inflated the balloon became.

Assessment

Performance Design an experiment that quantitatively demonstrates how concentration or temperature affects the rate of chemical reaction. Use **PASC,** p. 95.

Test Your Model

Concentration	50 %	30 %	10 %
Observations	Balloon is biggest	Balloon is blown up	Balloon is smallest

Temperature	Cold	Room Temperature	Hot
Observations	very slow	medium rate	very fast

Communicating Your Data

Facilitate student discussion of results.

Oops! Accidents in SCIENCE

SOMETIMES GREAT DISCOVERIES HAPPEN BY ACCIDENT!

Content Background

When Chardonnet made his discovery in 1878, the French silk industry was in danger because something was causing the silkworms to die. Louis Pasteur was working to solve the mystery while, at the same time, Chardonnet was working to find a replacement for natural silk. He derived the solution from which he finally produced his artificial silk from the pulp of mulberry leaves, the natural food of silkworms. When he displayed the product at the Paris Exposition in 1889, he got backing for it immediately. It wasn't called rayon until about 1924.

Discussion

Learn from Mistakes Ask students why it might have been obvious to Chardonnet that his accident might lead to artificial silk. because he had been searching for an artificial silk anyway Discuss how this outcome might give students a new perspective on making mistakes. Remind students that we learn from mistakes and mistakes can often give a whole new outlook on a problem. L2

Analyze the Event

Eventually, the diseases striking silkworms were identified and controlled. Why do you think Chardonnet's artificial silk remained so popular? Possible answers: because now the amount of silk produced could be easily controlled. As much or as little fabric could be made as was necessary to meet demand. No longer did people have to worry about silkworms getting sick. L2

A Clumsy Move Pays Off

Hilaire de Chardonnet

Great scientific discoveries can happen in some very unlikely ways. Most people might not think that an accidental spill left uncleaned would become significant, but that's exactly what led a chemist named Hilaire de Chardonnet (hee LAYR • duh • shar doh NAY) to his discovery. In 1878, Chardonnet accidentally knocked over some nitrate chemicals. He put off cleaning up the mess and ended up inventing artificial silk.

Silk is produced naturally by silkworms. In the mid-1800s, though, silkworms were dying from disease and the silk industry was suffering. Businesses were going under and people were put out of work. Many scientists were working to develop a solution to this problem. Chardonnet had been searching for a silk substitute for years—he just didn't plan to find it by knocking it over!

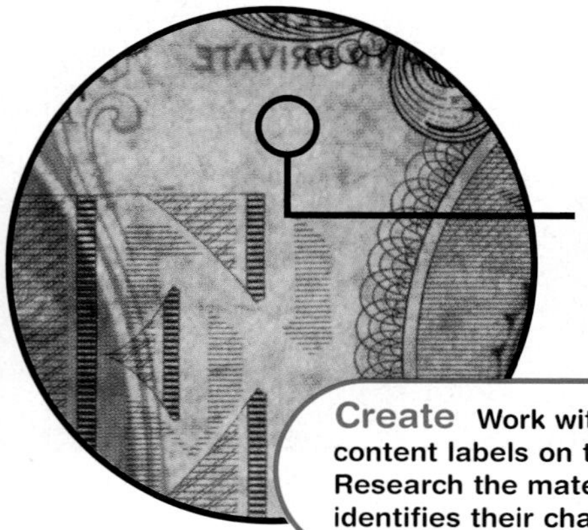

Rayon fiber

A Messy Discovery

Chardonnet was in his darkroom developing photographs when the accidental spill took place. He decided to clean up the spill later and finish what he was working on. By the time he returned to wipe up the spill, the chemical solution had turned into a thick, gooey mess. When he pulled the cleaning cloth away, the goop formed long, thin strands of fiber that stuck to the cloth. The chemicals had reacted with the cellulose in the wooden table and liquefied it. The strands of fiber looked just like the raw silk made by silkworms.

Within six years, Chardonnet had developed a way to make the fibers into an artificial silk. Other scientists extended his work, developing a fiber called rayon. Today's rayon is made from sodium hydroxide mixed with wood fibers, which is then stranded and woven into cloth.

Rayon has another real-world application. To help prevent counterfeiting, dollars are printed on paper that contains red and blue rayon fibers. If you can scratch off the red or blue, that means it's ink and your bill is counterfeit. If you can pick out the red or blue fiber with a needle, it's a real bill.

Create Work with a partner to examine the fabric content labels on the inside collars of your clothes. Research the materials, then make a data table that identifies their characteristics.

For more information, visit gpescience.com

Create Suggest students include in their tables information on the weather conditions for which each piece of clothing is used. Ask students to examine the textures and elasticity of the clothing and hypothesize how the polymers must be arranged. L2

Resources for Teachers and Students

Mistakes that Worked, by Charlotte Foltz Jones, Doubleday, 1994

They All Laughted . . . From Light Bulbs to Lasers, by Ira Flatlow, Perennial, 1993

Bright Ideas, by Sharon Dalgleish, Mason Crest Publishers, 2003

Reviewing Main Ideas

Section 1 Chemical Changes

1. In a chemical reaction, one or more substances are changed to new substances.
2. The substances that react are called reactants, and the new substances formed are called products. Charcoal, the reactant shown below, is almost pure carbon.

3. The law of conservation of mass states that in chemical reactions, matter is neither created nor destroyed, just rearranged.
4. The law of conservation of energy states that energy is neither created nor destroyed.

Section 2 Chemical Equations

1. Balanced chemical equations give the exact number of atoms involved in the reaction.
2. A balanced chemical equation has the same number of atoms of each element on both sides of the equation. This satisfies the law of conservation of mass.
3. When balancing chemical equations, change only the coefficients of the formulas, never the subscripts. To change a subscript would change the compound.

Section 3 Classifying Chemical Reactions

1. In synthesis reactions, two or more substances combine to form another substance.
2. In single-displacement reactions, one element replaces another in a compound.
3. In double-displacement reactions, ions in two compounds switch places, often forming a gas or insoluble compound.
4. Using the activity series chart, scientists can determine which metal can replace another metal.

Section 4 Reaction Rates and Energy

1. When energy is released in the form of heat, the reaction is exothermic. An endothermic reaction requires heat to get started. This flame is releasing light and heat energy.

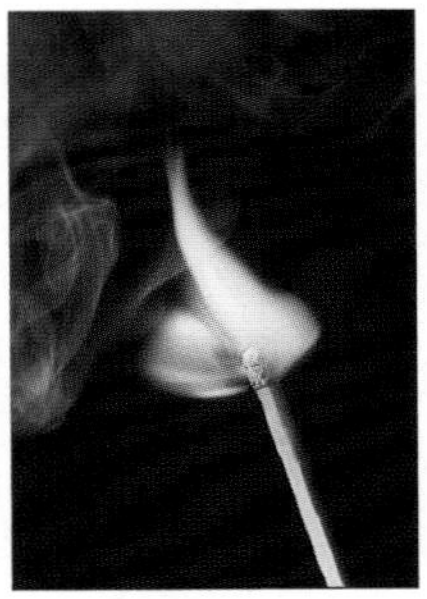

2. Temperature, concentration, and the presence of a catalyst can change the rate of reaction.
3. Activation energy is the minimum amount of energy needed to start a reaction.
4. Reactions may be sped up by adding catalysts, such as a nickel catalyst. A reaction can be slowed down by adding inhibitors.

FOLDABLES™ Use the Foldable that you made at the beginning of this chapter to help you review chemical reactions.

Reviewing Main Ideas

Summary statements can be used by students to review the major concepts of the chapter.

Science Online

Visit gpescience.com
More Section Review
Interactive Tutor
Vocabulary PuzzleMaker
More Chapter Review
Standardized Test Practice

Assessment Transparency

For additional assessment questions, use the *Assessment Transparency* located in the transparency book.

Assessment

Assessment Transparency — Chemical Reactions — Chapter 23

Directions: *Carefully review the diagrams and answer the following questions.*

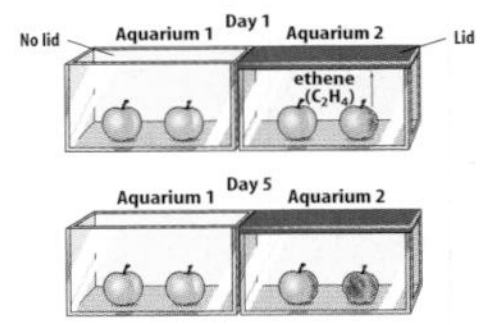

1. From the results of the experiment above, it is reasonable to assume that the production of ethene ___.
   A has no effect on the rotting of a peach in its immediate area
   B slows the rotting of a peach in its immediate area
   C quickens the rotting of a peach in its immediate area
   D slows the rotting process in the peach producing the gas
2. According to the information in the diagram, we can conclude that ethene consists of ___.
   F hydrogen and helium
   G carbon and hydrogen
   H carbon and oxygen
   J calcium and carbon
3. George wanted to use the peaches that he picked from the tree in his backyard to bake a pie. However, some were not quite ripe. George could best speed the ripening process by placing the peaches ___.
   A in the refrigerator
   B outside by the tree
   C inside an enclosed space
   D near a breezy window

L2

Chemical Reactions

FOLDABLES™ Have students use the Foldables that they made at the beginning of the chapter to help them review scientific processes.

Using Vocabulary

1. The two are opposite processes; in a synthesis reaction substances are put together and in a decomposition reaction they are taken apart.
2. In a chemical change, reactants change into products.
3. The two produce opposite outcomes; catalysts speed up chemical reactions, while inhibitors slow them down.
4. The two are opposite reactions; exothermic reactions release heat and endothermic reactions absorb heat.
5. Chemical reactions are processes in which new substances, called products, are formed.
6. In single-displacement reactions, only one element of one compound is replaced by another element. In double-displacement reactions, two elements in two compounds change places.
7. Not all chemical reactions are synthesis reactions, but all synthesis reactions are chemical reactions.

Checking Concepts

8. D	13. D
9. D	14. B
10. D	15. A
11. D	16. D
12. C	17. D

chapter 23 Review

Using Vocabulary

activation energy p. 735
balanced chemical equation p. 726
catalyst p. 740
chemical equation p. 723
chemical reaction p. 720
combustion reaction p. 730
decomposition reaction p. 731
double-displacement reaction p. 732
endothermic reaction p. 735
exothermic reaction p. 738
inhibitor p. 740
product p. 720
rate of reaction p. 738
reactant p. 720
single-displacement reaction p. 731
synthesis reaction p. 731

For each set of vocabulary words below, explain the relationship that exists.

1. synthesis reaction—decomposition reaction
2. reactant—product
3. catalyst—inhibitor
4. exothermic reaction—endothermic reaction
5. chemical reaction—product
6. single-displacement reaction—double-displacement reaction
7. chemical reaction—synthesis reaction

Checking Concepts

Choose the word or phrase that best answers the question.

8. Oxygen gas is always written as O_2 in chemical equations. What term is used to describe the "2" in this formula?
   A) catalyst **C)** product
   B) coefficient **D)** subscript

9. In an endothermic reaction, which has the lower energy?
   A) catalyst **C)** product
   B) inhibitor **D)** reactant

10. What law is based on the experiments of Lavoisier?
    A) atomic theory
    B) collision theory
    C) conservation of energy
    D) conservation of mass

11. What must an element be in order to replace another element in a compound?
    A) less inhibiting **C)** more inhibiting
    B) less reactive **D)** more reactive

12. How do you indicate that a substance in an equation is a solid?
    A) (*l*) **C)** (*s*)
    B) (*g*) **D)** (*aq*)

13. Classify the reaction:
    $2H_2(g) + O_2(g) \rightarrow 2H_2O(g)$.
    A) combustion
    B) decomposition
    C) single displacement
    D) synthesis

14. What compound is the food additive BHA?
    A) catalyst **C)** oxidized
    B) inhibitor **D)** reduced

15. Which symbol indicates that a substance is dissolved in water when writing an equation?
    A) (*aq*) **C)** (*g*)
    B) (*s*) **D)** (*l*)

16. What word would you use to describe HgO in the reaction that Lavoisier used to show conservation of mass?
    A) catalyst **C)** product
    B) inhibitor **D)** reactant

17. When hydrogen burns, what is oxygen's role?
    A) catalyst **C)** product
    B) inhibitor **D)** reactant

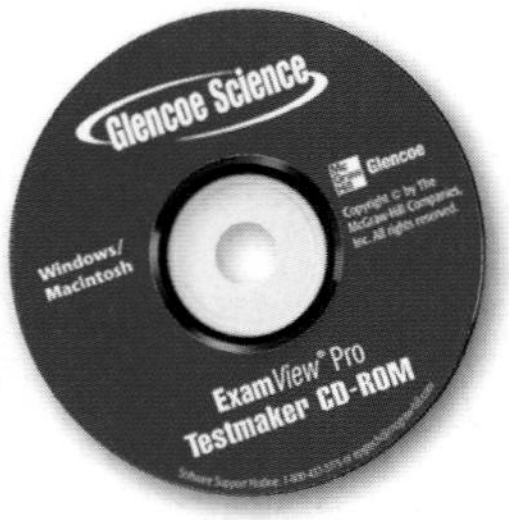

Use the Exam*View*® Pro Testmaker CD-ROM to:
- create multiple versions of tests
- create modified tests with one mouse click for inclusion students
- edit existing questions and add your own questions
- build tests aligned with state standards using built-in State Curriculum Tags
- change English tests to Spanish with one mouse click and vice versa

Interpreting Graphics

18. Copy and complete the concept map using the following terms: *oxidized, redox reactions, lost, reduced, oxidation, gained,* and *reduction.*

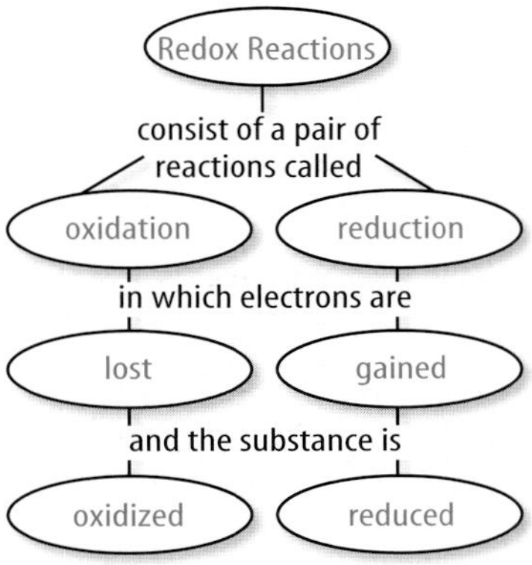

19. Sequence Sometimes a bond formed in a chemical reaction is weak and the product breaks apart as it forms. This is shown by a double arrow in chemical equations. Copy and complete the concept map, using the words *product(s)* and *reactant(s).* In the blank in the center, fill in the formulas for the substances appearing in the reversible reaction.

$$H_2(g) + I_2(g) \rightleftharpoons 2HI(g)$$

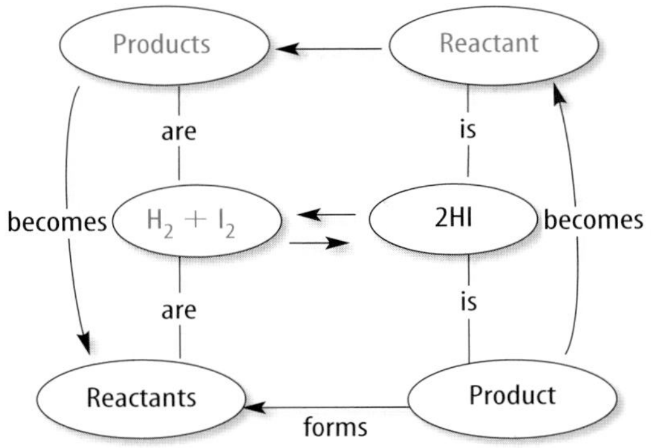

Thinking Critically

20. Write a balanced chemical equation for the reaction of propane $C_3H_8(g)$ burning in oxygen to form carbon dioxide and water vapor.

21. Interpret the balanced chemical equation from question 23 to explain the law of conservation of mass.

22. Hypothesize Zn is placed in a solution of $Cu(NO_3)_2$ and Cu is placed in a $Zn(NO_3)_2$ solution. In which of these will a reaction occur?

23. Predict what kind of energy process happens when lye, $NaOH(s)$, is put in water and the water gets hot.

24. Recognize Cause and Effect Sucrose, or table sugar, is a disaccharide. This means that sucrose is composed of two simple sugars chemically bonded together. Sucrose can be separated into its components by heating it in an aqueous sulfuric acid solution. Research what products are formed by breaking up sucrose. What role does the acid play?

25. Classify Make an outline with the general heading *Chemical Reactions.* Include the five types of reactions, with a description and example of each.

Applying Math

26. Use Numbers When 46 g of sodium were exposed to dry air, 62 g of sodium oxide formed. How many grams of oxygen from the air were used?

27. Calculate Mass Chromium is produced by reacting its oxide with aluminum. If 76 g of Cr_2O_3 and 27 g of Al completely react to form 51 g of Al_2O_3, how many grams of Cr are formed?

Assessment Resources

Reproducible Masters

Chapter *Fast File* Resources
- Chapter Review, pp. 39–40
- Chapter Tests, pp. 41–44
- Assessment Transparency Activity, p. 53

Glencoe Science Web site
- Chapter Review Test
- Standardized Test Practice

Glencoe Technology
- Assessment Transparency
- Exam*View*® Pro Testmaker
- MindJogger Videoquiz
- Interactive Chalkboard

chapter Review 23

Interpreting Graphics

18. See student page.

19. See student page.

Thinking Critically

20. $C_3H_8(g) + 5O_2(g) \rightarrow 3CO_2(g) + 4H_2O(g)$

21. There are 3 atoms of carbon, 8 atoms of hydrogen, and 10 atoms of oxygen on both sides of the equation.

22. Zinc reacts in the solution of copper nitrate and displaces copper to form $Zn(NO_3)_2$. In the second solution, no reaction is observed.

23. exothermic

24. Fructose and glucose; the acid is a catalyst.

25. Chemical Reactions
- **I.** Combustion Reaction
  A substance reacts with oxygen to produce energy as heat or light.
- **II.** Synthesis Reaction
  Two or more elements or compounds combine.
- **III.** Decomposition
  A compound is broken down into its elements or other compounds.
- **IV.** Single Displacement
  An element in one compound is replaced by another element.
- **V.** Double Displacement
  Two elements from two different compounds replace each other. Accept all reasonable examples.

Applying Math

Math Standards

National: 1, 2, 9, 10

26. $62\ g - 46\ g = 16\ g$ of O_2

27. 52 g

chapter 23 Standardized Test Practice

Answer Sheet An answer sheet can be found at **gpescience.com**.

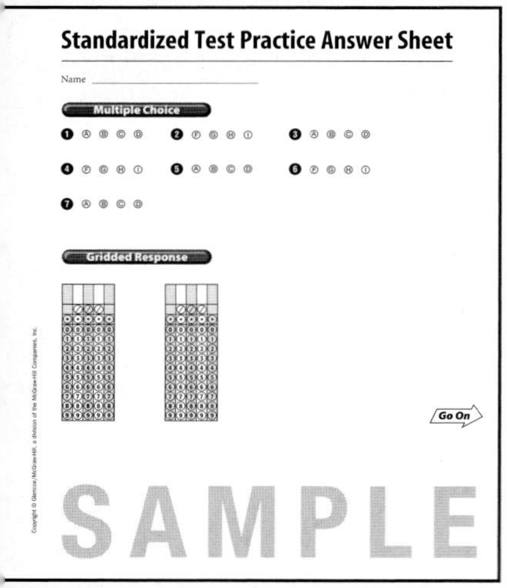

Multiple Choice

1. D
2. C
3. D
4. A
5. D

Gridded Response

6. 32
7. 89.4

chapter 23 Standardized Test Practice

Record your answers on the answer sheet provided by your teacher or on a sheet of paper.

Multiple Choice

Use the illustration below to answer question 1.

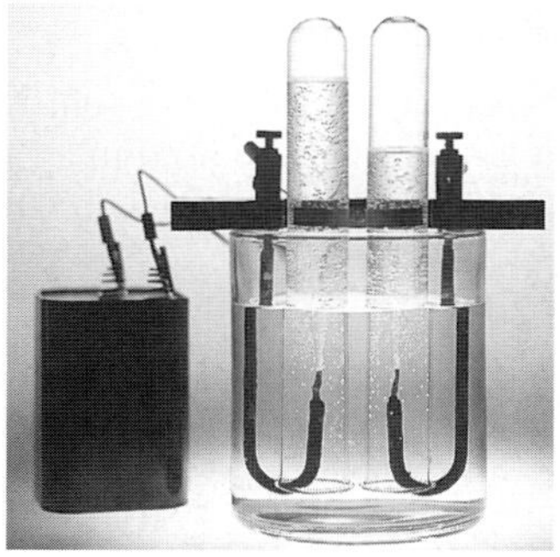

1. The photograph above shows a chemical reaction in which water decomposes into hydrogen gas and oxygen gas when an electric current is passed through it. Which of the following is the correct chemical equation for this reaction?

A. $H_2O(l) \longrightarrow H_2(g) + O(g)$

B. $H_2O(l) \longrightarrow 2H(g) + O(g)$

C. $2H_2O(l) \longrightarrow 2H_2(g) + 2O(g)$

D. $2H_2O(l) \longrightarrow 2H_2(g) + O_2(g)$

2. Which substance is the precipitate in the following reaction?

$Ba(NO_3)_2(aq) + K_2SO_4(aq) \longrightarrow BaSO_4(s) + 2KNO_3(aq)$

A. $Ba(NO_3)_2$

B. K_2SO_4

C. $BaSO_4$

D. KNO_3

3. Which reaction is endothermic?

A. iron rusting

B. burning wood

C. exploding dynamite

D. mixing Epsom salt in water

Use the figure below to answer question 4.

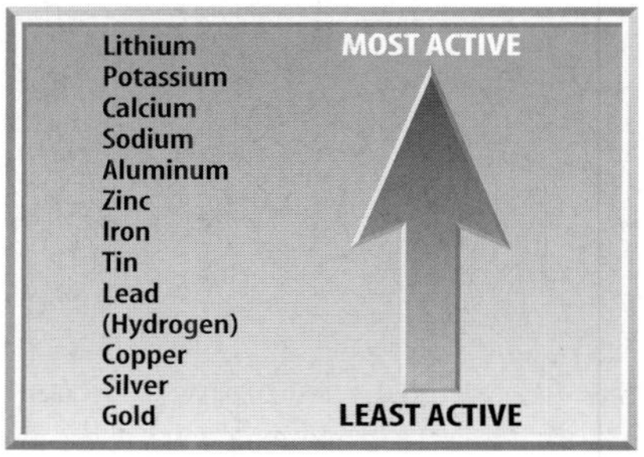

4. Which metal would most likely replace lead in a solution?

A. potassium

B. copper

C. silver

D. gold

5. Which type of reaction is the opposite of a synthesis reaction?

A. displacement

B. reversible

C. combustion

D. decomposition

Gridded Response

6. A reaction of 24 g of sodium hydroxide with 20 g of hydrogen chloride gives off 12 g of water. What mass of sodium chloride is formed in this reaction?

7. From an experiment to seperate water into hydrogen and oxygen, a student collected 10.0 g of hydrogen and 79.4 g of oxygen. How much water was originally involved in the process?

Short Response

8. What is a synthesis reaction?

Use the illustration to answer question 9.

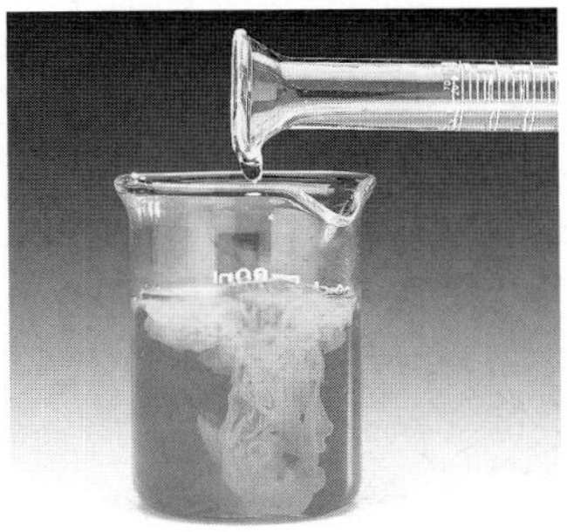

9. The illustration above shows the reaction of aqueous nickel(II) chloride, $NiCl_2$, and aqueous sodium hydroxide, NaOH, to form solid nickel(II) hydroxide, $Ni(OH)_2$, and aqueous sodium chloride, NaCl. State the conversation of mass as it applies to this chemical reaction.

10. Food preservatives are a type of inhibitor. Explain why this is useful in foods.

Extended Response

11. Explain what is wrong with the following balanced equation:

$4Al(s) + 6O(g) \longrightarrow 2Al_2O_3(s)$

What is the correct form of the equation?

Use the illustration to answer question 12.

12. The photograph above shows a chemical reaction between magnesium, Mg, and oxygen gas, O_2. This reaction is exergonic and exothermic. Explain what these terms mean and how you can tell that a chemical reaction is exergonic or exothermic.

13. The reaction of magnesium and oxygen gas forms magnesium oxide, MgO. Write the chemical equation for this reaction and explain the process you use to balance the equation.

Test-Taking Tip

Missing Information Questions often will ask about missing information. Notice what is missing as well as what is given.

chapter 23

Standardized Test Practice

Extended Response

11. The equation has oxygen as a single atom; however, oxygen gas is a diatomic molecule, O_2. The correct form of the equation is $4Al(s) + 3O_2(g) \longrightarrow 2Al_2O_3(s)$.
12. A chemical reaction is exergonic if it releases energy. A reaction is exothermic if it gives off energy in the form of heat. The reaction shown is exergonic because it releases heat and produces visible light. It is exothermic because it produces warmth and burning.
13. The unbalanced chemical equation is $Mg(s) + O_2(g) \longrightarrow MgO(s)$. To balance the equation, adjust the coefficient with MgO to balance oxygen and with Mg to balance magnesium. The equation is balanced as $2Mg(s) + O_2(g) \longrightarrow 2MgO(s)$.

Rubrics

For more help evaluating Short- and Extended-Response questions, see the rubrics on p. 9T.

Short Response

8. A synthesis reaction is a chemical reaction in which two or more substances combine to form another substance.

9. The number of atoms of nickel, chlorine, sodium, oxygen, and hydrogen that are present before the reaction equals the number of each present after the reaction.

10. An inhibitor slows down the rate of a reaction. Preservatives slow down the rate of food spoilage.

chapter 24 Organizer

Section/Objectives	Standards		Labs/Features
	National	State/Local	
Chapter Opener	See pp. 16T–17T for a Key to Standards.		**Launch Lab:** Magic Solutions, p. 751 **Foldables,** p. 751
Section 1 How Solutions Form 2 sessions 1 block 1. **Identify** the components of a solution. 2. **Explain** how things dissolve. 3. **Identify** the factors that affect the rates at which solids and gases dissolve in liquids.	National Content Standards: UCP.1–3, UCP.5, A.1, A.2, B.1, B.2, B.3		**Integrate Career,** p. 753 **Visualizing Metal Alloys,** p. 754 **MiniLAB:** Observing the Effect of Surface Area, p. 756 Video Lab **Applying Math:** Surface Area, p. 757
Section 2 Solubility and Concentration 1 session .5 block 4. **Define** the concept of solubility. 5. **Identify** how to express the concentration of solutions. 6. **List** and define three types of solutions. 7. **Describe** the effects of pressure and temperature on the solubility of gases.	National Content Standards: UCP.1–3, UCP.5, A.1, A.2, B.2, B.6		**Science Online,** p. 762
Section 3 Acids, Bases, and Salts 3 sessions 1.5 blocks 8. **Compare and contrast** acids and bases and identify the characteristics they have. 9. **Examine** some formulas and uses of common acids and bases. 10. **Determine** how the processes of ionization and dissociation apply to acids and bases.	National Content Standards: UCP.1, UCP.2, UCP.3, UCP.5, A.1, A.2, B.2, B.3		**MiniLAB:** Observing Acid Relief, p. 766 **Integrate Life Science,** p. 768 **Science Online,** p. 770
Section 4 Strength of Acids and Bases 2 sessions 1 block 11. **Determine** what is responsible for the strength of an acid or a base. 12. **Compare and contrast** strength and concentration. 13. **Examine** the relationship between pH and acid or base strength. 14. **Explain** electrical conductivity.	National Content Standards: UCP.1, UCP.2, UCP.3, UCP.5, A.1, A.2, B.2, B.3		**Lab:** Determining Acidity, p. 775 **Lab:** Saturated Solutions, pp. 776–777

Glencoe Exclusive!

StudentWorks Plus | TeacherWorks™ All-In-One Planner and Resource Center

Lab Materials	Reproducible Resources	Section Assessment	Technology
Launch Lab: white paper, cotton balls, phenolphthalein indicator, universal indicator, ammonia, vinegar	**Chapter *Fast File* Resources** Foldables Worksheet, p. 17 Directed Reading, p. 19 Note-taking Worksheets, pp. 35–37	Glencoe's Assessment Advantage	TeacherWorks includes: • Interactive Teacher Edition • Lesson Planner with calendar • Access to all program blacklines • Correlations to standards • Web links
MiniLAB: ground sugar cubes (2), whole sugar cubes (2), medium-sized glasses (2), distilled water, stirring rods (2)	**Chapter *Fast File* Resources** Transparency Activity, p. 46 MiniLAB, p. 3 Enrichment, p. 31 Reinforcement, p. 27 Directed Reading, p. 20	**Portfolio** Assessment, p. 758 **Performance** MiniLAB, p. 756 Applying Math p. 758 **Content** Section Review, p. 758	Section Focus Transparency Interactive Chalkboard CD-ROM StudentWorks Plus Video Lab
Need materials? Contact Science Kit at 1-800-828-7777 or www.sciencekit.com.	**Chapter *Fast File* Resources** Lab Activity, pp. 9–12 Transparency Activity, p. 47 MiniLAB, p. 4 Enrichment, p. 32 Reinforcement, p. 28 Directed Reading, p. 20 Transparency Activity, pp. 51–52	**Portfolio** Assessment, p. 763 **Performance** Applying Math p. 763 **Content** Section Review, p. 763	Section Focus Transparency Teaching Transparency Virtual Labs CD-ROM Interactive Chalkboard CD-ROM StudentWorks Plus
MiniLAB: 150 mL water, 250–mL beaker, 1*M* HCl, universal indicator (12 drops), antacid tablet, graduated cylinder, dropper	**Chapter *Fast File* Resources** Transparency Activity, p. 48 MiniLAB, p. 4 Enrichment, p. 33 Reinforcement, p. 29 Directed Reading, p. 21	**Portfolio** Curriculum Connection, p. 765 **Performance** MiniLAB, p. 766 Applying Math, p. 770 **Content** Section Review, p. 770	Section Focus Transparency Interactive Chalkboard CD-ROM StudentWorks Plus
Lab: homemade cabbage indicator, coffee filter, waxed paper, grease pencil or masking tape, teaspoons (3), alum, cream of tartar, fruit preservative **Lab:** distilled water, test tubes, test tube holder, test-tube rack, thermometer, sugar, copper-wire stirrer, graduated cylinder, beaker, hot plate, ring stand	**Chapter *Fast File* Resources** Transparency Activity, p. 49 Enrichment, p. 34 Reinforcement, p. 30 Directed Reading, pp. 21–22 Lab Activity, pp. 13–16 Lab Worksheets, pp. 5–6, 7–8	**Performance** Applying Math, p. 774 **Content** Section Review, p. 774	Section Focus Transparency Interactive Chalkboard CD-ROM StudentWorks Plus

End of Chapter Assessment

Glencoe's Assessment Advantage

Blackline Masters	Technology	Professional Series
Chapter *Fast File* Resources Chapter Review, pp. 39–40 Chapter Tests, pp. 41–44 **Standardized Test Practice,** pp. 100–103	MindJogger Videoquiz Virtual Labs CD-ROM Exam*View*® Pro Testmaker TeacherWorks CD-ROM Interactive Chalkboard CD-ROM	**Performance Assessment in the Science Classroom (PASC)**

Transparencies

Section Focus

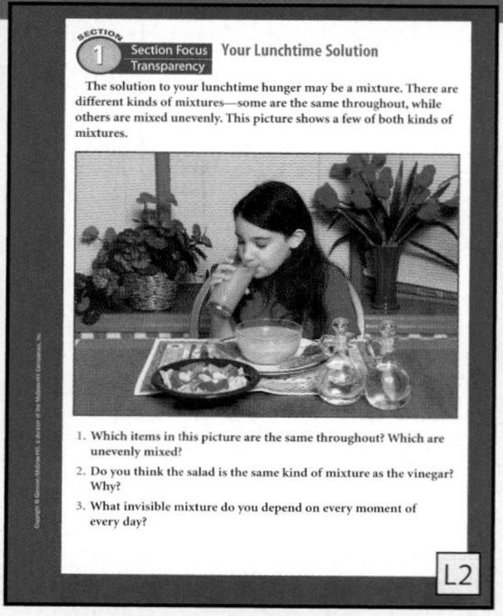
Section 1 Section Focus Transparency — Your Lunchtime Solution

The solution to your lunchtime hunger may be a mixture. There are different kinds of mixtures—some are the same throughout, while others are mixed unevenly. This picture shows a few of both kinds of mixtures.

1. Which items in this picture are the same throughout? Which are unevenly mixed?
2. Do you think the salad is the same kind of mixture as the vinegar? Why?
3. What invisible mixture do you depend on every moment of every day?

L2

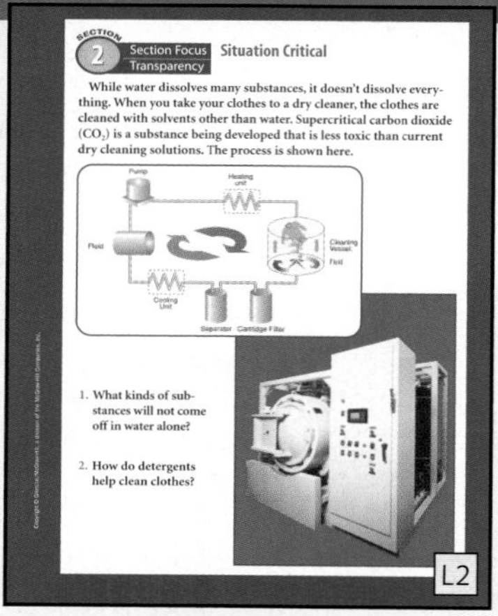
Section 2 Section Focus Transparency — Situation Critical

While water dissolves many substances, it doesn't dissolve everything. When you take your clothes to a dry cleaner, the clothes are cleaned with solvents other than water. Supercritical carbon dioxide (CO_2) is a substance being developed that is less toxic than current dry cleaning solutions. The process is shown here.

1. What kinds of substances will not come off in water alone?
2. How do detergents help clean clothes?

L2

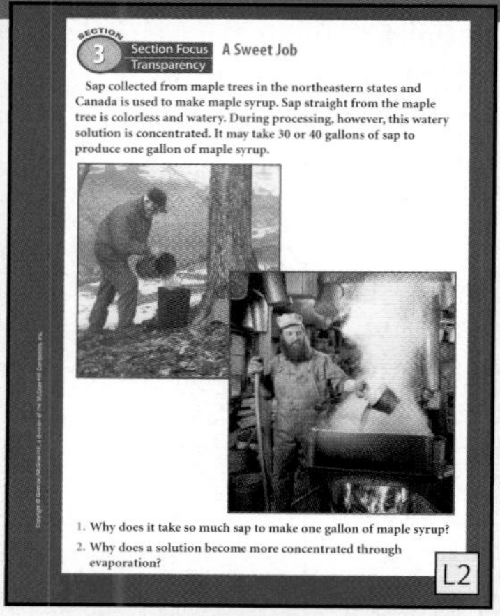
Section 3 Section Focus Transparency — A Sweet Job

Sap collected from maple trees in the northeastern states and Canada is used to make maple syrup. Sap straight from the maple tree is colorless and watery. During processing, however, this watery solution is concentrated. It may take 30 or 40 gallons of sap to produce one gallon of maple syrup.

1. Why does it take so much sap to make one gallon of maple syrup?
2. Why does a solution become more concentrated through evaporation?

L2

This is a representation of key blackline masters available in the Teacher Classroom Resources. See Resource Manager boxes within the chapter for additional information.

Assessment

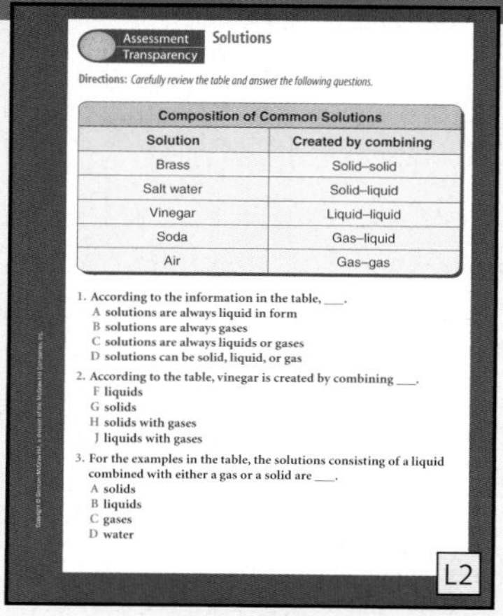
Assessment Transparency — Solutions

Directions: *Carefully review the table and answer the following questions.*

Composition of Common Solutions	
Solution	**Created by combining**
Brass	Solid–solid
Salt water	Solid–liquid
Vinegar	Liquid–liquid
Soda	Gas–liquid
Air	Gas–gas

1. According to the information in the table, ___.
   A solutions are always liquid in form
   B solutions are always gases
   C solutions are always liquids or gases
   D solutions can be solid, liquid, or gas
2. According to the table, vinegar is created by combining ___.
   F liquids
   G solids
   H solids with gases
   J liquids with gases
3. For the examples in the table, the solutions consisting of a liquid combined with either a gas or a solid are ___.
   A solids
   B liquids
   C gases
   D water

L2

Teaching

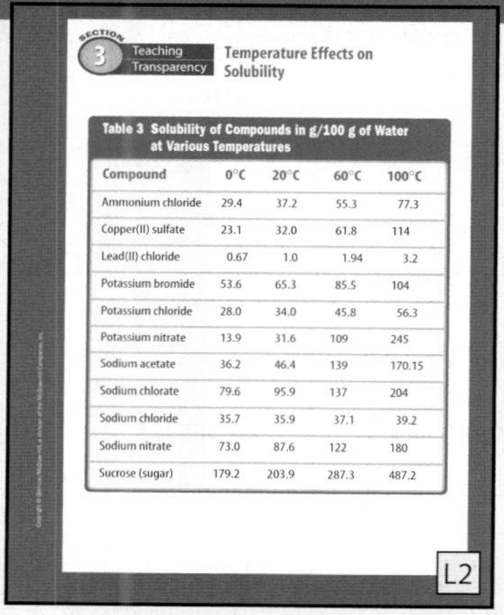
Section 3 Teaching Transparency — Temperature Effects on Solubility

Table 3 Solubility of Compounds in g/100 g of Water at Various Temperatures

Compound	0°C	20°C	60°C	100°C
Ammonium chloride	29.4	37.2	55.3	77.3
Copper(II) sulfate	23.1	32.0	61.8	114
Lead(II) chloride	0.67	1.0	1.94	3.2
Potassium bromide	53.6	65.3	85.5	104
Potassium chloride	28.0	34.0	45.8	56.3
Potassium nitrate	13.9	31.6	109	245
Sodium acetate	36.2	46.4	139	170.15
Sodium chlorate	79.6	95.9	137	204
Sodium chloride	35.7	35.9	37.1	39.2
Sodium nitrate	73.0	87.6	122	180
Sucrose (sugar)	179.2	203.9	287.3	487.2

L2

Key to Teaching Strategies

The following designations will help you decide which activities are appropriate for your students.

- L1 Level 1 activities should be appropriate for students with learning difficulties.
- L2 Level 2 activities should be within the ability range of all students.
- L3 Level 3 activities are designed for above-average students.
- ELL ELL activities should be within the ability range of English Language Learners.
- COOP LEARN Cooperative Learning activities are designed for small group work.
- LS Multiple Learning Styles logos, as described on page 12T, are used throughout to indicate strategies that address different learning styles.
- P These strategies represent student products that can be placed into a best-work portfolio.
- PBL Problem-Based Learning activities apply real-world situations to learning.

Hands-on Activities

Student Text Lab Worksheet

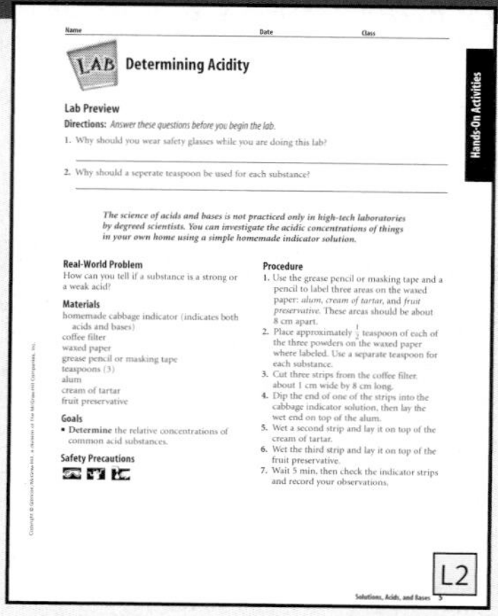
LAB Determining Acidity

Lab Preview

Real-World Problem

Materials

Goals

Safety Precautions

Procedure

Hands-On Activities

L2

Laboratory Activities

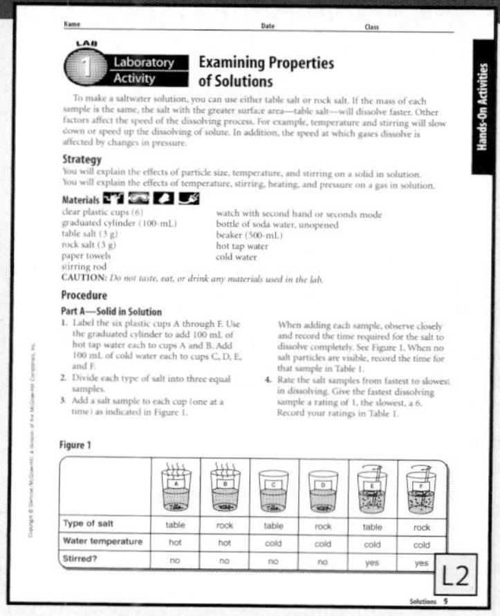
Laboratory Activity 1 — Examining Properties of Solutions

Strategy

Materials

Procedure

Part A—Solid in Solution

Figure 1

Hands-On Activities

L2

Meeting Different Ability Levels

Content Outline

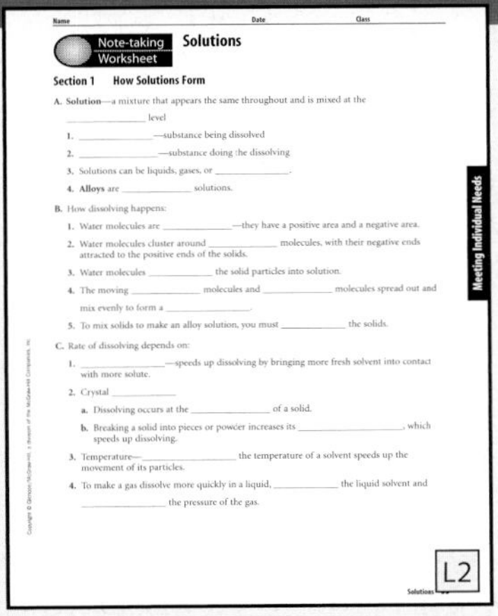

Reinforcement

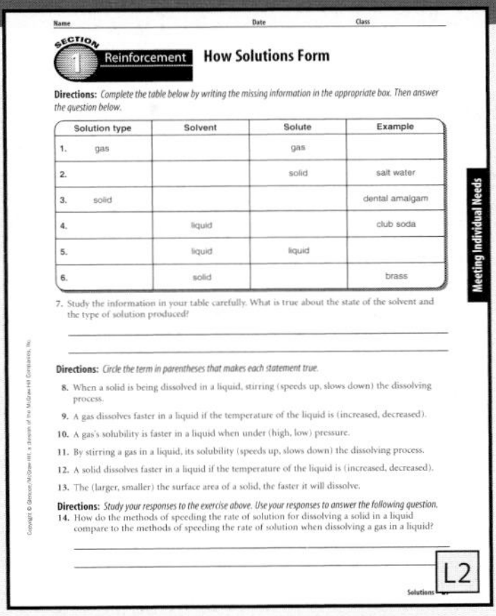

Enrichment

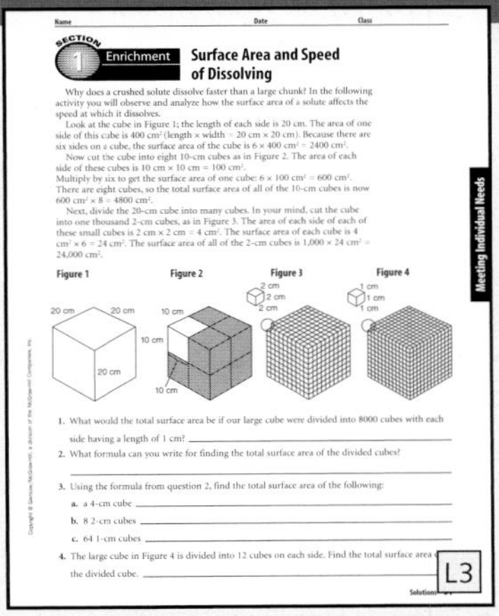

Directed Reading (English/Spanish)

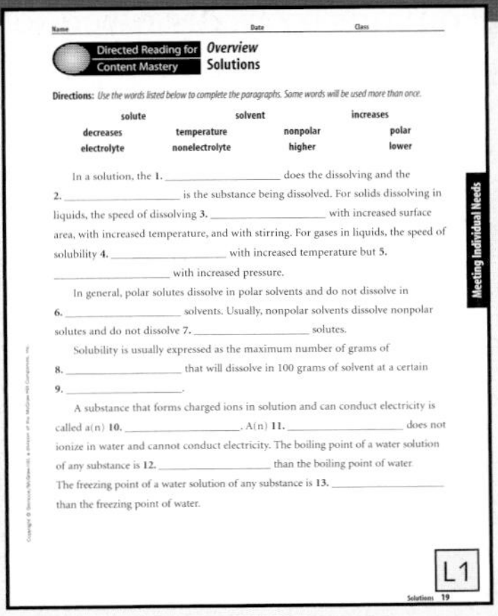

Study Guide

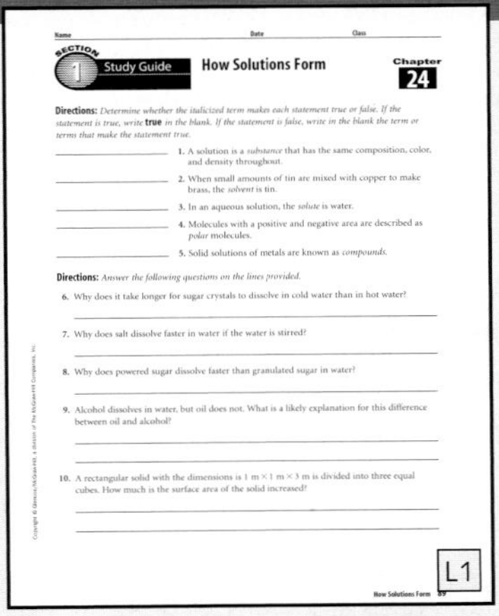

Reading Essentials

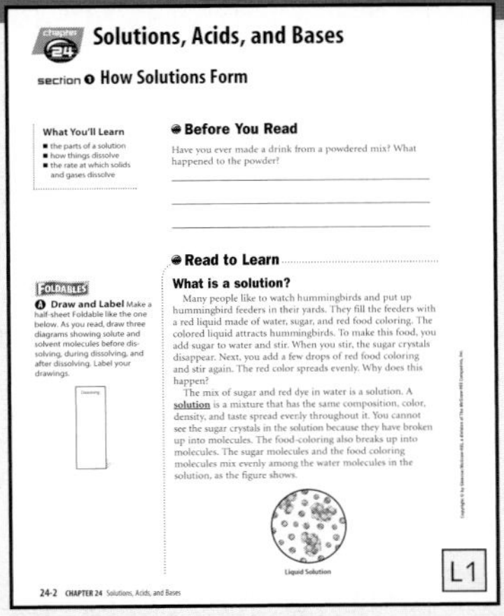

Assessment

Test Practice Workbook

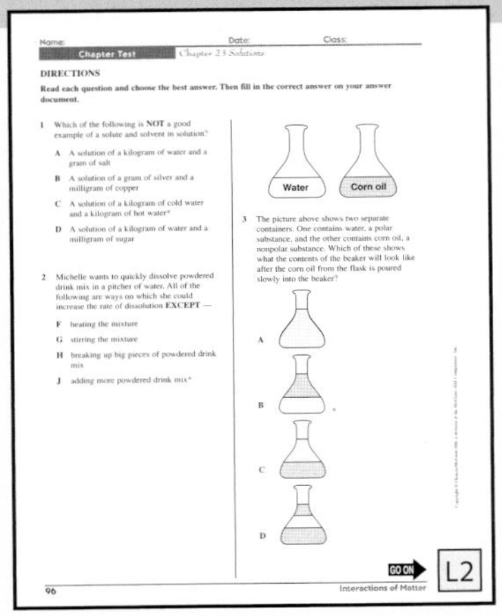

Chapter Review

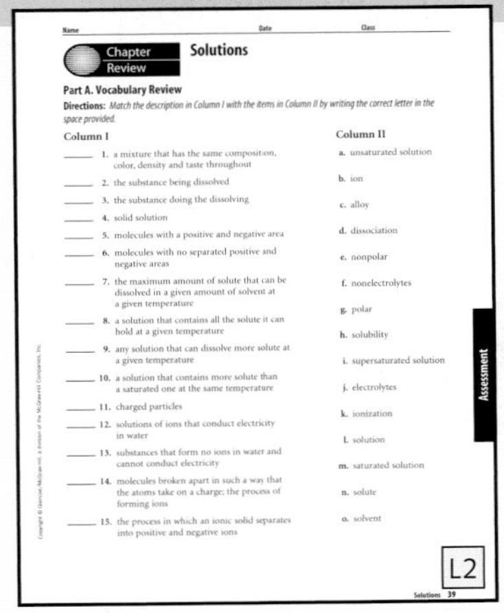

Chapter Tests

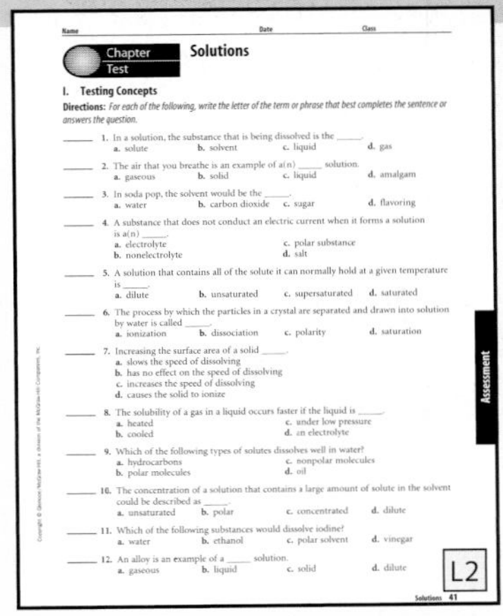

Science Content Background

section 1 How Solutions Form

How Substances Dissolve

Attractive forces between the atoms, ions, or molecules of a substance hold liquid and solid substances together. When a substance is surrounded by a solvent, particles of the substance may be attracted to the solvent molecules by various forces. If these attractive forces are strong enough to overcome the internal attractive forces of the solute, the substance will be soluble to some extent. A substance with an extremely low solubility is usually said to be insoluble.

The process of dissolving, called dissolution, involves energy. Energy is absorbed when the structure of a molecular solid or liquid is broken down or the ions of an ionic crystal are separated. Energy is released when the particles of solute form new bonds with the solvent. In the cold packs used by athletic trainers, more energy is absorbed in the first part of the dissolution process than is released in the second. For that reason, the overall process is endothermic, and the liquid becomes colder.

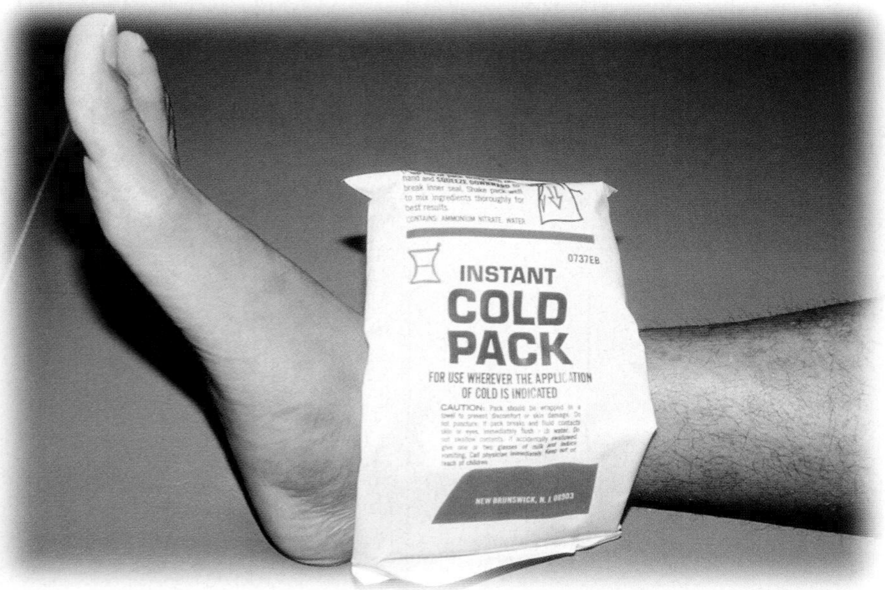

David R. Frazier/ Photo Researchers,Inc.

section 2 Solubility and Concentration

Types of Solutions

A solution is saturated when equilibrium between the undissolved solute and dissolved solute is established at a particular temperature. It is important to state the temperature of a saturated solution. Because a solution that is saturated at one temperature may not be saturated at another temperature. In the state known as solution equilibrium, the solute is dissolving into the solution and coming out of solution at exactly the same rate.

If a solution contains more dissolved solute than it usually can hold at a given temperature, the solution is said to be supersaturated. Supersaturated solutions are unstable and disturbances such as jarring, stirring, scratching the walls of the container, or dropping in a "seed" crystal cause the solution to return to the saturated state.

section 3 Acids, Bases, and Salts

Solutions of Acids and Bases

A good operational definition of acids and bases is that acids increase the concentration of hydronium ions (H_3O^+) when dissolved in water and bases increase the concentration of hydroxide ions when dissolved in water. Other characteristics come from work by Robert Boyle in the 1600s. Acids have a sour taste, are corrosive, turn litmus from blue to red, and lose their acidity when they react with alkaline (basic) materials. Bases feel slippery, change litmus from red to blue, and become less *alkaline* when they react with acids. The word alkaline became synonymous with basic because alkalines are the "basis" for making salts.

section 4 Strength of Acids and Bases

pH of a Solution

The term pH is derived from the German *potenz* (power) and H for hydrogen. It refers to the power of 10 used to express the molar H_3O^+ concentration. The approximate pH of a solution can be determined by using an acid-base indicator. Bromothymol blue, for instance, changes color in the pH range 6.0–7.6 from yellow in its acid form to blue in its base form. Phenolphthalein changes in the pH range of 8.2–9.8 from colorless in its acid form to pink in its base form. A mixture of indicators called universal indicator can be used that measures the range of pH from 0–14.

A salt is an ionic compound that is formed when an acid neutralizes a base. Salt solutions can be neutral, acidic, or basic, depending on the acid-base properties of the constituents. As a general rule, salts formed by the reaction of a strong acid with a strong base are neutral, salts formed by reaction of a strong acid with a weak base are acidic, and salts formed by the reaction of a weak acid with a strong base are basic.

Teacher to Teacher

Pam K. Hintz,
Elgin/New Leipzig Public School
Elgin, North Dakota

"To show how solutions can be useful in analytical applications, I prepare a simple chromatography demonstration. I place a dot of permanent marker near the bottom of a strip of coffee filter paper and a dot of water-based marker ink on another strip. Then I dip the strips in separate beakers with a small amount of water (water line below the ink dots) and let them sit for about 45 minutes. We take a minute for the students to predict what will happen and we come back to the beakers at the end of class. Students should see that the water-based ink dissolved in the water and, as the water was absorbed up the paper, separated out to show the colors that combined to make the ink. Chromatography techniques like this one are used to isolate and analyze the individual components of unknown substances."

Pam K. Hintz

chapter content resources

Internet Resources

For additional content background, visit **gpescience.com** to:

- access your book online
- find references to related articles in popular science magazines
- access Web links with related content background
- access current events with science journal topics

Print Resources

Clean Solvents: alternative media for chemical reactions and processing, by M. A. Abraham, American Chemical Society (symposium series 819), 2000

Elements, compounds, and mixtures, by B. J. Knapp, Grolier Educational, 1998

Properties of Solvents, by X. Marcus, Wiley & Sons, 1998

Acids, Bases, and Salts, Brian J. Knapp, Grolier Educational, Danbury, CT, 1998

Acids, Bases, and Salts (CHEMLAB), Keith Walshaw, Atlantic Europe Publishing Co., 1998

chapter 24

Chapter Vocabulary

solution, p. 752
solute, p. 753
solvent, p.753
aqueous solution, p. 753
solubility, p. 759
concentration, p. 760
saturated solution, p. 761
unsaturated solution, p. 761
supersaturated solution, p. 762
acid, p. 764
indicator, p. 764
base, p. 766
strong acid, p. 771
weak acid, p. 771
strong base, p. 772
weak base, p. 772
pH, p. 773

Science Journal Student responses will vary at the beginning, but all students should come to recognize that all liquids are not necessarily solutions and all solutions are not necessarily liquids.

INTERACTIVE CHALKBOARD with Image Bank

PowerPoint® Presentations

This CD-ROM is an editable Microsoft® PowerPoint® presentation that includes:

- a pre-made presentation for every chapter
- interactive graphics
- animations
- audio clips
- image bank
- all new section and chapter questions
- Standardized Test Practice
- transparencies
- Foldables directions
- links to gpescience.com

chapter 24

Solutions, Acids, and Bases

chapter preview

sections

1. How Solutions Form
2. Solubility and Concentration
3. Acids, Bases, and Salts
4. Strength of Acids and Bases
   Lab *Determining Acidity*
   Lab *Saturated Solutions*
   Virtual Lab *How is the solubility of a compound determined?*

Mixed-Up Chemistry

This diver is swimming in a solution. Seas are solutions that contain dissolved solids, such as calcium and magnesium, and dissolved gases, such as carbon dioxide, in water. In this chapter, you will learn about solutions, acids, and bases.

Science Journal Are all liquids solutions, and are all solutions liquids? Answer this question in your Science Journal. Check your answer later and revise it if you've learned differently.

750

Theme Connection

Systems and Interactions Solutions are systems whose properties are determined by the interactions between the molecules or ions of the solute and the molecules or ions of the solvent.

About the Photo

Underwater Solutes This diver may not know it, but the underwater environment is full of solutes in solution. Water dissolves many substances, and the salty seawater itself is a solution. The oxygen tank that makes this dive possible also contains a solution–a gas solution of nitrogen or possibly helium mixed with oxygen.

Start-Up Activities

Launch LAB

Magic Solutions

To prevent spies from learning military secrets, scientists developed a special ink that is invisible on paper at room temperature. When the paper is warmed by a candle or lightbulb, the message appears. In this lab, you will create an invisible message.

1. Write a message or draw a picture on a white sheet of paper using a cotton swab dipped in either phenolphthalein indicator or universal indicator. In your Science Journal, record which indicator you used.
2. Allow the paper to dry thoroughly.
3. Dip a clean cotton ball in household ammonia (a base) or vinegar (an acid) and rub it across your paper. Record which solution you used and your observations in your Science Journal.
4. Compare your results with those of others.
5. **Think Critically** In your Science Journal, infer how the magic solution works.

FOLDABLES™ Study Organizer

Solutions, Acids, and Bases Make the following Foldable to help you identify the main characteristics of solutions, acids, and bases.

STEP 1 **Fold** a sheet of paper vertically from side to side. Make the front edge about 1.25 cm longer than the back edge.

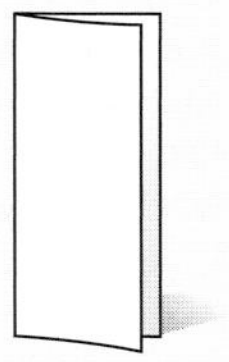

STEP 2 **Turn** lengthwise and **fold** into thirds.

STEP 3 **Unfold and cut** only the top layer along both folds to make three tabs.

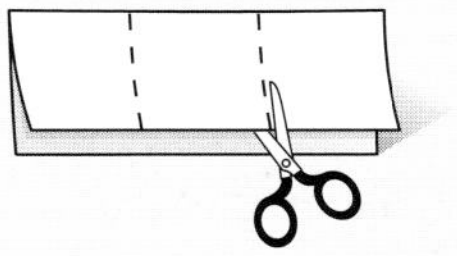

STEP 4 **Label** each tab.

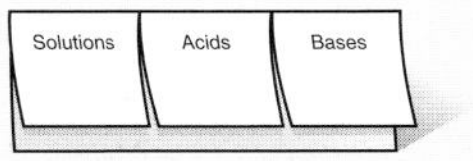

Reading for Main Ideas As you read the chapter, list the characteristics of solutions, acids, and bases.

Science Online — Preview this chapter's content and activities at gpescience.com

Launch LAB

Purpose Use the Launch Lab to introduce students to the concept of acids and bases. L2 IN **Kinesthetic**

Materials white paper, cotton balls, cotton swabs, phenolphthalein indicator, universal indicator, ammonia, vinegar

Teaching Strategy

To extend this activity, students could use vinegar and baking soda dissolved in water to write a message. The message is then revealed using red cabbage indicator. If acidic and basic solutions are used, the messages will show up as different colors.

Think Critically

Sample answer: The writing appeared when vinegar or ammonia was rubbed across an indicator. The pH changed, which allowed the writing to appear.

Assessment

Oral Ask students to explain how indicators can show if a solution is acidic or basic. The indicator will be one color for acids and another color for bases.

FOLDABLES™ Study Organizer Dinah Zike Study Fold

Student preparation materials for this Foldable are available in the **Chapter *Fast File* Resources.**

section 1

How Solutions Form

Reading Guide

What You'll Learn

- **Identify** the components of a solution.
- **Explain** how things dissolve.
- **Identify** the factors that affect the rates at which solids and gases dissolve in liquids.

Why It's Important

Solutions play an important role in your everyday life. Examples of everyday solutions are sports drinks, dishwashing detergents, and shampoos.

Review Vocabulary

homogeneous mixture: solid, liquid, or gas that contains two or more substances blended evenly throughout

New Vocabulary

- solution
- solute
- solvent
- aqueous solution

What is a solution?

Hummingbirds are fascinating creatures. They can hover for long periods while they sip nectar from flowers through their long beaks. To attract hummingbirds, many people use feeder bottles containing a red liquid, as shown in **Figure 1.** The liquid is a solution of sugar and red food coloring in water.

Suppose you are making some hummingbird food. When you add sugar to water and stir, the sugar crystals disappear. When you add a few drops of red food coloring and stir, the color spreads evenly throughout the sugar water. Why does this happen?

Hummingbird food is one of many solutions. A **solution** is a mixture that has the same composition, color, density, and even taste throughout. The reason you no longer see the sugar crystals and the reason the red dye spreads out evenly is that they have formed a completely homogeneous mixture. The sugar crystals broke up into sugar molecules, the red dye into its molecules, and both mixed evenly among the water molecules.

Figure 1 The liquid solution in the hummingbird feeder contains sugar, food coloring, and other substances.

Section 1 Resource Manager

Chapter *FAST FILE* Resources

Transparency Activity, p. 46

Note-taking Worksheets, pp. 35–37

Directed Reading for Content Mastery, pp. 19–20

Enrichment, p. 31

Lab Activity, pp. 9–12

MiniLAB, p. 3

Reinforcement, p. 13

Reading and Writing Skill Activities, p. 17

Mathematics Skill Activities, p. 13

1 Motivate

INTERACTIVE CHALKBOARD An editable Microsoft® PowerPoint® presentation is available on **Interactive Chalkboard** CD-ROM.

Bellringer

Section Focus Transparencies also are available on the Interactive Chalkboard CD-ROM. L2 ELL

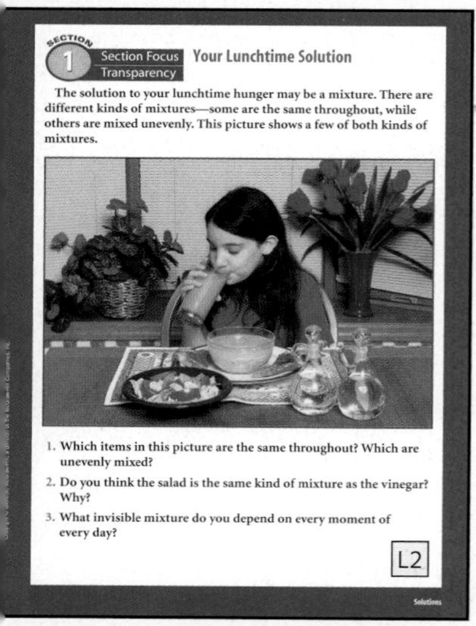
Section 1 Section Focus Transparency **Your Lunchtime Solution**

The solution to your lunchtime hunger may be a mixture. There are different kinds of mixtures—some are the same throughout, while others are mixed unevenly. This picture shows a few of both kinds of mixtures.

1. Which items in this picture are the same throughout? Which are unevenly mixed?
2. Do you think the salad is the same kind of mixture as the vinegar? Why?
3. What invisible mixture do you depend on every moment of every day?

L2

Solutions

Reading Preview

Tie to Prior Knowledge

Mixtures Have students recall what they know about heterogeneous and homogeneous mixtures. In a heterogeneous mixture, the mixed materials are not distributed evenly. A homogeneous mixture is one in which the particles are distributed evenly at the molecular or ionic level. L2

Word Analysis Point out that several words in this section are followed by syllables in parentheses. These syllables show how to pronounce the words correctly. Model the process with *aqueous* (A kwee us) *solution.* Point out that *aqua* means "water" and is derived from Latin.

Solutes and Solvents

In a solution, one substance is dissolved in another. In the hummingbird solution, sugar which is the substance being dissolved, is the **solute.** Water, which is the substance doing the dissolving, is the **solvent.** When a solid dissolves in a liquid, the solid is the solute and the liquid is the solvent. In salt water, salt is the solute and water is the solvent. In carbonated soft drinks, carbon dioxide gas is one of the solutes and water is the solvent. When a liquid dissolves in another liquid, the substance present in the larger amount is usually called the solvent. A solution in which water is the solvent is called an **aqueous** (A kwee us) **solution.**

Reading Check *How do you know which substance is the solute in a solution?*

Nonliquid Solutions Solutions also can be gaseous or even solid. Examples are shown in **Figure 1** and **Figure 2.** Did you know that the air you breathe is a solution? In fact, all mixtures of gases are solutions. Air is a solution of 78 percent nitrogen, 21 percent oxygen, and small amounts of other gases such as argon, carbon dioxide, and hydrogen. The sterling silver and brass used in musical instruments are an example of a solid solution. The sterling silver contains 92.5 percent silver and 7.5 percent copper. The brass is a solution of copper and zinc metals. Solid solutions are known as alloys. They are made by melting the metal solute and solvent together. Most coins, as shown in **Figure 3,** are alloys.

INTEGRATE Career

Surface-Coating Chemist A scientist who develops products such as house paints and polyurethane wood finishers is called a surface-coating chemist. Paints, varnishes, and synthetic clear coatings are solutions. These products are designed to protect the surface of an object from the environment. Make a list of five items that have a protective coating that was applied as a solution.

Figure 2 Solutions also can be mixtures of solids or gases.
Identify *the parts of a solution.*

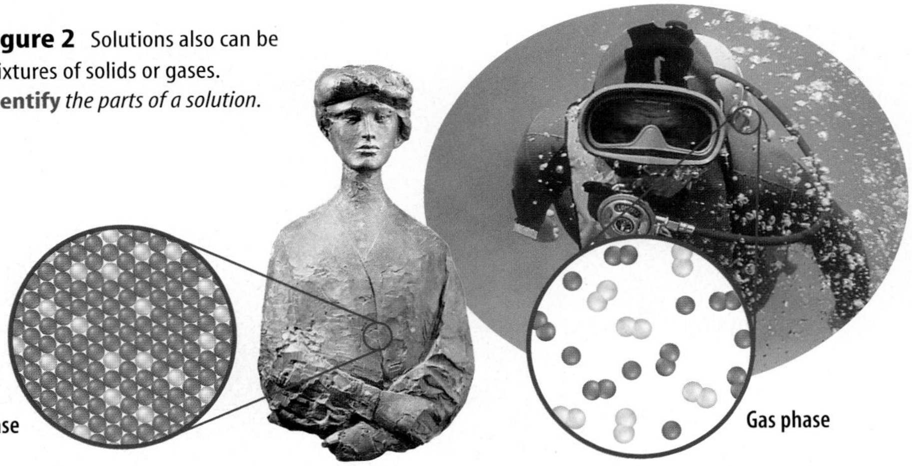

Bronze is a solid solution of copper and tin.

A diver breathes a gas solution containing compressed air.

2 Teach

Caption Answer

Figure 2 solute and solvent

Reading Check

Answer It is the substance being dissolved and is usually the substance that is present in the lesser amount.

Activity

Salt Residue Have students stir table salt into 50 mL of water until no more salt dissolves. Then have them add 5 mL of powdered chalk and stir again. Have them pour the liquid through filter paper. They should observe the chalk on the filter paper. Have them evaporate the filtered liquid and observe the residue remaining (salt). Explain that if filter paper can separate a substance out of a liquid, the substance was not dissolved. The chalk did not dissolve; the salt did. L2 ELL

LS **Visual-Spatial**

INTEGRATE Career

Surface-Coating Chemist Suggested answers: polyurethane on wood floors, parking lot line marks, house paint, and nail polish

These chemists usually have a degree in chemistry and specialize in surface coatings. Many colleges offer four-year degrees in chemistry, but fewer colleges offer courses in surface coatings.

Research Have students research to find colleges and universities that offer classes in surface coating.

Science Journal

Everyday Solvents and Solutes Have students recall that solvents and solutes are all around them. Ask them to list in their Science Journals solvents and solutes they encounter in their daily lives. Their bodies contain solutes dissolved in water. Paint thinner, spot removers, and nail polish remover are all solvents that do not contain water. L2 LS **Linguistic**

Reading Strategy

Set the Purpose Have students outline this section using text headings as guides. Set the purpose by asking them to make sure their outlines contain main ideas. Remind them that main ideas are often signaled by words and phrases in bold.

NATIONAL GEOGRAPHIC

Visualizing Metal Alloys

Have students examine the pictures and read the captions. Then ask the following questions.

Why is it necessary for vending machines to be able to recognize a coin by its size, weight, and electrical conductivity? All three properties are difficult to duplicate in counterfeit coins or slugs. It also compensates for the machine's lack of visual recognition.

Look at the photograph of the two types of dollars. Do they appear to be made from the same alloy? No, the Susan B. Anthony dollar appears to be made of a material, such as nickel or silver, that is silver in color. The Sacagawea dollar is copper in color, similar to the element copper.

Activity

Coin Composition Have students find the composition of the Susan B. Anthony dollar. Construct a circle graph for the Susan B. Anthony dollar similar to the one shown in the text for the Sacagawea dollar. L2 LS **Logical-Mathematical**

NATIONAL GEOGRAPHIC VISUALIZING METAL ALLOYS

Figure 3

Have you ever accidentally put a non-United States coin into a vending machine? Of course, the vending machine didn't accept it. If a vending machine is that selective, how can it be fooled by two coins that look and feel very different? This is exactly the case with the silver Susan B. Anthony dollar and the new golden Sacagawea dollar. Vending machines can't tell them apart.

◀ Vending machines recognize coins by size, weight, and electrical conductivity. The size and weight of the Susan B. Anthony coin were easy to copy. Copying the coin's electrical conductivity was more difficult.

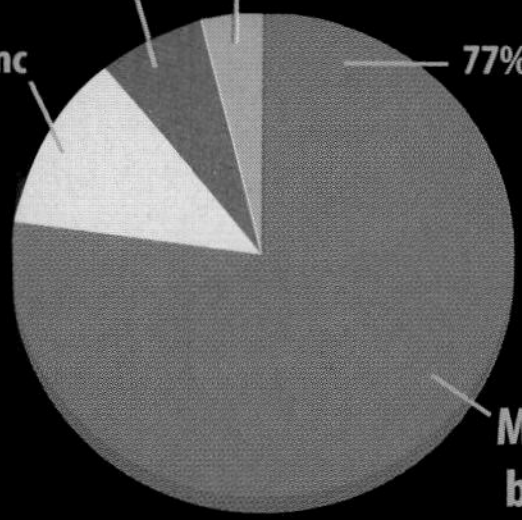

▲ The dollar's copper core is half the coin's thickness. It is sandwiched between two layers of manganese brass alloy.

▲ Over 30,000 samples of coin coatings were tested to find an alloy and thickness that would copy the conductivity of the Susan B. Anthony dollar. The final composition of the alloy is shown in the graph above. The key ingredient? Manganese.

Differentiated Instruction

Challenge Have students find out how vending machines check the size, weight, and electrical conductivity of coins. Have students report their findings to their class. L3 LS **Linguistic**

Teacher FYI

Alloys Steel is an alloy of mostly iron with various other metals and semimetals added. Chromium, carbon, and nickel are solutes added to molten iron, which is cooled to make a solid alloy.

How Substances Dissolve

Fruit drinks and sports drinks are examples of solutions made by dissolving solids in liquids. Like hummingbird food, both contain sugar as well as other substances that add color and flavor. How do solids such as sugar dissolve in water?

The dissolving of a solid in a liquid occurs at the surface of the solid. To understand how water solutions form, keep in mind two things you have learned about water. Like the particles of any substance, water molecules are constantly moving. Also, water molecules are polar, which means they have a positive area and a negative area. Molecules of sugar also are polar.

How It Happens Molecules of sugar dissolving in water are shown in **Figure 4.** First, water molecules cluster around sugar molecules with their negative ends attracted to the positive ends of the sugar. Then, the water molecules pull the sugar molecules into solution. Finally, the water molecules and the sugar molecules mix evenly, forming a solution.

Reading Check *How do water molecules help sugar molecules dissolve?*

The process described in **Figure 4** repeats as layer after layer of sugar molecules move away from the crystal, until all the molecules are evenly spread out. The same three steps occur for most solid solutes dissolving in a liquid solvent.

Dissolving Liquids and Gases The same process takes place when a gas dissolves in a liquid. Particles of liquids and gases move much more freely than do particles of solids. When gases dissolve in gases or when liquids dissolve in liquids, this movement spreads solutes evenly throughout the solvent, resulting in a homogenous solution.

Dissolving Solids in Solids How can you mix solids to make alloys? Although solid particles do move a little, this movement is not enough to spread them evenly throughout the mixture. The solid metals are first melted and then mixed together. In this liquid state, the metal atoms can spread out evenly and will remain mixed when cooled.

Figure 4 Dissolving sugar in water can be thought of as a three-step process.

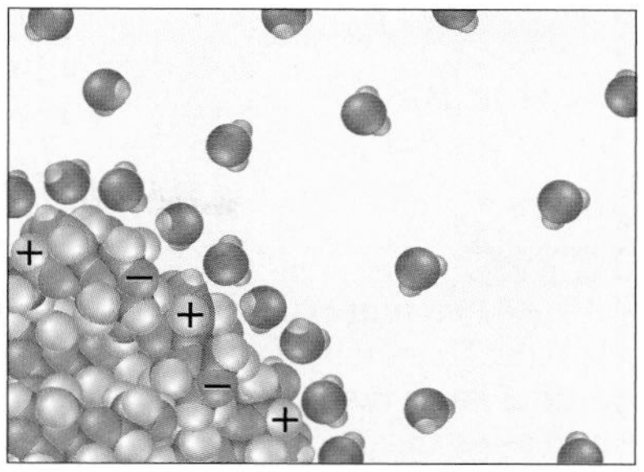

Step 1 Moving water molecules cluster around the sugar molecules as their negative ends are attracted to the positive ends of the sugar molecules.

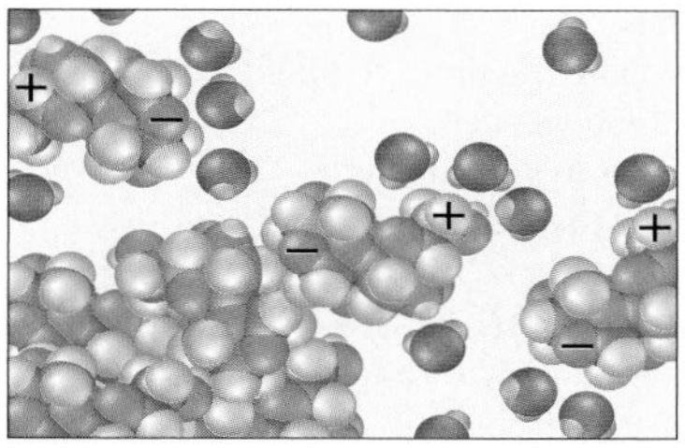

Step 2 Water molecules pull the sugar molecules into solution.

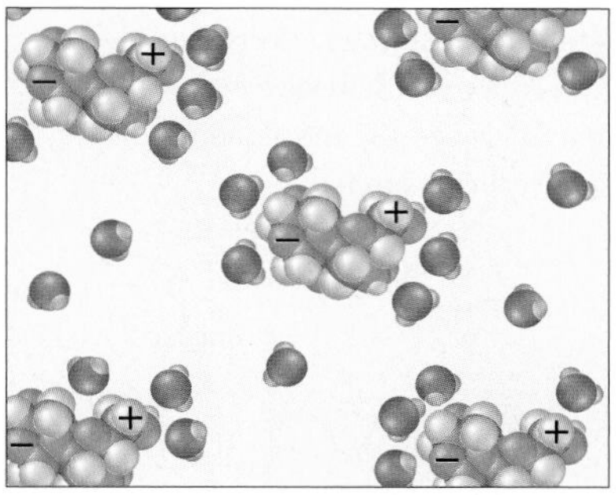

Step 3 Water molecules and sugar molecules spread out to form a homogeneous mixture.

Visual Learning

Figure 4 Place a box of foam spheres in the center of a group of students who have linked arms. Tell students that they are solvent particles and the spheres are solute particles. In order for a sphere to dissove, it must be held by a student. Discuss the three dissolving steps presented on the page. Then have students act out the steps with the spheres as you call out Step 1, Step 2, and Step 3. The activity can also be used to discuss the advantage of making the solute more available by stirring it among the solvent particles. L2 ELL IS **Kinesthetic**

Reading Check

Answer The negative ends of the water molecules pull on the positive ends of sugar molecules.

Quick Demo
Water Polarity

Materials balloon, wool cloth

Estimated Time 5 minutes

Procedure To show the polarity of water, blow up a balloon and rub its surface with a wool cloth. Turn on the water faucet so it delivers a thin steady stream. Bring the statically charged balloon near the stream, but do not touch the balloon to it. Have students observe that the stream bends dramatically. L2 ELL IS **Visual-Spatial**

Cultural Diversity

Sandbox Trees The sap from the tall sandbox trees, found in the jungles of Central and South America, is acidic. People who fish throw this sap into lakes and streams, which have been dammed, to stun the fish so they can gather them for food. Then they remove the dams. The sap becomes sufficiently dilute, and the fish recover completely.

Differentiated Instruction

Learning Disabled As you do the various demonstrations, help students follow what you are doing by moving slowly and deliberately through each step and explaining what you are doing as you do it. Make sure all students can see what you do and can see the results. Make sure you describe the results to the class. L1 ELL **Auditory-Musical**

SECTION 1 How Solutions Form 755

Mini LAB

Video Lab available.

Purpose Students will observe differences in the rates of dissolution of particles with different surface areas. L2 ELL LS **Visual-Spatial**

Materials four sugar cubes, distilled water, two glasses, two stirring rods per group

Teaching Strategy Have students do the activity twice, once stirring the sugar and once not stirring. Stirring increases rate of dissolving.

Analysis

1. The granules dissolved faster than the cubes even though they were treated identically.
2. The greater the surface area of the solute, the faster it dissolves.

Assessment

Oral Have students use their MiniLAB results and **Figure 5** to explain how the surface area of the two cubes increases when they are ground. Use **Performance Assessment in the Science Classroom,** p. 89.

Try at Home

Discussion

Surface Area Discuss with students how rapidly surface area increases as an object is divided into smaller pieces. Have students calculate the surface area of a 2-cm cube. $6 \times 4\ \text{cm}^2 = 24\ \text{cm}^2$ Ask students to predict how much larger the surface area would be if the cube were divided into 1-cm cubes. How many 1-cm cubes would there be? 8 What is their surface area? $8 \times 6 \times 1\ \text{cm}^2 = 48\ \text{cm}^2$ L2

Mini LAB

Observing the Effect of Surface Area

Procedure

1. Grind up two **sugar cubes.**
2. Place the ground sugar particles into a **medium-sized glass** and place two **unground sugar cubes** into a **similar glass.**
3. Add an equal amount of **water** at room temperature to each glass.

Analysis

1. Compare the times required to dissolve each.
2. What can you conclude about the dissolving rate and surface area?

Try at Home

Rate of Dissolving

When two substances form a solution, the dissolving occurs at different rates. Sometimes the rate at which a solute dissolves into a solvent is fast, while other times it is slow. There are several things you can do to speed up the rate of dissolving—stirring, reducing crystal size, and increasing temperature.

Stirring How does stirring speed up the dissolving process? Think about how you make a drink from a powdered mix. After you add the mix to water, you stir it. Stirring a solution speeds up the dissolving process because it brings more fresh solvent into contact with more solute. The fresh solvent attracts the particles of solute, causing the solid solute to dissolve faster.

Crystal Size Another way to speed the dissolving of a solid in a liquid is to grind large crystals into smaller ones. Suppose you want to use a 5-g crystal of rock candy to sweeten your water. If you put the whole crystal into a glass of water, it might take several minutes to dissolve, even with stirring. However, if you first grind the crystal of rock candy into a powder, it will dissolve in the same amount of water in a few seconds.

Why does breaking up a solid cause it to dissolve faster? Breaking the solid into many smaller pieces greatly increases its surface area, as you can see in **Figure 5.** Because dissolving takes place at the surface of the solid, increasing the surface area allows more solvent to come into contact with more solid solute. Therefore, the speed of the dissolving process increases.

Figure 5 Crystal size affects solubility. Large crystals dissolve in water slowly because the amount of surface area is limited.

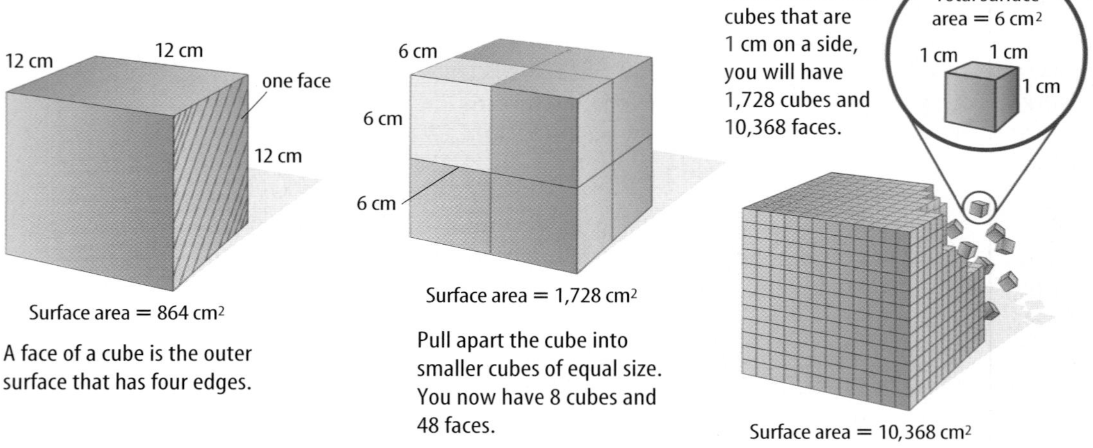

Active Reading

Quickwrites Let students discover what they already know about solutions, solvents, and solutes. Have students list their ideas and thoughts about these topics freely in a paragraph. Then, during or after a learning experience, share those ideas and thoughts with the class. L2

756 **CHAPTER 24** Solutions, Acids, and Bases

Applying Math — Calculate

SURFACE AREA The length, height, and width of a cube are each 1 cm. If the cube is cut in half to form two rectangles, how much new surface area has been created?

IDENTIFY the known values and the unknown value

Identify the known values:

- The cube has dimensions of $l = h = w = 1$ cm.
- The rectangular solid has a width $w = 0.5$ cm.
- The rectangular solid has a length and height $l = h = 1$ cm.

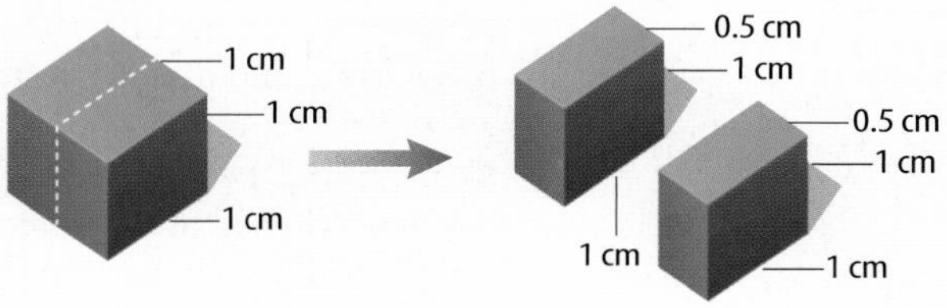

- The cube and the rectangular solids each have six faces: front and back ($h \times w$); left and right ($h \times l$); and top and bottom ($w \times l$). The total surface area of the cube or the rectangular solid is the sum of these areas, or $2(h \times w) + 2(h \times l) + 2(w \times l)$.

Identify the unknown value:

Find the total surface area of the two rectangular solids.

SOLVE the problem

The surface area of the cube is:
$2(1\text{ cm} \times 1\text{ cm}) + 2(1\text{ cm} \times 1\text{ cm}) + 2(1\text{ cm} \times 1\text{ cm}) = 6\text{ cm}^2$

The surface area of the rectangular solid is:
$2(1\text{ cm} \times 0.5\text{ cm}) + 2(1\text{ cm} \times 1\text{ cm}) + 2(0.5\text{ cm} \times 1\text{ cm}) = 4\text{ cm}^2$

Because there are two rectangular solids, their total surface area is:
$4\text{ cm}^2 + 4\text{ cm}^2 = 8\text{ cm}^2$

To find out how much new surface area has been created, compare the two results:
$8\text{ cm}^2 - 6\text{ cm}^2 = 2\text{ cm}^2$

CHECK the answer

Does your answer seem reasonable? Consider what you've done by splitting the cube in two. You have created two new faces, each with a surface area of 1 cm^2; therefore, the answer 2 cm^2 is correct.

Practice Problems

1. A cube of salt with a length, height, and width of 5 cm is attached along a face to another cube of salt with the same dimensions. What is the combined surface area of the new rectangular solid?
2. How much surface area has been lost?

For more practice problems go to page 879, and visit Math Practice at gpescience.com.

Applying Math

Math Standards

National: 4, 6, 9

Answers to Practice Problems

1. Solve the equations
   - For the attached cubes:
     $h = 5$ cm, $l = 5$ cm, $w = 10$ cm
     $2(5\text{ cm} \times 10\text{ cm}) + 2(5\text{ cm} \times 5\text{ cm}) + 2(10\text{ cm} \times 5\text{ cm}) = 250\text{ cm}^2$
   - For the original cubes:
     $h = l = w = 5$ cm
     $2(5\text{ cm} \times 5\text{ cm}) + 2(5\text{ cm} \times 5\text{ cm}) + 2(5\text{ cm} \times 5\text{ cm}) = 150\text{ cm}^2$
2. Because there were two cubes, $150\text{ cm}^2 + 150\text{ cm}^2 = 300\text{ cm}^2$, so 50 cm^2 of surface area was lost.

Fun Fact

Moisturizers have long been used to protect and rehydrate the skin. These products contain compounds called humectants and emollients that increase the water content of the skin in different ways. Humectants add water to the skin by attracting water vapor from the air. Emollients cover the skin with a layer of material that is immiscible with water. This prevents water from within the skin from evaporating.

Differentiated Instruction

Challenge Air is a solution of gases, primarily nitrogen. Ask students to discover the other gases and the relative amounts of each in air. Students can then present their research to the class in a format of their choosing. Although charts and graphs make good visual representation, challenge students to invent another creative way to illustrate their findings. L2

Post Reading

Clarify Text Have students use the Review Summary to check their notes for completion and accuracy. Remind them to look back in the text to cross-check and clarify their notes.

3 Assess

DAILY INTERVENTION

Check for Understanding

Kinesthetic Have two or three students stand in a group and have another student pull at the hand of a student in the group. Relate this activity to the job of a solvent pulling a solute into solution. Have students identify which person is the solvent and which is the solute. L1

Reteach

Surface Area Bring in two boxes of different sizes to represent different surface areas. Use a new crayon and color all six sides of the larger box. Then use another new crayon and color all six sides of the smaller box. Explain that the difference in surface area affected the amount of crayon that was needed to color it. L2 IS **Visual Spatial**

Assessment

Content Have students work in groups to write a story or a poem about what happens to one NaCl crystal as it is put into water and dissolves. Use **Performance Assessment in the Science Classroom,** p. 157. L2 P

Temperature In addition to stirring and decreasing particle size, a third way to increase the rate at which most solids dissolve is to increase the temperature of the solvent. Think about making hot chocolate from a mix. You can make the sugar in the chocolate mix dissolve faster by putting it in hot water instead of cold water. Increasing the temperature of a solvent speeds up the movement of its particles. This increase causes more solvent particles to bump into the solute. As a result, solute particles break loose and dissolve faster.

Controlling the Process Think about how the three factors you just learned about affect the rate of dissolving. Can these factors combine to further increase the rate, or perhaps control the rate of dissolving? Each technique—stirring, crushing, and heating—is known to speed up the rate of dissolving by itself. However, when two or more techniques are combined, the rate of dissolving is even faster. Consider a sugar cube placed in cold water. You know that the sugar cube eventually will dissolve. You can predict that heating the water will increase the rate by some amount. You also can predict that heat and stirring will increase the rate further. Finally, you can predict that crushing the cube combined with heating and stirring will result in the fastest rate of dissolving. Knowing how much each technique affects the rate will allow you to control the rate of dissolving more precisely.

section 1 review

Summary

What is a solution?

- A solution is a uniform mixture.
- A solution has the same composition, color, density, and taste throughout.

Solutes and Solvents

- In a solution, the solute is the substance that is being dissolved; the solvent is the substance that is doing the dissolving.

How Substances Dissolve

- The process of dissolving happens at the surface and is aided by polarity and molecular movement.

Rate of Dissolving

- Stirring, surface area, and temperature affect the rate of dissolving.

Self Check

1. **List** possible ways that phases of matter could combine to form a solution.
2. **Describe** how temperature affects the rate of dissolving.
3. **Describe** how the metal atoms in an alloy are mixed.
4. **Think Critically** Amalgams, which sometimes are used in tooth fillings, are alloys of mercury with other metals. Is an amalgam a solution? Explain.

Applying Math

5. **Find Surface Area** Calculate the surface area of a rectangular solid with dimensions $\ell = 2$ cm, $w = 1$ cm, and $h = 0.5$ cm.
6. **Calculate Percent Increase** If the length of the rectangle in question 5 is increased by 10 percent, by how much will the surface area increase?

More Section Review gpescience.com

section 1 review

1. Possible answer: liquid/liquid, solid/liquid, gas/liquid, gas/gas, solid/solid.
2. Increasing temperature causes particles to move faster which causes solutes to dissolve faster.
3. Metals are melted, mixed evenly, then cooled to a solid.
4. Yes, one metal acts as the solute while the other metal acts as a solvent.
5. $2(2\text{ cm} \times 1\text{ cm}) + 2(2\text{ cm} \times 0.5\text{ cm}) + 2(1\text{ cm} \times 0.5\text{ cm}) = 7\text{ cm}^2$
6. new $l = 2.2$ cm; therefore, new surface area = 7.6 cm. $\left[\frac{(7.6\text{ cm} - 7\text{ cm})}{7\text{ cm}}\right] \times 100 = 8.5\%$ increase

section 2

Solubility and Concentration

Reading Guide

What You'll Learn

- **Define** the concept of solubility.
- **Identify** how to express the concentration of solutions.
- **List** and define three types of solutions.
- **Describe** the effects of pressure and temperature on the solubility of gases.

Why It's Important

Solutions such as medicine and lemonade work and taste a particular way because of the specific solution concentrations.

Review Vocabulary

substance: element or compound that cannot be broken down into simpler components

New Vocabulary

- solubility
- concentration
- saturated solution
- unsaturated solution
- supersaturated solution

How much can dissolve?

You can stir several teaspoons of salt into water, and the salt will dissolve. However, if you continue adding salt, eventually the point is reached when no more salt dissolves and the excess salt sinks to the bottom of the glass. This indicates how soluble salt is in water. **Solubility** (sol yuh BIH luh tee) is the maximum amount of a solute that can be dissolved in a given amount of solvent at a given temperature.

Reading Check *What is solubility?*

Comparing Solubilities The amount of a solute that can dissolve in a solvent depends on the nature of these substances. **Figure 6** shows two beakers with the same volume of water and two different solutes. In one beaker, 1 g of solute A dissolves completely, but additional solute does not dissolve and falls to the bottom of the beaker. On the other hand, 1 g of solute B dissolves completely, and two more grams also dissolve before solute begins to fall to the bottom. You can conclude that substance B is more soluble than substance A, if the temperature of the water is the same in both beakers. **Table 1** shows how the solubility of several substances varies at 20°C. For solutes that are gases, the pressure also must be given.

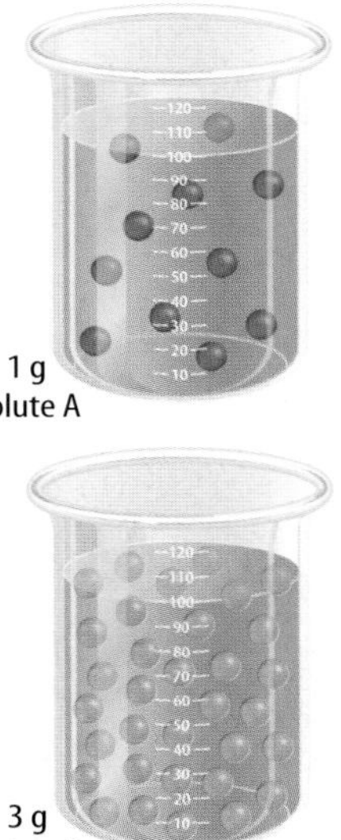

Figure 6 Substance B is more soluble in water than substance A is at the same temperature.

Section 2 Resource Manager

Chapter *Fast File* Resources

Transparency Activity, p. 47
Directed Reading for Content Mastery, p. 21
MiniLAB, p. 4
Enrichment, p. 32
Reinforcement, p. 28

1 Motivate

INTERACTIVE CHALKBOARD PowerPoint® Presentations An editable Microsoft® PowerPoint® presentation is available on **Interactive Chalkboard** CD-ROM.

Bellringer

Section Focus Transparencies also are available on the Interactive Chalkboard CD-ROM. L2 ELL

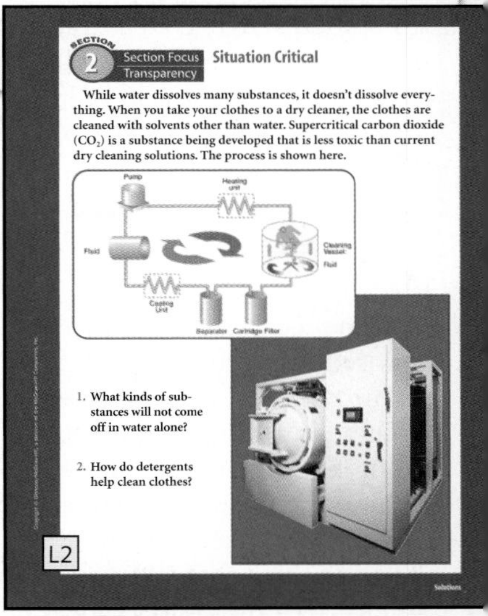

Reading Preview

Tie to Prior Knowledge

Nutritious Milk Students are familiar with milk as a nutritious food. Bring in a milk carton and go over the percent concentrations of various nutrients dissolved in the milk. Point out that solute percentages can provide important information. L2

Preview Vocabulary Read the vocabulary words to students. Then, have them practice saying the words to a partner. Tell them that learning to pronounce words before reading will help them become more fluent readers. Point out that there is a pronunciation key for *solubility* in the first paragraph.

2 Teach

Reading Check

Answer the maximum amount of solute that can be dissolved in a given amount of solvent at a given temperature

IDENTIFYING Misconceptions

Concentrated Acids Some people think that all concentrated acids are 100% acid. Explain to students that concentrated hydrochloric acid is 37% HCl, concentrated nitric acid is 70% HNO_3, and sulfuric acid is 96% H_2SO_4.

Activity

Ranking Concentration Bring a colored drink to class and dilute it into several glasses of equal volume but different concentration. Have students place the solutions in sequence from low to high concentration. (The basis for the sequencing is the intensity of the color.) Once the students are satisfied with the sequence, tell them the concentrations of the solutions in %v/v.
L1 ELL LS **Visual-Spatial**

Virtual Labs

Solute *How is the solubility of a compound determined?*

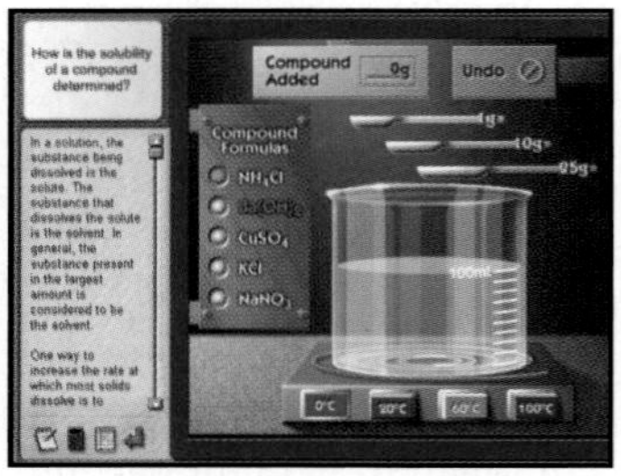

Table 1 Solubility of Substances in Water at 20°C

Substance	Solubility in g/100 g of Water
Solid Substances	
Salt (sodium chloride)	35.9
Baking soda (sodium bicarbonate)	9.6
Washing soda (sodium carbonate)	21.4
Lye (sodium hydroxide)	109.0
Sugar (sucrose)	203.9
Gaseous Substances*	
Hydrogen	0.00017
Oxygen	0.005
Carbon dioxide	0.16

*at normal atmospheric pressure

Concentration

Suppose you add one teaspoon of lemon juice to a glass of water to make lemonade. Your friend adds four teaspoons of lemon juice to another glass of the same size. What is the difference between these two glasses of lemonade? The difference between the two drinks is the amount of water present compared to the amount of lemon juice. The **concentration** describes how much solute is present in a solution compared to the amount of solvent. A concentrated solution is one in which a large amount of solute is dissolved in the solvent. A dilute solution is one that has a small amount of solute in the solvent.

Precise Concentrations How much real fruit juice is there in one of those boxed fruit drinks? You can read the label to find out. *Concentrated* and *dilute* are not precise terms. Concentrations of solutions can be described precisely. One way is to state the percentage by volume of the solute. The percentage by volume of the juice in the bottled drink shown in **Figure 7** is 10 percent. Adding 10 mL of juice to 90 mL of water makes 100 mL of this drink. Commonly, fruit-flavored drinks can have ten percent or less fruit juice. Generally, if two or more liquids are being mixed, the concentration is given in percentage by volume.

Figure 7 The concentrations of fruit juices often are given in percent by volume, as these are. Concentrations commonly range from 10 percent to 100 percent juice.
Identify *the product that has the highest concentration.*

Differentiated Instruction

Learning Disabled To show students the difference between saturated and unsaturated solutions, add 36 g of sodium chloride to 100-mL of room temperature water. Stir the salt until it is completely dissolved. Place a small amount of this solution in a petri dish. Place a small amount of the same solution in a second petri dish and add water to make it unsaturated. Place both petri dishes on the overhead projector. Have a student drop a crystal of salt into each dish and slowly stir both solutions. The crystal will dissolve in the unsaturated solution, but it will remain visible in the saturated solution.

Types of Solutions

How much solute can dissolve in a given amount of solvent? That depends on a number of factors, including the solubility of the solute. Here you will examine the types of solutions based on the amount of a solute dissolved.

Saturated Solutions If you add 35 g of copper(II) sulfate, $CuSO_4$, to 100 g of water at 20°C, only 32 g will dissolve. You have a saturated solution because no more copper(II) sulfate can dissolve. A **saturated solution** is a solution that contains all the solute it can hold at a given temperature. However, if you heat the mixture to a higher temperature, more copper(II) sulfate can dissolve. Generally, as the temperature of a liquid solvent increases, the amount of solid solute that can dissolve in it also increases. **Table 2** shows the amounts of a few solutes that can dissolve in 100 g of water at different temperatures to form saturated solutions. Some of these data also are shown on the accompanying graph.

Table 2 Solubility of Compounds in g/100 g of Water

Compound	0°C	20°C	100°C
Copper(II) sulfate	23.1	32.0	114
Potassium bromide	53.6	65.3	104
Potassium chloride	28.0	34.0	56.3
Potassium nitrate	13.9	31.6	245
Sodium chlorate	79.6	95.9	204
Sodium chloride	35.7	36.0	39.2
Sucrose (sugar)	179.2	203.9	487.2

Solubility Curves Each line on the graph from **Table 2** is called a solubility curve for a particular substance. You can use a solubility curve to determine how much solute will dissolve at any temperature given on the graph. For example, about 78 g of KBr (potassium bromide) will form a saturated solution in 100 g of water at 47°C. How much NaCl (sodium chloride) will form a saturated solution with 100 g of water at the same temperature?

Temperature Effects on Solubility

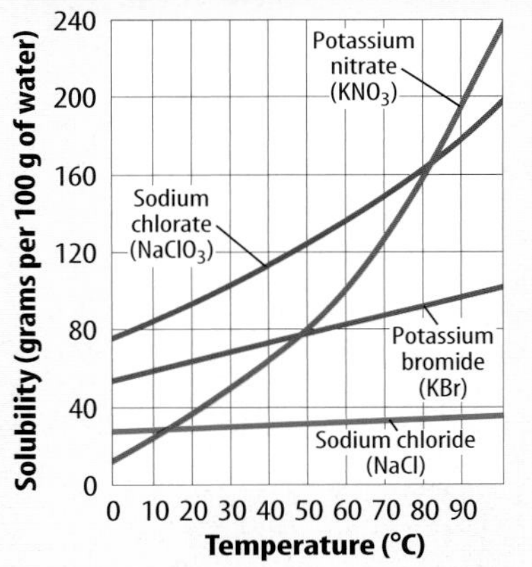

Unsaturated Solutions An **unsaturated solution** is any solution that can dissolve more solute at a given temperature. Each time a saturated solution is heated to a higher temperature, it generally becomes unsaturated. The term *unsaturated* isn't precise. If you look at **Table 2,** you'll see that at 20°C, 35.9 g of NaCl (sodium chloride) forms a saturated solution in 100 g of water. However, an unsaturated solution of NaCl could be any amount less than 35.9 g in 100 g of water at 20°C.

Reading Check *What happens to a saturated solution if it is heated?*

Text Question Answer

approximately 37 g of NaCl

Inquiry Lab

Saturation Point

Purpose Students witness the saturation point of a solution of their choice and have the opportunity to compare results with others for a wider experience.

Possible Materials water, rubbing alcohol, juices or drinks for solvents; granular sugar, powdered sugar, flour, salt for solutes, balance

Estimated Time 30 minutes

Give each student a beaker and have them add 50 mL of the solvent of their choice. Then instruct them to begin adding 5g of solute of their choice, slowly and with stirring. Have students keep close track of how much solute they add until the solution becomes saturated. Encourage students to repeat the activity to find out how other solutes work with the solvent they chose or how other solvents work with the solute they chose. Prepare a class chart of the results.

Teaching Strategies

- Discuss this activity before starting and let the students brainstorm possible solutes and solvents.
- Do not limit their possible materials to only those substances that will dissolve.
- Encourage students to investigate the variables that apply to this activity, such as volume of solvent, degree of agitation, and temperature. L2

For additional inquiry activities, see *Science Inquiry Lab Manual.*

Reading Strategy

Use Graphs Have students write a sentence comparing the general effect of increasing temperature on the solubility of sodium chloride and potassium nitrate. Tell students that all the information needed for this task can be found in **Table 2.** Discuss students' sentences and analyze their accuracy based on **Table 2.**

Curriculum Connection

Math Ask students to refer to **Table 2** and answer the following question. If you were to graph the solubility of a solute on the *y* axis and the temperature of the solution on the *x* axis, which solute would have the line with the steepest slope, potassium chloride or sodium chloride? potassium chloride L2

Reading Check

Answer It may become unsaturated.

Caption Answer

Figure 7 the product labeled "100% pure orange juice"

Make a Model

Beaker Solutions On the board draw three identical oversized beakers. Draw the same number of small circles in each beaker. These represent particles of a solvent. Ask students to copy your drawings and add, using a different color of pen or pencil, circles in the beakers to represent unsaturated, saturated, and supersaturated solutions. L1 LS **Analytical-Mathematical**

Quick Demo

Gas in Solution

Materials full, unopened bottle of soda (any size)

Estimated Time 10 minutes

Procedure Open a soda bottle. Point out that when a soda is sealed, pressure keeps the gas in solution. Once opened, pressure is reduced and then bubbles become visible again.

Use an Analogy

Saturated Class Describe the types of solutions using the analogy of adding students to a classroom. In a room with 25 desks, a class with fewer than 25 students is analogous to an unsaturated solution. More students can be added to fill the desks. The 25th student takes the last desk and makes the classroom saturated. Adding more students beyond 25 causes some students to be displaced from desks and fall out into the aisles, representing precipitation. L1

Supersaturated Solutions If you make a saturated solution of potassium nitrate at 100°C and then let it cool to 20°C, part of the solute comes out of solution. This is because the solvent cannot hold as much solute at the lower temperature. Most other saturated solutions behave in a similar way when cooled. However, if you cool a saturated solution of sodium acetate from 100°C to 20°C without disturbing it, no solute comes out. At this point, the solution is supersaturated. A **supersaturated solution** is one that contains more solute than a saturated solution at the same temperature. Supersaturated solutions are unstable. For example, if a seed crystal of sodium acetate is dropped into the supersaturated solution, excess sodium acetate crystallizes out, as shown in **Figure 8.**

Solution Energy As the supersaturated solution of sodium acetate crystallizes, the solution becomes hot. Energy is given off as the sodium acetate forms crystals. Some portable heat packs use crystallization from supersaturated solutions to produce heat. After crystallization, the heat pack can be reused by heating it to again dissolve all the solute.

Substances, such as ammonium nitrate, draw energy from their surroundings to dissolve. This is what happens when a cold pack is activated to treat minor injuries or to reduce swelling. When the inner bags of ammonium nitrate and water are broken, the ammonium nitrate draws energy from the water, which causes the temperature of the water to drop, which makes the the pack cool.

Reading Check *Why is energy given off between ions and water molecules?*

Science Online

Topic: Crystallization

Visit gpescience.com for Web links to information about crystals and crystallization.

Activity Find instructions for a safe "do-it-yourself" home crystallization experiment. Grow the crystals as directed and share the results with the class.

Figure 8 A supersaturated solution is unstable.
Explain *why this is so.*

A seed crystal of sodium acetate is added to a supersaturated solution of sodium acetate.

Excess solute immediately crystallizes from solution.

The crystallization reaction draws solute from the solution.

LAB DEMONSTRATION

Purpose to show that dissolved ionic compounds conduct an electrical current

Materials conductivity tester, distilled water, NaCl, Epsom salt, rubbing alcohol, sugar

Preparation List the solutes on the board. Dissolve each in distilled water.

Procedure Test the conductivity of each solution. Make sure students can see the results of each test.

Expected Outcome NaCl and Epsom salt solutions will conduct electricity; alcohol and sugar solutions will not.

Assessment

What occurs in the conducting solutions? Ions are moving out of crystals and into water where they can move in the solution and conduct electricity.

Why don't the other solutions conduct electricity? The solutes in the other solutions don't form ions. L2

762 CHAPTER 24 Solutions, Acids, and Bases

Solubility of Gases

When you shake an opened bottle of soda, it bubbles up and may squirt out. Shaking or pouring a solution of a gas in a liquid causes gas to come out of solution. Agitating the solution exposes more gas molecules to the surface, where they escape from the liquid.

Pressure Effects What might you do if you want to dissolve more gas in a liquid? One thing you can do is increase the pressure of that gas over the liquid. Soft drinks are bottled under increased pressure. This increases the amount of carbon dioxide that dissolves in the liquid. When the pressure is released, the carbon dioxide bubbles out, as shown in **Figure 9.**

Figure 9 Solutions of gases behave differently from those of solids or liquids. This soda is bottled under pressure to keep carbon dioxide in solution. When the bottle is opened, pressure is released and carbon dioxide bubbles out of solution.

Temperature Effects Another way to increase the amount of gas that dissolves in a liquid is to cool the liquid. This is just the opposite of what you do to increase the speed at which most solids dissolve in a liquid. Imagine what happens to the carbon dioxide when a bottle of soft drink is opened. Even more carbon dioxide will bubble out of a soft drink as it gets warmer.

section 2 review

Summary

How much can dissolve?
- Solubility tells how much solute can dissolve in a solvent at a particular temperature.

Concentration
- A concentrated solution has a larger amount of dissolved solute. A dilute solution has a smaller amount of dissolved solute.

Types of Solutions
- Saturated, unsaturated, and supersaturated solutions are defined by how much solute is dissolved.
- Solubility curves help predict how much solute can dissolve at a particular temperature.
- Some supersaturated solutions absorb or give off energy.

Solubility of Gases
- Pressure and temperature affect gases in solution. High pressure and low temperature allow more gas to dissolve.

Self Check

1. **Explain** Do all solutes dissolve to the same extent in the same solvent? How do you know?
2. **Interpret** from **Table 2** the mass of sugar that would have to be dissolved in 100 g of water to form a saturated solution at 20°C.
3. **Determine** which solution is more concentrated: 17 g of solute X dissolved in 100 mL of water at 23°C or 26 g of solute Z dissolved in 100 mL of water at 23°C.
4. **Identify** the type of solution you have if, at 35°C, the solute continues to dissolve as you add more.
5. **Think Critically** Explain how keeping a carbonated beverage capped helps keep it from going "flat."

Applying Math

6. **Calculate Cost** By volume, orange drink is ten percent each of orange juice and corn syrup. A 1.5-L can of the drink costs $0.95. A 1.5-L can of orange juice is $1.49, and 1.5 L of corn syrup is $1.69. Per serving, does it cost less to make your own orange drink or buy it ?

Reading Check

Answer New bonds are formed.

Caption Answer

Figure 8 because a change in temperature causes solute to fall out

Post Reading

Question a Partner Place students in pairs and have them read their sentences related to **Table 2** to each other. Have each partner ask the other questions about their sentences, probing for deeper meaning and understanding.

3 Assess

DAILY INTERVENTION

Check for Understanding

Honey Crystals Describe, or bring to class if available, an old jar of honey. Ask students to describe why there are crystals of sugar forming in the previously smooth solution. As the water evaporates from the solution, the dissolved sugar becomes more concentrated. As the concentration exceeds the saturation limit, sugar will begin to precipitate, crystallizing out of the solution. L2 IN **Linguistic**

Reteach

Aromas Open a small bottle of ammonia in the back of the room without telling students. Ask if anyone can detect any type of chemical aroma. As the ammonia fumes mix in the air, point out to students that the air is diluting the ammonia. L2

section 2 review

1. No; you can determine this experimentally.
2. 203.9 g
3. solute Z
4. unsaturated
5. When capped, carbon dioxide stays in solution, which keeps the soda "fizzy."
6. Making it is cheaper. If you were making 1,500 mL of orange drink you would need 150 mL of orange juice @ $1.49/1,500 mL = 14.9 cents per 150 mL; 150 mL of syrup @ $1.69/1,500 mL = 16.9 cents per 150 mL; so, to make 1,500 mL of drink you need only 14.9 + 16.9 cents = 31.8 cents of ingredients per 1,500 mL of drink

Assessment

Performance Have students use the data in **Table 2** to plot solubility versus temperature for sucrose. The line slopes up. and the second line slopes down. Use **PASC,** p. 111. L2 P

section 3 Acids, Bases, and Salts

1 Motivate

INTERACTIVE CHALKBOARD An editable Microsoft® PowerPoint® presentation is available on **Interactive Chalkboard** CD-ROM.

Bellringer

Section Focus Transparencies also are available on the Interactive Chalkboard CD-ROM. L2 ELL

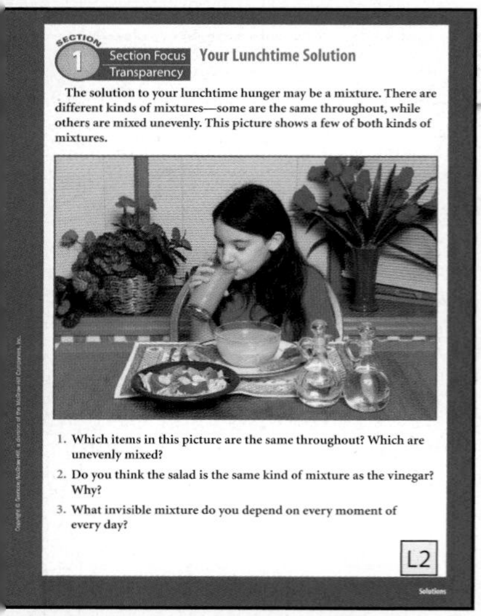

Reading Preview

Tie to Prior Knowledge

Material States Ask students to describe situations in which the boiling point or the freezing point of a material was changed. If they have trouble, explain that adding antifreeze to automobile radiators raises the boiling point. Explain that they will learn how this process works. L2

Activate Background Knowledge Ask students if they have heard of acid indigestion. Tell them this is a burning feeling in your stomach and sometimes people take pink or white chalky medicine to neutralize the burning. Tell them that they will learn about acids and bases and how they interact.

Reading Guide

What You'll Learn

- **Compare and contrast** acids and bases and identify the characteristics they have.
- **Examine** some formulas and uses of common acids and bases.
- **Determine** how the processes of ionization and dissociation apply to acids and bases.

Why It's Important

Acids and bases are found almost everywhere—from fruit juice and gastric juice to soaps.

Review Vocabulary

electrolyte: compound that breaks apart in water, forming charged particles (ions) that can conduct electricity

New Vocabulary

- acid
- indicator
- base

Acids

What comes to mind when you hear the word *acid?* Do you think of a substance that can burn your skin or even burn a hole through a piece of metal? Do you think about sour foods such as those shown in **Figure 10?** Although some acids can burn and are dangerous to handle, most acids in foods are safe to eat. What acids have in common, however, is that they contain at least one hydrogen atom that can be removed when the acid is dissolved in water.

Figure 10 The acids in these common foods give each their distinctive sour taste.

Properties of Acids When an acid dissolves in water, some of the hydrogen is released as hydrogen ions, H^+. An **acid** is a substance that produces hydrogen ions in a water solution. It is the ability to produce these ions that gives acids their characteristic properties. When an acid dissolves in water, H^+ ions interact with water molecules to form H_3O^+ ions, which are called hydronium ions (hi DROH nee um • I ahnz).

Acids have several common properties. For one thing, all acids taste sour. The familiar, sour taste of many foods is due to acids. However, taste never should be used to test for the presence of acids. Some acids can damage tissue by producing painful burns. Acids are corrosive. Some acids react strongly with certain metals, eating away the metals and forming metallic compounds and hydrogen gas. Acids also react with indicators to produce predictable changes in color. An **indicator** is an organic compound that changes color in acids and bases. For example, the indicator litmus paper turns red in acid.

Section 3 Resource Manager

Chapter *Fast File* Resources

Transparency Activity, pp. 48, 51–52
Directed Reading for Content Mastery, p. 20
Lab Activity, pp. 13–16
Enrichment, p. 33
Reinforcement, p. 29

Physical Science Critical Thinking/Problem Solving, p. 1

Cultural Diversity, p. 37

Common Acids Many foods contain acids. In addition to citric acid in citrus fruits, lactic acid is found in yogurt and buttermilk, and food, such as pickles, contain vinegar, also known as acetic acid. Your stomach uses acid to help digest your food. At least four acids (sulfuric, phosphoric, nitric, and hydrochloric) play roles in industrial applications.

Reading Check ***Which four acids are important for industry?***

Table 3 lists the names and formulas of a few acids, their uses, and some properties. Three acids are used to make fertilizers; most of the nitric acid and sulfuric acid and approximately 90 percent of phosphoric acid produced are used for this purpose. Many acids can burn, but sulfuric acid can burn by removing water from your skin as easily as it takes water from sugar, as shown in **Figure 11.**

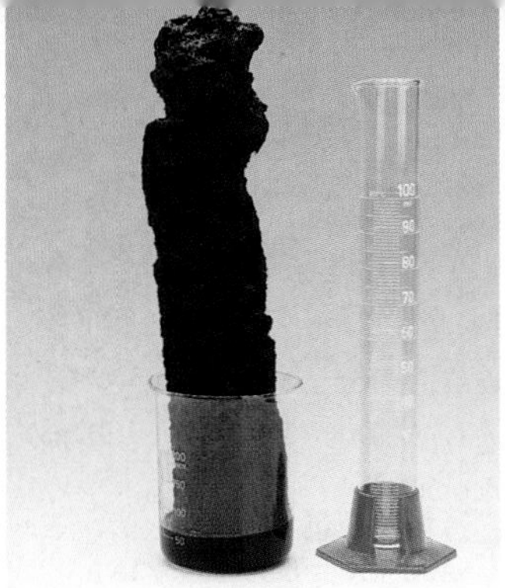

Figure 11 When sulfuric acid is added to sugar, the mixture foams, removing hydrogen and oxygen atoms as water and leaving air-filled carbon.

Table 3 Common Acids and Their Uses

Name, Formula	Use	Other Information
Acetic acid, CH_3COOH	Food preservation and preparation	When in solution with water, it is known as vinegar.
Acetylsalicylic acid, $HOOC–C_6H_4–OOCCH_3$	Pain relief, fever relief, to reduce inflammation	Known as aspirin
Ascorbic acid, $H_2C_6H_6O_6$	Antioxidant, vitamin	Called vitamin C
Carbonic acid, H_2CO_3	Carbonated drinks	Involved in cave, stalactite, and stalagmite formation
Hydrochloric acid, HCl	Digestion as gastric juice in stomach, to clean steel in a process called pickling	Commonly called muriatic acid
Nitric acid, HNO_3	To make fertilizers	Used to produce nitrogen fertilizers
Phosphoric acid, H_3PO_4	To make detergents, fertilizers, and soft drinks	Slightly sour but pleasant taste, detergents containing phosphates cause water pollution
Sulfuric acid, H_2SO_4	Car batteries, to manufacture fertilizers and other chemicals	Dehydrating agent, causes burns by removing water from cells

2 Teach

Activity

Acid Formulas Have students note the formulas of the inorganic acids listed in **Table 3.** Ask what they observe about the way formulas of these acids are typically written. Chemists commonly indicate that a compound is an acid by writing the formula with "H" as the first element. L2 LS **Logical-Mathematical**

Use Science Words

Word Meaning Have students use the word *indicator* in a sentence, and then explain how the meaning of *indicator* in their sentence parallels its meaning in the context of acid and base identification. L2 LS **Linguistic**

Visual Learning

Table 3 If an acid contains a structure that includes COOH, it is an organic acid. Other acids, including H_2CO_3, are inorganic. Have students work in small groups to classify the acids from **Table 3** as organic or inorganic. All are inorganic except acetic acid and acetylsalicylic acid. L2 LS **Linguistic**

Reading Check

Answer sulfuric, phosphoric, nitric, and hydrochloric acids

Visual Learning

Figure 11 This reaction produces irritating fumes and should not be attempted in the classroom.

Reading Strategy

Tables Have students keep a data table labeled Acids and Bases. Ask students to list common and chemical names of acids and bases under the appropriate headings. Remind them to read the text carefully as they complete their charts.

Curriculum Connection

Art Etching is using the reaction between an acid and a metal to make a piece of art. Have students find out more about this process and make posters illustrating it. A metal plate, usually copper or zinc, is coated with acid-resistant resin. The artist draws lines through the resin, then puts the plate in an acid bath. The acid reacts with the metal exposed by the drawing and not through the resin. L2 P LS **Visual-Spatial**

Mini LAB

Purpose to observe how an indicator changes color as a base is neutralized L2 ELL
LS **Kinesthetic**

Materials water, 250-mL beaker, 1 *M* HCl, universal indicator, antacid tablets, graduated cylinder, dropper

Teaching Strategy A blue or violet color may occur when the HCl is added, depending on the brand of antacid used.

Analysis

1. The color changed from red to orange to yellow to green.
2. The base neutralized the HCl, changing the color of the indicator.

Assessment

Portfolio Have students write complete lab reports of this activity in their Science Journals. Encourage them to include both diagrams and written descriptions. Make sure they include the materials used, the procedure, and all of their observations. Use **Performance Assessment in the Science Classroom**, p. 119. P L2

Quick Demo

Test a Base

Materials drain cleaner, distilled water, litmus

Estimated Time 15 minutes

Procedure Add a small amount (less than 5 mL) of drain cleaner to distilled water. Test the solution with litmus to demonstrate the base properties of the cleaner. **WARNING:** *Keep the solution out of reach of students. Dispose of it properly.* L2 ELL
LS **Visual-Spatial**

Caption Answer

Figure 12 slipperiness

Mini LAB

Observing Acid Relief

WARNING: *Do not eat antacid tablets.*

Procedure

1. Add 150 mL of **water** to a **250-mL beaker.**
2. Add three drops of **1*M* HCl** and 12 drops of **universal indicator.**
3. Observe the color of the solution.
4. Add an **antacid tablet** and observe for 15 min.

Analysis

1. Describe any changes that took place in the solution.
2. Explain why these changes occurred.

Bases

You might not be as familiar with bases as you are with acids. Although you eat some foods that are acidic, you don't consume many bases. Some foods, such as egg whites, are slightly basic. Another example of basic materials is baking powder, which is found in some foods. Medicines, such as milk of magnesia and antacids, are basic, too. Still, you come in contact with many bases every day. Each time you wash your hands using soap, you are using a base. One characteristic of bases is that they feel slippery, like soapy water. Bases are important in many types of cleaning materials, as shown in **Figure 12.** Bases are important in industry, also. For example, sodium hydroxide is used in the paper industry to separate fibers of cellulose from wood pulp. The freed cellulose fibers are made into paper.

Bases can be defined in two ways. Any substance that forms hydroxide ions, OH^-, in a water solution is a **base.** In addition, a base is any substance that accepts H^+ from acids. The definitions are related, because the OH^- ions produced by some bases do accept H^+ ions.

Reading Check *What are the two definitions of a base?*

Properties of Bases One way to think about bases is as the complements, or opposites, of acids. Although acids and bases share some common features, bases have their own characteristic properties. In the pure, undissolved state, many bases are crystalline solids. In solution, bases feel slippery and have a bitter taste. Like strong acids, strong bases are corrosive, and contact with skin can result in severe burns. Taste and touch never should be used to test for the presence of a base or an acid. Finally, like acids, bases react with indicators to produce changes in color. The indicator litmus turns blue in bases.

Figure 12 Bases commonly are found in many cleaning products used around the home.
Identify *the property of bases evident in soaps.*

Teacher FYI

Base Attractions All bases attract H^+ to a pair of unshared electrons in their structures. OH^- ions have a negative charge, which helps attract positive H^+ ions. Bases containing nitrogen have an unshared pair of electrons around the nitrogen. Typically, nitrogen-containing bases are not as strong as OH^--containing bases.

Figure 13 Two applications of bases are shown here.

Aluminum hydroxide is a base used in water-treatment plants. Its sticky surface collects impurities, making them easier to filter from the water.

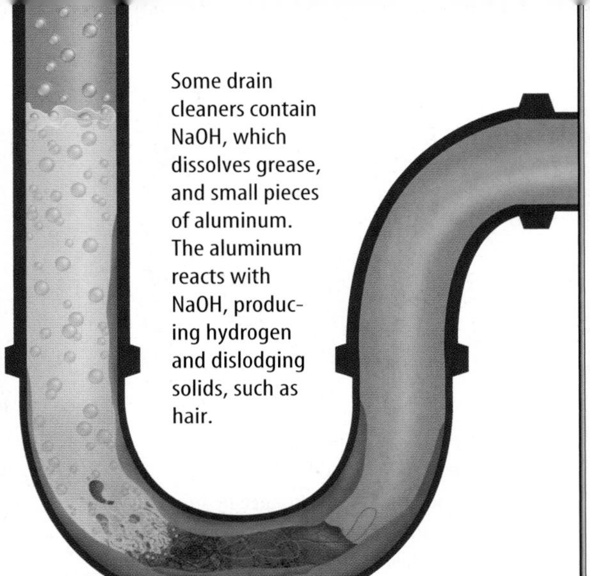

Some drain cleaners contain NaOH, which dissolves grease, and small pieces of aluminum. The aluminum reacts with NaOH, producing hydrogen and dislodging solids, such as hair.

Common Bases You probably are familiar with many common bases because they are found in cleaning products used in the home. These and some other bases are shown in **Table 4,** which also includes their uses and some information about them. **Figure 13** shows two uses of bases that you might not be familiar with.

Table 4 Common Bases and Their Uses

Name, Formula	Use	Other Information
Aluminum hydroxide, $Al(OH)_3$	Color-fast fabrics, antacid, water purification as shown in **Figure 13**	Sticky gel that collects suspended clay and dirt particles on its surface
Calcium hydroxide, $Ca(OH)_2$	Leather-making, mortar and plaster, to lessen acidity of soil	Called caustic lime
Magnesium hydroxide, $Mg(OH)_2$	Laxative, antacid	Called milk of magnesia when in water
Sodium hydroxide, NaOH	To make soap, oven cleaner, drain cleaner, textiles, and paper	Called lye and caustic soda; generates heat (exothermic) when combined with water, reacts with metals to form hydrogen
Ammonia, NH_3	Cleaners, fertilizer, to make rayon and nylon	Irritating odor that is damaging to nasal passages and lungs

IDENTIFYING Misconceptions

OH Bases Most of the bases examined in this section have OH bonded to a metal. Students may have seen the OH symbols connected to other compounds called alcohols. This does not make alcohols fit the definition of a base. The —OH in an alcohol is called a hydroxyl group and is not the same thing as the hydroxide ion, OH^-.

Fun Fact

The formula for caffeine, the stimulant found in coffee, tea, and many soft drinks, is $C_8H_{10}N_4O_2$. Caffeine is a weak acid with a pH of 6.9. Caffeinated beverages may stimulate the secretion of stomach acid, which may worsen ulcer symptoms.

Use an Analogy

Football Pass In a football game, a quarterback holding the ball cannot complete a pass unless a receiver catches the ball. An H^+ ion from an acid is like the football. The quarterback (the acid) must have a receiver (the base) to receive the football (the H^+ ion) to complete the pass (the reaction between the acid and the base). This could be demonstrated in class with a foam football labeled H^+. L1 ELL IN **Kinesthetic**

Differentiated Instruction

Challenge Amino acids make up the building blocks of proteins. Write out the structure of the amino acid glycine, NH_2CH_2 COOH. Ask students to identify the areas of the molecule that cause it to have acidic properties. The H at the end of COOH can be donated to produce H^+ ions. Also ask students to look for another area that allows it to have base properties. The N atom has unshared electrons that can attract and accept H^+ ions, as bases do. L3 IN **Logical-Mathematical**

INTEGRATE Life Science

Acidic Stings HCOOH, or formic acid, has the simplest structure of the organic acids. One of the first preparations of this acid included the crushing and heating of ants and the recovery of the vapor that contained the acid.

Discussion

Natural Acids and Bases Talk about other examples of acids and bases in nature. Students may not know of specific examples, but the discussion could focus on logical possibilities such as defense mechanisms.

Make a Model

Ionization To illustrate the dissociation that takes place when an acid is dissolved in water, have students hold a capped ink pen in the right hand. On your signal, have them use the left hand to remove the cap and cover it in that hand. In this model, water (the left hand) detaches H^+ (the pen cap) from an acid (the pen) and surrounds and holds it. This same process takes place with billions of acid molecules as they dissociate in water. L1 ELL IN **Kinesthetic**

Visual Learning

Figure 14 With students, review the two parts of the illustration. Draw a diagram on the chalkboard showing how hydrogen chloride gas molecules form hydronium ions in water. Draw a similar diagram for formic acid. L2 IN **Visual-Spatial**

Caption Answer

Figure 15 It would speed it up by providing more surface area, allowing more of the antacid to come in contact quickly with stomach acid.

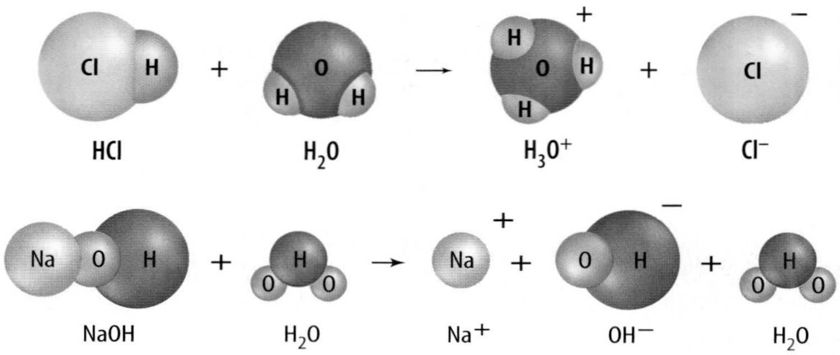

When sodium hydroxide dissolves in water, a sodium ion and a hydroxide ion are produced.

When hydrogen chloride dissolves in water, a hydronium ion and a chloride ion are produced.

Figure 14 When acids and bases are dissolved in water, they produce ions. Acids produce hydronium ions in water. Bases produce hydroxide ions in water.

INTEGRATE Life Science

Acidic Stings Some ants add sting to their bite by injecting a solution of formic acid. In fact, formic acid was named for ants, which make up the genus *Formica.* Still, ants are considered tasty treats by many animals. For example, one woodpecker called a flicker has saliva that is basic enough to take the sting out of ants. Research the chemical formula and physical properties of formic acid.

Solutions of Acids and Bases

Many of the products that rely on the chemistry of acids and bases are solutions, such as the cleaning products and food products mentioned previously. Because of its polarity, water is the main solvent in these cleaning products.

Dissociation of Acids You have learned that substances such as HCl, HNO_3, and H_2SO_4 are acids because of their ability to produce hydrogen ions (H^+) in water. When an acid dissolves in water, the negative areas of nearby water molecules attract the positive hydrogen in the acid. The acid dissociates into ions and the hydrogen atom combines with a water molecule to form hydronium ions (H_3O^+). Dissociation is the process in which an ionic solid separates into its positive and negative ions. An acid can more accurately be described as a compound that produces hydronium ions when dissolved in water, as shown in **Figure 14.**

Dissociation of Bases Compounds that can form hydroxide ions (OH^-) in water are classified as bases. If you look at **Table 4,** you will find that most of the substances listed contain –OH in their formulas. When bases that contain –OH dissolve in water, the negative areas of nearby water molecules attract the positive ion in the base. The positive areas of nearby water molecules attract the –OH of the base. The base dissociates into a positive ion and a negative ion—a hydroxide ion (OH–). This process also is shown in **Figure 14.** Unlike in acid dissociation, water molecules do not combine with the ions formed from the base.

Reading Check *What ions form when acids and bases dissolve in water?*

Science Journal

Oil of Vitriol Sulfate compounds used to be called vitriols because the compounds look glassy. The old name for sulfuric acid was *oil of vitriol.* The words *vitriol* and *vitriolic* have taken on broader meanings. Ask students to write the meaning of *vitriol* in their Science Journals and explain how it is connected to sulfuric acid. *Vitriol* means "something caustic," or "virulence of feeling or speech." L2

Differentiated Instruction

Visually Impaired **Figure 14** is referred to several times in the teaching suggestions; therefore, this figure should be made accessible to visually impaired students. Bring models of the molecules in the figure and have sighted students work with visually impaired students to clarify the structures.

768 CHAPTER 24 Solutions, Acids, and Bases

Neutralization Advertisements for antacids claim that these products neutralize the excess stomach acid that causes indigestion. Normally, gastric juice is acidic. Too much acid can produce discomfort. Antacids contain bases or other compounds containing sodium, calcium, magnesium, or aluminum that react with acids to lower acid concentration. **Figure 15** shows what happens when you ingest an antacid tablet containing sodium bicarbonate, $NaHCO_3$. The acid (HCl) is neutralized by the base ($NaHCO_3$).

Neutralization is a chemical reaction between an acid and a base that takes place in a water solution. When HCl is neutralized by NaOH, hydronium ions from the acid combine with hydroxide ions from the base to produce water.

$$H_3O^+(aq) + OH^- \rightarrow 2H_2O(l)$$

Acid-Base Reactions The following general equation represents acid-base reactions in water. A few common salts are listed in **Table 5.**

Acid-Base Reactions

acid + base → salt + water

Salt Formation The acid-base equation accounts for only half of the ions in the solution. The remaining ions react to form a salt. A salt is a compound formed when the negative ions from an acid combine with the positive ions from a base. In the reaction between HCl and NaOH, the salt formed in water solution is sodium chloride.

$$Na^+(aq) + Cl^-(aq) \rightarrow NaCl(aq)$$

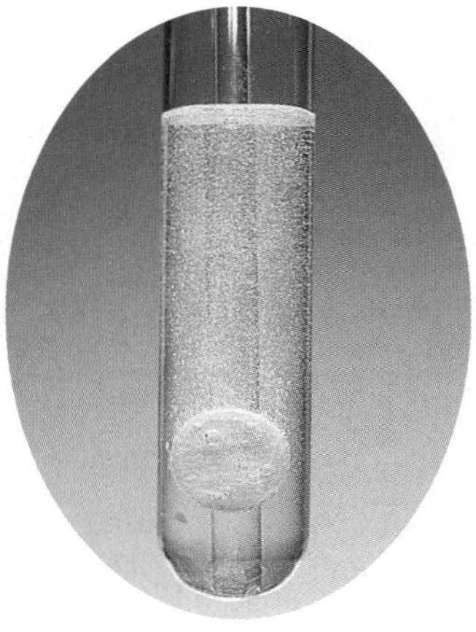

Figure 15 An antacid tablet reacts in your stomach much as it does in this dilute HCl. Many antacid tablets are made to be chewed before they are swallowed. **Explain** *how chewing the tablet would affect the rate of the reaction.*

Table 5 Some Common Salts and Their Uses

Name, Formula	Common Name	Uses
Sodium chloride, NaCl	Salt	Food, manufacture of chemicals
Sodium hydrogen carbonate, $NaHCO_3$	Sodium bicarbonate, baking soda	Food, antacids
Calcium carbonate, $CaCO_3$	Calcite, chalk	Manufacture of paint and rubber tires

Quick Demo
Produce a Salt

Materials zinc metal piece, HCl (5 mL, 1*M*), 2 test tubes, wood splint

Estimated Time 15 minutes

Procedure Place a pea-size piece of zinc metal in a medium-sized test tube. Add about 5 mL of 0.1*M* HCl to the zinc metal. **WARNING:** *Handle HCl with care. Wear goggles, an apron, and gloves.* Using a test-tube holder, invert another test tube over the first to collect the gas (H_2) that is generated. Then bring a glowing splint near the mouth of the second tube. The hydrogen will give a small "bark" as the hydrogen and oxygen react. **WARNING:** *Wear goggles, ensure that students wear goggles, and demonstrate a safe distance from students.* Ask students to balance the equation and name the salt that is produced. $Zn + 2HCl \rightarrow H_2 + ZnCl_2$; zinc chloride L3

LS **Logical-Mathematical**

Discussion

Base/Acid Prediction Ask students to use the information in **Table 3** to predict the acid and base that most likely produced each salt.

NaCl: NaOH; HCl
$NaHCO_3$: NaOH; H_2CO_3
$CaCO_3$: $Ca(OH)_2$; H_2CO_3
KNO_3: KOH; HNO_3
K_2CO_3: KOH; H_2CO_3
Na_3PO_4: NaOH; H_3PO_4
NH_4Cl: NH_3; HCl

Science Journal

Epsom Salt Another salt students may know is Epsom salt. Have them find out the chemical formula for Epsom salt, what it is used for, and how it was named. Have them record their findings in their Science Journals. Epsom salt is $MgSO_4 \cdot 7H_2O$. It is used for soaking bruises and sprains. It was named after the mineral-rich waters of Epsom, England, which contained magnesium sulfate. L2 LS **Linguistic**

Differentiated Instruction

Learning Disabled React a small amount of dilute HCl with the same amount of dilute NaOH. Gently boil away the liquid. Collect the white residue and show the resulting salt (NaCl) of the neutralization reaction. **WARNING:** *Do not taste the salt as it may contain impurities.* L1 LS **Visual-Spatial**

Figure 16 Ammonia reacts with water to produce some hydroxide ions; therefore, it is a base.

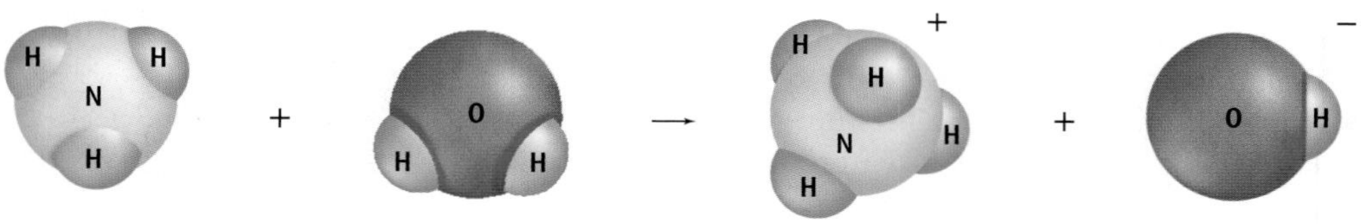

Science Online

Topic: Cleaner Chemistry
Visit gpescience.com for Web links to information about the dangers of mixing ammonia cleaners with chlorine or hydrochloric acid cleaners.

Activity Visit the cleaning products and laundry sections of the grocery store. Read the labels on several products. Make a list of products that include warnings on the labels and those that do not. Share your findings with the class.

An Exception Ammonia is a base that does not contain −OH. In a water solution, dissociation takes place when the ammonia molecule attracts a hydrogen ion from a water molecule, forming an ammonium ion (NH_4^+). This leaves a hydroxide ion (OH^-), as shown in **Figure 16.**

Reading Check *How does ammonia react in a water solution?*

Ammonia is a common household cleaner. However, products containing ammonia never should be used with other cleaners that contain chlorine or sodium hypochlorite, such as some bathroom toilet-bowl cleaners and bleach. A reaction between sodium hypochlorite and ammonia produces the toxic gases hydrazine and chloramine. Breathing these gases can severely damage lung tissues and cause death.

The reactions of acids and bases are important to the chemistry of living systems, the environment, and many industrial processes.

section 3 review

Summary

Acids

- Acids, when dissolved in water, release H^+, which forms hydronium ions (H_3O^+).
- Acids are sour tasting, corrosive, and reactive with indicators.

Bases

- Bases, when dissolved in water, form OH^-.
- Bases are slippery, have a bitter taste, are corrosive, and are reactive with indicators.

Solutions of Acids and Bases

- The polar nature of water allows acids and bases to dissolve in water.
- Dissociation is the separation of substances, such as acids and bases, into ions in water.

Self Check

1. **Identify** three important acids and three important bases and describe their uses.
2. **Describe** an indicator.
3. **Predict** what metallic compound forms when sulfuric acid reacts with magnesium metal.
4. **Infer** If an acid donates H^+ and a base produces OH^-, what compound is likely to be produced when acids react with bases?
5. **Think Critically** Vinegar contains acetic acid, CH_3COOH. What salt is formed if acetic acid reacts with sodium hydroxide, NaOH?

Applying Math

6. **Calculate** the molecular weight of acetylsalicylic acid, $C_9H_8O_4$.

More Section Review gpescience.com

Reading Check

Answer NH_3 removes H^+ from water to leave behind OH^- ions and form NH_4^+.

Post Reading

Science Journal In their Science Journals have students summarize the process by which bases neutralize acids. Tell students to look back in the text to ensure accuracy. Remind students that rereading is often essential for comprehension. Many people must look at technical texts several times to understand what they have read.

3 Assess

DAILY INTERVENTION

Check for Understanding

Linguistic Conduct a discussion about the properties of acids and bases by going around the room and having each student make a true statement about what they've learned in this section. L2

Reteach

Litmus Test Provide several unlabeled dilute solutions of acids and bases. Give students litmus paper to test the solutions to determine which are acids and which are bases. Litmus is red in an acid and blue in a base. L2 LS **Visual-Spatial**

Assessment

Performance Ask students to write the balanced chemical equation for the reaction of ammonium hydroxide, NH_4OH with hydrogen chloride, HCl. $NH_4OH + HCl \rightarrow NH_4Cl + H_2O$ L2

section 3 review

1. Accept all reasonable responses.
2. an organic compound that changes color in acid or base
3. magnesium sulfate
4. HOH, which is water
5. sodium acetate
6. 180.16

section 4

Strength of Acids and Bases

Reading Guide

What You'll Learn
- **Determine** what is responsible for the strength of an acid or a base.
- **Compare and contrast** strength and concentration.
- **Examine** the relationship between pH and acid or base strength.
- **Examine** electrical conductivity.

Why It's Important
Understanding the strength of acids and bases helps you use them safely.

Review Vocabulary
acid strength: the ability of an acid to dissociate completely

New Vocabulary
- strong acid
- weak acid
- strong base
- weak base
- pH

Strong and Weak Acids and Bases

Some acids must be handled with great care. For example, sulfuric acid found in car batteries can burn your skin, yet you drink acids such as citric acid in orange juice. Obviously, some acids are stronger than others. One measure of acid strength is the ability to dissociate in solution.

The strength of an acid or base depends on how many acid or base particles dissociate into ions in water. When a **strong acid** dissolves in water, almost 100 percent of the acid molecules dissociate into ions. HCl, HNO_3, and H_2SO_4 are examples of strong acids. When a **weak acid** dissolves in water, only a small fraction of the acid molecules dissociates into ions. Acetic acid and carbonic acid are examples of weak acids.

Ions in solution can conduct an electric current are called electrolytes. The more ions a solution contains, the more current it can conduct. The ability of a solution to conduct a current can be demonstrated using a lightbulb connected to a battery with leads placed in the solution, as shown in **Figure 17.** The strong acid solution conducts more current. The weak acid solution does not conduct as much current as a strong acid solution.

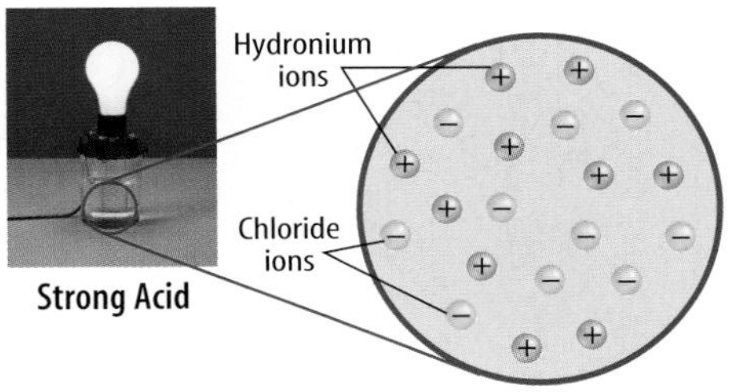

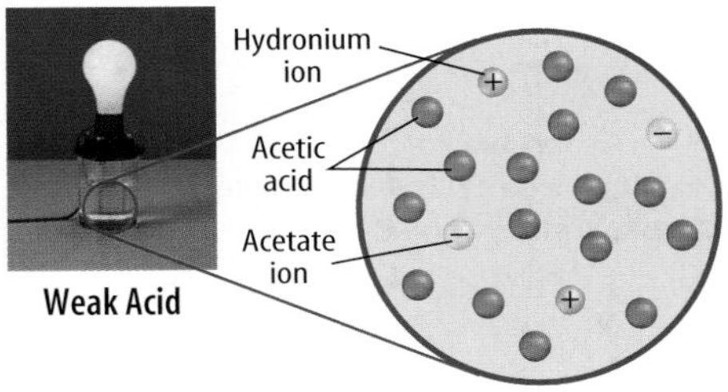

Figure 17 HCl is a strong acid. The bulb burns brightly. Acetic acid is a weak acid. The bulb is dimmer.

Section 4 Resource Manager

Chapter *Fast File* Resources
- Transparency Activity, p. 45
- Directed Reading for Content Mastery, p. 20
- Enrichment, p. 31
- Lab Activity, pp. 9–11
- Reinforcement, p. 28
- Lab Worksheet, pp. 5–6

Physical Science Critical Thinking/Problem Solving, p. 16

1 Motivate

INTERACTIVE CHALKBOARD PowerPoint® Presentations An editable Microsoft® PowerPoint® presentation is available on **Interactive Chalkboard** CD-ROM.

Bellringer

Section Focus Transparencies also are available on the Interactive Chalkboard CD-ROM. L2 ELL

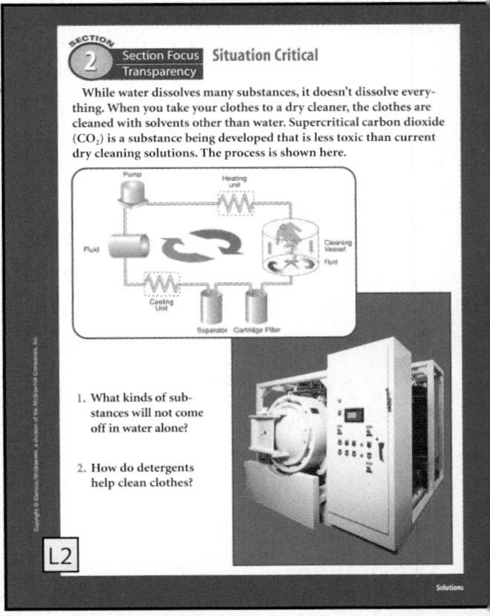
SECTION 2 Section Focus Transparency **Situation Critical**

While water dissolves many substances, it doesn't dissolve everything. When you take your clothes to a dry cleaner, the clothes are cleaned with solvents other than water. Supercritical carbon dioxide (CO_2) is a substance being developed that is less toxic than current dry cleaning solutions. The process is shown here.

1. What kinds of substances will not come off in water alone?
2. How do detergents help clean clothes?

L2

Solutions

Reading Preview

Tie to Prior Knowledge

Acid Strength Ask students to name acids they have encountered that weren't harmful and acids that were. Possible answers: Fruit juices with weak acids are not harmful; battery acid is harmful. Tell students that in this section, they will learn why some acids are stronger than others. L2

Activate Background Knowledge Tell students that pH is a measurement to rate the strength of acids and bases, indicating "positive hydrogen ions" or "H^+ ions." Tell them that swimming pool and spa owners must test their water to find out if it is too acidic or basic and then adjust the water with chemicals. Ask students why it is important to have the proper ph.

2 Teach

Fun Fact

Hydrochloric acid is essential for digestion and is secreted by the lining of the stomach in quantities of 1.2 to 1.5 L per day.

IDENTIFYING Misconceptions

Strong Disconnect In connection with acid, the word *strong* means that the acid forms ions easily. Some students may confuse the concept, thinking it is a contradiction to use the word *strong* with something that comes apart easily.

Use Science Words

Word Usage Have students complete the following sentence: A __________ will ionize only to a small extent because its molecules have a strong hold on their H atoms. weak acid L1 ELL LS

Reading Strategy

Paired Reading Allow partners to read the text about strong and weak acids and bases. After reading, one partner should explain the reaction equation formula while showing the change in units on each side. The other partner should check the explanation with the text. Have students alternate roles as they read and explain the four paragraphs and equations.

Figure 18 You can have a dilute solution of a strong acid and a concentrated solution of a weak acid.

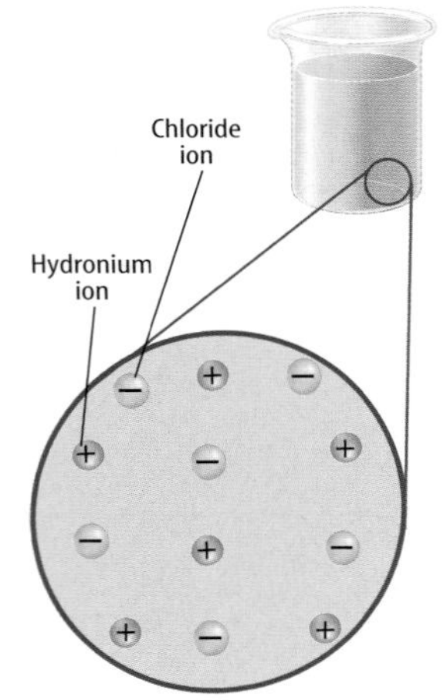

This shows a dilute solution of HCl.

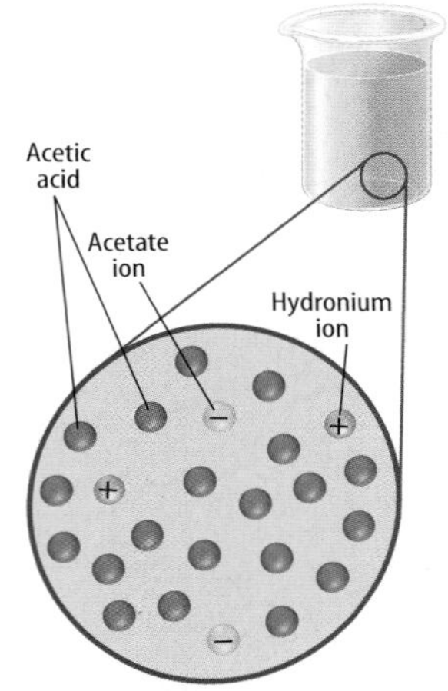

This shows a concentrated solution of acetic acid.

Strong and Weak Acids Equations describing dissociation are written in two ways. In strong acids, such as HCl, nearly all the acid dissociates. This is shown by writing the equation using a single arrow pointing toward the ions that are formed.

$$HCl(g) + H_2O(l) \rightarrow H_3O^+(aq) + Cl^-(aq)$$

Almost 100 percent of the particles in solution are H_3O^+ and Cl^- ions, and only a negligible number of HCl molecules are present.

Equations describing the dissociation of weak acids, such as acetic acid, are written using double arrows pointing in opposite directions. This means that only some of the CH_3COOH dissociates and the reaction does not go to completion.

$$CH_3COOH(aq) + H_2O(l) \rightleftharpoons H_3O^+(aq) + CH_3COO^-(aq)$$

In an acetic acid solution, most of the particles are CH_3COOH molecules, and only a few CH_3COO^- and H^+ ions are in solution.

Strong and Weak Bases Remember that many bases are ionic compounds that dissociate to produce ions when they dissolve. A **strong base** dissociates completely in solution. The following equation shows the dissociation of sodium hydroxide, a strong base.

$$NaOH(s) + H_2O(l) \rightarrow Na^+(aq) + OH^-(aq)$$

The dissociation of ammonia, which is a weak base, is shown using double arrows to indicate that not all the ammonia dissociates. A **weak base** is one that does not dissociate completely.

$$NH_3(aq) + H_2O(l) \rightleftharpoons NH_4^+(aq) + OH^-(aq)$$

Because ammonia produces only a few ions and most of the ammonia remains in the form of NH_3, ammonia is a weak base.

Strength and Concentration Sometimes, when talking about acids and bases, the terms *strength* and *concentration* can be confused. The terms *strong* and *weak* are used to classify acids and bases. The terms refer to the ease with which an acid or base dissociates in solution. *Strong* acids and bases dissociate completely; *weak* acids and bases dissociate only partially. In contrast, the terms *dilute* and *concentrated* are used to indicate the concentration of a solution, which is the amount of acid or base dissolved in the solution. It is possible to have dilute solutions of strong acids and bases and concentrated solutions of weak acids and bases, as shown in **Figure 18.**

Differentiated Instruction

English-Language Learners The difference between ionization and dissociation is subtle. Review these terms by stressing that ionization happens when nonionic substances break apart, interact with water, and produce ions. Dissociation is the separation of ionic substances, such as a salt. Use a model to visually represent these concepts.

Teacher FYI

Logarithmic Value The value of pH is based on a logarithmic scale. Each unit increment is a tenfold change in hydrogen ion concentration. So, if one solution has a pH of 3 and another has a pH of 2, the second is 10 times more acidic than the first.

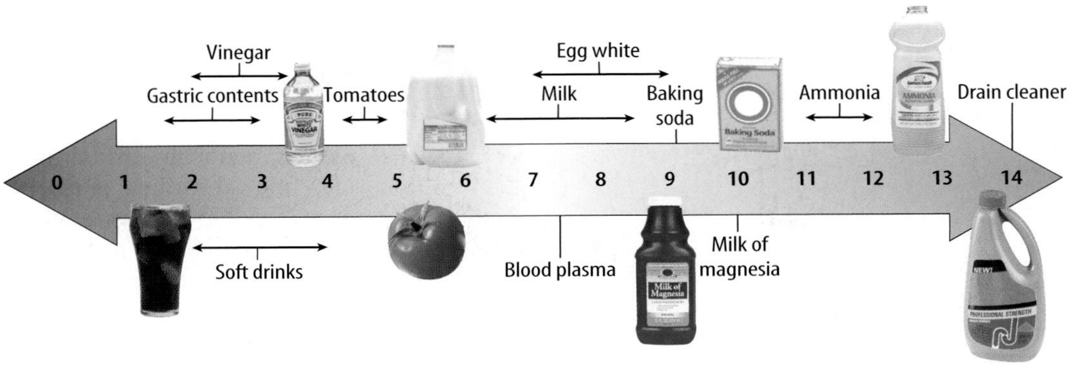

Figure 19 The pH scale helps classify solutions as acidic or basic.

pH of a Solution

If you have a swimming pool or keep tropical fish, you know that the pH of the water must be controlled. Also, many shampoo products claim to control pH, making them suitable for your type of hair. The **pH** of a solution is a measure of the concentration of H^+ ions in it. The greater the H^+ concentration is, the lower the pH is and the more acidic the solution is. The pH measures how acidic or basic a solution is. To indicate pH, a scale ranging from 0 to 14 has been devised, as shown in **Figure 19.**

Reading Check *If a solution has a pH of 8.5, does it have more hydroxide ions or hydronium ions?*

As the scale shows, solutions with a pH lower than 7 are described as acidic, and the lower the value is, the more acidic the solution is. Solutions with a pH greater than 7 are basic, and the higher the pH is, the more basic the solution is. A solution with a pH of exactly 7 indicates that the concentrations of H^+ ions and OH^- ions are equal. These solutions are considered neutral. Pure water at 25°C has a pH of 7.

One way to determine pH is by using indicator paper. This paper undergoes a color change in the presence of H_3O^+ ions and OH^- ions in solution. The final color of the pH paper is matched with colors in a chart to find the pH, as shown in **Figure 20.** Is this an accurate way to determine pH?

An instrument called a pH meter is another tool to determine the pH of a solution. This meter is operated by immersing the electrode in the solution to be tested and reading the dial. Small, battery-operated pH meters with digital readouts, as shown in **Figure 20,** are precise and convenient for use outside the laboratory when testing the pH of soils and streams.

Figure 20 The pH of a sample can be measured in several ways. Indicator paper gives an approximate value quickly, however, a pH meter is quick and more precise.

Activity

Measure pH Provide samples, other than those shown in **Figure 19,** with which students can measure pH using universal pH paper. Examples may include spoiled milk, lemon juice, soap solutions, and dissolved antacids. L2 ELL IN **Visual-Spatial**

Quick Demo

Examine pH Changes

Materials indicator paper (litmus or universal), vinegar, milk of magnesia, pH meter

Estimated Time 20 minutes

Procedure Use litmus paper or universal indicator paper to show that vinegar has an acidic pH value. Then add a small amount of milk of magnesia to the vinegar. Check the pH again to see whether it has changed. As the milk of magnesia is added, OH^- is brought into the solution. OH^- ions react with the H_3O^+ ions, so the pH should rise. Continue adding milk of magnesia until this effect is noticed on the pH indicator. If one is available, do this demonstration with a pH meter. L2 ELL IN **Visual-Spatial**

Discussion

Indicators and pH Ask students to think of a reason why someone would use an indicator paper instead of a pH meter to obtain a pH value. Indicator paper may be used when controlling costs is an issue. A box of indicator paper is less expensive than a pH meter.

Reading Check

Answer hydroxide ions

Differentiated Instruction

Challenge Have students write chemical equations that show HCO_3^- acting to neutralize the addition of OH^- ions and the addition of H^+ ions. This would show how one of the blood buffers works. $HCO_3^- + OH^- \rightarrow H_2O + CO_3^{2-}$; $HCO_3^- + H^+ \rightarrow H_2CO_3$ L3 IN **Logical-Mathematical**

Science Journal

Sour Milk Have students describe the changes in pH that occur in milk as it spoils. They may need to examine the process in a nutrition reference or biology source. Lactose, commonly called milk sugar, is changed through bacterial action into lactic acid. This change lowers the pH of the solution. L2 IN **Logical-Mathematical**

Reading Check

Answer Buffers are solutions containing ions that react with acids or bases to minimize their effects. This is important because our blood needs to maintain a pH of about 7.4.

Post Reading

Draw Conclusions Have students explain why symbols for elements and formulas are used to show chemical reactions. What actions do single arrows and double arrows indicate? Point out that people of all languages can understand the notations. How are letters in words and symbols similar?

3 Assess

DAILY INTERVENTION

Check for Understanding

Visual-Spatial Bring in a can of frozen orange juice and a gallon container. Explain to the students that the orange juice in the can is a concentrated form, then add water and explain that the orange juice is now diluted.

Reteach

Acid Strength Place a small piece of magnesium ribbon in two seperate Petri dishes. In the first one, add a few drops of 1*M* HCl. In the second, add a few drops of acetic acid. **WARNING:** *Wear goggles, an apron, and gloves when working with HCl.* Ask which is a strong acid. The HCl is a strong acid because it reacts with magnesium to produce more hydrogen gas. L2 LS **Visual-Spatial**

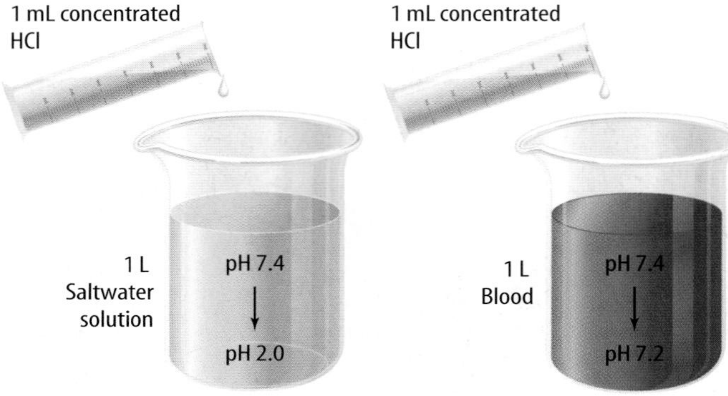

Figure 21 This experiment shows how well blood plasma acts as a buffer. Adding 1 mL of concentrated HCl to 1 L of saltwater solution changes the pH from 7.4 to 2.0. Adding the same amount of concentrated HCl to 1 L of blood plasma changes the pH from 7.4 to 7.2.

Blood pH

INTEGRATE Life Science

Your blood circulates throughout your body carrying oxygen, removing carbon dioxide, and absorbing nutrients from food that you have eaten. In order to carry out its many functions properly, the pH of blood must remain between 7.0 and 7.8. The main reason for this is that some enzymes cannot work outside this pH range. An enzyme is a protein molecule that acts as a catalyst for many reactions in the body. Yet you can eat foods that are acidic without changing the pH of your blood. How can this be? The answer is that your blood contains compounds called buffers that enable small amounts of acids or bases to be absorbed without harmful effects.

Buffers are solutions containing ions that react with additional acids or bases to minimize their effects on pH. One buffer system in blood involves bicarbonate ions, HCO_3^-. Because of these buffer systems, small amounts of even concentrated acid will not change pH much, as shown in **Figure 21.** Buffers help keep your blood close to a nearly constant pH of 7.4.

Reading Check *What are buffers and how are they important for health?*

section 4 review

Summary

Strong and Weak Acids and Bases

- When strong acids dissolve in water, nearly all the acid particles dissociate into ions. When weak acids dissolve in water, few particles dissociate.
- When strong bases dissolve in water, nearly all base particles dissociate. When weak bases dissove, only a few particles dissociate.
- Ions in solution can conduct electricity.
- Strength refers to the ability of an acid or base to dissociate in water; concentration refers to how much acid or base is in solution.

pH of a Solution

- pH describes a substance as acidic or basic.
- Buffers are substances that minimize the effects of an acid or base on pH.

Self Check

1. **Describe** what determines the strength of an acid. A base?
2. **Explain** how to make a dilute solution of a strong acid.
3. **Explain** how electricity can be conducted by solutions.
4. **Describe** pH values of 9.1, 1.2, and 5.7 as basic, acidic, or very acidic.
5. **Think Critically** The proper pH range for a swimming pool is between 7.2 and 7.8. Some pools use two substances, $NaHCO_3$ and HCl, to maintain this range. How would you adjust the pH if you found it was 8.2? 6.9?

Applying Math

6. **Use Equations** To determine the difference in acid strength, calculate 10^n, where n = difference between pHs. How much more acidic is a solution of pH 2.4 than a solution of pH 4.4?

More Section Review gpescience.com

Assessment

Oral Sometimes soil pH must be changed to encourage plant growth. Ask students whether adding $Ca(OH)_2$, sometimes referred to as slaked lime, would raise or lower the pH of soil. The OH^- ions released by $Ca(OH)_2$ would raise the pH. Use **PASC**, p. 89. L2

section 4 review

1. The strength of an acid is determined by its ability to produce H^+ ions in solution. The strength of a base is determined by its ability to produce OH^- ions in solution.
2. You can dilute hydrochloric acid, a strong acid, by adding a small amount of acid to a much larger amount of water.
3. An ionic compound breaks into its ions, which conduct electricity.
4. 9.1–basic; 1.2–very acidic; 5.7–acidic
5. pH of 8.2–add HCl; pH of 6.9–add $NaHCO_3$
6. $4.4 - 2.4 = 2.0$
   $10^2 = 100$

LAB

Determining Acidity

The science of acids and bases is not practiced only in high-tech laboratories by degreed scientists. You can investigate the acidic concentrations of things in your own home using a simple homemade indicator solution.

Real-World Problem

How can you tell if a substance is a strong or weak acid?

Goal

- **Determine** the relative concentrations of common acidic substances.

Materials

homemade cabbage indicator (indicates both acids and bases)
coffee filter
waxed paper
grease pencil or masking tape
teaspoons (3)
alum
cream of tartar
fruit preservative

Safety Precautions

Procedure

1. Use the grease pencil or masking tape and a pencil to label three areas on the waxed paper *alum, cream of tartar,* and *fruit preservative.* These areas should be about 8 cm apart.
2. Place approximately $\frac{1}{2}$ teaspoon of each of the three powders on the waxed paper where labeled. Use a separate teaspoon for each substance.
3. Cut three strips from the coffee filter, about 1 cm wide by 8 cm long.
4. Dip the end of one of the strips into the cabbage indicator solution, then lay the wet end on top of the alum.
5. Wet a second strip and lay it in on top of the cream of tartar.
6. Wet the third strip and lay on top of the fruit preservative.
7. Wait 5 min, then check the indicator strips and record your observations.

Conclude and Apply

1. **Determine** if all three substances were acids. Did the indicator strips turn a similar color?
2. **Explain** why each substance produced a different color.
3. **Propose** a possible rank of the concentrations.
4. **Predict** what you would have observed if you used sodium hydroxide instead of alum.

Communicating Your Data

Compare your results with other groups in the class. Discuss any differences in the results you obtained.

BENCH TESTED

Real-World Problem

Purpose Students will test several substances and rank the relative acid concentration by the color of the indicator. L2

Process Skills Lab techniques, observe, sequence, draw conclusions.

Time Required 30 minutes

Procedure

Alternative Materials Other common acidic substances such as vinegar, catsup, soda pop

Safety Precautions Have students wash hands after the experiment.

Teaching Strategies

- Prepare the indicator ahead of class according to the following recipe. Fill a glass quart jar with uncooked purple cabbage leaves that have been torn into small pieces. Heat distilled water to boiling, then fill the jar with the cabbage. Allow to cool to room temperature. Pour the cooled cabbage solution through a tea strainer into a second container and discard the cabbage leaves.
- Acids turn this indicator red, bases turn it green.

Conclude and Apply

1. yes, shades of red
2. Each substance has a different acid concentration.
3. Actual rank (most concentrated to least) is fruit preservative, cream of tartar, alum. Students may rank least to most concentrated if they interpret the colors in reverse sequence.
4. Sodium hydroxide is a base, so the indicator would turn green. Students may indicate simply a different color.

Assessment

Process This investigation indicated the relative concentration of several acids. Using these results, can you draw conclusions about the strength of the acids? No reliable conclusion can be made. Concentration and strength are independent of each other. L2

Communicating Your Data

Conduct a discussion of the results and possible differences in outcomes. L2

BENCH TESTED

Real-World Problem

Purpose Students compare the solubility of a solute at various temperatures. L2 ELL

LS **Logical-Mathematical**

Process Skills measure, use numbers, communicate, make and use graphs, make and use tables, infer

Time Required 40 minutes

Procedure

Alternate Materials In addition to sugar, other solutes such as $CuSO_4$ (**WARNING:** *toxic*) or KBr could be used.

Safety Precautions Students should use test tube holders when handling hot test tubes. They should not stir solutions with a thermometer.

Teaching Strategy Keep the hot plate setting low so the temperature changes will be slow.

Tie to Prior Knowledge Remind students about dissolving sugar in hot tea versus cold tea.

Troubleshooting Experiment with making the copper stirrers before the lab. Coil the copper wire around a pencil and check to be sure the coil fits into the test tubes being used.

LAB

Saturated Solutions

Goal

- **Observe** the effects of temperature on the amount of solute that dissolves.

Materials

distilled water at room temperature
large test tubes
Celsius thermometer
table sugar
copper wire stirrer, bent into a spiral
test-tube holder
graduated cylinder (25-mL)
beaker (250-mL) with 150 mL of water
electric hot plate
test-tube rack
ring stand

Safety Precautions

WARNING: *Do NOT touch the test tubes or hot-plate surface when hot plate is turned on or cooling down. When heating a solution in a test tube, keep it pointed away from yourself and others. Do NOT remove goggles until cleanup, including washing hands, is completed.*

Real-World Problem

Two major factors to consider when you are dissolving a solute in water are temperature and the ratio of solute to solvent. What happens to a solution as the temperature changes? How does solubility change as temperature is increased? To be able to draw conclusions about the effect of temperature, you must keep other variables constant. For example, you must be sure to stir each solution in a similar manner.

Procedure

1. Place 20 mL of distilled water in a test tube. Add 30 g of sugar.
2. Stir. Does the sugar dissolve?
3. If it dissolves completely, add another 5 g of sugar to the test tube. Does it dissolve?
4. Continue adding 5-g amounts of sugar until no more sugar dissolves.
5. Now place the beaker of water on the hot plate and hang the thermometer from the ring stand so that the bulb is immersed about halfway into the beaker, making sure it does not touch the sides or bottom. Record the starting temperature.

Alternative Inquiry Lab

Change Variables Make this Lab an Inquiry Lab by asking students what they think will happen if two or more different kinds of solutes are dissolved in a solvent? In other words, how will this experiment result if multiple solutes are dissolved in the water? Let the students investigate solutes of their choosing with safety guidance from the teacher. Some students may want to go further and investigate solute solubility in different solvents. Have students record their alternative activities and results in their Science Journals. L2

Using Scientific Methods

6. Using a test-tube holder, place the test tube into the water.
7. Gradually increase the temperature of the hot plate while stirring the solution in the test tube, until all the sugar dissolves.
8. Note the temperature at which this happens.
9. Add another 5 g of sugar and continue. Note the temperature at which this additional sugar dissolves.
10. Continue in this manner until you have at least four data points. Note the total amount of sugar that has dissolved. Record your data in the data table.

Analyze Your Data

1. **Graph** your results using a line graph. Plot grams of solute per 20 g of water on the *y*-axis and plot temperature on the *x*-axis.
2. **Interpret Data** Using your graph, estimate the solubility of sugar at 100°C and at 0°C, the boiling and freezing point of water, respectively.

Dissolving Sugar in Water

Temperature	Total Grams of Sugar Dissolved
20°C–25°C	about 40 g
30°C–35°C	about 45 g
50°C	about 50 g
55°C–60°C	about 55 g

Conclude and Apply

1. **Explain** how the saturation change as the temperature was increased.
2. **Compare** your results with the data in **Table 2.**

Communicating Your Data

Compare your results with those of other groups and discuss any differences noted. Why might these differences have occurred? **For more help, refer to the Science Skill Handbook.**

Analyze Your Data

Expected Outcome At higher temperatures, more sugar will dissolve.

Answers to Questions

1. Check student graphs against their results for accuracy.
2. approximately 98 g per 20 mL at 100°C and 35.8 g per 20 mL at 0°C

Error Analysis It may be difficult to tell whether the solute is dissolved when the solution is near saturation. Be sure students pause at each temperature long enough to give the solute time to dissolve. Otherwise, the amount of solute may be less than expected for saturation.

Conclude and Apply

1. The amount of solute needed to cause saturation was greater with increasing temperature steps.
2. Answers will vary.

Assessment

Oral Have students explain how the relationship between saturation and temperature shown in this activity can be used in making candy. Large amounts of sugar may be dissolved at a very high temperature, then cooled quickly to form sugar crystals used in candy making. Students should also observe how stirring influences crystal size. Use **Performance Assessment in the Science Classroom,** p. 93. L2

Communicating Your Data

Keeping the temperature constant while observing possible saturation is difficult. It is easy to go beyond the saturation level without knowing it. If the temperature increases at different rates, results will be different.

LAB 777

TIME

Content Background

Acid rain is caused by water falling through polluted air. A number of factors determine the severity of the effects of acid rain. Among them are the amount and type of chemicals contained in the clouds and the contours and composition of the soil on which it falls. For example, soils formed over limestone or chalk can tolerate much higher levels of acid than those based on granite or sandstone. The alkalinity of limestone and chalk neutralizes acids before they can have a corrosive effect. Quartzite granite does not react with the acids, leaving them in the soil to be washed into streams and lakes. There is some disagreement over the extent of the harm caused by acid rain, but not over the fact that it is harmful.

Activity

Place a clean glass container in a safe place outside prior to an expected rainstorm. Collect a rain sample and check the pH using pH paper. Have students find the position of the pH of rainwater on the chart in **Figure 19.** L2 LS **Kinesthetic**

Investigate the Issue

Research the patterns of acid rain across the country and the presumed sources. Note them on a national map and use it to discuss how the local area is affected. Find out whether you are in an area of acid rainfall, a source area or both. L2

TIME SCIENCE AND Society

SCIENCE ISSUES THAT AFFECT YOU!

Acid Rain

Protecting Earth from the Damaging Effects of Chemically Loaded Precipitation

Acid precipitation is rain, snow, or sleet that is more acidic than unpolluted precipitation. It's caused by the burning of fossil fuels, such as coal, oil, and natural gas. In the United States, most gasoline and electricity come from fossil fuels. People burn fossil fuels each time they drive a car, heat a building, or turn on a light.

Normally, raindrops pick up particles and natural chemicals in the air. When rain falls, it mixes with the carbon dioxide in the atmosphere, giving clean rain a slightly acidic pH of 5.6. Then, natural chemicals found in the air and soil balance out the acidity, giving most lakes and streams a pH between 6.0 and 8.0. But when pollutants are introduced, these natural bases are not strong enough to neutralize these solutions. Wind can carry this acidic moisture for hundreds of miles before it falls to Earth as acid rain.

Eating Away at History

Like all acids, acid rain can corrode, or eat away at, substances. Many historical monuments, such as the Mayan temples in Mexico and the Parthenon in Greece, have been slowly but steadily damaged by acid rain. This kind of damage can be fixed, though it costs billions of dollars to ensure that ancient monuments and buildings are not destroyed.

Some Solutions

In some countries, high acid levels in lakes and streams have been lowered by adding lime to the water. Lime, a natural base, balances out the damaging chemicals. In the United States, all new cars must have catalytic converters, which help reduce the amount of exhaust pollution that vehicles give off.

You also can make a difference. Turning off the lights when you are not using them means a power plant does not have to produce as much electricity. By carpooling, using public transportation, and walking, there is less pollution from cars. The results of all these individual actions can make a huge difference in preserving our environment.

List Go to a local park or forest. List any effects of acid rain that you see. Make a list of the things you do that use energy or cause pollution. Think about what your family can do to reduce pollution and save energy. Share your list with an adult.

TIME
For more information, visit gpescience.com

List If your local park shows symptoms of acid rain, try to determine the source of the acid rain. In many cases, the sources of acid rain are also major contributors to the local economy. Find out if the economic activity of your community produces acid rain-causing pollutants and what steps local industries and government have taken to address the problem. L3

Resources for Teachers and Students

Acid Rain, Sally Morgan, Franklin Watts: New York, 1999

Acid Rain, Louise Petheram, Bridgestone Books, Mankato, MN, 2003

Reviewing Main Ideas

Section 1 How Solutions Form

1. A solution is a mixture that has the same composition, color, density, and taste throughout.
2. The substance being dissolved is called a solute, and the substance that does the dissolving is called a solvent.
3. The rate of dissolving can be increased by stirring, increasing surface area, or increasing temperature.
4. Under similar conditions, small particles of solute dissolve faster than large particles.

Section 2 Solubility and Concentration

1. Some compounds are more soluble than others, and this can be measured.
2. *Concentrated* and *dilute* are not precise terms used to describe concentrations of solutions.
3. Concentrations can be expressed as percent by volume.
4. An unsaturated solution can dissolve more solute, while a saturated solution, such as this tea, cannot. A supersaturated solution is made by raising the temperature of a saturated solution and adding more solute. If it is cooled carefully, the supersaturated solution will retain the dissolved solute.

Section 3 Acids, Bases, and Salts

1. An acid is a substance that produces hydrogen ions, H^+, in solution. A base produces hydroxide ions, OH^-, in solution.
2. Most foods can be classified as acidic or basic. Properties of acids and bases are due, in part, to the presence of the H^+ and OH^- ions.

3. Salts form when negative ions from an acid combine with positive ions from a base.
4. Dissociation is the process where an ionic solid separates into its positive and negative ions.

Section 4 Strength of Acids and Bases

1. The strength of an acid or base is determined by how completely it forms ions when it is in solution.
2. Strength and concentration are not the same thing. Concentration involves the relative amounts of solvent and solute in a solution, whereas strength is related to the extent to which a substance dissociates.

FOLDABLES™ Use the Foldable that you made at the beginning of this chapter to help you review the characteristics of solutions, acids, and bases.

Reviewing Main Ideas

Summary statements can be used by students to review the major concepts of the chapter.

Science Online

Visit gpescience.com
More Section Review
Interactive Tutor
Vocabulary PuzzleMaker
More Chapter Review
Standardized Test Practice

Assessment Transparency

For additional assessment questions, use the *Assessment Transparency* located in the transparency book.

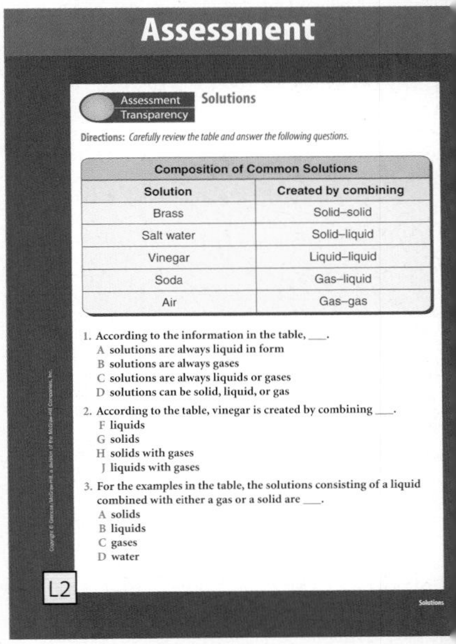

Assessment

Assessment Transparency **Solutions**

Directions: *Carefully review the table and answer the following questions.*

Composition of Common Solutions	
Solution	**Created by combining**
Brass	Solid–solid
Salt water	Solid–liquid
Vinegar	Liquid–liquid
Soda	Gas–liquid
Air	Gas–gas

1. According to the information in the table, ___.
   A solutions are always liquid in form
   B solutions are always gases
   C solutions are always liquids or gases
   D solutions can be solid, liquid, or gas
2. According to the table, vinegar is created by combining ___.
   F liquids
   G solids
   H solids with gases
   J liquids with gases
3. For the examples in the table, the solutions consisting of a liquid combined with either a gas or a solid are ___.
   A solids
   B liquids
   C gases
   D water

L2

Solutions

FOLDABLES™ Have students use their Foldables to review the content of the chapter.

Using Vocabulary

1. solute, solvent
2. acid
3. supersaturated solution
4. base
5. solubility
6. strong acid
7. pH
8. aqueous

Checking Concepts

9. B
10. C
11. B
12. A
13. C
14. D
15. A
16. C
17. B
18. C

Interpreting Graphics

19. ammonia
20. see student page.

chapter 24 Review

Using Vocabulary

acid p. 764	solution p. 752
aqueous solution p. 751	solvent p. 751
base p. 766	strong acid p. 771
concentration p. 760	strong base p. 772
indicator p. 764	supersaturated solution p. 762
pH p. 773	unsaturated solution p. 761
saturated solution p. 761	weak acid p. 771
solubility p. 759	weak base p. 772
solute p. 751	

Fill in the vocabulary word(s) that correctly completes each sentence.

1. In lemonade, sugar is the _________ and water is the _________.
2. A(n) _________ is a substance that produces hydrogen ions, H^+, in solution.
3. Adding a seed crystal may cause solute to crystallize from a(n) _________.
4. A(n) _________ produces hydroxide ions, OH^-, in solution.
5. If more of substance B dissolves in water than substance A, then substance B has a higher _________ than substance A.
6. When a(n) _________ dissolves in water, nearly all the acid molecules dissociate into ions.
7. The measure of the concentration of H^+ ions in solution is called the _________.
8. A solution in which water is the solvent is called a(n) _________ solution.

Checking Concepts

Choose the word or phrase that best answers the question.

9. What term is **NOT** appropriate to use when describing solutions?
   A) gaseous **C)** liquid
   B) heterogeneous **D)** solid

10. What is another name for sodium hydroxide (NaOH)?
   A) ammonia **C)** lye
   B) caustic lime **D)** milk of magnesia

11. When iodine is dissolved in alcohol, what term is used to describe the alcohol?
   A) alloy **C)** solution
   B) solvent **D)** solute

12. What word is used to describe a solution that is 85 percent copper and 15 percent tin?
   A) alloy **C)** saturated
   B) solvent **D)** solute

13. What is a common name for hydrochloric acid?
   A) battery acid **C)** muriatic acid
   B) citric acid **D)** vinegar

14. Which acid ionizes only partially in water?
   A) HCl **C)** HNO_3
   B) H_2SO_4 **D)** CH_3COOH

15. Carrots have a pH of 5.0. How would you describe them?
   A) acidic **C)** an indicator
   B) basic **D)** neutral

16. What is the pH of pure water at 25°C?
   A) 0 **C)** 7
   B) 5 **D)** 14

17. What can you increase to make a gas more soluble in a liquid?
   A) particle size **C)** stirring
   B) pressure **D)** temperature

18. If a solute crystallizes out of a solution when a seed crystal is added, what kind of solution is it?
   A) dilute **C)** supersaturated
   B) saturated **D)** unsaturated

Vocabulary PuzzleMaker gpescience.com

Interpreting Graphics

Use the table below to answer question 19.

19. **Explain** which substance listed in the table would be most effective for neutralizing battery acid.

pH Readings

Substance	pH
Battery acid	1.5
Lemon juice	2.5
Apple	3
Milk	6.7
Seawater	8.5
Ammonia	12

Use the table below to answer question 20.

Limits of Solubility

Compound	Type of Solution	Solubility in 100 g Water at 20°C
$CuSO_4$	saturated	32.0 g
KCl	supersaturated	38.0 g
KNO_3	saturated	31.6 g
$NaClO_3$	unsaturated	45.8 g

20. **Identify** Using the data in **Table 2,** complete the table. Use the terms *saturated, unsaturated,* and *supersaturated* to describe the type of solution.

Thinking Critically

21. **Describe** what happens to hydrogen chloride, HCl, when it is dissolved in water to form hydrochloric acid.
22. **Explain** why ammonia is considered a base, even though it contains no hydroxide ions. Is it a strong or weak base?
23. **Explain** why a concentrated acid is not necessarily a strong acid.
24. **Compare and Contrast** How would the pH of a dilute solution of HCl compare with the pH of a concentrated solution of the same acid?
25. **Explain** why the statement, "Water is the solvent in a solution," is not always true.

Applying Math

26. **Use Proportions** To make an indicator solution, a student mixes 3 mL of a concentrated solution with 97 mL of water. How much concentrate is needed to make 3 L of the indicator?

Use the graph below to answer question 27.

Temperature Effects on Solubility

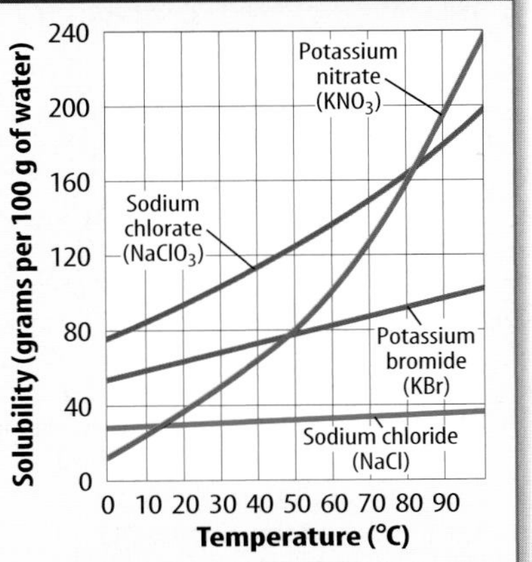

27. **Interpret Data** Determine the temperature at which a solution of 80 g of potassium nitrate (KNO_3) in 100 mL of water is saturated.
28. **Measure in SI** You dissolve 153 g of potassium nitrate in enough water to make 1 L of solution. Then, you use a graduated cylinder to measure 80 mL of solution. What mass of potassium nitrate is in the 80-mL sample?
29. **Use Numbers** How would you make a 25-percent solution by volume of an apple-juice drink?

chapter 24 Review

Thinking Critically

21. Water interacts forming H30+ and Cl- ions in the dissociation process.
22. Ammonia can accept H+ ions from water, forming NH4+ ions and thus producing OH- in water. It is a weak base.
23. A concentrated acid has a large amount of acid dissolved in a solution. A strong acid easily donates H+ ions. A concentrated acid could be a large amount of weak acid in a solution.
24. A concentrated solution of HCl has a low pH. A dilute solution has a higher pH that is still below 7.
25. Water can be the solute in a solution. For example, water may be dissolved in alcohol.

Applying Math

Math Standards

National: 1, 2, 9

26. 90 mL
27. 50°C
28. 153 g/1000 mL x 80.0 mL
    = 12.2 g KNO3 [Please stack fraction. This is a pick up of answer #23 from ch 615]
29. Place 25 mL of concentrated apple juice in 75 mL of water.

Assessment Resources

Reproducible Masters

Chapter *Fast File* Resources
- Chapter Review, pp. 39–40
- Chapter Tests, pp. 41–44
- Assessment Transparency Activity, p. 51

Glencoe Science Web site
- Chapter Review Test
- Standardized Test Practice

Glencoe Technology
- Assessment Transparency
- Exam*View*® Pro Testmaker
- MindJogger Videoquiz
- Interactive Chalkboard

Answer Sheet An answer sheet can be found at **gpescience.com**.

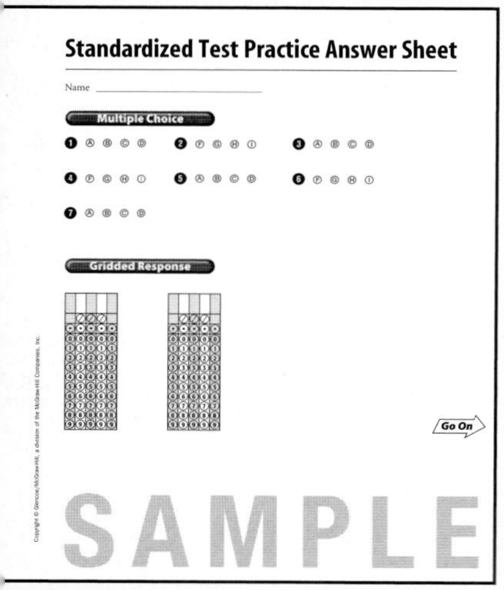

Short Response

1. D
2. D
3. B
4. C
5. A

Gridded Response

6. 32 g
7. 0.10

Record your answers on the answer sheet provided by your teacher or on a sheet of paper.

Multiple Choice

The graph below shows the solubility of various salts in water.

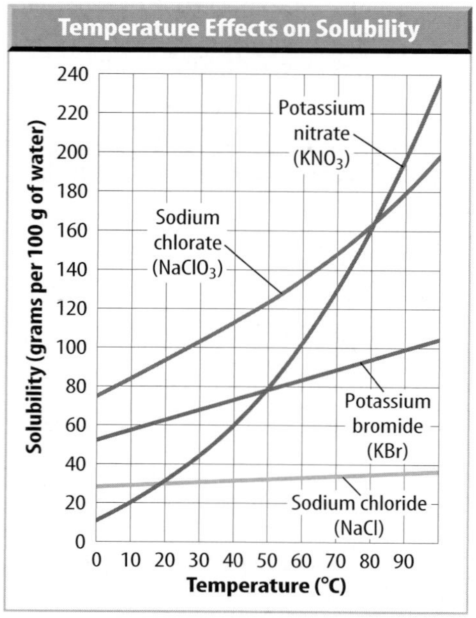

1. Which compound will make a saturated solution when added to 100 g of water?
   A. 20 g NaCl if the water is 50°C
   B. 60 g of KNO_3 if the water is 100°C
   C. 80 g $NaClO_3$ if the water is 30°C
   D. 100 g KBr if the water is 90°C

2. A label on a flask reads 130 g KNO_3/100 g of water. A thermometer reading shows a room temperature of 23°C. No crystals are seen on the bottom of the flask. How is this solution best described?
   A. concentrated
   B. dilute
   C. saturated
   D. supersaturated

3. What allows you to eat acidic foods without changing your blood pH?
   A. blood plasma
   B. buffers
   C. enzymes
   D. protein molecules

4. The following graph is a titration curve. The data indicate the changes that happened to the solution as drops of a strong base were added.

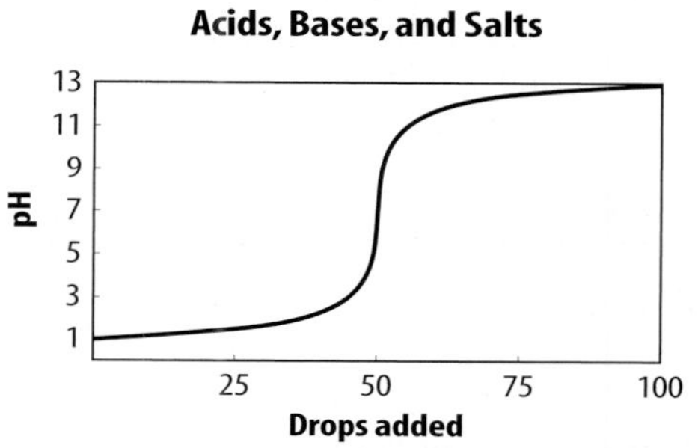

At the instant of neutralization, what is in the beaker (besides water)?
   A. acid only
   B. base only
   C. salt only
   D. equal amounts of each

5. Which chemical formula below describes a hydronium ion?
   - **A.** H_3O^+
   - **B.** OH^-
   - **C.** COOH
   - **D.** H_2O

Gridded Response

6. The solubility of potassium chloride in water is 34 g per 100 g of water at 20°C. A warm solution containing 100 g of potassium chloride in 200 g of water is cooled to 20°C. How many grams of potassium chloride will come out of solution?

7. When the pH of a solution drops from 3.0 to 1.0, the hydronium ion concentration increases by a factor of 100 fold from 0.0010. What is the concentration at pH = 1.0?

Short Response

8. The drawing below shows carbon dioxide gas dissolved in water.

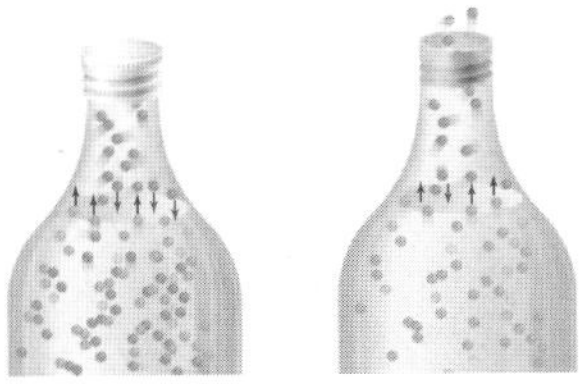

   What are two ways you could make more gas dissolve in the water?

9. Name the salt that is produced by each of the following acid-base pairs.
   $HCl + NaOH$; $HNO_3 + KOH$;
   $H_2SO_4 + Ca(OH)_2$

Extended Response

10. One of the solutions has a pH of 10, the other pH of 12. In one beaker, the bulb glows more brightly than does the other.

   Explain why the bulbs glow with different intensities. Use the words *strong* and *weak* in your answer.

11. You are given a clear water solution containing potassium nitrate. How could you determine whether the solution is unsaturated, saturated, or supersaturated?

12. Explain why a weak acid in solution has a higher pH than a strong acid of the same concentration.

Test-Taking Tip

Answer Bubbles Double-check that you are filling in the correct answer bubble for the question number you are working on.

Short Response

8. You could cool the liquid or increase the pressure of the carbon dioxide over the liquid.
9. sodium chloride; potassium nitrate; calcium sulfate

Extended Response

10. The base with the higher pH is a stronger base and therefore dissociates more completely than does the one with the lower pH. The stronger base releases more OH- ions and conducts more electricity.
11. You could add a single crystal of potassium nitrate to the solution. If the crystal dissolved, the solution is unsaturated. If the crystal sank to the bottom, the solution is saturated. If, when the crystal is added, more potassium nitrate crystallizes out, the solution was supersaturated.
12. The pH of a weak acid is higher because a weak acid produces fewer H_3O^+ ions than a strong acid at the same concentration.

Rubrics

For more help evaluating Short- and Extended-Response questions, see the rubrics on p. 9T.

chapter 25 Organizer

Section/Objectives	Standards		Labs/Features
	National	State/Local	
Chapter Opener	See pp. 16T–17T for a Key to Standards.		**Launch Lab:** The Size of a Nucleus, p. 785 **Foldables,** p. 785
Section 1 Radioactivity 1 session .5 block 1. **Describe** the structure of an atom and its nucleus. 2. **Explain** what radioactivity is. 3. **Compare and contrast** properties of radioactive and stable nuclei. 4. **Discuss** the discovery of radioactivity.	National Content Standards: UCP.1, UCP.2, UCP.3, UCP.5, A.1, A.2, B.1, B.2, G.3		**MiniLAB:** Modeling the Strong Force, p. 789 **Science Online,** p. 790
Section 2 Nuclear Decay 1 session .5 block 5. **Compare and contrast** alpha, beta, and gamma radiation. 6. **Define** the half-life of a radioactive material. 7. **Describe** the process of radioactive dating.	National Content Standards: UCP.1, UCP.2, UCP.3, UCP.5, A.1, A.2, B.1, B.2		
Section 3 Detecting Radioactivity 2 sessions 1 block 8. **Describe** how radioactivity can be detected in cloud and bubble chambers. 9. **Explain** how an electroscope can be used to detect radiation. 10. **Explain** how a Geiger counter can measure nuclear radiation.	National Content Standards: UCP.1, UCP.2, UCP.3, UCP.5, A.1, A.2, B.1, B.2, F.1		**Applying Math:** The Age of Rocks, p. 798 **Integrate Social Studies,** p. 799
Section 4 Nuclear Reactions 3 sessions 1.5 block 11. **Explain** nuclear fission and how it can begin a chain reaction. 12. **Discuss** how nuclear fusion occurs in the Sun. 13. **Describe** how radioactive tracers can be used to diagnose medical problems. 14. **Discuss** how nuclear reactions can help treat cancer.	National Content Standards: UCP.1, UCP.2, UCP.3, UCP.5, A.1, A.2, B.1, B.2, B.4, F.1, G.3		**MiniLAB:** Modeling a Nuclear Reaction, p. 802 **Science Online,** p. 803 **Integrate Chemistry,** p. 804 **Visualizing PET Scans,** p. 805 **Lab:** Chain Reactions, p. 807 Video Lab **Lab:** Modeling Transmutations, pp. 808–809 **Science and History:** The Nuclear Alchemists, p. 810

StudentWorks Plus

Glencoe Exclusive! TeacherWorks™ All-In-One Planner and Resource Center

Lab Materials	Reproducible Resources	Section Assessment	Technology
Launch Lab: grains of sugar, piece of dark paper, meterstick, tape	**Chapter *Fast File* Resources** Directed Reading Overview, p. 19 Foldables Worksheet, p. 17 Note-taking Worksheets, pp. 35–37	Glencoe's Assessment Advantage	TeacherWorks includes: • Interactive Teacher Edition • Lesson Planner with calendar • Access to all program blacklines • Correlations to standards • Web links
MiniLAB: small candies (15 yellow, 13 red, 2 green)	**Chapter *Fast File* Resources** Transparency Activity, p. 46 MiniLAB, p. 3 Enrichment, p. 31 Reinforcement, p. 27 Directed Reading, p. 20 **Science Inquiry Labs,** pp. 19–20	**Portfolio** Make a Model, p. 787 **Performance** Applying Math, p. 790 **Content** Section Review, p. 790	Section Focus Transparency Interactive Chalkboard CD-ROM StudentWorks Plus
Need materials? Contact Science Kit at 1-800-828-7777 or www.sciencekit.com.	**Chapter *Fast File* Resources** Transparency Activity, p. 47 Enrichment, p. 32 Reinforcement, p. 28 Directed Reading, p. 20 Transparency Activity, pp. 51–52	**Performance** Applying Math, p. 795 **Content** Section Review, p. 795	Section Focus Transparency Teaching Transparency Virtual Labs CD-ROM Interactive Chalkboard CD-ROM StudentWorks Plus
	Chapter *Fast File* Resources Transparency Activity, p. 48 Enrichment, p. 33 Reinforcement, p. 29 Directed Reading, p. 21 **Mathematics Skill Activities,** p. 31	**Portfolio** Check for Understanding, p. 800 **Performance** Applying Math, p. 798 Applying Math, p. 800 **Content** Section Review, p. 800	Section Focus Transparency Interactive Chalkboard CD-ROM StudentWorks Plus
MiniLAB: marbles (32), 400-mL beakers (2), modeling clay **Lab:** dominoes, stopwatch **Lab:** brown rice, white rice, colored candies, dried beans, dried seeds, glue, poster board	**Chapter *Fast File* Resources** Transparency Activity, p. 49 MiniLAB, p. 4 Enrichment, p. 34 Reinforcement, p. 30 Directed Reading, pp. 21, 22 Lab Worksheet, pp. 5–6, 7–8 **Home and Community Involvement,** p. 37	**Portfolio** Activity, p. 805 **Performance** MiniLAB, p. 802 Applying Math, p. 806 **Content** Section Review, p. 806	Section Focus Transparency Interactive Chalkboard CD-ROM StudentWorks Plus Video Lab

End of Chapter Assessment

Glencoe's Assessment Advantage

Blackline Masters	Technology	Professional Series
Chapter *Fast File* Resources Chapter Review, pp. 39–40 Chapter Tests, pp. 41–44 **Standardized Test Practice,** pp. 104–107	MindJogger Videoquiz Virtual Labs CD-ROM Exam*View*® Pro Testmaker TeacherWorks CD-ROM Interactive Chalkboard CD-ROM	**Performance Assessment in the Science Classroom (PASC)**

Transparencies

Section Focus

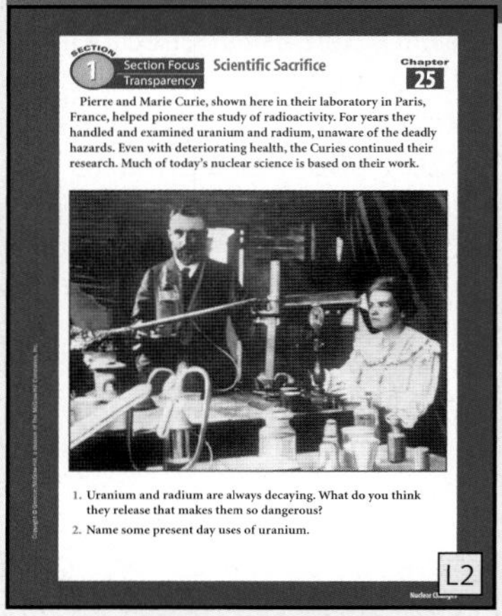
Section 1 Section Focus Transparency — Scientific Sacrifice — Chapter 25

Pierre and Marie Curie, shown here in their laboratory in Paris, France, helped pioneer the study of radioactivity. For years they handled and examined uranium and radium, unaware of the deadly hazards. Even with deteriorating health, the Curies continued their research. Much of today's nuclear science is based on their work.

1. Uranium and radium are always decaying. What do you think they release that makes them so dangerous?
2. Name some present day uses of uranium.

L2

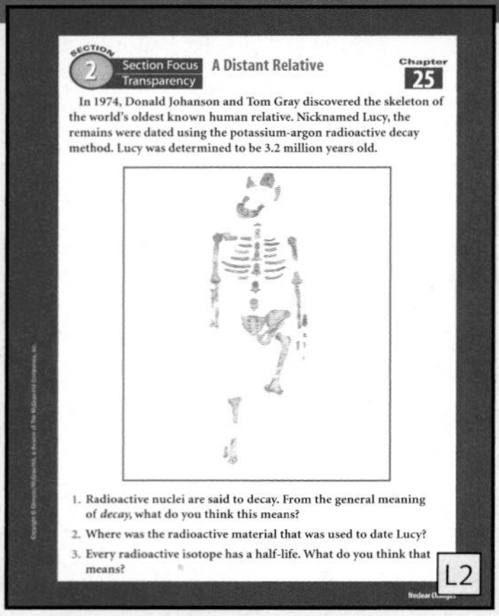
Section 2 Section Focus Transparency — A Distant Relative — Chapter 25

In 1974, Donald Johanson and Tom Gray discovered the skeleton of the world's oldest known human relative. Nicknamed Lucy, the remains were dated using the potassium-argon radioactive decay method. Lucy was determined to be 3.2 million years old.

1. Radioactive nuclei are said to decay. From the general meaning of *decay*, what do you think this means?
2. Where was the radioactive material that was used to date Lucy?
3. Every radioactive isotope has a half-life. What do you think that means?

L2

Section 3 Section Focus Transparency — Home Safety — Chapter 25

Radon is a radioactive gas that exists naturally in soil and rock. This odorless and colorless gas can seep through cracks into basements. At high levels, radon is a serious health risk. A home radon detector, like the one shown below, is a practical way to check radon levels.

1. The can looks pretty simple. How do you think the detector works?
2. What kinds of risk might the accumulation of radon pose?
3. Using the word *radon* as a guide, name the element that decays and releases radon.

L2

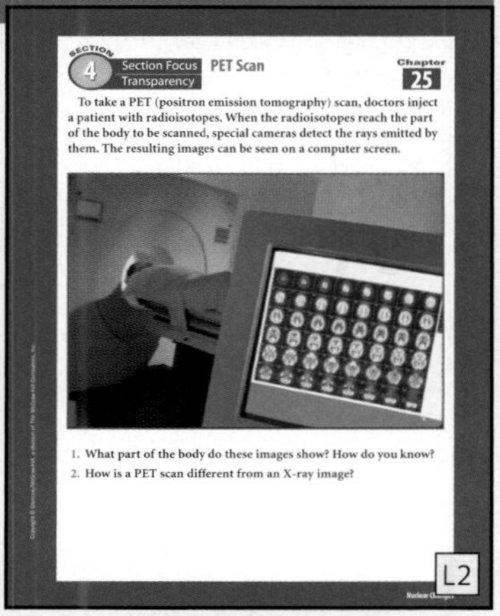
Section 4 Section Focus Transparency — PET Scan — Chapter 25

To take a PET (positron emission tomography) scan, doctors inject a patient with radioisotopes. When the radioisotopes reach the part of the body to be scanned, special cameras detect the rays emitted by them. The resulting images can be seen on a computer screen.

1. What part of the body do these images show? How do you know?
2. How is a PET scan different from an X-ray image?

L2

This is a representation of key blackline masters available in the Teacher Classroom Resources. See Resource Manager boxes within the chapter for additional information.

Assessment

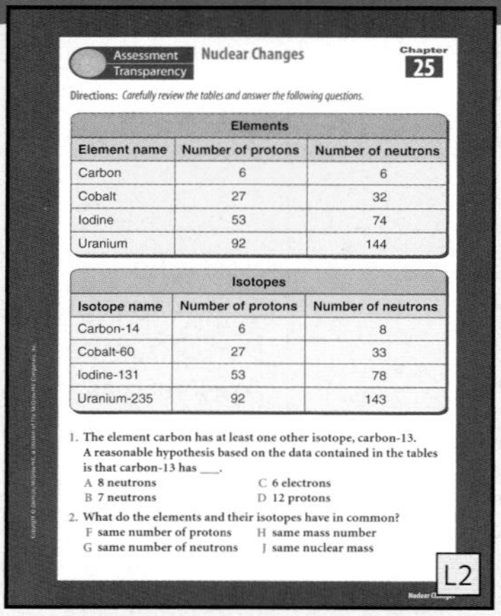
Assessment Transparency — Nuclear Changes — Chapter 25

Directions: Carefully review the tables and answer the following questions.

Elements

Element name	Number of protons	Number of neutrons
Carbon	6	6
Cobalt	27	32
Iodine	53	74
Uranium	92	144

Isotopes

Isotope name	Number of protons	Number of neutrons
Carbon-14	6	8
Cobalt-60	27	33
Iodine-131	53	78
Uranium-235	92	143

1. The element carbon has at least one other isotope, carbon-13. A reasonable hypothesis based on the data contained in the tables is that carbon-13 has ___.
   A 8 neutrons C 6 electrons
   B 7 neutrons D 12 protons
2. What do the elements and their isotopes have in common?
   F same number of protons H same mass number
   G same number of neutrons J same nuclear mass

L2

Teaching

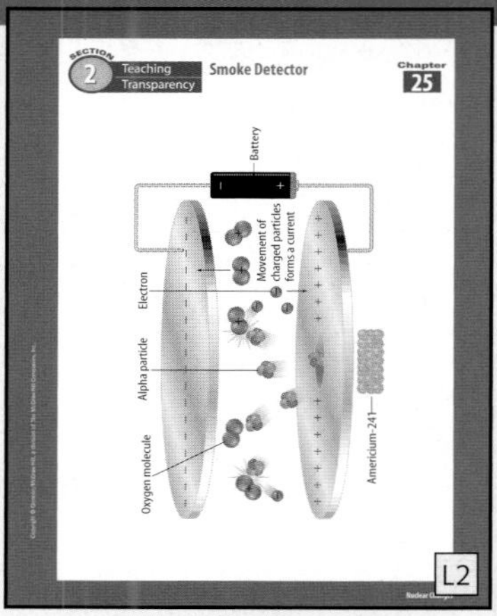
Section 2 Teaching Transparency — Smoke Detector — Chapter 25

L2

Key to Teaching Strategies

The following designations will help you decide which activities are appropriate for your students.

L1 Level 1 activities should be appropriate for students with learning difficulties.

L2 Level 2 activities should be within the ability range of all students.

L3 Level 3 activities are designed for above-average students.

ELL ELL activities should be within the ability range of English Language Learners.

COOP LEARN Cooperative Learning activities are designed for small group work.

LS Multiple Learning Styles logos, as described on page 12T, are used throughout to indicate strategies that address different learning styles.

P These strategies represent student products that can be placed into a best-work portfolio.

PBL Problem-Based Learning activities apply real-world situations to learning.

Hands-on Activities

Student Text Lab Worksheet

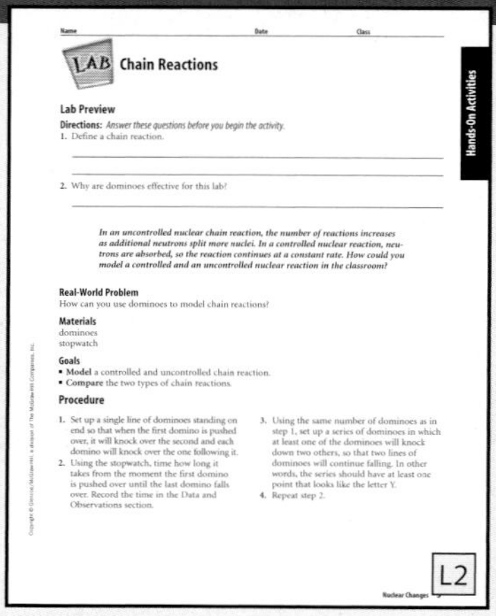
LAB Chain Reactions

Lab Preview

Directions: Answer these questions before you begin the activity.

1. Define a chain reaction.
2. Why are dominoes effective for this lab?

In an uncontrolled nuclear chain reaction, the number of reactions increases as additional neutrons split more nuclei. In a controlled nuclear reaction, neutrons are absorbed, so the reaction continues at a constant rate. How could you model a controlled and an uncontrolled nuclear reaction in the classroom?

Real-World Problem

How can you use dominoes to model chain reactions?

Materials

dominoes
stopwatch

Goals

- **Model** a controlled and uncontrolled chain reaction.
- **Compare** the two types of chain reactions.

Procedure

L2

Laboratory Activities

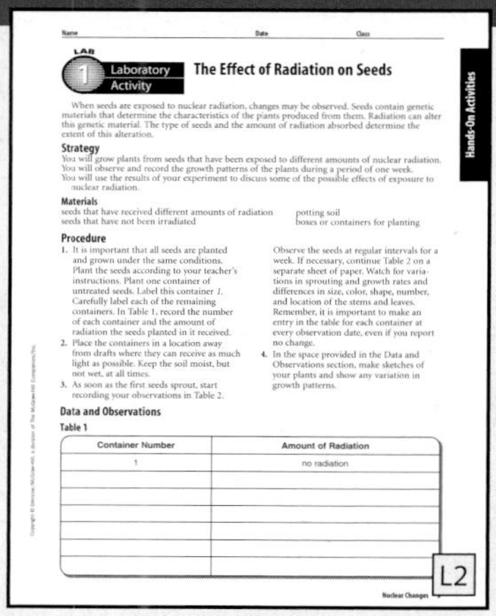
Lab 1 Laboratory Activity — The Effect of Radiation on Seeds

Strategy

Materials

Procedure

Data and Observations

Table 1

Container Number	Amount of Radiation
1	no radiation

L2

Resource Manager

Meeting Different Ability Levels

Content Outline

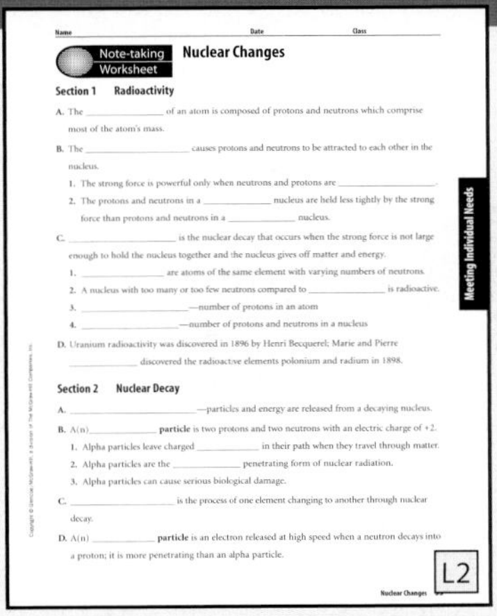
Note-taking Worksheet — Nuclear Changes

Section 1 Radioactivity

Section 2 Nuclear Decay

L2

Reinforcement

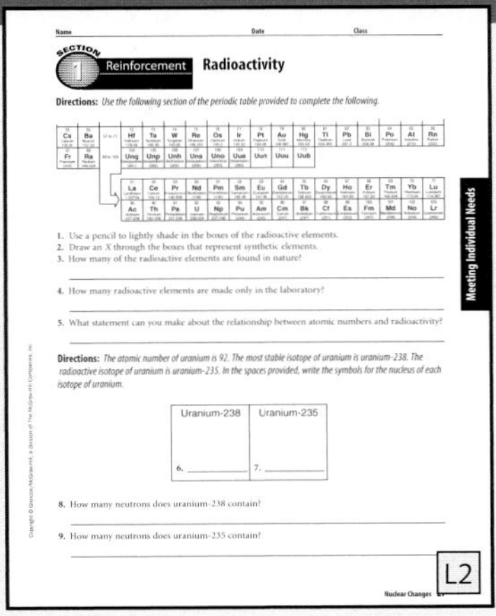
Section 1 Reinforcement — Radioactivity

Uranium-238 Uranium-235

L2

Enrichment

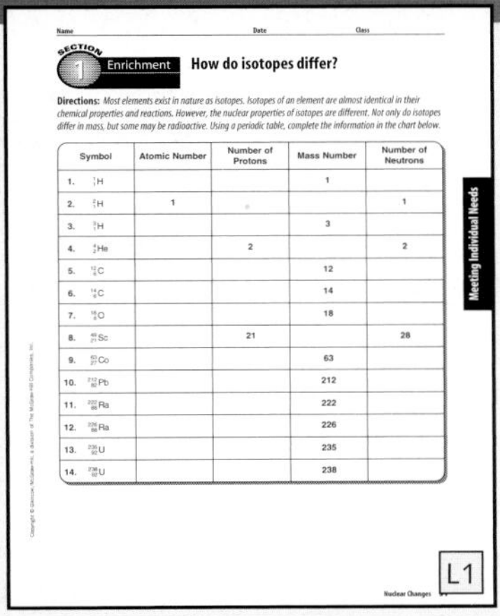
Section 1 Enrichment — How do isotopes differ?

Symbol	Atomic Number	Number of Protons	Mass Number	Number of Neutrons

L1

Directed Reading (English/Spanish)

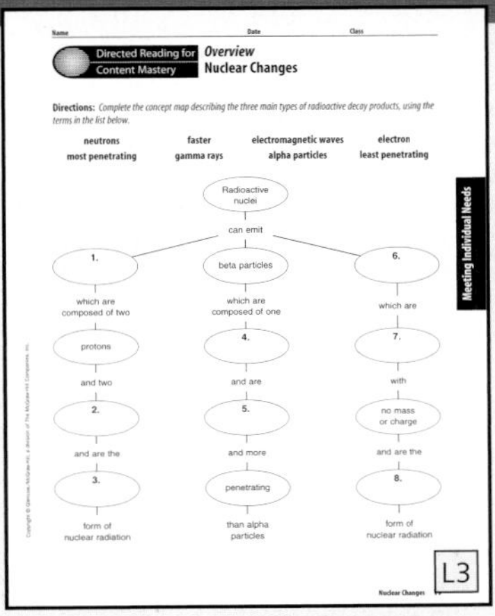
Directed Reading for Content Mastery — Overview — Nuclear Changes

neutrons, faster, electromagnetic waves, electron, most penetrating, gamma rays, alpha particles, least penetrating

L3

Study Guide

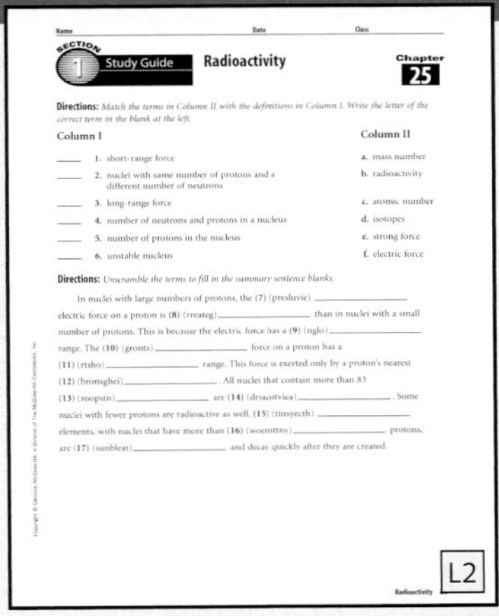
Section 1 Study Guide — Radioactivity — Chapter 25

Column I — Column II

L2

Reading Essentials

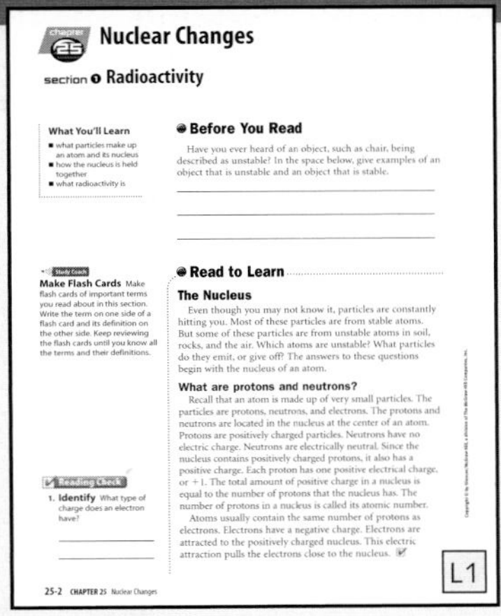
Chapter 25 Nuclear Changes

section 1 Radioactivity

Before You Read

Read to Learn

The Nucleus

What are protons and neutrons?

L1

Assessment

Test Practice Workbook

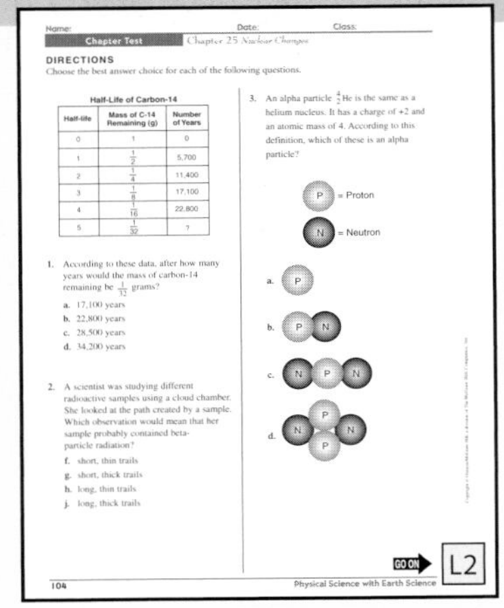
Chapter Test — Chapter 25 Nuclear Changes

Half-Life of Carbon-14

L2

Chapter Review

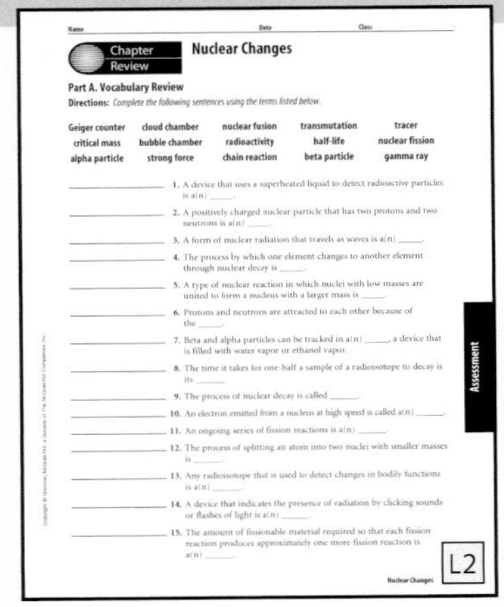
Chapter Review — Nuclear Changes

Part A. Vocabulary Review

L2

Chapter Tests

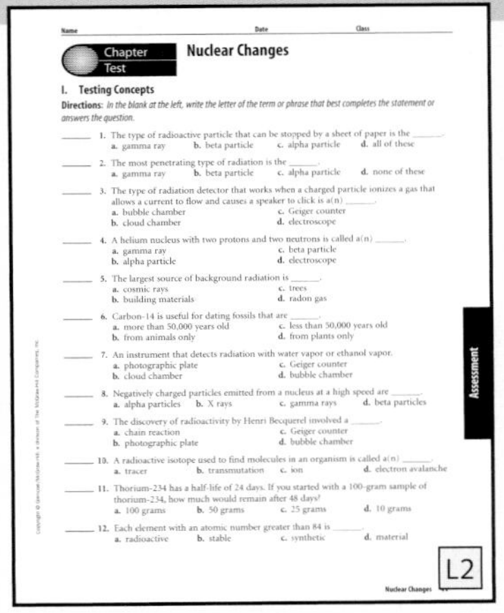
Chapter Test — Nuclear Changes

I. Testing Concepts

L2

Science Content Background

section 1 Radioactivity

The Nucleus

There are six "flavors" of quarks—the fundamental components of matter. The up, charm, and top quarks have a charge of +2/3. The down, strange, and bottom quarks have a charge of −1/3. Protons are made of two up quarks and one down quark. Neutrons are made of one up quark and two down quarks. Quarks are bound tightly together by the strong force so they are not observed as free particles.

In periodic tables, the atomic mass of an element usually is not written as a whole number. For example, silicon is shown as having an atomic mass of 28.086. The atomic mass on the periodic table is the average of the masses of all the isotopes of an element weighted by the relative occurrence of each isotope.

Carbon is the standard for the atomic mass of elements. It is defined as having a mass of 12 atomic mass units.

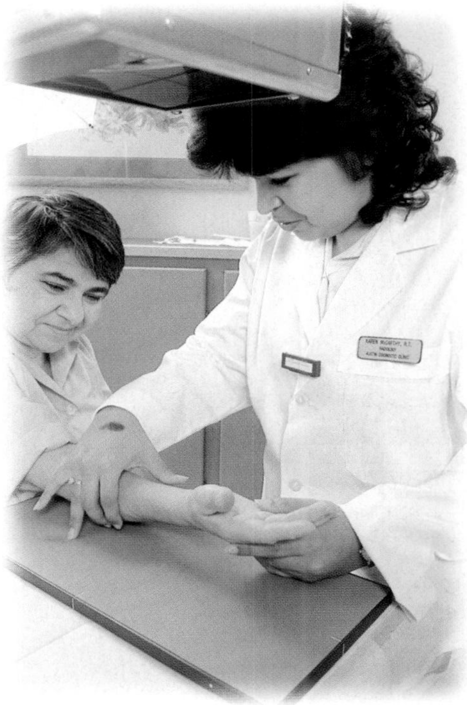

B. Daemmrich/The Image Works

Discovery of Radioactivity

Initial investigators of radioactivity were not aware of the long-term health risks associated with the handling of radioactive materials. Unfortunately this may have contributed to the death of Marie Curie due to leukemia in 1934.

chapter content resources

Internet Resources

For additional content background, visit **gpescience.com** to:

- access your book online
- find references to related articles in popular science magazines
- access Web links with related content background
- access current events with science journal topics

Print Resources

Contemporary College Physics, by Edwin R. Jones and Richard L. Childers, McGraw-Hill, 2001

How Things Work, 2nd Edition, Louis A. Bloomfield, John Wiley & Sons, 2001

section 2 Nuclear Decay

Gamma Rays

Gamma rays penetrate human tissue. Some cellular necrosis is not a problem as most cells can be replaced. The larger threat is from gamma rays that pass through tissues and change DNA. These changes can make a cell function less efficiently. When the cell reproduces, it produces more cells with less than optimal functioning. Aging is caused by the buildup of these kinds of cells. In rarer circumstances, DNA is damaged in a way that results in a malfunction in the control of the growth of the cell, resulting in rapid cell growth and division—a condition known as cancer.

Teacher to Teacher
Cindy L. Marr
Frazier High School
Perryopolis, PA

"Use coated candies to simulate radioactive decay. Pour 60-100 candies on a paper plate. Each candy represents a radioactive atom. Candies with letters showing are "radioactive," and the others have "decayed." Count the radioactive atoms, record the number in a data table, and then remove the decayed atoms. Pour the remaining candies on the plate again. Repeat the procedure until all the "atoms" have "decayed." Plot the data (atoms left v. trial number) and draw a smooth curve through the points. Obtain the half-life by selecting two values on the *y*-axis, one twice as large as the other, and finding the difference between corresponding values on the *x*-axis."

Cindy Marr

Putting food into sealed bags and exposing it to gamma rays can reduce the need for chemical preservatives or canning procedures. However, many people object to food irradiation. Some believe it will make food radioactive, which is not true. Others are concerned with the effects of eating foods that have been exposed to ionizing radiation.

section 3

Detecting Radioactivity

Measuring Radiation

Many radiation detectors use the tendency of radiation to ionize atoms as a means for detection. Ionization can be as simple as knocking an electron off an atom or it might involve the more complex breakup of a molecule into positive and negative pieces.

Health care workers who use X rays and people who work with radioactivity often wear radiation badges and carry pocket dosimeters. The badges are worn for periods of one to three months and then analyzed to assess how much radiation the person has received during that period. Pocket dosimeters tell the wearer how much radiation he or she has received in a shorter time period, such as one day of work.

Background Radiation

Cosmic radiation in space is an obstacle that must be overcome before astronauts can spend longer periods in space. The majority of cosmic rays are protons, but heavier nuclei are common. Some cosmic rays are gamma rays.

section 4

Nuclear Reactions

Nuclear Fusion

Research is under way to develop reactors that use nuclear fusion to generate electricity. Unlike fission reactors, a fusion reactor would generate very little long-lived radioactive material. However, extremely high temperatures are needed for the fusion reactions to occur and the plasma created is difficult to confine under these conditions. One way to contain the plasma is to use strong magnetic fields that prevent the plasma from touching the inside surfaces of the reactor.

Telegraph Colour Library/FPG International

chapter 25

Chapter Vocabulary

strong force, p. 787
radioactivity, p. 788
alpha particle, p. 791
transmutation, p. 792
beta particle, p. 793
gamma ray, p. 793
half-life, p. 794
cloud chamber, p. 796
bubble chamber, p. 797
Geiger counter, p. 798
nuclear fission, p. 801
chain reaction, p. 802
critical mass, p. 802
nuclear fusion, p. 803
tracer, p. 804

Science Journal Student responses might include brightness, warmth and heat, intensity, and feeling more energetic on a sunny day.

INTERACTIVE CHALKBOARD with Image Bank

PowerPoint® Presentations

This CD-ROM is an editable Microsoft® PowerPoint® presentation that includes:
- a pre-made presentation for every chapter
- interactive graphics
- animations
- audio clips
- image bank
- all new section and chapter questions
- Standardized Test Practice
- transparencies
- Foldables directions
- links to gpescience.com

chapter 25

Nuclear Changes

chapter preview

sections

1 Radioactivity
2 Nuclear Decay
3 Detecting Radioactivity
4 Nuclear Reactions
Lab *Chain Reactions*
Lab *Modeling Transmutations*
Virtual Lab *How can you simulate the radioactive half-life of an element?*

Planet Power

Although less than one billionth of the energy emitted by the Sun falls on Earth, the energy Earth receives from the Sun powers the entire planet. Without the Sun's energy, life on Earth could not exist. This energy is produced inside the Sun by nuclear fusion—a nuclear reaction in which atomic nuclei join together.

Science Journal In your Science Journal, write a paragraph describing your impressions of the Sun.

784

Theme Connection

Stability and Change Although the nucleus of an atom is stable during normal chemical reactions, it undergoes profound changes during nuclear reactions. These can be so profound that they change the identity of the element.

About the Photo

The Sun This is a photograph of the Sun, which is composed mostly of hydrogen. The enormous amount of energy emitted by the Sun comes from nuclear fusion, in which hydrogen atoms fuse into helium atoms, releasing energy.

Start-Up Activities

Launch LAB

The Size of a Nucleus

Do you realize you are made up mostly of empty space? Your body is made of atoms, and atoms are made of electrons whizzing around a small nucleus of protons and neutrons. The size of an atom is the size of the space in which the electrons move around the nucleus. In this lab, you'll find out how the size of an atom compares with the size of a nucleus.

1. Pour several grains of sugar onto a sheet of dark paper.
2. Choose one of the grains of sugar to represent the nucleus of an atom. Tape this grain to the center of the sheet of paper.
3. Place the sheet of paper in a large open space.
4. Use a meterstick to measure a distance of 10 m from the sugar grain. This distance represents the radius of the electron cloud around an atom.
5. **Think Critically** In your Science Journal, compare the size of an atom to the size of a nucleus. If an electron is much smaller than a nucleus, explain why an atom contains mostly empty space.

FOLDABLES Study Organizer

Radioactivity and Nuclear Reactions Make the following Foldable to help you understand radioactivity and nuclear reactions.

STEP 1 **Fold** a sheet of paper in half lengthwise.

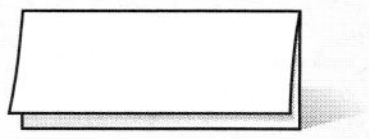

STEP 2 **Fold** paper down 2.5 cm from the top. (Hint: From the tip of your index finger to your middle knuckle is about 2.5 cm.)

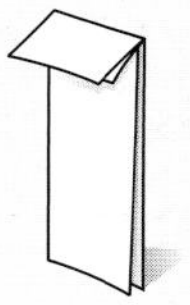

STEP 3 **Open and draw** lines along the 2.5-cm fold. **Label** as shown.

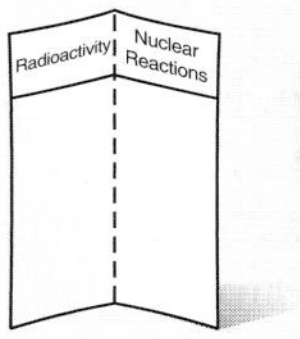

Summarize in a Table As you read the chapter, write what you learn about radioactivity in the left column and what you learn about nuclear reactions in the right column.

Science Online — Preview this chapter's content and activities at gpescience.com

Launch LAB

Purpose Use this Launch Lab to introduce students to what the interior of an atom is like.

Preparation Choose an outdoor location that will safely accommodate all the groups. To avoid confusion, assign a location for each group.

Materials meterstick, sugar, sheet of dark paper

Teaching Strategies Ask one student to be a group leader and assign the tasks of choosing and measuring the sugar grain and measuring the 10-m distance to group members.

Think Critically

The space in which the electrons move is much larger than the nucleus. Since the electron is much smaller than the nucleus, the space occupied by the electrons and the nucleus is much smaller than the space occupied by the atom.

Assessment

Content Sometimes it is said that an atom is mostly empty space. Ask students to write a paragraph discussing whether this statement is true. The sizes of the nucleus and electrons in an atom are much smaller than the size of the atom. However, electrons move throughout the space occupied by the atom. Use **Performance Assessment in the Science Classroom,** p. 89.

FOLDABLES Study Organizer **Dinah Zike Study Fold**

Student preparation materials for this Foldable are available in the Chapter ***Fast File*** Resources.

1 Motivate

An editable Microsoft® PowerPoint® presentation is available on **Interactive Chalkboard** CD-ROM.

Bellringer

Section Focus Transparencies also are available on the Interactive Chalkboard CD-ROM. L2 ELL

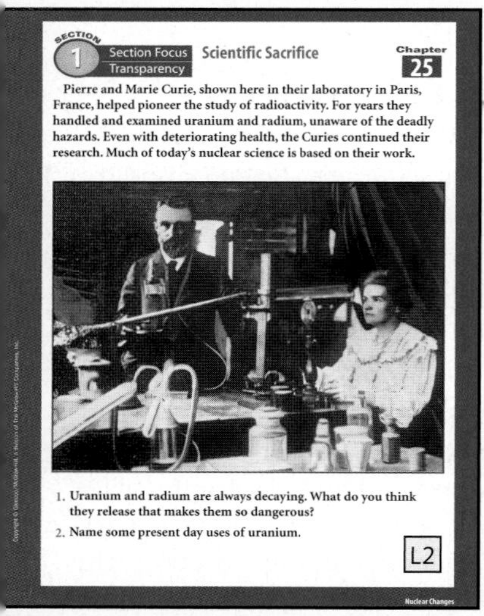
Section 1 Section Focus Transparency — Scientific Sacrifice — Chapter 25

Pierre and Marie Curie, shown here in their laboratory in Paris, France, helped pioneer the study of radioactivity. For years they handled and examined uranium and radium, unaware of the deadly hazards. Even with deteriorating health, the Curies continued their research. Much of today's nuclear science is based on their work.

1. Uranium and radium are always decaying. What do you think they release that makes them so dangerous?
2. Name some present day uses of uranium.

L2

Nuclear Changes

Reading Preview

Tie to Prior Knowledge

Parts of an Atom Ask students to recall the parts of an atom. Students are probably aware that an atom is composed of electrons swirling around a nucleus of protons and neutrons. In this section they will learn about the force that holds the nucleus together and why some nuclei are radioactive.

Vocabulary Usage Use the new vocabulary words in sentences. Then ask students to predict meaning. Have them check the meaning in the text to validate or modify predictions.

section 1 Radioactivity

Reading Guide

What You'll Learn

- **Describe** the structure of an atom and its nucleus.
- **Explain** what radioactivity is.
- **Compare and contrast** properties of radioactive and stable nuclei.
- **Discuss** the discovery of radioactivity.

Why It's Important

Radioactivity is everywhere because every element on the periodic table has some atomic nuclei that are radioactive.

Review Vocabulary

long-range force: a force that becomes weaker with distance, but never vanishes

New Vocabulary

- strong force
- radioactivity

The Nucleus

Every second you are being bombarded by energetic particles. Some of these particles come from unstable atoms in soil, rocks, and the atmosphere. What types of atoms are unstable? What type of particles do unstable atoms emit? The answers to these questions begin with the nucleus of an atom.

Recall that atoms are composed of protons, neutrons, and electrons. The nucleus of an atom contains the protons, which have a positive charge, and neutrons, which have no electric charge. The total amount of charge in a nucleus is determined by the number of protons, which also is called the atomic number. You might remember that an electron has a charge that is equal but opposite to a proton's charge. Atoms usually contain the same number of protons as electrons. Negatively charged electrons are electrically attracted to the positively charged nucleus and swarm around it.

Figure 1 The size of a nucleus in an atom can be compared to a marble sitting in the middle of an empty football stadium.

Protons and Neutrons in the Nucleus Protons and neutrons are packed together tightly in a nucleus. The region outside the nucleus in which the electrons are located is large compared to the size of the nucleus. As **Figure 1** shows, the nucleus occupies only a tiny fraction of the space in the atom. If an atom were enlarged so that it was 1 km in diameter, its nucleus would have a diameter of only a few centimeters. But the nucleus contains almost all the mass of the atom, because the mass of one proton or neutron is almost 2,000 times greater than the mass of an electron.

Section 1 Resource Manager

Chapter *FAST FILE* Resources

Transparency Activity, p. 46
Note-taking Worksheets, pp. 35–37
Directed Reading for Content Mastery, pp. 19–20
Enrichment, p. 31
Reinforcement, p. 27
Science Inquiry Labs, pp. 19–20

Figure 2 The particles in the nucleus are attracted to each other by the strong force.

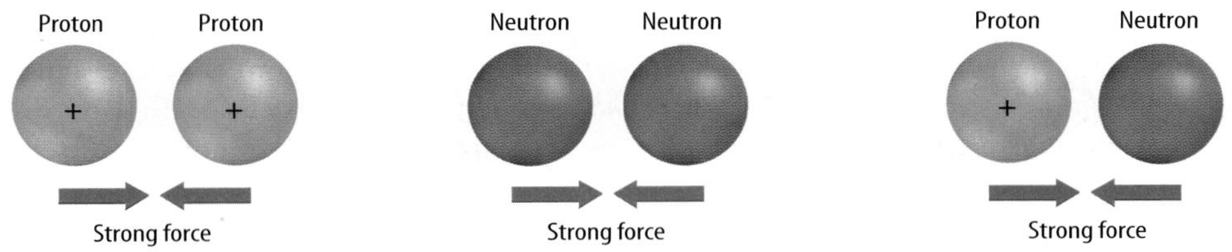

The Strong Force

How do you suppose protons and neutrons are held together so tightly in the nucleus? Positive electric charges repel each other, so why don't the protons in a nucleus push each other away? Another force, called the **strong force,** causes protons and neutrons to be attracted to each other, as shown in **Figure 2.**

The strong force is one of the four basic forces in nature and is about 100 times stronger than the electric force. The attractive forces between all the protons and neutrons in a nucleus keep the nucleus together. However, protons and neutrons have to be close together, like they are in the nucleus, to be attracted by the strong force. The strong force is a short-range force that quickly becomes extremely weak as protons and neutrons get farther apart. The electric force is a long-range force, so protons that are far apart still are repelled by the electric force, as shown in **Figure 3.**

Reading Check *What causes the attraction between protons and neutrons?*

Figure 3 The total force between two protons depends on how far apart they are. **Infer** *whether the total force between two protons could become zero.*

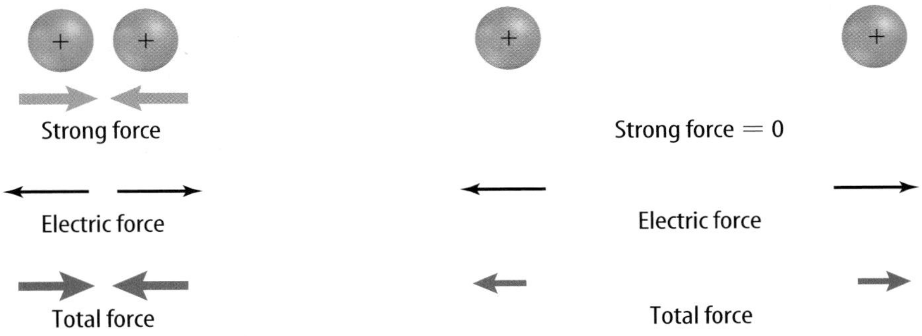

When protons are close together, they are attracted to each other. The attraction due to the short-range strong force is much stronger than the repulsion due to the long-range electric force.

When protons are too far apart to be attracted by the strong force, they still are repelled by the electric force between them. Then the total force between them is repulsive.

2 Teach

Activity

Atomic Structure To review atomic structure, display a periodic table. Have students choose an element and draw its structure on the board using different colors for protons, neutrons, and electrons. Tell students that physicists often refer to the number of protons (atomic number) as "Z." L1 ELL IS **Visual-Spatial**

Make a Model

The Nucleus The strong force is significant only for a distance that is less than the width of a few protons and neutrons. Have students model the nucleus of a nitrogen atom by drawing closely packed circles as nucleons. (Tracing around a penny works well.) Students should draw seven neutrons and seven protons, randomly placed and colored differently. By multiplying the diameter of a circle by three, they can see about how far the strong force can be felt. L2 ELL IS **Kinesthetic** P

Reading Check

Answer the strong force

Caption Answer

Figure 3 Yes, if they were separated by a distance such that the attractive strong force was balanced by the repulsive electric force.

Reading Strategy

Directed Reading Have students skim the text prior to reading. They should note titles, figures, and bold print. Ask them to predict what they will learn and write their predictions in their Science Journals. Have students check off or modify their prediction statements as they read.

Teacher FYI

Four Fundamental Forces Scientists have identified four fundamental forces of nature. The strong force holds neutrons and protons together; the electromagnetic force acts between particles with electric charge; the weak force is involved in the neutron decay process; and the weakest force is gravity.

SECTION 1 Radioactivity **787**

Visual Learning

Figure 4 Point out to students that in the large nucleus the protons near the center of the nucleus feel a slightly greater strong force than those near the edge of the nucleus. Protons near the edge have no neighbors on the outer side of the nucleus to pull on them. This can be a source of instability in the nucleus. L2 LS **Visual-Spatial**

Quick Demo
Strong Force v. Magnetism

Materials magnets

Estimated Time 2–5 minutes

Procedure Use magnets to review the concepts of repulsion and attraction. With magnetism, like poles repel and unlike poles attract. Similarly, two protons (both positively charged) repel each other. With the strong force, however, the charge doesn't matter; all protons and neutrons attract one another at very short distances. L2 ELL LS **Visual-Spatial**

Discussion

Periodic End Why is there an end to the periodic table? As the number of protons in the nucleus increases, the relative effect of the electromagnetic repulsion between protons increases, causing large nuclei to be unstable. Beyond a certain point, the electromagnetic repulsion makes large nuclei too unstable to exist. L3 LS **Logical-Mathematical**

IDENTIFYING Misconceptions

Radioactive Energy Students may think that radioactive materials glow. Explain that energy is given off, but not in the form of light. Radiation can, however, induce fluorescence in some materials.

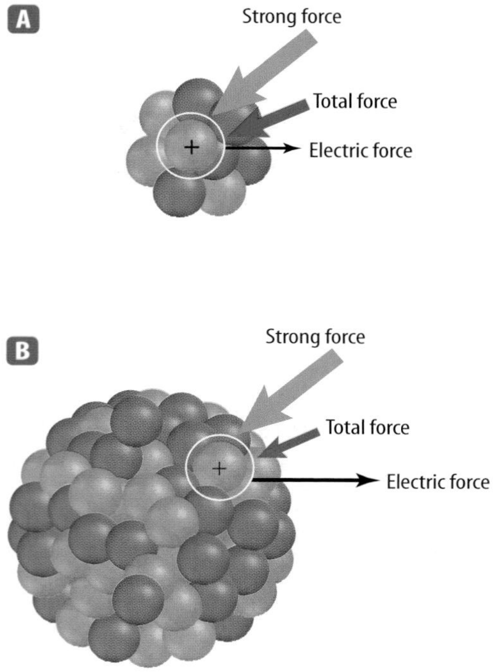

Figure 4 Protons and neutrons are held together less tightly in large nuclei. The circle shows the range of the attractive strong force. **A** Small nuclei have few protons, so the repulsive force on a proton due to the other protons is small. **B** In large nuclei, the attractive strong force is exerted only by the nearest neighbors, but all the protons exert repulsive forces. The total repulsive force is large.

Attraction and Repulsion Some atoms, such as uranium, have many protons and neutrons in their nuclei. These nuclei are held together less tightly than nuclei containing only a few protons and neutrons. To understand this, look at **Figure 4A.** If a nucleus has only a few protons and neutrons, they are all close enough together to be attracted to each other by the strong force. Because only a few protons are in the nucleus, the total electric force causing protons to repel each other is small. As a result, the overall force between the protons and the neutrons attracts the particles to each other.

Forces in a Large Nucleus However, if nuclei have many protons and neutrons, each proton or neutron is attracted to only a few neighbors by the strong force, as shown in **Figure 4B.** The other protons and neutrons are too far away. Because only the closest protons and neutrons attract each other in a large nucleus, the strong force holding them together is about the same as in a small nucleus. However, all the protons in a large nucleus exert a repulsive electric force on each other. Thus, the electric repulsive force on a proton in a large nucleus is larger than it would be in a small nucleus. Because the repulsive force increases in a large nucleus while the attractive force on each proton or neutron remains about the same, protons and neutrons are held together less tightly in a large nucleus.

Radioactivity

Many types of nuclei are held together permanently and are stable. However, there are many other types of nuclei that are unstable. These nuclei break apart, or decay, by emitting particles and energy. This process of nuclear decay is called **radioactivity.** A nucleus that decays is called a radioactive nucleus.

Nuclei that contain large numbers of protons and neutrons tend to be unstable. In fact, all nuclei that contain more than 83 protons are radioactive. However, many other nuclei that contain fewer than 83 protons also are radioactive. Even some nuclei with only one or a few protons are radioactive.

Almost all elements with more than 92 protons don't exist naturally on Earth. They have been produced only in laboratories and are called synthetic elements. These synthetic elements are unstable and decay soon after they are created.

Cultural Diversity

Hideki Yukawa In 1949 Japanese scientist Hideki Yukawa received the Nobel Prize in physics for his work on nuclear forces. In 1935 he predicted the existence of particles he called mesons, that would transfer energy between protons and neutrons and hold the nucleus together. His theory also stated that the nuclear force must be stronger than electromagnetic forces over short distances in order to overcome the repulsion between protons. The mesons Yukawa predicted, now known as pions, were discovered in 1937.

Converting Mass into Energy When an unstable nucleus decays, energy is emitted. If energy is conserved and cannot be created or destroyed, where does this energy come from? Recall that in nuclear reactions, mass can be converted into energy. As an unstable nucleus decays, a small amount of mass is converted into energy. As a result, the mass of the initial nucleus is slightly larger than the mass of the final nucleus plus the mass of any particles that are emitted. A large amount of energy is produced by the conversion of only a small amount of mass.

Isotopes The atoms of an element all have the same number of protons in their nuclei. For example, the nuclei of all carbon atoms contain six protons. However, naturally occurring carbon nuclei can have six, seven, or eight neutrons. Nuclei that have the same number of protons but different numbers of neutrons are called isotopes. The element carbon has three isotopes that occur naturally. The atoms of all isotopes of an element have the same number of electrons and have the same chemical properties. **Figure 5** shows two isotopes of helium.

Nuclear Numbers A nucleus can be described by the number of protons and neutrons it contains. The number of protons in a nucleus is called the atomic number. Because the mass of all the protons and neutrons in a nucleus is nearly the same as the mass of the atom, the number of protons and neutrons is called the mass number.

Reading Check *What is the atomic number of a nucleus?*

A nucleus can be represented by a symbol that includes its atomic number, mass number, and the symbol of the element it belongs to. The symbol for the nucleus of the stable isotope of carbon is shown below as an example.

$$\text{mass number} \rightarrow \; {}^{12}_{6}\text{C} \leftarrow \text{element symbol}$$
$$\text{atomic number} \rightarrow$$

This isotope is called carbon-12. The number of neutrons in the nucleus is the mass number minus the atomic number. So the number of neutrons in the carbon-12 nucleus is $12 - 6 = 6$. Carbon-12 has six protons and six neutrons. Now, compare the isotope carbon-12 to this radioactive isotope of carbon:

$$\text{mass number} \rightarrow \; {}^{14}_{6}\text{C} \leftarrow \text{element symbol}$$
$$\text{atomic number} \rightarrow$$

The radioactive isotope is carbon-14. How many neutrons does carbon-14 have?

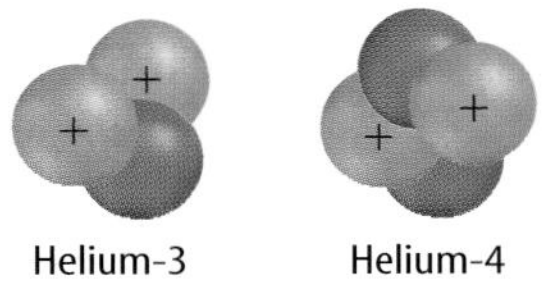

Figure 5 These two isotopes of helium each have the same number of protons, but different numbers of neutrons.
Identify *the ratio of protons to neutrons in each of these isotopes of helium.*

Mini LAB

Modeling the Strong Force

Procedure

1. Gather **15 yellow candies** to represent neutrons and **13 red** and **2 green candies** to represent protons.
2. Model a small nucleus by placing 2 red protons and 3 neutrons around a green proton so they touch.
3. Model a larger nucleus by arranging the remaining candies around the other green proton so they are touching.

Analysis

1. Compare the number of protons and neutrons touching a green proton in both models.
2. Suppose the strong force on a green proton is due to protons and neutrons that touch it. Compare the strong force on a green proton in both models.

Try at Home

Caption Answers

Figure 5 Helium-3: 2 to 1, Helium-4: 2 to 2

Text Question Answer

8

Reading Check

Answer the number of protons

Mini LAB

Purpose Students construct models to discover how the size of the nucleus affects the strong force on protons. L2 LS **Kinesthetic**

Materials small candies (15 yellow, 13 red, two green)

Teaching Strategy Remind students that both green and red candies represent protons; the green candy is used to draw attention to a single proton in each model.

Analysis

1. About the same number touch the green proton in both models.
2. The strong force on the green proton is the same in each model. The electromagnetic force, however, would increase in the larger nucleus, making it less stable.

Assessment

Process Show students a drawing of a uranium nucleus and ask whether it is stable. It is too large to be stable. Use **PASC,** p. 89.

Try at Home

Differentiated Instruction

Challenge Have students determine the size of the nuclei of helium, neon, argon, krypton, xenon, radon, and uranium. Calculate the ratio of the diameter of each nucleus to its atomic mass and graph using the atomic mass on the x-axis and the ratio on the y-axis. Does the ratio remain constant as the size of the nucleus increases? Explain why this would be true. L3

Visually Impaired Allow visually impaired students to hold magnets and feel the attraction and repulsion to help them understand what happens when two protons are close together. Explain that the strong force is like your hands holding the repelling magnets close together.

Post Reading

Extended Research Radioactivity is used for sterilization, protecting works of art, and fire detectors. Have students research one of the many applications of radioactivity and create a written report. Students should present findings to the class.

INTEGRATE History

Content Background

Marie Curie is credited with coining the term radioactivity in a paper written with Pierre in which they presented the discovery of polonium. Marie was the first person ever to receive two Nobel prizes. She shared the first in physics in 1903 with Pierre and Becquerel for their discovery of radioactivity. She received the second in 1911 in chemistry for her discovery and isolation of radium and polonium. (Pierre died in 1906, so he did not share in the chemistry prize.)

3 Assess

DAILY INTERVENTION

Check for Understanding

Logical-Mathematical Why don't elements with atomic numbers greater than 92 exist naturally on Earth in significant quantities? because they are so unstable that if they are created, they decay almost immediately L3 LS

Reteach

Reviewing Isotopes Write on the board the chemical symbol, atomic mass, and atomic number of an isotope. Have students tell the number of protons and neutrons the element has and predict whether the isotope is radioactive. Do this for several isotopes. L2 ELL LS **Visual-Spatial**

Assessment

Content Have students work in groups to create games that teach about radioactive elements. Games should reinforce the concept that unstable nuclei cause radioactivity. Use **Performance Assessment in the Science Classroom,** p. 169.

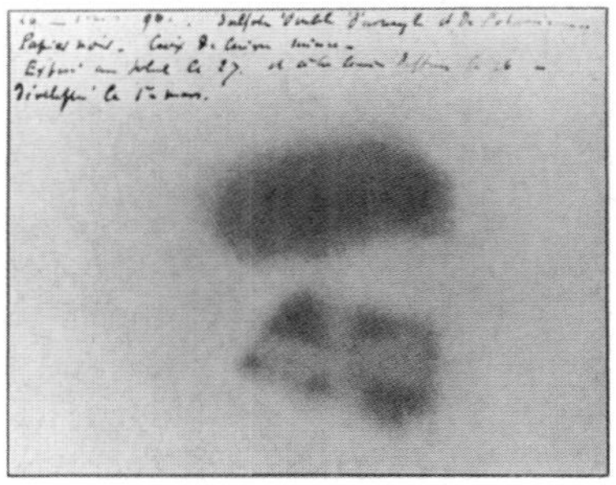

Figure 6 The dark spots on this photographic plate were made by the radiation emitted by radioactive uranium atoms. Uranium salt had been placed next to the plate by Henri Becquerel in 1896.

INTEGRATE History

The Discovery of Radioactivity In 1896, Henri Becquerel left uranium salt in a desk drawer with a photographic plate. Later, when he developed the plate, shown in **Figure 6,** he found an outline of the clumps of the uranium salt. He hypothesized that the uranium salt had emitted some unknown invisible rays, or radiation, that had darkened the film.

Two years after Becquerel's discovery, Marie and Pierre Curie discovered two new elements, polonium and radium, that also were radioactive. To obtain a sample of radium large enough to be studied, they developed a process to extract radium from the mineral pitchblende. After more than three years, they were able to obtain about 0.1 g of radium from several tons of pitchblende. Years of additional processing gradually produced more radium that was made available to other researchers all over the world.

Science Online

Topic: Marie Curie
Visit gpescience.com for Web links to information about the life of Marie Curie.

Activity Create a timeline showing important events in the life of Marie Curie.

section 1 review

Summary

The Strong Force

- The short-ranged strong force causes neutrons and protons to be attracted to each other.
- The long-ranged electric force causes protons to repel each other.
- The combination of the strong and electric forces causes protons and neutrons in a large nucleus to be held together less tightly than in a small nucleus.

Radioactivity and Isotopes

- Radioactivity is the process of nuclear decay.
- Isotopes of an element have the same number of protons, but different numbers of neutrons.
- The atomic number is the number of protons in a nucleus. The mass number is the number of protons and neutrons in a nucleus.

Self Check

1. **Describe** the properties of the strong force.
2. **Compare** the strong force between protons and neutrons in a small nucleus and a large nucleus.
3. **Explain** why large nuclei are unstable.
4. **Identify** the contributions of the three scientists who discovered the first radioactive elements.
5. **Think Critically** What is the ratio of protons to neutrons in lead-214? Explain whether you would expect this isotope to be radioactive or stable.

Applying Math

6. **Calculate a Ratio** What is the ratio of neutrons to protons in a nucleus of radon-222?
7. **Use Percentages** A silicon rod contains 30.21 g of silicon-28, 1.53 g of silicon-29, and 1.02 g of silicon-30. Calculate the percentage of each isotope in the rod.

More Section Review gpescience.com

section 1 review

1. short range, attractive, exists between protons, neutrons, and protons and neutrons
2. The strong force is exerted by nearest neighbors, so it is nearly the same in both nuclei.
3. Large nuclei have so many protons that the strong force is unable to overcome the total electrical repulsion.
4. Becquerel found that uranium salt emitted radiation. Marie and Pierre Curie discovered polonium and radium.
5. $82/132 = 0.62$; might be radioactive because the ratio of protons to neutrons differs from the 2-to-3 (0.67) ratio for stable heavy elements
6. $86/136 = 0.63$
7. total mass of rod = 32.76 g. Percentage of silicon-28 = $30.21/32.76 = 92.2\%$; silicon-29 = $1.53/32.76 = 4.7\%$; silicon-30 = $1.02/32.76 = 3.1\%$

section 2

Nuclear Decay

Reading Guide

What You'll Learn
- **Compare and contrast** alpha, beta, and gamma radiation.
- **Define** the half-life of a radioactive material.
- **Describe** the process of radioactive dating.

Why It's Important

Nuclear decay produces nuclear radiation that can both harm people and be useful.

Review Vocabulary

electromagnetic wave: a transverse wave consisting of vibrating electric and magnetic fields

New Vocabulary
- alpha particle
- transmutation
- beta particle
- gamma ray
- half-life

Nuclear Radiation

When an unstable nucleus decays, particles and energy called nuclear radiation are emitted from it. The three types of nuclear radiation are alpha, beta (BAY tuh), and gamma radiation. Alpha and beta radiation are particles. Gamma radiation is an electromagnetic wave.

Alpha Particles

When alpha radiation occurs, an **alpha particle**—made of two protons and two neutrons, as shown in **Table 1**—is emitted from the decaying nucleus. An alpha particle is the same as the nucleus of a helium atom. It has a charge of +2 and an atomic mass of 4. Its symbol is the same as the symbol of a helium nucleus, ^4_2He.

Reading Check *What does an alpha particle consist of?*

Compared to beta and gamma radiation, alpha particles are much more massive. They also have the most electric charge. As a result, alpha particles lose energy more quickly when they interact with matter than the other types of nuclear radiation do. When alpha particles pass through matter, they exert an electric force on the electrons in atoms in their path. This force pulls electrons away from atoms and leaves behind charged ions. Alpha particles lose energy quickly during this process. As a result, alpha particles are the least penetrating form of nuclear radiation. Alpha particles can be stopped by a sheet of paper.

Table 1 Alpha Particles

Symbol	^4_2He
Mass	4
Charge	+2

Section 2 Resource Manager

Chapter *Fast File* Resources

Transparency Activity, p. 47, 51–52

Lab Activity, pp. 9–12, 13–16

Enrichment, p. 32

MiniLAB, p. 3

Reinforcement, p. 28

Mathematics Skill Activities, p. 3

1 Motivate

INTERACTIVE CHALKBOARD PowerPoint® Presentations An editable Microsoft® PowerPoint® presentation is available on **Interactive Chalkboard** CD-ROM.

Bellringer

Section Focus Transparencies also are available on the Interactive Chalkboard CD-ROM. L2 ELL

SECTION 2 Section Focus Transparency **A Distant Relative** Chapter 25

In 1974, Donald Johanson and Tom Gray discovered the skeleton of the world's oldest known human relative. Nicknamed Lucy, the remains were dated using the potassium-argon radioactive decay method. Lucy was determined to be 3.2 million years old.

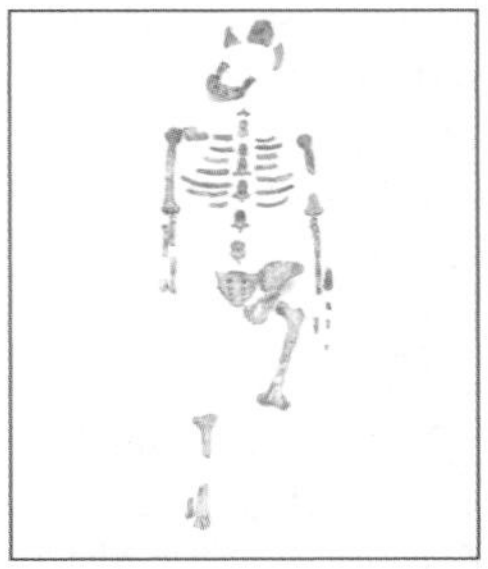

1. **Radioactive nuclei are said to decay. From the general meaning of *decay*, what do you think this means?**
2. **Where was the radioactive material that was used to date Lucy?**

L2 **Every radioactive isotope has a half-life. What do you think that means?**

Nuclear Changes

Reading Preview

Tie to Prior Knowledge

Gamma Radiation Tell students that gamma radiation is one kind of radiation emitted during radioactive decay.

Word Associations Ask students to look for the new vocabulary words in the text to identify meanings. Have students link words together by creating a paragraph that uses all the terms.

Reading Check

Answer two protons and two neutrons

2 Teach

Visual Learning

Figure 7 Point out to students that the metal plate of the ionization chamber serves as shielding for the radioactive source underneath. Bring in a smoke detector that uses americium-241. Light some flash paper or a candle to produce enough smoke to make the smoke detector beep. L2 ELL LS **Visual-Spatial**

Activity

Nuclear Time Line With students, make a class time line of the important events in nuclear decay and radiation, beginning with Henri Becquerel's discovery of radioactivity. The time line could include contributions by Pierre and Marie Curie, Ernest Rutherford, Irène and Frédéric Joliot-Curie, Kasimir Fajans, Leo Szilard, Otto Hahn, Fritz Strassman, and Lise Meitner. L3 LS **Visual-Spatial**

Teacher FYI

Smoke Detectors The detector shown in **Figure 7** is called an ionization detector. Another form of detector, the optical smoke detector, relies on detecting light scattering off particles in smoke.

Caption Answer

Figure 8 yes

Figure 7 When alpha particles collide with molecules in the air, positively charged ions and electrons result. The ions and electrons move toward charged plates, creating a current in the smoke detector.

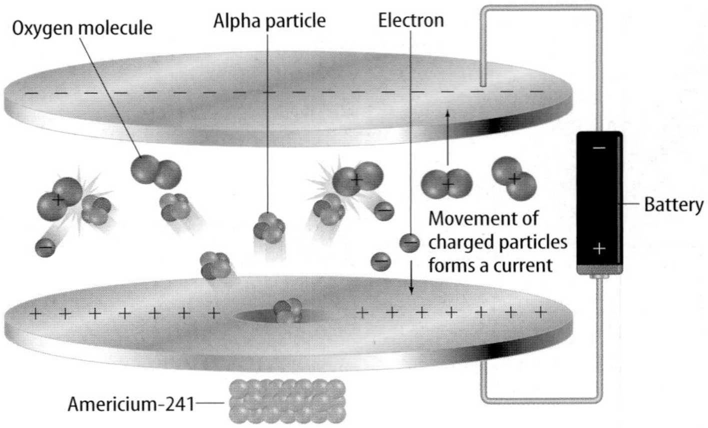

Damage from Alpha Particles Alpha particles can be dangerous if they are released by radioactive atoms inside the human body. Biological molecules inside your body are large and easily damaged. A single alpha particle can damage many fragile biological molecules. Damage from alpha particles can cause cells not to function properly, leading to illness and disease.

Smoke Detectors Some smoke detectors give off alpha particles that ionize the surrounding air. Normally, an electric current flows through this ionized air to form a circuit, as in **Figure 7.** But if smoke particles enter the ionized air, they will absorb the ions and electrons. The circuit is broken and the alarm goes off.

Transmutation When an atom emits an alpha particle, it has two fewer protons, so it is a different element. **Transmutation** is the process of changing one element to another through nuclear decay. In alpha decay, two protons and two neutrons are lost from the nucleus. The new element has an atomic number two less than that of the original element. The mass number of the new element is four less than the original element. **Figure 8** shows a nuclear transmutation caused by alpha decay. The charge of the original nucleus equals the sum of the charges of the nucleus and the alpha particle that are formed.

Figure 8 In this transmutation, polonium emits an alpha particle and changes into lead.
Determine *whether the charges and mass numbers of the products equal the charge and mass number of the polonium nucleus.*

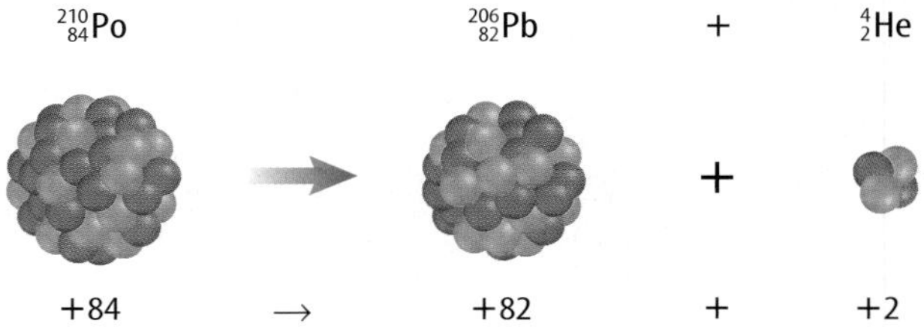

Reading Strategy

Question Have students preview the text and turn headings into questions. "Damage from Alpha Particles" could be turned into "How can alpha particles cause damage?" As students read, have them answer questions. Later have them revisit questions and answer from memory.

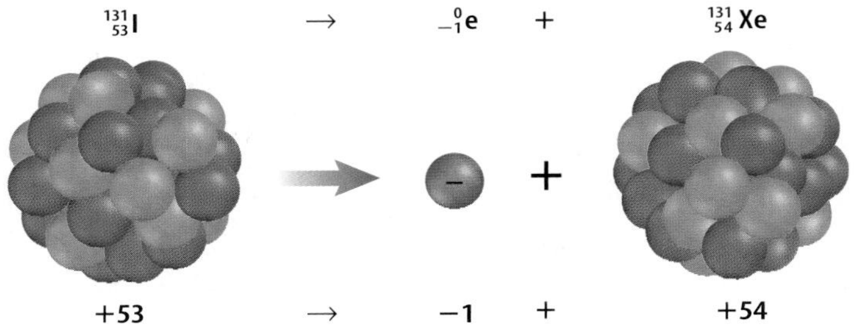

Figure 9 Nuclei that emit beta particles undergo transmutation. In beta decay shown here, iodine changes to xenon.
Compare *the total atomic number and mass number of the products with the atomic number and mass number of the iodine nucleus.*

Beta Particles

A second type of radioactive decay is called beta decay, which is summarized in **Table 2.** Sometimes in an unstable nucleus a neutron decays into a proton and emits an electron. The electron is emitted from the nucleus and is called a **beta particle.** Beta decay is caused by another basic force called the weak force.

Because the atom now has one more proton, it becomes the element with an atomic number one greater than that of the original element. Atoms that lose beta particles undergo transmutation. However, because the total number of protons and neutrons does not change during beta decay, the mass number of the new element is the same as that of the original element. **Figure 9** shows a transmutation caused by beta decay.

Damage from Beta Particles Beta particles are much faster and more penetrating than alpha particles. They can pass through paper but are stopped by a sheet of aluminum foil. Just like alpha particles, beta particles can damage cells when they are emitted by radioactive nuclei inside the human body.

Table 2 Beta Particles

Symbol	$^{0}_{-1}e$
Mass	0.0005
Charge	−1

Gamma Rays

The most penetrating form of nuclear radiation is gamma radiation. **Gamma rays** are electromagnetic waves with the highest frequencies and the shortest wavelengths in the electromagnetic spectrum. They have no mass and no charge and travel at the speed of light. They usually are emitted from a nucleus when alpha decay or beta decay occurs. The properties of gamma rays are summarized in **Table 3.**

Thick blocks of dense materials, such as lead and concrete, are required to stop gamma rays. However, gamma rays cause less damage to biological molecules as they pass through living tissue. Suppose an alpha particle and a gamma ray travel the same distance through matter. The gamma ray produces fewer ions because it has no electric charge.

Table 3 Gamma Rays

Symbol	γ
Mass	0
Charge	0

Caption Answer

Figure 9 The electron has a mass number of 0 and a charge of -1, so the mass number of the products equals 131, and the charge of the products equals +53.

Inquiry Lab

Electromagnetic Radiation

Purpose to demonstrate the penetration of electromagnetic radiation, using light

Possible Materials flashlight, blue plastic wrap, red plastic wrap, clear plastic wrap, white T-shirt, aluminum foil, other materials students choose

Estimated Time 10–15 min

Teaching Stratiegies Have students shine a flashlight through various materials to observe if the light penetrates the material and hits the wall. Students can change the wavelength of the light by placing blue or red plastic wrap over the flashlight. If the light penetrates, measure how far back they can move and still see the light on the wall, then make a table summarizing their results. Repeat with any other materials they choose. Have them draw conclusions about the penetration of different wavelengths of light.

Discussion

Emitting Particles Have students summarize the effect on an atom's atomic mass (A) and atomic number (Z) if the atom emits an alpha particle, a beta particle, or a gamma ray. When an alpha particle is released, A decreases by four and Z decreases by two. When a beta particle is released, A is unchanged and Z increases by one. When gamma rays are released, A and Z are unchanged. L2 IN **Logical-Mathematical**

Differentiated Instruction

English-Language Learners Have ELL students draw three lithium atoms with three electrons around the nucleus with a pencil. Have them erase one electron from each lithium atom, and explain that an ion is a atom missing an electron, and that ions have the capacity to transfer electrons, which is electricity.

Science Journal

Radiation Have students find out who chose alpha, beta, and gamma to name different kinds of radiation, why, and when, and write this information in their journals. Ernest Rutherford gave these names to these types of radiation for, as he said, simplicity. He named alpha and beta radiation between 1895 and 1898 and gamma rays in 1903. L2 IN **Linguistic**

Caption Answer

Figure 10 one

Use an Analogy

Half-Lives Tell students to each hold up a large sheet of paper. After ten seconds, have students tear their sheets of paper in half and place one half on their desks. During the next ten seconds, have them tear off half the part that is left and place it on the desk. Continue counting ten-second intervals while students continue tearing their papers in half until they can no longer continue. Explain that, like the ever-smaller pieces of paper, the concentration of radioactive isotopes in a substance continuously decreases. L2

ELL LS **Kinesthetic**

Reading Check

Answer the nucleus left after the isotope decays

Quick Demo

Radiation Detection

Materials Geiger counter, different samples of rock and bone

Estimated Time five minutes

Procedure Use the Geiger counter to detect radiation in samples of rock and bone, and to confirm that all materials have some radioactive material.

Virtual Labs

Half-Life *How can you simulate the radioactive half-life of and element?*

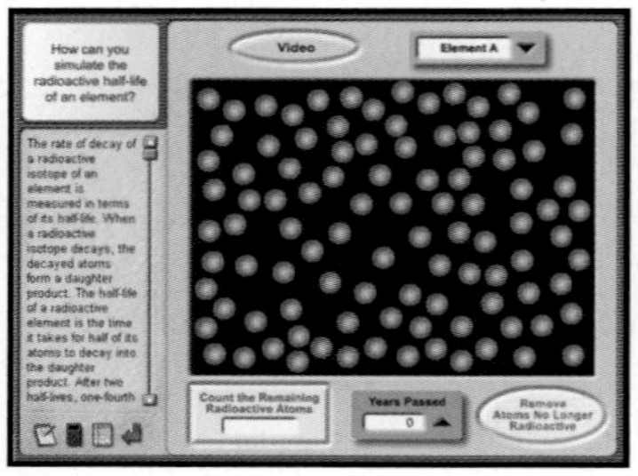

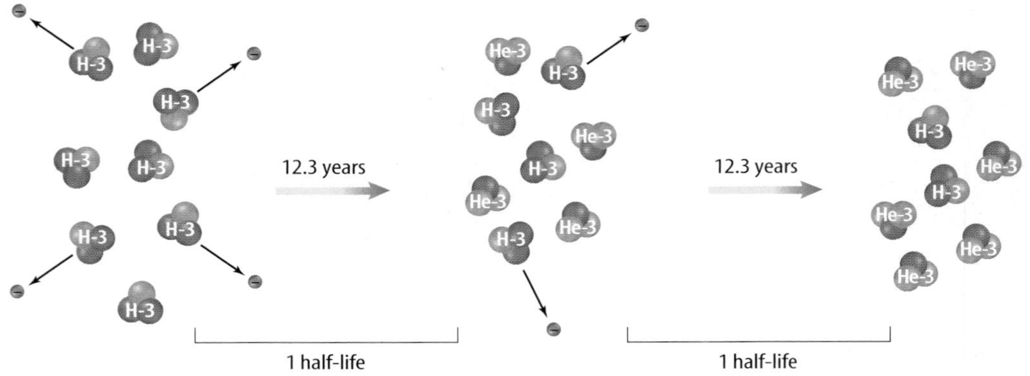

Figure 10 The half-life of $^{3}_{1}H$ is 12.3 years. During each half-life, half of the atoms in the sample decay into helium.
Infer *how many hydrogen atoms will be left in the sample after the next half-life.*

Radioactive Half-Life

If an element is radioactive, how can you tell when its atoms are going to decay? Some radioisotopes decay to stable atoms in less than a second. However, the nuclei of certain radioactive isotopes require millions of years to decay. A measure of the time required by the nuclei of an isotope to decay is called the half-life. The **half-life** of a radioactive isotope is the amount of time it takes for half the nuclei in a sample of the isotope to decay. The nucleus left after the isotope decays is called the daughter nucleus. **Figure 10** shows how the number of decaying nuclei decreases after each half-life.

Half-lives vary widely among the radioactive isotopes. For example, polonium-214 has a half-life of less than a thousandth of a second, but uranium-238 has a half-life of 4.5 billion years. The half-lives of some other radioactive elements are listed in **Table 4.**

Reading Check *What is a daughter nucleus?*

Table 4 Sample Half-Lives

Isotope	Half-Life
$^{3}_{1}H$	12.3 years
$^{212}_{82}Pb$	10.6 hr
$^{14}_{6}C$	5,730 years
$^{211}_{84}Po$	0.5 s
$^{235}_{92}U$	7.04×10^{8} years
$^{131}_{53}I$	8.04 days

Radioactive Dating

Some geologists, biologists, and archaeologists, among others, are interested in the ages of rocks and fossils found on Earth. The ages of these materials can be determined using radioactive isotopes and their half-lives. First, the amounts of the radioactive isotope and its daughter nucleus in a sample of material are measured. Then, the number of half-lives that need to pass to give the measured amounts of the isotope and its daughter nucleus is calculated. The number of half-lives is the amount of time that has passed since the isotope began to decay. Also, it is usually the amount of time that has passed since the object was formed, or the age of the object. Different isotopes are useful in dating different types of materials.

Curriculum Connection

History Have students do research to learn how radioactive dating has been used to determine the ages of artifacts found in archaeological digs. Students might research Pompeii, China's terra-cotta army, or Easter Island. L3 LS **Linguistic**

Differentiated Instruction

Challenge Have students investigate the process scientists use to determine the levels of radioactive isotopes and daughter nuclei present in a sample when performing carbon or uranium dating. Put the process in a flow chart. L3

794 CHAPTER 25 Nuclear Changes

Carbon Dating The radioactive isotope carbon-14 often is used to estimate the ages of plant and animal remains. Carbon-14 has a half-life of 5,730 years and is found in molecules such as carbon dioxide. Plants use carbon dioxide when they make food, so all plants contain carbon-14. When animals eat plants, carbon-14 is added to their bodies.

The decaying carbon-14 in a plant or animal is replaced when an animal eats or when a plant makes food. As a result, the ratio of the number of carbon-14 atoms to the number of carbon-12 atoms in the organism remains nearly constant. But when an organism dies, its carbon-14 atoms decay without being replaced. The ratio of carbon-14 to carbon 12 then decreases with time. By measuring this ratio, the age of an organism's remains can be estimated. However, only material from plants and animals that lived within the past 50,000 years contains enough carbon-14 to be measured.

Uranium Dating Radioactive dating also can be used to estimate the ages of rocks. Some rocks contain uranium, which has two radioactive isotopes with long half-lives. Each of these uranium isotopes decays into a different isotope of lead. The number of these uranium isotopes and their daughter nuclei are measured. From the ratios of these amounts, the number of half-lives since the rock was formed can be calculated.

section 2 review

Summary

Nuclear Radiation

- When an unstable nucleus decays it emits nuclear radiation that can be alpha particles, beta particles, or gamma rays.
- An alpha particle consists of two protons and two neutrons.
- A beta particle is an electron and is emitted when a neutron decays into a proton.
- Gamma rays are electromagnetic waves of very high frequency that usually are emitted when alpha decay or beta decay occurs.

Half-Life and Radioactive Dating

- The half-life of a radioactive isotope is the amount of time for half the nuclei in a sample of the isotope to decay.
- The amounts of radioactive isotopes and their daughter nuclei are needed to date materials.

Self Check

1. **Infer** how the mass number and the atomic number of a nucleus change when it emits a beta particle.
2. **Determine** the daughter nucleus formed when a radon-222 nucleus emits an alpha particle.
3. **Describe** how each of the three types of radiation can be stopped.
4. **Think Critically** Sample 1 contains nuclei with a half-life of 10.6 hr and sample 2 contains an equal number of nuclei with a half-life of 0.5 s. After 3 half-lives pass for each sample, which sample contains more of the original nuclei?

Applying Math

5. **Use Percentages** What is the percentage of radioactive nuclei left after 3 half-lives pass?
6. **Use Fractions** If the half-life of iodine-131 is 8 days, how much of a 5-g sample is left after 32 days?

More Section Review gpescience.com

Post Reading

Visualizations Ask students to use the information gained from the reading, along with prior knowledge, to create mental images of alpha particles, beta particles, gamma rays, and radioactive decay. Have students sketch their visualizations.

3 Assess

DAILY INTERVENTION

Check for Understanding

Linguistic Have students find out more about the forces and radiation involved in beta decay. Beta decay involves the weak force and is accompanied by the release of particles called neutrinos, which have high energy but very little mass. L3

Reteach

Half-Life Have students tell how long it would take for three-fourths of a sample of each isotope in **Table 4** to decay. twice the listed half-life L2 LS **Logical-Mathematical**

Assessment

Have students make drawings illustrating how radioactive isotopes decay.

section 2 review

1. The atomic number increases by one and the mass number doesn't change.
2. $^{222}_{86}\text{Rn} \rightarrow {}^{218}_{84}\text{Po} + {}^{4}_{2}\text{He}$; polonium
3. alpha particles: sheet of paper; beta particles: sheet of metal foil; gamma rays: thick blocks of lead or concrete
4. They contain the same number. After three half lives, each sample contains one eighth of the original number of nuclei, which was the same for both samples.
5. 12.5%
6. 32 days = 4 half-lives = 1/16 of original number of nuclei left; 1/16 x 5 g = 0.3 g left

section 3

Detecting Radioactivity

Reading Guide

What You'll Learn
- **Describe** how radioactivity can be detected in cloud and bubble chambers.
- **Explain** how an electroscope can be used to detect radiation.
- **Explain** how a Geiger counter can measure nuclear radiation.

Why It's Important
Devices that detect and measure radioactivity are used to monitor exposure to humans.

Review Vocabulary
ion: an atom that has gained or lost electrons

New Vocabulary
- cloud chamber
- bubble chamber
- Geiger counter

Radiation Detectors

Because you can't see or feel alpha particles, beta particles, or gamma rays, you must use instruments to detect their presence. Some tools that are used to detect radioactivity rely on the fact that radiation forms ions in the matter it passes through. The tools detect these newly formed ions in several ways.

Cloud Chambers A **cloud chamber,** shown in **Figure 11,** can be used to detect alpha or beta particle radiation. A cloud chamber is filled with water or ethanol vapor. When a radioactive sample is placed in the cloud chamber, it gives off charged alpha or beta particles that travel through the water or ethanol vapor. As each charged particle travels through the chamber, it knocks electrons off the atoms in the air, creating ions. It leaves a trail of ions in the chamber. The water or ethanol vapor condenses around these ions, creating a visible path of droplets along the track of the particle. Beta particles leave long, thin trails, and alpha particles leave shorter, thicker trails.

Reading Check *Why are trails produced by alpha and beta particles seen in cloud chambers?*

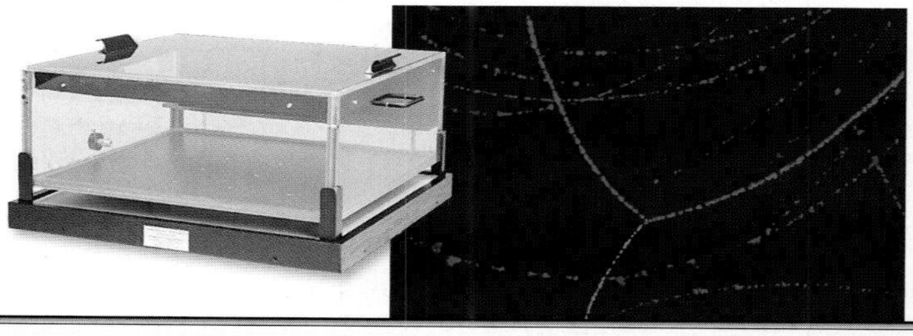

Figure 11 If a sample of radioactive material is placed in a cloud chamber, a trail of condensed vapor will form along the paths of the emitted particles.

796

1 Motivate

INTERACTIVE CHALKBOARD An editable Microsoft® PowerPoint® presentation is available on **Interactive Chalkboard** CD-ROM.

Bellringer

Section Focus Transparencies also are available on the Interactive Chalkboard CD-ROM. L2 ELL

SECTION 3 Section Focus Transparency **Home Safety** Chapter 25

Radon is a radioactive gas that exists naturally in soil and rock. This odorless and colorless gas can seep through cracks into basements. At high levels, radon is a serious health risk. A home radon detector, like the one shown below, is a practical way to check radon levels.

1. The can looks pretty simple. How do you think the detector works?
2. What kinds of risk might the accumulation of radon pose?
3. Using the word *radon* as a guide, name the element that decays and releases radon.

L2

Nuclear Changes

Reading Preview

Tie to Prior Knowledge

Detecting Radiation Our five senses allow us to see, hear, smell, taste, and feel, but none of our senses can tell us when we are being exposed to radioactivity. In this section, students will learn about four methods for detecting radiation.

Vocabulary Usage Have students find the figures that illustrate each new vocabulary term. *Cloud chamber, bubble chamber,* and *Geiger counter* all are shown in the text. Ask them to say the vocabulary word as they focus on the associated picture. Pairing pictures with words helps support vocabulary development.

Section 3 Resource Manager

Chapter *FAST FILE* Resources
- Transparency Activity, p. 48
- Directed Reading for Content Mastery, p. 21
- Enrichment, p. 33
- Reinforcement, p. 29
- **Mathematics Skill Activities,** p. 31

Bubble Chambers Another way to detect and monitor the paths of nuclear particles is by using a bubble chamber. A **bubble chamber** holds a superheated liquid, which doesn't boil because the pressure in the chamber is high. When a moving particle leaves ions behind, the liquid boils along the trail. The path shows up as tracks of bubbles, like the ones in **Figure 12.**

Figure 12 Particles of nuclear radiation can be detected as they leave trails of bubbles in a bubble chamber.

Electroscopes Do you remember how an electroscope can be used to detect electric charges? When an electroscope is given a negative charge, its leaves repel each other and spread apart, as in **Figure 13A.** They will remain apart until their extra electrons have somewhere to go and discharge the electroscope. The excess charge can be neutralized if it combines with positive charges. Nuclear radiation moving through the air can remove electrons from some molecules in air, as shown in **Figure 13B,** and cause other molecules in air to gain electrons. When this occurs near the leaves of the electroscope, some positively charged molecules in the air can come in contact with the electroscope and attract the electrons from the leaves, as **Figure 13C** shows. As these negatively charged leaves lose their charges, they move together. **Figure 13D** shows this last step in the process. The same process also will occur if the electroscope leaves are positively charged. Then the electrons move from negative ions in the air to the electroscope leaves.

Figure 13 Nuclear radiation can cause an electroscope to lose its charge.

A The electroscope leaves are charged with negative charge.

B Nuclear radiation, such as alpha particles, can create positive ions.

C Negative charges move from the leaves to positively charged ions.

D The electroscope leaves lose their negative charge and come together.

2 Teach

Reading Check

Answer The charged particles knock electrons off atoms in the air, leaving a trail of ions. The vapor condenses around these ions.

Use an Analogy

Vapor Trails Tell students that the vapor trails sometimes seen behind jet airplanes are made up of water droplets that have condensed around the jet's exhaust fumes. Like the trails in cloud chambers, vapor trails provide a visual record of the path of the object that caused them.

Visual Learning

Figure 12 Point out to students that at the lower part of this bubble chamber photograph, particles collide and create a spray of charged particles. A magnetic field perpendicular to the page deflects the particles so that those curling to the left must have an opposite charge to those curling to the right. Note that only charged particles are visible.

IDENTIFYING Misconceptions

Fundamental Particles Students might assume that electrons, protons, and neutrons are the smallest possible particles. Explain that electrons are fundamental particles, but that protons and neutrons are composite particles made up of smaller particles called quarks.

Teacher FYI

Bubble Chamber The bubble chamber, developed in the 1950s, was used by scientists for many years to observe the particles in matter. It has since been replaced by newer, more complex detectors.

Quick Demo

Tracking Radiation Exposure

Materials Radiation film badge

Time Required 2–5 minutes

Procedure People whose work involves possible exposure to radiation are required to wear film badges that record the amount of radiation the person has received. You can obtain one of these badges from the radiation laboratory at a hospital. Explain to students that a small piece of film is encased in a plastic holder. The casing is light-tight so the film responds only to alpha, beta, and gamma radiation, not visible light. Every month, the film is removed and the amount of radiation it (and therefore the wearer) has received is measured. New film is then inserted in the holder. L3 LS **Visual-Spatial**

Applying Math

Math Standards

National: 1, 6, 9

Answer to Practice Problem

5.2 billion years

Reading Strategy

Quick Write After students read about bubble chambers, electroscopes, measuring radiation, and background radiation, have them respond to this prompt: How is radiation detected and what causes background radiation? Allow five minutes for students to respond. Let students share their quick writes.

Measuring Radiation

It is important to monitor the amount of radiation a person is being exposed to because large doses of radiation can be harmful to living tissue. A **Geiger counter** is a device that measures the amount of radiation by producing an electric current when it detects a charged particle.

Applying Math — Use Logarithms

THE AGE OF ROCKS The radioactive nucleus uranium-238 produces the daughter nucleus lead-206 with a half-life of 4.5 billion years. The age of a mineral sample can be calculated from the equation:

$$\text{age} = (1.44H)\ln\left[1 + \frac{N_L}{N_U}\right]$$

In this equation, H is the half-life of uranium 238, N_L is the number of lead-206 atoms in the sample, and N_U is the number of uranium-238 atoms in the sample. Find the age of a sample in which the ratio N_L/N_U is measured to be 0.55.

IDENTIFY known values and unknown values

Identify the known values:

the ratio of the number of uranium-238 atoms to the number of lead-206 atoms is 0.55 means $\frac{N_L}{N_U} = 0.55$

a half-life of 4.5 billion years means $H = 4.5$ billion years

Identify the unknown value:

what is the age of the sample? means age = ? years

SOLVE the problem

Substitute the known values into the equation for the age:

$$\text{age} = (1.44H)\ln\left[1 + \frac{N_L}{N_U}\right] = (1.44 \times 4.5 \text{ billion yrs}) \ln\,[1 + 0.55]$$
$$= (6.48 \text{ billion yrs}) \ln(1.55)$$

To calculate ln(1.55), enter 1.55 on your calculator and press the "ln" button. The result is 0.438. Substitute this value in the above equation:

$$\text{age} = (6.48 \text{ billion yrs})(0.438) = 2.84 \text{ billion yrs}$$

CHECK the answer

Does your answer seem reasonable? The ratio $N_L/N_U = 0.55$, means that less than one half-life has elapsed. The calculated age is less than one half-life.

Practice Problems

Find the age of a sample in which the ratio N_L/N_U has been measured to be 1.21.

For more practice problems go to page 879, and visit Math Practice at gpescience.com.

Teacher FYI

Radiation Units There are several units for measuring radiation. The curie and the becquerel are based on the number of disintegrations per second. The roentgen, the rad, and the gray measure the effect radiation has on the absorbing material. The rem is used to measure biological damage to humans.

Active Reading

Metacognition Journal In this strategy, each student analyzes his or her own thought processes. Have students divide a sheet of paper in half. On the left, have them record what they have learned about radiation detection. On the right, have them record the reason they learned it.

Figure 14 Electrons that are stripped off gas molecules in a Geiger counter move to a positively charged wire in the device. This causes current to flow in the wire. The current then is used to produce a click or a flash of light.

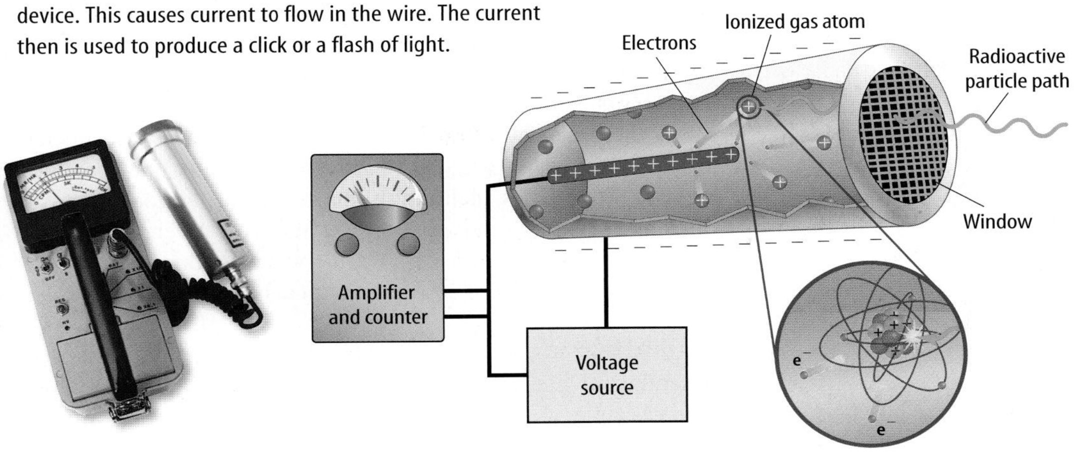

Geiger Counters A Geiger counter, shown in **Figure 14,** has a tube with a positively charged wire running through the center of a negatively charged copper cylinder. This tube is filled with gas at a low pressure. When radiation enters the tube at one end, it knocks electrons from the atoms of the gas. These electrons then knock more electrons off other atoms in the gas, and an "electron avalanche" is produced. The free electrons are attracted to the positive wire in the tube. When a large number of electrons reaches the wire, a short, intense current is produced in the wire. This current is amplified to produce a clicking sound or flashing light. The intensity of radiation present is determined by the number of clicks or flashes of light each second.

Reading Check *How does a Geiger counter indicate that radiation is present?*

Background Radiation

It might surprise you to know that you are bathed in radiation that comes from your environment. This radiation, called background radiation, is not produced by humans. Instead it is low-level radiation emitted mainly by naturally occurring radioactive isotopes found in Earth's rocks, soils, and atmosphere. Building materials such as bricks, wood, and stones contain traces of these radioactive materials. Traces of naturally occurring radioactive isotopes are found in the food, water, and air consumed by all animals and plants. As a result, animals and plants also contain small amounts of these isotopes.

INTEGRATE Social Studies

Artificial Rainmaking It may be possible to ease the health and economic hardships caused by severe droughts by artificially making rain. The formation of raindrops in a cloud is similar to the formation of droplets in a cloud chamber. Rain forms when cold droplets freeze around microscopic particles of dust, and then melt as they fall through warmer air. Research artificial rainmaking and report your findings to your class.

INTEGRATE Social Studies

Artificial Rainmaking Scientists have tried three ways to make artificial rain. Have students research artificial rain to learn how the methods work. One method is spraying water into warm clouds. Another method is to drop dry ice into clouds. The third method is to drop silver iodide crystals or similar crystals into clouds. None of these methods have been very successful.

Discussion

Radiation Badges What occupations might require a radiation badge to monitor exposure to radiation? Possible answers: nuclear power plant workers; sailors on nuclear-powered ships and submarines; doctors, nurses, dentists, airport security workers (X-ray exposure); scientists doing research with radioactive materials

Reading Check

Answer by a clicking sound or flashing light

Activity

Background Radiation Have students do research to find out about sources of background radiation in their community. L2 LS **Linguistic**

Post Reading

Fix-Up Strategy Ask students to re-read a part of the text they found difficult. When they encounter problems with comprehension, tell students to read ahead for clarification. Remind students to slow down when confronting difficult text and speed up when they want a sense of the overall idea.

Differentiated Instruction

Visually Impaired If you have a Geiger counter, let your visually impaired students hear the difference in the clicking between different materials. If you don't have a Geiger counter, do a web search for Geiger counter sounds and download a sound file for them to hear.

Teacher FYI

The G-M Counter The Geiger counter was invented by a German physicist named Hans Geiger. In 1928, Geiger, along with Walther Müller, improved the detector, so it is often called the Geiger-Müller counter, or simply the G-M counter.

Visual Learning

Figure 15 According to this circle graph, how much of the background radiation received by an average person in the United States comes from sources outside the body? at least 89 percent

3 Assess

DAILY INTERVENTION

Check For Understanding

Visual-Spatial Ask students to draw sketches of pictures that might be obtained with a cloud chamber and a bubble chamber. For each sketch, have the students explain the lines they have drawn and which type of particle would cause that type of line. L2 LS P

Reteach

Natural Radioactivity Have students explain why radiation occurs naturally in the human body. Radioactive isotopes of elements used by the body occur in nature and are used in the same way as the stable isotopes of the same elements. L2 LS **Logical-Mathematical**

Assessment

Process Have students create a concept map for each of the four methods of radiation detection mentioned in this section. Use **Performance Assessment in the Science Classroom,** p. 161.

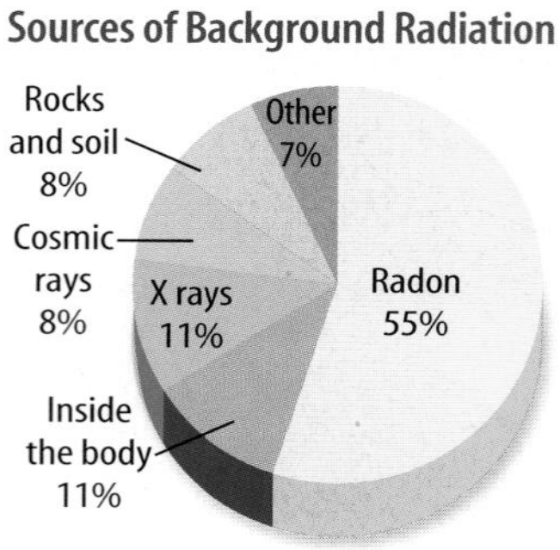

Figure 15 This circle graph shows the average amount of background radiation from different sources received by a person living in the United States.

Sources of Background Radiation Background radiation comes from several sources, as shown in **Figure 15.** The largest source comes from the decay of radon gas. Radon, which emits an alpha particle when it decays, is produced in Earth's crust by the decay of uranium-238. Radon gas can seep into houses and basements from the surrounding soil and rocks.

Some background radiation comes from high-speed nuclei, called cosmic rays, that strike Earth's atmosphere. They produce showers of particles, including alpha, beta, and gamma radiation. Most of this radiation is absorbed by the atmosphere. Higher up there is less atmosphere to absorb this radiation, so the background radiation from cosmic rays increases with altitude.

Radiation in Your Body Some of the elements that are essential for life have naturally occurring radioactive isotopes. For example, about one out of every trillion carbon atoms is carbon-14, which emits a beta particle when it decays. With each breath, you inhale about 3 million carbon-14 atoms.

The amount of background radiation a person receives can vary greatly. The amount depends on the type of rocks underground, the type of materials used to construct the person's home, and the elevation at which the person lives, among other things. However, because it comes from naturally occurring processes, background radiation never can be eliminated.

section 3 review

Summary

Radiation Detectors

- Alpha and beta particles can be detected by the trail of ions they form when they pass through a cloud chamber or a bubble chamber.
- The presence of alpha or beta particles can cause an electroscope to become discharged.
- A Geiger counter is used to measure radiation levels. It produces a clicking sound or a flash of light when alpha or beta particles enter the Geiger counter tube.

Background Radiation

- Background radiation is low-level radiations emitted mainly by radioactive isotopes in Earth's rocks, soils, and atmosphere.
- The largest source of background radiation is from the alpha decay of radon gas.

Self Check

1. **Describe** why a charged electroscope will discharge when placed near a radioactive material.
2. **Compare and contrast** cloud and bubble chambers.
3. **Describe** the process that occurs in a Geiger counter when radiation is detected.
4. **Explain** why background radiation never can be completely eliminated.
5. **Think Critically** If the radioactive isotope radon-222 has a half-life of only four days, how can radon gas be continually present inside houses?

Applying Math

6. **Use Percentages** The amount of radiation can be measured in units called millirems. If 25 millirems from cosmic rays is 8.0 percent of the average background radiation, what is the amount of the average background radiation in millirems?

More Section Review gpescience.com

section 3 review

1. Nuclear radiation causes some molecules in air to become positively charged. Negative charges on the electroscope leaves move from the leaves to the positively charged ions.
2. Both show the paths of ions created by radiation. In bubble chambers a liquid boils along the trail of the ions. In cloud chambers, vapor condenses around the ions.
3. A charged particle strikes a gas molecule in the tube, knocking off electrons. These electrons are attracted to a positively charged wire in the tube, producing more electrons as they collide with gas molecules. The current is amplified to produce a click.
4. Natural sources of background radiation include the decay of radioactive materials in rocks and soil, and cosmic rays, which cannot be eliminated.
5. Radon gas is continually produced by the decay of the isotope uranium-238, which has a half-life of 4.5 billion years.
6. Set up a ratio: (25 millirem)/x = 0.08; so x = (25 millirem)/0.08 = 312 millirem

800 CHAPTER 25 Nuclear Changes

section 4

Nuclear Reactions

Reading Guide

What You'll Learn
- **Explain** nuclear fission and how it can begin a chain reaction.
- **Discuss** how nuclear fusion occurs in the Sun.
- **Describe** how radioactive tracers can be used to diagnose medical problems.
- **Discuss** how nuclear reactions can help treat cancer.

Why It's Important

Almost all of the different atoms that you are made of were formed by the nuclear reactions inside ancient, distant stars.

Review Vocabulary

kinetic energy: energy of motion; increases as the mass or speed of an object increases

New Vocabulary
- nuclear fission
- chain reaction
- critical mass
- nuclear fusion
- tracer

Nuclear Fission

In the 1930s, physicist Enrico Fermi thought that by bombarding nuclei with neutrons, nuclei would absorb neutrons and heavier nuclei would be produced. However, in 1938, Otto Hahn and Fritz Strassmann found that when a neutron strikes a uranium-235 nucleus, the nucleus splits apart into smaller nuclei.

In 1939 Lise Meitner was the first to offer a theory to explain these results. She proposed that the uranium-235 nucleus is so distorted when the neutron strikes it that it divides into two smaller nuclei, as shown in **Figure 16.** The process of splitting a nucleus into several smaller nuclei is **nuclear fission.** The word *fission* means "to divide."

Reading Check *What initiates nuclear fission of a uranium-235 nucleus?*

Only large nuclei, such as the nuclei of uranium and plutonium, undergo nuclear fission. A fission reaction usually produces several individual neutrons in addition to the smaller nuclei. The total mass of the products is slightly less than the mass of the original nucleus and the neutron. This small amount of missing mass is converted to a tremendous amount of energy during the fission reaction.

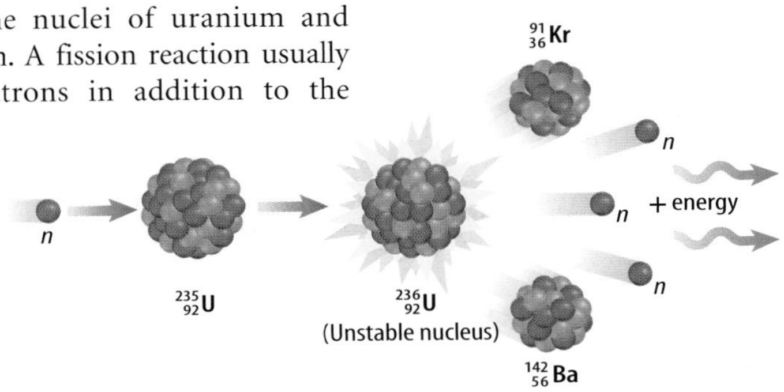

Figure 16 When a neutron hits a uranium-235 nucleus, the uranium nucleus splits into two smaller nuclei and two or three free neutrons. Energy also is released.

Section 4 Resource Manager

Chapter *FAST FILE* Resources
- Transparency Activity, p. 49
- MiniLAB, p. 4
- Directed Reading for Content Mastery, pp. 21–22
- Enrichment, p. 34
- Lab Worksheet, pp. 5–6, 7–8
- Reinforcement, p. 30

Home and Community Involvement, p. 37

Reading and Writing Skill Activities, p. 47

1 Motivate

INTERACTIVE CHALKBOARD — An editable Microsoft® PowerPoint® presentation is available on **Interactive Chalkboard** CD-ROM.

Bellringer

Section Focus Transparencies also are available on the Interactive Chalkboard CD-ROM. L2 ELL

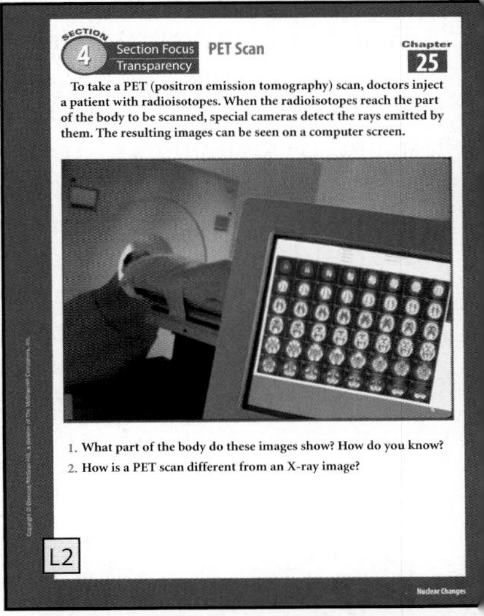

Reading Preview

Tie to Prior Knowledge

Breaking and Combining Fission means breaking things apart and fusion means putting things together. Ask students to give examples of processes they know that fit these definitions. In this section they will learn about nuclear fission and nuclear fusion.

Connections Connect new vocabulary words to more familiar terms. For instance, *nuclear fission* might be linked to *splitting nucleus*. Write the vocabulary term and the associated word on a chart. Ask students to visualize the associated word when they hear or see the vocabulary term.

2 Teach

Reading Check

Answer A neutron striking the nucleus causes it to split.

Quick Demo
Atomic Forces

Materials kinetic toy—several ball bearings suspended by two strings in contact with each other.

Time Required 1–3 min

Procedure Explain the forces at work in splitting an atom. The kinetic energy of a neutron is high enough to disrupt the strong force in the target nucleus, causing the atom to split into more stable configurations. At this point demonstrate the kinetic energy of the neutron by lifting one of the outside balls and dropping it to see the kinetic energy transmitted through the intermediary balls to the opposite outside ball and observe that ball flying out from the group.

Mini LAB

Purpose Students model a nuclear reaction. L2 ELL IS **Kinesthetic**

Materials marbles, beaker, modeling clay

Teaching Strategy Emphasize that the marbles taken out represent nuclei that decay but do not disappear; they change into nuclei of a different element.

Analysis
1. one minute
2. No. The waste products might be radioactive. They will not undergo fission.

Assessment

Oral What was the half-life of the marbles with clay? How many were left after 5 min? 1 min; one Use **PASC,** p. 101.

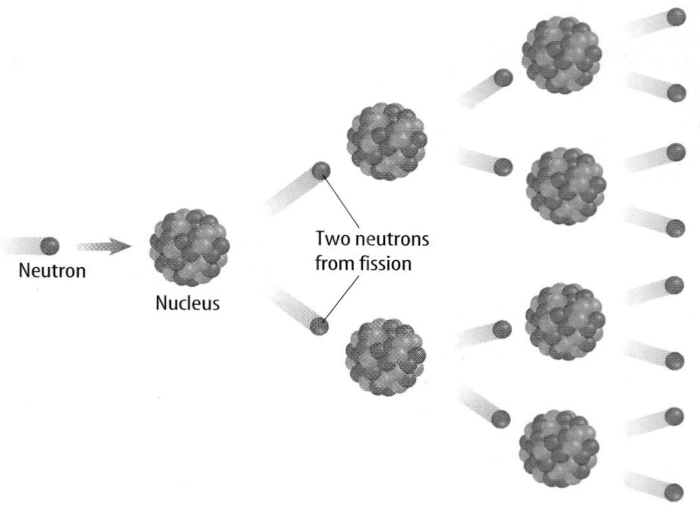

Figure 17 A chain reaction occurs when neutrons emitted from a split nucleus cause other nuclei to split and emit additional neutrons.

Mini LAB

Modeling a Nuclear Reaction

Procedure
1. Place **32 marbles,** each with an attached lump of **clay,** into a large **beaker.** These marbles with clay represent unstable atoms.
2. During a 1-min period, remove half of the marbles and pull off the clay. Place the removed marbles into another beaker and place the lumps of clay into a pile. Marbles without clay represent stable atoms. The clay represents waste from the reaction—smaller atoms that still might decay and give off energy.
3. Repeat this procedure four more times.

Analysis
1. What is the half-life of this reaction?
2. Explain whether the waste products could undergo nuclear fission.

Mass and Energy Albert Einstein proposed that mass and energy were related in his special theory of relativity. According to this theory, mass can be converted to energy and energy can be converted to mass. The relation between mass and energy is given by this equation:

Mass-Energy Equation

$$\text{Energy (joules)} = \text{mass (kg)} \times [\text{speed of light (m/s)}]^2$$
$$E = mc^2$$

A small amount of mass can be converted into an enormous amount of energy. For example, if one gram of mass is converted to energy, about 100 trillion joules of energy are released.

Chain Reactions When a nuclear fission reaction occurs, the neutrons emitted can strike other nuclei in the sample and cause them to split. These reactions then release more neutrons, causing additional nuclei to split, as shown in **Figure 17.** The series of repeated fission reactions caused by the release of neutrons in each reaction is a **chain reaction.**

If the chain reaction is uncontrolled, an enormous amount of energy is released in an instant. However, a chain reaction can be controlled by adding materials that absorb neutrons. If enough neutrons are absorbed, the reaction will continue at a constant rate.

For a chain reaction to occur, a critical mass of material that can undergo fission must be present. The **critical mass** is the amount of material required so that each fission reaction produces approximately one more fission reaction. If less than the critical mass of material is present, a chain reaction will not occur.

Science Journal

Nuclear Energy? Advocates claim that nuclear reactors are a safe, clean method of producing electricity. Opponents argue that because of the danger from spent nuclear fuel and nuclear waste, reactors should be permanently shut down. Have students write their opinions on this issue in their Science Journals. L2 IS **Linguistic**

Differentiated Instruction

Physically Disabled Pair students who cannot manipulate the marbles with students who can. Have the student with disabilities in each pair calculate the number of marbles to be processed during each one-minute period, and keep track of the number of marbles processed.

802 CHAPTER 25 Nuclear Changes

Nuclear Fusion

Even though nuclear fission reactions release tremendous amounts of energy, even more energy can be released by nuclear fusion reactions. In a **nuclear fusion** reaction, two nuclei with small masses combine to form a nucleus of larger mass. Nuclear fission reactions release millions of times more energy than can be released by chemical reactions.

The reason nuclear reactions release so much more energy than chemical reactions is that the strong force is much stronger than the electric force. This means that the nuclear potential energy stored in atomic nuclei is much greater than the chemical potential energy stored in chemical bonds between atoms.

Temperature and Fusion For nuclear fusion to occur, positively charged nuclei must get close to each other. However, nuclei repel each other because they have the same positive electric charge. If nuclei are moving fast, they can have enough kinetic energy to overcome the repulsive electrical force between them and get close to each other.

Remember that the kinetic energy of atoms or molecules increases as their temperature increases. Only at temperatures of millions of degrees Celsius are nuclei moving so fast that they can get close enough for fusion to occur. These extremely high temperatures are found in the center of stars, such as the Sun.

Nuclear Fusion and the Sun The Sun is composed mainly of hydrogen. Most of the energy given off by the Sun is produced by a process involving the fusion of hydrogen nuclei. This process occurs in several stages, and one of the stages is shown in **Figure 18.** The net result of this process is that four hydrogen nuclei are converted into one helium nucleus. As these nuclear reactions occur, a small amount of mass is changed into an enormous amount of energy. Earth receives a small amount of this energy as thermal energy and light.

As the Sun ages, the hydrogen nuclei are used up as they are converted into helium. So far, only about one percent of the Sun's mass has been converted into energy. It is estimated that the Sun has enough hydrogen to keep this reaction going for another 5 billion years.

Science Online

Topic: Fusion Reactors
Visit gpescience.com for Web links to information about the use of nuclear fusion as a future energy source.

Activity Write a paragraph describing the different types of fusion reactors that have been developed.

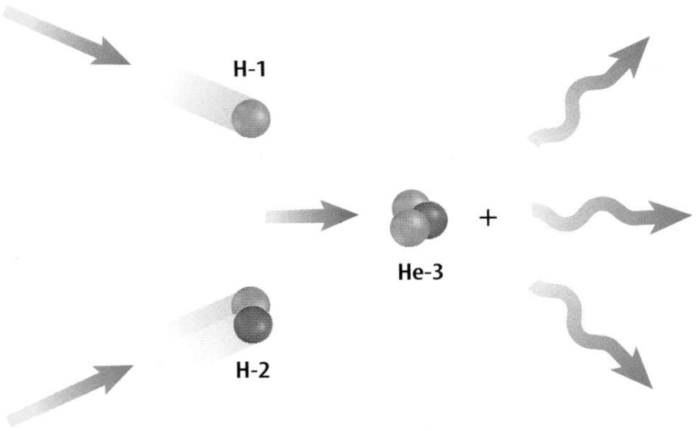

Figure 18 The fusion of hydrogen to form helium takes place in several stages in the Sun. One of these stages is shown here. An isotope of helium is produced when a proton and the hydrogen isotope H-2 undergo fusion.

Make a Model

Clay Nuclei Have students model fusion by using small balls of clay to show how two nuclei can join to become one larger nucleus. They should use different colors of clay to represent protons and neutrons. An easy reaction to model is the one in which a deuterium nucleus (hydrogen with one neutron) and a tritium nucleus (hydrogen with two neutrons) combine to form a helium nucleus and one neutron. Point out that when the number of protons changes, a nucleus of a new element is formed. L2
LS **Kinesthetic**

Teacher FYI

Hydrogen Bomb Scientists have been unable to achieve controlled fusion because the high temperature needed to initiate the reaction creates plasma that is difficult to contain. A hydrogen bomb, however, uses uncontrolled fusion. Inside the hydrogen bomb's casing, an atomic bomb uses fission to create the extreme temperatures needed to start the fusion reaction.

Use Science Words

Word Meaning Have students explain why the fusion of hydrogen nuclei on the Sun is called a thermonuclear reaction. *Thermo-* comes from a Greek word meaning "heat." Forcing hydrogen nuclei to fuse requires extreme heat. L3 LS **Linguistic**

Fun Fact

The submarines of the U.S. Navy are powered by nuclear reactors.

Reading Strategy

Infer This skill involves reading carefully to interpret meaning. Students might read: If less critical mass of material is present, a chain reaction will not occur. They could infer: If there's more critical mass, a chain reaction will occur. Have them practice making inferences.

SECTION 4 Nuclear Reactions 803

INTEGRATE Chemistry

Radioactive Decay Equations The atomic number of barium is 56 and the atomic number of krypton is 36. These add up to 92. Uranium-235 breaks into neodymium (atomic number 60) and germanium (atomic number 32).

Research Potassium-40 decays to form two other isotopes. Research to learn what these isotopes are. argon-40 and calcium-40

Discussion

Tracers How is the use of tracers similar to the use of radio collars in tracking wild animals? The collars emit an electromagnetic signal that can be detected with an antenna and receiver. This allows scientists to determine the movement of the animal. Similarly, a radioactive tracer emits radiation, which allows physicians to track its movement in the body. L2 LS **Logical-Mathematical**

Reading Check

Answer by detecting the radioactivity they emit

Caption Answer

Figure 19 Iodine is naturally taken up by the thyroid. Also, it allows doctors to determine how well the thyroid is functioning without having to actually look at it.

INTEGRATE Health **Content Background**

A malfunctioning thyroid may produce too much or too little of the hormones necessary for your body to function properly. These conditions are called hyperthyroidism and hypothyroidism, respectively. Iodine is a main ingredient in the two most important hormones produced by the thyroid. A hyperthyroid patient given radioactive iodine will show an excessive level of thyroid radioactivity. The opposite occurs in hypothyroidism.

INTEGRATE Chemistry

Radioactive Decay Equations A uranium-235 atom can fission, or break apart, to form barium and krypton. Use a periodic table to find the atomic numbers of barium and krypton. What do they add up to? A uranium-235 atom can fission in several other ways such as producing neodymium and another element. What is the other element?

Using Nuclear Reactions in Medicine

If you were going to meet a friend in a crowded area, it would be easier to find her if she told you that she would be wearing a red hat. In a similar way, scientists can find one molecule in a large group of molecules if they know that it is "wearing" something unique. Although a molecule can't wear a red hat, if it has a radioactive atom in it, it can be found easily in a large group of molecules, or even in a living organism. Radioactive isotopes can be located by detecting the radiation they emit.

When a radioisotope is used to find or keep track of molecules in an organism, it is called a **tracer.** Scientists can use tracers to follow where a particular molecule goes in your body or to study how a particular organ functions. Tracers also are used in agriculture to monitor the uptake of nutrients and fertilizers. Examples of tracers include carbon-11, iodine-131, and sodium-24. These three radioisotopes are useful tracers because they are important in certain body processes. As a result, they accumulate inside the organism being studied.

Reading Check *How are tracers located inside the human body?*

INTEGRATE Health **Iodine Tracers in the Thyroid** The thyroid gland is located in your neck and produces chemical compounds called hormones. These hormones help regulate several body processes, including growth. Because the element iodine accumulates in the thyroid, the radioisotope iodine-131 can be used to diagnose thyroid problems. As iodine-131 atoms are absorbed by the thyroid, their nuclei decay, emitting beta particles and gamma rays. The beta particles are absorbed by the surrounding tissues, but the gamma rays penetrate the skin. The emitted gamma rays can be detected and used to determine whether the thyroid is healthy, as shown in **Figure 19.** If the detected radiation is not intense, then the thyroid has not properly absorbed the iodine-131 and is not functioning properly. This could be due to the presence of a tumor. **Figure 20** shows how radioactive tracers are used to study the brain.

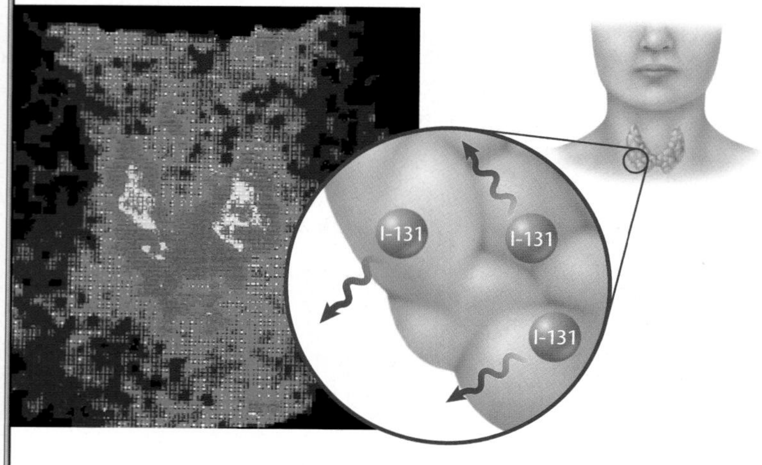

Figure 19 Radioactive iodine-131 accumulates in the thyroid gland and emits gamma rays, which can be detected to form an image of a patient's thyroid. **List** *some advantages of being able to use iodine-131 to form an image of a thyroid.*

Differentiated Instruction

Challenge Have students investigate other ways that tracers are used in medicine and prepare a report on one method. If possible, they should interview a physician who uses tracers to find out drawbacks and benefits of the procedure. Possible topics are tracers used to detect problems with the heart, kidneys, or digestion. L3 LS **Linguistic**

Visual Learning

Figure 19 Point out that the picture to the left shows the thyroid after the person has ingested the iodine-131 tracer. The red and orange colors indicate areas in which the iodine is well absorbed. Have students each find his or her thyroid gland, which is located in the neck between the larynx and the trachea. L2 LS **Visual-Spatial**

NATIONAL GEOGRAPHIC

VISUALIZING PET SCANS

Figure 20

The diagram below shows an imaging technique known as Positron Emission Tomography, or PET. Positrons are emitted from the nuclei of certain radioactive isotopes when a proton changes to a neutron. PET can form images that show the level of activity in different areas of the brain. These images can reveal tumors and regions of abnormal brain activity.

A When positrons are emitted from the nucleus of an atom, they can hit electrons from other atoms and become transformed into gamma rays.

B The radioactive isotope fluorine-18 emits positrons when it decays. Fluorine-18 atoms are chemically attached to molecules that are absorbed by brain tissue. These compounds are injected into the patient and carried by blood to the brain.

C Inside the patient's brain, the decay of the radioactive fluorine-18 nuclei emits positrons that collide with electrons. The gamma rays that are released are sensed by the detectors.

D A computer uses the information collected by the detectors to generate an image of the activity level in the brain. This image shows normal activity in the right side of the brain (red, yellow, green) but below-normal activity in the left (purple).

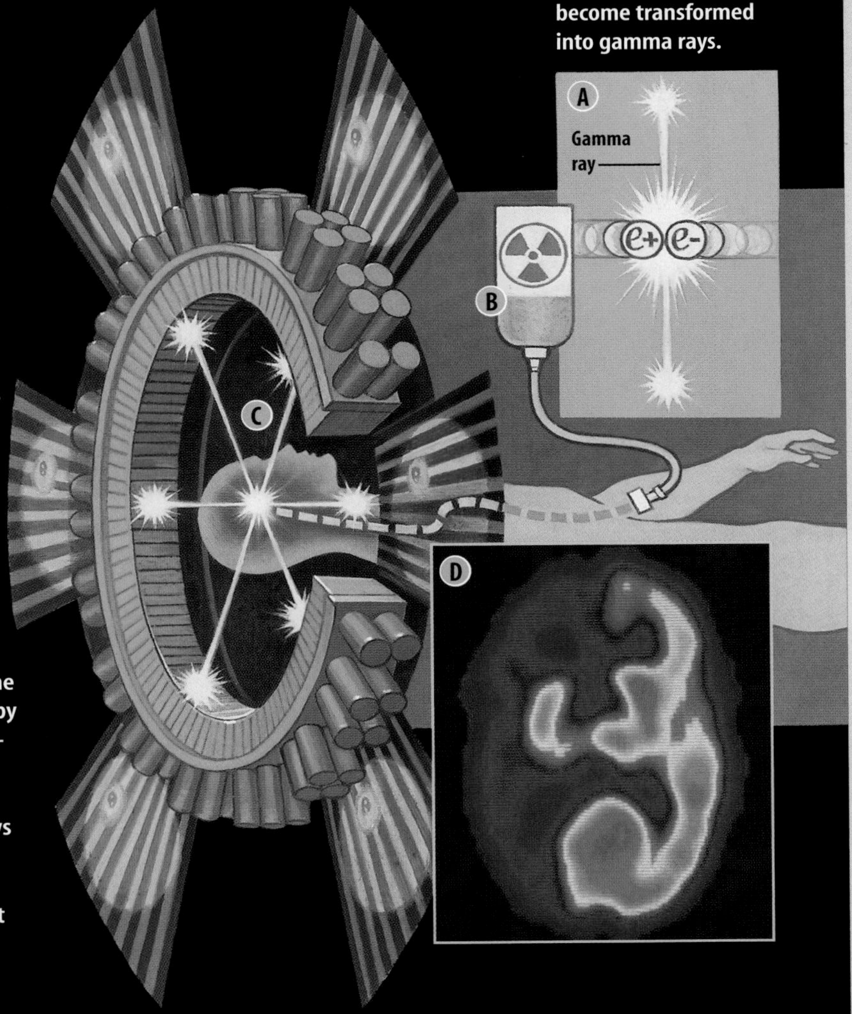

NATIONAL GEOGRAPHIC

Visualizing PET Scans

Have students examine the pictures and read the captions. Then ask the following questions:

What is a positron? A positron has the same mass as an electron but a positive charge. It can be considered a positively charged electron.

What is formed when a positron and electron combine? gamma rays

Why is it important for the fluorine-18 to be chemically attached to substances that are normally absorbed by the brain? The fluorine-18 needs to be absorbed in the brain tissue because that is the area that is being studied.

Activity

Positron Posters Have the students research how positrons are formed. Suggest students make posters illustrating their findings and present their posters to the class. L2 IS **Visual-Spatial** P

Post Reading

Debate Have students research nuclear reactions to determine the pros and cons of nuclear energy use. Engage the class in a debate with the following prompt: Do the benefits of using nuclear energy outweigh the risks?

3 Assess

DAILY INTERVENTION

Check for Understanding

Logical-Mathematical Ask students to explain why chain reactions do not occur in naturally existing material. Fission occurs only for certain rare isotopes. The percentage of these isotopes in naturally existing material is so low that a chain reaction is unlikely. LS

Reteach

Chain Reactions Have students discuss why a critical mass is necessary to keep a fission reaction going but not to keep a fusion reaction going. In a fission reaction, a particle bombards a nucleus and splits it into two nuclei plus several neutrons. If these neutrons hit other fissionable nuclei, those nuclei will split and produce new particles. This chain reaction will continue as long as there is enough fissionable material nearby. The amount needed to keep the reaction going is the critical mass. A fusion reaction is not a chain reaction. L2 LS **Logical-Mathematical**

Assessment

Content Many benefits result from nuclear applications in medicine, but there are disadvantages, too. Ask students to write newspaper articles explaining how radiation can cause as well as treat cancer. Possible answers: It can cause mutations in cell structures, leading to tumor formation, or it can kill cancer cells. Use **PASC,** p. 141.

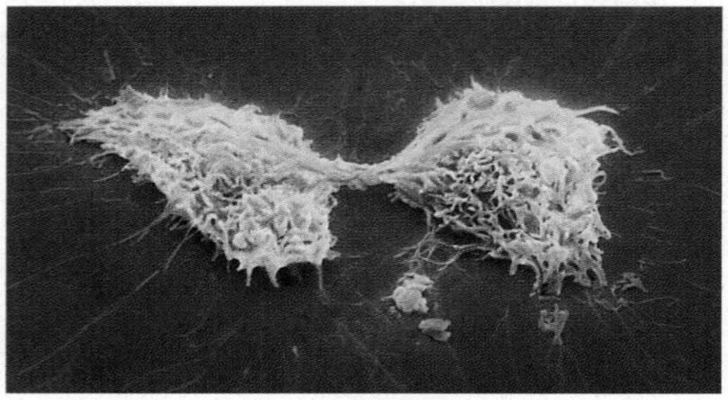

Figure 21 Cancer cells, such as the ones shown here, can be killed with carefully measured doses of radiation.

Treating Cancer with Radioactivity

When a person has cancer, a group of cells in that person's body grows out of control and can form a tumor. Radiation can be used to stop some types of cancerous cells from growing. Remember that the radiation that is given off during nuclear decay is strong enough to ionize nearby atoms. If a source of radiation is placed near cancer cells, such as those shown in **Figure 21,** atoms in the cells can be ionized. If the ionized atoms are in a critical molecule, such as the DNA or RNA of a cancer cell, then the molecule might no longer function properly. The cell then could die or stop growing.

When possible, a radioactive isotope such as gold-198 or iridium-192 is implanted within or near the tumor. Other times, tumors are treated from outside the body. Typically, an intense beam of gamma rays from the decay of cobalt-60 is focused on the tumor for a short period of time. The gamma rays pass through the body and into the tumor. How can physicians be sure that only the cancer cells will absorb radiation? Because cancer cells grow quickly, thev are more susceptible to absorbing radiation and being damaged than healthy cells are. However, other cells in the body that grow quickly also are damaged, which is why cancer patients who have radiation therapy sometimes experience severe side effects.

section 4 review

Summary

Nuclear Fission

- Nuclear fission occurs when a neutron strikes a nucleus, causing it to split into smaller nuclei.
- A chain reaction requires a critical mass of fissionable material.

Nuclear Fusion

- Nuclear fusion occurs when two nuclei combine to form another nucleus.
- Nuclear fusion occurs at temperatures of millions of degrees, which occur inside the Sun.

Medical Uses of Radiation

- Radioactive isotopes are used as tracers to locate various atoms or molecules in organisms.
- Radiation emitted by radioactive isotopes is used to kill cancer cells.

Self Check

1. **Infer** whether mass is conserved in a nuclear reaction.
2. **Explain** why fusion reactions can occur inside stars.
3. **Explain** how a chain reaction can be controlled.
4. **Describe** two properties of a tracer isotope used for monitoring the functioning of an organ in the body.
5. **Think Critically** Explain why high temperatures are needed for fusion reactions to occur, but not for fission reactions to occur.

Applying Math

6. **Calculate Number of Nuclei** In a chain reaction, two neutrons are emitted by each nucleus that is split. If one nucleus is split in the first step of the reaction, how many nuclei will have been split after the fifth step?

More Section Review gpescience.com

section 4 review

1. No. Some of the mass in the initial nuclei is converted into energy.
2. Fusion reactions require extremely high temperatures to get started. These temperatures occur in the interior of stars.
3. By absorbing some of the neutrons emitted when fission occurs.
4. The isotope must be absorbed by the organ being studied, and must have a half-life sufficiently long for the study to be completed before it decays away.
5. In order for the strong force to act and fusion to occur, nuclei must be moving fast enough to overcome the electrical repulsion between them. The necessary speeds occur only at high temperatures. Fission does not require high speeds because neutrons are not electrically repulsed by the nucleus.
6. step1 :1; step 2 : 2; step 3 : 4; step 4 : 8; step 5 : 16

LAB

Chain Reactions

In an uncontrolled nuclear chain reaction, the number of reactions increases as additional neutrons split more nuclei. In a controlled nuclear reaction, neutrons are absorbed, so the reaction continues at a constant rate. How could you model a controlled and an uncontrolled nuclear reaction in the classroom?

Real-World Problem

How can you use dominoes to model chain reactions?

Goals

- **Model** a controlled and uncontrolled chain reaction.
- **Compare** the two types of chain reactions.

Materials

dominoes
stopwatch

Procedure

1. Set up a single line of dominoes standing on end so that when the first domino is pushed over, it will knock over the second and each domino will knock over the one following it.
2. Using the stopwatch, time how long it takes from the moment the first domino is pushed over until the last domino falls over. Record the time.
3. Using the same number of dominoes as in step 1, set up a series of dominoes in which at least one of the dominoes will knock down two others, so that two lines of dominoes will continue falling. In other words, the series should have at least one point that looks like the letter Y.
4. Repeat step 2.

Conclude and Apply

1. **Compare** the amount of time it took for all of the dominoes to fall in each of your two arrangements.
2. **Determine** the average number of dominoes that fell per second in both domino arrangements.
3. **Identify** which of your domino arrangements represented a controlled chain reaction and which represented an uncontrolled chain reaction.
4. **Describe** how the concept of critical mass was represented in your model of a controlled chain reaction.
5. Assuming that they had equal amounts of material, which would finish faster—a controlled or an uncontrolled nuclear chain reaction? Explain.

Communicating Your Data

Explain to friends or members of your family how a controlled nuclear chain reaction can be used in nuclear power plants to generate electricity.

BENCH TESTED

Video Lab available.

Real-World Problem

Purpose Students model controlled and uncontrolled chain reactions. L2 IN **Kinesthetic**

Process Skills collect data, make models, compare and contrast, draw conclusions

Time Required 40 min

Procedure

Teaching Strategy Students can collect additional data by forming large groups and using all of their dominoes to form longer chains.

Conclude and Apply

1. The Y-shaped arrangement fell faster.
2. Answers will vary.
3. The straight arrangement represented a controlled reaction because any neutron that split off was absorbed. The Y-shaped arrangement represented an uncontrolled reaction.
4. Critical mass was represented because the reaction stopped when the fissionable material (dominoes) was used up.
5. An uncontrolled reaction would finish faster because a single reaction could produce two reactions which could produce four reactions and so on.

Communicating Your Data

Students should prepare an illustration of a controlled and an uncontrolled reaction to help explain what is taking place.

Assessment

Content Have students write and perform a skit that demonstrates controlled and uncontrolled reactions. Use **Performance Assessment in the Science Classroom,** p. 147.

BENCH TESTED

Real-World Problem

Purpose Students will model the decay of a uranium atom through the process of transmutation. L2 LS **Kinesthetic**

Process Skills make a model, compare and contrast, identify, infer

Time Required one 45-minute class period

Possible Materials Students can use any small objects in place of the rice, beans, or candy. A strong bonding glue should be used when constructing the model.

Safety Precautions Never eat foods used in the lab.

Discussion

Radioactive Substances Ask students to think about radioactive substances such as uranium and plutonium. Have them consider the exposure to radiation some people have been exposed to such as after nuclear testing or the Chernobyl accident. Why is radiation dangerous? Where does radiation come from? What effects would come from having radioactive materials in their homes? What radioactive substance might be found in their basements (radon)?

LAB Model and Invent

Modeling Transmutations

Goal
- **Model** decay of a uranium atom.

Possible Materials
brown rice
white rice
colored candies
dried beans
dried seeds
glue
poster board

Safety Precautions

WARNING: *Never eat foods used in the lab.*

Data Source
Refer to your textbook for general information about transmutation.

Real-World Problem

Imagine what would happen if the oxygen atoms around you began changing into nitrogen atoms. Without oxygen, most living organisms, including people, could not live. Fortunately, more than 99.9 percent of all oxygen atoms are stable and do not decay. Usually, when an unstable nucleus decays, an alpha or beta particle is thrown out of its nucleus, and the atom becomes a new element. A uranium-238 atom, for example, will undergo eight alpha decays and six beta decays to become lead. This process of one element changing into another element is called transmutation. How could you create a model of a uranium-238 atom and the decay process it undergoes during transmutation? What types of materials could you use to represent the protons and neutrons in a U-238 nucleus? How could you use these materials to model transmutation?

Make a Model

1. **Choose** two materials of different colors or shapes for the protons and neutrons of your nucleus model. Choose a material for the negatively charged beta particle.

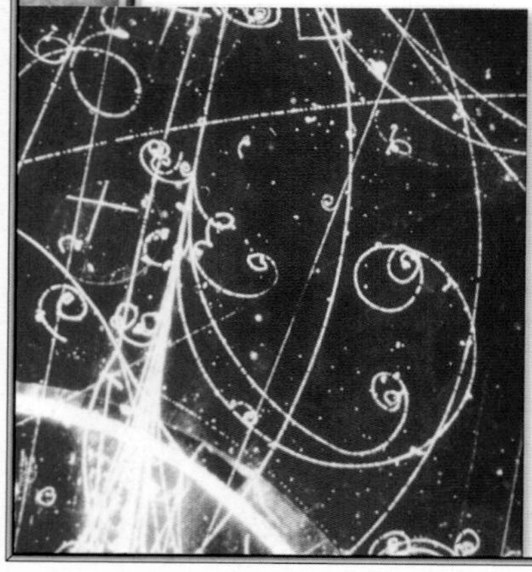

Differentiated Instruction

Physically Challenged If students cannot manipulate the materials, have them design a model, and ask other students to work with them to make the model.

Using Scientific Methods

2. **Decide** how to model the transmutation process. Will you create a new nucleus model for each new element? How will you model an alpha or beta particle leaving the nucleus?

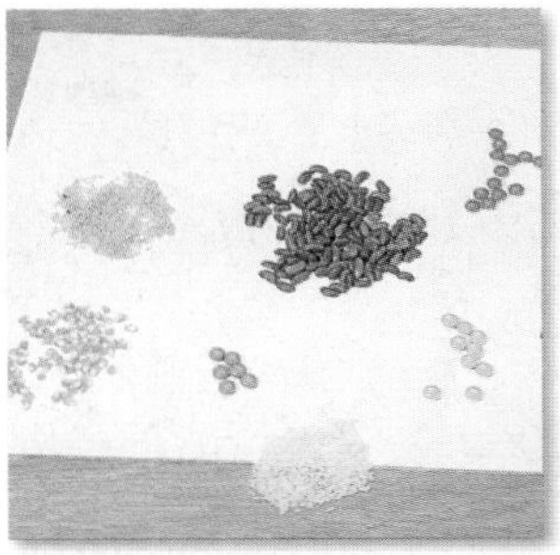

3. **Create** a transmutation chart to show the results of each transmutation step of a uranium-238 atom with the identity, atomic number, and mass number of each new element formed and the type of radiation particle emitted at each step. A uranium-238 atom will undergo the following decay steps before transmuting into a lead-206 atom: alpha decay, beta decay, beta decay, alpha decay, alpha decay, alpha decay, alpha decay, alpha decay, beta decay, beta decay, alpha decay, beta decay, beta decay, alpha decay.
4. **Describe** your model plan and transmutation chart to your teacher and ask how they can be improved.
5. **Present** your plan and chart to your class. Ask classmates to suggest improvements in both.
6. Construct your model of a uranium-238 nucleus showing the correct number of protons and neutrons.

Test Your Model

1. Using your nucleus model, demonstrate the transmutation of a uranium-238 nucleus into a lead-206 nucleus by following the decay sequence outlined in the previous section.
2. Show the emission of an alpha particle or beta particle between each transmutation step.

Analyze Your Data

1. **Compare** how alpha and beta decay change an atom's atomic number.
2. **Compare** how alpha and beta decay change the mass number of an atom.

Conclude and Apply

1. **Calculate** the ratio of neutrons to protons in lead-206 and uranium-238. In which nucleus is the ratio closer to 1.5?
2. **Identify** Alchemists living during the Middle Ages spent much time trying to turn lead into gold. Identify the decay processes needed to accomplish this task.

Communicating Your Data

Show your model to the class and explain how your model represents the transmutation of U-238 into Pb-206.

Make a Model

Possible Procedures

- Use white rice for protons and brown rice for neutrons.
- Make a model of the nucleus of a uranium-238 atom in the upper left corner of the poster board by gluing the appropriate rice to the board.
- Draw an arrow with the type of decay above it pointing to the resulting isotope.
- Repeat all 14 steps of decay.
- Make rice model of lead-206 nucleus in lower right corner.

Teaching Strategy Have references available for students to use that show the transmutation of uranium into lead.

Test Your Model

Expected Outcome Students will build a model that demonstrates the transmutation of uranium.

Analyze Your Data

1. Alpha decay decreases the atomic number by two; beta decay increases the atomic number by one.
2. Alpha decay decreases the mass number by four; beta decay causes no change in the mass number.

Conclude and Apply

1. For lead-206, the ratio is 1.51. For uranium-238, the ratio is 1.59. Lead-206 has a ratio closer to 1.5.
2. Two alpha decays and one beta decay would be required to turn an atom of lead into an atom of gold.

Assessment

Process Ask students to make pamphlets identifying ways the transmutation of uranium and plutonium are used. nuclear power plant, nuclear weapons, nuclear submarines, and spacecraft Use **Performance Assessment in the Science Classroom,** p. 129.

Communicating Your Data

Encourage students to use computer-generated diagrams to accompany their models.

TIME

Content Background

After Henri Becquerel's discovery of radioactivity in 1896, no one as yet suspected that atoms were not indivisible. At first it was thought that radioactivity was the result of chemical processes that occurred in the atoms involved. However, in 1902, Ernest Rutherford and Frederick Soddy discovered that radioactive thorium produced other elements, and realized that thorium atoms were decaying.

In the early 1930s, Enrico Fermi started a series of experiments in which he bombarded nuclei of various elements with neutrons, in an attempt to produce artificial radioactivity. When uranium was bombarded with neutrons, several radioactive products were produced. In 1938, Otto Hahn and Fritz Strassmann announced that the products of the neutron bombardment of uranium were smaller nuclei. This was the first demonstration of nuclear fission.

Historical Significance

The discovery of radioactivity and the development of methods to control nuclear fission have resulted in techniques for using nuclear radiation to treat diseases, as well as nuclear power plants. However, the development of nuclear weapons has had a profound impact on relations between the United States and other countries.

TIME **SCIENCE** AND HISTORY

SCIENCE CAN CHANGE THE COURSE OF HISTORY!

The Nuclear Alchemists

The colored tracks are alpha particles emitted from a speck of radium salt placed on a special photographic plate.

For centuries, ancient alchemists tried in vain to convert common metals into gold. However, in the early 20th century, some scientists realized there was a way to convert atoms of some elements into other elements—nuclear fission.

A Startling Discovery

As the twentieth century dawned, most scientists thought atoms could not be broken apart. In 1902, New Zealand physicist Ernest Rutherford and his colleague Frederick Soddy showed that heavy elements uranium and thorium decayed into slightly lighter elements, with the production of helium gas. "Don't call it transmutation. They'll have our heads off as alchemists!" Rutherford warned Soddy. In 1908, Rutherford showed that the alpha particles emitted in radioactive decay were the same as helium nuclei.

Something's Missing

In 1938 in Germany, Otto Hahn and Fritz Strassmann found the uranium-235 nucleus would split if struck by a neutron. The process was called nuclear fission.

Enrico Fermi lead the development of the first nuclear reactor.

A year later, Austrian physicist Lise Meitner pointed out that the total mass of the particles produced when the uranium nucleus split was less than that of the original uranium nucleus. According to the special theory of relativity, this small amount of missing mass results in the release of a tremendous amount of energy when fission occurs. But is there any way this energy can be controlled?

Lise Meitner was the first to explain how nuclear fission occurs.

Controlling a Chain Reaction

Only a few years later, Italian physicist Enrico Fermi, working with colleagues in the United States, found the answer. Fermi realized that the neutrons released when fission occurs could lead to a chain reaction. However, materials that absorb neutrons could be used to control the chain reaction. In late 1942, Fermi and his colleagues built the first nuclear reactor by using cadmium rods to absorb neutrons and control the chain reaction. The tremendous energy released by nuclear fission could be controlled.

Research Find out more about the contributions these scientists made to understanding radioactivity and the nucleus. What other discoveries did Rutherford and Fermi make?

TIME
For more information, visit gpescience.com

Research Rutherford also discovered alpha rays and beta rays, the existence of the atomic nucleus, and predicted the existence of the neutron. Fermi discovered that neutron bombardment causes nuclear transformations, formulated the theory of beta decay, and predicted the existence of the neutrino.

Resources for Teachers and Students

How Do We Know the Nature of the Atom?, Natalie Goldstein, Rosen Publishing Group, Incorporated, 2001

Ernest Rutherford and the Atom, John L. Heilbron, Oxford, 2003

Reviewing Main Ideas

Section 1 Radioactivity

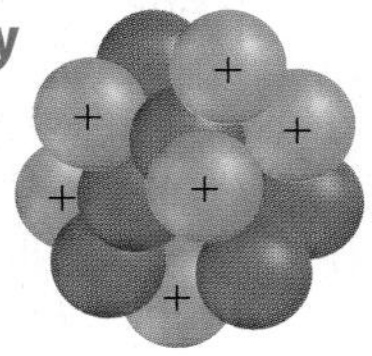
Nucleus

1. The protons and neutrons in an atomic nucleus, like the one to the right, are held together by the strong force.
2. The ratio of protons to neutrons indicates whether a nucleus will be stable or unstable. Large nuclei tend to be unstable.
3. Radioactivity is the emission of energy or particles from an unstable nucleus.
4. Radioactivity was discovered accidentally by Henri Becquerel about 100 years ago.

Section 2 Nuclear Decay

1. Unstable nuclei can decay by emitting alpha particles, beta particles, and gamma rays.
2. Alpha particles consist of two protons and two neutrons. A beta particle is an electron.
3. Gamma rays are the highest frequency electromagnetic waves.
4. Half-life is the amount of time in which half of the nuclei of a radioactive isotope will decay.
5. Because all living things contain carbon, the radioactive isotope carbon-14 can be used to date the remains of organisms that lived during the past 50,000 years, such as this skeleton.

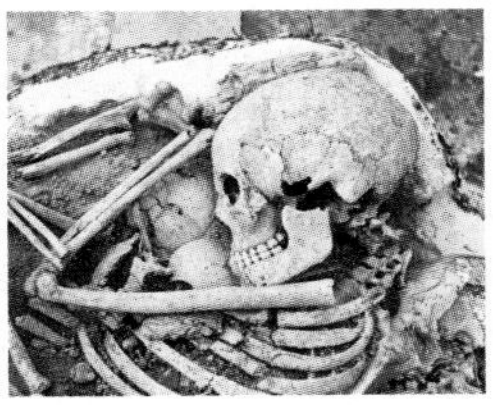

6. Radioactive isotopes of uranium are used to date rocks.

Section 3 Detecting Radioactivity

1. Radioactivity can be detected with a cloud chamber, a bubble chamber, an electroscope, or a Geiger counter.
2. A Geiger counter measures the amount of radiation by producing electric current when it is struck by a charged particle.
3. Background radiation is low-level radiation emitted by naturally occurring isotopes found in Earth's rocks and soils, the atmosphere, and inside your body.

Section 4 Nuclear Reactions

1. When nuclear fission occurs, a nucleus splits into smaller nuclei. Neutrons and a large amount of energy are emitted.
2. Neutrons emitted when a nuclear fission reaction occurs can cause a chain reaction. A chain reaction can occur only if a critical mass of material is present.
3. Nuclear fusion occurs at high temperatures when light nuclei collide and form heavier nuclei, releasing a large amount of energy.
4. Radioactive tracers that are absorbed by specific organs can help diagnose health problems. Nuclear radiation is used to kill cancer cells.

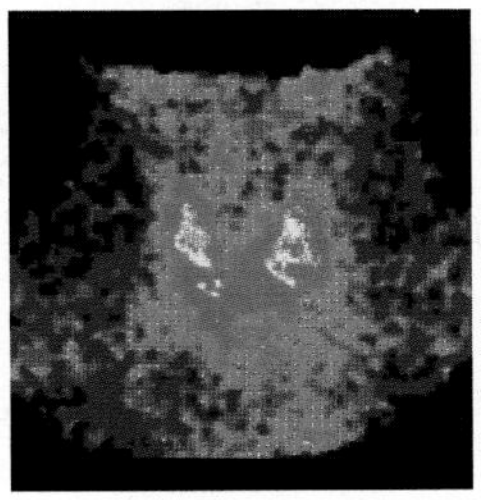

FOLDABLES™ Use the Foldable that you made at the beginning of this chapter to help you review advantages and disadvantages of using radioactive materials and nuclear reactions.

chapter Study Guide 25

Reviewing Main Ideas

Summary statements can be used by students to review the major concepts of the chapter.

Science Online

Visit gpescience.com
More Section Review
Interactive Tutor
Vocabulary PuzzleMaker
More Chapter Review
Standardized Test Practice

Assessment Transparency

For additional assessment questions, use the *Assessment Transparency* located in the transparency book.

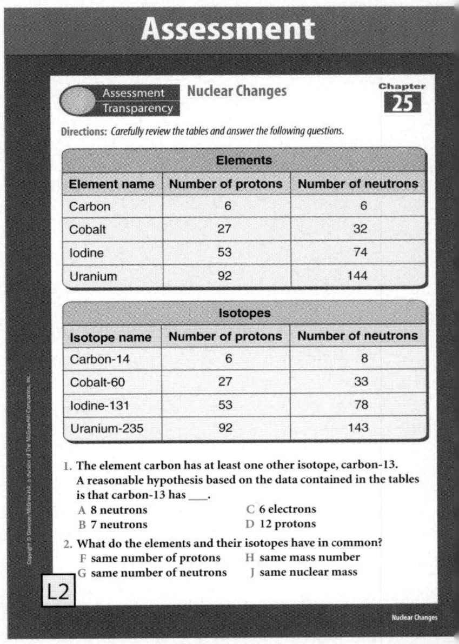
Assessment

Assessment Transparency **Nuclear Changes** Chapter 25

Directions: *Carefully review the tables and answer the following questions.*

Elements		
Element name	**Number of protons**	**Number of neutrons**
Carbon	6	6
Cobalt	27	32
Iodine	53	74
Uranium	92	144

Isotopes		
Isotope name	**Number of protons**	**Number of neutrons**
Carbon-14	6	8
Cobalt-60	27	33
Iodine-131	53	78
Uranium-235	92	143

1. The element carbon has at least one other isotope, carbon-13. A reasonable hypothesis based on the data contained in the tables is that carbon-13 has ___.
   A 8 neutrons C 6 electrons
   B 7 neutrons D 12 protons
2. What do the elements and their isotopes have in common?
   F same number of protons H same mass number
   G same number of neutrons J same nuclear mass

L2

Nuclear Changes

FOLDABLES™ Have students use their Foldables to review the content of the chapter. Is radioactivity necessarily a good thing or a bad thing? Explain why.

Using Vocabulary

1. Both are used to detect subatomic particles. In both, charged particles create ions. In a cloud chamber, vapor condenses around these ions. In a bubble chamber, a liquid boils along the trail of ions.
2. A chain reaction is an ongoing series of fission reactions. Critical mass is the minimum amount of fissionable material required for a fission chain to occur.
3. Nuclear fission is the splitting of a nucleus. Nuclear fusion is the combining of two nuclei.
4. Radioactivity is the emission of high-energy radiation or particles from the nucleus of a radioactive atom. Half-life is the time required for half of a sample of radioactive material to decay.
5. An alpha particle is made of two protons and two neutrons. A beta particle is a high-speed electron. A gamma ray is high-energy electromagnetic radiation. All are types of nuclear radiation.
6. A Geiger counter is a device that measures radioactivity by producing an electric current when radiation is present. A tracer is a radioactive isotope that can be detected as it moves in an organism.
7. Nuclear fission is the splitting of a nucleus. Transmutation is the process of changing one element to another.
8. An electroscope detects radiation by responding to ionization of the surrounding air, which causes its leaves to separate. In a Geiger counter, electric current is produced when the instrument detects radiation.
9. The strong force binds atomic nuclei together. Radioactivity occurs when a nucleus emits alpha, beta, or gamma radiation.

Checking Concepts

10. A
11. B
12. B
13. A
14. A
15. A
16. D

chapter 25 Review

Using Vocabulary

alpha particle p. 791
beta particle p. 793
bubble chamber p. 797
chain reaction p. 802
cloud chamber p. 796
critical mass p. 802
gamma ray p. 793
Geiger counter p. 798
half-life p. 794
nuclear fission p. 801
nuclear fusion p. 803
radioactivity p. 788
strong force p. 787
tracer p. 804
transmutation p. 792

Use what you know about the vocabulary words to explain the differences in the following sets of words. Then explain how the words are related.

1. cloud chamber—bubble chamber
2. chain reaction—critical mass
3. nuclear fission—nuclear fusion
4. radioactivity—half-life
5. alpha particle—beta particle—gamma ray
6. Geiger counter—tracer
7. nuclear fission—transmutation
8. electroscope—Geiger counter
9. strong force—radioactivity

Checking Concepts

Choose the word or phrase that best answers the question.

10. What keeps particles in a nucleus together?
    A) strong force
    B) repulsion
    C) electrical force
    D) atomic glue
11. Which device would be most useful for measuring the amount of radiation in a nuclear laboratory?
    A) a cloud chamber
    B) a Geiger counter
    C) an electroscope
    D) a bubble chamber
12. What is an electron that is produced when a neutron decays called?
    A) an alpha particle
    B) a beta particle
    C) gamma radiation
    D) a negatron
13. Which of the following describes an isotope's half-life?
    A) a constant time interval
    B) a varied time interval
    C) an increasing time interval
    D) a decreasing time interval
14. For which of the following could carbon-14 dating be used?
    A) a bone fragment
    B) a marble column
    C) dinosaur fossils
    D) rocks

Use the illustration below to answer question 15.

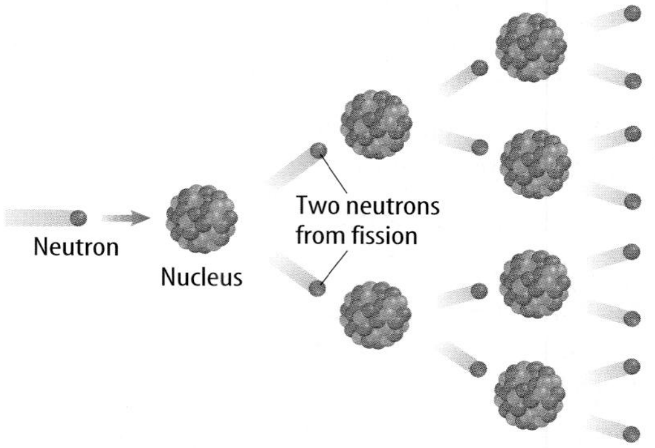

15. Which term describes an ongoing series of fission reactions such as the one pictured above?
    A) chain reaction
    B) decay reaction
    C) positron emission
    D) fusion reaction
16. Which of the following describes atoms with the same number of protons and a different number of neutrons?
    A) unstable
    B) synthetic
    C) radioactive
    D) isotopes

Vocabulary PuzzleMaker gpescience.com

Use the Exam*View*® Pro Testmaker CD-ROM to:

- create multiple versions of tests
- create modified tests with one mouse click for inclusion students
- edit existing questions and add your own questions
- build tests aligned with state standards using built-in State Curriculum Tags
- change English tests to Spanish with one mouse click and vice versa

Interpreting Graphics

17. Copy and complete the following concept map on radioactivity.

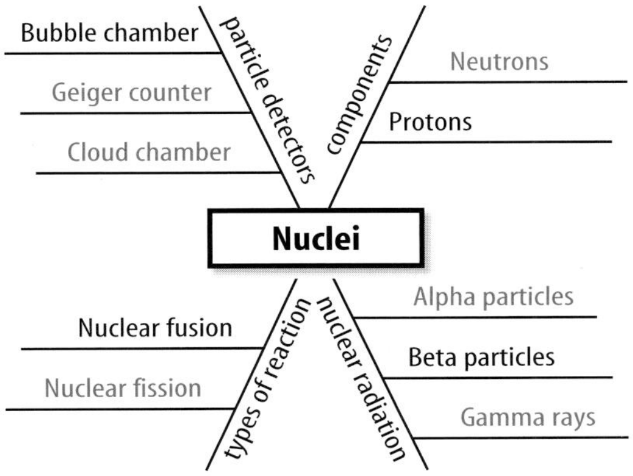

18. **Make a table** summarizing the use of radioactive isotopes or nuclear radiation in the following applications: radioactive dating, monitoring the thyroid gland, and treating cancer. Include a description of the radioactive isotope or radiation involved.

Use the data in the table below to answer question 19.

Isotope Half-Lives

Isotope	Mass Number	Half-Life
Radon-222	222	4 days
Thorium-234	234	24 days
Iodine-131	131	8 days
Bismuth-210	210	5 days
Polonium-210	210	138 days

19. **Graph** the data in the table above with the x-axis the mass number and the y-axis the half-life. Infer from your graph whether there is a relationship between the half-life and the mass number. If so, how does half-life depend on mass number?

Thinking Critically

20. **Explain** why the amount of background radiation a person receives can vary greatly from place to place.
21. **Infer** how the atomic number of a nucleus changes when the nucleus emits only gamma radiation.
22. **Identify** the properties of alpha particles that make them harmful to living cells.
23. **Determine** the type of nuclear radiation that is emitted by each of the following nuclear reactions:
    a. uranium-238 to thorium-234
    b. boron-12 to carbon-12
    c. cesium-130 to cesium-130
    d. radium-226 to radon-222
24. **Determine** how the motion of an alpha particle is affected when it passes between a positively charged electrode and a negatively charged electrode. How is the motion of a gamma ray affected?
25. **Infer** how the background radiation a person receives changes when they fly in a jet airliner.

Applying Math

26. **Use a Ratio** The mass of an alpha particle is 4.0026 mass units, and the mass of a beta particle is 0.000548 mass units. How many times larger is the mass of an alpha particle than the mass of a beta particle?
27. **Calculate Number of Half-Lives** How many half-lives have elapsed when the amount of a radioactive isotope in a sample is reduced to 3.125 percent of the original amount in the sample.

chapter Review 25

Interpreting Graphics

17. Check students' work.
18. radioactive dating: carbon-14; monitoring the thyroid gland: iodine-131; treating cancer: gamma rays
19. Graphs should show that there is no relation between mass number and half-life.

Thinking Critically

20. The amount of background radiation a person receives depends on their elevation above sea level, the material their house is made from, and the type of minerals in the ground.
21. The atomic number doesn't change when gamma radiation is emitted.
22. Alpha particles have the most mass and the greatest charge, and cause more ions to be formed as they travel in matter.
23. a. alpha particle, b. beta particle, c. gamma radiation, d. alpha particle
24. The alpha particle is deflected toward the negative electrode; the gamma ray is not affected.
25. The background radiation increases, because there is less atmosphere at higher elevations to absorb cosmic rays.

Applying Math

Math Standards

National: 1, 6, 9

26. about 7,300 times larger
27. five half-lives

Assessment Resources

Reproducible Masters

Chapter *Fast File* Resources
Chapter Review, pp. 39–40
Chapter Tests, pp. 41–44
Assessment Transparency Activity, p. 51

Glencoe Science Web site
Chapter Review Test
Standardized Test Practice

Glencoe Technology

Assessment Transparency
Exam*View*® Pro Testmaker
MindJogger Videoquiz
Interactive Chalkboard

Answer Sheet An answer sheet can be found at **gpescience.com**.

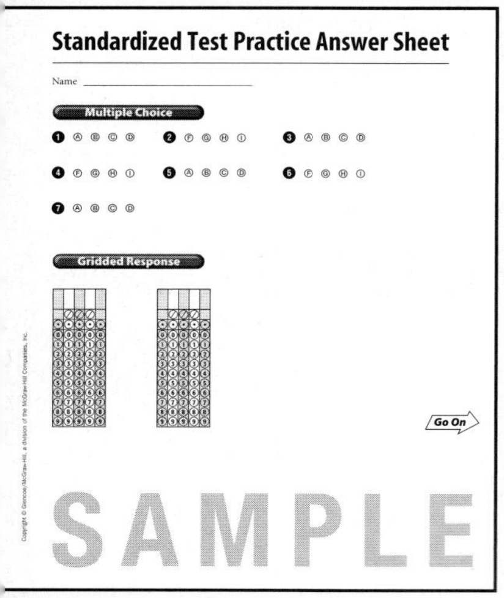

Multiple Choice

1. D
2. C
3. A
4. A
5. B
6. C
7. D
8. B

Gridded Response

9. 10

chapter 25 Standardized Test Practice

Record your answers on the answer sheet provided by your teacher or on a sheet of paper.

Multiple Choice

1. If a radioactive material has a half-life of 10 years, what fraction of the material will remain after 30 years?
   A. one-half
   B. one-third
   C. one-fourth
   D. one-eighth

2. Which of the following statements is true about all the isotopes of an element?
   A. They have the same mass number.
   B. They have different numbers of protons.
   C. They have different numbers of neutrons.
   D. They have the same number of neutrons.

3. How does the beta decay of a nucleus cause the nucleus to change?
   A. The number of protons increases.
   B. The number of neutrons increases.
   C. The number of protons decreases.
   D. The number of protons plus the number of neutrons decreases.

Use the illustration below to answer question 4.

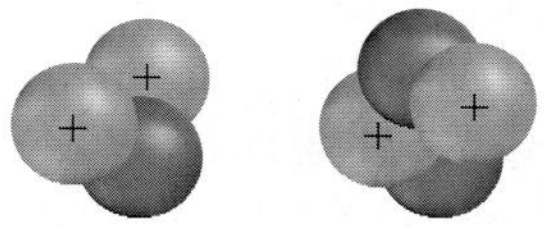

Helium-3 Helium-4

4. Which is a true statement about the two nuclei?
   A. They have the same atomic number.
   B. They have the same mass number.
   C. They have different numbers of electrons.
   D. They have different numbers of protons.

5. What is the atomic number of a nucleus equal to?
   A. the number of neutrons
   B. the number of protons
   C. the number of neutrons and protons
   D. the number of neutrons minus the number of protons

Use the illustration below to answer questions 6 and 7.

$^{210}_{84}Po$ $^{206}_{82}Pb$ + $^{4}_{2}He$

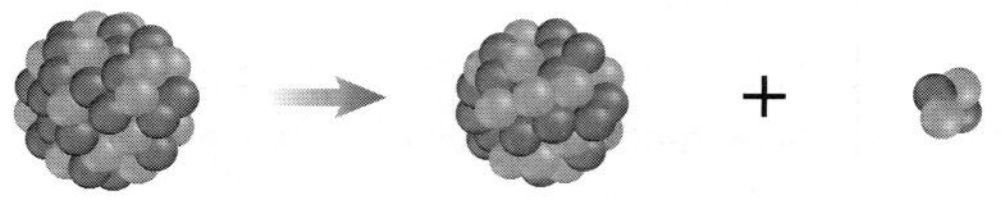

6. What process is shown by this illustration?
   A. nuclear fusion
   B. chain reaction
   C. transmutation
   D. beta decay

Test-Taking Tip

Understand the Question Be sure you understand the question before you read the answer choices. Make special note of words like NOT or EXCEPT. Read and consider all the answer choices before you mark your answer sheet.

Short Response

10. iodine-131
11. lithium-7

7. How do the total charge and total mass number of the products compare to the charge and mass number of the polonium nucleus?
   A. The charges are equal but the mass numbers are not equal.
   B. The mass numbers are equal but the charges are not equal.
   C. Neither the mass numbers or the charges are equal
   D. The mass numbers and charges are equal.

8. Radioactive isotopes of which element are used to study the brain?
   A. uranium
   B. fluorine
   C. carbon
   D. lead

Gridded Response

Use the table below to answer questions 9 and 10.

Half-Lives of Isotopes	
Isotope	**Half-life**
Carbon-14	5,730 years
Potassium-40	1.28 billion years
Iodine-131	8.04 days
Radon-222	4 days

9. How many grams of an 80-g sample of carbon-14 will be left after 17,190 years?

Short Response

10. A sample containing which radioactive isotope will have one-eighth of the isotope left after 24 days?

11. When the boron isotope boron-10 is bombarded with neutrons, it absorbs a neutron and then emits an alpha particle. Identify the isotope that is formed in this process.

Extended Response

12. Compare the strength of the strong force and the strength of the electric force on a proton in a small nucleus and in a large nucleus.

Use the illustration below to answer question 13.

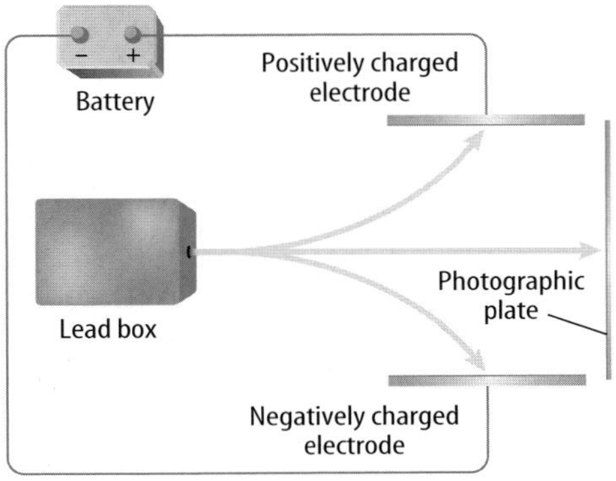

13. In the figure above, nuclear radiation is escaping from a small hole in the lead box.
   PART A Which type of nuclear radiation is deflected toward the positively-charged electrode, and why is this radiation deflected toward this electrode?
   PART B Explain why the radiation that struck the photographic plate was not deflected by the electrodes.

Rubrics

For more help evaluating Short- and Extended-Response questions, see the rubrics on p. 9T.

Extended Response

12. Compared to a small nucleus, in a large nucleus the repulsive electric force on a proton has increased more than the attractive strong force has increased.

13. *Sample answer:*
   Part A: The Beta particles are negatively charged, and because like charges repel and unlike charges attract, they are deflected away from the negatively charged electrode and toward the postively charged electrode.
   Part B: Gamma rays have no charge and their motion is not affected by the charged electrodes.

STANDARDIZED TEST PRACTICE 815

chapter 26 Organizer

Section/Objectives	Standards: National	Standards: State/Local	Labs/Features
Chapter Opener	See pp. 16T–17T for a Key to Standards.		**Launch Lab:** Stars in the Sky, p. 817 **Foldables,** p. 817
Section 1 Observing the Universe 2 sessions 1 block 1. **Describe** a constellation as a pattern of stars. 2. **Compare and contrast** types of optical telescopes. 3. **Explain** how a radio telescope differs from an optical one.	National Content Standards: UCP.1-3, UCP.5, A.1, A.2, B.2, B.4, E.1, F.6		**MiniLAB:** Modeling a Telescope, p. 819 **Applying Math:** The Magnifying Power of Telescopes, p. 820 **Science Online,** p. 821
Section 2 Evolution of Stars 2 sessions 1 block 4. **Explain** how stars form. 5. **Classify** the stages of stellar evolution using a Hertzsprung-Russel (H-R) diagram. 6. **Describe** the Sun and explain how it has and will evolve.	National Content Standards: UCP.1-5, A.1, A.2, B.2, B.4, B.6, E.1, F.6		**MiniLAB:** Counting Stars, p. 824 **Visualizing H-R Diagrams of Star Clusters,** p. 826 **Integrate Life Science,** p. 827 **Lab:** Star Cluster Age, p. 830
Section 3 Galaxies and the Milky Way 1 session .5 block 7. **Explain** that the same natural laws that apply in the Milky Way Galaxy also apply in other galaxies. 8. **Compare** the three main types of galaxies. 9. **Describe** the Milky Way Galaxy and the Sun's position in it.	National Content Standards: UCP.1-5, A.1, A.2, D.4, G.3		**Science Online,** p. 834
Section 4 Cosmology 2 sessions 1 block 10. **Describe** the most accepted theory about the origin of the universe. 11. **Define** dark matter. 12. **Explain** how dark energy may cause the universe to expand forever.	National Content Standards: UCP.1-5, A.1, A.2, B.6, D.4, E.1, 3.2, G.3		**Integrate Language Arts,** p. 837 **Lab:** Expansion of the Universe, pp. 840–841 Video Lab **Science and Language Arts:** Stars, p. 842

StudentWorks Plus

Glencoe Exclusive! TeacherWorks™ All-In-One Planner and Resource Center

Lab Materials	Reproducible Resources	Section Assessment	Technology
Launch Lab: cardboard tube	**Chapter *Fast File* Resources** Foldables Worksheet, p. 15 Directed Reading Overview, p. 17 Note-taking Worksheets, pp. 33–35	Glencoe's Assessment Advantage	TeacherWorks includes: • Interactive Teacher Edition • Lesson Planner with calendar • Access to all program blacklines • Correlations to standards • Web links
MiniLAB: construction paper, tape, double-sided tape, two lenses of different focal lengths	**Chapter *Fast File* Resources** Transparency Activity, p. 44, 49–50 MiniLAB, p.3 Enrichment, p. 29 Reinforcement, p. 25 Directed Reading, p. 18	**Portfolio** Science Journal, p. 821 **Performance** MiniLAB, p .819 Applying Math, p. 820 Applying Math, p. 822 **Content** Section Review, p. 822	Section Focus Transparency Teaching Transparency Interactive Chalkboard CD-ROM StudentWorks Plus
MiniLAB: blue construction paper, metric ruler, rice kernels **Lab:** H-R diagrams of star clusters having different ages	**Chapter *Fast File* Resources** Transparency Activity, p. 45 MiniLAB, p. 4 Lab Activity, pp. 9–12, 13–14 Enrichment, p. 30 Reinforcement, p. 26 Directed Reading, p. 18 Lab Worksheets, pp. 5–6	**Portfolio** Activity, p. 826 Differentiated Instruction, p. 826 **Performance** MiniLAB, p .824 Applying Math, p. 829 **Content** Section Review, p. 829	Section Focus Transparency Interactive Chalkboard CD-ROM StudentWorks Plus
Need materials? Contact Science Kit at 1-800-828-7777 or www.sciencekit.com.	**Chapter *Fast File* Resources** Transparency Activity, p. 46 Enrichment, p. 31 Reinforcement, p. 27 Directed Reading, p. 19	**Portfolio** Check for Understanding, p. 835 **Performance** Applying Math, p. 835 **Content** Section Review, p. 835	Section Focus Transparency Interactive Chalkboard CD-ROM StudentWorks Plus
Lab: balloon, permanent marker, medium-sized binder clip	**Chapter *Fast File* Resources** Transparency Activity, p. 47 Enrichment, p. 32 Reinforcement, p. 28 Directed Reading, p. 19,20 Lab Worksheets, pp. 7–8	**Portfolio** Check for Understanding, p. 839 **Performance** Applying Math, p. 839 **Content** Section Review, p. 839	Section Focus Transparency Interactive Chalkboard CD-ROM StudentWorks Plus Video Lab

End of Chapter Assessment

Glencoe's Assessment Advantage

Blackline Masters	Technology	Professional Series
Chapter *Fast File* Resources Chapter Review, pp. 37–38 Chapter Tests, pp. 39–42 **Standardized Test Practice,** pp. 108–111	MindJogger Videoquiz Exam*View*® Pro Testmaker TeacherWorks CD-ROM Interactive Chalkboard CD-ROM	**Performance Assessment in the Science Classroom (PASC)**

Transparencies

Section Focus

Section 1 Section Focus Transparency — Very Large Telescope — Chapter 26

This telescope consists of a system of four separate optical telescopes. Each telescope has an 8.2-m aperture. The telescope is on a 2,635-m high mountain in northern Chile. It can be used as four independent telescopes or as a single instrument.

1. Explain adaptive optics.
2. Explain active optics.
3. What is the benefit of using four telescopes?

L2

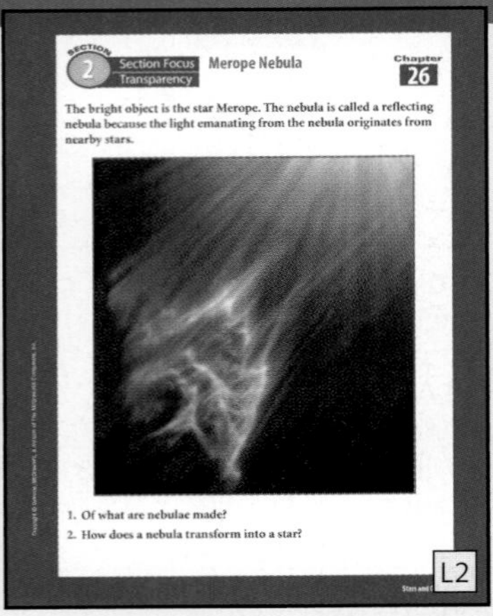
Section 2 Section Focus Transparency — Merope Nebula — Chapter 26

The bright object is the star Merope. The nebula is called a reflecting nebula because the light emanating from the nebula originates from nearby stars.

1. Of what are nebulae made?
2. How does a nebula transform into a star?

L2

Section 3 Section Focus Transparency — Coma Cluster — Chapter 26

The Coma cluster is a rich cluster of galaxies with over a thousand member galaxies known. The central region, dominated by two giant elliptical galaxies, is pictured here. Most of the objects in this picture are galaxies. Only the very bright objects with spikes and the smallest circular dots are foreground stars in the Milky Way.

1. Why are the galaxies smaller than the stars in this transparency?
2. Can you tell from the transparency that the galaxies are in a cluster?
3. How are galaxies formed?

L2

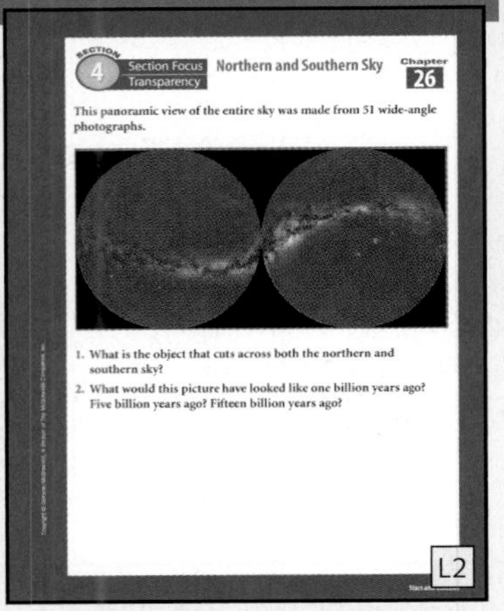
Section 4 Section Focus Transparency — Northern and Southern Sky — Chapter 26

This panoramic view of the entire sky was made from 51 wide-angle photographs.

1. What is the object that cuts across both the northern and southern sky?
2. What would this picture have looked like one billion years ago? Five billion years ago? Fifteen billion years ago?

L2

This is a representation of key blackline masters available in the Teacher Classroom Resources. See Resource Manager boxes within the chapter for additional information.

Assessment

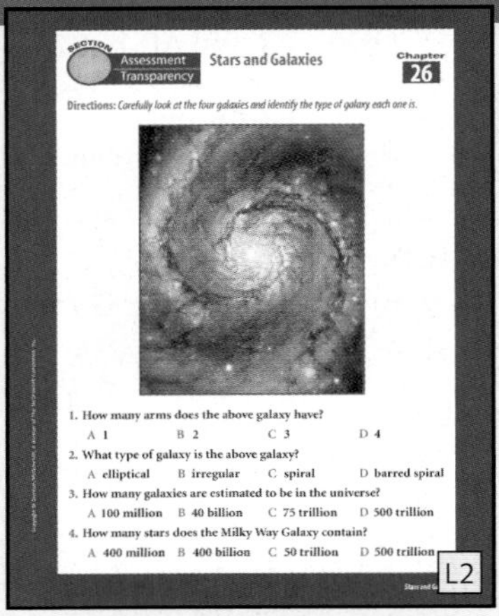
Section Assessment Transparency — Stars and Galaxies — Chapter 26

Directions: *Carefully look at the four galaxies and identify the type of galaxy each one is.*

1. How many arms does the above galaxy have?
   A 1 B 2 C 3 D 4
2. What type of galaxy is the above galaxy?
   A elliptical B irregular C spiral D barred spiral
3. How many galaxies are estimated to be in the universe?
   A 100 million B 40 billion C 75 trillion D 500 trillion
4. How many stars does the Milky Way Galaxy contain?
   A 400 million B 400 billion C 50 trillion D 500 trillion

L2

Teaching

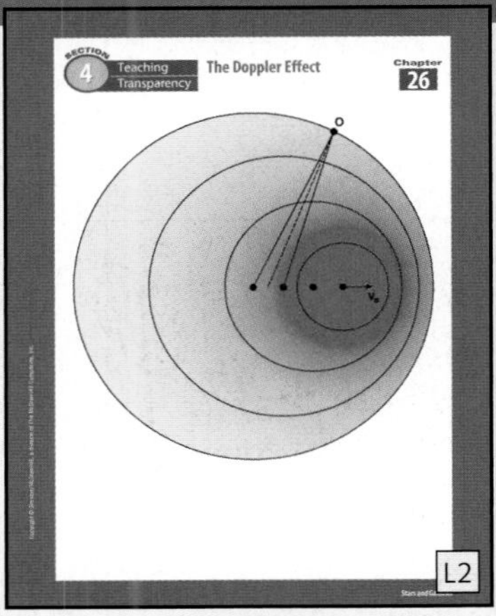
Section 4 Teaching Transparency — The Doppler Effect — Chapter 26

L2

Key to Teaching Strategies

The following designations will help you decide which activities are appropriate for your students.

- L1 Level 1 activities should be appropriate for students with learning difficulties.
- L2 Level 2 activities should be within the ability range of all students.
- L3 Level 3 activities are designed for above-average students.
- ELL ELL activities should be within the ability range of English Language Learners.
- COOP LEARN Cooperative Learning activities are designed for small group work.
- LS Multiple Learning Styles logos, as described on page 12T, are used throughout to indicate strategies that address different learning styles.
- P These strategies represent student products that can be placed into a best-work portfolio.
- PBL Problem-Based Learning activities apply real-world situations to learning.

Hands-on Activities

Student Text Lab Worksheet

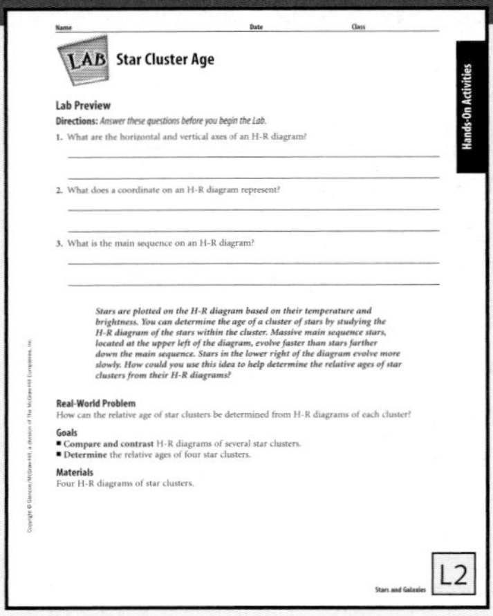
LAB Star Cluster Age

Lab Preview
Directions: *Answer these questions before you begin the Lab.*
1. What are the horizontal and vertical axes of an H-R diagram?
2. What does a coordinate on an H-R diagram represent?
3. What is the main sequence on an H-R diagram?

Stars are plotted on the H-R diagram based on their temperature and brightness. You can determine the age of a cluster of stars by studying the H-R diagram of the stars within the cluster. Massive main sequence stars, located at the upper left of the diagram, evolve faster than stars farther down the main sequence. Stars in the lower right of the diagram evolve more slowly. How could you use this idea to help determine the relative ages of star clusters from their H-R diagrams?

Real-World Problem
How can the relative age of star clusters be determined from H-R diagrams of each cluster?

Goals
- Compare and contrast H-R diagrams of several star clusters.
- Determine the relative ages of four star clusters.

Materials
Four H-R diagrams of star clusters.

L2

Laboratory Activities

LAB 1 Laboratory Activity — How to Measure the Distance to a Star

Below are replications of two photographs of the same section of the sky taken six months apart. As you can see, one of the stars appears to have moved, while the others have not. The star that moved was much closer to Earth than the other stars, so the motion of Earth around the Sun caused the apparent position of the star to shift.

This shift in the position of the star is called the stellar parallax. The figure below shows why the position of the star appeared to shift when viewed six months later.

Strategy
In this lab, you will make a device for measuring the distance of a distant object on the ground by measuring its parallax.

Materials
metersticks (2)
paper clips (3)
rubber bands

L2

Resource Manager

Meeting Different Ability Levels

Content Outline

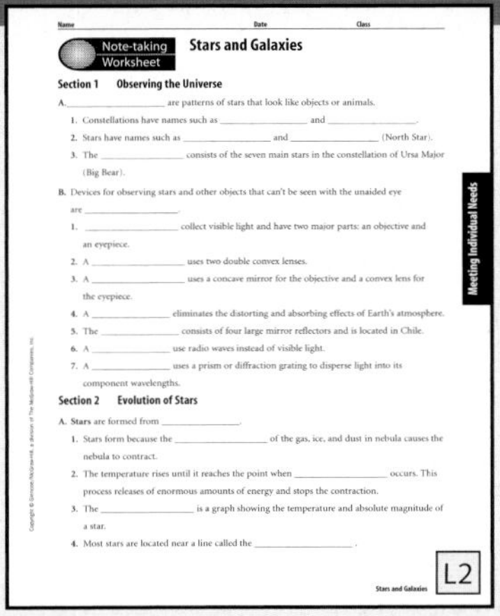

Name Date Class

Note-taking Worksheet — **Stars and Galaxies**

Section 1 Observing the Universe

A. ______ are patterns of stars that look like objects or animals.

1. Constellations have names such as ______ and ______.
2. Stars have names such as ______ and ______ (North Star).
3. The ______ consists of the seven main stars in the constellation of Ursa Major (Big Bear).

B. Devices for observing stars and other objects that can't be seen with the unaided eye are ______.

1. ______ collect visible light and have two major parts: an objective and an eyepiece.
2. A ______ uses two double convex lenses.
3. A ______ uses a concave mirror for the objective and a convex lens for the eyepiece.
4. A ______ eliminates the distorting and absorbing effects of Earth's atmosphere.
5. The ______ consists of four large mirror reflectors and is located in Chile.
6. A ______ use radio waves instead of visible light.
7. A ______ uses a prism or diffraction grating to disperse light into its component wavelengths.

Section 2 Evolution of Stars

A. Stars are formed from ______.

1. Stars form because the ______ of the gas, ice, and dust in nebula causes the nebula to contract.
2. The temperature rises until it reaches the point when ______ occurs. This process releases of enormous amounts of energy and stops the contraction.
3. The ______ is a graph showing the temperature and absolute magnitude of a star.
4. Most stars are located near a line called the ______.

Meeting Individual Needs

Stars and Galaxies L2

Reinforcement

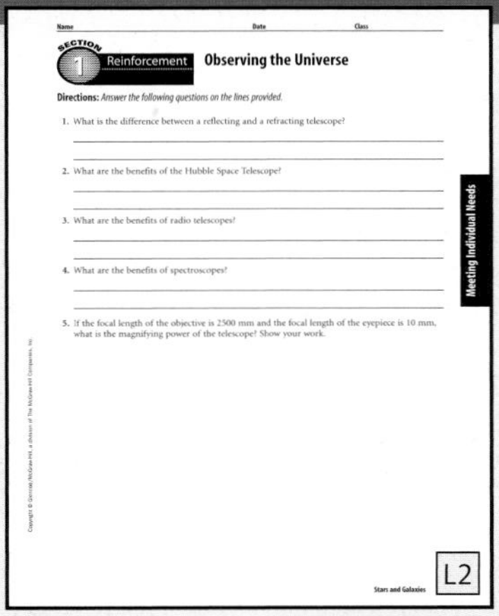

Name Date Class

Section 1 Reinforcement — **Observing the Universe**

Directions: Answer the following questions on the lines provided.

1. What is the difference between a reflecting and a refracting telescope?
2. What are the benefits of the Hubble Space Telescope?
3. What are the benefits of radio telescopes?
4. What are the benefits of spectroscopes?
5. If the focal length of the objective is 2500 mm and the focal length of the eyepiece is 10 mm, what is the magnifying power of the telescope? Show your work.

Meeting Individual Needs

Stars and Galaxies L2

Enrichment

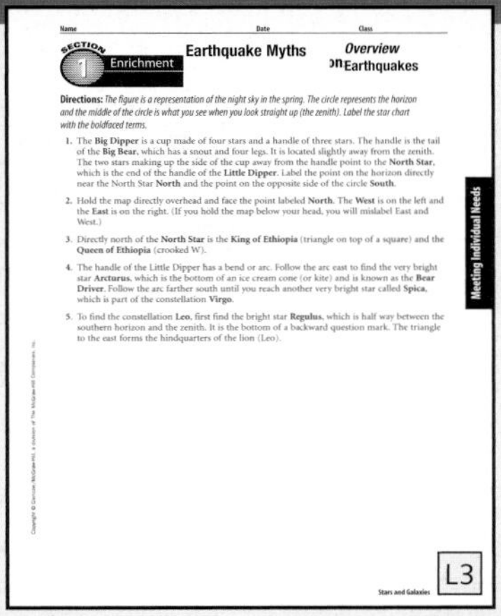

Name Date Class

Section 1 Enrichment — **Earthquake Myths** *Overview* on Earthquakes

Directions: The figure is a representation of the night sky in the spring. The circle represents the horizon and the middle of the circle is what you see when you look straight up (the zenith). Label the star chart with the boldfaced terms.

1. The **Big Dipper** is a cup made of four stars and a handle of three stars. The handle is the tail of the **Big Bear**, which has a snout and four legs. It is located slightly away from the zenith. The two stars making up the side of the cup away from the handle point to the **North Star**, which is the end of the handle of the **Little Dipper**. Label the point on the horizon directly near the North Star **North** and the point on the opposite side of the circle **South**.
2. Hold the map directly overhead and face the point labeled **North**. The **West** is on the left and the **East** is on the right. (If you hold the map below your head, you will mislabel East and West.)
3. Directly north of the **North Star** is the **King of Ethiopia** (triangle on top of a square) and the **Queen of Ethiopia** (crooked W).
4. The handle of the Little Dipper has a bend or arc. Follow the arc east to find the very bright star **Arcturus**, which is the bottom of an ice cream cone (or kite) and is known as the **Bear Driver**. Follow the arc farther south until you reach another very bright star called **Spica**, which is part of the constellation **Virgo**.
5. To find the constellation **Leo**, first find the bright star **Regulus**, which is half way between the southern horizon and the zenith. It is the bottom of a backward question mark. The triangle to the east forms the hindquarters of the lion (Leo).

Meeting Individual Needs

Stars and Galaxies L3

Directed Reading (English/Spanish)

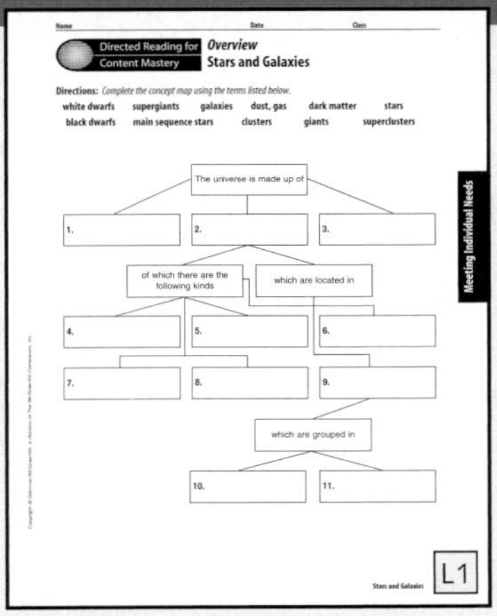

Name Date Class

Directed Reading for Content Mastery — *Overview* **Stars and Galaxies**

Directions: Complete the concept map using the terms listed below.

white dwarfs, supergiants, galaxies, dust, gas, dark matter, stars, black dwarfs, main sequence stars, clusters, giants, superclusters

Meeting Individual Needs

Stars and Galaxies L1

Study Guide

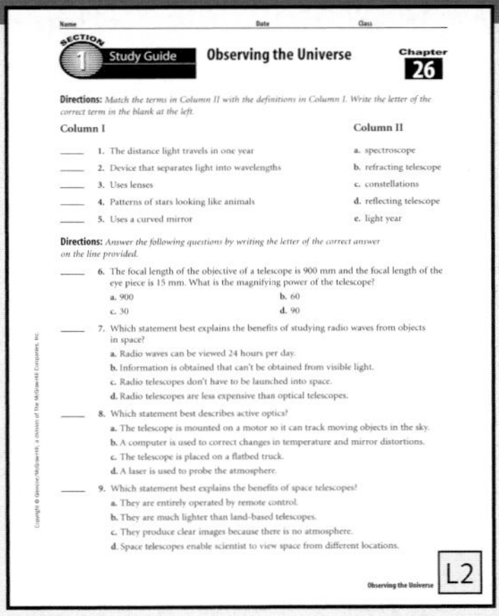

Name Date Class

Section 1 Study Guide — **Observing the Universe** Chapter 26

Directions: Match the terms in Column II with the definitions in Column I. Write the letter of the correct term in the blank at the left.

Column I	Column II
____ 1. The distance light travels in one year	a. spectroscope
____ 2. Device that separates light into wavelengths	b. refracting telescope
____ 3. Uses lenses	c. constellations
____ 4. Patterns of stars looking like animals	d. reflecting telescope
____ 5. Uses a curved mirror	e. light year

Directions: Answer the following questions by writing the letter of the correct answer on the line provided.

____ 6. The focal length of the objective of a telescope is 900 mm and the focal length of the eye piece is 15 mm. What is the magnifying power of the telescope?
a. 900 b. 60
c. 30 d. 90

____ 7. Which statement best explains the benefits of studying radio waves from objects in space?
a. Radio waves can be viewed 24 hours per day.
b. Information is obtained that can't be obtained from visible light.
c. Radio telescopes don't have to be launched into space.
d. Radio telescopes are less expensive than optical telescopes.

____ 8. Which statement best describes active optics?
a. The telescope is mounted on a motor so it can track moving objects in the sky.
b. A computer is used to correct changes in temperature and mirror distortions.
c. The telescope is placed on a flatbed truck.
d. A laser is used to probe the atmosphere.

____ 9. Which statement best explains the benefits of space telescopes?
a. They are entirely operated by remote control.
b. They are much lighter than land-based telescopes.
c. They produce clear images because there is no atmosphere.
d. Space telescopes enable scientist to view space from different locations.

Observing the Universe L2

Reading Essentials

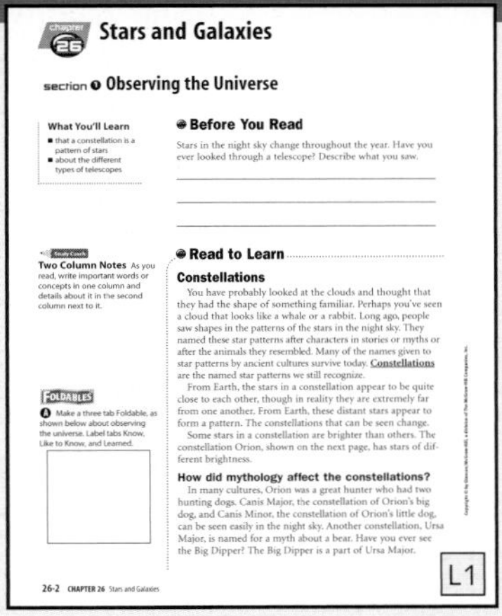

Chapter 26 **Stars and Galaxies**

section 1 **Observing the Universe**

What You'll Learn
- that a constellation is a pattern of stars
- about the different types of telescopes

Before You Read

Stars in the night sky change throughout the year. Have you ever looked through a telescope? Describe what you saw.

Study Coach — **Two Column Notes** As you read, write important words or concepts in one column and details about it in the second column next to it.

Read to Learn

Constellations

You have probably looked at the clouds and thought that they had the shape of something familiar. Perhaps you've seen a cloud that looks like a whale or a rabbit. Long ago, people saw shapes in the patterns of the stars in the night sky. They named these star patterns after characters in stories or myths or after the animals they resembled. Many of the names given to star patterns by ancient cultures survive today. **Constellations** are the named star patterns we still recognize.

From Earth, the stars in a constellation appear to be quite close to each other, though in reality they are extremely far from one another. From Earth, these distant stars appear to form a pattern. The constellations that can be seen change.

Some stars in a constellation are brighter than others. The constellation Orion, shown on the next page, has stars of different brightness.

FOLDABLES — A Make a three-tab Foldable, as shown below about observing the universe. Label tabs Know, Like to Know, and Learned.

How did mythology affect the constellations?

In many cultures, Orion was a great hunter who had two hunting dogs. Canis Major, the constellation of Orion's big dog, and Canis Minor, the constellation of Orion's little dog, can be seen easily in the night sky. Another constellation, Ursa Major, is named for a myth about a bear. Have you ever seen the Big Dipper? The Big Dipper is a part of Ursa Major.

26-2 CHAPTER 26 Stars and Galaxies L1

Assessment

Test Practice Workbook

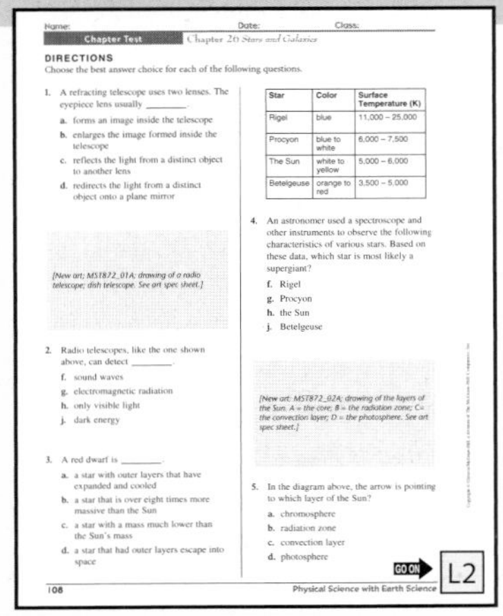

Name: Date: Class:

Chapter Test — *Chapter 26 Stars and Galaxies*

DIRECTIONS
Choose the best answer choice for each of the following questions.

1. A refracting telescope uses two lenses. The eyepiece lens usually ______.
a. forms an image inside the telescope
b. enlarges the image formed inside the telescope
c. reflects the light from a distinct object to another lens
d. redirects the light from a distinct object onto a plane mirror

[New art: MST872_01A; drawing of a radio telescope; dish telescope. See art spec sheet.]

2. Radio telescopes, like the one shown above, can detect ______.
f. sound waves
g. electromagnetic radiation
h. only visible light
j. dark energy

3. A red dwarf is ______.
a. a star with outer layers that have expanded and cooled
b. a star that is over eight times more massive than the Sun
c. a star with a mass much lower than the Sun's mass
d. a star that had outer layers escape into space

Star	Color	Surface Temperature (K)
Rigel	blue	11,000 – 25,000
Procyon	blue to white	6,000 – 7,500
The Sun	white to yellow	5,000 – 6,000
Betelgeuse	orange to red	3,500 – 5,000

4. An astronomer used a spectroscope and other instruments to observe the following characteristics of various stars. Based on these data, which star is most likely a supergiant?
f. Rigel
g. Procyon
h. the Sun
j. Betelgeuse

[New art: MST872_02A; drawing of the layers of the Sun. A = the core; B = the radiation zone; C = the convection layer; D = the photosphere. See art spec sheet.]

5. In the diagram above, the arrow is pointing to which layer of the Sun?
a. chromosphere
b. radiation zone
c. convection layer
d. photosphere

GO ON L2

108 Physical Science with Earth Science

Chapter Review

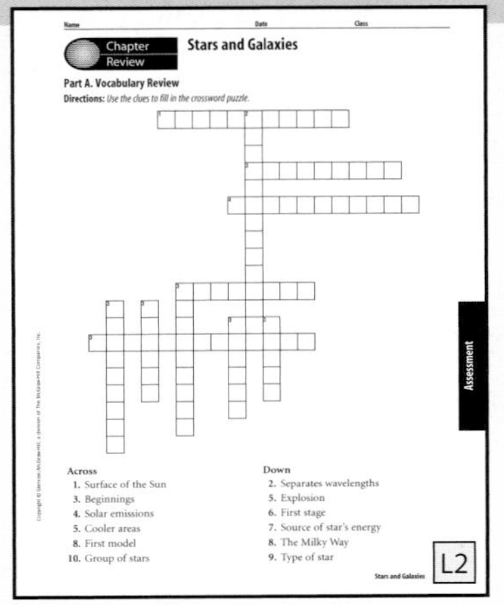

Name Date Class

Chapter Review — **Stars and Galaxies**

Part A. Vocabulary Review

Directions: Use the clues to fill in the crossword puzzle.

Across	Down
1. Surface of the Sun	2. Separates wavelengths
3. Beginnings	3. Explosion
4. Solar emissions	6. First stage
5. Cooler areas	7. Source of star's energy
8. First model	8. The Milky Way
10. Group of stars	9. Type of star

Assessment

Stars and Galaxies L2

Chapter Tests

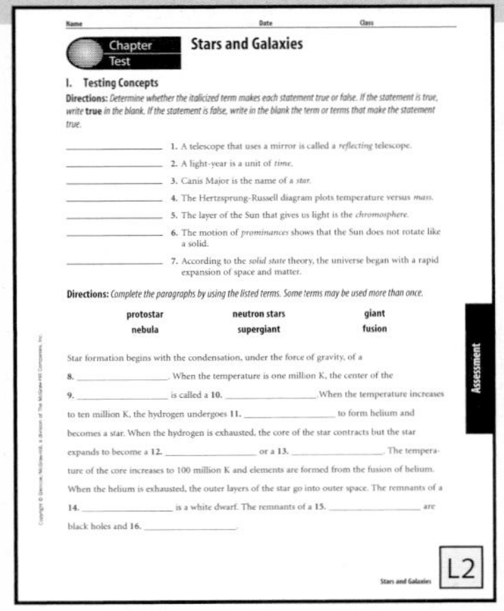

Name Date Class

Chapter Test — **Stars and Galaxies**

I. Testing Concepts

Directions: Determine whether the italicized term makes each statement true or false. If the statement is true, write true *in the blank. If the statement is false, write in the blank the term or terms that make the statement true.*

______ 1. A telescope that uses a mirror is called a *reflecting* telescope.
______ 2. A light-year is a unit of *time*.
______ 3. Canis Major is the name of a *star*.
______ 4. The Hertzsprung-Russell diagram plots temperature versus *mass*.
______ 5. The layer of the Sun that gives us light is the *chromosphere*.
______ 6. The motion of *prominences* shows that the Sun does not rotate like a solid.
______ 7. According to the *solid state* theory, the universe began with a rapid expansion of space and matter.

Directions: Complete the paragraphs by using the listed terms. Some terms may be used more than once.

protostar, neutron stars, giant, nebula, supergiant, fusion

Star formation begins with the condensation, under the force of gravity, of a 8. ______. When the temperature is one million K, the center of the 9. ______ is called a 10. ______. When the temperature increases to ten million K, the hydrogen undergoes 11. ______ to form helium and becomes a star. When the hydrogen is exhausted, the core of the star contracts but the star expands to become a 12. ______ or a 13. ______. The temperature of the core increases to 100 million K and elements are formed from the fusion of helium. When the helium is exhausted, the outer layers of the star go into outer space. The remnants of a 14. ______ is a white dwarf. The remnants of a 15. ______ are black holes and 16. ______.

Assessment

Stars and Galaxies L2

Science Content Background

section 1 Observing the Universe

Optical Telescopes

In addition to magnifying power, there are two other powers that are important to consider when selecting a telescope. The light gathering power (*B*) is a measure of how much light an objective lens can concentrate into the image. It is based on the aperture (diameter) of the objective lens or mirror and is also affected by the focal length of the telescope. In general, the light gathering power increases with the square of the objective's aperture. The equation for *B* is $B = c(a/f_o)^2$.

The resolving power (α) of a telescope is the ability to separate objects which are very close together. It is a measure of the resolution of the image or fineness of detail. The smaller the value of resolving power, the better it is. Resolving power increases with an increase in aperture. The equation for α is $\alpha = 11.6/a$ when *a* is in cm.

section 2 Evolution of Stars

The Sun

The *Solar and Heliospheric Observatory (SOHO)* observes the Sun 24 hours a day from a position about 1.5 million km closer to the Sun than Earth. It studies the Sun's surface, atmosphere, and interior. Some observations indicate that the Sun goes through measurable changes prior to ejecting material through coronal storms. If these storms can be predicted, humans can prepare for the disruption of communication, power generation, and electronics. SOHO has helped scientists determine that the boundary between the convection zone and radiation zone is located 71.3 percent outward from the Sun's center.

section 3 Galaxies and the Milky Way

Galaxy Center

Studies of other galaxies indicate the possibility that massive black holes exist at galactic centers. In these studies, radio telescopes were connected across an entire continent, drastically increasing the telescopes' resolving power. When aimed at nearby galaxy M106, data indicated the existence of a disk of gas with properties consistent with the existence of a black hole equal in mass to 36 million suns.

section 4 Cosmology

Dark Energy

In a universe with accelerating expansion, the redshifts of distant objects are less than would be expected. Using Type I supernovas as a standard, scientists determine their distance independent of redshift values. Then by comparing distance to the redshift of the light from these supernovas, scientists have calculated a rate of expansion in the past that is lower than the expected value. This means that the expansion of the universe is accelerating. It is not known what is causing this, but it is neither matter nor radiation. The accelerating expansion is caused by an unknown type of energy called dark energy. Because gravity weakens as matter becomes farther apart, dark energy might eventually dominate the universe and keep it expanding forever.

chapter content resources

Internet Resources

For additional content background, visit **gpescience.com** to:

- access your book online
- find references to related articles in popular science magazines
- access Web links with related content background
- access current events with science journal topics

Print Resources

Discovering the Universe, by Neil F. Comins, and William J. Kaufmann, W.H. Freeman, 2003

A Dictionary of Astronomy, Ian Ridpath (ed.), Oxford University Press, 1998

Star Chart Map, American Map Corporation, 1995

IDENTIFYING Misconceptions

Find Out What Students Think

Students may think that . . .

Stars within a constellation must be close to one another in space.

Students might not be aware that stars can be very far away from each other and still appear to be side by side. Also, they might think that brighter stars are closer and that if two stars that appear to be side by side have the same brightness, they must be close to each other. These misconceptions come about because of the lack of depth perception when looking at stars in the sky and because the stars in a constellation are connected by mythology.

Discussion

Organize the class into groups and have each group work together to research the distance to several stars in a well-known constellation, such as Orion. **Possible answer: Betelgeuse is 427 light-years, Bellatrix is 243 light-years, Rigel is 773 light-years, the three stars that form the belt are about 1,025 light-years, and Meissa, Salph, and Na'ir al Saif are about 1,025 light-years from Earth.**

Promote Understanding

Demonstration

- Take students to a large, open room, such as the gym or cafeteria or outside if weather permits.
- Have most of the students stand at random locations in the room or on the grass outside the school.
- Have a student close one eye and look across the room or field and note that two or three people can look as if they are standing next each other, but are actually different distances away.
- Relate the appearance of people standing in widely separated positions appearing to be side by side to the fact that stars within a constellation can be separated by a great distance and still appear to be side by side.

Assess

After completing the chapter, see *Identifying Misconceptions* in the Study Guide at the end of the chapter.

chapter 26

Chapter Vocabulary

constellation, p. 818
refracting telescope, p. 819
reflecting telescope, p. 820
radio telescope, p. 821
light-year, p. 821
spectroscope, p. 822
main sequence, p. 823
giant, p. 825
white dwarf, p. 825
solar mass, p. 827
photosphere, p. 827
sunspots, p. 828
galaxy, p. 831
Milky Way, p. 831
Local Group, p. 832
cosmology, p. 836
big bang theory, p. 837
dark matter, p. 838
dark energy, p. 839

Science Journal Students may know that our Sun is one of many billions of stars in the Milky Way Galaxy. They might know that the Sun is an average star in size and age.

INTERACTIVE CHALKBOARD with Image Bank

PowerPoint® Presentations

This CD-ROM is an editable Microsoft® PowerPoint® presentation that includes:

- a pre-made presentation for every chapter
- interactive graphics
- animations
- audio clips
- image bank
- all new section and chapter questions
- Standardized Test Practice
- transparencies
- Foldables directions
- links to gpescience.com

chapter 26

Stars and Galaxies

chapter preview

sections

1 **Observing the Universe**
2 **Evolution of Stars**
Lab Star Cluster Age
3 **Galaxies and the Milky Way**
4 **Cosmology**
Lab Expansion of the Universe

Colliding Galaxies

These two spiral galaxies, known as "the mice," have been colliding for about 160 million years. Eventually, they will merge into one giant, elliptical galaxy.

Science Journal In your Science Journal, write a paragraph about what you know about the Sun as a star.

816

Theme Connection

Scale and Structure and Stability and Change Two themes are involved in this chapter. One pertains to the immense scale of space and the overall structure of the universe. The second pertains to the apparent stability of the universe when viewed over a short span of time and the gradual changes of stars, galaxies, and the universe when viewed over the total time the universe has been in existence.

About the Photo

Colliding Galaxies This *Hubble* photo is a mosaic of four filtered images combined to approximate natural color. Orange areas are cores of the two galaxies. A band of dark dust lies between the cores and dust filaments criss-cross the areas where bright, blue star clusters are forming. In some areas, dust scatters the blue light, making it appear reddish.

Start-Up Activities

Launch LAB

Stars in the Sky

Have you ever looked up at the night sky and been amazed at the number of stars you could see? But if you live in a well lighted area, you may not have seen very many stars at all. In this lab, you will explore a quick way to estimate how many stars you can see in different parts of the sky.

1. Ask an adult to help you locate an area near your home suitable for star gazing where there are not very many lights.
2. Hold a cardboard tube up to one eye and look through it at one area of the sky.
3. Count the number of stars you can see easily through the tube.
4. Look at three other areas of the sky in the same way and count those stars. Try looking to the south, west, straight up, and in a random direction.
5. Compare your data with those of two or three other students.
6. **Think Critically** In your Science Journal, report whether a similar number of stars were easily visible no matter where you looked or whether the number of stars varied. Explain any similarities or differences noted by you or other students.

FOLDABLES Study Organizer

Cosmology Make the following Foldable to help identify what you know, what you want to know, and what you learned about stars, galaxies, and cosmology.

STEP 1 **Fold** a vertical sheet of paper from side to side. Make the front edge about $\frac{1}{2}$ inch longer than the back edge.

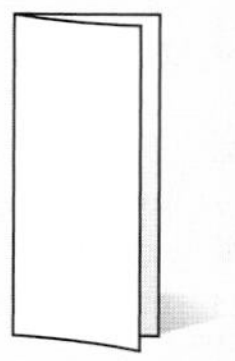

STEP 2 **Turn** lengthwise and **fold** into thirds.

STEP 3 **Unfold and cut** only the top layer along both folds to make three tabs. Label each tab as shown.

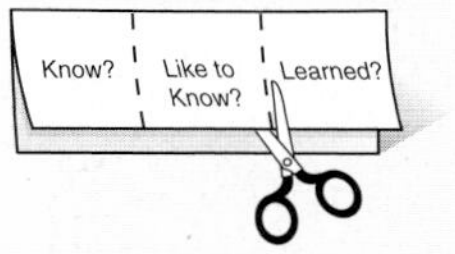

Questioning Before you read the chapter, write what you know about cosmology under the left tab of your Foldable, and write questions about what you'd like to know under the center tab. After you read the chapter, list what you learned under the right tab.

Science Online — Preview this chapter's content and activities at gpescience.com

Launch LAB

Purpose Use this Launch Lab to introduce students to the number of stars that are visible in different areas of the sky. L2 LS **Kinesthetic**

Preparation Obtain several cardboard tubes from empty rolls of paper towels.

Materials cardboard tubes

Alternative Materials rolled-up construction paper

Teaching Strategy Use a cardboard tube and look in different directions in the classroom to demonstrate observations of the sky.

Safety Precaution Caution students to use the cardboard tube carefully when viewing.

Think Critically

Student answers should indicate that the numbers of stars visible in different areas varies. Possible answer: Stars are visible in every direction, but more stars are visible in some areas than in others.

Assessment

Oral Are the number of stars visible in different parts of the sky the same? Explain. Possible answers: No, some areas of the sky appear to have more stars. This is caused by comparing observations in the direction of the rim of our galaxy's disk (the Milky Way) to areas above or below it.

FOLDABLES Study Organizer **Dinah Zike Study Fold**

Student preparation materials for this Foldable are available in the Chapter *Fast File* Resources.

1 Motivate

An editable Microsoft® PowerPoint® presentation is available on **Interactive Chalkboard** CD-ROM.

Bellringer

Section Focus Transparencies also are available on the Interactive Chalkboard CD-ROM. L2 ELL

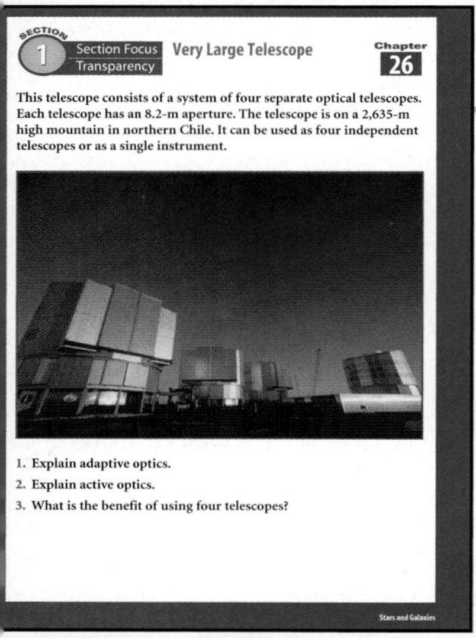
Section 1 Section Focus Transparency — Very Large Telescope — Chapter 26

This telescope consists of a system of four separate optical telescopes. Each telescope has an 8.2-m aperture. The telescope is on a 2,635-m high mountain in northern Chile. It can be used as four independent telescopes or as a single instrument.

1. Explain adaptive optics.
2. Explain active optics.
3. What is the benefit of using four telescopes?

Stars and Galaxies

Reading Preview

Tie to Prior Knowledge

Constellations Ask students if they have seen any constellations in the night sky. Ask if they could recognize the patterns of stars that comprise Orion the hunter or the Big Dipper. Ask a volunteer to draw on the chalkboard any familiar constellation. L2

Graphic Organizer On the board draw a hierarchical chart for Telescopes. Create three levels with the following words in boxes, connected with lines to show their relationships. Top level: *Telescopes* Second level: *Optical Telescopes/Radio Telescopes/Space Telescopes* Third level under Optical: *Reflecting Telescopes/Refracting Telescopes*

section 1

Observing the Universe

Reading Guide

What You'll Learn

- **Describe** a constellation as a pattern of stars.
- **Compare and contrast** types of optical telescopes.
- **Explain** how a radio telescope differs from an optical one.

Why It's Important

You can observe different parts of the universe from your home.

Review Vocabulary

electromagnetic spectrum: the entire range of wavelengths of electromagnetic energy

New Vocabulary

- constellation
- refracting telescope
- reflecting telescope
- radio telescope
- light-year
- spectroscope

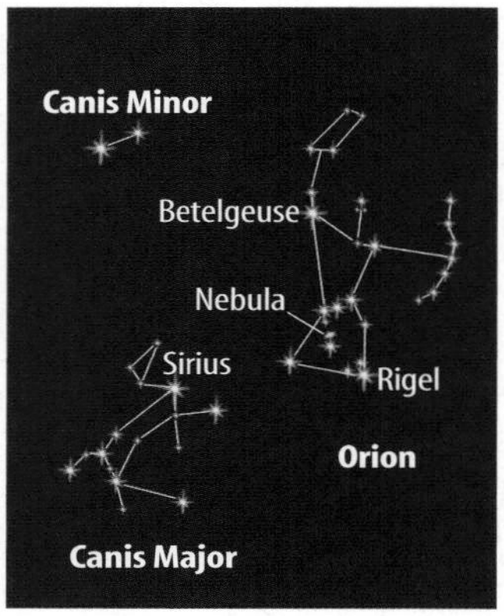

Figure 1 These three constellations contain some of the brightest stars visible from the northern hemisphere—Betelgeuse, Rigel, and Sirius.

Constellations

Have you ever watched clouds drift by on a summer day and tried to find shapes and patterns in them? One might look like a ship and another might resemble a rabbit or a bear. Long ago, people did much the same thing with stars. They named these patterns of stars after characters in stories, animals, or tools. Many of the names given to these star patterns by ancient cultures survive today and are called **constellations.** Astronomers use these constellations to locate and name stars.

From Earth, the stars in a constellation appear relatively close to one another. You can see that some of the stars are brighter than others, but you can't see how far they are from you or from each other. Usually, they lie at greatly different distances and just happen to line up and form a pattern.

In **Figure 1,** three constellations are shown with some of their brighter stars. The constellations visible in the evening sky change throughout the year.

INTEGRATE History **Mythology** In many cultures, Orion was a great hunter who had two hunting dogs, Canis Major (big dog) and Canis Minor (little dog). In another myth, two bears traveled around Earth's north pole. The constellations Ursa Major and Ursa Minor (big and little bears) were named for them. Indeed, they do swing around the north pole. In fact, Polaris, the polestar, is in Ursa Minor. If you have seen the Big Dipper you have seen most of Ursa Major, because the dipper is part of this constellation.

Section 1 Resource Manager

Chapter *Fast File* Resources

Transparency Activity, pp. 44, 49–50
Note-taking Worksheets, pp. 33–35
MiniLAB, p. 3
Enrichment, p. 29
Reinforcement, p. 25
Directed Reading for Content Mastery, pp. 17–18
Home and Community Involvement, p. 25
Physical Science Critical Thinking/Problem Solving, p. 4
Cultural Diversity, pp. 51–52

Telescopes Constellations and the stars that make them up are visible with the unaided eye. However, to see other objects in space, or to see some objects better, you need a telescope. Scientists and amateur astronomers use many different types of telescopes. Optical telescopes are used to study objects in visible light, and radio telescopes are used to study objects in the radio wavelengths. What do you think would be used to study X rays?

Optical Telescopes There are two basic types of optical telescopes. One type uses only lenses to study light and the other uses lenses and mirrors. Optical telescopes collect visible light and produce magnified images of objects. Light is collected by an objective lens or mirror. Because starlight is so distant, the light forms an image at the focus of the telescope. The focus is where light that is bent by the objective lens or reflected by the objective mirror comes together. A second lens, the eyepiece lens, then magnifies the image. The distance from the objective to the focus is the focal length of the telescope. You can find the magnifying power (M_p) of a telescope by dividing the focal length of the objective (f_o) by the focal length of the eyepiece (f_e).

$$M_p = f_o / f_e$$

Refracting Optical Telescopes A **refracting telescope** uses a convex lens, which is curved outward like the surface of a ball, as an objective, shown in **Figure 2.** When the lens curves outward on both sides, it is a double convex lens. Light passes through the objective lens. The eyepiece, which also can be a double convex lens, then magnifies the image. There is a limit to how large a refracting telescope can be. Since the objective lens can be supported only at its edges, it could sag in the middle if it is too large. When a larger telescope is needed, a reflecting telescope is used.

Reading Check *What type of optical telescope uses a lens as an objective?*

Mini LAB

Modeling a Telescope

Procedure

1. Obtain two **lenses of different focal length** from your teacher.
2. Place **double-sided tape** around the edge of one lens.
3. Place the lens along the short side of a piece of **construction paper** and roll the paper around the lens to form a tube. Tape the tube securely.
4. Repeat steps 2 and 3 with the other lens.
5. Insert the small tube into the large tube with the lenses on opposite ends.
6. Look through the eyepiece lens (small tube) and slide it in and out until you see a clear image.

Analysis

1. Observe an object with and without your telescope. Estimate how many times larger it appears through the telescope.
2. Obtain the focal lengths of your lenses from your teacher. Calculate the magnifying power of your telescope using the equation on this page. Compare this value to your estimate.

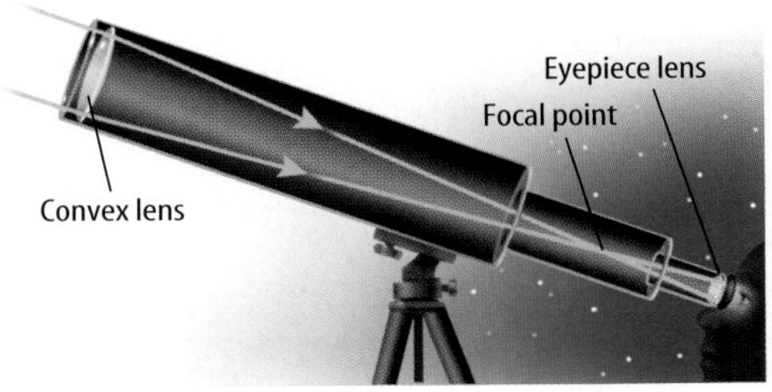

Figure 2 Two lenses are all that is needed for a refracting telescope. The tube and tripod aid in viewing.
Identify *the curvature of an objective lens.*

Test Question Answer

X-ray telescope

2 Teach

Mini LAB

Purpose Students will design and build a telescope. Students will then observe objects and calculate the magnifying power of their telescopes by solving a one-step equation. L2 IN **Kinesthetic**

Materials construction paper, two lenses of different focal lengths, tape, double-sided tape

Teaching Strategy Construct a telescope prior to students' attempts.

Safety Precautions

- Caution students to handle lenses with care and not to use broken or chipped ones.
- Students should wear eye protection.

Analysis

1. Lenses with focal lengths of 30 mm and 5 mm should make objects look six times larger.
2. If the actual magnifying power is six, an estimate of four should be considered close enough.

Assessment

Performance Ask students to determine the focal length needed for an objective lens if the eyepiece focal length is 6 mm and you want a magnifying power of 150. Possible answer: 900 mm Use PASC, p 101. L2 **Logical—Mathematical**

Differentiated Instruction

English-Language Learners Help your English-language learners by showing them photographs and drawings of refracting telescopes. Encourage them to build the telescope and to see if it works. Provide drawings of how to determine the focal lengths of the two lenses and help them fit the two sections of their telescopes together.

Reading Strategy

Determine Importance Have students copy the hierarchical chart for telescopes that was used to introduce the vocabulary words. Then, as they read the text, have them determine the important details for each type of telescope and add these to their chart.

Reading Check

Answer refracting

Caption Answer

Figure 2 convex

Quick Demo
Image Formation

Materials a glass, 15-cm focal length lens

Estimated Time 5 minutes

Procedure Darken the room so that the only light comes in the window. Have a student hold up a sheet of white paper so students can see it. Use the lens to demonstrate how an image is formed. Hold the lens up to the window so that light coming in the window falls on the sheet of paper and forms an image. Explain that the lens is like the objective of a telescope. L2 ELL **Visual-Spatial**

Applying Math

Math Standards

National: 1, 9

Teaching Strategies

- Place a simple equation on the chalkboard (a = 2b). Tell students the value of b is 12. Rewrite the equation as a = 2 × 12. Ask students to solve the equation for a. Answer: 24
- Now write another simple equation on the chalkboard a = b/c. Tell them the value of b is 10 and the value of c is 5. Rewrite the equation as a = 10/5. Ask them to solve the equation for a. Answer: 2
- Relate these simple example equations to the one for the magnifying power of a telescope.

Answers to Practice Problems

1. Mp = 2500 mm/50 mm = 50; Mp = 2500 mm/10 mm = 250
2. Mp = 900 mm/12 mm = 75

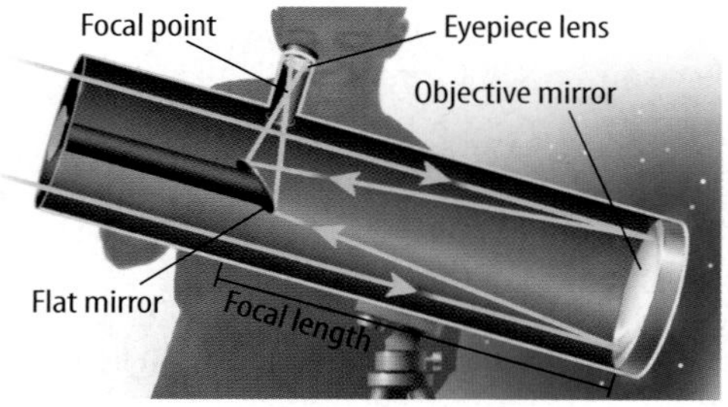

Figure 3 Reflecting telescopes use concave mirrors to gather light.

Reflecting Optical Telescopes A **reflecting telescope** uses a mirror as an objective to reflect light to the focus. **Figure 3** shows how light passes through the open end of a reflecting telescope and strikes a concave mirror at the base of the telescope. Often, a smaller mirror is used to reflect light into the eyepiece where it is magnified for viewing. However, in very large reflecting telescopes, the astronomer sits inside the telescope and looks through the eyepiece at the focus. Because mirrors can be supported from underneath a much larger telescope can be built.

Applying Math — Use Equations

THE MAGNIFYING POWER OF TELESCOPES If the focal lengths of a telescope's objective and eyepiece are known, the magnifying power can be calculated from the equation:

$$M_p = f_o/f_e$$

In this equation, M_p is the magnifying power of the telescope, f_o is the focal length of the objective, and f_e is the focal length of the eyepiece. Find the magnifying power of a telescope with a focal length of 1200 mm using eyepieces of 20 mm and 6 mm.

IDENTIFY known values and unknown values.

Identify the known values.

the focal length of the objective is 1,200 mm, this means $f_o = 1{,}200$ mm

the focal lengths of the eyepieces are 20 mm and 6 mm, this means $f_e = 20$ mm; 6 mm

Identify the unknown value

what is the magnifying power of the telescope means $M_p = ?$

SOLVE the problem

Substitute the known values into the equation for magnifying power:

$M_p = 1{,}200 \text{ mm}/20 \text{ mm} = 60$ $\qquad$ $M_p = 1{,}200 \text{ mm}/6 \text{ mm} = 200$

Notice that the units cancel, and that magnifying power has no unit.

CHECK the answer

Does your answer seem reasonable? Do images look 60 times larger than the object when using the 20 mm eyepiece and 200 times larger when using the 6 mm eyepiece?

Practice Problems

1. Find the magnifying power of a telescope with a focal length of 2,500 mm when using eyepieces with focal lengths of 50 mm and 10 mm.
2. Find the magnifying power for a telescope with a focal length of 900 mm when using an eyepiece with a focal length of 12 mm.

For more practice problems, go to page 879 and visit Math Practice at gpescience.com.

Teacher FYI

The Hubble Space Telescope The *Hubble Space Telescope* is a reflecting telescope with an objective mirror 240 cm in diameter. It is in orbit 610 km above the Earth's surface. Radio emissions send commands to the telescope and send images taken by the *Hubble Space Telescope* back to Earth.

820 CHAPTER 26 Stars and Galaxies

New Telescope Design The most recent innovations in optical telescopes involve active and adaptive optics. With active optics, a computer is used to correct changes in temperature, mirror distortions, and bad viewing conditions. Adaptive optics uses a laser to probe the atmosphere and relay information to a computer about air turbulence. The computer then adjusts the telescope's mirror thousands of times per second to lessen the effects of atmospheric turbulence. The European Southern Observatory's *Very Large Telescope* in Chile, the largest optical telescope in use, uses adaptive optics.

Figure 4 27 dish antennae of the VLA are mounted on railroad tracks for rapid repositioning. The 304-m dish antenna in Arecibo, Puerto Rico is shown in the inset.

Radio Telescopes Radio waves, like visible light, are a form of electromagnetic energy emitted by stars and other objects in space. Radio waves can be detected even during the day, when the Sun's light makes it impossible to see the fainter visible light from other stars. Radio waves pass freely through Earth's atmosphere, even on completely cloudy days.

A telescope that collects and amplifies radio waves is a **radio telescope.** Because radio waves have long wavelengths, a radio telescope must be built with a very large objective, usually some form of dish antenna. Astronomers often build several radio telescopes close together and connect them to form one large telescope. The VLA (very large array), shown in **Figure 4,** is an example of this.

Science Online

Topic: New Telescope Design

Visit gpescience.com for Web links to information about the development of new telescopes.

Activity Write and illustrate a paragraph about one of the new designs being considered for Earth-based telescopes or Earth-orbital telescopes.

Reading Check *What type of telescope is used to study radio waves?*

Hubble Space Telescope Even using active and adaptive optics, the atmosphere limits what Earth-based telescopes can achieve. For this reason, astronomers use space telescopes, such as the *Hubble Space Telescope* shown in **Figure 5.**

The clear images provided by *Hubble* are changing scientists' ideas about space. One object viewed by *Hubble* is the massive galaxy cluster Abell 2218, which is about 2 billion light-years away. This cluster acts as a gravity lens that magnifies the light of even more distant galaxies. Such large distances in space are measured in a unit called a **light-year,** the distance that light travels in one year—about 9.5 trillion km. Even though it may seem confusing, remember that a light-year measures distance, not time.

Figure 5 The *Hubble Space Telescope* orbits Earth at an altitude of 610 km.

Activity

View Through a Telescope Provide students with two lenses (one with a 30-mm focal length and one with a 10-mm focal length). Have students hold the thicker lens (the 10-mm focal length lens) up to their eyes and place the other lens directly in line with the first but farther from their eyes. Have students move the lenses back and forth until they can see an image clearly. Ask them to write a description of what they see in their Science Journals. Students should see that the image is reversed and inverted. They should note that objects appear about three times larger and that a tube is not needed to have a telescope. L2 ELL IN **Visual-Spatial**

Reading Check

Answer radio telescope.

Discussion

Light Pollution One problem amateur astronomers have with observing from their homes is light pollution. Light from homes, street lights, malls, and city lights make observing almost impossible. Ask students to research the problem of light pollution and then have them discuss possible solutions to the problem. Homeowners could turn off security lights when requested by a neighbor who wants to observe. Hoods can be placed on lights so they only shine downward. Certain light bulbs can be used that give off just a few wavelengths of light. L2

Post Reading

Extended Research Have students look up information and read about the newest developments in space telescopes. As a class, have students brainstorm questions of interest such as these: What is the history and future of the *Hubble Telescope*? How many space telescopes are currently in use? Do other countries have space telescopes?

Visual Learning

Figure 5 Help students understand the information shown in **Figure 5.** Point out where the objective mirror is located on the *Hubble Space Telescope*. Show students the solar panels that provide power to the telescope in orbit. Explain that several teams of astronauts have visited the *Hubble Space Telescope* in the Space Shuttle and that astronauts have repaired and updated the satellite telescope. L2 ELL IN **Visual-Spatial**

Science Journal

What have we learned? Have students write an article for a newspaper in their Science Journals about some of the discoveries that have been made and are still being made by the *Hubble Space Telescope*. Possible answer: photographs of some of the dimmest galaxies ever seen, photographs of galaxy interactions, photographs of Pluto and Charon. L1 IN **Linguistic** P

Reading Check

Answer A spectroscope disperses the light into a spectrum.

Caption Answer

Figure 6 It disperses light into individual wavelengths.

3 Assess

DAILY INTERVENTION

Check for Understanding

Visual-Spatial Have students collect images of different types of telescopes and bring them to class. Separate the class into groups of four or five and have each group compile a photographic journal of the different types of telescopes. Students can separate the journal into sections with a basic diagram of the type of telescope shown in that section illustrated on the title page. Each photograph could also have a caption, in which the telescope is named and described. L2

Reteach

Light Years Away Place images of five different space objects on the chalkboard and label the distance to each object in light-years. Ask students when the light from each object started toward Earth. L1

Assessment

Process Provide students with models of the two basic types of optical telescopes. Have them describe which type is more appropriate for building a large optical telescope and have them explain why. Possible answer: Reflecting, because the large objective mirror can be supported from the bottom. **PASC,** p. 89. L3

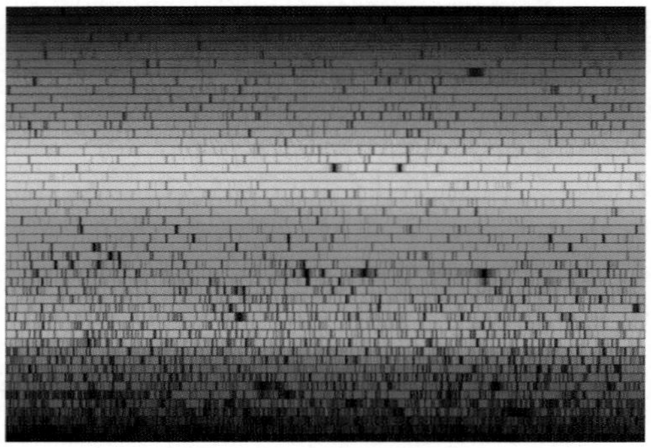

Figure 6 The dark lines in stellar spectra tell astronomers what elements are present in the stars being studied.
Explain *how a spectroscope produces a spectrum of colors.*

Spectroscopes

A **spectroscope** is a device that uses a prism or diffraction grating to disperse the light into its component wavelengths. When connected to a telescope, it disperses the light from the star or other celestial object collected by the telescope into its electromagnetic spectrum. This tells astronomers a great deal about a star. For example, they can determine its chemical composition, its surface temperature, and whether it is moving away from or toward Earth. Astronomers can even tell how fast the star is moving in relation to Earth.

Reading Check *What does a spectroscope do?*

Spectra A spectroscope disperses light into its individual wavelengths, or its spectrum. Visible light yields a spectrum of colors, including red, orange, yellow, green, blue, indigo, and violet, the colors of a rainbow. In fact, a rainbow is actually a visible spectrum of sunlight that has been dispersed by droplets of water in Earth's atmosphere. A spectrum displays all wavelengths in the light being studied, shown in **Figure 6.** You have learned that a star's spectrum indicates its surface temperature. For example, if the blue section is brightest, the star has a relatively high surface temperature. If the red section is brightest, the temperature of the star is much lower.

section 1 review

Summary

Constellations

- Constellations are patterns of stars that are used today to name and locate stars.

Telescopes

- Refracting telescopes use lenses to collect light and magnify the image.
- Reflecting telescopes use a mirror to collect light and a lens to magnify the image.
- A radio telescope collects and amplifies radio waves.

Spectroscopes

- A spectroscope disperses light into its spectrum.

Self Check

1. **Define** constellation.
2. **Compare and contrast** refractor telescopes and reflector telescopes.
3. **Describe** the objective of a radio telescope.
4. **Explain** how radio waves differ from visible light.
5. **Think Critically** Why do astronomers change eyepieces rather than objectives when they wish to increase the magnifying power of a telescope?

Applying Math

6. **Use Numbers** If the magnifying powers (M_p) of refracting and reflecting telescopes are 20 and 100, respectively, how much greater is the M_p of the reflecting telescope?

More Section Review gpescience.com

section 1 review

1. a pattern of stars that resembles a recognizable object, person, or animal.
2. Both are optical telescopes. Refractor telescopes use an objective lens; reflectors use an objective mirror.
3. a large dish antenna
4. They have a much longer wavelength.
5. It is easy to take out one eyepiece and replace it with another. In order to change an objective, an entirely different telescope must be used.
6. five times greater

section 2

Evolution of Stars

Reading Guide

What You'll Learn
- **Explain** how stars form.
- **Classify** the stages of stellar evolution using a Hertzsprung-Russel (H-R) diagram.
- **Describe** the Sun and explain how it has and will evolve.

Why It's Important
The Sun is the star that provides energy for life on Earth.

Review Vocabulary
absolute magnitude: a measure of the amount of light given off by a star

New Vocabulary
- main sequence
- giant
- white dwarf
- solar mass
- photosphere
- sunspots

How do stars form?

Star formation begins with condensation of a large cloud of gas, ice, and dust called a nebula. These particles exert a gravitational force on each other, and the nebula contracts. Gravitational instability within the nebula causes it to break up into smaller cloud fragments. As a cloud fragment condenses its temperature increases. When the interior temperature reaches 1 million K, the center of the cloud is called a protostar. When the temperature reaches 10 million K, hydrogen fuses to form helium and a star is born.

H-R Diagram In the early 1900s, Ejnar Hertzsprung and Henry Russell studied the relationship between absolute magnitude and temperature of stars. They noticed that higher-temperature stars radiate more energy and have higher absolute magnitudes. As stars form, even while they are still protostars, they can be plotted on the Hertzsprung-Russell (H-R) diagram, like the one shown in **Figure 7.** About 90 percent of all stars fall on a line drawn from the upper left to the lower right of the H-R diagram, called the **main sequence.** The other 10 percent of stars fall elsewhere on the graph and will be discussed later.

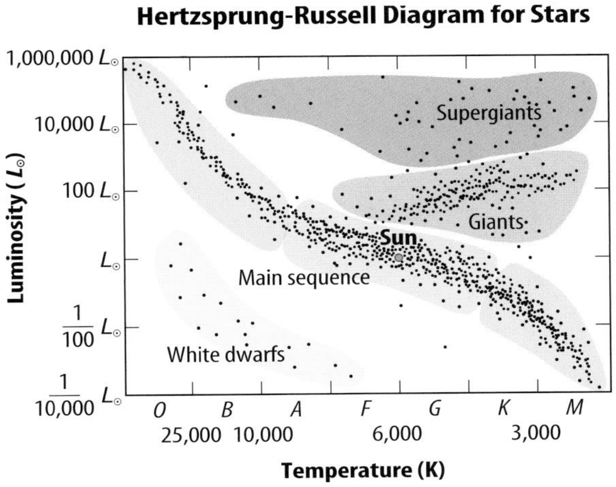

Figure 7 The Sun is located in the center of the main sequence on this H-R diagram. It is cooler than young stars like Vega and Sirius, but warmer than the giant Betelgeuse.

Section 2 Resource Manager

Chapter *FAST FILE* Resources
Transparency Activity, p. 45
MiniLAB, p. 4
Lab Activity, pp. 9–12, 13–14
Enrichment, p. 30
Reinforcement, p. 26
Directed Reading for Content Mastery, p. 18
Performance Assessment in the Science Classroom, p. 52
Reading and Writing Skills Activities, pp. 3–4

1 Motivate

INTERACTIVE CHALKBOARD PowerPoint® Presentations An editable Microsoft® PowerPoint® presentation is available on **Interactive Chalkboard** CD-ROM.

Bellringer

Section Focus Transparencies also are available on the Interactive Chalkboard CD-ROM. L2 ELL

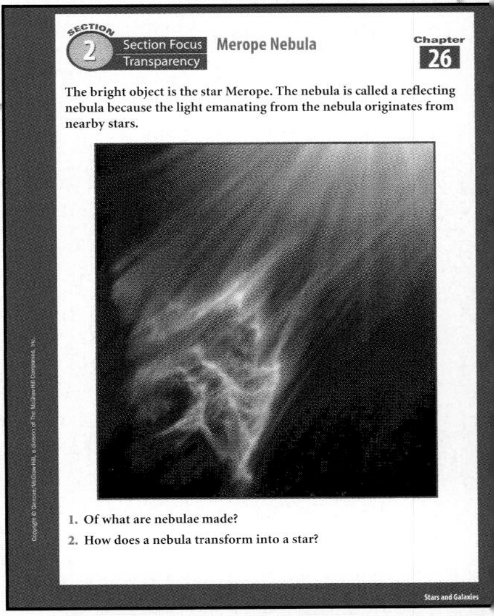

Reading Preview

Tie to Prior Knowledge

Star Colors Explain to students that the color of a star can indicate its temperature. Ask them to consider three different colors of stars—red, yellow, and blue. Ask them which star would be hottest and which would be coolest. The blue star would be hottest and the red would be coolest. L2

Activate Background Knowledge Use **Figure 7** to orient students to the new, star-related vocabulary. Explain the meaning of *luminosity*, which is used in the scale. Ask questions to help students think about types of stars, such as: In what group are most of the stars?

2 Teach

Reading Check

Answer main sequence

Mini LAB

Purpose Students will model counting stars in the sky. L2 IN **Kinesthetic**

Materials blue construction paper, metric ruler, 1 tablespoon of rice kernels

Teaching Strategy Prepare a transparency of the grid students will draw. Randomly make dark marks on the grid and show students how to evaluate the total number of dots.

Analysis

1. Answers will vary, but should equal the total number counted in three squares divided by 3 and then multiplied by 20.
2. Students should realize that they could count the number of stars observed through a cardboard tube over several sections of the sky of a known area, obtain an average, and multiply it by the total area of the sky.

Assessment

Oral Ask students to propose a more accurate method. Possible answer: Several teams of students could use one of the grids and count the number of rice kernels in different grid sections. They could then average all of the counted grids from the several teams and multiply this value by 20.

Try at Home

Mini LAB

Counting Stars

Procedure

1. Draw a grid of twenty squares, with each square measuring 5 cm on a side. The final grid will be 25 cm long and 20 cm wide.
2. Randomly scatter about one **tablespoon** of **white rice** over the grid.
3. Select three squares and count the number of rice grains that are either completely within each square or partly touching its right side or bottom. Calculate the average number in each square.
4. Multiply the average by 20.

Analysis

1. How many rice grains are located within the grid?
2. How does this process model counting stars?

Try at Home

How do stars change?

A star like our Sun probably had a diameter about 100 times its present size while a protostar. As a star continues to form, it shrinks and increases in density, raising its interior temperature. Once fusion begins and the star attains stellar equilibrium, it settles onto the main sequence. In general, stellar equilibrium is the balance between outward pressure due to energy released in fusion and inward pressure due to gravity. Once this state of equilibrium is lost, the star enters the next stage of its life.

Main Sequence As long as the star's gravity balances outward pressures, the star remains on the main sequence. Stars are thought to spend most of their lives on the main sequence, which explains why this is the largest group on the H-R diagram. The Sun has been a main sequence star for about 5 billion years and will continue in this stage for about another 5 billion years.

Reading Check *The Sun is classified as which type of star?*

When its hydrogen fuel is depleted, a star loses its equilibrium and its main sequence status. What it becomes next is determined by the total mass of the star. An average star like the Sun will become a giant, then a white dwarf, and finally a black dwarf. Stars more massive than the Sun can become supergiants and end up as neutron stars or black holes. Stars much lower in mass than the Sun, like the red dwarf star *Proxima Centauri,* could remain on the main sequence for 16 trillion years. Most stars on the main sequence are red dwarfs, and they probably make up about 80 percent of all stars in the universe.

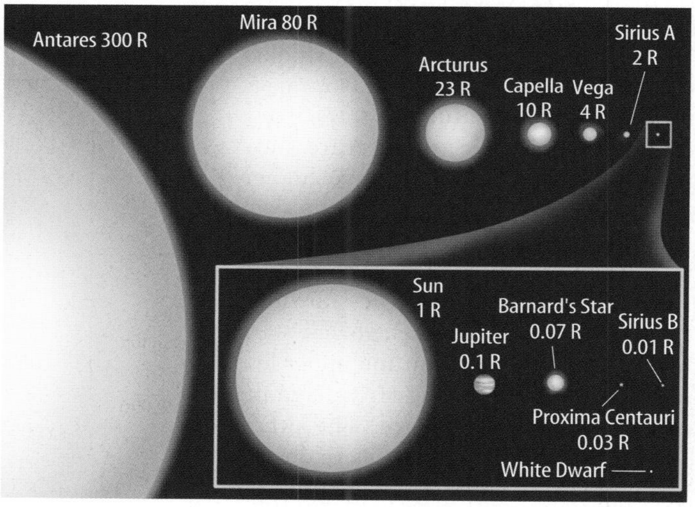

Figure 8 Only part of the giant star Antares is shown here. Super giant stars, such as Betelgeuse, are too large to be shown at all.

Visual Learning

Figure 8 Help students understand the information presented in **Figure 8**. The relative sizes of several stars are shown to scale in this illustration. Point out that white dwarf stars are very hot, but they are so small that they are difficult to see in the sky. Although they are cool, giants emit light from such a large area that they look bright even from great distances. L2 ELL IN **Visual-Spatial**

Science Journal

Main Sequence Stars Have students write a brief summary about three hypothetical protostars having solar masses of 15, 1, and 0.1. Ask students where they would place these stars on the main sequence, and predict the relative length of time each will stay there. Possible answer: 15—upper left (will stay shortest time), 1—middle, and 0.1—lower right (will stay longest time) L2 IN **Linguistic**

Giants and Dwarfs When hydrogen in a star's core is used up, its outward pressure is overcome by gravity. Its core contracts and increases in temperature. The outer layers expand and cool. In this late stage of its life cycle, an average star like our Sun is called a **giant.** In about five billion years, our Sun will become a giant like the one shown in **Figure 8.**

The giant's core continues to contract and become hotter. Eventually, the core uses up its helium and contracts even more. When temperature reaches 100 million K, helium fuses, forming carbon. Now the star is enormous and its surface is much cooler. Its outer layers escape into space leaving behind the hot, dense core that continues to contract. At this final stage in an average star's evolution, it is a **white dwarf.** A white dwarf, also shown in **Figure 8,** is about the size of Earth.

Supergiants, Neutron Stars, and Black Holes Stars that are over eight times more massive than our Sun take a different course. Their cores reach temperatures high enough to cause fusion that produces heavier and heavier elements. The star expands into a supergiant, such as Betelgeuse shown in **Figure 9.** Eventually, iron accumulates in the core. Since iron does not fuse readily, there is no outward radiation of energy to counteract the inward pull of gravity. The core collapses violently, and the outer portion of the star explodes, producing a supernova.

A supernova is a gigantic explosion in which the temperature in the collapsing core reaches 10 billion K and atomic nuclei are split into neutrons and protons. Protons merge with electrons to form neutrons, and the collapsing core becomes a neutron star. A typical neutron star is the size of a major city on Earth, but has a mass greater than the Sun's.

Very massive stars, with masses greater than 25 times that of the Sun, face a different end. In this case, the final collapse of the core continues past the neutron-star stage, forming a black hole—an object so dense that nothing can escape its gravity if it gets too close.

Supernovas The heavy elements you are made of formed during supernova explosions. Type I supernovas form from hydrogen-poor, low mass stars that have pulled in matter from a nearby red giant star. This process, called carbon detonation, causes carbon fusion almost everywhere inside the star and is thought to destroy the star completely. In contrast, Type II supernovas form from hydrogen-rich, high mass stars. They leave behind a collapsed core that can then condense further to form a neutron star or black hole.

Figure 9 Betelgeuse is located in the constellation of Orion. Its diameter is larger than the diameter of Jupiter's orbit around the Sun.
Classify *What kind of star is Betelgeuse?*

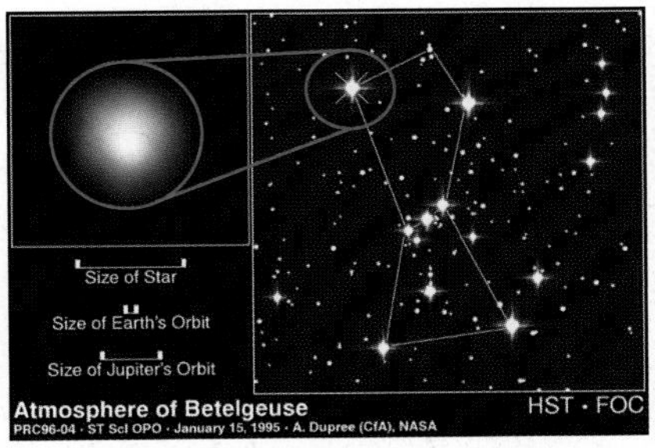

Activity

Giants Betelgeuse is 630, Antares is 500, Aldebaran is 40, and Sirius A is 2 times larger than the Sun. Have students use construction paper to draw and cut out representative circles for each of these stars and the Sun. Ask students to speculate on whether these stars are supergiants, giants, or main sequence stars. Possible answer: Betelgeuse is a supergiant, Antares and Aldebaran are giants, Sirius A and the Sun are main sequence stars. L1 ELL LS **Visual-Spatial**

Caption Answer

Figure 9 supergiant

Use Science Words

Word Meaning When a star suddenly brightens by thousands or even millions of times, it is called a nova or a supernova. Ask students to research the meaning of the word *nova* and to discover why it is used when talking about stars that suddenly get brighter. Possible answer: Since many of these stars were not seen before they became so bright, early astronomers thought they might be a new star. "Nova" means new and is used to describe these "new" stars. L1

Discussion

Supernovas Have students research the cause of Type I supernovas. Ask students to discuss the processes that are involved in the formation of this type of supernova. Possible answer: If a white dwarf pulls too much material from its companion star, it contracts and heats up to a temperature at which carbon fuses into more massive atoms. This fusion occurs through out the star and the star explodes. L2

Teacher FYI

Black Holes Contrary to what some people think, a black hole does not suck in matter from all directions. Only objects closer to the black hole than a certain point, called the event horizon, are undetectable, because no mass or radiation can escape.

Active Reading

Quickwrites This strategy lets students use spontaneous writing to discover what they already know. Have students write a list of ideas about black holes, then share these ideas with the class. Next, have students write their ideas freely in a paragraph without worrying about punctuation, spelling, and grammar.

Reading Strategy

Sequence As they read the following pages, have students write the steps in the evolution of giant stars and supergiant stars. Ask them to identify the names of phases and the cause of each change in their evolution.

SECTION 2 Evolution of Stars **825**

NATIONAL GEOGRAPHIC

Visualizing H–R Diagrams of Star Clusters

Have students examine the pictures and read the captions. Then ask the following questions.

Compare the brightness, temperature, and age of stars in the upper right and left corners of the H-R diagram for the Pleiades. Possible answer: Stars in the upper right corner are cooler and older than stars in the upper left corner. Stars in both corners are relatively bright stars.

Compare the H-R diagrams of the Pleiades and M5. What major differences can you identify? Possible answer: The H-R diagram for M5 shows red giants and white dwarfs. It has no hot, blue stars, and lacks a well-defined main sequence.

How can the age of globular clusters like M5 help astronomers estimate the age of the universe? Possible answer: Globular clusters contain some of the oldest stars in the galaxy. The universe must be at least as old as these stars.

Activity

View the Pleiades The Pleiades is located in the constellation Taurus. Have students find the Pleiades in the night sky by facing south, then looking above and to the right of the constellation Orion. The first bright star they will see is Aldebaran in Taurus. The Pleiades are just up and to the right. Viewing conditions affect the number of visible stars, but students should see the brightest stars, which are Alcyone, Merope, Maia, and Electra. Students should describe their observations using a written format of their choice and include a drawing of what they saw. P

NATIONAL GEOGRAPHIC **VISUALIZING H-R DIAGRAMS OF STAR CLUSTERS**

Figure 10

The Pleiades star cluster blazed into existence a mere 100 million years ago, when dinosaurs reigned on Earth and mammals were just gaining a foothold. The Pleiades, located in the back of the constellation Taurus, is among the earliest of celestial objects to be known and recorded by humans. Many myths sprang up to explain their origin. Today, astronomers study star clusters like the Pleiades because they offer valuable insights into how the universe is evolving.

Pleiades

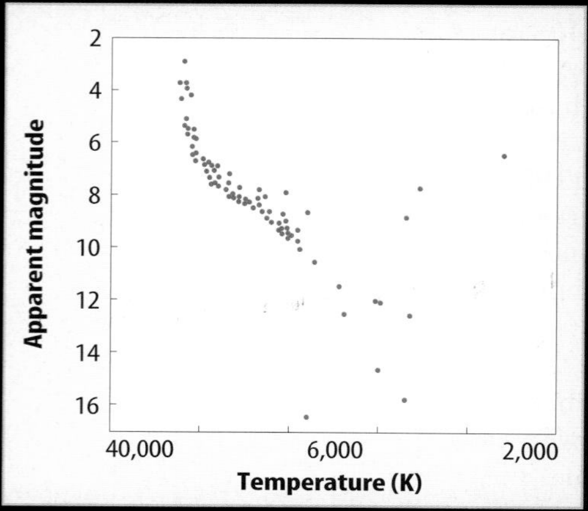

Because star clusters are believed to have formed from the same nebula, they are assumed to be about the same distance away. For this reason they are plotted using apparent magnitude instead of absolute magnitude or luminosity. Note that a lower magnitude number represents a brighter star. The H-R diagram for the Pleiades shows a well-defined main sequence. Stars in the upper left are hot, blue, and massive. As stars age, they burn all available hydrogen and eventually become red giants. The presence of hot, blue stars and the lack of red giants indicate that the Pleiades is a relatively young star cluster.

M5 is a globular cluster, located roughly 24,500 light-years from Earth. It has a compact appearance and vastly more stars than are found in open clusters like the Pleiades. Astronomers believe M5 is one of the oldest star clusters in our galaxy, with an estimated age of 13 billion years.

M5 Globular Cluster

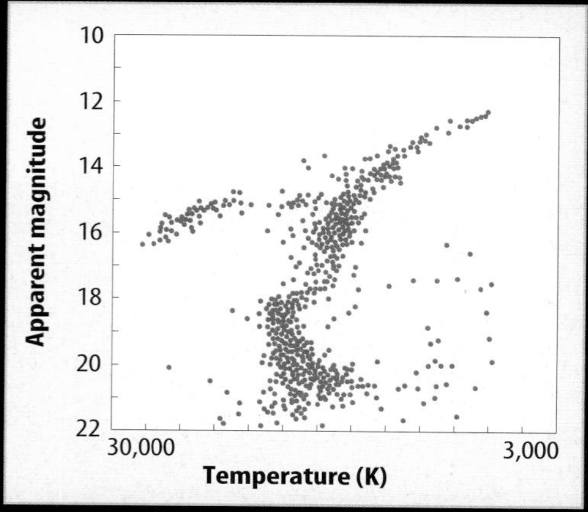

Compare the H-R diagram for M5 to the H-R diagram for the Pleiades. The stars in cluster M5, which were once hot and blue, have evolved into cooler, highly luminous red giants that appear in the upper right of the diagram. Sun-sized stars evolve from main sequence to red giants over billions of years, indicating that M5 is an ancient star cluster.

Differentiated Instruction

Challenge Astronomers recently discovered brown dwarfs within the Pleiades star cluster. Have students research these unique objects. Students should discover the characteristics of brown dwarfs, why they are difficult to find, and how they differ from both stars and gas planets. Have students create a chart comparing the characteristics of brown dwarfs, main sequence stars, red giants, and white dwarfs, including relative diameter, temperature, luminosity, and mass. P

The Sun—A Main Sequence Star

The Sun is a middle-aged star and is plotted just about in the middle of the main sequence on the H-R diagram. It is average in size, temperature, and absolute magnitude. A **solar mass** is simply the mass of the Sun. For most stars, the relationship between mass and luminosity can be approximated by

$$\frac{L}{L_\odot} = \left(\frac{M}{M_\odot}\right)^{3.5}$$

where $L_\odot$ and $M_\odot$ are the luminosity and mass of the Sun. The H-R diagrams, shown in **Figure 10,** are used to compare very young stars to very old stars.

Structure of the Sun Although scientists cannot see inside the Sun, they have developed some theories about its interior. Much of what they know comes from studying its outer layers and its surface. The solar interior is composed of the core, the radiation layer, and the convection layer. The surface of the Sun is called the **photosphere.** This is the layer of the Sun that gives us light. The atmosphere above the photosphere is composed of the chromosphere and the corona. The Sun's structure is shown in **Figure 11.**

Solar Interior The innermost layer of the Sun is the core. This is where fusion occurs. The energy produced at the core may take millions of years to reach the photosphere where it is radiated into space.

The layer of the Sun just above the core is the radiation zone. In this layer, gases are completely ionized. Since no electrons remain on atoms to capture photons, this layer of the Sun is transparent to radiation. Energy formed by fusion travels easily through the radiation zone.

As you move farther outward from the Sun's core, the temperature drops and some electrons remain bound to their atoms. Here the gas becomes opaque to radiation and by the time you reach the outer edge of the radiation zone, all of the photons generated in the core have been absorbed. The energy from these photons is carried to the Sun's surface by convection through the next layer, the convection zone. Hotter gases from the bottom of this zone move upward toward the Sun's surface and cooler gases sink, setting up convection cells.

INTEGRATE Life Science

Energy for Life Plants use energy from the Sun and produce carbohydrates in a process called photosynthesis. When we burn fossil fuels, such as coal, we are using energy from the Sun that is stored in fossilized plant materials. Scientists also are trying to make direct use of solar energy by using solar cells. Research some applications of solar energy and share your results with your class.

Figure 11 The Sun's interior is divided into three parts: the core, the radiation zone, and the convection zone.
List *three of the Sun's spheres or layers, starting with the surface and moving outward.*

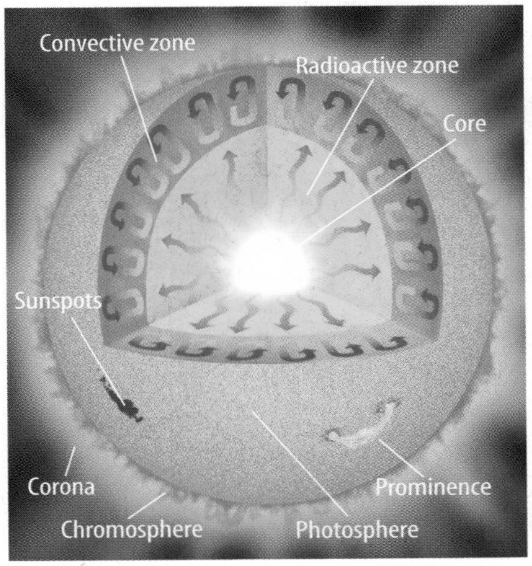

IDENTIFYING Misconceptions

The Sun is a Star Students often look at the Sun as the source of light and heat for Earth, but not as a star. The only reason the Sun is so bright compared to other stars is that it is so close to us. It is a star of average size, average temperature, and average brightness. Have students find the Sun on the H-R diagram. They will see that it (often referred to as Sol) is plotted along with many other main sequence stars.

INTEGRATE Life Science

Energy for Life Decayed organic materials deposited on seafloors were buried under layers of sediment. Then, the heat and pressure of these overlying sediments transformed them into the hydrocarbon fuels: oil, coal, and gas. Burning these fuels releases their stored energy. In burning they combine with oxygen from the atmosphere to form mostly carbon dioxide and water.

Caption Answer

Figure 11 photosphere, chromosphere, corona

LAB DEMONSTRATION

Purpose Students estimate the rate of movement of sunspots.

Materials clipboard, piece of cardboard, refracting telescope, small tripod, scissors, plain white paper

Preparation Cut a hole in the cardboard so it fits over the end of the telescope.

Procedure Set up the telescope with the eyepiece facing away from the Sun. Cover the finder scope. Project an image of the Sun onto the white paper on the clipboard. Trace any sunspots that appear on the lighted disk. Repeat the procedure daily for a week. Caution students to never look at the Sun through a telescope or directly with the unaided eye.

Expected Outcome Students will see sunspots moving across the Sun.

Assessment

What is the rate of sunspot movement over the week? Possible answer: Sunspots crossed about half the Sun in one week.

Make a Model

Structure of the Sun Have students make a model of the Sun's interior and surface using different colors of modeling clay. Encourage them to include some of the solar phenomena that occur on the photosphere, such as sunspots. L2 ELL IS **Visual-Spatial**

Reading Check

Answer darker, cooler spots on the Sun's photoshere

Quick Demo

Sunspots

Materials transparency of black line image

Estimated Time 5 minutes

Procedure Demonstrate why sunspots look dark on the Sun even though they are very hot. Have students look at an overhead projector screen. Ask them what color it is. Then turn on the projector. Ask them again what color is shown. Then place the black line transparency on the projector. Ask them what color the lines of the drawing are. Possible answers: Students will have said that the screen is white and bright white. Then they will say the lines are black. Explain to them that the lines look black because they are not as bright as the rest of the screen. Point out that the black lines are no blacker than the unlit portion of the screen. Sunspots look dark because they are not giving off as much light as the rest of the Sun. L2 ELL **Visual-Spatial**

Post Reading

Discussion Have students discuss what they learned about the evolution of stars. For example, were they surprised to discover that some stars shrink and some stars expand as they die? What do they think about black holes? Does the information learned from the reading match up with what they have seen on television and in movies about black holes?

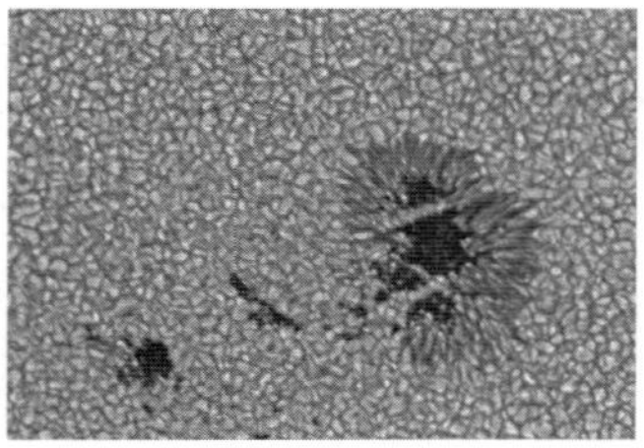

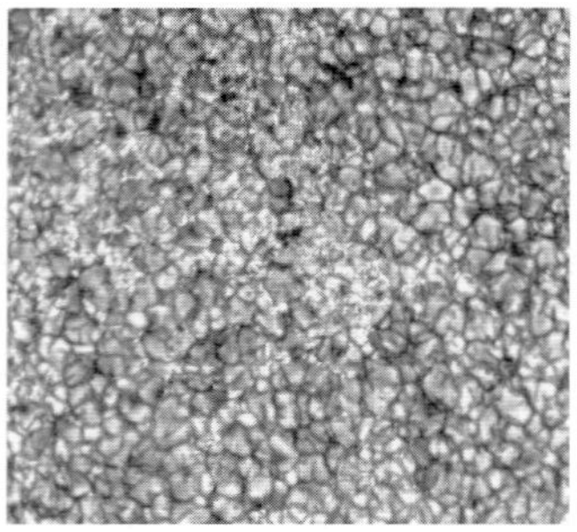

Figure 12 Sunspots, above, are often 2,000 K cooler than the surrounding granules, shown below.

Photosphere The Sun's photosphere, or surface, is at the top of the convection zone and has a mottled appearance, called granulation. This is caused by rising hot material and sinking cooler material within the convection cells. Each granule shown in **Figure 12** is about 1,000 km across and is a direct result of convection cells in the convection zone.

Sunspots Some areas of the Sun appear darker than others. These darker areas of the Sun's photosphere, called **sunspots** are cooler than surrounding areas. Scientists can observe the movement of individual sunspots as they move with the Sun's rotation. They show that the Sun doesn't rotate as a solid body—it rotates faster at its equator than at its poles. Sunspots near the equator take about 25 days to go around the sun, but at about 60 degrees north or south latitude, they take about 31 days. **Figure 12** shows a closeup view of some sunspots.

Reading Check *What is a sunspot?*

Sunspots aren't permanent features of the Sun. They appear and disappear over periods of days, weeks, or months. The number of sunspots changes in a fairly regular pattern called the sunspot, or solar activity, cycle. Periods of sunspot maximum occur about every 11 years, with periods of sunspot minimum occurring in between. At a sunspot minimum, sunspots appear at high latitudes. As the cycle progresses, they appear closer to the Sun's equator. By the next minimum, they again cluster at high latitudes.

Figure 13 This prominence of dense plasma appears suspended in the Sun's chromosphere as it loops back to the surface.

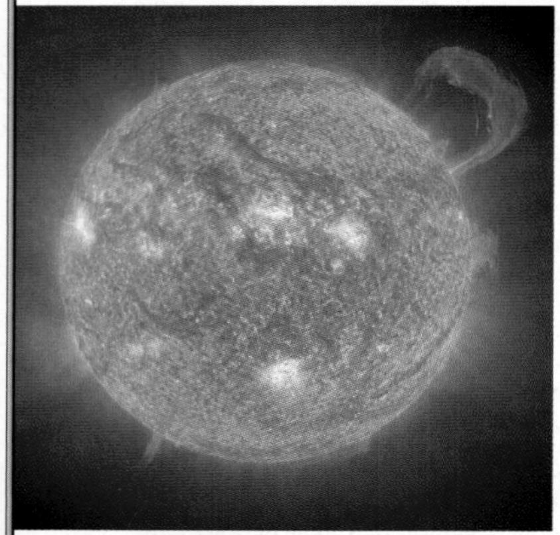

Prominences and Flares Intense magnetic fields associated with sunspots can cause huge arching columns of gas called prominences to erupt, as shown in **Figure 13.** Convection in the convection zone causes magnetized gases to flow upward toward the photosphere. Sometimes the magnetic field strength is great enough that magnetic field lines shoot out from the surface near a pair of sunspots and cause a prominence of solar material to loop from one spot to the other. Some prominences blast material from the sun into space at speeds ranging from 600 km/s to more than 1,000 km/s.

Gases near a sunspot sometimes brighten suddenly, shooting gas outward at high speed in what are called solar flares. Temperatures within these flares can reach 100 million K. Particles produced in a flare possess so much energy that the Sun's magnetic field cannot hold them as it can hold prominences and they blast into space.

Differentiated Instruction

Hearing Impaired Help your hearing-impaired students better understand the structure of the Sun. As you present the different layers of the Sun and what happens to energy at each layer, draw a cross-section of the Sun's interior on the chalkboard. Use a different color of chalk for each layer and include several of the photosphere's surface phenomena, such as sunspots and flares. L2 ELL IS **Visual-Spatial**

Visual Learning

Figure 12 Help students understand the information presented in **Figure 12.** The granulation shown on the surface of the Sun is caused by rising and falling gases in the convection layer. Rising columns of gas are hotter and brighter and sinking gases are cooler and darker. The sunspots also are darker, cooler regions on the photosphere. L2 ELL IS **Visual-Spatial**

828 CHAPTER 26 Stars and Galaxies

CMEs Sometimes large bubbles of ionized gas are emitted from the Sun. These are known as CMEs (coronal mass ejections). During sunspot minimums there is usually one CME per week, but during a sunspot maximum, there are two to three per day. When a CME is released in the direction of Earth, it appears as a halo around the Sun, as shown in **Figure 14.** As it passes Earth, the planet is exposed to a sudden shock wave of increased solar wind. Earth's atmosphere protects us, but occurrences of auroras increase. When scientists note a CME, they post an alert to watch for auroras at lower latitudes than normal.

Auroras take place when high-energy particles in CMEs and the solar wind are carried past Earth's magnetic field. This generates large electric currents that flow toward Earth's poles. These electric currents ionize gases in Earth's atmosphere. When these ions recombine with electrons and drop to a lower energy level, they produce light. This light is called the aurora borealis, or northern lights, when it occurs in the northern hemisphere. In the southern hemisphere, it is called the aurora australis. CMEs present little danger to life on Earth, but some of the highly charged solar wind material disrupts Earth's magnetosphere and interferes with orbiting satellites and radio signals.

Figure 14 CMEs like this one can hurl a million tons of matter into space each second. They can damage satellites and endanger astronauts.

section 2 review

Summary

How do stars form?

- Stars form from a large cloud of gas, ice, and dust. Once the temperature inside the nebula reaches 10 million K, fusion begins.
- The H-R diagram plots temperature v. absolute magnitude of stars.

How do stars change?

- Once fusion begins, a star develops stellar equilibrium and becomes a main sequence star.
- When the hydrogen fuel is depleted, a star loses stellar equilibrium and evolves into a giant, or a supergiant.

The Sun—A Main Sequence Star

- The Sun's energy is produced by fusion.
- Sunspots are dark, cooler regions on the Sun's photosphere.
- Other solar features that can affect Earth are prominences, flares, and CMEs.

Self Check

1. **Explain** how stars form from nebulae.
2. **Describe** the different evolution stages of stars as shown on the H-R diagram.
3. **Describe** the structure of the Sun.
4. **Explain** the difference between Type I and Type II supernovas.
5. **Think Critically** What happens to stellar equilibrium to make a main sequence star evolve into a giant star?

Applying Math

6. **Use Percentages** Eighty percent of all stars are red dwarfs. Out of a random sample of 2,000 stars in the galaxy, about how many will plot on the H-R diagram as a red dwarf?
7. **Use Numbers** If the Sun will remain a main sequence star for a total of 10 billion years and Proxima Centauri will remain one for 16 trillion years, how many times longer will Proxima Centauri be a main sequence star?

More Section Review gpescience.com

3 Assess

DAILY INTERVENTION

Check for Understanding

Visual-Spatial Show students images of three different stars. Show Betelgeuse, which is cooler and hundreds of times larger than the Sun; Sirius A, which is a little hotter and twice as large as the Sun; and Sirius B, which is much hotter, but much smaller than the Sun. Ask them to classify the three stars. Possible answer: Betelgeuse is a supergiant, Sirius A is a main sequence star, and Sirius B is a white dwarf. L2 ELL

Reteach

Sunspots Ask students to draw an image of sunspots on the Sun and to explain why they are visible on the Sun's photosphere. Possible answer: Students should draw an image of the Sun with dark spots visible on the Sun's photosphere. Students may draw dark spots surrounded by an area that is not quite as dark. They are darker than surrounding areas of the Sun because they are about 1,000 degrees cooler. L1 ELL **Visual-Spatial**

Assessment

Oral The most common type of star in the universe is the red dwarf, a main sequence star. Ask students why many of the bright stars we can see in the sky are giants. Possible answer: Most easily visible stars are giants because they have large surface areas that emit large amounts of light and can be seen from great distances. Use **PASC,** p. 89 L2

section 2 review

1. Nebulae fragment, condense and flatten. Matter concentrates in the center where temperature increases. At about 10,000,000°C, hydrogen fuses into helium, producing heat and light.
2. Once a star achieves stellar equilibrium, it is a main sequence star. Stars can change into giants or supergiants. Giants evolve into white dwarfs. Supergiants will undergo supernova explosions and become neutron stars or black holes.
3. The Sun's interior has three layers; the core, the radiation layer, and the convection layer. The photosphere is the Sun's surface. Above the surface is the atmosphere containing the chromosphere and the corona.
4. Type I supernovas form from hydrogen-poor, low-mass stars that have pulled in material from a nearby red giant star; they are destroyed completely. Type II supernovas form from hydrogen-rich, high-mass stars; they leave cores that form neutron stars or black holes.
5. Stellar equilibrium is lost when hydrogen is exhausted. The core contracts, temperatures rise, and the outer layers of the star expand .
6. 1,600 stars
7. 1,600 times longer

BENCH TESTED

Real-World Problem

Purpose Students will compare and contrast H-R diagrams and determine the relative ages of four star clusters.

Process Skills compare and contrast, infer, interpret scientific illustrations, use graphs

Time Required 30 minutes

Procedure

Teaching Strategies Make transparencies of different star clusters. Select clusters having different ages. For example, the h and chi Persei double cluster (NGC 869 and 864), the Hyades, NGC 188 (in Cepheus), and 47 Tucanae (NGC 104). These H-R diagrams are available in many astronomy books and Internet sites.

Troubleshooting Remind students of the locations of giants, white dwarfs, and main sequence stars on the H-R diagram.

Conclude and Apply

1. Different types of stars are shown on H-R diagrams of different star clusters.
2. The youngest star cluster will not have giants or white dwarfs. High-mass stars will have evolved off the main sequence with some having evolved to white dwarfs in the oldest star cluster.
3. The number of low-mass stars on the main sequence and what has happened to high-mass stars help determine the relative ages of the star clusters.
4. Answers will vary.
5. Check how many high-mass stars have evolved off the main sequence.

LAB

Star Cluster Age

Stars are plotted on the H-R diagram based on their temperature and brightness. You can determine the age of a cluster of stars by studying the H-R diagram of the stars within the cluster. Massive main sequence stars, located at the upper left of the diagram, evolve faster than stars farther down the main sequence. Stars in the lower right of the diagram evolve more slowly. How could you use this idea to help determine the relative ages of star clusters from their H-R diagrams?

Real-World Problem

How can the relative age of star clusters be determined from H-R diagrams of each cluster?

Goals

- **Compare and contrast** H-R diagrams of several star clusters.
- **Determine** the relative ages of four star clusters.

Materials

four H-R diagrams of star clusters

Procedure

1. Study the four H-R diagrams your teacher gives you.
2. Note which types of stars remain on the main sequence and which stars have evolved off the main sequence.
3. Based on the evolution of the stars within each star cluster, decide which cluster is youngest and which is oldest. Also decide the relative ages of the other two star clusters. *HINT: The oldest cluster will have some that have evolved to white dwarfs.*

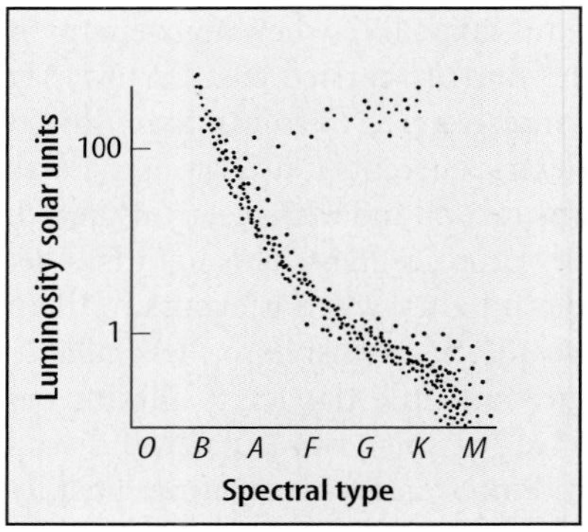

Conclude and Apply

1. **Compare and contrast** H-R diagrams of four star clusters.
2. **Determine** which star cluster was youngest and which was oldest.
3. **Explain** how you determined the ages of these two star clusters.
4. **Determine** the relative ages of the remaining two star clusters.
5. **Explain** how you determined the ages of these two star clusters.

Communicating Your Data

Explain to your friends how the relative ages of star clusters can be found by studying H-R diagrams.

Assessment

Process Show students a transparency of the H-R diagram of the Pleiades star cluster. Ask them to determine its relative age compared to the other star clusters they evaluated in this lab. Possible answer: The Pleiades is older than the h and chi Persei double cluster, but younger than the Hyades star cluster. Use **PASC**, p. 99. L2 ELL **Visual-Spatial**

Communicating Your Data

Have students discuss with one another any differences they used to help determine the relative ages of the four star clusters.

section 3

Galaxies and the Milky Way

Reading Guide

***What* You'll Learn**
- **Explain** that the same natural laws that apply in the Milky Way Galaxy also apply in other galaxies.
- **Compare** the three main types of galaxies.
- **Describe** the Milky Way galaxy and the Sun's position in it.

***Why* It's Important**
The Milky Way galaxy is your galaxy and you can see part of it stretching across the evening sky.

Review Vocabulary
ellipse: oblong, closed curve

New Vocabulary
- galaxy
- Milky Way
- Local Group

Galaxies

One reason to study astronomy is to learn about your place in the universe. Long ago, people thought Earth was at the center of the universe. You know this isn't true, but do you know where you are in the universe?

You are on Earth, and Earth orbits the Sun. But the Sun orbits something also and it interacts with other objects in the universe. The Sun is one star among billions of stars in a galaxy. A **galaxy** is a large group of stars, gas, and dust held together by gravity, shown in **Figure 15.** Our galaxy, called the **Milky Way,** contains 400 billion stars, by most recent estimates, including the Sun. Countless other galaxies exist throughout the universe—an estimated 40 billion galaxies can be seen. Each of these galaxies contains the same elements, forces, and types of energy as our galaxy. There are three major types of galaxies: spiral, elliptical, and irregular.

Spiral Galaxies Take another look at **Figure 15.** Notice that spiral galaxies have spiral arms that wind outward from the galaxy's center. These spiral arms are made up of bright stars, dust, and gas. Our neighbor, the Andromeda galaxy, is visible to the unaided eye as a fuzzy patch in the constellation Andromeda. It is a normal spiral galaxy with its arms starting close to center. Barred spirals are another type of galaxy that have spiral arms extending from a large central bar of stars, dust, and gas that passes through the center, or hub, of the galaxy. Astronomers are not certain whether the Milky Way is normal or barred spiral.

Figure 15 Spiral galaxy 4414. Galaxies often are millions of light-years apart.
Explain *what is meant by* a million light-years.

Section 3 Resource Manager

Chapter *Fast File* Resources
- Transparency Activity, p. 46
- Enrichment, p. 31
- Reinforcement, p. 27
- Directed Reading for Content Mastery, p. 19
- **Earth Science Critical Thinking/ Problem Solving,** p. 8
- **Lab Management and Safety,** p. 66

1 Motivate

INTERACTIVE CHALKBOARD An editable Microsoft® PowerPoint® presentation is available on **Interactive Chalkboard** CD-ROM.

Bellringer

Section Focus Transparencies also are available on the Interactive Chalkboard CD-ROM. L2 ELL

Section 3 Section Focus Transparency — Coma Cluster — Chapter 26

The Coma cluster is a rich cluster of galaxies with over a thousand member galaxies known. The central region, dominated by two giant elliptical galaxies, is pictured here. Most of the objects in this picture are galaxies. Only the very bright objects with spikes and the smallest circular dots are foreground stars in the Milky Way.

1. Why are the galaxies smaller than the stars in this transparency?
2. Can you tell from the transparency that the galaxies are in a cluster?
3. How are galaxies formed?

Stars and Galaxies

Reading Preview

Tie to Prior Knowledge

The Milky Way Ask students if they have viewed the night sky when it was really dark. If so, they might have seen a band of dim light stretching across the sky. Ask students what this band of light could be. Stars; the light of many stars contained in our Milky Way. L2

Predict Ask students to predict what the connections might be among the terms *galaxy*, *Milky Way*, and *Local Group*. Ask why *Local Group* is capitalized. Have the students preview the text to see if their predictions were correct.

SECTION 3 Galaxies and the Milky Way 831

2 Teach

Caption Answer

Figure 15 the distance light travels in one million years

Figure 16 dwarf elliptical

Activity

Types of Galaxies Show students photographs of different types of galaxies. Have students discuss which type is shown in each photograph. Have them list the different types in their Science Journals. Encourage students to describe each galaxy. L2 ELL IN **Visual-Spatial**

Inquiry Lab

Counting Stars

Question What volume of salt grains represents the number of stars in the Milky Way galaxy?

Possible Materials salt, sand, pipettes, 10-mL graduated cylinder, colored paper, calculator

Estimated Time 20 minutes

Teaching Strategies

- Warn students never to eat anything during science class.
- Students can measure 0.1 mL of salt grains and pour them onto colored paper. They can spread the grains and estimate their number by counting by fives. For easier counting, the grains can be divided into sections.
- There are 5,000 salt grains in 1 mL of salt. Students can divide the number of Milky Way stars (400 billion) by 5,000 to calculate the volume of salt grains needed to represent the number of stars in the galaxy. 80,000,000 mL or 80,000 L
- Encourage students to visualize the volume of salt grains by calculating the number of 38-L (10-gallon) aquariums it would fill. approximately 2,105 aquariums

For additional inquiry activities, see Science Inquiry Lab Manual.

Figure 16 In ultraviolet light, this elliptical galaxy reveals a core of thousands of old, helium-burning stars.
***Identify** the most common type of galaxies in the universe.*

Elliptical Galaxies Astronomers once thought that spiral galaxies were the most common galaxies because they are relatively large and easy to see. But as observations of the universe became more detailed, it became clear that most galaxies are elliptical galaxies, and most of these are dwarf galaxies. They are just too small and dim to be easily seen.

These galaxies are shaped like large, three-dimensional ellipses. Many are football-shaped, but others are spherical as shown in **Figure 16.** These giant elliptical galaxies can be over 9 million light-years across and contain trillions of stars. However, most dwarf ellipticals are only about 3,000 light-years across and contain fewer than a million stars.

Irregular Galaxies Most galaxies that aren't elliptical or spiral are considered irregular galaxies. They take many different shapes and contain 100 million to 10 billion stars, making them larger than dwarf ellipticals but smaller than spirals. Irregular galaxies are less common than spirals or ellipticals.

Two irregular galaxies called the Clouds of Magellan orbit the Milky Way. One of these, known as the Large Magellanic Cloud, is shown in **Figure 17.** Several other dwarf galaxies also are affected by the Milky Way's gravity. One of these, the elliptical Sagittarius dwarf, is being absorbed by the Milky Way. This dwarf galaxy lies about 60,000 light-years from the center of the Milky Way on the opposite side of the galaxy from us and 20,000 light-years below the galactic plane.

The Local Group Just as stars are grouped together within galaxies, galaxies are grouped into clusters. Clusters of galaxies are even grouped into superclusters. Our Milky Way galaxy belongs to a cluster called the **Local Group.** It is a relatively small cluster containing about 45 galaxies of various types and sizes, most of which are dwarf elliptical galaxies. The largest galaxy in the Local Group is the Andromeda galaxy, a spiral galaxy a little larger than ours that lies about 2.6 million light-years away. If the Andromeda galaxy and the Milky Way galaxy continue to travel through space as they are, they may collide in the distant future.

Figure 17 The irregular structure of the Large Magellanic Cloud might have been produced by interactions with the Milky Way galaxy.

Visual Learning

Figure 17 Explain to students that before today's powerful telescopes were available, these objects were thought to be nebulae or "clouds." Today we know they are galaxies in the local group. Because of their locations in the southern skies, these galaxies are not visible from the United States. They were named for explorer Ferdinand Magellan, who observed them on his voyage. L2 ELL IN **Visual-Spatial**

Differentiated Instruction

Learning Disabled Have each of your learning-disabled students work with another student. Encourage the teams of students to make flash cards of each of the major types of galaxies. Provide student teams time in class to quiz each other on galaxy types. Suggest that students identify the type and one key property that led to its classification. L1 ELL IN **Visual-Spatial**

How do galaxies form?

Astronomers aren't sure how galaxies originally formed. It is thought that fluctuations in density of primordial matter in the universe began to form blobs of gas that would eventually form into galaxies. These blobs might have had masses equivalent to the mass of the dwarf galaxies. In fact, one idea is that the dwarf galaxies may be remnants of these earlier blobs of matter.

Most astronomers now believe that the galaxies we see closer to us grew by absorbing or merging with other smaller objects. One bit of evidence that supports this idea is that more distant galaxies tend to be much smaller than those closer to the Milky Way. It makes sense to conclude that these smaller galaxies that existed long ago merged to make the larger, more organized galaxies of the universe today. Also, we have evidence that galaxies do collide.

Colliding Galaxies In some galaxy clusters, the galaxies are concentrated very close together. In the Virgo Cluster, for example, thousands of galaxies orbit within 10 million light-years of each other. Do these galaxies collide? If so, what happens to them and to the stars within them? It seems that little happens to the individual stars within the galaxies. There is so much open space between the stars that the individual stars of the two galaxies just move past each other.

Reading Check *What happens to individual stars in colliding galaxies?*

However, galaxy collisions have a strong effect on the overall structure and shape of the colliding galaxies. They may lose all of their spiral shape, if they had any.

It is thought that the two galaxies shown in **Figure 18** will eventually collide. The smaller galaxy on the right does not seem to have enough energy to escape the larger one to the left. When galaxies interact by passing close to each other or by colliding, there is a burst of star formation in each. Their interstellar gas and dust clouds are shocked and squeezed, leading to star formation. This can be detected by the blue light emitted by young, hot stars.

Figure 18 In about a billion years, these two galaxies will merge. Much of their spiral structures probably will be lost.

Use an Analogy

Merging Galaxies Explain to students that water droplets running down a windowpane and merging into larger droplets that run even faster is analogous to the way large galaxies form by absorbing and merging with smaller galaxies. L2

ELL LS **Visual-Spatial**

Reading Strategy

Close Reading Read the text on The Local Group to students and show them how to take apart the text in phrases to understand the content. Then, make notes on the board as you read the text titled We live in a Supercluster.

in a Cluster—named Local Group
in a Galaxy—named Milky Way
in a star system—named solar system
on a planet—named Earth

Discussion

Sagittarius Dwarf Galaxy Astronomers have said that small galaxies like the Sagittarius dwarf elliptical galaxy are the building blocks of larger galaxies like the Milky Way. Have students research this galaxy and the infrared survey used to learn about it, called the Two-Micron All Sky Survey (2MASS). Have them discuss what (2MASS) means for the future of these two galaxies and other nearby galaxies, such as the Large and Small Magellanic Clouds. Possible answer: The stars, gas, and dust and any other objects in the smaller galaxies near the Milky Way will be absorbed and the Milky Way will continue to grow. L2

Reading Check

Answer Probably nothing; because stars are so far apart, they will move past each other.

Quick Demo

It's a Spiral

Materials pinwheel

Estimated Time 5 minutes

Procedure Hold a pinwheel toy in front of the class. Demonstrate how the blades of the pinwheel seem to spiral out from its center. Now gently blow on the pinwheel to make it turn. Relate this shape and movement to the shape of the Milky Way Galaxy and its slow turning movement. L2 ELL LS **Visual-Spatial**

Reading Check

Answer spiral or barred spiral

Visual Learning

Figure 20 Help students understand the information presented in **Table 1** The illustration shows the Milky Way as if you were looking down on it. It is a spiral galaxy with a radius of 50,000 light-years. The Sun is about halfway out at a distance of 26,000 light-years from the center. Note the bar shape to the nucleus; recent indications are that the Milky Way is a barred spiral. L2 ELL LS **Visual-Spatial**

Caption Answer

Figure 20 a cubic volume of space that is one light-year in length, width, and depth.

Post Reading

Discussion Have students look back into the text of this section and illustrate the Milky Way. Ask them to label the light-year distances of the Sun to the center, the length of the spiral arms, and the distance through the central bulge. In small groups, have them present their drawings as prompts for discussion.

Science Online

Topic: The Milky Way Galaxy

Visit gpescience.com for Web links to information about the Milky Way galaxy.

Activity Draw a model of the Milky Way galaxy showing its possible barred structure. Include the approximate location of the Sun and information about the Sagittarius dwarf galaxy.

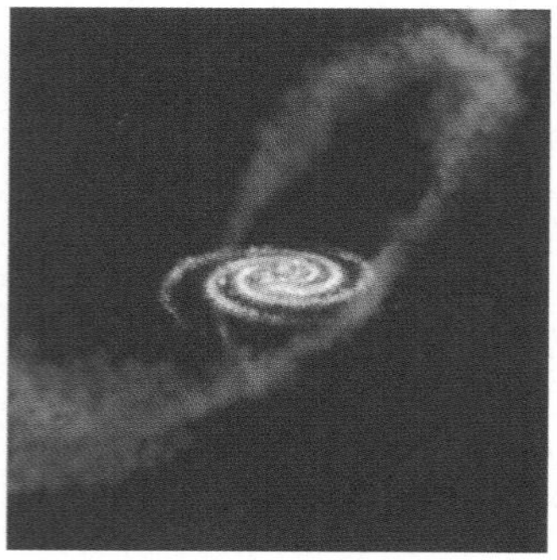

Figure 19 The swirls of red seen in this model are stars in the remnants of the Sagittarius dwarf elliptical galaxy.

The Milky Way

Recall that the Milky Way galaxy contains about 400 billion stars, including our Sun. The Sun makes one complete orbit around the center of the Milky Way in about 225 million years, traveling at a speed of 220 km/s. This means that since it formed, the Sun has made a little over 22 orbits of the Milky Way.

The Milky Way is usually classified as a normal spiral galaxy. However, recent evidence suggests that it might be a barred spiral. It is difficult to know for sure because astronomers can never see our galaxy from the outside. You can't see the normal spiral or barred shape of the Milky Way because the Sun and Earth are located within one of its spiral arms. However, you can see the Milky Way stretching across the sky as a faint band of light. All of the stars you can see belong to the Milky Way galaxy.

Reading Check *What type of galaxy is the Milky Way?*

Evidence indicates that the Milky Way, like many galaxies, grows by absorbing other galaxies. It has been gobbling up the Sagittarius dwarf elliptical galaxy for 2 billion years. If we could see infrared light, we could see stars and other material from this galaxy becoming part of our section of the Milky Way, as shown in **Figure 19.** Eventually, the Milky Way probably will absorb both Clouds of Magellan and several other dwarf galaxies.

Structure of the Milky Way The Milky Way galaxy, shown in **Figure 20,** measures about 100,000 light-years from one side to the other. The Sun lies about 26,000 light-years from the galactic center on the edge of one of the spiral arms. The Milky Way's disk is about 1,000 light-years thick—it would take 1,000 years to travel from top to bottom even at the speed of light. The central bulge of the Milky Way is about 10,000 light-years in diameter.

Figure 20 Star density is greatest near the center of the Milky Way, with over 1,400 stars in every cubic light-year of space. The Sun is located about halfway out on the Orion arm of the Milky Way galaxy.
Explain *what is meant by* a cubic light-year.

Cultural Diversity

The Milky Way The fluid form of the Milky Way is reflected in the interpretations of many different cultures. Akkadians called it the River of the Snake. In Judea, Armenia, and Syria, it was called a long bandage. In China and Japan, it was called the Celestial River. Polynesians called it the Long, Blue, Cloud-Eating Shark. In India, it was known as the Bed of the Ganges.

Curriculum Connection

Math A parsec (pc) is the distance to a star that has a parallax angle of one second of arc. Each parsec equals 3.26 light-years. Ask students to calculate the radius of the Milky Way and the distance from its center to the Sun in parsecs. Possible answer: Students should use the equation: dpc = dly /3.26. The Sun is 26,000 ly from the center; 26,000/3.26 = 8000 pc L3 LS **Logical-Mathematics**

Spiral Arms The arms of a spiral galaxy look like pinwheels that begin near the galactic center and extend outward through the disk of the galaxy. These spiral arms contain both young stars and prestellar material, such as glowing nebulae. Young open star clusters are present too. This is the part of a spiral galaxy where stars are forming. Astronomers do not yet fully understand what causes the spiral structure to form. They speculate that it might be caused by instabilities in the gas near the galactic bulge or gravitational effects of other galaxies that are or were nearby, or might be just an extension of the shape of the galactic bulge, itself. They just don't know.

Galaxy Center What strange objects lurk in the very dense population of stars at a galaxy's core? Recent theories suggest that extremely massive black holes might exist at the cores of galaxies. The problem is that this part of a galaxy is hidden from view by material that exists in between the densely packed stars. The total energy emitted from an object called Sgr A* (saj-ay-star), located in the nucleus of the Milky Way, is equivalent to the energy that would be emitted by a million suns. The leading theory about this object, shown in **Figure 21,** is that it is a supermassive black hole, containing the mass of 3 million suns.

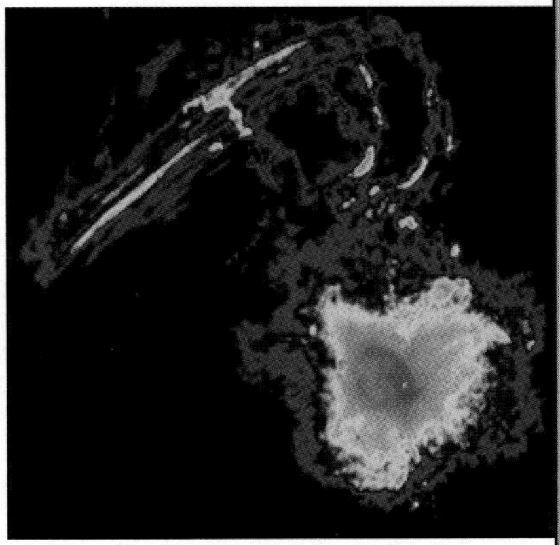

Figure 21 This bright radio source captured by the VLA is indirect evidence of a black hole at the center of our galaxy.

section 3 review

Summary

Galaxies
- A galaxy is a large group of stars, gas, and dust held together by gravity.
- The three main types of galaxies are elliptical, irregular, and spiral.

How do galaxies form?
- Astronomers believe that galaxies form by absorbing or merging with smaller objects.
- Young, hot stars form when galaxies collide, but individual stars within each galaxy are not affected much.

The Milky Way Galaxy
- The Milky Way galaxy contains about 400 billion stars and has a spiral shape.
- The Milky Way galaxy is about 100,000 light-years across and the Sun lies about 26,000 light-years from its center.
- Supermassive black holes are thought to exist in the centers of galaxies.

Self Check

1. **Compare and contrast** the Milky Way galaxy to other galaxies in the universe.
2. **Describe** the three main types of galaxies.
3. **Draw** the overall structure of the Milky Way galaxy and indicate where the Sun is located.
4. **Describe** the most common type of galaxy.
5. **Think Critically** How might the Sun be affected if the Andromeda galaxy and the Milky Way galaxy collide.

Applying Math

6. **Use Numbers** Assume there are 400 billion stars in the Milky Way galaxy, plus or minus 200 billion. Based on this estimate, what is the range of the number of stars that might exist in the Milky Way?
7. **Use Percentages** A dwarf elliptical galaxy has fewer than 1 million stars and a small irregular galaxy contains 100 million stars. What percent of the number of stars found in a small irregular galaxy are found in a dwarf elliptical galaxy?

More Section Review gpescience.com

3 Assess

DAILY INTERVENTION

Check for Understanding

Visual-Spatial Have students draw an illustration of the Milky Way galaxy as a spiral or a barred spiral galaxy. Ask students to position where Earth and the Sun are located. Possible answer: Students should indicate that the Sun and everything on Earth would be located about halfway out of the center of the Milky Way. L1 P

Reteach

Milky Way's Center If there are about 1,400 stars in every cubic light-year at the galaxy's center, how many more stars are there than in the area of the Milky Way where the Sun is located? Possible answer: Since the closest star to the Sun is over 4 light-years away, the center of the Milky Way contains about 1,400 more stars per cubic light-year than is found in the area near the Sun. L2 LS **Logical-Mathematical**

Assessment

Oral The most common type of galaxy in the universe is the dwarf elliptical. Why did astronomers once think that spiral galaxies were the most common? Spiral galaxies are much larger and brighter than dwarf ellipticals, therefore it was easier to see them than the smaller dwarf eliptical galaxies. Use **Performance Assessment in the Science Classroom,** p. 93. L2

section 3 review

1. All galaxies are large families of stars, gas, and dust. The Milky Way is a spiral galaxy; larger than dwarf ellipticals, but not as large as giant elliptical galaxies.
2. Elliptical galaxies have a spherical or elliptical shape with no structure. Spiral galaxies have a central hub with arms spiraling out from it. Irregular galaxies have no structure and can be any shape.
3. Student drawings should show a spiral pattern, with a central hub and the Sun about halfway out from the center.
4. Dwarf ellipticals are small, and resemble round to elliptically shaped balls.
5. Little will happen to individual stars like the Sun; they will just move past each other.
6. 200 billion to 600 billion stars
7. less than 1 percent

section 4

Cosmology

1 Motivate

INTERACTIVE CHALKBOARD An editable Microsoft® PowerPoint® presentation is available on **Interactive Chalkboard** CD-ROM.

Bellringer

Section Focus Transparencies also are available on the Interactive Chalkboard CD-ROM. L2 ELL

Section 4 Section Focus Transparency — Northern and Southern Sky — Chapter 26

This panoramic view of the entire sky was made from 51 wide-angle photographs.

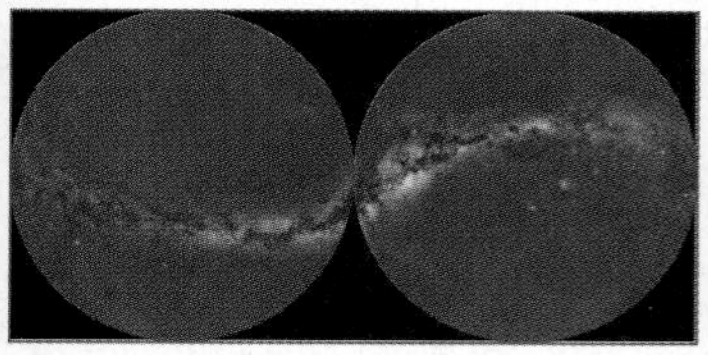

1. What is the object that cuts across both the northern and southern sky?
2. What would this picture have looked like one billion years ago? Five billion years ago? Fifteen billion years ago?

Reading Preview

Tie to Prior Knowledge

The Big Bang Ask students how the universe began. Some will reply that it started with a big bang. Ask them what this big bang was. One theory explains that the universe was smaller than it is today. A large explosion caused the universe to rapidly expand. L2

SQ3R This five-step strategy helps promote active reading. Have students first **S**urvey the section, focusing on headings. Students should then develop **Q**uestions about key concepts. Next, students should **R**ead the section, keeping their questions in mind. Last, have students **R**ecite the vocabulary words and **R**eview their definitions.

Reading Guide

***What* You'll Learn**
- **Describe** the most accepted theory about the origin of the universe.
- **Define** dark matter.
- **Explain** how dark energy may cause the universe to expand forever.

***Why* It's Important**

Conditions that existed when the universe began led to the formation of galaxies like the Milky Way.

Review Vocabulary

universe: the space that contains all known matter and energy

New Vocabulary
- cosmology
- big bang theory
- dark matter
- dark energy

How did it begin?

The study of the universe—how it began, how it evolves, and what it is made of—is known as **cosmology.** Several models of the origin and evolution of the universe have been proposed.

One model, proposed in 1948, is called the steady state theory. In this theory, the universe has always existed and it always will. As the universe expands, new matter is created. The density of the universe remains the same or in steady state.

A second idea is called the oscillating model. In this model, the universe expanded rapidly, then slowed, and eventually contracted. This oscillating process continues back and forth through time. Some scientists currently believe that enough matter exists to cause the universe to eventually contract.

Figure 22 This map produced by the WMAP team has been called a "baby picture" of the universe. It is oval because it is a projection, just as maps of Earth can be projected as ovals. **Infer** *why this map is called a "baby picture" of the universe.*

Section 4 Resource Manager

Chapter *Fast File* Resources
- Transparency Activity, p. 47
- Enrichment, p. 32
- Reinforcement, p. 28
- Directed Reading for Content Mastery, pp. 19J, 20
- Lab Worksheets, pp. 7–8
- Life Science Critical Thinking/ Problem Solving, p. 14
- Mathematics Skill Activities, pp. 47–48

The Big Bang Theory

The most accepted theory of how the universe formed is the **big bang theory.** It states that the universe started with a big bang, or explosion, and has been expanding ever since. The big bang is not like an explosion of matter into empty space; it is the rapid expansion of space itself.

When did it begin? A NASA-related mission, called the Wilkinson Microwave Anisotropy Probe (WMAP), produced a map of the oldest light in the universe. Based on the map, shown in **Figure 22,** and other data, the WMAP team proposed a more specific age of the universe. Their findings indicate that the universe began about 13.7 billion years ago with a big bang. The team believes its data are correct within a one percent margin of error. They measured temperature variations over the entire universe found in the cosmic microwave background radiation. This radiation is thought to have been produced about 400,000 years after the big bang when temperatures became low enough for atoms to form. Bright areas of the map are thought to indicate places that collapsed, forming the galaxies that we see today.

Reading Check *When did the universe begin?*

Expansion of the Universe

The motion of stars within the Milky Way can be detected by using the Doppler effect. For example, sound waves from a moving source are compressed as the object approaches and stretched as it recedes. Doppler shifts occur in light as well as sound. If a star approaches Earth, its wavelengths of light are compressed, causing a blue shift. If a star moves away, its wavelengths are stretched, causing a red shift. Using the Doppler shift, scientists found that some galaxies in the Local Group are moving toward, some are moving away, and others are moving with the Milky Way. A red shift is also seen in the light from distant galaxies, but this is explained differently.

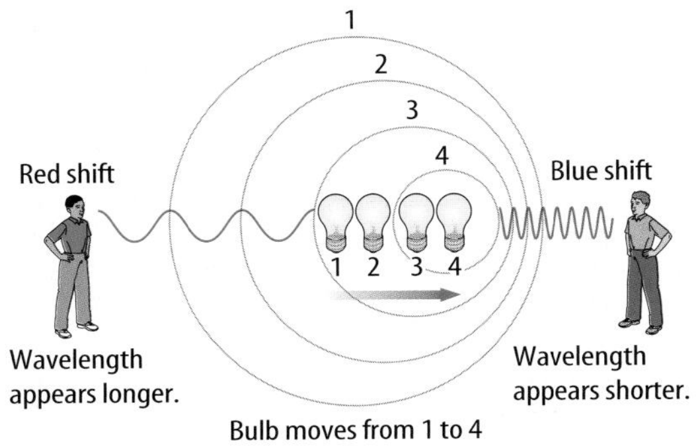

Figure 23 The observer on the right experiences a blue shift as wavelengths of light emitted by an approaching object are compressed. The observer on the left experiences a red shift as wavelengths are stretched.

INTEGRATE Language Arts

Science as Literature
Many famous scientists have written about science for the general public. Among them are physicists Albert Einstein and George Gamow. More recently, physicist Stephen Hawking wrote "A Brief History of Time," which describes current theories of how the universe began. Research the work of Steven Hawking and his contributions to cosmology and write a brief biography.

2 Teach

Caption Answer

Figure 22 It is a picture of the earliest radiation produced in the universe.

Reading Check

Answer 13.7 billion years ago

INTEGRATE Language Arts

Science as Literature Many writers of science fiction were originally scientists. For example, Isaac Asimov was a professor of biochemistry before turning to writing full time. Also, Arthur C. Clarke, best known for the book and film "2001—A Space Odyssey", was the scientist who first proposed placing a satellite in geostationary orbit for weather and communications. In fact, the geostationary orbit at 42,000 km was named for him by the International Astronomical Union. Other science fiction writers combine careers, such as Jerry Pournelle, who writes both science fiction and a nonfiction column in computer science.

Fun Fact

The rotation rate of the Sun can be determined from the Doppler effect. Light from the left side of the Sun shows a slight blue shift and light from the right side shows a slight red shift. The amount of the shift is related to the rate of rotation for the Sun.

Reading Strategy

Clarify Text Have a student read the text about Expansion of the Universe while others demonstrate the Doppler effect shown in **Figure 23.** Have them continue this modeling process as other students take turns reading the subsequent topics. Conclude with the concept of acceleration of expansion of the universe.

Visual Learning

Figure 22 Help students understand that the oval shape of this photo is a projection designed to show the whole sky. This is similar to the way Earth globes are projected as ovals. Also, the image was made using microwaves that were translated into visual wavelengths. Red shows warmer areas and blue shows cooler areas, the reverse of star colors. L2 ELL LS **Visual-Spatial**

SECTION 4 Cosmology **837**

Quick Demo
Doppler Effect

Materials a ball that whistles when thrown.

Estimated Time 5 minutes

Procedure Attach a strong piece of rope to the ball and carefully twirl the ball around your head. Stand about 5m away from students. As the ball twirls around, students will hear a higher pitch as the ball approaches them and a lower pitch as the ball moves away. Relate the changing wavelengths of sound waves to the changing wavelengths of light caused by a star coming toward or going away from Earth. L2 ELL IN **Visual-Spatial**

Activity

Expansion of the Universe Have students cut stars out of a piece of cotton and attach them at various positions on a 5-cm wide strip of spandex. Tell them to hold the ends of the spandex strip in both hands and slowly pull on both ends. Students will observe the distance between the stars (galaxy clusters) increases as space expands. L1 ELL IN **Visual-Spatial**

Discussion

Dark Matter and Dark Energy Have students research the existence of dark matter and dark energy. Have them discuss the presence of both dark matter and dark energy. Possible answer: The rate at which the Sun orbits the center of the Milky Way is incorrect if only the visible mass of the Milky Way is taken into account. The expansion of the universe appears to be greater now than in the past. There must be an energy source for this accelerated expansion. L3

Reading Check

Answer regular matter

Caption Answer

Figure 6 voids

Figure 24 This *Hubble* view looks deep into space and time when the universe was more chaotic and oddly shaped galaxies were common. Dark matter might have influenced galaxies to take the classic spiral and elliptical forms we see today.

***Hubble* Red Shift** The Doppler shift does not explain the shift in wavelength of light coming from distant galaxies. This shift is known as the *Hubble* red shift. It is caused by the stretching of space itself as the universe expands. Light waves traveling through space lengthen as space expands. The fact that this red shift is seen in the light from all galaxies outside the Local Group indicates that the entire universe is expanding.

What is the universe made of?

The way in which galaxies like the Milky Way rotate and move should depend on the amounts of mass they contain. The problem is that if only the visible or otherwise detectable mass (called regular matter) is counted, the Milky Way and other galaxies shouldn't be rotating, moving, and interacting with other galaxies the way they are. It appears that regular matter makes up only a very small amount of the known universe. Much of the mass that must be present cannot be seen. However, its effect on other galaxies can be seen, shown in **Figure 24.** This unseen and little-understood matter that affects galaxies has been named **dark matter.**

Reading Check *Which type of matter is considered to make up the least amount of the universe?*

Differentiated Instruction

Hearing Impaired Help your hearing impaired students achieve success in note taking by setting up paired partners. Pair each of your hearing impaired students with another student. During the lesson, they should work together to write down all notes. The hearing impaired student should concentrate on information on the board and the other student on information presented by voice. L2 IN **Linguistic**

Teacher FYI

Standard Candles A standard candle, like a Type I supernova, is always considered to have the same absolute brightness. If a standard candle is recognized in another galaxy, its apparent brightness is compared to its absolute brightness. This comparison can be used to determine the distance to the galaxy in which the supernova exists.

Dark Matter Although scientists are uncertain about what dark matter is, the concept helps them explain how the universe may have formed. Temperature variations, as shown on the WMAP map, could have led to density fluctuations in the early universe. As the universe expanded, gravity from dark matter pulled matter together in regions with higher density. Galaxies could have formed in the denser regions and voids could have formed elsewhere. This structure is seen when sections of the universe are mapped, as shown in **Figure 25.**

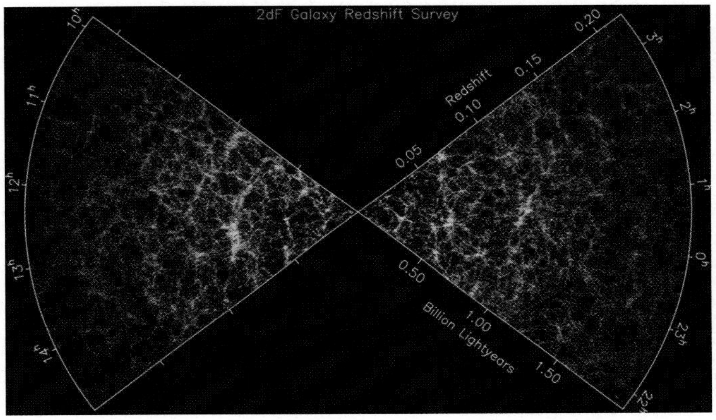

Figure 25 These maps of sections of the universe show areas densely populated with galaxies and other areas almost empty. **Identify** *What are the almost-empty areas called?*

Dark Energy Data indicate that the expansion of the universe is accelerating. Explaining this acceleration is difficult. One hypothesis is that a form of energy, called **dark energy,** might be causing the acceleration. When matter was closer together in the early universe, gravity could easily overcome expansion caused by dark energy. Now, with matter farther apart, gravity is insufficient to overcome it and expansion accelerates. This does not mean, however, that dark energy is related to dark matter.

section 4 review

Summary

How did it begin?

- Cosmology is the study of how the universe began and evolves.
- The big bang theory is the most accepted theory about the beginning of the universe.
- The universe is estimated to be 13.7 billion years old.

Expansion of the Universe

- The Doppler effect indicates whether stars are coming toward Earth or moving away.
- The Hubble red shift is caused by the expansion of space and the entire universe.

What is the universe made of?

- The universe might contain dark matter and dark energy.

Self Check

1. **Define** cosmology.
2. **Describe** the big bang theory.
3. **Explain** how the expansion of space could cause a red shift in the light from distant galaxies.
4. **Describe** the Doppler effect.
5. **Think Critically** How could the presence of some repulsing force cause the universe to expand forever?

Applying Math

6. **Use Percentages** The currently accepted age of the universe is 13.7 billion years plus or minus one percent. How much time does this one percent represent?
7. **Use Percentages** What percent of the universe's age is the first 400,000 years?

Post Reading

Summarize Have students work in pairs to summarize the effects of the opposing forces of gravity and expansion of space on matter. Have them consider colliding galaxies and the star sequences of giant and supergiant stars. Encourage them to look back in the text to check for accuracy.

3 Assess

DAILY INTERVENTION

Check for Understanding

Linguistic Have students write a paragraph about why astronomers think the universe had a beginning. Galaxy clusters are expanding away from all other galaxy clusters. This implies that they were all closer together in the past when all matter was together. L2 P

Reteach

Expansion of the Universe What is true of light coming from distant galaxies? Light from galaxies outside of the Local Group has been lengthened by the expansion of space. L2

Assessment

Content Explain how the Doppler effect can tell scientists whether a star is approaching or moving away from Earth. Light that is moving away is shifted toward the red end of the spectrum; if it is moving toward us, light is compressed and is shifted toward the blue end of the spectrum. L2

section 4 review

1. the study of how the universe began, how it continues to evolve, and what it is made of
2. The universe started with a big bang and has been expanding ever since.
3. As space expands, it causes the light waves to expand as well, thus lengthening the wavelengths or shifting them toward the red end of the spectrum.
4. The Doppler effect is caused by the movement of an object. If it is moving away, its light is lengthened in wavelength; if it is moving toward you, its light is shortened in wavelength.
5. As matter expands more and more, the expansion force would overcome any attractive force that exists between the matter.
6. 137 million years
7. 0.003 percent

BENCH TESTED

Video Lab available for this Lab.

Real-World Problem

Purpose Students will model the stretching of the wavelength of light caused by expansion of the universe.

Process Skills Make a model, analyze results, collect data, draw and label, draw conclusions, infer, interpret data, make and use tables, observe, organize data, recognize cause and effect.

Time Required 35 minutes

Possible Materials round balloon, permanent marker, medium-sized binder clip

Safety Precautions

- Caution students not to over inflate the balloon, it could burst.
- Caution students to handle the binder clip carefully; it can slip out of their hands.

Make a Model

Possible Procedures Slightly inflate the balloon and clip it shut. Mark the location of the galaxy clusters. Use a metric ruler to measure the distances between the galaxy clusters. Record these measurements. Draw a wavy line from the reference galaxy cluster to each of the other galaxy clusters. Measure and record the wavelength of each wavy line. Inflate the balloon. Measure and record the distances between galaxy clusters and the wavelengths of the wavy lines.

Teaching Strategies Have a balloon already marked so students can compare their balloons to it.

Troubleshooting Have students blow up their balloons and let them deflate prior to beginning the exercise.

LAB

Model and Invent

Expansion of the Universe

Goals

- **Model** the stretching of the wavelengths of light caused by the expansion of the universe.
- **Measure** the amount of wavelength lengthening produced in the model.
- **Measure** increases in distances between galaxy clusters caused by the expansion of the model.

Possible Materials

round balloon
permanent marker (black or dark blue)
medium-sized binder clip (3 cm)

Safety Precautions

Real-World Problem

You have read that the universe is expanding. In fact, recent calculations indicate that it is expanding more quickly now than it did in the past. Astronomers are able to measure this expansion because it stretches the wavelengths of light coming from distant objects. Can you make a model that demonstrates how this happens?

Make a Model

1. Work in teams of two or more. **Collect** all needed materials.
2. Sketch an image on the balloon slightly inflated. **Model** the positions of galaxy clusters by placing three or four dots at four different locations and different distances apart on the surface of the balloon. Mark the locations R (for reference), A, B, and C.
3. Make a table for data.
4. Check to see if the binder clip can hold air in the balloon long enough for you to make measurements and to draw on the balloon.
5. Obtain your teacher's approval of your sketches and data table before proceeding.

Test Your Model

1. Slightly inflate your balloon so that it is not very big.
2. Use the binder clip to temporarily seal the balloon (or have your partner hold it closed). Do not tie it.
3. **Measure** the distance from your reference galaxy cluster (R) to each of the other galaxy clusters and record these distances on your data table.

Data

Location	First Distance Measurement	Second Distance Measurement	Change in Distance	First λ Measurement	Second λ Measurement	Change in λ
A						
B						
C						

Fun Fact

If the accelerated expansion of the universe continues, eventually the only stars that will be visible to observers on Earth will be those in the Milky Way Galaxy and those in the galaxies of the Local Group.

Differentiated Instruction

Physically Challenged If students cannot manipulate the binder clips, have them work with other students. A physically challenged student can hold the balloon after the clip has been attached or the balloon has been tied shut. A physically challenged student could inflate the balloon while another student attaches the binder clip or ties the end of the balloon shut. L2

840 CHAPTER 26 Stars and Galaxies

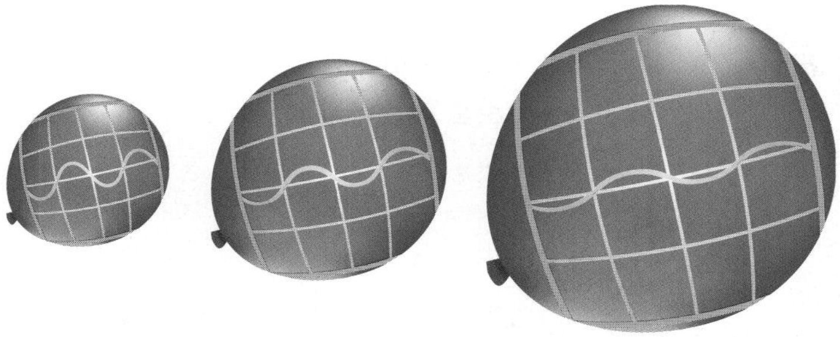

4. Draw a wavy line from your reference galaxy cluster to each of the other galaxy clusters marked to represent the wavelength (λ) of light coming from each galaxy cluster. Measure and record the wavelength of each wavy line.
5. Inflate your balloon farther (be careful not to inflate it too much). Replace the binder clip or tie the end shut.
6. **Measure** and record the distances from your reference galaxy cluster to each of the other galaxy clusters.
7. **Measure** and record the wavelength of each wavy line on your inflated model.

Analyze Your Data

1. **Calculate** the change in distance and the change in wavelength for each galaxy cluster and record it on your data table.
2. **Analyze** whether objects moved on your model or whether your entire model expanded.

Conclude and Apply

1. **Explain** any changes in distance or wavelength noted.
2. **Conclude** whether the objects moved apart because of their individual motions or because the model expanded.
3. **Infer** how measurements on your model can be related to measurements of the universe.

Communicating Your Data

Enter the data from your model on a table that shows the data from all teams of students.

Test Your Model

Expected Outcome Students will use expansion of the balloon as a model of the expansion of the universe.

Analyze Your Data

1. Answers will vary depending on the size of the balloon, how much they inflate it, and where they locate their galaxy clusters.
2. Individual points representing the galaxy clusters did not move on the balloon, the entire model of the universe expanded.

Conclude and Apply

1. As the model expanded, the distances between the galaxy clusters increased. The wavelength of light traveling between galaxy clusters increased.
2. The galaxy clusters moved apart because the entire model expanded.
3. If the universe is thought of as a balloon, the fabric of the universe is the skin of the balloon. Distances and wavelength of light would increase in the universe just as the measurement of these factors increased on the balloon model.

Assessment

Process Ask students to hypothesize as to what would happen if the universe stopped expanding and started to shrink. Possible answer: The distances between galaxy clusters and the wavelength traveling from between galaxy clusters would decrease. Use **Performance Assessment in the Science Classroom,** p. 93. L2

Communicating Your Data

Encourage students to perform the exercise more than once to check their data. Have them discuss their results with another team and find out if that team obtained similar data. If not, have them discuss possible reasons for any differences noted.

Understanding Literature

Imagery The primary sense evoked by Sara Teasdale in this poem is sight. The reader is aware of the darkness and the varied colors of stars that are seen moving steadily across the sky. The senses of sound and smell are also triggered as she describes the pine trees as being "still" and having a "spicy" smell.

Respond to the Reading

1. Teasdale writes that the stars have beating hearts. She describes their movement across the sky as a march up a great hill.
2. The author expresses feelings of awe and gratitude for the beauty she witnesses. The tone is reverence.
3. **Linking Science and Writing** Review stellar characteristics with students, including the process of nuclear fusion, the relationship between temperature and color, and the life cycle of stars. Review the connection between Earth's rotation and the apparent movement of stars.

INTEGRATE Astronomy

Light Pollution Unless you have viewed the stars on a clear, dark night like the author, you may not fully understand her emotion. Astronomers are very concerned about light pollution. Every observatory in the southwest is affected, as city lights brighten skies. L2

Science and Language Arts

Stars

Sara Teasdale

Alone in the night
On a dark hill
With pines around me
Spicy and still,

And a heaven full of stars
Over my head,
White and topaz
And misty red;

Myriads with beating
Hearts of fire
That aeons
Cannot vex or tire;

Up the dome of heaven
Like a great hill,
I watch them marching
Stately and still,

And I know that I
Am honored to be
Witness
Of so much majesty.

Understanding Literature

Imagery Imagery refers to how a literary work invites the reader to see, hear, smell, touch, or taste something in his mind. Authors often use related images throughout a work, encouraging the reader to consider the subject using more than one sense. Of what specific senses does this poet make the reader aware?

Respond to the Reading

1. How does the author use personification to make the stars in the poem seem alive?
2. Tone refers to the overall mood of a literary work. Describe the tone of this poem.
3. **Linking Science and Writing** The poet refers to the color, age, energy source, and apparent movement of stars. Write a paragraph relating what you have learned about these properties to how they are mentioned in the poem.

INTEGRATE Astronomy

On a clear, dark night, it is possible to see as many as 1,500 stars with the unaided eye. However, this number is far lower because of light pollution. Light from houses, shopping areas, signs, and street lights floods the sky, making it difficult to see the stars. Inside major cities, fewer than 50 stars may be visible in the night sky.

Resources for Teachers and Students

Nightwatch: A Practical Guide to Viewing the Universe, by Terence Dickinson, Firefly Books, Ltd, 1998.

The Book of Constellations: Discover the Secrets in the Stars, by Robin Kerrod, Barron's Educational Series, 2002.

Reviewing Main Ideas

Section 1 Observing the Universe

1. Constellations are patterns of stars that resemble things familiar to the observer.
2. Optical telescopes collect visible light and magnify viewed objects.
3. A refracting telescope uses lenses to collect light and magnify the image, and a reflecting telescope uses a mirror to collect light and a lens to magnify the image.
4. A radio telescope collects and amplifies radio waves.

Section 2 Evolution of Stars

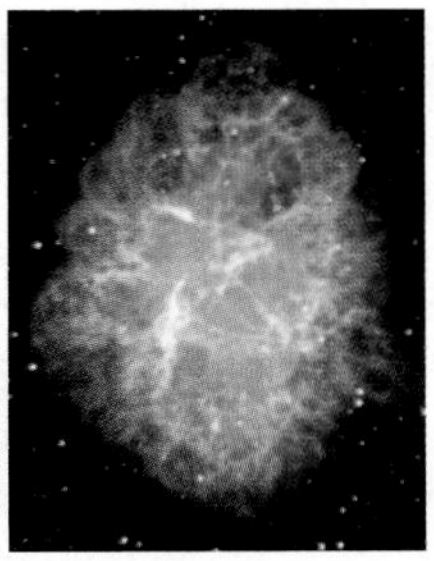

1. Stars form from a large cloud of gas, ice, and dust, called a nebula like the one shown here. When the temperature inside the contracting nebula reaches 10 million K, fusion begins, and a star is born.
2. Stars are classified as main sequence stars, giants, and white dwarfs on the H-R diagram.
3. When a star reaches stellar equilibrium it is considered a main sequence star. When the hydrogen fuel is depleted, a star loses equilibrium and evolves into a giant or supergiant.
4. After losing its outer layers, a giant becomes a white dwarf. A supergiant can evolve into a neutron star or a black hole.
5. The Sun's energy is produced at its core by nuclear fusion.

Section 3 Galaxies and the Milky Way

1. A galaxy is a large group of stars, gas, and dust held together by gravity. The Local Group of galaxies is a cluster that contains the Milky Way Galaxy.
2. The three main types of galaxies are elliptical, irregular, and spiral as shown here.
3. Astronomers believe that galaxies form by absorbing or merging with smaller objects. They continue to evolve by colliding or merging with other galaxies.
4. The Milky Way galaxy is about 100,000 light-years across and the Sun lies about 26,000 light-years from its center.

Section 4 Cosmology

1. The big bang theory is the most accepted theory of how the universe began.
2. The universe is 13.7 billion years old and appears to be expanding faster now than in the past.
3. The Hubble red shift is caused by the expansion of space, not the movement of galaxies.

FOLDABLES™ Use the Foldable that you made at the beginning of this chapter to help you review what you learned about cosmology.

chapter 26 Study Guide

Reviewing Main Ideas

Summary statements can be used by students to review the major concepts of the chapter.

Science Online

Visit gpescience.com
More Section Review
Interactive Tutor
Vocabulary PuzzleMaker
More Chapter Review
Standardized Test Practice

Assessment Transparency

For additional assessment questions, use the *Assessment Transparency* located in the transparency book.

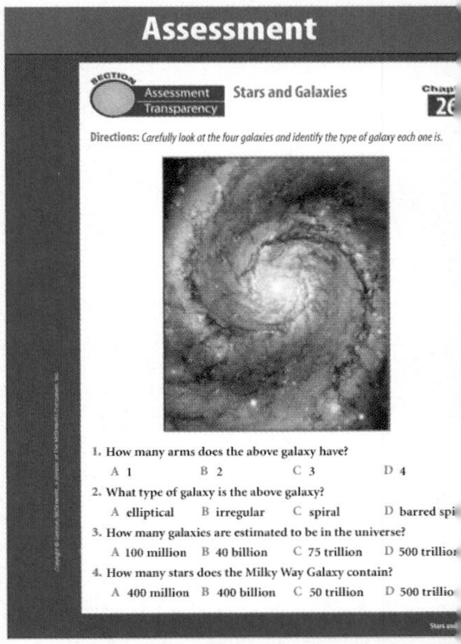

Assessment

Section Assessment Transparency — Stars and Galaxies — Chapter 26

Directions: *Carefully look at the four galaxies and identify the type of galaxy each one is.*

1. How many arms does the above galaxy have?
   A 1 B 2 C 3 D 4
2. What type of galaxy is the above galaxy?
   A elliptical B irregular C spiral D barred spi
3. How many galaxies are estimated to be in the universe?
   A 100 million B 40 billion C 75 trillion D 500 trillion
4. How many stars does the Milky Way Galaxy contain?
   A 400 million B 400 billion C 50 trillion D 500 trillio

FOLDABLES™ Have students use their Foldables to review what they learned about stars, galaxies, and cosmology.

Identifying Misconceptions

Assess

After students have done the activity on page F at the beginning of the chapter and completed the chapter, have them perform this activity.

Materials various-sized plastic or paper drinking cups

Procedure Randomly place the cups of different sizes over the top of a large flat table. Have a student close one eye and kneel at one end of the table. Ask them to identify which cups seem to be close to each other.

Expected Outcome Students using only one eye will lose some of their ability to judge distance and will select several cups that look like they are next to each other only to discover that they can be quite far away from each other on the table, just as stars can be in the galaxy. L2

Using Vocabulary

1. constellations
2. reflecting telescope
3. light-year
4. main sequence
5. giant
6. photosphere
7. sunspots
8. galaxy
9. Milky Way
10. cosmology

Checking Concepts

11. D
12. C
13. A
14. C
15. A
16. B
17. B
18. A
19. B

chapter 26 Review

Using Vocabulary

big bang theory p. 837
constellation p. 818
cosmology p. 836
dark energy p. 839
dark matter p. 838
galaxy p. 831
giant p. 825
light-year p. 821
Local Group p. 832
main sequence p. 823
Milky Way p. 831
photosphere p. 827
radio telescope p. 821
reflecting telescope p. 820
refracting telescope p. 819
solar mass p. 827
spectroscope p. 822
sunspots p. 828
white dwarf p. 825

Match the correct vocabulary word(s) with each definition given below.

1. patterns of stars
2. an optical telescope that uses a mirror to collect light
3. the distance light travels in one year
4. plotted from the upper left to the lower right on the H-R diagram
5. star in which the core contracts and outer layers expand and cool
6. layer of the Sun from which light is emitted
7. dark, cooler areas on the Sun's photosphere
8. large group of stars, gas, and dust held together by gravity
9. spiral galaxy that contains the solar system
10. study of the evolution of the universe

Checking Concepts

Choose the word or phrase that best answers the question.

11. Which telescope uses lenses to collect light and form an image?
    A) adaptive **B)** radio **C)** reflecting **D)** refracting

12. Which form of energy are optical telescopes used to study?
    A) infrared radiation
    B) radio waves
    C) visible light
    D) X rays

13. Which magnifies the image in a telescope?
    A) eyepiece **B)** focal length **C)** focus **D)** objective

14. Which is the most common type of star in the universe?
    A) giant **B)** neutron **C)** red dwarf **D)** white dwarf

15. Which forms from a star that is over 25 times the mass of the Sun?
    A) black hole **B)** giant star **C)** neutron star **D)** white dwarf

16. Which is a feature of the Sun that can reach 100 million K?
    A) CME **B)** flare **C)** prominence **D)** sunspot

Use the illustration below to answer question 17.

17. Which type of galaxy is most common?
    A) barred spiral
    B) dwarf elliptical
    C) irregular
    D) spiral

18. Which is the most accepted theory of how the universe formed?
    A) big bang **B)** collision **C)** oscillating **D)** steady state

Vocabulary PuzzleMaker gpescience.com

Use the Exam*View*® Pro Test Bank CD-ROM to:

- create multiple versions of tests
- create modified tests with one mouse click for inclusion students
- edit existing questions and add your own questions
- build tests aligned with state standards using built-in State Curriculum Tags
- change English tests to Spanish with one mouse click and vice versa

19. Which adds to the gravity of a galaxy, but cannot be seen or detected?
A) dark energy
B) dark matter
C) regular energy
D) regular matter

Interpreting Graphics

20. **Make a table** summarizing the absolute brightness (magnitude) and temperatures of stars on this H-R diagram.

Hertzsprung-Russell Diagram for Stars

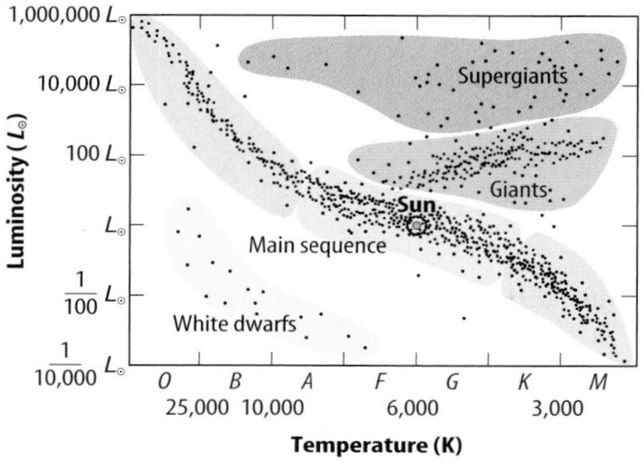

21. **Draw and label** scale models of the following stars: the Sun; Antares, 500 times larger than the Sun; and Sirius B 0.01 times the Sun's diameter.

22. **Draw and label** a concept map showing the life history of a star like the Sun.

23. **Draw and label** the parts in a reflecting telescope.

Thinking Critically

24. **Explain** how energy created in the core of the Sun is eventually emitted from the photosphere.

25. **Compare and contrast** elliptical, irregular, and spiral galaxies.

26. **Discuss** the benefits of using a radio telescope.

27. **Explain** why high sunspot activity on the Sun can affect Earth's magnetic field.

28. **Explain** how the Sun's position in the Milky Way affects how we perceive our galaxy.

Applying Math

29. **Solve One-Step Equations** Use the equation $M_p = f_o/f_e$, to determine the magnifying power of a telescope in which the focal lengths of the objective and eyepiece are 1500 mm and 9 mm, respectively.

Use the illustration below to answer question 30.

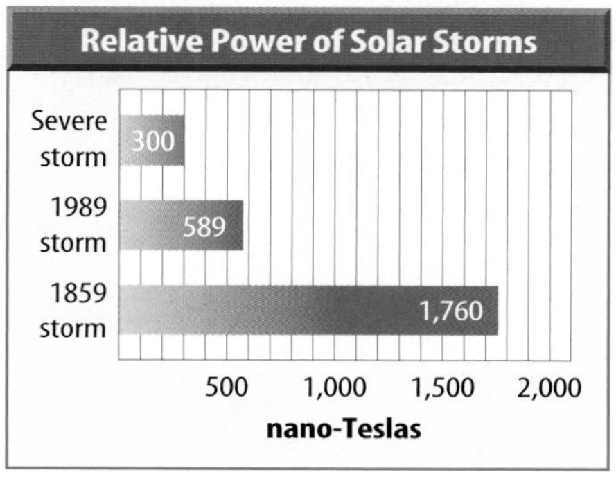

30. A solar storm that took place in 1859 is called "the perfect storm," because of its great power. The diagram shows the relative destructive power of some solar storms. Using this diagram, calculate approximately how much more destructive was the solar storm of 1859 than the one of 1989.

31. **Calculate** how long ago the light we see today left a star that is 25 light-years away. Calculate the distance in km to that star.

Assessment Resources

Reproducible Masters

Chapter *Fast File* Resources
Chapter Review, pp. 37–38
Chapter Tests, pp. 39–42
Assessment Transparency Activity, p. 51

Glencoe Science Web site
Chapter Review Test
Standardized Test Practice

Glencoe Technology
Assessment Transparency
Exam*View*® Pro Testmaker
MindJogger Videoquiz
Interactive Chalkboard

Interpreting Graphics

20.

H–R Diagram Summary		
Star Type	*Absolute Brightness*	*Temperature*
Giant	*High*	*Low*
Main sequence	*Varies with mass*	*Varies with mass*
White dwarf	*Low*	*High*

21. Antares should be about 7.5 m in diameter. The Sun should be about 1.5 cm and Sirius B should be about 1.5 mm.

22. Student maps should include the following: nebula, main sequence, giant, white dwarf, black dwarf.

23. Student drawings should show and should label the objective, the eyepiece, the focus, and the focal length.

Thinking Critically

24. Energy emitted at the core of the Sun radiates through the transparent radiation layer and then is transferred to the surface by convection cells.

25. All are families of stars, dust, and gas held together by gravity. Elliptical galaxies look like round or elliptical balls, spiral galaxies have spiral arms, and irregular galaxies have no regular structure.

26. Radio telescopes can be used during the day and in all kinds of weather.

27. Sunspots are magnetic storms on the Sun and increase the amount of charged material in the solar wind that can affect Earth's magnetic field.

28. The Sun's position within one of its spiral arms obscures visibility of the entire Milky Way.

Applying Math

Math Standards
National: 2, 9

29. Mp = 167
30. about three times
31. 25 years; 237.5 trillion km

Answer Sheet An answer sheet can be found at **gpescience.com**.

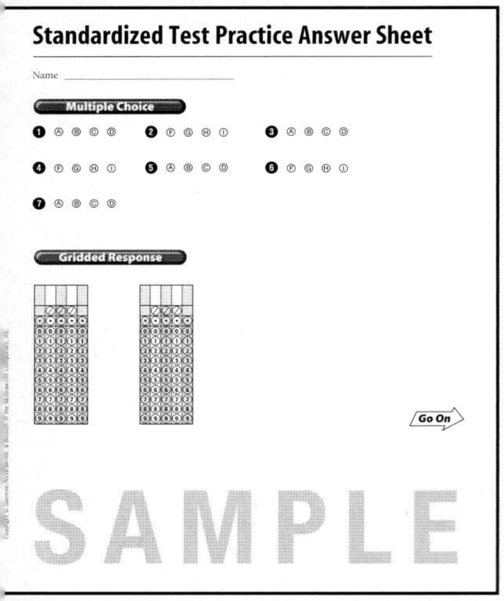

Multiple Choice

1. D
2. A
3. B
4. D
5. D
6. A

Gridded Response

7. 120
8. 52.8 m^2

chapter 26 Standardized Test Practice

Record your answers on the answer sheet provided by your teacher or on a sheet of paper.

Multiple Choice

1. What is used as an objective in a reflecting telescope?

A. antenna

B. camera

C. lens

D. mirror

Use the photo below to answer question 2.

2. Which type of telescope is shown?

A. optical

B. radio

C. ultraviolet

D. X-ray

Test-Taking Tip

Concentrate Stay focused during the test and don't rush, even if you notice that other students are finishing the test early.

3. Which group contains most stars on the H-R diagram ?

A. giant

B. main sequence

C. supergiant

D. white dwarf

4. Which stage of stellar evolution occurs when the outer layers escape, leaving behind the hot core?

A. black hole

B. giant

C. main sequence

D. white dwarf

Use the illustration below to answer question 5.

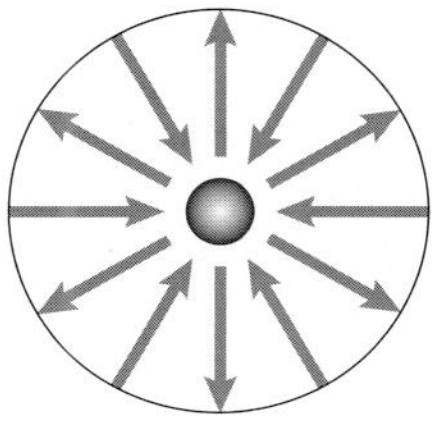

5. What occurs inside a main sequence star?

A. Energy from fusion exceeds gravity.

B. Fusion shuts down.

C. Gravity exceeds energy from fusion.

D. It attains stellar equilibrium.

846 STANDARDIZED TEST PRACTICE

6. Which may be responsible for the accelerating expansion of the universe?
   - **A.** dark energy
   - **B.** dark matter
   - **C.** regular energy
   - **D.** regular matter

Gridded Response

7. If the focal length of a telescope objective is 2,400 mm and the focal length of the eyepiece is 20 mm, what is the magnifying power of the telescope?

8. Use this equation, $A = \pi r^2$. What is the area in square meters of one of the four 8.2-meter reflectors in the *Very Large Telescope*?

Short Response

Use the illustration below to answer question 9.

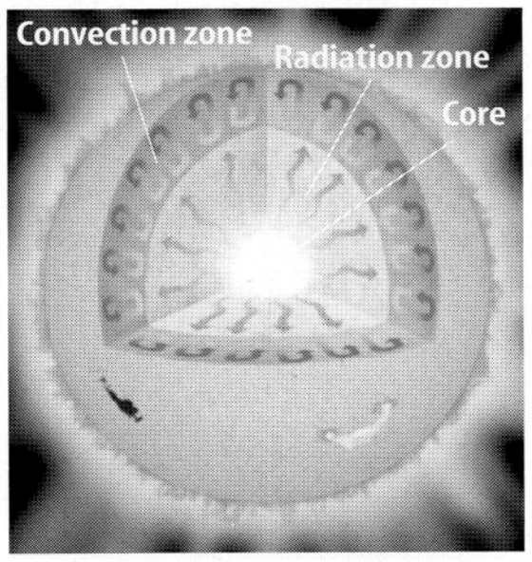

9. Describe the structure of the Sun's interior.

10. What does a spectroscope do to starlight that enables astronomers to determine the star's composition?

11. What does the H-R diagram show about the stars plotted on it?

12. What are coronal mass ejections?

13. What is the Local Group?

14. How do astronomers think that galaxies like the Milky Way formed?

15. What is cosmology?

16. Why have astronomers proposed the existence of dark energy in the universe?

Extended Response

Use the photo below to help answer question 17.

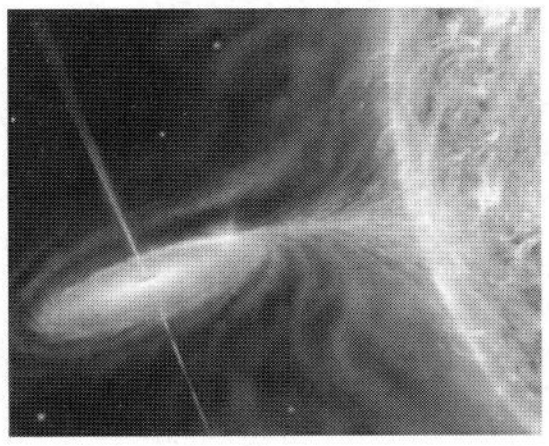

17. **PART A** What are the evolutionary stages of a star like the Sun?

    PART B What are the evolutionary stages of a star more than eight times the mass of the Sun?

Short Response

12. Coronal mass ejections (CMEs) are large bubble of ionized gas are emitted from the Sun.
13. A relatively small cluster of about 45 galaxies that includes the Milky Way Galaxy. Most galaxies in the Local Group are dwarf elliptical galaxies.
14. Most astronomers believe that relatively nearby galaxies grew by absorbing or merging with other smaller objects.
15. The study how the universe began, how it continues to evolve, and what it is made of.
16. The existence of dark energy is used to explain the apparent accelerating expansion of the universe.

Extended Response

17. **Part A:** After a star like the Sun reaches the main sequence, it will eventually evolve to a giant star, then a planetary nebula. After that it will evolve to a white dwarf and end as a black dwarf.

    Part B: A star eight times more massive than the Sun will become a main sequence star quicker and stay there for a much shorter period. After main sequence, it will evolve into a supergiant, a neutron star, and eventually a black hole.

Rubrics

For more help evaluating Short- and Extended-Response questions, see the rubrics on p. 9T.

Short Response

10. A spectroscope disperses the light into its component wavelengths, producing a spectrum. Astronomers use the contained wavelengths to determine the chemical composition of the star from which the light was collected.

11. The temperature or color of the star is plotted against its absolute magnitude.

9. The central area of the Sun is the core where fusion occurs. Above the core, energy radiates outward through the radiation layer. Energy moves through the convection layer to the Sun's surface by convection.

Student Resources

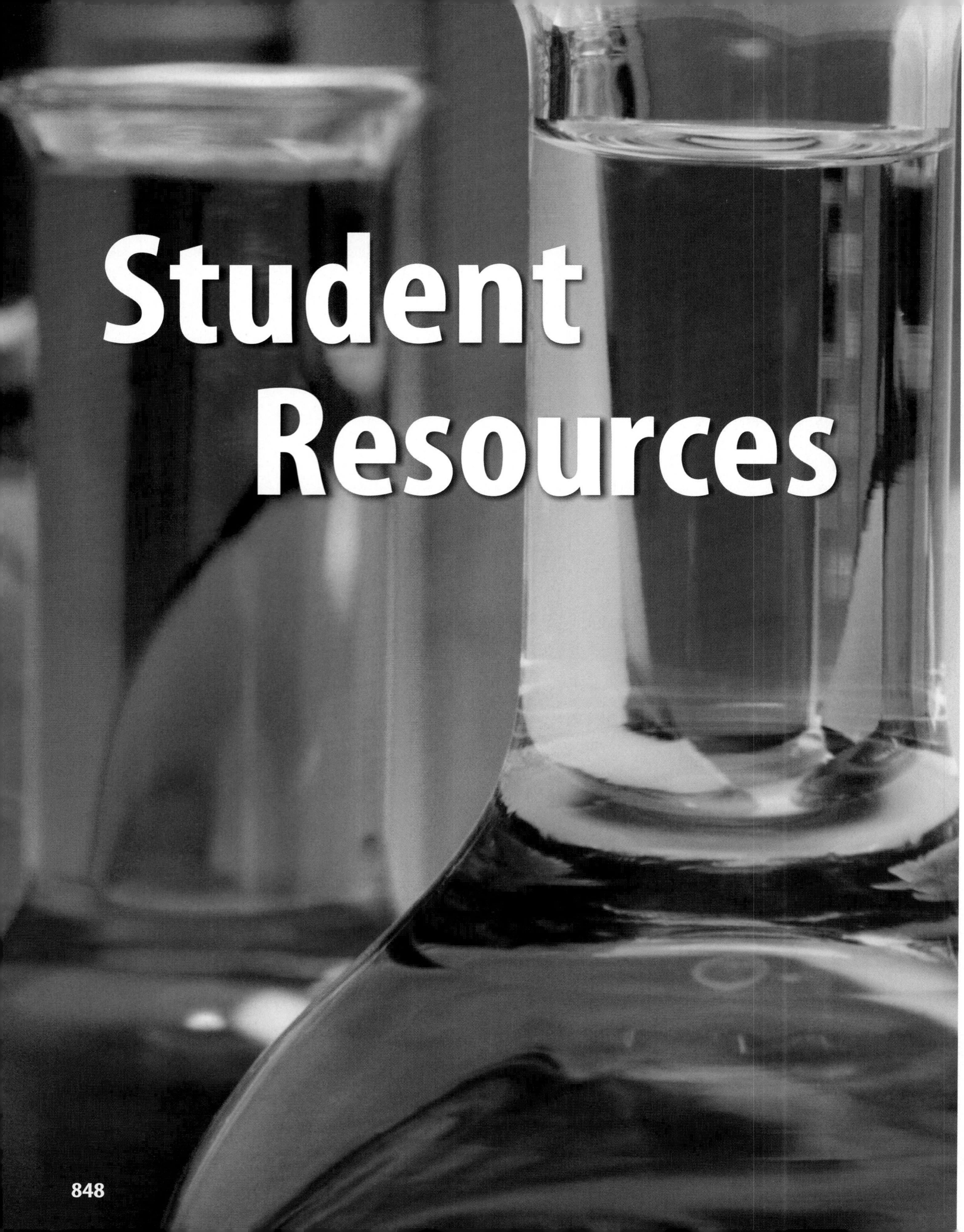

CONTENTS

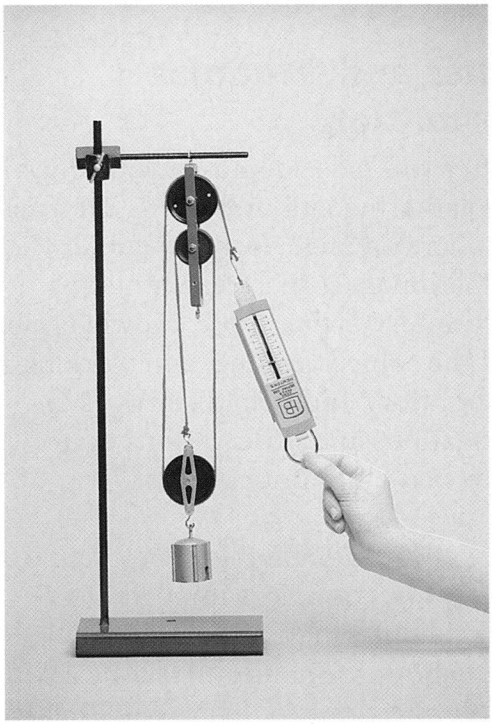

Scientific Methods

Scientists use an orderly approach called the scientific method to solve problems. This includes organizing and recording data so others can understand them. Scientists use many variations in this method when they solve problems.

Identify a Question

The first step in a scientific investigation or experiment is to identify a question to be answered or a problem to be solved. For example, you might ask which gasoline is the most efficient.

Gather and Organize Information

After you have identified your question, begin gathering and organizing information. There are many ways to gather information, such as researching in a library, interviewing those knowledgeable about the subject, testing, and working in the laboratory and field. Fieldwork is investigations and observations done outside of a laboratory.

Researching Information Before moving in a new direction, it is important to gather the information that already is known about the subject. Start by asking yourself questions to determine exactly what you need to know. Then you will look for the information in various reference sources, like the student is doing in **Figure 1.** Some sources may include textbooks, encyclopedias, government documents, professional journals, science magazines, and the Internet. Always list the sources of your information.

Figure 1 The Internet can be a valuable research tool.

Evaluate Sources of Information Not all sources of information are reliable. You should evaluate all your sources of information, and use only those you know to be dependable. For example, if you are researching ways to make homes more energy efficient, a site written by the U.S. Department of Energy would be more reliable than a site written by a company that is trying to sell a new type of weatherproofing material. Also, remember that research always is changing. Consult the most current resources available to you. For example, a 1985 resource about saving energy would not reflect the most recent findings.

Sometimes scientists use data that they did not collect themselves, or conclusions drawn by other researchers. These data must be evaluated carefully. Ask questions about how the data were obtained, if the investigation was carried out properly, and if it has been duplicated exactly with the same results. Would you reach the same conclusion from the data? Only when you have confidence in the data can you believe it is true and feel comfortable using it.

Interpret Scientific Illustrations As you research a topic in science, you will see drawings, diagrams, and photographs to help you understand what you read. Some illustrations are included to help you understand an idea that you can't see easily by yourself, like the tiny particles in an atom in **Figure 2.** A drawing helps many people to remember details more easily and provides examples that clarify difficult concepts or give additional information about the topic you are studying. Most illustrations have labels or a caption to identify or to provide more information.

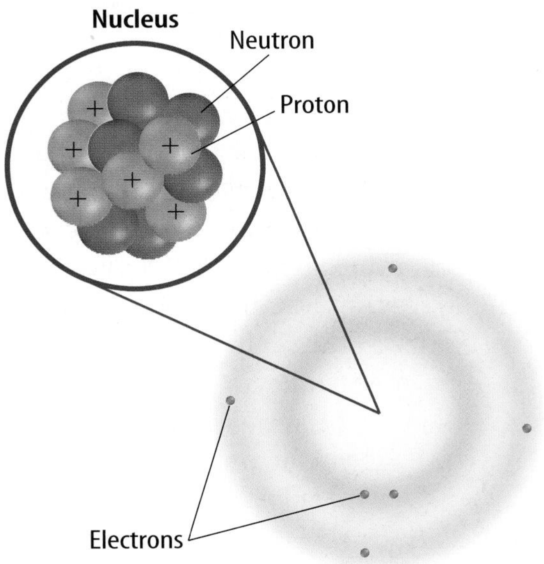

Figure 2 This drawing shows an atom of carbon with its six protons, six neutrons, and six electrons.

Concept Maps One way to organize data is to draw a diagram that shows relationships among ideas (or concepts). A concept map can help make the meanings of ideas and terms more clear, and help you understand and remember what you are studying. Concept maps are useful for breaking large concepts down into smaller parts, making learning easier.

Network Tree A type of concept map that not only shows a relationship, but how the concepts are related is a network tree, shown in **Figure 3.** In a network tree, the words are written in the ovals, while the description of the type of relationship is written across the connecting lines.

When constructing a network tree, write down the topic and all major topics on separate pieces of paper or notecards. Then arrange them in order from general to specific. Branch the related concepts from the major concept and describe the relationship on the connecting line. Continue to more specific concepts until finished.

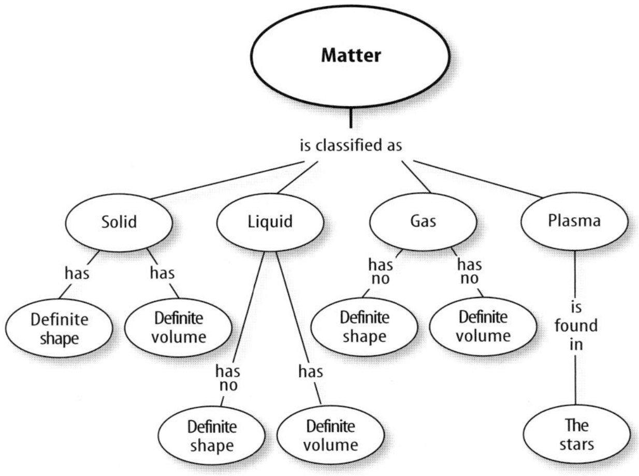

Figure 3 A network tree shows how concepts or objects are related.

Events Chain Another type of concept map is an events chain. Sometimes called a flow chart, it models the order or sequence of items. An events chain can be used to describe a sequence of events, the steps in a procedure, or the stages of a process.

When making an events chain, first find the one event that starts the chain. This event is called the initiating event. Then, find the next event and continue until the outcome is reached, as shown in **Figure 4.**

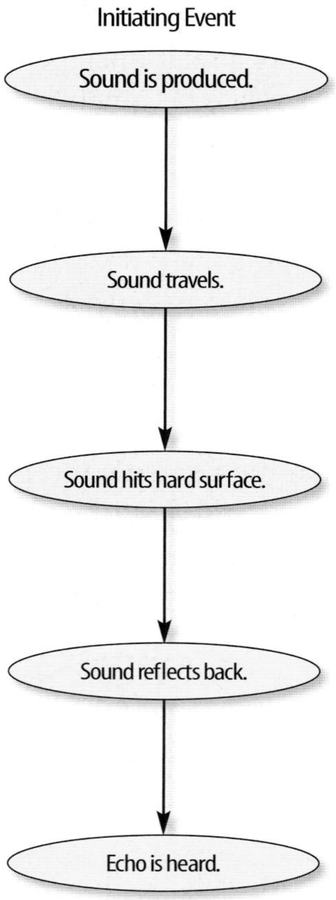

Figure 4 Events-chain concept maps show the order of steps in a process or event. This concept map shows how a sound makes an echo.

Cycle Map A specific type of events chain is a cycle map. It is used when the series of events do not produce a final outcome, but instead relate back to the beginning event, such as in **Figure 5.** Therefore, the cycle repeats itself.

To make a cycle map, first decide what event is the beginning event. This is also called the initiating event. Then list the next events in the order that they occur, with the last event relating back to the initiating event. Words can be written between the events that describe what happens from one event to the next. The number of events in a cycle map can vary, but usually contain three or more events.

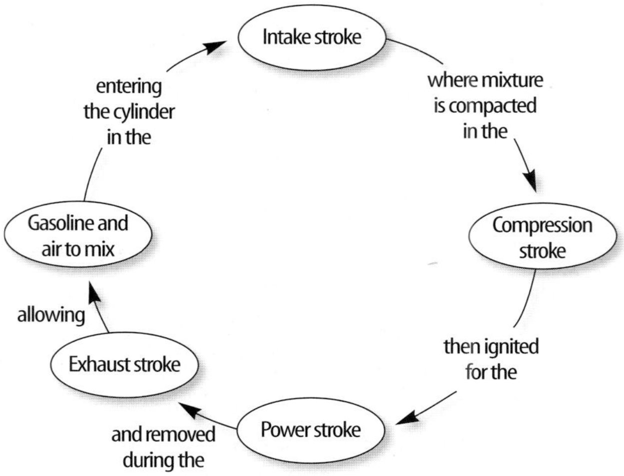

Figure 5 A cycle map shows events that occur in a cycle.

Spider Map A type of concept map that you can use for brainstorming is the spider map. When you have a central idea, you might find that you have a jumble of ideas that relate to it but are not necessarily clearly related to each other. The spider map on sound in **Figure 6** shows that if you write these ideas outside the main concept, then you can begin to separate and group unrelated terms so they become more useful.

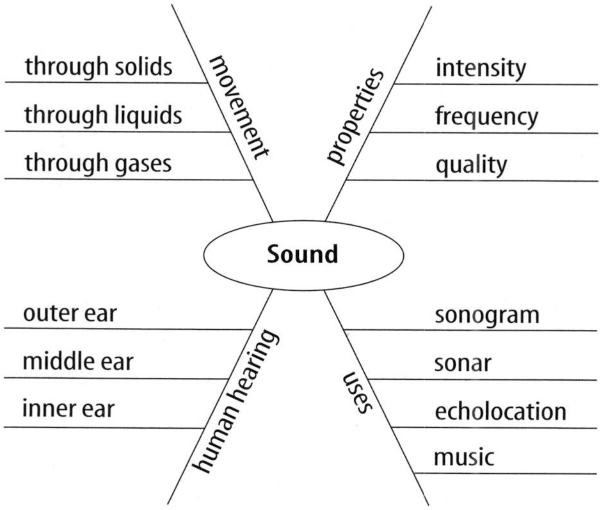

Figure 6 A spider map allows you to list ideas that relate to a central topic but not necessarily to one another.

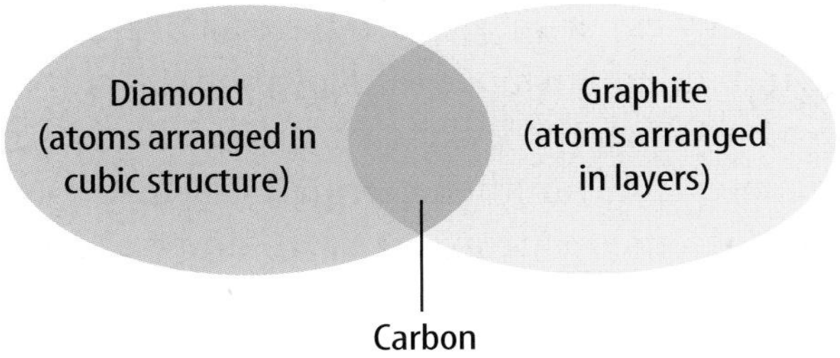

Figure 7 This Venn diagram compares and contrasts two substances made from carbon.

Venn Diagram To illustrate how two subjects compare and contrast you can use a Venn diagram. You can see the characteristics that the subjects have in common and those that they do not, shown in **Figure 7.**

To create a Venn diagram, draw two overlapping ovals that that are big enough to write in. List the characteristics unique to one subject in one oval, and the characteristics of the other subject in the other oval. The characteristics in common are listed in the overlapping section.

Make and Use Tables One way to organize information so it is easier to understand is to use a table. Tables can contain numbers, words, or both.

To make a table, list the items to be compared in the first column and the characteristics to be compared in the first row. The title should clearly indicate the content of the table, and the column or row heads should be clear. Notice that in **Table 1** the units are included.

Table 1 Recyclables Collected During Week

Day of Week	Paper (kg)	Aluminum (kg)	Glass (kg)
Monday	5.0	4.0	12.0
Wednesday	4.0	1.0	10.0
Friday	2.5	2.0	10.0

Make a Model One way to help you better understand the parts of a structure, the way a process works, or to show things too large or small for viewing is to make a model. For example, an atomic model made of a plastic-ball nucleus and pipe-cleaner electron shells can help you visualize how the parts of an atom relate to each other. Other types of models can by devised on a computer or represented by equations.

Form a Hypothesis

A possible explanation based on previous knowledge and observations is called a hypothesis. After researching gasoline types and recalling previous experiences in your family's car you form a hypothesis—our car runs more efficiently because we use premium gasoline. To be valid, a hypothesis has to be something you can test by using an investigation.

Predict When you apply a hypothesis to a specific situation, you predict something about that situation. A prediction makes a statement in advance, based on prior observation, experience, or scientific reasoning. People use predictions to make everyday decisions. Scientists test predictions by performing investigations. Based on previous observations and experiences, you might form a prediction that cars are more efficient with premium gasoline. The prediction can be tested in an investigation.

Design an Experiment A scientist needs to make many decisions before beginning an investigation. Some of these include: how to carry out the investigation, what steps to follow, how to record the data, and how the investigation will answer the question. It also is important to address any safety concerns.

Test the Hypothesis

Now that you have formed your hypothesis, you need to test it. Using an investigation, you will make observations and collect data, or information. This data might either support or not support your hypothesis. Scientists collect and organize data as numbers and descriptions.

Follow a Procedure In order to know what materials to use, as well as how and in what order to use them, you must follow a procedure. **Figure 8** shows a procedure you might follow to test your hypothesis.

Procedure

1. Use regular gasoline for two weeks.
2. Record the number of kilometers between fill-ups and the amount of gasoline used.
3. Switch to premium gasoline for two weeks.
4. Record the number of kilometers between fill-ups and the amount of gasoline used.

Figure 8 A procedure tells you what to do step by step.

Identify and Manipulate Variables and Controls In any experiment, it is important to keep everything the same except for the item you are testing. The one factor you change is called the independent variable. The change that results is the dependent variable. Make sure you have only one independent variable, to assure yourself of the cause of the changes you observe in the dependent variable. For example, in your gasoline experiment the type of fuel is the independent variable. The dependent variable is the efficiency.

Many experiments also have a control—an individual instance or experimental subject for which the independent variable is not changed. You can then compare the test results to the control results. To design a control you can have two cars of the same type. The control car uses regular gasoline for four weeks. After you are done with the test, you can compare the experimental results to the control results.

Collect Data

Whether you are carrying out an investigation or a short observational experiment, you will collect data, as shown in **Figure 9.** Scientists collect data as numbers and descriptions and organize it in specific ways.

Observe Scientists observe items and events, then record what they see. When they use only words to describe an observation, it is called qualitative data. Scientists' observations also can describe how much there is of something. These observations use numbers, as well as words, in the description and are called quantitative data. For example, if a sample of the element gold is described as being "shiny and very dense" the data are qualitative. Quantitative data on this sample of gold might include "a mass of 30 g and a density of 19.3 g/cm^3."

Figure 9 Collecting data is one way to gather information directly.

Figure 10 Record data neatly and clearly so it is easy to understand.

When you make observations you should examine the entire object or situation first, and then look carefully for details. It is important to record observations accurately and completely. Always record your observations immediately as you make them, so you do not miss details or make a mistake when recording results from memory. Never put unidentified observations on scraps of paper. Instead they should be recorded in a notebook, like the one in **Figure 10.** Write your data neatly so you can easily read it later. At each point in the experiment, record your observations and label them. That way, you will not have to determine what the figures mean when you look at your notes later. Set up any tables that you will need to use ahead of time, so you can record any observations right away. Remember to avoid bias when collecting data by not including personal thoughts when you record observations. Record only what you observe.

Estimate Scientific work also involves estimating. To estimate is to make a judgment about the size or the number of something without measuring or counting. This is important when the number or size of an object or population is too large or too difficult to accurately count or measure.

Sample Scientists may use a sample or a portion of the total number as a type of estimation. To sample is to take a small, representative portion of the objects or organisms of a population for research. By making careful observations or manipulating variables within that portion of the group, information is discovered and conclusions are drawn that might apply to the whole population. A poorly chosen sample can be unrepresentative of the whole. If you were trying to determine the rainfall in an area, it would not be best to take a rainfall sample from under a tree.

Measure You use measurements every day. Scientists also take measurements when collecting data. When taking measurements, it is important to know how to use measuring tools properly. Accuracy also is important.

Length To measure length, the distance between two points, scientists use meters. Smaller measurements might be measured in centimeters or millimeters.

Length is measured using a metric ruler or meterstick. When using a metric ruler, line up the 0-cm mark with the end of the object being measured and read the number of the unit where the object ends. Look at the metric ruler shown in **Figure 11.** The centimeter lines are the long, numbered lines, and the shorter lines are millimeter lines. In this instance, the length would be 4.50 cm.

Figure 11 This metric ruler has centimeter and millimeter divisions.

Mass The SI unit for mass is the kilogram (kg). Scientists can measure mass using units formed by adding metric prefixes to the unit gram (g), such as milligram (mg). To measure mass, you might use a triple-beam balance similar to the one shown in **Figure 12.** The balance has a pan on one side and a set of beams on the other side. Each beam has a rider that slides on the beam.

When using a triple-beam balance, place an object on the pan. Slide the largest rider along its beam until the pointer drops below zero. Then move it back one notch. Repeat the process for each rider proceeding from the larger to smaller until the pointer swings an equal distance above and below the zero point. Sum the masses on each beam to find the mass of the object. Move all riders back to zero when finished.

Instead of putting materials directly on the balance, scientists often take a tare of a container. A tare is the mass of a container into which objects or substances are placed for measuring their masses. To mass objects or substances, find the mass of a clean container. Remove the container from the pan, and place the object or substances in the container. Find the mass of the container with the materials in it. Subtract the mass of the empty container from the mass of the filled container to find the mass of the materials you are using.

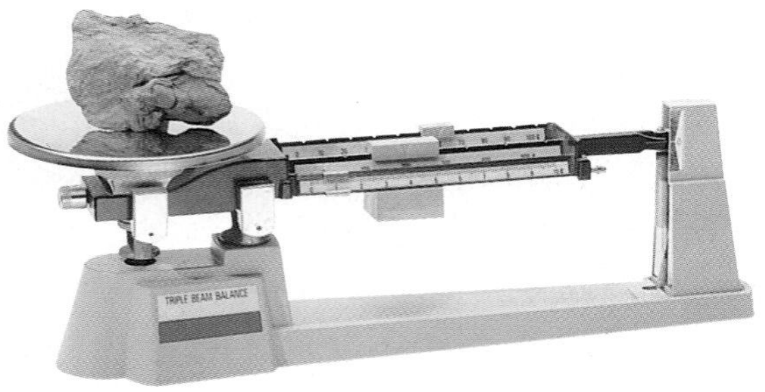

Figure 12 A triple-beam balance is used to determine the mass of an object.

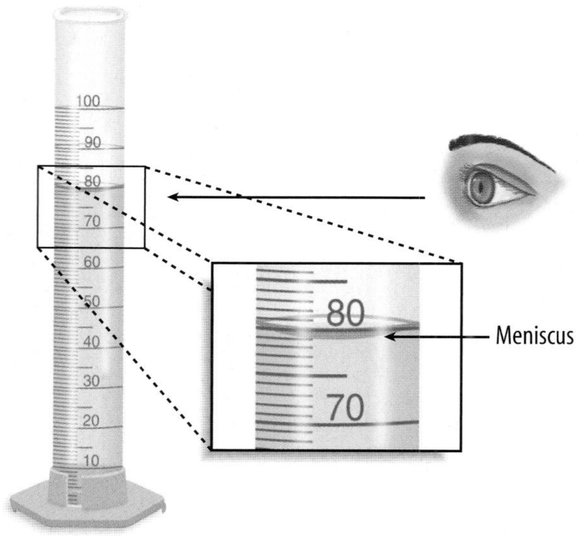

Figure 13 Graduated cylinders measure liquid volume.

Liquid Volume To measure liquids, the unit used is the liter (L). When a smaller unit is needed, scientists might use a milliliter (mL). Because a milliliter takes up the volume of a cube measuring 1 cm on each side it also can be called a cubic centimeter ($cm^3 = cm \times cm \times cm$).

You can use beakers and graduated cylinders to measure liquid volume. A graduated cylinder, shown in **Figure 13,** is marked from bottom to top in milliliters. In the lab, you might use a 10-mL graduated cylinder or a 100-mL graduated cylinder. When measuring liquids, notice that the liquid has a curved surface. Look at the surface at eye level, and measure the bottom of the curve. This is called the meniscus. The graduated cylinder in **Figure 13** contains 79.0 mL, or 79.0 cm^3, of a liquid.

Temperature Scientists often measure temperature using the Celsius scale. Pure water has a freezing point of 0°C and boiling point of 100°C. The unit of measurement is degrees Celsius. Two other scales often used are the Fahrenheit and Kelvin scales.

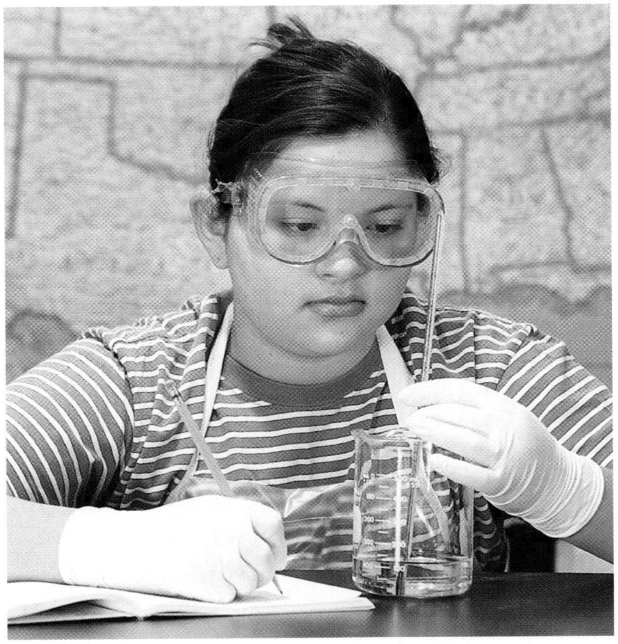

Figure 14 A thermometer measures the temperature of an object.

Scientists use a thermometer to measure temperature. Most thermometers in a laboratory are glass tubes with a bulb at the bottom end containing a liquid such as colored alcohol. The liquid rises or falls with a change in temperature. To read a glass thermometer like the thermometer in **Figure 14,** rotate it slowly until a red line appears. Read the temperature where the red line ends.

Form Operational Definitions An operational definition defines an object by how it functions, works, or behaves. For example, when you are playing hide and seek and a tree is home base, you have created an operational definition for a tree.

Objects can have more than one operational definition. For example, a ruler can be defined as a tool that measures the length of an object (how it is used). It can also be a tool with a series of marks used as a standard when measuring (how it works).

Analyze the Data

To determine the meaning of your observations and investigation results, you will need to look for patterns in the data. Then you must think critically to determine what the data mean. Scientists use several approaches when they analyze the data they have collected and recorded. Each approach is useful for identifying specific patterns.

Interpret Data The word *interpret* means "to explain the meaning of something." When analyzing data from an experiement, try to find out what the data show. Identify the control group and the test group to see whether or not changes in the independent variable have had an effect. Look for differences in the dependent variable between the control and test groups.

Classify Sorting objects or events into groups based on common features is called classifying. When classifying, first observe the objects or events to be classified. Then select one feature that is shared by some members in the group, but not by all. Place those members that share that feature in a subgroup. You can classify members into smaller and smaller subgroups based on characteristics. Remember that when you classify, you are grouping objects or events for a purpose. Keep your purpose in mind as you select the features to form groups and subgroups.

Compare and Contrast Observations can be analyzed by noting the similarities and differences between two more objects or events that you observe. When you look at objects or events to see how they are similar, you are comparing them. Contrasting is looking for differences in objects or events.

Recognize Cause and Effect A cause is a reason for an action or condition. The effect is that action or condition. When two events happen together, it is not necessarily true that one event caused the other. Scientists must design a controlled investigation to recognize the exact cause and effect.

Draw Conclusions

When scientists have analyzed the data they collected, they proceed to draw conclusions about the data. These conclusions are sometimes stated in words similar to the hypothesis that you formed earlier. They may confirm a hypothesis, or lead you to a new hypothesis.

Infer Scientists often make inferences based on their observations. An inference is an attempt to explain observations or to indicate a cause. An inference is not a fact, but a logical conclusion that needs further investigation. For example, you may infer that a fire has caused smoke. Until you investigate, however, you do not know for sure.

Apply When you draw a conclusion, you must apply those conclusions to determine whether the data support the hypothesis. If your data do not support your hypothesis, it does not mean that the hypothesis is wrong. It means only that the result of the investigation did not support the hypothesis. Maybe the experiment needs to be redesigned, or some of the initial observations on which the hypothesis was based were incomplete or biased. Perhaps more observation or research is needed to refine your hypothesis. A successful investigation does not always come out the way you originally predicted.

Avoid Bias Sometimes a scientific investigation involves making judgments. When you make a judgment, you form an opinion. It is important to be honest and not to allow any expectations of results to bias your judgments. This is important throughout the entire investigation, from researching to collecting data to drawing conclusions.

Communicate

The communication of ideas is an important part of the work of scientists. A discovery that is not reported will not advance the scientific community's understanding or knowledge. Communication among scientists also is important as a way of improving their investigations.

Scientists communicate in many ways, from writing articles in journals and magazines that explain their investigations and experiments, to announcing important discoveries on television and radio. Scientists also share ideas with colleagues on the Internet or present them as lectures, like the student is doing in **Figure 15.**

Figure 15 A student communicates to his peers about his investigation.

SAFETY SYMBOLS	HAZARD	EXAMPLES	PRECAUTION	REMEDY
DISPOSAL	Special disposal procedures need to be followed.	certain chemicals, living organisms	Do not dispose of these materials in the sink or trash can.	Dispose of wastes as directed by your teacher.
BIOLOGICAL	Organisms or other biological materials that might be harmful to humans	bacteria, fungi, blood, unpreserved tissues, plant materials	Avoid skin contact with these materials. Wear mask or gloves.	Notify your teacher if you suspect contact with material. Wash hands thoroughly.
EXTREME TEMPERATURE	Objects that can burn skin by being too cold or too hot	boiling liquids, hot plates, dry ice, liquid nitrogen	Use proper protection when handling.	Go to your teacher for first aid.
SHARP OBJECT	Use of tools or glassware that can easily puncture or slice skin	razor blades, pins, scalpels, pointed tools, dissecting probes, broken glass	Practice common-sense behavior and follow guidelines for use of the tool.	Go to your teacher for first aid.
FUME	Possible danger to respiratory tract from fumes	ammonia, acetone, nail polish remover, heated sulfur, moth balls	Make sure there is good ventilation. Never smell fumes directly. Wear a mask.	Leave foul area and notify your teacher immediately.
ELECTRICAL	Possible danger from electrical shock or burn	improper grounding, liquid spills, short circuits, exposed wires	Double-check setup with teacher. Check condition of wires and apparatus.	Do not attempt to fix electrical problems. Notify your teacher immediately.
IRRITANT	Substances that can irritate the skin or mucous membranes of the respiratory tract	pollen, moth balls, steel wool, fiberglass, potassium permanganate	Wear dust mask and gloves. Practice extra care when handling these materials.	Go to your teacher for first aid.
CHEMICAL	Chemicals can react with and destroy tissue and other materials	bleaches such as hydrogen peroxide; acids such as sulfuric acid, hydrochloric acid; bases such as ammonia, sodium hydroxide	Wear goggles, gloves, and an apron.	Immediately flush the affected area with water and notify your teacher.
TOXIC	Substance may be poisonous if touched, inhaled, or swallowed.	mercury, many metal compounds, iodine, poinsettia plant parts	Follow your teacher's instructions.	Always wash hands thoroughly after use. Go to your teacher for first aid.
FLAMMABLE	Flammable chemicals may be ignited by open flame, spark, or exposed heat.	alcohol, kerosene, potassium permanganate	Avoid open flames and heat when using flammable chemicals.	Notify your teacher immediately. Use fire safety equipment if applicable.
OPEN FLAME	Open flame in use, may cause fire.	hair, clothing, paper, synthetic materials	Tie back hair and loose clothing. Follow teacher's instruction on lighting and extinguishing flames.	Notify your teacher immediately. Use fire safety equipment if applicable.

Eye Safety
Proper eye protection should be worn at all times by anyone performing or observing science activities.

Clothing Protection
This symbol appears when substances could stain or burn clothing.

Animal Safety
This symbol appears when safety of animals and students must be ensured.

Handwashing
After the lab, wash hands with soap and water before removing goggles.

Introduction to Science Safety

Confucius, an ancient and well-known Chinese philosopher, is credited with a statement that could serve as a legacy of all types of human wisdom. It seems especially appropriate for the active learning you will experience in this science program.

"I hear and I forget, I see and I remember, I do and I understand."

This is the basis for the safety routine that will be used in all the labs in this book. It is assumed that you will use all of your senses as you "experience" the labs. However, with such experience comes the potential for injury. The purpose of this section of the book is to help keep you safe by involving you in the safety process.

How will your teacher help?

It will be your teacher's responsibility to decide which science labs are safe and appropriate for you. Your teacher will identify the hazards involved in each activity and likely will ask for your assistance for ways to reduce the dangers as much as possible. He or she will involve you regularly in safety discussions about your understanding of the actual and potential dangers and the safety measures needed to keep everyone safe. Ideally, this will become a habit with each lab in which you take part.

Your teacher also will explain the safety features of your room as well as the most important safety equipment and routines for addressing safety issues. He or she will also require that you complete a *Student Lab-Safety Form* for each lab to make certain you are prepared to perform the lab safely.

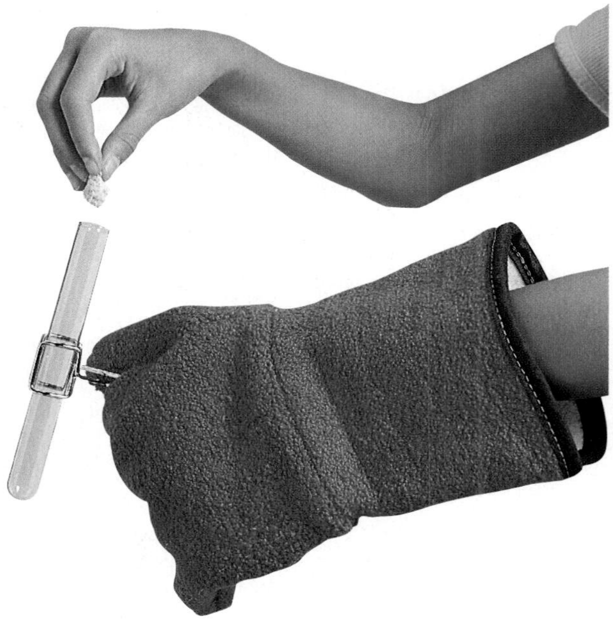

Your teacher will review your comments, make corrections, and sign or initial this form **BEFORE** you will be permitted to begin the lab.

The ultimate purpose of the safety discussions and the *Student Lab-Safety Form* will be to ***help you take some responsibility for your own safety*** and to help you to develop good habits when you prepare and perform science experiments and labs.

How can you help?

Since your teacher cannot anticipate every safety hazard that might occur and he or she cannot be everywhere in the room at the same time, you need to take some responsibility for your own safety. The following general information should apply to nearly every science lab in which you will be involved as part of this class.

Adapted from Gerlovich, et al. (2004). The Total Science Safety System D. JaKel, Inc. http://www.netins.net/showcase/jakel. Used with Permission

You must:

- Review any *Safety Symbols* in the labs and be certain that you know what they mean.
- Follow all teacher instructions for safety and make certain that you understand all the hazards related to the labs you are about to do.
- Be able to explain the purpose of the lab.
- Be able to explain, or demonstrate, all reasonable emergency procedures, such as:
  - how to evacuate the room during emergencies;
  - how to react to any chemical emergencies;
  - how to deal with fire emergencies;
  - how to perform a scientific investigation safely;
  - how to anticipate some safety concerns and be prepared to address them;
  - how to use equipment properly and safely.
- Be able to locate and use all safety equipment as directed by your teacher, such as:
  - fire extinguishers;
  - fire blankets;
  - eye protective equipment (goggles, safety glasses, face shield);
  - eyewash;
  - drench shower.
- Complete the Student Lab-Safety Form before starting any science lab.
- Ask questions about any safety concerns that you might have BEFORE starting any lab of science investigation.

Remember! Your teacher will review your comments, make corrections, and sign or initial the *Student Lab-Safety Form* **BEFORE** you will be permitted to begin the lab. A copy of this form appears below.

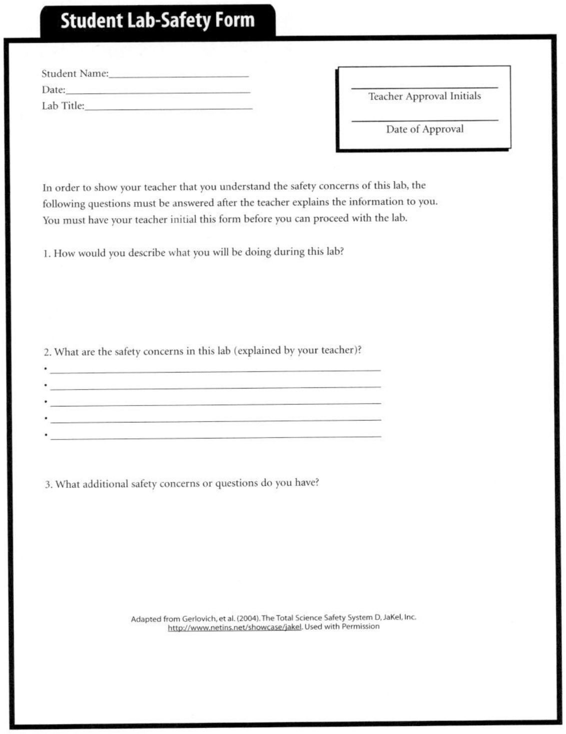

Student Lab-Safety Form

Student Name:________________
Date:________________
Lab Title:________________

Teacher Approval Initials

Date of Approval

In order to show your teacher that you understand the safety concerns of this lab, the following questions must be answered after the teacher explains the information to you. You must have your teacher initial this form before you can proceed with the lab.

1. How would you describe what you will be doing during this lab?

2. What are the safety concerns in this lab (explained by your teacher)?

- ________________
- ________________
- ________________
- ________________
- ________________

3. What additional safety concerns or questions do you have?

Adapted from Gerlovich, et al. (2004). The Total Science Safety System D, JaKel, Inc. http://www.netins.net/showcase/jakel. Used with Permission

Adapted from Gerlovich, et al. (2004). The Total Science Safety System D. JaKel, Inc. http://www.netins.net/showcase/jakel. Used with Permission

Reduce Fractions

$\frac{66 \div 6}{90 \div 6} = \frac{11}{15}$

Add and Subtract Fractions

$\frac{4}{9} + \frac{2}{9} = \frac{6}{9}$

$\frac{6 \div 3}{9 \div 3} = \frac{2}{3}$

Math Review

Use Fractions

A fraction compares a part to a whole. In the fraction $\frac{2}{3}$, the 2 represents the part and is the numerator. The 3 represents the whole and is the denominator.

Reduce Fractions To reduce a fraction, you must find the largest factor that is common to both the numerator and the denominator, the greatest common factor (GCF). Divide both numbers by the GCF. The fraction has then been reduced, or it is in its simplest form.

Example Twelve of the 20 chemicals in the science lab are in powder form. What fraction of the chemicals used in the lab are in powder form?

Step 1 Write the fraction.

$\frac{\text{part}}{\text{whole}} = \frac{12}{20}$

Step 2 To find the GCF of the numerator and denominator, list all of the factors of each number.

Factors of 12: 1, 2, 3, 4, 6, 12 (the numbers that divide evenly into 12)

Factors of 20: 1, 2, 4, 5, 10, 20 (the numbers that divide evenly into 20)

Step 3 List the common factors.

1, 2, 4

Step 4 Choose the greatest factor in the list.

The GCF of 12 and 20 is 4.

Step 5 Divide the numerator and denominator by the GCF.

$\frac{12 \div 4}{20 \div 4} = \frac{3}{5}$

In the lab, $\frac{3}{5}$ of the chemicals are in powder form.

Practice Problem At an amusement park, 66 of 90 rides have a height restriction. What fraction of the rides, in its simplest form, has a height restriction?

Add and Subtract Fractions To add or subtract fractions with the same denominator, add or subtract the numerators and write the sum or difference over the denominator. After finding the sum or difference, find the simplest form for your fraction.

Example 1 In the forest outside your house, $\frac{1}{8}$ of the animals are rabbits, $\frac{3}{8}$ are squirrels, and the remainder are birds and insects. How many are mammals?

Step 1 Add the numerators.

$\frac{1}{8} + \frac{3}{8} = \frac{(1 + 3)}{8} = \frac{4}{8}$

Step 2 Find the GCF.

$\frac{4}{8}$ (GCF, 4)

Step 3 Divide the numerator and denominator by the GCF.

$\frac{4 \div 4}{8 \div 4} = \frac{1}{2}$

$\frac{1}{2}$ of the animals are mammals.

Example 2 If $\frac{7}{16}$ of the Earth is covered by freshwater, and $\frac{1}{16}$ of that is in glaciers, how much freshwater is not frozen?

Step 1 Subtract the numerators.

$\frac{7}{16} - \frac{1}{16} = \frac{(7 - 1)}{16} = \frac{6}{16}$

Step 2 Find the GCF.

$\frac{6}{16}$ (GCF, 2)

Step 3 Divide the numerator and denominator by the GCF.

$\frac{6 \div 2}{16 \div 2} = \frac{3}{8}$

$\frac{3}{8}$ of the freshwater is not frozen.

Practice Problem A bicycle rider is riding at a rate of 15 km/h for $\frac{4}{9}$ of his ride, 10 km/h for $\frac{2}{9}$ of his ride, and 8 km/h for the remainder of the ride. How much of his ride is he riding at a rate greater than 8 km/h?

Unlike Denominators To add or subtract fractions with unlike denominators, first find the least common denominator (LCD). This is the smallest number that is a common multiple of both denominators. Rename each fraction with the LCD, and then add or subtract. Find the simplest form if necessary.

Example 1 A chemist makes a paste that is $\frac{1}{2}$ table salt (NaCl), $\frac{1}{3}$ sugar ($C_6H_{12}O_6$), and the remainder is water (H_2O). How much of the paste is a solid?

Step 1 Find the LCD of the fractions.

$\frac{1}{2} + \frac{1}{3}$ (LCD, 6)

Step 2 Rename each numerator and each denominator with the LCD.

Step 3 Add the numerators.

$\frac{3}{6} + \frac{2}{6} = \frac{(3 + 2)}{6} = \frac{5}{6}$

$\frac{5}{6}$ of the paste is a solid.

Example 2 The average precipitation in Grand Junction, CO, is $\frac{7}{10}$ inch in November, and $\frac{3}{5}$ inch in December. What is the total average precipitation?

Step 1 Find the LCD of the fractions.

$\frac{7}{10} + \frac{3}{5}$ (LCD, 10)

Step 2 Rename each numerator and each denominator with the LCD.

Step 3 Add the numerators.

$\frac{7}{10} + \frac{6}{10} = \frac{(7 + 6)}{10} = \frac{13}{10}$

$\frac{13}{10}$ inches total precipitation, or $1\frac{3}{10}$ inches.

Practice Problem On an electric bill, about $\frac{1}{8}$ of the energy is from solar energy and about $\frac{1}{10}$ is from wind power. How much of the total bill is from solar energy and wind power combined?

Example 3 In your body, $\frac{7}{10}$ of your muscle contractions are involuntary (cardiac and smooth muscle tissue). Smooth muscle makes $\frac{3}{15}$ of your muscle contractions. How many of your muscle contractions are made by cardiac muscle?

Step 1 Find the LCD of the fractions.

$\frac{7}{10} - \frac{3}{15}$ (LCD, 30)

Step 2 Rename each numerator and each denominator with the LCD.

$7 \times 3 = 21, \quad 10 \times 3 = 30$

$3 \times 2 = 6, \quad 15 \times 2 = 30$

Step 3 Subtract the numerators.

$\frac{21}{30} - \frac{6}{30} = \frac{(21 - 6)}{30} = \frac{15}{30}$

Step 4 Find the GCF.

$\frac{15}{30}$ (GCF, 15)

$\frac{1}{2}$

$\frac{1}{2}$ of all muscle contractions are cardiac muscle.

Example 4 Tony wants to make cookies that call for $\frac{3}{4}$ of a cup of flour, but he only has $\frac{1}{3}$ of a cup. How much more flour does he need?

Step 1 Find the LCD of the fractions.

$\frac{3}{4} - \frac{1}{3}$ (LCD, 12)

Step 2 Rename each numerator and each denominator with the LCD.

$\frac{3 \times 3}{4 \times 3} = \frac{9}{12}$

$\frac{1 \times 4}{3 \times 4} = \frac{4}{12}$

Step 3 Subtract the numerators.

$\frac{9}{12} - \frac{4}{12} = \frac{(9 - 4)}{12} = \frac{5}{12}$

$\frac{5}{12}$ of a cup of flour

Practice Problem Using the information provided to you in Example 3 above, determine how many muscle contractions are voluntary (skeletal muscle).

Unlike Denominators

Problem 1

$1 \times 5 = 5, 8 \times 5 = 40$

$1 \times 4 = 4, 10 \times 4 = 40$

$\frac{5}{40} + \frac{4}{40} = \frac{9}{40}$

Problem 2

If $\frac{7}{10}$ are involuntary, the remainder are voluntary.

$\frac{10}{10} - \frac{7}{10} = \frac{3}{10}$

Multiply Fractions

$\frac{3}{14} \times \frac{5}{16} = \frac{(3 \times 5)}{(14 \times 16)} = \frac{15}{224}$

Find a Reciprocal

$\frac{9}{4}$

Divide Fractions

The reciprocal of $\frac{7}{10}$ is $\frac{10}{7}$.

$\frac{3}{11} \times \frac{10}{7} = \frac{(3 \times 10)}{(11 \times 7)} = \frac{30}{77}$

Multiply Fractions To multiply with fractions, multiply the numerators and multiply the denominators. Find the simplest form if necessary.

Example Multiply $\frac{3}{5}$ by $\frac{1}{3}$.

Step 1 Multiply the numerators and denominators.

$$\frac{3}{5} \times \frac{1}{3} = \frac{(3 \times 1)}{(5 \times 3)} = \frac{3}{15}$$

Step 2 Find the GCF.

$\frac{3}{15}$ (GCF, 3)

Step 3 Divide the numerator and denominator by the GCF.

$$\frac{3 \div 3}{15 \div 3} = \frac{1}{5}$$

$\frac{3}{5}$ multiplied by $\frac{1}{3}$ is $\frac{1}{5}$.

Practice Problem Multiply $\frac{3}{14}$ by $\frac{5}{16}$.

Find a Reciprocal Two numbers whose product is 1 are called multiplicative inverses, or reciprocals.

Example Find the reciprocal of $\frac{3}{8}$.

Step 1 Inverse the fraction by putting the denominator on top and the numerator on the bottom.

$\frac{8}{3}$

The reciprocal of $\frac{3}{8}$ is $\frac{8}{3}$.

Practice Problem Find the reciprocal of $\frac{4}{9}$.

Divide Fractions To divide one fraction by another fraction, multiply the dividend by the reciprocal of the divisor. Find the simplest form if necessary.

Example 1 Divide $\frac{1}{9}$ by $\frac{1}{3}$.

Step 1 Find the reciprocal of the divisor.

The reciprocal of $\frac{1}{3}$ is $\frac{3}{1}$.

Step 2 Multiply the dividend by the reciprocal of the divisor.

$$\frac{\frac{1}{9}}{\frac{1}{3}} = \frac{1}{9} \times \frac{3}{1} = \frac{(1 \times 3)}{(9 \times 1)} = \frac{3}{9}$$

Step 3 Find the GCF.

$\frac{3}{9}$ (GCF, 3)

Step 4 Divide the numerator and denominator by the GCF.

$$\frac{3 \div 3}{9 \div 3} = \frac{1}{3}$$

$\frac{1}{9}$ divided by $\frac{1}{3}$ is $\frac{1}{3}$.

Example 2 Divide $\frac{3}{5}$ by $\frac{1}{4}$.

Step 1 Find the reciprocal of the divisor.

The reciprocal of $\frac{1}{4}$ is $\frac{4}{1}$.

Step 2 Multiply the dividend by the reciprocal of the divisor.

$$\frac{\frac{3}{5}}{\frac{1}{4}} = \frac{3}{5} \times \frac{4}{1} = \frac{(3 \times 4)}{(5 \times 1)} = \frac{12}{5}$$

$\frac{3}{5}$ divided by $\frac{1}{4}$ is $\frac{12}{5}$ or $2\frac{2}{5}$.

Practice Problem Divide $\frac{3}{11}$ by $\frac{7}{10}$.

Use Ratios

When you compare two numbers by division, you are using a ratio. Ratios can be written 3 to 5, 3:5, or $\frac{3}{5}$. Ratios, like fractions, also can be written in simplest form.

Ratios can represent one type of probability, called odds. This is a ratio that compares the number of ways a certain outcome occurs to the number of possible outcomes. For example, if you flip a coin 100 times, what are the odds that it will come up heads? There are two possible outcomes, heads or tails, so the odds of coming up heads are 50:100. Another way to say this is that 50 out of 100 times the coin will come up heads. In its simplest form, the ratio is 1:2.

Example 1 A chemical solution contains 40 g of salt and 64 g of baking soda. What is the ratio of salt to baking soda as a fraction in simplest form?

Step 1 Write the ratio as a fraction.

$$\frac{\text{salt}}{\text{baking soda}} = \frac{40}{64}$$

Step 2 Express the fraction in simplest form.

The GCF of 40 and 64 is 8.

$$\frac{40}{64} = \frac{40 \div 8}{64 \div 8} = \frac{5}{8}$$

The ratio of salt to baking soda in the sample is 5:8.

Example 2 Sean rolls a 6-sided die 6 times. What are the odds that the side with a 3 will show?

Step 1 Write the ratio as a fraction.

$$\frac{\text{number of sides with a 3}}{\text{number of possible sides}} = \frac{1}{6}$$

Step 2 Multiply by the number of attempts.

$$\frac{1}{6} \times 6 \text{ attempts} = \frac{6}{6} \text{ attempts} = 1 \text{ attempt}$$

1 attempt out of 6 will show a 3.

Practice Problem Two metal rods measure 100 cm and 144 cm in length. What is the ratio of their lengths in simplest form?

Use Decimals

A fraction with a denominator that is a power of ten can be written as a decimal. For example, 0.27 means $\frac{27}{100}$. The decimal point separates the ones place from the tenths place.

Any fraction can be written as a decimal using division. For example, the fraction $\frac{5}{8}$ can be written as a decimal by dividing 5 by 8. Written as a decimal, it is 0.625.

Add or Subtract Decimals When adding and subtracting decimals, line up the decimal points before carrying out the operation.

Example 1 Find the sum of 47.68 and 7.80.

Step 1 Line up the decimal places when you write the numbers.

$$\begin{array}{r} 47.68 \\ +\ 7.80 \\ \hline \end{array}$$

Step 2 Add the decimals.

$$\begin{array}{r} {}^{1\,1} \\ 47.68 \\ +\ 7.80 \\ \hline 55.48 \end{array}$$

The sum of 47.68 and 7.80 is 55.48.

Example 2 Find the difference of 42.17 and 15.85.

Step 1 Line up the decimal places when you write the number.

$$\begin{array}{r} 42.17 \\ -15.85 \\ \hline \end{array}$$

Step 2 Subtract the decimals.

$$\begin{array}{r} {}^{3\,11\,1} \\ 42.17 \\ -15.85 \\ \hline 26.32 \end{array}$$

The difference of 42.17 and 15.85 is 26.32.

Practice Problem Find the sum of 1.245 and 3.842.

Use Ratios

$$\frac{100 \text{ cm}}{144 \text{ cm}} = \frac{100 \div 4}{144 \div 4} = \frac{25}{36}$$

25:36

Add or Subtract Decimals

$$\begin{array}{r} {}^{1} \\ 1.245 \\ +\ 3.842 \\ \hline 5.087 \end{array}$$

Multiply Decimals To multiply decimals, multiply the numbers like you multiply numbers without decimals. Count the decimal places in each factor. The product will have the same number of decimal places as the sum of the decimal places in the factors.

Example Multiply 2.4 by 5.9.

Step 1 Multiply the factors like two whole numbers.
$24 \times 59 = 1416$

Step 2 Find the sum of the number of decimal places in the factors. Each factor has one decimal place, for a sum of two decimal places.

Step 3 The product will have two decimal places.
14.16

The product of 2.4 and 5.9 is 14.16.

Practice Problem Multiply 4.6 by 2.2.

Divide Decimals When dividing decimals, change the divisor to a whole number. To do this, multiply both the divisor and the dividend by the same power of ten. Then place the decimal point in the quotient directly above the decimal point in the dividend. Then divide as you do with whole numbers.

Example Divide 8.84 by 3.4.

Step 1 Multiply both factors by 10.
$3.4 \times 10 = 34,\ 8.84 \times 10 = 88.4$

Step 2 Divide 88.4 by 34.

$$\begin{array}{r} 2.6 \\ 34\overline{)88.4} \\ -\underline{68} \\ 20\,4 \\ -\underline{20\,4} \\ 0 \end{array}$$

8.84 divided by 3.4 is 2.6.

Practice Problem Divide 75.6 by 3.6.

Use Proportions

An equation that shows that two ratios are equivalent is a proportion. The ratios $\frac{2}{4}$ and $\frac{5}{10}$ are equivalent, so they can be written as $\frac{2}{4} = \frac{5}{10}$. This equation is a proportion.

When two ratios form a proportion, the cross products are equal. To find the cross products in the proportion $\frac{2}{4} = \frac{5}{10}$, multiply the 2 and the 10, and the 4 and the 5. Therefore $2 \times 10 = 4 \times 5$, or $20 = 20$.

Because you know that both ratios are equal, you can use cross products to find a missing term in a proportion. This is known as solving the proportion.

Example The heights of a tree and a pole are proportional to the lengths of their shadows. The tree casts a shadow of 24 m when a 6-m pole casts a shadow of 4 m. What is the height of the tree?

Step 1 Write a proportion.
$$\frac{\text{height of tree}}{\text{height of pole}} = \frac{\text{length of tree's shadow}}{\text{length of pole's shadow}}$$

Step 2 Substitute the known values into the proportion. Let h represent the unknown value, the height of the tree.
$$\frac{h}{6} = \frac{24}{4}$$

Step 3 Find the cross products.
$h \times 4 = 6 \times 24$

Step 4 Simplify the equation.
$4h = 144$

Step 5 Divide each side by 4.
$$\frac{4h}{4} = \frac{144}{4}$$
$h = 36$

The height of the tree is 36 m.

Practice Problem The ratios of the weights of two objects on the Moon and on Earth are in proportion. A rock weighing 3 N on the Moon weighs 18 N on Earth. How much would a rock that weighs 5 N on the Moon weigh on Earth?

Multiply Decimals

Multiply 4.6 and 2.2 by 10.

$46 \times 22 = 1012$

Each factor had one decimal place.

10.12

Divide Decimals

Multiply both factors by 10.

Divide 756 by 36.

$$\begin{array}{r} 21 \\ 36\overline{)756} \\ \underline{72} \\ 36 \\ \underline{36} \\ 0 \end{array}$$

Use Proportions

$$\frac{3}{18} = \frac{5}{w}$$

$w \times 3 = 5 \times 18$

$$\frac{3w}{3} = \frac{90}{3}$$

$w = 30$

Use Percentages

The word *percent* means "out of one hundred." It is a ratio that compares a number to 100. Suppose you read that 77 percent of the Earth's surface is covered by water. That is the same as reading that the fraction of the Earth's surface covered by water is $\frac{77}{100}$. To express a fraction as a percent, first find the equivalent decimal for the fraction. Then, multiply the decimal by 100 and add the percent symbol.

Example Express $\frac{13}{20}$ as a percent.

Step 1 Find the equivalent decimal for the fraction.

$$\begin{array}{r} 0.65 \\ 20\overline{)13.00} \\ \underline{12\ 0} \\ 1\ 00 \\ \underline{1\ 00} \\ 0 \end{array}$$

Step 2 Rewrite the fraction $\frac{13}{20}$ as 0.65.

Step 3 Multiply 0.65 by 100 and add the % symbol.

$0.65 \times 100 = 65 = 65\%$

So, $\frac{13}{20} = 65\%$.

This also can be solved as a proportion.

Example Express $\frac{13}{20}$ as a percent.

Step 1 Write a proportion.

$\frac{13}{20} = \frac{x}{100}$

Step 2 Find the cross products.

$1300 = 20x$

Step 3 Divide each side by 20.

$\frac{1300}{20} = \frac{20x}{20}$

$65\% = x$

Practice Problem In one year, 73 of 365 days were rainy in one city. What percent of the days in that city were rainy?

Solve One-Step Equations

A statement that two expressions are equal is an equation. For example, $A = B$ is an equation that states that A is equal to B.

An equation is solved when a variable is replaced with a value that makes both sides of the equation equal. To make both sides equal the inverse operation is used. Addition and subtraction are inverses, and multiplication and division are inverses.

Example 1 Solve the equation $x - 10 = 35$.

Step 1 Find the solution by adding 10 to each side of the equation.

$x - 10 = 35$

$x - 10 + 10 = 35 + 10$

$x = 45$

Step 2 Check the solution.

$x - 10 = 35$

$45 - 10 = 35$

$35 = 35$

Both sides of the equation are equal, so $x = 45$.

Example 2 In the formula $a = bc$, find the value of c if $a = 20$ and $b = 2$.

Step 1 Rearrange the formula so the unknown value is by itself on one side of the equation by dividing both sides by b.

$a = bc$

$\frac{a}{b} = \frac{bc}{b}$

$\frac{a}{b} = c$

Step 2 Replace the variables a and b with the values that are given.

$\frac{a}{b} = c$

$\frac{20}{2} = c$

$10 = c$

Step 3 Check the solution.

$a = bc$

$20 = 2 \times 10$

$20 = 20$

Both sides of the equation are equal, so $c = 10$ is the solution when $a = 20$ and $b = 2$.

Practice Problem In the formula $h = gd$, find the value of d if $g = 12.3$ and $h = 17.4$.

Use Percentages

$\frac{73}{365} = \frac{x}{100}$

$\frac{7300}{365} = \frac{365x}{365}$

$20\% = x$

Solve One-Step Equations

$h = gd$

$\frac{17.4}{12.3} = \frac{12.3d}{12.3}$

$1.41 \approx d$

MATH SKILL HANDBOOK 867

Use Statistics

mean

$8 + 4 + 12 + 8 + 11 + 14 + 16 = 73$

$73 \div 7 \approx 10.4$

median

4, 8, 8, 11, 12, 14, 16

mode

4, 8, 8, 11, 12, 14, 16

range

4, 8, 8, 11, 12, 14, 16

$16 - 4 = 12$

Text Question Answer

purple

Use Statistics

The branch of mathematics that deals with collecting, analyzing, and presenting data is statistics. In statistics, there are three common ways to summarize data with a single number—the mean, the median, and the mode.

The **mean** of a set of data is the arithmetic average. It is found by adding the numbers in the data set and dividing by the number of items in the set.

The **median** is the middle number in a set of data when the data are arranged in numerical order. If there were an even number of data points, the median would be the mean of the two middle numbers.

The **mode** of a set of data is the number or item that appears most often.

Another number that often is used to describe a set of data is the range. The **range** is the difference between the largest number and the smallest number in a set of data.

A **frequency table** shows how many times each piece of data occurs, usually in a survey. **Table 2** below shows the results of a student survey on favorite color.

Table 2 Student Color Choice

Color	Tally	Frequency
Red	||||	4
Blue	卌	5
Black	||	2
Green	|||	3
Purple	卌 ||	7
Yellow	卌 |	6

Based on the frequency table data, which color is the favorite?

Example The speeds (in m/s) for a race car during five different time trials are 39, 37, 44, 36, and 44.

To find the mean:

Step 1 Find the sum of the numbers.

$39 + 37 + 44 + 36 + 44 = 200$

Step 2 Divide the sum by the number of items, which is 5.

$200 \div 5 = 40$

The mean is 40 m/s.

To find the median:

Step 1 Arrange the measures from least to greatest.

36, 37, 39, 44, 44

Step 2 Determine the middle measure.

36, 37, 39, 44, 44

The median is 39 m/s.

To find the mode:

Step 1 Group the numbers that are the same together.

44, 44, 36, 37, 39

Step 2 Determine the number that occurs most in the set.

44, 44, 36, 37, 39

The mode is 44 m/s.

To find the range:

Step 1 Arrange the measures from greatest to least.

44, 44, 39, 37, 36

Step 2 Determine the greatest and least measures in the set.

44, 44, 39, 37, 36

Step 3 Find the difference between the greatest and least measures.

$44 - 36 = 8$

The range is 8 m/s.

Practice Problem Find the mean, median, mode, and range for the data set 8, 4, 12, 8, 11, 14, 16.

Use Geometry

The branch of mathematics that deals with the measurement, properties, and relationships of points, lines, angles, surfaces, and solids is called geometry.

Perimeter The **perimeter** (P) is the distance around a geometric figure. To find the perimeter of a rectangle, add the length and width and multiply that sum by two, or $2(l + w)$. To find perimeters of irregular figures, add the length of the sides.

Example 1 Find the perimeter of a rectangle that is 3 m long and 5 m wide.

Step 1 You know that the perimeter is 2 times the sum of the width and length.
$P = 2(3\text{ m} + 5\text{ m})$

Step 2 Find the sum of the width and length.
$P = 2(8\text{ m})$

Step 3 Multiply by 2.
$P = 16\text{ m}$

The perimeter is 16 m.

Example 2 Find the perimeter of a shape with sides measuring 2 cm, 5 cm, 6 cm, 3 cm.

Step 1 You know that the perimeter is the sum of all the sides.
$P = 2 + 5 + 6 + 3$

Step 2 Find the sum of the sides.
$P = 2 + 5 + 6 + 3$
$P = 16$

The perimeter is 16 cm.

Practice Problem Find the perimeter of a rectangle with a length of 18 m and a width of 7 m.

Practice Problem Find the perimeter of a triangle measuring 1.6 cm by 2.4 cm by 2.4 cm.

Area of a Rectangle The **area** (A) is the number of square units needed to cover a surface. To find the area of a rectangle, multiply the length times the width, or $l \times w$. When finding area, the units also are multiplied. Area is given in square units.

Example Find the area of a rectangle with a length of 1 cm and a width of 10 cm.

Step 1 You know that the area is the length multiplied by the width.
$A = (1\text{ cm} \times 10\text{ cm})$

Step 2 Multiply the length by the width. Also multiply the units.
$A = 10\text{ cm}^2$

The area is 10 cm^2.

Practice Problem Find the area of a square whose sides measure 4 m.

Area of a Triangle To find the area of a triangle, use the formula:

$$A = \frac{1}{2}(\text{base} \times \text{height})$$

The base of a triangle can be any of its sides. The height is the perpendicular distance from a base to the opposite endpoint, or vertex.

Example Find the area of a triangle with a base of 18 m and a height of 7 m.

Step 1 You know that the area is $\frac{1}{2}$ the base times the height.
$A = \frac{1}{2}(18\text{ m} \times 7\text{ m})$

Step 2 Multiply $\frac{1}{2}$ by the product of 18×7. Multiply the units.
$A = \frac{1}{2}(126\text{ m}^2)$
$A = 63\text{ m}^2$

The area is 63 m^2.

Practice Problem Find the area of a triangle with a base of 27 cm and a height of 17 cm.

Perimeter

Problem 1
$P = 2(18\text{ m} + 7\text{ m})$
$P = 2(25\text{ m})$
$P = 50\text{ m}$

Problem 2
$P = 1.6\text{ cm} + 2.4\text{ cm} + 2.4\text{ cm}$
$P = 6.4\text{ cm}$

Area of a Rectangle

$A = (4\text{ m} \times 4\text{ m})$
$A = 16\text{ m}^2$

Area of a Triangle

$A = \frac{1}{2}(27\text{ cm} \times 17\text{ cm})$
$A = \frac{1}{2}(459\text{ cm}^2)$
$A = 229.5\text{ cm}^2$

Circumference of a Circle

$C = 2\pi r$

$C = 2\pi(19)$

$C = 38\pi$

$C \approx 119.4$

Area of a Circle

$A = \pi r^2$

$A = \pi(16\ m)^2$

$A = \pi\ 256\ m^2$

$A \approx 804.2\ m^2$

Circumference of a Circle The **diameter** (d) of a circle is the distance across the circle through its center, and the **radius** (r) is the distance from the center to any point on the circle. The radius is half of the diameter. The distance around the circle is called the **circumference** (C). The formula for finding the circumference is:

$$C = 2\pi r \ \ or \ \ C = \pi d$$

The circumference divided by the diameter is always equal to 3.1415926... This nonterminating and nonrepeating number is represented by the Greek letter π (pi). An approximation often used for π is 3.14.

Example 1 Find the circumference of a circle with a radius of 3 m.

Step 1 You know the formula for the circumference is 2 times the radius times π.
$C = 2\pi(3)$

Step 2 Multiply 2 times the radius.
$C = 6\pi$

Step 3 Multiply by π.
$C = 19$ m

The circumference is 19 m.

Example 2 Find the circumference of a circle with a diameter of 24.0 cm.

Step 1 You know the formula for the circumference is the diameter times π.
$C = \pi(24.0)$

Step 2 Multiply the diameter by π.
$C = 75.4$ cm

The circumference is 75.4 cm.

Practice Problem Find the circumference of a circle with a radius of 19 cm.

Area of a Circle The formula for the area of a circle is:
$A = \pi r^2$

Example 1 Find the area of a circle with a radius of 4.0 cm.

Step 1 $A = \pi(4.0)^2$

Step 2 Find the square of the radius.
$A = 16\pi$

Step 3 Multiply the square of the radius by π.
$A = 50\ cm^2$

The area of the circle is 50 cm^2.

Example 2 Find the area of a circle with a radius of 225 m.

Step 1 $A = \pi(225)^2$

Step 2 Find the square of the radius.
$A = 50625\pi$

Step 3 Multiply the square of the radius by π.
$A = 158962.5$

The area of the circle is 158,962 m^2.

Example 3 Find the area of a circle whose diameter is 20.0 mm.

Step 1 You know the formula for the area of a circle is the square of the radius times π, and that the radius is half of the diameter.
$A = \pi\left(\frac{20.0}{2}\right)^2$

Step 2 Find the radius.
$A = \pi(10.0)^2$

Step 3 Find the square of the radius.
$A = 100\pi$

Step 4 Multiply the square of the radius by π.
$A = 314\ mm^2$

The area is 314 mm^2.

Practice Problem Find the area of a circle with a radius of 16 m.

Math Skill Handbook

Volume The measure of space occupied by a solid is the **volume** (V). To find the volume of a rectangular solid multiply the length times width times height, or $V = l \times w \times h$. It is measured in cubic units, such as cubic centimeters (cm^3).

Example Find the volume of a rectangular solid with a length of 2.0 m, a width of 4.0 m, and a height of 3.0 m.

Step 1 You know the formula for volume is the length times the width times the height.
$V = 2.0 \text{ m} \times 4.0 \text{ m} \times 3.0 \text{ m}$

Step 2 Multiply the length times the width times the height.
$V = 24 \text{ m}^3$

The volume is 24 m^3.

Practice Problem Find the volume of a rectangular solid that is 8 m long, 4 m wide, and 4 m high.

To find the volume of other solids, multiply the area of the base times the height.

Example 1 Find the volume of a solid that has a triangular base with a length of 8.0 m and a height of 7.0 m. The height of the entire solid is 15.0 m.

Step 1 You know that the base is a triangle, and the area of a triangle is $\frac{1}{2}$ the base times the height, and the volume is the area of the base times the height.
$V = \left[\frac{1}{2}(b \times h)\right] \times 15$

Step 2 Find the area of the base.
$V = \left[\frac{1}{2}(8 \times 7)\right] \times 15$
$V = \left(\frac{1}{2} \times 56\right) \times 15$

Step 3 Multiply the area of the base by the height of the solid.
$V = 28 \times 15$
$V = 420 \text{ m}^3$

The volume is 420 m^3.

Example 2 Find the volume of a cylinder that has a base with a radius of 12.0 cm, and a height of 21.0 cm.

Step 1 You know that the base is a circle, and the area of a circle is the square of the radius times π, and the volume is the area of the base times the height.
$V = (\pi r^2) \times 21$
$V = (\pi 12^2) \times 21$

Step 2 Find the area of the base.
$V = 144\pi \times 21$
$V = 452 \times 21$

Step 3 Multiply the area of the base by the height of the solid.
$V = 9{,}490 \text{ cm}^3$

The volume is 9,500 cm^3.

Example 3 Find the volume of a cylinder that has a diameter of 15 mm and a height of 4.8 mm.

Step 1 You know that the base is a circle with an area equal to the square of the radius times π. The radius is one-half the diameter. The volume is the area of the base times the height.
$V = (\pi r^2) \times 4.8$
$V = \left[\pi\left(\frac{1}{2} \times 15\right)^2\right] \times 4.8$
$V = (\pi 7.5^2) \times 4.8$

Step 2 Find the area of the base.
$V = 56.25\pi \times 4.8$
$V \approx 176.63 \times 4.8$

Step 3 Multiply the area of the base by the height of the solid.
$V = 847.8$

The volume is 847.8 mm^3.

Practice Problem Find the volume of a cylinder with a diameter of 7 cm in the base and a height of 16 cm.

Volume

Problem 1
$V = 8 \text{ m} \times 4 \text{ m} \times 4 \text{ m}$
$V = 128 \text{ m}^3$

Problem 2
$V = \pi r^2 \times \text{height}$
$V = \left[\pi\left(\frac{1}{2} \times 7\right)^2\right] \times 16$
$V = [\pi(3.5)^2] \times 16$
$V = [\pi(12.25)] \times 16$
$V \approx 38.48 \times 16$
$V \approx 615.75$

Math Skill Handbook

MATH SKILL HANDBOOK 871

Measure in SI

smaller; 1000; one thousandth

Dimensional Analysis

$x\text{ mg} = 1\,\cancel{\text{kg}} \times \frac{1000\,\cancel{\text{g}}}{1\,\cancel{\text{kg}}} \times \frac{1000\text{ mg}}{1\,\cancel{\text{g}}} =$

1,000,000 mg

1,000,000 mg = 1 kg

Science Applications

Measure in SI

The metric system of measurement was developed in 1795. A modern form of the metric system, called the International System (SI), was adopted in 1960 and provides the standard measurements that all scientists around the world can understand.

The SI system is convenient because unit sizes vary by powers of 10. Prefixes are used to name units. Look at **Table 3** for some common SI prefixes and their meanings.

Table 3 Common SI Prefixes

Prefix	Symbol	Meaning	
kilo-	k	1,000	thousand
hecto-	h	100	hundred
deka-	da	10	ten
deci-	d	0.1	tenth
centi-	c	0.01	hundredth
milli-	m	0.001	thousandth

Example How many grams equal one kilogram?

Step 1 Find the prefix *kilo-* in **Table 3.**

Step 2 Using **Table 3,** determine the meaning of *kilo-*. According to the table, it means 1,000. When the prefix *kilo-* is added to a unit, it means that there are 1,000 of the units in a "kilounit."

Step 3 Apply the prefix to the units in the question. The units in the question are grams. There are 1,000 grams in a kilogram.

Practice Problem Is a milligram larger or smaller than a gram? How many of the smaller units equal one larger unit? What fraction of the larger unit does one smaller unit represent?

Dimensional Analysis

Convert SI Units In science, quantities such as length, mass, and time sometimes are measured using different units. A process called dimensional analysis can be used to change one unit of measure to another. This process involves multiplying your starting quantity and units by one or more conversion factors. A conversion factor is a ratio equal to one and can be made from any two equal quantities with different units. If 1,000 mL equal 1 L then two ratios can be made.

$$\frac{1{,}000\text{ mL}}{1\text{ L}} = \frac{1\text{ L}}{1{,}000\text{ mL}} = 1$$

One can convert between units in the SI system by using the equivalents in **Table 3** to make conversion factors.

Example 1 How many cm are in 4 m?

Step 1 Write conversion factors for the units given. From **Table 3,** you know that 100 cm = 1 m. The conversion factors are

$$\frac{100\text{ cm}}{1\text{ m}} \quad \textit{and} \quad \frac{1\text{ m}}{100\text{ cm}}$$

Step 2 Decide which conversion factor to use. Select the factor that has the units you are converting from (m) in the denominator and the units you are converting to (cm) in the numerator.

$$\frac{100\text{ cm}}{1\text{ m}}$$

Step 3 Multiply the starting quantity and units by the conversion factor. Cancel the starting units with the units in the denominator. There are 400 cm in 4 m.

$$4\,\cancel{\text{m}} \times \frac{100\text{ cm}}{1\,\cancel{\text{m}}} = 400\text{ cm}$$

Practice Problem How many milligrams are in one kilogram? (Hint: You will need to use two conversion factors from **Table 3.**)

Table 4 Unit System Equivalents

Type of Measurement	Equivalent
Length	1 in = 2.54 cm 1 yd = 0.91 m 1 mi = 1.61 km
Mass and weight*	1 oz = 28.35 g 1 lb = 0.45 kg 1 ton (short) = 0.91 tonnes (metric tons) 1 lb = 4.45 N
Volume	1 in^3 = 16.39 cm^3 1 qt = 0.95 L 1 gal = 3.78 L
Area	1 in^2 = 6.45 cm^2 1 yd^2 = 0.83 m^2 1 mi^2 = 2.59 km^2 1 acre = 0.40 hectares
Temperature	$°C = \frac{(°F - 32)}{1.8}$ K = °C + 273

*Weight is measured in standard Earth gravity.

Convert Between Unit Systems **Table 4** gives a list of equivalents that can be used to convert between English and SI units.

Example If a meterstick has a length of 100 cm, how long is the meterstick in inches?

Step 1 Write the conversion factors for the units given. From **Table 4,** 1 in = 2.54 cm.

$$\frac{1\text{ in}}{2.54\text{ cm}} \quad \textit{and} \quad \frac{2.54\text{ cm}}{1\text{ in}}$$

Step 2 Determine which conversion factor to use. You are converting from cm to in. Use the conversion factor with cm on the bottom.

$$\frac{1\text{ in}}{2.54\text{ cm}}$$

Step 3 Multiply the starting quantity and units by the conversion factor. Cancel the starting units with the units in the denominator. Round your answer to the nearest tenth.

$$100\ \cancel{\text{cm}} \times \frac{1\text{ in}}{2.54\ \cancel{\text{cm}}} = 39.37\text{ in}$$

The meterstick is about 39.4 in long.

Practice Problem A book has a mass of 5 lbs. What is the mass of the book in kg?

Practice Problem Use the equivalent for in and cm (1 in = 2.54 cm) to show how 1 in^3 = 16.39 cm^3.

Convert Between Unit Systems

Problem 1

$$5\ \cancel{\text{lb}} \times \frac{0.45\text{ kg}}{1\ \cancel{\text{lb}}} = 2.25\text{ kg}$$

Problem 2

$$\frac{(1\text{ in})^3}{(2.54\text{ cm})^3} = \frac{1\text{ in} \times 1\text{ in} \times 1\text{ in}}{2.54\text{ cm} \times 2.54\text{ cm} \times 2.54\text{ cm}} = \frac{1\text{ in}^3}{16.39\text{ cm}^3}$$

Precision and Significant Digits

Problem 1
7; 4

Problem 2
$5.28 \times 5.2 = 27.456$

5.28 has 3 significant digits.

5.2 has 2 significant digits.

When multiplying and dividing, the answer is rounded to the smallest number of significant digits of the numbers being multiplied or divided—in this case, 2.

27.456 is rounded to 27.

Scientific Notation

Problem 1
4; 4

Problem 2
0.000007

Problem 3
5.39×10^2

Precision and Significant Digits

When you make a measurement, the value you record depends on the precision of the measuring instrument. This precision is represented by the number of significant digits recorded in the measurement. When counting the number of significant digits, all digits are counted except zeros at the end of a number with no decimal point such as 2,050, and zeros at the beginning of a decimal such as 0.03020. When adding or subtracting numbers with different precision, round the answer to the smallest number of decimal places of any number in the sum or difference. When multiplying or dividing, the answer is rounded to the smallest number of significant digits of any number being multiplied or divided.

Example The lengths 5.28 and 5.2 are measured in meters. Find the sum of these lengths and record your answer using the correct number of significant digits.

Step 1 Find the sum.

5.28 m	2 digits after the decimal
+ 5.2 m	1 digit after the decimal
10.48 m	

Step 2 Round to one digit after the decimal because the least number of digits after the decimal of the numbers being added is 1.

The sum is 10.5 m.

Practice Problem How many significant digits are in the measurement 7,071,301 m? How many significant digits are in the measurement 0.003010 g?

Practice Problem Multiply 5.28 and 5.2 using the rule for multiplying and dividing. Record the answer using the correct number of significant digits.

Scientific Notation

Many times numbers used in science are very small or very large. Because these numbers are difficult to work with scientists use scientific notation. To write numbers in scientific notation, move the decimal point until only one non-zero digit remains on the left. Then count the number of places you moved the decimal point and use that number as a power of ten. For example, the average distance from the Sun to Mars is 227,800,000,000 m. In scientific notation, this distance is 2.278×10^{11} m. Because you moved the decimal point to the left, the number is a positive power of ten.

The mass of an electron is about 0.000 000 000 000 000 000 000 000 000 000 911 kg. Expressed in scientific notation, this mass is 9.11×10^{-31} kg. Because the decimal point was moved to the right, the number is a negative power of ten.

Example Earth is 149,600,000 km from the Sun. Express this in scientific notation.

Step 1 Move the decimal point until one non-zero digit remains on the left.
1.496 000 00

Step 2 Count the number of decimal places you have moved. In this case, eight.

Step 3 Show that number as a power of ten, 10^8.

Earth is 1.496×10^8 km from the Sun.

Practice Problem How many significant digits are in 149,600,000 km? How many significant digits are in 1.496×10^8 km?

Practice Problem Parts used in a high performance car must be measured to 7×10^{-6} m. Express this number as a decimal.

Practice Problem A CD is spinning at 539 revolutions per minute. Express this number in scientific notation.

Make and Use Graphs

Data in tables can be displayed in a graph—a visual representation of data. Common graph types include line graphs, bar graphs, and circle graphs.

Line Graph A line graph shows a relationship between two variables that change continuously. The independent variable is changed and is plotted on the x-axis. The dependent variable is observed, and is plotted on the y-axis.

Example Draw a line graph of the data below from a cyclist in a long-distance race.

Table 5 Bicycle Race Data

Time (h)	Distance (km)
0	0
1	8
2	16
3	24
4	32
5	40

Step 1 Determine the x-axis and y-axis variables. Time varies independently of distance and is plotted on the x-axis. Distance is dependent on time and is plotted on the y-axis.

Step 2 Determine the scale of each axis. The x-axis data ranges from 0 to 5. The y-axis data ranges from 0 to 50.

Step 3 Using graph paper, draw and label the axes. Include units in the labels.

Step 4 Draw a point at the intersection of the time value on the x-axis and corresponding distance value on the y-axis. Connect the points and label the graph with a title, as shown in **Figure 20.**

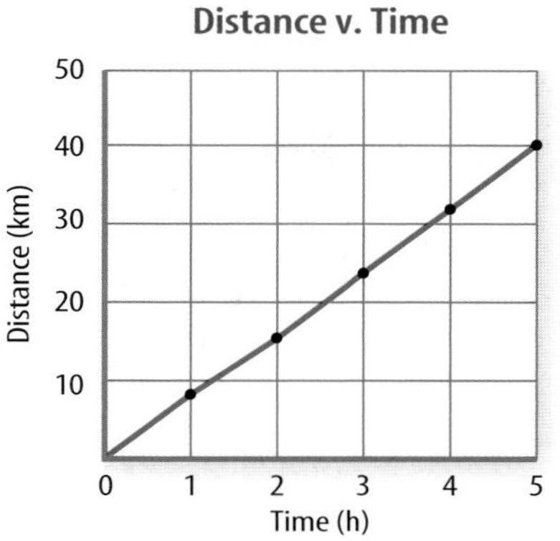

Figure 20 This line graph shows the relationship between distance and time during a bicycle ride.

Practice Problem A puppy's shoulder height is measured during the first year of her life. The following measurements were collected: (3 mo, 52 cm), (6 mo, 72 cm), (9 mo, 83 cm), (12 mo, 86 cm). Graph this data.

Find a Slope The slope of a straight line is the ratio of the vertical change, rise, to the horizontal change, run.

$$\text{Slope} = \frac{\text{vertical change (rise)}}{\text{horizontal change (run)}} = \frac{\text{change in } y}{\text{change in } x}$$

Example Find the slope of the graph in **Figure 20.**

Step 1 You know that the slope is the change in y divided by the change in x.

$$\text{Slope} = \frac{\text{change in } y}{\text{change in } x}$$

Step 2 Determine the data points you will be using. For a straight line, choose the two sets of points that are the farthest apart.

$$\text{Slope} = \frac{(40-0)\text{ km}}{(5-0)\text{ h}}$$

Step 3 Find the change in y and x.

$$\text{Slope} = \frac{40\text{ km}}{5\text{h}}$$

Step 4 Divide the change in y by the change in x.

$$\text{Slope} = \frac{8\text{ km}}{\text{h}}$$

The slope of the graph is 8 km/h.

Line Graph

x	y
3	52
6	72
9	83
12	86

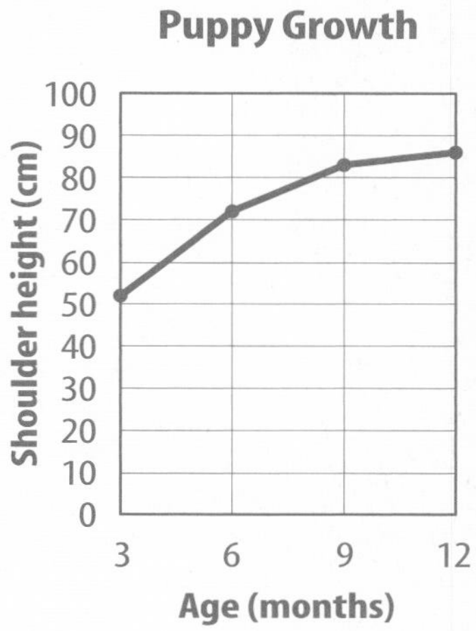

Math Skill Handbook

MATH SKILL HANDBOOK 875

Bar Graph To compare data that does not change continuously you might choose a bar graph. A bar graph uses bars to show the relationships between variables. The x-axis variable is divided into parts. The parts can be numbers such as years, or a category such as a type of animal. The y-axis is a number and increases continuously along the axis.

Example A recycling center collects 4.0 kg of aluminum on Monday, 1.0 kg on Wednesday, and 2.0 kg on Friday. Create a bar graph of this data.

Step 1 Select the x-axis and y-axis variables. The measured numbers (the masses of aluminum) should be placed on the y-axis. The variable divided into parts (collection days) is placed on the x-axis.

Step 2 Create a graph grid like you would for a line graph. Include labels and units.

Step 3 For each measured number, draw a vertical bar above the x-axis value up to the y-axis value. For the first data point, draw a vertical bar above Monday up to 4.0 kg.

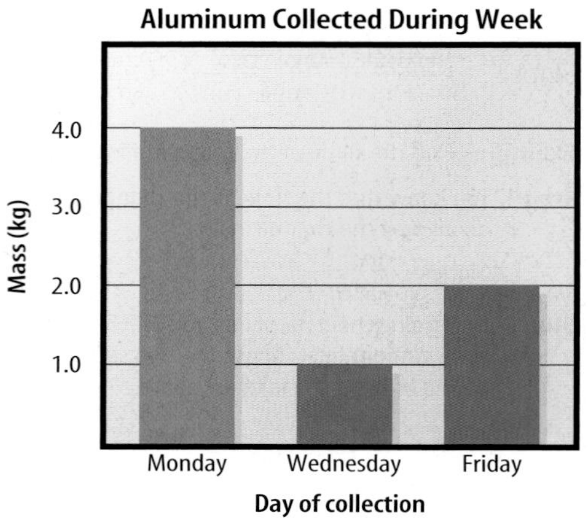

Practice Problem Draw a bar graph of the gases in air: 78% nitrogen, 21% oxygen, 1% other gases.

Circle Graph To display data as parts of a whole, you might use a circle graph. A circle graph is a circle divided into sections that represent the relative size of each piece of data. The entire circle represents 100%, half represents 50%, and so on.

Example Air is made up of 78% nitrogen, 21% oxygen, and 1% other gases. Display the composition of air in a circle graph.

Step 1 Multiply each percent by 360° and divide by 100 to find the angle of each section in the circle.

$$78\% \times \frac{360°}{100} = 280.8°$$

$$21\% \times \frac{360°}{100} = 75.6°$$

$$1\% \times \frac{360°}{100} = 3.6°$$

Step 2 Use a compass to draw a circle and to mark the center of the circle. Draw a straight line from the center to the edge of the circle.

Step 3 Use a protractor and the angles you calculated to divide the circle into parts. Place the center of the protractor over the center of the circle and line the base of the protractor over the straight line.

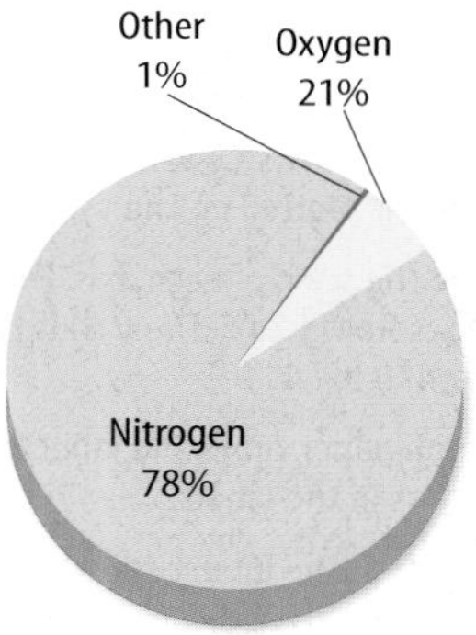

Practice Problem Draw a circle graph to represent the amount of aluminum collected during the week shown in the bar graph to the left.

Bar Graph

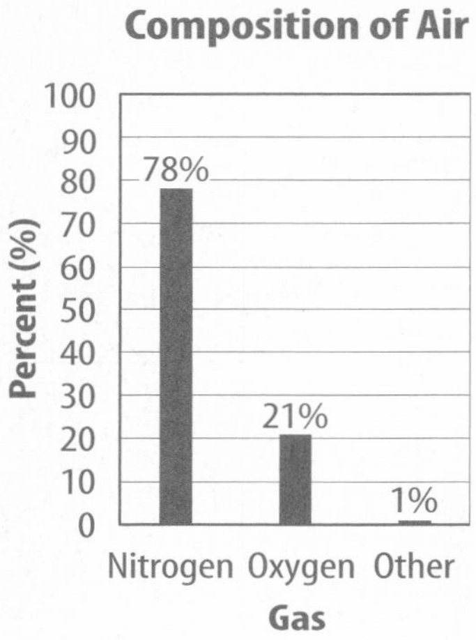

Circle Graph

The total amount of aluminum collected is:

$$4.0\text{ kg} + 1.0\text{ kg} + 2.0\text{ kg} = 7.0\text{ kg}$$

$$\frac{4.0\text{ kg}}{7.0\text{ kg}} = \frac{x}{360°};\ x = 206°$$

$$\frac{1.0\text{ kg}}{7.0\text{ kg}} = \frac{x}{360°};\ x = 51°$$

$$\frac{2.0\text{ kg}}{7.0\text{ kg}} = \frac{x}{360°};\ x = 103°$$

Monday is 57% of graph, Wednesday is 14% of graph, and Friday is 29% of graph.

Formulas

Chapter 1 The Nature of Science

density = mass/volume
Kelvin = °Celsius + 273
% Error = [(Accepted value − Experimental value)/Accepted value] × 100

Chapter 3 Motion, Acceleration, and Forces

average speed = total distance/total time
acceleration = (final velocity − initial velocity)/(final time − initial time)

Chapter 4 The Laws of Motion

acceleration = net force/mass
net force = mass × acceleration
gravitational force = mass × (acceleration due to gravity)
weight = mass × 9.8 m/s^2
momentum (p) = mass × velocity

Chapter 5 Energy

kinetic energy = $\frac{1}{2}$ mass × $(\text{velocity})^2$
gravitational potential energy (GPE) = mass × 9.8 m/s^2 × height
mechanical energy = gravitational potential energy + kinetic energy

Chapter 6 Work and Machines

work = force × distance
power = work/time
power = energy transferred/time
mechanical advantage = output force/input force
efficiency % = (output work/input work) × 100
Ideal mechanical advantage of a lever = length of input arm/length of output arm
Ideal mechanical advantage of a wheel and axle = radius of wheel/radius of axle
Ideal mechanical advantage of an inclined plane = length of slope/height of slope

Chapter 9 Heat and States of Matter

change in thermal energy = mass × change in temperature × specific heat
or
$Q = m \times (T_{final} - T_{initial}) \times C_p$
latent heat of melting = mass × heat of fusion
latent heat of vaporization = mass × heat of vaporization

Math Skill Handbook

MATH SKILL HANDBOOK 877

Chapter 10 Waves

wave speed = wavelength × frequency
frequency = number of wavelengths/time
wavelength = wave speed/frequency

Chapter 11 Sound and Light

index of refraction = speed of light in a vacuum/speed of light in a substance or $n = c/v$

Chapter 13 Electricity

electric current = voltage difference/resistance
electric power = current × voltage difference
electric energy = power × time

EXTRA Math Problems

For help and hints with these problems, visit Math Practice at gpescience.com.

Chapter 1 The Nature of Science

1. How many centimeters are in four meters?
2. How many deciliters are in 500 mL?
3. How many liters are in 2540 cm^3?
4. A young child has a mass of 40 kg. What is the mass of the child in grams?
5. Iron has a density of 7.9 g/cm^3. What is the mass in kg of an iron statue that has a volume of 5.4 L?
6. A 2-L bottle of soda has a volume of 2000 cm^3. What is the volume of the bottle in cubic meters?
7. A big summer movie has a running time of 96 minutes. What is the movie's running time in seconds?
8. The temperature in space is approximately 3 K. What is this temperature in degrees Celsius?
9. The x-axis of a certain graph is distance traveled in meters and the y-axis is time in seconds. Two points are plotted on this graph with coordinates (2, 43) and (5, 68). What is the elapsed time between the two points?
10. A circle graph has labeled segments of: 57%, 21%, 13%, and 6%. What percentage does the unlabeled segment have?

Chapter 2 Science, Technology, and Society

11. A car can travel 14 km on 1 L of gasoline. What percentage of its fuel efficiency does another car have if it travels 10 km on 1 L of gasoline?
12. What is the fuel efficiency of a car if it gets 45 percent of the fuel efficiency of another car that travels 15 km on 1 L of gasoline?
13. If new information technology causes a three percent reduction in the 40,000,000 HIV infections worldwide, how many people would be infected?
14. A circle graph shows the comparative effects of five new technologies. The circle graph has segments labeled 45 percent, 32 percent, 12 percent, and 3 percent. What is the correct label of the fifth segment?
15. Data from a new Web site takes 17 min to download. How many seconds does it take?
16. If a new internet connection reduces a download time of 17 min by 85 percent, how much time (in minutes and seconds) will it take now?
17. Because of a new health center in a town, the cases of influenza are 25 percent fewer. If the town usually has 300 cases per month, how many cases should you expect during the next month?
18. If a person can sell 10 computers per day and a new technology allows her to triple her sales, how many computers can she expect to sell the next day?
19. If it normally takes 45 min to travel to a nearby town using an older train, but a new technologically advanced train can make the trip in one-third of the time, how long will the trip take?
20. A technologically advanced engine runs at twice the efficiency of an older engine. If the older engine allows a car to travel at a fuel efficiency of 8 km/L, what is the fuel efficiency of the advanced engine?

Chapter 3 Motion, Acceleration, and Forces

21. John rides his bike 2.3 km to school. After school, he rides an additional 1.4 km to the mall in the opposite direction. What is his total distance traveled?
22. A squirrel runs 4.8 m across a lawn, stops, then runs 2.3 m back in the opposite direction. What is the squirrel's displacement from its starting point?

Answers

Chapter 1

1. 400 cm
2. 5 dL
3. 2.54 L
4. 40,000 g
5. 42.7 kg
6. 0.002 m^3
7. 5,760 s
8. −270°C
9. 25 s
10. 3%

Chapter 2

11. 71%
12. 6.8 km/L
13. 38,800,000
14. 8%
15. 1,020 s
16. 2 min, 33 s
17. 225
18. 30
19. 15 minutes
20. 16 km/L

Chapter 3

21. 3.7 km
22. 2.5 m

Answers

Chapter 3 cont.

23. 15 cm/s
24. 84.6 km/h
25. 100 km/h
26. 3 m/s
27. 0.5 m/s^2
28. −0.3 m/s^2
29. 3,000 N toward team B
30. 4 h
31. 7.92 h
32. 2.5 m/s^2
33. −5 m/s^2

Chapter 4

34. 467.5 N
35. 20 m/s^2
36. 19.6 N
37. 245 N
38. 140 N
39. 114 N
40. 215,000 kg·m/s
41. 30 m/s
42. 6,000 N
43. 5 m/s^2
44. 784 N
45. 36,000 kg·m/s

Chapter 5

46. 122.5 J
47. 12 kg
48. 80 J
49. 123,000 J
50. 2,350 J
51. 2,000 kg
52. 327,000 J

Extra Math Problems

23. An ant travels 75 cm in 5 s. What was the ant's speed?
24. It took you 6.5 h to drive 550 km. What was your speed?
25. A bus leaves at 9 A.M. with a group of tourists. They travel 350 km before they stop for lunch. Then they travel an additional 250 km until the end of their trip at 3 P.M. What was the average speed of the bus?
26. Halfway through a cross-country meet, a runner's speed is 4 m/s. In the last stretch, she increases her speed to 7 m/s. What is her change in speed?
27. It takes a car one minute to go from rest to 30 m/s. What is the acceleration of this car?
28. You are running at a speed of 10 km/h and hit a patch of mud. Two seconds later your speed is 8 km/h. What is your acceleration in units of m/s^2?
29. During a tug-of-war, Team A is applying a force of 5000 N while Team B is applying a force of 8000 N. What is the net force applied to the rope?
30. You are in a car traveling an average speed of 60 km/h. The total trip is 240 km. How long does the trip take?
31. You are riding in a train that is traveling at a speed of 120 km/h. How long will it take to travel 950 km?
32. A car goes from rest to a speed of 90 km/h in 10 s. What is the car's acceleration in m/s^2?
33. A cart rolling at a speed of 10 m/s comes to a stop in 2 s. What is the cart's acceleration?

Chapter 4 The Laws of Motion

34. A 85-kg mass has an acceleration of 5.5 m/s^2. What is the net force applied?
35. A 3200-N force is applied to a 160-kg mass. What is the acceleration of the mass?
36. A 2-kg object is dropped from a height of 1000 m. What is the force of air resistance on the object when it reaches terminal velocity?
37. How much force is needed to lift a 25-kg mass?
38. If you are pushing on a box with a force of 20 N and there is a force of 7 N on the box due to sliding friction, what is the net force on the box?
39. The acceleration due to gravity on the moon is about 1.6 m/s^2. If you weigh 539 N on Earth, how much would you weigh on the moon?
40. If a 5000-kg mass is moving at a speed of 43 m/s, what is its momentum?
41. How fast must a 50-kg mass travel to have a momentum of 1500 kg m/s?
42. What is the net force on a 4000-kg car that doubles its speed from 15 m/s to 30 m/s over 10 seconds?
43. A book with a mass of 1 kg is sliding on a table. If the frictional force on the book is 5 N, calculate the book's acceleration. Is it speeding up or slowing down?
44. What is the weight of a person with a mass of 80 kg?
45. A car with a mass of 1,200 kg has a speed of 30 m/s. What is the car's momentum?

Chapter 5 Energy

46. What is the kinetic energy of a 5-kg object moving at 7 m/s?
47. An object has kinetic energy of 600 J and a speed of 10 m/s. What is its mass?
48. If you throw a 0.4-kg ball at a speed of 20 m/s, what is the ball's kinetic energy?
49. A rollercoaster car moving around a high turn has 100,000 J of GPE and 23,000 J of KE. What is its mechanical energy?
50. If you have a mass of 80 kg and you are standing on a platform 3 m above the ground, what is your gravitational potential energy?
51. A car is traveling at 30 m/s with a kinetic energy of 900 kJ. What is its mass?
52. At top of a hill, a rollercoaster has 67,500 J of kinetic energy and 290,000 J of potential energy. Gradually the roller coaster comes to a stop due to friction. If the roller coaster has 30,000 J of potential when it stops, how much heat energy is generated by friction from the top of the hill until it stops?

53. A 2-kg book is moved from a shelf that is 2 m off the ground to a shelf that is 1.5 m off the ground. What is its change in GPE?

54. A system has a total mechanical energy of 350 J and kinetic energy of 220 J. What is its potential energy?

55. An object held in the air has a GPE of 470 J. The object then is dropped. Halfway down, what is the object's kinetic energy?

56. A car with a mass of 900 kg is traveling at a speed of 25 m/s. What is the kinetic energy of the car in joules?

57. What is the gravitational potential energy of a diver with a mass of 60 kg who is 10 m above the water?

58. If your weight is 500 N, and you are standing on a floor that is 20 m above the ground, what is your gravitational potential energy?

Chapter 6 Work and Machines

59. When moving a couch, you exert a force of 400 N and push it 4 m. How much work have you done?

60. How much work is needed to lift a 50-kg weight to a shelf 3 m above the floor?

61. By applying a force of 50 N, a pulley system can lift a box with a mass of 20 kg. What is the mechanical advantage of the pulley system?

62. How much energy do you save per hour if you replace a 60-watt lightbulb with a 55-watt lightbulb?

63. Suppose you supply energy to a machine at a rate of 700 W and that the machine converts 560 J into heat every second. At what rate does the machine do work?

64. You exert a force of 200 N on a machine over a distance of 0.3 m. If the machine moves an object a distance of 0.5 m, how much force does the machine exert on the object? Assume friction can be ignored.

65. What is the efficiency of a machine if you do work on the machine at a rate of 1200 W and the machine does work at a rate of 300 W?

66. What is the IMA of a seesaw with a 1.6-m effort arm and a 1.2-m resistance arm?

67. What is the IMA of a wheel with a radius of 0.35 m and an axle radius of 0.04 m?

68. An inclined plane has an IMA of 1.5 and a height of 2.0 m. How long is this inclined plane?

69. What power is used by a machine to perform 800 J of work in 25 s?

70. A person pushes a box up a ramp that is 3 m long, and 1 m high. If the box has a mass of 20 kg, and the person pushes with a force of 80 N, what is the efficiency of the ramp?

71. A first class lever has a mechanical advantage of 5. How large would a force need to be to lift a rock with a mass of 100 kg?

Chapter 7 The Earth-Moon-Sun System

72. Earth's diameter is 12,714 km from pole to pole and 12,756 km at the equator. How much less is Earth's diameter from pole to pole than that at the equator?

73. Earth's circumference is 40,075 km at the equator and 40,008 km through the two poles. How much greater is Earth's circumference around the equator?

74. Earth's average density is 5.52 g/cm^3. If the Moon's average density is 3.31 g/cm^3, what percentage of Earth's density is the Moon's density?

75. If a day on Earth lasts 23 h and 56 min, how many minutes are in one day?

76. Earth is one AU (149,600,000 km) from the Sun. If Jupiter is 5.2 AUs from the Sun, how many kilometers is Jupiter from the Sun?

77. If Earth rotates 15° each hour, how many degrees will it rotate in three hours?

78. Earth is tilted 23.5°. If the Sun is 50° above the southern horizon when it is directly over the equator, how high in the sky will the Sun be on the first day of summer?

79. If the Sun has a diameter of 1,392,000 km and is about 400 times larger than the Moon, what is the approximate diameter of the Moon?

Answers

Chapter 5 cont.

53. 9.8 J
54. 130 J
55. 235 J
56. 281,000 J
57. 5,880 J
58. 10,000 J

Chapter 6

59. 1,600 J
60. 120 J
61. 3.92
62. 18,000 J
63. 140 W
64. 1,120 N
65. 25%
66. 1.33
67. 8.75
68. 3.0 m
69. 32 W
70. 81.7%
71. 196 N

Chapter 7

72. 42 km
73. 67 km
74. 60%
75. 1,436 min
76. 777,920,000 km
77. 45°
78. 73.5°
79. 3,480 km

Answers

Chapter 7 cont.

80. 12.4 synodic months
81. 208 times

Chapter 8

82. $\frac{3}{4}$
83. $\frac{1}{4}$
84. 152 kPa
85. 0.608 kPa
86. 0.002 kPa
87. 20%
88. 4
89. 1408
90. 15.1%
91. 1,429,500,000 km
92. 47.5 times
93. 4.2 times

Chapter 9

94. 20,920 J
95. 2 kg
96. 13,280 J
97. 418,400 J
98. 6 kg
99. 343 K
100. 710 J/(kg K)
101. 198 K
102. 1,300 J
103. 20,900 J
104. 397 J/(kg K)

Chapter 10

105. 0.04 m

80. If there are 29.5 days in one synodic month, how many synodic months are there in one year of 365 days?

81. The South Pole-Aitken Basin on the Moon is 12 km deep and 2,500 km wide. How many times wider is the basin than it is deep?

Chapter 8 The Solar System

82. What fraction of a complete orbit (360°) would a planet move through if its H.L. changes from 32° to 302°?

83. What fraction of a complete orbit (360°) would a planet move through if its H.L. changes from 152° to 242°?

84. Earth's atmospheric pressure is 101.3 kPa. What is atmospheric pressure on the surface of Titan if it is 1.5 times that of Earth?

85. What is the atmospheric pressure on the surface of Mars if it is 0.6 percent of Earth's?

86. If the atmospheric pressure of Triton's atmosphere is 0.002 percent of Earth's, what is the atmospheric pressure on the surface of Triton?

87. If a planet has an H.L. of 73°, what percentage of the total orbit (360°) would this represent?

88. If the diameters of Earth and Uranus are 12,756 km and 51,118 km respectively, approximately how many Earths could fit across Uranus's diameter?

89. The volume of sphere is $4/3(\pi r^3)$. If the radius of Earth is 6,378 km and the radius of Jupiter is 71,492, how many Earths would fit inside Jupiter?

90. The volume of sphere is $4/3(\pi r^3)$. If the radius of Mars is 3,394 km and the radius of Earth is 6,378 km, what percentage of Earth's volume is Mars's volume?

91. On average, Earth is 150 million km (1 AU) from the Sun. If Saturn is 9.53 AU from the Sun, what is the distance from the Sun to Saturn?

92. If Venus takes 0.62 years to orbit the Sun and Saturn takes 29.42 years to orbit the Sun, how many times will Venus orbit the Sun during each orbit of Saturn?

93. If Earth is tilted 23.5° and Uranus is tilted 97.9°, how many times greater is the axial tilt of Uranus than that of Earth?

Chapter 9 Heat and States of Matter

94. Water has a specific heat of 4184 J/(kg K). How much energy is needed to increase the temperature of a kilogram of water 5°C?

95. The temperature of a block of iron, which has a specific heat of 450 J/(kg K), increases by 3 K when 2700 J of energy are added to it. What is the mass of this block of iron?

96. How much energy is needed to heat 1 kg of sand, which has a specific heat of 664 J/(kg K), from 30°C to 50°C?

97. 1 kg of water (specific heat = 4184 J/(kg K)) is heated from freezing (0°C) to boiling (100°C). What is the change in thermal energy?

98. A concrete statue (specific heat = 600 J/(kg K)) sits in sunlight and warms up to 40°C. Overnight, it cools to 15°C and loses 90,000 J of thermal energy. What is its mass?

99. A glass of water has temperature of 70°C. What is its temperature in K?

100. A substance with a mass of 10 kg loses 106.5 kJ of heat when its temperature drops 15°C. What is this substance's specific heat?

101. Air is cooled from room temperature (25°C) to 100 K. What is the temperature change in K?

102. To remove 800 J of heat from a refrigerator, the compressor in the refrigerator does 500 J of work. How much heat is released into the surrounding room?

103. How much heat is needed to raise the temperature of 100 g of water by 50 K, if the specific heat of water is 4,184 J/kg K?

104. A sample of an unknown metal has a mass of 0.5 kg. Adding 1,985 J of heat to the metal raises its temperature by 10 K. What is the specific heat of the metal?

Chapter 10 Waves

105. What is the wavelength of a wave with a frequency of 0.4 kHz traveling at 16 m/s?

106. Two waves are traveling in the same medium with a speed of 340 m/s. What is the difference in frequency of the waves if the one has a wavelength of 5 m and the other has a wavelength of 0.2 m?

107. Transverse wave A has an amplitude of 7 cm. This wave constructively interferes with wave B. While the two waves overlap, the amplitude of the resulting wave is 10 cm. What is the amplitude of wave B?

108. What is the wavelength of a wave with a frequency of 5 Hz traveling at 15 m/s?

109. What is the velocity of a wave that has a wavelength of 6 m and a frequency of 3 Hz?

110. A ray of light hits a mirror at an angle of 35° to the normal. What is the angle of the reflected ray to the normal?

111. A wave has a wavelength of 250 cm and a frequency of 4 Hz. What is its speed?

112. A wave has a frequency of 5.6 MHz. What is the frequency of this wave in Hz?

113. A light ray strikes a mirror and is reflected. The angle between the incident and reflected rays is 86°. What is the angle of the incident ray to the normal?

114. What is the frequency of a wave with a wavelength of 7 m traveling at 21 m/s?

Chapter 11 Sound and Light

115. A sound wave with a frequency of 440 Hz travels in steel with a speed of 5200 m/s. What is the wavelength of the sound wave?

116. A wave traveling in water has a wavelength of a 750 m and a frequency of 2 Hz. How fast is this wave moving?

117. At 0°C sound travels through air with a speed of about 331 m/s and through aluminum with a speed of 4877 m/s. How many times longer is the wavelength of a sound wave in aluminum compared to the wavelength of a sound wave in air if both waves have the same frequency?

118. The speed of sound in air at 0°C is 331 m/s, and at 20°C is 344 m/s. What is the percentage change in the speed of sound at 20°C compared to 0°C?

119. The wreck of the *Titanic* is at a depth of about 3800 m. A sonar unit on a ship above the *Titanic* emits a sound wave that travels at a speed of 1500 m/s. How long does it take a sound wave reflected from the *Titanic* to return to the ocean surface?

120. A sonar unit on a ship emits a sound wave. The echo from the ocean floor is detected two seconds later. If the speed of sound in water is 1500 m/s, how deep is the ocean beneath the ship?

121. A tsunami travels across the ocean at a speed of 500 km/h. If the distance between the wave crests is 200 km, what is the frequency of the wave?

122. A light ray strikes a plane mirror. The angle between the light ray and the surface of the mirror is 25°. What angle does the reflected ray make with the normal?

123. If the index of refraction of the mineral rock salt is 1.52, and the speed of light in a vacuum is 300,000 km/s, what is the speed of light in rock salt?

124. In the human eye, there are about 7,000,000 cone cells distributed over an area of 5 cm^2. If cone cells are evenly distributed over this region, how many cone cells are distributed over an area of 2 cm^2? Express your answer in scientific notation.

125. The magnification of a mirror or lens equals the image size divided by the object size. If a plant cell with a diameter of 0.0035 mm is magnified so that the diameter of the image is 0.028 cm, what is the magnification?

126. Light enters the human eye through the pupil. In the dark, the pupil is dilated and has a diameter of about 1 cm. The Keck telescope has a mirror with a diameter of 10 m. If both the pupil and the Keck mirror are circles, what is the ratio of the area of the Keck telescope mirror to the area of a dilated human pupil?

Answers

Chapter 10 cont.

106. 1,632 Hz
107. 3 cm
108. 3 m
109. 18 m/s
110. 35°
111. 1 m/s
112. 5,600,000 Hz
113. 43°
114. 3 Hz

Chapter 11

115. 11.8 m
116. 150 m/s
117. 14.7
118. 3.9%
119. 5.1 s
120. 1,500 m
121. 2.5 wavelengths/h
122. 65°
123. 197,000 km/s
124. 2.8×10^6
125. 80×
126. 1,000,000:1

Answers

Chapter 11 cont.

127. 1.2 cm

Chapter 12

128. 13 min 53 sec
129. 3000 km
130. 2946 km
131. 5 min 36 s; 6 min 32 s
132. 13 min 1 s
133. 60%
134. 8.7×10^8 m^3
135. 2600 km
136. 5.6 times faster
137. $V_{Earth} = 1.087 \times 10^{12}$ km^3; $V_{core} = 1.774 \times 10^{11}$ km^3; 16.3%

Chapter 13

138. 5.6 V
139. 3 A
140. 2 Ω
141. 360 W
142. 5.8 A
143. 220 V
144. 330 kWh
145. 8 h
146. $0.32
147. 0.75 h
148. 240 Ω
149. 0.833 A
150. 906 W
151. 1 kWh : 0.30 kWh

Extra Math Problems

127. A light source is placed a distance of 1.2 m from a concave mirror on the optical axis. The reflected light rays are parallel and form a light beam. What is the focal length of the mirror?

Chapter 12 Earth's Internal Processes

128. How long after an earthquake will a seismograph 3,000 km away from the epicenter record S-waves that travel at 3.6 km/s?

129. If it takes 48 min and 20 s for P-waves traveling at 6.0 km/s to reach and be recorded by a seismograph, how far away is the epicenter?

130. If S-waves lag behind P-waves by 1 min 52 s for every 1000 km of distance from the earthquake epicenter, how far away from the earthquake epicenter is a seismograph that measures a time-lag of 5 min 30 s between the arrivals of P-waves and S-waves.?

131. With a P-wave-S-wave lag time of 1 min 52 sec, how much difference between the arrival times of P-waves and S-waves would be measured at 3,000 km? At 3,500 km?

132. If surface waves travel at 3.2 km/s, when would you expect them to arrive at a seismograph that is 2,500 km distant from the earthquake epicenter?

133. If S-waves travel at 3.6 km/s and P-waves travel at 6.0 km/s through Earth's crust, what percentage of the speed of P-waves would you expect S-waves to travel at other depths inside Earth?

134. The volume of a cone is $\frac{1}{3}\pi r^2 h$. If Paricutín is 424 m high and has a base 2.8 km across, what is the volume of the cinder cone?

135. If two plates diverge at a rate of 1.3 cm/year, how much farther apart in kilometers will the two plates be after 200 million years?

136. How many times faster are plates moving at 7.3 cm/year than are plates moving at 1.3 cm/year?

137. The volume of a sphere is $4/3(\pi r^3)$. The radius of Earth is 6,378 km, and the radius of its core (including both outer and inner cores) is 3,486 km. What are the volumes of both? What percentage of the total volume of Earth is its core?

Chapter 13 Electricity

138. A circuit has a resistance of 4 Ω. What voltage difference will cause a current of 1.4 A to flow in the circuit?

139. How many amperes of current will flow in a circuit if the voltage difference is 9 V and the resistance in the circuit is 3 Ω?

140. If a voltage difference of 3 V causes a 1.5 A current to flow in a circuit, what is the resistance in the circuit?

141. The current in an appliance is 3 A and the voltage difference is 120 V. How much power is being supplied to the appliance?

142. What is the current into a microwave oven that requires 700 W of power if the voltage difference is 120 V?

143. What is the voltage difference in a circuit that uses 2420 W of power if 11 A of current flows into the circuit?

144. How much energy is used when a 110 kW appliance is used for 3 hours?

145. A television has a power rating of 210 W. If the television uses 1.68 kWh of energy, for how long has the television been on?

146. How much does it cost to light six 100-W lightbulbs for six hours if the price of electrical energy is $0.09/kWh?

147. An electric clothes dryer uses 4 kW of electric power. How long did it take to dry a load of clothes if electric power costs $0.09/kWh, and the cost of using the dryer was $0.27?

148. What is the resistance of a lightbulb that draws 0.5 amp of current when plugged into a 120-V outlet?

149. How much current flows through a 100-W lightbulb that is plugged into a 120-V outlet?

150. Eight amps of current flow through a hair dryer connected to a 120-V outlet. How much electrical power does the hair dryer use?

151. Compare the electrical energy that is used by a 100-W lightbulb that burns for 10 h, and a 1,200-W hair dryer that is used for 15 min.

Extra Math Problems

Chapter 14 Magnetism

152. How many turns are in the secondary coil of a step-down transformer that reduces a voltage from 900 V to 300 V and has 15 turns in the primary coil?

153. A step-down transformer reduces voltage from 2400 V to 120 V. What is the ratio of the number of turns in the primary coil to the number of turns in the secondary coil of the transformer?

154. The current produced by an AC generator switches direction twice for each revolution of the coil. How many times does a 110-Hz alternating current switch direction each second?

155. What is the output voltage from a step-down transformer with 200 turns in the primary coil and 100 turns in the secondary coil if the input voltage was 750 V?

156. What is the output voltage from a step-up transformer with 25 turns in the primary coil and 75 turns in the secondary coil if the input voltage was 120 V?

157. How many turns are in the primary coil of a step-down transformer that reduces a voltage from 400 V to 100 V and has 80 turns in the secondary coil?

158. How many turns are in the secondary coil of a step-up transformer that increases voltage from 30 V to 150 V and has seven turns in the primary coil?

159. The coil of a 60-Hz generator makes 60 revolutions each second. How many revolutions does the coil make in five minutes?

160. If a generator coil makes 6000 revolutions in two minutes, how many revolutions does it make each second?

Chapter 15 Electromagnetic Radiation

161. Express the number 20,000 in scientific notation.

162. An electromagnetic wave has a wavelength of 0.054 m. What is the wavelength in scientific notation?

163. Earth is about 4,500,000,000 years old. Express this number in scientific notation.

164. The speed of electromagnetic waves in air is 300,000 km/s. What is the frequency of electromagnetic waves that have a wavelength of 5×10^{-3} km?

165. The speed of radio waves in water Is about 2.26×10^5 km/s. What is the frequency of radio waves that have a wavelength of 3.0 km?

166. Radio waves with a frequency of 125,000 Hz have a wavelength of 1.84 km when traveling in ice. What is the speed of the radio waves in ice?

167. Some infrared waves have a frequency of 10,000,000,000,000 Hz. Express this frequency in scientific notation.

168. An infrared wave has a frequency of 1×10^{13} Hz and a wavelength of 3×10^{-5} m. Express this wavelength as a decimal number.

169. An AM radio station broadcasts at a frequency of 620 kHz. Express this frequency in Hz using scientific notation.

170. An FM radio station broadcasts at a frequency of 101 MHz. Express this frequency in Hz using scientific notation.

Chapter 16 Energy Sources

171. A gallon of gasoline contains about 2800 g of gasoline. If burning one gram of gasoline releases about 48 kJ of energy, how much energy is released when a gallon of gasoline is burned? (1 kJ = 1000 J)

172. An automobile engine converts the energy released by burning gasoline into mechanical energy with an efficiency of about 25%. If burning 1 kg of gasoline releases about 48,000 kJ of energy, how much mechanical energy is produced by the engine when 1 kg of gasoline is burned?

173. You heat a cup of water in a 750-W microwave oven for 40 s, and warm the water by 20°C. If it takes about 20 kJ of energy to raise the temperature of a cup of water by 20°C, what is the efficiency of the microwave oven?

Answers

Chapter 14

152. 5
153. 20:1
154. 220
155. 375 V
156. 360 V
157. 320
158. 35
159. 18,000
160. 50

Chapter 15

161. 2×10^4
162. 5.4×10^{-2}
163. 4.5×10^9
164. 6×10^7 Hz
165. 7.5×10^{-4} Hz
166. 2.30×10^5 km/s
167. 1×10^{13} Hz
168. 0.00003 m
169. 6.2×10^5 Hz
170. 1.01×10^8 Hz

Chapter 16

171. 134,400 kJ
172. 12,000 kJ
173. 67%

Answers

Chapter 16 cont.

174. 5 m^2
175. 68%
176. 3
177. 4,000 kg
178. 32
179. 10.8%
180. 5.7

Chapter 17

181. 3 times
182. 1.6 cm per day
183. 10.13 kPa
184. 78.8%
185. 3°
186. 202.6 kPa
187. 0.3%
188. 12 minutes
189. One every 25,000 years
190. nitrogen = 280.8°; oxygen = 75.6°; argon = 3.6°.

Chapter 18

191. 675 g

Extra Math Problems

174. On average, solar energy strikes Earth's surface with an intensity of about 200 W/m^2. If solar cells are 10% efficient, how large an area would have to be covered by solar cells to generate enough electrical power to light a 100-W lightbulb?

175. What is the overall efficiency of a hydroelectric plant if the process of falling water turning a turbine is 80% efficient, the turbine spinning an electric generator is 95% efficient, and the transmission through power lines is 90% efficient?

176. When a certain $^{235}_{92}U$ nucleus is struck by a neutron, it forms the two nuclei $^{91}_{36}Kr$ and $^{142}_{56}Ba$. How many neutrons are emitted when this occurs?

177. A nuclear reactor contains 100,000 kg of enriched uranium. About 4% of the enriched uranium is the isotope uranium-235. What is the mass of uranium-235 in the reactor core?

178. Suppose the number of uranium-235 nuclei that are split doubles at each stage of a chain reaction. If the chain reaction starts with one nucleus split in the first stage, how many nuclei will have been split after six stages?

179. From 1970 to 1995 the carbon dioxide concentration in Earth's atmosphere increased from about 325 parts per million to about 360 parts per million. What was the percentage change in the concentration of carbon dioxide?

180. About 85% of the energy used in the U.S. comes from fossil fuels. How many times greater is the amount of energy used from fossil fuel than the amount used from all other energy sources?

Chapter 17 Weather and Climate

181. If a snowy surface reflects 90 percent of the solar radiation that strikes it and bare soil reflects 30 percent, how many times more solar radiation is reflected from a snowy surface than from bare soil?

182. The amount of rainfall over five days is 4 cm, 2 cm, 0.4 cm, 0.2 cm, and 1.3 cm. What is the average rainfall per day?

183. Air pressure at Earth's surface is 101.3 kPa. What is the air pressure at 16 km if it is $\frac{1}{10}$ the air pressure at Earth's surface?

184. Much of northern Florida receives 1,300 mm of rain on average per year and the southern part of the Everglades receives 1,650 mm of rain on average per year. What percentage is the rainfall in northern Florida of the rainfall in the southern part of the Everglades?

185. If the tilt of Earth's axis has varied from 21.5° to 24.5° over time, what is the value of the range of Earth's axial tilt?

186. Air pressure at Earth's surface is 101.3 kPa. If air pressure in an average car tire is equal to two atmospheres, what is the pressure in an average car tire?

187. Most of Earth's atmosphere is within 30 km of Earth's surface. If Earth's atmosphere extends about 10,000 km above Earth's surface, what percentage of the atmosphere's depth contains most of Earth's atmosphere?

188. If a tornado travels at 50 km/h and cuts a path of destruction 10 km long, how many minutes did it take to do this?

189. If there have been eight glacial periods during the past 200,000 years, what is the rate at which these have occurred?

190. The three main gases in Earth's atmosphere are nitrogen—78 percent, oxygen—21 percent, and argon and trace gases—1 percent. If a circle graph were drawn to represent these data, how many degrees would represent each section?

Chapter 18 Classification of Matter

191. Two solutions, one with a mass of 450 g and the other with a mass of 350 g, are mixed. A chemical reaction occurs and 125 g of solid crystals are produced that settle on the bottom of the container. What is the mass of the remaining solution?

192. Carbon reacts with oxygen to form carbon dioxide according to the following equation: $C + O_2 \rightarrow CO_2$. When 120 g of carbon reacts with oxygen, 440 g of carbon dioxide are formed. How much oxygen reacted with the carbon?

193. Salt water is distilled by boiling it and condensing the vapor. After distillation, 1,164 g of water have been collected and 12 g of salt are left behind in the original container. What was the original mass of the salt water?

194. Calcium carbonate, $CaCO_3$, decomposes according to the reaction: $CaCO_3 \rightarrow CaO + CO_2$. When 250 g of $CaCO_3$ decompose completely, the mass of CaO is 56% of the mass of the products of this reaction. What is the mass of CO_2 produced?

195. Water breaks down into hydrogen gas and oxygen gas according to the reaction: $2H_2O \rightarrow 2H_2 + O_2$. In this reaction the mass of oxygen produced is eight times greater than the mass of hydrogen produced. If 36 g of water form hydrogen and oxygen gas, what is the mass of hydrogen gas produced?

196. The size of particles in a solution is about 1 nm (1 nm = 0.000000001 m). Write 0.000000001 m in scientific notation.

197. A chemical reaction produces two new substances, one with a mass of 34 g and the other with a mass of 39 g. What was the total mass of the reactants?

198. The human body is about 65% oxygen. If a person has a mass of 75.0 kg, what is the mass of oxygen in their body?

199. A 112-g serving of ice cream contains 19 g of fat. What percentage of the serving is fat?

200. The mass of the products produced by a chemical reaction is measured. The reaction is repeated five times, with the same mass of reactants used each time. The measured product masses are 50.17 g, 50.12 g, 50.17 g, 50.10 g, and 50. 14 g. What is the average of these measurements?

Chapter 19 Properties of Atoms and the Periodic Table

201. Boron has a mass number of 11 and an atomic number of 5. How many neutrons are in a boron atom?

202. A magnesium atom has 12 protons and 12 neutrons. What is its mass number?

203. Iodine-127 has a mass number of 127 and 74 neutrons. What percentage of the particles in an iodine-127 nucleus are protons?

204. How many neutrons are in an atom of phosphorus-31?

205. What is the ratio of neutrons to protons in the isotope radium-234?

206. About 80% of all magnesium atoms are magnesium-24, about 10% are magnesium-25, and about 10% are magnesium-26. What is the average atomic mass of magnesium?

207. The half-life of the radioactive isotope rubidium-87 is 48,800,000,000 years. Express this half-life in scientific notation.

208. The radioactive isotope nickel-63 has a half-life of 100 years. How much of a 10.0-g sample of nickel-63 is left after 300 years?

209. A sample of the radioactive isotope cobalt-62 is prepared. The sample has a mass of 1.00 g. After three minutes, the mass of cobalt-62 remaining is 0.25 g. What is the half-life of cobalt-62?

210. A neutral phosphorus atom has 15 electrons. How many electrons are in the third energy level?

Chapter 20 Earth Materials

211. If oxygen makes up 46.6 percent of the mass of Earth's crust and silicon makes up 27.7 percent, what is the total percent of the crust's mass for oxygen and silicon?

212. If oxygen and silicon make up 74.3 percent of the mass of Earth's crust, what percent of this percentage is silicon's percentage?

213. How many total atoms of aluminum and oxygen combined make up one molecule of corundum (Al_2O_3)?

Answers

Chapter 18 cont.

192. 320 g
193. 1,176 g
194. 110 g
195. 4 g
196. 1×10^{-9}
197. 73 g
198. 48.8 g
199. 17%
200. 50.14 g

Chapter 19

201. 6
202. 24
203. 42%
204. 16
205. 1.66 or 73:44
206. 24.3 amu
207. 4.88×10^{10}
208. 1.25 g
209. 1.5 minutes
210. 5

Chapter 20

211. 74.3%
212. 37.3%
213. 5

EXTRA MATH PROBLEMS 887

Answers

Chapter 20 cont.

214. 1:4
215. 31 times
216. 4
217. 8
218. 85%
219. 96 cm^2
220. 8:1

Chapter 21

221. 51.2 years
222. 13.3%
223. 39.2 years
224. 1.8×10^7 kg/day
225. 1.2×10^7 kg/day
226. 4.5 years
227. 8.88×10^{14} m^3
228. 3.98×10^{14} m^3
229. 1/8
230. 48,000 years

Chapter 22

231. $(NH_4)_2SO_4$
232. $-2 + 2 = 0$
233. Fe_2O_3
234. 36
235. +5

214. What is the ratio of silicon to oxygen in a molecule of olivine ($(Mg, Fe)_2SiO_4$)?

215. Other than the common eight elements that make up Earth's crust, all other elements make up only 1.5 percent. If oxygen makes up 46.6 percent of Earth's crust, how many times greater is the amount of oxygen in Earth's crust than those other elements.

216. The Mohs scale of hardness consists of ten categories, each associated with a mineral standard. How many categories are between hardness 7–quartz and hardness 2–gypsum?

217. The volume of sphere is $4/3\ \pi r^3$. If a particle of gravel has a radius of 2 mm and a sand grain has a radius of 1 mm, how much bigger is the volume of the gravel?

218. If a sedimentary rock has a porosity of 15 percent, how much volume do the mineral grains and cement take up?

219. If you have a halite cube that measures 4 cm on each side, what is the total surface area of the cube?

220. What is the ratio of oxygen atoms to potassium atoms in one molecule of K-feldspar, ($KAlSiO_8$)?

Chapter 21 Earth's Changing Surface

221. If soil erosion averages 2.5 cm per year and the average soil profile is 3.2 m thick with 40 percent of topsoil, how long will it take for the topsoil to erode away?

222. The average soil profile in your area is 2.1 m thick. Topsoil erodes at 2.0 cm per year. What percent of the soil profile is topsoil if it erodes in 14 years?

223. Soil erosion in your area averages 3.5 cm per year. The average soil profile is 3.7 m thick and 35 percent of that is topsoil. Soil replacement through weathering is 0.2 cm per year. How long will it take for the topsoil to erode?

224. Observations taken at the mouth of a stream include a flow rate of 120 m^3/s and a suspended sediment load of 1.8 kg/m^3. How many kilograms of sediment potentially could drop out of this stream each day?

225. Observations taken at the mouth of a stream include a flow rate of 85 m^3/s and a suspended sediment load of 1.6 kg/m^3. How many kilograms of sediment potentially could drop out of this stream each day?

226. Suppose a community with a human population of 800 has a water consumption rate of 900 L per person per day. This community relies on an aquifer that is thought to contain 1.2 billion L of water. Assuming no change in average water consumption or significant recharge of the aquifer, how many years will this water supply last?

227. An aquifer is 400 km in length, 185 km in width, and 80 km thick. Sampling of the aquifer material shows it has an average porosity of 15 percent. What is the volume of porosity?

228. An aquifer with dimensions of 350 km in length, 175 km in width, and 65 km thick. Sampling of the aquifer material shows it has an average porosity of 10 percent. What is the volume of porosity?

229. If three half-lives for an isotope have passed, what fraction of the original isotope would be present in the igneous rock?

230. If the half-life of an isotope is 12,000 years and the amount of the isotope present in the rock is only $\frac{1}{16}$ of the original amount present, how old is the igneous rock containing the isotope?

Chapter 22 Chemical Bonds

231. What is the formula of the compound formed when ammonium ions, NH_4^+, and phosphate ions, PO_4^{3-}, combine?

232. Show that the sum of positive and negative charges in a unit of calcium chloride ($CaCl_2$) equals zero.

233. What is the formula for iron(III) oxide?

234. How many hydrogen atoms are in three molecules of ammonium phosphate, $(NH_4)_3PO_4$?

235. The overall charge on the polyatomic phosphate ion, PO_4^{3-}, is 3−. What is the oxidation number of phosphorus in the phosphate ion?

236. The overall charge on the polyatomic dichromate ion, $Cr_2O_7^{2-}$, is 2−. What is the oxidation number of chromium in this polyatomic ion?

237. What is the formula for lead(IV) oxide?

238. What is the formula for potassium chlorate?

239. What is the formula for carbon tetrachloride?

240. What percentage of the mass of a sulfuric acid molecule, H_2SO_4, is sulfur?

Chapter 23 Chemical Reactions

241. Lithium reacts with oxygen to form lithium oxide according to the equation: $4Li + O_2 \rightarrow 2Li_2O$. If 27.8 g of Li react completely with 32.0 g of O_2, how many grams of Li_2O are formed?

242. What coefficients balance the following equation: $\_Zn(OH)_2 + \_H_3PO_4 \rightarrow \_Zn_3(PO_4)_2 + \_H_2O$?

243. Aluminum hydroxide, $Al(OH)_3$, decomposes to form aluminum oxide, Al_2O_3, and water according to the reaction: $2Al(OH)_3 \rightarrow Al_2O_3 + 3H_2O$. If 156.0 g of $Al(OH)_3$ decompose to from 102.0 g of Al_2O_3, how many grams of H_2O are formed?

244. In the following balanced chemical reaction one of the products is represented by the symbol *X*: $BaCO_3 + C + H_2O \rightarrow Ba(OH)_2 + H_2O + 2X$. What is the formula for the compound represented by *X*?

245. When propane, C_3H_8, is burned, carbon dioxide and water vapor are produced according to the following reaction: $C_3H_8 + 5O_2 \rightarrow 3CO_2 + 4H_2O$. How much propane is burned if 160.0 g of O_2 are used and 132.0 g of CO_2 and 72.0 g of H_2O are produced?

246. Increasing the temperature usually causes the rate of a chemical reaction to increase. If the rate of a chemical reaction doubles when the temperature increases by 10°C, by what factor does the rate of reaction increase if the temperature increases by 30°C?

247. When acetylene gas, C_2H_2, is burned, carbon dioxide and water are produced. Find the coefficients that balance the chemical equation for the combustion of acetylene: $\_C_2H_2 + \_O_2 \rightarrow \_CO_2 + \_H_2O$.

248. What coefficients balances the following equation: $\_CS_2 + \_O_2 \rightarrow \_CO_2 + \_SO_2$?

249. When methane, CH_4, is burned, 50.1 kJ of energy per gram are released. When propane, C_3H_8, is burned, 45.8 kJ of energy are released. If a mixture of 1 g of methane and 1 g of propane is burned, how much energy is released per gram of mixture?

250. A chemical reaction produces 0.050 g of a product in 0.18 s. In the presence of a catalyst, the reaction produces 0.050 g of the same product in 0.007 s. How much faster is the rate of reaction in the presence of the enzyme?

Chapter 24 Solutions, Acids, and Bases

251. A cup of orange juice contains 126 mg of vitamin C and 1/2 cup of strawberries contain 42 mg of vitamin C. How many cups of strawberries contain as much vitamin C as one cup of orange juice?

252. What is the total surface area of a 2-cm cube?

253. A cube has 2-cm sides. If it is split in half, what is the total surface area of the two pieces?

254. At 20°C, the solubility in water of potassium bromide, KBr, is 65.3 g/100 mL. What is the maximum amount of potassium bromide that will dissolve in 237 mL of water?

255. At 20°C, the solubility of sodium chloride, NaCl, in water is 35.9 g/100 mL. If the maximum amount of sodium chloride is dissolved in 500 mL of water at 20°C, the mass of the dissolved sodium chloride is what percentage of the mass of the solution?

256. The difference between the pH of an acidic solution and the pH of pure water is 3. What is the pH of the solution?

Answers

Chapter 22 cont.

236. +6
237. PbO_2
238. $KClO_3$
239. CCl_4
240. 32.6%

Chapter 23

241. 59.8 g
242. 3, 2, 1, 6
243. 54.0 g
244. CO
245. 44.0 g
246. 8
247. 2, 5, 4, 2
248. 1, 3, 1, 2
249. 48.0 kJ/g
250. 25.7 times
251. 1.5
252. 24 cm^2
253. 32 cm^2
254. 155 g
255. 26.4%

Chapter 24

256. 4

Answers

Chapter 24 cont.

257. 4.7
258. 26.0 mL
259. $H_2SO_4 + 2KOH \rightarrow K_2SO_4 + 2H_2O$
260. $3HBr + Al(OH)_3 \rightarrow AlBr_3 + 3H_2O$

Chapter 25

261. 36
262. 30
263. 0.65 or 95:146
264. 1
265. 1
266. $^{222}_{86}Rn$
267. 2.1 s
268. 16.08 days
269. 17,190 years
270. 37.2 minutes

Chapter 26

271. 90 times
272. 32.5 mm
273. about 12.5 days
274. 69 hours and 44 minutes
275. 6.25 times
276. 2.6 times
277. 3000 times
278. 1.5 times
279. 62.5%
280. 6.3 billion years younger

257. The pH of rain that fell over a region had measured values of 4.6, 5.1, 4.8, 4.5, 4.5, 4.9, 4.7, and 4.8. What was the mean value of the measured pH?

258. If 5.5% of 473.0 mL of vinegar is acetic acid, how many milliliters of acetic acid are there?

259. Write the balanced chemical equation for the neutralization of H_2SO_4, sulfuric acid, by KOH, potassium hydroxide.

260. Write the balanced chemical equation for the neutralization of HBr, hydrobromic acid, by $Al(OH)_3$, aluminum hydroxide.

Chapter 25 Nuclear Changes

261. How many protons are in the nucleus $^{81}_{36}Kr$?

262. How many neutrons are in the nucleus $^{56}_{26}Fe$?

263. What is the ratio of neutrons to protons in the nucleus $^{241}_{95}Am$?

264. How many alpha particles are emitted when the nucleus $^{222}_{86}Rn$ decays to $^{218}_{84}Po$?

265. How many beta particles are emitted when the nucleus $^{40}_{19}K$ decays to the nucleus $^{40}_{20}Ca$?

266. An alpha particle is the same as the helium nucleus $^{4}_{2}He$. What nucleus is produced when the nucleus $^{226}_{88}Ra$ decays by emitting an alpha particle?

267. How long will it take a sample of $^{194}_{84}Po$ to decay to 1/8 of its original amount if $^{194}_{84}Po$ has a half-life of 0.7 s?

268. The half-life of $^{131}_{53}I$ is 8.04 days. How much time would be needed to reduce 1 g of $^{131}_{53}I$ to 0.25 g?

269. A sample of radioactive carbon-14 sample has decayed to 12.5% of its original amount. If the half-life of carbon-14 is 5730 years, how old is this sample?

270. A sample of $^{38}_{17}Cl$ is observed to decay to 25% of the original amount in 74.4 minutes. What is the half-life of $^{38}_{17}Cl$?

Chapter 26 Stars and Galaxies

271. If the focal length of a telescope's objective is 900 mm and the focal length of its eyepiece is 10 mm, what is the magnifying power of this telescope?

272. If the focal length of a telescope's objective is 700 mm and the magnifying power of the telescope is 40 times, what is the focal length of an eyepiece?

273. If it takes 25 days for a sunspot to travel once around the Sun, about how many days would it take to travel across the face of the Sun?

274. If a solar prominence blasts material from the Sun at a speed of 600 km/s, how long in hours and minutes would it take for material to arrive at Earth 150 million km away?

275. How many times larger in area is a 250-mm-diameter objective than a 100-mm diameter objective?

276. How many times larger in area is an 8-m-diameter objective than a 5-m-diameter objective?

277. How many times larger is an elliptical galaxy that is nine million light-years across than one that is 3,000 light-years across?

278. A telescope's objective has a focal length of 1,200 mm. It is used with two eyepieces that have focal lengths of 12 mm and 18 mm. How many times greater is the magnifying power of the telescope when the 12-mm eyepiece is used?

279. A telescope's objective has a focal length of 1500 mm. It is used with two eyepieces that have focal lengths of 20 mm and 12.5 mm. What percentage of the magnifying power obtained using the 12.5-mm eyepiece is achieved using the 20-mm eyepiece?

280. If the age of the universe was thought to be 20 billion years, but is now considered to be 13.7 billion years, how much younger is the universe thought to be now?

Rocks

Rock Type	Rock Name	Characteristics
Igneous (intrusive)	Granite	Large mineral grains of quartz, feldspar, hornblende, and mica. Usually light in color.
	Diorite	Large mineral grains of feldspar, hornblende, and mica. Less quartz than granite. Intermediate in color.
	Gabbro	Large mineral grains of feldspar, augite, and olivine. No quartz. Dark in color.
Igneous (extrusive)	Rhyolite	Small mineral grains of quartz, feldspar, hornblende, and mica, or no visible grains. Light in color.
	Andesite	Small mineral grains of feldspar, hornblende, and mica or no visible grains. Intermediate in color.
	Basalt	Small mineral grains of feldspar, augite, and possibly olivine or no visible grains. No quartz. Dark in color.
	Obsidian	Glassy texture. No visible grains. Volcanic glass. Fracture looks like broken glass.
	Pumice	Frothy texture. Floats in water. Usually light in color.
Sedimentary (detrital)	Conglomerate	Coarse grained. Gravel or pebble-size grains.
	Sandstone	Sand-sized grains 1/16 to 2 mm.
	Siltstone	Grains are smaller than sand but larger than clay.
	Shale	Smallest grains. Often dark in color. Usually platy.
Sedimentary (chemical or organic)	Limestone	Major mineral is calcite. Usually forms in oceans and lakes. Often contains fossils.
	Coal	Forms in swampy areas. Compacted layers of organic material, mainly plant remains.
Sedimentary (chemical)	Rock Salt	Commonly forms by the evaporation of seawater.
Metamorphic (foliated)	Gneiss	Banding due to alternate layers of different minerals, of different colors. Parent rock often is granite.
	Schist	Parallel arrangement of sheetlike minerals, mainly micas. Forms from different parent rocks.
	Phyllite	Shiny or silky appearance. May look wrinkled. Common parent rocks are shale and slate.
	Slate	Harder, denser, and shinier than shale. Common parent rock is shale.
Metamorphic (nonfoliated)	Marble	Calcite or dolomite. Common parent rock is limestone.
	Soapstone	Mainly of talc. Soft with greasy feel.
	Quartzite	Hard with interlocking quartz crystals. Common parent rock is sandstone.

Minerals

Minerals					
Mineral (formula)	**Color**	**Streak**	**Hardness**	**Breakage Pattern**	**Uses and Other Properties**
Graphite (C)	black to gray	black to gray	1–1.5	basal cleavage (scales)	pencil lead, lubricants for locks, rods to control some small nuclear reactions, battery poles
Galena (PbS)	gray	gray to black	2.5	cubic cleavage perfect	source of lead, used for pipes, shields for X rays, fishing equipment sinkers
Hematite (Fe_2O_3)	black or reddish-brown	reddish-brown	5.5–6.5	irregular fracture	source of iron; converted to pig iron, made into steel
Magnetite (Fe_3O_4)	black	black	6	conchoidal fracture	source of iron, attracts a magnet
Pyrite (FeS_2)	light, brassy, yellow	greenish-black	6–6.5	uneven fracture	fool's gold
Talc ($Mg_3 Si_4O_{10}(OH)_2$)	white, greenish	white	1	cleavage in one direction	used for talcum powder, sculptures, paper, and tabletops
Gypsum ($CaSO_4{\cdot}2H_2O$)	colorless, gray, white, brown	white	2	basal cleavage	used in plaster of paris and dry wall for building construction
Sphalerite (ZnS)	brown, reddish-brown, greenish	light to dark brown	3.5–4	cleavage in six directions	main ore of zinc; used in paints, dyes, and medicine
Muscovite ($KAl_3Si_3O_{10}(OH)_2$)	white, light gray, yellow, rose, green	colorless	2–2.5	basal cleavage	occurs in large, flexible plates; used as an insulator in electrical equipment, lubricant
Biotite ($K(Mg,Fe)_3(AlSi_3O_{10})(OH)_2$)	black to dark brown	colorless	2.5–3	basal cleavage	occurs in large, flexible plates
Halite (NaCl)	colorless, red, white, blue	colorless	2.5	cubic cleavage	salt; soluble in water; a preservative

Minerals

Mineral (formula)	Color	Streak	Hardness	Breakage Pattern	Uses and Other Properties
Calcite ($CaCO_3$)	colorless, white, pale blue	colorless, white	3	cleavage in three directions	fizzes when HCl is added; used in cements and other building materials
Dolomite ($CaMg(CO_3)_2$)	colorless, white, pink, green, gray, black	white	3.5–4	cleavage in three directions	concrete and cement; used as an ornamental building stone
Fluorite (CaF_2)	colorless, white, blue, green, red, yellow, purple	colorless	4	cleavage in four directions	used in the manufacture of optical equipment; glows under ultraviolet light
Hornblende ($(CaNa)_{2-3}(Mg,Al,Fe)_5$-$(Al,Si)_2Si_6O_{22}(OH)_2$)	green to black	gray to white	5–6	cleavage in two directions	will transmit light on thin edges; 6-sided cross section
Feldspar ($(KAlSi_3O_8)$ $(NaAlSi_3O_8)$, $(CaAl_2Si_2O_8)$)	colorless, white to gray, green	colorless	6	two cleavage planes meet at 90° angle	used in the manufacture of ceramics
Augite ($((Ca,Na)(Mg,Fe,Al)(Al,Si)_2O_6)$)	black	colorless	6	cleavage in two directions	square or 8-sided cross section
Olivine ($((Mg,Fe)_2SiO_4)$)	olive, green	none	6.5–7	conchoidal fracture	gemstones, refractory sand
Quartz (SiO_2)	colorless, various colors	none	7	conchoidal fracture	used in glass manufacture, electronic equipment, radios, computers, watches, gemstones

Physical Science Reference Tables

Standard Units

Symbol	Name	Quantity
m	meter	length
kg	kilogram	mass
Pa	pascal	pressure
K	kelvin	temperature
mol	mole	amount of a substance
J	joule	energy, work, quantity of heat
s	second	time
C	coulomb	electric charge
V	volt	electric potential
A	ampere	electric current
Ω	ohm	resistance

Physical Constants and Conversion Factors

Acceleration due to gravity	g	9.8 m/s/s or m/s^2
Avogadro's Number	N_A	6.02×10^{23} particles per mole
Electron charge	e	1.6×10^{-19} C
Electron rest mass	m_e	9.11×10^{-31} kg
Gravitation constant	G	6.67×10^{-11} N $\times$ m^2/kg^2
Mass-energy relationship		1 u (amu) $= 9.3 \times 10^2$ MeV
Speed of light in a vacuum	c	3.00×108 m/s
Speed of sound at STP	331 m/s	
Standard Pressure	1 atmosphere 101.3 kPa 760 Torr or mmHg 14.7 lb/in.^{2}	

Wavelengths of Light in a Vacuum

Violet	$4.0 - 4.2 \times 10^{-7}$ m
Blue	$4.2 - 4.9 \times 10^{-7}$ m
Green	$4.9 - 5.7 \times 10^{-7}$ m
Yellow	$5.7 - 5.9 \times 10^{-7}$ m
Orange	$5.9 - 6.5 \times 10^{-7}$ m
Red	$6.5 - 7.0 \times 10^{-7}$ m

The Index of Refraction for Common Substances

($\lambda = 5.9 \times 10^{-7}$ m)

Air	1.00
Alcohol	1.36
Canada Balsam	1.53
Corn Oil	1.47
Diamond	2.42
Glass, Crown	1.52
Glass, Flint	1.61
Glycerol	1.47
Lucite	1.50
Quartz, Fused	1.46
Water	1.33

Heat Constants

	Specific Heat (average) (kJ/kg × °C) (J/g × °C)	Melting Point (°C)	Boiling Point (°C)	Heat of Fusion (kJ/kg) (J/g)	Heat of Vaporization (kJ/kg) (J/g)
Alcohol (ethyl)	2.43 (liq.)	−117	79	109	855
Aluminum	0.90 (sol.)	660	2467	396	10500
Ammonia	4.71 (liq.)	−78	−33	332	1370
Copper	0.39 (sol.)	1083	2567	205	4790
Iron	0.45 (sol.)	1535	2750	267	6290
Lead	0.13 (sol.)	328	1740	25	866
Mercury	0.14 (liq.)	−39	357	11	295
Platinum	0.13 (sol.)	1772	3827	101	229
Silver	0.24 (sol.)	962	2212	105	2370
Tungsten	0.13 (sol.)	3410	5660	192	4350
Water (solid)	2.05 (sol.)	0	–	334	–
Water (liquid)	4.18 (liq.)	–	100	–	–
Water (vapor)	2.01 (gas)	–	–	–	2260
Zinc	0.39 (sol.)	420	907	113	1770

Standard Units

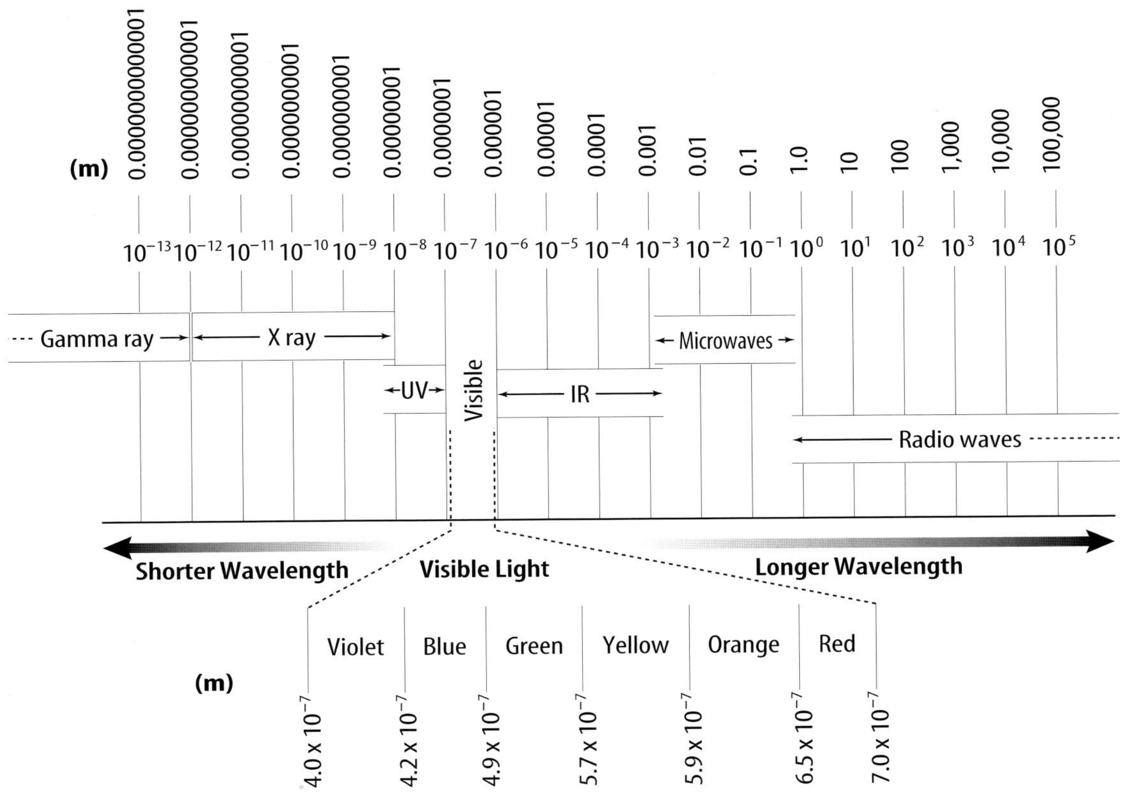

Radioactive Decay

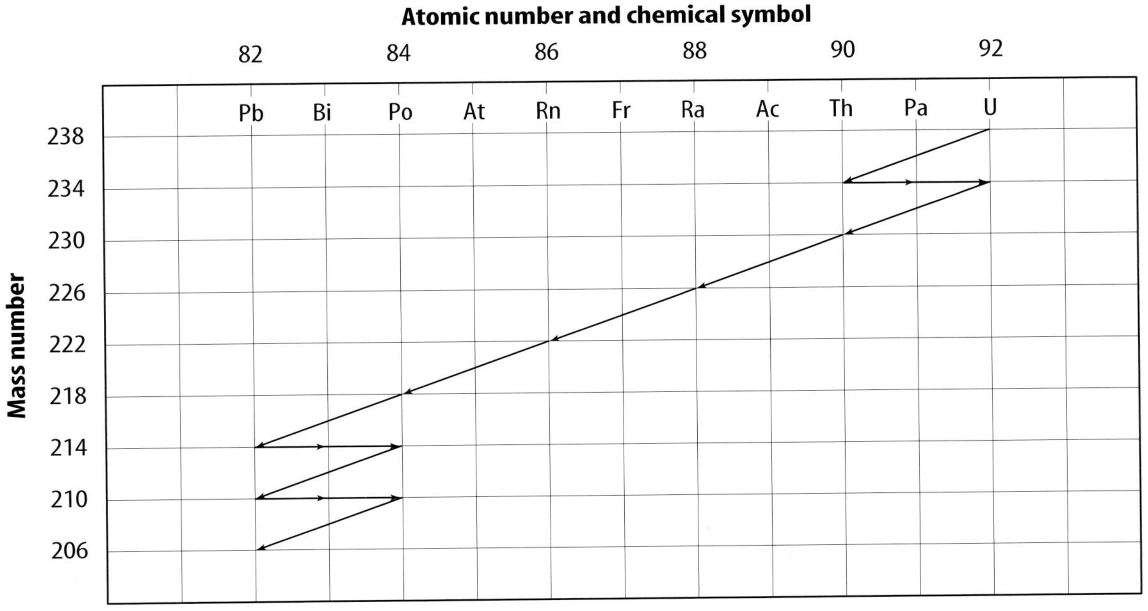

^4_2He (α particle) Helium nucleus emission

$^{\ 0}_{-1}e$ (β particle) electron emission

PERIODIC TABLE OF THE ELEMENTS

Columns of elements are called groups. Elements in the same group have similar chemical properties.

Element — Hydrogen
Atomic number — 1
Symbol — H
Atomic mass — 1.008
State of matter

Gas
Liquid
Solid
Synthetic

The first three symbols tell you the state of matter of the element at room temperature. The fourth symbol identifies elements that are not present in significant amounts on Earth. Useful amounts are made synthetically.

	1	2	3	4	5	6	7	8	9
1	Hydrogen 1 H 1.008								
2	Lithium 3 Li 6.941	Beryllium 4 Be 9.012							
3	Sodium 11 Na 22.990	Magnesium 12 Mg 24.305							
4	Potassium 19 K 39.098	Calcium 20 Ca 40.078	Scandium 21 Sc 44.956	Titanium 22 Ti 47.867	Vanadium 23 V 50.942	Chromium 24 Cr 51.996	Manganese 25 Mn 54.938	Iron 26 Fe 55.845	Cobalt 27 Co 58.933
5	Rubidium 37 Rb 85.468	Strontium 38 Sr 87.62	Yttrium 39 Y 88.906	Zirconium 40 Zr 91.224	Niobium 41 Nb 92.906	Molybdenum 42 Mo 95.94	Technetium 43 Tc (98)	Ruthenium 44 Ru 101.07	Rhodium 45 Rh 102.906
6	Cesium 55 Cs 132.905	Barium 56 Ba 137.327	Lanthanum 57 La 138.906	Hafnium 72 Hf 178.49	Tantalum 73 Ta 180.948	Tungsten 74 W 183.84	Rhenium 75 Re 186.207	Osmium 76 Os 190.23	Iridium 77 Ir 192.217
7	Francium 87 Fr (223)	Radium 88 Ra (226)	Actinium 89 Ac (227)	Rutherfordium 104 Rf (261)	Dubnium 105 Db (262)	Seaborgium 106 Sg (266)	Bohrium 107 Bh (264)	Hassium 108 Hs (277)	Meitnerium 109 Mt (268)

The number in parentheses is the mass number of the longest-lived isotope for that element.

Rows of elements are called periods. Atomic number increases across a period.

The arrow shows where these elements would fit into the periodic table. They are moved to the bottom of the table to save space.

Lanthanide series	Cerium 58 Ce 140.116	Praseodymium 59 Pr 140.908	Neodymium 60 Nd 144.24	Promethium 61 Pm (145)	Samarium 62 Sm 150.36
Actinide series	Thorium 90 Th 232.038	Protactinium 91 Pa 231.036	Uranium 92 U 238.029	Neptunium 93 Np (237)	Plutonium 94 Pu (244)

Metal

Metalloid

Nonmetal

The color of an element's block tells you if the element is a metal, nonmetal, or metalloid.

Science Online
Visit gpescience.com for updates to the periodic table.

10	11	12	13	14	15	16	17	18
								Helium 2 **He** 4.003
			Boron 5 **B** 10.811	Carbon 6 **C** 12.011	Nitrogen 7 **N** 14.007	Oxygen 8 **O** 15.999	Fluorine 9 **F** 18.998	Neon 10 **Ne** 20.180
			Aluminum 13 **Al** 26.982	Silicon 14 **Si** 28.086	Phosphorus 15 **P** 30.974	Sulfur 16 **S** 32.065	Chlorine 17 **Cl** 35.453	Argon 18 **Ar** 39.948
Nickel 28 **Ni** 58.693	Copper 29 **Cu** 63.546	Zinc 30 **Zn** 65.409	Gallium 31 **Ga** 69.723	Germanium 32 **Ge** 72.64	Arsenic 33 **As** 74.922	Selenium 34 **Se** 78.96	Bromine 35 **Br** 79.904	Krypton 36 **Kr** 83.798
Palladium 46 **Pd** 106.42	Silver 47 **Ag** 107.868	Cadmium 48 **Cd** 112.411	Indium 49 **In** 114.818	Tin 50 **Sn** 118.710	Antimony 51 **Sb** 121.760	Tellurium 52 **Te** 127.60	Iodine 53 **I** 126.904	Xenon 54 **Xe** 131.293
Platinum 78 **Pt** 195.078	Gold 79 **Au** 196.967	Mercury 80 **Hg** 200.59	Thallium 81 **Tl** 204.383	Lead 82 **Pb** 207.2	Bismuth 83 **Bi** 208.980	Polonium 84 **Po** (209)	Astatine 85 **At** (210)	Radon 86 **Rn** (222)
Darmstadtium 110 **Ds** (281)	Roentgenium * 111 **Rg** (272)	Ununbium * 112 **Uub** (285)		Ununquadium * 114 **Uuq** (289)				

* The names and symbols for elements 111–114 are temporary. Final names will be selected when the elements' discoveries are verified.

Europium 63 **Eu** 151.964	Gadolinium 64 **Gd** 157.25	Terbium 65 **Tb** 158.925	Dysprosium 66 **Dy** 162.500	Holmium 67 **Ho** 164.930	Erbium 68 **Er** 167.259	Thulium 69 **Tm** 168.934	Ytterbium 70 **Yb** 173.04	Lutetium 71 **Lu** 174.967
Americium 95 **Am** (243)	Curium 96 **Cm** (247)	Berkelium 97 **Bk** (247)	Californium 98 **Cf** (251)	Einsteinium 99 **Es** (252)	Fermium 100 **Fm** (257)	Mendelevium 101 **Md** (258)	Nobelium 102 **No** (259)	Lawrencium 103 **Lr** (262)

Weather Map Symbols

Sample Station Model

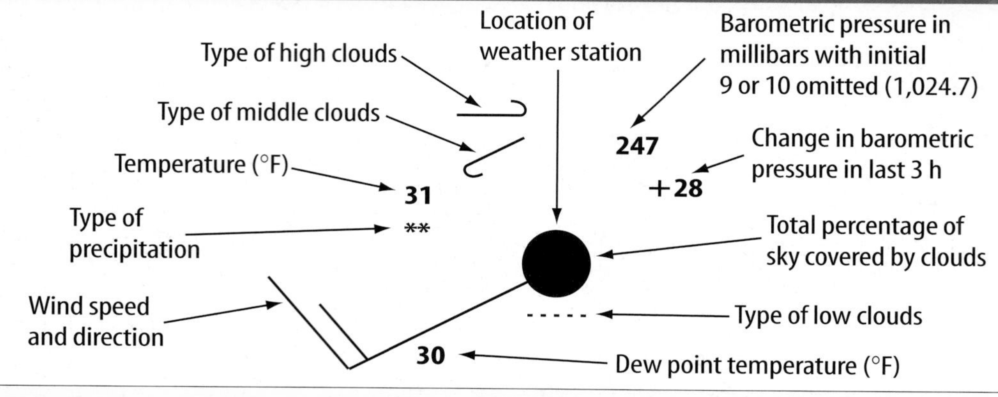

Sample Plotted Report at Each Station

Precipitation		Wind Speed and Direction		Sky Coverage		Some Types of High Clouds	
≡	Fog	○	0 calm	○	No cover		Scattered cirrus
★	Snow		1–2 knots		1/10 or less		Dense cirrus in patches
●	Rain		3–7 knots		2/10 to 3/10		Veil of cirrus covering entire sky
	Thunderstorm		8–12 knots		4/10		Cirrus not covering entire sky
,	Drizzle		13–17 knots	◑	–		
▽	Showers		18–22 knots		6/10		
			23–27 knots		7/10		
			48–52 knots		Overcast with openings		
		1 knot = 1.852 km/h		●	Completely overcast		

Some Types of Middle Clouds		Some Types of Low Clouds		Fronts and Pressure Systems	
	Thin altostratus layer	⌓	Cumulus of fair weather	(H) or High (L) or Low	Center of high- or low-pressure system
	Thick altostratus layer	‿	Stratocumulus		Cold front
	Thin altostratus in patches	-----	Fractocumulus of bad weather		Warm front
	Thin altostratus in bands	—	Stratus of fair weather		Occluded front
					Stationary front

Cómo usar el glosario en español:
1. Busca el término en inglés que desees encontrar.
2. El término en español, junto con la definición, se encuentran en la columna de la derecha.

Pronunciation Key

Use the following key to help you sound out words in the glossary.

a	**ba**ck (BAK)	**ew**	f**oo**d (FEWD)
ay	**da**y (DAY)	**yoo**	p**u**re (PYOOR)
ah	**fa**ther (FAH thur)	**yew**	f**ew** (FYEW)
ow	fl**ow**er (FLOW ur)	**uh**	comm**a** (CAH muh)
ar	**car** (CAR)	**u (1 con)**	r**u**b (RUB)
e	l**e**ss (LES)	**sh**	**sh**elf (SHELF)
ee	l**ea**f (LEEF)	**ch**	na**t**ure (NAY chur)
ih	tr**i**p (TRIHP)	**g**	**g**ift (GIHFT)
i (i 1 con 1 e)	**i**dea (i DEE uh)	**j**	**g**em (JEM)
oh	g**o** (GOH)	**ing**	s**ing** (SING)
aw	s**o**ft (SAWFT)	**zh**	vi**si**on (VIH zhun)
or	**or**bit (OR buht)	**k**	**c**a**k**e (KAYK)
oy	c**oi**n (COYN)	**s**	**s**eed, **c**ent (SEED, SENT)
oo	f**oo**t (FOOT)	**z**	**z**one, rai**s**e (ZOHN, RAYZ)

English — A — Español

absolute dating: process of assigning a precise numerical age to an organism, object, or event, based on an absolute reference. (p. 669)

acceleration: rate of change of velocity; can be calculated by dividing the change in the velocity by the time it takes the change to occur. (p. 76)

accuracy: compares a measurement to the real or accepted value. (p. 14)

acid: any substance that produces hydrogen ions, H^+, in a water solution. (p. 764)

activation energy: the minimum amount of energy needed to start a reaction (p. 735)

agricultural biotechnology: scientific techniques, such as genetic engineering, used to increase farm crop yields and nutritional values of foods by creating, modifying, or improving plants, animals, and microorganisms. (p. 45)

air resistance: force that opposes the motion of objects that move through the air. (p. 85)

alpha particle: particle consisting of two protons and two neutrons that is emitted from a decaying atomic nucleus. (p. 791)

alternating current (AC): electric current that reverses its direction of flow in a regular pattern. (p. 442)

amplitude: maximum distance a wave causes the particles in a medium to move from the rest position. (p. 298)

datación absoluta: proceso de asignar una edad numérica precisa a un organismo, objeto o evento, basado en una referencia absoluta. (p. 669)

aceleración: tasa de cambio de la velocidad; se calcula dividiendo el cambio en la velocidad por el tiempo que toma para que ocurra el cambio. (p. 76)

exactitud: comparación de una medición con el valor real o aceptado. (p. 14)

ácido: sustancia que produce iones de hidrógeno, H^+, en una solución de agua. (p. 764)

energía de activación: cantidad mínima de energía necesaria para comenzar una reacción. (p. 735)

biotecnología agrícola: técnicas científicas, como la ingeniería genética, utilizadas para incrementar la producción de las cosechas de las granjas y los valores nutricionales de los alimentos al crear, modificar o mejorar las plantas, animales y microorganismos. (p. 45)

resistencia del aire: fuerza que se opone al movimiento de los objetos que se mueven por el aire. (p. 85)

partícula alfa: partícula compuesta por dos protones y dos neutrones y que es emitida por un núcleo atómico en descomposición. (p. 791)

corriente alterna (CA): corriente eléctrica que invierte su dirección de flujo en un patrón regular. (p. 442)

amplitud: distancia máxima a la que una onda causa que las partículas en un medio salgan de su posición de reposo. (p. 298)

aqueous solution: a solution in which water is the solvent. (p. 753)

Solución acuosa: solución en la que el agua es el solvente. (p. 753)

aquifer: rock unit that transmits water through its pore space. (p. 664)

Acuífero: unidad rocosa que conduce agua a través de su espacio poroso. (p. 664)

asteroids: rocky solar system objects of widely varying size usually found between the orbits of Mars and Jupiter in an area called the asteroid belt. (p. 236)

Asteroides: objetos rocosos del sistema solar que varían ampliamente en tamaño y usualmente se encuentran entre las órbitas de Marte y Júpiter en un área llamada el cinturón de asteroides. (p. 236)

asthenosphere: weaker, semi-solid, plasticlike layer beneath Earth's lithosphere on which lithospheric plates move. (p. 372)

astenosfera: capa débil, semisólida, similar al plástico que se encuentra por debajo de la litosfera terrestre en la cual se mueven las placas litosféricas. (p. 372)

astronomical unit: about 150 million km, which equals the average distance from Earth to the Sun; used to measure distances within the solar system. (p. 220)

unidad astronómica: cerca de 150 millones de km, lo cual equivale a la distancia promedio de la tierra al sol; utilizada para medir distancias entre el sistema solar. (p. 220)

atom: the smallest particle of an element that still retains the properties of the element. (p. 589)

átomo: la partícula más pequeña de un elemento que mantiene las propiedades del elemento. (p. 589)

atomic number: number of protons in an atom's nucleus. (p. 585)

número atómico: número de protones en el núcleo de un átomo. (p. 585)

average atomic mass: weighted-average mass of the mixture of an element's isotopes. (p. 587)

masa atómica promedio: masa de peso promedio resultado de la mezcla de los isótopos de un elemento. (p. 587)

average speed: total distance an object travels divided by the total time it takes to travel that distance. (p. 72)

velocidad promedio: distancia que recorre un objeto dividida por el tiempo que dura en recorrer dicha distancia. (p. 72)

B

balanced chemical equation: chemical equation with the same number of atoms of each element on both sides of the equation. (p. 726)

ecuación química Fnceada: ecuación química con el mismo número de átomos de cada elemento en los dos lados de la ecuación. (p. 726)

balanced forces: forces on a object that combine to give a zero net force and do not change the motion of the object. (p. 82)

fuerzas equilibradas: fuerzas en un objeto que se combinan para dar una fuerza neta de cero y no cambiar el movimiento del objeto. (p. 82)

base: any substance that forms hydroxide ions, OH^-, in a water solution. (p. 766)

base: sustancia que forma iones de hidróxido, OH^-, en una solución de agua. (p. 766)

beta particle: electron that is emitted from a decaying atomic nucleus. (p. 793)

partícula beta: electrón emitido por un núcleo atómico en descomposición. (p. 793)

bias: occurs when a scientist's expectations change how the results of an experiment are viewed. (p. 10)

predisposición: ocurre cuando las expectativas de un científico cambian la forma en que son vistos los resultados de un experimento. (p. 10)

big bang theory: the theory that the universe started with a big bang, or explosion, and has been expanding ever since. (p. 837)

teoría de la gran explosión: teoría que explica que el universo comenzó con una gran explosión y que se ha estado expandiendo desde entonces. (p. 837)

binary compound: compound that is composed of two elements. (p. 703)

compuesto binario: compuesto conformado por dos elementos. (p. 703)

biomass: renewable organic matter from plants and animals, such as wood and animal manure, that can be burned to provide heat. (p. 506)

biomasa: materia orgánica renovable proveniente de plantas y animales, tales como madera y estiércol animal, que puede ser incinerada para producir calor. (p. 506)

biosphere: everything organic, including plants, animals, and humans. (p. 529)

bubble chamber: radiation detector, consisting of a container of superheated liquid under high pressure, that is used to detect the paths of charged particles. (p. 797)

biosfera: cualquier entidad orgánica, incluyendo plantas, animales y humanos. (p. 529)

cámara de burbujas: detector de radiación que consiste de un contenedor de un líquido sobrecalentado a alta presión, usado para detectar la trayectoria de las partículas cargadas. (p. 797)

C

carrier wave: specific frequency that a radio station is assigned and uses to broadcast signals. (p. 469)

catalyst: substance that speeds up a chemical reaction without being permanently changed itself. (p. 740)

cathode-ray tube: sealed vacuum tube that produces one or more beams of electrons that produce an image when they strike the coating on the inside of a TV screen. (p. 472)

cementation: sedimentary rock-forming process in which minerals precipitate out of water and fill the spaces between clasts. (p. 625)

centripetal acceleration: acceleration of an object toward the center of a curved or circular path. (p. 110)

centripetal force: a net force that is directed toward the center of a curved or circular path. (p. 110)

chain reaction: ongoing series of fission reactions. (p. 802)

charging by contact: process of transferring charge between objects by touching or rubbing. (p. 395)

charging by induction: process of rearranging electrons on a neutral object by bringing a charged object close to it. (p. 396)

chemical bond: force that holds atoms together in a compound. (p. 694)

chemical change: change of one substance into a new substance. (p. 564)

chemical equation: shorthand method to describe chemical reactions using chemical formulas and other symbols. (p. 723)

chemical formula: chemical shorthand that uses symbols to tell what elements are in a compound and their ratios. (p. 689)

chemical potential energy: energy stored in chemical bonds. (p. 131)

chemical property: any characteristic of a substance, such as flammability, that indicates whether it can undergo a certain chemical change. (p. 563)

chemical reaction: process in which one or more substances are changed into new substances. (p. 720)

onda transportadora: frecuencia específica que se le asigna a una estación de radio y que la usa para emitir señales. (p. 469)

catalizador: sustancia que acelera una reacción química sin cambiar el mismo permanentemente. (p. 740)

tubo de rayos catódicos: tubo vacío sellado que produce uno o más haces de electrones para producir una imagen al chocar con el revestimiento del interior de una pantalla de televisor. (p. 472)

cementación: proceso de formación de rocas sedimentarias en el que los minerales se precipitan del agua y rellenan los espacios entre los clastos. (p. 625)

aceleración centrípeta: aceleración de un objeto dirigida hacia el centro de un trayecto curvo o circular. (p. 110)

fuerza centrípeta: fuerza neta dirigida hacia el centro de un trayecto curvo o circular. (p. 110)

reacción en cadena: serie continua de reacciones de fisión. (p. 802)

carga por contacto: proceso de transferir carga entre objetos por contacto o frotaciòn. (p. 395)

carga por inducción: proceso de redistribución de los electrones en un objeto neutro acercándoles un objeto con carga. (p. 396)

enlace químico: fuerza que mantiene a los átomos juntos dentro de un compuesto. (p. 694)

cambio químico: transformación de una sustancia en una nueva sustancia. (p. 564)

ecuación química: método simplificado para describir reacciones químicas usando fórmulas químicas y otros símbolos. (p. 723)

fórmula química: nomenclatura química que usa símbolos para expresar qué elementos están en un compuesto y en qué proporción. (p. 689)

energía química potencial: energía almacenada en los enlaces químicos. (p. 131)

propiedad química: cualquier característica de una sustancia, como por ejemplo la combustibilidad, que indique si puede someterse a determinado cambio químico. (p. 563)

reacción química: proceso en el cual una o más sustancias son cambiadas por nuevas sustancias. (p. 720)

cinder cone volcano: small, violently erupting volcano formed by accumulation of large pyroclastic materials around a vent. (p. 377)

circuit: closed conducting loop through which an electric current can flow. (p. 401)

clasts: bits and pieces of rock that vary widely in size and composition, are broken down by weathering, and may become consolidated into sedimentary rock. (p. 624)

cleavage: physical property of a mineral that causes it to break along planes that cut across relatively weak chemical bonds, creating a well-defined, smooth, flat surface. (p. 610)

cloud chamber: radiation detector that uses water or ethanol vapor to detect the paths of charged particles. (p. 796)

colloid (KAHL oyd): heterogeneous mixture whose particles never settle. (p. 556)

combustion reaction: a type of chemical reaction that occurs when a substance reacts with oxygen to produce energy in the form of heat and light. (p. 730)

comet: mass of dust, rock particles, frozen water, methane, and ammonia that travels through space and develops a bright, distinctive tail of light as it approaches the Sun and is pushed on by the solar wind. (p. 236)

composite volcano: large volcano formed by alternating lava flows and violently erupting pyroclastic materials. (p. 378)

compound: substance formed from two or more elements in which the exact combination and proportion of elements is always the same. (p. 554)

compound machine: machine that is a combination of two or more simple machines. (p. 174)

compressional wave: a wave for which the matter in the medium moves back and forth along the direction that the wave travels. (p. 290)

computer simulation: performance-testing method using a computer to imitate the process or procedure or to gather data. (p. 55)

concave lens: a lens that is thicker at the edges than in the middle; causes light rays to diverge and forms reduced, upright, virtual images; usually used in combination with other lenses. (p. 335)

concave mirror: a reflective surface that curves inward and can magnify objects or create beams of light. (p. 332)

volcán de cono de ceniza: volcán pequeño, de erupción violenta formado por la acumulación de materiales piroclásticos grandes alrededor de una chimenea. (p. 377)

circuito: circuito conductor cerrado a través del cual puede fluir una corriente eléctrica. (p. 401)

clastos: toda clase de objetos rocosos que varían ampliamente en tamaño y composición, son degradados por el clima y pueden consolidarse en rocas sedimentarias. (p. 624)

clivaje: propiedad física de un mineral que causa que éste se rompa en planos que toman el camino más corto entre los enlaces químicos relativamente débiles, creando una superficie bien definida, suave y plana. (p. 610)

cámara de vapor: detector de radiaciones que usa vapor de agua o de etanol para detectar la trayectoria de las partículas cargadas. (p. 796)

coloide: mezcla heterogénea cuyas partículas nunca se sedimentan. (p. 556)

reacción de combustión: un tipo de reacción química que ocurre cuando una sustancia reacciona con oxígeno para producir energía en forma de calor y luz. (p. 730)

cometa: masa de polvo, partículas de roca, agua congelada, metano y amoniaco que viaja a través del espacio; desarrolla una cauda de luz brillante y distintiva a medida que se acerca al sol, y es empujada por vientos solares. (p. 236)

volcán compuesto: volcán grande formado por flujos alternantes de lava y materiales piroclásticos erupcionados violentamente. (p. 378)

compuesto: sustancia formada por dos o más elementos en la que la combinación y proporción exacta de los elementos es siempre la misma. (p. 554)

máquina compuesta: máquina compuesta por dos o más máquinas simples. (p. 174)

onda de compresión: onda para la cual la materia en el medio se mueve hacia adelante y hacia atrás en la dirección en que viaja la onda. (p. 290)

simulación computarizada: método de prueba del desempeño utilizando una computadora para imitar el proceso o procedimiento o para recopilar datos. (p. 55)

lente cóncavo: lente que es más delgado en los bordes que en el centro; hace que los rayos de luz se desvíen y forma imágenes reducidas, verticales y virtuales, generalmente utiliza en combinación con otros lentes. (p. 335)

espejo cóncavo: superficie reflexiva que se curva hacia el interior y que puede amplificar los objetos o crear rayos de luz. (p. 332)

concentration: how much solute is present in a solution compared to the amount of solvent. (p. 706)

concentración: cantidad de soluto que está presente en una solución en comparación con la cantidad de solvente. (p. 706)

conduction: transfer of thermal energy by collisions between particles in matter at a higher temperature and particles in matter at a lower temperature. (p. 266)

conducción: transferencia de energía térmica por colisiones entre partículas de materia a una temperatura alta y partículas de materia a una temperatura más baja. (p. 266)

conductor: material, such as copper wire, in which electrons can move easily. (p. 395)

conductor: material, como el alambre de cobre, a través del cual los electrones se pueden mover con facilidad. (p. 395)

constant: in an experiment, a variable that does not change when other variables change. (p. 9)

constante: en un experimento, una variable que no cambia cuando cambian otras variables. (p. 9)

constellation: star pattern that appears to form images, is used by astronomers to locate and name stars, and often is named for a mythological figure. (p. 818)

constelación: patrón estelar que parece formar imágenes; es usado por los astrónomos para ubicar y nombrar las estrellas, y con frecuencia se denomina con base en una figura mitológica (p. 818)

constraints: design limitations placed on products by outside factors, such as available materials, cost, and environmental impact. (p. 55)

restricciones: limitaciones de diseño impuestas en los productos por factores externos, como los materiales disponibles, el costo y el impacto ambiental. (p. 55)

continental climate: climate with little direct ocean influence and steep temperature gradients. (p. 532)

clima continental: clima con una pequeña influencia oceánica directa y gradientes abruptos de temperatura. (p. 532)

control: standard used for comparison of test results in an experiment. (p. 9)

control: estándar usado para la comparación de resultados de pruebas en un experimento. (p. 9)

control system: device or collection of devices used to monitor a system and limit system failures. (p. 56)

sistema de control: dispositivo o conjunto de dispositivos utilizados para monitorear un sistema y limitar sus fallas. (p. 56)

convection: transfer of thermal energy in a fluid from one place to another. (p. 267)

convección: transferencia de energía térmica en un fluido de un lugar a otro. (p. 267)

convergent boundary: plate tectonic boundary where lithospheric plates collide. (p. 539)

límite convergente: límite de la placa tectónica donde las placas litosféricas colisionan. (p. 539)

convex lens: a lens that is thicker in the middle than at the edges and can form real or virtual images. (p. 333)

lente convexo: lente que es más delgado en el centro que en los bordes y que puede formar imágenes reales o virtuales. (p. 333)

convex mirror: a reflective surface that curves outward and forms a reduced, upright, virtual image. (p. 333)

espejo convexo: una superficie reflexiva que se curva hacia el exterior y forma una imagen reducida, vertical y virtual. (p. 333)

cosmology: study of how the universe began, what it is made of, and how it continues to evolve. (p. 836)

cosmología: estudio del origen del universo, de su composición y de la forma como continúa evolucionando. (p. 836)

covalent bond: attraction formed between atoms when they share electrons. (p. 697)

enlace covalente: atracción formada entre átomos que comparten electrones. (p. 697)

crest: the highest points on a transverse wave. (p. 294)

cresta: los puntos más altos en una onda transversal. (p. 294)

critical mass: amount of fissionable material required so that each fission reaction produces approximately one more fission reaction. (p. 802)

masa crítica: cantidad de material fisionable requerido de manera que cada reacción de fisión produzca aproximadamente una reacción de fisión adicional. (p. 802)

D

dark energy: energy that might be causing accelerated expansion of the universe. (p. 837)

dark matter: unseen mass that adds to the gravity of a galaxy, but cannot be detected or seen. (p. 838)

decibel: unit for sound intensity; abbreviated dB. (p. 322)

decomposition reaction: chemical reaction in which one substance breaks down into two or more substances. (p. 731)

density: mass per unit volume of a material. (p. 19)

dependent variable: factor that changes as a result of changes in the other variables. (p. 9)

deposition: process in which eroded materials are dropped by their transporting agents. (p. 654)

diffraction: the bending of waves around an obstacle; can also occur when waves pass through a narrow opening. (p. 304)

direct current (DC): electric current that flows in only one direction. (p. 442)

discontinuity: boundary marking an abrupt density change between Earth's layers. (p. 371)

displacement: distance and direction of an object's change in position from the starting point. (p. 71)

distance: how far an object moves. (p. 71)

distillation: process that can separate two substances in a mixture by evaporating a liquid and recondensing its vapor. (p. 563)

divergent boundary: plate tectonic boundary where lithospheric plates are moving apart. (p. 358)

Doppler effect: change in pitch or frequency that occurs when a source of a sound is moving relative to a listener. (p. 330)

double-displacement reaction: chemical reaction that produces a precipitate, water, or a gas when two ionic compounds in solution are combined. (p. 732)

drainage basin: land area that gathers water for a major river. (p. 655)

energía oscura: energía que podría estar causando la expansión acelerada del universo. (p. 837)

materia oscura: masa no vista que se suma a la gravedad de una galaxia pero que no puede detectarse o verse. (p. 838)

decibel: unidad que mide la intensidad del sonido; se abrevia dB. (p. 322)

reacción de descomposición: reacción química en la cual una sustancia se descompone en dos o más sustancias. (p. 731)

densidad: masa por unidad de volumen de un material. (p. 19)

variable dependiente: factor que varía como resultado de los cambios en las otras variables. (p. 9)

deposición: proceso en el que los materiales erosionados son decantados a partir de sus agentes transportadores. (p. 654)

difracción: curvatura de las ondas alrededor de un obstáculo, la cual también puede ocurrir cuando éstas pasan a través de una abertura angosta. (p. 304)

corriente directa (CD): corriente eléctrica que fluye en una sola dirección. (p. 442)

discontinuidad: límite que marca un cambio abrupto de densidad entre las capas de la Tierra. (p. 371)

desplazamiento: distancia y dirección del cambio de posición de un objeto desde el punto inicial. (p. 71)

distancia: qué tan lejos se mueve un objeto. (p. 71)

destilación: proceso que puede separar dos sustancias de una mezcla por medio de la evaporación de un líquido y la recondensación de su vapor. (p. 563)

límite divergente: límite de las placas tectónicas donde las placas litosféricas se alejan. (p. 358)

efecto Doppler: cambio en la altura o frecuencia que ocurre cuando una fuente de sonido se mueve en relación con un oyente. (p. 330)

reacción de doble desplazamiento: reacción química que produce un precipitado, agua o gas cuando se combinan dos compuestos iónicos en una solución. (p. 732)

cuenca de drenaje: área terrestre que capta agua para un río grande. (p. 655)

E

Earth: third planet from the Sun; the only planet known to support life and to have water on its surface as a gas, a liquid, and a solid. (p. 225)

tierra: tercer planeta más cercano al ; el único planeta que se sabe que alberga vida y que tiene agua en su superficie en estado sólido, líquido y gaseoso. (p. 225)

ecliptic: yearly path of Earth around the Sun; also, the Sun's apparent path through the zodiac. (p. 192)

efficiency: ratio of the output work done by the machine to the input work done on the machine, expressed as a percentage. (p. 164)

elastic potential energy: energy stored when an object is compressed or stretched. (p. 131)

elastic rebound: sudden energy release that accompanies fault movement and causes earthquakes, or seismic vibrations. (p. 363)

electric current: the net movement of electric charges in a single direction, measured in amperes (A). (p. 400)

electric motor: device that converts electrical energy to mechanical energy by using the magnetic forces between an electromagnet and a permanent magnet to make a shaft rotate. (p. 435)

electric power: rate at which electrical energy is converted to another form of energy; expressed in watts (W). (p. 410)

electromagnet: temporary magnet made by wrapping a wire coil, carrying a current, around an iron core. (p. 432)

electromagnetic induction: process in which electric current is produced in a wire loop by a changing magnetic field. (p. 438)

electromagnetic waves: waves created by vibrating electric charges, can travel through a vacuum or through matter, and have a wide variety of frequencies and wavelengths. (p. 456)

electron cloud: area around the nucleus of an atom where the atom's electrons are most likely to be found. (p. 583)

electron dot diagram: uses the symbol for an element and dots representing the number of electrons in the element's outer energy level. (p. 594)

electrons: particles surrounding the center of an atom that have a charge of 1−. (p. 579)

element: substance with atoms that are all alike. (p. 552)

ellipse: elongated, closed curve with two foci; shape of Earth's orbit around the Sun. (p. 188)

El Niño: a warming of the Pacific Ocean every three to five years, which dramatically alters worldwide weather patterns, and occurs when prevailing trade winds weaken near the equator. (p. 539)

eclíptico: trayectoria anual de la tierra alrededor del Sol; también, la trayectoria aparente del Sol a través del zodíaco. (p. 192)

eficiencia: relación del trabajo efectuado por una máquina y el trabajo hecho en ésta, expresada en porcentaje. (p. 164)

energía elástica potencial: energía almacenada cuando un objeto es comprimido o estirado. (p. 131)

rebote elástico: liberación súbita de energía que acompaña al movimiento de las fallas y que causa terremotos o vibraciones sísmicas. (p. 363)

corriente eléctrica: movimiento neto de cargas eléctricas en una sola dirección, medido en amperios (A). (p. 400)

motor eléctrico: dispositivo que convierte la energía eléctrica en energía mecánica usando las fuerzas magnéticas entre un electroimán y un imán permanente para que el eje gire. (p. 435)

potencia eléctrica: proporción a la cual la energía eléctrica se convierte en otra forma de energía; se expresa en vatios (V). (p. 410)

electroimán: imán temporal que se hace envolviendo una bobina de cable que conduce una corriente, alrededor de un núcleo de hierro. (p. 432)

inducción electromagnética: proceso en el cual una corriente eléctrica es producida en un circuito cerrado de cable mediante un campo magnético cambiante. (p. 438)

ondas electromagnéticas: ondas creadas por la vibración de cargas eléctricas, que pueden viajar a través del vacío o de la materia y que tienen una amplia variedad de frecuencias y de longitudes de onda. (p. 456)

nube de electrones: área alrededor del núcleo de un átomo en donde hay más probabilidad de encontrar los electrones de los átomos. (p. 583)

diagrama de punto de electrones: usa el símbolo de un elemento y puntos que representan el número de electrones en el nivel de energía externo del elemento. (p. 594)

electrones: partículas que rodean el centro de un átomo que tienen la carga de 1−. (p. 579)

elemento: sustancia en la cual todos los átomos son iguales. (p. 552)

elipse: curva alargada y cerrada con dos distancias focales; forma de la órbita terrestre alrededor del Sol. (p. 188)

El Niño: calentamiento del Océano Pacífico cada tres a cinco años, el cual altera dramáticamente los patrones climáticos en todo del mundo y que ocurre cuando los vientos alisios se debilitan cerca del ecuador. (p. 539)

endothermic reaction: chemical reaction that requires heat energy in order to proceed. (p. 735)

energy: the ability to do work and cause a change to occur. (p. 128)

engineer: researcher who uses scientific information or ideas to solve problems or human needs and bring technology to consumers. (p. 53)

entropy: a measure of how spread out, or dispersed energy is. (p. 276)

epicenter: point on Earth's surface directly above an earthquake's focus. (p. 364)

equinox: occurs twice yearly (March and September), when the Sun is directly above Earth's equator, and the number of daylight hours equals the number of nighttime hours worldwide. (p. 195)

erosion: removal of surface material through weathering by agents such as wind and water. (p. 654)

exothermic reaction: chemical reaction in which energy is primarily given off in the form of heat. (p. 738)

experiment: organized procedure for testing a hypothesis; tests the effect of one thing on another under controlled conditions. (p. 8)

extrasolar planet: planet in orbit around another star. (p. 222)

extraterrestrial life: life on other worlds. (p. 239)

extrusive igneous rock: rock formed from rapidly cooling lava that has erupted at Earth's surface or formed from consolidated solid materials expelled from volcanoes. (p. 620)

reacción endotérmica: reacción química que requiere energía de calor para proceder. (p. 735)

energía: capacidad de realizar un trabajo y hacer que ocurra un cambio. (p. 128)

ingeniero: investigador que utiliza información científica o ideas para solucionar problemas o necesidades humanas y brindar tecnología a los consumidores. (p. 53)

entropía: una medida del grado de diseminación o dispersión de la energía. (p. 276)

epicentro: punto de la superficie terrestre directamente encima del foco de un terremoto. (p. 364)

equinoccio: fenómeno que ocurre dos veces al año (marzo y septiembre), cuando el Sol está directamente sobre el ecuador terrestre y en el que el número de horas en el día es igual al número de horas en la noche en todo el mundo. (p. 195)

erosión: remoción del material superficial a través del desgaste por agentes como el viento y el agua. (p. 654)

reacción exotérmica: reacción química en la cual la energía es inicialmente emitida en forma de calor. (p. 738)

experimento: procedimiento organizado para probar una hipótesis; prueba el efecto de una cosa sobre otra bajo condiciones controladas. (p. 8)

planeta extrasolar: planeta en órbita alrededor de otra estrella. (p. 222)

vida extraterrestre: vida en otros mundos. (p. 239)

roca ígnea extrusiva: roca formada a partir de lava que fue erupcionada a la superficie terrestre y que se enfrió rápidamente o formada a partir de materiales sólidos consolidados expulsados de los volcanes. (p. 620)

F

fault: crack in Earth's crust along which movement has taken place. (p. 364)

first law of motion: states that if the net force on an object is zero, then an object at rest remains at rest, or, if the object is moving, it continues moving with constant velocity. (p. 98)

first law of thermodynamics: states that the increase in thermal energy of a system equals the work done on the system plus the heat added to the system. (p. 274)

focus: point of origin of an earthquake. (p. 363)

foliated: type of metamorphic rock whose grains are arranged in layers or bands. (p. 631)

falla: fisura en la corteza terrestre a lo largo de la cual ha tenido lugar un movimiento. (p. 364)

primera ley del movimiento: ley que establece que si la fuerza neta sobre un objeto es cero, entonces un objeto en reposo permanece en reposo, o, si el objeto está moviéndose, éste continúa moviéndose con una velocidad constante. (p. 98)

primera ley de la termodinámica: establece que el aumento en la energía térmica de un sistema es igual al trabajo realizado sobre el sistema más el calor agregado a éste. (p. 274)

foco: punto de origen de un terremoto. (p. 363)

foliado: tipo de roca metamórfica cuyos granos están dispuestos en capas o bandas. (p. 631)

force: a push or pull exerted on an object. (p. 81)

fossil fuels: oil, natural gas, and coal; formed from the decayed remains of ancient plants and animals. (p. 487)

fossils: remains or traces of organisms found in the geologic rock record; can be direct remains such as bones, mold and cast formations, and trace impressions. (p. 671)

fracture: physical property of a mineral that causes it to break into uneven pieces. (p. 610)

frequency: the number of wavelengths that pass a fixed point each second; expressed in hertz (Hz). (p. 295)

friction: a force that opposes the sliding motion between objects that are in contact. (p. 83)

fuerza: impulso o tracción sobre un objeto. (p. 81)

combustibles fósiles: petróleo, gas natural y carbón formados por los restos descompuestos de plantas y animales ancestrales. (p. 487)

fósiles: restos o vestigios de organismos que se encuentran en el registro geológico; pueden ser restos directos como huesos, moldes, impresiones fosilizadas e impresiones de huellas. (p. 671)

fractura: propiedad física de un mineral que causa que éste se rompa en piezas asimétricas. (p. 610)

frecuencia: el número de longitudes de onda que pasan por un punto fijo en un segundo; expresa en hertz (Hz). (p. 295)

fricción: una fuerza que se opone al movimiento deslizante entre los objectos que están el contacto. (p. 83)

G

galaxy: large group of stars, gas, and dust held together by gravity; most commonly can be elliptical, spiral, and irregular. (p. 831)

galvanometer: a device that uses an electromagnet to measure electric current. (p. 434)

gamma ray: electromagnetic wave with no mass and no charge that travels at the speed of light and is usually emitted with alpha or beta particles from a decaying atomic nucleus; has a wavelength less than about ten trillionths of a meter. (pp. 467, 793)

Geiger counter: radiation detector that produces a click or a flash of light when a charged particle is detected. (p. 798)

generator: device that uses electromagnetic induction to convert mechanical energy to electrical energy. (p. 400)

geocentric model: Earth-centered model of the solar system. (p. 218)

geothermal energy: thermal energy in hot magma; can be converted by a power plant into electrical energy. (p. 505)

giant: late stage in a star's life cycle that occurs when its hydrogen fuel is depleted, its core contracts, and its outer layers expand and cool. (p. 825)

Global Positioning System (GPS): a system of satellites and ground monitoring stations that enable a receiver to determine its location at or above Earth's surface. (p. 475)

galaxia: grupo grande de estrellas, gas y polvo mantenidos juntos por la gravedad; comúnmente pueden ser elípticas, espirales e irregulares. (p. 831)

galvanómetro: dispositivo que usa un electroimán para medir la corriente eléctrica. (p. 434)

rayo gama: onda electromagnética sin masa ni carga que viaja a la velocidad de la luz y que usualmente es emitida con partículas alfa o beta a partir de un núcleo atómico en descomposición; tiene una electromagnética con longitudes de onda menores a diez trillonésimas de metro. (pp. 467, 793)

contador Geiger: detector de radiación que produce un sonido seco o un destello de luz al detectar una partícula cargada. (p. 798)

generador: dispositivo que usa inducción electromagnética para convertir energía mecánica en energía eléctrica. (p. 400)

modelo geocéntrico: modelo del sistema solar centrado en la tierra. (p. 218)

energía geotérmica: energía térmica en el magma caliente, la cual se puede convertir mediante una planta industrial en energía eléctrica. (p. 505)

gigante: última etapa en el ciclo de vida de una estrella que ocurre cuando su combustible hidrógeno es agotado, su núcleo se contrae y sus capas externas se expanden y enfrían. (p. 825)

Sistema de Posicionamiento Global (GPS): sistema de satélites y estaciones de monitoreo en tierra que permiten que un receptor determine su ubicación en o sobre la superficie terrestre. (p. 475)

global warming: increased atmospheric heating from activities such as fossil fuel burning, which have increased air pollution and concentrations of trace gases and dust and modified the water and carbon cycles. (p. 538)

graph: visual display of information or data that can provide a quick way to communicate a lot of information and allow scientists to observe patterns. (p. 22)

gravitational potential energy: energy stored by objects due to their position above Earth's surface; depends on the distance above Earth's surface and the object's mass. (p. 132)

gravity: attractive force between two objects that depends on the masses of the objects and the distance between them. (p. 104)

greenhouse effect: atmospheric warming involving heat absorption by trace gases such as carbon dioxide and water vapor. (p. 520)

group: vertical column in the periodic table. (p. 592)

H

half-life: amount of time it takes for half the nuclei in a sample of a radioactive isotope to decay. (p. 794)

hardness: physical property of a mineral that measures resistance to scratching. (p. 611)

heat: thermal energy that flows from a warmer material to a cooler material. (p. 257)

heat of fusion: amount of energy required to change a substance from the solid phase to the liquid phase. (p. 262)

heat of vaporization: the amount of energy required for the liquid at its boiling point to become a gas. (p. 262)

heliocentric model: Sun-centered model of the solar system. (p. 219)

heterogeneous (het uh ruh JEE nee us) mixture: mixture, such as mixed nuts or a dry soup mix, in which different materials are unevenly distributed and are easily identified. (p. 555)

homogeneous (hoh moh JEE nee us) mixture: solid, liquid, or gas that contains two or more substances blended evenly throughout. (p. 556)

hydrate: compound that has water chemically attached to its ions and written into its chemical formula. (p. 708)

calentamiento global: aumento de la temperatura atmosférica por actividades como la quema de combustibles fósiles, lo cual incrementa la polución del aire y las concentraciones de gases traza y polvo y modifica los ciclos del agua y del carbono. (p. 538)

gráfica: presentación visual de información que puede suministrar una forma rápida de comunicar gran cantidad de información y que permite que los científicos puedan observar los patrones. (p. 22)

energía gravitacional potencial: energía almacenada por objetos debido a su posición sobre la superficie terrestre, la cual depende de la distancia sobre la superficie terrestre y de la masa del objeto. (p. 132)

gravedad: fuerza de atracción entre dos objetos que depende de las masas de los objetos y de la distancia entre ellos. (p. 104)

efecto de invernadero: calentamiento atmosférico que involucra la absorción de calor por gases traza como el dióxido de carbono y el vapor de agua. (p. 520)

grupo: columna vertical en la tabla periódica. (p. 592)

vida media: tiempo requerido para que se descomponga la mitad de los núcleos de una muestra de isótopo radiactivo. (p. 794)

dureza: propiedad física de un mineral que mide la resistencia al desgaste. (p. 611)

calor: energía térmica que fluye de un material caliente a uno frío. (p. 257)

calor de fusión: cantidad de energía necesaria para cambiar una sustancia del estado sólido al líquido. (p. 262)

calor de vaporización: cantidad de energía necesaria para que un líquido en su punto de ebullición se convierta en gas. (p. 262)

modelo heliocéntrico: modelo del sistema solar centrado en el sol. (p. 219)

mezcla heterogénea: mezcla, tal como una mezcla de nueces o una mezcla seca para hacer sopa, en la cual diferentes materiales están distribuidos en forma desigual y se pueden identificar fácilmente. (p. 555)

mezcla homogénea: sólido, liquido, o gas que contiene dos o más sustancias mezcladas de manera uniforme en toda la mezcla. (p. 556)

hidrato: compuesto que contiene agua químicamente conectada a sus iones y representada en su fórmula química. (p. 708)

hydroelectricity: electricity produced from the energy of falling water. (p. 503)

hypothesis: educated guess using what you know and what you observe. (p. 8)

hidroelectricidad: electricidad producida a partir de la energía generada por una caída de agua. (p. 503)

hipótesis: suposición fundamentada que se basa en lo que se sabe y lo que se observa. (p. 8)

I

inclined plane: simple machine that consists of a sloping surface, such as a ramp, that reduces the amount of force needed to lift something by increasing the distance over which the force is applied. (p. 172)

independent variable: factor that, as it changes, affects the measure of another variable. (p. 9)

index of refraction: property of a material indicating how much light slows down when traveling in the material. (p. 329)

indicator: organic compound that changes color in acids and bases. (p. 764)

inertia: resistance of an object to a change in its motion. (p. 99)

infiltration: process by which water enters Earth to become groundwater, controlled by the slope of the land, type of surface material, and type and amount of vegetation. (p. 663)

infrared waves: electromagnetic waves that have a wavelength between about 1 mm and 750 billionths of a meter. (p. 464)

inhibitor: substance that slows down a chemical reaction or prevents it from occurring by combining with a reactant. (p. 740)

input force: force exerted on a machine. (p. 162)

instantaneous speed: speed of an object at a given point in time; is constant for an object moving with constant speed, and changes with time for an object that is slowing down or speeding up. (p. 71)

insulator: material in which electrons are not able to move easily. (p. 395); material in which heat flows slowly. (p. 270)

intensity: amount of energy that flows through a certain area in a specific amount of time. (p. 322)

interference: occurs when two or more waves overlap and combine to form a new wave. (p. 306)

internal combustion engine: heat engine that burns fuel inside the engine in chambers or cylinders. (p. 275)

intrusive igneous rock: coarse-grained rock formed from slowly cooling magma below Earth's surface. (p. 617)

plano inclinado: máquina simple que consiste de una superficie inclinada, tal como una rampa, que reduce la fuerza necesaria para levantar un objeto aumentando la distancia sobre la cual se aplica dicha fuerza. (p. 172)

variable independiente: factor que, a medida que cambia, afecta la medida de otra variable. (p. 9)

índice de refracción: propiedad de un material para indicar la cantidad de luz que se frena al pasar a través del material. (p. 329)

indicador: compuesto orgánico que cambia de color en presencia de ácidos y bases. (p. 764)

inercia: resistencia de un objeto a cambiar su movimiento. (p. 99)

infiltración: proceso mediante el cual el agua entra en la tierra para convertirse en agua subterránea, controlado por la pendiente del suelo, el tipo de material superficial y el tipo y cantidad de vegetación. (p. 663)

ondas infrarrojas: ondas electromagnéticas que tienen una longitud de onda entre aproximadamente 1 mm y 750 billonésimas de metro. (p. 464)

inhibidor: sustancia que reduce una reacción química o previene que ocurra por una combinación con un reactivo. (p. 740)

fuerza de entrada: fuerza ejercida sobre una máquina. (p. 162)

velocidad instantánea: velocidad de un objeto en un punto dado en el tiempo; es constante para un objeto que se mueve a una velocidad constante y cambia con el tiempo en un objeto que está reduciendo o aumentando su velocidad. (p. 71)

aislador: material a través del cual los electrones no se pueden mover con facilidad. (p. 395); material en el cual el calor fluye lentamente. (p. 270)

intensidad: cantidad de energía que fluye a través de cierta área en un tiempo específico. (p. 322)

interferencia: ocurre cuando dos o más ondas se sobreponen y combinan para formar una nueva onda. (p. 306)

motor de combustión interna: motor de calor que quema combustible en su interior en cámaras o cilindros. (p. 275)

roca ígnea intrusiva: roca áspera y granulosa formada a partir de un enfriamiento lento del magma debajo de la superficie terrestre. (p. 617)

ion: charged particle that has either more or fewer electrons than protons. (pp. 692, 707)

ionic bond: attraction formed between oppositely charged ions in an ionic compound. (p. 696)

isotopes: atoms of the same element that have different numbers of neutrons. (p. 586)

ion: partícula cargada que tiene ya sea más o menos electrones que protones. (pp. 692, 707)

enlace iónico: atracción formada entre iones con cargas opuestas en un compuesto iónico. (p. 696)

isótopos: átomos del mismo elemento que tienen diferente número de neutrones. (p. 586)

J

jet stream: high-speed, powerful air current that affects many weather processes, such as the development of storms. (p. 525)

joule: SI unit of energy. (p. 130)

Jupiter: largest and fifth planet from the Sun; has continuous, swirling, high-pressure gas storms, the largest of which is the Great Red Spot. (p. 231)

corriente a presión: corriente de aire poderosa y de alta velocidad que afecta a muchos procesos climáticos, como el desarrollo de las tormentas. (p. 525)

julio: unidad SI de energía. (p. 130)

Júpiter: quinto planeta más cercano al Sol, también es el más grande; tiene tormentas gaseosas arremolinadas y continuas de alta presión, la más grande de las cuales es la Gran Mancha Roja. (p. 231)

K

Kelvin: the SI unit for temperature, abbreviated K; a temperature change of 1 Kelvin is the same as a temperature change of 1°C. (p. 255)

kinetic energy: energy a moving object has because of its motion; depends on the mass and speed of the object. (p. 130)

kinetic theory: explanation of the behavior of molecules in matter; states that all matter is made of constantly moving particles that collide without losing energy. (p. 254)

Kelvin: la unidad del sistema internacional de medidas para la temperatura, cuya abreviatura es K; un cambio en la temperatura de 1 grado kelvin es lo mismo que un cambio en la temperatura de 1°C. (p. 255)

energía cinética: energía que tiene un cuerpo debido a su movimiento, la cual depende de la masa y velocidad del objeto. (p. 130)

teoría cinética: explicación del comportamiento de las moléculas en la materia, la cual establece que todas las sustancias están compuestas de partículas en constante movimiento que colindan sin perder energía. (p. 254)

L

La Niña: climatic phenomenon that occurs when Pacific trade winds are very strong and temperatures colder than normal; the opposite of El Niño. (p. 539)

latent heat: energy used to melt snow or evaporate water. (p. 520)

law of conservation of charge: states that charge can be transferred from one object to another but cannot be created or destroyed. (p. 393)

law of conservation of energy: states that energy can never be created or destroyed. (p. 139)

law of conservation of mass: states that the mass of all substances present before a chemical change equals the mass of all the substances remaining after the change. (p. 567)

La Niña: fenómeno climático que ocurre cuando los vientos alisios del pacífico son muy fuertes y la temperatura disminuye más de lo normal; lo opuesto a El Niño. (p. 539)

calor latente: energía utilizada para derretir nieve o evaporar agua. (p. 520)

ley de la conservación de carga: establece que la carga puede ser transferida entre un objeto y otro pero no puede ser creada o destruida. (p. 393)

ley de la conservación de energía: establece que la energía nunca puede ser creada ni destruida. (p. 139)

ley de conservación de la masa: establece que la masa de todas las sustancias presente antes de un cambio químico es igual a la masa de todas las sustancias resultantes después del cambio. (p. 567)

law of conservation of momentum: states that if a group of objects exerts forces only on each other, then the total momentum of the objects doesn't change (p. 117)

lee rain shadow: area of reduced precipitation on one side of a mountain range. (p. 533)

lever: simple machine consisting of a bar free to pivot about a fixed point called the fulcrum. (p. 166)

light-year: distance light travels in one year—about 9.5 billion km. (p. 820)

Local Group: cluster of about 45 galaxies, including the Milky Way. (p. 831)

longshore current: movement of water parallel to the shoreline caused by waves colliding with the shore at an angle, which results in net sediment transport parallel to the shoreline. (p. 659)

loudness: human perception of sound intensity. (p. 322)

lunar eclipse: occurs during full moon, when the Moon enters Earth's umbra and Earth casts a curved shadow on the Moon's surface. (p. 202)

ley de la conservación del movimiento: ley que establece que si en un grupo de objetos se ejercen fuerzas sólo en unos sobre otros, entonces el momento total de los objetos no cambia. (p. 117)

sombra lluviosa a sotavento: área de precipitación reducida en un lado de un sistema montañoso. (p. 533)

palanca: máquina simple que consiste de una barra que puede girar sobre un punto fijo llamado pivote. (p. 166)

año luz: distancia que viaja la luz en un año—cerca de 9 500 millones de km. (p. 820)

Grupo Local: agrupación de cerca de 45 galaxias, incluyendo la Vía Láctea. (p. 831)

corriente costera: movimiento de agua paralelo a la línea costera causado por olas que colisionan con la costa en ángulo, lo cual resulta en transporte neto de sedimentos paralelo a la línea costera. (p. 659)

volumen de sonido: percepción humana de la intensidad del sonido. (p. 322)

eclipse lunar: fenómeno que ocurre durante la luna llena, cuando la Luna entra en el cono de sombra de la Tierra y ésta proyecta una sombra curva sobre la superficie de la Luna. (p. 202)

M

machine: device that makes doing work. easier by increasing the force applied to an object, changing the direction of an applied force, or increasing the distance over which a force can be applied. (p. 160)

magma: molten rock material found inside Earth. (p. 613)

magnetic domain: group of atoms in a magnetic material with the magnetic poles of the atoms pointing in the same direction. (p. 429)

magnetic field: surrounds a magnet and exerts a force on other magnets and objects made of magnetic materials. (p. 425)

magnetic pole: region on a magnet where the magnetic force exerted by a magnet is strongest; like poles repel and opposite poles attract. (p. 425)

magnetism: the properties and interactions of magnets. (p. 424)

main sequence: section of an H-R diagram that is plotted from the upper left to the lower right and contains 90 percent of all known stars. (p. 823)

maria: relatively flat, dark-colored regions on the Moon's surface. (p. 203)

máquina: artefacto que facilita la ejecución del trabajo aumentando la fuerza que se aplica a un objeto, cambiando la dirección de una fuerza aplicada o aumentando la distancia sobre la cual se puede aplicar una fuerza. (p. 160)

magma: material rocoso derretido que se encuentra en el interior de la Tierra. (p. 613)

dominio magnético: grupo de átomos en un material magnético en el cual los polos magnéticos de los átomos apuntan en la misma dirección. (p. 429)

campo magnético: rodea a un imán y ejerce una fuerza sobre otros imanes y objetos hechos de materiales magnéticos. (p. 425)

polo magnético: zona en un imán en donde la fuerza magnética ejercida por un imán es la más fuerte; los polos iguales se repelen y los polos opuestos se atraen. (p. 425)

magnetismo: propiedades e interacciones de los imanes. (p. 424)

secuencia principal: sección de un diagrama H-R que es graficado desde la parte superior izquierda hasta la parte inferior derecha y contiene el 90% de todas las estrellas conocidas. (p. 823)

maría: egiones relativamente planas y de color oscuro sobre la superficie de la luna. (p. 203)

Glossary/Glosario

maritime climate: climate with a strong ocean influence and milder temperatures. (p. 532)

Mars: fourth planet from the Sun; called the red planet because of high concentrations of iron oxide. (p. 225)

mass: amount of matter in an object. (p. 19)

mass number: sum of the number of protons and neutrons in an atom's nucleus. (p. 585)

mechanical advantage (MA): ratio of the output force exerted by a machine to the input force applied to the machine. (p. 164)

mechanical energy: sum of the potential energy and kinetic energy in a system. (p. 136)

medium: matter in which a wave travels. (p. 289)

Mercury: closest planet to the Sun; has a larger than expected iron core. (p. 223)

meteoroid: rocky solar system object formed from pieces of comets and asteroids. (pp. 236, 633)

microwaves: radio waves with wavelengths of between about 1 m and 1 mm. (p. 463)

mid-ocean ridge (MOR): a continuous system of twin mountain ranges with a rift valley between them that extends around Earth on the seafloor; formed where two oceanic plates are forced apart due to magma rising from Earth's mantle; a source of new rock. (p. 356)

Milky Way: our spiral-shaped galaxy, which contains the solar system and about 400 billion stars, including the Sun, and measures about 100,000 light-years across. (p. 831)

mineral: naturally occurring, inorganic, crystalline solid with a predictable chemical composition and a characteristic set of physical properties. (p. 609)

model: can be used to represent an idea, object, or event that is too big, too small, too complex, or too dangerous to observe or test directly. (p. 11)

molecule: a neutral particle that forms as a result of electron sharing. (p. 697)

momentum: property of a moving object that equals its mass times its velocity. (p. 116)

moon phase: changing appearance of the Moon as viewed from Earth, depending on the relative positions of the Sun, the Moon, Earth, and the observer. (p. 199)

clima marítimo: clima con una fuerte influencia oceánica y temperaturas templadas. (p. 532)

marte: cuarto planeta más cercano al Sol; llamado el planeta rojo debido a altas concentraciones de óxido de hierro. (p. 225)

masa: cantidad de materia en un objeto. (p. 19)

número de masa: suma del número de protones y neutrones en el núcleo de un átomo. (p. 585)

ventaja mecánica (MA): relación de la fuerza ejercida por una máquina y la fuerza aplicada a dicha máquina. (p. 164)

energía mecánica: suma de la energía potencial y energía cinética en un sistema. (p. 136)

medio: materia a través de la cual viaja una onda. (p. 289)

Mercurio: planeta más cercano al sol; tiene un núcleo de hierro más grande de lo esperado. (p. 223)

meteorito: objeto rocoso del sistema solar formado de pedazos de cometas y asteroides. (pp. 236, 633)

microondas: ondas de radio con longitudes de onda entre aproximadamente 1 mm y 1 m. (p. 463)

canto del mediados de-océano (MOR): un sistema continuo de la montaña gemela se extiende con un valle de la grieta entre ellos que extienda alrededor de la tierra en el seafloor; formado donde están dos placas oceánicas separado forzado debido al magma que se levanta de la capa de la tierra; una fuente de la roca nueva. (p. 356)

Vía Láctea: nuestra galaxia en forma de espiral, la cual contiene al sistema solar y cerca de 400 000 millones de estrellas, incluyendo al Sol, y tiene una extensión de aproximadamente 100 000 años luz. (p. 831)

mineral: sólido de origen natural, inorgánico y cristalino con una composición química predecible y un conjunto característico de propiedades físicas. (p. 609)

modelo: puede ser usado para representar una idea, objeto o evento que es demasiado grande, demasiado pequeño, demasiado complejo o demasiado peligroso para ser observado o probado directamente. (p. 11)

molécula: partícula neutra que se forma al compartir electrones. (p. 697)

ímpetu: propiedad de un objeto en movimiento que es igual a su masa por su velocidad. (p. 116)

fase lunar: cambio en la apariencia de la Luna según es vista desde la Tierra, dependiendo de las posiciones relativas del Sol, la Luna, la Tierra y el observador. (p. 199)

Glossary/Glosario

N

Neptune: eighth planet from the Sun; has storms similar to Jupiter's and appears blue because of atmospheric methane. (p. 235)

net force: sum of the forces that are acting on an object. (p. 82)

neutron: neutral particle, composed of quarks, inside the nucleus of an atom. (p. 579)

nonpolar molecule: molecule that shares electrons equally and does not have oppositely charged ends. (p. 700)

nonrenewable resources: natural resource, such as fossil fuels, that cannot be replaced by natural processes as quickly as it is used. (p. 493)

nuclear fission: process of splitting an atomic nucleus into two or more nuclei with smaller masses. (p. 801)

nuclear fusion: reaction in which two or more atomic nuclei form a nucleus with a larger mass. (p. 803)

nuclear reactor: uses energy from a controlled nuclear chain reaction to generate electricity. (p. 494)

nuclear waste: radioactive by-product that results when radioactive materials are used. (p. 498)

nucleus: positively charged center of an atom that contains protons and neutrons and is surrounded by a cloud of electrons. (p. 579)

Neptuno: octavo planeta más cercano al Sol; tiene tormentas similares a las de Júpiter y parece azul debido al metano atmosférico. (p. 235)

fuerza neta: suma de fuerzas que actúan sobre un objeto. (p. 82)

neutrón: partícula neutra, compuesta por quarks, dentro del núcleo de un átomo. (p. 579)

molécula no polar: molécula que comparte equitativamente los electrones y que no tiene extremos con cargas opuestas. (p. 700)

recursos no renovables: recursos naturales, tales como combustibles fósiles, que no pueden ser reemplazados por procesos naturales tan pronto como son usados. (p. 493)

fisión nuclear: proceso de división de un núcleo atómico en dos o más núcleos con masas más pequeñas. (p. 801)

fusión nuclear: reacción en la cual dos o más núcleos atómicos forman un núcleo con mayor masa. (p. 803)

reactor nuclear: usa energía de una reacción nuclear controlada en cadena para generar electricidad. (p. 494)

desperdicio nuclear: subproducto radioactivo que resulta del uso de materiales radiactivos. (p. 498)

núcleo: centro de un átomo con carga positiva que contiene protones y neutrones y está rodeado por una nube de electrones. (p. 579)

O

Ohm's law: states that the current in a circuit equals the voltage difference divided by the resistance. (p. 405)

opaque: material that absorbs or reflects all light and does not transmit any light. (p. 327)

output force: force applied by a machine. (p. 162)

oxidation number: positive or negative number that indicates how many electrons an atom has gained, lost, or shared to become stable. (p. 703)

ley de Ohm: establece que la corriente en un circuito es igual a la diferencia de voltaje dividida por la resistencia. (p. 405)

opaco: material que absorbe o refleja toda la luz pero no la transmite. (p. 327)

fuerza de salida: fuerza aplicada por una máquina. (p. 162)

número de oxidación: número positivo o negativo que indica cuántos electrones ha ganado, perdido o compartido un átomo para poder ser estable. (p. 703)

P

parallel circuit: circuit in which electric current has more than one path to follow. (p. 406)

circuito paralelo: circuito en el cual la corriente eléctrica tiene más de una trayectoria para seguir. (p. 406)

period: the amount of time it takes one wavelength to pass a fixed point; expressed in seconds. (p. 295); horizontal row in the periodic table. (p. 595)

período: la cantidad de tiempo que requiere una longitud de onda para pasar un punto fijo; expresa en segundos. (p. 295); fila horizontal en la tabla periódica. (p. 595)

periodic table: organized list of all known elements that are arranged by increasing atomic number and by changes in chemical and physical properties. (p. 588)

tabla periódica: lista organizada de todos los elementos conocidos y que han sido ordenados de manera ascendente por número atómico y por cambios en sus propiedades químicas y físicas. (p. 588)

permeability: a measure of the ability of a fluid to pass through a material. (p. 665)

permeabilidad: medida de la capacidad de un fluido para pasar a través de un material. (p. 665)

petroleum: liquid fossil fuel formed from decayed remains of ancient organisms; can be refined into fuels and used to make plastics. (p. 489)

petróleo: combustible fósil líquido que se forma a partir de residuos en descomposición de organismos ancestrales y que puede ser refinado para producir combustibles y usado para hacer plásticos. (p. 489)

pH: a measure of the concentration of hydronium ions in a solution using a scale ranging from 0 to 14, with 0 being the most acidic and 14 being the most basic. (p. 773)

pH: medida de la concentración de iones de hidronio en una solución, usando una escala de 0 a 14, en la cual 0 es la más ácida y 14 la más básica. (p. 773)

photon: particle that electromagnetic waves sometimes behave like; has energy that increases as the frequency of the electromagnetic wave increases. (p. 460)

fotón: partícula como la cual algunas veces se comportan las ondas electromagnéticas; tiene energía que aumenta a medida que la frecuencia de la onda electromagnética aumenta. (p. 460)

photosphere: light-emitting surface of the Sun. (p. 827)

fotosfera: superficie solar que emite luz. (p. 827)

photovoltaic cell: device that converts solar energy into electricity; also called a solar cell. (p. 501)

células fotovoltaicas: dispositivo que convierte la energía solar en electricidad; también llamada celda solar. (p. 501)

physical change: any change in size, shape, or state of matter in which the identity of the substance remains the same. (p. 562)

cambio físico: cualquier cambio en tamaño, forma o estado de una sustancia en la cual la identidad de la sustancia sigue siendo la misma. (p. 562)

physical property: any characteristic of a material, such as size or shape, that you can observe or attempt to observe without changing the identity of the material. (p. 560)

propiedad física: cualquier característica de un material, tal como tamaño o forma, que se puede haber observar o tratado de observar sin cambiar la identidad del material. (p. 560)

pigment: colored material that is used to change the color of other substances. (p. 342)

pigmento: material de color que se usa para cambiar el color de otras sustancias. (p. 342)

pilot plant: scaled-down version of real production equipment that closely models actual manufacturing conditions and is used to test a new manufacturing process. (p. 56)

planta piloto: versión a escala reducida de un equipo de producción real que simula cercanamente las condiciones reales de fabricación y es utilizada para probar un proceso de fabricación nuevo. (p. 56)

pitch: how high or low a sound seems; related to the frequency of the sound waves. (p. 323)

altura: qué tan alto o bajo parece un sonido; tiene relación con la frecuencia de las ondas sonoras. (p. 323)

plane mirror: flat, smooth mirror that reflects light to form upright, virtual images. (p. 331)

espejo plano: espejo plano y liso que refleja la luz para formar imágenes verticales y virtuales. (p. 331)

plasma: matter consisting of positively and negatively charged particles. (p. 261)

plasma: materia consistente de partículas con cargas positivas y negativas. (p. 261)

Pluto: smallest and ninth planet from the Sun; has a thin atmosphere and a solid, ice-rock surface. (p. 236)

Plutón: noveno planeta y el más lejano al Sol, también el más pequeño; tiene una atmósfera delgada y una superficie sólida de hielo y roca. (p. 236)

polar molecule: molecule with a slightly positive end and a slightly negative end as a result of electrons being shared unequally. (p. 700)

molécula polar: molécula con un extremo ligeramente positivo y otro ligeramente negativo como resultado de un compartir desigual de los electrones. (p. 700)

polyatomic ion: positively or negatively charged, covalently bonded group of atoms. (p. 707)

porosity: empty space in sedimentary rock in which water, oil, and natural gas are stored within Earth. (p. 625)

potential energy: stored energy an object has due to its position. (p. 131)

power: amount of work done, or the amount of energy transferred, divided by the time required to do the work or transfer the energy; measured in watts (W). (p. 157)

precision: describes how closely measurements are to each other and how carefully the measurements were made. (p. 14)

principle of superposition: states that the oldest rocks in an undisturbed sequence of rocks are at the bottom of the undisturbed sequence. (p. 670)

product: in a chemical reaction, the new substance that is formed. (p. 720)

proton: particle, composed of quarks, inside the nucleus of an atom that has a charge of 1+. (p. 579)

prototype: first full-scale model built to performance-test a new product. (p. 56)

pulley: simple machine that consists of a grooved wheel with a rope, chain, or cable running along the groove; can be either fixed or movable. (p. 169)

ion poliatómico: grupo de átomos enlazados covalentemente, con carga positiva o negativa. (p. 707)

porosidad: espacio vacío en la roca sedimentaria en el que el agua, el petróleo y el gas natural son almacenados dentro de la Tierra. (p. 625)

energía potencial: energía almacenada que un objeto tiene debido a su posición. (p. 131)

potencia: cantidad de trabajo realizado o cantidad de energía transferida, dividida por el tiempo requerido para realizar el trabajo o transferir la energía; medida en vatios (V). (p. 157)

precisión: descripción de la cercanía de las mediciones una respecto a otra y del cuidado con el que se hacen éstas. (p. 14)

principio de superposición (estratigráfico): principio que establece que las rocas más antiguas en una secuencia de rocas sin perturbaciones están en la parte más baja de la secuencia no perturbada. (p. 670)

producto: es la nueva sustancia que se forma en una reacción química. (p. 720)

protón: partícula, compuesta por quarks, dentro del núcleo de un átomo que tiene una carga de 1+. (p. 579)

prototipo: el primer modelo a escala completa construido para probar el desempeño de un producto nuevo. (p. 56)

polea: máquina simple que consiste de una rueda acanalada con una cuerda, cadena o cable que se desliza por el canal y que puede ser fija o móvil. (p. 169)

Q

quarks: particles of matter that make up protons and neutrons. (p. 579)

quarks: partículas de materia que constituyen los protones y neutrones. (p. 579)

R

radiant energy: energy carried by an electromagnetic wave. (p. 459)

radiation: transfer of thermal energy by electromagnetic waves. (p. 269)

radioactivity: process that occurs when a nucleus decays and emits alpha, beta, or gamma radiation. (p. 788)

radio telescope: telescope that collects and magnifies radio waves. (p. 821)

radio waves: electromagnetic waves with wavelengths longer than about 1 mm, used for communications. (p. 463)

energía radiante: energía transportada por una onda electromagnética. (p. 459)

radiación: transferencia de energía térmica mediante ondas electromagnéticas. (p. 269)

radiactividad: proceso que ocurre cuando un núcleo se descompone y emite radiación alfa, beta o gama. (p. 788)

radio telescopio: telescopio que colecta y magnifica las ondas de radio. (p. 821)

ondas de radio: ondas electromagnéticas con longitudes de onda más largas de aproximadamente 1 mm y que se usan en las comunicaciones. (p. 463)

rarefaction: the least dense regions of a compressional wave. (p. 294)

rate of reaction: the speed at which reactants are consumed and products are produced in a given reaction. (p. 738)

reactant: in a chemical reaction, the substance that reacts. (p. 720)

reflecting telescope: optical instrument that uses a concave mirror to collect light and a lens to magnify an image. (p. 820)

refracting telescope: optical instrument that uses double convex lenses to collect light and magnify an image. (p. 819)

refraction: the bending of a wave as it changes speed in moving from one medium to another. (p. 302)

regolith: layer of debris on the Moon's surface formed by the accumulation of meteoric material. (p. 203)

relative dating: process of dating objects or events in time order, or sequence, based on logical relationships; may or may not involve the use of numbers. (p. 669)

renewable resource: energy source that is replaced almost as quickly as it is used. (p. 501)

resistance: tendency for a material to oppose electron flow and change electrical energy into thermal energy and light; measured in ohms (Ω). (p. 403)

resonance: the process by which an object is made to vibrate by absorbing energy at its natural frequencies. (p. 309)

revolution: movement of Earth in its orbit around the Sun; used to measure time in years. (p. 192)

rift valley: long, linear, dropped-down valley between twin, parallel mountain ranges produced by faulting. (p. 356)

rock: consolidated, natural mixture of minerals, volcanic glass, or rock fragments. (p. 617)

rock cycle: continuous process that forms and changes rocks on Earth's surface and deep below the surface. (p. 634)

rotation: spinning of Earth on its axis; used to measure time in days. (p. 192)

rarefacción: las regiones menos densas de una onda de compresión. (p. 294)

fasa de reacción: velocidad a la que los reactantes son consumidos y los productos son generados en una reacción dada. (p. 738)

reactante: es la sustancia que reacciona en una reacción química. (p. 720)

felescopio de reflexión: instrumento óptico que utiliza un espejo cóncavo para captar la luz y una lente para magnificar una imagen. (p. 820)

felescopio de refracción: instrumento óptico que utiliza lentes convexas dobles para captar la luz y magnificar una imagen. (p. 819)

refracción: curvatura de una onda al cambiar su velocidad al pasar de un medio a otro. (p. 302)

regolito: capa de escombros sobre la superficie lunar formada por la acumulación de material meteórico. (p. 203)

datación relativa: proceso de datar objetos o eventos en un orden o secuencia temporal, basado en relaciones lógicas; puede o no involucrar el uso de números. (p. 669)

recursos renovables: fuente de energía que es reemplazada casi tan pronto como es usada. (p. 501)

resistencia: tendencia de un material de oponerse al fluido de los electrones y convertir la energía eléctrica en energía térmica y luz; se mide en ohmios (Ω). (p. 403)

resonancia: el proceso por el cual un objeto vibra al absorber energía en sus frecuencias naturales. (p. 309)

revolución: movimiento de la Tierra en su órbita alrededor del sol, utilizado para medir el tiempo en años. (p. 192)

valle de hendidura: valle alargado, lineal y deprimido producido por una falla que se encuentra entre dos sistemas montañosos paralelos. (p. 356)

roca: mezcla natural y consolidada de minerales, obsidiana o fragmentos de roca. (p. 617)

ciclo de la roca: proceso continuo que forma y cambia las rocas sobre y debajo de la superficie terrestre. (p. 634)

rotación: giro de la Tierra sobre su eje, utilizado para medir el tiempo en días. (p. 192)

S

saturated solution: any solution that contains all the solute it can hold at a given temperature. (p. 761)

solución saturada: cualquier solución que contiene todo el soluto que puede retener a una temperatura determinada. (p. 761)

Saturn: second-largest and sixth planet from the Sun; has the most complex system of rings. (p. 234)

Saturno: sexto planeta más cercano al Sol, también el segundo más grande; tiene el sistema de anillos más complejo. (p. 234)

scientific law: statement about what happens in nature that seems to be true all the time; does not explain why or how something happens. (p. 12)

ley científica: enunciado acerca de lo que ocurre en la naturaleza, lo cual parece ser cierto en todo momento, sin explicar cómo o por qué algo ocurre. (p. 12)

scientific methods: organized set of investigation procedures that can include stating a problem, forming a hypothesis, researching and gathering information, testing a hypothesis, analyzing data, and drawing conclusions. (p. 7)

métodos científico: conjunto organizado de procedimientos de investigación que puede incluir el planteamiento de un problema, formulación de una hipótesis, investigación y recopilación de información, comprobación de la hipótesis, análisis de datos y elaboración de conclusiones. (p. 7)

screw: simple machine that consists of an inclined plane wrapped in a spiral around a cylindrical post. (p. 173)

tornillo: máquina simple que consiste de un plano inclinado envuelto en espiral alrededor de un poste cilíndrico. (p. 173)

sea breeze: cooling breeze that blows from the sea toward land during the afternoon. (p. 533)

brisa marina: brisa refrescante que sopla del mar hacia la tierra durante la tarde. (p. 533)

second law of motion: states that the acceleration of an object is in the same direction as the net force on the object, and that the acceleration equals the net force divided by the mass. (p. 102)

segunda ley de movimiento: establece que la aceleración de un objeto es en la misma dirección que la fuerza neta del objeto y que la aceleración es igual a la fuerza neta dividida por su masa. (p. 102)

second law of thermodynamics: states that is impossible for heat to flow from a cool object to a warmer object unless work is done. (p. 274)

segunda ley de la termodinámica: establece que es imposible que el calor fluya de un objeto frío a uno caliente, a menos que se realice un trabajo. (p. 274)

sediment transport: movement of eroded materials by wind, water, and/or glaciers from one location to another. (p. 654)

transporte de sedimentos: movimiento de materiales erosionados por el viento, agua o glaciares de un lugar a otro. (p. 654)

Sedna: unofficial name for object 2003 VB12, a distant planetoid with a very elliptical orbit. (p. 237)

Sedna: nombre no oficial para el objeto 2003 VB12, un planetoide distante con una órbita muy elíptica. (p. 237)

series circuit: circuit in which electric current has only one path to follow. (p. 407)

circuito en serie: circuito en el cual la corriente eléctrica tiene una sola trayectoria para seguir. (p. 407)

shadow zone: "dead zone" between 105 and 140 degrees from an earthquake's epicenter, where nothing is recorded on a seismogram. (p. 371)

zona de sombra: "zona muerta" entre 105 y 140 grados del epicentro de un terremoto, donde nada es registrado sobre un sismograma. (p. 371)

shield volcano: broad, flat volcano formed by layers of free-flowing, high-temperature, basaltic lava. (p. 377)

volcán de escudo: or capas de lava basáltica que fluyeron libremente a alta temperatura. (p. 377)

simple machine: machine that does work with only one movement—lever, pulley, wheel and axle, inclined plane, screw, and wedge. (p. 166)

máquina simple: máquina que realiza el trabajo con un solo movimiento: palanca, polea, rueda y eje, plano inclinado, tornillo y cuña. (p. 166)

single-displacement reaction: chemical reaction in which one element replaces another element in a compound. (p. 731)

reacción de un solo desplazamiento: reacción química en la cual un elemento reemplaza a otro elemento en un compuesto. (p. 731)

sliding friction: frictional force that opposes the motion of two surfaces sliding past each other. (p. 84)

fricción deslizante: fuerza de fricción que se opone al movimiento de dos superficies que se deslizan entre sí. (p. 84)

society: group of people who share similar values and beliefs. (p. 46)

sociedad: grupo de personas que comparten valores y creencias similares. (p. 46)

soil: mixture of weathered rock, decaying organic matter, water, and air that overlies bedrock and is capable of supporting plant life. (p. 650)

solar eclipse: occurs during new moon, when the Moon passes directly between the Sun and Earth, casting a shadow on part of Earth. (p. 201)

solenoid: a wire wrapped into a cylindrical coil. (p. 432)

solstice: occurs twice yearly (June and December), when the Sun reaches its greatest distance north or south of the equator. (p. 195)

solubility: maximum amount of a solute that can be dissolved in a given amount of solvent at a given temperature. (p. 759)

solute: in a solution, the substance being dissolved. (p. 753)

solution: homogeneous mixture that remains constantly and uniformly mixed and has particles that are so small they cannot be seen with a microscope. (pp. 556, 752)

solvent: in a solution, the substance in which the solute is dissolved. (p. 753)

specific heat: amount of thermal energy needed to raise the temperature of 1 kg of a material 1°C. (p. 257)

spectroscope: device that disperses light into its component wavelengths, using a prism or diffraction grating. (p. 822)

speed: distance an object travels per unit of time. (p. 71)

sphere: three-dimensional, round object whose surface is the same distance from the center in all directions. (p. 186)

standing wave: a wave pattern that forms when waves of equal wavelength and amplitude, but traveling in opposite directions, continuously interfere with each other; has points called nodes that do not move. (p. 308)

static electricity: the accumulation of excess electric charge on an object. (p. 392)

static friction: frictional force that prevents two surfaces from sliding past each other. (p. 84)

streak: color of a mineral in powdered form; helps identify a mineral and can be observed by rubbing a mineral on a white porcelain tile. (p. 611)

strong acid: any acid that dissociates almost completely in solution. (p. 771)

strong base: any base that dissociates completely in solution. (p. 772)

suelo: mezcla de rocas degradadas, materia orgánica en descomposición, agua y aire que yace sobre el lecho rocoso y que es capaz de soportar la vida vegetal. (p. 650)

eclipse solar: ocurre durante la luna nueva, cuando la Luna pasa directamente entre Sol y la Tierra, proyectando una sombra sobre una parte de la Tierra. (p. 201)

solenoide: cable envuelto en forma de bobina cilíndrica. (p. 432)

solsticio: fenómeno que ocurre dos veces al año (junio y diciembre), cuando el sol alcanza su mayor distancia al norte o al sur del ecuador. (p. 195)

solubilidad: máxima cantidad de soluto que puede ser disuelto en una cantidad dada de solvente a una temperatura determinada. (p. 759)

soluto: en una solución, la sustancia que está disuelta. (p. 753)

solución: mezcla homogénea que permanece constante y uniformemente mezclada y que tiene partículas tan pequeñas que no pueden ser vistas en un microscopio. (pp. 556, 752)

solvente: en una solución, la sustancia en la cual se disuelve el soluto. (p. 753)

calor específico: cantidad de energía térmica necesaria para aumentar un grado centígrado la temperatura de un kilogramo de material. (p. 257)

espectroscopio: dispositivo que dispersa la luz en las longitudes de onda que la componen, utilizando un prisma o rejilla de difracción. (p. 822)

velocidad: distancia que recorre un objeto por unidad de tiempo. (p. 71)

esfera: objeto redondo tridimensional cuya superficie está a la misma distancia desde el centro hacia todas las direcciones. (p. 186)

onda estacionaria: patrón de una onda que se forma cuando ondas con la misma longitud de onda y amplitud, pero que viajan en direcciones opuestas, interfieren continuamente entre sí; tiene puntos llamados nodos que no se mueven. (p. 308)

electricidad estática: la acumulación del exceso de carga eléctrica en un objeto. (p. 392)

fricción estática: fuerza que evita que dos superficies en contacto se deslicen una sobre otra. (p. 84)

veta: color de un mineral en forma de polvo; ayuda a identificar un mineral y puede observarse al frotar un mineral sobre una losa de porcelana blanca. (p. 611)

ácido fuerte: cualquier ácido que se disocie casi por completo en una solución. (p. 771)

base fuerte: cualquier base que se disocie completamente en una solución. (p. 772)

strong force: attractive force that acts between protons and neutrons in an atomic nucleus. (p. 878)

subduction: occurs when lithospheric plates converge and the edge of one plate is forced downward beneath another; recycles old lithosphere. (p. 359)

substance: element or compound that cannot be broken down into simpler components and maintain the properties of the original substance. (p. 552)

subtropical high: persistent, relatively stationary, high-pressure system. (p. 525)

sunspots: cool, darker areas of the Sun's photosphere. (p. 827)

supersaturated solution: any solution that contains more solute than a saturated solution at the same temperature. (p. 762)

suspension: heterogeneous mixture containing a liquid in which visible particles settle. (p. 558)

synthesis reaction: chemical reaction in which two or more substances combine to form a different substance. (p. 731)

fuerza de atracción: fuerza de atracción que actúa entre protones y neutrones en un núcleo atómico. (p. 878)

subducción: fenómeno que ocurre cuando las placas litosféricas convergen y el borde de una placa es forzado a pasar por debajo del otro; recicla la litosfera antigua. (p. 359)

sustancia: elemento o compuesto que no se puede descomponer en componentes más simples y que mantiene las propiedades de la sustancia original. (p. 552)

alto subtropical: sistema persistente de alta presión relativamente estacionario. (p. 525)

manchas solares: áreas frías y más oscuras de la fotosfera solar. (p. 827)

solución sobresaturada: cualquier solución que contenga más solutos que una solución saturada a la misma temperatura. (p. 762)

suspensión: mezcla heterogénea que contiene un líquido en el cual las partículas visibles se sedimentan. (p. 558)

reacción síntesis: reacción química en la cual se combinan dos o más sustancias para formar una sustancia diferente. (p. 731)

T

technology: application of science to help people. (p. 13)

temperature: measure of the average kinetic energy of all the particles in an object. (p. 255)

temperature inversion: an increase of temperature with height, resulting in very stable air that resists the rising needed for cloud formation or dispersal of air pollution. (p. 519)

texture: describes the size and arrangement of rock components and can help indicate how a rock formed. (p. 617)

theory: explanation of things or events that is based on knowledge gained from many observations and investigations. (p. 12)

thermal energy: sum of the kinetic and potential energy of the particles in an object; is transferred by conduction, convection, and radiation. (p. 256)

third law of motion: states that when one object exerts a force on a second object, the second object exerts a force on the first object that is equal in strength and in the opposite direction. (p. 113)

tecnología: aplicación de la ciencia en beneficio de la población. (p. 13)

temperatura: medida de la energía cinética promedio de todas las partículas en un objeto. (p. 255)

inversión de temperatura: incremento de la temperatura con la altura, resultando en aire muy estable que resiste la elevación necesaria para la formación de nubes o dispersión de la polución del aire. (p. 519)

textura: patrón que describe el tamaño y disposición de los componentes rocosos y que puede ayudar a indicar cómo está formada la roca. (p. 617)

teoría: explicación de las cosas o eventos que se basa en el conocimiento obtenido a partir de numerosas observaciones e investigaciones. (p. 12)

energía térmica: suma de la energía cinética y potencial de las partículas en un objeto, la cual se transfiere por conducción, convección y radiación. (p. 256)

tercera ley de movimiento: establece que cuando un objeto ejerce una fuerza sobre un segundo objeto, el segundo objeto ejerce una fuerza igual de fuerte sobre el primer objeto y en dirección opuesta. (p. 113)

Glossary/Glosario

tide: rise and fall in Earth's sea level, caused by a giant wave formed by the gravitational pull of the Sun and Moon. (p. 199)

time zone: 15°-wide area on Earth's surface in which the time is the same. (p. 190)

tracer: radioactive isotope, such as iodine-131, that can be detected by the radiation it emits after it is absorbed by a living organism. (p. 804)

transceiver: device that transmits one radio signal and receives another radio signal at the same time, allowing a cordless phone user to talk and listen at the same time. (p. 473)

transform boundary: plate tectonic boundary that exists as a large fault, or crack, along which lithospheric plates move in a horizontal direction. (p. 360)

transformer: device that uses electromagnetic induction to increase or decrease the voltage of an alternating current. (p. 443)

translucent: material that transmits some light but not enough to see objects clearly through it. (p. 327)

transmutation: process of changing one element to another through radioactive decay. (p. 792)

transparent: material that transmits almost all the light striking it so that objects can be clearly seen through it. (p. 327)

transverse wave: wave for which the matter in the medium moves back and forth at right angles to the direction the wave travels; has crests and troughs. (p. 290)

troposphere: lowest layer of Earth's atmosphere where most weather occurs and temperature normally decreases with height. (p. 519)

trough: the lowest points on a transverse wave. (p. 294)

turbine: large wheel that rotates when pushed by steam, wind, or water and provides mechanical energy to a generator. (p. 440)

Tyndall effect: scattering of a light beam as it passes through a colloid. (p. 557)

marea: elevación y caída del nivel del mar en la Tierra, causadas por una ola gigante formada por la atracción gravitacional del Sol y de la Luna. (p. 199)

zona horaria:área sobre la superficie terrestre de 15° de ancho en la que la hora es la misma. (p. 190)

indicador radiactivo: isótopo radioactivo, tal como el yodo-131, que puede ser detectado por la radiación que emite después de ser absorbido por un organismo vivo. (p. 804)

radio transmisor-receptor: dispositivo que transmite y recibe una señal de radio al mismo tiempo, permitiendo que un usuario de un teléfono inalámbrico pueda hablar y escuchar al mismo tiempo. (p. 473)

límite de transformación: límite de la placa tectónica que existe como una gran falla o grieta, a lo largo del cual las placas litosféricas se mueven en dirección horizontal. (p. 360)

transformador: dispositivo que usa inducción electromagnética para aumentar o disminuir el voltaje de una corriente alterna. (p. 443)

translúcido: material que transmite alguna luz pero no la suficiente para ver claramente los objetos a través del mismo. (p. 327)

transmutación: proceso de cambio de un elemento a otro mediante la descomposición radioactiva. (p. 792)

transparente: material que transmite casi toda la luz, chocándola de tal manera que los objetos pueden ser claramente vistos a través del mismo. (p. 327)

onda transversal: onda para la cual la materia en el medio se mueve hacia adelante y hacia atrás en ángulos rectos respecto a la dirección en que viaja la onda; ésta tiene cresta y depresiones. (p. 290)

troposfera: capa más baja de la atmósfera terrestre donde ocurre la mayoría de los fenómenos climáticos y la temperatura disminuye normalmente con la altura. (p. 519)

depresión: los puntos más bajos en una onda transversal. (p. 294)

turbina: rueda grande que gira al ser impulsada por vapor, viento o agua y que suministra energía mecánica a un generador. (p. 440)

efecto Tyndall: difusión de un rayo de luz al pasar a través de un coloide. (p. 557)

U

ultraviolet waves: electromagnetic waves with wavelengths between about 400 billionths and 10 billionths of a meter. (p. 465)

ondas ultravioleta: ondas electromagnéticas con longitudes de onda entre aproximadamente 10 y 400 billonésimas de metro. (p. 465)

unbalanced forces: forces that combine to produce a net force that is not equal to zero and cause the velocity of an object to change. (p. 82)

unconformity: gap in the rock record representing a period of erosion or non-deposition. (p. 671)

uniformitarianism: Hutton's concept that the laws of nature act today as they have in the past. (p. 670)

unsaturated solution: any solution that can dissolve more solute at a given temperature. (p. 671)

Uranus: seventh planet from the Sun; appears blue-green because of atmospheric methane, and its axis of rotation is tilted on its side. (p. 235)

fuerzas desbalanceadas: fuerzas que se combinan para producir una fuerza neta diferente a cero y causan que cambie la velocidad de un objeto. (p. 82)

discordancia: brecha en el registro rocoso que representa un periodo de erosión o falta de deposición. (p. 671)

uniformitarianismo: concepto de Hutton respecto a que las leyes de la naturaleza que actúan hoy día son iguales a las del pasado. (p. 670)

solución no saturada: cualquier solución que puede disolver más solutos a una temperatura determinada. (p. 671)

Urano: séptimo planeta más cercano al Sol; tiene una apariencia verde-azul debido al metano atmosférico, y cuyo eje de rotación está inclinado hacia un lado. (p. 235)

V

variable: factor that can cause a change in the results of an experiment. (p. 9)

vector: a physical quantity that is specified by both a size and a direction. (p. 71)

velocity: the speed and direction of a moving object. (p. 73)

Venus: second planet outward from the Sun; has a dense, atmosphere of mostly carbon dioxide and very high surface temperatures. (p. 224)

viscosity: a fluid's resistance to flow. (p. 375)

visible light: electromagnetic waves with wavelengths of 750 to 400 billionths of a meter that can be detected by human eyes. (p. 465)

voltage difference: related to the force that causes electric charges to flow; measured in volts (V). (p. 400)

volume: amount of space occupied by an object. (p. 18)

variable: factor que puede causar un cambio en los resultados de un experimento. (p. 9)

vector: cantidad física que está especificada por un tamaño y una dirección. (p. 71)

velocidad direccional: la rapidez y dirección de un objeto en movimiento. (p. 73)

Venus: segundo planeta más cercano al Sol; tiene una atmósfera densa compuesta principalmente de dióxido de carbono y una temperatura superficial muy alta. (p. 224)

viscosidad: resistencia de un fluido al flujo. (p. 375)

luz visible: ondas electromagnéticas con longitudes de onda entre 400 y 750 billonésimas de metro y que pueden ser detectadas por el ojo humano. (p. 465)

diferencia de voltaje: se refiere a la fuerza que causa que las cargas eléctricas fluyan; se mide en voltios (V). (p. 400)

volumen: espacio ocupado por un objeto. (p. 18)

W

water table: boundary separating the saturated zone from the unsaturated zone. (p. 664)

wave: a repeating disturbance or movement that transfers energy through matter or space. (p. 288)

wavelength: distance between one point on a wave and the nearest point just like it. (p. 295)

weak acid: any acid that only partly dissociates in solution. (p. 771)

tabla de agua: límite que separa la zona saturada de la zona insaturada. (p. 664)

onda: alteración o movimiento repetitivo que transfiere energía a través de la materia o el espacio. (p. 288)

longitud de onda: distancia entre un punto en una onda y el punto semejante más cercano. (p. 295)

ácido débil: cualquier ácido que solamente se disocie parcialmente en una solución. (p. 771)

weak base: any base that does not dissociate completely in solution. (p. 772)

weather fronts: zones in which air masses interact. (p. 526)

weathering: process of physical or chemical breakdown of materials at or near Earth's surface, influenced by factors such as the nature of the parent material, climate, and time. (p. 646)

wedge: simple machine that is an inclined plane with one or two sloping sides. (p. 173)

weight: gravitational force exerted on an object. (p. 106)

westerlies: global winds that blow from the west in the middle latitudes. (p. 524)

wheel and axle: simple machine that consists of a shaft or axle attached to the center of a larger wheel, so that the shaft and the wheel rotate together. (p. 171)

white dwarf: giant star that has lost its outer layers, leaving behind a hot, dense core that continues to contract under gravity. (p. 825)

work: transfer of energy that occurs when a force makes an object move; measured in joules. (p. 154)

base débil: cualquier base que no se disocie completamente en una solución. (p. 772)

frentes climáticos: zonas en las que interactúan las masas de aire. (p. 526)

desgaste: proceso de fraccionamiento físico o químico de materiales en o cerca de la superficie terrestre, influenciado por factores como la naturaleza del material de origen, el clima y el tiempo. (p. 646)

cuña: máquina simple que consiste de un plano inclinado con uno o dos lados en declive. (p. 173)

peso: fuerza gravitacional ejercida sobre un objeto. (p. 106)

vientos del oeste: vientos globales que soplan desde el oeste en las latitudes medias. (p. 524)

rueda y eje: máquina simple que consiste de una barra o eje sujeto al centro de una rueda de mayor tamaño de manera que el eje y la rueda giran juntos. (p. 171)

enana blanca: estrella gigante que ha perdido sus capas externas, dejando un núcleo denso y caliente que continúa contrayéndose bajo la gravedad. (p. 825)

trabajo: transferencia de energía que se produce cuando una fuerza hace mover un objeto y que se mide en julios. (p. 154)

X

X rays: electromagnetic waves with wavelengths between about 10 billionths of a meter and 10 trillionths of a meter, that are often used for medical imaging. (p. 467)

rayos X: ondas electromagnéticas con longitudes de onda entre 10 billonésimas de metro y 10 trillonésimas de metro, las cuales se utilizan con frecuencia para producir imágenes de uso médico. (p. 467)

Italic numbers = illustration/photo **Bold numbers = vocabulary term**
lab = a page on which the entry is used in a lab
act = a page on which the entry is used in an activity

A

B

Index

D

Index

E

G

Index

I

J

K

L

N

O

P

Q

R

Index

T

U

V

W

Index

Credits

Magnification Key: Magnifications listed are the magnifications at which images were originally photographed.
LM–Light Microscope
SEM–Scanning Electron Microscope
TEM–Transmission Electron Microscope

Acknowledgments: Glencoe would like to acknowledge the artists and agencies who participated in illustrating this program: Absolute Science Illustration; Andrew Evansen; Argosy; Articulate Graphics; Craig Attebery represented by Frank & Jeff Lavaty; CHK America; John Edwards and Associates; Gagliano Graphics; Pedro Julio Gonzalez represented by Melissa Turk & The Artist Network; Robert Hynes represented by Mendola Ltd.; Morgan Cain & Associates; JTH Illustration; Laurie O'Keefe; Matthew Pippin represented by Beranbaum Artist's Representative; Precision Graphics; Publisher's Art; Rolin Graphics, Inc.; Wendy Smith represented by Melissa Turk & The Artist Network; Kevin Torline represented by Berendsen and Associates, Inc.; WILDlife ART; Phil Wilson represented by Cliff Knecht Artist Representative; Zoo Botanica.

Photo Credits

cover (bkgd)Getty Images, (l)Jack Fields/Photo Researchers, (r)Alfred Pasieka/Photo Researchers; **vii** NASA/Science Source/Photo Researchers; **viii** Peticolas-Megna/Fundamental Photographs; **ix** NASA/JPL; **x** Ray Ellis/Photo Researchers; **xi** SuperStock; **xii** Photo Researchers; **xiii** Richard Megna/Fundamental Photographs; **xiv** (t)Matt Meadows, (b)NASA; **xv** Shuttle Mission Imagery/Liaison Agency; **xvi** NASA; **xvii** Joe Lertola; **xx** Tim Courlas/Horizons; **1** James H. Karales/Peter Arnold, Inc.; **2–3** Jon Feingersh/The Stock Market; **3** Dorling Kindersley; **4–5** Roger Ressmeyer/CORBIS; **6** Shuttle Mission Imagery/Getty Images News Services; **7** Will McIntyre/Photo Researchers; **9** James L. Amos/CORBIS; **10** David Young-Wolff/PhotoEdit; **11** (l)Roger Ressmeyer/CORBIS, (r)Douglas Mesney/CORBIS; **12** J. Marshall/The Image Works; **13** (t)Jonathan Nourok/PhotoEdit, (b)Tony Freeman/PhotoEdit; **14** First Image; **15** courtesy Bureau International Des Poids et Mesures; **16** Matt Meadows; **17** (t)Amanita Pictures, (l)Runk/Schoenberger from Grant Heilman, (r)CORBIS; **20** Stephen R. Wagner; **24** First Image; **28 29** Matt Meadows; **30** Rosalie Winard; **31** (l)TSADO/NCDC/NOAA/Tom Stack & Associates, (r)David Ball/CORBIS; **32** Amanita Pictures; **35** courtesy Bureau International Des Poids et Mesures; **36–37** David Luzzi, University of Pennsylvania/Photo Researchers; **38** Bettmann/CORBIS; **39** Reuters/CORBIS; **40** Getty Images; **41** (l)Reunion des Musees Nationaux/Art Resource, NY, (r)file photo; **42** Torlief Svensson/CORBIS; **43** Getty Images; **44** (t)Getty Images, (cl)George D. Lepp/CORBIS; **44** (cr)Richard Price/Getty Images, (bl)Lester Lefkowitz/CORBIS, (br)Joel Stettenheim/CORBIS; **46** Jill Connelly/AP/Wide World Photos; **47** Najlah Feanny/CORBIS; **48** Randy Brandon/Peter Arnold, Inc.; **49** (t)Pascal Le Segretain/CORBIS, (b)CORBIS; **52** Jim Reed/CORBIS; **53** (t)Hulton-Deutsch Collection/CORBIS, (b)Orlin Wagner/AP/Wide World Photos; **54** Roger Ressmeyer/CORBIS; **55** NASA/Science Source/Photo Researchers; **56** Toshiyuki Aizawa/Reuters/CORBIS; **57** Steve Dunwell/Index Stock Imagery; **58 59** Matt Meadows; **60** (t)AP, National Inventors Hall of Fame, (b)Rita Maas/Getty Images; **61** (t)Arthur Tilley/Getty Images, (bl)E. Dygas/Getty Images, (br)Roger Ressmeyer/CORBIS; **64** (l)Torlief Svensson/CORBIS, (r)Najlah Feanny/CORBIS; **65** (l)Ed Pritchard/Getty Images, (r)NASA/Science Source/Photo Researchers, Inc.; **66–67** John Terence Turner/FPG; **67** (l)Artville, (r)Charles L. Perrin; **68–69** Lester Lefkowitz/CORBIS; **70** Icon Images; **73** (t)SuperStock, (b)Robert Holmes/CORBIS; **78** (t)RDF/Visuals Unlimited, (c)Ron Kimball, (b)Richard Megna/Fundamental Photographs; **79** (l)The Image Finders, (r)Richard Hutchings; **80** Dan Feicht/Cedar Point Amusement Park; **81** Globus Brothers Studios, NYC; **82** Tim Courlas/Horizons; **84** Bob Daemmrich; **85** (t)James Sugar/Black Star/PictureQuest, (b)Michael Newman/PhotoEdit; **86** Keith Kent/Peter Arnold; **87** First Image; **88 89** Icon Images; **90** Sylvain Grandadam/Stone; **91** (t bl)Tony Freeman/PhotoEdit, (br)Keith Kent/Peter Arnold; **96–97** Tim Wright/CORBIS; **98** David Young-Wolff/PhotoEdit; **99** Neal Haynes/Rex USA, Ltd.; **100** (tl tr)Bob Daemmrich; (b)courtesy Insurance Institute for Highway Safety; **101** Donald Johnston/Stone; **103** Pictor; **105** StockTrek/CORBIS; **106** Peticolas-Megna/Fundamental Photographs; **107** NASA; **109** (tl)KS Studios, (tr)David Young-Wolff/PhotoEdit, (b)Richard Megna/Fundamental Photographs; **110** Pictor; **113** Steven Sutton/Duomo; **114** Philip Bailey/The Stock Market; **115** (l)NASA, (tr)(br)North American Rockwell, (cr)Teledyne Ryan Aeronautical; **117** (l)Jeff Smith/Fotosmith, (r)Richard Megna/Fundamental Photographs; **118** Matt Meadows; **119** Tim Courlas/Horizons; **120** (t)Tony Craddock/Photo Researchers, (b)Bettmann/CORBIS; **121** (l)Neal Haynes/Rex USA, Ltd., (r)Richard Megna/Fundamental Photographs; **126–127** Jim Cummins/CORBIS; **128** Runk/Schoenberger from Grant Heilman; **129** (l)Tony Walker/PhotoEdit, (c)Mark Burnett, (r)D. Boone/CORBIS; **133** KS Studios; **137** Walter H. Hodge/Peter Arnold, Inc.; **138** RFD/Visuals Unlimited; **142** Rudi Von Briel; **144 145** Matt Meadows; **146** (r)TIME, (l)Brompton Studios; **147** (tl)SuperStock, (bl)Jana R. Jirak/Visuals Unlimited, (r)Telegraph Colour Library/FPG; **152** Jakob Helbig/Getty Images; **153** Timothy Fuller; **154** Tim Courlas/Horizons; **155** (t)Tim Courlas/Horizons, (b)Michael Newman/PhotoEdit; **157** Michelle Bridwell/PhotoEdit; **159** Jules Frazier/Getty Images; **160** Michael Newman/Getty Images; **161** (t)Mark Burnett, (b)Tony Freeman/PhotoEdit; **162** Joseph P. Sinnot/Fundamental Photographs; **163** Richard Megna/Fundamental Photographs; **167** (t)Mark Burnett, (l)Tom Pantages, (r)Tony Freeman/PhotoEdit; **168** (t)Richard T. Nowitz, (c)David Madison/Stone, (b)John Henley/The Stock Market; **169** A.J. Copley/Visuals Unlimited; **171** Mark Burnett; **172** Tom Pantages; **173** (tl)file photo, (tr)Mark Burnett; **184–185** Richard Cummins/CORBIS; **189** NASA; **196** Matt Meadows; **201** Roger Ressmeyer/CORBIS; **202** NASA Kennedy Space Center; **203** NASA Goddard Space Flight Center; **205** (t)NASA/JPL/USGS, (c)NASA/CORBIS, (b)Julian Baum/Photo Researchers; **208** Bettmann/CORBIS; **210** (t)Bill Sanderson/Photo Researchers, (b)Ronald Royer/Science Photo Library; **211** (t)NASA Kennedy Space Center, (b)NASA/CORBIS; **215** NASA/GSFC; **216–217** Detlev Van Ravenswaay/SPL/Photo Researchers; **223** (t)NASA, (b)NASA/JPL/Northwestern University; **224** (t)NASA/JPL, (b)JPL/NASA; **225** NASA; **226** (t bl)JPL/NASA, (br)NASA/JPL/Malin Space Science Systems; **227** JPL/NASA; **228** (t)JPL/NASA, (b)Cornell/JPL/NASA; **229** JPL/NASA; **231** CICLOPS/University of Arizona/NASA; **232** JPL/NASA; **233** (t)CORBIS, (c)NASA-HQ-GRIN, (b)NASA-JPL; **234** (t)NASA/JPL, (b)NASA/JPL/University of Colorado; **235** (l)Goddard Space Flight Center/NASA, (r)JPL/NASA; **236** (t)Dr. R. Albrecht, ESA/ESO Space Telescope European Coordinating Facility/NASA, (b)JPL/NASA; **237** Caltech/JPL/NASA; **238** OAR/National Undersea Research Program (NURP); Texas A&M University; **239** Marshall Space Flight Center/NASA; **240** (t)Lunar and Planetary Institute, (b)JPL/NASA; **241** JPL/NASA; **242 243** Matt Meadows; **244** Gordon Garradd/Photo Researchers; **245** (l)HQ/GRIN/NASA, (r)JPL/NASA; **246** CICLOPS/University of Arizona/NASA; **249** JPL/NASA; **250–251** Nonstock Inc.; **250** John Eastcott & Yva Momatiuk/Woodfin Camp & Associates; **252–253** Charles E. Rotkin/CORBIS; **253** Matt Meadows; **257** Aaron Haupt Photography; **261** JISAS/Lockheed/Science Photo Library/Photo Researchers; **262** Doug Martin; **263** Getty Images; **264** (t)Mark C. Burnett/Photo Researchers, (b)CORBIS; **265** Mark E. Gibson/Visuals Unlimited; **266** Zefa Visual Media/Index Stock; **267** Charles D. Winters/Photo Researchers; **268** (t)Earth Imaging/Stone, (bl)K&K Arman/Bruce Coleman, Inc./PictureQuest, (br)Charles & Josette Lenars/CORBIS; **270** Science Photo Library/Photo Researchers; **271** Leonard Lee Rue III/Bruce Coleman, Inc./PictureQuest; **273** Steve Callahan/Visuals Unlimited; **278** Tim Courlas/Horizons; **280** (t b)NASA, (c)Roy Johnson/Tom Stack & Associates; **281** (l)Breck P. Kent/Animals Animals, (r)Michael Newman/PhotoEdit; **286–287** Jason Childs/Getty Images; **288** James H. Karales/Peter Arnold, Inc.; **292** (t)Galen Rowell, (b)Stephen R. Wagner; **301** Richard Hutchings/Photo Researchers; **302** (t)Richard Megna/Fundamental Photographs, (b)SIU/Visuals Unlimited; **304** (t)John S. Shelton, (b)Richard Megna/Fundamental Photographs; **305** Richard Megna/Fundamental Photographs; **308** Kodansha; **310** Doug Martin; **311** Tim Courlas/Horizons Companies; **312** Ralph White/CORBIS; **313** (tl)Stan Osolinski/The Stock Market, (tr)Bruce Heinemann/PhotoDisc, (b)SIU/Visuals Unlimited; **318–319** AFP/CORBIS; **322** (l)Mark A. Schneider/Visuals Unlimited, (cl)Rafael Macia/Photo Researchers, (cr)David Young-Wolff/PhotoEdit, (r)SuperStock; **326** Doug Martin; **327** First Image; **329** (t)Stephen Frisch/Stock Boston/PictureQuest, (b)David Parker/Photo Researchers; **330** Charles O'Rear/CORBIS; **331** David Young-Wolff/PhotoEdit; **333** David Parker/Photo Researchers; **338** Matt Meadows; **340** First Image; **341** (t)Ralph C. Eagle, Jr./Photo Researchers, (b)Diane Hirsch/Fundamental Photographs; **342** Matt Meadows; **344** John Wang/Getty Images; **345** David Young-Wolff/PhotoEdit; **346** (t)Archivo Iconografico, S.A./CORBIS, (b)Ashmolean Museum, Oxford, UK/Bridgeman Art Library, London/New York; **347** (t)Jeff Greenberg/Visuals Unlimited, (b)Dick Poe/Visuals Unlimited; **352–353** Alfio Scigliano/CORBIS; **354** Mark Garlick/Photo Researchers; **355** NOAA/NGDC; **356** The Floor of the Oceans by Bruce C. Heezen and Marie Tharp, ©1977 by Marie Tharp. Reproduced by permission of Marie Tharp; **362** USGS, National Earthquake Information Center; **363** AP/Wide World Photos; **368** (tl)Bob Riha/Getty Images, (tr)Otto Greule Jr./Getty Images, (bl)Steven Powell, Star Seismic LLC, (br)Jerome Favre/AP/Wide World Photos; **382** Roger Ressmeyer/CORBIS; **383** Gary Braasch/CORBIS; **388–389** National Geographic Society Image Collection; **389** National Geographic Society Image Collection; **390–391** John Lawrence/Getty Images; **391** Michael Newman/PhotoEdit; **393** Geoff Butler; **395** KS Studios; **396** Tim Courlas; **397** T. Wiewandt/DRK Photo; **398** Dale Sloat/PhotoTake NYC/PictureQuest; **403** Ray Ellis/Photo Researchers; **404** Thomas Veneklasen; **406 407 408** Geoff Butler; **410** (tl)Geoff Butler, (tr)Tony Freeman/PhotoEdit, (c b)Aaron Haupt; **414 415** Geoff Butler; **416** Bernard Gotfryd/Woodfin Camp & Assoc.; **417** (t)file photo, (bl)Lester Lefkowitz/CORBIS, (br)Harold Stucker/Black Star; **422–423** Kennan Ward/CORBIS; **424** Don Smetzer/Getty Images; **425 426** Richard Megna/Fundamental Photographs; **429** (l)Stephen Frisch/Stock Boston, (r)Mark Burnett; **430** Mark Burnett; **433** Icon Images; **435** (t)Allen Zak, (b)Tim Courlas; **438** Tim Courlas; **440** (t)Tom Campbell/Getty Images, (b)Russell D. Curtis/Photo Researchers; **441** (tl)Clement Mok/PictureQuest, (tr)Joseph Palmieri/Pictor, (cl)Tim Ridley/DK Images, (cr)Robin Adshead/Military Picture Library/CORBIS, (b)Brian Gordon Green; **442** Mark Burnett; **445** Tim Courlas; **446 447** KS Studios; **448** (t)Brian Blauser/Stock Shop, (b)Laurence Dutton/Getty Images; **449** (l)Richard Megna/Fundamental Photographs, (r)Jeff Greenberg/Peter Arnold, Inc.; **454–455** Bob Burch/Index Stock Imagery; **459** Mat Jacob/The Image Works; **464** (t)Pete Saloutos/The Stock Market, (bl)NASA/GSFC/JPL, MISR and AirMISR Teams, (br)NASA/GSFC/MITI/ERSDAC/JAROS, and USA/Japan ASTER Science Team; **465** AP/Wide World Photos; **467** Telegraph Colour Library/FPG; **469** StudiOhio; **470** (t bl)First Image, (br)PhotoDisc; **471** (tl)Stephen Frisch/Stock Boston/PictureQuest, (tr)Mark Richards/PhotoEdit/PictureQuest, (bl)CORBIS, (bc)Dorling Kindersley, Ltd., (br)Michael Newman/PhotoEdit/PictureQuest; **472** Nino Mascardi/The Image Bank; **473** Photolink/PhotoDisc; **474** VCG/FPG; **476** Len Delessio/Index Stock; **477** Jim Wark/Index Stock; **478** (t)Getty Images, (b)Bettman/CORBIS; **479** (t)Martin Dohrn/Science Photo Library/Photo Researchers, (c)Mickey Pfleger/Photo 20-20, (b)Joe McDonald/Tom Stack & Associates; **482** PhotoDisc; **484–485** Sandy Felsenthal/CORBIS; **486** Bill Heinsohn/Stone; **488** Robert E. Pratt; **489** Amanita Pictures; **490** (t)Digital Vision/PictureQuest, (b)Doug Martin; **494** Robert Essel/The Stock Market; **495** Photo Researchers; **498** AFP/CORBIS; **499** Tim Wright/CORBIS; **501** Amanita Pictures; **503** S.K. Patrick/Tom Stack & Associates; **504** (t)John Elk III/Stock Boston, (b)Lester Lefkowitz/The Stock Market; **506** Martin Bond/Science Photo Library/Photo Researchers; **508** Timothy Fuller; **509** Martin B. Withers/Frank Lane Picture Agency/CORBIS; **510** Dan Lamont/CORBIS; **511** (t)Amanita Pictures, (c)Kathy Ferguson/PhotoEdit, (b)US Department of Energy/Science Photo Library/Photo Researchers; **515** Robert Essel/The Stock Market; **516–517** Byron Aughenbaugh/Getty Images; **531** (cw from top) Cartesia/Getty Iamges, Bernhard Edmaier/Photo Researchers, Bernhard Edmaier/Photo Researchers, Michele Westmorland/CORBIS, Wendy Dennis/Visuals Unlimited, Anthony Bannister/CORBIS; **539** APF/Getty Images; **540** Bill Ross/CORBIS; **541** Philippe Colombi/Getty Images; **542** AP/Wide World Photos; **548–549** Granger Collection, NY; **549** National Geographic Society Image Collection; **550–551** Michael Newman/PhotoEdit; **551** Matt Meadows; **552** (t)Siede Pries/Getty Images, (c)Ryan McVay/Getty Images, (b)Getty Images; **553** (tl)James L. Amos/CORBIS, (tr)Stockbyte/PictureQuest, (cl)Yann Arthus-Bertrand/CORBIS, (cr)CalTech, (bl)Robert Fried/Stock Boston/PictureQuest, (br)Dorling Kindersley, Ltd.; **554** (t)Richard Megna/Fundamental Photographs, (b)Icon Images; **555** (l c)Icon Images, (r)Andrew Syred/Science Photo Library/Photo Researchers; **556** (l)Getty Images, (r)C. Squared Studios/Getty Images; **557** (tl)Chuck Keeler, Jr./

CORBIS, (tr)Kaj R. Svensson/Science Photo Library/Photo Researchers, (b)Kip & Pat Peticolas/Fundamental Photographs; **558** Larry Mayer/Getty News Images; **560** Matt Meadows; **561** (t)Amanita Pictures, (b)Doug Martin; **562** Richard Megna/Fundamental Photographs; **563** Jed & Kaoru Share/Getty Images; **564** Richard Megna/ Fundamental Photographs; **565** (l)M. Romesser, (r)SuperStock; **567** Chris Rogers/CORBIS; **568 569** Matt Meadows; **570** (t)Dominic Oldershaw, (c)Doug Martin, (b)Frank Siteman/Stock Boston/PictureQuest; **571** (tl)Icon Images, (tr)Will Ryan/CORBIS, (bl)Tony Freeman/PhotoEdit, (br)Icon Images; **575** (tl tr)Doug Martin, (b)Chris Rogers/ CORBIS; **576–577** Walter Bibikow/Index Stock Imagery, NY; **580** (tl)Science Photo Library/Photo Researchers, (tr)Hank Morgan/Photo Researchers, (b)Photo Researchers; **581** Sheila Terry/Photo Researchers; **588** Science Museum/Science & Society Picture Library; **596** CORBIS; **597** The Image Bank; **598** Tom Pantages; **599** PhotoEdit; **600** (t)Roger Ressmeyer/ CORBIS, (b)Maria Stenzel/National Geographic Image Collection; **606–607** Hans Peter Merten/Robert Harding World Imagery/Getty Images; **610** (t)Doug Martin, (b)Marli Miller/Visuals Unlimited; **611** (l)Ken Lucas/Visuals Unlimited, (r)Alfred Pasieka/Photo Researchers; **612** NPS Photo; **613** (t to b) Mark A. Schneider/Photo Researchers, Carolina Biological/Visuals Unlimited, Marli Miller/Visuals Unlimited, Marli Miller/Visuals Unlimited, John R. Foster/ Photo Researchers; **614** (t)Mark A. Schneider/Visuals Unlimited, (b)Martin Land/Photo Researchers; **616** (t)Icon Images, (b)Charles D. Winters/Photo Researchers; **617** Marli Miller/Visuals Unlimited; **619** Breck P. Kent/Earth Scenes; **620** Marli Miller/Visuals Unlimited; **622** (tl tr bl)Breck P. Kent/Earth Scenes, (br)Amanita Pictures; **623** (t)NPS Photo, (b)Wally Eberhart/Visuals Unlimited; **624** Darrell Gulin/ CORBIS; **630** Kevin Schafer/CORBIS; **631** Breck P. Kent/ Earth Scenes; **633** (t)Max Dannenbaum/Getty Images, (c)NASA, (b)NASA/GSFC/LaRC/JPL/MISR Team; **636 637** Matt Meadows; **638** (t)Albert Copley/Visuals Unlimited, (b)CORBIS; **639** (tl)Lawrence Lawry/Photo Researchers, (tr)Larry Stepanowicz/Visuals Unlimited, (b)Brad Lewis/Visuals Unlimited; **640** John R. Foster/Photo Researchers; **641** Breck P. Kent/Earth Scenes; **642** Marli Miller/Visuals Unlimited; **643** Breck P. Kent/Earth Scenes; **644–645** Tom Bean/CORBIS; **646** Robert Gill/CORBIS; **648** Owen Franken/CORBIS; **649** (tl tr)Doug Martin, (b)Adam Woolfitt/CORBIS; **652** Yann Arthus-Bertrand/ CORBIS; **655** NASA/Goddard Space Flight Center/LaRC/JPL; **656** (t)Francois Gohier/Photo Researchers, (b)Martin Bond/ Science Photo Library/Photo Researchers; **657** (t c)NASA/ Goddard Space Flight Center Scientific Visualization Studio, (b)NASA/GSFC/METI/ERSDAC/JAROS, and U.S./Japan ASTER Science Team; **662** Yann Arthus-Bertrand/CORBIS; **666** (t)Gary Hincks/Photo Researchers, (cl)Carl & Ann Purcell/CORBIS, (cr)Stephen Alvarez/Getty Images, (b)Mark Gormus/AP/Wide World Photos; **678** (t)Peter Cade/Getty Images, (b)Ron Thomas/Getty Images; **679** (l)Barry Runk from Grant Heilman Photography, (r)Jon Turk/Visuals Unlimited; **684–685** Norbert Wu; **685** Spencer Collection, New York Public Library, Astor, Lenox & Tilden Foundation; **686–687** Tom Sanders/CORBIS; **687** Amanita Pictures; **688** (l)CORBIS, (r)John Evans; **689** (l c)Richard Megna/ Fundamental Photographs, (r)Syndicated Features Limited/ The Image Works; **693** First Image; **694** John Paul Kay/Peter Arnold; **696** Paul Silverman/Fundamental Photographs; **698** John Evans; **699** Patricia Lanza; **700** Amanita Pictures; **701** (l)Richard Megna/Fundamental Photographs, (r)Matt Meadows; **702** Mark Burnett; **703** Bettmann/CORBIS; **708** Amanita Pictures; **710 711** Matt Meadows; **712** Daniel Belknap; **713** Syndicated Features Limited/The Image Works; **718–719** Transglobe/Index Stock; **722** Mansell Collection/ TimePix; **723 726** Richard Megna/Fundamental Photographs; **727** Doug Martin/Photo Researchers; **729** Richard Megna/ Fundamental Photographs; **730** Emory Kristof/National Geographic Image Collection; **731** (t)Charles D. Winters/ Photo Researchers, (b)Stephen Frisch/Stock Boston/ PictureQuest; **732** Richard Megna/Fundamental Photographs; **733** Royalty-Free/CORBIS; **734** Tim Matsui/ Liaison Agency; **735 736** Matt Meadows; **737** (t)Roger Ressmeyer/NASA/CORBIS, (l c)Bettmann/CORBIS, (r)NASA/CORBIS; **739** SuperStock; **741** Timothy Fuller; **742 743** Matt Meadows; **744** (t)Bibliotheque du Museum D'Histoire Naturelle, (b)Brad Maushart/Graphistock; **745** (l)Charles D. Winters/Photo Researchers, (r)Joseph P. Sinnot/Fundamental Photographs; **748** Charles D. Winters/ Photo Researchers; **749** (l)Richard Megna/Fundamental Photographs, (r)Firefly Productions/The Stock Market; **750–751** Stephen Frink/Index Stock Imagery; **752** Annie Griffiths Belt/CORBIS; **753** (l)Christie's Images, (r)Flip Schulke/Black Star; **754** (t)Bettmann/CORBIS, (c)Brian Gordon Green, (b)Michael Newman/PhotoEdit/ PictureQuest; **760** Mark Thayer; **762** Richard Megna/ Fundamental Photographs; **764 765** Matt Meadows; **766** Geoff Butler; **767** Rick Poley/Index Stock; **769** Charles D. Winters/Photo Researchers; **771** Matt Meadows; **773** (from top left) CORBIS, Elaine Shay, CORBIS, Brent Turner/BLT Productions, Icon Images, Matt Meadows, Elaine Shay, StudiOhio, (c)Dominic Oldershaw, (bl)Matt Meadows, (br)Mark Burnett/Stock Boston/PictureQuest; **775** Matt Meadows; **776** Tim Courlas/Horizons; **777** Matt Meadows; **778** TIME; **779** (l)Icon Images, (r)KS Studios; **783** Matt Meadows; **784–785** Paul Souders/Getty Images; **785** Aaron Haupt; **786** (t)First Image, (b)David Frazier/The Image Works; **790** American Institute of Physics/Emilio Segrè Visual Archives; **792** Amanita Pictures; **796** (l)courtesy Supersaturated Environments; **796** (r)Science Photo Library/ Photo Researchers; **797** (t)CERN, P. Loiez/Science Photo Library/Photo Researchers, (bl bcl bcr br)Richard Megna/ Fundamental Photographs; **799** Hank Morgan/Photo Researchers; **804** Oliver Meckes/Nicole Ottawa/Photo Researchers; **805** UCLA School of Medicine; **806** J.L. Carson/ Custom Medical Stock Photo; **807** Tim Courlas/Horizons Companies; **808** (l)Fermilab/Visuals Unlimited, (r)Matt Meadows; **809** Matt Meadows; **810** (t)C. Powell, P. Fowler & D. Perkins/Science Photo Library/Photo Researchers, Inc., (bl br)CORBIS; **811** (l)Martha Cooper/Peter Arnold, Inc., (r)Oliver Meckes/Nicole Ottawa/Photo Researchers; **848** PhotoDisc; **849** Hickson-Bender; **850** Tom Pantages; **854** Michell D. Bridwell/PhotoEdit; **855** (t)Mark Burnett, (b)Dominic Oldershaw; **856** StudiOhio; **857** Timothy Fuller; **858** Aaron Haupt Photography; **860** KS Studios; **861** Matt Meadows

PERIODIC TABLE OF THE ELEMENTS

Columns of elements are called groups. Elements in the same group have similar chemical properties.

Legend	
Gas	
Liquid	
Solid	
Synthetic	

Element	Hydrogen
Atomic number	1
Symbol	H
Atomic mass	1.008
State of matter	[Gas]

The first three symbols tell you the state of matter of the element at room temperature. The fourth symbol identifies elements that are not present in significant amounts on Earth. Useful amounts are made synthetically.

	1	2	3	4	5	6	7	8	9
1	Hydrogen 1 H 1.008 [Gas]								
2	Lithium 3 Li 6.941 [Solid]	Beryllium 4 Be 9.012 [Solid]							
3	Sodium 11 Na 22.990 [Solid]	Magnesium 12 Mg 24.305 [Solid]							
4	Potassium 19 K 39.098 [Solid]	Calcium 20 Ca 40.078 [Solid]	Scandium 21 Sc 44.956 [Solid]	Titanium 22 Ti 47.867 [Solid]	Vanadium 23 V 50.942 [Solid]	Chromium 24 Cr 51.996 [Solid]	Manganese 25 Mn 54.938 [Solid]	Iron 26 Fe 55.845 [Solid]	Cobalt 27 Co 58.933 [Solid]
5	Rubidium 37 Rb 85.468 [Solid]	Strontium 38 Sr 87.62 [Solid]	Yttrium 39 Y 88.906 [Solid]	Zirconium 40 Zr 91.224 [Solid]	Niobium 41 Nb 92.906 [Solid]	Molybdenum 42 Mo 95.94 [Solid]	Technetium 43 Tc (98) [Synthetic]	Ruthenium 44 Ru 101.07 [Solid]	Rhodium 45 Rh 102.906 [Solid]
6	Cesium 55 Cs 132.905 [Solid]	Barium 56 Ba 137.327 [Solid]	Lanthanum 57 La 138.906 [Solid]	Hafnium 72 Hf 178.49 [Solid]	Tantalum 73 Ta 180.948 [Solid]	Tungsten 74 W 183.84 [Solid]	Rhenium 75 Re 186.207 [Solid]	Osmium 76 Os 190.23 [Solid]	Iridium 77 Ir 192.217 [Solid]
7	Francium 87 Fr (223) [Solid]	Radium 88 Ra (226) [Solid]	Actinium 89 Ac (227) [Solid]	Rutherfordium 104 Rf (261) [Synthetic]	Dubnium 105 Db (262) [Synthetic]	Seaborgium 106 Sg (266) [Synthetic]	Bohrium 107 Bh (264) [Synthetic]	Hassium 108 Hs (277) [Synthetic]	Meitnerium 109 Mt (268) [Synthetic]

The number in parentheses is the mass number of the longest-lived isotope for that element.

Rows of elements are called periods. Atomic number increases across a period.

The arrow shows where these elements would fit into the periodic table. They are moved to the bottom of the table to save space.

Lanthanide series	Cerium 58 Ce 140.116 [Solid]	Praseodymium 59 Pr 140.908 [Solid]	Neodymium 60 Nd 144.24 [Solid]	Promethium 61 Pm (145) [Synthetic]	Samarium 62 Sm 150.36 [Solid]
Actinide series	Thorium 90 Th 232.038 [Solid]	Protactinium 91 Pa 231.036 [Solid]	Uranium 92 U 238.029 [Solid]	Neptunium 93 Np (237) [Synthetic]	Plutonium 94 Pu (244) [Synthetic]